Algebra 1

Program Highlights

Vertically Aligned Content	Sample Page(s)
• PreK-12 Alignment	T10
• Research Base for Glencoe Mathematics	T12
• College and Work Readiness	T14
• Program Philosophy	T16

Balanced Instruction Delivers Rich, Rigorous Content to All Students	Sample Page(s)
• Chapter 0, Preparing for Algebra 1	P1–P45
• Friendly Lesson Design	5–9
• Engaging Algebra and Graphing Technology Labs	53, 90
• Step-by-Step Selected Solutions	77–80, R12–R93

Right Amount of Rigor	Sample Page(s)
• Leveled Exercise Sets	77–80
• Multiple Representations	116, 267
• **H**igher **O**rder **T**hinking Problems (H.O.T. Problems)	130, 229
• Leveled Resources	72A–72B, 132

Assessment and Tiered Intervention	Sample Page(s)
• Diagnostic Teaching	210F, 217, 221
• Formative Assessment	225, 227, 230, 244
• Summative Assessment	275
• Tier 1–3 Response to Intervention (RtI)	211, 244, 275

State-of-the-Art Technology	Sample Page(s)
• Personal Tutors for Each Example	132, 153
• Math Online at glencoe.com	72, 132, 139
• FREE! Hotmath.com Online Tutorials	R12–R93

Refer to the back of this endsheet for your *QuickPass* Code.

More Than Just a Textbook

Internet Resources

StudentWorks™ *Plus* Online This interactive **eBook** includes the complete Student Edition with audio, Math in Motion, Personal Tutor, Self-Check Quizzes, and much more – all at point of use!

Step 1 **Connect to** IL Math Online glencoe.com

Step 2 **Connect to resources by using simple and convenient** QuickPass **codes.**

IL5476c1

"IL" for "Illinois"

This edition, ISBN 978-0-07-890547-6

Enter the appropriate chapter number. c1 = Chapter 1

For Students

Connect to the Student Edition **eBook** that contains all of the following online resources. You don't need to take your textbook home every night.

- Personal Tutor
- Self-Check Quizzes
- Chapter Readiness Quizzes
- Math in Motion: Animation
- Math in Motion: BrainPOP®
- Math in Motion: Interactive Lab
- Extra Examples
- Chapter Test Practice
- Standardized Test Practice
- Study to Go
- Vocabulary Review Games
- Graphing Calculator Keystrokes
- Multilingual eGlossary
- Scavenger Hunts
- Workbooks
- Hotmath Math Homework Help Homework Help

For Teachers

- Teaching Today
- **AdvanceTracker**
  - Diagnostic, formative, and summative assessment
  - Progress reports
  - Differentiated instruction
- State Resources
- Professional Development at www.mhpdonline.com
  - Video Clips
  - Online Credit Courses
- Research
  - White Papers
  - Efficacy Studies

For Parents

Connect to www.glencoe.com to access **StudentWorks *Plus* Online** and all of the resources for students and teachers listed above.

Glencoe McGraw-Hill

Teacher Edition

Illinois Algebra 1

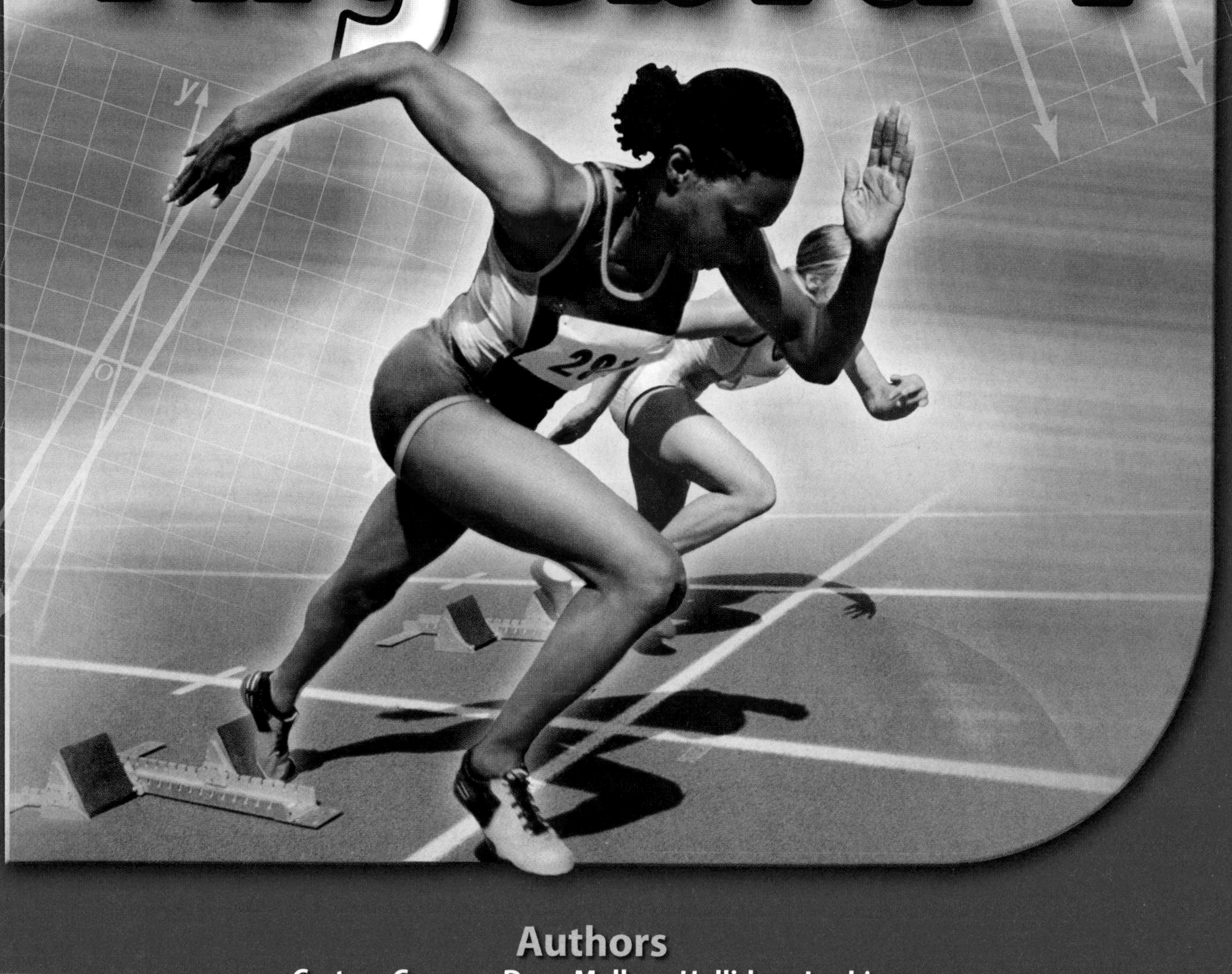

Authors

Carter • Cuevas • Day • Malloy • Holliday • Luchin

McGraw Hill Glencoe

About the Cover

On your mark, get set, GO! Math is everywhere, even on a track. The lanes on a track never cross or intersect. Lines that continue infinitely and never intersect are called parallel lines. You will learn more about parallel lines, intersecting lines, and the equations that represent them in Chapter 4.

The McGraw·Hill Companies

Glencoe

Send all inquiries to:
Glencoe/McGraw-Hill
8787 Orion Place
Columbus, OH 43240-4027

ISBN: 978-0-07-890547-6 (Illinois Teacher Edition)
MHID: 0-07-890547-8 (Illinois Teacher Edition)
ISBN: 978-0-07-890544-5 (Illinois Student Edition)
MHID: 0-07-890544-3 (Illinois Student Edition)

Printed in the United States of America.

3 4 5 6 7 8 9 10 QWD/LEH 17 16 15 14 13 12 11 10 09

CONTENTS IN BRIEF

Lead Authors

Macmillan/McGraw-Hill and Glencoe/McGraw-Hill K–12 Mathematics Lead Authors

Our lead authors ensure that the Macmillan/McGraw-Hill and Glencoe/McGraw-Hill mathematics programs are truly vertically aligned by beginning with the end in mind—success in Algebra 1 and beyond. By "backmapping" the content from the high school programs, all of our mathematics programs are well articulated in their scope and sequence, ensuring that the content in each program provides a solid foundation for moving forward. These authors also worked closely with the entire K–12 author team to ensure vertical alignment of the instructional approach and visual design.

Dr. John A. Carter, Ph.D.
Assistant Principal for Teaching and Learning
Adlai E. Stevenson High School
Lincolnshire, Illinois

Areas of Expertise: Using technology and manipulatives to visualize concepts; Mathematics Achievement of English-Language Learners

Dr. Gilbert J. Cuevas, Ph.D.
Professor of Mathematics Education
Texas State University–San Marcos
San Marcos, Texas

Areas of Expertise: Applying concepts and skills in mathematically rich contexts; Mathematical Representations

Dr. Roger Day, Ph.D., NBCT
Mathematics Department Chairperson
Pontiac Township High School
Pontiac, Illinois

Areas of Expertise: Understanding and applying probability and statistics; Mathematics Teacher Education

Dr. Carol Malloy, Ph.D.
Associate Professor
University of North Carolina at Chapel Hill
Chapel Hill, NC

Areas of Expertise: Representations and critical thinking; Student Success in Algebra 1

Additional Algebra 1 Authors

The entire Algebra 1 author team strives to create a program that can be used by all types of Algebra 1 teachers with all types of Algebra 1 students. Each author brings their special expertise to making a program that will contribute to the success of every student who uses this instructional resource.

Dr. Berchie Holliday, Ed.D.
National Mathematics Consultant
Silver Spring, MD
Areas of Expertise: Using mathematics to model and understand real-world data, the effect of graphics on the mathematical understanding

Beatrice Luchin
Mathematics Consultant
League City, TX
Areas of Expertise: Using reading strategies to aid in mathematical understanding

Contributing Author

This program is the beneficiary of the imagination of Dinah Zike through the contribution of the Foldables Study Organizers.

Dinah Zike
Educational Consultant
Dinah-Might Activities, Inc.
San Antonio, Texas

IL Math Online Meet the Authors at **glencoe.com**

Consultants and Reviewers

Glencoe/McGraw-Hill wishes to thank the following professionals for their feedback. They were instrumental in providing valuable input toward the development of this program in these specific areas.

Mathematical Content

Viken Hovsepian
Professor of Mathematics
Rio Hondo College
Whittier, California

Grant A. Fraser, Ph.D.
Professor of Mathematics
California State University, Los Angeles
Los Angeles, California

Arthur K. Wayman, Ph.D.
Professor of Mathematics Emeritus
California State University, Long Beach
Long Beach, California

Gifted and Talented

Shelbi K. Cole
Research Assistant
University of Connecticut
Storrs, Connecticut

College Readiness

Robert Lee Kimball, Jr.
Department Head, Math and Physics
Wake Technical Community College
Raleigh, North Carolina

English-Language Learners

Susana Davidenko
State University of New York
Cortland, New York

Alfredo Gómez
Mathematics/ESL teacher
Fowler High School
Syracuse, New York

Graphing Calculator

Ruth M. Casey
T^3 National Instructor
Frankfort, Kentucky

Jerry Cummins
Former President
National Council of Supervisors of Mathematics
Western Springs, Illinois

Mathematical Fluency

Robert M. Capraro
Associate Professor
Texas A&M University
College Station, Texas

Pre-AP

Dixie Ross
Mathematics Teacher
Pflugerville High School
Pflugerville, Texas

Reading and Writing

ReLeah Cossett Lent
Author and Educational Consultant
Morganton, Georgia

Lynn T. Havens
Director of Project CRISS
Kalispell, Montana

Consultants and Reviewers

Each Reviewer reviewed at least two chapters of the Student Edition, giving feedback and suggestions for improving the effectiveness of the mathematics instruction.

Sherri Abel
Mathematics Teacher
Eastside High School
Taylors, South Carolina

Kelli Ball, NBCT
Mathematics Teacher
Owasso 7th Grade Center
Owasso, Oklahoma

Cynthia A. Burke
Mathematics Teacher
Sherrard Junior High School
Wheeling, West Virginia

Patrick M. Cain, Sr.
Assistant Principal
Stanhope Elmore High School
Millbrook, Alabama

Robert D. Cherry
Mathematics Instructor
Wheaton Warrenville South High School
Wheaton, Illinois

Tammy Cisco
8th Grade Mathematics/Algebra Teacher
Celina Middle School
Celina, Ohio

Amber L. Contrano
High School Teacher
Naperville Central High School
Naperville, Illinois

Catherine Creteau
Mathematics Department
Delaware Valley Regional High School
Frenchtown, New Jersey

Glenna L. Crockett
Mathematics Department Chair
Fairland High School
Fairland, Oklahoma

Jami L. Cullen
Mathematics Teacher/Leader
Hilltonia Middle School
Columbus, Ohio

Franco DiPasqua
Director of K-12 Mathematics
West Seneca Central Schools
West Seneca, New York

Kendrick Fearson
Mathematics Department Chair
Amos P. Godby High School
Tallahassee, Florida

Lisa K. Gleason
Mathematics Teacher
Gaylord High School
Gaylord, Michigan

Debra Harley
Director of Math & Science
East Meadow School District
Westbury, New York

Tracie A. Harwood
Mathematics Teacher
Braden River High School
Bradenton, Florida

Bonnie C. Hill
Mathematics Department Chair
Triad High School
Troy, Illinois

Clayton Hutsler
Teacher
Goodwyn Junior High School
Montgomery, Alabama

Gureet Kaur
7th Grade Mathematics Teacher
Quail Hollow Middle School
Charlotte, North Carolina

Rima Seals Kelley, NBCT
Mathematics Teacher/Department Chair
Deerlake Middle School
Tallahassee, Florida

Holly W. Loftis
8th Grade Mathematics Teacher
Greer Middle School
Lyman, South Carolina

Katherine Lohrman
Teacher, Math Specialist, New Teacher Mentor
John Marshall High School
Rochester, New York

Carol Y. Lumpkin
Mathematics Educator
Crayton Middle School
Columbia, South Carolina

Ron Mezzadri
Supervisor of Mathematics K–12
Fair Lawn Public Schools
Fair Lawn, New Jersey

Bonnye C. Newton
SOL Resource Specialist
Amherst County Public Schools
Amherst, Virginia

Kevin Olsen
Mathematics Teacher
River Ridge High School
New Port Richey, Florida

Kara Painter
Mathematics Teacher
Downers Grove South High School
Downers Grove, Illinois

Sheila L. Ruddle, NBCT
Mathematics Teacher, Grades 7 and 8
Pendleton County Middle/High School
Franklin, West Virginia

Angela H. Slate
Mathematics Teacher/Grade 7, Pre-Algebra, Algebra
LeRoy Martin Middle School
Raleigh, North Carolina

Cathy Stellern
Mathematics Teacher
West High School
Knoxville, Tennessee

Dr. Maria J. Vlahos
Mathematics Division Head for Grades 6–12
Barrington High School
Barrington, Illinois

Susan S. Wesson
Mathematics Consultant/Teacher (Retired)
Pilot Butte Middle School
Bend, Oregon

Mary Beth Zinn
High School Mathematics Teacher
Chippewa Valley High Schools
Clinton Township, Michigan

Teacher Handbook

Focus on Algebra 1

- Rigorous mathematics content
- Review for students who need it
- In-depth preparation for college and cutting-edge careers
- Aligned to standards from NCTM, College Board, and American Diploma Project
- Multiple Representations
- Next-generation technology

Bloom Works Inc./Alamy

Table of Contents

True Vertical Alignment in 3 Ways

1 Content Design

Vertical content alignment is a process that ensures you and your students experience an articulated, coherent sequence of content from grade level to grade level. This provides you with the assurance that content is introduced, reinforced, and assessed at appropriate times in the series, eliminating gaps and unnecessary duplication. You are able to target your instruction to student needs because you are not teaching content intended to be covered later or that students have previously mastered.

2 Instructional Design

Our strong vertical alignment in instructional approach from PreKindergarten through Algebra 2 provides a smooth transition for students from elementary to middle school to high school. Our common vocabulary, technology, manipulatives, and lesson planning reduces the confusion students often encounter when transitioning between grade levels without this built-in articulation.

3 Visual Design

The student pages have a consistent visual design from grade to grade. This aids students' transition from elementary school to middle school and from middle school to Algebra 2. Students are more likely to succeed when they are already familiar with how to navigate student pages.

Grades PreK–2

Grades 3–5

5 Keys to Success

1 Backmapping

According to College Board research, about 80% of students who successfully complete Algebra 1 and Geometry by 10th grade attend and succeed in college (Changing the Odds: Factors Increasing Access to College, 1990). ***Math Connects*** **K–8** and the ***Glencoe Mathematics*** high school series were conceived and developed by backmapping with the final result in mind–student success in Algebra 1 and beyond.

2 Balanced, In-Depth Content

The content was developed to specifically target the skills and topics that give students the most difficulty, such as Problem Solving, in each grade span.

Grades K–2	Grades 3–5
1. Problem Solving	**1.** Problem Solving
2. Money	**2.** Fractions
3. Time	**3.** Measurement
4. Measurement	**4.** Decimals
5. Fractions	**5.** Time
6. Computation	**6.** Algebra

Grades 6–8	Grades 9–12
1. Fractions	**1.** Problem Solving
2. Problem Solving	**2.** Fractions
3. Measurement	**3.** Algebra
4. Algebra	**4.** Geometry
5. Computation	**5.** Computation
	6. Probability

– *K–12 Math Market Analysis Survey,* Open Book Publishing, 2006

3 Ongoing Assessment

Diagnostic, formative, and summative assessment includes: data-driven instruction; intervention options; and performance tracking, as well as remediation, acceleration, and enrichment tools throughout the program.

4 Intervention and Differentiated Instruction

A three-tiered Response to Intervention (RtI) is provided.

TIER 1 **Daily Intervention** Options for Differentiated Instruction in the Teacher Edition address concepts for different modalities or learning styles.

TIER 2 **Strategic Intervention** Teachers can use the myriad of intervention tips and ancillary materials, such as the *Strategic Intervention Guide* (1–5) and *Study Guide and Intervention* (6–Algebra 2).

TIER 3 **Intensive Intervention** For students who are two or more years below grade level, ***Math Triumphs*** provides step-by-step instruction, vocabulary support, and data-driven decision making to help students succeed.

5 Professional Development

Many opportunities are included for teacher professional development. Additional learning opportunities in various formats–video, online, and on-site instruction–are fully aligned and articulated from Kindergarten through Algebra 2.

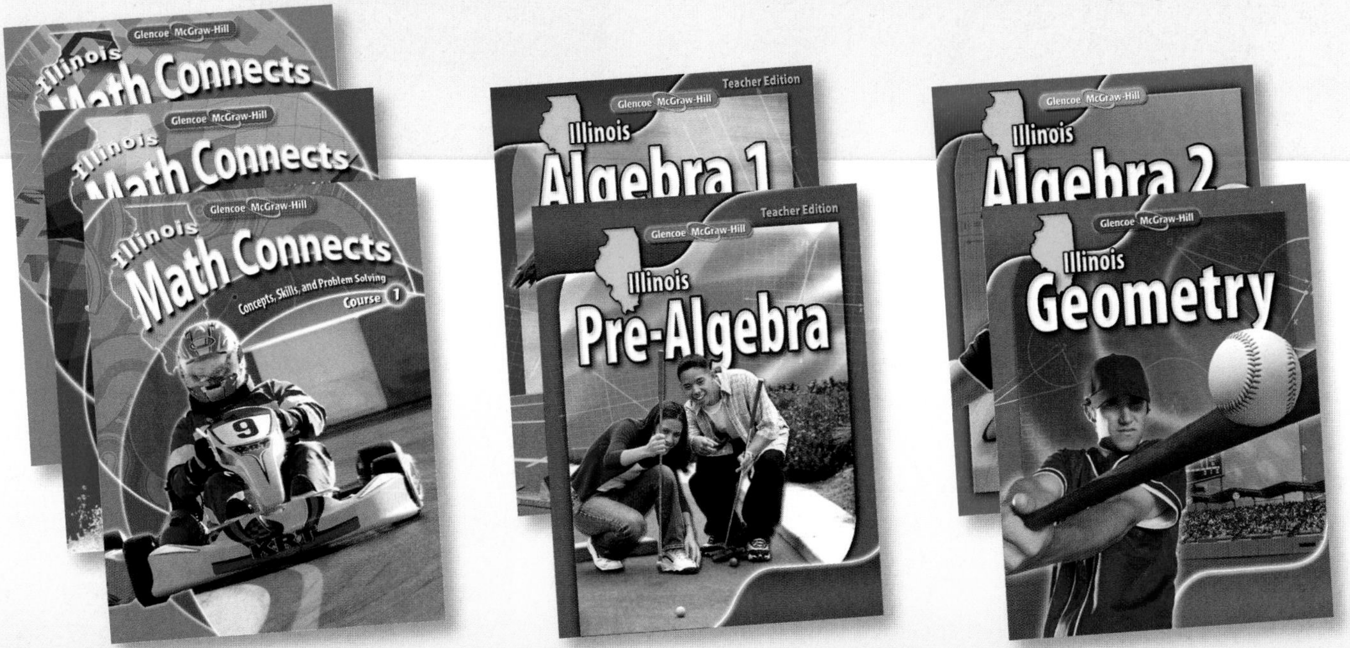

Grades 6–8 | **Pre-Algebra and Algebra 1** | **Geometry and Algebra 2**

The Research Base for Glencoe's High School Mathematics Programs

Continuous research with teachers, students, academicians, and leading experts helps to build a solid foundation for all of our PreK–12 programs, including **Glencoe *Algebra 1*, *Geometry*,** and ***Algebra 2*.**.

1 Program Development Research

- Evaluating state and local standards
- Qualitative market research
- Academic content research

For more detailed information about our classroom research results, please consult the Glencoe *High School Mathematics Program Efficacy Research Report.*

2 Formative Research

- Pedagogical research base
- Classroom field tests
- Teacher advisory boards
- Academic consultants and reviewers

3 Summative Research

- Evidence of increased test scores
- Quasi-experimental program efficacy research
- Longitudinal studies
- Qualitative program evaluations

Access all of our current research at glencoe.com.

Michael Newman/PhotoEdit

Preparing Students for College and the World of Work

According to a recent study, there is a large gap between what students learn in high school and what they are expected to know when they begin college (ACT, 2007). Because of this gap, it is reported that 42% of students entering community colleges and 20% of freshmen in four-year colleges enroll in at least one remedial course (NCES, 2004b). Because of the high economic cost of remedial education, eleven states have recently passed laws preventing or discouraging public four-year colleges from offering remedial courses (Jenkins & Boswell, 2002).

Does remediation work? Some research has shown that the need for remediation is the leading predictor that a student will drop out of college. While 58% of students who need no remedial courses earn a bachelor's degree within eight years, only 17% of students who enroll in remedial reading courses receive a bachelor's degree within the same time period. In fact, students enrolling in those courses are 41% more likely to drop out of college.

How Can Students be Better Prepared for College?

A strong high school curriculum is a good predictor of college readiness (Adelman, 2006). Students who take at least three years of college-preparatory mathematics using programs like *Glencoe Algebra 1, Glencoe Geometry,* and *Glencoe Algebra 2* are less likely to need remedial courses than students who do not (Abraham & Creech, 2002).

What is College Readiness?

The following definition of college readiness was developed by David Conley at the University of Oregon.

- **Habits of Mind** These are the skills needed for learning college-level content. These critical thinking skills include analysis, interpretation, problem solving, and reasoning. Each day, students who use Glencoe mathematics programs have the opportunity to hone critical higher-order thinking skills through the use of **H.O.T. Problems**.

- **Key Content Knowledge** *Glencoe Algebra 1, Glencoe Geometry,* and *Glencoe Algebra 2* have been aligned to rigorous state and national standards, including the NCTM Principles & Standards for School Mathematics, the College Board Standards for College Success, and the American Diploma Project's Benchmarks. Correlations to these standards can be found at glencoe.com.

- **Academic Behaviors** These include general skills such as reading comprehension, time management, note-taking, and metacognition. Throughout each Glencoe program, **Reading Math** tips and **Vocabulary Links** help students with reading comprehension in mathematics. Glencoe's new **Study Notebooks** are designed to help students hone note-taking skills by helping them organize information for better retention. And the **Anticipation Guides** in the Chapter Resource Masters aid students with metacognition by analyzing what they know before starting the chapter and what they know once it has been completed.

- **Contextual Skills** These are practical skills like understanding the admissions process and financial aid, placement testing, and communicating with professors. Throughout Glencoe mathematics programs, students are required to write, explain, justify, prove, and analyze. Along with **Writing in Math** exercises that help students improve their mathematical writing skills, these exercises help students communicate more effectively.

What About Students Who Don't Plan to Go to College?

In today's technological world, math is no longer just for students who go to college. ACT examined the skills needed to succeed as a freshman in college and compared them to skills needed for job-training programs one might take to train for a job that supports a family of four. They found that students need to be educated to a comparable level in algebra, geometry, data analysis, and statistics for success in either situation. (ACT, 2006)

And this is not only true for technological careers. According to the Associated General Contractors of America, electricians, pipe fitters, sheet metal workers, draftspersons, and surveyors need algebra, geometry, trigonometry, and physics to be successful. (Achieve, 2007)

Does College Readiness Lead to Success in the World of Work?

Work readiness is the ability of entry-level employees to add value in front-line jobs. The U.S. Chamber of Commerce has created a National Work Readiness Credential that involves nine sub-skills, one of which is using math to solve problems. In a recent study, 53.5% of employers who responded reported that high school graduate entrants into the workforce are "deficient" in mathematics, while 30.4% felt that knowledge of mathematics is "very important." (*Are They Really Ready to Work?*, 2006)

According to J. Willard Marriott, Jr., Chairman and CEO of Marriott International, Inc., "Our nation's long-term ability to succeed in exporting to the growing global marketplace hinges on the abilities of today's students." If excellence is the standard for global competitiveness, students leaving high school must go with the knowledge and skills required to make an impact in today's society. To this end, *Glencoe Algebra 1*, *Glencoe Geometry*, and *Glencoe Algebra 2* have been designed to prepare students for success both in and after high school, no matter where their journey takes them.

Sources

Abraham, A. & Creech, J. (2002). *Reducing Remedial Education.* Atlanta, GA: Southern Regional Education Board.

Achieve, Inc. (2007). *Do All Students Need Challenging Math in High School?*

ACT, Inc. (2006). *Readiness for College and Readiness for Work: Same or Different?* Iowa City, IA.

ACT, Inc. (2007). *National Curriculum Survey.* Iowa City, IA.

Adelman, C. (2006). *The Toolbox Revisited: Paths to Degree Completion from High School Through College.* Washington, DC: U.S. Department of Education.

The Conference Board, Corporate Voices for Working Families, the Partnership for 21st Century Skills, and the Society for Human Resource Management (2006). *Are They Really Ready to Work?*

Conley, D. (2007). *Toward a More Comprehensive Conception of College Readiness.* Eugene, OR: Educational Policy Improvement Center.

Jenkins, D., & Boswell, K. (2002) *State Policies on Community College Remedial Education.* Denver, CO: Education Commission of the States.

National Center for Education Statistics (NCES) (2004). *The Condition of Education 2004: Remediation and Degree Completion.* Washington, DC: U.S. Department of Education.

Teacher Handbook

Program Philosophy

Balanced Instruction, Vertically Aligned from Grade PreK through Algebra 2

The vertical alignment of ***Math Connects*** PreK–8 through ***Algebra 2*** incorporates a balance of instruction throughout. These programs provide students a balanced approach to mathematics by:

- investigating concepts and building conceptual understanding.
- developing, reinforcing, and mastering computational and procedural skills.
- applying mathematics to problem-solving situations.

This sequence of Student Edition pages illustrates the vertically-aligned development of the conceptual understanding and corresponding computational and procedural skills for an important algebra topic.

Primary Students use two-color counters to model addition sentences. This activity forms a basis for future understanding of and success in solving algebraic equations.

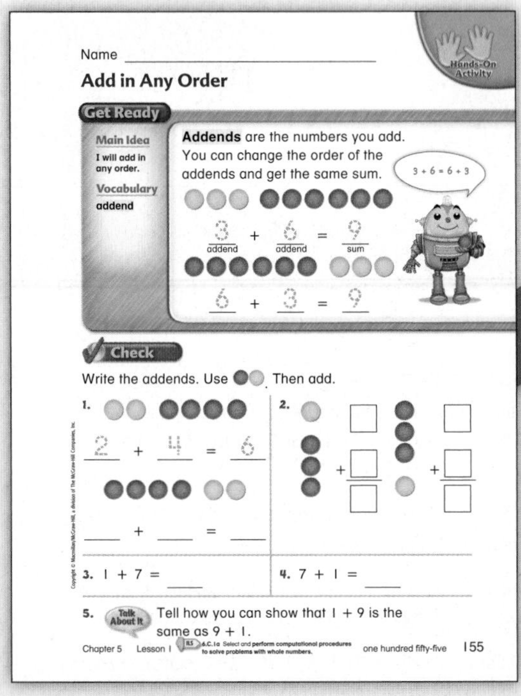

Name ______________________

Add in Any Order

Get Ready

Main Idea
I will add in any order.

Vocabulary
addend

Addends are the numbers you add. You can change the order of the addends and get the same sum.

3 + 6 = 9 (addend, addend, sum)

6 + 3 = 9

Check

Write the addends. Use counters. Then add.

1. 2 + 4 = 6; ___ + ___ = ___
2.
3. 1 + 7 = ___
4. 7 + 1 = ___
5. Talk About It: Tell how you can show that 1 + 9 is the same as 9 + 1.

Chapter 5 Lesson 1 ILS 6.C.1a Select and perform computational procedures to solve problems with whole numbers. one hundred fifty-five 155

Copyright © Macmillan/McGraw-Hill, a division of The McGraw-Hill Companies, Inc.

Math Connects, Grade 1, Student Edition, page 155

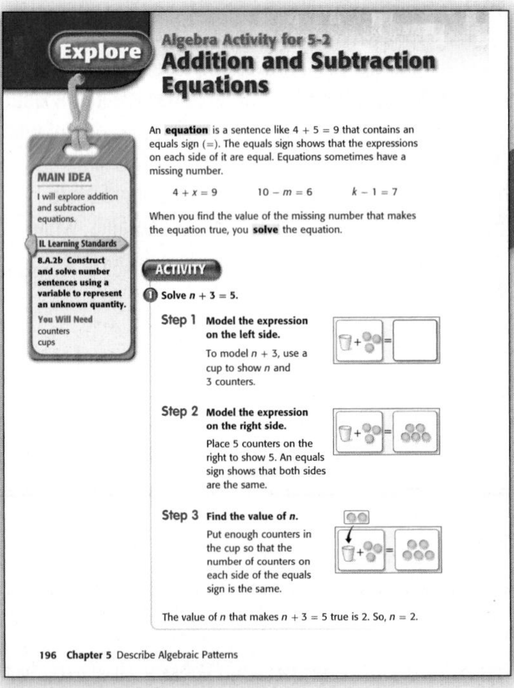

Explore

Algebra Activity for 5-2

Addition and Subtraction Equations

MAIN IDEA
I will explore addition and subtraction equations.

IL Learning Standards
8.A.2b Construct and solve number sentences using a variable to represent an unknown quantity.

You Will Need
counters
cups

An **equation** is a sentence like $4 + 5 = 9$ that contains an equals sign (=). The equals sign shows that the expressions on each side of it are equal. Equations sometimes have a missing number.

$4 + x = 9$ $\quad 10 - m = 6$ $\quad k - 1 = 7$

When you find the value of the missing number that makes the equation true, you **solve** the equation.

ACTIVITY

1 **Solve $n + 3 = 5$.**

Step 1 **Model the expression on the left side.** To model $n + 3$, use a cup to show n and 3 counters.

Step 2 **Model the expression on the right side.** Place 5 counters on the right to show 5. An equals sign shows that both sides are the same.

Step 3 **Find the value of n.** Put enough counters in the cup so that the number of counters on each side of the equals sign is the same.

The value of n that makes $n + 3 = 5$ true is 2. So, $n = 2$.

196 **Chapter 5** Describe Algebraic Patterns

Math Connects, Grade 4, Student Edition, page 196

Intermediate Students build on their experience with counters to using cups and counters to model and solve addition and subtraction equations. The exercises are designed to help students bridge the gap from using cups and counters to solving equations symbolically.

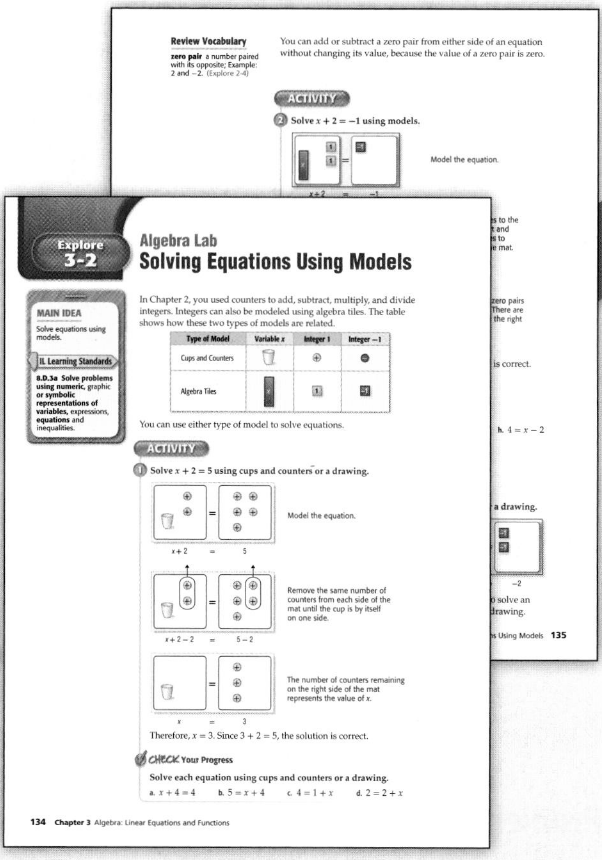

Review Vocabulary

zero pair a number paired with its opposite; Example: 2 and −2. (Explore 2-4)

You can add or subtract a zero pair from either side of an equation without changing its value, because the value of a zero pair is zero.

ACTIVITY

2 Solve $x + 2 = -1$ using models.

Explore 3-2

Algebra Lab

Solving Equations Using Models

MAIN IDEA

Solve equations using models.

IL Learning Standards

8.D.3a Solve problems using numeric, graphic or symbolic representations of variables, expressions, equations and inequalities.

In Chapter 2, you used counters to add, subtract, multiply, and divide integers. Integers can also be modeled using algebra tiles. The table shows how these two types of models are related.

Type of Model	Variable x	Integer 1	Integer −1
Cups and Counters			
Algebra Tiles			

You can use either type of model to solve equations.

ACTIVITY

1 Solve $x + 2 = 5$ using cups and counters or a drawing.

Model the equation.

Remove the same number of counters from each side of the mat until the cup is by itself on one side.

The number of counters remaining on the right side of the mat represents the value of x.

Therefore, $x = 3$. Since $3 + 2 = 5$, the solution is correct.

CHECK Your Progress

Solve each equation using cups and counters or a drawing.

a. $x + 4 = 4$ b. $5 = x + 4$ c. $4 = 1 + x$ d. $2 = 2 + x$

134 Chapter 3 Algebra: Linear Equations and Functions

Math Connects, Course 2,
Student Edition, pages 134–135

Middle School Students represent the variable *x* as a cup, as a counter, or as a written *x*. In this Algebra Lab, students make the transition from cups and counters to the more abstract algebra tiles. In the next lesson, students solve simple equations symbolically.

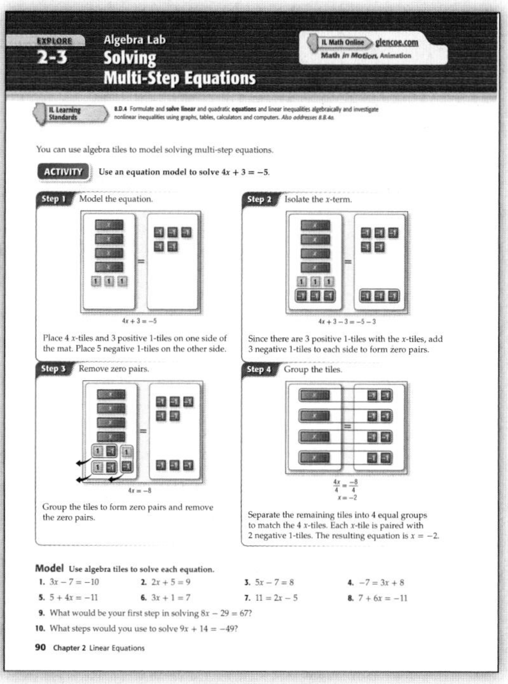

EXPLORE 2-3

Algebra Lab

Solving Multi-Step Equations

You can use algebra tiles to model solving multi-step equations.

ACTIVITY Use an equation model to solve $4x + 3 = -5$.

Step 1 Model the equation.

Place 4 x-tiles and 3 positive 1-tiles on one side of the mat. Place 5 negative 1-tiles on the other side.

Step 2 Isolate the x-term.

Since there are 3 positive 1-tiles with the x-tiles, add 3 negative 1-tiles to each side to form zero pairs.

Step 3 Remove zero pairs.

Group the tiles to form zero pairs and remove the zero pairs.

Step 4 Group the tiles.

Separate the remaining tiles into 4 equal groups to match the 4 x-tiles. Each x-tile is paired with 2 negative 1-tiles. The resulting equation is $x = -2$.

Model Use algebra tiles to solve each equation.

1. $3x - 7 = -10$ 2. $2x + 5 = 9$ 3. $5x - 7 = 8$ 4. $-7 = 3x + 8$
5. $5 + 4x = -11$ 6. $3x + 1 = 7$ 7. $11 = 2x - 5$ 8. $7 + 6x = -11$
9. What would be your first step in solving $8x - 29 = 67$?
10. What steps would you use to solve $9x + 14 = -49$?

90 Chapter 2 Linear Equations

Algebra 1,
Student Edition, page 90

Algebra 1 Students continue the use of algebra tiles to investigate solving multi-step equations. In the next lesson, students apply the procedure developed in the Algebra Lab to a symbolic approach.

Continuity of Instruction The instructional sequence described demonstrates the power of backward mapping from the desired result, success in Algebra 1 and beyond. This process of development avoids gaps and overlaps between grade levels and ensures that at each grade level the concepts and skills are built on the strong foundation developed in previous grades. The same approach was used across all strands throughout the entire PreK–12 series.

Teacher Handbook

Program Philosophy

Balanced Approach

- Concepts
- Skills
- Problem solving

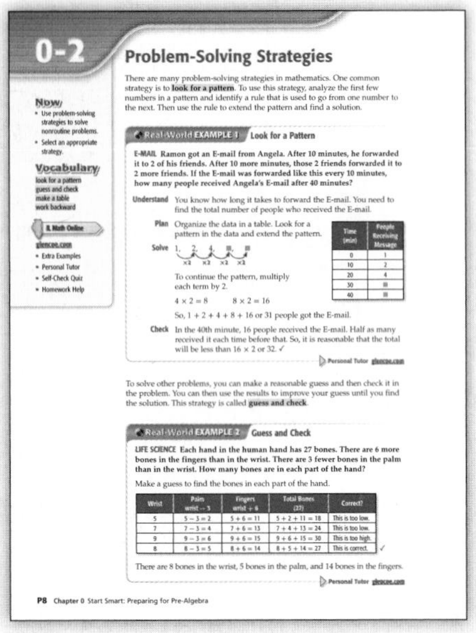

0-2

Problem-Solving Strategies

There are many problem-solving strategies in mathematics. One common strategy is to **look for a pattern**. To use this strategy, analyze the first few numbers in a pattern and identify a rule that is used to go from one number to the next. Then use the rule to extend the pattern and find a solution.

Now
- Use problem-solving strategies to solve nonroutine problems.
- Select an appropriate strategy.

Vocabulary
look for a pattern
guess and check
make a table
work backward

Math Online
glencoe.com
- Extra Examples
- Personal Tutor
- Self-Check Quiz
- Homework Help

Real-World EXAMPLE 1 Look for a Pattern

E-MAIL Ramon got an E-mail from Angela. After 10 minutes, he forwarded it to 2 of his friends. After 10 more minutes, those 2 friends forwarded it to 2 more friends. If the E-mail was forwarded like this every 10 minutes, how many people received Angela's E-mail after 40 minutes?

Understand You know how long it takes to forward the E-mail. You need to find the total number of people who received the E-mail.

Plan Organize the data in a table. Look for a pattern in the data and extend the pattern.

Time (min)	People Receiving Message
0	1
10	2
20	4
30	■
40	■

Solve 1, 2, 4, ■, ■ (×2 ×2 ×2 ×2)

To continue the pattern, multiply each term by 2.

$4 \times 2 = 8$ $8 \times 2 = 16$

So, $1 + 2 + 4 + 8 + 16$ or 31 people got the E-mail.

Check In the 40th minute, 16 people received the E-mail. Half as many received it each time before that. So, it is reasonable that the total will be less than 16×2 or 32. ✓

Personal Tutor glencoe.com

To solve other problems, you can make a reasonable guess and then check it in the problem. You can then use the results to improve your guess until you find the solution. This strategy is called **guess and check**.

Real-World EXAMPLE 2 Guess and Check

LIFE SCIENCE Each hand in the human hand has 27 bones. There are 6 more bones in the fingers than in the wrist. There are 3 fewer bones in the palm than in the wrist. How many bones are in each part of the hand?

Make a guess to find the bones in each part of the hand.

Wrist	Palm wrist − 3	Fingers wrist + 6	Total Bones (27)	Correct?
5	5 − 3 = 2	5 + 6 = 11	5 + 2 + 11 = 18	This is too low.
7	7 − 3 = 4	7 + 6 = 13	7 + 4 + 13 = 24	This is too low.
9	9 − 3 = 6	9 + 6 = 15	9 + 6 + 15 = 30	This is too high.
8	8 − 3 = 5	8 + 6 = 14	8 + 5 + 14 = 27	This is correct. ✓

There are 8 bones in the wrist, 5 bones in the palm, and 14 bones in the fingers.

Personal Tutor glencoe.com

P8 Chapter 0 Start Smart: Preparing for Pre-Algebra

Pre-Algebra
Student Edition, page P8

Relevant Problem Solving

Students are provided with ongoing opportunities to apply their math skills and solve problems using visual thinking, logical reasoning, number sense, and algebra.

Problem-Solving Strategies

Problem-Solving Strategy Lessons help students learn different problem-solving strategies for attacking word problems.

Real-World Problem Solving, Algebra 1

Real-World Problem-Solving Graphic Novels

Motivating, teen-relevant problem solving in graphic novel format provides practice with number sense, algebraic thinking, geometry, measurement, statistics and probability, and mathematical reasoning.

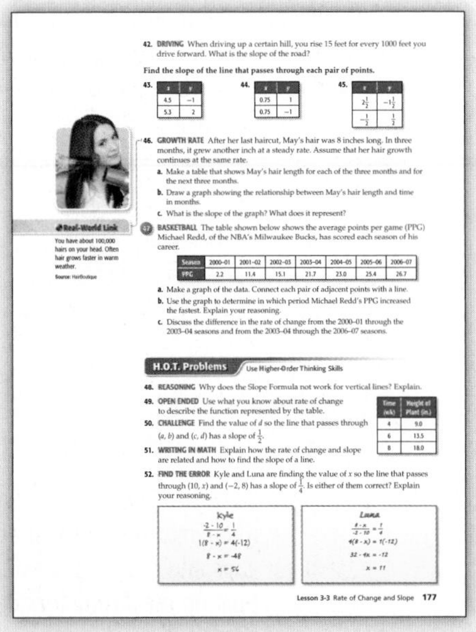

42. **DRIVING** When driving up a certain hill, you rise 15 feet for every 1000 feet you drive forward. What is the slope of the road?

Find the slope of the line that passes through each pair of points.

43.

x	y
4.5	−1
5.3	2

44.

x	y
0.75	1
0.75	−1

45.

x	y
$2\frac{1}{2}$	$-1\frac{1}{2}$
$-\frac{1}{2}$	$\frac{1}{2}$

46. **GROWTH RATE** After her last haircut, May's hair was 8 inches long. In three months, it grew another inch at a steady rate. Assume that her hair growth continues at the same rate.
   a. Make a table that shows May's hair length for each of the three months and for the next three months.
   b. Draw a graph showing the relationship between May's hair length and time in months.
   c. What is the slope of the graph? What does it represent?

Real-World Link
You have about 100,000 hairs on your head. Often hair grows faster in warm weather.
Source: HairBoutique

47. **BASKETBALL** The table shown below shows the average points per game (PPG) Michael Redd, of the NBA's Milwaukee Bucks, has scored each season of his career.

Season	2000–01	2001–02	2002–03	2003–04	2004–05	2005–06	2006–07
PPG	2.2	11.4	15.1	21.7	23.0	25.4	26.7

   a. Make a graph of the data. Connect each pair of adjacent points with a line.
   b. Use the graph to determine in which period Michael Redd's PPG increased the fastest. Explain your reasoning.
   c. Discuss the difference in the rate of change from the 2000–01 through the 2003–04 seasons and from the 2003–04 through the 2006–07 seasons.

H.O.T. Problems Use Higher-Order Thinking Skills

48. **REASONING** Why does the Slope Formula not work for vertical lines? Explain.
49. **OPEN ENDED** Use what you know about rate of change to describe the function represented by the table.

Time (wk)	Height of Plant (in.)
4	9.0
6	13.5
8	18.0

50. **CHALLENGE** Find the value of d so the line that passes through (a, b) and (c, d) has a slope of $\frac{1}{2}$.
51. **WRITING IN MATH** Explain how the rate of change and slope are related and how to find the slope of a line.
52. **FIND THE ERROR** Kyle and Luna are finding the value of x so the line that passes through $(10, x)$ and $(-2, 8)$ has a slope of $\frac{1}{4}$. Is either of them correct? Explain your reasoning.

Kyle
$\frac{-2-10}{8-x} = \frac{1}{4}$
$1(8-x) = 4(-12)$
$8-x = -48$
$x = 56$

Luna
$\frac{8-x}{-2-10} = \frac{1}{4}$
$4(8-x) = 1(-12)$
$32-4x = -12$
$x = 11$

Lesson 3-3 Rate of Change and Slope 177

Algebra 1
Student Edition, page 177

H.O.T. Problems

H.O.T. Problems require students to use **Higher Order Thinking** skills to solve problems.

Multiple Representations

Problems using **Multiple Representations** help students visualize concepts and increase understanding. Verbal, numerical, algebraic, tabular, graphical, and analytical representations can be found throughout.

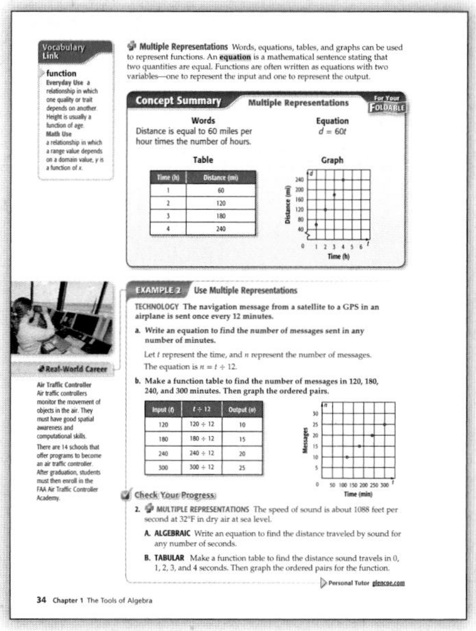
Vocabulary Link

function
Everyday Use a relationship in which one quality or trait depends on another. Height is usually a function of age.
Math Use a relationship in which a range value depends on a domain value, y is a function of x.

Multiple Representations Words, equations, tables, and graphs can be used to represent functions. An **equation** is a mathematical sentence stating that two quantities are equal. Functions are often written as equations with two variables—one to represent the input and one to represent the output.

Concept Summary Multiple Representations — For Your FOLDABLE

Words
Distance is equal to 60 miles per hour times the number of hours.

Equation
$d = 60t$

Table

Time (h)	Distance (mi)
1	60
2	120
3	180
4	240

Graph

EXAMPLE 2 Use Multiple Representations

TECHNOLOGY **The navigation message from a satellite to a GPS in an airplane is sent once every 12 minutes.**

a. **Write an equation to find the number of messages sent in any number of minutes.**

Let t represent the time, and n represent the number of messages. The equation is $n = t \div 12$.

b. **Make a function table to find the number of messages in 120, 180, 240, and 300 minutes. Then graph the ordered pairs.**

Input (t)	$t \div 12$	Output (n)
120	$120 \div 12$	10
180	$180 \div 12$	15
240	$240 \div 12$	20
300	$300 \div 12$	25

Real-World Career

Air Traffic Controller Air traffic controllers monitor the movement of objects in the air. They must have good spatial awareness and computational skills.

There are 14 schools that offer programs to become an air traffic controller. After graduation, students must then enroll in the FAA Air Traffic Controller Academy.

Check Your Progress

2. MULTIPLE REPRESENTATIONS The speed of sound is about 1088 feet per second at 32°F in dry air at sea level.

A. **ALGEBRAIC** Write an equation to find the distance traveled by sound for any number of seconds.

B. **TABULAR** Make a function table to find the distance sound travels in 0, 1, 2, 3, and 4 seconds. Then graph the ordered pairs for the function.

Personal Tutor glencoe.com

34 Chapter 1 The Tools of Algebra

Pre-Algebra
Student Edition, page 34

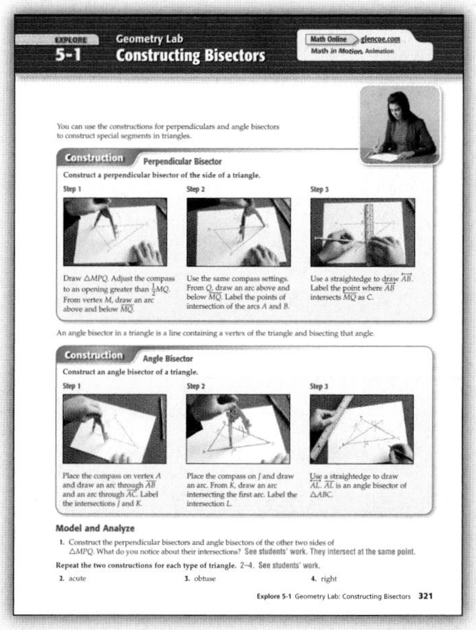
EXPLORE 5-1 Geometry Lab
Constructing Bisectors

Math Online glencoe.com
Math in Motion, Animation

You can use the constructions for perpendiculars and angle bisectors to construct special segments in triangles.

Construction Perpendicular Bisector

Construct a perpendicular bisector of the side of a triangle.

Step 1
Draw $\triangle MPQ$. Adjust the compass to an opening greater than $\frac{1}{2}MQ$. From vertex M, draw an arc above and below $\overline{MQ}$.

Step 2
Use the same compass settings. From Q, draw an arc above and below $\overline{MQ}$. Label the points of intersection of the arcs A and B.

Step 3
Use a straightedge to draw $\overleftrightarrow{AB}$. Label the point where $\overleftrightarrow{AB}$ intersects $\overline{MQ}$ as C.

An angle bisector in a triangle is a line containing a vertex of the triangle and bisecting that angle.

Construction Angle Bisector

Construct an angle bisector of a triangle.

Step 1
Place the compass on vertex A and draw an arc through $\overline{AB}$ and an arc through $\overline{AC}$. Label the intersections J and K.

Step 2
Place the compass on J and draw an arc. From K, draw an arc intersecting the first arc. Label the intersection L.

Step 3
Use a straightedge to draw $\overline{AL}$. $\overline{AL}$ is an angle bisector of $\triangle ABC$.

Model and Analyze

1. Construct the perpendicular bisectors and angle bisectors of the other two sides of $\triangle MPQ$. What do you notice about their intersections? See students' work. They intersect at the same point.

Repeat the two constructions for each type of triangle. 2–4. See students' work.

2. acute
3. obtuse
4. right

Explore 5-1 Geometry Lab: Constructing Bisectors 321

Geometry
Student Edition, page 321

Hands-On Labs

Some labs introduce mathematical topics, while others extend topics just presented. **Algebra, Geometry, Measurement, Statistics,** and **Probability** labs use models to bridge the gap between concrete understanding and mathematical symbolism.

Math in Motion

Math in Motion are online illustrations of key concepts through Animations, Interactive Labs, and BrainPOPs®.

Graphing Technology Labs

Graphing technology labs allow students to gain understanding of mathematics through graphical representations.

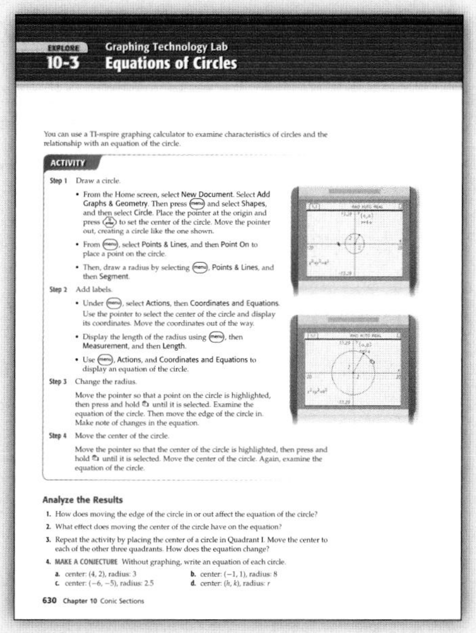
EXPLORE 10-3 Graphing Technology Lab
Equations of Circles

You can use a TI-nspire graphing calculator to examine characteristics of circles and the relationship with an equation of the circle.

ACTIVITY

Step 1 Draw a circle.

- From the Home screen, select New Document. Select Add Graphs & Geometry. Then press (menu) and select Shapes, and then select Circle. Place the pointer at the origin and press (enter) to set the center of the circle. Move the pointer out, creating a circle like the one shown.
- From (menu), select Points & Lines, and then Point On to place a point on the circle.
- Then, draw a radius by selecting (menu), Points & Lines, and then Segment.

Step 2 Add labels.

- Under (menu), select Actions, then Coordinates and Equations. Use the pointer to select the center of the circle and display its coordinates. Move the coordinates out of the way.
- Display the length of the radius using (menu), then Measurement, and then Length.
- Use (menu), Actions, and Coordinates and Equations to display an equation of the circle.

Step 3 Change the radius.

Move the pointer so that a point on the circle is highlighted, then press and hold until it is selected. Examine the equation of the circle. Then move the edge of the circle in. Make note of changes in the equation.

Step 4 Move the center of the circle.

Move the pointer so that the center of the circle is highlighted, then press and hold until it is selected. Move the center of the circle. Again, examine the equation of the circle.

Analyze the Results

1. How does moving the edge of the circle in or out affect the equation of the circle?
2. What effect does moving the center of the circle have on the equation?
3. Repeat the activity by placing the center of a circle in Quadrant I. Move the center to each of the other three quadrants. How does the equation change?
4. MAKE A CONJECTURE Without graphing, write an equation of each circle.
   a. center: (4, 2), radius: 3
   b. center: (−1, 1), radius: 8
   c. center: (−6, −5), radius: 2.5
   d. center: (h, k), radius: r

630 Chapter 10 Conic Sections

Algebra 2
Student Edition, page 630

Comprehensive Assessment System

Data-Driven Decision Making

Frequent and meaningful assessment of student progress is offered within the curriculum structure and printed teacher support materials. See pages T22 and T23 for digital assessment solutions.

PRINT SOLUTIONS

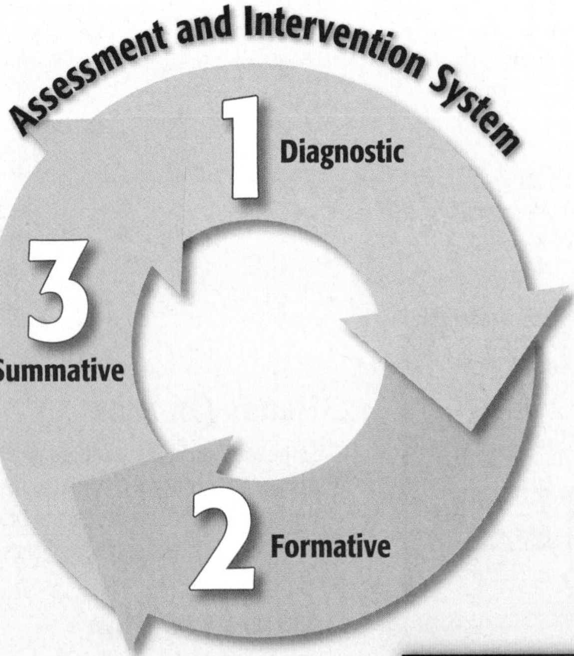

1 Diagnostic

Initial Assessment Assess students' knowledge **at the beginning of the year** with the *Diagnostic and Placement Tests*. This booklet will help you determine whether your students need additional materials and resources to meet grade-level standards.

Entry–Level Assessment Assess students' prior knowledge **at the beginning of a chapter or lesson** with one of the following options.

Student Edition
- Get Ready

Teacher Edition
- Differentiated Instruction
- 5-Minute Check

Additional Resources
- Chapter Resource Masters, Anticipation Guide

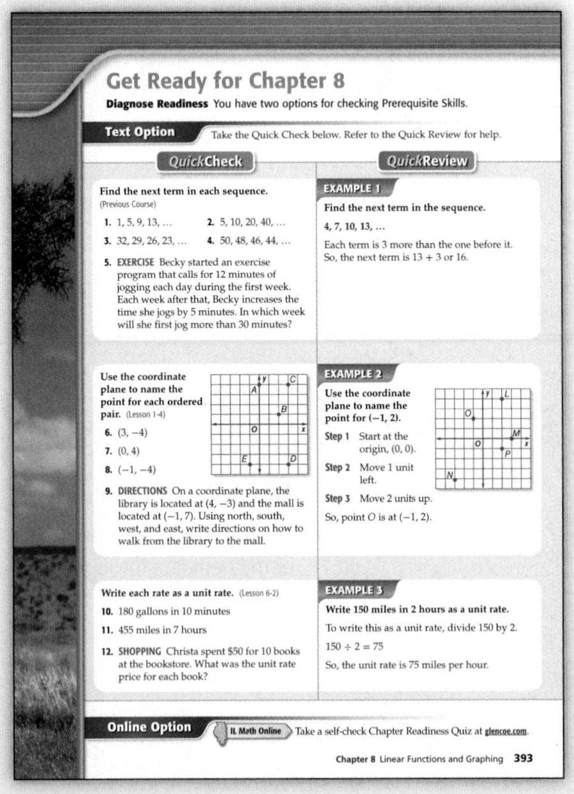

Get Ready for Chapter 8

Diagnose Readiness You have two options for checking Prerequisite Skills.

Text Option Take the Quick Check below. Refer to the Quick Review for help.

*Quick*Check

Find the next term in each sequence. (Previous Course)

1. 1, 5, 9, 13, …
2. 5, 10, 20, 40, …
3. 32, 29, 26, 23, …
4. 50, 48, 46, 44, …
5. EXERCISE Becky started an exercise program that calls for 12 minutes of jogging each day during the first week. Each week after that, Becky increases the time she jogs by 5 minutes. In which week will she first jog more than 30 minutes?

Use the coordinate plane to name the point for each ordered pair. (Lesson 1-4)

6. (3, −4)
7. (0, 4)
8. (−1, −4)
9. DIRECTIONS On a coordinate plane, the library is located at (4, −3) and the mall is located at (−1, 7). Using north, south, west, and east, write directions on how to walk from the library to the mall.

Write each rate as a unit rate. (Lesson 6-2)

10. 180 gallons in 10 minutes
11. 455 miles in 7 hours
12. SHOPPING Christa spent $50 for 10 books at the bookstore. What was the unit rate price for each book?

*Quick*Review

EXAMPLE 1

Find the next term in the sequence.

4, 7, 10, 13, …

Each term is 3 more than the one before it. So, the next term is 13 + 3 or 16.

EXAMPLE 2

Use the coordinate plane to name the point for (−1, 2).

Step 1 Start at the origin, (0, 0).

Step 2 Move 1 unit left.

Step 3 Move 2 units up.

So, point *O* is at (−1, 2).

EXAMPLE 3

Write 150 miles in 2 hours as a unit rate.

To write this as a unit rate, divide 150 by 2.

150 ÷ 2 = 75

So, the unit rate is 75 miles per hour.

Online Option IL Math Online Take a self-check Chapter Readiness Quiz at glencoe.com.

Chapter 8 Linear Functions and Graphing 393

Pre-Algebra
Student Edition, page 393

2 Formative

Progress Monitoring Determine if students are progressing adequately as you teach each lesson. Use the assessments to differentiate lesson instruction and practice.

Student Edition

- Check Your Understanding
- Find the Error
- Writing in Math
- Mid-Chapter Quiz
- Study Guide and Review
- Foldables®

Teacher Edition

- Differentiated Instruction
- Step 4 (Assess) of the Teaching Plan
- Response to Intervention

Additional Resources

Chapter Resource Masters

- Mid-Chapter Test
- 4 Quizzes
- Standardized Test Practice

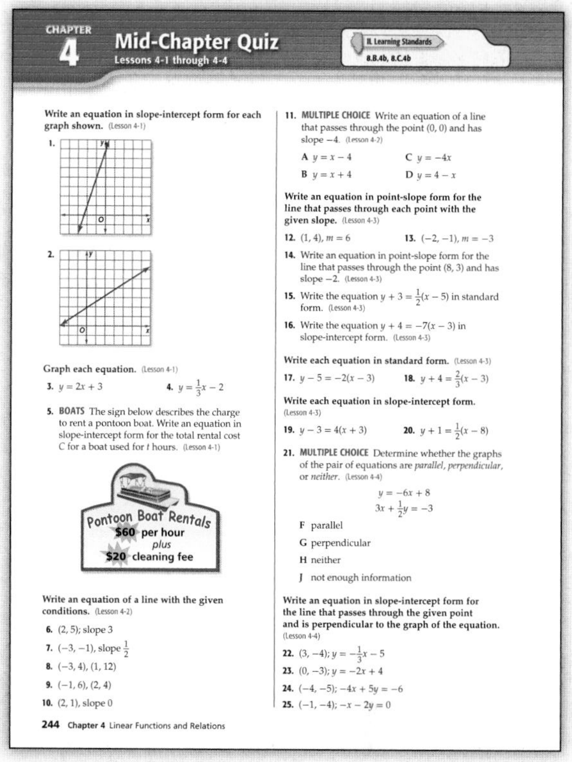

CHAPTER 4 **Mid-Chapter Quiz**
Lessons 4-1 through 4-4

IL Learning Standards 8.B.4b, 8.C.4b

Write an equation in slope-intercept form for each graph shown. (Lesson 4-1)

1.

2.

Graph each equation. (Lesson 4-1)

3. $y = 2x + 3$
4. $y = \frac{1}{3}x - 2$

5. **BOATS** The sign below describes the charge to rent a pontoon boat. Write an equation in slope-intercept form for the total rental cost C for a boat used for t hours. (Lesson 4-1)

Pontoon Boat Rentals
$60 per hour
plus
$20 cleaning fee

Write an equation of a line with the given conditions. (Lesson 4-2)

6. (2, 5); slope 3
7. (−3, −1), slope $\frac{1}{2}$
8. (−3, 4), (1, 12)
9. (−1, 6), (2, 4)
10. (2, 1), slope 0

11. **MULTIPLE CHOICE** Write an equation of a line that passes through the point (0, 0) and has slope −4. (Lesson 4-2)
A $y = x - 4$ C $y = -4x$
B $y = x + 4$ D $y = 4 - x$

Write an equation in point-slope form for the line that passes through each point with the given slope. (Lesson 4-3)

12. (1, 4), $m = 6$
13. (−2, −1), $m = -3$
14. Write an equation in point-slope form for the line that passes through the point (8, 3) and has slope −2. (Lesson 4-3)
15. Write the equation $y + 3 = \frac{1}{2}(x - 5)$ in standard form. (Lesson 4-3)
16. Write the equation $y + 4 = -7(x - 3)$ in slope-intercept form. (Lesson 4-3)

Write each equation in standard form. (Lesson 4-3)

17. $y - 5 = -2(x - 3)$
18. $y + 4 = \frac{2}{3}(x - 3)$

Write each equation in slope-intercept form. (Lesson 4-3)

19. $y - 3 = 4(x + 3)$
20. $y + 1 = \frac{1}{2}(x - 8)$

21. **MULTIPLE CHOICE** Determine whether the graphs of the pair of equations are *parallel*, *perpendicular*, or *neither*. (Lesson 4-4)

$$y = -6x + 8$$
$$3x + \frac{1}{2}y = -3$$

F parallel
G perpendicular
H neither
J not enough information

Write an equation in slope-intercept form for the line that passes through the given point and is perpendicular to the graph of the equation. (Lesson 4-4)

22. (3, −4); $y = -\frac{1}{3}x - 5$
23. (0, −3); $y = -2x + 4$
24. (−4, −5); $-4x + 5y = -6$
25. (−1, −4); $-x - 2y = 0$

244 Chapter 4 Linear Functions and Relations

Algebra 1
Student Edition, page 244

3 Summative

Summative Evaluation Assess student success in learning the concepts in each chapter.

Student Edition

- Practice Test
- Standardized Test Practice
- Foldables™

Teacher Edition

- Response to Intervention

Additional Resources

Chapter Resource Masters

- Vocabulary Test
- 6 Leveled Chapter Tests
- Extended Response Test

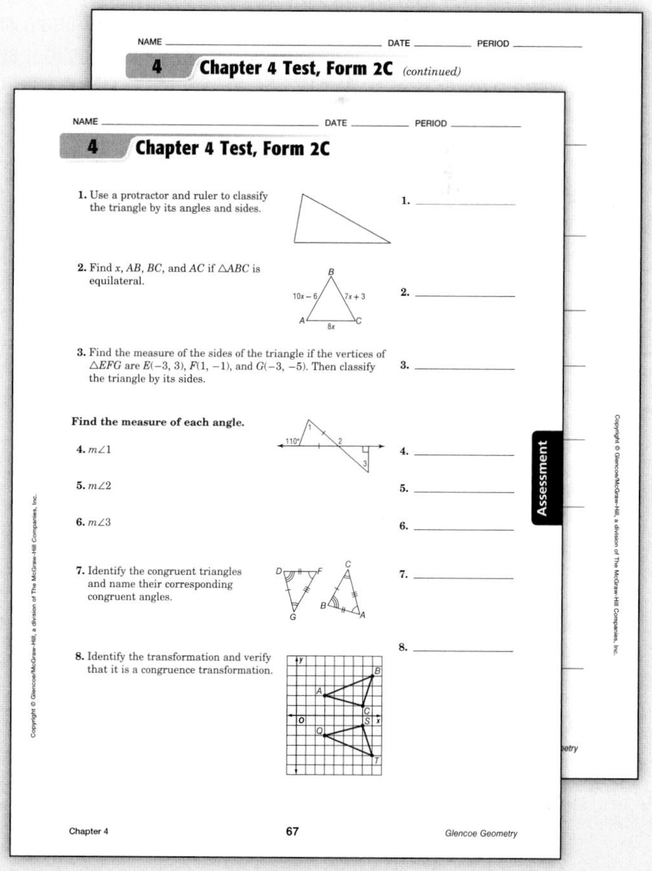

NAME ________ DATE ________ PERIOD ________

4 **Chapter 4 Test, Form 2C** *(continued)*

NAME ________ DATE ________ PERIOD ________

4 **Chapter 4 Test, Form 2C**

1. Use a protractor and ruler to classify the triangle by its angles and sides. 1. ________
2. Find x, AB, BC, and AC if $\triangle ABC$ is equilateral. 2. ________

3. Find the measure of the sides of the triangle if the vertices of $\triangle EFG$ are $E(-3, 3)$, $F(1, -1)$, and $G(-3, -5)$. Then classify the triangle by its sides. 3. ________

Find the measure of each angle.

4. $m\angle 1$ 4. ________
5. $m\angle 2$ 5. ________
6. $m\angle 3$ 6. ________
7. Identify the congruent triangles and name their corresponding congruent angles. 7. ________

8. Identify the transformation and verify that it is a congruence transformation. 8. ________

Assessment

Chapter 4 67 Glencoe Geometry

Geometry
Chapter 4 Resource Masters, pages 67–68

Comprehensive Assessment System

Data-Driven Decision Making

Digital assessment options are provided to create, customize, administer, and instantly score a variety of assessments. These digital solutions offer the same quality assessments and reporting as the print resources in easy-to-use technology tools.

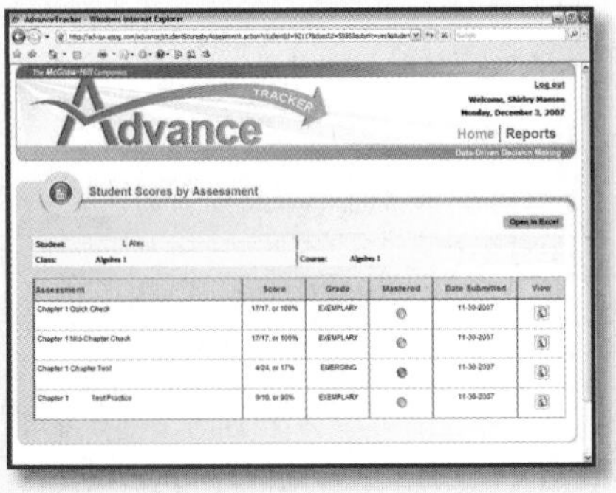

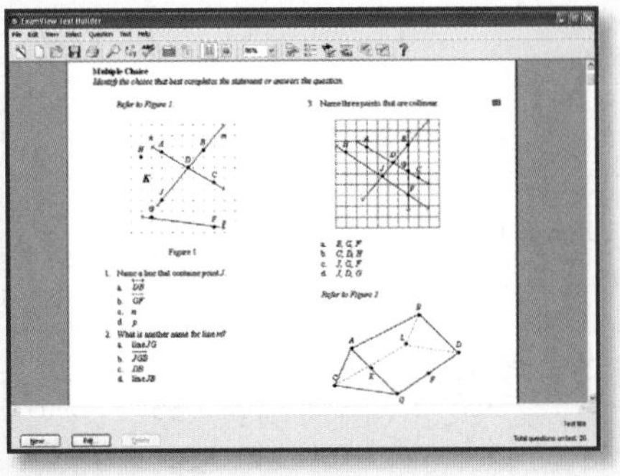

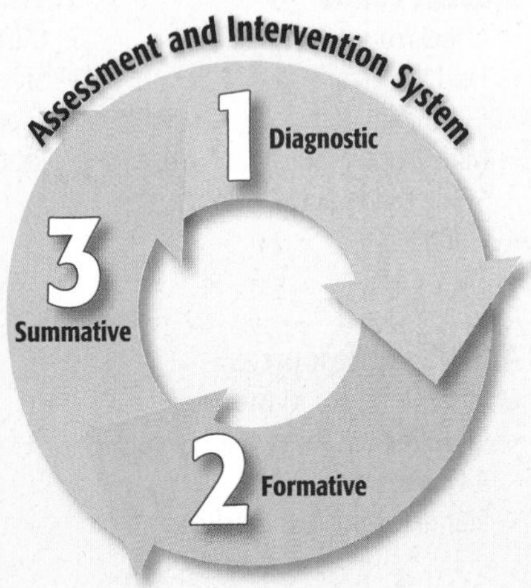

AdvanceTracker helps teachers administer online tests, diagnose student achievement, and create prescriptive reports for a student or class.

Exam*View*® Assessment Suite allows teachers to create and customize their own assessment and assignments. Print in one or two columns to match state test.

1 Diagnostic

Initial Assessment Assess students' knowledge **at the beginning of the year** with the *Diagnostic and Placement Tests.* These assessments will help you determine whether your students need additional materials and resources to meet grade-level standards.

ExamView Assessment Suite

- Diagnostic and Placement Tests

Advance Tracker

- Diagnostic and Placement Tests

Entry–Level Assessment Assess students' prior knowledge **at the beginning of a chapter or lesson.**

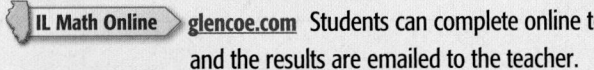

IL Math Online glencoe.com Students can complete online tests and the results are emailed to the teacher.

- Chapter Readiness

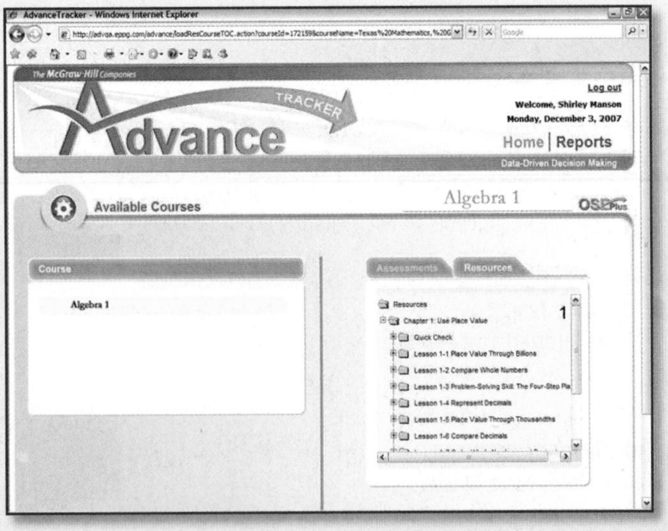

Algebra 1, AdvanceTracker

2 Formative

Progress Monitoring Determine if students are progressing adequately as you teach each lesson. Use the assessments to differentiate lesson instruction and practice.

ExamView® Assessment Suite

Advance Tracker
- Mid-Chapter Test
- Study Guide and Review

MindJogger, Super DVD

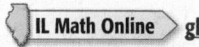

IL Math Online glencoe.com
- Self-Check Quizzes

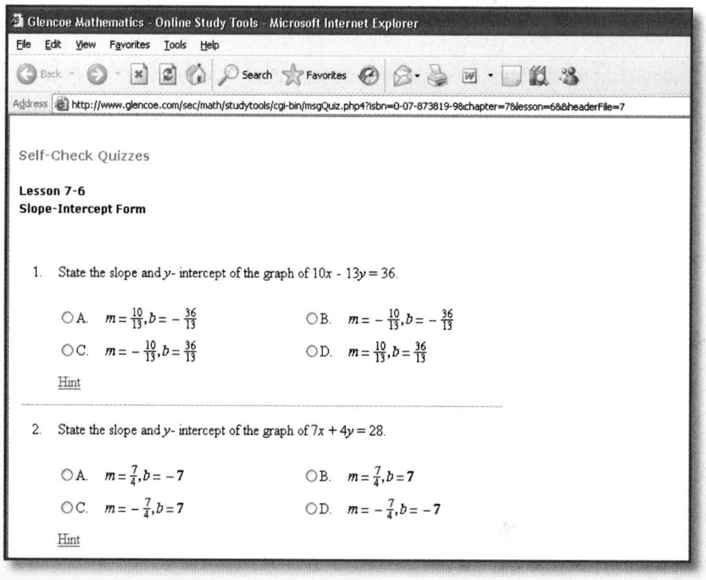

Pre-Algebra, Self-Check Quiz

3 Summative

Summative Evaluation Assess students' success in learning the concepts in each chapter.

ExamView® Assessment Suite
- Chapter Tests
- Cumulative Standardized Test Practice

Advance Tracker
- Chapter Tests
- Cumulative Standardized Test Practice

IL Math Online glencoe.com
- Chapter Tests

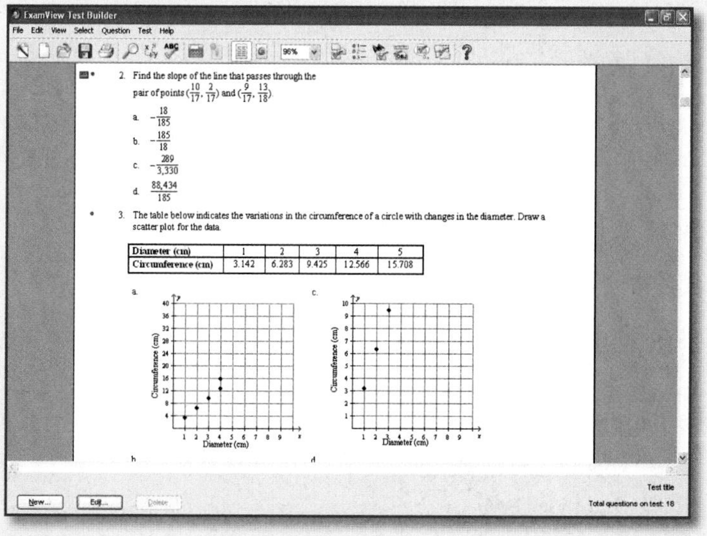

Algebra 2, ExamView® Assessment Suite

Differentiated Instruction

Reaching All Learners

Every chapter and lesson includes suggestions for identifying and meeting your students' needs. Strategies include differentiation in pacing and student grouping, alternate approaches, ways to enhance instruction with manipulatives, questions to promote higher-order thinking, and language hints.

Personalize instruction for:

- **AL** Students who are approaching grade level
- **ELL** English language learners
- **BL** Students who are beyond grade level

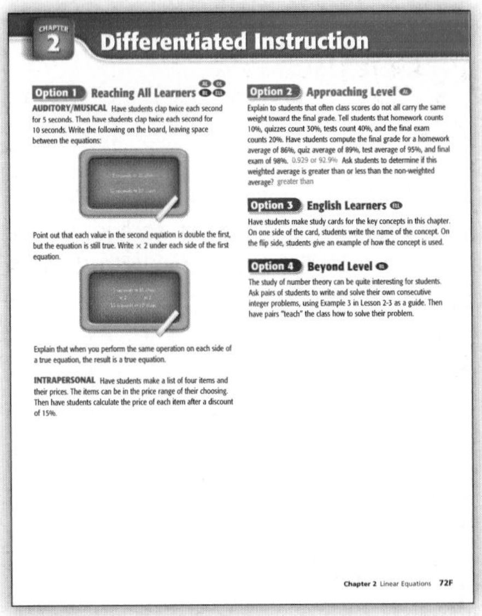
Chapter 2 Differentiated Instruction

Algebra 1
Teacher Edition, page 72F

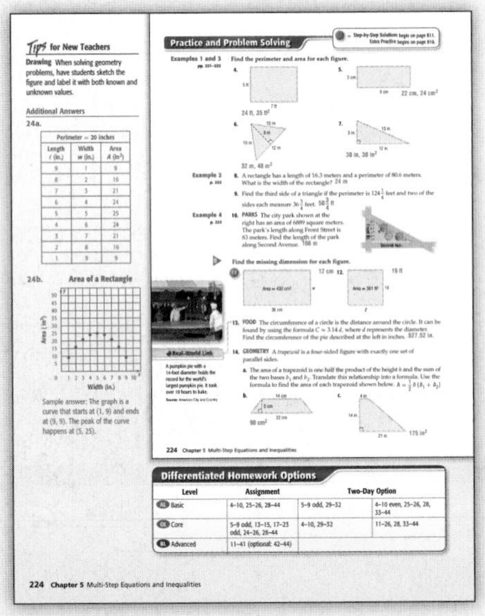
Practice and Problem Solving

Differentiated Homework Options

Pre-Algebra
Teacher Edition, page 224

Leveled Exercise Sets

The assignments for each lesson are leveled for students.

- **AL** Approaching Grade Level
- **OL** On Grade Level
- **BL** Beyond Grade Level

Leveled Resources

All of the blackline masters and transparencies that accompany the program, as well as all of the Teacher Edition pages, are available on the **TeacherWorks Plus™ CD-ROM.** Resources and assignments are leveled for students who are:

- **AL** Approaching Grade Level
- **OL** On Grade Level
- **BL** Beyond Grade Level
- **ELL** English Language Learners

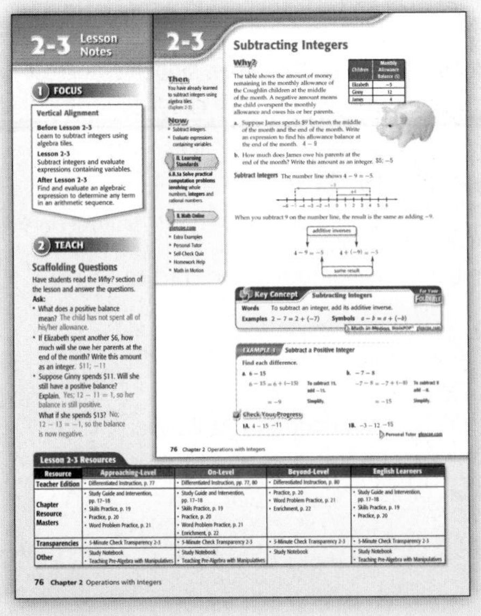
2-3 Lesson Notes

2-3 Subtracting Integers

Lesson 2-3 Resources

Pre-Algebra
Teacher Edition, page 76

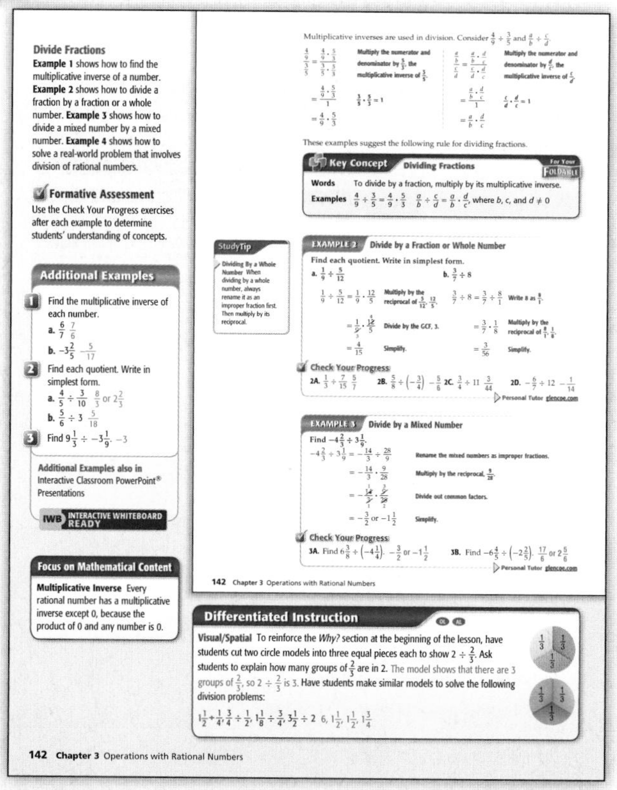

Pre-Algebra
Teacher Edition, page 142

Meeting Students' Needs

Diagnostic Teaching Every chapter and lesson includes suggestions for identifying and meeting your students' needs. Strategies include differentiation in pacing and student grouping, alternate approaches, ways to enhance instruction with manipulatives, questions to promote higher order thinking, and language hints.

Personalize instruction for:

- Struggling students
- English language learners
- Students with special needs
- Students who are above or beyond grade level in their comprehension of mathematics

Advanced Learners

Acceleration and Enrichment Resources and assignments that are coded for students who are above or beyond level may be used with advanced learners. The **Enrichment Masters** provide students with valuable opportunities for extending your lessons. **Differentiated Instruction** in the Teacher Edition provide additional opportunities for extension.

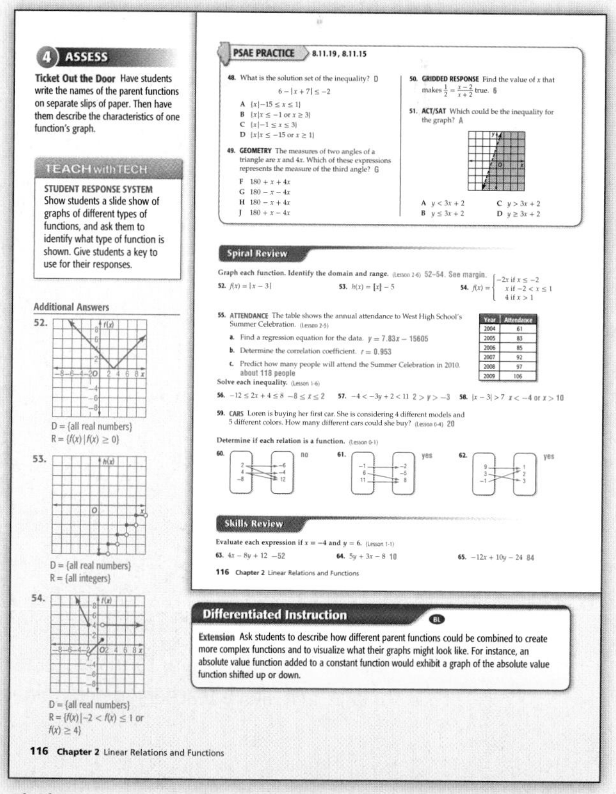

Algebra 2
Teacher Edition, page 116

Response to Intervention

Tiered Intervention

A comprehensive approach to intervention is provided throughout the Teacher Editions, beginning with a diagnostic review and continuing with prescriptions at all three RtI levels.

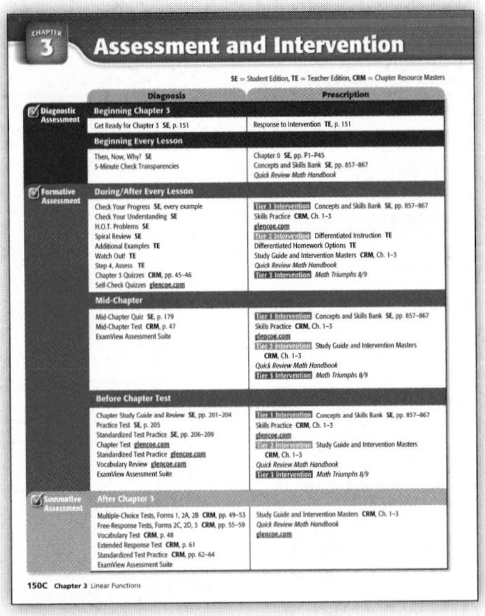
Chapter 3 Assessment and Intervention

Algebra 1
Teacher Edition, page 150C

Assessment and Intervention

Each chapter includes diagnosis and prescription suggestions for each of the three tiers of intervention.

- **TIER 1** Leveled exercise sets and leveled resources
- **TIER 2** Study Guide and Intervention and differentiated instruction options
- **TIER 3** Intensive Intervention, ***Math Triumphs***

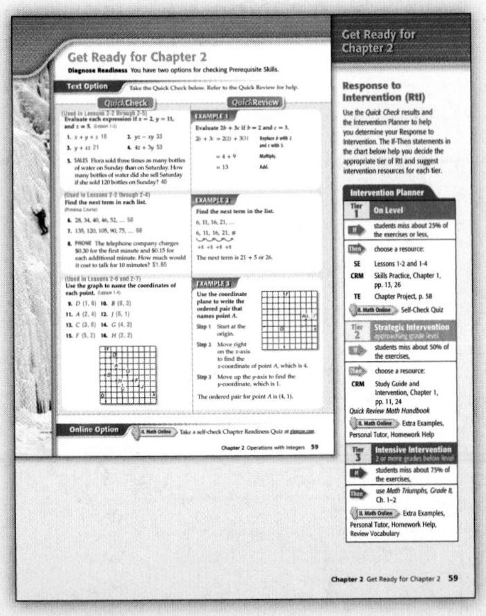
Get Ready for Chapter 2

Pre-Algebra
Teacher Edition, page 59

Beginning Each Chapter

Based on the results of the *Quick Check* at the beginning of each chapter, the Intervention Planner provides suggestions for intervening with your students. The If-Then statements help you decide which tier of RtI to use.

During Each Lesson

Multiple opportunities for formative assessment are included in each chapter that allows teachers to determine if intervention is needed.

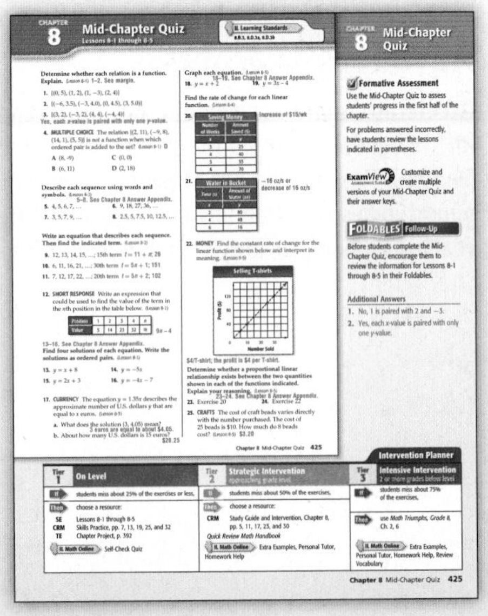
Chapter 8 Mid-Chapter Quiz

Pre-Algebra
Teacher Edition, page 425

After the Chapter

If students are still struggling after completing the chapter, students are provided with several options to help them get back on track.

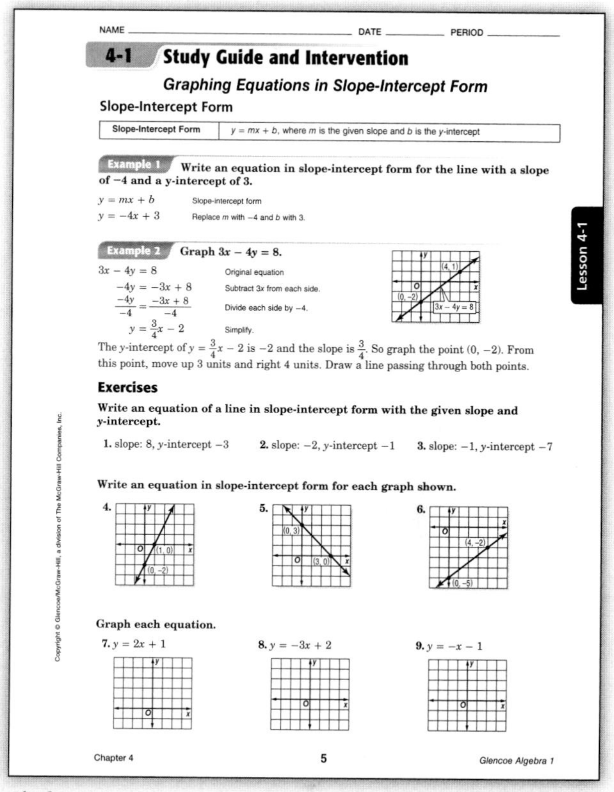

NAME ______________________ DATE __________ PERIOD __________

4-1 Study Guide and Intervention

Graphing Equations in Slope-Intercept Form

Slope-Intercept Form

Slope-Intercept Form	$y = mx + b$, where m is the given slope and b is the y-intercept

Example 1 **Write an equation in slope-intercept form for the line with a slope of −4 and a y-intercept of 3.**

$y = mx + b$ Slope-intercept form

$y = -4x + 3$ Replace m with −4 and b with 3.

Example 2 **Graph $3x - 4y = 8$.**

$3x - 4y = 8$ Original equation

$-4y = -3x + 8$ Subtract $3x$ from each side.

$\frac{-4y}{-4} = \frac{-3x + 8}{-4}$ Divide each side by −4.

$y = \frac{3}{4}x - 2$ Simplify.

The y-intercept of $y = \frac{3}{4}x - 2$ is −2 and the slope is $\frac{3}{4}$. So graph the point (0, −2). From this point, move up 3 units and right 4 units. Draw a line passing through both points.

Lesson 4-1

Exercises

Write an equation of a line in slope-intercept form with the given slope and y-intercept.

1. slope: 8, y-intercept −3 **2.** slope: −2, y-intercept −1 **3.** slope: −1, y-intercept −7

Write an equation in slope-intercept form for each graph shown.

Graph each equation.

7. $y = 2x + 1$ **8.** $y = -3x + 2$ **9.** $y = -x - 1$

Chapter 4 5 *Glencoe Algebra 1*

Algebra 1
Chapter 4 Resource Master, page 5

Study Guide and Intervention Masters

Reinforces important mathematical skills by providing additional worked-out examples and problems. This Tier 2 RtI addresses students' needs up to one year below grade level.

Math Triumphs
Foundations for Algebra

Math Triumphs

For students who are two or more years below grade level, ***Math Triumphs*** provides step-by-step instruction, vocabulary support, and data-driven decision making to help students succeed.

Planning for Success

Teacher Handbook

Ease of Use

A strong instructional model is provided that includes differentiated instructional options, reteaching, reinforcement, and extension options, Tips for New Teachers to help address various learners, Advanced items, and assessment linked with instruction.

Convenient Lesson Planning at Your Fingertips

The **Chapter Planner** helps you plan your instruction by showing the objectives to be covered, suggested pacing, and coverage of Focal Points.

TeacherWorks™ Plus

This electronic lesson planner contains multi-purpose management software including the Teacher Edition pages, program blackline masters, and daily calendars that make planning a snap.

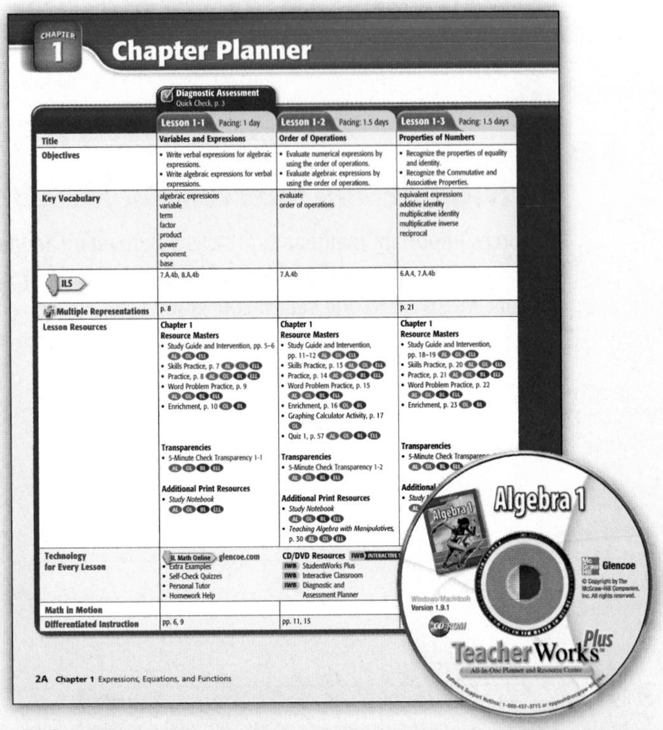
CHAPTER 1 Chapter Planner

Diagnostic Assessment Quick Check, p. 3

	Lesson 1-1 Pacing: 1 day	Lesson 1-2 Pacing: 1.5 days	Lesson 1-3 Pacing: 1.5 days
Title	Variables and Expressions	Order of Operations	Properties of Numbers
Objectives	• Write verbal expressions for algebraic expressions. • Write algebraic expressions for verbal expressions.	• Evaluate numerical expressions by using the order of operations. • Evaluate algebraic expressions by using the order of operations.	• Recognize the properties of equality and identity. • Recognize the Commutative and Associative Properties.
Key Vocabulary	algebraic expressions, variable, term, factor, product, power, exponent, base	evaluate, order of operations	equivalent expressions, additive identity, multiplicative identity, multiplicative inverse, reciprocal
ILS	7.A.4b, 8.A.4b	7.A.4b	6.A.4, 7.A.4b
Multiple Representations	p. 8		p. 21
Lesson Resources	Chapter 1 Resource Masters • Study Guide and Intervention, pp. 5–6 • Skills Practice, p. 7 • Practice, p. 8 • Word Problem Practice, p. 9 • Enrichment, p. 10 Transparencies • 5-Minute Check Transparency 1-1 Additional Print Resources • Study Notebook	Chapter 1 Resource Masters • Study Guide and Intervention, pp. 11–12 • Skills Practice, p. 13 • Practice, p. 14 • Word Problem Practice, p. 15 • Enrichment, p. 16 • Graphing Calculator Activity, p. 17 • Quiz 1, p. 57 Transparencies • 5-Minute Check Transparency 1-2 Additional Print Resources • Study Notebook • Teaching Algebra with Manipulatives, p. 30	Chapter 1 Resource Masters • Study Guide and Intervention, pp. 18–19 • Skills Practice, p. 20 • Practice, p. 21 • Word Problem Practice, p. 22 • Enrichment, p. 23 Transparencies • 5-Minute Check Transparency
Technology for Every Lesson	IL Math Online glencoe.com • Extra Examples • Self-Check Quizzes • Personal Tutor • Homework Help	CD/DVD Resources • StudentWorks Plus • Interactive Classroom • Diagnostic and Assessment Planner	
Math in Motion			
Differentiated Instruction	pp. 6, 9	pp. 11, 15	

2A Chapter 1 Expressions, Equations, and Functions

Algebra 1
Teacher Edition, page 2A

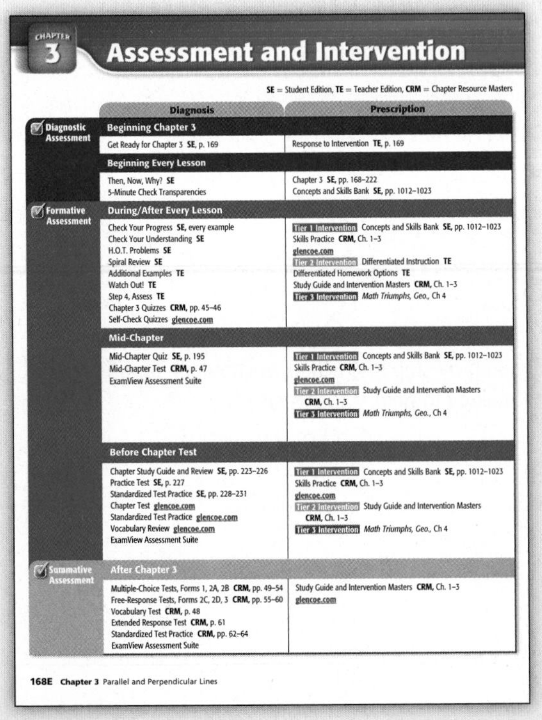
CHAPTER 3 Assessment and Intervention

SE = Student Edition, TE = Teacher Edition, CRM = Chapter Resource Masters

	Diagnosis	Prescription
Diagnostic Assessment	**Beginning Chapter 3**	
	Get Ready for Chapter 3 **SE**, p. 169	Response to Intervention **TE**, p. 169
	Beginning Every Lesson	
	Then, Now, Why? **SE** 5-Minute Check Transparencies	Chapter 3 **SE**, pp. 168–222 Concepts and Skills Bank **SE**, pp. 1012–1023
Formative Assessment	**During/After Every Lesson**	
	Check Your Progress **SE**, every example Check Your Understanding **SE** H.O.T. Problems **SE** Spiral Review **SE** Additional Examples **TE** Watch Out! **TE** Step 4, Assess **TE** Chapter 3 Quizzes **CRM**, pp. 45–46 Self-Check Quizzes glencoe.com	Tier 1 Intervention Concepts and Skills Bank **SE**, pp. 1012–1023 Skills Practice **CRM**, Ch. 1–3 glencoe.com Tier 2 Intervention Differentiated Instruction **TE** Differentiated Homework Options **TE** Study Guide and Intervention Masters **CRM**, Ch. 1–3 Tier 3 Intervention *Math Triumphs, Geo.*, Ch 4
	Mid-Chapter	
	Mid-Chapter Quiz **SE**, p. 195 Mid-Chapter Test **CRM**, p. 47 ExamView Assessment Suite	Tier 1 Intervention Concepts and Skills Bank **SE**, pp. 1012–1023 Skills Practice **CRM**, Ch. 1–3 glencoe.com Tier 2 Intervention Study Guide and Intervention Masters **CRM**, Ch. 1–3 Tier 3 Intervention *Math Triumphs, Geo.*, Ch 4
	Before Chapter Test	
	Chapter Study Guide and Review **SE**, pp. 223–226 Practice Test **SE**, p. 227 Standardized Test Practice **SE**, pp. 228–231 Chapter Test glencoe.com Standardized Test Practice glencoe.com Vocabulary Review glencoe.com ExamView Assessment Suite	Tier 1 Intervention Concepts and Skills Bank **SE**, pp. 1012–1023 Skills Practice **CRM**, Ch. 1–3 glencoe.com Tier 2 Intervention Study Guide and Intervention Masters **CRM**, Ch. 1–3 Tier 3 Intervention *Math Triumphs, Geo.*, Ch 4
Summative Assessment	**After Chapter 3**	
	Multiple-Choice Tests, Forms 1, 2A, 2B **CRM**, pp. 49–54 Free-Response Tests, Forms 2C, 2D, 3 **CRM**, pp. 55–60 Vocabulary Test **CRM**, p. 48 Extended Response Test **CRM**, p. 61 Standardized Test Practice **CRM**, pp. 62–64 ExamView Assessment Suite	Study Guide and Intervention Masters **CRM**, Ch. 1–3 glencoe.com

168E Chapter 3 Parallel and Perpendicular Lines

Geometry,
Teacher Edition, page 168E

Vertical Alignment

Topics are presented to build upon prior grade level skills and concepts and to serve as a foundation for future topics.

Professional Development

Targeted professional development has been articulated throughout the program. Actual classroom video clips are especially helpful when planning lessons and differentiating instruction. See page T32 for more information.

Four-Step Teaching Plan

Organizes your instruction as you **Focus** and **Teach** and help your students **Practice** and **Assess** what they've learned.

Vertical Alignment

Vertical Alignment at the beginning of each lesson shows the objectives that lead into and follow the current lesson's content for a coherent PreK–12 scope and sequence.

Scaffolding Questions

Each lesson contains **Scaffolding Questions** for you to use to help students investigate and understand the main ideas of the lesson.

Additional Examples

Each **Additional Example** mirrors the example in the Student Edition. The Additional Examples are also available as a PowerPoint® presentation on the **Interactive Classroom** CD-ROM.

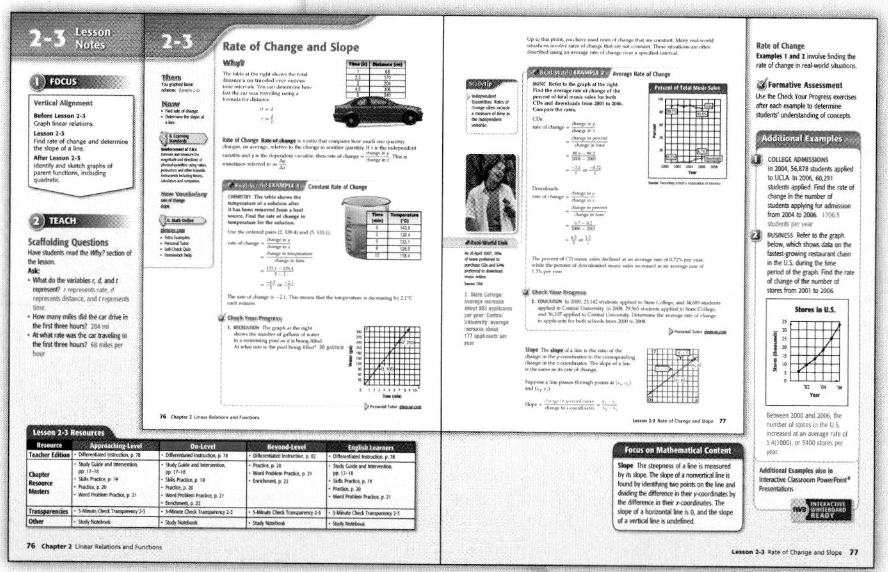

Algebra 2
Teacher Edition, pages 76–77

Differentiated Homework Options

Because most classrooms include students at a wide range of ability levels, **Differentiated Homework Options** allow you to customize your assignments.

Assessment Activities

Formative Assessment activities provide alternate ways to determine student comprehension at the end of each lesson.

- **Ticket Out the Door** Students must answer the given question and hand to the teacher as they leave the classroom.
- **Yesterday's News** Students connect what they learned today to yesterday's lesson.
- **Crystal Ball** Students predict how today's lesson will relate to the next lesson.
- **Name the Math** Students tell what mathematics is used in a problem.

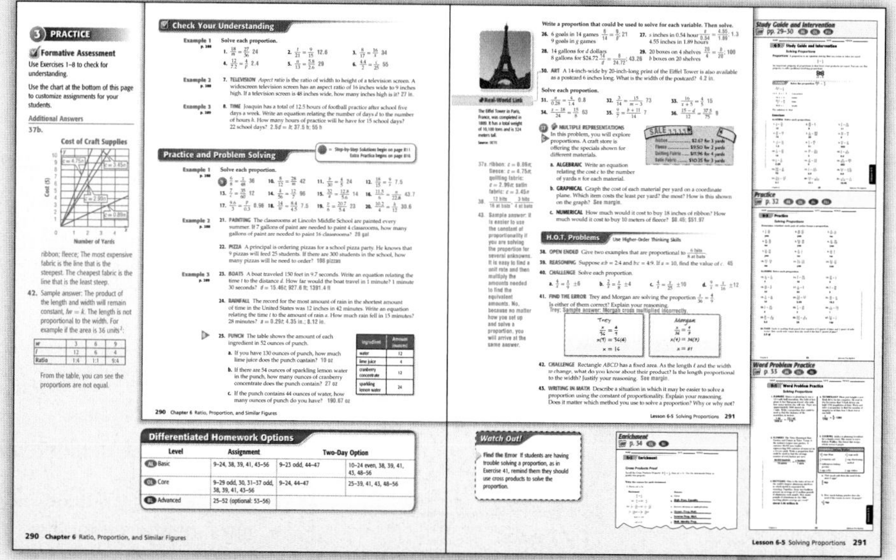

Pre-Algebra
Teacher Edition, pages 290–291

Planning for Success

State-of-the-Art Technology

Fully integrated technology resources are provided for teachers, students, and parents.

For Teachers

TeacherWorks™ Plus is your all-in-one planner and resource center.

- entire Teacher Edition
- all print ancillaries
- electronic lesson planner

Exam*View*® Assessment Suite allows teachers to create and customize their own assessment and assignments.

New features:
- correlated to state standards
- online content update
- one- or two-column formatting

Use **Interactive Classroom** to guide instruction using PowerPoint ™

- In-Class Examples
- 5-Minute Check Transparencies
- Math in Motion
- links to IL Math Online

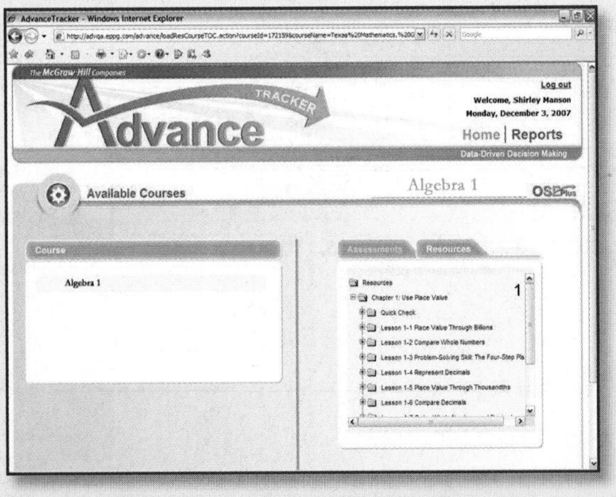

Algebra 1

Advance Tracker Learner Management System helps you track progress and differentiate your instruction.

- formative assessments aligned to standards
- links to intervention help

For Students

StudentWorks™ Plus is your students' backpack solution.

- entire Student Edition
- all student worksheets
- links to IL Math Online

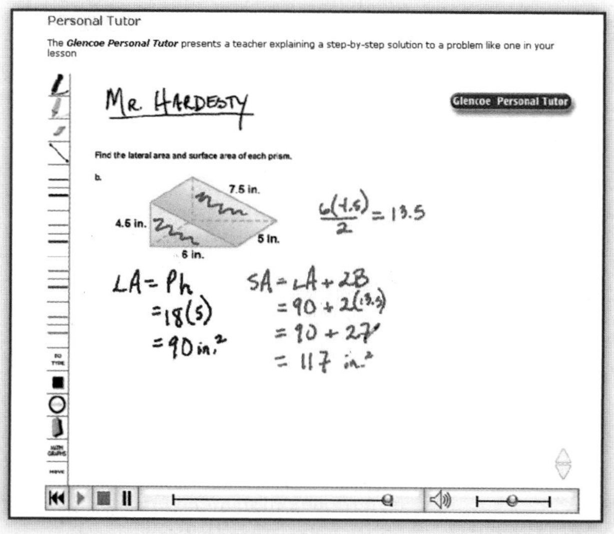

Pre-Algebra
Web site, Personal Tutor

IL Math Online provides a wealth of resources–convenient for students and parents!

- Self-Check Quizzes
- Personal Tutor
- Math in Motion
- eGlossary (14 languages)
- And much, much more!

IL Math Online The **eBook** is easy to use, easy to read, and packed with features.

- links to online study tools and resources right from the page
- includes audio

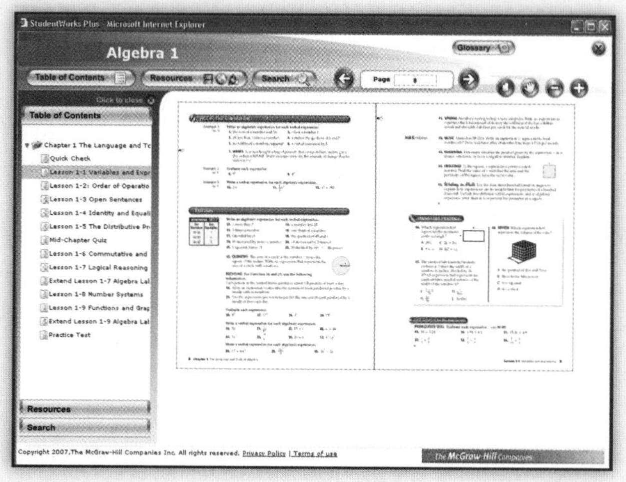

Algebra 1
eBook, pages 8–9

PreK–12 Data-Driven Professional Development

McGraw-Hill Professional Development (MHPD) provides a comprehensive plan for mathematics that is fully aligned and articulated with ***Math Connects PreK–8*** and the ***Glencoe Mathematics*** high school series.

Professional Development Needs	Online Courses	DVD Workshops	Video Library	Program Walkthroughs	Ready-Access Math
Has immediate classroom application	✓	✓	✓	✓	✓
Builds content knowledge	✓	✓			✓
Promotes best teaching practices		✓	✓		
Supports new and experienced teachers	✓	✓	✓	✓	✓
Allows customization of courses	✓	✓			✓
Can be self-paced	✓	✓		✓	✓
Adaptable for various timeframes	✓	✓	✓	✓	✓
Is grade-level specific			✓	✓	✓
Promotes a learning community	✓	✓			✓
Provides vertically-aligned content	✓	✓	✓		✓
Helps with RtI (Response to Intervention), Tiers 1–3	✓	✓	✓		✓

Use students' mathematics achievement data to help develop a targeted Professional Development Plan.

Accredited Online Courses

(available for purchase)

- Watch video clips of math classrooms Complete interactive exercises Develop electronic portfolios.
- Complete each 3- to 5-hour online module one segment at a time.
- University credit (additional tuition charge)

DVD Workshops

- Watch video clips of classroom mathematics lessons and commentaries by leading educators.
- Complete lessons and activities.

MHPD Online

- Access this online Professional Development resource for K–12 educators.
- Link to relevant Web sites.
- Download grade-level student resources.

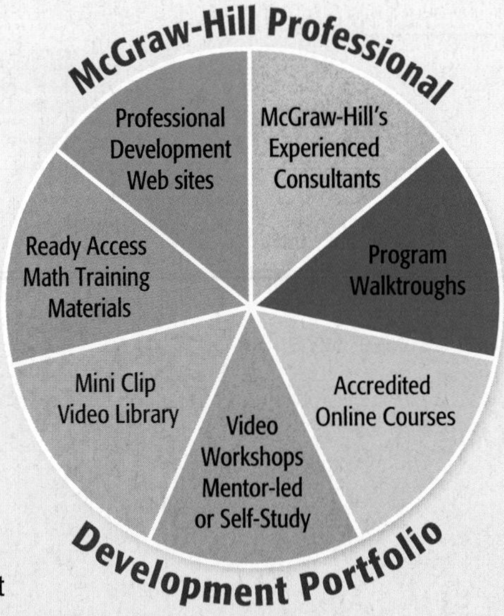

Program Walkthroughs

- Walk through program features of the Student Edition, Teacher Edition, and program ancillaries, including technology options.
- Online or video-enhanced DVD

Ready-Access Math, Personalized Professional Development

- Access training materials for nearly 300 mathematics professional development lessons.
- Create a customized sequence of professional development sessions.
- Deliver 45–60 minute after-school professional development sessions.

PSAE Pacing

Glencoe/McGraw-Hill's ***Illinois Algebra 1*** Student Edition is organized for Prairie State Achievement Exam (PSAE) success.

1. **Chapter 0** gets students ready for Algebra 1 with a review of topics from previous courses that are prerequisites for Algebra 1.
2. **Chapters 1–12** Each chapter has coherent groups of lessons focused on related skills and concepts from the Illinois Learning Standards.

The organization and pacing of ***Illinois Algebra 1*** helps ensure in-depth coverage of all standards, and success on the PSAE.

image 100/Alamy

Pacing Guide Each chapter includes multiple days for review and assessment.	
Chapter 0	15 days
Chapter 1	15 days
Chapter 2	12 days
Chapter 3	9 days
Chapter 4	11 days
Chapter 5	10 days
Chapter 6	16 days
Chapter 7	13 days
Chapter 8	10 days
Chapter 9	15 days
Chapter 10	13 days
Chapter 11	12 days
Chapter 12	9 days
Total:	160 days
PSAE	

WELCOME TO

Illinois Algebra 1

Master the Illinois Program of Studies in 3 Easy Steps

1 Practice the Standards Daily

IL Learning Standards

6.A.4 Identify and apply the associative, commutative, **distributive** and identity **properties of real numbers, including special numbers**

Each lesson addresses the Illinois Learning Standard covered in that lesson.

PSAE Practice Questions aligned to the standards in a format like those on the Prairie State Achievement Examination provide you with ongoing opportunities to sharpen your test-taking skills.

Chicago Harbor on Lake Michigan

2 Practice the Standards throughout the Chapter

PSAE Example Every chapter contains a completely worked-out Prairie State Achievement Examination Example to help you solve problems that are similar to those you might find on that test.

PSAE Practice Every chapter contains two full pages of PSAE Practice with Test-Taking Tips.

3 Practice the Standards Before the Test

Countdown PLUS to the Illinois PSAE If you've followed steps 1 and 2, you should be more than ready for the test. But just in case you want to make sure, use pages IL1–IL20 to practice questions that are similar to those on the test. Lesson references are included should you need a little refresher.

Illinois Reviewers

Each Illinois Reviewer reviewed at least two chapters of the Student Edition, giving feedback and suggestions for improving the effectiveness of the mathematics instruction.

Robert D. Cherry
Mathematics Instructor
Wheaton Warrenville South High School
Wheaton, Illinois

Amber L. Contrano
High School Teacher
Naperville Central High School
Naperville, Illinois

Bonnie C. Hill
Mathematics Department Chair
Triad High School
Troy, Illinois

Kara Painter
Mathematics Teacher
Downers Grove South High School
Downers Grove, Illinois

Dr. Maria J. Vlahos
Mathematics Division Head for Grades 6–12
Barrington High School
Barrington, Illinois

Correlation Between the Illinois Mathematics Goals and Standards, and Glencoe's *Illinois Algebra 1, Illinois Geometry, and Illinois Algebra 2*

Lessons in which the standard is the primary focus are indicated in **bold.**

Number	Skills and Concepts	Algebra 1 Lesson(s)	Geometry Lesson(s)	Algebra 2 Lesson(s)
STATE GOAL 6: Demonstrate and apply a knowledge and sense of numbers, including numeration and operations (addition, subtraction, multiplication, division), patterns, ratios and proportions.				
A. Demonstrate knowledge and use of numbers and their representations in a broad range of theoretical and practical settings.				
6.A.4	Identify and apply the associative, commutative, distributive and identity properties of real numbers, including special numbers such as pi and square roots.	**1-3, 1-4**	10-1	
6.A.5	Perform addition, subtraction and multiplication of complex numbers and graph the results in the complex plane.			**5-4**
B. Investigate, represent and solve problems using number facts, operations (addition, subtraction, multiplication, division) and their properties, algorithms and relationships.				
6.B.4	Select and use appropriate arithmetic operations in practical situations including calculating wages after taxes, developing a budget and balancing a checkbook.	0-3, 2-2, 2-3, Extend 2-6, 5-6, Extend 6-5	**Extend 11-2**	
6.B.5	Identify, represent and apply numbers expressed in exponential, logarithmic and scientific notation using contemporary technology.			Explore 8-2, Extend 8-3, Extend 8-6, Explore 8-8, Extend 8-8, Concepts and Skills 3
C. Compute and estimate using mental mathematics, paper-and-pencil methods, calculators and computers.				
6.C.4	Determine whether exact values or approximations are appropriate (e.g., bid a job, determine gas mileage for a trip).	0-1, 2-8, 2-9	Throughout the text; for example, 7-7, 8-4, 10-6, 11-4, 12-7	
6.C.5	Determine the level of accuracy needed for computations involving measurement and irrational numbers.		**Extend 1-2**	
D. Solve problems using comparison of quantities, ratios, proportions and percents.				
6.D.4	Solve problems involving recipes or mixtures, financial calculations and geometric similarity using ratios, proportions and percents.	**2-6, Extend 2-6, 2-7**	7-1	
6.D.5	Solve problems involving loans, mortgages and other practical applications involving geometric patterns of growth.			8-1, **Explore 8-8**, 8-8, **Extend 8-8**
STATE GOAL 7: Estimate, make and use measurements of objects, quantities and relationships and determine acceptable levels of accuracy.				
A. Measure and compare quantities using appropriate units, instruments and methods.				
7.A.4a	Apply units and scales to describe and compare numerical data and physical objects.	0-13, **2-6**, 3-4, 5-4, 9-8, 10-7, 12-2	1-2, 1-4, 2-6, 4-2, 6-3, 7-2, 7-3, 7-4, 7-5, 7-6, 7-7, Extend 8-7, 9-6, Extend 9-6, 10-1, 11-5, Extend 12-4, 12-8	

Number	Skills and Concepts	Algebra 1 Lesson(s)	Geometry Lesson(s)	Algebra 2 Lesson(s)
7.A.4b	Apply formulas in a wide variety of theoretical and practical real-world measurement applications involving perimeter, area, volume, angle, time, temperature, mass, speed, distance, density and monetary values.	**0-7, 0-8, 0-9,** 1-1, 1-2, 1-3, 1-8, 2-1, 2-8, 2-9, 3-1, 3-4, 7-1, 7-3, 7-4, 8-6, 10-4, 10-5, **10-6**, 11-3, 11-4, 11-5, 11-7	0-1, 0-2, **1-3, 1-4, 1-5, 1-6, Extend 1-6, 1-7, Extend 1-7**, Explore 8-2, 8-2, **11-1, Explore 11-2, 11-2, 11-3, Explore 11-4, 11-4**, Extend 11-4, 11-5, 12-2, **12-4, 12-5, 12-6**	
7.A.5	Apply nonlinear scales (e.g., Richter, decibel, pH) to solve practical problems.			**8-6**
B. Estimate measurements and determine acceptable levels of accuracy.				
7.B.4	Estimate and measure the magnitude and directions of physical quantities (e.g., velocity, force, slope) using rulers, protractors and other scientific instruments including timers, calculators and computers.	2-8, Explore 3-3, 3-3, 3-4, Explore 4-1, 8-2, 8-4, 8-6, 9-1, Extend 9-1, 9-2, 10-1, 10-2, 10-3, 10-4, 11-1, 11-3, 11-7	2-6, Explore 3-3, 3-3, 8-7, Extend 8-7, 9-4	
7.B.5	Estimate perimeter, area, volume, and capacity of irregular shapes, regions and solids and explain the reasoning supporting the estimate.		**Extend 11-4**, 12-4, 12-5, 12-6	
C. Select and use appropriate technology, instruments and formulas to solve problems, interpret results and communicate findings.				
7.C.4a	Make indirect measurements, including heights and distances, using proportions (e.g., finding the height of a tower by its shadow).	**2-6, 10-7**	**7-3, 7-7**	
7.C.4b	Interpret scale drawings and models using maps and blueprints.	**2-6**	**7-7**	
7.C.4c	Convert within and between measurement systems and monetary systems using technology where appropriate.	**Concepts and Skills 1**	**0-1, 0-2**	
7.C.5a	Use dimensional analysis to determine units and check answers in applied measurement problems.		**0-1, 0-2**, 1-2, 7-7	**Extend 6-1**
7.C.5b	Determine how changes in one measure may affect other measures (e.g., what happens to the volume and surface area of a cube when the side of the cube is halved).		1-6, 1-7, 11-4, 11-5, 12-3, 12-4, **Extend 12-4**, 12-5, 12-6, 12-8	
STATE GOAL 8: Use algebraic and analytical methods to identify and describe patterns and relationships in data, solve problems and predict results.				
A. Describe numerical relationships using variables and patterns.				
8.A.4a	Use algebraic methods to convert repeating decimals to fractions.			**11-4**
8.A.4b	Represent mathematical patterns and describe their properties using variables and mathematical symbols.	1-1, 2-7, **3-5**, Extend 3-5, **3-6**, 4-5, 7-1, 7-2, 7-6, 7-7, 7-8, 8-1, 8-3, 8-4, 8-5, 8-6, **Extend 9-1**, 9-5, 9-6, **9-8, 9-9**, Explore 10-8, Explore 11-1, 11-5, 11-6, 12-3	2-1, **Extend 7-1, Extend 7-5**, Extend 9-4	
8.A.5	Solve mathematical problems involving recursive patterns and use models that employ such relationships.			**11-5**

Number	Skills and Concepts	Algebra 1 Lesson(s)	Geometry Lesson(s)	Algebra 2 Lesson(s)
B. Interpret and describe numerical relationships using tables, graphs and symbols.				
8.B.4a	Represent algebraic concepts with physical materials, words, diagrams, tables, graphs, equations and inequalities and use appropriate technology.	1-5, 1-6, Extend 1-7, Extend 1-8, 2-1, Explore 2-2, 2-2, Explore 2-3, 2-3, 2-4, 2-5, Extend 2-6, 2-8, 5-1, Explore 5-2, 5-2, 5-3, 5-4, 5-5, Extend 5-6, 6-1, Extend 6-1, 6-2, 6-3, 6-4, 6-5, 6-8, Extend 6-8, Explore 7-4, Explore 7-5, Explore 7-7, Explore 8-2, Explore 8-3, Extend 8-3, Extend 10-2, Extend 11-3		
8.B.4b	Use the basic functions of absolute value, square root, linear, quadratic and step to describe numerical relationships.	**3-1, 3-2, Extend 3-2,** 3-5, 4-4, **4-7, Extend 4-7, 9-1, 9-3, 10-1, Extend 10-1**		
8.B.5	Use functions including exponential, polynomial, rational, parametric, logarithmic, and trigonometric to describe numerical relationships.			**6-3, Extend 6-3, 6-4, Extend 6-4, 8-1, 8-3,** Extend 8-3, **9-3, 9-4, Extend 9-4, 13-2, 13-4, 13-5, 13-7, Explore 13-8, 13-8, 13-9**
C. Solve problems using systems of numbers and their properties.				
8.C.4a	Analyze and report the effects of changing coefficients, exponents and other parameters on functions and their graphs.	**Extend 4-1, 9-3**		
8.C.4b	Apply algebraic properties and procedures with matrices, vectors, functions and sequences using data found in business, industry and consumer situations.	**1-7**, 3-1, 3-2, **3-5**, 4-1, 4-2, 4-3, 4-7, **6-6, 6-7**, 7-4, 7-5, 8-2, 8-5, 9-5, 9-6, 9-7, **9-8, 9-9**, 10-3, 10-4, 11-2, 11-8	**8-7, Extend 8-7**	
8.C.5	Use polynomial, exponential, logarithmic and trigonometric functions to model situations.			6-3, 6-4, **Extend 6-4**, 8-1, 8-3, **Extend 8-3**, 13-7, 13-8
D. Use algebraic concepts and procedures to represent and solve problems.				
8.D.4	Formulate and solve linear and quadratic equations and linear inequalities algebraically and investigate nonlinear inequalities using graphs, tables, calculators and computers.	**2-1, Explore 2-2, 2-2, Explore 2-3, 2-3, 2-4, 5-1, 5-2, 5-3, 5-4, 5-6, Extend 5-6, 8-3, 8-4, 8-5, 8-6, 9-2, Extend 9-2, 9-4, 9-5**		

Number	Skills and Concepts	Algebra 1 Lesson(s)	Geometry Lesson(s)	Algebra 2 Lesson(s)
8.D.5	Formulate and solve nonlinear equations and systems including problems involving inverse variation and exponential and logarithmic growth and decay.			3-1, Extend 3-1, 3-2, 3-3, 3-5, **5-2, 5-3, 5-5, 5-6, 6-5, 6-6, 6-7, 7-7, Extend 7-7, 8-2, 8-4, 8-8, 9-5, 9-6, Extend 9-6, 10-7, Explore 14-5, 14-5**
STATE GOAL 9: Use geometric methods to analyze, categorize and draw conclusions about points, lines, planes and space.				
A. Demonstrate and apply geometric concepts involving points, lines, planes and space.				
9.A.4a	Construct a model of a three-dimensional figure from a two-dimensional pattern.		**Extend 1-7, Explore 12-1**	
9.A.4b	Make perspective drawings, tessellations and scale drawings, with and without the use of technology.	**2-6**	**Extend 1-7, 7-7, Extend 9-4**	
9.A.5	Use geometric figures and their properties to solve problems in the arts, the physical and life sciences and the building trades, with and without the use of technology.		Throughout the text; for example, 1-1, 3-1, 4-4, 8-3, 12-1	
B. Identify, describe, classify and compare relationships using points, lines, planes and solids.				
9.B.4	Recognize and apply relationships within and among geometric figures.		4-1, 4-3, 4-4, 4-5, Extend 4-5, Explore 4-7, 4-7, 5-5, 6-1, Extend 6-1, 7-2, 7-3, 7-4, 7-5, 7-6, 9-1, 9-2, Explore 9-3, 9-3, Explore 9-4, 9-4, 9-6, Extend 9-6, 10-1, 10-2, 10-3, 10-4, 10-5, Extend 10-5, 10-6, 10-7, 11-5, 12-8	
9.B.5	Construct and use two- and three-dimensional models of objects that have practical applications (e.g., blueprints, topographical maps, scale models).		**7-7, Extend 12-1**	
C. Construct convincing arguments and proofs to solve problems.				
9.C.4a	Construct and test logical arguments for geometric situations using technology where appropriate.		**2-2, 2-3, Extend 2-3,** 2-4, Extend 12-4	
9.C.4b	Construct and communicate convincing arguments for geometric situations.		**2-2**	

Number	Skills and Concepts	Algebra 1 Lesson(s)	Geometry Lesson(s)	Algebra 2 Lesson(s)
9.C.4c	Develop and communicate mathematical proofs (e.g., two-column, paragraph, indirect) and counter examples for geometric statements.		**2-1, 2-5, 2-6**, 2-7, 2-8, 3-2, 3-5, 3-6, 4-2, 4-3, 4-4, Extend 4-4, 4-5, Extend 4-5, 4-6, 4-7, **4-8**, 5-1, 5-2, 5-3, **5-4**, 5-6, 6-2, 6-3, 6-4, 6-5, 6-6, 7-2, 7-3, 7-4, 7-6, 8-1, 8-2, Extend 8-2, 8-6, 9-4, 9-5, 9-6, 10-2, 10-3, 10-4, 10-5, 10-6, 10-7, 10-8	
9.C.5a	Perform and describe an original investigation of a geometric problem and verify the analysis and conclusions to an audience.		Throughout the text; for example, 1-5, 4-6, 7-1, 8-2, 11-3	
9.C.5b	Apply physical models, graphs, coordinate systems, networks and vectors to develop solutions in applied contexts (e.g., bus routing, areas of irregular shapes, describing forces and other physical quantities).		0-7, 8-7, Extend 8-7, Extend 12-1, Extend 13-6	10-2, 10-3, 10-4, 10-5, 10-6
D. Use trigonometric ratios and circular functions to solve problems.				
9.D.4	Analyze and solve problems involving triangles (e.g., distances which cannot be measured directly) using trigonometric ratios.	**Explore 10-8, 10-8**	**8-4, Extend 8-4, 8-5, 8-6, Extend 8-6**	
9.D.5	Analyze and solve problems involving periodic patterns (e.g., sound waves, tide variations) using circular functions and communicate results orally and in writing.			**13-6**, 13-7
STATE GOAL 10: Collect, organize and analyze data using statistical methods; predict results; and interpret uncertainty using concepts of probability.				
A. Organize, describe and make predictions from existing data.				
10.A.4a	Represent and organize data by creating lists, charts, tables, frequency distributions, graphs, scatterplots and box-plots.	**0-13**	13-1, **Concepts and Skills 6**	
10.A.4b	Analyze data using mean, median, mode, range, variance and standard deviation of a data set, with and without the use of technology.	**0-12**, Extend 2-7, **12-2**, Extend 12-6	**Concepts and Skills 5**	
10.A.4c	Predict from data using interpolation, extrapolation and trend lines, with and without the use of technology.	**4-5, 4-6**		
10.A.5	Construct a statistics-based presentation, individually and as members of a team, to communicate and justify the results of a project.			**12-2**
B. Formulate questions, design data collection methods, gather and analyze data and communicate findings.				
10.B.4	Design and execute surveys or experiments, gather data to answer relevant questions, and communicate results and conclusions to an audience using traditional methods and contemporary technology.	**Explore 12-1, 12-1, 12-2**		
10.B.5	Design a statistical experiment to answer a question about a realistic situation, conduct the experiment, use statistics to interpret the data, and communicate the results, individually and as members of a team.		**13-4**	**12-1, 12-2**

Number	Skills and Concepts	Algebra 1 Lesson(s)	Geometry Lesson(s)	Algebra 2 Lesson(s)
C. Determine, describe and apply the probabilities of events.				
10.C.4a	Solve problems of chance using the principles of probability including conditional settings.	0-11, **12-5**, 12-6	0-3, 13-2, 13-3, **13-5, 13-6**	
10.C.4b	Design and conduct simulations (e.g., waiting times at restaurant, probabilities of births, likelihood of game prizes), with and without the use of technology.	**12-7**	**13-4**	
10.C.4c	Propose and interpret discrete probability distributions, with and without the use of technology.	**12-6**		
10.C.5a	Compute conditional probabilities and the probabilities of independent events.		**13-5, 13-6**	**12-3**, 12-7
10.C.5b	Compute probabilities in counting situations involving permutations and combinations.		**13-2**	**0-5**, Extend 11-6, 12-4
10.C.5c	Make predictions using probabilities associated with normally distributed events.			**12-5, Extend 12-5**

Tim Bieber/Getty Images

Farm in Galena, Illinois

CHAPTER 0

Preparing for Algebra

Chapter 0 Support

Helping You Learn

IL Math Online

Jupiter Images/Comstock Images/Alamy

Unit 1
Foundations for Functions

CHAPTER 1

Expressions, Equations, and Functions

Chapter 1 Support

Helping You Learn

- **New Vocabulary** 5, 10, 16, 23, 31, 38, 45, 54
- **Key Concepts** 6, 10, 16, 17, 18, 23, 26, 45
- **Check Your Progress** 5, 6, 10, 11, 12, 17, 18, 19, 24, 25, 26, 31, 32, 33, 39, 40, 45, 46, 47, 48, 54, 55, 56
- **Check Your Understanding** 7, 12, 19, 27, 34, 41, 49, 56
- **Multiple Representations** 8, 21, 36
- **H.O.T. Problems** 8, 14, 21, 28, 36, 43, 51, 58
- **Skills Review** 9, 15, 22, 29, 37, 44, 52, 59

IL Math Online

- **Math in Motion: Animation** 60
- **Math in Motion: BrainPOP®** 18, 23
- **Math in Motion: Interactive Labs** 32
- **Graphing Technology Personal Tutor** 53
- **Personal Tutor** 5, 6, 10, 11, 12, 16, 18, 19, 23, 24, 25, 26, 31, 32, 33, 38, 39, 40, 45, 46, 47, 48, 54, 55, 56
- **Self-Check Quizzes** 5, 10, 16, 23, 31, 38, 45, 54
- **Extra Examples** 5, 10, 16, 23, 31, 38, 45, 54
- **Homework Help** 5, 10, 16, 23, 31, 38, 45, 54

Preparing for PSAE

- **Extended Response** 15
- **Multiple Choice** 9, 15, 22, 29, 30, 32, 37, 44, 52, 59, 67
- **Short/Gridded Response** 9, 15, 22, 29, 37, 44, 52, 59
- **Worked-Out Example** 32

Bob Daemmrich/PhotoEdit

Linear Equations

Chapter 2 Support

Helping You Learn

IL Math Online

Preparing for PSAE

Unit 2
Linear Functions and Relations

CHAPTER 3 Linear Functions

Wolfgang Kaehler

Chapter 3 Support

Helping You Learn

IL Math Online

Preparing for PSAE

Unit 2
Linear Functions and Relations

CHAPTER 4

Linear Functions and Relations

Alex Segre/Alamy

ILS

Chapter 4 Support

Helping You Learn

IL Math Online

Preparing for PSAE

Unit 2
Linear Functions and Relations

Digital Vision Ltd./SuperStock

CHAPTER 5 Linear Inequalities

Chapter 5 Support

Helping You Learn

IL Math Online

Preparing for PSAE

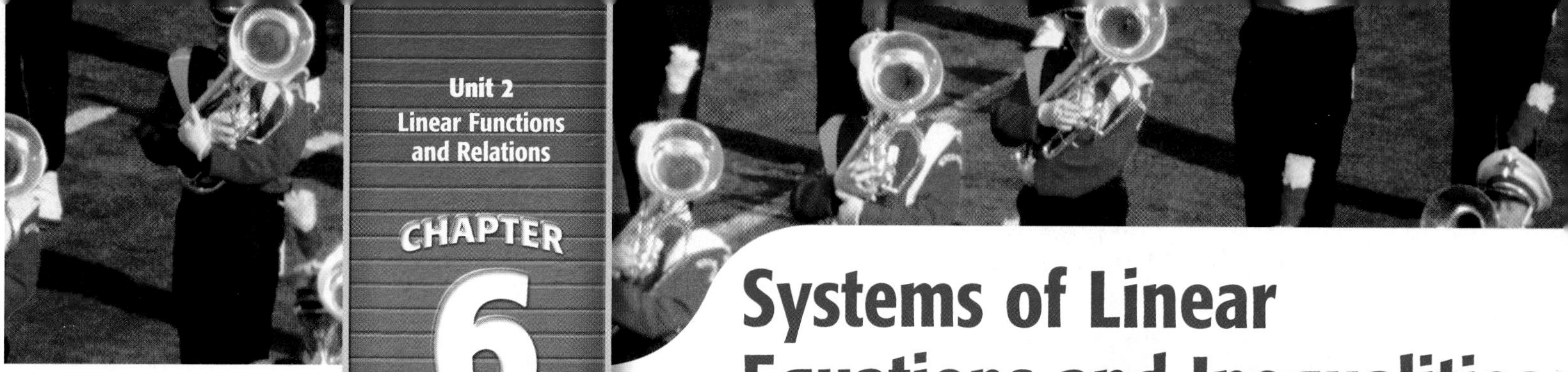

Masterfile

Unit 2
Linear Functions and Relations

CHAPTER 6

Systems of Linear Equations and Inequalities

ILS

Chapter 6 Support

Helping You Learn

IL Math Online

Preparing for PSAE

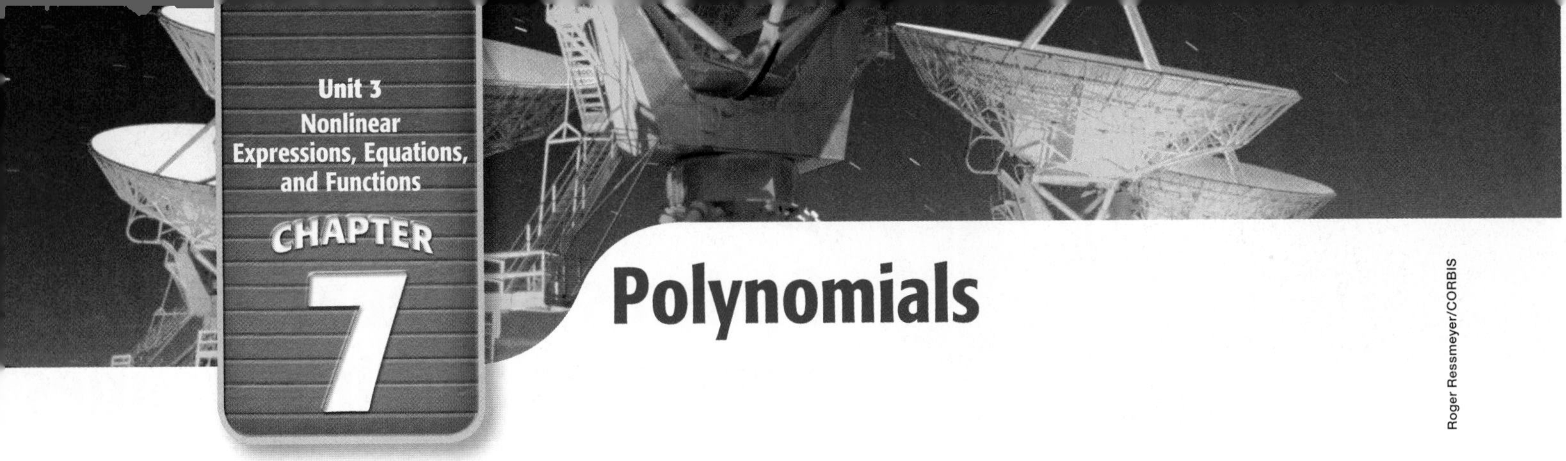

Unit 3
Nonlinear Expressions, Equations, and Functions

CHAPTER 7

Polynomials

Chapter 7 Support

Helping You Learn

- **New Vocabulary** 401, 408, 416, 424, 447, 453
- **Key Concepts** 402, 403, 404, 408, 409, 410, 416, 417, 448, 453, 454, 455
- **Check Your Progress** 401, 402, 403, 404, 408, 409, 410, 411, 412, 416, 417, 418, 424, 425, 426, 433, 434, 435, 439, 440, 441, 448, 449, 452, 453, 454, 455
- **Check Your Understanding** 404, 412, 419, 426, 435, 441, 450, 455
- **Multiple Representations** 406, 414, 428, 443, 451, 457
- **H.O.T. Problems** 406, 414, 421, 428, 437, 443, 451, 457
- **Skills Review** 407, 415, 422, 429, 438, 444, 452, 458

IL Math Online

- **Math in Motion: Animation** 423, 431, 445, 448, 453, 455
- **Math in Motion: BrainPOP®** 408
- **Personal Tutor** 401, 402, 403, 404, 408, 409, 410, 411, 412, 416, 417, 418, 424, 425, 426, 433, 434, 435, 439, 440, 441, 447, 448, 449, 453, 454, 455
- **Self-Check Quizzes** 401, 408, 416, 424, 433, 439, 447, 453
- **Extra Examples** 401, 408, 416, 424, 433, 439, 447, 453
- **Homework Help** 401, 408, 416, 424, 433, 439, 447, 453

Preparing for PSAE

- **Extended Response** 415
- **Multiple Choice** 407, 415, 422, 429, 430, 438, 440, 444, 452, 458, 463
- **Short/Gridded Response** 407, 422, 429, 438, 444, 458
- **Worked-Out Example** 440

Jon Arnold Images Ltd/Alamy

Unit 3
Nonlinear Expressions, Equations, and Functions

CHAPTER 8

Factoring and Quadratic Equations

Chapter 8 Support

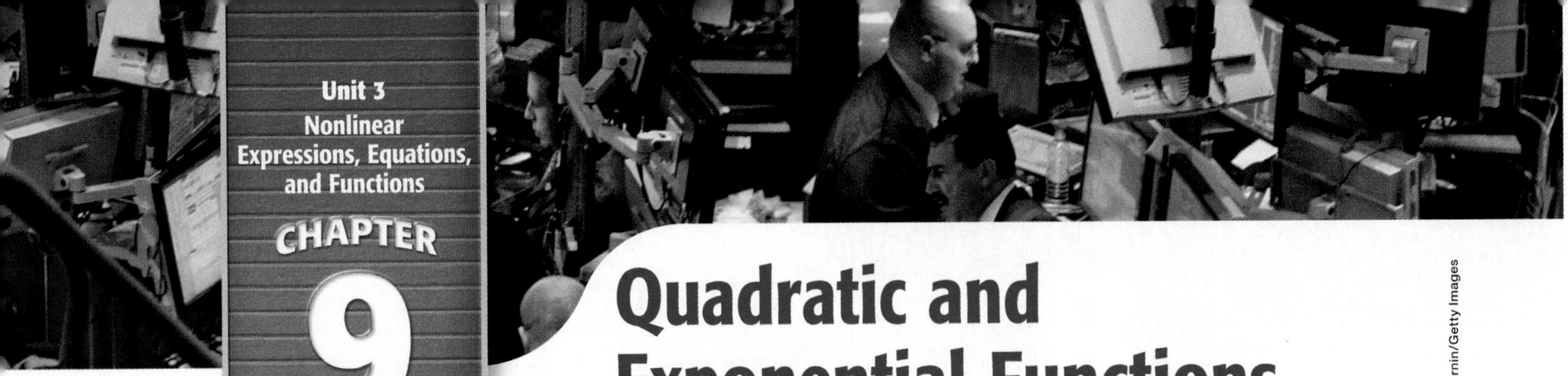

Stephen Chernin/Getty Images

Unit 3
Nonlinear Expressions, Equations, and Functions

CHAPTER 9

Quadratic and Exponential Functions

Chapter 9 Support

Helping You Learn

- **New Vocabulary** 525, 537, 544, 552, 558, 567, 573, 578
- **Key Concepts** 525, 528, 529, 537, 544, 545, 552, 558, 561, 567, 573, 574, 580, 584
- **Check Your Understanding** 531, 540, 547, 554, 562, 570, 575, 581, 587
- **Multiple Representations** 534, 541, 548, 556, 563
- **H.O.T. Problems** 534, 541, 548, 556, 563, 571, 576, 582, 588
- **Skills Review** 535, 542, 549, 557, 564, 572, 577, 583, 589

IL Math Online

- **Math in Motion: Animation** 536, 537, 544, 552
- **Graphing Technology Personal Tutor** 543, 550, 565, 590
- **Personal Tutor** 525, 526, 527, 529, 530, 537, 538, 539, 544, 545, 546, 552, 553, 554, 558, 559, 560, 561, 567, 568, 569, 573, 578, 579, 580, 584, 585, 586
- **Self-Check Quizzes, Extra Examples, Homework Help** 525, 537, 544, 552, 558, 567, 573, 578, 584

Preparing for PSAE

- **Extended Response** 542
- **Multiple Choice** 535, 542, 546, 549, 557, 559, 564, 566, 572, 577, 583, 589
- **Short/Gridded Response** 535, 549, 557, 564, 572, 577, 583, 589
- **Worked-Out Example** 546

Unit 4
Advanced Functions and Equations

CHAPTER 10

Radical Functions and Geometry

Stockbyte/PunchStock

Chapter 10 Support

Helping You Learn

- **New Vocabulary** 605, 612, 624, 630, 636, 642, 649
- **Key Concepts** 605, 606, 612, 613, 621, 624, 630, 631, 636, 638, 642, 649, 651
- **Check Your Progress** 605, 606, 607, 612, 613, 614, 619, 620, 621, 625, 630, 631, 636, 637, 638, 642, 643, 644, 649, 650, 651
- **Check Your Understanding** 608, 615, 621, 626, 632, 638, 644, 652
- **Multiple Representations** 609, 627, 646, 654
- **H.O.T. Problems** 609, 616, 622, 627, 634, 640, 646, 654
- **Skills Review** 610, 617, 623, 628, 635, 641, 647, 655

IL Math Online

- **Math in Motion: Animation** 642, 648
- **Graphing Technology Personal Tutor** 611, 618
- **Personal Tutor** 605, 606, 607, 612, 613, 614, 619, 620, 621, 624, 625, 630, 631, 636, 637, 638, 642, 643, 644, 649, 650, 651
- **Self-Check Quizzes** 605, 612, 619, 624, 630, 636, 642, 649
- **Extra Examples** 605, 612, 619, 624, 630, 636, 642, 649
- **Homework Help** 605, 612, 619, 624, 630, 636, 642, 649

Preparing for PSAE

- **Extended Response** 655
- **Multiple Choice** 610, 617, 623, 628, 629, 635, 641, 647, 655, 661
- **Short/Gridded Response** 610, 617, 623, 628, 635, 641, 647
- **Worked-Out Example** 614

Unit 4
Advanced Functions and Equations

CHAPTER 11

Rational Functions and Equations

Doug Pensinger/Getty Images

ILS

Chapter 11 Support

Helping You Learn

- **New Vocabulary** 670, 678, 684, 706, 714, 720
- **Key Concepts** 670, 671, 673, 678, 679, 680, 685, 692, 693, 706, 708
- **Check Your Progress** 670, 671, 672, 678, 679, 680, 684, 685, 686, 687, 692, 693, 694, 700, 701, 702, 706, 707, 708, 709, 710, 714, 715, 716, 720, 721, 722, 723
- **Check Your Understanding** 673, 681, 687, 695, 702, 710, 717, 724
- **Multiple Representations** 704
- **H.O.T. Problems** 675, 682, 689, 697, 704, 712, 718, 725
- **Skills Review** 676, 683, 690, 698, 705, 713, 719, 726

IL Math Online

- **Math in Motion: Animation** 701, 723
- **Math in Motion: Interactive Labs** 685
- **Graphing Technology Personal Tutor** 691
- **Personal Tutor** 670, 671, 672, 678, 679, 680, 684, 685, 692, 693, 694, 700, 701, 702, 706, 708, 709, 710, 714, 715, 716, 720, 721, 722, 723
- **Self-Check Quizzes** 670, 678, 684, 692, 700, 706, 714, 720
- **Extra Examples** 670, 678, 684, 692, 700, 706, 714, 720
- **Homework Help** 670, 678, 684, 692, 700, 706, 714, 720

Preparing for PSAE

- **Extended Response** 698, 705
- **Multiple Choice** 676, 683, 685, 690, 698, 705, 713, 719, 726
- **Short/Gridded Response** 676, 683, 690, 713, 719, 726
- **Worked-Out Example** 685

Dex Image/Alamy

Unit 5
Data Analysis

CHAPTER 12

Statistics and Probability

Chapter 12 Support

Helping You Learn

IL Math Online

Preparing for PSAE

Student Handbook

Contents

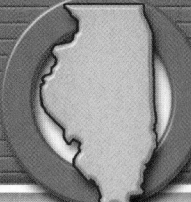

PSAE

Countdown to the Illinois PSAE

The **Countdown to the Illinois PSAE** helps prepare your students for the PSAE.

Countdown PLUS to the

Illinois PSAE

Prairie State Achievement Examination

In the spring of your eleventh-grade year, you will take the Prairie State Achievement Examination (PSAE) for Mathematics. The PSAE covers the Illinois Assessment Framework Objectives. The Prairie State Achievement Examination in Mathematics consists of two components. The first is the ACT Assessment Mathematics test. The second is the WorkKeys® Applied Mathematics test. You will apply the concepts and skills that you have learned throughout the year.

Multiple-Choice Items

For multiple-choice questions, you will select the correct response from five answer choices. Your teacher will provide you with an answer sheet to fill in your answer choices.

Radius Images/Masterfile

Should I Study for the PSAE?

The good news is that you've been studying all along for the PSAE—a little bit every day. Here are some of the ways your textbook has been preparing you for the test.

- **Every Day** Each lesson had practice questions that are similar to the questions on the PSAE.
- **Every Week** The Mid-Chapter Quiz and Practice Test had several practice questions. Also, the following pages include a section called Countdown Plus to the PSAE. These pages give you practice questions similar to those found on the test that specifically address the Prairie State Achievement Examination.
- **Every Chapter** Each chapter had two full pages of practice questions that are similar to the questions on the PSAE.

How Should I Use Countdown PLUS?

You can use these pages in the weeks before the test to determine if you are ready. Begin 20 weeks before the PSAE. You should plan to complete one practice page each week to help you review the Prairie State Achievement Examination.

If you are struggling with any of the items, lesson references are provided so that you can go back and review from the pages in your textbook.

Countdown PLUS to the PSAE

Week 20

Monday

1. Which expression finds the number of b boxes given the number of n notebooks packed inside? (Lesson 1-1) (8.11.02) **C**

Notebooks, n	498	174	222	96	288
Boxes, b	83	29	37	16	48

Ⓐ $6b$
Ⓑ $\frac{b}{6}$
Ⓒ $\frac{1}{6}n$
Ⓓ $6 + n$
Ⓔ $6n$

Wednesday

3. Which simplified algebraic expression represents the verbal expression: three times the difference of $4x$ and 7 decreased by twice the sum of 4 and $5x$? (Lesson 1-4) (6.11.13) **B**

Ⓐ $-22x + 13$
Ⓑ $2x - 29$
Ⓒ $2x - 13$
Ⓓ $9x - 3$
Ⓔ $17x - 15$

Tuesday

2. Which expression has the same value as the given expression? (Lesson 1-3) (6.11.02) **K**

$$\frac{3}{8}[(12 - 4) \div 3] + (2.5 + 6.5 + 7.5)$$

Ⓕ $\left[\left(\frac{5}{6} \cdot 12\right) + (6 \cdot 0)\right] + (6 \cdot 6 - 1)$
Ⓖ $(2 \cdot 4.5 \cdot 5) - \left[4.5 + \left(\frac{3}{5} \cdot 5\right) + 2.5\right]$
Ⓗ $(6.3 + 7.5 + 3.7) \cdot 2$
Ⓙ $7\frac{1}{2} + 6\frac{3}{4} + 8\frac{1}{2} + 5\frac{3}{4} - \left(3\frac{1}{4} + 4\frac{1}{4}\right)$
Ⓚ $\left(\frac{1}{9} \cdot 5 \cdot 9 \cdot 7\right) \div 2$

Thursday

4. Which label could be used for the vertical axis to represent the data shown in the graph? (Lesson 1-6) (8.11.13) **J**

Ⓕ Cumulative Sales
Ⓖ Distance
Ⓗ Height of a Person
Ⓙ Speed
Ⓚ Total Income

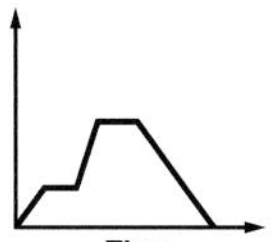

Friday

5. **WorkKeys® Level 5** You want to put a square border of fencing around a circular garden in your backyard. The square of fencing would touch the circle on each side. The circular garden has an area of about 50.24 ft^2. If the fencing costs \$2.25 per foot, how much will it cost? Use 3.14 for π. (Lesson 1-2) (7.11.03) **D**

Ⓐ \$18 Ⓑ \$27 Ⓒ \$36 Ⓓ \$72 Ⓔ \$144

Choice Analysis

1. A number of n notebooks within a given number of b boxes
B Incorrect variable chosen.
C CORRECT
D Incorrect operation chosen.
E Incorrect operation chosen.

2. F The value of the expression is 45.
G The value of the expression is 37.
H The value of the expression is 35.
J The value of the expression is 21.
K CORRECT

3. A reversed terms of algebraic expression
B CORRECT
C Verbal expression incorrectly translated.
D Distributive Property incorrectly applied.
E Distributive Property incorrectly applied.

4. F Cumulative sales won't decrease over time.
G Distance never decreases.
H Height won't decrease to the starting height.
J CORRECT
K The amount of total income over time never decreases.

5. A Cost of fence for one side.
B Added diameter and 4, not multiplied.
C Used radius instead of the diameter.
D CORRECT
E Used circumference formula instead of area formula.

Week 20

NEED EXTRA HELP?					
If You Missed Question...	1	2	3	4	5
Go to Lesson...	1-1	1-3	1-4	1-6	1-2
IL Assessment Objectives	8.11.02	6.11.02	6.11.13	8.11.13	7.11.03

Choice Analysis

1. A The solution is $x = 4.6$.
B The solution is $x = 4.6$.
C The solution is $x = 4.6$.
D CORRECT The solution is $x = 4.65$.
E The solution is $x = 4.6$.

2. F Total grams in new amount.
G CORRECT
H This is the amount of grams in new amount if the proportion incorrectly uses 8.4 g as the amount left of original amount.
J This is the amount of grams left if the proportion incorrectly uses 8.4 g as the amount left of the original amount.
K This is the number of grams used from the original amount.

3. A The scale is 1 inch = 50 miles.
B The scale is 1 inch = 20 miles.
C The scale is 1 inch = 30 miles.
D CORRECT
E The scale is 1 inch = 40 miles.

4. F 0.25 of 40 miles is 10 miles.
G 0.5 of 40 miles is 20 miles.
H CORRECT
J The correct scale is 1 inch = 40 miles.
K 1.5 of 40 miles is 60 miles.

5. A Found the difference of both containers at one-third full.
B CORRECT
C Found the difference of both full containers.
D Added the amounts instead of subtracted.
E Did not convert to gallons as requested.

Countdown PLUS to the PSAE

Week 19

Monday

1. Which equation does not have the same solution as the others? (Lesson 2-4) (8.11.01) **D**

Ⓐ $1.5x + 2.3 = 5x - 13.8$
Ⓑ $\frac{x+5}{3} = 2x - 6$
Ⓒ $5(2x + 3) = \frac{1}{3}\left(6x + 5\frac{2}{5}\right) + 50$
Ⓓ $3x - 28 = -2x + 37.1 - 9x$
Ⓔ $\frac{1}{7}(14x - 91) = -4(9 - x) + 3x$

Tuesday

2. During an experiment, 70% of an amount is used leaving 3.6 grams. If you start with a greater amount in the same experiment, how many grams are used if 100.8 grams remain? (Lesson 2-6) (6.11.18) **G**

Ⓕ 336 grams
Ⓖ 235.2 grams
Ⓗ 144 grams
Ⓙ 43.2 grams
Ⓚ 8.4 grams

Wednesday

3. The actual distance between three cities in Illinois are shown in the table.

From	To	Approximate Distance
Decatur	Springfield	39 miles
Springfield	Chicago	201 miles

Five maps of Illinois were created each using a different scale. Which map uses its scale correctly? In each choice, the distance on each map from Decatur to Springfield is given before the distance from Springfield to Chicago. (Lesson 2-6) (9.11.03) **D**

Ⓐ 0.78 in.; 4.02 in.
Ⓑ 0.975 in.; 5.025 in.
Ⓒ 1.3 in.; 6.7 in.
Ⓓ 1.56 in.; 8.05 in.
Ⓔ 1.95 in.; 10.05 in.

Thursday

4. A detail of a road map from Illinois is shown. On the map, the distance from Monticello to Decatur is 0.7 inches and the distance between Champaign and Decatur is 1.25 inches. What is the scale of the map? (Lesson 2-6) (9.11.03) **H**

Ⓕ 0.25 inch = 11 miles
Ⓖ 0.5 inch = 15 miles
Ⓗ 0.75 inch = 30 miles
Ⓙ 1 inch = 45 miles
Ⓚ 1.5 inches = 50 miles

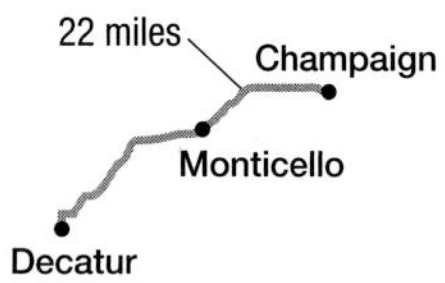

Friday

5. WorkKeys® Level 4 Lou has a container that holds 8 quarts 4 cups of water. Bradley has a container that holds twice as many gallons as the container. Both contaiers are $\frac{2}{3}$ full with water. How many more gallons of water are in Bradley's container than Lou's? (Lesson 2-6) (7.11.02) **B**

Ⓐ 0.75 gallons Ⓑ 1.5 gallons Ⓒ 2.25 gallons Ⓓ 4.5. gallons Ⓔ 6 quarts

Week 19

NEED EXTRA HELP?					
If You Missed Question...	1	2	3	4	5
Go to Lesson...	2-4	2-6	2-6	2-6	2-6
IL Assessment Objectives	8.11.0	6.11.18	9.11.03	9.11.03	7.11.02

Week 18

Monday

1. Which of the following equations is an example of the Associative Property? (Lesson 1-3) (6.11.05) **D**

Ⓐ $(a + b) + (c + d) = (c + d) + (a + b)$
Ⓑ $w + (x + y) = (x + y) + w$
Ⓒ $m \cdot p \cdot q = q \cdot p \cdot m$
Ⓓ $e + (f + g) = (e + f) + g$
Ⓔ $(rs)v = v(rs)$

Tuesday

2. The value of a coin increased 29% in three years to $10,500. About how much did the coin increase in value during that time? (Lesson 2-7) (6.11.18) **F**

Ⓕ $2,360.47
Ⓖ $4,288.73
Ⓗ $4,395.65
Ⓙ $8,139.53
Ⓚ $12,860.47

Wednesday

3. In a book store in Abbott, Illinois, a 6.25% sales tax is added to the purchase price of each book. The book store is having a sale. During the sale, the registers are programmed to use the following function to calculate the total cost of each book including slaes tax, p: $f(p) = \frac{17}{64}p$. What is the percent of discount? (Lesson 1-7) (6.11.18) **A**

Ⓐ 75%
Ⓑ 73%
Ⓒ 68.75%
Ⓓ 26%
Ⓔ 25%

Thursday

4. The volume of the given cone is about 415.9 cubic centimeters. What is the area of its base to the nearest tenth of a centimeter? Use 3.14 for π. (Lesson 2-8) (7.11.03) **J**

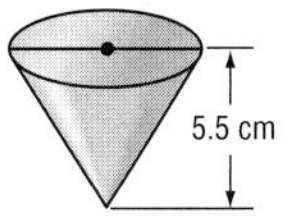

Ⓕ about 25.2 cm^2
Ⓖ about 53.4 cm^2
Ⓗ about 75.4 cm^2
Ⓙ about 226.9 cm^2
Ⓚ about 452.2 cm^2

Friday

5. **WorkKeys® Level 7** You spend 25% of your monthly income after taxes toward your mortgage. This amount is $450 more than the amount you save each month. You save 15% of your monthly earnings after taxes. You pay $225 more for food and expenses each month than savings. How much is spent each month on food and expenses? (Lesson 2-3) (6.11.18) **B**

Ⓐ $1,350 Ⓑ $900 Ⓒ $675 Ⓓ $450 Ⓔ $393.75

Week 18

NEED EXTRA HELP?					
If You Missed Question...	1	2	3	4	5
Go to Lesson...	1-3	2-7	1-7	2-8	2-3
IL Assessment Objectives	6.11.05	6.11.18	6.11.18	7.11.03	6.11.18

Choice Analysis

1. A Commutative Property.
B Commutative Property.
C Commutative Property.
D CORRECT
E Commutative Property.

2. F CORRECT
G Incorrectly used $10,500 as the value before the increase in the proportion.
H Found an increase of 71% instead of the given 29%.
J Actual value of the coin three years ago.
K Added the values instead of finding the difference.

3. A CORRECT
B Changed fraction in formula to percent form, then subtracted from 100%.
C Subtracted the sales tax percent from the percent discount.
D Changed fraction in formula to percent form.
E This is the percent of the price that is paid before tax.

4. F Divides both sides of formula by 3 instead of multiplying.
G Finds circumference.
H Uses the volume formula for a cylinder to find the length of the radius.
J CORRECT
K Adds 3.14 and the height instead of multiplying.

5. A Added $225 to mortgage amount instead of savings.
B CORRECT
C Found only the amount saved each month.
D Subtracted $225 instead of adding.
E Added percents in equation instead of subtracting.

Choice Analysis

1. A Related function, $f(x) = 4x - 8$.
B Related function, $f(x) = 4x - 8$.
C Related function, $f(x) = 4x - 8$.
D Related function, $f(x) = 4x - 8$.
E CORRECT

2. F amount of inches used
G Switched x- and y-values.
H Switched x- and y-values then subtracted incorrect amount.
J CORRECT
K amount of feet used

3. A This is the cost of 1 shirt when 200 shirts are purchased.
B CORRECT
C Added costs, instead of subtracting to find difference.
D Divided the cost of 200 shirts by 7 instead of 200.
E Subtracted the total costs of the purchases, not unit rates.

4. F CORRECT
G Used first given term in sequence as first term.
H Used fourth given term in sequence as first term.
J Used a proportion with the amount after 7 shirts sold and all of the shirts sold.
K Used a proportion with the amount after 4 shirts sold and all of the shirts sold.

5. A Added 17 min. to Driver A's time.
B Assumed Driver B finished only 17 minutes before Driver A each time.
C Assumed Driver B finished 7 minutes before Driver A.
D CORRECT
E Assumed Driver B finished 17 minutes before Driver A each set of 30 miles.

Countdown PLUS to the PSAE

Week 17

Monday

1. Which equation does not represent the relationship shown on the graph? (Lesson 3-2) (8.11.07) **E**

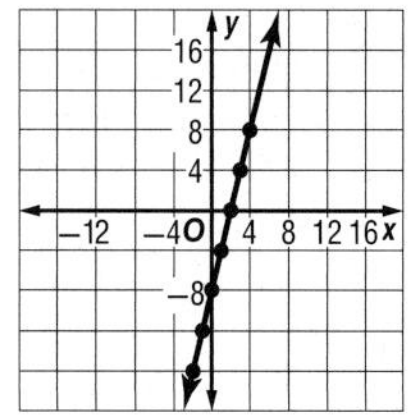

Ⓐ $17x + 5 = 21x - 3$
Ⓑ $14x - 2 = 18x - 10$
Ⓒ $11x + 3 = 15x - 5$
Ⓓ $9x + 7 = 5x + 15$
Ⓔ $8x - 2 = 12x - 9$

Wednesday

3. The Paper Store has pricing as shown. Customers can buy one package of paper or up to 500 packages. How much does the price of a package of paper change if you buy 200 packages instead of 1 package? (Lesson 3-5) (8.11.04) **B**

Paper Pricing

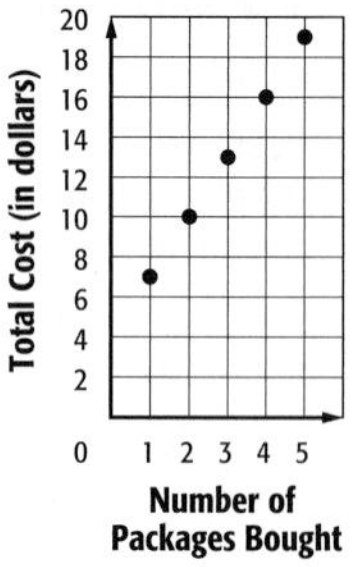

Ⓐ \$3.02
Ⓑ \$3.98
Ⓒ \$10.02
Ⓓ \$79.29
Ⓔ \$597

Tuesday

2. For every 1.5 feet of rope Ira buys to make into a rug, he uses 16.2 inches. So, the amount of rope he buys varies directly with the amount of rope he uses. If he buys 5.5 feet of rope, how much will be left over? (Lesson 3-4) (6.11.19) **J**

Ⓕ 59.4 inches
Ⓖ 73 inches
Ⓗ 0.4 feet
Ⓙ 0.55 feet
Ⓚ 4.95 feet

Thursday

4. Ted sells souvenir shirts at the stadium. He records the amount of money in his register from the fourth shirt sold and creates the following arithmetic sequence: 266, 284, 295, 306, …. If Ted sells out of shirts after his register has \$1598, how many shirts did he sell? (Lesson 3-5) (8.11.04) **F**

Ⓕ 78 shirts
Ⓖ 74 shirts
Ⓗ 72 shirts
Ⓙ 36 shirts
Ⓚ 24 shirts

Friday

5. **WorkKeys® Level 6** During the race, there is a checkpoint every 60 miles. The time the driver reaches each checkpoint is recorded. The first three checkpoint times for Driver A are shown in the graph. Driver B reached the first checkpoint 17 minutes before Driver A. Driver B continues at the same rate through the race. About what is the speed of Driver B? (Lesson 3-3) (7.11.07) **D**

Driver A

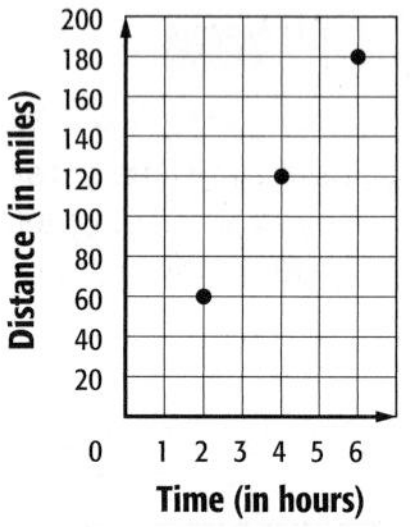

Ⓐ 27 mph
Ⓑ 30 mph
Ⓒ 32 mph
Ⓓ 35 mph
Ⓔ 42 mph

Week 17

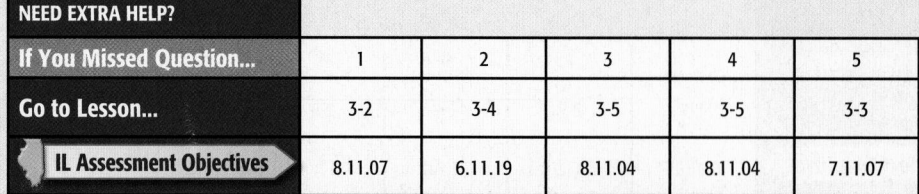

NEED EXTRA HELP?					
If You Missed Question...	1	2	3	4	5
Go to Lesson...	3-2	3-4	3-5	3-5	3-3
IL Assessment Objectives	8.11.07	6.11.19	8.11.04	8.11.04	7.11.07

Week 16

Monday

1. A survey was given to 142 students attending Ramsey High School. Students were asked their favorite school subject. The table shows most of the total votes. If a circle graph was made from the totals, by about how many degrees would the languages and math sections differ? (Lesson 0-13) (10.11.01) **C**

Ⓐ 14°
Ⓑ 36°
Ⓒ 55°
Ⓓ 91°
Ⓔ 127°

Survey Results

Subject	Totals
Languages	14
Mathematics	?
Sciences	43
Social Studies	49

Tuesday

2. The letters A, B, C, and D were each written on more than one index card and placed in a bag. The probability of randomly selecting an index card with an A from the bag is $\frac{2}{5}$, the probability of a B is $\frac{1}{10}$, and the probability of a C is $\frac{1}{6}$. If a card was picked and returned a total of 60 times, about how many of those cards would have a D written on them? (Lesson 0-12) (10.11.08) **J**

Ⓕ 1
Ⓖ 6
Ⓗ 10
Ⓙ 20
Ⓚ 24

Wednesday

3. Seven of the eight numbers in the set of data are shown below.

81, 46, 90, 85, 94, 72, 83

The mean of the complete set of data is 79. Which of the following measures of central tendency best represents the entire set of data? (Lesson 0-12) (10.11.05) **B**

I Mode II Median III Mean

Ⓐ I only
Ⓑ II only
Ⓒ III only
Ⓓ I and III
Ⓔ II and III

Thursday

4. The restaurant has 3.25 pounds of potatoes but needs a total of 16.97 pounds. It has 4.1 pounds of asparagus but needs a total of 14.3 pounds. The potatoes cost \$1.45 per pound and the asparagus costs \$2.20 per pound. The restaurant owner set aside \$30 for the purchase. About how much more money does he need? (Lesson 0-1) (6.11.10) **K**

Ⓕ about \$3 more
Ⓖ about \$7 more
Ⓗ about \$9.50 more
Ⓙ about \$12 more
Ⓚ about \$18.50 more

Friday

5. **WorkKeys® Level 5** You are making two similar, rectangular sandboxes. The area of the rectangular base of the smaller sandbox is 156 square centimeters and the area of the larger rectangular base is 2496 square centimeters. The length of the larger rectangular base is 48 centimeters. What is the width of the smaller rectangular base? (Lesson 2-6) (6.11.17) **B**

Ⓐ 3 cm Ⓑ 12 cm Ⓒ 13 cm Ⓓ 44 cm Ⓔ 52 cm

Choice Analysis

1. A Divided the total votes for languages and math by 360°.
B This is the degrees for the language section.
C CORRECT
D This is the degrees for the mathematics section.
E Totaled instead of subtracted.

2. F $P(\text{picking D}) = \frac{1}{3}$; student chose numerator.
G This is the number of B cards picked.
H This is the number of C cards picked.
J CORRECT
K This is the number of A cards picked.

3. A Mode of 81 is not the best indicator for the data set.
B CORRECT
C 79 represents only one portion of the data.
D The mean represents only one portion of the data.
E The mean represents only one portion of the data.

4. F Underestimated price and quantity for both products.
G Underestimated price for both products.
H Underestimated price and quantity for asparagus.
J Underestimated the amount they had and price for both.
K CORRECT

5. A Divided length by 16 instead of 4.
B CORRECT
C This is the width of the smaller, similar rectangle.
D Subtracted by 4 instead of dividing.
E This is the length of the larger, similar rectangle.

Week 16

NEED EXTRA HELP?					
If You Missed Question...	1	2	3	4	5
Go to Lesson...	0-13	0-12	0-12	0-1	2-6
IL Assessment Objectives	10.11.01	10.11.08	10.11.05	6.11.10	6.11.17

Choice Analysis

1. A CORRECT
B Read graph incorrectly.
C Read graph incorrectly.
D Read graph incorrectly.
E Read graph incorrectly.

2. F $y = -4x + 2$; slope is not the opposite reciprocal
G $y = -2x + 2$; slope is not the opposite reciprocal
H $y = 4x - 2$; slope is not the opposite reciprocal
J CORRECT
K $y = -2x - 2$; slope is not the opposite reciprocal

3. A Switched *x*- and *y*-coordinates in formula.
B Subtracted 50 from both sides of the formula instead of adding.
C CORRECT
D Add in slope formula instead of subtracting.
E Had a difference of 2 in the denominator of the slope formula instead of 1.

4. F Divided 77° by 70° highlighted in plot.
G Used slope of 10; did not divide in slope by run of 2.
H CORRECT
J Used slope of $\frac{5}{2}$.
K Subtracted instead of divided by 65 from line of fit equation.

5. A Subtracted yearly amount of dues.
B CORRECT
C Subtracted only 2 months of rent and 2 months association dues.
D Subtracted only 1 month of rent and 1 month association dues.
E Subtracted 3 months of rent and 3 months toward the association dues. Then divided by 100.

Week 15

Monday

1. Karla and Trista each want to ship a present to their Aunt. The cost for shipping is shown in the graph. Karla's present weighs 5.5 pounds. Trista's present weighs 7.3 pounds. How much do they each save if they mail the presents together in one package? (Lesson 4-7) (8.11.13) **A**

Ⓐ $5
Ⓑ $7.50
Ⓒ $10
Ⓓ $15
Ⓔ $20

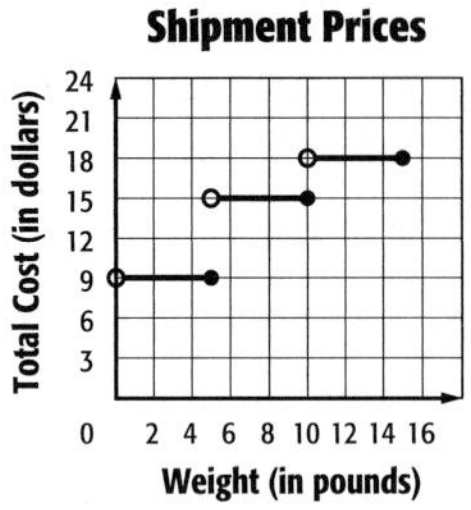

Tuesday

2. Which of the following pairs of given points create a line that is perpendicular to the line shown? (Lesson 4-4) (8.11.11) **J**

Ⓕ (−4, 18), (0, 2)
Ⓖ (3, 4), (−4, 10)
Ⓗ (−1, −6), (2, 6)
Ⓙ (1, 4), (−2, −2)
Ⓚ (0, −2), (1, −4)

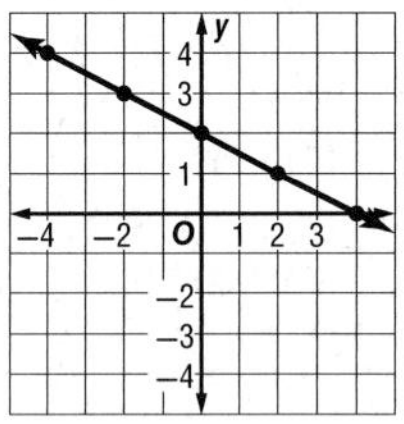

Wednesday

3. Which equation can be used to predict the number of tickets sold at the twelfth basketball game of the season? (Lesson 4-5) (8.11.07) **C**

Ⓐ $y = 150x - 29{,}998$
Ⓑ $y = 150x - 200$
Ⓒ $y = 150x - 100$
Ⓓ $y = 83\frac{1}{3}x - 33\frac{1}{3}$
Ⓔ $y = 75x - 50$

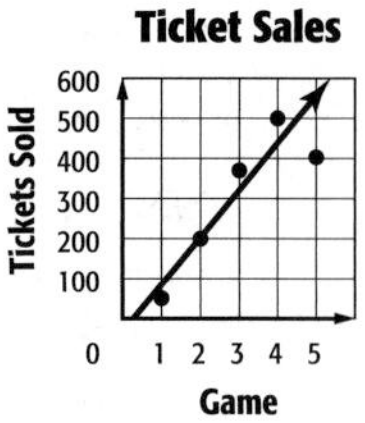

Thursday

4. For each of 10 days in May, Darren recorded the number of miles and the temperature in which he walked. This information is shown. Using the scatter plot and the line of fit decide about how far Darren walked in 77° weather. (Lesson 4-5) (8.11.07) **H**

Ⓕ 1.1 miles
Ⓖ 1.2 miles
Ⓗ 2.4 miles
Ⓙ 2.8 miles
Ⓚ 7 miles

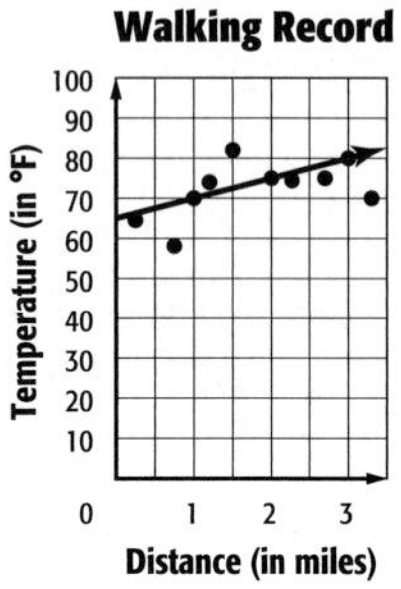

Friday

5. **WorkKeys® Level 4** Each month the doctor rents an office and pays $2500 for rent, $100 per parking space he rents for his patients, and toward the annual building association dues of $3450 paid in equal monthly installments. How many parking spaces did the doctor reserve for his patients if he paid $15,562.50 for 3 months rent? (Lesson 4-1) (6.11.13) **B**

Ⓐ 15 spaces Ⓑ 24 spaces Ⓒ 33 spaces Ⓓ 42 spaces Ⓔ 72 spaces

Week 15

NEED EXTRA HELP?					
If You Missed Question...	1	2	3	4	5
Go to Lesson...	4-7	4-4	4-5	4-5	4-1
IL Assessment Objectives	8.11.13	8.11.11	8.11.07	8.11.07	6.11.13

Week 14

Monday

1. Tyrone is standing next to a tree and in the tree's shadow creating the similar triangles shown. How far is Tyrone standing from the tree? (Lesson 2-6) (9.11.12) **D**

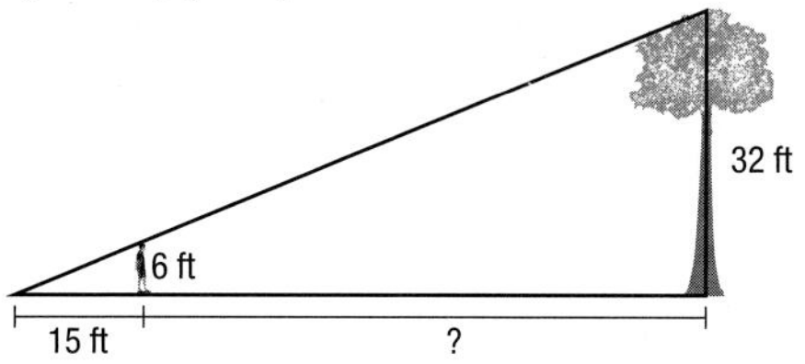

Ⓐ 2.8 ft
Ⓑ 12.8 ft
Ⓒ 17.8 ft
Ⓓ 65 ft
Ⓔ 80 ft

Tuesday

2. On Monday, Cody drove 113.6 miles and used 3.55 gallons of gasoline. Each gallon of gasoline costs $3.49. If Cody had only driven one fourth of the distance of his trip on Monday, about how much will he spend on gasoline for the entire round trip? (Lesson 0-1) (6.11.17) **J**

Ⓕ about $12.39
Ⓖ about $16
Ⓗ about $64
Ⓙ about $112
Ⓚ about $880

Wednesday

3. On a blueprint, the height of the wall is drawn as 4.7 inches. The actual height of the wall in the building is 16.45 feet. A second wall is to be built parallel to the first with an actual height 3.55 feet higher. What is the height of the second wall on the blueprint? (Lesson 2-6) (6.11.17) **C**

Ⓐ 20 inches
Ⓑ 6 inches
Ⓒ 5.7 inches
Ⓓ 3.7 inches
Ⓔ 1 inch

Thursday

4. On a map, the actual distances of 1,440 miles, 288 miles, and 800 miles must be represented. Which of the following scales produces the total distance as 79 inches on the map? (Lesson 2-6) (6.11.17) **G**

Ⓕ scale: 1 inch = 33 miles
Ⓖ scale: 1 inch = 32 miles
Ⓗ scale: 1 inch = 30 miles
Ⓙ scale: 1 inch = 25 miles
Ⓚ scale: 1 inch = 20 miles

Friday

5. **WorkKeys® Level 3** Kendra and Nicolleta attend The School of the Art Institute of Chicago. They each needed to bring canvas to class. Kendra brought 1.6 meters of canvas and Nicolleta brought 1.7 yards. Who brought more canvas to class? By how much? (Lesson CSB1) (6.11.10) **A**

Ⓐ Kendra, by 2.8 inches
Ⓑ Kendra, by $2.\overline{3}$ feet
Ⓒ Kendra, by $0.\overline{7}$ yards
Ⓓ Nicolleta, 0.07 m
Ⓔ Nicolleta, by 7 cm

Choice Analysis

1. A Reversed numbers in proportion.
B Multiplied the heights and divided the product by 15.
C Reversed numbers in proportion and added found measure to the given 15 ft.
D CORRECT
E Total length of tree's shadow

2. F Exact amount spent for one fourth of trip
G Estimate for one fourth of trip
H Estimate for one complete one way of trip
J CORRECT
K Used the estimate of total miles of round trip

3. A actual height of the second wall in feet
B Divided the sum of the blueprint and the actual heights of the first wall by the scale.
C CORRECT
D Subtracted 3.55 ft from 16.45 ft.
E Just found the scale of 3.55 ft.

4. F Total distance = 76.61 in.
G CORRECT
H Total distance = 83 in.
J Total distance = 101.12 in.
K Total distance = 126.4 in.

5. A CORRECT
B $5.\overline{3}$ ft − 5.1 ft = $0.2\overline{3}$ feet
C $1.\overline{7}$ yd − 1.7 yd = $0.0\overline{7}$ yd
D Kendra has more by 0.07 m.
E Kendra has more by 7 cm.

Week 14

NEED EXTRA HELP?

If You Missed Question...	1	2	3	4	5
Go to Lesson...	2-6	0-1	2-6	2-6	CSB1
IL Assessment Objectives	9.11.12	6.11.17	6.11.17	6.11.17	6.11.10

Choice Analysis

1. **A** Simplifies to $34 > 2x$.
   B Simplifies to $33 < x$.
   C CORRECT
   D Simplifies to $33 > x$.
   E Simplifies to $34 < x$.

2. **F** Students confuse when to use open and closed circles.
   G CORRECT
   H This would be the solution for $x < 3$ and $x > -1\frac{2}{3}$.
   J This would be the solution for $x < 3$ or $x > -1\frac{2}{3}$, all real numbers.
   K This would be the solution for $x > 3$ and $x < -1\frac{2}{3}$, no real numbers.

3. **A** Used higher pay rate, but did not subtract taxes and rounded 5.9 to 5 weeks.
   B Used higher pay rate, but did not subtract taxes.
   C Used current pay rate and did not subtract taxes.
   D CORRECT
   E Used current pay rate.

4. **F** The amount added to 2.7 lb cannot be greater than the 5.1 lb the containers can hold.
   G The amount added to 2.7 lb cannot be greater than 5.1 lb.
   H The amount added must fit into both containers, not one or the other.
   J CORRECT
   K The amount added to 2.7 lb cannot be greater than the amount the containers can hold.

5. **A** $8b + 12w > 400$; $396 < 400$
   B $8b + 12w > 400$; $364 < 400$
   C $8b + 12w > 400$; $388 < 400$
   D $8b + 12w > 400$; $392 < 400$
   E CORRECT

Countdown PLUS to the PSAE

Week 13

Monday

1. Which inequality has the solution $34 > x$? (Lesson 5-3) (8.11.01) **C**

Ⓐ $3x - 10 > 5x - 44$
Ⓑ $7x + 8 < 8x - 25$
Ⓒ $4(x + 2) > 6(x - 10)$
Ⓓ $-2x - 21 < -3(x - 4)$
Ⓔ $-8(x - 7) < -5x - 46$

Tuesday

2. Which is the graph of the solution for $|3x - 2| > 7$? (Lesson 5-5) (8.11.08) **G**

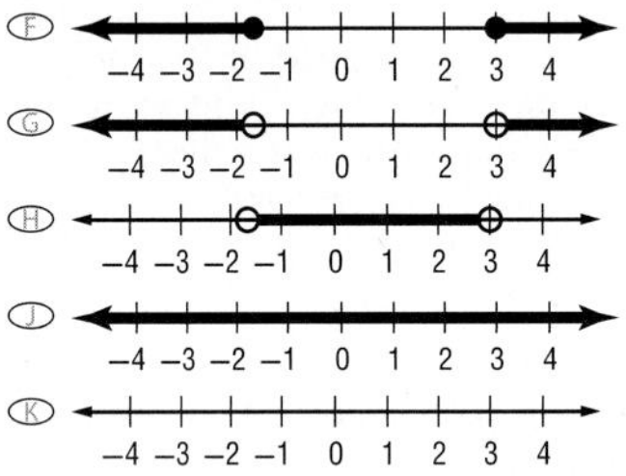

Wednesday

3. Anthony needs to save $5,000 for his next semester of college. He works as a math tutor five days each week for 6 hours a day and earns $25 an hour. Each day he works, $30 is subtracted from his earnings for taxes. If he can get a raise of $3.25 an hour, about how many full weeks would it take to earn the necessary amount for his tuition? (Lesson 5-2) (8.11.16) **D**

Ⓐ 5 weeks
Ⓑ 6 weeks
Ⓒ 7 weeks
Ⓓ 8 weeks
Ⓔ 9 weeks

Thursday

4. Julia has a container that holds a maximum of 5.1 pounds. Her sister has a container that holds a maximum of 9.4 pounds. Both containers are filled with 2.7 pounds of rice. Julia wants to buy a bag of rice to evenly divide between the two containers. Which compound inequality will help her decide the amount that can be added to each container? (Lesson 5-4) (8.11.19) **J**

Ⓕ $5.1 \le x + 2.7 \le 9.4$
Ⓖ $5.1 \le x + 2.7$ or $x + 2.7 \le 9.4$
Ⓗ $5.1 \ge x + 2.7$ or $x + 2.7 \le 9.4$
Ⓙ $5.1 \ge x + 2.7$ and $x + 2.7 \le 9.4$
Ⓚ $5.1 \le x + 2.7$ and $x + 2.7 \ge 9.4$

Friday

5. **WorkKeys® Level 4** You paid a $400 entrance fee to sell hand-made items at the trade show. You sell leather bookmarks for $8 each and leather wallets for $12 each. Which of the following combinations earn more than the entrance fee? (Lesson 5-6) (8.11.16) **E**

Ⓐ 21 bookmarks, 19 wallets
Ⓑ 20 bookmarks, 17 wallets
Ⓒ 20 bookmarks, 19 wallets
Ⓓ 19 bookmarks, 20 wallets
Ⓔ 18 bookmarks, 24 wallets

IL8

Week 13

NEED EXTRA HELP?					
If You Missed Question...	1	2	3	4	5
Go to Lesson...	5-3	5-5	5-2	5-4	5-6
IL Assessment Objectives	8.11.01	8.11.08	8.11.16	8.11.19	8.11.16

Week 12

Monday

1. Which is the solution to the following system of equations?
Twelve times a number x increased by the product of four and a number y.
Three times the number y more than the opposite of the number x.
(Lesson 6-2) (8.11.17) **C**

Ⓐ No solution
Ⓑ Infinite number of solutions
Ⓒ $(2, -3)$
Ⓓ $(-3, 2)$
Ⓔ $\left(3\frac{1}{4}, 2\right)$

Tuesday

2. Diana bought a total of 10 moving boxes in two different sizes. Some hold a total of 4 pounds and others hold a total of 3 pounds. Once packed, the total combined weight of the moving boxes was 36 pounds. Which augmented matrix can represent the number of each type of box sold if x represents the number of larger boxes purchased? (Lesson 6-7) (8.11.17) **G**

Ⓕ $\left[\begin{array}{cc|c} 1 & 0 & 4 \\ 0 & 1 & 6 \end{array}\right]$
Ⓖ $\left[\begin{array}{cc|c} 1 & 0 & 6 \\ 0 & 1 & 4 \end{array}\right]$
Ⓗ $\left[\begin{array}{cc|c} 1 & 0 & 2 \\ 0 & 1 & 8 \end{array}\right]$
Ⓙ $\left[\begin{array}{cc|c} 1 & 0 & 8 \\ 0 & 1 & 2 \end{array}\right]$
Ⓚ $\left[\begin{array}{cc|c} 1 & 0 & 7 \\ 0 & 1 & 3 \end{array}\right]$

Wednesday

3. Suppose local businesses decide to donate \$6 per student so that each school can grow a garden. How much more will West Caroll receive than the other two districts combined? (Lesson 6-6) (6.11.03) **E**

Ⓐ \$14,514
Ⓑ \$6510
Ⓒ \$6066
Ⓓ \$5484
Ⓔ \$3546

	Students in School Districts
Mulberry Grove	420
West Carroll	1,505
Arthur	494

Thursday

4. Given $y < x - 4$, which inequality will create a system of inequalities with (5, 0) as one of the solutions? (Lesson 6-8) (8.11.16) **J**

Ⓕ $y - x > 5$
Ⓖ $2y - 2x > 14$
Ⓗ $-2x + y > -3$
Ⓙ $4x + y > 3$
Ⓚ $y + 3x > 15$

Friday

5. **WorkKeys® Level 6** Sara has 5 less than four times the number of points Tracie has. Together they have a total of 50 points. Which student has more points and by how many? (Lesson 6-5) (8.11.17) **B**

Ⓐ Tracie, 18 points more
Ⓑ Sara, 18 points more
Ⓒ Tracie, 32 points more
Ⓓ Sara, 32 points more
Ⓔ Tracie, 11 points more

Choice Analysis

1. A This occurs when the lines are parallel and these are not.
B This occurs when the two equations name the same line and these do not.
C CORRECT
D Reversed coordinates.
E Substituted the value of x as the y-value.

2. F (4, 6); total weight = 34 lb
G CORRECT
H (2, 8); total weight = 32 lb
J (8, 2); total weight = 38 lb
K (7, 3); total weight = 37 lb

3. A Added amount to 3 schools.
B Subtracted Arthur only.
C Subtracted Mulberry Grove only.
D Total of two smaller schools.
E CORRECT

4. F The inequalities are parallel lines without any intersection.
G The inequalities are parallel lines without any intersection.
H (5, 0) is not a solution.
J CORRECT
K (5, 0) is not a solution.

5. A Tracie has fewer points than Sara.
B CORRECT
C Tracie has fewer points than Sara.
D Added not subtracted when simplifying equations.
E Total points Tracie has.

Week 12

NEED EXTRA HELP?					
If You Missed Question...	1	2	3	4	5
Go to Lesson...	6-2	6-7	6-6	6-8	6-5
IL Assessment Objectives	8.11.17	8.11.17	6.11.03	8.11.16	8.11.17

Choice Analysis

1. A Solution is $\left(3, 1\frac{5}{8}\right)$.

B Solution is $\left(3, \frac{1}{3}\right)$.

C Solution is $(2, -1)$.

D CORRECT

E Solution is $\left(\frac{3}{7}, 4\right)$.

2. F Percent of lunches not sold that are from Lunch 4 School A

G Percent of lunches sold that are from Lunch 3 School A

H Percent of lunches not sold that are from Lunch 1 School A

J Percent of lunches not sold that are from Lunch 2 School A

K CORRECT

3. A Hours volunteered Weeks 2-3

B Used number of hours as percent.

C Hours volunteered in Week 1

D CORRECT

E Hours volunteered Weeks 4-5

4. F Switched the coordinates in the point-slope form of a line.

G Subtracted 500 from both sides of the point-slope form of a line.

H Switched slope and x-coordinate in point-slope form of a line.

J CORRECT

K Added y-coordinate and $116\frac{2}{3}$ in point-slope form of a line.

5. A Needs $380 just for expenses.

B Needs $80 just for expenses.

C Savings = $300

D CORRECT

E Savings = $420

Week 11

Monday

1. Which system of equations has a solution with coordinates that are opposites? (Lesson 6-3) (8.11.17) **D**

Ⓐ $4(a - 2b) = 10$ and $7a + 8b = 23$
Ⓑ $6a - 3b = 17$ and $4a + 3b = 13$
Ⓒ $4a - 3b = 11$ and $3(2a + b) = 9$
Ⓓ $5a - 4b = 27$ and $-5a + 2b = -21$
Ⓔ $-7a + 2b = 5$ and $7a + 3b = 15$

Tuesday

2. The matrices show the number of school lunches prepared and the number of those lunches that were purchased in two schools. About what percent of the lunches not sold in School A were from the third lunch? (Lesson 6-6) (6.11.03) **K**

Ⓕ 7.1%
Ⓖ 13.2%
Ⓗ 14.3%
Ⓙ 28.6%
Ⓚ 50%

Schools	A	B	A	B
Lunch 1	66	72	64	70
Lunch 2	54	68	50	67
Lunch 3	37	75	30	70
Lunch 4	84	75	83	72
	Lunches Prepared		Lunches Purchased	

Wednesday

3. Layla recorded her total volunteer hours in a line graph. What percent of the total hours are the hours she volunteered between weeks 3 and 4? (Lesson 0-13) (10.11.01) **D**

Ⓐ 0%
Ⓑ 5%
Ⓒ 10%
Ⓓ 25%
Ⓔ 40%

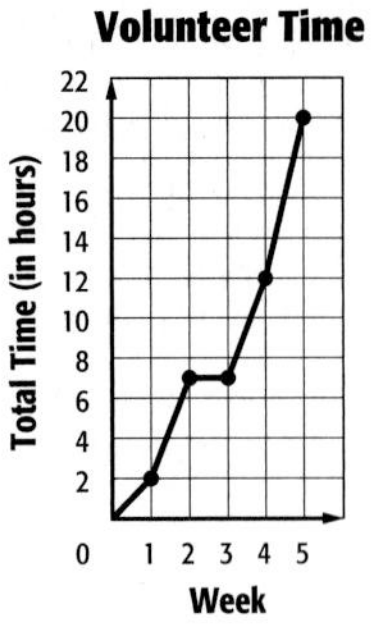

Thursday

4. Tyler opened a new business and kept track of his sales amounts. Using this scatter plot, what will Tyler predict for the amount of sales in month 10? (Lesson 4-5) (10.11.01) **J**

Ⓕ −$57,165.67
Ⓖ −$550
Ⓗ $393.33
Ⓙ $1,550
Ⓚ $1,783

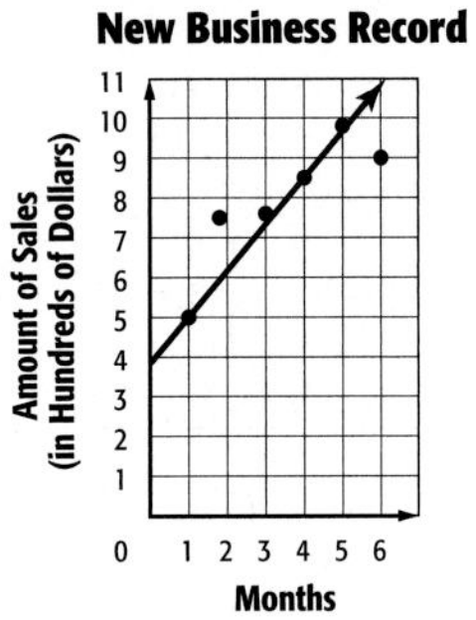

Friday

5. **WorkKeys® Level 3** You created the inequality $y \geq 4x - 480$, in which x is your weekly salary and y is the amount remaining each month after expenses are paid. Which amount of weekly salary leaves a savings of $320? (Lesson 5-6) (8.11.16) **D**

Ⓐ $25
Ⓑ $100
Ⓒ $195
Ⓓ $200
Ⓔ $225

Week 11

NEED EXTRA HELP?

If You Missed Question...	1	2	3	4	5
Go to Lesson...	6-3	6-6	0-13	4-5	5-6
IL Assessment Objectives	8.11.17	6.11.03	10.11.01	10.11.01	8.11.16

Week 10

Monday

1. Circle A is inscribed in a square. Which simplified polynomial represents the unshaded area? (Lesson 7-1) (7.11.03) **D**

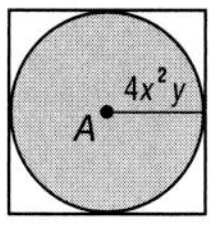

Ⓐ $4x^2y(2 - \pi)$
Ⓑ $8x^2y(8x^2y - \pi)$
Ⓒ $8x^4y^3(2 - \pi)$
Ⓓ $16x^4y^2(4 - \pi)$
Ⓔ $16x^4y^2(1 - \pi)$

Tuesday

2. Which expression does not simplify to $\frac{1}{2}m^8p^{14}$? (Lesson 7-1) (8.11.01) **K**

Ⓕ $\frac{1}{2}(m^4p^7)^2$
Ⓖ $(2mp)^2\left(\frac{1}{2}m^2p^4\right)^3$
Ⓗ $\left(\frac{1}{4}mp\right)^2(2mp^3)^3(m^5p^3)$
Ⓙ $\left(\frac{1}{4}m^2p^3\right)^3(32m^2p^5)$
Ⓚ $\left(\frac{1}{6}m^4p\right)^2\left[(2p^3)^2\right]^2$

Wednesday

3. The manager wanted to keep record of the total number of hours his employees worked. He knows that Tom works 5 hours more than Joe, Joe works 6 hours less than Zack, and Zack works 3 hours more than Tom. Which simplified expression is the total number of hours the three employees work? Let j represent the number of hours Joe works. (Lesson 7-5) (8.11.14) **C**

Ⓐ $j + 11$
Ⓑ $3j + 12$
Ⓒ $3j + 15$
Ⓓ $3j + 27$
Ⓔ $j^3 + 27$

Thursday

4. Set each pair of expressions equal to each other to make an equation. Then, solve each equation. Which variable does not have a value less than 1? (Lesson 7-6) (8.11.16) **J**

Ⓕ $3a(5a - 4) - a(a - 2)$ and $-10a(-a - 3) + 4(a^2 - 2a - 5)$
Ⓖ $-3(2c^2 - 4c + 3) - c(c + 6)$ and $-5(c^2 - c - 1) - 2c(c + 4)$
Ⓗ $2e(-3e + 4) + 7(e^2 - 4e + 7)$ and $-2e(e - 4) + 3(e^2 - 6e + 8)$
Ⓙ $m(-2m + 5) + 4(m^2 - 2m + 8)$ and $m(m - 5) - (-m^2 - 9m - 5)$
Ⓚ $-5v(-2v + 5) - 8(v^2 - v - 4)$ and $6(-2v^2 - 5v - 3) + 2v(7v - 9)$

Friday

5. **WorkKeys® Level 5** A company is painting their circular logo on each side of their large warehouse. The logo has a radius of 4.15×10^3 centimeters. What is the area of the logo? (Lesson 7-3) (7.11.03) **D**

Ⓐ 17.2225π cm^2
Ⓑ 8300π cm^2
Ⓒ $17{,}222.5\pi$ cm^2
Ⓓ $172{,}225\pi$ cm^2
Ⓔ $172{,}225{,}000\pi$ cm^2

Week 10

NEED EXTRA HELP?					
If You Missed Question...	1	2	3	4	5
Go to Lesson...	7-1	7-1	7-5	7-6	7-3
IL Assessment Objectives	7.11.03	8.11.01	8.11.14	8.11.16	7.11.03

Choice Analysis

1. A Correct area formulas not used.
B Used circumference formula instead of area of circle.
C Adds exponents instead of multiplying and multiplies exponents and coefficients.
D CORRECT
E Used radius as side length of square instead of diameter.

2. F Added exponents instead of multiplying.
G Multiplied exponents instead of added in last step.
H Did not correctly square fraction or cube 2.
J Did not reduce the fraction correctly.
K CORRECT

3. A Subtracted Joe's time from total.
B Did not include the 3 hours Zack worked more than Joe.
C CORRECT
D Incorrectly added 6 hours, meaning Joe worked 6 hours more than Zack.
E Multiplied instead of added.

4. F $a = \frac{5}{8}$
G $c = -\frac{5}{9}$
H $e = -2\frac{1}{2}$
J CORRECT; $m = 3\frac{6}{7}$
K $v = -1\frac{19}{31}$

5. A Exponents were subtracted.
B Circumference formula used.
C Only one 10^3 was used.
D CORRECT
E Exponents were multiplied.

Choice Analysis

1. A Only divide in the first term by the GCF to simplify.

B When raising each power to -2, the exponents are multiplied by -2.

C 4 from the second term cubed equals 64 not 16 as in the third term.

D The reciprocal of the previous term is squared.

E CORRECT

2. F Assumed width of rectangle was $3.5x$.

G CORRECT

H Answered in terms of perimeter and assumed perimeter of triangle was half of rectangle's.

J Amount used for rectangle

K Total tin used for both

3. A Used circumference formula with $r = 2x$.

B Used $r = 2x$.

C Found the area of the outer section of the larger circle.

D CORRECT

E Found total area as if smaller circle was not inscribed.

4. F The median and the mode

G The range

H CORRECT

J Only added one 11 and found the mean of 7 numbers.

K Mean of the 6 given numbers

5. A CORRECT

B Balance if not charged the overdraft fee

C Balance after spending $14.25

D Balance as if deposited $4.97 without any withdrawals

E Balance without any withdrawals, only deposits

Countdown PLUS to the PSAE

Week 9

Monday

1. What is the pattern for the sequence? (Lesson 7-2) (8.11.04) **E**

$$\frac{16a^{-3}b^2c^{-4}}{8a^{-2}b^{-4}c^5}, \frac{a^2c^{18}}{4b^{12}}, \frac{16b^{24}}{a^4c^{36}}, \frac{a^8c^{72}}{256b^{48}}, \ldots$$

Ⓐ Divide by the previous term.
Ⓑ Multiply each factor by -2.
Ⓒ Cube the previous term.
Ⓓ Square the previous term.
Ⓔ Square the reciprocal of the previous term.

Tuesday

2. Tina is a metal sculptor. From tin, she cut out a rectangle with a length of $2x$ and a width that is 3.5 times greater than its length. She then cut out a triangle using the length from the rectangle as its base and the width as its height. How much tin did she use for the triangle? (Lesson 7-4) (7.11.03) **G**

Ⓕ $3.5x^2$ of tin
Ⓖ $7x^2$ of tin
Ⓗ $9x$ of tin
Ⓙ $14x^2$ of tin
Ⓚ $21x^2$ of tin

Wednesday

3. Use 3.14 for π. What is the area of the larger circle? (Lesson 7-4) (7.11.03) **D**

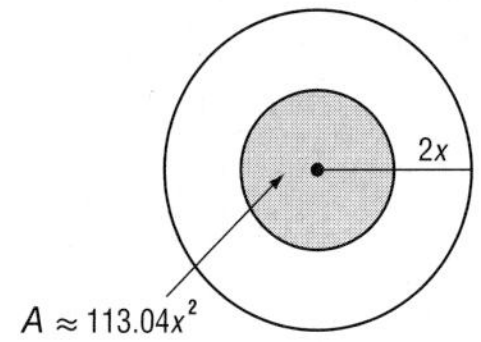

Ⓐ about $12.56x$
Ⓑ about $50.24x^2$
Ⓒ about $87.92x^2$
Ⓓ about $200.96x^2$
Ⓔ about $314x^2$

Thursday

4. The mode of the set of data is 11. The set contains 8 numbers. What is the mean of the set of data? (Lesson 0-12) (10.11.05) **H**

11, 15, 9, 18, 21, 9

Ⓕ 11
Ⓖ 12
Ⓗ 13.125
Ⓙ 13.429
Ⓚ $13.8\overline{3}$

Friday

5. WorkKeys® Level 4 Kyle attends Eastern Illinois University in Charleston. He arrived to school early to purchase his books and supplies from the school store and spent $14.25 and then $54.75. The balance of his checking account before these transactions was $68.97. He is charged an overdraft fee of $25. If he then deposits $30 what is the balance of his checking account? (Lesson 0-3) (6.11.10) **A**

Ⓐ $4.97　Ⓑ $30.03　Ⓒ $54.72　Ⓓ $73.94　Ⓔ $98.97

Week 9

NEED EXTRA HELP?					
If You Missed Question...	1	2	3	4	5
Go to Lesson...	7-2	7-4	7-4	0-12	0-3
IL Assessment Objectives	8.11.04	7.11.03	7.11.03	10.11.05	6.11.10

Week 8

Monday

1. A square has an area of $36x^2 + 60x + 25$. What is the difference when the length of the rectangle shown below is subtracted from the length of one side of the square? (Lesson 8-6) (7.11.03) **C**

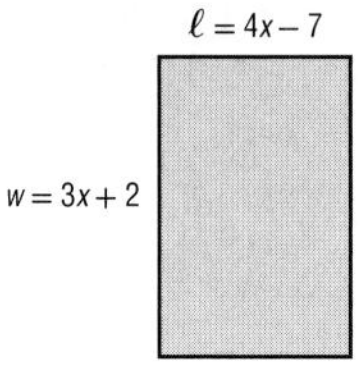

Ⓐ $10x - 2$
Ⓑ $5x + 12$
Ⓒ $2x + 12$
Ⓓ $-2x - 12$
Ⓔ 12

Tuesday

2. The formula $h = -16t^2 + (\text{initial velocity})t$ where t is the time in seconds is used to represent the height of a ball thrown in the air with an initial velocity measured in feet per second. Not including the initial height of the person throwing the ball, which initial velocity will make the ball land on the ground in about 3 seconds? (Lesson 8-2) (8.11.18) **H**

Ⓕ 60 feet per second
Ⓖ 54 feet per second
Ⓗ 50 feet per second
Ⓙ 44 feet per second
Ⓚ 40 feet per second

Wednesday

3. Which is the pattern for the following sequence? (Lesson 8-1) (8.11.04) **E**

$$3m, 6m^2p, 12m^3p^2, 24m^4p^3, \ldots$$

Ⓐ Multiply two previous factors.
Ⓑ Divide by $2mp$.
Ⓒ Add $3mp$.
Ⓓ Square the previous factor.
Ⓔ Multiply by $2mp$.

Thursday

5. The length of a picture is 4 inches greater than its width. A mat is being placed around the picture adding 0.5 inch to each side. If the area of the picture and the mat is 60 square inches, what is the length of the mat? (Lesson 8-3) (7.11.03) **J**

Ⓕ 5 inches
Ⓖ 6 inches
Ⓗ 9 inches
Ⓙ 10 inches
Ⓚ 11 inches

Friday

4. **WorkKeys® Level 5** You run a store exclusively for charity. You created formulas to price donated items for sale in the store, where x represents an amount in dollars. Which formula will price the item greater than \$2.50 but less than \$5.00? (Lesson 8-5) (8.11.02) **D**

Ⓐ $16x^3 - 100x$
Ⓑ $16x^3 - 400x$
Ⓒ $32x^3 - 968x$
Ⓓ $45x^3 - 405x$
Ⓔ $75x^3 - 300x$

Choice Analysis

1. A The length from the square $6x + 5$ was added to the length of the rectangle.
B Incorrect length of the square $9x + 5$ was used.
C CORRECT
D The length from the square was subtracted from the length of the rectangle.
E Incorrect length of the square $4x + 5$ was used.

2. F Lands in 3.75 seconds.
G Lands in 3.375 seconds.
H CORRECT; Lands in 3.125 seconds.
J Lands in 2.75 seconds. So, it lands before 3 seconds.
K Lands in 2.5 seconds. So, it lands before 3 seconds.

3. A The third term would than be $18m^3p$, not $12m^3p^2$.
B If the sequence was reversed and the last given term is the first, …, this is the pattern.
C Cannot add $3m$ and $3mp$, because they are not like terms.
D The third term would be $3m(3m) = 9m^2$, not $6m^2p$.
E CORRECT

4. F Price is \$2.50 per item.
G Price is \$5.00 per item.
H Price is \$5.50 per item.
J CORRECT, price is \$3.00.
K Price is \$2.00 per item.

5. A width of just the picture
B Mat's width = 5 + 0.5 + 0.5
C length of just the picture
D CORRECT
E Added all four 0.5 inches to length of picture.

Week 8

NEED EXTRA HELP?					
If You Missed Question...	1	2	3	4	5
Go to Lesson...	8-6	8-2	8-1	8-5	8-3
IL Assessment Objectives	7.11.03	8.11.18	8.11.04	7.11.03	8.11.02

Choice Analysis

1. A Only the solution of 3.5 remains the same.
B One of the solutions, 3.5, remains the same for each.
C One of the solutions, 3.5, remains the same for each.
D This reflects the sequence in reverse order.
E CORRECT

2. F CORRECT
G This is the difference in the negative amounts of time.
H This is the time it takes to reach the ground at 39 feet per second.
J This is the time it takes to reach the ground at 60 feet per second.
K Added instead of subtracting times.

3. A Linear; Only works when $x = 1$.
B Linear; Only works when $x = 2$.
C CORRECT
D Quadratic; Only works when $x = 4$.
E Quadratic; Only works when $x = 2$.

4. F $x = -2$ and 2
G $x = -2$
H CORRECT, $x = 2$
J $x = -2$ and 1.5
K $x = -2$ and -4

5. A Students divide incorrectly.
B CORRECT
C Students subtract the cost of one ticket instead of dividing the cost of one ticket.
D Students add the cost of one ticket instead of dividing the cost of one ticket.
E Students multiply by the cost of one ticket instead of dividing the cost of one ticket.

Countdown PLUS to the PSAE

Week 7

Monday

1. What pattern do you notice about the equations listed in the sequence? (Lesson 8-4) (8.11.04) **E**

$2x^2 - x - 21 = 0, 2x^2 - 3x - 14 = 0,$
$2x^2 - 11x + 14 = 0, 2x^2 - 13x + 21 = 0, \ldots$

Ⓐ both solutions remain the same
Ⓑ both solutions decrease
Ⓒ both solutions increase
Ⓓ one solution remains the same while the other decreases
Ⓔ one solution remains the same while the other increases

Tuesday

2. A ball is dropped from the top of a 100-foot building. The equation $-16t^2 + 39t + 100$ models its drop to the ground. What is the difference in seconds if the ball was dropped at an initial velocity of 60 feet per second? (Lesson 8-4) (8.11.18) **F**

Ⓕ 1 second
Ⓖ 1.25 seconds
Ⓗ 4 seconds
Ⓙ 5 seconds
Ⓚ 9 seconds

Wednesday

3. At the DuPage Children's Museum in Naperville, the admission is $7.50 per adult. On Friday afternoon, a total of $345 was collected from the sale of adult tickets. How many adult tickets had been sold? (Lesson 2-2) (6.11.10) **C**

Ⓐ 45 tickets
Ⓑ 46 tickets
Ⓒ 338 tickets
Ⓓ 353 tickets
Ⓔ 2,588 tickets

Thursday

4. Which equation when solved does not have a solution of -2? (Lesson 8-6) (8.11.16) **H**

Ⓕ $x^2 - 2 = 2$
Ⓖ $x^2 + 4x = -4$
Ⓗ $x^2 - 4x + 4 = 0$
Ⓙ $2x^2 + x = 6$
Ⓚ $x^2 + 6x = -8$

Friday

5. **WorkKeys® Level 4** Your company prints designs on fabric. You program a function into a machine to find the number of designs that will be printed on each yard of fabric. The table shows the number of designs per yard. Which function was used? (Lesson 8-2) (8.11.12) **B**

Yardage	Designs
0	0
1	65
2	140
3	225
4	320

Ⓐ $60x + 5$
Ⓑ $50x + 40$
Ⓒ $5x^2 + 60x$
Ⓓ $6x^2 + 56x$
Ⓔ $10x^2 + 20x$

Week 7

NEED EXTRA HELP?					
If You Missed Question...	1	2	3	4	5
Go to Lesson...	8-4	8-4	8-2	8-6	2-2
IL Assessment Objectives	8.11.04	8.11.18	6.11.10	8.11.16	8.11.12

Week 6

Monday

1. Which sequence has a seventh term that is less than and greater than 0? (Lesson 9-8) (8.11.04) **A**

Ⓐ 1875, 75, −15, …
Ⓑ 36, 29, 22, …
Ⓒ $-\frac{5}{9}, 1\frac{2}{3}, -5, \ldots$
Ⓓ −3, 3, 9, …
Ⓔ −18, −7, 4, …

Tuesday

2. Which pair of quadratic functions when graphed creates a pair of opposite parabolas? (Lesson 9-3) (8.11.07) **K**

Ⓕ $y = -\frac{1}{3}x^2 - 2$ and $y = -3x^2 - 2$
Ⓖ $y = -4x^2 - 6$ and $y = -4x^2 + 6$
Ⓗ $y = -6x^2 - 7$ and $y = \frac{1}{6}x^2 + 7$
Ⓙ $y = 5x^2 - 3$ and $y = 5x^2 + 3$
Ⓚ $y = -9x^2 - 6$ and $y = 9x^2 - 6$

Wednesday

3. Which is the function for the graph shown? (Lesson 9-1) (8.11.07) **B**

Ⓐ $y = -4x + 2$
Ⓑ $y = x^2 - 4x + 2$
Ⓒ $y = 2x^2 - 5x + 2$
Ⓓ $y = 3x^2 - 6x - 2$
Ⓔ $y = 3x^2 - 4x + 2$

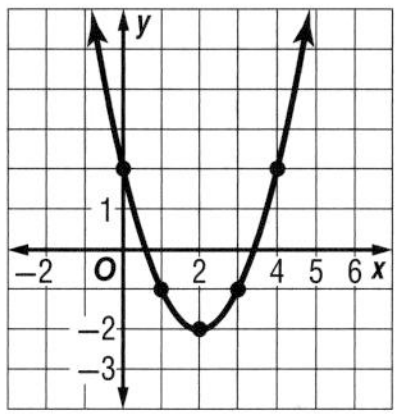

Thursday

4. Suppose the number of monthly visitors to Illinois State Park in Marseilles, was as recorded in the table. Which equation can be used to predict the number of visitors in month 10? (Lesson 9-9) (8.11.07) **F**

Month	May	June	July	Aug	Sept
Visitors	100	144	196	256	324

Ⓕ $y = 4x^2$
Ⓖ $y = 8x^2$
Ⓗ $y = 4x - 8$
Ⓙ $y = 8x - 4$
Ⓚ $y = 4 \cdot 8^x$

Friday

5. **WorkKeys® Level 3** The graph shows the path of a ball that was kicked up from the ground. Which point on the graph tells Dan how long the ball was in the air before landing on the ground? (Lesson 9-2) (8.11.13) **E**

Ⓐ Point *A*
Ⓑ Point *B*
Ⓒ Point *C*
Ⓓ Point *D*
Ⓔ Point *E*

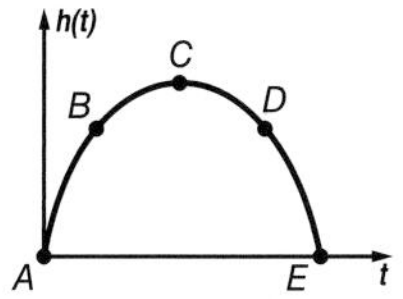

Choice Analysis

1. A CORRECT
B The seventh term is −6.
C The seventh term is −405.
D The seventh term is 33.
E The seventh term is 48.

2. F Only difference is dilation of parabolas.
G Only difference is the *y*-intercepts.
H Differences in dilation and *y*-intercepts.
J Only difference is the *y*-intercepts.
K CORRECT

3. A This is a linear equation.
B CORRECT
C Does not share more than (0, 2).
D *y*-intercept is (0, −2).
E Does not share more than (0, 2).

4. F CORRECT
G Used the second difference as *a*.
H The first differences are not equal. So, the values do not represent a linear function.
J The first differences are not equal. So, the values do not represent a linear function.
K The second differences were equal. So, the values do not represent an exponential function.

5. A Point actually represents −1 seconds, not realistic.
B This is a time the ball is still in the air.
C This is the time the ball reaches the highest point.
D This is a time the ball is still in the air.
E CORRECT

Week 6

NEED EXTRA HELP?					
If You Missed Question...	1	2	3	4	5
Go to Lesson...	9-8	9-3	9-1	9-9	9-2
IL Assessment Objectives	8.11.04	8.11.07	8.11.07	8.11.07	8.11.13

Choice Analysis

1. **A** This is notation for the parent function being transformed as described.
   B This is a linear function.
   C CORRECT
   D Notation for each transformation is reversed in the equation.
   E Transformations combined into −4 and distributed −4 through the entire equation for the given parabola.
2. **F** Ordered least to greatest.
   G CORRECT
   H Incorrectly thought −5 is greater than −1.4.
   J Incorrectly thought equations with two solutions are greater than the equation with one solution.
   K Found incorrect values for x.
3. **A** The area is $x^2 + 5x + 6.25$.
   B CORRECT
   C The area is $x^2 - 5x + 6.25$.
   D The area is $x^2 - 4.8x + 5.76$.
   E The area is $x^2 - 3x + 2.25$.
4. **F** Line does not enter Quadrant II.
   G Line does not enter Quadrant IV.
   H Line does not enter Quadrant II.
   J Line does not enter Quadrant I.
   K CORRECT
5. **A** These dimensions represent the sixth rectangle in the sequence.
   B These are the combined lengths and widths of the sixth rectangle in the sequence.
   C CORRECT
   D These are the combined lengths and widths of the seventh rectangle in the sequence.
   E These dimensions represent the eighth rectangle in the sequence.

Week 5

Monday

1. If the graph shown below is translated four units down and reflected across the x-axis, which will be its new equation? (Lesson 9-3) (8.11.07) **C**

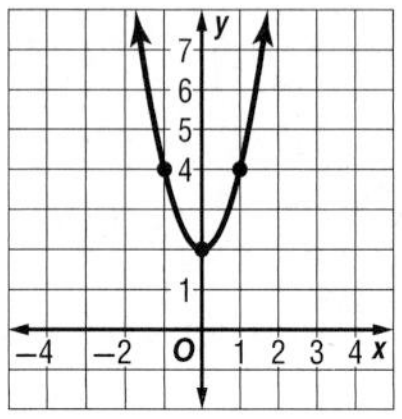

Ⓐ $y = -x^2 - 4$
Ⓑ $y = -2x - 2$
Ⓒ $y = -2x^2 - 2$
Ⓓ $y = -8x^2 - 2$
Ⓔ $y = -8x^2 - 8$

Tuesday

2. What is the order of the equations so that the solutions are in order from greatest to least? (Lesson 9-5) (8.11.16) **G**

I. $11x^2 - 5x - 30$
II. $x^2 - 4x + 4$
III. $3x^2 + 13x - 10$

Ⓕ III, I, II
Ⓖ II, I, III
Ⓗ II, III, I
Ⓙ I, III, II
Ⓚ I, II, III

Wednesday

3. The area of a square is $x^2 - 5.2x + 6.76$. Which expression represents the length of each side of that square? (Lesson 9-4) (8.11.01) **B**

Ⓐ $x + 2.5$
Ⓑ $x - 2.6$
Ⓒ $x - 2.5$
Ⓓ $x - 2.4$
Ⓔ $x - 1.5$

Thursday

4. Which linear equation when graphed does not enter Quadrant III on the coordinate plane? (Lesson 3-1) (8.11.11) **K**

Ⓕ $y = 4x - 5$
Ⓖ $y = 2x + 3$
Ⓗ $y = 2x - 4$
Ⓙ $y = -2x - 2$
Ⓚ $y = -3x + 4$

Friday

5. **WorkKeys® Level 6** You created an art piece of different rectangles. Each rectangle in the art piece is a term in a sequence. The rectangle below was used in the creation of the sequence: 34, 102, 306, 918, …. What are the dimensions of the rectangle represented by the seventh term in this sequence? (Lesson 9-8) (8.11.04) **C**

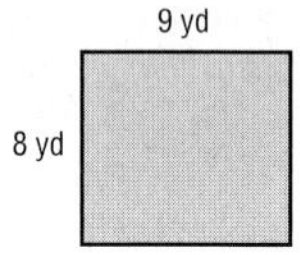

Ⓐ 2,065 yd and 2,066 yd
Ⓑ 4,130 yd and 4,132 yd
Ⓒ 6,196 yd and 6,197 yd
Ⓓ 12,393 yd and 12,394 yd
Ⓔ 18,589 yd and 18,590 yd

Week 5

NEED EXTRA HELP?					
If You Missed Question...	1	2	3	4	5
Go to Lesson...	9-3	9-5	9-4	3-1	9-8
IL Assessment Objectives	8.11.07	8.11.16	8.11.01	8.11.11	8.11.04

Countdown PLUS to the PSAE

Week 4

Monday

1. The distance on a coordinate plane between point A at (1, 3) and a point B is $\sqrt{32}$ units. If the x-coordinate of B is -3, what is the y-coordinate? (Lesson 10-6) (9.11.09) **D**

Ⓐ $3 + \sqrt{32}$
Ⓑ $\sqrt{28} - 3$
Ⓒ 1
Ⓓ -1
Ⓔ $3 - 4\sqrt{2}$

Tuesday

2. Diane is 5 feet tall and flying a kite at Lake Le-Aqua-Na State Recreation Area near Lena. The kite string she is holding has extended 11 feet in the air and has created a 36° angle parallel to the ground. How high is the kite from the ground to the nearest tenth? (Lesson 10-8) (9.11.19) **J**

Ⓕ 5 feet
Ⓖ 6.5 feet
Ⓗ 8.9 feet
Ⓙ 11.5 feet
Ⓚ 13.9 feet

Wednesday

3. Which function is shown in the graph? (Lesson 10-1) (8.11.07) **E**

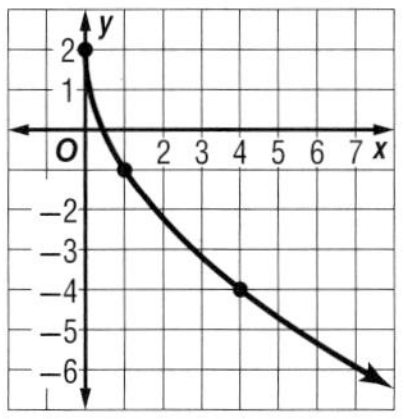

Ⓐ $y = x + 2$
Ⓑ $y = x^2 + 2$
Ⓒ $y = x^2 - 2x + 2$
Ⓓ $y = 3\sqrt{x} + 2$
Ⓔ $y = -3\sqrt{x} + 2$

Thursday

4. Which measure represents side x in the similar triangles? (Lesson 10-7) (9.11.19) **J**

Ⓕ 3.2
Ⓖ 11.3
Ⓗ 12.2
Ⓙ 16.5
Ⓚ 25.5

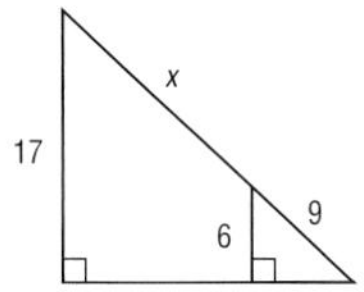

Friday

5. **WorkKeys® Level 5** Sebastian is 5 feet tall and his shadow is 1 foot 6 inches long. He is standing next to a tree that is casting a shadow that is 5.4 feet long. What is the difference in Sebastian's height and the height of the tree? (Lesson 10-7) (9.11.19) **C**

Ⓐ 1.62 feet
Ⓑ 6.62 feet
Ⓒ 13 feet
Ⓓ 18 feet
Ⓔ 23 feet

Week 4

NEED EXTRA HELP?					
If You Missed Question...	1	2	3	4	5
Go to Lesson...	10-6	10-8	10-1	10-7	10-7
IL Assessment Objectives	9.11.09	9.11.19	8.11.07	9.11.19	9.11.19

Choice Analysis

1. A Added distance to y-coordinate of point A
B Used the sum of x and y coordinates instead of difference
C Arithmetic error
D CORRECT
E guess

2. F This is Diane's height.
G This is the height of the kite from the top of Diane's head found using the sine ratio.
H The cosine ratio was used to find the height of the kite from Diane.
J CORRECT
K The cosine ratio was used to find the height of the kite from Diane and then added to Diane's height.

3. A This is a linear function.
B This is a quadratic function that would create a full parabola.
C This is a quadratic function that would create a full parabola.
D This would have the curve reflected over the x-axis.
E CORRECT

4. F Incorrectly arranged measures in proportion. This incorrect measure represents the larger hypotenuse.
G Incorrectly arranged proportion and added found amount to 9.
H Incorrectly arranged proportion and added found amount to 9.
J CORRECT
K Total length of larger hypotenuse

5. A Incorrectly arranged proportion; used incorrect amount as difference.
B Incorrectly arranged proportion; added incorrect amount to height of boy.
C CORRECT
D Height of tree
E Added instead of subtracting.

Choice Analysis

1. **A** Negative slope; $m = -\frac{45}{323}$
   B Positive slope greater than 1; $m = 12$
   C CORRECT
   D Negative slope; $m = -2\frac{81}{92}$
   E Positive slope greater than 1; $m = 1\frac{541}{549}$
2. **F** This is the numerator of the difference once the fraction has been renamed using the LCD, $x^2 + 6x + 8$.
   G This expression is multiplied by the numerator of the difference when it is renamed with the LCD.
   H This is the reciprocal.
   J CORRECT
   K This is the denominator from the first term.
3. **A** Reversed volumes and heights.
   B CORRECT
   C Height of second cone
   D Height of first cone
   E Total of heights instead of difference
4. **F** Dimensions are $2x$, $4x + 2$, $3x + 4$.
   G CORRECT
   H Dimensions are $2x$, $4x - 3$, $3x - 4$.
   J Dimensions are $2x$, $4x - 4$, $3x - 2$.
   K Dimensions are $2x$, $4x - 2$, $3x + 4$.
5. **A** Difference in the total time before teams and the total time after teams were created.
   B Total of the times from each team
   C Students incorrectly added the numerators and denominators without renaming.
   D This is the difference in the times before the teams were created.
   E CORRECT

Countdown PLUS to the PSAE

Week 3

Monday

1. Which of the lines that pass through the given pairs of points have a positive slope less than 1? (Lesson 11-7) (8.11.09) **C**

(A) $\left(-3\frac{3}{8}, 2\frac{1}{4}\right)$ and $\left(4\frac{7}{10}, 1\frac{1}{8}\right)$
(B) $\left(-1\frac{3}{10}, -2\frac{5}{7}\right)$ and $\left(-1\frac{1}{5}, -1\frac{3}{7}\right)$
(C) $\left(1\frac{1}{2}, 4\frac{3}{4}\right)$ and $\left(2\frac{7}{8}, 5\frac{5}{6}\right)$
(D) $\left(3\frac{1}{2}, -4\right)$ and $\left(1\frac{1}{5}, 2\frac{5}{8}\right)$
(E) $\left(3\frac{4}{5}, 6\frac{2}{3}\right)$ and $\left(-2\frac{3}{10}, -5\frac{4}{9}\right)$

Tuesday

2. What is the difference between the terms in the given sequence? (Lesson 11-6) (8.11.04) **J**

$$\frac{4x}{x+4}, \frac{5x^2 + 12x}{x^2 + 6x + 8}, \frac{6x^2 + 16x}{x^2 + 6x + 8}, \ldots$$

(F) $x(x + 4)$
(G) $x + 4$
(H) $\frac{x+2}{x}$
(J) $\frac{x}{x+2}$
(K) $\frac{x}{x+4}$

Wednesday

3. The volume of Cone A is about 847.8 cubic centimeters. The volume of Cone B is about 753.6 cubic centimeters. What is the difference in length of the radii of both cones? (Lesson 11-3) (7.11.03) **B**

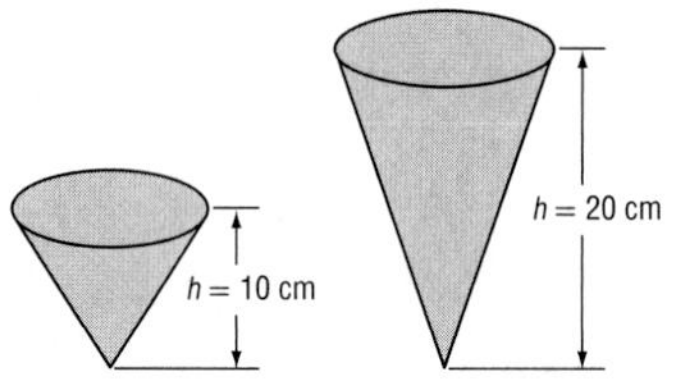

Cone A   Cone B

(A) 2 cm
(B) 3 cm
(C) 6 cm
(D) 9 cm
(E) 15 cm

Thursday

4. The volumes of different rectangular prisms are given. Which rectangular prism has a dimension of $4x - 2$? (Lesson 11-3) (8.11.06) **G**

(F) $24x^3 + 44x^2 + 16x$
(G) $24x^3 - 44x^2 + 16x$
(H) $24x^3 - 50x^2 + 24x$
(J) $24x^3 - 40x^2 + 16x$
(K) $24x^3 + 20x^2 - 16x$

Friday

5. **WorkKeys® Level 6** Darla and Willard work during the morning shift at a company. Darla can create 6500 products in 2 hours 10 minutes. Willard can create 6500 of the same products in 1 hour 30 minutes. Scott and Heidi work during the evening shift. Scott can create 6500 of the same products in 2 hours 30 minutes. Heidi can create 6500 of the same products in 1 hour 15 minutes. If both people from each shift become a team and work together to create 6500 products, what is the difference in time to finish? (Lesson 11-8) (7.11.07) **E**

(A) 5 hours 42 minutes
(B) 1 hour 43 minutes
(C) 20 minutes
(D) 5 minutes
(E) 3 minutes

Week 3

NEED EXTRA HELP?					
If You Missed Question...	1	2	3	4	5
Go to Lesson...	11-7	11-6	11-3	11-3	11-8
IL Assessment Objectives	8.11.09	8.11.04	7.11.03	8.11.06	7.11.07

Week 2

Monday

1. The table lists the number of tickets sold during each movie showing in a movie theater in Skokie. The mean of the number of tickets sold for the seven movie showings is $25\frac{1}{7}$. What is the difference between the median and the mean? (Lesson 12-2) (10.11.05) **E**

Ⓐ $51\frac{1}{7}$
Ⓑ 26
Ⓒ $1\frac{6}{7}$
Ⓓ $1\frac{1}{7}$
Ⓔ $\frac{6}{7}$

Movie Times	Tickets Sold
8 A.M.	12
10:30 A.M.	24
1 P.M.	14
3:30 P.M.	27
6 P.M.	?
8:30 P.M.	35
11 P.M.	38

Wednesday

3. A simple random sample of students were asked their favorite type of book to read. About what percent liked to read either nonfiction or mystery? (Lesson 12-2) (10.11.01) **B**

Ⓐ about 54%
Ⓑ about 53%
Ⓒ about 47%
Ⓓ about 37%
Ⓔ about 17%

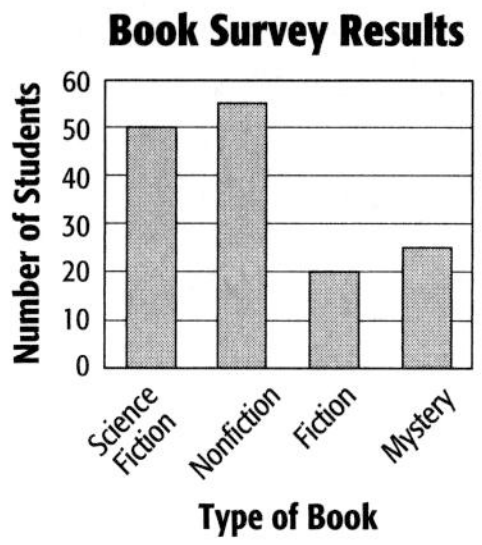

Tuesday

2. Stephanie answered 15 out of 22 multiple-choice items correctly by guessing. Each multiple-choice item has 2 answer choices. Which simulation cannot be used to find how many of the next 22 multiple-choice items she would answer correctly while guessing? (Lesson 12-7) (10.11.08) **H**

Ⓕ spinning a spinner with 2 equal sectors
Ⓖ a spinner with 4 equal sectors
Ⓗ a number cube with 4 of the sides covered
Ⓙ flipping a coin
Ⓚ flipping a red and yellow counter

Thursday

4. A store randomly called 1,000 people who purchased a DVD player and asked the number of days it was used between Friday and Sunday. The data is shown. What is the probability that the customers used the DVD player during at most 2 of these days? (Lesson 12-6) (10.11.07) **K**

Ⓕ about 5.6%
Ⓖ about 31.5%
Ⓗ about 41.8%
Ⓙ about 47%
Ⓚ about 52.8%

DVD Player Usage

Days Used	Probability
0	?
1	0.103
2	0.315
3	0.472

Friday

5. **WorkKeys® Level 3** Teresa writes each letter of the word MATHEMATICS on a separate index card. If she draws two cards without replacement, what is the probability she will draw a vowel and then a consonant in that order? (Lesson 12-5) (10.11.08) **C**

Ⓐ about 6.4%
Ⓑ about 23.1%
Ⓒ about 25.5%
Ⓓ about 28%
Ⓔ about 100%

Choice Analysis

1. A Sum of median and mean
B This is the median.
C This is the difference of the mean and a median of 27.
D This is the difference of the mean and a median of 24.
E CORRECT

2. F The two halves equally represent the two answer choices.
G The two halves equally represent the two answer choices.
H CORRECT
J The two sides equally represent the two answer choices.
K The two sides equally represent the two answer choices.

3. A Incorrectly rounded up $53.\overline{3}\%$.
B CORRECT
C Percent who liked science fiction or fiction
D Percent who liked nonfiction
E Percent who liked mystery

4. F Found difference of the probabilities of at most 2 days used and only 3 days used.
G Found probability that was used 2 of the 3 days.
H Found probability that was used 1 or 2 of the 3 days.
J guess
K CORRECT

5. A Found the sum $\frac{4}{11}$ and $\frac{7}{10}$ and then subtracted 100%.
B Assumed replacement.
C CORRECT
D Assumed 10 cards and replacement.
E Added $\frac{4}{11}$ and $\frac{7}{11}$ to find the probability of picking either a consonant or vowel.

Week 2

NEED EXTRA HELP?					
If You Missed Question...	1	2	3	4	5
Go to Lesson...	12-2	12-7	12-2	12-6	12-5
IL Assessment Objectives	10.11.05	10.11.08	10.11.01	10.11.07	10.11.08

Choice Analysis

1. **A** Subtracted 2.25 lb and 2.2 lb as if Susan had 1 kg of flour.
   B CORRECT
   C Divided 1.4 kg by 2.2 lb instead of multiplying.
   D Multiplied 1.4 kg times 16 oz.
   E Subtracted unlike amounts.

2. **F** guess
   G Confused percent with actual number of people.
   H CORRECT
   J Added the number of people and the spin.
   K Assumed 1 meant a total set of 20 people.

3. **A** Confuse people who visit at most once a day with those who only visit once a day.
   B Substitute the probability of visiting twice with the probability of visiting zero times.
   C CORRECT
   D Only subtracted the probability of visiting once, not including the probability of visiting zero times.
   E Students thought visiting each day meant visiting only Sunday and Tuesday.

4. **F** guess
   G guess
   H guess
   J CORRECT
   K The percent of people that had been there before

5. **A** CORRECT
   B This is the measure of the angle the ladder forms with the ground.
   C Divided 13.7 and 22 then multiplied by 100.
   D This is the measure of the angle the building makes with the house.
   E guess

Week 1

Monday

1. Sandra has 1.4 kilogram of flour and Kaitlyn has 36 ounces of flour. Who has more flour? By about how much? (Lesson CSB1) (7.11.01) **B**

Ⓐ about 0.05 pounds
Ⓑ about 0.83 pounds
Ⓒ about 1.61 pounds
Ⓓ about 26.9 ounces
Ⓔ about 13.6 ounces

Tuesday

2. A restaurant offers 4 lunch meals. A spinner divided into fourths was used to simulate the probability of customers purchasing each meal. Each of 20 spins was recorded in the table. Yellow represents the chicken sandwich. Out of 120 customers, what is the probability that the chicken sandwich meal will be purchased? (Lesson 12-7) (10.11.07) **H**

Ⓕ 1 person
Ⓖ 5 people
Ⓗ 6 people
Ⓙ 7 people
Ⓚ 20 people

Color	Number of Spins
red	5
blue	6
yellow	?
green	8

Wednesday

3. A food store randomly asked 800 customers the number of days they visited the food store between Sunday and Tuesday. The data is shown. The survey showed 280 people visited only once in those three days. What is the difference in the number of customers who visit at most once and the number of customers who visit once a day each of the days? (Lesson 12-6) (10.11.07) **C**

Ⓐ 16 people
Ⓑ 48 people
Ⓒ 72 people
Ⓓ 88 people
Ⓔ 160 people

Food Store Visits	
Days Visited	**Probability**
3	0.46
2	0.17
1	?
0	?

Thursday

4. Suppose each of the guests on the first six school groups to The Adler Planetarium & Astronomy Museum in Chicago were asked if this was their first visit. Each group had 40 students. The numbers of students in each group to respond no are as follows: 24, 36, 17, 18, 21, and 35. What percentage of the groups had not been to the site before? (Lesson 12-2) (10.11.01) **J**

Ⓕ about 7.9%
Ⓖ about 9.4%
Ⓗ about 10.5%
Ⓙ about 37.1%
Ⓚ about 62.9%

Friday

5. **WorkKeys® Level 5** A ladder is leaning against the side of a house. The ladder reaches 22 feet up the side of the house. The ladder is placed 13.7 feet from the side of the house. What angle does the ladder form with the house? (Lesson 10-8) (9.11.19) **A**

Ⓐ 32°
Ⓑ 58°
Ⓒ 62°
Ⓓ 90°
Ⓔ 148°

Week 1

NEED EXTRA HELP?					
If You Missed Question...	1	2	3	4	5
Go to Lesson...	CSB1	12-7	12-6	12-2	10-8
IL Assessment Objectives	7.11.01	10.11.07	10.11.07	10.11.01	9.11.19

CHAPTER 0

Preparing for Algebra

Chapter 0 contains lessons on topics from previous courses. You can use this chapter in various ways.

- Begin the school year by taking the Pretest. If you need additional review, complete the lessons in this chapter. To verify that you have successfully reviewed the topics, take the Posttest.
- As you work through the text, you may find that there are topics you need to review. When this happens, complete the individual lessons that you need.
- Use this chapter for reference. When you have questions about any of these topics, flip back to this chapter to review definitions or key concepts.

CHAPTER 0 **Notes**

Using Chapter 0

The concepts presented in Chapter 0 are review from previous courses. You may wish to use all or some of the chapter at the beginning of the school year to refresh students' skills. Or you may wish to begin with Chapter 1 and use the Chapter 0 lessons as needed to reinforce prerequisite skills as you progress through the program.

Foldables Study Organizer

Each chapter of *Glencoe Algebra 1* features a Foldable Study Organizer students can make to organize their notes. Encourage students to use these tools to make their study time more productive.

Get Started on Chapter 0

You will review several concepts, skills, and vocabulary terms as you study Chapter 0. To get ready, identify important terms and organize your resources.

FOLDABLES® Study Organizer

Throughout this text, you will be invited to use Foldables to organize your notes.

Why should you use them?

- They help you organize, display, and arrange information.
- They make great study guides, specifically designed for you.
- You can use them as your math journal for recording main ideas, problem-solving strategies, examples, or questions you may have.
- They give you a chance to improve your math vocabulary.

How should you use them?

- Write general information – titles, vocabulary terms, concepts, questions, and main ideas – on the front tabs of your Foldable.
- Write specific information – ideas, your thoughts, answers to questions, steps, notes, and definitions – under the tabs.
- Use the tabs for:
  - math concepts in parts, like types of triangles,
  - steps to follow, or
  - parts of a problem, like *compare* and *contrast* (2 parts) or *what*, *where*, *when*, *why*, and *how* (5 parts).
- You may want to store your Foldables in a plastic zipper bag that you have three-hole punched to fit in your notebook.

When should you use them?

- Set up your Foldable as you begin a chapter, or when you start learning a new concept.
- Write in your Foldable every day.
- Use your Foldable to review for homework, quizzes, and tests.

New Vocabulary

English		Español
integer	p. P7	entero
absolute value	p. P11	valor absolute
opposites	p. P11	opuestos
reciprocal	p. P18	recíproco
perimeter	p. P23	perímetro
circle	p. P24	círculo
diameter	p. P24	diámetro
center	p. P24	centro
circumference	p. P24	circunferencia
radius	p. P24	radio
area	p. P26	area
volume	p. P29	volumen
surface area	p. P31	area de superficie
probability	p. P33	probabilidad
sample space	p. P33	espacio muestral
complements	p. P33	complementos
tree diagram	p. P34	diagrama de árbol
odds	p. P35	probabilidades
mean	p. P37	media
median	p. P37	mediana
mode	p. P37	moda
range	p. P38	rango
quartile	p. P38	cuartil
lower quartile	p. P38	cuartil inferior
upper quartile	p. P38	cuartil superior
bar graph	p. P40	gráfica de barras
histogram	p. P40	histograma
line graph	p. P41	gráfica lineal
circle graph	p. P41	gráfica circular
outliers	p. P42	valores atípicos

Multilingual eGlossary glencoe.com

IL Math Online glencoe.com

- Study the chapter online
- Explore **Math in Motion**
- Get extra help from your own **Personal Tutor**
- Use **Extra Examples** for additional help
- Take a **Self-Check Quiz**
- **Review Vocabulary** in fun ways

Determine whether you need an estimate or an exact answer. Then solve.

1. **SHOPPING** Addison paid \$1.29 for gum and \$0.89 for a package of notebook paper. She gave the cashier a \$5 bill. If the tax was \$0.14, how much change should Addison receive? exact; \$2.68

2. **DISTANCE** Luis rode his bike 1.2 miles to his friend's house, then 0.7 mile to the video store, then 1.9 miles to the library. If he rode the same route back home, about how far did he travel in all? estimate; about 8 mi

Find each sum or difference.

3. $20 + (-7)$ 13
4. $-15 + 6$ −9
5. $-9 - 22$ −31
6. $18.4 - (-3.2)$ 21.6
7. $23.1 + (-9.81)$ 13.29
8. $-5.6 + (-30.7)$ −36.3

Find each product or quotient.

9. $11(-8)$ −88
10. $-15(-2)$ 30
11. $63 \div (-9)$ −7
12. $-22 \div 11$ −2

Replace each ● with <, >, or = to make a true sentence.

13. $\frac{7}{20}$ ● $\frac{2}{5}$ <
14. 0.15 ● $\frac{1}{8}$ >

15. Order 0.5, $-\frac{1}{7}$, −0.2, and $\frac{1}{3}$ from least to greatest. $-0.2, -\frac{1}{7}, \frac{1}{3}, 0.5$

Find each sum or difference. Write in simplest form.

16. $\frac{5}{6} + \frac{2}{3}$ $1\frac{1}{2}$
17. $\frac{11}{12} - \frac{3}{4}$ $\frac{1}{6}$
18. $\frac{1}{2} + \frac{4}{9}$ $\frac{17}{18}$
19. $-\frac{3}{5} + \left(-\frac{1}{5}\right)$ $-\frac{4}{5}$

Find each product or quotient.

20. $2.4(-0.7)$ −1.68
21. $-40.5 \div (-8.1)$ 5

Name the reciprocal of each number.

22. $\frac{4}{11}$ $\frac{11}{4}$
23. $-\frac{3}{7}$ $-\frac{7}{3}$

Find each product or quotient. Write in simplest form.

24. $\frac{2}{21} \div \frac{1}{3}$ $\frac{2}{7}$
25. $\frac{1}{5} \cdot \frac{3}{20}$ $\frac{3}{100}$
26. $\frac{6}{25} \div \left(-\frac{3}{5}\right)$ $-\frac{2}{5}$
27. $\frac{1}{9} \cdot \frac{3}{4}$ $\frac{1}{12}$
28. $-\frac{2}{21} \div \left(-\frac{2}{15}\right)$ $\frac{5}{7}$
29. $2\frac{1}{2} \cdot \frac{2}{15}$ $\frac{1}{3}$

Express each percent as a fraction in simplest form.

30. 20% $\frac{1}{5}$
31. 7.5% $\frac{3}{40}$

Use the percent proportion to find each number.

32. 18 is what percent of 72? 25%
33. 35 is what percent of 200? 17.5%
34. 24 is 60% of what number? 40

35. **TEST SCORES** James answered 14 items correctly on a 16-item quiz. What percent did he answer correctly? 87.5%

36. **BASKETBALL** Emily made 75% of the baskets that she attempted. If she made 9 baskets, how many attempts did she make? 12

Find the perimeter and area of each figure.

37. 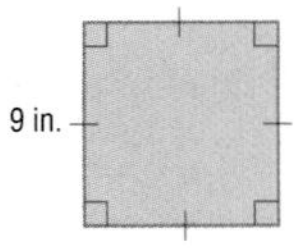

36 in.; 81 in^2

38. 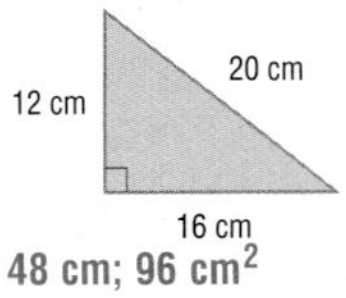

48 cm; 96 cm^2

39. A parallelogram has side lengths of 7 inches and 11 inches. Find the perimeter. 36 in.

40. **GARDENS** Find the perimeter of the garden. 23 m

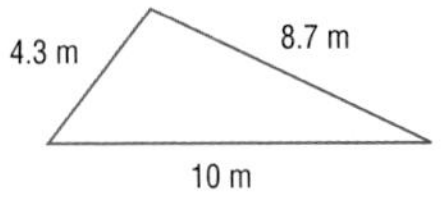

CHAPTER 0 Pretest

Using the Pretest

The Chapter 0 Pretest assesses students' understanding of the concepts presented in Chapter 0. You may use the pretest to determine whether students need to complete each lesson in Chapter 0 before beginning the content in Chapter 1.

Chapter 0 Pretest P3

Additional Answers

57.

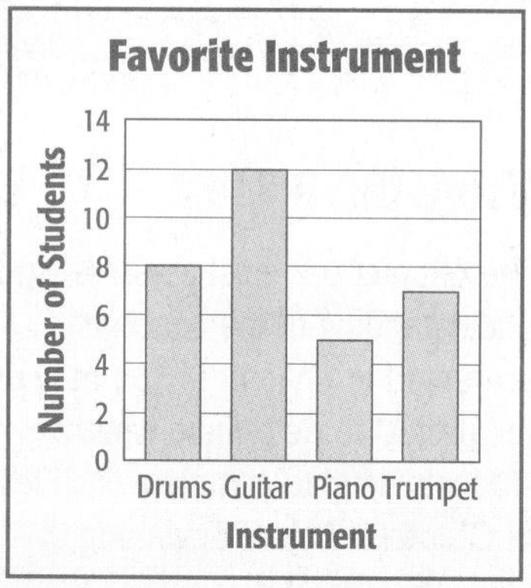

58.

Stem	Leaf
3	5 8
4	2 4 6 7
5	0 0 5 6 9
6	2

Key: 3|5 = 35

59. **Money Spent at the Fair**

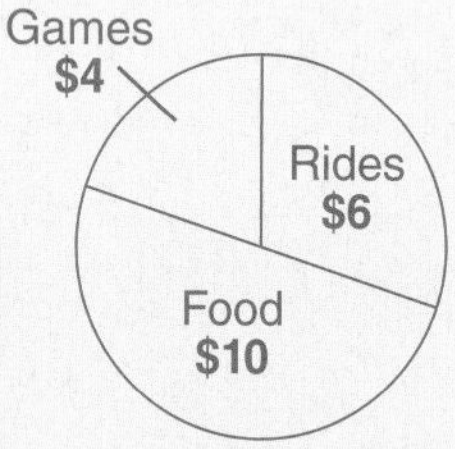

Find the circumference and area of each circle. Round to the nearest tenth.

41.

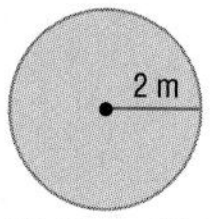

12.6 m; 12.6 m^2

42.

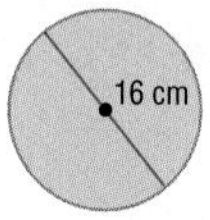

50.3 cm; 201.1 cm^2

43. BIRDS The floor of a birdcage is a circle with a circumference of about 47.1 inches. What is the diameter of the birdcage floor? Round to the nearest inch. 15 in.

Find the volume and surface area of each rectangular prism given the measurements below.

44. $\ell = 3$ cm, $w = 1$ cm, $h = 3$ cm 9 cm^3; 30 cm^2

45. $\ell = 6$ ft, $w = 2$ ft, $h = 5$ ft 60 ft^3; 104 ft^2

46. Find the volume and surface area of the rectangular prism. 30 cm^3; 62 cm^2

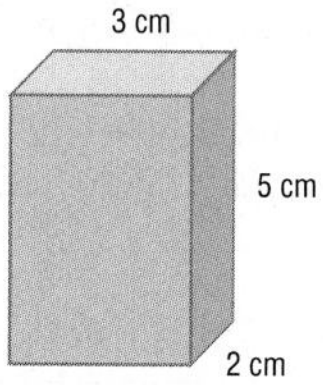

One pencil is randomly selected from a case containing 3 red, 4 green, 2 black, and 6 blue pencils. Find each probability.

47. P(green) $\frac{4}{15}$

48. P(red or blue) $\frac{3}{5}$

49. Use a tree diagram to find the sample space for the event *a die is rolled, and a coin is tossed*. State the number of possible outcomes. 12

One coin is randomly selected from a jar containing 20 pennies, 15 nickels, 3 dimes, and 12 quarters. Find the odds of each outcome. Write in simplest form.

50. a penny 2:3

51. a penny or nickel 7:3

52. A coin is tossed 50 times. The results are shown in the table. Find the experimental probability of heads. Write as a fraction in simplest form. $\frac{11}{25}$

Lands Face-Up	Number of Times
head	22
tails	28

Find the mean, median, and mode for each set of data.

53. {10, 11, 18, 24, 30} 18.6; 18; no mode

54. {4, 8, 9, 9, 10, 14, 16} 10; 9; 9

55. Find the range, median, lower quartile, and upper quartile for {16, 19, 21, 24, 25, 31, 35}. 19; 24; 19; 31

56. SCHOOL Devonte's scores on his first four Spanish tests are 92, 85, 90, and 92. What test score must Devonte earn on the fifth test so that the mean will be exactly 90? 91

57. MUSIC The table shows the results of a survey in which students were asked to choose which of four instruments they would like to learn. Make a bar graph of the data. See margin.

Favorite Instrument	
Instrument	**Number of Students**
drums	8
guitar	12
piano	5
trumpet	7

58. Make a stem-and-leaf plot of the data: 42, 50, 38, 59, 50, 44, 46, 62, 47, 35, 55, and 56. See margin.

59. EXPENSES The table shows how Dylan spent his money at the fair. Make a circle graph of the data. See margin.

Money Spent at the Fair	
How Spent	**Amount ($)**
rides	6
food	10
games	4

0-1 Plan for Problem Solving

Using the **four-step problem-solving plan** can help you solve any word problem.

Objective

Use the four-step problem-solving plan.

IL Learning Standards

6.C.4 Determine whether exact values or approximations are appropriate.

New Vocabulary

four-step problem-solving plan
defining a variable

Key Concept — Four-Step Problem-Solving Plan (For Your FOLDABLE)

Step 1 Understand the problem.
Step 2 Plan the solution.
Step 3 Solve the problem.
Step 4 Check the solution.

Each step of the plan is important.

Step 1 Understand the Problem

To solve a verbal problem, first read the problem carefully and explore what the problem is about.

- Identify what information is given.
- Identify what you need to find.

Step 2 Plan the Solution

One strategy you can use is to write an equation. Choose a variable to represent one of the unspecified numbers in the problem. This is called **defining a variable**. Then use the variable to write expressions for the other unspecified numbers in the problem.

Step 3 Solve the Problem

Use the strategy you chose in Step 2 to solve the problem.

Step 4 Check the Solution

Check your answer in the context of the original problem.

- Does your answer make sense?
- Does it fit the information in the problem?

EXAMPLE 1

FLOORS Ling's hallway is 10 feet long and 4 feet wide. He paid $200 to tile his hallway floor. How much did Ling pay per square foot for the tile?

Understand We are given the measurements of the hallway and the total cost of the tile. We are asked to find the cost of each square foot of tile.

Plan Write an equation. Let f represent the cost of each square foot of tile. The area of the hallway is 10×4 or 40 ft^2.

40	times	the cost per square foot	equals	200
40	$\cdot$	f	$=$	200

Solve $40 \cdot f = 200$. Find f mentally by asking, "What number times 40 is 200?"

$f = 5$

The tile cost $5 per square foot.

Check If the tile costs $5 per square foot, then 40 square feet of tile costs $5 \cdot 40$ or $200. The answer makes sense.

0-1 Lesson Notes

1 FOCUS

Vertical Alignment

Lesson 0-1
Use the four-step problem-solving plan.

After Lesson 0-1
Use the four-step plan to analyze and solve real-world problems.

2 TEACH

Examples 1 and 2 show how to use the four-step plan to solve real-world problems.

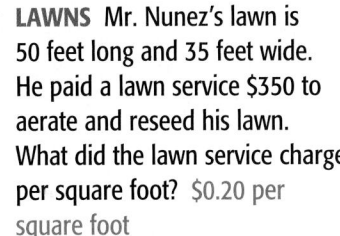

Additional Example

1 **LAWNS** Mr. Nunez's lawn is 50 feet long and 35 feet wide. He paid a lawn service $350 to aerate and reseed his lawn. What did the lawn service charge per square foot? $0.20 per square foot

TEACH with TECH

INTERACTIVE WHITEBOARD Use the board as you step through an example. Use a new page on the whiteboard to organize notes for each of the 4 steps. Save and post on your class Web site.

Additional Example

2 **BOOKS** A used book store had a sale on all paperbacks for \$0.45 each. The store had \$72.45 in sales. How many books did the store sell? 161 books

Tips for New Teachers

Estimation Point out to students that if a problem involves having enough money to purchase items, it is a good idea to round up at least one of the items to ensure that there is enough money for the purchases.

3 ASSESS

Formative Assessment

Use Exercises 1–6 to assess whether students understand how to use the four-step problem-solving plan.

Name the Math Ask students to describe the four steps they would use to solve a problem.

When an exact value is needed, you can use estimation to check your answer.

EXAMPLE 2

TRAVEL Emily's family drove 254.6 miles. Their car used 19 gallons of gasoline. Describe the car's gas mileage.

Understand We are given the total miles driven and how much gasoline was used. We are asked to find the gas mileage of the car.

Plan Write an equation. Let G represent the car's gas mileage.

gas mileage = number of miles ÷ number of gallons used

$G = 254.6 \div 19$

Solve $G = 254.6 \div 19$

$= 13.4$ mi/gal

The car's gas mileage is 13.4 miles per gallon.

Check Use estimation to check your solution.

260 mi ÷ 20 gal = 13 mi/gal

Since the solution 13.4 is close to the estimate, the answer is reasonable.

Real-World Link

In a recent year, an average of \$2.9 billion was spent on grooming and boarding dogs in the United States.

Source: American Pet Products Manufacturers Association

Exercises

Determine whether you need an estimate or an exact answer. Then use the four step problem-solving plan to solve.

1. **DRIVING** While on vacation, the Jacobson family drove 312.8 miles the first day, 177.2 miles the second day, and 209 miles the third day. About how many miles did they travel in all? estimate; about 700 mi
2. **PETS** Ms. Hernandez boarded her dog at a kennel for 4 days. It cost \$18.90 per day, and she had a coupon for \$5 off. What was the final cost for boarding her dog? exact; \$70.60
3. **MEASUREMENT** William is using a 1.75-liter container to fill a 14-liter container of water. About how many times will he need to fill the smaller container? estimate; about 7 times
4. **SEWING** Fabric costs \$5.15 per yard. The drama department needs 18 yards of the fabric for their new play. About how much should they expect to pay? estimate; about \$100
5. **FINANCIAL LITERACY** The table shows donations to help purchase a new tree for the school. How much money did the students donate in all? exact; \$98.75

Number of Students	Amount of Each Donation
20	\$2.50
15	\$3.25

6. **SHOPPING** Is \$12 enough to buy a half gallon of milk for \$2.30, a bag of apples for \$3.99, and four cups of yogurt that cost \$0.79 each? Explain. Estimate; yes, the total cost is about \$2 + \$4 + \$4 or \$10.

0-2 Real Numbers

Objective

Classify and use real numbers.

New Vocabulary

positive number
negative number
natural number
whole number
integer
rational number
square root
perfect square
irrational number
real number
graph
coordinate

A number line can be used to show the sets of natural numbers, whole numbers, integers, and rational numbers. Values greater than 0, or **positive numbers**, are listed to the right of 0, and values less than 0, or **negative numbers**, are listed to the left of 0.

natural numbers: 1, 2, 3, …

whole numbers: 0, 1, 2, 3, …

integers: …, −3, −2, −1, 0, 1, 2, 3, …

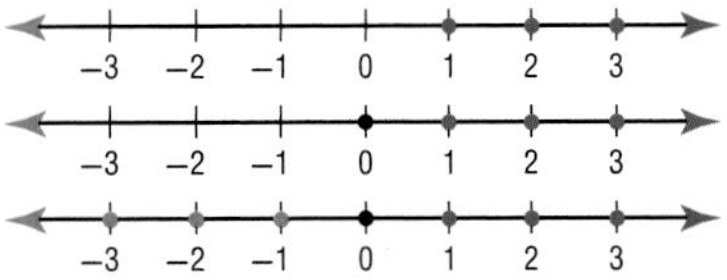

rational numbers: numbers that can be expressed in the form $\frac{a}{b}$, where a and b are integers and $b \neq 0$

A **square root** is one of two equal factors of a number. For example, one square root of 64, written as $\sqrt{64}$, is 8 since $8 \cdot 8$ or 8^2 is 64. Another square root of 64 is −8 since $(-8) \cdot (-8)$ or $(-8)^2$ is also 64. A number like 64, with a square root that is a rational number, is called a **perfect square**. The square roots of a perfect square are rational numbers.

A number such as $\sqrt{3}$ is the square root of a number that is not a perfect square. It cannot be expressed as a terminating or repeating decimal; $\sqrt{3} \approx 1.73205\ldots$. Numbers that cannot be expressed as terminating or repeating decimals, or in the form $\frac{a}{b}$, where a and b are integers and $b \neq 0$, are called **irrational numbers**. Irrational numbers and rational numbers together form the set of **real numbers**.

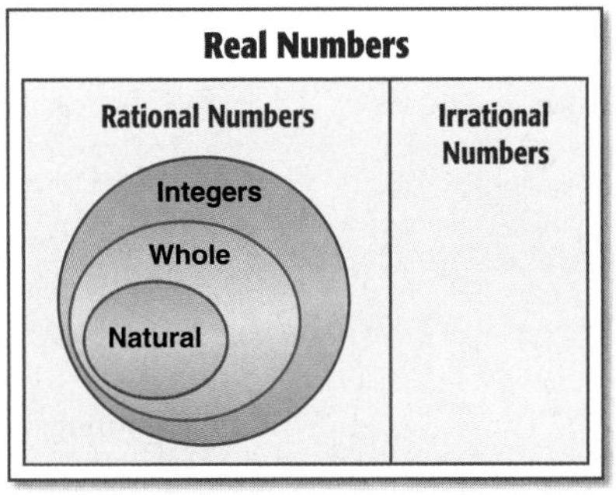

Math *in Motion*, Animation glencoe.com

EXAMPLE 1 Classify Real Numbers

Name the set or sets of numbers to which each real number belongs.

a. $\frac{5}{22}$

Because 5 and 22 are integers and $5 \div 22 = 0.2272727\ldots$ or $0.2\overline{27}$, which is a repeating decimal, this number is a rational number.

b. $\sqrt{81}$

Because $\sqrt{81} = 9$, this number is a natural number, a whole number, an integer, and a rational number.

c. $\sqrt{56}$

Because $\sqrt{56} = 7.48331477\ldots$, which is not a repeating or terminating decimal, this number is irrational.

0-2 Lesson Notes

1 FOCUS

Vertical Alignment

Lesson 0-2
Classify and use real numbers.

After Lesson 0-2
Graph real numbers as solutions to equations and inequalities.
Find square roots as solutions to quadratic equations.

2 TEACH

Example 1 shows how to classify real numbers. **Example 2** shows how to graph real numbers on a number line. **Example 3** shows how to write repeating decimals as fractions. **Example 4** shows how to simplify expressions involving square roots. **Example 5** shows how to estimate square roots to the nearest whole number.

Additional Example

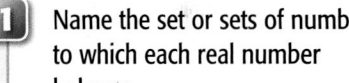

1 Name the set or sets of numbers to which each real number belongs.

a. $\frac{9}{10}$ rational number

b. $\sqrt{121}$ natural number, whole number, integer, rational number

c. $\sqrt{18}$ irrational number

TEACH with TECH

INTERACTIVE WHITEBOARD Draw a set diagram on the board showing how the set of real numbers is seperated into rational and irrational numbers, integers, whole numbers, etc. Create a list of 12 real numbers, and have students come to the board to drag them into the correct set in the diagram.

Additional Examples

2 Graph each set of numbers on a number line.

a. $\left\{-1\frac{1}{2}, -\frac{1}{4}, \frac{3}{4}, \frac{7}{4}\right\}$

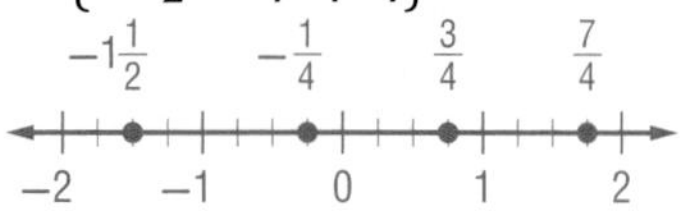

b. $x < 4$

c. $b \geq -0.5$

3 Write $0.\overline{23}$ as a fraction in simplest form. $\frac{23}{99}$

Tips for New Teachers

Number Lines Instruct students to be consistent in the scales on their number lines. Remind them to show tick marks at equal intervals.

To graph a set of numbers means to draw, or plot, the points named by those numbers on a number line. The number that corresponds to a point on a number line is called the coordinate of that point. The rational numbers and the irrational numbers complete the number line.

EXAMPLE 2 Graph Real Numbers

Graph each set of numbers on a number line.

a. $\left\{-\frac{4}{3}, -\frac{1}{3}, \frac{2}{3}, \frac{5}{3}\right\}$

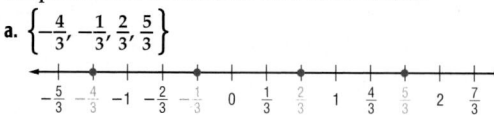

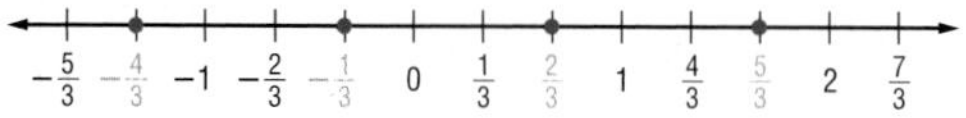

b. $x > -2$

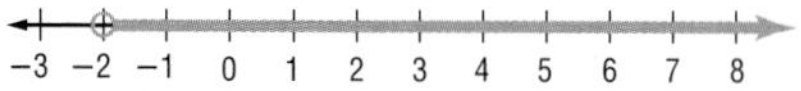

The heavy arrow indicates that all numbers to the right of −2 are included in the graph. The circle at −2 indicates that −2 is not included in the graph.

c. $b \leq 4.5$

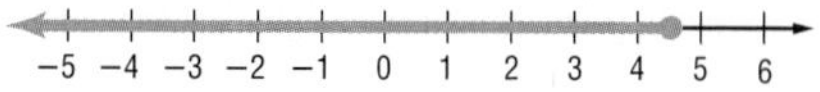

The heavy arrow indicates that all points to the left of 4.5 are included in the graph. The dot at 4.5 indicates that 4.5 is included in the graph.

d. $h \geq -3\frac{2}{5}$

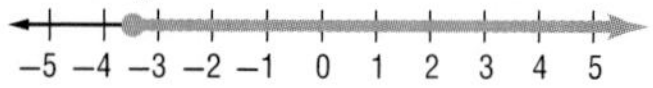

The heavy arrow indicates that all points to the right of $-3\frac{2}{5}$ are included in the graph. The dot at $-3\frac{2}{5}$ indicates that $-3\frac{2}{5}$ is included in the graph.

StudyTip

Finite and Infinite The set of numbers in Example 2a is *finite*, that is, the elements can be counted. However, the set of numbers in Example 2b is *infinite*. Its graph includes all values in the range including integers like 3 and −1, as well as rational numbers like $\frac{3}{8}$ and $-\frac{12}{13}$ and irrational numbers like $\sqrt{10}$ and π.

Any repeating decimal can be written as a fraction.

EXAMPLE 3 Write Repeating Decimals as Fractions

Write $0.\overline{7}$ as a fraction in simplest form.

Step 1 $N = 0.777...$ — **Let *N* represent the repeating decimal.**

$10N = 10(0.777...)$ — **Since only one digit repeats, multiply each side by 10.**

$10N = 7.777...$ — **Simplify.**

Step 2 Subtract N from $10N$ to eliminate the part of the number that repeats.

$10N = 7.777...$

$\underline{-(N = 0.777...)}$

$9N = 7$ — **Subtract.**

$\frac{9N}{9} = \frac{7}{9}$ — **Divide each side by 9.**

$N = \frac{7}{9}$ — **Simplify.**

Perfect squares can also be used to simplify square roots of rational numbers.

Key Concept — Perfect Square

For Your FOLDABLE

Words Rational numbers with square roots that are rational numbers.

Examples 25 is a perfect square since $\sqrt{25} = 5$.

144 is a perfect square since $\sqrt{144} = 12$.

EXAMPLE 4 Square Roots

Simplify each square root.

a. $-\sqrt{\frac{49}{256}}$

$-\sqrt{\frac{49}{256}} = -\sqrt{\left(\frac{7}{16}\right)^2}$ **$7^2 = 49$ and $16^2 = 256$**

$= -\frac{7}{16}$ **Simplify.**

b. $\sqrt{\frac{4}{121}}$

$\sqrt{\frac{4}{121}} = \sqrt{\left(\frac{2}{11}\right)^2}$ **$2^2 = 4$ and $11^2 = 121$**

$= \frac{2}{11}$ **Simplify.**

StudyTip

Perfect Squares Keep a list of perfect squares in your notebook. Refer to it when you need to simplify a square root.

You can estimate square roots of numbers that are not perfect squares.

EXAMPLE 5 Estimate Square Roots

Estimate each square root to the nearest whole number.

a. $\sqrt{15}$

Find the two perfect squares closest to 15. List some perfect squares.

1, 4, 9, 16, 25, 36, …

15 is between 9 and 16.

$9 < 15 < 16$ **Write an inequality.**

$\sqrt{9} < \sqrt{15} < \sqrt{16}$ **Take the square root of each number.**

$3 < \sqrt{15} < 4$ **Simplify.**

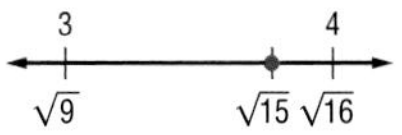

Since 15 is closer to 16 than 9, the best whole-number estimate for $\sqrt{15}$ is 4.

Additional Examples

4 Simplify each square root.

a. $\sqrt{\frac{64}{16}}$ 2

b. $-\sqrt{\frac{25}{144}}$ $-\frac{5}{12}$

5 Estimate each square root to the nearest whole number.

a. $\sqrt{34}$ 6

b. $\sqrt{97}$ 10

Lesson 0-2 Real Numbers P9

3 ASSESS

Formative Assessment

Use Exercises 1–35 to assess whether students understand real numbers.

Ticket Out the Door Ask students to write one rational number and one irrational number on a sheet of paper. Have them label each as rational or irrational.

Additional Answers

13. 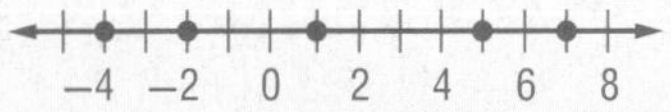

14. 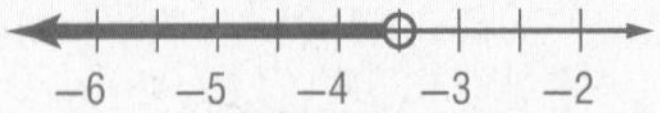

15. 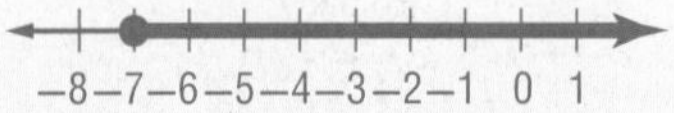

16. 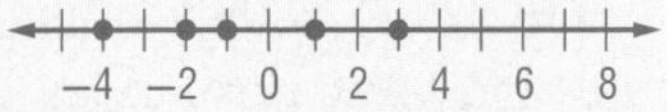

17. 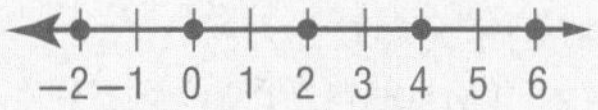

18. 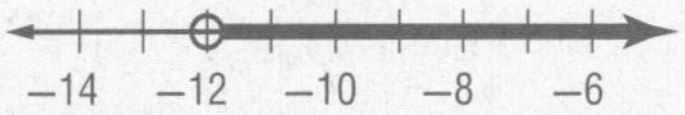

b. $\sqrt{130}$

Find the two perfect squares closest to 130. List some perfect squares.

81, 100, 121, 144, …

130 is between 121 and 144.

$121 < 130 < 144$ **Write an inequality.**

$\sqrt{121} < \sqrt{130} < \sqrt{144}$ **Take the square root of each number.**

$11 < \sqrt{130} < 12$ **Simplify.**

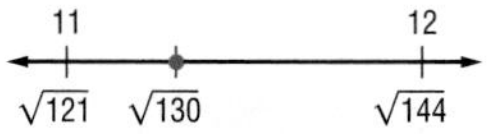

StudyTip

Draw a Diagram Graphing points on a number line can help you analyze your estimate for accuracy.

Since 130 is closer to 121 than 144, the best whole-number estimate for $\sqrt{130}$ is 11.

CHECK $\sqrt{130} \approx 11.4018\ldots$ **Use a calculator.**

Rounded to the nearest whole number, $\sqrt{130}$ is 11. So our estimate is valid.

Exercises

Name the set or sets of numbers to which each real number belongs.

1. $-\sqrt{64}$
2. $\frac{8}{3}$ rationals
3. $\sqrt{28}$ irrationals
4. $\frac{56}{7}$
5. $-\sqrt{22}$ irrationals
6. $\frac{36}{6}$
7. $-\frac{5}{12}$
8. $\frac{18}{3}$
9. $\sqrt{10.24}$ rationals
10. $\frac{-54}{19}$ rationals
11. $\sqrt{\frac{82}{20}}$ irrationals
12. $-\frac{72}{8}$

1. integers, rationals
4. naturals, wholes, integers, rationals
6. naturals, wholes, integers, rationals
7. rationals
8. wholes, naturals, integers, rationals
12. integers, rationals

Graph each set of numbers. 13–18. See margin.

13. $\{-4, -2, 1, 5, 7\}$
14. $x < -3.5$
15. $x \geq -7$
16. $\{-4, -2, -1, 1, 3\}$
17. $\{\ldots, -2, 0, 2, 4, 6\}$
18. $x > -12$

Write each repeating decimal as a fraction in simplest form.

19. $0.\overline{5}$ $\frac{5}{9}$
20. $0.\overline{4}$ $\frac{4}{9}$
21. $0.\overline{13}$ $\frac{13}{99}$
22. $0.\overline{21}$ $\frac{7}{33}$

Simplify each square root.

23. $-\sqrt{25}$ -5
24. $\sqrt{1.44}$ 1.2
25. $\pm\sqrt{\frac{16}{49}}$ $\pm\frac{4}{7}$
26. $\sqrt{361}$ 19
27. $\sqrt{49}$ 7
28. $\pm\sqrt{0.64}$ ± 0.8
29. $-\sqrt{6.25}$ -2.5
30. $\sqrt{\frac{169}{196}}$ $\frac{13}{14}$
31. $\sqrt{\frac{25}{324}}$ $\frac{5}{18}$

Estimate each square root to the nearest whole number.

32. $\sqrt{31}$ 6
33. $\sqrt{24}$ 5
34. $\sqrt{112}$ 11
35. $\sqrt{152}$ 12

0-3 Operations with Integers

Objective

Add, subtract, multiply, and divide integers.

IL Learning Standards

6.B.4 Select and use appropriate arithmetic operations in practical situations including calculating wages after taxes, developing a budget and balancing a checkbook.

New Vocabulary

absolute value
opposites
additive inverses

An integer is any number from the set {..., −3, −2, −1, 0, 1, 2, 3, ...}. You can use a number line to add integers.

EXAMPLE 1

Use a number line to find −3 + (−4).

Step 1 Draw an arrow from 0 to −3.

Step 2 Draw a second arrow 4 units to the left to represent adding −4.

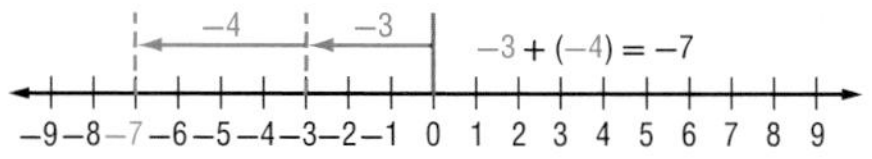

The second arrow ends at −7. So, −3 + (−4) = −7.

You can also use absolute value to add integers. The **absolute value** of a number is its distance from 0 on the number line.

Same Signs (+ + or − −)		Different Signs (+ − or − +)	
3 + 5 = 8	3 and 5 are positive. Their sum is positive.	3 + (−5) = −2	−5 has the greater absolute value. Their sum is negative.
−3 + (−5) = −8	−3 and −5 are negative. Their sum is negative.	−3 + 5 = 2	5 has the greater absolute value. Their sum is positive.

EXAMPLE 2

Find −11 + (−7).

$-11 + (-7) = -(\lvert -11 \rvert + \lvert -7 \rvert)$	**Add the absolute values. Both numbers are negative, so the sum is negative.**
$= -(11 + 7)$	**Absolute values of nonzero numbers are always positive.**
$= -18$	**Simplify.**

Every positive integer can be paired with a negative integer. These pairs are called **opposites**. A number and its opposite are **additive inverses**. Additive inverses can be used when you subtract integers.

EXAMPLE 3

Find 18 − 23.

$18 - 23 = 18 + (-23)$	**To subtract 23, add its inverse.**
$= -(\lvert -23 \rvert - \lvert 18 \rvert)$	**Subtract the absolute values. Because |−23| is greater than |18|, the result is negative.**
$= -(23 - 18)$	**Absolute values of nonzero numbers are always positive.**
$= -5$	**Simplify.**

TEACH with TECH

WIKI On your secure classroom wiki have all students contribute to the notes on this chapter and save as a reference.

0-3 Lesson Notes

1 FOCUS

Vertical Alignment

Lesson 0-3
Add, subtract, multiply, and divide integers.

After Lesson 0-3
Evaluate expressions and solve equations that involve operations with integers.

2 TEACH

Example 1 shows how to use a number line to add integers. **Example 2** shows how to use absolute values to add integers. **Example 3** shows how to subtract integers. **Example 4** shows how to multiply and divide integers.

Additional Examples

1 Use a number line to find −2 + 3. 1

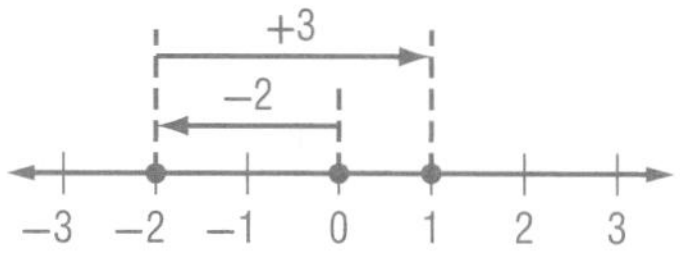

2 Find −15 + (−4). −19

3 Find 11 − 15. −4

Watch Out!

Preventing Errors Remind students to subtract the lesser absolute value from the greater absolute value when adding integers with different signs. The sum will have the sign of the number with the greater absolute value.

Additional Example

4 Find each product or quotient.

a. −9(4) −36

b. −112 ÷ (−8) 14

c. −11(−11) 121

d. 96 ÷ (−6) −16

3 ASSESS

Formative Assessment

Use Exercises 1–23 to assess whether students understand how to add, subtract, multiply, and divide integers.

Crystal Ball Ask students how they think today's lesson on adding and subtracting integers will help with tomorrow's lesson on adding and subtracting rational numbers.

StudyTip

Products and Quotients The product or quotient of two numbers having the *same sign* is positive. The product or quotient of two numbers having *different signs* is negative.

Same Signs (+ + or − −)		Different Signs (+ − or − +)	
3(5) = 15	3 and 5 are positive. Their product is positive.	3(−5) = −15	3 and −5 have different signs. Their product is negative.
−3(−5) = 15	−3 and −5 are negative. Their product is positive.	−3(5) = −15	−3 and 5 have different signs. Their product is negative.

EXAMPLE 4

Find each product or quotient.

a. 4(−5)
$4(-5) = -20$ **different signs ⟶ negative product**

b. −51 ÷ (−3)
$-51 \div (-3) = 17$ **same sign ⟶ positive quotient**

c. −12(−14)
$-12(-14) = 168$ **same sign ⟶ positive product**

d. −63 ÷ 7
$-63 \div 7 = -9$ **different signs ⟶ negative quotient**

Exercises

Find each sum or difference.

1. $-8 + 13$ **5**
2. $11 + (-19)$ **−8**
3. $-19 - 8$ **−27**
4. $-77 + (-46)$ **−123**
5. $12 - 34$ **−22**
6. $41 + (-56)$ **−15**
7. $50 - 82$ **−32**
8. $-47 - 13$ **−60**
9. $-80 + 102$ **22**

Find each product or quotient.

10. $5(18)$ **90**
11. $60 \div 12$ **5**
12. $-12(15)$ **−180**
13. $-64 \div (-8)$ **8**
14. $8(-22)$ **−176**
15. $54 \div (-6)$ **−9**
16. $30(14)$ **420**
17. $-23(5)$ **−115**
18. $-200 \div 2$ **−100**

19. WEATHER The outside temperature was −4°F in the morning and 13°F in the afternoon. By how much did the temperature increase? **17°**

20. DOLPHINS A dolphin swimming 24 feet below the ocean's surface dives 18 feet straight down. How many feet below the ocean's surface is the dolphin now? **42 ft**

21. MOVIES A movie theater gave out 50 coupons for $3 off each movie. What is the total amount of discounts provided by the theater? **$150**

22. WAGES Emilio earns $11 per hour. He works 14 hours a week. His employer withholds $32 from each paycheck for taxes. If he is paid weekly, what is the amount of his paycheck? **$122**

23. FINANCIAL LITERACY Talia is working on a monthly budget. Her monthly income is $500. She has allocated $200 for savings, $100 for vehicle expenses, and $75 for clothing. How much is available to spend on entertainment? **$125**

0-4 Adding and Subtracting Rational Numbers

Objective

Add and subtract rational numbers.

You can use different methods to compare rational numbers. One way is to compare two fractions with common denominators. Another way is to compare decimals.

EXAMPLE 1

Replace • with <, >, or = to make $\frac{2}{3} \bullet \frac{5}{6}$ a true sentence.

Method 1 Write the fractions with the same denominator.

The least common denominator of $\frac{2}{3}$ and $\frac{5}{6}$ is 6.

$\frac{2}{3} = \frac{4}{6}$

$\frac{5}{6} = \frac{5}{6}$

Since $\frac{4}{6} < \frac{5}{6}$, $\frac{2}{3} < \frac{5}{6}$.

Method 2 Write as decimals.

Write $\frac{2}{3}$ and $\frac{5}{6}$ as decimals. You may want to use a calculator.

2 [÷] 3 [ENTER] .6666666667

so, $\frac{2}{3} = 0.\overline{6}$

5 [÷] 6 [ENTER] .8333333333

so, $\frac{5}{6} = 0.8\overline{3}$

Since $0.\overline{6} < 0.8\overline{3}$, $\frac{2}{3} < \frac{5}{6}$.

You can order rational numbers by writing all of the fractions as decimals.

EXAMPLE 2

Order $5\frac{2}{9}$, $5\frac{3}{8}$, 4.9, and $-5\frac{3}{5}$ from least to greatest.

$5\frac{2}{9} = 5.\overline{2}$ $5\frac{3}{8} = 5.375$

$4.9 = 4.9$ $-5\frac{3}{5} = -5.6$

$-5.6 < 4.9 < 5.\overline{2} < 5.375$. So, from least to greatest, the numbers are $-5\frac{3}{5}$, 4.9, $5\frac{2}{9}$, and $5\frac{3}{8}$.

To add or subtract fractions with the same denominator, add or subtract the numerators and write the sum or difference over the denominator.

0-4 Lesson Notes

1 FOCUS

Vertical Alignment

Lesson 0-4
Compare and order rational numbers.
Add and subtract rational numbers.

After Lesson 0-4
Solve equations that involve adding and subtracting rational numbers.

2 TEACH

Example 1 shows how to compare rational numbers. **Example 2** shows how to order rational numbers. **Example 3** shows how to find the sum and difference of fractions with like denominators. **Example 4** shows how to find the sum and difference of fractions with unlike denominators. **Example 5** shows how to use a number line to add rational numbers. **Example 6** shows how to find the sum of rational numbers. **Example 7** shows how to subtract rational numbers.

Additional Examples

1. Replace • with <, >, or = to make $\frac{4}{5} \bullet \frac{5}{8}$ a true statement. >
2. Order $3\frac{3}{8}$, $-3\frac{3}{7}$, $3.\overline{45}$, and $-3\frac{2}{5}$ from least to greatest. $-3\frac{3}{7}$, $-3\frac{2}{5}$, $3\frac{3}{8}$, $3.\overline{45}$

Additional Examples

3 Find each sum or difference. Write in simplest form.

a. $\frac{5}{11} + \frac{3}{11}$ $\frac{8}{11}$

b. $\frac{11}{18} - \frac{7}{18}$ $\frac{2}{9}$

c. $\frac{3}{8} - \frac{5}{8}$ $-\frac{1}{4}$

4 Find each sum or difference. Write in simplest form.

a. $\frac{4}{5} + \frac{7}{10}$ $1\frac{1}{2}$

b. $\frac{5}{6} - \frac{5}{18}$ $\frac{5}{9}$

c. $\frac{3}{10} - \frac{3}{4}$ $-\frac{9}{20}$

TEACH with TECH

INTERACTIVE WHITEBOARD Create a template that you can use to show addition of fractions, such as:

$$\frac{\square}{\square} + \frac{\square}{\square} = \frac{\square + \square}{\square} = \frac{\square}{\square}$$

Display the template on the board and use it as you work through examples.

StudyTip

Mental Math If the denominators of the fractions are the same, you can use mental math to determine the sum or difference.

EXAMPLE 3

Find each sum or difference. Write in simplest form.

a. $\frac{3}{5} + \frac{1}{5}$

$\frac{3}{5} + \frac{1}{5} = \frac{3+1}{5}$ — The denominators are the same. Add the numerators.

$= \frac{4}{5}$ — Simplify.

b. $\frac{7}{16} - \frac{1}{16}$

$\frac{7}{16} - \frac{1}{16} = \frac{7-1}{16}$ — The denominators are the same. Subtract the numerators.

$= \frac{6}{16}$ — Simplify.

$= \frac{3}{8}$ — Rename the fraction.

c. $\frac{4}{9} - \frac{7}{9}$

$\frac{4}{9} - \frac{7}{9} = \frac{4-7}{9}$ — The denominators are the same. Subtract the numerators.

$= -\frac{3}{9}$ — Simplify.

$= -\frac{1}{3}$ — Rename the fraction.

To add or subtract fractions with unlike denominators, first find the least common denominator (LCD). Rename each fraction with the LCD, and then add or subtract. Simplify if possible.

EXAMPLE 4

Find each sum or difference. Write in simplest form.

a. $\frac{1}{2} + \frac{2}{3}$

$\frac{1}{2} + \frac{2}{3} = \frac{3}{6} + \frac{4}{6}$ — The LCD for 2 and 3 is 6. Rename $\frac{1}{2}$ as $\frac{3}{6}$ and $\frac{2}{3}$ as $\frac{4}{6}$.

$= \frac{3+4}{6}$ — Add the numerators.

$= \frac{7}{6}$ or $1\frac{1}{6}$ — Simplify.

b. $\frac{3}{8} - \frac{1}{3}$

$\frac{3}{8} - \frac{1}{3} = \frac{9}{24} - \frac{8}{24}$ — The LCD for 8 and 3 is 24. Rename $\frac{3}{8}$ as $\frac{9}{24}$ and $\frac{1}{3}$ as $\frac{8}{24}$.

$= \frac{9-8}{24}$ — Subtract the numerators.

$= \frac{1}{24}$ — Simplify.

c. $\frac{2}{5} - \frac{3}{4}$

$\frac{2}{5} - \frac{3}{4} = \frac{8}{20} - \frac{15}{20}$ — The LCD for 5 and 4 is 20. Rename $\frac{2}{5}$ as $\frac{8}{20}$ and $\frac{3}{4}$ as $\frac{15}{20}$.

$= \frac{8-15}{20}$ — Subtract the numerators.

$= -\frac{7}{20}$ — Simplify.

StudyTip

Number Line To use a number line, put your pencil at the first number. Then move left to find the difference. To find the sum, move your pencil to the right.

You can use a number line to add rational numbers.

EXAMPLE 5

Use a number line to find 2.5 + (−3.5).

Step 1 Draw an arrow from 0 to 2.5.

Step 2 Draw a second arrow 3.5 units to the left.

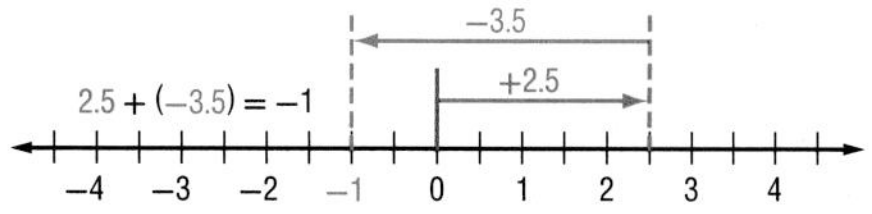

The second arrow ends at −1.

So, 2.5 + (−3.5) = −1.

You can also use absolute value to add rational numbers.

Same Signs (+ + or − −)		Different Signs (+ − or − +)	
3.1 + 2.5 = 5.6	3.1 and 2.5 are positive, so the sum is positive.	3.1 + (−2.5) = 0.6	3.1 has the greater absolute value, so the sum is positive.
−3.1 + (−2.5) = −5.6	−3.1 and −2.5 are negative, so the sum is negative.	−3.1 + 2.5 = −0.6	−3.1 has the greater absolute value, so the sum is negative.

EXAMPLE 6

Find each sum.

a. −13.12 + (−8.6)

$-13.12 + (-8.6) = -(|-13.12| + |-8.6|)$ **Both numbers are negative, so the sum is negative.**

$= -(13.12 + 8.6)$ **Absolute values of nonzero numbers are always positive.**

$= -21.72$ **Simplify.**

b. $\frac{7}{16} + \left(-\frac{3}{8}\right)$

$\frac{7}{16} + \left(-\frac{3}{8}\right) = \frac{7}{16} + \left(-\frac{6}{16}\right)$ **The LCD is 16. Replace $-\frac{3}{8}$ with $-\frac{6}{16}$.**

$= \left(\left|\frac{7}{16}\right| - \left|-\frac{6}{16}\right|\right)$ **Subtract the absolute values. Because $\left|\frac{7}{16}\right|$ is greater than $\left|-\frac{6}{16}\right|$, the result is positive.**

$= \frac{7}{16} - \frac{6}{16}$ **Absolute values of nonzero numbers are always positive.**

$= \frac{1}{16}$ **Simplify.**

Additional Examples

5 Use a number line to find −1.25 + 1.5. 0.25;

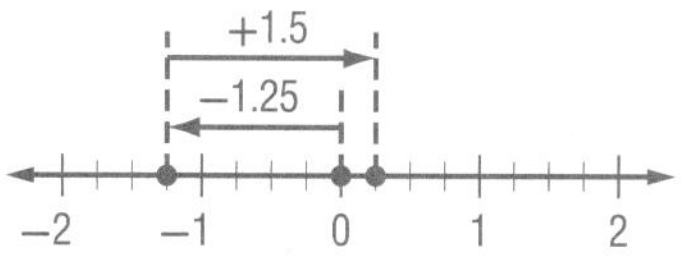

6 Find each sum.

a. −12.6 + (−3.9) −16.5

b. $-\frac{2}{3} + \frac{5}{9}$ $-\frac{1}{9}$

Watch Out!

Preventing Errors Calculation errors are common when adding rational numbers with decimals. Encourage students to align decimals and to annex zeros as placeholders when the decimals have different place values.

Lesson 0-4 Adding and Subtracting Rational Numbers P15

Additional Example

7 Find $-17.55 - (-24.5)$. 6.95

3 ASSESS

Formative Assessment

Use Exercises 1–41 to assess whether students understand how to compare and order rational numbers, and add and subtract rational numbers.

Yesterday's News Ask students to describe how yesterday's lesson on operations with integers helped with today's lesson on adding and subtracting rational numbers.

To subtract a negative rational number, add its inverse.

EXAMPLE 7

Find $-32.25 - (-42.5)$.

$-32.25 - (-42.5) = -32.25 + 42.5$	**To subtract −42.5, add its inverse.**
$= \lvert 42.5 \rvert - \lvert -32.25 \rvert$	**Subtract the absolute values. Because |42.5| is greater than |−32.25|, the result is positive.**
$= 42.5 - 32.25$	**Absolute values of nonzero numbers are always positive.**
$= 10.25$	**Simplify.**

Exercises

Replace each • with <, >, or = to make a true sentence.

1. $-\frac{5}{8} \bullet \frac{3}{8}$ <
2. $\frac{4}{5} \bullet 0.71$ >
3. $\frac{5}{6} \bullet 0.875$ <
4. $1.2 \bullet 1\frac{2}{9}$ <
5. $\frac{8}{15} \bullet 0.5\overline{3}$ =
6. $-\frac{7}{11} \bullet -\frac{2}{3}$ >

Order each set of rational numbers from least to greatest.

7. $3.8, 3.06, 3\frac{1}{6}, 3\frac{3}{4}$ $3.06, 3\frac{1}{6}, 3\frac{3}{4}, 3.8$
8. $2\frac{1}{4}, 1\frac{7}{8}, 1.75, 2.4$ $1.75, 1\frac{7}{8}, 2\frac{1}{4}, 2.4$
9. $0.11, -\frac{1}{9}, -0.5, \frac{1}{10}$ $-0.5, -\frac{1}{9}, \frac{1}{10}, 0.11$
10. $-4\frac{3}{5}, -3\frac{2}{5}, -4.65, -4.09$ $-4.65, -4\frac{3}{5}, -4.09, -3\frac{2}{5}$

Find each sum or difference. Write in simplest form.

11. $\frac{2}{5} + \frac{1}{5}$ $\frac{3}{5}$
12. $\frac{3}{9} + \frac{4}{9}$ $\frac{7}{9}$
13. $\frac{5}{16} - \frac{4}{16}$ $\frac{1}{16}$
14. $\frac{6}{7} - \frac{3}{7}$ $\frac{3}{7}$
15. $\frac{2}{3} + \frac{1}{3}$ 1
16. $\frac{5}{8} + \frac{7}{8}$ $1\frac{1}{2}$
17. $\frac{4}{3} + \frac{4}{3}$ $2\frac{2}{3}$
18. $\frac{7}{15} - \frac{2}{15}$ $\frac{1}{3}$
19. $\frac{1}{3} - \frac{2}{9}$ $\frac{1}{9}$
20. $\frac{1}{2} + \frac{1}{4}$ $\frac{3}{4}$
21. $\frac{1}{2} - \frac{1}{3}$ $\frac{1}{6}$
22. $\frac{3}{7} + \frac{5}{14}$ $\frac{11}{14}$
23. $\frac{7}{10} - \frac{2}{15}$ $\frac{17}{30}$
24. $\frac{3}{8} + \frac{1}{6}$ $\frac{13}{24}$
25. $\frac{13}{20} - \frac{2}{5}$ $\frac{1}{4}$

Find each sum or difference. Write in simplest form if necessary.

26. $-1.6 + (-3.8)$ −5.4
27. $-32.4 + (-4.5)$ −36.9
28. $-38.9 + 24.2$ −14.7
29. $-9.16 - 10.17$ −19.33
30. $26.37 + (-61.1)$ −34.73
31. $72.5 - (-81.3)$ 153.8
32. $43.2 + (-27.9)$ 15.3
33. $79.3 - (-14)$ 93.3
34. $1.34 - (-0.458)$ 1.798
35. $-\frac{1}{6} - \frac{2}{3}$ $-\frac{5}{6}$
36. $\frac{1}{2} - \frac{4}{5}$ $-\frac{3}{10}$
37. $-\frac{2}{5} + \frac{17}{20}$ $\frac{9}{20}$
38. $-\frac{4}{5} + \left(-\frac{1}{3}\right)$ $-1\frac{2}{15}$
39. $-\frac{1}{12} - \left(-\frac{3}{4}\right)$ $\frac{2}{3}$
40. $-\frac{7}{8} - \left(-\frac{3}{16}\right)$ $-\frac{11}{16}$

41. GEOGRAPHY About $\frac{7}{10}$ of the surface of Earth is covered by water. The rest of the surface is covered by land. How much of Earth's surface is covered by land? $\frac{3}{10}$

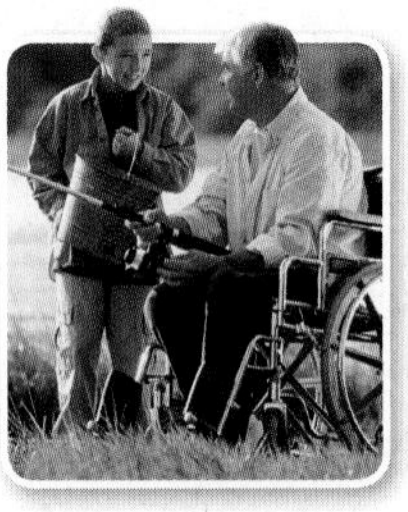

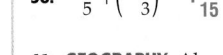

Real-World Link

About 97% of the water is saltwater from oceans. Of the freshwater, only 1% is on the surface from lakes, rivers, and swamps.

Source: U.S. Geological Survey

0-5 Multiplying and Dividing Rational Numbers

Objective

Multiply and divide rational numbers.

New Vocabulary

multiplicative inverses
reciprocals

The product or quotient of two rational numbers having the *same sign* is positive. The product or quotient of two rational numbers having *different signs* is negative.

EXAMPLE 1

Find each product or quotient.

a. $7.2(-0.2)$

different signs → negative product

$7.2(-0.2) = -1.44$

b. $-23.94 \div (-10.5)$

same sign → positive quotient

$-23.94 \div (-10.5) = 2.28$

To multiply fractions, multiply the numerators and multiply the denominators. If the numerators and denominators have common factors, you can simplify before you multiply by canceling.

EXAMPLE 2

Find each product.

a. $\frac{2}{5} \cdot \frac{1}{3}$

$\frac{2}{5} \cdot \frac{1}{3} = \frac{2 \cdot 1}{5 \cdot 3}$ Multiply the numerators. Multiply the denominators.

$= \frac{2}{15}$ Simplify.

b. $\frac{3}{5} \cdot 1\frac{1}{2}$

$\frac{3}{5} \cdot 1\frac{1}{2} = \frac{3}{5} \cdot \frac{3}{2}$ Write $1\frac{1}{2}$ as an improper fraction.

$= \frac{3 \cdot 3}{5 \cdot 2}$ Multiply the numerators. Multiply the denominators.

$= \frac{9}{10}$ Simplify.

c. $\frac{1}{4} \cdot \frac{2}{9}$

$\frac{1}{4} \cdot \frac{2}{9} = \frac{1}{\cancel{4}_2} \cdot \frac{\cancel{2}^1}{9}$ Divide by the GCF, 2.

$= \frac{1 \cdot 1}{2 \cdot 9}$ or $\frac{1}{18}$ Multiply the numerators. Multiply the denominators and simplify.

EXAMPLE 3

Find $-\left(\frac{3}{4}\right)\left(\frac{3}{8}\right)$.

$\left(-\frac{3}{4}\right)\left(\frac{3}{8}\right) = -\left(\frac{3}{4} \cdot \frac{3}{8}\right)$ different signs → negative product

$= -\left(\frac{3 \cdot 3}{4 \cdot 8}\right)$ or $\frac{9}{32}$ Multiply the numerators. Multiply the denominators and simplify.

0-5 Lesson Notes

1 FOCUS

Vertical Alignment

Lesson 0-5
Multiply and divide rational numbers.

After Lesson 0-5
Evaluate expressions and solve equations that involve multiplying and dividing rational numbers.

2 TEACH

Example 1 shows how to find the product or quotient of decimals with the same signs or different signs. **Example 2** shows how to find the product of fractions. **Example 3** shows how to find the product of fractions with different signs. **Example 4** shows how to find the reciprocal of a number. **Example 5** shows how to divide fractions.

Additional Examples

1 Find each product or quotient.

a. $-5.4(0.05)$ -0.27

b. $-6.84 \div (-2.4)$ 2.85

2 Find each product.

a. $\frac{4}{7} \cdot \frac{4}{5}$ $\frac{16}{35}$

b. $\frac{1}{4} \cdot 3\frac{5}{6}$ $\frac{23}{24}$

c. $\frac{3}{8} \cdot \frac{2}{3}$ $\frac{1}{4}$

3 Find $\left(\frac{7}{10}\right)\left(-\frac{2}{3}\right)$. $-\frac{7}{15}$

TEACH with TECH

INTERACTIVE WHITEBOARD Find a Web site with an applet that gives an area model of multiplying fractions. Demonstrate the model with several examples and explain how it shows multiplying the numerators and multiplying the denominators.

Additional Examples

4 Name the reciprocal of each number.

a. $\frac{4}{9}$ $\frac{9}{4}$

b. $2\frac{7}{8}$ $\frac{8}{23}$

5 Find each quotient.

a. $\frac{3}{5} \div \frac{1}{4}$ $2\frac{2}{5}$

b. $\frac{3}{10} \div \frac{2}{9}$ $1\frac{7}{20}$

c. $\frac{7}{8} \div 2\frac{1}{3}$ $\frac{3}{8}$

d. $-\frac{2}{3} \div \frac{4}{5}$ $-\frac{5}{6}$

Watch Out!

Preventing Errors Remind students that they must rewrite division by a fraction as multiplication by the reciprocal *before* they can divide by the common factors in the numerators and denominators.

Two numbers whose product is 1 are called **multiplicative inverses** or **reciprocals**.

EXAMPLE 4

Name the reciprocal of each number.

a. $\frac{3}{8}$

$\frac{3}{8} \cdot \frac{8}{3} = 1$ **The product is 1.**

The reciprocal of $\frac{3}{8}$ is $\frac{8}{3}$.

b. $2\frac{4}{5}$

$2\frac{4}{5} = \frac{14}{5}$ **Write $2\frac{4}{5}$ as $\frac{14}{5}$.**

$\frac{14}{5} \cdot \frac{5}{14} = 1$ **The product is 1.**

The reciprocal of $2\frac{4}{5}$ is $\frac{5}{14}$.

To divide one fraction by another fraction, multiply the dividend by the reciprocal of the divisor.

EXAMPLE 5

Find each quotient.

a. $\frac{1}{3} \div \frac{1}{2}$

$\frac{1}{3} \div \frac{1}{2} = \frac{1}{3} \cdot \frac{2}{1}$ **Multiply $\frac{1}{3}$ by $\frac{2}{1}$, the reciprocal of $\frac{1}{2}$.**

$= \frac{2}{3}$ **Simplify.**

b. $\frac{3}{8} \div \frac{2}{3}$

$\frac{3}{8} \div \frac{2}{3} = \frac{3}{8} \cdot \frac{3}{2}$ **Multiply $\frac{3}{8}$ by $\frac{3}{2}$, the reciprocal of $\frac{2}{3}$.**

$= \frac{9}{16}$ **Simplify.**

c. $\frac{3}{4} \div 2\frac{1}{2}$

$\frac{3}{4} \div 2\frac{1}{2} = \frac{3}{4} \div \frac{5}{2}$ **Write $2\frac{1}{2}$ as a mixed number.**

$= \frac{3}{4} \cdot \frac{2}{5}$ **Multiply $\frac{3}{4}$ by $\frac{2}{5}$, the reciprocal of $2\frac{1}{2}$.**

$= \frac{6}{20}$ or $\frac{3}{10}$ **Simplify.**

d. $-\frac{1}{5} \div \left(-\frac{3}{10}\right)$

$-\frac{1}{5} \div \left(-\frac{3}{10}\right) = -\frac{1}{5} \cdot \left(-\frac{10}{3}\right)$ **Multiply $-\frac{1}{5}$ by $-\frac{10}{3}$, the reciprocal of $-\frac{3}{10}$.**

$= \frac{10}{15}$ or $\frac{2}{3}$ **Same sign ⟶ positive quotient; simplify.**

StudyTip

Use Estimation You can justify your answer by using estimation. $\frac{3}{8}$ is close to $\frac{1}{2}$ and $\frac{2}{3}$ is close to 1. So, the quotient is close to $\frac{1}{2}$ divided by 1 or $\frac{1}{2}$.

StudyTip

Negative Fractions A negative fraction can be written as $-\frac{1}{2}$ or $\frac{-1}{2}$.

Exercises

Find each product or quotient. Round to the nearest hundredth if necessary.

1. $6.5(0.13)$ **0.85**

2. $-5.8(2.3)$ **−13.34**

3. $42.3 \div (-6)$ **−7.05**

4. $-14.1(-2.9)$ **40.89**

5. $-78 \div (-1.3)$ **60**

6. $108 \div (-0.9)$ **−120**

7. $0.75(-6.4)$ **−4.8**

8. $-23.94 \div 10.5$ **−2.28**

9. $-32.4 \div 21.3$ **−1.52**

Find each product. Simplify before multiplying if possible.

10. $\frac{3}{4} \cdot \frac{1}{5}$ $\frac{3}{20}$

11. $\frac{2}{5} \cdot \frac{3}{7}$ $\frac{6}{35}$

12. $-\frac{1}{3} \cdot \frac{2}{5}$ $-\frac{2}{15}$

13. $-\frac{2}{3} \cdot \left(-\frac{1}{11}\right)$ $\frac{2}{33}$

14. $2\frac{1}{2} \cdot \left(-\frac{1}{4}\right)$ $-\frac{5}{8}$

15. $3\frac{1}{2} \cdot 1\frac{1}{2}$ $\frac{21}{4}$ or $5\frac{1}{4}$

16. $\frac{2}{9} \cdot \frac{1}{2}$ $\frac{1}{9}$

17. $\frac{3}{2} \cdot \left(-\frac{1}{3}\right)$ $-\frac{1}{2}$

18. $\frac{1}{3} \cdot \frac{6}{5}$ $\frac{2}{5}$

19. $-\frac{9}{4} \cdot \frac{1}{18}$ $-\frac{1}{8}$

20. $\frac{11}{3} \cdot \frac{9}{44}$ $\frac{3}{4}$

21. $\left(-\frac{30}{11}\right) \cdot \left(-\frac{1}{3}\right)$ $\frac{10}{11}$

22. $-\frac{3}{5} \cdot \frac{5}{6}$ $-\frac{1}{2}$

23. $\left(-\frac{1}{3}\right)\left(-7\frac{1}{2}\right)$ $\frac{5}{2}$ or $2\frac{1}{2}$

24. $\frac{2}{7} \cdot 4\frac{2}{3}$ $\frac{4}{3}$ or $1\frac{1}{3}$

Name the reciprocal of each number.

25. $\frac{6}{7}$ $\frac{7}{6}$ or $1\frac{1}{6}$

26. $\frac{1}{22}$ 22

27. $-\frac{14}{23}$ $-\frac{23}{14}$ or $-1\frac{9}{14}$

28. $2\frac{3}{4}$ $\frac{4}{11}$

29. $-5\frac{1}{3}$ $-\frac{3}{16}$

30. $3\frac{3}{4}$ $\frac{4}{15}$

Find each quotient.

31. $\frac{2}{3} \div \frac{1}{3}$ 2

32. $\frac{16}{9} \div \frac{4}{9}$ 4

33. $\frac{3}{2} \div \frac{1}{2}$ 3

34. $\frac{3}{7} \div \left(-\frac{1}{5}\right)$ $-\frac{15}{7}$ or $-2\frac{1}{7}$

35. $-\frac{9}{10} \div 3$ $-\frac{3}{10}$

36. $\frac{1}{2} \div \frac{3}{5}$ $\frac{5}{6}$

37. $2\frac{1}{4} \div \frac{1}{2}$ $\frac{9}{2}$ or $4\frac{1}{2}$

38. $-1\frac{1}{3} \div \frac{2}{3}$ −2

39. $\frac{11}{12} \div 1\frac{2}{3}$ $\frac{11}{20}$

40. $4 \div \left(-\frac{2}{7}\right)$ −14

41. $-\frac{1}{3} \div \left(-1\frac{1}{5}\right)$ $\frac{5}{18}$

42. $\frac{3}{25} \div \frac{2}{15}$ $\frac{9}{10}$

43. **PIZZA** A large pizza at Pizza Shack has 12 slices. If Bobby ate $\frac{1}{4}$ of the pizza, how many slices of pizza did he eat? **3 slices**

44. **MUSIC** Samantha practices the flute for $4\frac{1}{2}$ hours each week. How many hours does she practice in a month? **18 hours**

45. **BAND** How many band uniforms can be made with $131\frac{3}{4}$ yards of fabric if each uniform requires $3\frac{7}{8}$ yards? **34 uniforms**

46. **CARPENTRY** How many boards, each 2 feet 8 inches long, can be cut from a board 16 feet long if there is no waste? **6 boards**

47. **SEWING** How many 9-inch ribbons can be cut from $1\frac{1}{2}$ yards of ribbon? **6 ribbons**

3 ASSESS

Formative Assessment

Use Exercises 1–47 to assess whether students understand how to multiply and divide rational numbers.

Ticket Out the Door Ask students to write a problem in which the product or quotient of two rational numbers is negative.

Lesson 0-5 Multiplying and Dividing Rational Numbers P19

0-6 Lesson Notes

1 FOCUS

Vertical Alignment

Before Lesson 0-6
Use and apply the percent proportion.

Lesson 0-6
Use proportions to solve problems involving percent of change.

2 TEACH

Example 1 shows how to express a percent as a fraction. **Example 2** shows how to use the percent proportion to find the part. **Example 3** shows how to use the percent proportion to find the percent in a real-world problem. **Example 4** shows how to use the percent proportion to find the whole.

Additional Examples

1 Express each percent as a fraction.

a. 43% $\frac{43}{100}$

b. 130% $\frac{13}{10}$

c. 0.2% $\frac{1}{500}$

2 24% of 25 is what number? 6

0-6 The Percent Proportion

Objective

Use and apply the percent proportion.

New Vocabulary

percent

percent proportion

A **percent** is a ratio that compares a number to 100. To write a percent as a fraction, express the ratio as a fraction with a denominator of 100. Fractions should be expressed in simplest form.

EXAMPLE 1

Express each percent as a fraction or mixed number.

a. 79%

$79\% = \frac{79}{100}$ Definition of percent

b. 107%

$107\% = \frac{107}{100}$ Definition of percent

$= 1\frac{7}{100}$ Simplify.

c. 0.5%

$0.5\% = \frac{0.5}{100}$ Definition of percent

$= \frac{5}{1000}$ Multiply the numerator and denominator by 10 to eliminate the decimal.

$= \frac{1}{200}$ Simplify.

In the **percent proportion**, the ratio of a part of something to the whole (base) is equal to the percent written as a fraction.

part → $\frac{a}{b} = \frac{p}{100}$ ← percent
whole →

Example: 25% (percent) of 40 (whole) is 10 (part).

You can use the percent proportion to find the part.

EXAMPLE 2

40% of 30 is what number?

$\frac{a}{b} = \frac{p}{100}$ The percent is 40, and the base is 30. Let a represent the part.

$\frac{a}{30} = \frac{40}{100}$ Replace b with 30 and p with 40.

$100a = 30(40)$ Find the cross products.

$100a = 1200$ Simplify.

$\frac{100a}{100} = \frac{1200}{100}$ Divide each side by 100.

$a = 12$ Simplify.

The part is 12. So, 40% of 30 is 12.

TEACH with TECH

INTERACTIVE WHITEBOARD Create a template that you can use to show the percent proportion, such as $\frac{\square}{\square} = \frac{\square}{100}$. Write an example of a percent application. Have students select the values to be entered in each square of the template.

You can also use the percent proportion to find the percent of the base.

EXAMPLE 3

SURVEYS Kelsey took a survey of students in her lunch period. 42 out of the 70 students Kelsey surveyed said their family had a pet. What percent of the students had pets?

$\frac{a}{b} = \frac{p}{100}$ **The part is 42, and the base is 70. Let *p* represent the percent.**

$\frac{42}{70} = \frac{p}{100}$ **Replace *a* with 42 and *b* with 70.**

$4200 = 70p$ **Find the cross products.**

$\frac{4200}{70} = \frac{70p}{70}$ **Divide each side by 70.**

$60 = p$ **Simplify.**

The percent is 60, so $\frac{60}{100}$ or 60% of the students had pets.

StudyTip

Percent Proportion In percent problems, the whole, or base usually follows the word *of*.

EXAMPLE 4

67.5 is 75% of what number?

$\frac{a}{b} = \frac{p}{100}$ **The percent is 75, and the part is 67.5. Let *b* represent the base.**

$\frac{67.5}{b} = \frac{75}{100}$ **Replace *a* with 67.5 and *p* with 75.**

$6750 = 75b$ **Find the cross products.**

$\frac{6750}{75} = \frac{75b}{75}$ **Divide each side by 75.**

$90 = b$ **Simplify.**

The base is 90, so 67.5 is 75% of 90.

Exercises

Express each percent as a fraction or mixed number in simplest form.

1. 5% $\frac{1}{20}$

2. 60% $\frac{3}{5}$

3. 11% $\frac{11}{100}$

4. 120% $\frac{6}{5}$

5. 78% $\frac{39}{50}$

6. 2.5% $\frac{1}{40}$

7. 0.6% $\frac{3}{500}$

8. 0.4% $\frac{1}{250}$

9. 1400% $\frac{14}{1}$

Use the percent proportion to find each number.

10. 25 is what percent of 125? 20%

11. 16 is what percent of 40? 40%

12. 14 is 20% of what number? 70

13. 50% of what number is 80? 160

14. What number is 25% of 18? 4.5

15. Find 10% of 95. 9.5

16. What percent of 48 is 30? 62.5%

17. What number is 150% of 32? 48

18. 5% of what number is 3.5? 70

19. 1 is what percent of 400? 0.25%

20. Find 0.5% of 250. 1.25

21. 49 is 200% of what number? 24.5

22. 15 is what percent of 12? 125%

23. 36 is what percent of 24? 150%

Additional Examples

3 **PARTY FAVORS** In a bag of party favors, 39 out of 60 are whistles. What percent of the party favors are whistles? 65%

4 38.25 is 45% of what number? 85

Tips for New Teachers

Reasoning Encourage students to check that their answers are reasonable. For example, have them identify the part and the whole in each problem. Then have them reason: If the percent is less than 100%, the part should be less than the whole; if the percent is greater than 100%, the part should be greater than the whole.

3 ASSESS

Formative Assessment

Use Exercises 1–31 to assess whether students understand how to use the percent proportion to solve problems involving percents.

Name the Math Ask students to explain how they would use the percent proportion to find what percent of 40 is 14.

StudyTip

Word Problems When a problem starts with the result and asks for something that happened earlier, work backward.

24. BASKETBALL Madeline usually makes 85% of her shots in basketball. If she attempts 20, how many will she likely make? **17 shots**

25. TEST SCORES Brian answered 36 items correctly on a 40-item test. What percent did he answer correctly? **90%**

26. CARD GAMES Juanita told her dad that she won 80% of the card games she played yesterday. If she won 4 games, how many games did she play? **5 games**

27. SOLUTIONS A glucose solution is prepared by dissolving 6 milliliters of glucose in 120 milliliters of pure solution. What is the percent of glucose in the resulting solution? **5%**

28. DRIVER'S ED Kara needs to get a 75% on her driving education test in order to get her license. If there are 35 questions on the test, how many does she need to answer correctly? **27 questions**

29. HEALTH The U.S. Food and Drug Administration require food manufacturers to label their products with a nutritional label. The label shows the information from a package of macaroni and cheese.

Nutrition Facts

Serving Size 1 cup (228g)		
Servings per container 2		
Amount per serving		
Calories 250	Calories from Fat 110	
		%Daily value*
Total Fat	12g	18%
Saturated Fat	3g	15%
Cholesterol	30mg	10%
Sodium	470mg	20%
Total Carbohydrate	31g	10%
Dietary Fiber	0g	0%
Sugars	5g	
Protein	5g	
Vitamin A 4%	•	Vitamin C 2%
Calcium 20%	•	Iron 4%

a. The label states that a serving contains 3 grams of saturated fat, which is 15% of the daily value recommended for a 2000-Calorie diet. How many grams of saturated fat are recommended for a 2000-Calorie diet? **20 g**

b. The 470 milligrams of sodium (salt) in the macaroni and cheese is 20% of the recommended daily value. What is the recommended daily value of sodium? **2350 mg**

c. For a healthy diet, the National Research Council recommends that no more than 30 percent of the total Calories come from fat. What percent of the Calories in a serving of this macaroni and cheese come from fat? **44%**

30. TEST SCORES The table shows the number of points each student in Will's study group earned on a recent math test. There were 88 points possible on the test. Express all answers to the nearest tenth of a percent.

Name	Will	Penny	Cheng	Minowa	Rob
Score	72	68	81	87	75

a. Find Will's percent correct on the test. **81.8%**

b. Find Cheng's percent correct on the test. **92.0%**

c. Find Rob's percent correct on the test. **85.2%**

d. What was the highest percentage? The lowest? **Minowa 98.9%; Penny 77.3%**

31. PET STORE In a pet store, 15% of the animals are hamsters. If the store has 40 animals, how many of them are hamsters? **6 animals**

0-7 Perimeter

Objective

Find the perimeter of two-dimensional figures.

IL Learning Standards

7.A.4b Apply formulas in a wide variety of theoretical and practical real-world measurement applications involving perimeter, area, volume, angle, time, temperature, mass, speed, distance, density and monetary values.

New Vocabulary

perimeter
circle
diameter
circumference
center
radius

Perimeter is the distance around a figure. Perimeter is measured in linear units.

Rectangle

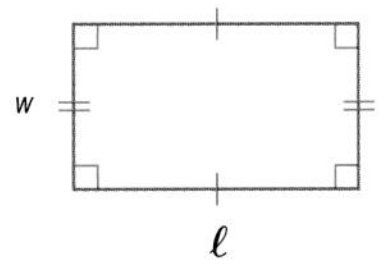

$P = 2(\ell + w)$ or
$P = 2\ell + 2w$

Parallelogram

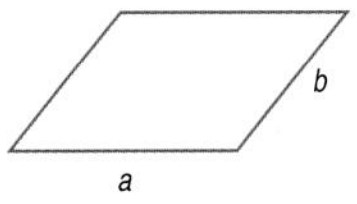

$P = 2(a + b)$ or
$P = 2a + 2b$

Square

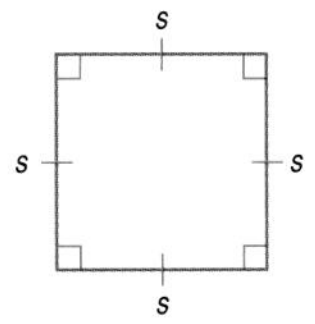

$P = 4s$

Triangle

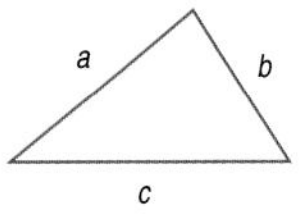

$P = a + b + c$

EXAMPLE 1

Find the perimeter of each figure.

a. a rectangle with a length of 5 inches and a width of 1 inch

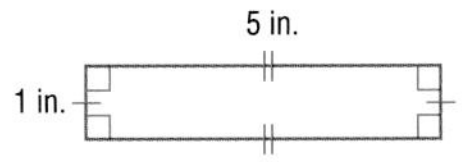

$P = 2(\ell + w)$	**Perimeter formula**
$= 2(5 + 1)$	$\ell = 5, w = 1$
$= 2(6)$	**Add.**
$= 12$	The perimeter is 12 inches.

b. a square with a side length of 7 centimeters

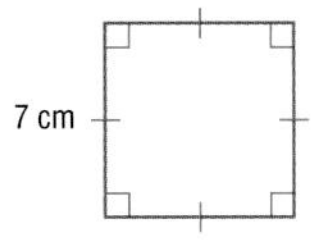

$P = 4s$	**Perimeter formula**
$= 4(7)$	**Replace *s* with 7.**
$= 28$	The perimeter is 28 centimeters.

TEACH with TECH

BLOG On your secure classroom blog, have students create a blog entry to list and describe real-world applications of perimeter.

0-7 Lesson Notes

1 FOCUS

Vertical Alignment

Lesson 0-7
Find the perimeter of two-dimensional figures.

After Lesson 0-7
Represent and find perimeter using polynomials.

2 TEACH

Example 1 shows how to find the perimeter of a rectangle and a square. **Example 2** shows how to find the perimeter of a parallelogram and a triangle. **Example 3** shows how to find the circumference of a circle.

Additional Example

1 Find the perimeter of each figure.

a. a rectangle with a length of 3 feet and a width of 13 feet

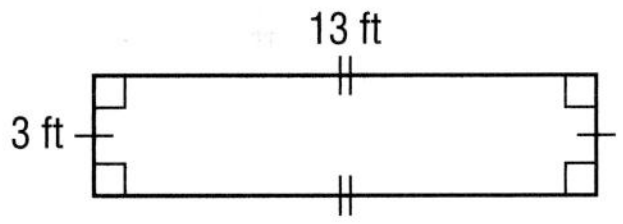

32 feet

b. a square with a side length of 11 millimeters 44 millimeters

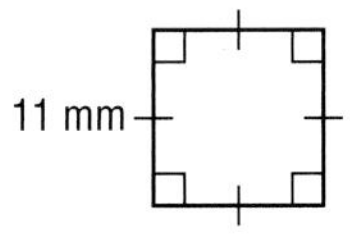

Additional Examples

2 Find the perimeter of each figure.

a.

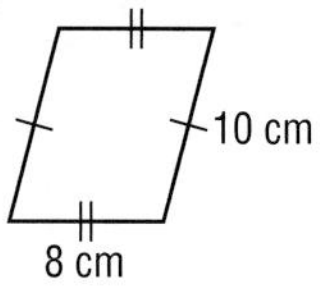

36 centimeters

b.

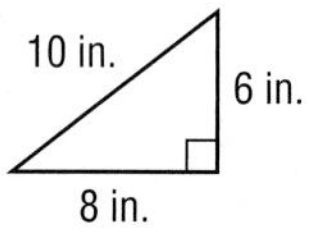

24 inches

3 Find the circumference of each circle to the nearest tenth.

a. The radius is 9 inches. about 56.5 inches

b. The diameter is 12 millimeters. about 37.7 millimeters

c.

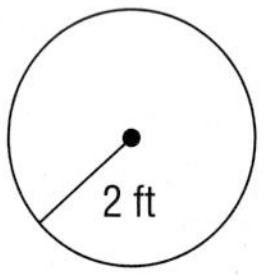

about 12.6 ft

EXAMPLE 2

Find the perimeter of each figure.

a.

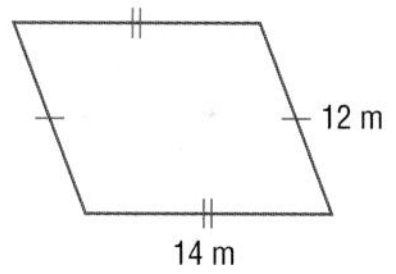

$P = 2(a + b)$ **Perimeter formula**

$= 2(14 + 12)$ **$a = 14$, $b = 12$**

$= 2(26)$ **Add.**

$= 52$ **Multiply.**

The perimeter of the parallelogram is 52 meters.

b.

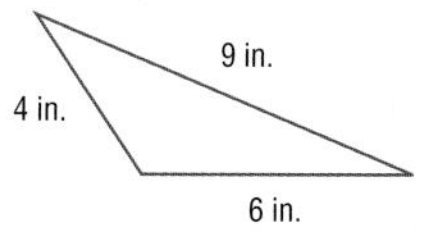

$P = a + b + c$ **Perimeter formula**

$= 4 + 6 + 9$ **$a = 4$, $b = 6$, $c = 9$**

$= 19$ **Add.**

The perimeter of the triangle is 19 inches.

StudyTip

Pi To perform a calculation that involves π, use a calculator.

A **circle** is the set of all points in a plane that are the same distance from a given point.

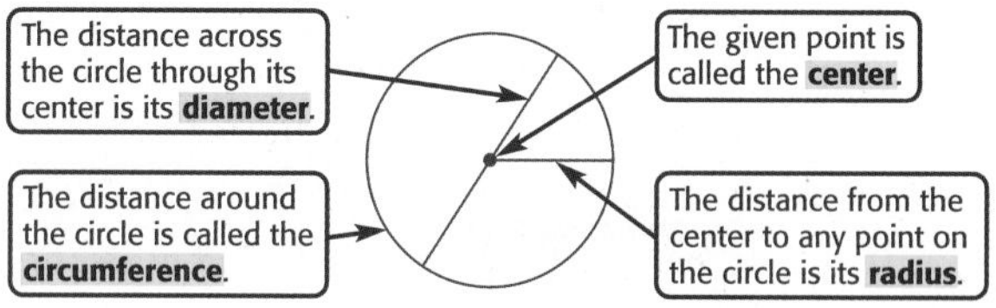

The formula for the circumference of a circle is $C = \pi d$ or $C = 2\pi r$.

EXAMPLE 3

Find each circumference to the nearest tenth.

a. The radius is 4 feet.

$C = 2\pi r$ **Circumference formula**

$= 2\pi(4)$ **Replace r with 4.**

$= 8\pi$ **Simplify.**

The exact circumference is 8π feet.

8 [π] [ENTER] 25.13274123

The circumference is about 25.1 feet.

b. The diameter is 15 centimeters.

$C = \pi d$ **Circumference formula**

$= \pi(15)$ **Replace d with 15.**

$= 15\pi$ **Simplify.**

≈ 47.1 **Use a calculator to evaluate 15π.**

The circumference is about 47.1 centimeters.

c.

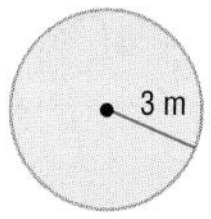

$C = 2\pi r$ **Circumference formula**

$= 2\pi(3)$ **Replace r with 3.**

$= 6\pi$ **Simplify.**

≈ 18.8 **Use a calculator to evaluate 6π.**

The circumference is about 18.8 meters.

P24 **Chapter 0** Preparing for Algebra

Exercises

Find the perimeter of each figure.

1. 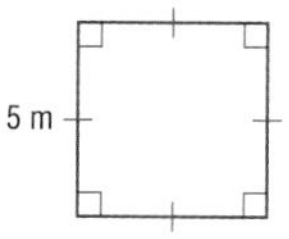

20 m

2. 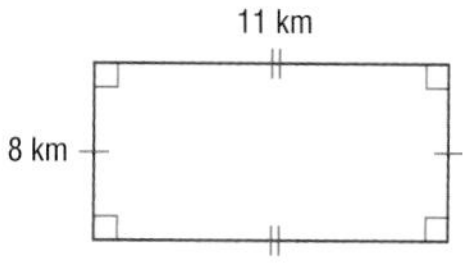

38 km

3. 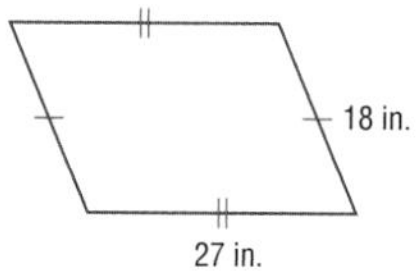

90 in.

4. 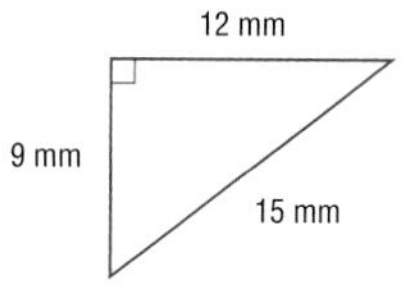

36 mm

5. a square with side length 8 inches **32 in.**

6. a rectangle with length 9 centimeters and width 3 centimeters **24 cm**

7. a triangle with sides 4 feet, 13 feet, and 12 feet **29 ft**

8. a parallelogram with side lengths $6\frac{1}{4}$ inches and 5 inches **$22\frac{1}{2}$ in.**

9. a quarter-circle with a radius of 7 inches **25.0 in.**

Find the circumference of each circle. Round to the nearest tenth.

10. 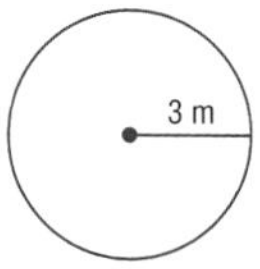

18.8 m

11. 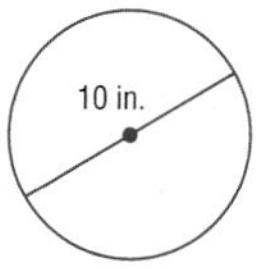

31.4 in.

12. 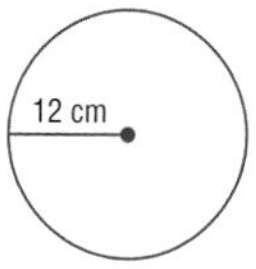

75.4 cm

13. GARDENS A square garden has a side length of 5.8 meters. What is the perimeter of the garden? **23.2 m**

14. ROOMS A rectangular room is $12\frac{1}{2}$ feet wide and 14 feet long. What is the perimeter of the room? **53 ft**

15. CYCLING The tire for a 10-speed bicycle has a diameter of 27 inches. Find the distance traveled in 10 rotations of the tire. Round to the nearest tenth. **848.2 in.**

16. GEOGRAPHY Earth's circumference is approximately 25,000 miles. If you could dig a tunnel to the center of the Earth, how long would the tunnel be? Round to the nearest tenth mile. **3978.9 mi**

Find the perimeter of each figure. Round to the nearest tenth.

17. 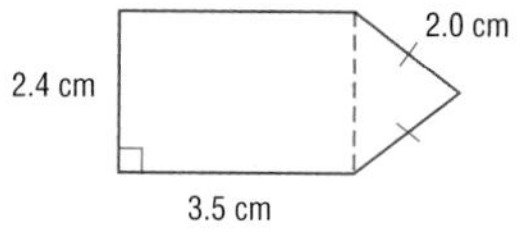

13.4 cm

18. 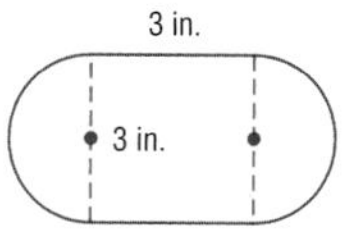

15.4 in.

19. 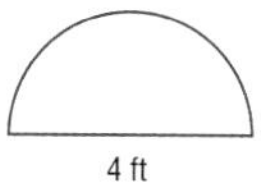

10.3 ft

20. 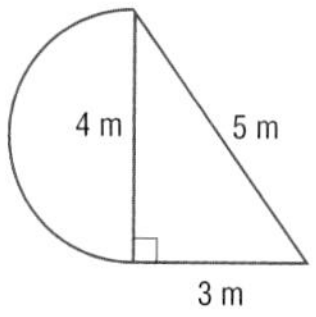

14.3 m

StudyTip

Congruent Marks The hash marks on the figures indicate sides that have the same length.

Watch Out!

Student Misconceptions Radius and diameter are often confused when using the formulas for circumference. Remind students to check that they used radius and diameter appropriately.

3 ASSESS

Formative Assessment

Use Exercises 1–20 to assess whether students understand how to find perimeter and circumference.

Ticket Out the Door Ask students to write a sentence that compares finding the perimeter of a square to finding the circumference of a circle.

Lesson 0-7 Perimeter **P25**

0-8 Lesson Notes

1 FOCUS

Vertical Alignment

Before Lesson 0-8
Find the area of two-dimensional figures.

Lesson 0-8
Represent and find area using polynomials.

2 TEACH

Example 1 shows how to find the area of a rectangle and a square. **Example 2** shows how to find the area of a parallelogram and a triangle. **Example 3** shows how to find the area of a circle when given the radius or diameter.

Additional Example

1 Find the area of each figure.

a. a rectangle that has a length of 14 inches and a width of 5 inches 70 square inches

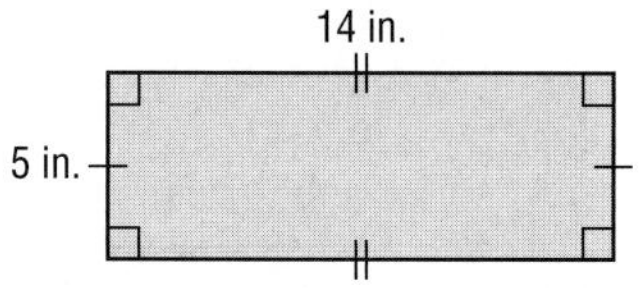

b. a square that has a side length of 6 meters 36 square meters

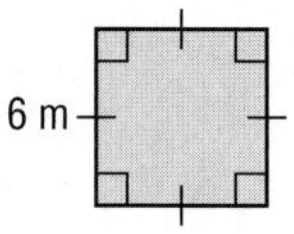

0-8 Area

Objective

Find the area of two-dimensional figures.

IL Learning Standards

7.A.4b Apply formulas in a wide variety of theoretical and practical real-world measurement applications involving perimeter, **area**, volume, angle, time, temperature, mass, speed, distance, density and monetary values.

New Vocabulary
area

Area is the number of square units needed to cover a surface. Area is measured in square units.

Rectangle

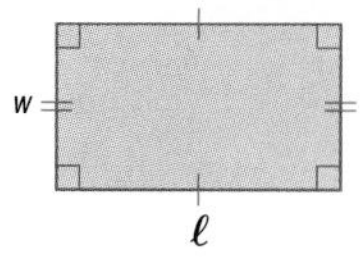

$A = \ell w$

Parallelogram

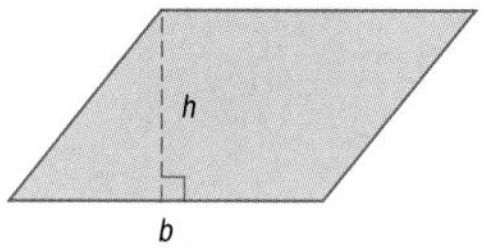

$A = bh$

Square

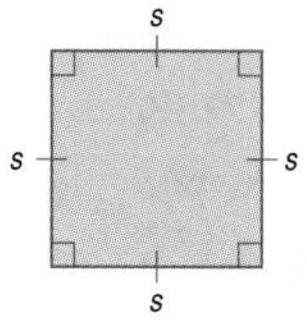

$A = s^2$

Triangle

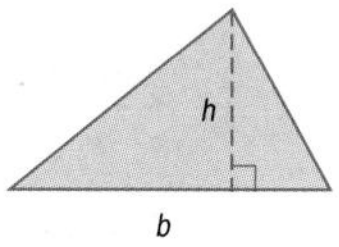

$A = \frac{1}{2}bh$

EXAMPLE 1

Find the area of each figure.

a. a rectangle that has a length of 7 yards and a width of 1 yard

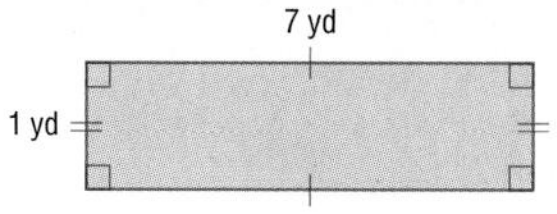

$A = \ell w$	**Area formula**
$= 7(1)$	**$\ell = 7$, $w = 1$**
$= 7$	The area of the rectangle is 7 square yards.

b. a square that has a side length of 2 meters

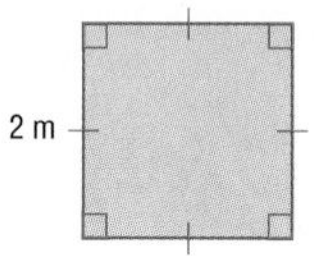

$A = s^2$	**Area formula**
$= 2^2$	**$s = 2$**
$= 4$	The area is 4 square meters.

TEACH with TECH

INTERACTIVE WHITEBOARD Display a parallelogram on the board and an altitude. Trace over the triangle formed by the altitude, one side of the parallelogram, and a portion of the base. Then trace over the quadrilateral formed by the altitude, the remaining portion of the base, and the other two sides. Drag the triangle and the quadrilateral to show students that the pieces form a rectangle. Thus, area of the parallelogram is the same as the area of the rectangle with the same base and height.

EXAMPLE 2

Find the area of each figure.

a. a parallelogram that has a base of 11 feet and a height of 9 feet

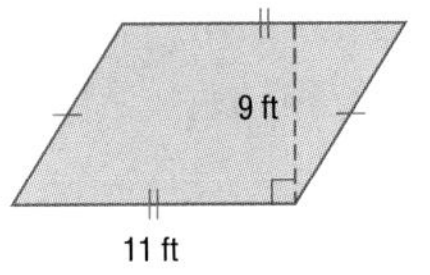

$A = bh$ **Area formula**

$= 11(9)$ **$b = 11, h = 9$**

$= 99$ **Multiply.**

The area is 99 square feet.

b. a triangle that has a base of 12 millimeters and a height of 5 millimeters

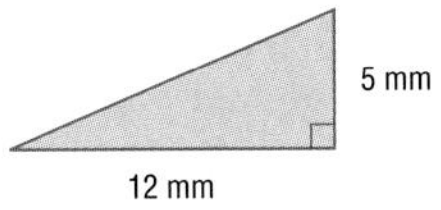

$A = \frac{1}{2}bh$ **Area formula**

$= \frac{1}{2}(12)(5)$ **$b = 12, h = 5$**

$= 30$ **Multiply.**

The area is 30 square millimeters.

The formula for the area of a circle is $A = \pi r^2$.

EXAMPLE 3

Find the area of each circle to the nearest tenth.

a. The radius is 3 centimeters.

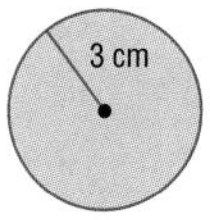

$A = \pi r^2$ **Area formula**

$= \pi(3)^2$ **Replace r with 3.**

$= 9\pi$ **Simplify.**

≈ 28.3 **Use a calculator to evaluate 9π.**

The area is about 28.3 square centimeters.

b. The diameter is 21 meters.

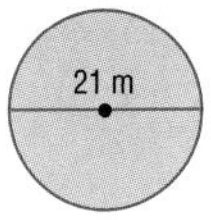

$A = \pi r^2$ **Area formula**

$= \pi(10.5)^2$ **Replace r with 10.5.**

$= 110.25\pi$ **Simplify.**

≈ 346.4 **Use a calculator to evaluate 110.25π.**

The area is about 346.4 square meters.

StudyTip

Mental Math You can use mental math to check your solutions. Square the radius and then multiply by 3.

Additional Examples

2 Find the area of each figure.

a. a parallelogram that has a base of 9 yards and a height of 7 yards

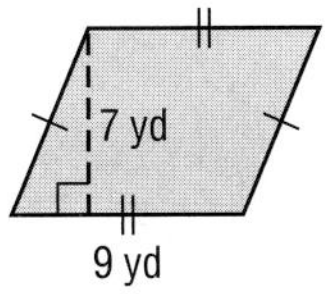

63 square yards

b. a triangle that has a base of 13 centimeters and a height of 8 centimeters

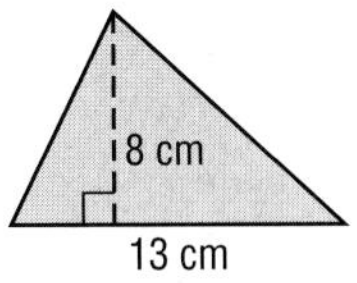

52 square centimeters

3 Find the area of each circle to the nearest tenth.

a. The radius is 4 kilometers.

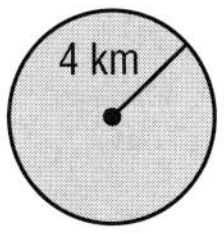

about 50.3 square kilometers

b. The diameter is 15 feet.

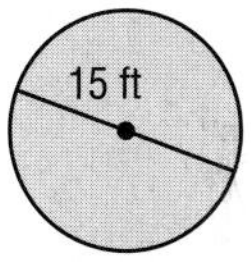

about 176.7 square feet

Lesson 0-8 Area **P27**

Watch Out!

Preventing Errors For Exercise 18, remind students that the inverse of squaring a number is taking the square root of the number.

3 ASSESS

Formative Assessment

Use Exercises 1–23 to assess whether students understand the concept of area and how to find it.

Crystal Ball Ask students to write how they think today's lesson on area will relate to a future lesson on surface area.

Exercises

Find the area of each figure.

1. 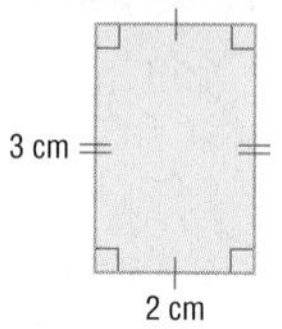

6 cm^2

2. 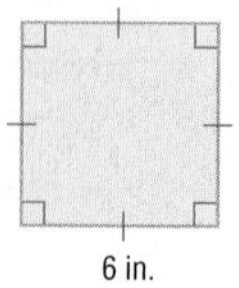

36 in^2

3. 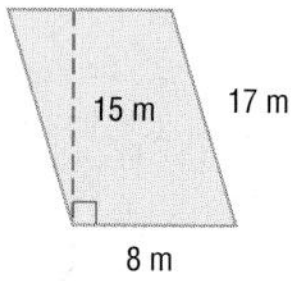

120 m^2

Find the area of each figure. Round to the nearest tenth if necessary.

4. a triangle with a base 12 millimeters and height 11 millimeters 66 mm^2

5. a square with side length 9 feet 81 ft^2

6. a rectangle with length 8 centimeters and width 2 centimeters 16 cm^2

7. a triangle with a base 6 feet and height 3 feet 9 ft^2

8. a quarter-circle with a diameter of 4 meters 3.1 m^2

9. a semi-circle with a radius of 3 inches 14.1 in^2

Find the area of each circle. Round to the nearest tenth.

10. 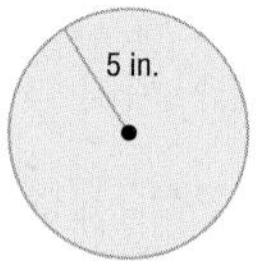

78.5 in^2

11. 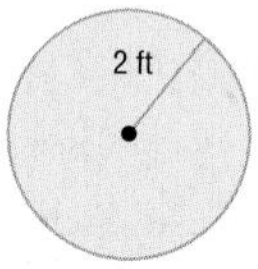

12.6 ft^2

12. 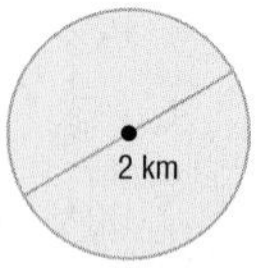

3.1 km^2

13. The radius is 4 centimeters. 50.3 cm^2

14. The radius is 7.2 millimeters. 162.9 mm^2

15. The diameter is 16 inches. 201.1 in^2

16. The diameter is 25 feet. 490.9 ft^2

17. **RECREATION** The Granville Parks and Recreation Department uses an empty city lot for a community vegetable garden. Each participant is allotted a space of 18 feet by 90 feet for a garden. What is the area of each plot? 1620 ft^2

18. **CAMPING** The square floor of a tent has an area of 49 square feet. What is the side length of the tent? 7 ft

19. **PUBLIC SAFETY** The sound emitted from the siren of a tornado warning system can be heard for a 2.5-mile radius. Find the area of the region that hears the siren. Round to the nearest tenth square mile. 19.6 mi^2

20. **HISTORY** Stonehenge is an ancient monument in Wiltshire, England. The giant stones of Stonehenge are arranged in a circle 30 meters in diameter. Find the area of the circle. Round to the nearest tenth square meter. 706.9 m^2

Real-World Link

It is estimated that Stonehenge was built around 2300 B.C. The construction of the monument took place in three phases.

Source: Window on Britain

Find the area of each figure. Round to the nearest tenth.

21. 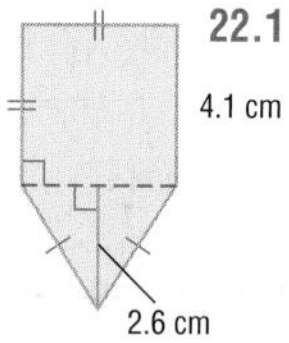

22.1 cm^2

22. 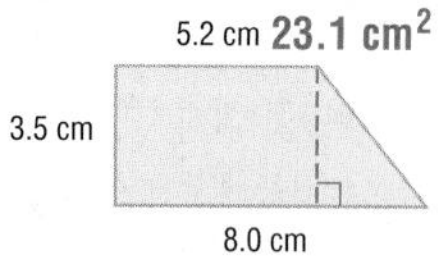

23.1 cm^2

23. 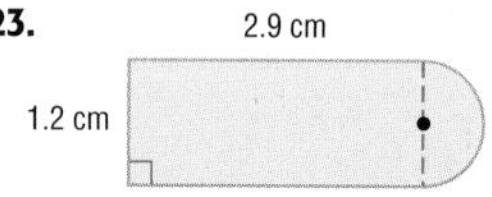

4.0 cm^2

0-9 Volume

Objective

Find the volume of rectangular prisms.

IL Learning Standards

7.A.4b Apply formulas in a wide variety of theoretical and practical real-world measurement applications involving perimeter, area, **volume**, angle, time, temperature, mass, speed, distance, density and monetary values.

New Vocabulary

volume

Volume is the measure of space occupied by a solid. Volume is measured in cubic units.

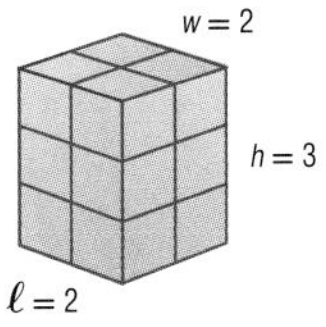

To find the volume of a rectangular prism, multiply the length times the width times the height. The formula for the volume of a rectangular prism is shown below.

$$V = \ell \cdot w \cdot h$$

The prism at the right has a volume of $2 \cdot 2 \cdot 3$ or 12 cubic units.

EXAMPLE 1

Find the volume of each rectangular prism.

a. The length is 8 centimeters, the width is 1 centimeter, and the height is 5 centimeters.

$V = \ell \cdot w \cdot h$ **Volume formula**

$= 8 \cdot 1 \cdot 5$ **Replace ℓ with 8, w with 1, and h with 5.**

$= 40$ **Simplify.**

The volume is 40 cubic centimeters.

b.

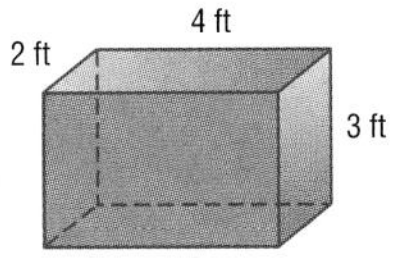

The prism has a length of 4 feet, width of 2 feet, and height of 3 feet.

$V = \ell \cdot w \cdot h$ **Volume formula**

$= 4 \cdot 2 \cdot 3$ **Replace ℓ with 4, w with 2, and h with 3.**

$= 24$ **Simplify.**

The volume is 24 cubic feet.

The volume of a solid is the product of the area of the base and the height of the solid. For a cylinder, the area of the base is πr^2. So the volume is $V = \pi r^2 h$.

EXAMPLE 2

Find the volume of the cylinder.

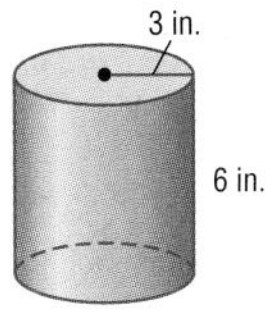

$V = \pi r^2 h$ **Volume of a cylinder**

$= \pi(3^2)6$ **$r = 3$, $h = 6$**

$= 54\pi$ **Simplify.**

≈ 169.6 **Use a calculator.**

The volume is 169.6 cubic inches.

0-9 Lesson Notes

1 FOCUS

Vertical Alignment

Lesson 0-9
Find the volume of rectangular prisms and cylinders.

After Lesson 0-9
Represent and find volume using polynomials.

2 TEACH

Example 1 shows how to find the volume of a rectangular prism. **Example 2** shows how to find the volume of a cylinder.

Additional Examples

1 Find the volume of each rectangular prism.

a. The length is 12 meters, the width is 9 meters, and the height is 4 meters.
432 cubic meters

b.

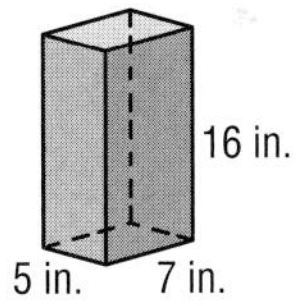

560 cubic inches

2 Find the volume of the cylinder.

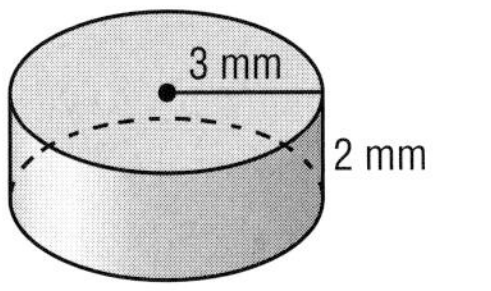

about 56.5 cubic millimeters

TEACH with TECH

WEB PAGE Add information about volumes of three-dimensional figures to your class Web page.

Watch Out!

Common Error Students may use square units rather than cubic units for volume. Remind them that they multiply three dimensions in a rectangular prism, and the square of the radius times height in a cylinder, so the result for both is cubic units.

3 ASSESS

Formative Assessment

Use Exercises 1–19 to assess whether students understand volume and how to find the volume of rectangular prisms and cylinders.

Name the Math Ask students to explain the procedure for finding the volume of a rectangular prism or a cylinder.

Exercises

Find the volume of each rectangular prism given the length, width, and height.

1. $\ell = 5$ cm, $w = 3$ cm, $h = 2$ cm **30 cm³**
2. $\ell = 10$ m, $w = 10$ m, $h = 1$ m **100 m³**
3. $\ell = 6$ yd, $w = 2$ yd, $h = 4$ yd **48 yd³**
4. $\ell = 2$ in., $w = 5$ in., $h = 12$ in. **120 in³**
5. $\ell = 13$ ft, $w = 9$ ft, $h = 12$ ft **1404 ft³**
6. $\ell = 7.8$ mm, $w = 0.6$ mm, $h = 8$ mm **37.44 mm³**

Find the volume of each rectangular prism.

7. 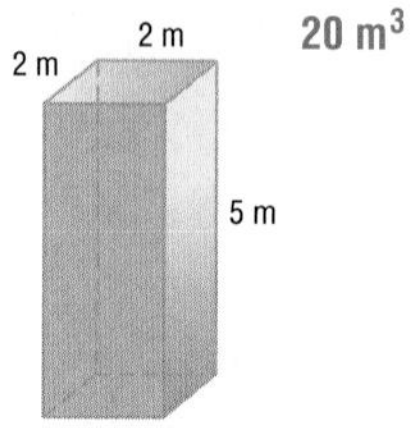

20 m³

8. 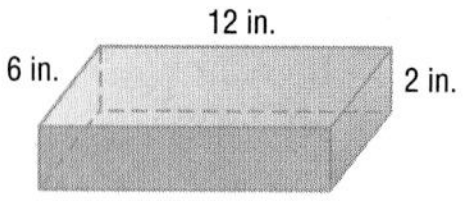

144 in³

9. **GEOMETRY** A cube measures 3 meters on a side. What is its volume? **27 m³**

10. **AQUARIUMS** An aquarium is 8 feet long, 5 feet wide, and 5.5 feet deep. What is the volume of the tank? **220 ft³**

11. **COOKING** What is the volume of a microwave oven that is 18 inches wide by 10 inches long with a depth of $11\frac{1}{2}$ inches? **2070 in³**

12. **BOXES** A cardboard box is 32 inches long, 22 inches wide, and 16 inches tall. What is the volume of the box? **11,264 in³**

13. **SWIMMING POOLS** A children's rectangular pool holds 480 cubic feet of water. What is the depth of the pool if its length is 30 feet and its width is 16 feet? **1 ft**

14. **BAKING** A rectangular cake pan has a volume of 234 cubic inches. If the length of the pan is 9 inches and the width is 13 inches, what is the height of the pan? **2 in.**

15. **GEOMETRY** The volume of the rectangular prism at the right is 440 cubic centimeters. What is the width? **4 cm**

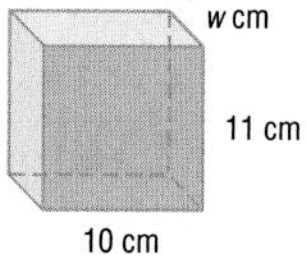

StudyTip

Draw a Diagram Draw a diagram to organize the information given in the problem.

Find the volume of each cylinder. Round to the nearest tenth.

16. 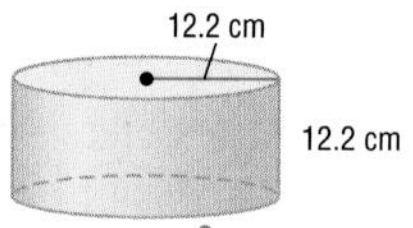

5704.7 cm³

17. 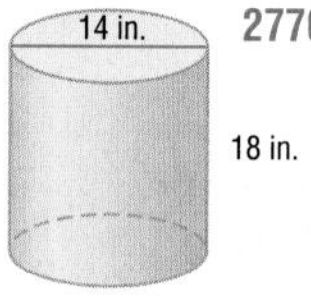

2770.9 in³

18. 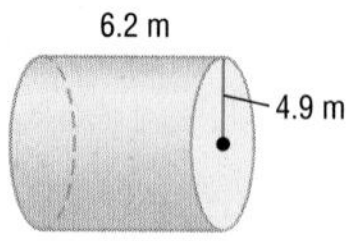

467.7 m³

19. **FIREWOOD** Firewood is usually sold by a measure known as a *cord*. A full cord may be a stack 8 × 4 × 4 feet or a stack 8 × 8 × 2 feet.
    a. What is the volume of a full cord of firewood? **128 ft³**
    b. A "short cord" of wood is 8 × 4 × the length of the logs. What is the volume of a short cord of $2\frac{1}{2}$-foot logs? **80 ft³**
    c. If you have an area that is 12 feet long and 2 feet wide in which to store your firewood, how high will the stack be if it is a full cord of wood? **5 ft 4 in.**

P30 Chapter 0 Preparing for Algebra

0-10 Surface Area

Objective

Find the surface area of rectangular prisms.

New Vocabulary

surface area

Surface area is the sum of the areas of all the surfaces, or faces, of a solid. Surface area is measured in square units.

Key Concept Surface Area

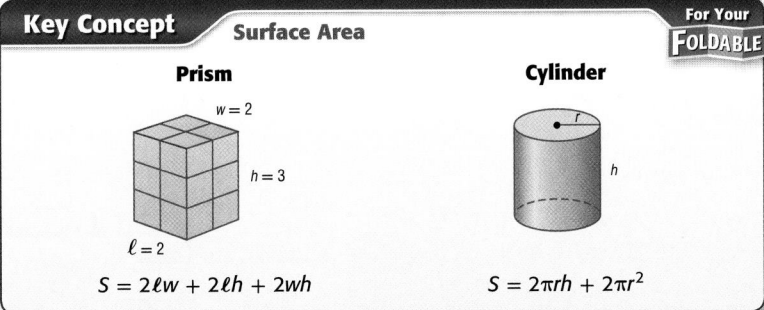

For Your FOLDABLE

Prism

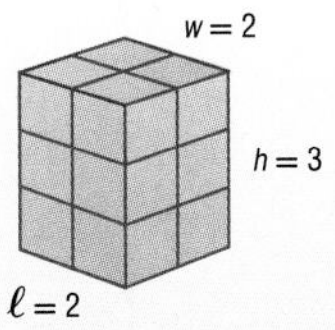

$S = 2\ell w + 2\ell h + 2wh$

Cylinder

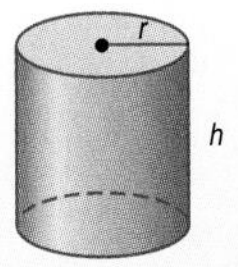

$S = 2\pi rh + 2\pi r^2$

EXAMPLE

Find the surface area of each solid. Round to the nearest tenth if necessary.

a.

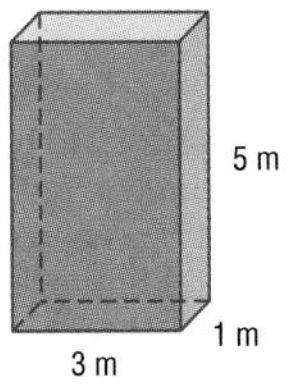

The prism has a length of 3 meters, width of 1 meter, and height of 5 meters.

$S = 2\ell w + 2\ell h + 2wh$	**Surface area formula**
$= 2(3)(1) + 2(3)(5) + 2(1)(5)$	**$\ell = 3, w = 1, h = 5$**
$= 6 + 30 + 10$	**Multiply.**
$= 46$	**Add.**

The surface area is 46 square meters.

b.

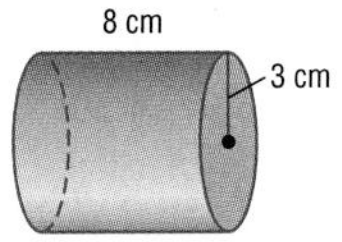

The height is 8 centimeters and the radius of the base is 3 centimeters. The surface area is the sum of the area of each base, $2\pi r^2$, and the area of the side, given by the circumference of the base times the height or $2\pi rh$.

$S = 2\pi rh + 2\pi r^2$	**Formula for surface area of a cylinder.**
$= 2\pi(3)(8) + 2\pi(3^2)$	**$r = 3, h = 8$**
$= 48\pi + 18\pi$	**Simplify.**
$\approx 207.3 \text{ cm}^2$	**Use a calculator.**

0-10 Lesson Notes

1 FOCUS

Vertical Alignment

Lesson 0-10
Find the surface area of rectangular prisms and cylinders.

After Lesson 0-10
Represent and find surface areas using polynomials.

2 TEACH

Example 1 shows how to use a formula to find the surface area of a rectangular prism and a cylinder.

Additional Example

1 Find the surface area of each solid. Round to the nearest tenth if necessary.

a.

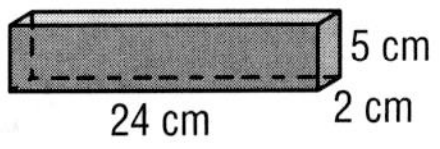

356 square centimeters

b.

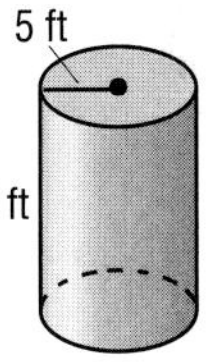

about 596.9 square feet

TEACH with TECH

VIDEO RECORDING Separate students into 4 groups. Have each group record themselves teaching how to find the surface area of a prism or a cylinder. Share the videos with the entire class.

Watch Out!

Preventing Errors It is easy for some students to overlook sides when finding the surface area of a rectangular prism. Suggest that they systematically list the sides of the prism to avoid this error.

3 ASSESS

Formative Assessment

Use Exercises 1–18 to assess whether students understand and can find the surface area of rectangular prisms and cylinders.

Yesterday's News Have students explain how the lesson on the area of two-dimensional figures helped them with today's lesson on the surface area of rectangular prisms.

Exercises

Find the surface area of each rectangular prism given the measurements below.

1. $\ell = 6$ in., $w = 1$ in., $h = 4$ in **68 in²**
2. $\ell = 8$ m, $w = 2$ m, $h = 2$ m **72 m²**
3. $\ell = 10$ mm, $w = 4$ mm, $h = 5$ mm **220 mm²**
4. $\ell = 6.2$ cm, $w = 1$ cm, $h = 3$ cm **55.6 cm²**
5. $\ell = 7$ ft, $w = 2$ ft, $h = \frac{1}{2}$ ft **37 ft²**
6. $\ell = 7.8$ m, $w = 3.4$ m, $h = 9$ m **254.64 m²**

StudyTip

Alternate Method Another way to find the surface area of a solid is to draw the net of the solid on grid paper.

Find the surface area of each solid.

7. 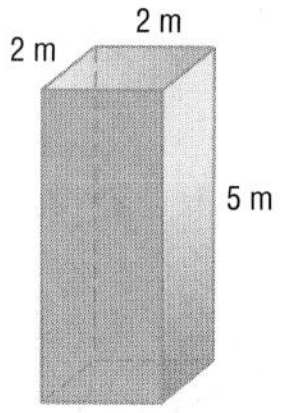

48 m²

8. 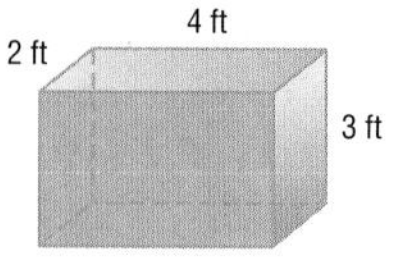

52 ft²

9. 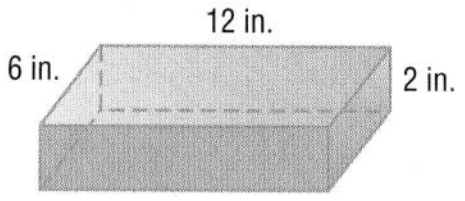

216 in²

10. 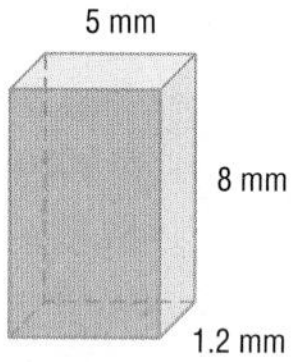

111.2 mm²

11. 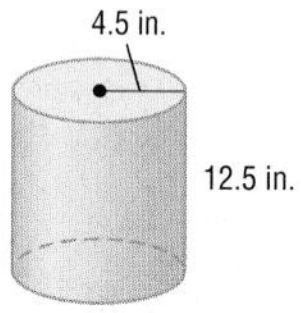

480.7 in²

12. 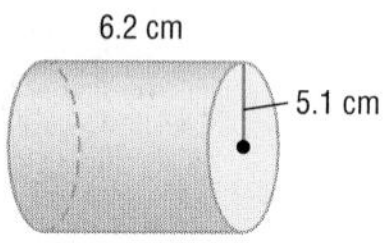

362.1 cm²

13. **GEOMETRY** What is the surface area of a cube with a side length of 2 meters? **24 m²**
14. **GIFTS** A gift box is a rectangular prism 14 inches long, 5 inches wide, and 4 inches high. If the box is to be covered in fabric, how much fabric is needed if there is no overlap? **292 in²**
15. **BOXES** A new refrigerator is shipped in a box 34 inches deep, 66 inches high, and $33\frac{1}{4}$ inches wide. What is the surface area of the box in square feet? Round to the nearest square foot. (*Hint:* 1 ft² = 144 in²) **77 ft²**
16. **PAINTING** A cabinet is 6 feet high, 3 feet wide, and 2 feet long. The entire outside surface of the cabinet is being painted except for the bottom. What is the surface area of the cabinet that is being painted? **66 ft²**
17. **SOUP** A soup can is 4 inches tall and has a diameter of $3\frac{1}{4}$ inches. How much paper is needed for the label on the can? Round your answer to the nearest tenth. **40.8 in²**
18. **CRAFTS** For a craft project, Sarah is covering all the sides of a box with stickers. The length of the box is 8 inches, the width is 6 inches, and the height is 4 inches. If each sticker has a length of 2 inches and a width of 4 inches, how many stickers does she need to cover the box? **26 stickers**

P32 Chapter 0 Preparing for Algebra

0-11 Simple Probability and Odds

Objective

Find the probability and odds of simple events.

IL Learning Standards

10.C.4a Solve problems of chance using the principles of probability including conditional settings.

New Vocabulary

probability
sample space
equally likely
tree diagram
odds
complements

The **probability** of an event is the ratio of the number of favorable outcomes for the event to the total number of possible outcomes. When you roll a die, there are six possible outcomes: 1, 2, 3, 4, 5, or 6. This list of all possible outcomes is called the **sample space**.

When there are n outcomes and the probability of each one is $\frac{1}{n}$, we say that the outcomes are **equally likely**. For example, when you roll a die, the 6 possible outcomes are equally likely because each outcome has a probability of $\frac{1}{6}$. The probabilty of an event is always between 0 and 1, inclusive. The closer a probability is to 1, the more likely it is to occur.

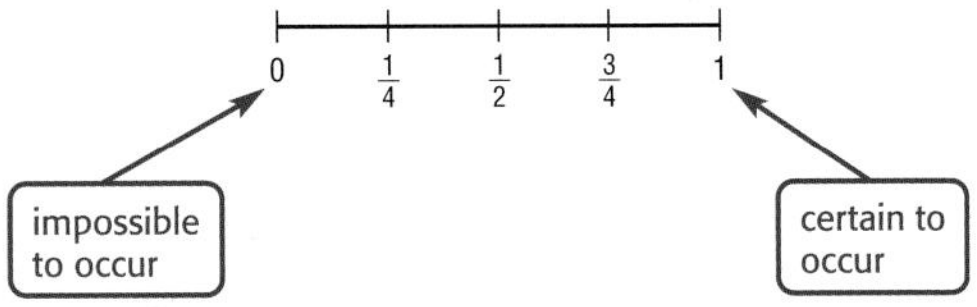

EXAMPLE 1

A die is rolled. Find each probability.

a. rolling a 1 or 5.

There are six possible outcomes. There are two favorable outcomes, 1 and 5.

$$\text{probability} = \frac{\text{number of favorable outcomes}}{\text{total number of possible outcomes}} = \frac{2}{6}$$

So, $P(1 \text{ or } 5) = \frac{2}{6}$ or $\frac{1}{3}$.

b. rolling an even number

Three of the six outcomes are even numbers. So, there are three favorable outcomes.

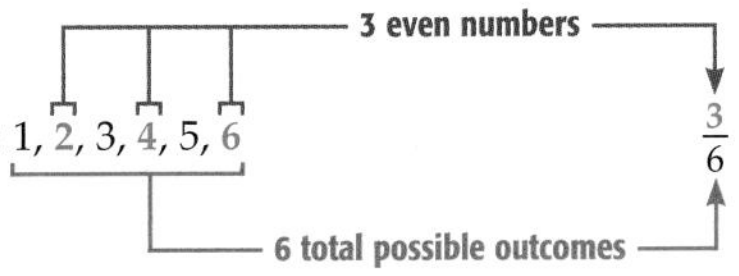

So, $P(\text{even number}) = \frac{3}{6}$ or $\frac{1}{2}$.

The events for rolling a 1 and for *not* rolling a 1 are called **complements**.

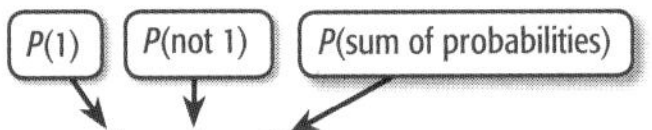

$$\frac{1}{6} + \frac{5}{6} = \frac{6}{6} \text{ or } 1$$

The sum of the probabilities for any two complementary events is always 1.

1 FOCUS

Vertical Alignment

Lesson 0-11
Find the probability and odds of simple events.

After Lesson 0-11
Find the probability of compound events. Use permutations and combinations to find probabilities.

2 TEACH

Example 1 shows how to find probability when rolling a die. **Example 2** shows how to find the probability that an event occurs or does not occur. **Example 3** shows how to use a tree diagram to count outcomes. **Example 4** shows how to use the Fundamental Counting Principle to find the number of possible choices. **Example 5** shows how to find the odds of an event.

Additional Example

1 A die is rolled. Find each probability.

a. rolling a 3 or an even number $\frac{2}{3}$

b. rolling at least a 2 $\frac{5}{6}$

Lesson 0-11 Simple Probability and Odds P33

Additional Examples

2 A bag contains 12 tiles with the letter A, 6 tiles with the letter S, 9 tiles with the letter P, and 5 tiles with the letter E. One tile is randomly drawn. Find each probability.

a. A $\frac{3}{8}$, 0.375, 37.5%

b. P or S $\frac{15}{32}$, about 0.47, or about 47%

c. not E $\frac{27}{32}$, about 0.84, or about 84%

3 A travel agency is offering specialty trips to Australia, Brazil, and India. The agency offers the trips in budget, luxury, and adventure. Use a tree diagram to determine the number of different trips possible.
9 possible trips

Place	Type	Outcomes
Australia	Adventure	A, A
	Budget	A, B
	Luxury	A, L
Brazil	Adventure	B, A
	Budget	B, B
	Luxury	B, L
India	Adventure	I, A
	Budget	I, B
	Luxury	I, L

TEACH with TECH

PORTABLE MEDIA PLAYER Have students find the total number of songs on their portable media player and the number of songs for each genre of music. Ask students to find the probability that a randomly chosen song will be from that genre.

EXAMPLE 2

A bowl contains 5 red chips, 7 blue chips, 6 yellow chips, and 10 green chips. One chip is randomly drawn. Find each probability.

a. blue

There are 7 blue chips and 28 total chips.

$P(\text{blue chip}) = \frac{7}{28}$ ← number of favorable outcomes / ← number of possible outcomes

$= \frac{1}{4}$

The probability can be stated as $\frac{1}{4}$, 0.25, or 25%.

b. red or yellow

There are 5 + 6 or 11 chips that are red or yellow.

$P(\text{red or yellow}) = \frac{11}{28}$ ← number of favorable outcomes / ← number of possible outcomes

≈ 0.39

The probability can be stated as $\frac{11}{28}$, about 0.39, or about 39%.

c. not green

There are 5 + 7 + 6 or 18 chips that are not green.

$P(\text{not green}) = \frac{18}{28}$ ← number of favorable outcomes / ← number of possible outcomes

$= \frac{9}{14}$ or about 0.64

The probability can be stated as $\frac{9}{14}$, about 0.64, or about 64%.

StudyTip

Alternate Method A chip drawn will either be green or not green. So, another method for finding *P*(not green) is to find *P*(green) and subtract that probability from 1.

One method used for counting the number of possible outcomes is to draw a **tree diagram**. The last column of a tree diagram shows all of the possible outcomes.

EXAMPLE 3

School baseball caps come in blue, yellow, or white. The caps have either the school mascot or the school's initials. Use a tree diagram to determine the number of different caps possible.

Color	Design	Outcomes
blue	mascot	blue, mascot
	initials	blue, initials
yellow	mascot	yellow, mascot
	initials	yellow, initials
white	mascot	white, mascot
	initials	white, initials

The tree diagram shows that there are 6 different caps possible.

This example is an illustration of the **Fundamental Counting Principle**, which relates the number of outcomes to the number of choices.

Key Concept — Fundamental Counting Principle

For Your FOLDABLE

Words If event M can occur in m ways and is followed by event N that can occur in n ways, then the event M followed by N can occur in $m \cdot n$ ways.

Example If there are 4 possible sizes for fish tanks and 3 possible shapes, then there are $4 \cdot 3$ or 12 possible fish tanks.

EXAMPLE 4

a. An ice cream shop offers one, two, or three scoops of ice cream from among 12 different flavors. The ice cream can be served in a wafer cone, a sugar cone, or in a cup. Use the Fundamental Counting Principle to determine the number of choices possible.

There are 3 ways the ice cream is served, 3 different servings, and there are 12 different flavors of ice cream.

Use the Fundamental Counting Principle to find the number of possible choices.

number of scoops		number of flavors		number of serving options		number of choices of ordering ice cream
3	·	12	·	3	=	108

So, there are 108 different ways to order ice cream.

b. Jimmy needs to make a 3-digit password for his log-on name on a Web site. The password can include any digit from 0-9, but the digits may not repeat. How many possible 3-digit passwords are there?

If the first digit is a 4, then the next digit cannot be a 4.

We can use the Fundamental Counting Principle to find the number of possible passwords.

1st digit		2nd digit		3rd digit		number of passwords
10	·	9	·	8	=	720

So, there are 720 possible 3-digit passwords.

The **odds** of an event occurring is the ratio that compares the number of ways an event can occur (successes) to the number of ways it cannot occur (failures).

StudyTip

Odds The sum of the number of successes and the number of failures equals the size of the sample space, or the number of possible outcomes.

EXAMPLE 5

Find the odds of rolling a number less than 3.

There are six possible outcomes; 2 are successes and 4 are failures.

So, the odds of rolling a number less than 3 are $\frac{1}{2}$ or 1:2.

Additional Examples

4 **a.** A printing shop is offering a special on business cards in white or off-white from among 18 different fonts. The ink on the cards can be raised or flat. Use the Fundamental Counting Principle to determine the number of choices possible. 72 choices

b. Kara needs to make a password consisting of 3 numbers followed by two letters. The numbers can be any digit 0–9 and the digits can repeat. The letters can be any letter, lowercase, and they cannot repeat. How many possible passwords are there? 650,000 passwords

5 Find the odds of rolling a number on a die that is greater than 2. 2:1

Watch Out!

Common Misconception The terms *odds* and *probability* are often confused and used interchangeably. Suggest that students read problems carefully for the use of these terms, and check that they applied the correct concept in solving the problems. Remind them that probabilities are never greater than 1, but that odds can be greater than 1.

3 ASSESS

Formative Assessment

Use Exercises 1–22 to assess whether students understand simple probability and odds.

Ticket Out the Door Ask students to find the probability and odds of randomly drawing a yellow marker out of a bag that contains 3 yellow markers, 2 blue markers, and 4 red markers. $\frac{1}{3}$; 1:2

Exercises

One coin is randomly selected from a jar containing 70 nickels, 100 dimes, 80 quarters, and 50 one-dollar coins. Find each probability.

1. P(quarter) $\frac{4}{15}$
2. P(dime) $\frac{1}{3}$
3. P(quarter or nickel) $\frac{1}{2}$
4. P(value greater than \$0.10) $\frac{13}{30}$
5. P(value less than \$1) $\frac{5}{6}$
6. P(value at most \$1) 1

One of the polygons below is chosen at random. Find each probability.

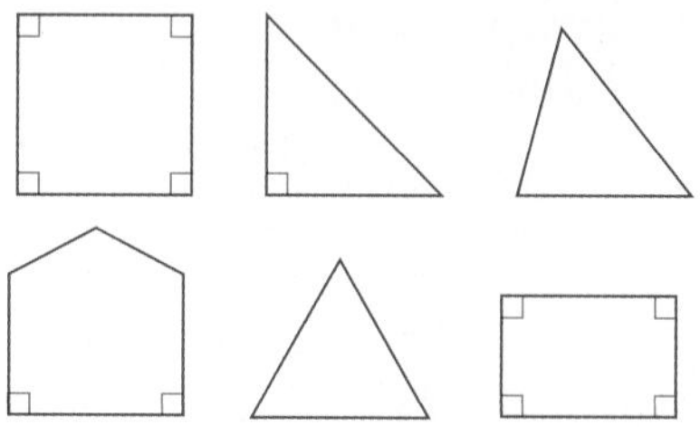

7. P(triangle) $\frac{1}{2}$
8. P(pentagon) $\frac{1}{6}$
9. P(not a quadrilateral) $\frac{2}{3}$
10. P(more than 2 right angles) $\frac{1}{3}$

StudyTip

Counting Outcomes When counting possible outcomes, make a column in your tree diagram for each part of the event.

Use a tree diagram to find the sample space for each event. State the number of possible outcomes.

11. The spinner at the right is spun and two coins are tossed. 20

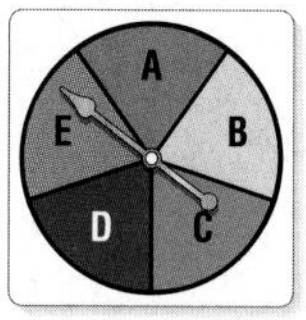

12. At a restaurant, you have several choices of sides to have with breakfast. You can choose white or whole wheat toast. You can choose sausage links, sausage patties, or bacon. 6
13. How many different 3-character codes are there using A, B, or C for the first character, 8 or 9 for the second character, and 0 or 1 for the third character? 12 codes

A bag is full of different colored marbles. The probability of randomly selecting a red marble from the bag is $\frac{1}{8}$. The probability of selecting a blue marble is $\frac{13}{24}$. Find each probability.

14. P(not red) $\frac{7}{8}$
15. P(not blue) $\frac{11}{24}$

Find the odds of each outcome if a computer randomly picks a letter in the name THE UNITED STATES OF AMERICA.

16. the letter *A* 1:7
17. the letter *T* 1:5
18. a vowel 11:13
19. a consonant 13:11

Margaret wants to order a sub at the local deli.

Subs	
ham, salami, roast beef, turkey, bologna, pepperoni	
Dressing	**Toppings**
mayonnaise, mustard, vinegar, oil	lettuce, onions, peppers, olives

20. Find the number of possible orders of a sub with one topping and one dressing option. 96 orders
21. Find the number of possible ham subs with mayonnaise, any combination of toppings or no toppings at all. 16 orders
22. Find the number of possible orders of a sub with any combination of dressing and/or toppings. $6 \cdot 16 \cdot 16$ or 1536 orders

0-12 Mean, Median, Mode, Range, and Quartiles

Objective

Calculate the measures of central tendency of a set of data.

IL Learning Standards

10.A.4b Analyze data using mean, median, mode, range, variance and standard deviation **of a data set, with and without the use of technology.**

New Vocabulary

measures of central tendency
mean
median
mode
measures of variation
range
quartiles
lower quartile
upper quartile

Measures of central tendency are numbers used to represent a set of data. Three types of measures of central tendency are mean, median, and mode. The **mean** is the sum of the numbers in a set of data divided by the number of items.

EXAMPLE 1

Katherine has a lemonade stand. She made a profit of $3.50 on Tuesday, $4.00 on Wednesday, $5.00 on Thursday, and $4.50 on Friday. What was her mean daily profit?

$$\text{mean} = \frac{\text{sum of daily profits}}{\text{number of days}}$$

$$= \frac{\$3.50 + \$4.00 + \$5.00 + \$4.50}{4}$$

$$= \frac{\$17.00}{4} \text{ or } \$4.25$$

Katherine's mean daily profit was $4.25.

The **median** is the middle number in a set of data when the data are arranged in numerical order. If there is an even number of data, the median is the mean of the two middle numbers.

EXAMPLE 2

The table shows the number of hits Marcus made for his team. Find the median of the data.

Team Played	Number of Hits by Marcus
Badgers	3
Hornets	6
Bulldogs	5
Vikings	2
Rangers	3
Panthers	7

To find the median, order the numbers from least to greatest. The median is in the middle.

2, 3, 3, 5, 6, 7

$\frac{3 + 5}{2} = 4$ ← There is an even number of items. Find the mean of the middle two.

The median number of hits is 4.

The **mode** is the number or numbers that appear most often in a set of data. If no item appears most often, the set has no mode.

EXAMPLE 3

The table shows the heights in inches of the members of a college men's basketball team. What is the mode of the heights?

Men's Basketball Team				
74	78	79	80	78
72	81	83	76	78
76	75	77	79	72

78 occurs three times. 72, 76, and 79 each occur twice. All the other heights occur once.

Since 78 occurs most frequently, the mode height is 78.

TEACH with TECH

INTERACTIVE WHITEBOARD Write a set of data on the board. Have a student arrange the data from least to greatest. Then separate the data into two groups to find the median. After discussing Example 6, use the data to find the quartiles.

0-12 Lesson Notes

1 FOCUS

Vertical Alignment

Lesson 0-12
Calculate the measures of central tendency and the measures of variation of a set of data.

After Lesson 0-12
Use measures of central tendency and variation to describe and analyze data.

2 TEACH

Example 1 shows how to find the mean of a set of data. **Example 2** shows how to find the median of a set of data. **Example 3** shows how to find the mode of a set of data. **Example 4** shows how to use mean to solve a problem. **Example 5** shows how to find the range of a set of data. **Example 6** shows how to find the quartiles of a set of data.

Additional Examples

1. **HIKING** Nyack hiked several trails on his camping trip. The lengths of the trails were 1.3 miles, 2.4 miles, 3.2 miles, and 1.7 miles. What was the mean length of the trails? 2.15 miles

2. **SWIMMING** The table shows the number of laps Ekta swam each day. Find the median of the data.

Day	Number of Laps
Monday	8
Tuesday	6
Wednesday	4
Thursday	9
Friday	5

6 laps

Additional Examples

3 **TEXT MESSAGES** The table shows the number of text messages Tumu received. What is the mode of the text messages? 31 messages

Text Messages					
15	28	31	17	24	33
11	24	15	31	19	6
24	31	21	18	31	15

4 **SPORTS** On their first five games of the season, the school basketball team made these scores: 58, 44, 38, 42, and 33. How many points must the team score on the next game to have an average score of 45? 55 points

5 **CELL PHONES** The number of minutes Sara talked on her phone each day this week is 63, 21, 24, 52, 74, 56, and 38. Find the range of the minutes. 53 minutes

6 Find the median, lower quartile, and upper quartile of the data shown below.
27, 35, 44, 13, 29, 44, 52, 28, 41
median: 35; lower quartile: 27.5; upper quartile: 44

You can use measures of central tendency to solve problems.

EXAMPLE 4

SCHOOL On her first five history tests, Yoko received the following scores: 82, 96, 92, 83, and 91. What must she earn on the sixth test to have an average (mean) of 90?

$$\text{mean} = \frac{\text{sum of the first five scores} + \text{sixth score}}{\text{total number of tests}}$$ **Write an equation.**

$$90 = \frac{82 + 96 + 92 + 83 + 91 + x}{6}$$ **Use x to represent the sixth score.**

$$90 = \frac{444 + x}{6}$$ **Simplify.**

$$540 = 444 + x$$ **Multiply each side by 6.**

$$96 = x$$ **Subtract 444 from each side.**

To have an average score of 90, Yoko must earn a 96 on the sixth test.

Measures of variation are used to describe the distribution of the data. One measure, the difference between the greatest and the least data values, is called the **range**.

StudyTip

Describing Data The measures of variation including range describe how the data in a set vary. This is another way to describe data.

EXAMPLE 5

The times in minutes it took Olivia to walk to school each day this week are 18, 15, 15, 12, and 14. Find the range of the times.

range = greatest value − least value **Write an equation.**

$= 18 - 12$ or 6 **The greatest value is 18, and the least value is 12.**

The range of the times is 6 minutes.

In a set of data, the **quartiles** are values that separate the data into four equal subsets, each containing one fourth of the data. Q_1, Q_2, and Q_3 are used to represent the three quartiles. Q_1 is the **lower quartile**. It divides the lower half of the data into two equal parts. Q_2 is the median since it separates the data into two equal parts. Q_3 is the **upper quartile**. It divides the upper half of the data into two equal parts.

EXAMPLE 6

Find the median, lower quartile, and upper quartile of the data shown below.

22, 16, 35, 26, 14, 17, 28, 29, 21, 17, 20

Order the data from least to greatest. Then use the list to determine the quartiles.

14, 16, 17, 17, 20, 21, 22, 26, 28, 29, 35

(arrows: 17 → Q_1, 21 → Q_2, 28 → Q_3)

The median (Q_2) is 21, the lower quartile (Q_1) is 17, and the upper quartile (Q_3) is 28.

Exercises

StudyTip

Calculating Measures of Central Tendency Remember to order the data from least to greatest before finding the median of the data.

Find the mean, median, and mode for each set of data. 6. 200; 200; 201 and 199

1. {1, 2, 3, 5, 5, 6, 13} 5; 5; 5
2. {3, 5, 8, 1, 4, 11, 3} 5; 4; 3
3. {52, 53, 53, 53, 55, 55, 57} 54; 53; 53
4. {8, 7, 5, 19} 9.75; 7.5; no mode
5. {3, 11, 26, 4, 1} 9; 4; no mode
6. {201, 201, 200, 199, 199}
7. {4, 5, 6, 7, 8} 6; 6; no mode
8. {3, 7, 21, 23, 63, 27, 29, 95, 23} $32\frac{1}{3}$; 23; 23

Find the range, median, lower quartile, and upper quartile for each set of data.

10. 37; 73; 66; 82

9. {4, 7, 11, 19, 26, 26, 32} 28; 19; 7; 26
10. {62, 65, 67, 68, 73, 80, 81, 83, 99}
11. {17, 9, 10, 17, 18, 5, 2} 16; 10; 5; 17
12. {33, 38, 29, 25, 41, 40} 16; 35.5; 29; 40
13. {10, 9, 8, 7, 6, 5, 4} 6; 7; 5; 9
14. {111, 109, 112, 114, 119, 112} 10; 112; 111; 114

15. **SCHOOL** The table shows the cost of some school supplies. Find the mean, median, and mode costs.

Cost of School Supplies	
Supply	**Cost**
pencils	$0.50
pens	$2.00
paper	$2.00
pocket folder	$1.25
calculator	$5.25
notebook	$3.00
eraser	$2.50
markers	$3.50

mean: $2.50; median: $2.25; mode: $2.00

16. **NUTRITION** The table shows the number of servings of fruits and vegetables that Cole eats one week. Find the range, median, lower quartile, and upper quartile. range: 5; median: 5; Q_1: 3; Q_3: 7

Fruit and Vegetable Servings	
Day	**Number of Servings**
Monday	5
Tuesday	7
Wednesday	5
Thursday	4
Friday	3
Saturday	3
Sunday	8

17. **SCHOOL** Bill's scores on his first four science tests are 86, 90, 84, and 91. What must Bill earn on the fifth test so that his average (mean) will be exactly 88? 89

18. **BOWLING** Sue's average for 9 games of bowling is 108. What is the lowest score she can receive for the tenth game to have an average of 110? 128

19. **SCHOOL** Olivia has an average score of 92 on five French tests. If she earns a score of 96 on the sixth test, what will her new average score be? about 92.7

20. **JOBS** The number of hours Maria and her friends each work at their part-time jobs is 20, 10, 8, 5, 25, 12 and 10 hours. Find the average amount of time Maria and her friends work at their jobs to the nearest hour. 13 hours

21. **MOVIES** At a movie theater, ten movies are playing and their lengths are 105, 95, 115, 120, 150, 130, 100, 125, 110, and 135 minutes. Find the average length of a movie playing at this theater to the nearest tenth. 118.5 min

22. **BASKETBALL** The heights of players of a girls' basketball team are shown. Find the average height of the team to the nearest tenth. 67.5 in.

Height of Players (in.)			
72	71	69	66
62	70	64	69
67	65	65	70

Tips for New Teachers

Sense-Making Advise students that the median is not included in the lower half or upper half of data when they are finding quartiles. If there is an odd number of values in the data set, the median is the middle number, and it is not included in either half. If there is an even number of values of the data set, the median is the mean of the two middle numbers.

3 ASSESS

Formative Assessment

Use Exercises 1–22 to assess whether students understand measures of central tendency and variation and how to calculate them.

Name the Math Ask students to explain how they would find the mean, median, mode, and range of the following data: 18, 10, 23, 11, 18.

0-13 Lesson Notes

1 FOCUS

Vertical Alignment

Before Lesson 0-13
Represent sets of data using different visual displays.

Lesson 0-13
Analyze data in visual displays. Recognize misleading graphs.

2 TEACH

Example 1 shows how to make a bar graph. **Example 2** shows how to make a histogram. **Example 3** shows how to make a line graph. **Example 4** shows how to make a stem-and-leaf plot. **Example 5** shows how to make a circle graph. **Example 6** shows how to make a box-and-whisker plot.

Additional Example

1 **MUSIC** The table shows the results of a student survey on favorite music. Make a bar graph to display the data.

Music	Frequency
Country	13
Hip-Hop	35
Metal	20
Rock	32

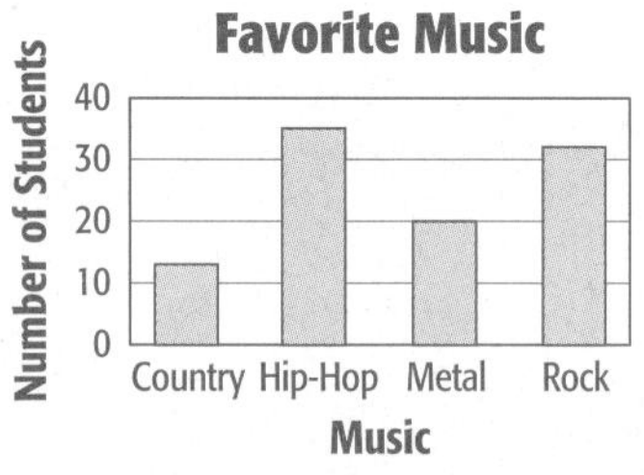

0-13 Representing Data

Objective

Represent sets of data using different visual displays.

IL Learning Standards

7.A.4a Apply units and scales to describe and compare numerical data and physical objects.
10.A.4a Represent and organize data by creating lists, charts, tables, frequency distributions, graphs, scatterplots and box-plots.

New Vocabulary

frequency table
bar graph
histogram
line graph
stem-and-leaf plot
circle graph
box-and-whisker plot
interquartile range
outliers

Data can be displayed and organized by different methods. In a **frequency table**, you use tally marks to record and display the frequency of events. A **bar graph** compares categories of data with bars representing the frequency.

EXAMPLE 1

The frequency table shows the results of a survey of students' favorite sports. Make a bar graph to display the data.

Sport	Tally	Frequency
basketball	𝍸 𝍸 𝍸	15
football	𝍸 𝍸 𝍸 𝍸 𝍸	25
soccer	𝍸 𝍸 𝍸 III	18
baseball	𝍸 𝍸 𝍸 𝍸 I	21
tennis	𝍸 𝍸 𝍸 I	16

Step 1 Draw a horizontal axis and a vertical axis. Label the axes as shown. Add a title.

Step 2 Draw a bar to represent each sport. The vertical scale is the number of students who chose each sport. The horizontal scale identifies the sport.

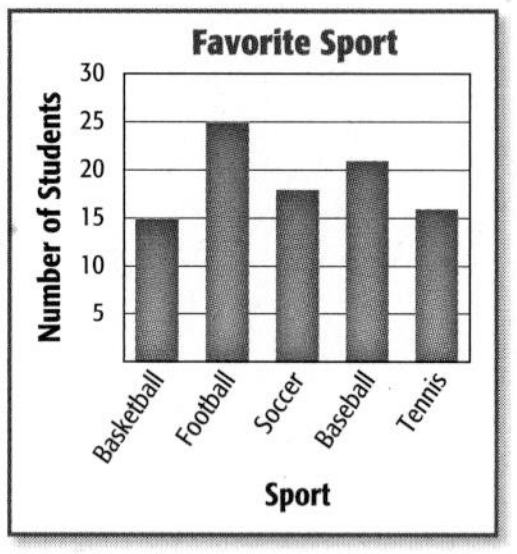

A **histogram** is a type of bar graph used to display numerical data that have been organized into equal intervals.

EXAMPLE 2

The frequency table shows the heights of students in a class. Make a histogram of the data.

Heights of Students		
Height (cm)	Tally	Frequency
131–140	IIII	4
141–150	𝍸 I	6
151–160	𝍸 III	8
161–170	𝍸	5
171–180	III	3

Step 1 Draw and label a horizontal and vertical axis. Include a title.

Step 2 Show the intervals from the frequency table on the horizontal axis.

Step 3 For each height interval, draw a bar whose height is given by the frequencies. There is no space between the bars.

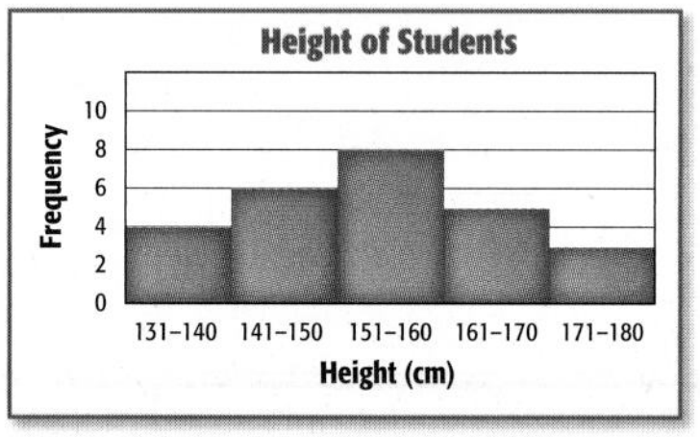

Another way to represent data is by using a line graph. A **line graph** usually shows how data change over a period of time.

EXAMPLE 3

Sales at the Marshall High School Store are shown in the table. Make a line graph of the data.

School Store Sales Amounts					
September	$670	December	$168	March	$412
October	$229	January	$290	April	$309
November	$300	February	$388	May	$198

Step 1 Draw a horizontal axis and a vertical axis and label them as shown. Include a title.

Step 2 Plot the points.

Step 3 Draw a line connecting each pair of consecutive points.

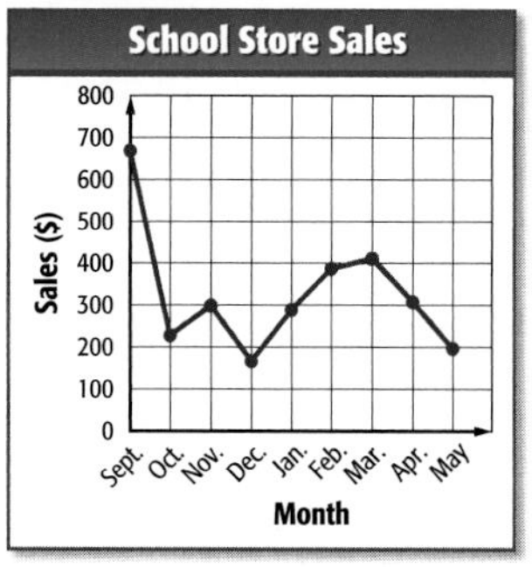

Data can also be organized and displayed by using a stem-and-leaf plot. In a **stem-and-leaf plot**, the greatest common place value is used for the *stems*. The numbers in the next greatest place value are used to form the *leaves*.

EXAMPLE 4

The speeds (mph) of 20 of the fastest land animals are listed at the right. Use the data to make a stem-and-leaf plot.

42	40	40	35	50
32	50	36	50	40
45	70	43	45	32
40	35	61	48	35

Source: *The World Almanac*

The greatest place value is tens. So, 32 miles per hour would have a stem of 3 and a leaf of 2.

Stem	Leaf
3	2 2 5 5 5 6
4	0 0 0 0 2 3 5 5 8
5	0 0 0
6	1
7	0

Key: 3|2 = 32

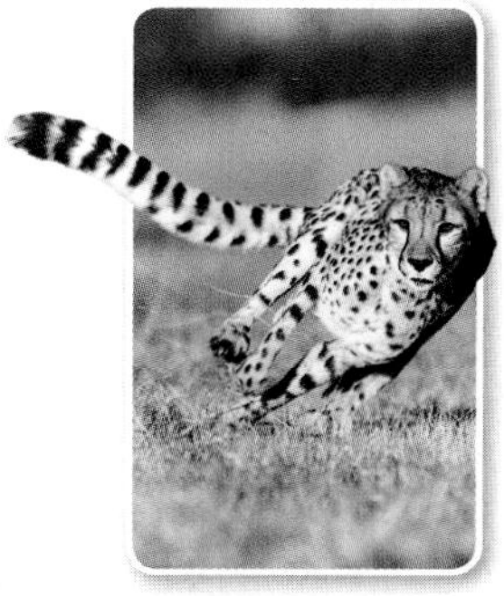

Real-World Link

The fastest animal on land is the cheetah. Cheetahs can run at speeds up to 60 miles per hour.

Source: Infoplease

A **circle graph** is a graph that shows the relationship between parts of the data and the whole. The circle represents all of the data.

Additional Examples

2 **VOLUNTEERS** Make a histogram of the ages of the volunteers at an animal shelter.

Ages	Frequency
16–25	6
26–35	4
36–45	9
46–55	12
56–65	8

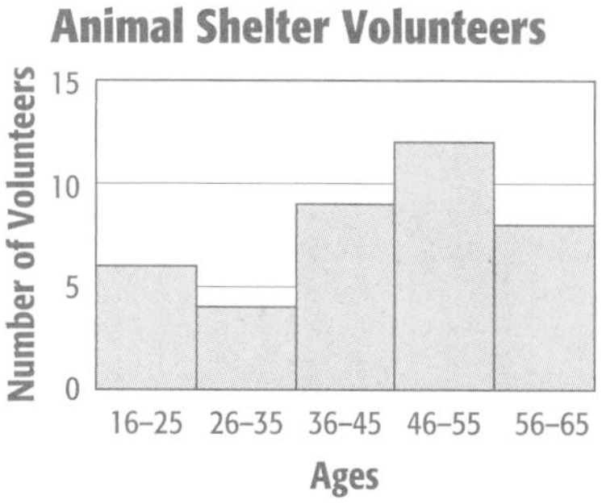

3 **WIND** Make a line graph of the wind speed forecast data.

Wind Speed Forecast (mph)			
Midnight	4	Noon	21
3:00 A.M.	5	3:00 P.M.	24
6:00 A.M.	8	6:00 P.M.	14
9:00 A.M.	11	9:00 P.M.	17

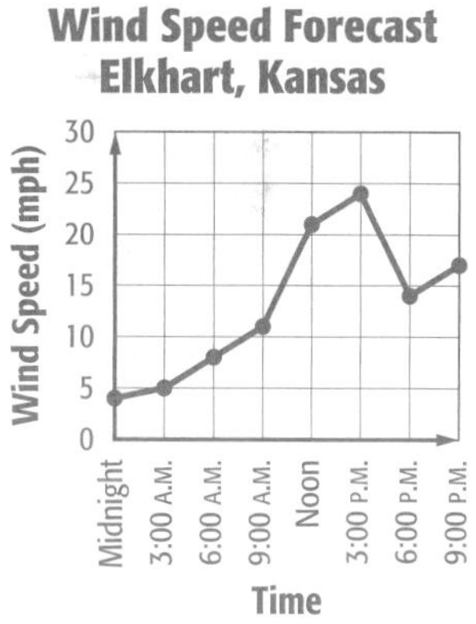

4 **SHIPPING** The weights (in pounds) of 25 packages shipped from a mailing center are listed below. Use the data to make a stem-and-leaf plot.

3	18	35	20	5
9	4	2	10	12
15	15	22	5	17
16	9	2	38	2
3	11	23	41	3

Additional Example Answer

4. Weights of Packages

Stem	Leaf
0	2 2 2 3 3 3 4 5 5 9 9
1	0 1 2 5 5 6 7 8
2	0 2 3
3	5 8
4	1

Key: 3|8 = 38 pounds

Additional Examples

5 The table shows how the Astronomy Club raised $500. Make a circle graph of the data.

Astronomy Club Fundraising	
Source	**Amount ($)**
Car Washes	125
Fish Fry	150
Game-a-thon	75
Poster Sales	150

Astronomy Club Fundraising

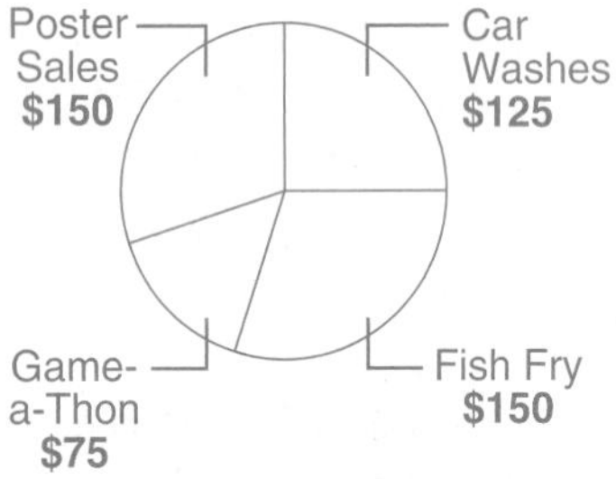

6 Draw a box-and-whisker plot for these data.

20, 17, 23, 26, 19, 28, 4, 20, 24

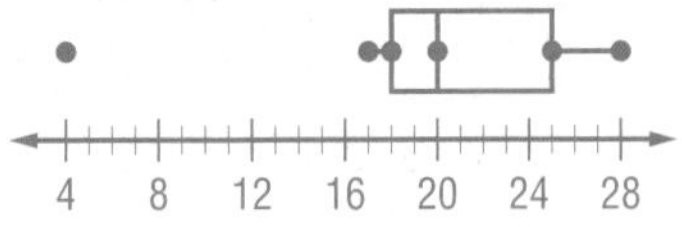

TEACH with TECH

BLOG On your secure classroom blog, have students write a blog entry explaining when they would use different types of data displays. Be sure students describe data sets that would best be shown using line graphs, bar graphs, and circle graphs.

EXAMPLE 5

The table shows how Lily spent 8 hours of one day at summer camp.

Summer Camp	
Activity	**Hours**
canoeing	3
crafts	1
eating	2
hiking	2

First, find the ratio that compares the number of hours for each activity to 8. Then multiply each ratio by 360° to find the number of degrees for each section of the graph.

Canoeing: $\frac{3}{8} \cdot 360° = 135°$

Crafts: $\frac{1}{8} \cdot 360° = 45°$

Eating: $\frac{2}{8} \cdot 360° = 90°$

Hiking: $\frac{2}{8} \cdot 360° = 90°$

Summer Camp

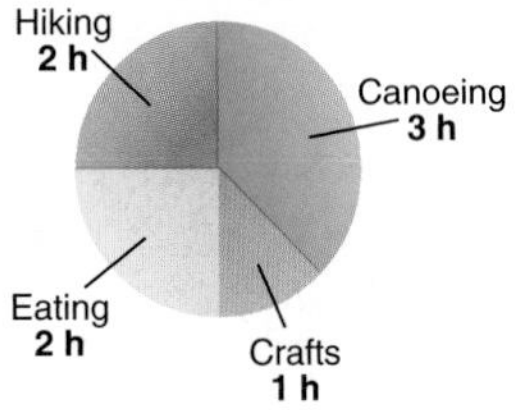

StudyTip

Interquartile Range When the interquartile range is a small value, the data in the set are close together. A large interquartile range means that the data are spread out.

Data can be organized and displayed by dividing a set of data into four parts using the median and quartiles. This is a **box-and-whisker plot**. The box in a box-and-whisker plot represents the interquartile range. The **interquartile range** is the difference between the upper and lower quartiles. Data that are more than 1.5 times the value of the interquartile range beyond the quartiles are called **outliers**.

EXAMPLE 6

Draw a box-and-whisker plot for these data. Describe how the outlier affects the quartile points.

14, 30, 16, 20, 18, 16, 20, 18, 22, 13, 8

Step 1 Order the data from least to greatest. Then determine the quartiles.

8, 13, **14**, 16, 16, **18**, 18, 20, **20**, 22, 30

Q_1 (14), Q_2 (18), Q_3 (20)

Determine the interquartile range.

$IQR = Q_3 - Q_1$

$= 20 - 14$ or 6

Check to see if there are any outliers.

$14 - 1.5(6) = 5$ $\quad$ $20 + 1.5(6) = 29$

Numbers less than 5 or greater than 29 are outliers.

The only outlier is 30.

Step 2 Draw a number line that includes the least and greatest numbers in the data. Place dots above the number line to represent the three quartile points, any outliers, the least number that is not an outlier, and the greatest number that is not an outlier.

Additional Answers

1.

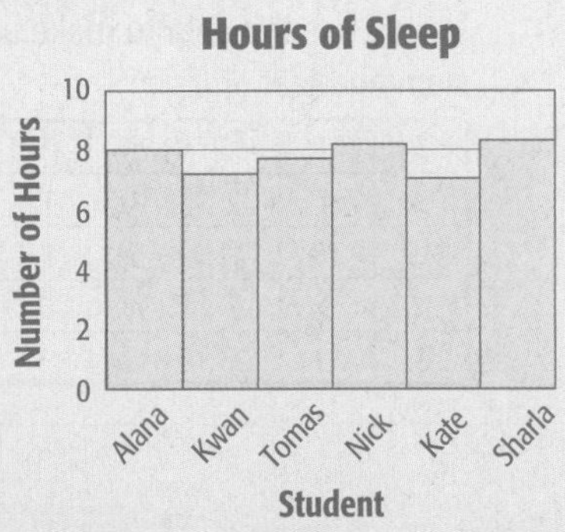

2.

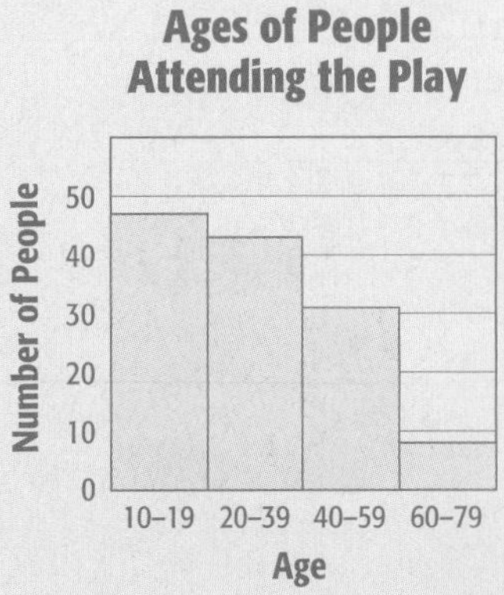

3.

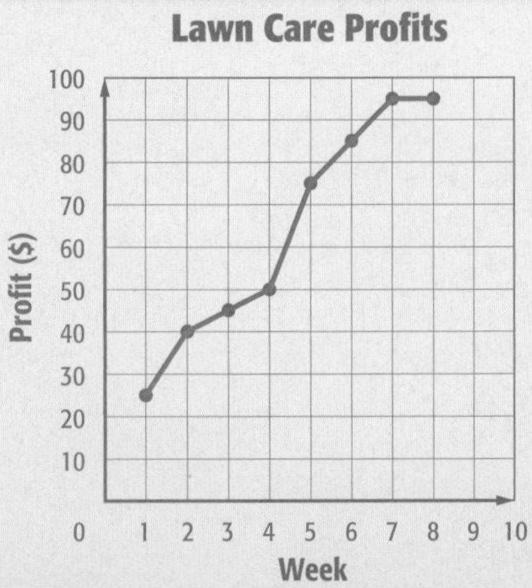

Step 3 Draw the box and the whiskers. The vertical rules go through the quartiles. The outliers are not connected to the whiskers.

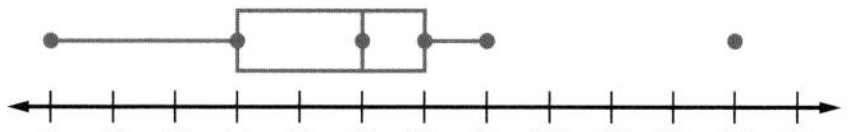

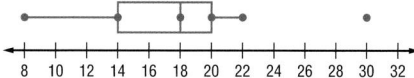

Step 4 Omit 30 from the data. Repeat Step 1 to determine Q_1, Q_2, and Q_3.
8, 13, **14,** 16, **16, 18,** 18, **20,** 20, 22

↑ Q_1 ↑ $Q_2 = 17$ ↑ Q_3

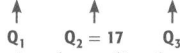

Removing the outlier does not affect Q_1 or Q_2 and thus does not affect the interquartile range. The value of Q_2 changes from 18 to 17.

Exercises

StudyTip

Best Representation A set of data can be represented by several different displays. There is usually one type of graph that is best for displaying the data.

1. **SURVEYS** Alana surveyed several students to find the number of hours of sleep they typically get each night. The results are shown in the table. Make a bar graph of the data. See margin.

Hours of Sleep					
Alana	8	Kwam	7.5	Tomas	7.75
Nick	8.25	Kate	7.25	Sharla	8.5

2. **PLAYS** The frequency table at the right shows the ages of people attending a high school play. Make a histogram to display the data. See margin.

Age	Tally	Frequency
0–19	卌 卌 卌 卌 卌 卌 卌 卌 卌 II	47
20–39	卌 卌 卌 卌 卌 卌 卌 卌 III	43
40–59	卌 卌 卌 卌 卌 卌 I	31
60–79	卌 III	8

3. **LAWN CARE** Marcus started a lawn care service. The chart shows how much money he made over summer break. Make a line graph of the data. See margin.

Lawn Care Profits ($)								
Week	1	2	3	4	5	6	7	8
Profit	25	40	45	50	75	85	95	95

Use each set of data to make a stem-and-leaf plot and a box-and-whisker plot. Describe how the outliers affects the quartile points.

4. {65, 63, 69, 71, 73, 59, 60, 70, 72, 66, 71, 58} 4–5. See margin.

5. {31, 30, 28, 26, 22, 34, 26, 31, 47, 32, 18, 33, 26, 23, 18}

6. **FINANCIAL LITERACY** The table shows how Ping spent his allowance of $40. Make a circle graph of the data. See margin.

Allowance	
How Spent	Amount ($)
savings	15
downloaded music	8
snacks	5
T-shirt	12

7. **JOGGING** The table shows the number of miles Hannah jogged each day for 10 days. Make a line graph of the data. See margin.

Day	1	2	3	4	5	6	7	8	9	10
Miles Jogged	2	2	3	3.5	4	4.5	2.5	3	4	5

Watch Out!

Preventing Errors In the Exercises, remind students that outliers do not form part of the whiskers of a box-and-whisker plot. Whiskers extend to the greatest value and the least value that are not outliers. Encourage students to carefully distinguish minimum and maximum values from outliers so they do not make outliers part of the whisker.

3 ASSESS

Formative Assessment

Use Exercises 1–7 to assess whether students understand how to make visual displays including bar graphs, histograms, line graphs, stem-and-leaf plots, circle graphs, and box-and-whisker plots.

Yesterday's News Ask students to explain how yesterday's lesson on measures of variation and central tendency helped with today's lesson on representing data in stem-and-leaf plots and box-and-whisker plots.

Additional Answers

6. **Allowance**

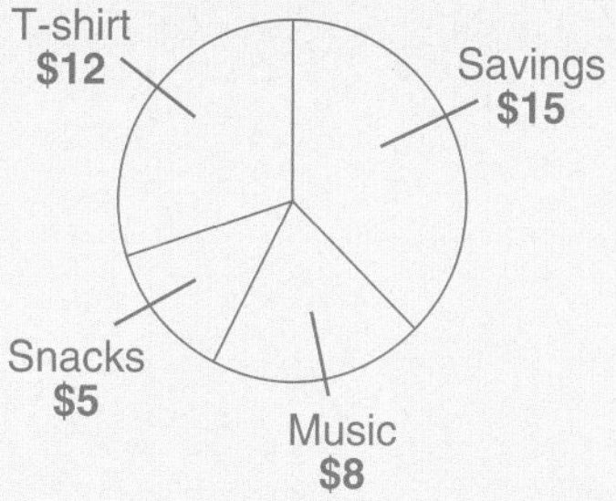

7. **Miles Jogged**

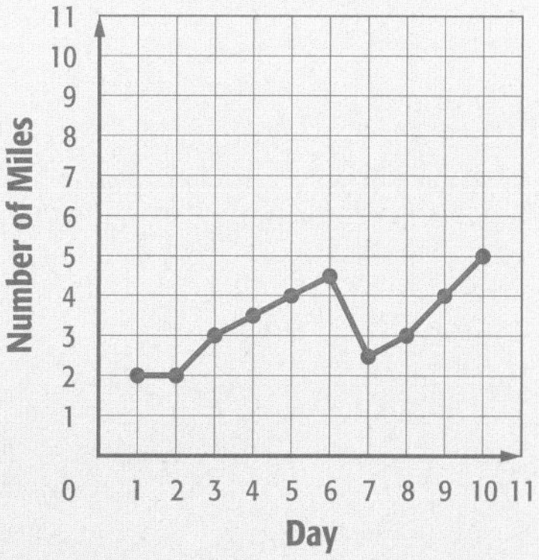

4.

Stem	Leaf
5	8 9
6	0 3 5 6 9
7	0 1 1 2 3

Key: 5|8 = 58

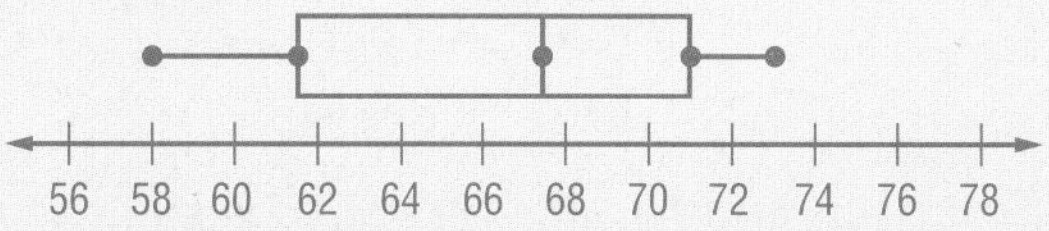

There are no outliers.

5.

Stem	Leaf
1	8 8
2	1 3 6 6 6 8
3	0 1 1 2 3 4
4	7

Key: 1|8 = 18

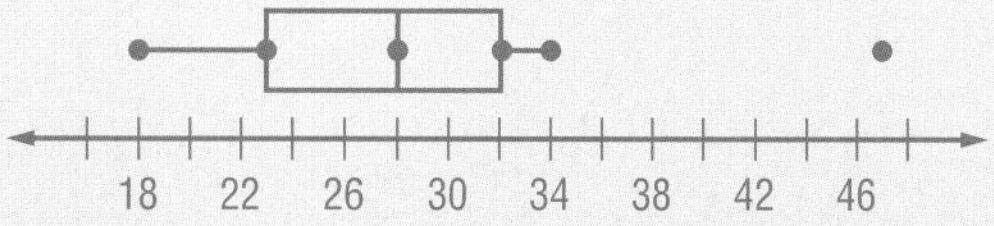

Removing 47 leaves Q_1 the same, changes Q_2 to 27 and Q_3 to 31.

CHAPTER 0 Posttest

Using the Posttest

Use the Chapter 0 Posttest to assess students' understanding of the concepts after you have presented the lessons in Chapter 0. If students are still having difficulty with one or more concepts, refer to *Math Triumphs 8/9* for strategies for reteaching.

CHAPTER 0 Posttest

Determine whether you need an estimate or an exact answer. Then use the four-step problem-solving plan to solve.

1. **DISTANCE** Fabio rode his scooter 2.3 miles to his friend's house, then 0.7 mile to the video store, then 2.1 miles to the library. If he rode the same route back home, about how far did he travel in all? **estimate; about 10 mi**

2. **SHOPPING** The regular price of a T-shirt is \$9.99. It is on sale for 15% off. Sales tax is 6%. If you give the cashier a \$10 bill, how much change will you receive? **exact; \$1**

Find each sum or difference.

3. $-31 + (-4)$ **−35**
4. $48 - 55$ **−7**
5. $-71 - (-10)$ **−61**
6. $31 - 42.9$ **−11.9**
7. $-11.5 + 8.1$ **−3.4**
8. $-0.38 - (-1.06)$ **0.68**

Find each product or quotient.

9. $-21(-5)$ **105**
10. $-81 \div (-3)$ **27**
11. $-120 \div 8$ **−15**
12. $-39 \div -3$ **13**

Replace each ● with <, >, or = to make a true sentence.

13. $-0.62 \bullet -\frac{6}{7}$ **>**
14. $\frac{12}{44} \bullet \frac{8}{11}$ **<**
15. Order $4\frac{4}{5}$, 4.85, $2\frac{5}{8}$, and 2.6 from least to greatest. **15. 2.6, $2\frac{5}{8}$, $4\frac{4}{5}$, 4.85**

Find each sum or difference. Write in simplest form.

16. $\frac{1}{7} + \frac{5}{7}$ **$\frac{6}{7}$**
17. $\frac{7}{8} - \frac{1}{8}$ **$\frac{3}{4}$**
18. $\frac{1}{6} + \left(-\frac{1}{2}\right)$ **$-\frac{1}{3}$**
19. $-\frac{1}{12} - \left(-\frac{3}{4}\right)$ **$\frac{2}{3}$**

Find each product or quotient.

20. $-1.2(9.3)$ **−11.16**
21. $-20.93 \div (-2.3)$ **9.1**
22. $10.5 \div (-1.2)$ **−8.75**
23. $(-3.4)(-2.8)$ **9.52**

Name the reciprocal of each number.

24. 6 **$\frac{1}{6}$**
25. $1\frac{2}{5}$ **$\frac{5}{7}$**
26. $-2\frac{3}{7}$ **$-\frac{7}{17}$**
27. $-\frac{1}{2}$ **−2**
28. $\frac{4}{3}$ **$\frac{3}{4}$**
29. $5\frac{1}{3}$ **$\frac{3}{16}$**

Find each product or quotient. Write in simplest form.

30. $\frac{2}{5} \cdot \frac{5}{9}$ **$\frac{2}{9}$**
31. $\frac{4}{5} \div \frac{1}{5}$ **4**
32. $-\frac{7}{8} \cdot 2$ **$-1\frac{3}{4}$**
33. $\frac{1}{3} \div 2\frac{1}{4}$ **$\frac{4}{27}$**
34. $-6 \cdot \left(-\frac{3}{4}\right)$ **$4\frac{1}{2}$**
35. $\frac{7}{18} \div \left(-\frac{14}{15}\right)$ **$-\frac{5}{12}$**

36. **PICNIC** Joseph is mixing $5\frac{1}{2}$ gallons of orange drink for his class picnic. Every $\frac{1}{2}$ gallon requires 1 packet of orange drink mix. How many packets of orange drink mix does Joseph need? **11 packets**

Express each percent as a fraction in simplest form.

37. 6% **$\frac{3}{50}$**
38. 140% **$\frac{7}{5}$**

Use the percent proportion to find each number.

39. 50% of what number is 31? **62**
40. What number is 110% of 51? **56.1**
41. Find 8% of 95. **7.6**

42. **SOLUTIONS** A solution is prepared by dissolving 24 milliliters of saline in 150 milliliters of pure solution. What is the percent of saline in the pure solution? **16%**

43. **SHOPPING** Marta got 60% off a pair of shoes. If the shoes cost \$9.75 (before sales tax), what was the original price of the shoes? **\$24.38**

Find the perimeter and area of each figure.

44.

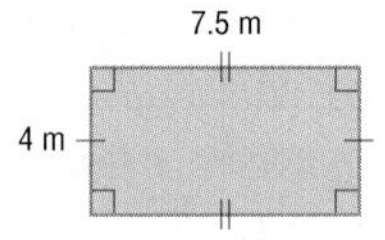

23 m; 30 m^2

45. **18 in.; 13.5 in^2**

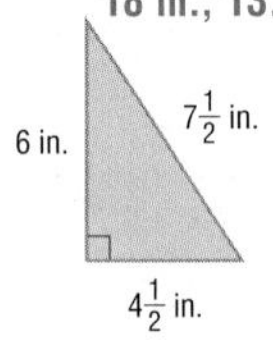

46. A parallelogram has a base of 20 millimeters and a height of 6 millimeters. Find the area. **120 mm^2**

47. **GARDENS** Find the perimeter of the garden. **13.5 m**

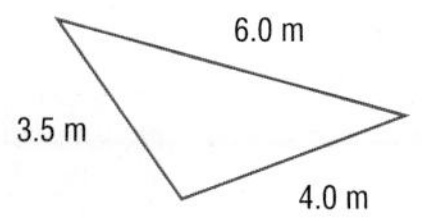

P44 Chapter 0 Preparing for Algebra

Find the circumference and area of each circle. Round to the nearest tenth.

48. 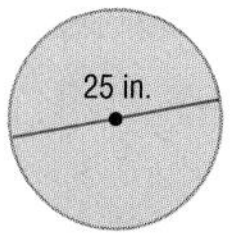

78.5 in.; 490.9 in^2

49. 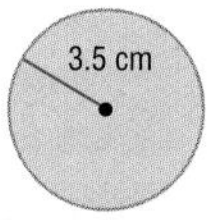

22.0 cm; 38.5 cm^2

50. **PARKS** A park has a circular area for a fountain that has a circumference of about 16 feet. What is the radius of the circular area? Round to the nearest tenth. 2.5 ft

Find the volume and surface area of each rectangular prism given the measurements below.

51. $\ell = 1.5$ m, $w = 3$ m, $h = 2$ m 9 m^3; 27 m^2

52. $\ell = 4$ in., $w = 1$ in., $h = \frac{1}{2}$ in. 2 in^3; 13 in^2

53. Find the volume and surface area of the rectangular prism. 7.8 m^3; 30.2 m^2

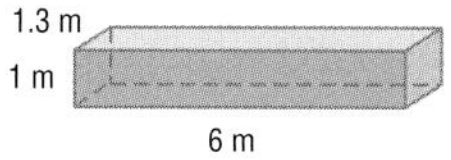

One marble is randomly selected from a jar containing 3 red, 4 green, 2 black, and 6 blue marbles. Find each probability.

54. P(red or blue) $\frac{3}{5}$ or 0.6

55. P(green or red) $\frac{7}{15}$

56. P(not black) $\frac{13}{15}$

57. P(not blue) $\frac{3}{5}$

58. A movie theater is offering snack specials. You can choose a small, medium, large, or jumbo popcorn with or without butter, and soda or bottled water. Use a tree diagram to find the sample space for the event. State the number of possible outcomes. 16 outcomes

One coin is randomly selected from a jar containing 20 pennies, 15 nickels, 3 dimes, and 12 quarters. Find the odds of each outcome. Write in simplest form.

59. a dime 3:47

60. a value less than \$0.25 19:6

61. a value greater than \$0.10 6:19

62. a value less than \$0.05 2:3

63. **SCHOOL** In a science class, each student must choose a lab project from a list of 15, write a paper on one of 6 topics, and give a presentation about one of 8 subjects. How many ways can students choose to do their assignments? 720 ways

64. **GAMES** Marcos has been dealt seven different cards. How many different ways can he play his cards if he is required to play one card at a time? 5040 ways

Find the mean, median, and mode for each set of data.

65. {99, 88, 88, 92, 100} 93.4; 92; 88

66. {30, 22, 38, 41, 33, 41, 30, 24} 32.375; 31.5; 30 and 41

67. Find the range, median, lower quartile, and upper quartile for {77, 75, 72, 70, 79, 77, 70, 76}. 9; 75.5; 71; 77

68. **TESTS** Kevin's scores on the first four science tests are 88, 92, 82, and 94. What score must he earn on the fifth test so that the mean will be 90? 94

69. **FOOD** The table shows the results of a survey in which students were asked to choose their favorite food. Make a bar graph of the data. See margin.

Favorite Foods	
Food	**Number of Students**
pizza	15
chicken nuggets	10
cheesy potatoes	8
ice cream	5

70. Make a box-and-whisker plot of the following data: 26, 18, 26, 29, 18, 20, 35, 32, 31, 24, 26, and 22. See margin.

71. **BUDGET** The table shows how Kat spends her allowance. Make a circle graph of the data. See margin.

Category	Amount (\$)
Savings	25
Clothes	10
Entertainment	15

Additional Answers

69.

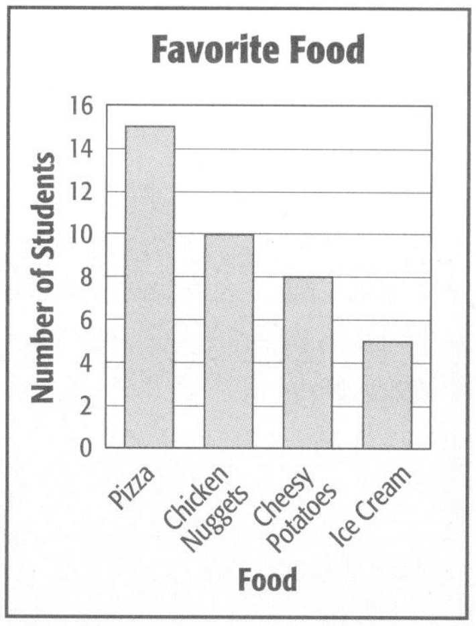

70.

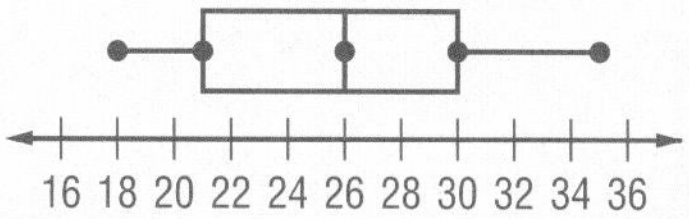

71.

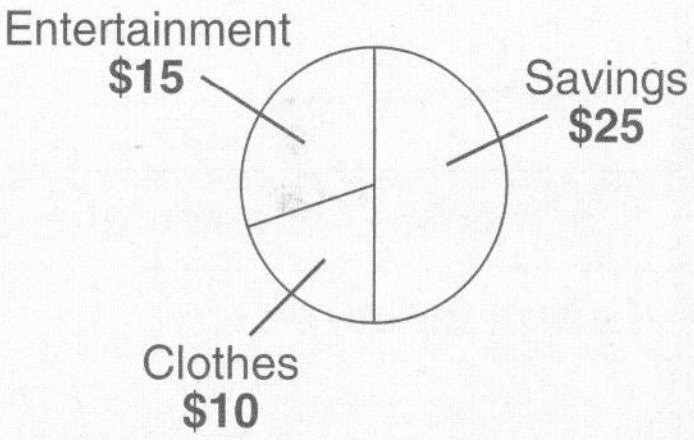

Chapter 0 Posttest P45

CHAPTER 1 Chapter Planner

Diagnostic Assessment
Quick Check, p. 3

	Lesson 1-1 Pacing: 1 day	Lesson 1-2 Pacing: 1.5 days	Lesson 1-3 Pacing: 1.5 days
Title	**Variables and Expressions**	**Order of Operations**	**Properties of Numbers**
Objectives	• Write verbal expressions for algebraic expressions. • Write algebraic expressions for verbal expressions.	• Evaluate numerical expressions by using the order of operations. • Evaluate algebraic expressions by using the order of operations.	• Recognize the properties of equality and identity. • Recognize the Commutative and Associative Properties.
Key Vocabulary	algebraic expressions variable term factor product power exponent base	evaluate order of operations	equivalent expressions additive identity multiplicative identity multiplicative inverse reciprocal
ILS	7.A.4b, 8.A.4b	7.A.4b	6.A.4, 7.A.4b
Multiple Representations	p. 8		p. 21
Lesson Resources	**Chapter 1 Resource Masters** • Study Guide and Intervention, pp. 5–6 AL OL ELL • Skills Practice, p. 7 AL OL ELL • Practice, p. 8 AL OL BL ELL • Word Problem Practice, p. 9 AL OL BL ELL • Enrichment, p. 10 OL BL **Transparencies** • 5-Minute Check Transparency 1-1 AL OL BL ELL **Additional Print Resources** • *Study Notebook* AL OL BL ELL	**Chapter 1 Resource Masters** • Study Guide and Intervention, pp. 11–12 AL OL ELL • Skills Practice, p. 13 AL OL ELL • Practice, p. 14 AL OL BL ELL • Word Problem Practice, p. 15 AL OL BL ELL • Enrichment, p. 16 OL BL • Graphing Calculator Activity, p. 17 OL • Quiz 1, p. 57 AL OL BL ELL **Transparencies** • 5-Minute Check Transparency 1-2 AL OL BL ELL **Additional Print Resources** • *Study Notebook* AL OL BL ELL • *Teaching Algebra with Manipulatives,* p. 30 AL OL ELL	**Chapter 1 Resource Masters** • Study Guide and Intervention, pp. 18–19 AL OL ELL • Skills Practice, p. 20 AL OL ELL • Practice, p. 21 AL OL BL ELL • Word Problem Practice, p. 22 AL OL BL ELL • Enrichment, p. 23 OL BL **Transparencies** • 5-Minute Check Transparency 1-3 AL OL BL ELL **Additional Print Resources** • *Study Notebook* AL OL BL ELL
Technology for Every Lesson	**IL Math Online** glencoe.com • Extra Examples • Self-Check Quizzes • Personal Tutor • Homework Help	**CD/DVD Resources** IWB INTERACTIVE WHITEBOARD READY IWB StudentWorks Plus IWB Interactive Classroom IWB Diagnostic and Assessment Planner	• TeacherWorks Plus • eSolutions Manual Plus • ExamView Assessment Suite
Math in Motion			BrainPOP
Differentiated Instruction	pp. 6, 9	pp. 11, 15	pp. 18, 22

Suggested Pacing

Time Periods	Instruction	Review & Assessment	Total
45-minute	12	2	14
90-minute	6	1	7

Expressions, Equations, and Functions

Lesson 1-4 Pacing: 1 day	Lesson 1-5 Pacing: 2 days	Lesson 1-6 Pacing: 1.5 days	Lesson 1-7 Pacing: 1.5 days
The Distributive Property	**Equations**	**Relations**	**Functions**
• Use the Distributive Property to evaluate expressions. • Use the Distributive Property to simplify expressions.	• Solve equations with one variable. • Solve equations with two variables.	• Represent relations. • Interpret graphs of relations.	• Determine whether a relation is a function. • Find function values.
like terms simplest form coefficient	open sentence equation solution replacement set set element solution set identify	coordinate system origin ordered pair relation domain range independent variable dependent variable	function discrete function continuous function vertical line test nonlinear function
6.A.4	8.B.4a	8.B.4a	8.C.4b
p. 28	p. 36		
Chapter 1 Resource Masters • Study Guide and Intervention, pp. 24–25 AL OL ELL • Skills Practice, p. 26 AL OL ELL • Practice, p. 27 AL OL BL ELL • Word Problem Practice, p. 28 AL OL BL ELL • Enrichment, p. 29 OL BL • Quiz 2, p. 57 AL OL BL ELL **Transparencies** • 5-Minute Check Transparency 1-4 AL OL BL ELL **Additional Print Resources** • *Study Notebook* AL OL BL ELL • *Teaching Algebra with Manipulatives*, pp. 31–32 AL OL ELL	**Chapter 1 Resource Masters** • Study Guide and Intervention, pp. 30–31 AL OL ELL • Skills Practice, p. 32 AL OL ELL • Practice, p. 33 AL OL BL ELL • Word Problem Practice, p. 34 AL OL BL ELL • Enrichment, p. 35 OL BL • Spreadsheet Activity, p. 36 AL OL BL ELL **Transparencies** • 5-Minute Check Transparency 1-5 AL OL BL ELL **Additional Print Resources** • *Study Notebook* AL OL BL ELL	**Chapter 1 Resource Masters** • Study Guide and Intervention, pp. 37–38 AL OL ELL • Skills Practice, p. 39 AL OL ELL • Practice, p. 40 AL OL BL ELL • Word Problem Practice, p. 41 AL OL BL ELL • Enrichment, p. 42 OL BL • Quiz 3, p. 58 AL OL BL ELL **Transparencies** • 5-Minute Check Transparency 1-6 AL OL BL ELL **Additional Print Resources** • *Study Notebook* AL OL BL ELL • *Teaching Algebra with Manipulatives*, p. 33 AL OL ELL	**Chapter 1 Resource Masters** • Study Guide and Intervention, pp. 43–44 AL OL ELL • Skills Practice, p. 45 AL OL ELL • Practice, p. 46 AL OL BL ELL • Word Problem Practice, p. 47 AL OL BL ELL • Enrichment, p. 48 OL BL • Quiz 4, p. 58 AL OL BL ELL **Transparencies** • 5-Minute Check Transparency 1-7 AL OL BL ELL **Additional Print Resources** • *Study Notebook* AL OL BL ELL • *Teaching Algebra with Manipulatives*, pp. 35–37 AL OL ELL
	IL Math Online glencoe.com • Extra Examples • Self-Check Quizzes • Personal Tutor • Homework Help	**CD/DVD Resources** IWB INTERACTIVE WHITEBOARD READY IWB StudentWorks Plus IWB Interactive Classroom IWB Diagnostic and Assessment Planner	• TeacherWorks Plus • eSolutions Manual Plus • ExamView Assessment Suite
BrainPOP	Interactive Lab		
pp. 25, 29	pp. 33, 37	pp. 43, 44	pp. 48, 52

Formative Assessment
Mid-Chapter Quiz, p. 30

CHAPTER 1

Chapter Planner

	Extend 1-7 Pacing: 0.5 day	**Lesson 1-8** Pacing: 1 day	**Extend 1-8** Pacing: 0.5 day
Title	**Graphing Technology Lab: Representing Functions**	**Logical Reasoning and Counterexamples**	**Algebra Lab: Sets**
Objectives	• Use a graphing calculator to represent a function as a graph and as a table.	• Identify the hypothesis and conclusion in a conditional statement. • Use counterexamples.	• Identify and write descriptions of specified subsets of a set of shapes.
Key Vocabulary		conditional statement if-then statements hypothesis conclusion deductive reasoning counterexample	
ILS	8.B.4a	7.A.4b	8.B.4a
Multiple Representations			
Lesson Resources	**Materials** • TI-Nspire calculator or software	**Chapter 1 Resource Masters** • Study Guide and Intervention, pp. 49–50 AL OL ELL • Skills Practice, p. 51 AL OL ELL • Practice, p. 52 AL OL BL ELL • Word Problem Practice, p. 53 AL OL BL ELL • Enrichment, p. 54 OL BL • Quiz 4, p. 58 AL OL BL ELL **Transparencies** • 5-Minute Check Transparency 1-8 AL OL BL ELL **Additional Print Resources** • *Study Notebook* AL OL BL ELL	**Materials** • paper • scissors • string • colored pencils **Additional Print Resources** • *Teaching Algebra with Manipulatives,* p. 38 AL OL ELL
Technology for Every Lesson	**IL Math Online** glencoe.com • Extra Examples • Self-Check Quizzes • Personal Tutor • Homework Help	**CD/DVD Resources** IWB INTERACTIVE WHITEBOARD READY IWB StudentWorks Plus IWB Interactive Classroom IWB Diagnostic and Assessment Planner	• TeacherWorks Plus • eSolutions Manual Plus • ExamView Assessment Suite
Math in Motion		Animation	
Differentiated Instruction		pp. 55, 59	

Summative Assessment
- Study Guide and Review, pp. 62–66
- Practice Test, p. 67

Quick Review Math Handbook*

is Glencoe's mathematical handbook for students and parents.

Hot Words includes a glossary of terms.

Hot Topics consists of two parts:

- explanations of key mathematical concepts
- exercises to check students' understanding.

Lesson	Hot Topics Section	Lesson	Hot Topics Section
1-1	6.1	1-5	6.4
1-2	1.1, 1.3, 6.3	1-6	6.7
1-3	6.2	1-7	6.7
1-4	6.2	1-8	5.2

**Also available in Spanish*

Teacher to Teacher

Larry Hummel
Central City High School
Central City, NE

USE BEFORE LESSON 1-6

"I like to introduce the CBL or CBR with a graphing calculator with Example 3. I give students a graph and see if they can duplicate it by moving back and forth in front of the range finder. It really makes them think about what the graph represents."

Project CRISS STUDY SKILL

Encourage students to write process notes as they study new concepts and algorithms.

Process notes help students work through the steps of problem solving by writing the steps in the left column and the sample steps for an example in the right column.

These process notes describe how to use the order of operations to evaluate an expression, which students study in Lesson 1-2.

Topic:	Notes
Step 1 Evaluate expressions inside grouping symbols.	$14 - 30 \div 5 + (6 - 2)^2$
Step 2 Evaluate all powers.	$= 14 - 30 \div 5 + (4)^2$
Step 3 Do all multiplications and/or divisions from left to right.	$= 14 - 30 \div 5 + 16$
Step 4 Do all additions and subtractions from left to right.	$= 14 - 6 + 16$ $= 8 + 16$ $= 24$

Creating Independence through Student-owned Strategies

Assessment and Intervention

SE = Student Edition, **TE** = Teacher Edition, **CRM** = Chapter Resource Masters

	Diagnosis	Prescription
Diagnostic Assessment	**Beginning Chapter 1**	
	Get Ready for Chapter 1 **SE**, p. 3	Response to Intervention **TE**, p. 3
	Beginning Every Lesson	
	Then, Now, Why? **SE** 5-Minute Check Transparencies	Chapter 0 **SE**, pp. P1–P45 Concepts and Skills Bank **SE**, pp. 857–867 *Quick Review Math Handbook*
Formative Assessment	**During/After Every Lesson**	
	Check Your Progress **SE**, every example Check Your Understanding **SE** H.O.T. Problems **SE** Spiral Review **SE** Additional Examples **TE** Watch Out! **TE** Step 4, Assess **TE** Chapter 1 Quizzes **CRM**, pp. 57–58 Self-Check Quizzes glencoe.com	**Tier 1 Intervention** Concepts and Skills Bank **SE**, pp. 857–867 Skills Practice **CRM**, Ch. 1 glencoe.com **Tier 2 Intervention** Differentiated Instruction **TE** Differentiated Homework Options **TE** Study Guide and Intervention Masters **CRM**, Ch. 1 *Quick Review Math Handbook* **Tier 3 Intervention** *Math Triumphs Alg. 1,* Ch. 1, 2, 3, 5, and 6
	Mid-Chapter	
	Mid-Chapter Quiz **SE**, p. 30 Mid-Chapter Test **CRM**, p. 59 ExamView Assessment Suite	**Tier 1 Intervention** Concepts and Skills Bank **SE**, pp. 857–867 Skills Practice **CRM**, Ch. 1 glencoe.com **Tier 2 Intervention** Study Guide and Intervention Masters **CRM**, Ch. 1 *Quick Review Math Handbook* **Tier 3 Intervention** *Math Triumphs Alg. 1,* Ch. 1, 2, 3, 5, and 6
	Before Chapter Test	
	Chapter Study Guide and Review **SE**, pp. 62–66 Practice Test **SE**, p. 67 Standardized Test Practice **SE**, pp. 68–71 Chapter Test glencoe.com Standardized Test Practice glencoe.com Vocabulary Review glencoe.com ExamView Assessment Suite	**Tier 1 Intervention** Concepts and Skills Bank **SE**, pp. 857–867 Skills Practice **CRM**, Ch. 1 glencoe.com **Tier 2 Intervention** Study Guide and Intervention Masters **CRM**, Ch. 1 *Quick Review Math Handbook* **Tier 3 Intervention** *Math Triumphs Alg. 1,* Ch. 1, 2, 3, 5, and 6
Summative Assessment	**After Chapter 1**	
	Multiple-Choice Tests, Forms 1, 2A, 2B **CRM**, pp. 61–68 Free-Response Tests, Forms 2C, 2D, 3 **CRM**, pp. 67–72 Vocabulary Test **CRM**, p. 60 Extended Response Test **CRM**, p. 73 Standardized Test Practice **CRM**, pp. 74–76 ExamView Assessment Suite	Study Guide and Intervention Masters **CRM**, Ch. 1 *Quick Review Math Handbook* glencoe.com

CHAPTER 1

Differentiated Instruction

Option 1 Reaching All Learners AL OL BL ELL

NATURALIST Challenge students to write open sentences about a plant or animal they are interested in. For example, the gestation period of armadillos can be described using the sentence 60 days $\leq$ gestation period $\leq$ 120 days.

AUDITORY/MUSICAL If students have difficulty with the concept of mapping, have those who are familiar with reading music make a mapping of the relation between different notes and the number of beats the notes contain. For example, a whole note is held for 4 beats, and a half note for 2 beats. In this case, the domain is the set that contains all of the types of notes and the range is the set that contains the number of beats the notes are held.

Option 2 Approaching Level AL

Play a song with a fast tempo (measured in beats per minute) for 10 seconds and then for 20 seconds. Ask students to count the number of beats each time. Help students understand that the number of beats played is the dependent variable because it is affected by the length of time the song is played. The length of time the song is played is the independent variable because it is unaffected by the number of beats played.

Option 3 English Learners ELL

Write the name and an example of each property of numbers studied in Lesson 1-3 on the board. Have students who are fluent in other languages tell the class how to express the names of these properties and their meanings in those languages.

Option 4 Beyond Level BL

On each of six cards write an equation that represents a function. For each of these six equations, write a table, graph, or mapping that is also a representation of the function on another card. Make a set of cards for each pair of students. Have partners play a matching game with the cards, taking turns turning two cards over until the same function is represented in both cards turned over.

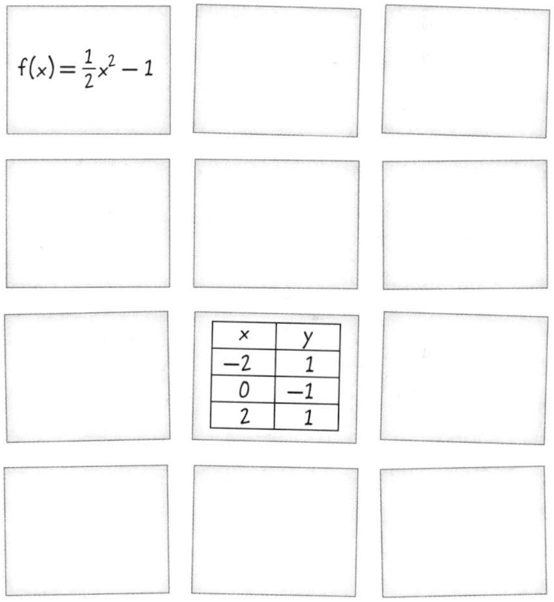

Focus on Mathematical Content

Vertical Alignment

Before Chapter 1

Related Topics before Grade 8

- perform operations on integers
- simplify integer expressions
- use concrete models to solve equations
- validate conclusions from mathematical properties and relationships
- simplify numeric expressions

Related Topics from Grade 8

- compare and order rational numbers
- locate points on a coordinate plane

Chapter 1

Related Topics from Algebra 1

- represent relationships among quantities using tables, graphs, verbal descriptions, and inequalities
- use symbols to represent unknowns and variables
- find specific function values and solve equations in problem situations
- use the Commutative, Associative, and Distributive Properties to simplify algebraic expressions
- interpret and make critical predictions from functional relationships
- describe independent and dependent quantities in functional relationships
- identify mathematical domains and ranges and determine reasonable domain and range values for given situations, both continuous and discrete
- connect equation notation with function notation

After Chapter 1

Preparation for Algebra 2

- use the necessary algebraic skills required to simplify algebraic expressions and inequalities in problem situations
- use properties and attributes of functions, and apply functions to problem situations

Lesson-by-Lesson Preview

1-1 Variables and Expressions

Algebraic expressions contain one or more numbers and variables along with arithmetic operations. They can be written as mathematical expressions or verbal expressions. They do not contain an equals sign.

- A variable is a symbol used to represent an unknown number or value. Though any letter can be used as a variable, many letters used as variables are chosen because they are the first letter of the quantity they represent, such as t for *time*.
- Algebraic expressions may contain powers. When evaluating a power, the exponent tells you how many times the base is used as a factor.

1-2 Order of Operations

When evaluating an expression, the set of rules that specifies which operation to do first is the order of operations.

- First, perform operations inside grouping symbols. Grouping symbols include parentheses, brackets, braces, and fraction bars. Perform operations inside the innermost grouping symbol first.
- Then, evaluate all powers.
- Next, perform all multiplications and/or divisions from left to right. Finally, perform all additions and/or subtractions from left to right.

1-3 Properties of Numbers

Identity and Equality Properties can be used to justify each step when evaluating expressions and solving equations.

- The Properties of Equality are often used to solve equations. These properties include the Reflexive, Symmetric, Transitive, and Substitution Properties.
- Two properties of addition are the Additive Identity and the Additive Inverse.
- Three properties of multiplication are the Multiplicative Identity, Multiplicative Inverse, and the Multiplicative Property of Zero.
- The Commutative Property states that the order in which numbers are added or multiplied does not change their sum or product.
- The Associative Property states that the way three or more numbers are grouped when adding or multiplying does not affect their sum or product.

Expressions, Equations, and Functions

- The Commutative and Associative Properties do not apply to either subtraction or division because order and grouping affect differences and quotients.

Using these properties can often help make mental calculations easier.

1-4 The Distributive Property

The Distributive Property can be used to evaluate numerical expressions and simplify algebraic expressions.

- The Distributive Property permits a factor outside the parentheses to be distributed to each term of an addition or subtraction expression inside the parentheses. So, $25(8 + 4)$ can be rewritten as $25(8) + 25(4)$, making it easier to evaluate the expression.
- When applying the Distributive Property to algebraic expressions, the coefficients of like terms can be combined and the expressions simplified. For example, the expression $13a + 29a$ can be rewritten as $(13 + 29)a$, which can be simplified as $42a$.

1-5 Equations

An equation is an algebraic statement that contains an equals sign.

- An open sentence is neither true nor false until the variables have been replaced with specific values.
- The process of finding a value for each variable that makes an equation true is called *solving the equation.* A solution set is a set of numbers that makes an equation true.

1-6 Relations

A relation can be represented as a set of ordered pairs, (x, y), as an equation, a table, a mapping, or a graph.

- A mapping lists the x-values in the domain and the y-values in the range. An arrow is drawn from each x-value in the domain to its corresponding y-value in the range.
- The domain contains values of the independent variable and the range contains values of the dependent variable.

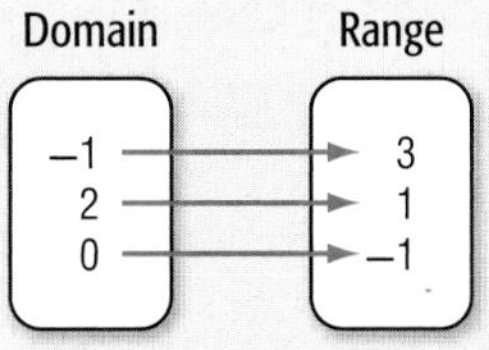

- A table lists the set of x-coordinates in the first column and their corresponding y-coordinates in the second column.
- A coordinate plane consists of a horizontal axis (the x-axis) and a vertical axis (the y-axis) and the intersection of the axes (the origin).

1-7 Functions

A function is a relationship between input and output in which each input value has exactly one output.

- The set of input values is the *domain* of the function, and the set of output values is the *range*.
- A vertical line test can be used to check if a graph is a function. If the graph does not touch any drawn vertical line more than once, it is a function.
- A discrete function's graph consists of points that are not connected. A continuous function's graph forms a line or smooth curve.
- In a function, if x represents the independent quantity (elements of the domain), $f(x)$ represents the dependent quantity (elements of the range).

1-8 Logical Reasoning and Counterexamples

Logical reasoning encompasses conditional statements, deductive reasoning, and counterexamples.

- A conditional statement has a hypothesis and a conclusion, and is often written in if-then form, with the "if" part of the statement the hypothesis, and the "then" part of the statement the conclusion.
- Deductive reasoning is a process that uses facts and rules to reach a valid conclusion.
- A counterexample is a specific example that can be used to show that a statement is false.

McGraw-Hill Professional Development

Targeted professional development has been articulated throughout *Algebra 1.* More quality, customized professional development is available from McGraw-Hill Professional Development. Visit glencoe.com for details on each product.

- **Online Lessons** emphasize the strategies and techniques used to teach Algebra 1. Includes streaming video, interactive pages, and online tools.
- **Video Workshops** allow mentors, coaches, or leadership personnel to facilitate on-site workshops on educational strategies in mathematics and mathematical concepts.
- **MHPD Online** (www.mhpdonline.com) offers online professional development with video clips of instructional strategies, links, student activities, and news and issues in education.
- **Teaching Today** (teachingtoday.glencoe.com) gives secondary teachers practical strategies and materials that inspire excellence and innovation in teaching.

CHAPTER 1

Notes

Chapter Project

Sports Expressions

Students use what they have learned about expressions, functions, and logical reasoning to work with concepts related to sports.

- Divide students into groups. Ask them to select one sport and then define a variable to represent a real-life quantity (such as time, cost, distance, scores, etc.) related to that sport. Have them use the variable to write a verbal expression (and then an algebraic expression) that represents the sport in some way.
- Ask each group to compile a menu that includes the cost for different types of food that can be typically purchased when attending their sport. Ask them to write and evaluate an expression to find the total cost of what their group would eat.
- Have each group find two variables related to their sport that are related (such as time and distance). Then have them identify the independent and dependent variable, create a set of ordered pairs, and finally graph the relation. Is the relationship a function? How do they know?
- Ask each group to write an *if-then* conditional statement related to their sport. Have them identify the hypothesis and conclusion and determine if the statement is always true. If it is not, have students write a counterexample.

CHAPTER 1

Expressions, Equations, and Functions

Then

You have learned how to perform operations on whole numbers.

Now

In Chapter 1, you will:

- Write algebraic expressions.
- Use the order of operations.
- Solve equations.
- Represent relations and functions.
- Use conditional statements and counterexamples.

IL Learning Standards

8.B.4a Represent algebraic concepts with physical materials, words, diagrams, tables, graphs, equations and inequalities and use appropriate technology.

Why?

SCUBA DIVING A scuba diving store rents air tanks and wet suits. An algebraic expression can be written to represent the total cost to rent this equipment. This expression can be evaluated to determine the total cost for a group of people to rent the equipment.

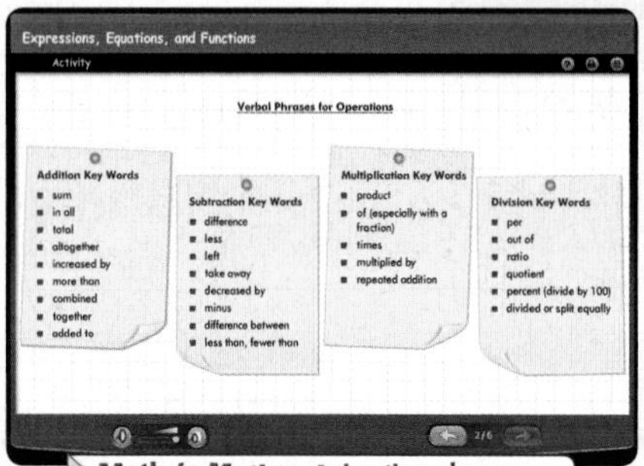

Math *in Motion*, Animation glencoe.com

Key Vocabulary Introduce the key vocabulary in the chapter using the routine below.

Define: An algebraic expression is an expression consisting of one or more numbers and variables along with one or more arithmetic operations.

Example: $x - 7$

Ask: What is the variable? x What is the operation? subtraction What is 7? a number

Get Ready for Chapter 1

Diagnose Readiness You have two options for checking Prerequisite Skills.

Text Option Take the Quick Check below. Refer to the Quick Review for help.

*Quick*Check

(Used in Lessons 1-2 and 1-5)

Write each fraction in simplest form. If the fraction is already in simplest form, write *simplest form*. (Lesson 0-4)

1. $\frac{24}{36}$ $\frac{2}{3}$ **2.** $\frac{34}{85}$ $\frac{2}{5}$ **3.** $\frac{36}{12}$ 3

4. $\frac{27}{45}$ $\frac{3}{5}$ **5.** $\frac{11}{18}$ simplest form **6.** $\frac{5}{65}$ $\frac{1}{13}$

7. $\frac{19}{1}$ 19 **8.** $\frac{16}{44}$ $\frac{4}{11}$ **9.** $\frac{64}{88}$ $\frac{8}{11}$

10. ICE CREAM Fifty-four out of 180 customers said that cookie dough ice cream was their favorite flavor. What fraction of customers was this? (Lesson 0-5) $\frac{3}{10}$

(Used in Lessons 1-1 through 1-6)

Find the perimeter of each figure. (Lesson 0-7)

11.

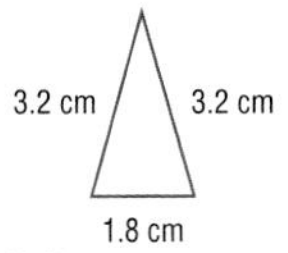

8.2 cm

12. $18\frac{1}{2}$ in.

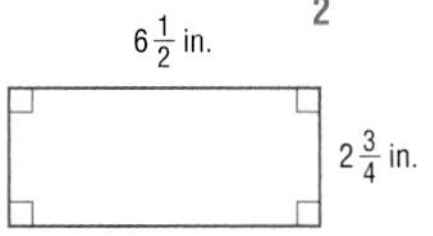

13. FENCING Jolon needs to fence a garden. The dimensions of the garden are 6 meters by 4 meters. How much fencing does Jolon need to purchase? 20 m

(Used in Lessons 1-1 through 1-6)

Evaluate. (Lesson 0-5)

14. $6 \cdot \frac{2}{3}$ 4 **15.** $4.2 \cdot 8.1$ 34.02 **16.** $\frac{3}{8} \div \frac{1}{4}$ $\frac{3}{2}$ or $1\frac{1}{2}$

17. $5.13 \div 2.7$ 1.9 **18.** $3\frac{1}{5} \cdot \frac{3}{4}$ **19.** $2.8 \cdot 0.2$ 0.56

20. CONSTRUCTION A board measuring 7.2 feet must be cut into three equal pieces. Find the length of each piece. 2.4 ft **18.** $\frac{12}{5}$ or $2\frac{2}{5}$

*Quick*Review

EXAMPLE 1

Write $\frac{24}{40}$ in simplest form.

Find the greatest common factor (GCF) of 24 and 40.

factors of 24: 1, 2, 3, 4, 6, 8, 12, 24
factors of 40: 1, 2, 4, 5, 8, 10, 20, 40

The GCF of 24 and 40 is 8.

$\frac{24 \div 8}{40 \div 8} = \frac{3}{5}$ **Divide the numerator and denominator by their GCF, 8.**

EXAMPLE 2

Find the perimeter.

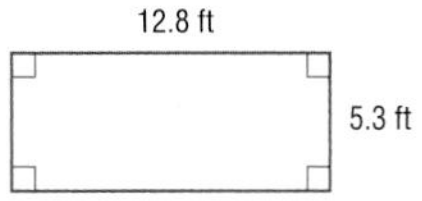

$P = 2\ell + 2w$

$= 2(12.8) + 2(5.3)$ **$\ell = 12.8$ and $w = 5.3$**

$= 25.6 + 10.6$ or 36.2 **Simplify.**

The perimeter is 36.2 feet.

EXAMPLE 3

Find $2\frac{1}{4} \div 1\frac{1}{2}$.

$2\frac{1}{4} \div 1\frac{1}{2} = \frac{9}{4} \div \frac{3}{2}$ **Write mixed numbers as improper fractions.**

$= \frac{9}{4}\left(\frac{2}{3}\right)$ **Multiply by the reciprocal.**

$= \frac{18}{12}$ or $1\frac{1}{2}$ **Simplify.**

Online Option IL Math Online Take a self-check Chapter Readiness Quiz at glencoe.com.

Get Ready for Chapter 1

Response to Intervention (RtI)

Use the *Quick Check* results and the Intervention Planner chart to help you determine your Response to Intervention. The If-Then statements in the chart below help you decide the appropriate tier of RtI and suggest intervention resources for each tier.

Intervention Planner

Tier 1 — On Level

If students miss about 25% of the exercises or less,

Then choose a resource:

SE Lessons 0-4, 0-5, and 0-7

IL Math Online Self-Check Quiz

Tier 2 — Strategic Intervention approaching grade level

If students miss about 50% of the exercises,

Then choose a resource:

Quick Review Math Handbook

IL Math Online Extra Examples, Personal Tutor, Homework Help

Tier 3 — Intensive Intervention 2 or more grades below level

If students miss about 75% of the exercises,

Then use *Math Triumphs Alg. 1,* Ch. 1, 2, 3, 5, and 6

IL Math Online Extra Examples, Personal Tutor, Homework Help, Review Vocabulary

Diagnose students' readiness for each chapter by using either the intext **Quick Check** or the online **Chapter Readiness Quiz.** Then use the **Intervention Planner** to choose the correct program resource to reinforce each student's prerequisite skills.

CHAPTER 1 Notes

FOLDABLES® Study Organizer

Dinah Zike's Foldables®

Focus Students write notes about expressions, equations, and functions as they are presented in each lesson of this chapter.

Teach Have students make and label their Foldables as illustrated. Have students write a summary of each lesson on its corresponding sheet. Under the summaries, they should include an example of the lesson's main concept. Point out that the ninth tab should be used to list the properties described in the chapter, and the last tab should be used to list the chapter's vocabulary.

When to Use It Encourage students to add to their Foldables as they work through the chapter and to use them to review for the chapter test.

Differentiated Instruction

CRM Student-Built Glossary, pp. 1–2 Students should complete the chart by providing the definition of each term and an example as they progress through Chapter 1. This study tool can also be used to review for the chapter test.

Get Started on Chapter 1

You will learn several new concepts, skills, and vocabulary terms as you study Chapter 1. To get ready, identify important terms and organize your resources. You may wish to refer to **Chapter 0** to review prerequisite skills.

FOLDABLES® Study Organizer

Expressions, Equations, and Functions Make this Foldable to help you organize your Chapter 1 notes about expressions, equations, and functions. Begin with five sheets of grid paper.

1. **Fold** each sheet of grid paper in half along the width. Then cut along the crease.

2. **Staple** the ten half-sheets together to form a booklet.

3. **Cut** nine lines from the bottom of the top sheet, eight lines from the second sheet, and so on.

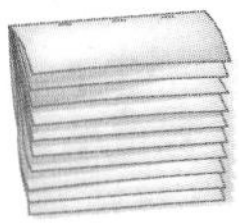

4. **Label** each of the tabs with a lesson number. The ninth tab is for the properties and the last tab is for the vocabulary.

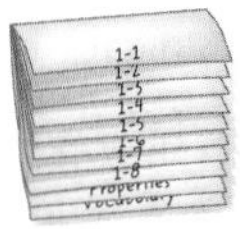

IL Math Online glencoe.com

- Study the chapter online
- Explore **Math in Motion**
- Get extra help from your own **Personal Tutor**
- Use **Extra Examples** for additional help
- Take a **Self-Check Quiz**
- **Review Vocabulary** in fun ways

New Vocabulary

English		Español
algebraic expression	• p. 5 •	expression algebraica
variable	• p. 5 •	variable
term	• p. 5 •	término
power	• p. 5 •	potencia
coefficient	• p. 26 •	coeficiente
equation	• p. 31 •	ecuación
solution	• p. 31 •	solución
identity	• p. 33 •	identidad
relation	• p. 38 •	relacíon
domain	• p. 38 •	domino
range	• p. 38 •	rango
independent variable	• p. 40 •	variable independiente
dependent variable	• p. 40 •	variable dependiente
function	• p. 45 •	función
nonlinear function	• p. 48 •	función no lineal
deductive reasoning	• p. 55 •	razonamiento deductivo
counterexample	• p. 56 •	contraejemplo

Review Vocabulary

additive inverse • p. P11 • inverso aditivo a number and its opposite

multiplicative inverse • p. P18 • inverso multiplicativo two numbers with a product of 1

perimeter • p. P23 • perímetro the distance around a geometric figure

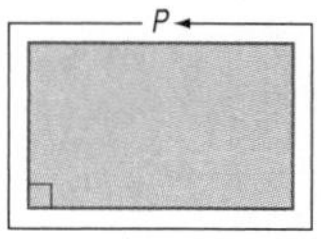

Multilingual eGlossary glencoe.com

1-1 Variables and Expressions

Then

You performed operations on integers. (Lesson 0-3)

Now

- Write verbal expressions for algebraic expressions.
- Write algebraic expressions for verbal expressions.

IL Learning Standards

7.A.4b Apply formulas in a wide variety of theoretical and practical real-world measurement applications involving perimeter, area, volume, angle, time, temperature, mass, speed, distance, density and monetary values.
8.A.4b Represent mathematical patterns and describe their properties using variables and mathematical symbols.

New Vocabulary

algebraic expression
variable
term
factor
product
power
exponent
base

IL Math Online

glencoe.com

- Extra Examples
- Personal Tutor
- Self-Check Quiz
- Homework Help

Why?

Cassie and her friends are at a baseball game. The stadium is running a Dime-A-Dog promotion where hot dogs are \$0.10 each. Suppose d represents the number of hot dogs Cassie and her friends eat. Then $0.10d$ represents the cost of the hot dogs they eat.

Write Verbal Expressions An **algebraic expression** consists of sums and/or products of numbers and variables. In the algebraic expression $0.10d$, the letter d is called a variable. In algebra, **variables** are symbols used to represent unspecified numbers or values. Any letter may be used as a variable.

$$0.10d \qquad 2x + 4 \qquad 3 + \frac{z}{6} \qquad p \cdot q \qquad 4cd \div 3mn$$

A **term** of an expression may be a number, a variable, or a product or quotient of numbers and variables. For example, $0.10d$, $2x$ and 4 are each terms.

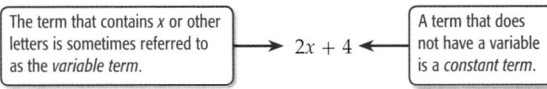

The term that contains x or other letters is sometimes referred to as the *variable term*. → $2x + 4$ ← A term that does not have a variable is a *constant term*.

In a multiplication expression, the quantities being multiplied are **factors**, and the result is the **product**. A raised dot or set of parentheses are often used to indicate a product. Here are several ways to represent the product of x and y.

$$xy \qquad x \cdot y \qquad x(y) \qquad (x)y \qquad (x)(y)$$

An expression like x^n is called a **power**. The word *power* can also refer to the exponent. The **exponent** indicates the number of times the base is used as a factor. In an expression of the form x^n, the **base** is x. The expression x^n is read "x to the nth power." When no exponent is shown, it is understood to be 1. For example, $a = a^1$.

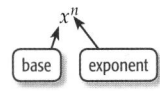

x^n — base (x), exponent (n)

EXAMPLE 1 Write Verbal Expressions

Write a verbal expression for each algebraic expression.

a. $3x^4$
three times x to the fourth power

b. $5z^2 + 16$
5 times z to the second power plus sixteen

Check Your Progress 1A–1B. Sample answers given.

1A. $16u^2 - 3$ 16 times u to the second power minus 3

1B. $\frac{1}{2}a + \frac{6b}{7}$ 1B. one half of a plus the quotient of 6 times b and 7

Personal Tutor glencoe.com

All of the **Lesson Resources** are leveled for students who are **approaching grade level, on grade level,** and **beyond grade level**, and for students who are **English language learners.**

1-1 Lesson Notes

1 FOCUS

Vertical Alignment

Before Lesson 1-1
Perform operations on integers.

Lesson 1-1
Write verbal expressions for algebraic expressions.
Write algebraic expressions for verbal expressions.

After Lesson 1-1
Evaluate algebraic expressions.

2 TEACH

Scaffolding Questions

Have students read the *Why?* section of the lesson.

Ask:

- How do you find the cost of the hot dogs that Cassie and her friends eat? multiply the number of hot dogs times \$0.10.
- What does the expression $0.10d$ stand for? 0.10 times d, the number of hot dogs
- What other variable could you use to represent the number of hot dogs? Sample answer: h

Write Verbal Expressions

Example 1 shows how to translate an algebraic expression into a verbal expression.

Lesson 1-1 Resources

Resource	Approaching-Level	On-Level	Beyond-Level	English Learners
Teacher Edition	• Differentiated Instruction, p. 6	• Differentiated Instruction, pp. 6, 9	• Differentiated Instruction, p. 9	• Differentiated Instruction, p. 6
Chapter Resource Masters	• Study Guide and Intervention, pp. 5–6 • Skills Practice, p. 7 • Practice, p. 8 • Word Problem Practice, p. 9	• Study Guide and Intervention, pp. 5–6 • Skills Practice, p. 7 • Practice, p. 8 • Word Problem Practice, p. 9 • Enrichment, p. 10	• Practice, p. 8 • Word Problem Practice, p. 9 • Enrichment, p. 10	• Study Guide and Intervention, pp. 5–6 • Skills Practice, p. 7 • Practice, p. 8
Transparencies	• 5-Minute Check Transparency 1-1	• 5-Minute Check Transparency 1-1	• 5-Minute Check Transparency 1-1	• 5-Minute Check Transparency 1-1
Other	• Study Notebook	• Study Notebook	• Study Notebook	• Study Notebook

Formative Assessment

Use the Check Your Progress exercises after each Example to determine students' understanding of concepts.

Additional Example

1 Write a verbal expression for each algebraic expression.

a. $8x^2$ eight times x squared

b. $y^5 - 16y$ the difference of y to the fifth power and 16 times y

Write Algebraic Expressions

Examples 2 and 3 show how to translate a verbal expression into an algebraic expression.

Additional Examples

2 Write an algebraic expression for each verbal expression.

a. 5 less than a number c $c - 5$

b. 9 plus the product of 2 and d $9 + 2d$

c. two fifths of the area a $\frac{2}{5}a$ or $\frac{2a}{5}$

3 **ENTERTAINMENT** Mr. Nehru bought two adult tickets and three student tickets for the planetarium show. Write an algebraic expression that represents the cost of the tickets. Let a be the cost of adult tickets and c be the cost of student tickets. The cost of the tickets is represented by $2a + 3c$.

Additional Examples also in Interactive Classroom PowerPoint® Presentations

IWB INTERACTIVE WHITEBOARD READY

StudyTip

Order of Operations Remember to follow the order of operations when writing a sentence to represent an algebraic expression.

Write Algebraic Expressions Another important skill is translating verbal expressions into algebraic expressions.

Key Concept — Translating Verbal to Algebraic Expressions (For Your FOLDABLE)

Operation	Verbal Phrases
Addition	more than, sum, plus, increased by, added to
Subtraction	less than, subtracted from, difference, decreased by, minus
Multiplication	product of, multiplied by, times, of
Division	quotient of, divided by

EXAMPLE 2 Write Algebraic Expressions

Write an algebraic expression for each verbal expression.

a. a number t more than 6

The words *more than* suggest addition.
Thus, the algebraic expression is $6 + t$ or $t + 6$.

b. 10 less than the product of 7 and f

Less than implies subtraction, and *product* suggests multiplication.
So the expression is written as $7f - 10$.

c. two thirds of the volume v

The word *of* with a fraction implies that you should multiply.
The expression could be written as $\frac{2}{3}v$ or $\frac{2v}{3}$.

Check Your Progress

2A. the product of p and 6 $6p$

2B. one third of the area a $\frac{1}{3}a$

Personal Tutor glencoe.com

Variables can represent quantities that are known and quantities that are unknown. They are also used in formulas, expressions, and equations.

Real-World Career

Sports Marketing
Sports marketers promote and manage athletes, teams, facilities and sports-related businesses and organizations. A minimum of a bachelor's degree in sports management or business administration is preferred.

Real-World EXAMPLE 3 Write an Expression

SPORTS MARKETING Mr. Martinez orders 250 key chains printed with his athletic team's logo and 500 pencils printed with their Web address. Write an algebraic expression that represents the cost of the order.

Let k be the cost of each key chain and p be the cost of each pencil. Then the cost of the key chains is $250k$ and the cost of the pencils is $500p$. The cost of the order is represented by $250k + 500p$.

Check Your Progress

3. COFFEE SHOP Katie estimates that $\frac{1}{8}$ of the people who order beverages also order pastries. Write an algebraic expression to represent this situation. $\frac{1}{8}b + b$

Personal Tutor glencoe.com

Differentiated Instruction (AL OL ELL)

If you identify students who have trouble writing mathematical or verbal expressions,

Then pair them with other students as mentors for practicing these skills. The transition from verbal expressions to algebraic expressions is easier for some students than others.

Check Your Understanding

Example 1 p. 5

1–3. Sample answers given.

Write a verbal expression for each algebraic expression.

1. $2m$ the product of 2 and m
2. $\frac{2}{3}r^4$ two thirds times a number raised to the fourth power.
3. $a^2 - 18b$ a squared minus 18 times b

Example 2 p. 6

Write an algebraic expression for each verbal expression.

4. the sum of a number and 14 $n + 14$
5. 6 less a number t $6 - t$
6. 7 more than 11 times a number $11n + 7$
7. 1 minus the quotient of r and 7 $1 - \frac{r}{7}$
8. two fifths of a number j squared $\frac{2}{5}j^2$
9. n cubed increased by 5 $n^3 + 5$

Example 3 p. 6

10. **GROCERIES** Mr. Bailey purchased some groceries that cost d dollars. He paid with a \$50 bill. Write an expression for the amount of change he will receive. $50 - d$

Practice and Problem Solving

● = Step-by-Step Solutions begin on page R12.
Extra Practice begins on page 815.

Example 1 p. 5

Write a verbal expression for each algebraic expression. 11–18. Sample answers given.

11. $4q$ four times a number q
12. $\frac{1}{8}y$ one eighth of y
13. $15 + r$ 15 plus r
14. $w - 24$ w minus 24
15. $3x^2$
16. $\frac{r^4}{9}$
17. $2a + 6$
18. $r^4 \cdot t^3$

15. 3 times x squared
16. r to the fourth power divided by 9
17. 6 more than the product 2 times a
18. the product of a number r raised to the fourth power and a number t cubed

Example 2 p. 6

Write an algebraic expression for each verbal expression.

19. x more than 7 $7 + x$
20. a number less 35 $n - 35$
21. 5 times a number $5n$
22. one third of a number $\frac{1}{3}n$
23. f divided by 10 $\frac{f}{10}$
24. the quotient of 45 and r $\frac{45}{r}$
25. three times a number plus 16 $3n + 16$
26. 18 decreased by 3 times d $18 - 3d$
27. k squared minus 11 $k^2 - 11$
28. 20 divided by t to the fifth power $\frac{20}{t^5}$

Example 3 p. 6

31–33. Sample answers given.

29. **GEOMETRY** The volume of a cylinder is π times the radius r squared multiplied by the height h. Write an expression for the volume. $\pi r^2 h$

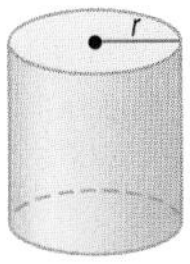

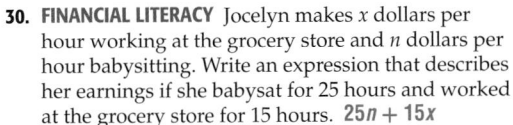

30. **FINANCIAL LITERACY** Jocelyn makes x dollars per hour working at the grocery store and n dollars per hour babysitting. Write an expression that describes her earnings if she babysat for 25 hours and worked at the grocery store for 15 hours. $25n + 15x$

Write a verbal expression for each algebraic expression.

31. $25 + 6x^2$
32. $6f^2 + 5f$
33. $\frac{3a^5}{2}$

31. twenty-five plus six times a number squared
32. six times a number squared plus five times the number
33. three times a number raised to the fifth power divided by two

34. **HEALTH** If the body mass index (BMI) is 25 or higher, then you are at a higher risk for heart disease. The BMI is the product of 703 and the quotient of the weight in pounds and the square of the height in inches.
    a. Write an expression that describes how to calculate the BMI. $703\frac{w}{h^2}$
    b. Calculate the BMI for a 140-pound person who is 65 inches tall.
    c. Calculate the BMI for a 155-pound person who is 5 feet 8 inches tall.

34b. BMI ≈ 23.3
34c. BMI ≈ 23.6

Focus on Mathematical Content

Writing Algebraic Expressions When writing algebraic expressions that involve multiplication, the multiplication symbol × should not be used, since it is easily confused with the variable x.

Teach with Tech features throughout the Teacher Edition offer tips on using various types of technology such as interactive whiteboards, document cameras, blogs, and more, to enhance your teaching.

TEACH with TECH

INTERACTIVE WHITEBOARD Write an algebraic expression on the board. Have students come to the board and use the highlighter tool to identify the variable. Copy the expression and have students replace the highlight with the value.

3 PRACTICE

Formative Assessment

Use Exercises 1–10 to check for understanding.

Use the chart at the bottom of this page to customize assignments for your students.

Differentiated Homework Options

Level	Assignment	Two-Day Option	
AL Basic	11–33, 38–40, 42–61	11–33 odd, 43–46	12–32 even, 38–40, 42, 47–61
OL Core	11–33 odd, 34–40, 42–61	11–33, 43–46	34–40, 42, 47–61
BL Advanced	34–55, (optional: 56–61)		

Study Guide and Intervention
CRM pp. 5–6 AL OL ELL

NAME ______________ DATE ________ PERIOD ________

1-1 Study Guide and Intervention
Variables and Expressions

Write Verbal Expressions An **algebraic expression** consists of one or more numbers and variables along with one or more arithmetic operations. In algebra, **variables** are symbols used to represent unspecified numbers or values. Any letter may be used as a variable.

Example Write a verbal expression for each algebraic expression.

a. $6n^2$
the product of 6 and n squared

b. $n^3 - 12m$
the difference of n cubed and twelve times m

Exercises

Write a verbal expression for each algebraic expression. 1–16. Sample answers are given.

1. $w - 1$ one less than w
2. $\frac{1}{3}a^3$ one third the cube of a
3. $81 + 2x$ eighty-one increased by twice x
4. $12d$ 12 times d
5. 8^4 eight to the fourth power
6. 6^2 the square of 6
7. $2n^2 + 4$ the sum of 4 and twice the square of n
8. $a^3 \cdot b^3$ a cubed times b cubed
9. $2x^3 - 3$ the difference of twice a number cubed and 3
10. $\frac{6k^3}{5}$ 6 times the cube of k divided by 5
11. $\frac{1}{4}b^2$ one-fourth the square of b
12. $7n^5$ seven times the fifth power of n
13. $3x + 4$ the sum of three times a number and 4
14. $\frac{2}{3}k^5$ two-thirds the fifth power of k
15. $3b^2 + 2a^3$ 3 times b squared plus 2 times a cubed
16. $4(n^2 + 1)$ 4 times the sum of the square of n and 1

Lesson 1-1

Practice
CRM p. 8 AL OL BL ELL

NAME ______________ DATE ________ PERIOD ________

1-1 Practice
Variables and Expressions

Write a verbal expression for each algebraic expression. 1–8. Sample answers are given.

1. $23f$ the product of 23 and f
2. 7^3 seven cubed
3. $5m^2 + 2$ 2 more than 5 times m squared
4. $4d^3 - 10$ 4 times d cubed minus 10
5. $x^3 \cdot y^4$ x cubed times y to the fourth power
6. $b^2 - 3c^3$ b squared minus 3 times c cubed
7. $\frac{k^5}{6}$ one sixth of the fifth power of k
8. $\frac{4n^2}{7}$ one seventh of 4 times n squared

Write an algebraic expression for each verbal expression.

9. the difference of 10 and u $10 - u$
10. the sum of 18 and a number $18 + x$
11. the product of 33 and j $33j$
12. 74 increased by 3 times y $74 + 3y$
13. 15 decreased by twice a number $15 - 2x$
14. 91 more than the square of a number $x^2 + 91$
15. three fourths the square of b $\frac{3}{4}b^2$
16. two fifths the cube of a number $\frac{2}{5}x^3$
17. **BOOKS** A used bookstore sells paperback fiction books in excellent condition for \$2.50 and in fair condition for \$0.50. Write an expression for the cost of buying x excellent-condition paperbacks and f fair-condition paperbacks. $2.50x + 0.50f$
18. **GEOMETRY** The surface area of the side of a right cylinder can be found by multiplying twice the number π by the radius times the height. If a circular cylinder has radius r and height h, write an expression that represents the surface area of its side. $2\pi rh$

Word Problem Practice
CRM p. 9 AL OL BL ELL

NAME ______________ DATE ________ PERIOD ________

1-1 Word Problem Practice
Variables and Expressions

1. **SOLAR SYSTEM** It takes Earth about 365 days to orbit the sun. It takes Uranus about 85 times as long. Write a numerical expression to describe the number of days it takes Uranus to orbit the sun. 365×85

2. **TECHNOLOGY** There are 1024 bytes in a kilobyte. Write an expression that describes the number of bytes in a computer chip with n kilobytes.
$1024 \times n$ or $1024n$

3. **THEATER** Howard Hughes, Professor Emeritus of Texas Wesleyan College, reportedly attended a record 6136 theatrical shows. Write an expression to represent the average number of theater shows attended if he accumulated the record over y years.
$\frac{6136}{y}$

4. **TIDES** The difference between high and low tides along the Maine coast in November is 19 feet on Monday and x feet on Tuesday. Write an expression to show the average rise and fall of the tide for Monday and Tuesday. $\frac{19 + x}{2}$

5. **BLOCKS** A toy manufacturer produces a set of blocks that can be used by children to build play structures. The product packaging team is analyzing different arrangements for packaging their blocks. One idea they have is to arrange the blocks in the shape of a cube, with b blocks along one edge.

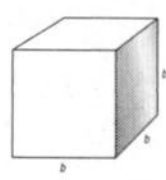

a. Write an expression representing the total number of blocks packaged in a cube measuring b blocks on one edge.
b^3

b. The packaging team decides to take one layer of blocks off the top of this package. Write an expression representing the number of blocks in the top layer of the package. b^2

c. The team finally decides that their favorite package arrangement is to take 2 layers of blocks off the top of a cube measuring b blocks along one edge. Write an expression representing the number of blocks left behind after the top two layers are removed.
$b^3 - 2b^2$ or $(b - 2) \times b^2$

Lesson 1-1

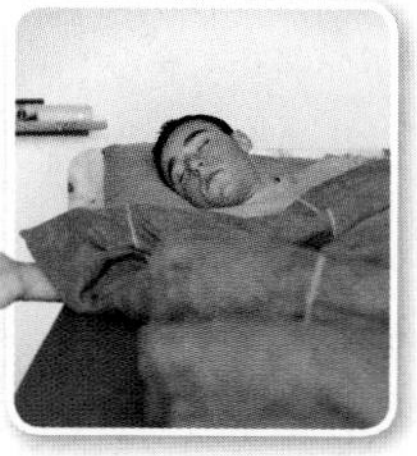

Real-World Link

About 20% of our dreams are about animals. About $\frac{3}{4}$ of our dreams involve people that we know.

Source: National Dream Hotline

36c. Sample answer: 4 touchdowns and 4 field goals

38. Algebraic expressions include variables, numbers, and symbols. Verbal expressions contain words.

39. Sample answer: x is the number of minutes it takes to walk between my house and school. $2x + 15$ represents the amount of time in minutes I spend walking each day since I walk to and from school and I take my dog on a 15 minute walk.

42. Sample answer: An algebraic expression is a math phrase that contains one or more numbers or variables. To write an algebraic expression from real-world situation, first assign variables. Then determine the arithmetic operations done on the variables. Finally, put the terms in order.

35. DREAMS Refer to the information at the left.

a. Write an expression to describe the number of dreams that feature people you know if you have d dreams. $\frac{3}{4}d$

b. Use the expression you wrote to predict the number of dreams that include people you know out of 28 dreams. 21

36. SPORTS In football, a touchdown is awarded 6 points and the team can then try for a point after a touchdown.

a. Write an expression that describes the number of points scored on touchdowns and points after touchdowns by one team in a game. $6T + p$

b. If a team wins a football game 27-0, write an equation to represent the possible number of touchdowns and points after touchdowns by the winning team. $6T + p = 27$

c. If a team wins a football game 7-21, how many possible number of touchdowns and points after touchdowns were scored during the game by both teams?

37. MULTIPLE REPRESENTATIONS In this problem, you will explore the multiplication of powers with like bases.

a. **TABULAR** Copy and complete the table.

10^2	×	10^1	=	10 × 10 × 10	=	10^3	
10^2	×	10^2	=	10 × 10 × 10 × 10	=	10^4	
10^2	×	10^3	=	10 × 10 × 10 × 10 × 10	=	?	10^5
10^2	×	10^4	=	?	=	?	10^6

10 × 10 × 10 × 10 × 10 × 10

b. **ALGEBRAIC** Write an equation for the pattern in the table. $10^2 \times 10^x = 10^{(2 + x)}$

c. **VERBAL** Make a conjecture about the exponent of the product of two powers. The exponent of the product of two powers is the sum of the exponents of the powers with the same base.

H.O.T. Problems
Use Higher-Order Thinking Skills

38. REASONING Explain the differences between an algebraic expression and a verbal expression.

39. OPEN ENDED Define a variable to represent a real-life quantity, such as time in minutes or distance in feet. Then use the variable to write an algebraic expression to represent one of your daily activities. Describe in words what your expression represents, and explain your reasoning.

40. FIND THE ERROR Consuelo and James are writing an algebraic expression for *three times the sum of n squared and 3*. Is either of them correct? Explain your reasoning.
Consuelo; James left out the parentheses around $n^2 + 3$.

Consuelo	James
$3(n^2 + 3)$	$3n^2 + 3$

41. CHALLENGE For the cube, x represents a positive whole number. Find the value of x such that the volume of the cube and 6 times the area of one of its faces have the same value. 6

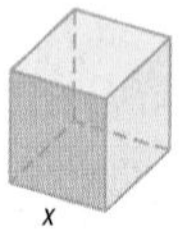

42. WRITING IN MATH Describe how to write an algebraic expression from a real-world situation. Include a definition of algebraic expression in your own words.

Enrichment
CRM p. 10 OL BL

NAME ______________ DATE ________ PERIOD ________

1-1 Enrichment

Toothpick Triangles

Variable expressions can be used to represent patterns and help solve problems. Consider the problem of creating triangles out of toothpicks shown below.

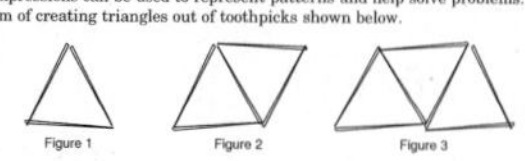

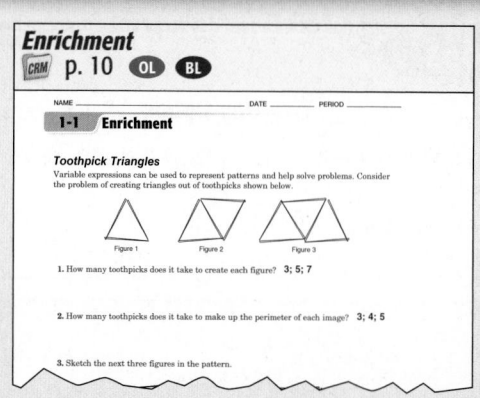

Figure 1 Figure 2 Figure 3

1. How many toothpicks does it take to create each figure? 3; 5; 7
2. How many toothpicks does it take to make up the perimeter of each image? 3; 4; 5
3. Sketch the next three figures in the pattern.

Multiple Representations In Exercise 37, students use a table and algebraic expressions to explore the multiplication of powers with like bases.

PSAE PRACTICE 7.11.03, 8.11.02

43. Which expression best represents the volume of the cube? D

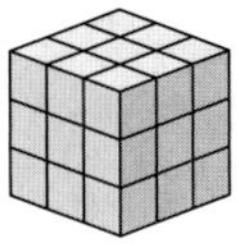

A the product of three and five
B three to the fifth power
C three squared
D three cubed

44. Which expression best represents the perimeter of the rectangle? H

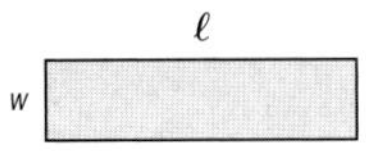

F $2\ell w$
G $\ell + w$
H $2\ell + 2w$
J $4(\ell + w)$

45. SHORT RESPONSE The yards of fabric needed to make curtains is 3 times the length of a window in inches, divided by 36. Write an expression that represents the yards of fabric needed in terms of the length of the window ℓ. $\frac{3\ell}{36}$

46. GEOMETRY Find the area of the rectangle. B

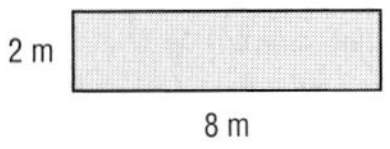

A 14 square meters
B 16 square meters
C 50 square meters
D 60 square meters

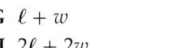

Spiral Review

47. AMUSEMENT PARKS A roller coaster enthusiast club took a poll to see what each member's favorite ride was. Make a bar graph of the results. (Lesson 0-13) See Ch. 1 Answer Appendix.

Our Favorite Rides

Ride	Big Plunge	Twisting Time	The Shiner	Raging Bull	The Bat	Teaser	The Adventure
Number of Votes	5	22	16	9	25	6	12

48. SPORTS The results for an annual 5K race are shown at the right. Make a box-and-whisker plot for the data. Write a sentence describing what the length of the box-and-whisker plot tells about the times for the race. (Lesson 0-13) See margin.

Annual 5-K Race Results

Joe	14:48	Carissa	19:58
Jessica	19:27	Jordan	14:58
Lupe	15:06	Taylor	20:47
Dante	20:39	Mi-Ling	15:48
Tia	15:54	Winona	21:35
Amber	20:49	Angel	16:10
Amanda	16:30	Catalina	20:21

Find the mean, median, and mode for each set of data. (Lesson 0-12)

49. {7, 6, 5, 7, 4, 8, 2, 2, 7, 8} mean = 5.6; median = 6.5; mode = 7

50. {−1, 0, 5, 2, −2, 0 ,−1, 2, −1, 0} 50. mean = 0.4; median = 0; mode = 0 and −1

51. {17, 24, 16, 3, 12, 11, 24, 15} mean = 15.25; median = 15.5; mode = 24

52. SPORTS Lisa has a rectangular trampoline that is 6 feet long and 12 feet wide. What is the area of her trampoline in square feet? (Lesson 0-8) 72 ft^2

Find each product or quotient. (Lesson 0-5)

53. $\frac{3}{5} \cdot \frac{7}{11}$ $\frac{21}{55}$

54. $\frac{4}{3} \div \frac{7}{6}$ $\frac{8}{7}$

55. $\frac{5}{6} \cdot \frac{8}{3}$ $\frac{20}{9}$

Skills Review

Evaluate each expression. (Lesson 0-4)

56. $\frac{3}{5} + \frac{4}{9}$ $\frac{47}{45}$

57. $5.67 - 4.21$ 1.46

58. $\frac{5}{6} - \frac{8}{3}$ $-1\frac{5}{6}$

59. $10.34 + 14.27$ 24.61

60. $\frac{11}{12} + \frac{5}{36}$ $\frac{19}{18}$

61. $37.02 - 15.86$ 21.16

Watch Out!

Find the Error For Exercise 40, students should see that grouping symbols are necessary for *the sum of n^2 and 3*. Suggest that students write a verbal expression for each algebraic expression and then compare these to the original verbal expression.

Preventing Errors Students often ignore the order of operations and read, write, and evaluate expressions from left to right. Remind students to always follow the order of operations.

4 ASSESS

Ticket Out the Door Give each student a slip of paper on which is written an algebraic expression. As they leave the room, ask each student to translate the algebraic expression into a verbal expression.

Additional Answer

48.

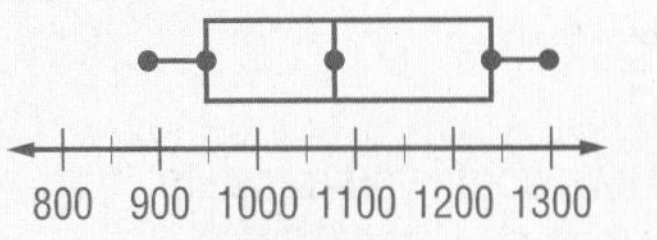

The length of the box-and-whisker plot shows how spread out the runners were.

Differentiated Instruction OL BL

Extension Suggest that students write an expression that represents their allowance. Ask them to write a verbal expression to represent their allowance and then an algebraic expression. Have them use their expressions to explain the difference between a verbal expression and an algebraic expression.

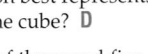

1-2 Lesson Notes

1 FOCUS

Vertical Alignment

Before Lesson 1-2
Express algebraic expressions verbally.

Lesson 1-2
Evaluate numerical expressions by using the order of operations.
Evaluate algebraic expressions by using the order of operations.

After Lesson 1-2
Evaluate expressions using properties of numbers.

2 TEACH

Scaffolding Questions

Have students read the *Why?* section of the lesson.

Ask:

- How would you translate 4(64.95) + 3(53.95)? Multiply 4 times 64.95 and then add the product of 3 times 53.95.
- What are the operations in the expression? multiplication and addition
- What does 4(64.95) represent? cost of four adult tickets

1-2 Order of Operations

Then
You expressed algebraic expressions verbally. (Lesson 1-1)

Now
- Evaluate numerical expressions by using the order of operations.
- Evaluate algebraic expressions by using the order of operations.

IL Learning Standards
7.A.4b Apply formulas in a wide variety of theoretical and practical real-world measurement applications involving perimeter, area, volume, angle, time, temperature, mass, speed, distance, density and monetary values.

New Vocabulary
evaluate
order of operations

IL Math Online
glencoe.com
- Extra Examples
- Personal Tutor
- Self-Check Quiz
- Homework Help

New Vocabulary is listed at the beginning of every lesson. Some lessons also have a Vocabulary Link, which shows how mathematical words are related to everyday words.

Why?

The admission prices for SeaWorld Adventure Park in Orlando, Florida, are shown in the table. If four adults and three children go the park, the expression below represents the cost of admission for the group.

$$4(64.95) + 3(53.95)$$

Ticket	Price ($)
Adult	64.95
Child	53.95

Evaluate Numerical Expressions To find the cost of admission, the expression 4(64.95) + 3(53.95) must be evaluated. To **evaluate** an expression means to find its value.

EXAMPLE 1 Evaluate Expressions

Evaluate 3^5.

$3^5 = 3 \cdot 3 \cdot 3 \cdot 3 \cdot 3$ — **Use 3 as a factor 5 times.**
$= 243$ — **Multiply.**

Check Your Progress

1A. 2^4 **16** **1B.** 4^5 **1024** **1C.** 7^3 **343**

Personal Tutor glencoe.com

The numerical expression that represents the cost of admission contains more than one operation. The rule that lets you know which operation to perform first is called the **order of operations**.

Key Concept Order of Operations *For Your FOLDABLE*

Step 1 Evaluate expressions inside grouping symbols.
Step 2 Evaluate all powers.
Step 3 Multiply and/or divide from left to right.
Step 4 Add and/or subtract from left to right.

EXAMPLE 2 Use Order of Operations

Evaluate $16 - 8 \div 2^2 + 14$.

$16 - 8 \div 2^2 + 14 = 16 - 8 \div 4 + 14$ — **Evaluate powers.**
$= 16 - 2 + 14$ — **Divide 8 by 4.**
$= 14 + 14$ — **Subtract 2 from 16.**
$= 28$ — **Add 14 and 14.**

Check Your Progress Evaluate each expression.

2A. $3 + 42 \cdot 2 - 5$ **82** **2B.** $20 - 7 + 8^2 - 7 \cdot 11$ **0**

Personal Tutor glencoe.com

Lesson 1-2 Resources

Resource	Approaching-Level	On-Level	Beyond-Level	English Learners
Teacher Edition	• Differentiated Instruction, p. 11	• Differentiated Instruction, pp. 11, 15	• Differentiated Instruction, p. 15	
Chapter Resource Masters	• Study Guide and Intervention, pp. 11–12 • Skills Practice, p. 13 • Practice, p. 14 • Word Problem Practice, p. 15 • Graphing Calculator Activity, p. 17	• Study Guide and Intervention, pp. 11–12 • Skills Practice, p. 13 • Practice, p. 14 • Word Problem Practice, p. 15 • Enrichment, p. 16 • Graphing Calculator Activity, p. 17	• Practice, p. 14 • Word Problem Practice, p. 15 • Enrichment, p. 16 • Graphing Calculator Activity, p. 17	• Study Guide and Intervention, pp. 11–12 • Skills Practice, p. 13 • Practice, p. 14 • Graphing Calculator Activity, p. 17
Transparencies	• 5-Minute Check Transparency 1-2	• 5-Minute Check Transparency 1-2	• 5-Minute Check Transparency 1-2	• 5-Minute Check Transparency 1-2
Other	• Study Notebook • Teaching Algebra with Manipulatives	• Study Notebook • Teaching Algebra with Manipulatives	• Study Notebook	• Study Notebook • Teaching Algebra with Manipulatives

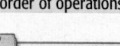

StudyTip

Grouping Symbols Grouping symbols such as parentheses ( ), brackets [ ], and braces { } are used to clarify or change the order of operations.

When one or more grouping symbols are used, evaluate within the innermost grouping symbols first.

EXAMPLE 3 Expressions with Grouping Symbols

Evaluate each expression.

a. $4 \div 2 + 5(10 - 6)$

$4 \div 2 + 5(10 - 6) = 4 \div 2 + 5(4)$	Evaluate inside parentheses.
$= 2 + 5(4)$	Divide 4 by 2.
$= 2 + 20$	Multiply 5 by 4.
$= 22$	Add 2 to 20.

b. $6\left[32 - (2 + 3)^2\right]$

$6\left[32 - (2 + 3)^2\right] = 6\left[32 - (5)^2\right]$	Evaluate innermost expression first.
$= 6[32 - 25]$	Evaluate power.
$= 6[7]$	Subtract 25 from 32.
$= 42$	Multiply.

c. $\dfrac{2^3 - 5}{15 + 9}$

$\dfrac{2^3 - 5}{15 + 9} = \dfrac{8 - 5}{15 + 9}$	Evaluate the power in the numerator.
$= \dfrac{3}{15 + 9}$	Subtract 5 from 8 in the numerator.
$= \dfrac{3}{24}$ or $\dfrac{1}{8}$	Add 15 and 9 in denominator, and simplify.

StudyTip

Grouping Symbols A fraction bar is considered a grouping symbol. So, evaluate expressions in the numerator and denominator before completing the division.

Check Your Progress

3A. $5 \cdot 4(10 - 8) + 20$ 60 **3B.** $15 - \left[10 + (3 - 2)^2\right] + 6$ 10 **3C.** $\dfrac{(4 + 5)^2}{3(7 - 4)}$ 9

Personal Tutor glencoe.com

Evaluate Algebraic Expressions To evaluate an algebraic expression, replace the variables with their values. Then find the value of the numerical expression using the order of operations.

EXAMPLE 4 Evaluate an Algebraic Expression

Evaluate $3x^2 + \left(2y + z^3\right)$ if $x = 4$, $y = 5$, $z = 3$.

$3x^2 + \left(2y + z^3\right)$

$= 3(4)^2 + \left(2 \cdot 5 + 3^3\right)$	Replace *x* with 4, *y* with 5, and *z* with 3.
$= 3(4)^2 + (2 \cdot 5 + 27)$	Evaluate 3^3.
$= 3(4)^2 + (10 + 27)$	Multiply 2 by 10.
$= 3(4)^2 + (37)$	Add 10 to 27.
$= 3(16) + 37$	Evaluate 4^2.
$= 48 + 37$	Multiply 3 by 16.
$= 85$	Add 48 to 37.

Check Your Progress

Evaluate each expression.

4A. $a^2(3b + 5) \div c$ if $a = 2, b = 6, c = 4$ 23 **4B.** $5d + (6f - g)$ if $d = 4, f = 3, g = 12$ 26

Personal Tutor glencoe.com

Evaluate Numerical Expressions

Example 1 shows how to evaluate numerical expressions with one term. **Examples 2 and 3** show how to use the order of operations to evaluate expressions with more than one operation or grouping symbol.

Formative Assessment

Use the Check Your Progress exercises after each Example to determine students' understanding of concepts.

Additional Examples

1 Evaluate 2^6. 64

2 Evaluate $48 \div 2^3 \cdot 3 + 5$. 23

3 Evaluate each expression.

a. $(8 - 3) \cdot 3(3 + 2)$ 75

b. $4[12 \div (6 - 2)]^2$ 36

c. $\dfrac{2^5 - 6 \cdot 2}{3^3 - 5 \cdot 3 - 2}$ 2

Focus on Mathematical Content

Grouping Symbols Grouping symbols include parentheses, ( ), brackets, [ ], braces, { }, and fraction bars, as in $\frac{5 + 7}{2}$. Evaluate expressions inside grouping symbols first when using the order of operations.

Evaluate Algebraic Expressions

Example 4 shows how to evaluate an algebraic expression by replacing the variables with their values and using the order of operations. **Example 5** shows how to find the value of a variable in a formula when the values of all the other variables are known.

Additional Example

4 Evaluate $2(x^2 - y) + z^2$ if $x = 4$, $y = 3$, and $z = 2$. 30

Differentiated Instruction AL

If students have difficulty evaluating complex algebraic expressions,

Then pair these students with advanced students and suggest that they work through the exercises step-by-step.

Additional Example

5 **ARCHITECTURE** Each side of the Great Pyramid of Giza, Egypt, is a triangle. The base of each triangle once measured 230 meters. The height of each triangle once measured 187 meters. The area of a triangle is one-half the product of the base b and its height h.

a. Write an expression that represents the area of one side of the Great Pyramid. $\frac{1}{2}(bh)$

b. Find the area of one side of the Great Pyramid. 21,505 m^2

Additional Examples also in Interactive Classroom PowerPoint® Presentations

IWB INTERACTIVE WHITEBOARD READY

Real-World Link

The National Oceanic & Atmospheric Administration (NOAA) developed the Science on a Sphere system to educate people about Earth's processes. There are five computers and four video projectors that power the sphere.

Source: NOAA

Real-World EXAMPLE 5 Write and Evaluate an Expression

ENVIRONMENTAL STUDIES Science on a Sphere (SOS)® demonstrates the effects of atmospheric storms, climate changes, and ocean temperature on the environment. The volume of a sphere is four thirds of π multiplied by the radius r to the third power.

a. Write an expression that represents the volume of a sphere.

Words	four thirds	of	π multiplied by radius to the third power
Variable	Let r = radius.		
Expression	$\frac{4}{3}$	$\times$	πr^3 or $\frac{4}{3}\pi r^3$

b. Find the volume of the 3-foot radius sphere used for SOS.

$V = \frac{4}{3}\pi r^3$ — **Volume of a sphere**

$= \frac{4}{3}\pi(3)^3$ — **Replace r with 3.**

$= \left(\frac{4}{3}\right)\pi(27)$ — **Evaluate $3^3 = 27$.**

$= 36\pi$ — **Multiply $\frac{4}{3}$ by 27.**

The volume of the sphere is 36π cubic feet.

Check Your Progress

5. FOREST FIRES According to the California Department of Forestry, an average of 539.2 fires each year are started by burning debris, while campfires are responsible for an average of 129.1 each year.

A. Write an algebraic expression that represents the number of fires, on average, in d years of debris burning and c years of campfires. $539.2d + 129.1c$

B. How many fires would there be in 5 years? 3342 fires

Personal Tutor glencoe.com

Check Your Understanding

Examples 1–3 pp. 10–11 — Evaluate each expression.

1. 9^2 81
2. 4^4 256
3. 3^5 243
4. $30 - 14 \div 2$ 23
5. $5 \cdot 5 - 1 \cdot 3$ 22
6. $(2 + 5)4$ 28
7. $[8(2) - 4^2] + 7(4)$ 28
8. $\frac{11 - 8}{1 + 7 \cdot 2}$ $\frac{3}{15}$ or $\frac{1}{5}$
9. $\frac{(4 \cdot 3)^2}{9 + 3}$ 12

Example 4 p. 11 — Evaluate each expression if $a = 4$, $b = 6$, and $c = 8$.

10. $8b - a$ 44
11. $2a + (b^2 \div 3)$ 20
12. $\frac{b(9 - c)}{a^2}$ $\frac{6}{16}$ or $\frac{3}{8}$

Example 5 p. 12

13. **BOOKS** Akira bought one new book for \$20 and three used books for \$4.95 each. Write and evaluate an expression to find how much money the books cost. $20 + 3 \times 4.95$; \$34.85
14. **FOOD** Koto purchased food for herself and her friends. She bought 4 cheeseburgers for \$2.25 each, 3 French fries for \$1.25 each, and 4 drinks for \$4.00. Write and evaluate an expression to find how much the food cost. $4 \times 2.25 + 3 \times 1.25 + 4 \times 4.00$; \$28.75

TEACH with TECH

DOCUMENT CAMERA Use numbers and operation tiles to create a numeric expression such as $6 \div (3^2 - 2 \cdot 3) + 3$. Have students remove the operation performed in each step and replace them with the number tiles that are equivalent (like removing the $2 \cdot 3$ tiles and replacing them with 6).

3 PRACTICE

Formative Assessment

Use Exercises 1–14 to check for understanding.

Use the chart at the bottom of the next page to customize assignments for your students.

Watch Out!

Student Misconceptions Caution that not all calculators follow the order of operations when evaluating expressions. Nonscientific calculators evaluate expressions in the order they are entered. All scientific calculators (including graphing calculators) follow the order of operations. However, for longer expressions, you may have to use grouping symbols or be creative when entering the expression in order to get the correct answer.

Practice and Problem Solving

● = **Step-by-Step Solutions** begin on page R12.
Extra Practice begins on page 815.

Examples 1–3 pp. 10–11

Evaluate each expression.

15. 7^2 **49**
16. 14^3 **2744**
17. 2^6 **64**
18. $35 - 3 \cdot 8$ **11**
19. $18 \div 9 + 2 \cdot 6$ **14**
20. $10 + 8^3 \div 16$ **42**
21. $24 \div 6 + 2^3 \cdot 4$ **36**
22. $(11 \cdot 7) - 9 \cdot 8$ **5**
23. $29 - 3(9 - 4)$ **14**
24. $(12 - 6) \cdot 5^2$ **150**
25. $3^5 - (1 + 10^2)$ **142**
26. $108 \div [3(9 + 3^2)]$ **2**
27. $[(6^3 - 9) \div 23]4$ **36**
28. $\frac{8 + 3^3}{12 - 7}$ **7**
29. $\frac{(1 + 6)9}{5^2 - 4}$ **3**

Example 4 p. 11

Evaluate each expression if $g = 2$, $r = 3$, and $t = 11$.

30. $g + 6t$ **68**
31. $7 - gr$ **1**
32. $r^2 + (g^3 - 8)^5$ **9**
33. $(2t + 3g) \div 4$ **7**
34. $t^2 + 8rt + r^2$ **394**
35. $3g(g + r)^2 - 1$ **149**

B

36. **GEOMETRY** Write an algebraic expression to represent the area of the triangle. Then evaluate it to find the area when $h = 12$ inches.
$\frac{1}{2}h(h + 6)$; 108 in^2

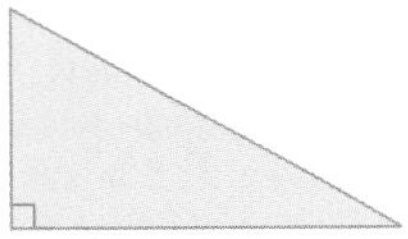

37. **AMUSEMENT PARKS** In 1997, there were 3344 amusement parks and arcades. This decreased by 148 by 2002. Write and evaluate an expression to find the number of amusement parks and arcades in 2002.
3344 − 148 = 3196

38. **SPORTS** Kamilah works at the Duke University Athletic Ticket Office. One week she sold 15 preferred season tickets, 45 blue zone tickets, and 55 general admission tickets. Write and evaluate an expression to find the amount of money Kamilah processed.
$15p + 45b + 55g$; 15(100) + 45(80) + 55(70) = $8950

Duke University Football Ticket Prices

Preferred Season Ticket	$100
Blue Zone	$80
General Admission	$70

Source: Duke University

Evaluate each expression.

39. 4^2 **16**
40. 12^3 **1728**
41. 3^6 **729**
42. 11^5 **161,051**
43. $(3 - 4^2)^2 + 8$ **177**
44. $23 - 2(17 + 3^3)$ **−65**
45. $3[4 - 8 + 4^2(2 + 5)]$ **324**
46. $\frac{2 \cdot 8^2 - 2^2 \cdot 8}{2 \cdot 8}$ **6**
47. $25 + \left[(16 - 3 \cdot 5) + \frac{12 + 3}{5}\right]$ **29**
48. $7^3 - \frac{2}{3}(13 \cdot 6 + 9)4$ **111**

Evaluate each expression if $a = 8$, $b = 4$, and $c = 16$.

49. $a^2bc - b^2$ **4080**
50. $\frac{c^2}{b^2} + \frac{b^2}{a^2}$ **$\frac{65}{4}$**
51. $\frac{2b + 3c^2}{4a^2 - 2b}$ **$\frac{97}{31}$**
52. $\frac{3ab + c^2}{a}$ **44**
53. $\left(\frac{a}{b}\right)^2 - \frac{c}{a - b}$ **0**
54. $\frac{2a - b^2}{ab} + \frac{c - a}{b^2}$ **$\frac{1}{2}$**

55. **SALES** One day, 28 small and 12 large merchant spaces were rented. Another day, 30 small and 15 large spaces were rented. Write and evaluate an expression to show the total rent collected.

55. 28(7) + 12(9.75) + 30(7) + 15(9.75); $669.25

Watch Out!

Preventing Errors Students may be reluctant to take time to show all the steps they use when evaluating an expression. Help them to see that these steps enable them to diagnose errors and to prevent calculation errors that may keep them from getting correct values.

Differentiated Homework Options

Level	Assignment	Two-Day Option	
AL Basic	15–35, 59–60, 62–81	15–35 odd, 65–68	16–34 even, 59–60, 62–64, 69–81
OL Core	15–35 odd, 36–38, 39–53 odd, 55–60, 62–81	15–35, 65–68	39–54, 36–38, 55–58, 59–60, 62–64
BL Advanced	36–75, (optional: 76–81)		

Real-World Link

The pyramid at the Louvre in Paris was designed by famed architect I.M. Pei. He also designed the Rock & Roll Hall of Fame in Cleveland, Ohio.

Source: Infoplease

56. SHOPPING Evelina is shopping for back-to-school clothes. She bought 3 skirts, 2 pairs of jeans, and 4 sweaters. Write and evaluate an expression to find out how much money Evelina spent on clothes, without including sales tax. **3(25.99) + 2(39.99) + 4(22.99); $249.91**

Clothing	
skirt	$25.99
jeans	$39.99
sweater	$22.99

57. PYRAMIDS The pyramid at the Louvre has a square base with a side of 35.42 meters and a height of 21.64 meters. The Great Pyramid in Egypt has a square base with a side of 230 meters and a height of 146.5 meters. The expression for the volume of a pyramid is $\frac{1}{3}Bh$, where B is the area of the base and h is the height.

a. Draw both pyramids and label the dimensions. **See margin.**

b. Write a verbal expression for the difference in volume of the two pyramids.

c. Write an algebraic expression for the difference in volume of the two pyramids. Find the difference in volume.

58. FINANCIAL LITERACY A sales representative receives an annual salary s, an average commission each month c, and a bonus b for each sales goal that she reaches.

a. Write an algebraic expression to represent her total earnings in one year if she receives four equal bonuses. **$s + 12c + 4b$**

b. Suppose her annual salary is $52,000 and her average commission is $1225 per month. If each of the four bonuses equals $1150, what does she earn annually? **$71,300**

H.O.T. Problems

Use Higher-Order Thinking Skills

59. FIND THE ERROR Tara and Curtis are simplifying $[4(10) - 3^2] + 6(4)$. Is either of them correct? Explain your reasoning.

Tara	Curtis
$= [4(10) - 9] + 6(4)$	$= [4(10) - 9] + 6(4)$
$= 4(1) + 6(4)$	$= (40 - 9) + 6(4)$
$= 4 + 6(4)$	$= 31 + 6(4)$
$= 4 + 24$	$= 31 + 24$
$= 28$	$= 55$

60. REASONING Explain how to evaluate $a[(b - c) \div d] - f$ if you were given values for a, b, c, d, and f. How would you evaluate the expression differently if the expression was $a \cdot b - c \div d - f$? **See margin.**

61. CHALLENGE Write an expression using the whole numbers 1 to 5 using all five digits and addition and/or subtraction to create a numeric expression with a value of 3. **5 + 4 − 3 − 2 − 1**

62. OPEN ENDED Write an expression that uses exponents, at least three different operations and two sets of parentheses. Explain the steps you would take to evaluate the expression. **See students' work.**

63. WRITING IN MATH Choose a geometric formula and explain how the order of operations applies when using the formula.

64. WRITING IN MATH Equivalent expression have the same value. Are the expressions (30 + 17) × 10 and 10 × 30 + 10 × 17 equivalent? Explain why or why not. **See margin.**

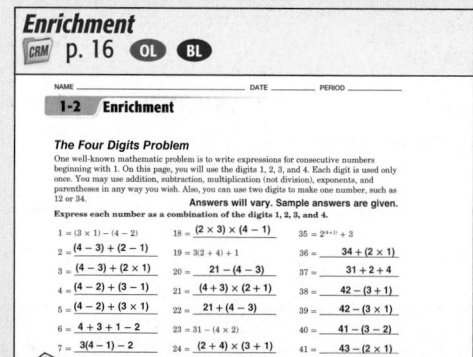

57b. one third times 230 m squared times 146.5 minus one third times 35.42 squared times 21.64

57c. $\frac{1}{3}(230)^2(146.5) - \frac{1}{3}(35.42)^2(21.64)$; $2{,}574{,}233.656\ m^3$

59. Curtis; Tara subtracted 10 − 9 before multiplying 4 by 10.

63. Sample answer: Area of a trapezoid $\frac{1}{2}h(b_1 + b_2)$; according to the order of operations you have to add the lengths of the bases together first and then multiply by the height and by $\frac{1}{2}$.

Watch Out!

Find the Error For Exercise 59, students should see that Tara and Curtis have done something different in the second step. Explain to students that once they have identified a difference, they do not need to look at subsequent steps.

Study Guide and Intervention

CRM pp. 11–12 AL OL ELL

NAME ______ DATE ______ PERIOD ______

1-2 Study Guide and Intervention

Order of Operations

Evaluate Numerical Expressions Numerical expressions often contain more than one operation. To evaluate them, use the rules for order of operations shown below.

Order of Operations	
	Step 1 Evaluate expressions inside grouping symbols.
	Step 2 Evaluate all powers.
	Step 3 Do all multiplication and/or division from left to right.
	Step 4 Do all addition and/or subtraction from left to right.

Example 1 Evaluate each expression.

a. 3^4

$3^4 = 3 \cdot 3 \cdot 3 \cdot 3$ Use 3 as a factor 4 times.
$= 81$ Multiply.

b. 6^3

$6^3 = 6 \cdot 6 \cdot 6$ Use 6 as a factor 3 times.
$= 216$ Multiply.

Example 2 Evaluate each expression.

a. $3[2 + (12 \div 3)^2]$

$3[2 + (12 \div 3)^2] = 3(2 + 4^2)$ Divide 12 by 3.
$= 3(2 + 16)$ Find 4 squared.
$= 3(18)$ Add 2 and 16.
$= 54$ Multiply 3 and 18.

b. $\frac{3 + 2^3}{4^2 \cdot 3}$

$\frac{3 + 2^3}{4^2 \cdot 3} = \frac{3 + 8}{4^2 \cdot 3}$ Evaluate power in numerator.
$= \frac{11}{4^2 \cdot 3}$ Add 3 and 8 in the numerator.
$= \frac{11}{16 \cdot 3}$ Evaluate power in denominator.
$= \frac{11}{48}$ Multiply.

Exercises

Evaluate each expression.

1. 5^2 **25**
2. 3^3 **27**
3. 10^4 **10,000**
4. 12^2 **144**
5. 8^3 **512**
6. 2^8 **256**
7. $(8 - 4) \cdot 2$ **8**
8. $(12 + 4) \cdot 6$ **96**
9. $10 + 8 \cdot 1$ **18**
10. $15 - 12 \div 4$ **12**
11. $12(20 - 17) - 3 \cdot 6$ **18**
12. $24 \div 3 \cdot 2 - 3^2$ **7**
13. $3^2 \div 3 + 2^2 \cdot 7 - 20 \div 5$ **27**
14. $\frac{4 + 3^2}{12 + 1}$ **1**
15. $250 \div [5(3 \cdot 7 + 4)]$ **2**
16. $\frac{2 \cdot 4^2 - 8 \div 2}{(5 + 2) \cdot 2}$ **2**
17. $\frac{4(5^2) - 4 \cdot 3}{4(4 \cdot 5 + 2)}$ **1**
18. $\frac{5^2 - 3}{20(3) + 2(3)}$ **$\frac{1}{3}$**

Lesson 1-2

Chapter 1 11 Glencoe Algebra 1

Practice

CRM p. 14 AL OL BL ELL

NAME ______ DATE ______ PERIOD ______

1-2 Practice

Order of Operations

Evaluate each expression.

1. 11^2 **121**
2. 8^3 **512**
3. 5^4 **625**
4. $(15 - 5) \cdot 2$ **20**
5. $9 \cdot (3 + 4)$ **63**
6. $5 + 7 \cdot 4$ **33**
7. $4(3 + 5) - 5 \cdot 4$ **12**
8. $22 \div 11 \cdot 9 - 3^2$ **9**
9. $6^2 + 3 \cdot 7 - 9$ **48**
10. $3[10 - (27 \div 9)]$ **21**
11. $2[5^2 + (36 \div 6)]$ **62**
12. $162 \div [6(7 - 4)^2]$ **3**
13. $\frac{5^2 \cdot 4 - 5 \cdot 4^2}{5(4)}$ **1**
14. $\frac{(2 \cdot 5)^2 + 4}{3^2 - 5}$ **26**
15. $\frac{7 + 3^2}{4^2 \cdot 2}$ **$\frac{1}{2}$**

Evaluate each expression if $a = 12$, $b = 9$, and $c = 4$.

16. $a^2 + b - c^2$ **137**
17. $b^2 + 2a - c^2$ **89**
18. $2c(a + b)$ **168**
19. $4a + 2b - c^2$ **50**
20. $(a^2 \div 4b) + c$ **8**
21. $c^2 \cdot (2b - a)$ **96**
22. $\frac{bc^2 + a}{c}$ **39**
23. $\frac{2c^3 - ab}{4}$ **5**
24. $2(a - b)^2 - 5c$ **−2**
25. $\frac{b^2 - 2c^2}{a + c - b}$ **7**

26. **CAR RENTAL** Ann Carlyle is planning a business trip for which she needs to rent a car. The car rental company charges $36 per day plus $0.50 per mile over 100 miles. Suppose Ms. Carlyle rents the car for 5 days and drives 180 miles.

a. Write an expression for how much it will cost Ms. Carlyle to rent the car. **5(36) + 0.5(180 − 100)**

b. Evaluate the expression to determine how much Ms. Carlyle must pay the car rental company. **$220.00**

27. **GEOMETRY** The length of a rectangle is $3n + 2$ and its width is $n - 1$. The perimeter of the rectangle is twice the sum of its length and its width.

a. Write an expression that represents the perimeter of the rectangle. **$2[(3n + 2) + (n - 1)]$**

b. Find the perimeter of the rectangle when $n = 4$ inches. **34 in.**

Chapter 1 14 Glencoe Algebra 1

Word Problem Practice

CRM p. 15 AL OL BL ELL

NAME ______ DATE ______ PERIOD ______

1-2 Word Problem Practice

Order of Operations

1. **SCHOOLS** Jefferson High School has 100 less than 5 times as many students as Taft High School. Write and evaluate an expression to find the number of students at Jefferson High School if Taft High School has 300 students. **$5t - 100$; 1400 students**

2. **GEOGRAPHY** Guadalupe Peak in Texas has an altitude that is 671 feet more than double the altitude of Mount Sunflower in Kansas. Write and evaluate an expression for the altitude of Guadalupe Peak if Mount Sunflower has an altitude of 4039 feet. **$2n + 671$; 8749 ft**

3. **TRANSPORTATION** The Plaid Taxi Cab Company charges $1.75 per passenger plus $3.45 per mile for trips less than 10 miles. Write and evaluate an expression to find the cost for Max to take a Plaid taxi 8 miles to the airport. **$1.75 + $3.45m; $29.35**

4. **GEOMETRY** The area of a circle is related to the radius of the circle such that the product of the square of the radius and a number π gives the area. Write and evaluate an expression for the area of a circular pizza below. Approximate π as 3.14. **πr^2; 153.86 in²**

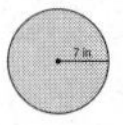

5. **BIOLOGY** Lavania is studying the growth of a population of fruit flies in her laboratory. She notices that the number of fruit flies in her experiment is five times as large after any six-day period. She observes 20 fruit flies on October 1. Write and evaluate an expression to predict the population of fruit flies Lavania will observe on October 31. **20×5^5; 62,500 flies**

6. **CONSUMER SPENDING** During a long weekend, Devon paid a total of x dollars for a rental car so he could visit his family. He rented the car for 4 days at a rate of $36 per day. There was an additional charge of $0.20 per mile after the first 200 miles driven.

a. Write an algebraic expression to represent the amount Devon paid for additional mileage only. **$x - (36 \times 4)$**

b. Write an algebraic expression to represent the number of miles over 200 miles that Devon drove the rented car. **$\frac{x - (36 \times 4)}{0.20}$**

c. How many miles did Devon drive overall if he paid a total of $174 for the car rental? **350 mi**

Lesson 1-2

Chapter 1 15 Glencoe Algebra 1

Enrichment

CRM p. 16 OL BL

NAME ______ DATE ______ PERIOD ______

1-2 Enrichment

The Four Digits Problem

One well-known mathematic problem is to write expressions for consecutive numbers beginning with 1. On this page, you will use the digits 1, 2, 3, and 4. Each digit is used only once. You may use addition, subtraction, multiplication (not division), exponents, and parentheses in any way you wish. Also, you can use two digits to make one number, such as 12 or 34.

Answers will vary. Sample answers are given.

Express each number as a combination of the digits 1, 2, 3, and 4.

1 = (3 × 1) − (4 − 2)	18 = **(2 × 3) × (4 − 1)**	35 = $2^{(4+1)} + 3$
2 = **(4 − 3) + (2 − 1)**	19 = 3(2 + 4) + 1	36 = **34 + (2 × 1)**
3 = **(4 − 3) + (2 × 1)**	20 = **21 − (4 − 3)**	37 = **31 + 2 + 4**
4 = **(4 − 2) + (3 − 1)**	21 = **(4 + 3) × (2 + 1)**	38 = **42 − (3 + 1)**
5 = **(4 − 2) + (3 × 1)**	22 = **21 + (4 − 3)**	39 = **42 − (3 × 1)**
6 = **4 + 3 + 1 − 2**	23 = 31 − (4 × 2)	40 = **41 − (3 − 2)**
7 = **3(4 − 1) − 2**	24 = **(2 + 4) × (3 + 1)**	41 = **43 − (2 × 1)**

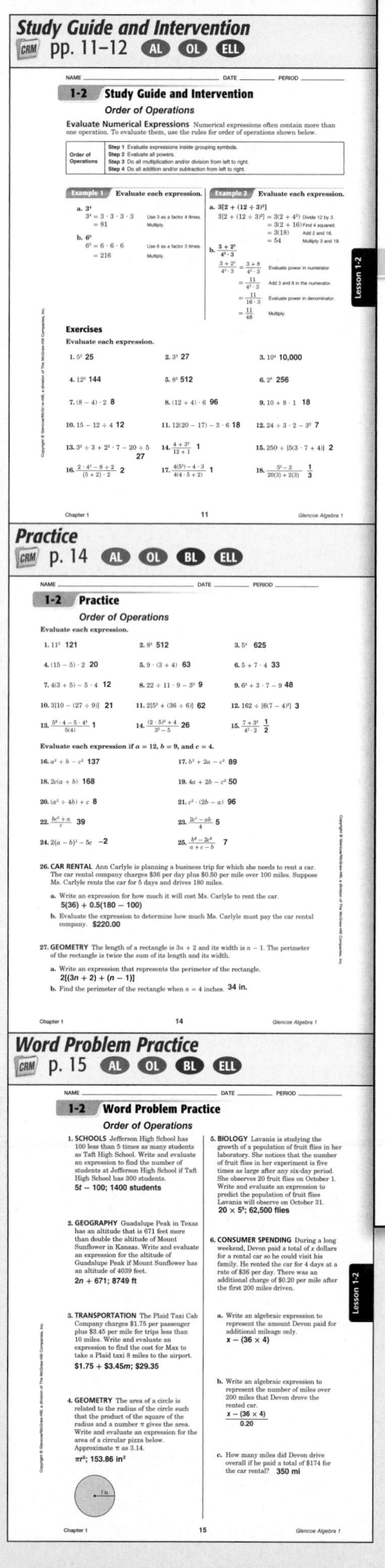

14 **Chapter 1** Expressions, Equations, and Functions

PSAE PRACTICE 8.11.02, 6.11.04, 10.11.07, 7.11.03

65. Let m represent the number of miles. Which algebraic expression represents the number of feet in m miles? **A**

A $5280m$

B $\frac{5280}{m}$

C $m + 5280$

D $5280 - m$

66. SHORT RESPONSE

Simplify: $[10 + 15(2^3)] \div [7(2^2) - 2]$

Step 1 $[10 + 15(8)] \div [7(4) - 2]$

Step 2 $[10 + 120] \div [28 - 2]$

Step 3 $130 \div 26$

Step 4 $\frac{1}{5}$

Which is the first *incorrect* step? Explain the error. **Step 4; the answer is 5.**

67. EXTENDED RESPONSE A local movie theater has advertised that one out of every four customers will receive a free popcorn with the purchase of a movie ticket. So far, 25 of the first 80 customers have won. **See margin.**

Part A Based on the results so far, what is the experimental probability that a customer will win?

Part B What is the theoretical probability that a customer will win?

Part C Explain the difference between theoretical and experimental probabilities.

68. GEOMETRY What is the perimeter of the triangle if $a = 9$ and $b = 10$? **G**

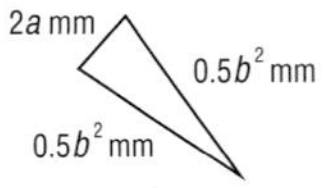

F 164 mm

G 118 mm

H 28 mm

J 4 mm

Spiral Review

Write a verbal expression for each algebraic expression. (Lesson 1-1)

69. $14 - 9c$ **14 minus 9 times c**

70. $k^3 + 13$ **k cubed plus 13**

71. $\frac{4 - v}{w}$ **the difference of 4 and v divided by w**

72. MONEY Destiny earns \$8 per hour babysitting and \$15 for each lawn she mows. Write an expression to show the amount of money she earns babysitting h hours and mowing m lawns. (Lesson 1-1) **$8h + 15m$**

Find the area of each figure. (Lesson 0-7)

73. **9π units²**

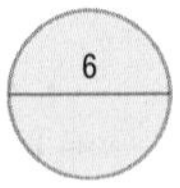

74. **18 units²**

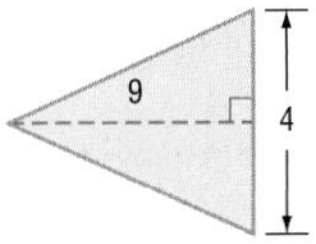

75. **$12b$ units²**

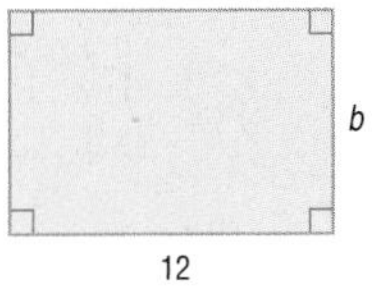

76. SCHOOL Aaron correctly answered 27 out of 30 questions on his last biology test. What percent of the questions did he answer correctly? (Lesson 0-5) **90%**

Skills Review

Find the value of each expression. (Lessons 0-4 and 0-5)

77. $5.65 - 3.08$ **2.57**

78. $6 \div \frac{4}{5}$ **$\frac{15}{2}$**

79. $4.85(2.72)$ **13.192**

80. $1\frac{1}{12} + 3\frac{2}{3}$ **$4\frac{3}{4}$**

81. $\frac{4}{9} \cdot \frac{3}{2}$ **$\frac{2}{3}$**

82. $7\frac{3}{4} - 4\frac{7}{10}$ **$3\frac{1}{20}$**

Differentiated Instruction BL

Extension Write the numbers 2, 3, 4, and 8 on the board. Tell students to make the number 8 by using each of the four numbers exactly once along with any operation and grouping symbol. Sample answers: $(4 + 8) \div 3 \cdot 2$; $8 \div 4 \cdot 3 + 2$

4 ASSESS

Name the Math Write a numerical and an algebraic expression on the board. Have students work with a partner and take turns explaining how to evaluate one of the expressions using the order of operations.

Formative Assessment

Check for student understanding of Lessons 1-1 and 1-2.

CRM Quiz 1, p. 57

Additional Answers

57a.

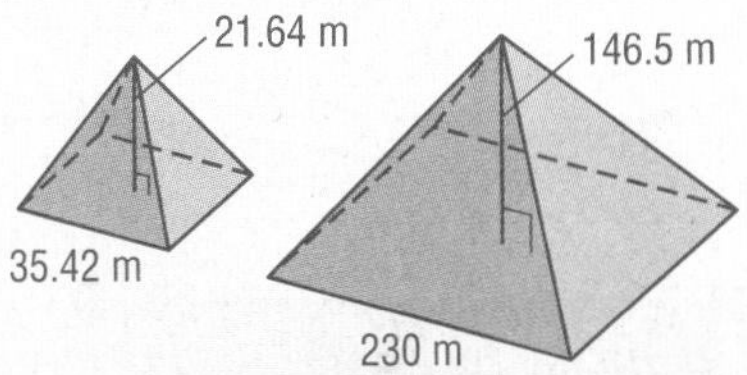

60. Sample answer: First I would subtract c from b and then divide by d. Then I would multiply that by a and then subtract f. Without grouping symbols, first a and b would be multiplied together, then c would be divided by d, and then c divided by d would be subtracted from a multiplied by b. Then f would be subtracted from the result.

64. The expressions are equivalent. To simplify the first expression, simplify the expression in the parentheses first to get 47. Then multiply by 10 to get 470. The order of operations states to multiply before adding. So, perform the multiplication first in the second expression. The result is 300 + 170. Then add to get 470.

67. $\frac{5}{16}$; $\frac{1}{4}$; Experimental probability is what happens in the trials. In this case the experimental probability is the probability that the customers have actually received popcorn. Theoretical probability is what is expected to happen.

1-3 Lesson Notes

1 FOCUS

Vertical Alignment

Before Lesson 1-3
Use the order of operations to simplify expressions.

Lesson 1-3
Recognize the properties of equality and identity.
Recognize the Commutative and Associative Properties.

After Lesson 1-3
Represent relationships among quantities using equations and inequalities.

2 TEACH

Scaffolding Questions

Have students read the *Why?* section of the lesson.

Ask:

- If the distance from Nate's house to the mall is 32 miles, what is the distance from the mall to Nate's house? 32 miles
- If the two distances are equal, how can you represent the distance using numbers? $32 = 32$
- What do you think the Reflexive Property means? A quantity is equal to itself.

1-3 Properties of Numbers

Then
You used the order of operations to simplify expressions. (Lesson 1-2)

Now
- Recognize the properties of equality and identity.
- Recognize the Commutative and Associative Properties.

IL Learning Standards

6.A.4 Identify and apply the associative, commutative, distributive **and identity properties of real numbers, including special numbers such as pi and square roots.**
7.A.4b Apply formulas in a wide variety of theoretical and practical real-world measurement applications involving perimeter, area, volume, angle, time, temperature, mass, speed, distance, density and monetary values.

New Vocabulary
equivalent expressions
additive identity
multiplicative identity
multiplicative inverse
reciprocal

IL Math Online
glencoe.com
- Extra Examples
- Personal Tutor
- Self-Check Quiz
- Homework Help
- Math in Motion

Why?

Nate lives 32 miles away from the mall. The distance from his house to the mall is the same as the distance from the mall to his house. This is an example of the *Reflexive Property*.

Properties of Equality and Identity The expressions $4k + 8k$ and $12k$ are called **equivalent expressions** because they represent the same number. The properties below allow you to write an equivalent expression for a given expression.

Key Concept Properties of Equality — For Your FOLDABLE

Property	Words	Symbols	Examples
Reflexive Property	Any quantity is equal to itself.	For any number a, $a = a$.	$5 = 5$ $4 + 7 = 4 + 7$
Symmetric Property	If one quantity equals a second quantity, then the second quantity equals the first.	For any numbers a and b, if $a = b$, then $b = a$.	If $8 = 2 + 6$, then $2 + 6 = 8$.
Transitive Property	If one quantity equals a second quantity and the second quantity equals a third quantity, then the first quantity equals the third quantity.	For any numbers a, b, and c, if $a = b$ and $b = c$, then $a = c$.	If $6 + 9 = 3 + 12$ and $3 + 12 = 15$, then $6 + 9 = 15$.
Substitution Property	A quantity may be substituted for its equal in any expression.	If $a = b$, then a may be replaced by b in any expression.	If $n = 11$, then $4n = 4 \cdot 11$

The sum of any number and 0 is equal to the number. Thus, 0 is called the **additive identity**.

Key Concept Addition Properties — For Your FOLDABLE

Property	Words	Symbols	Examples
Additive Identity	For any number a, the sum of a and 0 is a.	$a + 0 = 0 + a$ $= a$	$2 + 0 = 2$ $0 + 2 = 2$
Additive Inverse	A number and its opposite are additive inverses of each other.	$a + (-a) = 0$	$3 + (-3) = 0$ $4 - 4 = 0$

Lesson 1-3 Resources

Resource	Approaching-Level	On-Level	Beyond-Level	English Learners
Teacher Edition	• Differentiated Instruction, p. 18	• Differentiated Instruction, p. 22	• Differentiated Instruction, p. 22	
Chapter Resource Masters	• Study Guide and Intervention, pp. 18–19 • Skills Practice, p. 20 • Practice, p. 21 • Word Problem Practice, p. 22	• Study Guide and Intervention, pp. 18–19 • Skills Practice, p. 20 • Practice, p. 21 • Word Problem Practice, p. 22 • Enrichment, p. 23	• Practice, p. 21 • Word Problem Practice, p. 22 • Enrichment, p. 23	• Study Guide and Intervention, pp. 18–19 • Skills Practice, p. 20 • Practice, p. 21
Transparencies	• 5-Minute Check Transparency 1-3	• 5-Minute Check Transparency 1-3	• 5-Minute Check Transparency 1-3	• 5-Minute Check Transparency 1-3
Other	• Study Notebook	• Study Notebook	• Study Notebook	• Study Notebook

There are also special properties associated with multiplication. Consider the following equations.

$4 \cdot n = 4$

The solution of the equation is 1. Since the product of any number and 1 is equal to the number, 1 is called the **multiplicative identity**.

$6 \cdot m = 0$

The solution of the equation is 0. The product of any number and 0 is equal to 0. This is called the **Multiplicative Property of Zero**.

Two numbers whose product is 1 are called **multiplicative inverses** or **reciprocals**. Zero has no reciprocal because any number times 0 is 0.

Key Concept Multiplication Properties

For Your FOLDABLE

Property	Words	Symbols	Example
Multiplicative Identity	For any number a, the product of a and 1 is a.	$a \cdot 1 = 1$ $1 \cdot a = a$	$14 \cdot 1 = 14$ $1 \cdot 14 = 14$
Multiplicative Property of Zero	For any number a, the product of a and 0 is 0.	$a \cdot 0 = 0$ $0 \cdot a = 0$	$9 \cdot 0 = 0$ $0 \cdot 9 = 0$
Multiplicative Inverse	For every number $\frac{a}{b}$, where a, $b \neq 0$, there is exactly one number $\frac{b}{a}$ such that the product of $\frac{a}{b}$ and $\frac{b}{a}$ is 1.	$\frac{a}{b} \cdot \frac{b}{a} = 1$ $\frac{b}{a} \cdot \frac{a}{b} = 1$	$\frac{4}{5} \cdot \frac{5}{4} = \frac{20}{20}$ or 1 $\frac{5}{4} \cdot \frac{4}{5} = \frac{20}{20}$ or 1

StudyTip

Properties and Identities These properties are true for all real numbers. They are also referred to as *field properties*.

EXAMPLE 1 Evaluate Using Properties

Evaluate $7(4 - 3) - 1 + 5 \cdot \frac{1}{5}$. Name the property used in each step.

$7(4 - 3) - 1 + 5 \cdot \frac{1}{5} = 7(1) - 1 + 5 \cdot \frac{1}{5}$ — **Substitution: $4 - 3 = 1$**

$= 7 - 1 + 5 \cdot \frac{1}{5}$ — **Multiplicative Identity: $7 \cdot 1 = 7$**

$= 7 - 1 + 1$ — **Multiplicative Inverse: $5 \cdot \frac{1}{5} = 1$**

$= 6 + 1$ — **Substitution: $7 - 1 = 6$**

$= 7$ — **Substitution: $6 + 1 = 7$**

Check Your Progress

Name the property used in each step.

1A. $2 \cdot 3 + (4 \cdot 2 - 8)$
$= 2 \cdot 3 + (8 - 8)$? Substitution
$= 2 \cdot 3 + (0)$? Additive Inverse
$= 6 + 0$? Substitution
$= 6$? Additive Identity

1B. $7 \cdot \frac{1}{7} + 6(15 \div 3 - 5)$
$= 7 \cdot \frac{1}{7} + 6(5 - 5)$?
$= 7 \cdot \frac{1}{7} + 6(0)$?
$= 1 + 6(0)$?
$= 1 + 0$?
$= 1$?

1B. Substitution; Additive Inverse; Multiplicative Inverse; Multiplicative Property of Zero; Additive Identity

Personal Tutor glencoe.com

Properties of Equality and Identity

Example 1 shows how to use the identity and equality properties to justify each step when evaluating expressions.

Formative Assessment

Use the Check Your Progress exercises after each Example to determine students' understanding of concepts.

Additional Example

1 Evaluate $\frac{1}{4}(12 - 8) + 3(15 \div 5 - 2)$. Name the property used in each step.

$\frac{1}{4}(12 - 8) + 3(15 \div 5 - 2)$

$= \frac{1}{4}(4) + 3(15 \div 5 - 2)$
Substitution: $12 - 8 = 4$

$= \frac{1}{4}(4) + 3(3 - 2)$
Substitution: $15 \div 5 = 3$

$= \frac{1}{4}(4) + 3(1)$
Substitution: $3 - 2 = 1$

$= \frac{1}{4}(4) + 3$
Multiplicative Identity: $3(1) = 3$

$= 1 + 3 = 4$
Multiplicative Inverse: $\frac{1}{4}(4) = 1$

$= 4$
Substitution: $1 + 3 = 4$

Additional Examples also in Interactive Classroom PowerPoint® Presentations

IWB INTERACTIVE WHITEBOARD READY

Focus on Mathematical Content

Properties of Multiplication Some of the properties of multiplication include the Multiplicative Identity Property, the Multiplicative Property of Zero, and the Multiplicative Inverse Property. The Multiplicative Identity Property states that the product of any number and 1 is that number; the Multiplicative Property of Zero states that the product of any number and zero is 0; and the Multiplicative Inverse Property states that the product of a number and its reciprocal is 1.

TEACH with TECH

AUDIO RECORDING Have students work in pairs to record descriptions of the properties in their own words. Then have them listen to the recordings of other pairs.

Use Commutative and Associative Properties

Example 2 shows how to use the Commutative and Associative Properties for Addition to solve a real-world problem. **Example 3** shows how to use the Commutative and Associative Properties for Multiplication to evaluate a numerical expression.

Additional Example

2 **HORSEBACK RIDING** Migina made a list of trail lengths to find the total miles she rode. Find the total miles Migina rode her horse.

Trails	
Name	**Miles**
Bent Tree	4.25
Knob Hill	6.50
Meadowrun	9.00
Pinehurst	7.75

27.5 miles

Focus on Mathematical Content

Commutative and Associative Properties The Commutative Property states that the order in which you add or multiply numbers does not change their sum or product. The Associative Property states that the way you group 3 or more numbers when you add or multiply them does not change their sum or product.

Additional Answer (Check Your Progress)

2. $300 + 30.50 + 25.50 + 50$
$= 300 + 50 + 30.50 + 25.50$ Commutative (+)
$= (300 + 50) + (30.50 + 25.50)$ Associative (+)
$= 350 + 56$ Substitution
$= 406$ Substitution
The cost is \$406.

Use Commutative and Associate Properties Nikki walks 2 blocks to her friend Sierra's house. They walk another 4 blocks to school. At the end of the day, Nikki and Sierra walk back to Sierra's house, and then Nikki walks home.

The distance from Nikki's house to school	equals	the distance from the school to Nikki's house.
$2 + 4$	$=$	$4 + 2$

This is an example of the **Commutative Property** for addition.

Key Concept — **Commutative Property** *For Your FOLDABLE*

Words The order in which you add or multiply numbers does not change their sum or product.

Symbols For any numbers a and b, $a + b = b + a$ and $a \cdot b = b \cdot a$.

Examples $4 + 8 = 8 + 4$ $7 \cdot 11 = 11 \cdot 7$

Math *in Motion*, BrainPOP® glencoe.com

An easy way to find the sum or product of numbers is to group, or associate, the numbers using the **Associative Property**.

Key Concept — **Associative Property** *For Your FOLDABLE*

Words The way you group three or more numbers when adding or multiplying does not change their sum or product.

Symbols For any numbers a, b, and c, $(a + b) + c = a + (b + c)$ and $(ab)c = a(bc)$.

Examples $(3 + 5) + 7 = 3 + (5 + 7)$ $(2 \cdot 6) \cdot 9 = 2 \cdot (6 \cdot 9)$

Math *in Motion*, BrainPOP® glencoe.com

Real-World Link

A child's birthday party may cost about \$200 depending on the number of children invited.

Source: Family Corner

Real-World EXAMPLE 2 Apply Properties of Numbers

PARTY PLANNING Eric makes a list of items that he needs to buy for a party and their costs. Find the total cost of these items.

Party Supplies	
Item	**Cost (\$)**
balloons	6.75
decorations	14.00
food	23.25
beverages	20.50

Balloons		Decorations		Food		Beverages
6.75	+	14.00	+	23.25	+	20.50

$= 6.75 + 23.25 + 14.00 + 20.50$ Commutative (+)
$= (6.75 + 23.25) + (14.00 + 20.50)$ Associative (+)
$= 30.00 + 34.50$ Substitution
$= 64.50$ Substitution

The total cost is \$64.50.

Check Your Progress

2. **FURNITURE** Rafael is buying furnishings for his first apartment. He buys a couch for \$300, lamps for \$30.50, a rug for \$25.50, and a table for \$50. Find the total cost of these items. **See margin.**

Personal Tutor glencoe.com

Differentiated Instruction AL

If students have difficulty with the concepts of the Commutative and Associative Properties,

Then consider using manipulatives that will visually verify the properties for the Commutative Property. For example, show students that a big bucket of water and a small bucket of water equals a small bucket of water and a big bucket of water.

EXAMPLE 3 Use Multiplication Properties

Evaluate 5 • 7 • 4 • 2 using the properties of numbers. Name the property used in each step.

$5 \cdot 7 \cdot 4 \cdot 2 = 5 \cdot 2 \cdot 7 \cdot 4$	Commutative (×)
$= (5 \cdot 2) \cdot (7 \cdot 4)$	Associative (×)
$= 10 \cdot 28$	Substitution
$= 280$	Substitution

Check Your Progress

Evaluate each expression using the properties of numbers. Name the property used in each step. 3A, 3B. See margin.

3A. $2.9 \cdot 4 \cdot 10$

3B. $\frac{5}{3} \cdot 25 \cdot 3 \cdot 2$

Personal Tutor glencoe.com

Check Your Understanding

1–3. See Chapter 1 Answer Appendix.

Example 1 p. 17

Evaluate each expression. Name the property used in each step.

1. $(1 \div 5)5 \cdot 14$
2. $6 + 4(19 - 15)$
3. $5(14 - 5) + 6(3 + 7)$
4. **FINANCIAL LITERACY** Carolyn has 9 quarters, 4 dimes, 7 nickels, and 2 pennies, which can be represented as $9(25) + 4(10) + 7(5) + 2$. Evaluate the expression to find how much money she has. Name the property used in each step. See Chapter 1 Answer Appendix.

Examples 2 and 3 pp. 18–19

Evaluate each expression using the properties of numbers. Name the property used in each step. 5–8. See Chapter 1 Answer Appendix.

5. $23 + 42 + 37$
6. $2.75 + 3.5 + 4.25 + 1.5$
7. $3 \cdot 7 \cdot 10 \cdot 2$
8. $\frac{1}{4} \cdot 24 \cdot \frac{2}{3}$

Practice and Problem Solving

= Step-by-Step Solutions begin on page R12. Extra Practice begins on page 815.

Example 1 p. 17

Evaluate each expression. Name the property used in each step. 9–14. See Chapter 1 Answer Appendix.

9. $3(22 - 3 \cdot 7)$
10. $7 + (9 - 3^2)$
11. $\frac{3}{4}[4 \div (7 - 4)]$
12. $[3 \div (2 \cdot 1)]\frac{2}{3}$
13. $2(3 \cdot 2 - 5) + 3 \cdot \frac{1}{3}$
14. $6 \cdot \frac{1}{6} + 5(12 \div 4 - 3)$

Example 2 p. 18

15. **GEOMETRY** The expression $2 \cdot \frac{22}{7} \cdot 14^2 + 2 \cdot \frac{22}{7} \cdot 14 \cdot 7$ represents the approximate surface area of the cylinder at the right. Evaluate this expression to find the approximate surface area. Name the property used in each step. See Chapter 1 Answer Appendix.

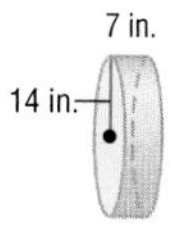

16. **HOTEL RATES** A traveler checks into a hotel on Friday and checks out the following Tuesday morning. Use the table to find the total cost of the room including tax. $291

Hotel Rates Per Day		
Day	**Room Charge**	**Sales Tax**
Monday–Friday	$72	$5.40
Saturday–Sunday	$63	$5.10

Additional Example

3 Evaluate 2 • 8 • 5 • 7 using the properties of numbers. Name the property used in each step.

$2 \cdot 8 \cdot 5 \cdot 7$	
$= 2 \cdot 5 \cdot 8 \cdot 7$	Commutative (×)
$= (2 \cdot 5) \cdot (8 \cdot 7)$	Associative (×)
$= 10 \cdot 56$	Substitution
$= 560$	Substitution

Additional Examples exactly parallel the examples in the text. Step-by-step solutions for these examples are included in ***Interactive Classroom***.

3 PRACTICE

Formative Assessment

Use Exercises 1–8 to check for understanding.

Use the chart at the bottom of this page to customize assignments for your students.

Additional Answers (Check Your Progress)

3A. $2.9 \cdot 4 \cdot 10$

$= 2.9 \cdot 10 \cdot 4$	Comm. (×)
$= (2.9 \cdot 10) \cdot 4$	Assoc. (×)
$= 29 \cdot 4$	Substitution
$= 116$	Substitution

3B. $\frac{5}{3} \cdot 25 \cdot 3 \cdot 2$

$= \frac{5}{3} \cdot 3 \cdot 25 \cdot 2$	Comm. (×)
$= \left(\frac{5}{3} \cdot 3\right) \cdot (25 \cdot 2)$	Assoc. (×)
$= 5 \cdot 50$	Substitution
$= 250$	Substitution

Differentiated Homework Options

Level	Assignment	Two-Day Option	
AL Basic	9–28, 54–56, 58–80	9–27 odd, 61–64	10–28 even, 54–56, 58–60
OL Core	9–29 odd, 30, 31–47 odd, 29–30, 48–56, 58–80	9–28, 61–64	29–56, 58–60, 65–80
BL Advanced	29–74, (optional: 75–80)		

Lesson 1-3 Properties of Numbers 19

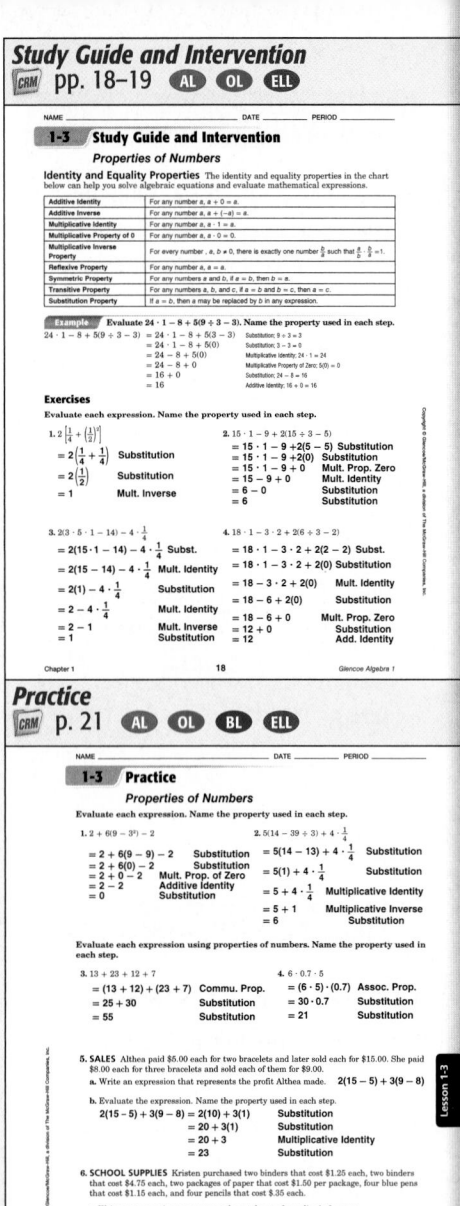

Examples 2 and 3 pp. 18–19

Evaluate each expression using properties of numbers. Name the property used in each step. 17–28. See Chapter 1 Answer Appendix.

17. $25 + 14 + 15 + 36$

18. $11 + 7 + 5 + 13$

19. $3\frac{2}{3} + 4 + 5\frac{1}{3}$

20. $4\frac{4}{9} + 7\frac{2}{9}$

21. $4.3 + 2.4 + 3.6 + 9.7$

22. $3.25 + 2.2 + 5.4 + 10.75$

23. $12 \cdot 2 \cdot 6 \cdot 5$

24. $2 \cdot 8 \cdot 10 \cdot 2$

25. $0.2 \cdot 4.6 \cdot 5$

26. $3.5 \cdot 3 \cdot 6$

27. $1\frac{5}{6} \cdot 24 \cdot 3\frac{1}{11}$

28. $2\frac{3}{4} \cdot 1\frac{1}{8} \cdot 32$

B

29. SCUBA DIVING The sign shows the equipment rented or sold by a scuba diving store.

a. Write two expressions to represent the total sales to rent 2 wet suits, 3 air tanks, 2 dive flags, and selling 5 underwater cameras.

b. What are the total sales? $149.35

29a. Sample answer: $2(10.95) + 3(7.5) + 2(5) + 5(18.99)$; $2(10.95 + 5) + 3(7.5) + 5(18.99)$

30. COOKIES Bobby baked 2 dozen chocolate chip cookies, 3 dozen sugar cookies, and a dozen oatmeal raisin cookies. How many total cookies did he bake? 72

Evaluate each expression if $a = -1$, $b = 4$, and $c = 6$.

31. $4a + 9b - 2c$ 20

32. $-10c + 3a + a$ −64

33. $a - b + 5a - 2b$ −18

34. $8a + 5b - 11a - 7b$ −5

35. $3c^2 + 2c + 2c^2$ 192

36. $3a - 4a^2 + 2a$ −9

Real-World Link

Fantasy football has about 10 million participants per year. Fans participate in drafts to pick their teams and then compete throughout the season.

Source: CNN

37. FOOTBALL A football team is on the 35-yard line. The quarterback is sacked at the line of scrimmage. The team gains 0 yards, so they are still at the 35-yard line. Which identity or property does this represent? Explain. Additive Identity; $35 + 0 = 35$

Find the value of x. Then name the property used.

38. $8 = 8 + x$ 0; Additive Identity

39. $3.2 + x = 3.2$ 0; Additive Identity

40. $10x = 10$ 1; Multiplicative Identity

41. $\frac{1}{2} \cdot x = \frac{1}{2} \cdot 7$ 7; Reflexive Property

42. $x + 0 = 5$ 5; Additive Identity

43. $1 \cdot x = 3$ 3; Multiplicative Identity

44. $5 \cdot \frac{1}{5} = x$ 1; Multiplicative Inverse

45. $2 + 8 = 8 + x$ 2; Commutative Property

46. $x + \frac{3}{4} = 3 + \frac{3}{4}$ 3; Reflexive Property

47. $\frac{1}{3} \cdot x = 1$ 3; Multiplicative Inverse

48. GEOMETRY Write an expression to represent the perimeter of the triangle. Then find the perimeter if $x = 2$ and $y = 7$.

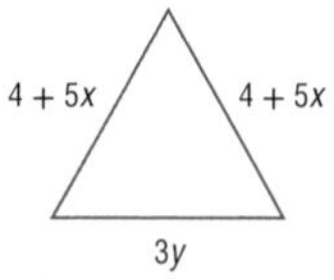

49. SPORTS Tickets to a baseball game cost \$25 each plus a \$4.50 handling charge per ticket. If Sharon has a coupon for \$10 off and orders 4 tickets, how much will she be charged? $108

48. $4 + 5x + 4 + 5x + 3y$; 49

50. RETAIL The table shows prices on children's clothing.

Shorts	Shirts	Tank Tops
\$7.99	\$8.99	\$6.99
\$5.99	\$4.99	\$2.99

a. Write three different expressions that represent 8 pairs of shorts and 8 tops. See margin.

b. Evaluate the three expressions in part **a** to find the costs of the 16 items. What do you notice about all the total costs?

c. If you buy 8 shorts and 8 tops, you receive a discount of 15%. Find the greatest and least amount of money you can spend on the 16 items at the sale.

50b. Sample answer: \$111.84; \$95.84; \$87.84; All totals have the same cent value.

50c. \$101.86; \$61.06

Study Guide and Intervention
CRM pp. 18–19 AL OL ELL

NAME ______ DATE ______ PERIOD ______

1-3 Study Guide and Intervention

Properties of Numbers

Identity and Equality Properties The identity and equality properties in the chart below can help you solve algebraic equations and evaluate mathematical expressions.

Additive Identity	For any number a, $a + 0 = a$.
Additive Inverse	For any number a, $a + (-a) = a$.
Multiplicative Identity	For any number a, $a \cdot 1 = a$.
Multiplicative Property of 0	For any number a, $a \cdot 0 = 0$.
Multiplicative Inverse Property	For every number , a, $b \neq 0$, there is exactly one number $\frac{b}{a}$ such that $\frac{a}{b} \cdot \frac{b}{a} = 1$.
Reflexive Property	For any number a, $a = a$.
Symmetric Property	For any numbers a and b, if $a = b$, then $b = a$.
Transitive Property	For any numbers a, b, and c, if $a = b$ and $b = c$, then $a = c$.
Substitution Property	If $a = b$, then a may be replaced by b in any expression.

Example Evaluate $24 \cdot 1 - 8 + 5(9 \div 3 - 3)$. Name the property used in each step.

$24 \cdot 1 - 8 + 5(9 \div 3 - 3) = 24 \cdot 1 - 8 + 5(3 - 3)$ Substitution; $9 \div 3 = 3$
$= 24 \cdot 1 - 8 + 5(0)$ Substitution; $3 - 3 = 0$
$= 24 - 8 + 5(0)$ Multiplicative Identity; $24 \cdot 1 = 24$
$= 24 - 8 + 0$ Multiplicative Property of Zero; $5(0) = 0$
$= 16 + 0$ Substitution; $24 - 8 = 16$
$= 16$ Additive Identity; $16 + 0 = 16$

Exercises

Evaluate each expression. Name the property used in each step.

1. $2\left[\frac{1}{4} + \left(\frac{1}{2}\right)^2\right]$
$= 2\left(\frac{1}{4} + \frac{1}{4}\right)$ Substitution
$= 2\left(\frac{1}{2}\right)$ Substitution
$= 1$ Mult. Inverse

2. $15 \cdot 1 - 9 + 2(15 \div 3 - 5)$
$= 15 \cdot 1 - 9 + 2(5 - 5)$ Substitution
$= 15 \cdot 1 - 9 + 2(0)$ Substitution
$= 15 \cdot 1 - 9 + 0$ Mult. Prop. Zero
$= 15 - 9 + 0$ Mult. Identity
$= 6 - 0$ Substitution
$= 6$ Substitution

3. $2(3 \cdot 5 \cdot 1 - 14) - 4 \cdot \frac{1}{4}$
$= 2(15 \cdot 1 - 14) - 4 \cdot \frac{1}{4}$ Subst.
$= 2(15 - 14) - 4 \cdot \frac{1}{4}$ Mult. Identity
$= 2(1) - 4 \cdot \frac{1}{4}$ Substitution
$= 2 - 4 \cdot \frac{1}{4}$ Mult. Identity
$= 2 - 1$ Mult. Inverse
$= 1$ Substitution

4. $18 \cdot 1 - 3 \cdot 2 + 2(6 \div 3 - 2)$
$= 18 \cdot 1 - 3 \cdot 2 + 2(2 - 2)$ Subst.
$= 18 \cdot 1 - 3 \cdot 2 + 2(0)$ Substitution
$= 18 - 3 \cdot 2 + 2(0)$ Mult. Identity
$= 18 - 6 + 2(0)$ Substitution
$= 18 - 6 + 0$ Mult. Prop. Zero
$= 12 + 0$ Substitution
$= 12$ Add. Identity

Chapter 1 18 Glencoe Algebra 1

Practice
CRM p. 21 AL OL BL ELL

NAME ______ DATE ______ PERIOD ______

1-3 Practice

Properties of Numbers

Evaluate each expression. Name the property used in each step.

1. $2 + 6(9 - 3^2) - 2$
$= 2 + 6(9 - 9) - 2$ Substitution
$= 2 + 6(0) - 2$ Substitution
$= 2 + 0 - 2$ Mult. Prop. of Zero
$= 2 - 2$ Additive Identity
$= 0$ Substitution

2. $5(14 - 39 \div 3) + 4 \cdot \frac{1}{4}$
$= 5(14 - 13) + 4 \cdot \frac{1}{4}$ Substitution
$= 5(1) + 4 \cdot \frac{1}{4}$ Substitution
$= 5 + 4 \cdot \frac{1}{4}$ Multiplicative Identity
$= 5 + 1$ Multiplicative Inverse
$= 6$ Substitution

Evaluate each expression using properties of numbers. Name the property used in each step.

3. $13 + 23 + 12 + 7$
$= (13 + 12) + (23 + 7)$ Commu. Prop.
$= 25 + 30$ Substitution
$= 55$ Substitution

4. $6 \cdot 0.7 \cdot 5$
$= (6 \cdot 5) \cdot (0.7)$ Assoc. Prop.
$= 30 \cdot 0.7$ Substitution
$= 21$ Substitution

5. **SALES** Althea paid \$5.00 each for two bracelets and later sold each for \$15.00. She paid \$8.00 each for three bracelets and sold each of them for \$9.00.
a. Write an expression that represents the profit Althea made. $2(15 - 5) + 3(9 - 8)$
b. Evaluate the expression. Name the property used in each step.
$2(15 - 5) + 3(9 - 8) = 2(10) + 3(1)$ Substitution
$= 20 + 3(1)$ Substitution
$= 20 + 3$ Multiplicative Identity
$= 23$ Substitution

6. **SCHOOL SUPPLIES** Kristen purchased two binders that cost \$1.25 each, two binders that cost \$4.75 each, two packages of paper that cost \$1.50 per package, four blue pens that cost \$1.15 each, and four pencils that cost \$.35 each.
a. Write an expression to represent the total cost of supplies before tax.
$2(1.25 + 4.75 + 1.50) + 4(1.15 + 0.35)$
b. What was the total cost of supplies before tax?
\$21.00

Lesson 1-3

Chapter 1 21 Glencoe Algebra 1

Word Problem Practice
CRM p. 22 AL OL BL ELL

NAME ______ DATE ______ PERIOD ______

1-3 Word Problem Practice

Properties of Numbers

1. **EXERCISE** Annika goes on a walk every day in order to get the exercise her doctor recommends. If she walks at a rate of 3 miles per hour for $\frac{1}{3}$ of an hour, then she will have walked $3 \times \frac{1}{3}$ miles. Evaluate the expression and name the property used.
1 mi; Multiplicative Inverse

2. **SCHOOL SUPPLIES** At a local school supply store, a highlighter costs \$1.25, a ballpoint pen costs \$0.80, and a spiral notebook costs \$2.75. Use mental math and the Associative Property of Addition to find the total cost if one of each item is purchased. \$4.80

3. **MENTAL MATH** The triangular banner has a base of 9 centimeters and a height of 6 centimeters. Using the formula for area of a triangle, the banner's area can be expressed as $\frac{1}{2} \times 9 \times 6$. Gabrielle finds it easier to write and evaluate $\left(\frac{1}{2} \times 6\right) \times 9$ to find the area. Is Gabrielle's expression equivalent to the area formula? Explain.

Yes; the Commutative and Associative Properties of Multiplication allow it to be rewritten.

4. **ANATOMY** The human body has 60 bones in the arms and hands, 84 bones in the upper body and head, and 62 bones in the legs and feet. Use the Associative Property to write and evaluate an expression that represents the total number of bones in the human body.
Sample answer: $(60 + 84) + 62 = 84 + (60 + 62) = 206$

5. **TOLL ROADS** Some toll highways assess tolls based on where a car entered and exited. The table below shows the highway tolls for a car entering and exiting at a variety of exits. Assume that the toll for the reverse direction is the same.

Entered	Exited	Toll
Exit 5	Exit 8	\$0.50
Exit 8	Exit 10	\$0.25
Exit 10	Exit 15	\$1.00
Exit 15	Exit 18	\$0.50
Exit 18	Exit 22	\$0.75

a. Running an errand, Julio travels from Exit 8 to Exit 5. What property would you use to determine the toll?
Symmetric Property of Equality

b. Gordon travels from home to work and back each day. He lives at Exit 15 on the toll road and works at Exit 22. Write and evaluate an expression to find his daily toll cost. What property or properties did you use?
$t = 2 \times (\$0.50 + \$0.75)$;
$t = \$2.50$; Substitution

Chapter 1 22 Glencoe Algebra 1

Enrichment
CRM p. 23 OL BL

NAME ______ DATE ______ PERIOD ______

1-3 Enrichment

Properties of Operations

Let's make up a new operation and denote it by ⊛, so that a ⊛ b means b^a.

2 ⊛ 3 = 3^2 = 9
(1 ⊛ 2) ⊛ 3 = 2^1 ⊛ 3 = 3^2 = 9

1. What number is represented by 2 ⊛ 3? $3^2 = 9$
2. What number is represented by 3 ⊛ 2? $2^3 = 8$
3. Does the operation ⊛ appear to be commutative? no
4. What number is represented by (2 ⊛ 1) ⊛ 3? 3
5. What number is represented by 2 ⊛ (1 ⊛ 3)? 9
6. Does the operation ⊛ appear to be associative? no

Let's make up another operation and denote it by ⊕, so that

$a \oplus b = (a + 1)(b + 1)$.

$3 \oplus 2 = (3 + 1)(2 + 1) = 4 \cdot 3 = 12$

(1 ⊕ … ⊕ 3 = (2 · 3) ⊕ 3 = … = 7 · 4 = …

Additional Answer

50a. Sample answer: $8(7.99) + 4(4.99) + 4(6.99)$; $8(5.99) + 4(8.99) + 4(2.99)$; $4(7.99) + 4(5.99) + 4(4.99) + 4(2.99)$

52c. The area of the rectangle is $x + 1 + 1 + x + 1 + 1 + x + 1 + 1 + x + 1 + 1$ or $4x + 8$. Therefore, $4(x + 2) = 4x + 8$.

53b. $\overline{AD} \cong \overline{AD}$ by the Reflexive Property. The Transitive Property shows that if $\overline{AB} \cong \overline{AC}$ and $\overline{AC} \cong \overline{DC}$, then $\overline{AB} \cong \overline{DC}$, and if $\overline{AB} \cong \overline{BD}$ and $\overline{AB} \cong \overline{AC}$, then $\overline{BD} \cong \overline{AC}$.

54. Sample answer: $5 = 3 + 2$ and $3 + 2 = 4 + 1$ so $5 = 4 + 1$; $5 + 7 = 8 + 4$, and $8 + 4 = 12$, so $5 + 7 = 12$.

57. Sometimes; when a number is subtracted by itself then it holds but otherwise it does not.

StudyTip

Proof A **proof** is a logical argument in which each statement you make is supported by a statement that is accepted as true.

51. GEOMETRY A regular octagon measures $(3x + 5)$ units on each side. What is the perimeter if $x = 2$? **88 units**

52. MULTIPLE REPRESENTATIONS You can use *algebra tiles* to model and explore algebraic expressions. The rectangular tile has an area of x, with dimensions 1 by x. The small square tile has an area of 1, with dimensions 1 by 1.

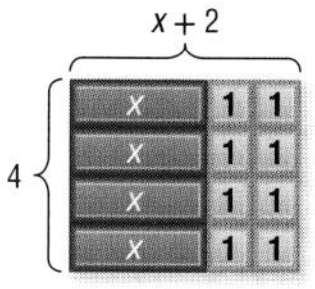

a. **CONCRETE** Make a rectangle with algebra tiles to model the expression $4(x + 2)$ as shown above. What are the dimensions of this rectangle? What is its area? **length: $x + 2$, width: 4; $4(x + 2)$**

b. **ANALYTICAL** What are the areas of the green region and of the yellow region? **4x; 8**

c. **VERBAL** Complete this statement: $4(x + 2) =$ __?__. Write a convincing argument to justify your statement.

53. GEOMETRY It is given that $\overline{AB} \cong \overline{CD}$, $\overline{AB} \cong \overline{BD}$, and $\overline{AB} \cong \overline{AC}$. Pedro wants to prove $\triangle ADB \cong \triangle ADC$. To do this, he must show that $\overline{AD} \cong \overline{AD}$, $\overline{AB} \cong \overline{DC}$ and $\overline{BD} \cong \overline{AC}$.

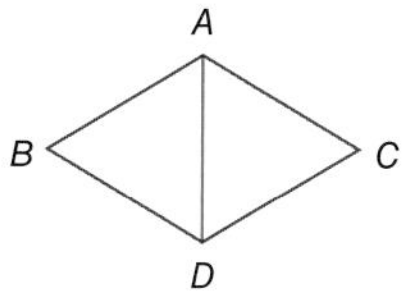

a. Copy the figure and label on your drawing that $\overline{AB} \cong \overline{CD}$, $\overline{AB} \cong \overline{BD}$, and $\overline{AB} \cong \overline{AC}$. **See margin.**

b. Explain how he can use the Reflexive and Transitive Properties to prove $\triangle ADB \cong \triangle ADC$.

c. If the length of $\overline{AC}$ is x cm, write an equation for the perimeter of the quadrilateral $ACDB$. $P = x + x + x + x$

H.O.T. Problems

Use Higher-Order Thinking Skills

54. OPEN ENDED Write two equations showing the Transitive Property of Equality. Justify your reasoning.

55. REASONING Explain why 0 has no multiplicative inverse. **Sample answer: You cannot divide by 0.**

56. REASONING The sum of any two whole numbers is always a whole number. So, the set of whole numbers {0, 1, 2, 3, 4, … } is said to be closed under addition. This is an example of the **Closure Property**. State whether each statement is *true* or *false*. If false, justify your reasoning.

a. The set of whole numbers is closed under subtraction. **False; $3 - 4 = -1$, which is not a whole number.**

b. The set of whole numbers is closed under multiplication. **true**

c. The set of whole numbers is closed under division. **False; $2 \div 3 = \frac{2}{3}$, which is not a whole number.**

57. CHALLENGE Does the Commutative Property *sometimes*, *always* or *never* hold for subtraction? Explain your reasoning.

58. REASONING Explain whether 1 can be an additive identity. Give an example to justify your answer. **No; $3 + 1 \neq 3$**

59. WHICH ONE DOESN'T BELONG? Identify the sentence that does not belong with the other three. Explain your reasoning. **See margin.**

$x + 12 = 12 + x$	$7h = h \cdot 7$	$1 + a = a + 1$	$(2j)k = 2(jk)$

60. WRITING IN MATH Determine whether the Commutative Property applies to division. Justify your answer. **See margin.**

Watch Out!

Preventing Errors Some students may have difficulty remembering the names of the properties in this lesson. Remind these students that they already know how to use the properties. Encourage them to think of word associations that will help them relate what they know to the correct names of the properties.

Tips for New Teachers

Reasoning Remind students to look for pairs of numbers that will make calculations easier when using the Commutative and Associative Properties.

Exercise Alert

Manipulatives Exercise 52 requires the use of algebra tiles.

Multiple Representations In Exercise 52, students use algebra tiles and algebraic expressions to discover how the Distributive Property applies to algebraic expressions.

Additional Answers

53a.

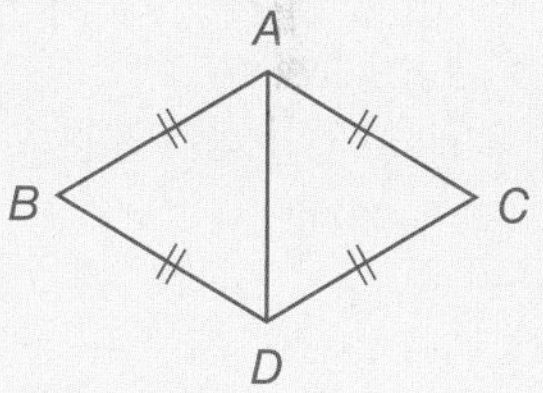

59. $(2j)k = 2(jk)$; The other three sentences illustrate the Commutative Property of Addition or Multiplication. This equation represents the Associative Property of Multiplication.

60. The Commutative Property does not apply to division. For $a \div b = b \div a$ to be true, a and b must be nonzero and equal or opposites.

Every effort is made to show **answers** on the reduced Student Edition page, or in the margin of the Teacher Edition.

4 ASSESS

Crystal Ball Ask students to write a brief statement on how they think the properties of identity and equality connect to the next lesson on the Distributive Property.

PSAE PRACTICE 7.11.03, 6.11.04, 6.11.10

61. A deck is shaped like a rectangle with a width of 12 feet and a length of 15 feet. What is the area of the deck? **D**

A 3 ft^2
B 27 ft^2
C 108 ft^2
D 180 ft^2

62. GEOMETRY A box in the shape of a rectangular prism has a volume of 56 cubic inches. If the length of each side is multiplied by 2, what will be the approximate volume of the box? **J**

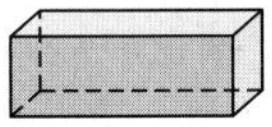

F 112 in^3 H 336 in^3
G 224 in^3 J 448 in^3

63. $27 \div 3 + (12 - 4) =$ **C**

A $\frac{-11}{5}$ C 17
B $\frac{27}{11}$ D 25

64. GRIDDED RESPONSE Ms. Beal had 1 bran muffin, 16 ounces of orange juice, 3 ounces of sunflower seeds, 2 slices of turkey, and half a cup of spinach. Find the total number of grams of protein she consumed. **39.5**

Protein Content

Food	Protein (g)
bran muffin (1)	3
orange juice (8 0z)	2
sunflower seeds (1 oz)	2
turkey (1 slice)	12
spinach (1 c)	5

Spiral Review

Evaluate each expression. (Lesson 1-2)

65. $3 \cdot 5 + 1 - 2$ **14**

66. $14 \div 2 \cdot 6 - 5^2$ **17**

67. $\frac{3 \cdot 9^2 - 3^2 \cdot 9}{3 \cdot 9}$ **6**

68. GEOMETRY Write an expression for the perimeter of the figure. (Lesson 1-1) **$10 + z$**

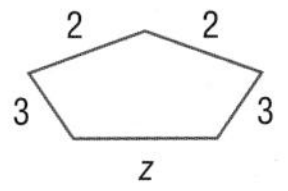

Find the perimeter and area of each figure. (Lessons 0-7 and 0-8)

69. a rectangle with length 5 feet and width 8 feet **26 ft; 40 ft^2**

70. a square with length 4.5 inches **18 in.; 20.25 in^2**

71. SURVEY Andrew took a survey of his friends to find out their favorite type of music. Of the 34 friends surveyed, 22 said they liked rock music the best. What percent like rock music the best? (Lesson 0-6) **about 64.7%**

Name the reciprocal of each number. (Lesson 0-5)

72. $\frac{6}{17}$ **$\frac{17}{6}$**

73. $\frac{2}{23}$ **$\frac{23}{2}$**

74. $3\frac{4}{5}$ **$\frac{5}{19}$**

Skills Review

Find each product. Express in simplest form. (Lesson 0-5)

75. $\frac{12}{15} \cdot \frac{3}{14}$ **$\frac{6}{35}$**

76. $\frac{5}{7} \cdot \left(-\frac{4}{5}\right)$ **$-\frac{4}{7}$**

77. $\frac{10}{11} \cdot \frac{21}{35}$ **$\frac{6}{11}$**

78. $\frac{63}{65} \cdot \frac{120}{126}$ **$\frac{12}{13}$**

79. $-\frac{4}{3} \cdot \left(-\frac{9}{2}\right)$ **6**

80. $\frac{1}{3} \cdot \frac{2}{5}$ **$\frac{2}{15}$**

Differentiated Instruction

OL BL

Extension Have students use a real-world situation to explain and demonstrate one of the properties of numbers. For example, Lee Ann pays \$8 + \$3 for a notebook and paper, and Rick pays \$9 + \$2 for a notebook and paper. If Lee Ann's total is equal to Rick's total and Rick paid \$11, then Lee Ann paid \$11 too. This illustrates the Transitive Property of Equality, which states that if $a = b$ and $b = c$, then $a = c$. In this case, $a = 8 + 3$, $b = 9 + 2$, and $c = 11$.

1-4 The Distributive Property

Then

You explored Associative and Commutative Properties. (Lesson 1-3)

Now

- Use the Distributive Property to evaluate expressions.
- Use the Distributive Property to simplify expressions.

IL Learning Standards

6.A.4 Identify and apply the associative, commutative, **distributive** and identity **properties of real numbers, including special numbers such as pi and square roots.**

New Vocabulary

like terms
simplest form
coefficient

IL Math Online

glencoe.com

- Extra Examples
- Personal Tutor
- Self-Check Quiz
- Homework Help
- Math in Motion

Why?

John burns approximately 420 Calories per hour by inline skating. The chart below shows the time he spent inline skating in one week.

Day	Mon	Tue	Wed	Thu	Fri	Sat	Sun
Time (h)	1	$\frac{1}{2}$	0	1	0	2	$2\frac{1}{2}$

To determine the total number of Calories that he burned inline skating that week, you can use the Distributive Property.

Evaluate Expressions There are two methods you could use to calculate the number of Calories John burned inline skating. You could find the total time spent inline skating and then multiply by the Calories burned per hour. Or you could find the number of Calories burned each day and then add to find the total.

Method 1 Rate Times Total Time

$$420\left(1 + \frac{1}{2} + 1 + 2 + 2\frac{1}{2}\right)$$
$$= 420(7)$$
$$= 2940$$

Method 2 Sum of Daily Calories Burned

$$420(1) + 420\left(\frac{1}{2}\right) + 420(1) + 420(2) + 420\left(2\frac{1}{2}\right)$$
$$= 420 + 210 + 420 + 840 + 1050$$
$$= 2940$$

Either method gives the same total of 2940 Calories burned. This is an example of the **Distributive Property**.

Key Concept For Your FOLDABLE

Distributive Property

Symbol For any numbers a, b, and c,
$a(b + c) = ab + ac$ and $(b + c)a = ba + ca$ and
$a(b - c) = ab - ac$ and $(b - c)a = ba - ca$.

Examples $3(2 + 5) = 3 \cdot 2 + 3 \cdot 5$ $4(9 - 7) = 4 \cdot 9 - 4 \cdot 7$
$3(7) = 6 + 15$ $4(2) = 36 - 28$
$21 = 21$ $8 = 8$

Math *in Motion*, BrainPOP® glencoe.com

The Symmetric Property of Equality allows the Distributive Property to be written as follows.

If $a(b + c) = ab + ac$, then $ab + ac = a(b + c)$.

1-4 Lesson Notes

1 FOCUS

Vertical Alignment

Before Lesson 1-4
Explore Associative and Commutative Properties.

Lesson 1-4
Use the Distributive Property to evaluate expressions.
Use the Distributive Property to simplify expressions.

After Lesson 1-4
Transform and solve equations.

2 TEACH

Scaffolding Questions

Have students read the *Why?* section of the lesson.

Ask:

- How can you represent the time John spent inline skating that week? $1 + \frac{1}{2} + 0 + 1 + 0 + 2 + 2\frac{1}{2}$

(continued on the next page)

Scaffolding Questions give direction and momentum to the lesson, clarify its purpose, and keep students on task.

Lesson 1-4 Resources

Resource	Approaching-Level	On-Level	Beyond-Level	English Learners
Teacher Edition	• Differentiated Instruction, p. 25	• Differentiated Instruction, p. 25	• Differentiated Instruction, p. 29	
Chapter Resource Masters	• Study Guide and Intervention, pp. 24–25 • Skills Practice, p. 26 • Practice, p. 27 • Word Problem Practice, p. 28	• Study Guide and Intervention, pp. 24–25 • Skills Practice, p. 26 • Practice, p. 27 • Word Problem Practice, p. 28 • Enrichment, p. 29	• Practice, p. 27 • Word Problem Practice, p. 28 • Enrichment, p. 29	• Study Guide and Intervention, pp. 24–25 • Skills Practice, p. 26 • Practice, p. 27
Transparencies	• 5-Minute Check Transparency 1-4	• 5-Minute Check Transparency 1-4	• 5-Minute Check Transparency 1-4	• 5-Minute Check Transparency 1-4
Other	• Study Notebook • Teaching Algebra with Manipulatives	• Study Notebook • Teaching Algebra with Manipulatives	• Study Notebook	• Study Notebook • Teaching Algebra with Manipulatives

- By what would you multiply the quantity to find the total number of Calories burned? 420
- How can you represent the total number of Calories burned as one quantity? $420\left(1+\frac{1}{2}+0+1+0+2+2\frac{1}{2}\right)$

Evaluate Expressions

Examples 1 and 2 show how to use the Distributive Property to rewrite and evaluate expressions.

Formative Assessment

Use the Check Your Progress exercises after each Example to determine students' understanding of concepts.

Additional Examples

1 **FITNESS** Julio walks 5 days a week. He walks at a fast rate for 7 minutes and cools down for 2 minutes. Use the Distributive Property to write and evaluate an expression that determines the total number of minutes Julio walks.

$5(7+2)$
$= 5(7) + 5(2)$ Distributive Prop.
$= 35 + 10$ Multiply.
$= 45$ Add.

2 Use the Distributive Property to rewrite $12 \cdot 82$. Then evaluate. $(10+2)82 = 820 + 164$ or 984

Additional Examples also in Interactive Classroom PowerPoint® Presentations

IWB INTERACTIVE WHITEBOARD READY

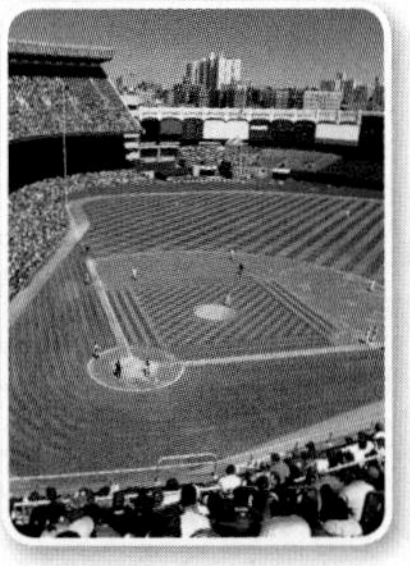

Real-World Link

The record attendance for a single baseball game was set in 1959. There were 92,706 spectators at a game between the Los Angeles Dodgers and the Chicago White Sox.

Source: *Baseball Almanac*

Real-World EXAMPLE 1 Distribute Over Addition

SPORTS A group of 7 adults and 6 children are going to a University of South Florida Bulls baseball game. Use the Distributive Property to write and evaluate an expression for the total ticket cost.

USF Bulls Baseball Tickets

Ticket	Cost ($)
Adult Single Game	5
Children Single Game (12 and under)	3
Groups of 10 or more Single Game	2
Senior Single Game (65 and over)	3

Source: USF

Understand You need to find the cost of each ticket and then find the total cost.

Plan 7 + 6 or 13 people are going to the game, so the tickets are $2 each.

Solve Write an expression that shows the product of the cost of each ticket and the sum of adult tickets and children's tickets.

$2(7+6) = 2(7) + 2(6)$ **Distributive Property**
$= 14 + 12$ **Multiply.**
$= 26$ **Add.**

The total cost is $26.

Check The total number of tickets needed is 13 and they cost $2 each. Multiply 13 by 2 to get 26. Therefore, the total cost of tickets is $26.

Check Your Progress

1. **SPORTS** A group of 3 adults, an 11-year old, and 2 children under 10 years old are going to a baseball game. Write and evaluate an expression to determine the cost of tickets for the group. $5(3) + 3(2+1) = 15 + 9$ or $24

Personal Tutor glencoe.com

You can use the Distributive Property to make mental math easier.

EXAMPLE 2 Mental Math

Use the Distributive Property to rewrite $7 \cdot 49$. Then evaluate.

$7 \cdot 49 = 7(50-1)$ **Think: $49 = 50 - 1$**
$= 7(50) - 7(1)$ **Distributive Property**
$= 350 - 7$ **Multiply.**
$= 343$ **Subtract.**

Check Your Progress

Use the Distributive Property to rewrite each expression. Then evaluate.

2A. $304(15)$ $(300+4)(15)$; 4560

2B. $44 \cdot 2\frac{1}{2}$ $(44)\left(2+\frac{1}{2}\right)$; 110

2C. $210(5)$ $(200+10)5$; 1050

2D. $52(17)$ $(50+2)17$; 884

Personal Tutor glencoe.com

Simplify Expressions You can use algebra tiles to investigate how the Distributive Property relates to algebraic expressions.

Focus on Mathematical Content

Distributive Property Multiplication can be distributed over addition or subtraction. If a, b, and c are any numbers, then $a(b \pm c) = a(b) \pm a(c)$. The variable a on the left side of the equation is distributed over the addition or subtraction of b and c.

TEACH with TECH

INTERACTIVE WHITEBOARD On the board, work through several examples using the Distributive Property. Save the examples and the work to a file, and send it to your students so that they can use it for reference outside of class.

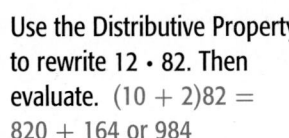

Tips for New Teachers

Mental Math Mental calculations with the Distributive Property prepare students for multiplying algebraic expressions in later chapters of this text. Consider having students complete additional practice with this skill.

Problem-SolvingTip

Make a Model It can be helpful to visualize a problem using algebra tiles or folded paper.

The rectangle at the right has 3 x-tiles and 6 1-tiles. The area of the rectangle is $x + 1 + 1 + x + 1 + 1 + x + 1 + 1$ or $3x + 6$. Therefore, $3(x + 2) = 3x + 6$.

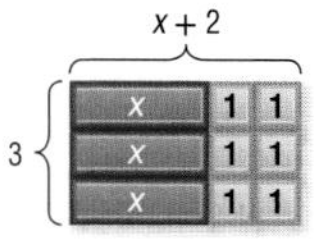

EXAMPLE 3 Algebraic Expressions

Rewrite each expression using the Distributive Property. Then simplify.

a. $7(3w - 5)$

$7(3w - 5) = 7 \cdot 3w - 7 \cdot 5$ — **Distributive Property**

$= 21w - 35$ — **Multiply.**

b. $(6v^2 + v - 3)4$

$(6v^2 + v - 3)4 = 6v^2(4) + v(4) - 3(4)$ — **Distributive Property**

$= 24v^2 + 4v - 12$ — **Multiply.**

Check Your Progress

3A. $(8 + 4n)2$ $8(2) + 4n(2)$; $16 + 8n$ **3B.** $-6(r + 3g - t)$

3C. $(2 - 5q)(-3)$ **3D.** $-4(-8 - 3m)$

3B. $-6(r) + (-6)(3g) + (-6)(-t)$; $-6r - 18g + 6t$
3C. $2(-3) + (-5q)(-3)$; $-6 + 15q$
3D. $(-4)(-8) + (-4)(-3m)$; $32 + 12m$

Personal Tutor glencoe.com

Review Vocabulary

term a number, a variable, or a product or quotient of numbers and variables (Lesson 1-1)

Like terms are terms that contain the same variables, with corresponding variables having the same power.

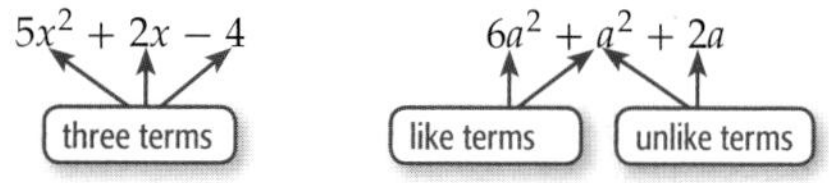

The Distributive Property and the properties of equality can be used to show that $4k + 8k = 12k$. In this expression, $4k$ and $8k$ are like terms.

$4k + 8k = (4 + 8)k$ — **Distributive Property**

$= 12k$ — **Substitution**

An expression is in **simplest form** when it contains no like terms or parentheses.

EXAMPLE 4 Combine Like Terms

a. Simplify $17u + 25u$.

$17u + 25u = (17 + 25)u$ — **Distributive Property**

$= 42u$ — **Substitution**

b. Simplify $6t^2 + 3t - t$.

$6t^2 + 3t - t = 6t^2 + (3 - 1)t$ — **Distributive Property**

$= 6t^2 + 2t$ — **Substitution**

Check Your Progress

Simplify each expression. If not possible, write *simplified*.

4A. $6n - 4n$ $2n$ **4B.** $b^2 + 13b + 13$ simplified

4C. $4y^3 + 2y - 8y + 5$ $4y^3 - 6y + 5$ **4D.** $7a + 4 - 6a^2 - 2a$ $-6a^2 + 5a + 4$

Personal Tutor glencoe.com

Simplify Expressions

Example 3 shows how to use the Distributive Property to rewrite expressions and then simplify the expressions. **Example 4** shows how to use the Distributive Property to combine like terms and then simplify the expressions. **Example 5** shows how to write and simplify an expression using properties.

Additional Examples

3 Rewrite each expression using the Distributive Property. Then simplify.

a. $12(y + 3)$

$12(y + 3)$

$= 12 \cdot y + 12 \cdot 3$ — Distributive Prop.

$= 12y + 36$ — Multiply.

b. $4(y^2 + 8y + 2)$

$4(y^2 + 8y + 2)$

$= 4(y^2) + 4(8y) + 4(2)$ — Distributive Prop.

$= 4y^2 + 32y + 8$ — Multiply.

4 **a.** Simplify $17a + 21a$. $38a$

b. Simplify $12b^2 - 8b^2 + 6b$. $4b^2 + 6b$

Differentiated Instruction

AL OL

If students have difficulty using the Distributive Property,

Then have them use algebra tiles to find products for problems such as $2(x + 1)$ or $5(x + 2)$. Have students work in pairs. Point out that one of the quantities being multiplied goes on the left side of the mat, and the other goes on the top. Using algebra tiles will help students visualize the Distributive Property.

Lesson 1-4 The Distributive Property 25

Additional Example

5 Use the expression *six times the sum of x and y increased by four times the difference of 5x and y.*

a. Write an algebraic expression for the verbal expression.
$6(x + y) + 4(5x - y)$

b. Simplify the expression and indicate the properties used.
$= 6(x) + 6(y) + 4(5x) - 4(y)$ Distributive Property
$= 6x + 6y + 20x - 4y$ Multiply.
$= 6x + 20x + 6y - 4y$ Commutative (+)
$= (6 + 20)x + (6 - 4)y$ Distributive Property
$= 26x + 2y$ Substitution

Watch Out!

Preventing Errors To make it easier for students to identify the coefficient of expressions such as $\frac{x^2}{3}$, remind them that since x^2 is in the numerator, they can rewrite the expression as $\frac{1}{3}x^2$. Write the following on the board for clarification.

$$\frac{1}{3} \cdot x^2 = \frac{1}{3} \cdot \frac{x^2}{1} = \frac{x^2}{3}$$

Additional Answers (Check Your Progress)

5A. $5(q^2 - r) + 8(3q + 2r)$

5B. $= 5(q^2) + 5(-r) + 8(3q) + 8(2r)$ Distributive Property
$= 5q^2 + (-5r) + 24q + 16r$ Multiply.
$= 5q^2 + 24q + 16r + (-5r)$ Commutative (+)
$= 5q^2 + 24q + [16 + (-5)]r$ Distributive Property
$= 5q^2 + 24q + 11r$ Substitution

EXAMPLE 5 Write and Simplify Expressions

Use the expression *twice the difference of 3x and y increased by five times the sum of x and 2y.*

a. Write an algebraic expression for the verbal expression.

Words	twice the difference of 3x and y	increased by	five times the sum of x and 2y
Variables	Let x and y represent the numbers.		
Expression	$2(3x - y)$	+	$5(x + 2y)$

b. Simplify the expression, and indicate the properties used.

$2(3x - y) + 5(x + 2y) = 2(3x) - 2(y) + 5(x) + 5(2y)$ **Distributive Property**
$= 6x - 2y + 5x + 10y$ **Multiply.**
$= 6x + 5x - 2y + 10y$ **Commutative (+)**
$= (6 + 5)x + (-2 + 10)y$ **Distributive Property**
$= 11x + 8y$ **Substitution**

Check Your Progress **5A, 5B. See margin.**

5. Write an algebraic expression *5 times the difference of q squared and r plus 8 times the sum of 3q and 2r.*

A. Write an algebraic expression for the verbal expression.

B. Simplify the expression, and indicate the properties used.

Personal Tutor glencoe.com

The **coefficient** of a term is the numerical factor. For example, in $6ab$, the coefficient is 6, and in $\frac{x^2}{3}$, the coefficient is $\frac{1}{3}$. In the term y, the coefficient is 1 since $1 \cdot y = y$ by the Multiplicative Identity Property.

StudyTip

Like Terms *Like terms* could be defined as terms with the same variables to the same powers.

Concept Summary

For Your FOLDABLE

Properties of Numbers

The following properties are true for any numbers *a*, *b*, and *c*.

Properties	Addition	Multiplication
Commutative	$a + b = b + a$	$ab = ba$
Associative	$(a + b) + c = a + (b + c)$	$(ab)c = a(bc)$
Identity	0 is the identity. $a + 0 = 0 + a = a$	1 is the identity. $a \cdot 1 = 1 \cdot a = a$
Zero	—	$a \cdot 0 = 0 \cdot a = 0$
Distributive	$a(b + c) = ab + ac$ and $(b + c)a = ba + ca$	
Substitution	If $a = b$, then a may be substituted for b.	

Check Your Understanding

Example 1 p. 24

1. **PILOT** A pilot at an air show charges \$25 per passenger for rides. If 12 adults and 15 children ride in one day, write and evaluate an expression to describe the situation. **25(12 + 15); \$675**

Example 2 p. 24

Use the Distributive Property to rewrite each expression. Then evaluate.

2. 14(51) **14(50 + 1); 714**
3. $6\frac{1}{9}(9)$ **$\left(6 + \frac{1}{9}\right)9$; 55**

Example 3 p. 25

Use the Distributive Property to rewrite each expression. Then simplify.

4. $2(4 + t)$ **$2(4) + 2(t)$; $8 + 2t$**
5. $(g - 9)5$ **$g(5) + (-9)(5)$; $5g - 45$**

Example 4 p. 25

Simplify each expression. If not possible, write *simplified*.

6. $15m + m$ **$16m$**
7. $3x^3 + 5y^3 + 14$ **simplified**
8. $(5m + 2m)10$ **$70m$**

Example 5 p. 26

Write an algebraic expression for each verbal expression. Then simplify, indicating the properties used.

9. 4 times the sum of 2 times x and six
10. one half of 4 times y plus the quantity of y and 3

9. $4(2x + 6)$
$= 4(2x) + 4(6)$ Distributive Property
$= 8x + 24$ Multiply.

10. $\frac{1}{2}(4y) + (y + 3)$
$= 2y + y + 3$ Multiply.
$= 3y + 3$ Simplify.

Practice and Problem Solving

(●) = **Step-by-Step Solutions** begin on page R12. **Extra Practice** begins on page 815.

Example 1 p. 24

11. **TIME MANAGEMENT** Margo uses dots to track her activities on a calendar. Red dots represent homework, yellow dots represent work, and green dots represent track practice. In a typical week, she uses 5 red dots, 3 yellow dots, and 4 green dots. How many activities does Margo do in 4 weeks? **48 activities**

12. **BLOOD SUPPLY** The Red Cross is holding blood drives in two locations. In one day, Center 1 collected 715 pints and Center 2 collected 1035 pints. Write and evaluate an expression to estimate the total number of pints of blood donated over a 3-day period. **3(715 + 1035); 5250 pt**

Example 2 p. 24

Use the Distributive Property to rewrite each expression. Then evaluate.

13. $(4 + 5)6$ **$6(4) + 6(5)$; 54**
14. $7(13 + 12)$
15. $6(6 - 1)$ **$6(6) - 6(1)$; 30**
16. $(3 + 8)15$
17. $14(8 - 5)$
18. $(9 - 4)19$
19. $4(7 - 2)$
20. $7(2 + 1)$
21. $7 \cdot 497$
22. 6(525)
23. $36 \cdot 3\frac{1}{4}$
24. $\left(4\frac{2}{7}\right)21$

Example 3 p. 25

Use the Distributive Property to rewrite each expression. Then simplify.

25. $2(x + 4)$ **$2(x) + 2(4)$; $2x + 8$**
26. $(5 + n)3$ **$5(3) + n(3)$; $15 + 3n$**
27. $(4 - 3m)8$ **$4(8) + (-3m)(8)$; $32 - 24m$**
28. $-3(2x - 6)$ **$-3(2x) + (-3)(-6)$; $-6x + 18$**

Example 4 p. 25

Simplify each expression. If not possible, write *simplified*.

29. $13r + 5r$ **$18r$**
30. $3x^3 - 2x^2$ **simplified**
31. $7m + 7 - 5m$ **$2m + 7$**
32. $5z^2 + 3z + 8z^2$
33. $(2 - 4n)17$ **$34 - 68n$**
34. $11(4d + 6)$ **$44d + 66$**
35. $7m + 2m + 5p + 4m$
36. $3x + 7(3x + 4)$ **$24x + 28$**
37. $4(fg + 3g) + 5g$

Example 5 p. 26

Write an algebraic expression for each verbal expression. Then simplify, indicating the properties used. 38–39. See margin.

38. the product of 5 and m squared, increased by the sum of the square of m and 5
39. 7 times the sum of a squared and b minus 4 times the sum of a squared and b

14. $7(13) + 7(12)$; 175
16. $3(15) + 8(15)$; 165
17. $14(8) - 14(5)$; 42
18. $19(9) - 19(4)$; 95
19. $4(7) - 4(2)$; 20
20. $7(2) + 7(1)$; 21
21. $7(500 - 3)$; 3479
22. $6(500 + 25)$; 3150
23. $36\left(3 + \frac{1}{4}\right)$; 117
24. $\left(4 + \frac{2}{7}\right)21$; 90
32. $13z^2 + 3z$
35. $13m + 5p$
37. $4fg + 17g$

3 PRACTICE

Formative Assessment

Use Exercises 1–10 to check for understanding.

Use the chart at the bottom of this page to customize assignments for your students.

Tips for New Teachers

Some students are confused when an expression is presented with the parentheses first, such as $(4 - 3)6$. Suggest that students rewrite the expression as $6(4 - 3)$ to avoid confusion.

Exercise Alert

Manipulatives Exercise 55 requires students to use algebra tiles.

Additional Answers

38. $5m^2 + (m^2 + 5)$
$= (5m^2 + m^2) + 5$ Associative (+)
$= 6m^2 + 5$ Substitution

39. $7(a^2 + b) - 4(a^2 + b)$
$= 7a^2 + 7b - 4a^2 - 4b$ Substitution
$= 7a^2 - 4a^2 + 7b - 4b$ Commutative (+)
$= (7 - 4)a^2 + (7 - 4)b$ Distributive Property
$= 3a^2 + 3b$ Substitution

Differentiated Homework Options

Level	Assignment	Two-Day Option	
AL Basic	11–47, 57–77	11–47 odd, 60–63	12–46 even, 57–59, 64–70
OL Core	11–47 odd, 48, 49–55 odd, 57–77	11–47, 60–63	48–55, 57–59, 64–77
BL Advanced	48–71, (optional: 72–77)		

Study Guide and Intervention
CRM pp. 24–25 AL OL ELL

NAME ________ DATE ________ PERIOD ________

1-4 Study Guide and Intervention

The Distributive Property

Evaluate Expressions The Distributive Property can be used to help evaluate expressions.

Distributive Property	For any numbers a, b, and c, a(b + c) = ab + ac and (b + c)a = ba + ca and a(b − c) = ab − ac and (b − c)a = ba − ca.

Example 1 Use the Distributive Property to rewrite 6(8 + 10). Then evaluate.

$6(8 + 10) = 6 \cdot 8 + 6 \cdot 10$ Distributive Property
$= 48 + 60$ Multiply.
$= 108$ Add.

Example 2 Use the Distributive Property to rewrite $-2(3x^2 + 5x + 1)$. Then simplify.

$-2(3x^2 + 5x + 1) = -2(3x^2) + (-2)(5x) + (-2)(1)$ Distributive Property
$= -6x^2 + (-10x) + (-2)$ Multiply.
$= -6x^2 - 10x - 2$ Simplify.

Exercises

Use the Distributive Property to rewrite each expression. Then evaluate.

1. 20(31) **620**
2. $12 \cdot 4\frac{1}{2}$ **54**
3. 5(311) **1555**
4. $5(4x - 9)$ **$20x - 45$**
5. $3(8 - 2x)$ **$24 - 6x$**
6. $12\left(6 - \frac{1}{2}x\right)$ **$72 - 6x$**
7. $12\left(2 + \frac{1}{2}x\right)$ **$24 + 6x$**
8. $\frac{1}{4}(12 - 4t)$ **$3 - t$**
9. $3(2x - y)$ **$6x - 3y$**
10. $2(3x + 2y - z)$ **$6x + 4y - 2z$**
11. $(x - 2)y$ **$xy - 2y$**
12. $2(3a - 2b + c)$ **$6a - 4b + 2c$**
13. $\frac{1}{4}(16x - 12y + 4z)$ **$4x - 3y + z$**
14. $(2 - 3x + x^2)3$ **$6 - 9x + 3x^2$**
15. $-2(2x^2 + 3x + 1)$ **$-4x^2 - 6x - 2$**

Practice
CRM p. 27 AL OL BL ELL

NAME ________ DATE ________ PERIOD ________

1-4 Practice

The Distributive Property

Use the Distributive Property to rewrite each expression. Then evaluate.

1. $9(7 + 8)$ **$9 \cdot 7 + 9 \cdot 8$; 135**
2. $7(6 - 4)$ **$7 \cdot 6 - 7 \cdot 4$; 14**
3. $(4 + 6)11$ **$4 \cdot 11 + 6 \cdot 11$; 110**
4. $9 \cdot 499$ **$9(500 - 1)$; 4491**
5. $7 \cdot 110$ **$7(100 + 10)$; 770**
6. $16\left(4\frac{1}{4}\right)$ **$16\left(4 + \frac{1}{4}\right)$; 68**

Use the Distributive property to rewrite each expression. Then simplify.

7. $(9 - p)3$ **$9 \cdot 3 - p \cdot 3$; $27 - 3p$**
8. $(5y - 3)7$ **$5y \cdot 7 - 3 \cdot 7$; $35y - 21$**
9. $15\left(f + \frac{1}{3}\right)$ **$15 \cdot f + 15 \cdot \frac{1}{3}$; $15f + 5$**
10. $16(3b - 0.25)$ **$16 \cdot 3b - 16 \cdot 0.25$; $48b - 4$**
11. $m(n + 4)$ **$m \cdot n + m \cdot 4$; $mn + 4m$**
12. $(c - 4)d$ **$c \cdot d - 4 \cdot d$; $cd - 4d$**

Simplify each expression. If not possible, write *simplified*.

13. $w + 14w - 6w$ **$9w$**
14. $3(5 + 6h)$ **$15 + 18h$**
15. $12b^2 + 9b^2$ **$21b^2$**
16. $25t^3 - 17t^3$ **$8t^3$**
17. $3a^2 + 6a + 2b^2$ **simplified**
18. $4(6p + 2q - 2p)$ **$16p + 8q$**

Write an algebraic expression for each verbal expression. Then simplify, indicating the properties used.

19. 4 times the difference of *f* squared and *g*, increased by the sum of *f* squared and 2*g*
$= 4(f^2 - g) + (f^2 + 2g)$
$= 4f^2 - 4g + f^2 + 2g$ Distributive Property
$= 5f^2 - 2g$ Substitution

20. 3 times the sum of *x* and *y* squared plus 5 times the difference of 2*x* and *y*
$= 3(x + y^2) + 5(2x - y)$
$= 3x + 3y^2 + 10x - 5y$ Distributive Property
$= 3y^2 - 2y + 10x$ Substitution

21. **DINING OUT** The Ross family recently dined at an Italian restaurant. Each of the four family members ordered a pasta dish that cost \$11.50, a drink that cost \$1.50, and dessert that cost \$2.75.

a. Write an expression that could be used to calculate the cost of the Ross' dinner before adding tax and a tip. **$4(11.5 + 1.5 + 2.75)$**

b. What was the cost of dining out for the Ross family? **\$63.00**

Lesson 1-4

Word Problem Practice
CRM p. 28 AL OL BL ELL

NAME ________ DATE ________ PERIOD ________

1-4 Word Problem Practice

The Distributive Property

1. **OPERA** Mr. Delong's drama class is planning a field trip to see Mozart's famous opera *Don Giovanni*. Tickets cost \$39 each, and there are 23 students and 2 teachers going on the field trip. Write and evaluate an expression to find the group's total ticket cost.
$39(23 + 2) = \$975$

2. **SALARY** The median salary for an engineer in the United States in 2007 is \$55,000. The median salary for a computer programmer is \$52,000. Write and evaluate an expression to estimate the total cost of salary for a business to hire an engineer and a programmer for 5 years.
$= 5(55{,}000 + 52{,}000)$
$= \$535{,}000$

3. **COSTUMES** Isabella's ballet class is performing a spring recital for which they need butterfly costumes. Each butterfly costume is made from $3\frac{3}{5}$ yards of fabric. Use the Distributive Property to find the number of yards of fabric needed for 5 costumes. (*Hint*: a mixed number can be written as the sum of an integer and a fraction.)
$5\left(3\frac{3}{5}\right) = 5\left(3 + \frac{3}{5}\right) = 5(3) + 5\left(\frac{3}{5}\right)$
$= 15 + 3 = 18$

4. **FENCES** Demonstrate the Distributive Property by writing two equivalent expressions to represent the perimeter of the fenced dog pen below.
$2n + 2m$ and $2(n + m)$

Dog Pen (sides *n* and *m*)

5. **MENTAL MATH** During a math facts speed contest, Jamal calculated the following expression faster than anyone else in his class.
197×4
When classmates asked him how he was able to answer so quickly, he told them he used the Distributive Property to think of the problem differently. Write and evaluate an expression using the Distributive Property that would help Jamal perform the calculation quickly.
$4(200 - 3) = 800 - 12 = 788$

6. **INVESTMENTS** Letisha and Noel each opened a checking account, a savings account, and a college fund. The chart below shows the amounts that they deposited into each account.

	Checking	Savings	College
Letisha	\$125	\$75	\$50
Noel	\$250	\$50	\$50

a. If Noel used only \$50 bills when he deposited the money to open his accounts, how many \$50 bills did he deposit? **7 \$50 bills**

b. If all accounts earn 1.5% interest per year and no further deposits are made, how much interest will Letisha have earned one year after her accounts were opened? **\$3.75**

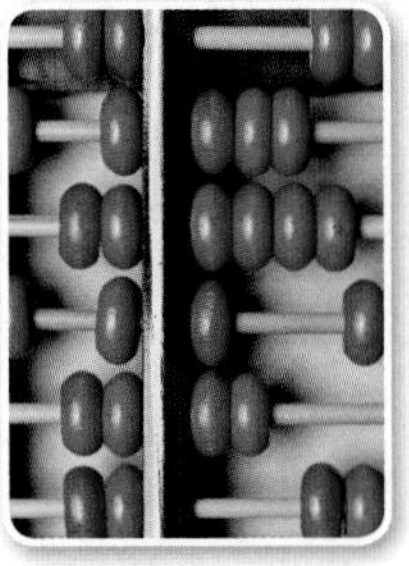

Math History Link

Kambei Mori (c. 1600–1628) Kambei Mori was a Japanese scholar who popularized the abacus. He changed the focus of mathematics from philosophy to computation.

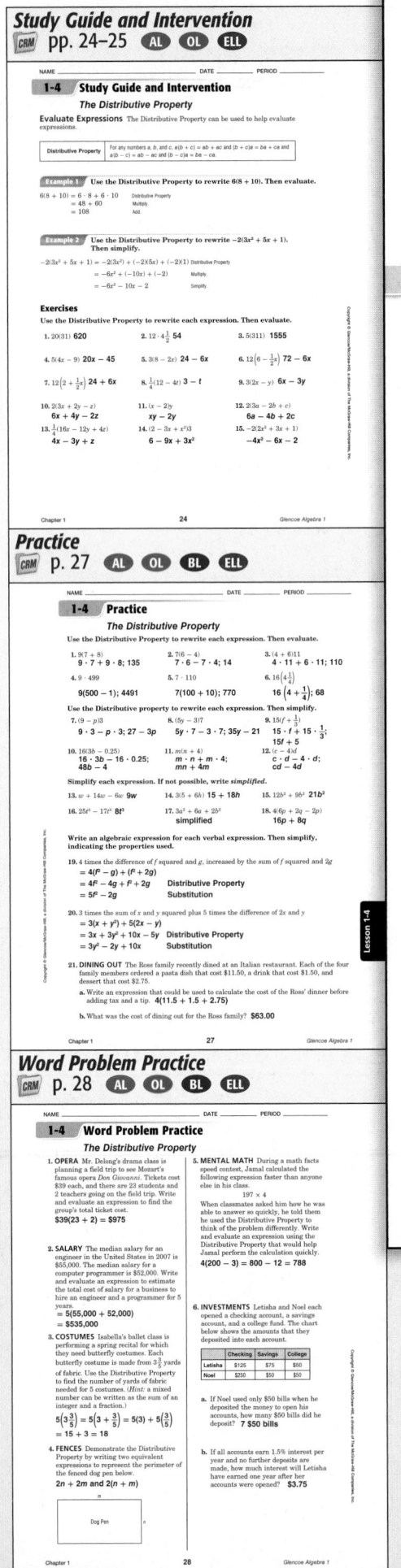

40. **GEOMETRY** Find the perimeter of an isosceles triangle with side lengths of $5 + x$, $5 + x$, and xy. Write in simplest form. **$xy + 10 + 2x$ units**

41. **GEOMETRY** A regular hexagon measures $3x + 5$ units on each side. What is the perimeter in simplest form? **$18x + 30$ units**

Simplify each expression. **43. $14m + 11g$ 44. $8a^2 + 4a$**

42. $6x + 4y + 5x$ **$11x + 4y$**
43. $3m + 5g + 6g + 11m$
44. $4a + 5a^2 + 2a^2 + a^2$
45. $5k + 3k^3 + 7k + 9k^3$ **$12k^3 + 12k$**
46. $6d + 4(3d + 5)$ **$18d + 20$**
47. $2(6x + 4) + 7x$ **$19x + 8$**

48. **FOOD** Kenji is picking up take-out food for his study group.

B a. Write and evaluate an expression to find the total cost of four sandwiches, three soups, three salads, and five drinks. **$4(2.49) + 3(1.29) + 3(0.99) + 5(1.49)$; \$24.25**

b. How much would it cost if Kenji bought four of each item on the menu? **\$25.04**

Menu	
Item	**Cost (\$)**
sandwich	2.49
cup of soup	1.29
side salad	0.99
drink	1.49

Use the Distributive Property to rewrite each expression. Then simplify.

49. $\left(\frac{1}{3} - 2b\right)27$ **$9 - 54b$**
50. $4(8p + 4q - 7r)$ **$32p + 16q - 28r$**
51. $6(2c - cd^2 + d)$ **$12c - 6cd^2 + 6d$**

Simplify each expression. If not possible, write *simplified*.

52. $6x^2 + 14x - 9x$ **$6x^2 + 5x$**
53. $4y^3 + 3y^3 + y^4$ **$7y^3 + y^4$**
54. $a + \frac{a}{5} + \frac{2}{5}a$ **$\frac{8}{5}a$**

55. **MULTIPLE REPRESENTATIONS** The area of the model is $2(x - 4)$ or $2x - 8$. The expression $2(x - 4)$ is in *factored form*.

C

	x	−1	−1	−1	−1
2	x	−1	−1	−1	−1

(top labels: x, −4)

a. **GEOMETRIC** Use algebra tiles to form a rectangle with area $2x + 6$. Use the result to write $2x + 6$ in factored form. **$2(x + 3)$**

b. **TABULAR** Use algebra tiles to form rectangles to represent each area in the table. Record the factored form of each expression.

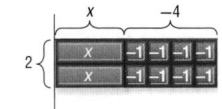

Area	Factored Form
$2x + 6$	**$2(x + 3)$**
$3x + 3$	**$3(x + 1)$**
$3x - 12$	**$3(x - 4)$**
$5x + 10$	**$5(x + 2)$**

c. **VERBAL** Explain how you could find the factored form of an expression. **Divide each term of the expression by the same number. Then write the expression as a product.**

H.O.T. Problems
Use Higher-Order Thinking Skills

56. **CHALLENGE** Use the Distributive Property to simplify $6x^2[(3x - 4) + (4x + 2)]$. **$42x^3 - 12x^2$**

57. **REASONING** Should the Distributive Property be a property of multiplication, addition, or both? Explain your answer.

58. **OPEN ENDED** Write a real-life example in which the Distributive Property would be useful. Write an expression that demonstrates the example.

59. **WRITING IN MATH** Use the data about skating on page 23 to explain how the Distributive Property can be used to calculate quickly. Also, compare the two methods of finding the total Calories burned.

57. Both; It should be considered a property of both. Both operations are used in $a(b + c) = ab + ac$.

58. Sample answer: A group goes to a concert at which the admission is \$25 for adults and \$16 for children. There are 4 adults and 4 children going to the concert. What is the total admission? $4(25 + 16)$

59. You can use the Distributive Property to calculate quickly by expressing any number as a sum or difference of a more convenient number. Answers should include the following: Both methods result in the correct answer. In one method you multiply then add, and in the other you add then multiply.

Enrichment
CRM p. 29 OL BL

NAME ________ DATE ________ PERIOD ________

1-4 Enrichment

The Maya

The Maya were a Native American people who lived from about 1500 B.C. to about 1500 A.D. in the region that today encompasses much of Central America and southern Mexico. Their many accomplishments include exceptional architecture, pottery, painting, and sculpture, as well as significant advances in the fields of astronomy and mathematics.

The Maya developed a system of numeration that was based on the number twenty. The basic symbols of this system are shown in the table at the right. The place in a Mayan numeral are written vertically—the bottom place represents *ones*, the place above represents *twenties*, the place above that represents 20 × 20, or *four hundreds*, and so on. For instance, this is how to write the number 997 in Mayan numerals.

← 2 × 400 = 800
← 9 × 20 = 180
← 17 × 1 = 17
997

Evaluate each expression when ...

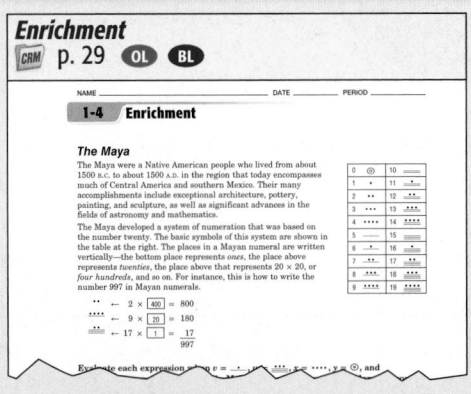

A Study Guide and Intervention, Practice, Word Problem Practice, and Enrichment Master are shown for every lesson. These masters can be found in the Chapter Resource Masters.

PSAE PRACTICE 8.11.21, 8.11.02, 6.11.05, 10.11.07

60. Which illustrates the Symmetric Property of Equality? **A**

A If $a = b$, then $b = a$.
B If $a = b$, and $b = c$, then $a = c$.
C If $a = b$, then $b = c$.
D If $a = a$, then $a + 0 = a$.

61. Anna is three years younger than her sister Emily. Which expression represents Anna's age if we express Emily's age as y years? **G**

F $y + 3$
G $y - 3$
H $3y$
J $\frac{3}{y}$

62. Which property is used below?
If $4xy^2 = 8y^2$ and $8y^2 = 72$, then $4xy^2 = 72$. **D**

A Reflexive Property
B Substitution Property
C Symmetric Property
D Transitive Property

63. SHORT RESPONSE A drawer contains the socks in the chart. What is the probability that a randomly chosen sock is blue?
$\frac{1}{3}$ or about 33.3%

Color	Number
white	16
blue	12
black	8

Spiral Review

Evaluate each expression. Name the property used in each step. (Lesson 1-3) **64–66. See margin.**

64. $14 + 23 + 8 + 15$
65. $0.24 \cdot 8 \cdot 7.05$
66. $1\frac{1}{4} \cdot 9 \cdot \frac{5}{6}$

67. SPORTS Braden runs 6 times a week for 30 minutes and lifts weights 3 times a week for 20 minutes. Write and evaluate an expression for the number of hours Braden works out in 4 weeks. (Lesson 1-2) **$\frac{4[6(30) + 3(20)]}{60}$; 16 hours**

SPORTS Refer to the table showing Blanca's cross-country times for the first 8 meets of the season. Round answers to the nearest second. (Lesson 0-12)

68. Find the mean of the data. **21:32**

69. Find the median of the data. **21:48**

70. Find the mode of the data. **21:48**

Cross Country

Meet	Time
1	22:31
2	22:21
3	21:48
4	22:01
5	21:48
6	20:56
7	20:34
8	20:15

71. SURFACE AREA What is the surface area of the cube? (Lesson 0-10)
384 in²

8 in.

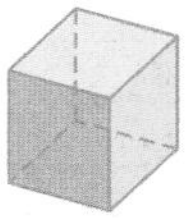

Skills Review

Evaluate each expression. (Lesson 1-2)

72. $12(7 + 2)$ **108**
73. $11(5) - 8(5)$ **15**
74. $(13 - 9) \cdot 4$ **16**
75. $3(6) + 7(6)$ **60**
76. $(1 + 19) \cdot 8$ **160**
77. $16(5 + 7)$ **192**

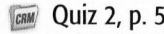

Multiple Representations In Exercise 55, students use models and a table to investigate factoring using the Distributive Property.

4 ASSESS

Name the Math Write $6(m + 8)$ on the board. Have students tell what procedure(s) they would use to simplify the expression.

Formative Assessment

Check for student understanding of Lessons 1-3 and 1-4.

CRM Quiz 2, p. 57

Additional Answers

64. $14 + 23 + 8 + 15$
$= (14 + 23) + (8 + 15)$ Associative (+)
$= 37 + 23$ Substitution
$= 60$ Substitution

65. $0.24 \cdot 8 \cdot 7.05$
$= (0.24 \cdot 8) \cdot 7.05$ Associative (×)
$= 1.92 \cdot 7.05$ Substitution
$= 13.536$ Substitution

66. $1\frac{1}{4} \cdot 9 \cdot \frac{5}{6}$
$= \left(1\frac{1}{4} \cdot 9\right)\frac{5}{6}$ Associative (×)
$= 11\frac{1}{4} \cdot \frac{5}{6}$ Substitution
$= 9\frac{3}{8}$ Substitution

Differentiated Instruction BL

Extension Ask students to demonstrate whether they can distribute division over addition in the same way that they distribute multiplication over addition. Sample answer: It depends on how the division is written.

$$24 \div (2 + 6) \stackrel{?}{=} 24 \div 2 + 24 \div 6$$
$$24 \div 8 \stackrel{?}{=} 12 + 4$$
$$3 \neq 16$$

$$(2 + 6) \div 24 \stackrel{?}{=} \frac{2}{24} + \frac{6}{24}$$
$$8 \div 24 \stackrel{?}{=} \frac{1}{12} + \frac{3}{12}$$
$$\frac{1}{3} = \frac{4}{12}$$

CHAPTER 1 Mid-Chapter Quiz

Formative Assessment

Use the Mid-Chapter Quiz to assess students' progress in the first half of the chapter.

For problems answered incorrectly, have students review the lessons indicated in parentheses.

ExamView Assessment Suite Customize and create multiple versions of your Mid-Chapter Quiz and their answer keys.

FOLDABLES Follow-Up

Before students complete the Mid-Chapter Quiz, encourage them to review the information for Lessons 1-1 through 1-4 in their Foldables.

CHAPTER 1 Mid-Chapter Quiz

Lessons 1-1 through 1-4

IL Learning Standards 7.A.4b, 8.A.4b, 6.A.4

Write a verbal expression for each algebraic expression. (Lesson 1-1)

1. $21 - x^3$ **1. twenty-one minus x to the third power**
2. $3m^5 + 9$ **2. the sum of three times m to the fifth power and nine**

Write an algebraic expression for each verbal expression. (Lesson 1-1)

3. five more than s squared $s^2 + 5$
4. four times y to the fourth power $4y^4$
5. **CAR RENTAL** The XYZ Car Rental Agency charges a flat rate of \$29 per day plus \$0.32 per mile driven. Write an algebraic expression for the rental cost of a car for x days that is driven y miles. (Lesson 1-1) $29x + 0.32y$

Evaluate each expression. (Lesson 1-2)

6. $24 \div 3 - 2 \cdot 3$ 2
7. $5 + 2^2$ 9
8. $4(3 + 9)$ 48
9. $36 - 2(1 + 3)^2$ 4
10. $\dfrac{40 - 2^3}{4 + 3(2^2)}$ 2
11. **AMUSEMENT PARK** The costs of tickets to a local amusement park are shown. Write and evaluate an expression to find the total cost for 5 adults and 8 children. (Lesson 1-2) $5(45) + 8(25) = 425$

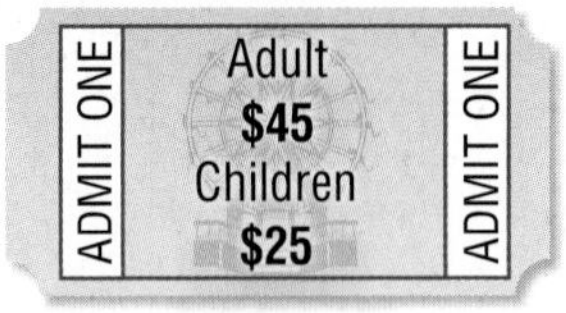

12. **MULTIPLE CHOICE** Write an algebraic expression to represent the perimeter of the rectangle shown below. Then evaluate it to find the perimeter when $w = 8$ cm. (Lesson 1-2) C

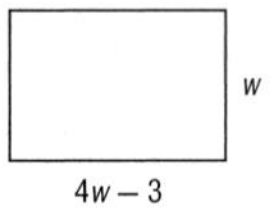

A 37 cm
B 232 cm
C 74 cm
D 45 cm

Evaluate each expression. Name the property used in each step. (Lesson 1-3) **13–17. See Ch.1 Answer Appendix for steps.**

13. $(8 - 2^3) + 21$ 21
14. $3(1 \div 3) \cdot 9$ 9
15. $[5 \div (3 \cdot 1)]\frac{3}{5}$ 1
16. $18 + 35 + 32 + 15$ 100
17. $0.25 \cdot 7 \cdot 4$ 7

Use the Distributive Property to rewrite each expression. Then evaluate. (Lesson 1-4)

18. $3(5 + 2)$ $3(5) + 3(2)$; 21
19. $(9 - 6)12$ $9(12) - 6(12)$; 36
20. $8(7 - 4)$ $8(7) - 8(4)$; 24

Use the Distributive Property to rewrite each expression. Then simplify. (Lesson 1-4)

21. $4(x + 3)$ $4(x) + 4(3)$; $4x + 12$
22. $(6 - 2y)7$ $6(7) - 2y(7)$; $42 - 14y$
23. $-5(3m - 2)$ $-5(3m) - 5(-2)$; $-15m + 10$
24. **DVD SALES** A video store chain has three locations. Use the information in the table below to write and evaluate an expression to estimate the total number of DVDs sold over a 4-day period. (Lesson 1-4) $4(145 + 211 + 184)$; 2160

Location	Daily Sales Numbers
Location 1	145
Location 2	211
Location 3	184

25. **MULTIPLE CHOICE** Rewrite the expression $(8 - 3p)(-2)$ using the Distributive Property. (Lesson 1-4) H

F $16 - 6p$
G $-10p$
H $-16 + 6p$
J $10p$

Intervention Planner

Tier 1 On Level

If students miss about 25% of the exercises or less,

Then choose a resource:

- **SE** Lessons 1-1, 1-2, 1-3, and 1-4
- **CRM** Skills Practice, pp. 7, 13, 20, and 26
- **TE** Chapter Project, p. 2

IL Math Online Self-Check Quiz

Tier 2 Strategic Intervention approaching grade level

If students miss about 50% of the exercises,

Then choose a resource:

- **CRM** Study Guide and Intervention, Chapter 1, pp. 5, 11, 18, and 24

Quick Review Math Handbook

IL Math Online Extra Examples, Personal Tutor, Homework Help

Tier 3 Intensive Intervention 2 or more grades below level

If students miss about 75% of the exercises,

Then use *Math Triumphs, Alg. 1*, Ch. 1, 2, 3, and 5

IL Math Online Extra Examples, Personal Tutor, Homework Help, Review Vocabulary

1-5 Equations

Then
You simplified expressions. (Lesson 1-1 through 1-4)

Now
- Solve equations with one variable.
- Solve equations with two variables.

IL Learning Standards

8.B.4a Represent algebraic concepts with physical materials, words, diagrams, tables, graphs, equations and inequalities and use appropriate technology.

New Vocabulary
open sentence
equation
solving
solution
replacement set
set
element
solution set
identity

IL Math Online

glencoe.com
- Extra Examples
- Personal Tutor
- Self-Check Quiz
- Homework Help
- Math in Motion

Why?

Mark's baseball team scored 3 runs in the first inning. At the top of the third inning, their score was 4. The open sentence below represents the change in their score.

$$3 + r = 4$$

The solution is 1. The team got 1 run in the second inning.

Solve Equations A mathematical statement that contains algebraic expressions and symbols is an **open sentence**. A sentence that contains an equals sign, =, is an **equation**.

expression → $3x + 7$ $3x + 7 = 13$ ← equation

Finding a value for a variable that makes a sentence true is called **solving** the open sentence. This replacement value is a **solution**.

A set of numbers from which replacements for a variable may be chosen is called a **replacement set**. A **set** is a collection of objects or numbers that is often shown using braces. Each object or number in the set is called an **element**, or member. A **solution set** is the set of elements from the replacement set that make an open sentence true.

EXAMPLE 1 Use a Replacement Set

Find the solution set of the equation $2q + 5 = 13$ if the replacement set is {2, 3, 4, 5, 6}.

Use a table to solve. Replace q in $2q + 5 = 13$ with each value in the replacement set.

q	$2q + 5 = 13$	True or False?
2	$2(2) + 5 = 13$	False
3	$2(3) + 5 = 13$	False
4	$2(4) + 5 = 13$	True
5	$2(5) + 5 = 13$	False
6	$2(6) + 5 = 13$	False

Since the equation is true when $q = 4$, the solution of $2q + 5 = 13$ is $q = 4$.

The solution set is {4}.

Check Your Progress

Find the solution set for each equation if the replacement set is {0, 1, 2, 3}.

1A. $8m - 7 = 17$ {3}

1B. $28 = 4(1 + 3d)$ {2}

Personal Tutor glencoe.com

1-5 Lesson Notes

1 FOCUS

Vertical Alignment

Before Lesson 1-5
Simplify expressions.

Lesson 1-5
Solve equations with one variable. Solve equations with two variables.

After Lesson 1-5
Explore different representations of relations.

2 TEACH

Scaffolding Questions

Have students read the *Why?* section of the lesson.

Ask:
- How would you translate the sentence $3 + r = 4$? Three plus r is equal to four.
- What does the variable r represent in the sentence? the number of runs in the second inning
- How do you know that the solution is 1? $3 + 1$ is equal to 4.

Lesson 1-5 Resources

Resource	Approaching-Level	On-Level	Beyond-Level	English Learners
Teacher Edition		• Differentiated Instruction, pp. 33, 37	• Differentiated Instruction, pp. 33, 37	
Chapter Resource Masters	• Study Guide and Intervention, pp. 30–31 • Skills Practice, p. 32 • Practice, p. 33 • Word Problem Practice, p. 34 • Spreadsheet Activity, p. 36	• Study Guide and Intervention, pp. 30–31 • Skills Practice, p. 32 • Practice, p. 33 • Word Problem Practice, p. 34 • Enrichment, p. 35 • Spreadsheet Activity, p. 36	• Practice, p. 33 • Word Problem Practice, p. 34 • Enrichment, p. 35 • Spreadsheet Activity, p. 36	• Study Guide and Intervention, pp. 30–31 • Skills Practice, p. 32 • Practice, p. 33 • Spreadsheet Activity, p. 36
Transparencies	• 5-Minute Check Transparency 1-5	• 5-Minute Check Transparency 1-5	• 5-Minute Check Transparency 1-5	• 5-Minute Check Transparency 1-5
Other	• Study Notebook	• Study Notebook	• Study Notebook	• Study Notebook

Solve Equations

Example 1 shows how to use a replacement set to solve equations. **Example 2** shows how to use the order of operations to solve an equation in a standardized test. **Example 3** shows that some equations have a unique solution and some have no solution. **Example 4** shows how to recognize an equation that is an identity.

Formative Assessment

Use the Check Your Progress exercises after each Example to determine students' understanding of concepts.

Additional Examples

1 Find the solution set of the equation $4a + 7 = 23$ if the replacement set is {2, 3, 4, 5, 6}. {4}

2 **STANDARDIZED TEST PRACTICE** Solve $3 + 4(2^3 - 2) = b$. B

A 19 **B** 27 **C** 33 **D** 42

3 Solve each equation.

a. $4 + (3^2 + 7) \div n = 8$ 4

b. $4n - (12 + 2) = n(6 - 2) - 9$ no solution

Additional Examples also in Interactive Classroom PowerPoint® Presentations

IWB INTERACTIVE WHITEBOARD READY

You can often solve an equation by applying the order of operations.

Test-Taking Tip

Rewrite the Equation If you are allowed to write in your testing booklet, it can be helpful to rewrite the equation with simplified terms.

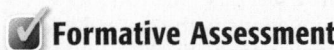

Every chapter includes a worked-out **Standardized Test Example** that is similar to problems found on the state assessments.

PSAE EXAMPLE 2 6.11.04

Solve $6 + (5^2 - 5) \div 2 = p$.

A 3 **B** 6 **C** 13 **D** 16

Read the Test Item

You need to apply the order of operations to the expression in order to solve for p.

Solve the Test Item

$6 + (5^2 - 5) \div 2 = p$	Original equation
$6 + (25 - 5) \div 2 = p$	Evaluate powers.
$6 + 20 \div 2 = p$	Subtract 5 from 25.
$6 + 10 = p$	Divide 20 by 2.
$16 = p$	Add. The correct answer is D.

Check Your Progress

2. Solve $t = 9^2 \div (5 - 2)$. J

F 3 **G** 6 **H** 14.2 **J** 27

Personal Tutor glencoe.com

Some equations have a unique solution. Other equations do not have a solution.

EXAMPLE 3 Solutions of Equations

Solve each equation.

a. $7 - (4^2 - 10) + n = 10$

Simplify the equation first and then look for a solution.

$7 - (4^2 - 10) + n = 10$	Original equation
$7 - (16 - 10) + n = 10$	Evaluate powers.
$7 - 6 + n = 10$	Subtract 10 from 16.
$1 + n = 10$	Subtract 6 from 7.

The only value for n that makes the equation true is 9. Therefore, this equation has a unique solution of 9.

Math in Motion, Interactive Lab glencoe.com

b. $n(3 + 2) + 6 = 5n + (10 - 3)$

$n(3 + 2) + 6 = 5n + (10 - 3)$	Original equation
$n(5) + 6 = 5n + (10 - 3)$	Add 3 + 2.
$n(5) + 6 = 5n + 7$	Subtract 3 from 10.
$5n + 6 = 5n + 7$	Commutative (×)

No matter what real value is substituted for n, the left side of the equation will always be one less than the right side. So, the equation will never be true. Therefore, there is no solution of this equation.

Check Your Progress **Solve each equation.**

3A. $(18 + 4) + m = (5 - 3)m$ 22

3B. $8 \cdot 4 \cdot k + 9 \cdot 5 = (36 - 4)k - (2 \cdot 5)$ no solution

Personal Tutor glencoe.com

Focus on Mathematical Content

Open Sentences An open sentence is a mathematical statement that contains two algebraic expressions and a symbol to compare them. An open sentence with an equals sign, =, is an equation.

An equation that is true for every value of the variable is called an **identity**.

ReadingMath

Reading Math Identities An identity is an equation that shows that a number or expression is equivalent to itself.

EXAMPLE 4 Identities

Solve $(2 \cdot 5 - 8)(3h + 6) = [(2h + h) + 6]2$.

$(2 \cdot 5 - 8)(3h + 6) = [(2h + h) + 6]2$	**Original Equation**
$(10 - 8)(3h + 6) = [(2h + h) + 6]2$	**Multiply $2 \cdot 5$.**
$2(3h + 6) = [(2h + h) + 6]2$	**Subtract 8 from 10.**
$6h + 12 = [(2h + h) + 6]2$	**Distributive Property**
$6h + 12 = [3h + 6]2$	**Add $2h + h$.**
$6h + 12 = 6h + 12$	**Distributive Property**

No matter what value is substituted for h, the left side of the equation will always be equal to the right side. So, the equation will always be true. Therefore, the solution of this equation could be any real number.

Check Your Progress

Solve each equation.

4A. $12(10 - 7) + 9g = g(2^2 + 5) + 36$ all real numbers

4B. $2d + (2^3 - 5) = 10(5 - 2) + d(12 \div 6)$ no solution

4C. $3(b + 1) - 5 = 3b - 2$ all real numbers

4D. $5 - \frac{1}{2}(c - 6) = 4$ 8

Personal Tutor glencoe.com

Solve Equations with Two Variables Some equations contain two variables. It is often useful to make a table of values and use substitution to find the corresponding values of the second variable.

EXAMPLE 5 Equations Involving Two Variables

MOVIE RENTALS Mr. Hernandez pays $10 each month for movies delivered by mail. He can also rent movies in the store for $1.50 per title. Write and solve an equation to find the total amount Mr. Hernandez spends this month if he rents 3 movies from the store.

The cost of the movie plan is a flat rate. The variable is the number of movies he rents from the store. The total cost is the price of the plan plus $1.50 times the number of movies from the store. Let C be the total cost and m be the number of movies.

$C = 1.50m + 10$	**Original equation**
$= 1.50(3) + 10$	**Substitute 3 for m.**
$= 4.50 + 10$	**Multiply.**
$= 14.50$	

Mr. Hernandez spends $14.50 on movie rentals in one month.

Check Your Progress

5. TRAVEL Amelia drives an average of 65 miles per hour. Write and solve an equation to find the time it will take her to drive 36 miles.
$d = 65t$; $t \approx 33$ min or 0.55 h

Personal Tutor glencoe.com

Additional Example

4 Solve $(5 + 8 \div 4) + 3k = 3(k + 32) - 89$. The solution could be any real number.

Solve Equations with Two Variables

Example 5 shows how to write and solve an equation with two variables to solve a real-world problem.

Additional Example

5 **GYM MEMBERSHIP** Dalila pays $16 per month for a gym membership. In addition, she pays $2 per Pilates class. Write and solve an equation to find the total amount Dalila spent this month if she took 12 Pilates classes. $c = 2p + 16$; $40

Examples illustrate lesson concepts and closely mirror the exercises. **Check Your Progress** exercises give students an opportunity to try a similar problem on their own.

TEACH with TECH

STUDENT RESPONSE SYSTEM Give students an equation and a set of four numbers. Ask students to check each of these numbers to see which is a solution of the equation. Give students a key, and have them respond with the choice that is a solution to the equation.

Differentiated Instruction

OL BL

If students have strong verbal skills,

Then challenge them to write and solve real-world equations involving one variable and two variables. Suggest that students write equations about a plant or animal in which they are interested.

3 PRACTICE

Formative Assessment

Use Exercises 1–10 to check for understanding.

Use the chart at the bottom of this page to customize assignments for your students.

Additional Answers

37.

x	$3x - 2$	y
−2	3(−2) − 2	−8
−1	3(−1) − 2	−5
0	3(0) − 2	−2
1	3(1) − 2	1
2	3(2) − 2	4

38.

x	$3.25x + 0.75$	y
−2	3.25(−2) + 0.75	−5.75
−1	3.25(−1) + 0.75	−2.5
0	3.25(0) + 0.75	0.75
1	3.25(1) + 0.75	4
2	3.25(2) + 0.75	7.25

48. solution
49. solution
50. not a solution
51. not a solution
52. solution
53. solution
54. not a solution
55. solution
56. solution

Check Your Understanding

Example 1 p. 31

Find the solution set for each equation if the replacement set is {11, 12, 13, 14, 15}.

1. $n + 10 = 23$ {13}
2. $7 = \frac{c}{2}$ {14}
3. $29 = 3x - 7$ {12}
4. $(k - 8)12 = 84$ {15}

Example 2 p. 32

5. **MULTIPLE CHOICE** Solve $\frac{d+5}{10} = 2$. B

A 10 B 15 C 20 D 25

Examples 3 and 4 pp. 32–33

Solve each equation.

6. $x = 4(6) + 3$ 27
7. $14 - 82 = w$ −68
8. $5 + 22a = 2 + 10 \div 2$ $\frac{1}{11}$
9. $(2 \cdot 5) + \frac{c^3}{3} = c^3 \div (1^5 + 2) + 10$ all real numbers

Example 5 p. 33

10. **RECYCLING** San Francisco has a recycling facility that accepts unused paint. Volunteers blend and mix the paint and give it away in 5-gallon buckets. Write and solve an equation to find the number of buckets of paint given away from the 30,000 gallons that are donated. $b = \frac{g}{5}$; 6000 buckets

Practice and Problem Solving

= **Step-by-Step Solutions** begin on page R12. **Extra Practice** begins on page 815.

Example 1 p. 31

Find the solution set of each equation if the replacement sets are y: {1, 3, 5, 7, 9} and z: {10, 12, 14, 16, 18}.

11. $z + 10 = 22$ {12}
12. $52 = 4z$ no solution
13. $\frac{15}{y} = 3$ {5}
14. $17 = 24 - y$ {7}
15. $2z - 5 = 27$ {16}
16. $4(y + 1) = 40$ {9}
17. $22 = \frac{60}{y} + 2$ {3}
18. $111 = z^2 + 11$ {10}

Examples 2–4 pp. 32–33

Solve each equation.

19. $a = 32 - 9(2)$ 14
20. $w = 56 \div (2^2 + 3)$ 8
21. $\frac{27 + 5}{16} = g$ 2
22. $\frac{12 \cdot 5}{15 - 3} = y$ 5
23. $r = \frac{9(6)}{(8 + 1)3}$ 2
24. $a = \frac{4(14 - 1)}{3(6) - 5} + 7$ 11
25. $(4 - 2^2 + 5)w = 25$ 5
26. $7 + x - (3 + 32 \div 8) = 3$ 3
27. $3^2 - 2 \cdot 3 + u = (3^3 - 3 \cdot 8)(2) + u$
28. $(3 \cdot 6 \div 2)v + 10 = 3^2v + 9$ no solution
29. $6k + (3 \cdot 10 - 8) = (2 \cdot 3)k + 22$
30. $(3 \cdot 5)t + (21 - 12) = 15t + 3^2$ all real numbers
31. $(2^4 - 3 \cdot 5)q + 13 = (2 \cdot 9 - 4^2)q + \left(\frac{3 \cdot 4}{12} - 1\right)$ 13
32. $\frac{3 \cdot 22}{18 + 4}r - \left(\frac{4^2}{9 + 7} - 1\right) = r + \left(\frac{8 \cdot 9}{3} \div 3\right)$ 4

27. no solution
29. all real numbers

33. **SCHOOL** A conference room can seat a maximum of 85 people. The principal and two counselors need to meet with the school's juniors to discuss college admissions. If each student must bring a parent with them, how many students can attend each meeting? Assume that each student has a unique set of parents.

33. 41 students

34. **GEOMETRY** The perimeter of a regular octagon is 128 inches. Find the length of each side. 16 in.

34 **Chapter 1** Expressions, Equations, and Functions

The Differentiated Homework Options provide leveled assignments. Many of the homework exercises are paired, so that the students can do the odds one day and the evens on the next day.

Differentiated Homework Options

Level	Assignment	Two-Day Option	
AL Basic	11–36, 64–67, 69–90	11–35 odd, 71–74	12–36 even, 64–67, 69–70, 75–90
OL Core	11–61 odd, 62–67, 69–90	11–36, 71–74	37–67, 69–70, 75–90
BL Advanced	37–84, (optional: 85–90)		

Example 5 p. 33

35. **SPORTS** A 200-pound athlete who trains for four hours per day requires 2836 Calories for basic energy requirements. During training, the same athlete requires 3091 Calories for extra energy requirements. Write an equation to find C, the total daily Calorie requirement for this athlete. Then solve the equation.

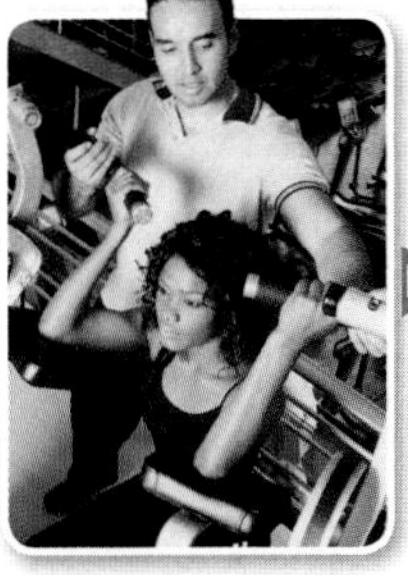

Real-World Link

Athletes in training should have a specific blend of sources for their Calories.
69% carbohydrates
20% fats
11% protein

Source: *Food and Sport*

35. $C = 2836 + 3091$; 5927 Calories/day

36. **ENERGY** An electric generator can power 3550 watts of electricity. Write and solve an equation to find how many 75-watt light bulbs a generator could power. **$3550 = 75x$; about 47 light bulbs**

B **Make a table of values for each equation if the replacement set is {−2, −1, 0, 1, 2}.**

37. $y = 3x - 2$ **37–38. See margin.**

38. $3.25x + 0.75 = y$

Solve each equation using the given replacement set.

39. $t - 13 = 7$; {10, 13, 17, 20} **20**

40. $14(x + 5) = 126$; {3, 4, 5, 6, 7} **4**

41. $22 = \frac{n}{3}$; {62, 64, 66, 68, 70} **66**

42. $35 = \frac{g - 8}{2}$; {78, 79, 80, 81} **78**

Solve each equation.

43. $\frac{3(9) - 2}{1 + 4} = d$ **5**

44. $j = 15 \div 3 \cdot 5 - 4^2$ **9**

45. $c + (3^2 - 3) = 21$ **$c = 15$**

46. $(3^3 - 3 \cdot 9) + (7 - 2^2)b = 24b$ **$b = 0$**

47. **HEALTH** Blood flow rate can be expressed as $F = \frac{p_1 - p_2}{r}$, where F is the flow rate, p_1 and p_2 are the initial and final pressure exerted against the blood vessel's walls, respectively, and r is the resistance created by the size of the vessel.

a. Write and solve an equation to determine the resistance of the blood vessel for an initial pressure of 100 millimeters of mercury, a final pressure of 0 millimeters of mercury, and a flow rate of 5 liters per minute. **$5 = \frac{100 - 0}{r}$; 20**

b. Use the equation to complete the table below.

Initial Pressure p_1 (mm Hg)	Final Pressure p_2 (mm Hg)	Resistance r (mm Hg/L/min)	Blood Flow Rate F (L/min)
100	0	**20**	5
100	0	30	**≈ 3.33**
165	5	40	4
90	**30**	10	6

48–56. See margin.

Determine whether the given number is a solution of the equation.

48. $x + 6 = 15$; 9

49. $12 + y = 26$; 14

50. $2t - 10 = 4$; 3

51. $3r + 7 = -5$; 2

52. $6 + 4m = 18$; 3

53. $-5 + 2p = -11$; −3

54. $\frac{q}{2} = 20$; 10

55. $\frac{w - 4}{5} = -3$; −11

56. $\frac{g}{3} - 4 = 12$; 48

57–60. See Chapter 1 Answer Appendix.

C **Make a table of values for each equation if the replacement set is {−2, −1, 0, 1, 2}.**

57. $y = 3x + 5$

58. $-2x - 3 = y$

59. $y = \frac{1}{2}x + 2$

60. $4.2x - 1.6 = y$

61. **GEOMETRY** The length of a rectangle is 2 inches greater than the width. The length of the base of an isosceles triangle is 12 inches, and the lengths of the other two sides are 1 inch greater than the width of the rectangle.

a. Draw a picture of each figure and label the dimensions.

b. Write two expressions to find the perimeters of the rectangle and triangle.

c. Find the width of the rectangle if the perimeters of the figures are equal. **$4 + 4w = 2w + 14$, $w = 5$ in.**

61a.

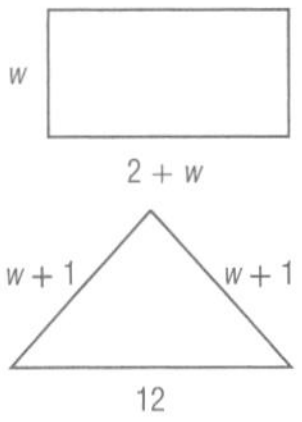

61b. perimeter of rectangle $= 2(2 + w) + 2w = 4 + 4w$; perimeter of triangle $= 2(w + 1) + 12 = 2w + 14$

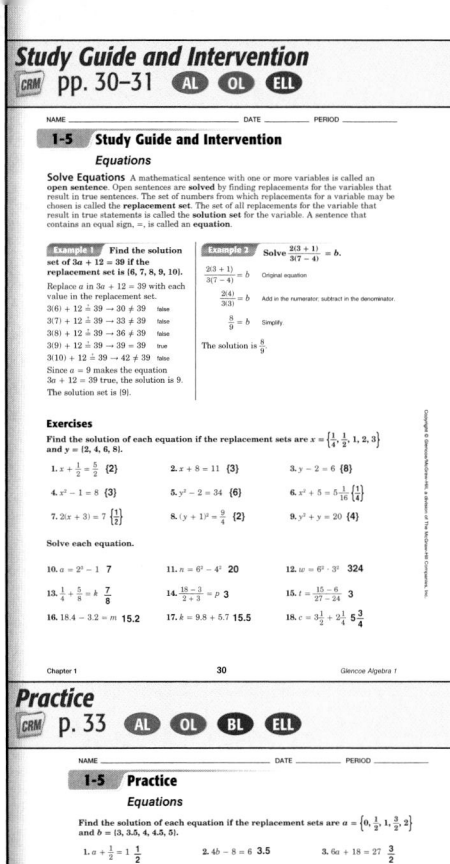

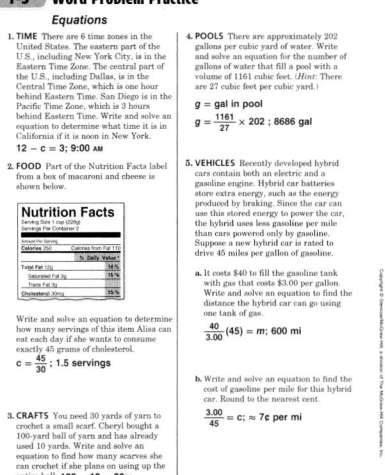

Study Guide and Intervention

CRM pp. 30–31 AL OL ELL

NAME ______ DATE ______ PERIOD ______

1-5 Study Guide and Intervention

Equations

Solve Equations A mathematical sentence with one or more variables is called an **open sentence**. Open sentences are **solved** by finding replacements for the variables that result in true sentences. The set of numbers from which replacements for a variable may be chosen is called the **replacement set**. The set of all replacements for the variable that result in true statements is called the **solution set** for the variable. A sentence that contains an equal sign, =, is called an **equation**.

Example 1 **Find the solution set of $3a + 12 = 39$ if the replacement set is {6, 7, 8, 9, 10}.**

Replace a in $3a + 12 = 39$ with each value in the replacement set.

$3(6) + 12 \stackrel{?}{=} 39 \rightarrow 30 \neq 39$ false
$3(7) + 12 \stackrel{?}{=} 39 \rightarrow 33 \neq 39$ false
$3(8) + 12 \stackrel{?}{=} 39 \rightarrow 36 \neq 39$ false
$3(9) + 12 \stackrel{?}{=} 39 \rightarrow 39 = 39$ true
$3(10) + 12 \stackrel{?}{=} 39 \rightarrow 42 \neq 39$ false

Since $a = 9$ makes the equation $3a + 12 = 39$ true, the solution is 9. The solution set is {9}.

Example 2 **Solve $\frac{2(3 + 1)}{3(7 - 4)} = b$.**

$\frac{2(3 + 1)}{3(7 - 4)} = b$ Original equation
$\frac{2(4)}{3(3)} = b$ Add in the numerator; subtract in the denominator.
$\frac{8}{9} = b$ Simplify.

The solution is $\frac{8}{9}$.

Exercises

Find the solution of each equation if the replacement sets are $x = \left\{\frac{1}{4}, \frac{1}{2}, 1, 2, 3\right\}$ and $y = \{2, 4, 6, 8\}$.

1. $x + \frac{1}{2} = \frac{5}{2}$ **{2}**
2. $x + 8 = 11$ **{3}**
3. $y - 2 = 6$ **{8}**
4. $x^2 - 1 = 8$ **{3}**
5. $y^2 - 2 = 34$ **{6}**
6. $x^2 + 5 = 5\frac{1}{16}$ **$\left\{\frac{1}{4}\right\}$**
7. $2(x + 3) = 7$ **$\left\{\frac{1}{2}\right\}$**
8. $(y + 1)^2 = \frac{9}{4}$ **{2}**
9. $y^2 + y = 20$ **{4}**

Solve each equation.

10. $a = 2^3 - 1$ **7**
11. $n = 6^2 - 4^2$ **20**
12. $w = 6^2 \cdot 3^2$ **324**
13. $\frac{1}{4} + \frac{5}{8} = k$ **$\frac{7}{8}$**
14. $\frac{18 - 3}{2 + 3} = p$ **3**
15. $t = \frac{15 - 6}{27 - 24}$ **3**
16. $18.4 - 3.2 = m$ **15.2**
17. $k = 9.8 + 5.7$ **15.5**
18. $c = 3\frac{1}{2} + 2\frac{1}{4}$ **$5\frac{3}{4}$**

Practice

CRM p. 33 AL OL BL ELL

NAME ______ DATE ______ PERIOD ______

1-5 Practice

Equations

Find the solution of each equation if the replacement sets are $a = \left\{0, \frac{1}{2}, 1, \frac{3}{2}, 2\right\}$ and $b = \{3, 3.5, 4, 4.5, 5\}$.

1. $a + \frac{1}{2} = 1$ **$\frac{1}{2}$**
2. $4b - 8 = 6$ **3.5**
3. $6a + 18 = 27$ **$\frac{3}{2}$**
4. $7b - 8 = 16.5$ **3.5**
5. $120 - 28a = 78$ **$\frac{3}{2}$**
6. $\frac{28}{b} + 9 = 16$ **4**

Solve each equation.

7. $x = 18.3 - 4.8$ **13.5**
8. $w = 20.2 - 8.95$ **11.25**
9. $\frac{37 - 9}{18 - 11} = d$ **4**
10. $\frac{97 - 25}{41 - 23} = k$ **4**
11. $y = \frac{4(22 - 4)}{3(6) + 6}$ **3**
12. $\frac{5(2^2) + 4(3)}{4(2^3 - 4)} = p$ **2**

13. **TEACHING** A teacher has 15 weeks in which to teach six chapters. Write and then solve an equation that represents the number of lessons the teacher must teach per week if there is an average of 8.5 lessons per chapter.
$n = \frac{6(8.5)}{15}$; 3.4

14. **CELL PHONES** Gabriel pays $40 a month for basic cell phone service. In addition, Gabriel can send text messages for $0.20 each. Write and solve an equation to find the total amount Gabriel spent this month if he sends 40 text messages.
c = 40 + 0.20 (40); $48.00

Lesson 1-5

Word Problem Practice

CRM p. 34 AL OL BL ELL

NAME ______ DATE ______ PERIOD ______

1-5 Word Problem Practice

Equations

1. **TIME** There are 6 time zones in the United States. The eastern part of the U.S., including New York City, is in the Eastern Time Zone. The central part of the U.S., including Dallas, is in the Central Time Zone, which is one hour behind Eastern Time. San Diego is in the Pacific Time Zone, which is 3 hours behind Eastern Time. Write and solve an equation to determine what time it is in California if it is noon in New York.
12 − c = 3; 9:00 AM

2. **FOOD** Part of the Nutrition Facts label from a box of macaroni and cheese is shown below.

Write and solve an equation to determine how many servings of this item Alisa can eat each day if she wants to consume exactly 45 grams of cholesterol.
$c = \frac{45}{30}$; 1.5 servings

3. **CRAFTS** You need 30 yards of yarn to crochet a small scarf. Cheryl bought a 100-yard ball of yarn and has already used 10 yards. Write and solve an equation to find how many scarves she can crochet if she plans on using up the entire ball. **100 − 10 = 30s; 3 scarves**

4. **POOLS** There are approximately 202 gallons per cubic yard of water. Write and solve an equation for the number of gallons of water that fill a pool with a volume of 1161 cubic feet. (*Hint:* There are 27 cubic feet per cubic yard.)
g = gal in pool
$g = \frac{1161}{27} \times 202$; 8686 gal

5. **VEHICLES** Recently developed hybrid cars contain both an electric and a gasoline engine. Hybrid car batteries store extra energy, such as the energy produced by braking. Since the car can use this stored energy to power the car, the hybrid uses less gasoline per mile than cars powered only by gasoline. Suppose a new hybrid car is rated to drive 45 miles per gallon of gasoline.

a. It costs $40 to fill the gasoline tank with gas that costs $3.00 per gallon. Write and solve an equation to find the distance the hybrid car can go using one tank of gas.
$\frac{40}{3.00}(45) = m$; 600 mi

b. Write and solve an equation to find the cost of gasoline per mile for this hybrid car. Round to the nearest cent.
$\frac{3.00}{45} = c$; ≈ 7¢ per mi

Enrichment

CRM p. 35 OL BL

NAME ______ DATE ______ PERIOD ______

1-5 Enrichment

Solution Sets

Consider the following open sentence.

It is the name of a month between March and July.

You know that a replacement for the variable *It* must be found in order to determine if the sentence is true or false. If *It* is replaced by either April, May, or June, the sentence is true. The set {April, May, June} is called the solution set of the open sentence given above. This set includes all replacements for the variable that make the sentence true.

Write the solution set for each open sentence.

1. It is the name of a state beginning with the letter A.
{Alabama, Alaska, Arizona, Arkansas}
2. It is a primary color.
{red, yellow, blue}
3. Its capital is Harrisburg. **{Pennsylvania}**
4. It is a New England state. **{Maine, New Hampshire, Vermont, Massachusetts, Rhode Island, Connecticut}**

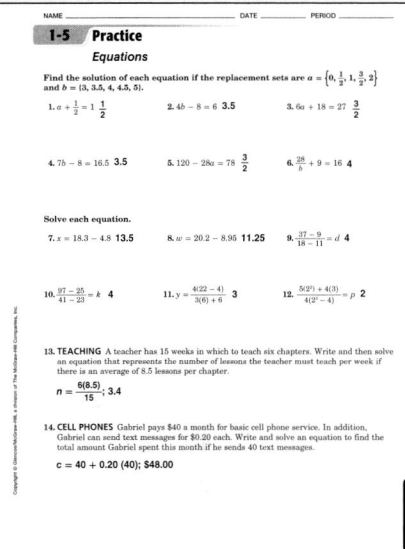

Exercise Alert

Manipulatives Exercise 63 requires centimeter cubes.

Multiple Representations In Exercise 63, students use models and tables to write equations.

Watch Out!

Find the Error For Exercise 67, students should see that Tom followed the order of operations and Li-Cheng did not. Remind students that they multiply and divide left to right before adding and subtracting left to right.

Additional Answers

63b.

Layers	1	2	3	4	5	6	7
Cubes	4	8	12	16	20	24	28

64. Sample answer: An equation contains an equals sign and an expression does not. An equation is made up of 2 expressions and an equals sign.

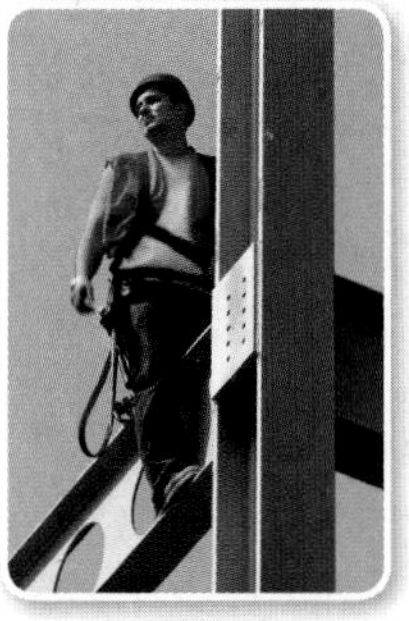

Real-World Link

In 2007, Chicago had three "supertall" skyscrapers (over 1000 feet) under construction that used a new method of steel construction. A web of supports stretch from the center to the outside wall supports. This method allows buildings to be built taller and with more features than ever before.

62. CONSTRUCTION The construction of a building requires 10 tons of steel per story.

a. Define a variable and write an equation for the number of tons of steel required if the building has 15 stories. **Sample answer: t = tons of steel; $t = 10(15)$**

b. How many tons of steel are needed? **150 tons of steel**

63. MULTIPLE REPRESENTATIONS In this problem, you will further explore writing equations.

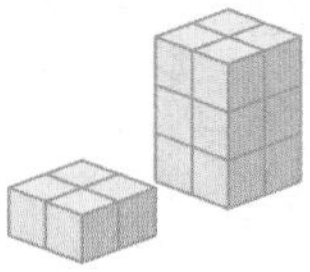

a. CONCRETE Use centimeter cubes to build a tower similar to the one shown at the right. **See students' work.**

b. TABULAR Copy and complete the table shown below. Record the number of layers in the tower and the number of cubes used in the table. **See margin.**

Layers	1	2	3	4	5	6	7
Cubes	?	?	?	?	?	?	?

c. ANALYTICAL As the number of layers in the tower increases, how does the number of cubes in the tower change? **Each layer adds 4 more cubes to the tower.**

d. ALGEBRAIC Write a rule that gives the number of cubes in terms of the number of layers in the tower. **The number of cubes = $4L$, where L is the number of layers in the tower.**

H.O.T. Problems

Use Higher-Order Thinking Skills

64. REASONING Compare and contrast an expression and an equation. **See margin.**

65. OPEN ENDED Write an equation that is an identity. **Sample answer: $3x + 12 = 3(x + 4)$**

66. REASONING Explain why an open sentence always has at least one variable.

67. FIND THE ERROR Tom and Li-Cheng are solving the equation $x = 4(3 - 2) + 6 \div 8$. Is either of them correct? Explain your reasoning.

Tom

$x = 4(3 - 2) + 6 \div 8$
$= 4(1) + 6 \div 8$
$= 4 + 6 \div 8$
$= 4 + \frac{6}{8}$
$= 4\frac{3}{4}$

Li-Cheng

$x = 4(3 - 2) + 6 \div 8$
$= 4(1) + 6 \div 8$
$= 4 + 6 \div 8$
$= 10 \div 8$
$= \frac{5}{4}$

68. CHALLENGE Find all of the solutions of $x^2 + 5 = 30$. **5, −5**

69. OPEN ENDED Write an equation that involves two or more operations with a solution of −7. **Sample answer: $3x - 2 = -23$**

70. WRITING IN MATH Explain how you can determine that an equation has no real numbers as a solution. How can you determine that an equation has all real numbers as solutions?

66. Sample answer: A sentence that contains no variable will be true or false, which means it cannot be an open sentence.

67. Tom; Li-Cheng added 6 + 4 instead of dividing 6 by 8. She did not follow the order of operations.

70. Sample answer: Equations with no real numbers for solutions may have the same variables on each side of the equation, but are different by some number or operation. Equations that have all of the real numbers as solutions are equations with the same variables and same numbers and operations on both sides of the equation.

36 Chapter 1 Expressions, Equations, and Functions

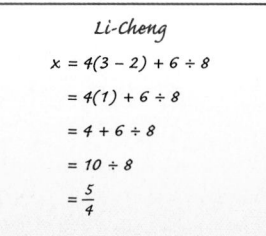

PSAE PRACTICE 6.11.18, 9.11.01, 7.11.07

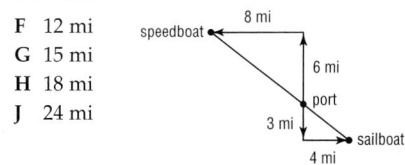

71. STATISTICS A researcher wants to find out how often teens in her town exercise. Which sample group should she survey to get results that best represent all the teens in the town? **C**

A a summer baseball league
B her nieces and nephews
C high school students chosen at random
D the teens at the mall one Saturday afternoon

72. SHORT RESPONSE The expected attendance for the Drama Club production is 65% of the student body. If the student body consists of 300 students, how many students are expected to attend? **195 students**

73. GEOMETRY A speedboat and a sailboat take off from the same port. The diagram shows their travel. What is the distance between the boats? **G**

F 12 mi
G 15 mi
H 18 mi
J 24 mi

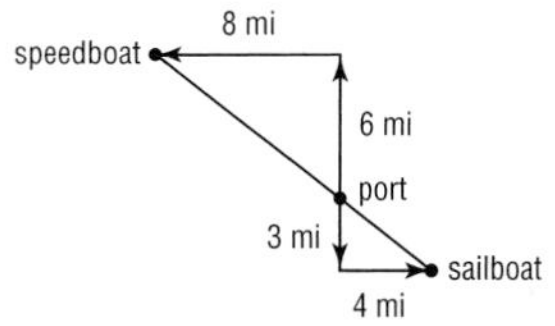

74. Michelle can read 1.5 pages per minute. How many pages can she read in two hours? **D**

A 90 pages
B 150 pages
C 120 pages
D 180 pages

Spiral Review

75. ZOO A zoo has about 500 children and 750 adults visit each day. Write an expression to represent about how many visitors the zoo will have over a month. (Lesson 1-4) **30(500 + 750)**

Find the value of p in each equation. Then name the property that is used. (Lesson 1-3)

76. $7.3 + p = 7.3$ **$p = 0$; Additive Identity**

77. $12p = 1$ **p a $\frac{1}{12}$; Multiplicative Inverse**

78. $1p = 4$ **$p = 4$; Multiplicative Identity**

79. MOVING BOXES The figure shows the dimensions of the boxes Steve uses to pack. How many cubic inches can each box hold? (Lesson 0-9) **1040 in^3**

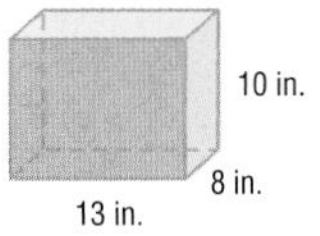

Express each percent as a fraction. (Lesson 0-6)

80. 35% $\frac{7}{20}$

81. 15% $\frac{3}{20}$

82. 28% $\frac{7}{25}$

For each problem, determine whether you need an estimate or an exact answer. Then solve. (Lessons 0-6 and 0-1)

83. TRAVEL The distance from Raleigh, North Carolina, to Philadelphia, Pennsylvania, is approximately 428 miles. The average gas mileage of José's car is 45 miles per gallon. About how many gallons of gas will be needed to make the trip? **estimate; 10 gal**

84. PART-TIME JOB An employer pays $8.50 per hour. If 20% of pay is withheld for taxes, what are the take-home earnings from 28 hours of work? **exact; $190.40**

Skills Review

Find each sum or difference. (Lesson 0–4)

85. $1.14 + 5.6$ **6.74**

86. $4.28 - 2.4$ **1.88**

87. $8 - 6.35$ **1.65**

88. $\frac{4}{5} + \frac{1}{6}$ $\frac{29}{30}$

89. $\frac{2}{7} + \frac{3}{4}$ $\frac{29}{28}$

90. $\frac{6}{8} - \frac{1}{2}$ $\frac{1}{4}$

4 ASSESS

Yesterday's News Ask students to write a brief statement on how yesterday's lesson on evaluating expressions helped them with today's lesson on finding solutions for open sentences.

The **Four-step Teaching Plan** shows you how to **Focus, Teach, Practice,** and **Assess** each lesson. Each lesson ends with a creative strategy for closing the lesson.

Differentiated Instruction OL BL

Extension Write the solution set {15} on the board. Have students write two equations, based on real-world situations, that match the solution set. For example, students could write, "Bryce scored 86 on a science test with p points for extra credit." $p + 71 = 86$; $86 - p = 71$

1-6 Lesson Notes

1 FOCUS

Vertical Alignment

Before Lesson 1-6
Solve equations with one or two variables.

Lesson 1-6
Represent relations.
Interpret graphs as relations.

After Lesson 1-6
Use algebraic, tabular, graphical, and verbal descriptions of linear functions.

2 TEACH

Scaffolding Questions

Have students read the *Why?* section of the lesson.

Ask:

- What happens to the pressure on your body as you dive deeper into the ocean? It increases.
- Does the pressure depend on the depth or does the depth depend on the pressure? Pressure depends on depth.
- Which variable do you think is the dependent variable? *P*, the pressure independent variable? *h*, the depth

1-6 Relations

Then
You solved equations with one or two variables.
(Lesson 1-5)

Now
- Represent relations.
- Interpret graphs of relations.

IL Learning Standards
8.B.4a Represent algebraic concepts with physical materials, words, diagrams, tables, graphs, equations and inequalities and use appropriate technology.

New Vocabulary
coordinate system
x- and *y*-axes
origin
ordered pair
x- and *y*-coordinates
relation
domain
range
independent variable
dependent variable

IL Math Online
glencoe.com
- Extra Examples
- Personal Tutor
- Self-Check Quiz
- Homework Help

Why?

The deeper in the ocean you are, the greater pressure is on your body. This is because there is more water over you. The force of gravity pulls the water weight down, creating a greater pressure.

The equation that relates the total pressure of the water to the depth is $P = rgh$, where
P = the pressure,
r = the density of water,
g = the acceleration due to gravity, and
h = the height of water above you.

Represent a Relation This relationship between the depth and the pressure exerted can be represented by a line on a coordinate grid.

A **coordinate system** is formed by the intersection of two number lines, the *horizontal axis* and the *vertical axis*.

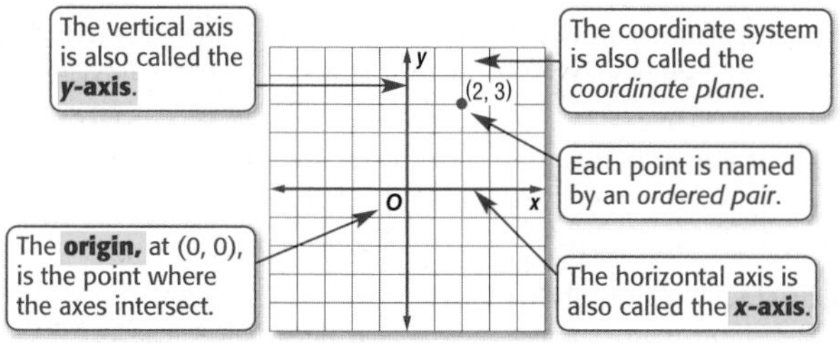
The vertical axis is also called the **y-axis**.
The coordinate system is also called the *coordinate plane*.
Each point is named by an *ordered pair*.
(2, 3)
y
x
O
The **origin**, at (0, 0), is the point where the axes intersect.
The horizontal axis is also called the **x-axis**.

A point is represented on a graph using ordered pairs.

- An **ordered pair** is a set of numbers, or *coordinates*, written in the form (x, y).
- The x-value, called the **x-coordinate**, represents the horizontal placement of the point.
- The y-value, or **y-coordinate**, represents the vertical placement of the point.

A set of ordered pairs is called a **relation**. A relation can be depicted in several different ways. An equation can represent a relation as well as graphs, tables, and mappings.

A **mapping** illustrates how each element of the *domain* is paired with an element in the *range*. The set of the first numbers of the ordered pairs is the **domain**. The set of second numbers of the ordered pairs is the **range** of the relation. This mapping represents the ordered pairs $(-2, 4)$, $(-1, 4)$, $(0, 6)$ $(1, 8)$, and $(2, 8)$.

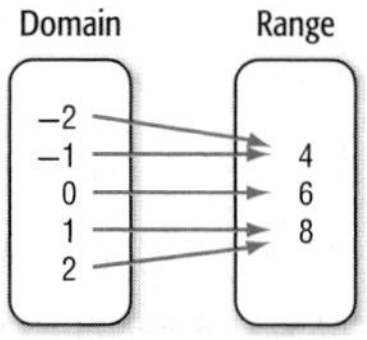
Domain
Range
−2
−1
0
1
2
4
6
8

Lesson 1-6 Resources

Resource	Approaching-Level	On-Level	Beyond-Level	English Learners
Teacher Edition		• Differentiated Instruction, p. 43	• Differentiated Instruction, pp. 43, 44	
Chapter Resource Masters	• Study Guide and Intervention, pp. 37–38 • Skills Practice, p. 39 • Practice, p. 40 • Word Problem Practice, p. 41	• Study Guide and Intervention, pp. 37–38 • Skills Practice, p. 39 • Practice, p. 40 • Word Problem Practice, p. 41 • Enrichment, p. 42	• Practice, p. 40 • Word Problem Practice, p. 41 • Enrichment, p. 42	• Study Guide and Intervention, pp. 37–38 • Skills Practice, p. 39 • Practice, p. 40
Transparencies	• 5-Minute Check Transparency 1-6	• 5-Minute Check Transparency 1-6	• 5-Minute Check Transparency 1-6	• 5-Minute Check Transparency 1-6
Other	• Study Notebook • Teaching Algebra with Manipulatives	• Study Notebook • Teaching Algebra with Manipulatives	• Study Notebook	• Study Notebook • Teaching Algebra with Manipulatives

StudyTip

Multiple Representations Each representation of the same relation serves a different purpose. Graphing the points can show the pattern between the points. A mapping shows you at a glance if elements are paired with the same element.

Study the different representations of the same relation below.

Ordered Pairs

(1, 2)
(−2, 4)
(0, −3)

Table

x	y
1	2
−2	4
0	−3

Graph

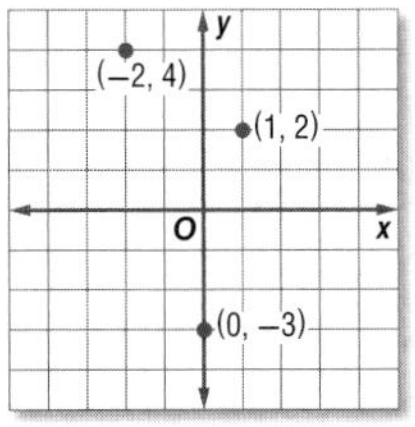

Mapping

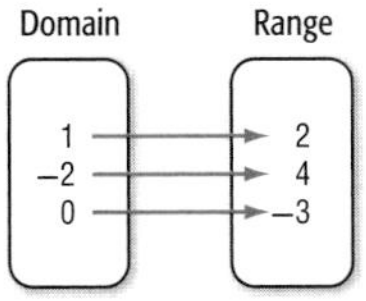

The x-values of a relation are members of the domain and the y-values of a relation are members of the range. In the relation above, the domain is {−2, 1, 0} and the range is {−3, 2, 4}.

EXAMPLE 1 **Representations of a Relation**

a. Express {(2, 5), (−2, 3), (5, −2), (−1, −2)} as a table, a graph, and a mapping.

Table
Place the x-coordinates into the first column of the table. Place the corresponding y-coordinates in the second column of the table.

x	y
2	5
−2	3
5	−2
−1	−2

Graph
Graph each ordered pair on a coordinate plane.

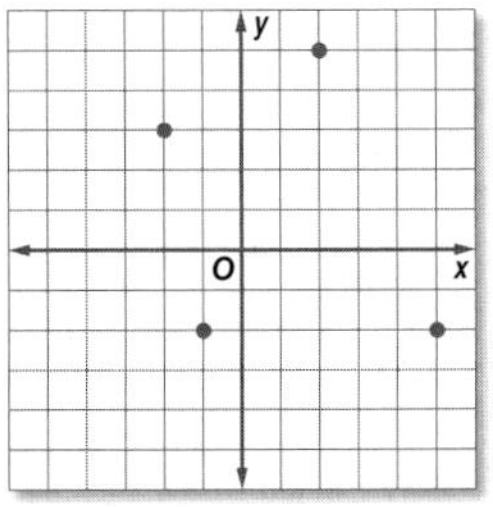

Mapping
List the x-values in the domain and the y-values in the range. Draw arrows from the x-values in the domain to the corresponding y-values in the range.

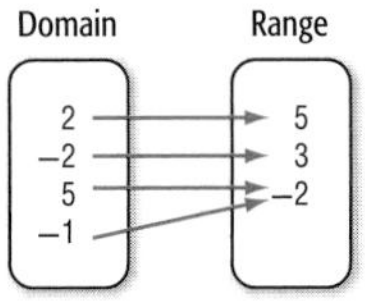

b. Determine the domain and the range of the relation.

The domain of the relation is {2, −2, 5, −1}. The range of the relation is {5, 3, −2}.

Check Your Progress

See margin.

1A. Express {(4, −3), (3, 2), (−4, 1), (0, −3)} as a table, graph, and mapping.

1B. Determine the domain and range. D: {4, 3, −4, 0}; R: {−3, 2, 1}

Personal Tutor glencoe.com

Represent a Relation

Example 1 shows how to represent a relation as a table, a graph, and a mapping. **Example 2** shows how to identify the independent and dependent variables in a relation.

Formative Assessment

Use the Check Your Progress exercises after each Example to determine students' understanding of concepts.

Additional Example

1 **a.** Express {(4, 3), (−2, −1), (2, −4), (0, −4)} as a table, a graph, and a mapping.

x	y
4	3
−2	−1
2	−4
0	−4

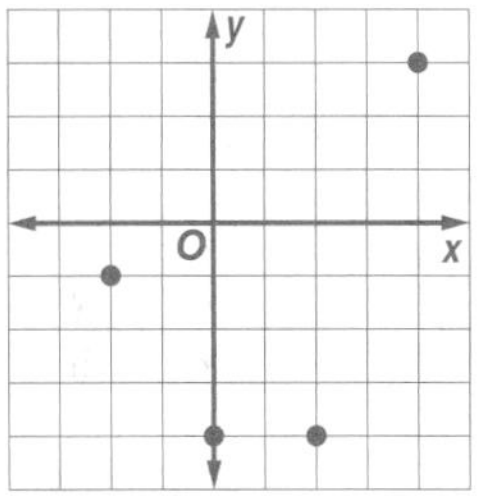

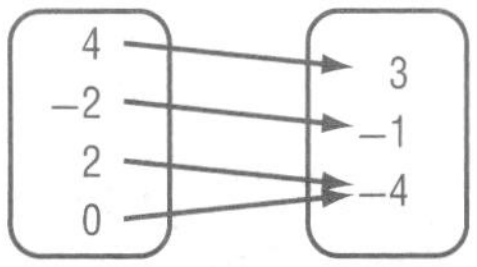

b. Determine the domain and range of the relation.
D = {4, −2, 2, 0};
R = {3, −1, −4}

Additional Examples also in Interactive Classroom PowerPoint® Presentations

IWB INTERACTIVE WHITEBOARD READY

Additional Answer, Check Your Progress

1A.

x	y
4	−3
3	2
−4	1
0	−3

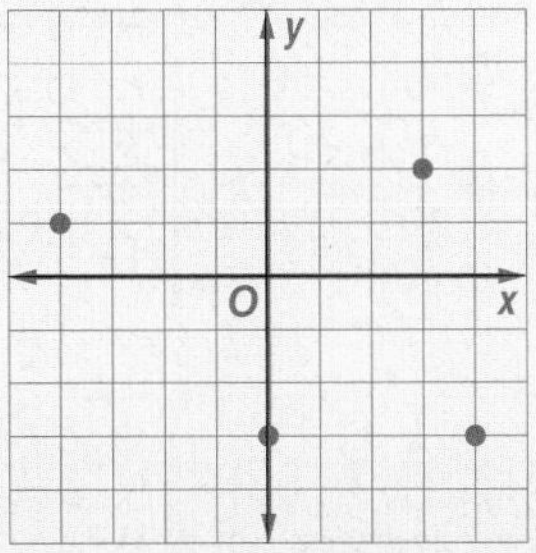

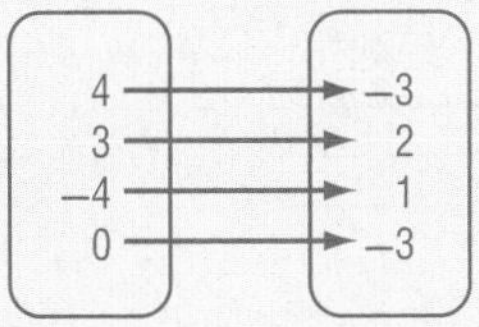

Focus on Mathematical Content

Domain and Range Domain refers to the x-coordinates, or inputs of a relation, and range refers to the y-coordinates or outputs. Repeated values for the domain and range should be listed only once.

Additional Example

2 Identify the independent and the dependent variables for each relation.

a. **CLIMATE** In warm climates, the average amount of electricity used rises as the daily average temperature increases and falls as the daily average temperature decreases. independent variable: temperature; dependent variable: amount of electricity used.

b. **CALORIES** The number of calories you burn increases as the number of minutes that you walk increases. independent variable: time; dependent variable: number of calories burned

Graphs of a Relation

Example 3 shows how to analyze and interpret graphs.

Additional Example

3 The graph represents the temperature in Ms. Ling's classroom on a winter day. Describe what happens in the graph.

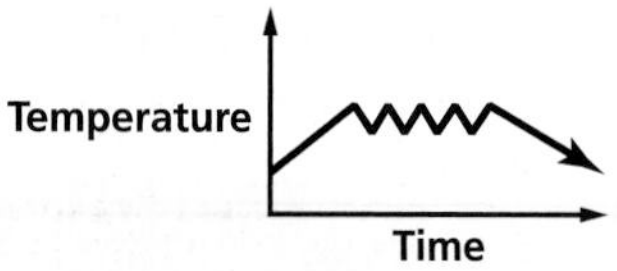

Sample answer: The temperature increases after the heat is turned on. Then the temperature fluctuates up and down because of the thermostat. Finally, the temperature drops when the heat is turned off.

In a relation, the value of the variable that determines the output is called the **independent variable**. The variable with a value that is dependent on the value of the independent variable is called the **dependent variable**. The domain contains values of the independent variable. The range contains the values of the dependent variable.

Real-World Link

In 1948, a movie ticket cost \$0.36. In 2006, the average ticket price in the United States was \$6.50.

Source: National Association of Theatre Owners

Real-World EXAMPLE 2 Independent and Dependent Variables

Identify the independent and dependent variables for each relation.

a. DANCE The dance committee is selling tickets to the Fall Ball. The more tickets that they sell, the greater the amount of money they can spend for decorations.

The number of tickets sold is the independent variable because it is unaffected by the money spent on decorations. The money spent on decorations is the dependent variable because it depends on the number of tickets sold.

b. MOVIES Generally, the average price of going to the movies has steadily increased over time.

Time is the independent variable because it is unaffected by the cost of attending the movies. The price of going to the movies is the dependent variable because it is affected by time.

Check Your Progress

Identify the independent and dependent variables for each relation.

2A. The air pressure inside a tire increases with the temperature.

2B. As the amount of rain decreases, so does the water level of the river.

2A. I: the temperature; D: the air pressure.
2B. I: the amount of rain; D: the water level.
3A. The graph indicates two periods where the car was stopped. The rate of the car is relatively fast in the first section and then slows down.
3B. As time increases, the income increases overall, although not at a constant rate.

Personal Tutor glencoe.com

Graphs of a Relation A relation can be graphed without a scale on either axis. These graphs can be interpreted by analyzing their shape.

EXAMPLE 3 Analyze Graphs

The graph represents the distance Francesca has ridden on her bike. Describe what happens in the graph.

Bike Ride

As time increases, the distance increases until the graph becomes a horizontal line.

So, time is increasing but the distance remains constant. At this section Francesca stopped. Then she continued to ride her bike.

Check Your Progress

Describe what is happening in each graph.

3A. Driving to School

3B. Change in Income

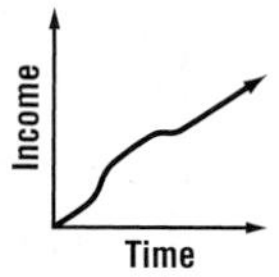

Personal Tutor glencoe.com

Additional Answer

1.

x	y
4	3
−2	2
5	−6

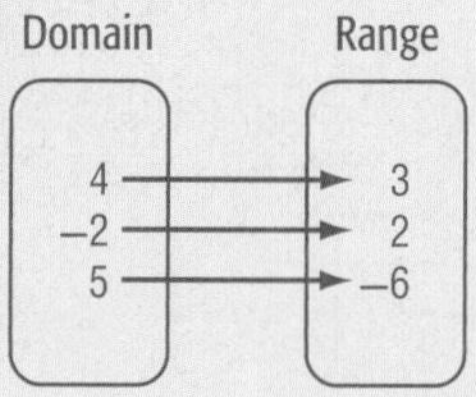

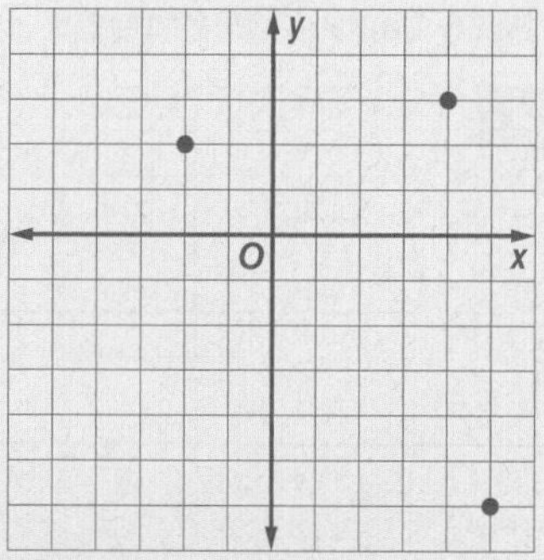

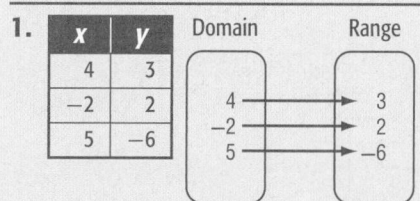

D = {−2, 4, 5}; R = {−6, 2, 3}

Check Your Understanding

Example 1 p. 39

Express each relation as a table, a graph, and a mapping. Then determine the domain and range. 1–2. See margin.

1. $\{(4, 3), (-2, 2), (5, -6)\}$
2. $\{(5, -7), (-1, 4), (0, -5), (-2, 3)\}$

Example 2 p. 40

Identify the independent and dependent variables for each relation.

3. Increasing the temperature of a compound inside a sealed container increases the pressure inside a sealed container. 3–6. See margin.
4. Mike's cell phone is part of a family plan. If he uses more minutes than his share, then there are fewer minutes available for the rest of his family.
5. Julian is buying concert tickets for him and his friends. The more concert tickets he buys the greater the cost.
6. A store is having a sale over Labor Day weekend. The more purchases, the greater the profits.

Example 3 p. 40

Describe what is happening in each graph. 7. See margin.

7. The graph represents the distance the track team runs during a practice.

8. The graph represents revenues generated through an online store.

Overall, the sales increase steadily but there are two sections where the sales decrease or remain constant.

Practice and Problem Solving

● = **Step-by-Step Solutions** begin on page R12. **Extra Practice** begins on page 815.

Example 1 p. 39

Express each relation as a table, a graph, and a mapping. Then determine the domain and range. 9–14. See Ch. 1 Answer Appendix.

9. $\{(0, 0), (-3, 2), (6, 4), (-1, 1)\}$
10. $\{(5, 2), (5, 6), (3, -2), (0, -2)\}$
11. $\{(6, 1), (4, -3), (3, 2), (-1, -3)\}$
12. $\{(-1, 3), (3, -6), (-1, -8), (-3, -7)\}$
13. $\{(6, 7), (3, -2), (8, 8), (-6, 2), (2, -6)\}$
14. $\{(4, -3), (1, 3), (7, -2), (2, -2), (1, 5)\}$

Example 2 p. 40

Identify the independent and dependent variables for each relation.

15. The Spanish classes are having a fiesta lunch. Each student that attends is to bring a Spanish side dish or dessert. The more students that attend, the more food there will be. 15–16. See Ch. 1 Answer Appendix.
16. The faster you drive your car, the longer it will take to come to a complete stop.

Example 3 p. 40

Describe what is happening in each graph. 17–18. See Ch. 1 Answer Appendix.

17. The graph represents the height of a bungee jumper.

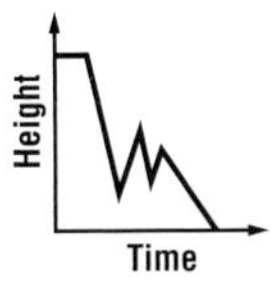

18. The graph represents the sales of lawn mowers.

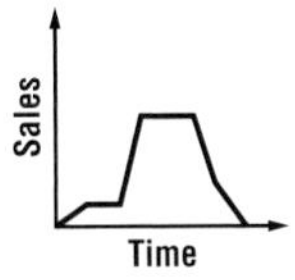

3 PRACTICE

Formative Assessment

Use Exercises 1–8 to check for understanding.

Use the chart at the bottom of this page to customize assignments for your students.

Tips for New Teachers

Reading Tip Point out to students that the letters D and R are often used to name the sets of numbers that represent the *domain* and *range*.

Additional Answers

2.

x	y
5	−7
−1	4
0	−5
−2	3

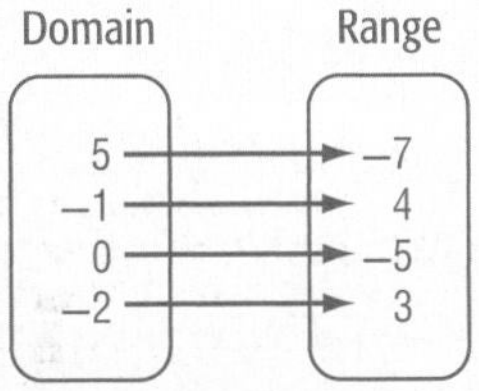

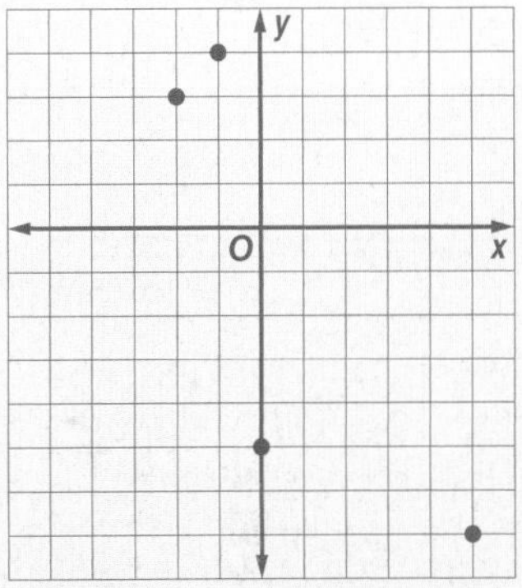

$D = \{-2, -1, 0, 5\}$;
$R = \{-7, -5, 3, 4\}$

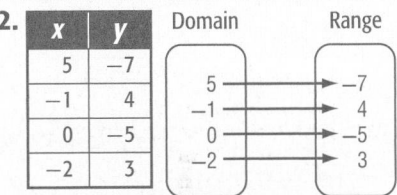

3. I: the temperature of the compound; D: the pressure of the compound
4. I: the number of minutes Mike uses on his cell phone; D: the number of minutes that are left
5. I: number of concert tickets; D: cost of tickets
6. I: number of customers who purchase something; D: the profits
7. The track team starts by running or walking, and then stops for a short period of time, then continues at the same pace. Finally, they run or walk at a slower pace.

Differentiated Homework Options

Level	Assignment	Two-Day Option	
AL Basic	9–20, 38, 40, 42–60	9–19 odd, 43–46	10–20 even, 38, 40, 42, 47–60
OL Core	9–31 odd, 32–38, 40, 42–60	9–20, 43–46	2–38, 40, 42, 47–60
BL Advanced	21–54, (optional: 55–60)		

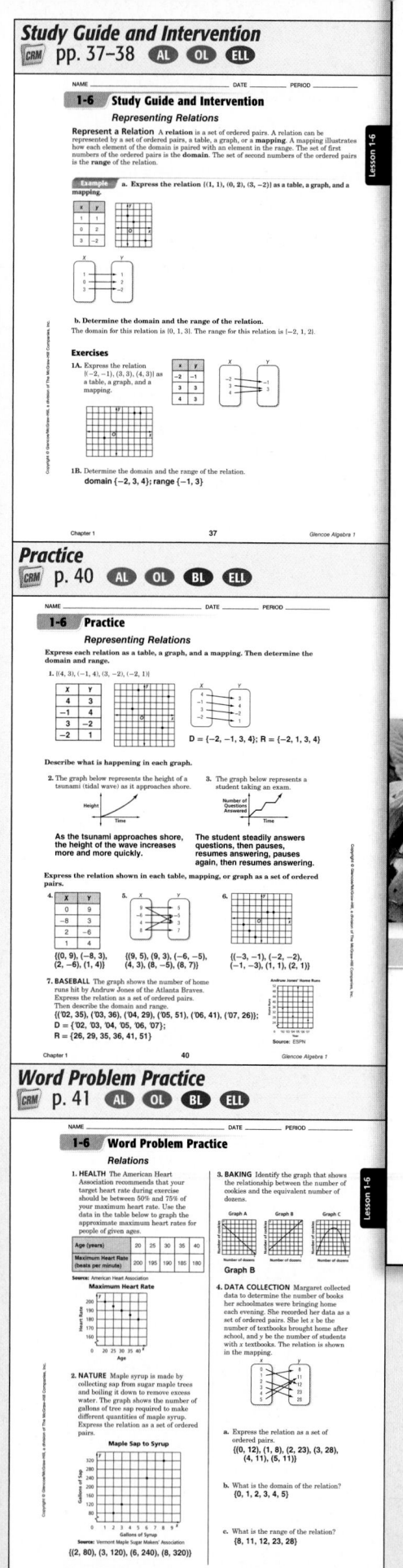

Study Guide and Intervention
CRM pp. 37–38 AL OL ELL

NAME ______ DATE ______ PERIOD ______

1-6 Study Guide and Intervention
Representing Relations

Lesson 1-6

Represent a Relation A **relation** is a set of ordered pairs. A relation can be represented by a set of ordered pairs, a table, a graph, or a **mapping**. A mapping illustrates how each element of the domain is paired with an element in the range. The set of first numbers of the ordered pairs is the **domain**. The set of second numbers of the ordered pairs is the **range** of the relation.

Example **a. Express the relation {(1, 1), (0, 2), (3, −2)} as a table, a graph, and a mapping.**

x	y
1	1
0	2
3	−2

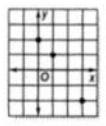
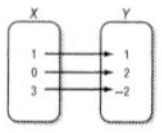

b. Determine the domain and the range of the relation.
The domain for this relation is {0, 1, 3}. The range for this relation is {−2, 1, 2}.

Exercises

1A. Express the relation {(−2, −1), (3, 3), (4, 3)} as a table, a graph, and a mapping.

x	y
−2	−1
3	3
4	3

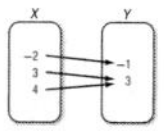

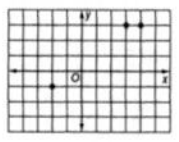

1B. Determine the domain and the range of the relation.
domain {−2, 3, 4}; range {−1, 3}

Chapter 1 37 *Glencoe Algebra 1*

Practice
CRM p. 40 AL OL BL ELL

NAME ______ DATE ______ PERIOD ______

1-6 Practice
Representing Relations

Express each relation as a table, a graph, and a mapping. Then determine the domain and range.

1. {(4, 3), (−1, 4), (3, −2), (−2, 1)}

X	Y
4	3
−1	4
3	−2
−2	1

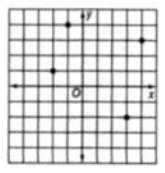
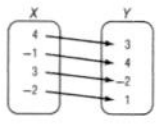

D = {−2, −1, 3, 4}; R = {−2, 1, 3, 4}

Describe what is happening in each graph.

2. The graph below represents the height of a tsunami (tidal wave) as it approaches shore.

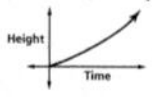

As the tsunami approaches shore, the height of the wave increases more and more quickly.

3. The graph below represents a student taking an exam.

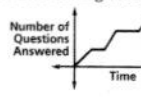

The student steadily answers questions, then pauses, resumes answering, pauses again, then resumes answering.

Express the relation shown in each table, mapping, or graph as a set of ordered pairs.

4.

X	Y
0	9
−8	3
2	−6
1	4

{(0, 9), (−8, 3), (2, −6), (1, 4)}

5.

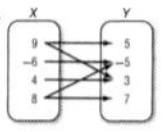

{(9, 5), (9, 3), (−6, −5), (4, 3), (8, −5), (8, 7)}

6.

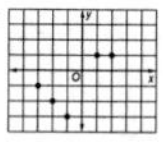

{(−3, −1), (−2, −2), (−1, −3), (1, 1), (2, 1)}

7. BASEBALL The graph shows the number of home runs hit by Andruw Jones of the Atlanta Braves. Express the relation as a set of ordered pairs. Then describe the domain and range.
{('02, 35), ('03, 36), ('04, 29), ('05, 51), ('06, 41), ('07, 26)};
D = {'02, '03, '04, '05, '06, '07};
R = {26, 29, 35, 36, 41, 51}

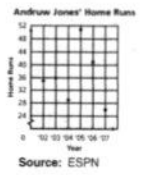

Source: ESPN

Chapter 1 40 *Glencoe Algebra 1*

Word Problem Practice
CRM p. 41 AL OL BL ELL

NAME ______ DATE ______ PERIOD ______

1-6 Word Problem Practice
Relations

Lesson 1-6

1. HEALTH The American Heart Association recommends that your target heart rate during exercise should be between 50% and 75% of your maximum heart rate. Use the data in the table below to graph the approximate maximum heart rates for people of given ages.

Age (years)	20	25	30	35	40
Maximum Heart Rate (beats per minute)	200	195	190	185	180

Source: American Heart Association

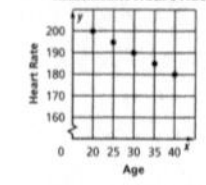

2. NATURE Maple syrup is made by collecting sap from sugar maple trees and boiling it down to remove excess water. The graph shows the number of gallons of tree sap required to make different quantities of maple syrup. Express the relation as a set of ordered pairs.

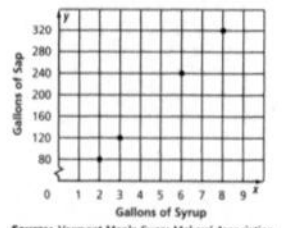

Source: Vermont Maple Sugar Makers' Association

{(2, 80), (3, 120), (6, 240), (8, 320)}

3. BAKING Identify the graph that shows the relationship between the number of cookies and the equivalent number of dozens.

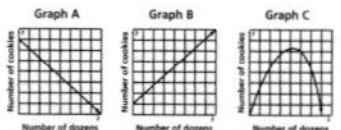

Graph B

4. DATA COLLECTION Margaret collected data to determine the number of books her schoolmates were bringing home each evening. She recorded her data as a set of ordered pairs. She let x be the number of textbooks brought home after school, and y be the number of students with x textbooks. The relation is shown in the mapping.

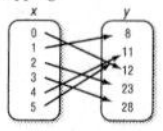

a. Express the relation as a set of ordered pairs.
{(0, 12), (1, 8), (2, 23), (3, 28), (4, 11), (5, 11)}

b. What is the domain of the relation?
{0, 1, 2, 3, 4, 5}

c. What is the range of the relation?
{8, 11, 12, 23, 28}

Chapter 1 41 *Glencoe Algebra 1*

19. The baseball card increases in value quickly.
20. The graph shows the car moving, and then stopping, and then moving at a faster pace. The car stops a second time, then continues moving.
27. {(1, 2.50), (2, 5.50), (5, 10.00), (8, 18.75)}; D = {1, 2, 5, 8}; R = {2.50, 5.50, 10.00, 18.75}
28. {(−2, 3), (−1, 2), (0, −1), (1, −2), (2, 1)}; $D = \{-2, -1, 0, 1, 2\}$; $R = \{3, 2, -1, -2, 1\}$
29. {(4, −1), (8, 9), (−2, −6), (7, −3)}
30. {(−5, 6), (−4, 9), (2, 1), (3, 9)}
31. {(4, −2), (−1, 3), (−2, −1), (1, 4)}

Describe what is happening in each graph.

19. The graph represents the value of a rare baseball card.

20. The graph represents the distance covered on an extended car ride.

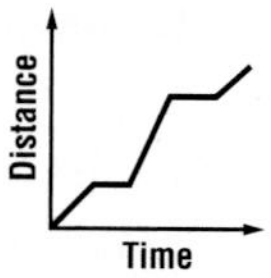

B **For Exercises 21–23, use the graph at the right.**

21. Name the ordered pair at point A and explain what it represents.

22. Name the ordered pair at point B and explain what it represents.

23. Identify the independent and dependent variables for the relation.
I: number of dogs walked; D: amount earned
21. (1, 5); The dog walker earns $5 for walking 1 dog.
22. (5, 25); The dog walker earns $25 for walking 5 dogs.

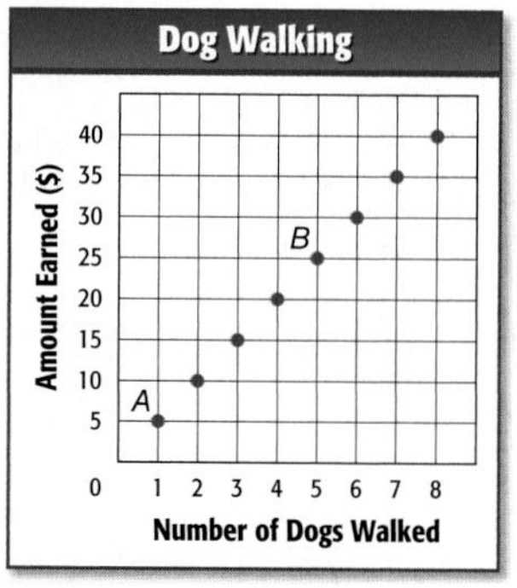

For Exercises 24–26, use the graph at the right.

24. Name the ordered pair at point C and explain what it represents.

25. Name the ordered pair at point D and explain what it represents.

26. Identify the independent and dependent variables. I: year; D: sales
24. (3, 2); In the year 2003, sales were about $2 million.
25. (5, 6); In the year 2005, sales were about $6 million.

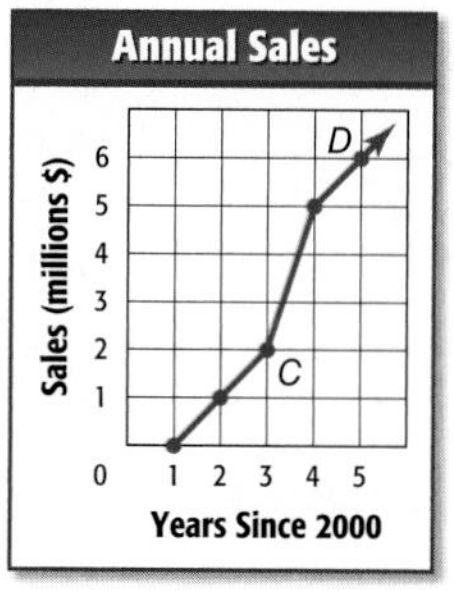

Real-World Link

Allow one gallon of water for each inch of fish you have in the tank.

Source: Tim's Tropicals

Express each relation as a set of ordered pairs. Describe the domain and range.

27.

Buying Aquarium Fish	
Number of Fish	**Total Cost**
1	$2.50
2	$5.50
5	$10.00
8	$18.75

28.

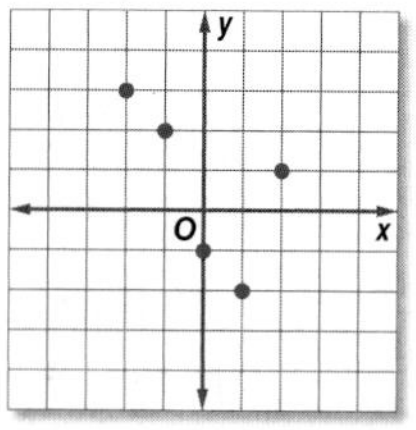

Express the relation in each table, mapping, or graph as a set of ordered pairs.

29.

x	y
4	−1
8	9
−2	−6
7	−3

30.

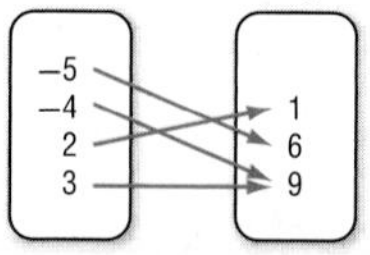

31.

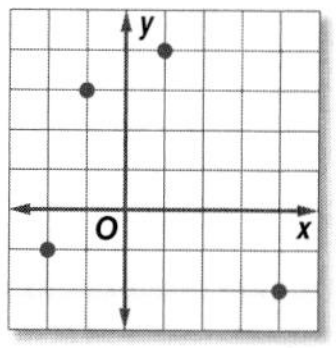

Enrichment
CRM p. 42 OL BL

NAME ______ DATE ______ PERIOD ______

1-6 Enrichment

Even and Odd Functions

We know that numbers can be either even or odd. It is also true that functions can be defined as even or odd. For a function to be even means that it is symmetric about the y-axis. That is, if you fold the graph along the y-axis, the two halves of the graph match exactly. For a function to be odd means that the function is symmetric about the origin. This means if you rotate the graph using the origin as the center, it will match its original position before completing a full turn.

The function $y = x^2$ is an even function.

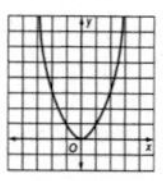

The function $y = x^5$ is an odd function. If you rotate the graph 180° the graph will lie on itself.

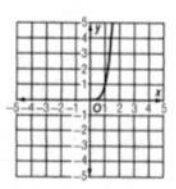

Additional Answers

32. Graph B; the graph indicates 2 stopping periods where the athlete prepared for the next event.

33. Sample answer:

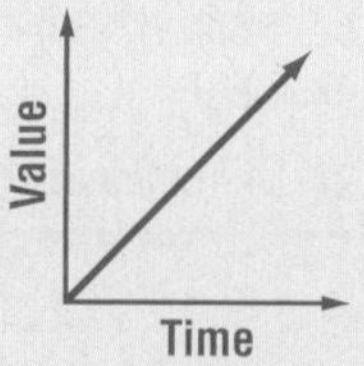

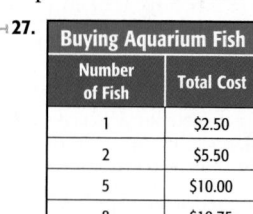

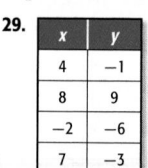

Real-World Link

A triathlon is a competitive sport in which participants swim 2.4 miles, bicycle 112 miles, and then run 26.2 miles. The athlete's total time includes transitioning from one activity to the next.

Source: Ironman World Championship

32. COMPETITIVE SPORTS Refer to the information at the left. Which of the following graphs best represents a participant in a triathlon? Explain. **See margin.**

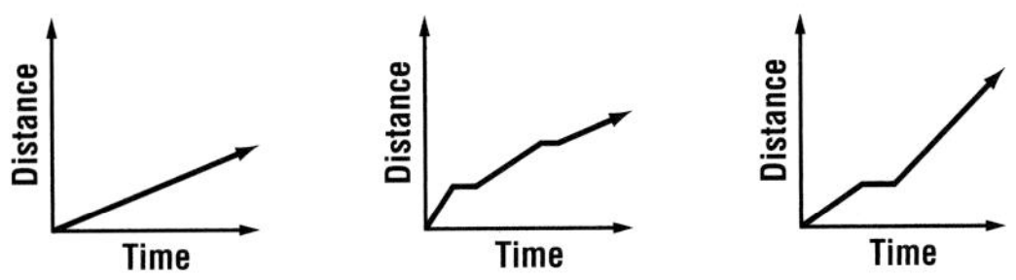

Draw a graph to represent each situation. **33–36. See margin.**

33. ANTIQUES A grandfather clock that is over 100 years old has increased in value rapidly from when it was first purchased.

34. CAR A car depreciates in value. The value decreases quickly in the first few years.

35. REAL ESTATE A house typically increases in value over time.

36. EXERCISE An athlete alternates between running and walking during a workout.

37. PHYSIOLOGY A typical adult has about 2 pounds of water for each 3 pounds of body weight. This can be represented by the equation $w = 2\left(\frac{b}{3}\right)$, where w is the weight of water in pounds and b is the body weight in pounds. **a–d. See Chapter 1 Answer Appendix.**

a. Make a table to show the relation between body and water weight for people weighing 100, 105, 110, 115, 120, 125, and 130 pounds. Round to the nearest tenth if necessary.

b. What are the independent and dependent variables?

c. State the domain and range, and then graph the relation.

d. Reverse the independent and dependent variables. Graph this relation. Explain what the graph indicates in this circumstance.

H.O.T. Problems

Use Higher-Order Thinking Skills

38, 40–42. See Chapter 1 Answer Appendix.

38. OPEN ENDED Describe a real-life situation that can be represented using a relation and discuss how one of the quantities in the relation depends on the other. Then represent the relation in three different ways.

39. CHALLENGE Describe a real-world situation where it is reasonable to have a negative number included in the domain or range. **See students' work.**

40. REASONING Compare and contrast dependent and independent variables.

41. CHALLENGE The table presents a relation. Graph the ordered pairs. Then reverse the y-coordinate and the x-coordinate in each ordered pair. Graph these ordered pairs on the same coordinate plane. Graph the line $y = x$. Describe the relationship between the two sets of ordered pairs.

x	y
0	1
1	3
2	5
3	7

42. WRITING MATH Use the data about the pressure of water on page 38 to explain the difference between dependent and independent variables.

Differentiated Instruction

OL BL

Social You may want to spend extra time on independent and dependent variables, since an understanding of these concepts provides the foundation for later work with functions. For Exercise 38, have students generate several real-world scenarios with dependent and independent variables. Then have students work in small groups to compare and contrast variables.

Tips for New Teachers

Sense-Making For Exercise 41, explain to students that reversing x- and y-coordinates results in the inverse of a relation. Point out that the inverse of a relation has the same number of ordered pairs as the relation.

Additional Answers

34. Sample answer:

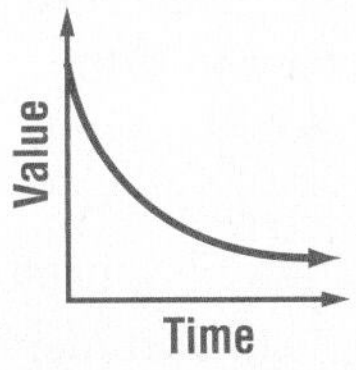

35. Sample answer:

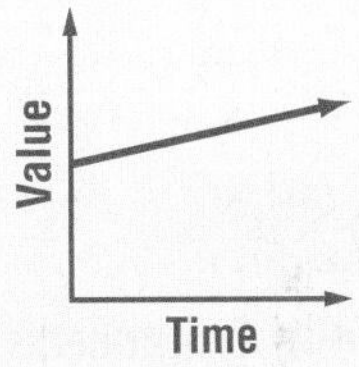

36. Sample answer:

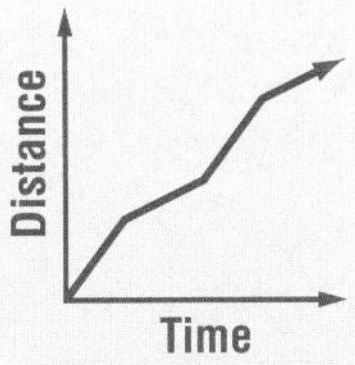

40. Sample answer: A dependent variable is determined by the independent variable for a given relation.

42. Sample answer: Real-world data can be recorded and visualized in a graph and by expressing an event in terms of another event. Graphs and mappings give you a visual representation of the situation which is easier to analyze and evaluate. The value of a dependent variable is dependent on the value of the independent variable. The independent variable is the depth of water. The pressure exerted under the water depends on the height or depth of the water.

PSAE PRACTICE 6.11.18, 8.11.01, 9.11.09, 6.11.13

43. A school's cafeteria employees surveyed 250 students asking what beverage they drank with lunch. They used the data to create the table below.

Beverage	Number of Students
milk	38
chocolate milk	112
juice	75
water	25

What percent of the students surveyed preferred drinking juice with lunch? **B**

A 25% C 35%
B 30% D 40%

44. Which of the following is equivalent to $6(3 - g) + 2(11 - g)$? **H**

F $2(20 - g)$ H $8(5 - g)$
G $8(14 - g)$ J $40 - g$

45. SHORT RESPONSE Grant and Hector want to build a clubhouse at the midpoint between their houses. If Grant's house is at point *G* and Hector's house is at point *H*, what will be the coordinates of the clubhouse? **(−1, −3)**

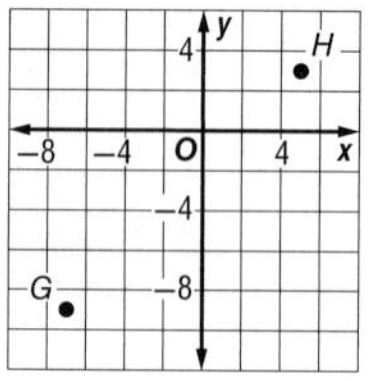

46. If $3b = 2b$, which of the following is true? **A**

A $b = 0$
B $b = \frac{2}{3}$
C $b = 1$
D $b = \frac{3}{2}$

Spiral Review

Solve each equation. (Lesson 1-5)

47. $6(a + 5) = 42$ **2**
48. $92 = k + 11$ **81**
49. $17 = \frac{45}{w} + 2$ **3**

50. HOT-AIR BALLOON A hot-air balloon owner charges $150 for a one-hour ride. If he gave 6 rides on Saturday and 5 rides on Sunday, write and evaluate an expression to describe his total income for the weekend. (Lesson 1-4) **150(6 + 5); $1650**

51. LOLLIPOPS A bag of lollipops contains 19 cherry, 13 grape, 8 sour apple, 15 strawberry, and 9 orange flavored lollipops. What is the probability of drawing a sour apple flavored lollipop? (Lesson 0-11) $\frac{1}{8}$

Find the perimeter of each figure. (Lesson 0-7)

52.
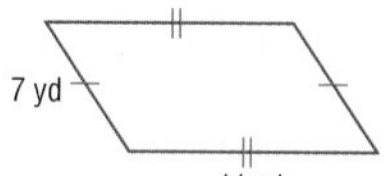

36 yd

53.
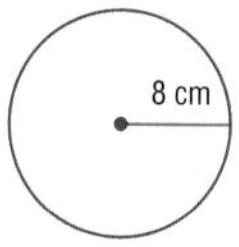

50.27 cm

54.
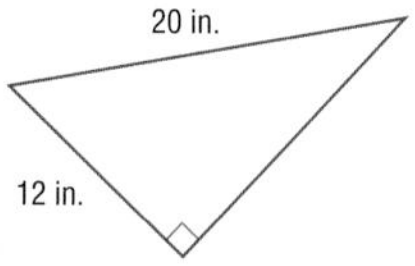

48 in.

Skills Review

Evaluate each expression. (Lesson 1-2)

55. 8^2 **64**
56. $(-6)^2$ **36**
57. $(2.5)^2$ **6.25**
58. $(-1.8)^2$ **3.24**
59. $(3 + 4)^2$ **49**
60. $(1 - 4)^2$ **9**

TEACH with TECH

INTERACTIVE WHITEBOARD Create a short quiz of several expressions (such as 6 • 5 − 4 ÷ 1) to determine if students understand the order of operations. You can do this at the board or use your SRS software. Ask students to perform the first, second, etc… operations. You can develop a key (such as A for add, B for subtract, C for multiply, and D for divide) for responses. You will be able to track how many students understand the order of operations.

4 ASSESS

Ticket out the Door Tell students that temperatures, in Fahrenheit, were 81°, 84°, 85°, 86°, and 88° on days 1–5. Ask students to identify the independent and dependent variables on a slip of paper.

Formative Assessment

Check for student understanding of Lessons 1-5 and 1-6.

CRM Quiz 3, p. 58

Extension Activities help you cultivate skills that students will need to have success in higher mathematics.

Differentiated Instruction BL

Extension Have students draw a graph that shows the height of water in a tub as it is filling, when the water is turned off, when a person gets into the water, then out, and as it is draining. Remind students to label the axes of their graphs. See students' graphs. Students can also exchange and discuss their graphs.

1-7 Functions

Then
You solved equations with elements from a replacement set. (Lesson 1-5)

Now
- Determine whether a relation is a function.
- Find function values.

IL Learning Standards

8.C.4b Apply algebraic properties and procedures with matrices, vectors, **functions** and sequences **using data found in business, industry and consumer situations.**

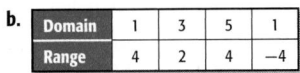

New Vocabulary
function
discrete function
continuous function
vertical line test
nonlinear function

IL Math Online

glencoe.com
- Extra Examples
- Personal Tutor
- Self-Check Quiz
- Homework Help

Why?

The distance a car travels from when the brakes are applied to the car's complete stop is the stopping distance. This includes time for the driver to react. The faster a car is traveling, the longer the stopping distance. The stopping distance is a function of the speed of the car.

Stopping Distance of a Passenger Car

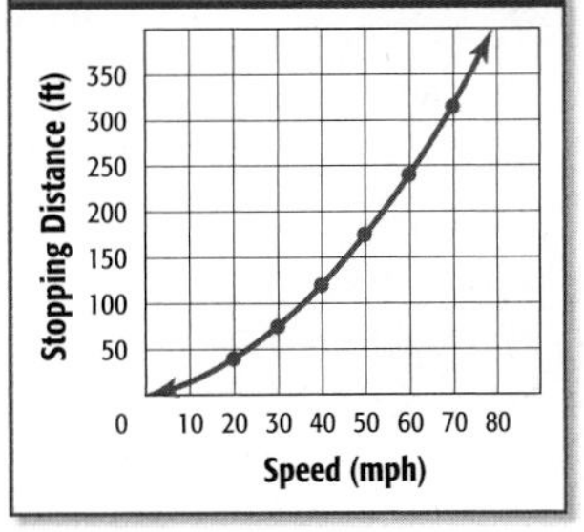

Identify Functions A **function** is a relationship between input and output. In a function, there is exactly one output for each input.

Key Concept — Function

For Your FOLDABLE

Words A function is a relation in which each element of the domain is paired with *exactly* one element of the range.

Examples

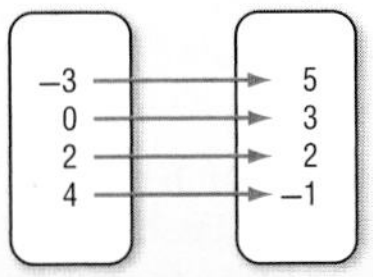

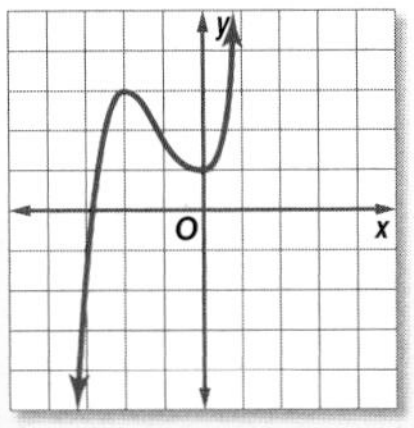

EXAMPLE 1 Identify Functions

Determine whether each relation is a function. Explain.

a.

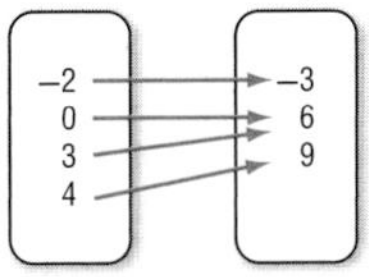

For each member of the domain, there is only one member of the range. So this mapping represents a function. It does not matter if more than one element of the domain is paired with one element of the range.

b.

Domain	1	3	5	1
Range	4	2	4	−4

The element 1 in the domain is paired with both 4 and −4 in the range. So, when x equals 1 there is more than one possible value for y. This relation is not a function.

Check Your Progress

1. $\{(2, 1), (3, -2), (3, 1), (2, -2)\}$ Not a function; sample answer: The value 2 in the domain is paired with 1 and −2.

Personal Tutor glencoe.com

1-7 Lesson Notes

1 FOCUS

Vertical Alignment

Before Lesson 1-7
Solve equations with elements from a replacement set.

Lesson 1-7
Determine whether a relation is a function.
Find function values.

After Lesson 1-7
Use algebraic, tabular, graphical, and verbal descriptions of linear functions.

2 TEACH

Scaffolding Questions

Have students read the *Why?* section of the lesson.

Ask:
- What does the ordered pair (30, 75) on the graph represent? the stopping distance of a car traveling at 30 mph
- About how many feet does it take to stop traveling at 60 mph? about 240 ft
- On what does the stopping distance depend? the speed of the car

Lesson 1-7 Resources

Resource	Approaching-Level	On-Level	Beyond-Level	English Learners
Teacher Edition	• Differentiated Instruction, p. 48	• Differentiated Instruction, p. 48	• Differentiated Instruction, pp. 48, 52	• Differentiated Instruction, p. 48
Chapter Resource Masters	• Study Guide and Intervention, pp. 43–44 • Skills Practice, p. 45 • Practice, p. 46 • Word Problem Practice, p. 47	• Study Guide and Intervention, pp. 43–44 • Skills Practice, p. 45 • Practice, p. 46 • Word Problem Practice, p. 47 • Enrichment, p. 48	• Practice, p. 46 • Word Problem Practice, p. 47 • Enrichment, p. 48	• Study Guide and Intervention, pp. 43–44 • Skills Practice, p. 45 • Practice, p. 46
Transparencies	• 5-Minute Check Transparency 1-7	• 5-Minute Check Transparency 1-7	• 5-Minute Check Transparency 1-7	• 5-Minute Check Transparency 1-7
Other	• Study Notebook • Teaching Algebra with Manipulatives	• Study Notebook • Teaching Algebra with Manipulatives	• Study Notebook	• Study Notebook • Teaching Algebra with Manipulatives

Identify Functions

Example 1 shows how to determine if a relation is a function. **Example 2** shows how to draw a graph of a real-world situation and how to determine whether the function is discrete or continuous. **Example 3** shows how to determine if an equation is a function by graphing and using the vertical line test.

Formative Assessment

Use the Check Your Progress exercises after each Example to determine students' understanding of concepts.

Additional Example

1 Determine whether each relation is a function. Explain.

a.

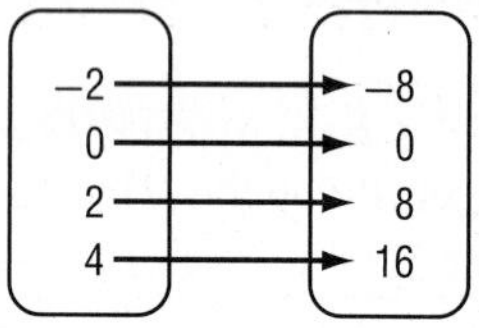

Function; each element of the domain is paired with exactly one member of the range.

b.

Domain	Range
−7	−12
−4	−9
2	3
5	0

Function; each element of the domain is paired with exactly one member of the range.

Additional Examples also in Interactive Classroom PowerPoint® Presentations

IWB INTERACTIVE WHITEBOARD READY

Real-World Link

The Icehotel, located in the Arctic Circle in Sweden, is a hotel made out of ice. The ice insulates the igloo-like hotel so the temperature is at least −8°C.

Source: Icehotel

A graph that consists of points that are not connected is a **discrete function**. A function graphed with a line or smooth curve is a **continuous function**.

EXAMPLE 2 Draw Graphs

ICE SCULPTING At an ice sculpting competition, each sculpture's height was measured to make sure that it was within the regulated height range of 0 to 6 feet. The measurements were as follows: Team 1, 4 feet; Team 2, 4.5 feet; Team 3, 3.2 feet; Team 4, 5.1 feet; Team 5, 4.8 feet.

a. Make a table of values showing the relation between the ice sculpting team and the height of their sculpture.

Team Number	1	2	3	4	5
Height (ft)	4	4.5	3.2	5.1	4.8

b. Determine the domain and range of the function.

The domain of the function is {1, 2, 3, 4, 5} because this set represents values of the independent variable. It is unaffected by the heights.

The range of the function is {4, 4.5, 3.2, 5.1, 4.8} because this set represents values of the dependent variable. This value depends on the team number.

c. Write the data as a set of ordered pairs. Then graph the data.

Use the table. The team number is the independent variable and the height of the sculpture is the dependent variable. Therefore, the ordered pairs are (1, 4), (2, 4.5), (3, 3.2), (4, 5.1), and (5, 4.8).

Because the team numbers and their corresponding heights cannot be between the points given, the points should not be connected.

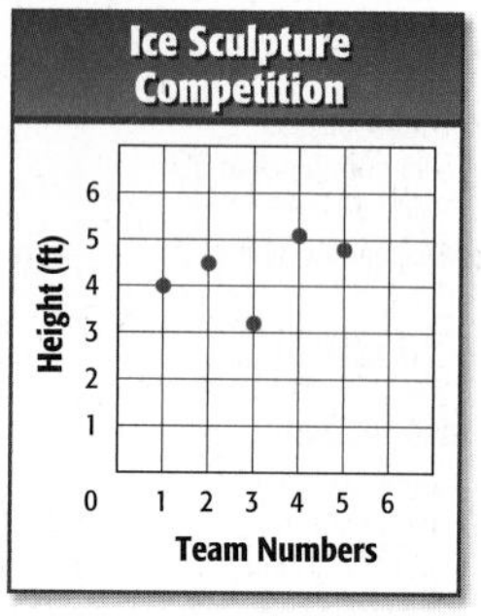

d. State whether the function is *discrete* or *continuous*. Explain your reasoning.

Because the points are not connected, the function is discrete.

Check Your Progress

2. A bird feeder will hold up to 3 quarts of seed. The feeder weighs 2.3 pounds when empty and 13.4 pounds when full. **2A–2D. See Ch. 1 Answer Appendix.**

A. Make a table that shows the bird feeder with 0, 1, 2, and 3 quarts of seed in it weighing 2.3, 6, 9.7, 13.4 pounds respectively.

B. Determine the domain and range of the function.

C. Write the data as a set of ordered pairs. Then graph the data.

D. State whether the function is *discrete* or *continuous*. Explain your reasoning.

Personal Tutor glencoe.com

Focus on Mathematical Content

Functions The set of *x*-values is the domain, and the corresponding set of *y*-values is the range. A function is a relation in which each element of the domain is paired with exactly one element of the range.

You can use the **vertical line test** to see if a graph represents a function. If a vertical line intersects the graph more than once, then the graph is not a function. Otherwise, the relation is a function.

Function

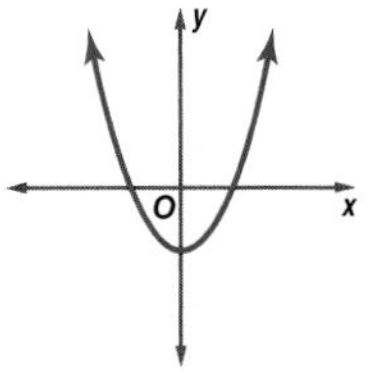

Not a Function

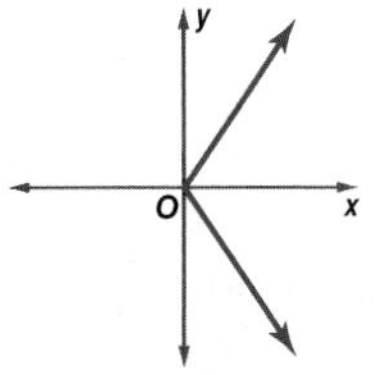

Function

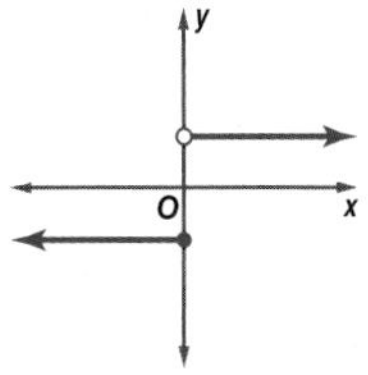

Recall from Lesson 1-6 that an equation is a representation of a relation. If the relation is a function, then the equation represents a function.

StudyTip

Vertical Line Test One way to perform the vertical line test is to use a pencil. Place your pencil vertically on the graph and move from left to right. If the pencil passes over the graph in only one place, then the graph represents a function.

EXAMPLE 3 Equations as Functions

Determine whether $-3x + y = 8$ represents a function.

First make a table of values. Then graph the equation.

x	−1	0	1	2
y	5	8	11	14

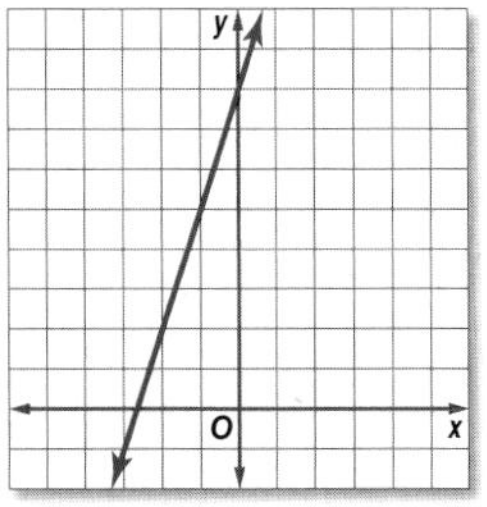

The graph is a line. Place a pencil at the left of the graph to represent a vertical line. Slowly move the pencil across the graph.

For any value of x, the vertical line passes through no more than one point on the graph. So, the graph and the equation represent a function.

Check Your Progress

Determine if each of the equations represents a function.

3A. $4x = 8$ no

3B. $4x = y + 8$ yes

Personal Tutor glencoe.com

A function can be represented in different ways.

Concept Summary Representations of a Function

For Your FOLDABLE

<table>
<tr><th>Table</th><th>Mapping</th><th>Equation</th><th>Graph</th></tr>
<tr>
<td>

x	y
−2	1
0	−1
2	1

</td>
<td>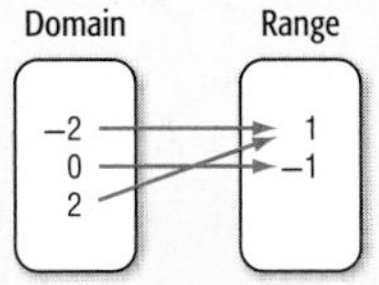</td>
<td>$f(x) = \frac{1}{2}x^2 - 1$</td>
<td>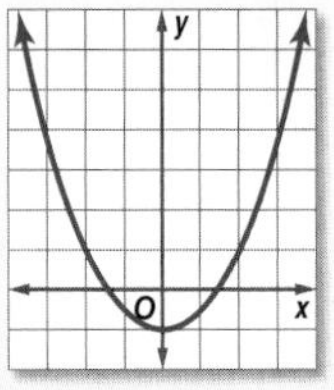</td>
</tr>
</table>

Additional Examples

2 **SCHOOL CAFETERIA** There are three lunch periods at a school. During the first period, 352 students eat. During the second period, 304 students eat. During the third period, 391 students eat.

a. Make a table showing the number of students for each of the three lunch periods.

Period	1	2	3
Number of Students	352	304	391

b. Determine the domain and range of the function.
D = {1, 2, 3}; R = {352, 304, 391}

c. Write the data as a set of ordered pairs. Then graph the data. {(1, 352), (2, 304), (3, 391)}

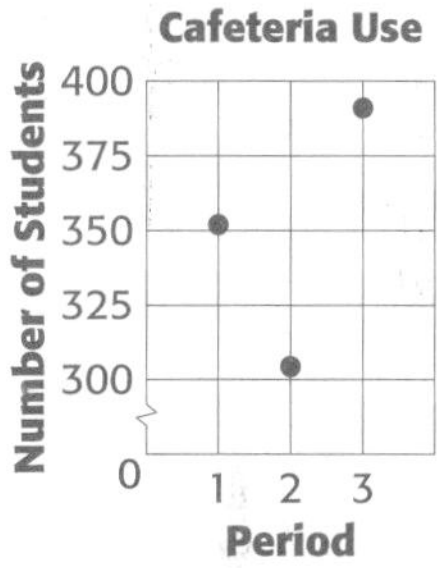

d. State whether the function is *discrete* or *continuous*. Explain your reasoning.
Because the points are not connected, the function is discrete.

3 Determine whether $x = -2$ represents a function. not a function

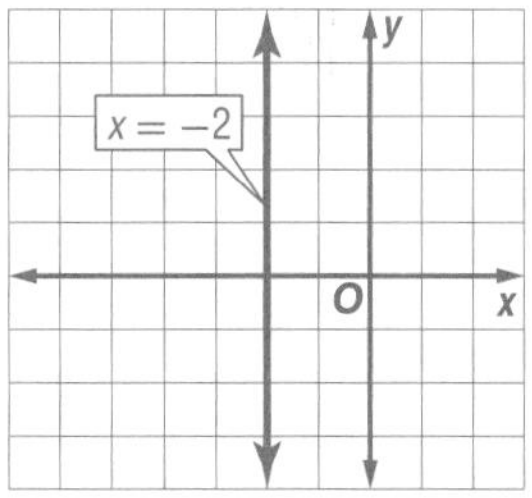

TEACH with TECH

INTERACTIVE WHITEBOARD Display a graph on the board and demonstrate the vertical line test. Draw a vertical line and drag it from left to right across the graph. Show students that if there is any place where a vertical line intersects the graph at more than one point, the graph is not a function.

Find Function Values

Example 4 shows how to find the element in the range that corresponds to a given element in the domain of a linear function. **Example 5** shows how to find the element in the range that corresponds to a given element in the domain of a nonlinear function.

Watch Out!

Preventing Errors Function notation is sometimes difficult for students to comprehend. Stress that $f(x)$ does not mean "f times x."

Additional Examples

4 For $f(x) = 3x - 4$, find each value.

a. $f(4)$ 8

b. $f(-5)$ -19

5 If $h(t) = 1248 - 160t + 16t^2$, find each value.

a. $h(3)$ 912

b. $h(2z)$ $1248 - 320z + 64z^2$

StudyTip

Function Notation Functions are indicated by the symbol $f(x)$. This is read f of x. Other letters, such as g or h, can be used to represent functions.

Find Function Values Equations that are functions can be written in a form called **function notation**. For example, consider $y = 3x - 8$.

Equation	Function Notation
$y = 3x - 8$	$f(x) = 3x - 8$

In a function, x represents the elements of the domain, and $f(x)$ represents the elements of the range. Suppose you want to find the value in the range that corresponds to the element 5 in the domain. This is written $f(5)$ and is read "f of 5." The value $f(5)$ is found by substituting 5 for x in the equation.

EXAMPLE 4 Function Values

For $f(x) = -4x + 7$, find each value.

a. $f(2)$

$f(2) = -4(2) + 7$ — $x = 2$

$= -8 + 7$ — Multiply.

$= -1$ — Add.

b. $f(-3) + 1$

$f(-3) + 1 = [-4(-3) + 7] + 1$ — $x = -3$

$= 19 + 1$ — Simplify.

$= 20$ — Add.

Check Your Progress

For $f(x) = 2x - 3$, find each value.

4A. $f(1)$ -1

4B. $6 - f(5)$ -1

4C. $f(-2)$ -7

4D. $f(-1) + f(2)$ -4

Personal Tutor glencoe.com

A function with a variable term that has an exponent other than 1 forms a **nonlinear function** and the graph is not a line.

EXAMPLE 5 Nonlinear Function Values

If $h(t) = -16t^2 + 68t + 2$, find each value.

a. $h(4)$

$h(4) = -16(4)^2 + 68(4) + 2$ — Replace t with 4.

$= -256 + 272 + 2$ — Multiply.

$= 18$ — Add.

b. $2[h(g)]$

$2[h(g)] = 2[-16(g)^2 + 68(g) + 2]$ — Replace t with g.

$= 2(-16g^2 + 68g + 2)$ — Simplify.

$= -32g^2 + 136g + 4$ — Distributive Property

Check Your Progress

If $f(t) = 2t^3$, find each value.

5A. $f(4)$ 128

5B. $3[f(t)] + 2$ $6t^3 + 2$

5C. $f(-5)$ -250

5D. $f(-3) - f(1)$ -56

Personal Tutor glencoe.com

Differentiated Instruction

AL OL BL ELL

If students are visual learners,

Then as a preview of later chapters, have students represent several nonlinear functions graphically to share with the class. Nonlinear functions could include quadratic, absolute value, and exponential functions, with a variety of examples for each. The emphasis should be on the shape of the graphs.

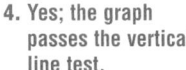

Check Your Understanding

Examples 1 and 3 pp. 45, 47

Determine whether each relation is a function. Explain.

1. 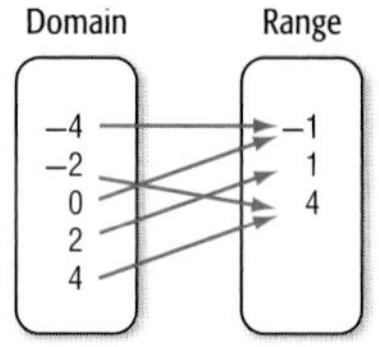

Yes; for each input there is exactly one output.

2.

Domain	Range
2	6
5	7
6	9
6	10

No; the domain value 6 is paired with both 9 and 10.

3. {(2, 2), (−1, 5), (5, 2), (2, −4)}

3. No; the domain value 2 is paired with 2 and −4.

4. $y = \frac{1}{2}x - 6$

4. Yes; the graph passes the vertical line test.

5. 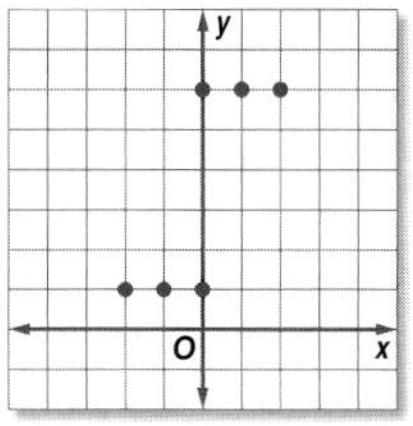

No; when $x = 0$, $y = 1$ and $y = 6$.

6. 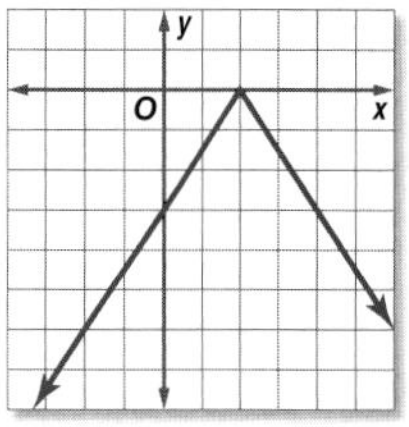

Yes; the graph passes the vertical line test.

7. 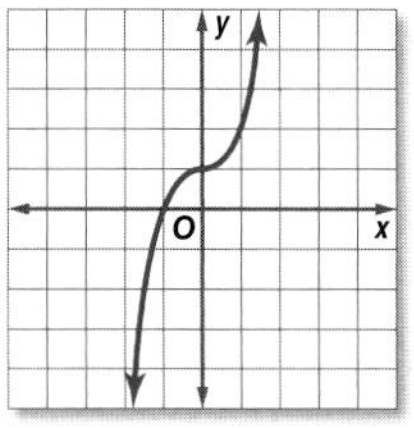

Yes; the graph passes the vertical line test.

8. 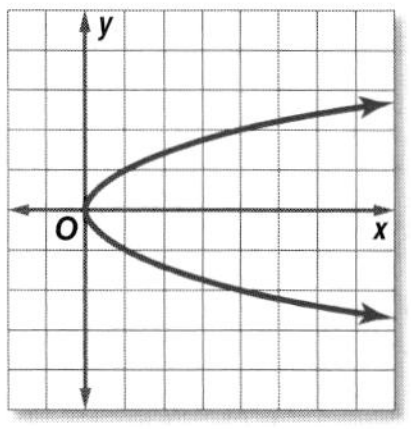

No; the graph does not pass the vertical line test.

Example 2 p. 46

9. SCHOOL ENROLLMENT The table shows the total enrollment in U.S. public schools.

School Year	2004–05	2005–06	2006–07	2007–08
Enrollment (in thousands)	48,560	48,710	48,948	49,091

Source: *The World Almanac*

a. Write a set of ordered pairs representing the data in the table if x is the number of school years since 2004–2005.

9a. {(0, 48,560), (1, 48,710), (2, 48,948), (3, 49,091)}

b. Draw a graph showing the relationship between the year and enrollment. **9b. See margin.**

c. Describe the domain and range of the data. The domain is the school year and the range is the enrollment.

10. CELL PHONES The cost of sending cell phone pictures is given by $y = 0.25x$, where x is the number of pictures that you send. Write the equation in function notation and then find $f(5)$ and $f(12)$. What do these values represent? Determine the domain and range of this function. See margin.

Examples 4 and 5 p. 48

If $f(x) = 6x + 7$ and $g(x) = x^2 - 4$, find each value.

11. $f(-3)$ -11 **12.** $f(m)$ $6m + 7$ **13.** $f(r - 2)$ $6r - 5$

14. $g(5)$ 21 **15.** $g(a) + 9$ $a^2 + 5$ **16.** $g(-4t)$ $16t^2 - 4$

17. $f(q + 1)$ $6q + 13$ **18.** $f(2) + g(-2)$ 19 **19.** $g(-b)$ $b^2 - 4$

3 PRACTICE

Formative Assessment

Use Exercises 1–19 to check for understanding.

Use the chart at the bottom of the next page to customize assignments for your students.

Additional Answers

9b. 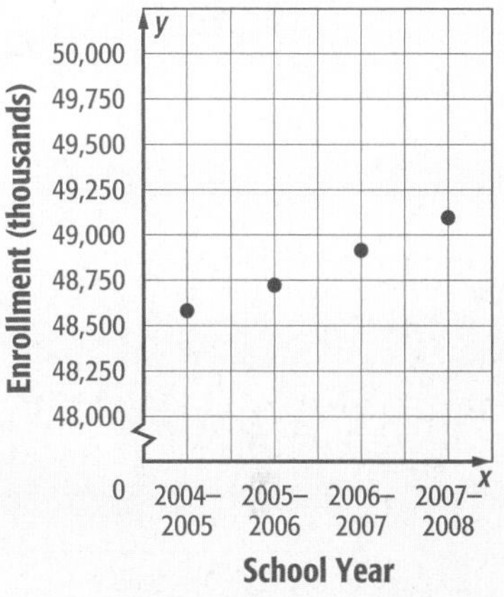

10. The domain is the school year and the range is the enrollment. $f(x) = 0.25x$; \$1.25, \$3.00; It costs \$1.25 to send 5 photos and \$3.00 to send 12 photos. The domain is the number of pictures sent and the cost is the range.

Watch Out!

Find the Error For Exercise 54, Corazon has confused the domain and range. To be a function, more than one element in the domain can be paired with one element in the range, but one element in the domain cannot be paired with more than one element in the range.

Additional Answers

26b. Home Value

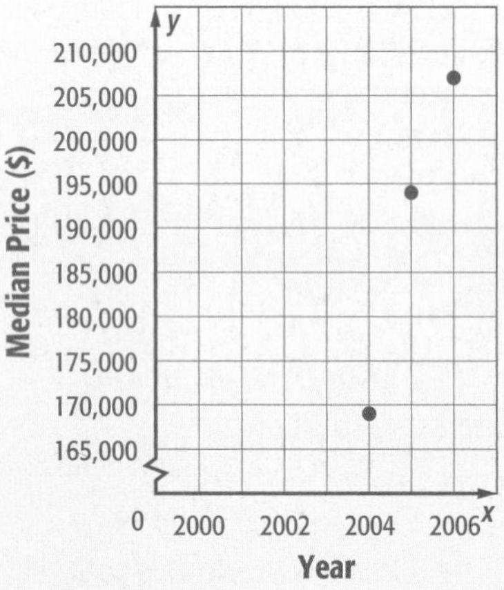

45a.

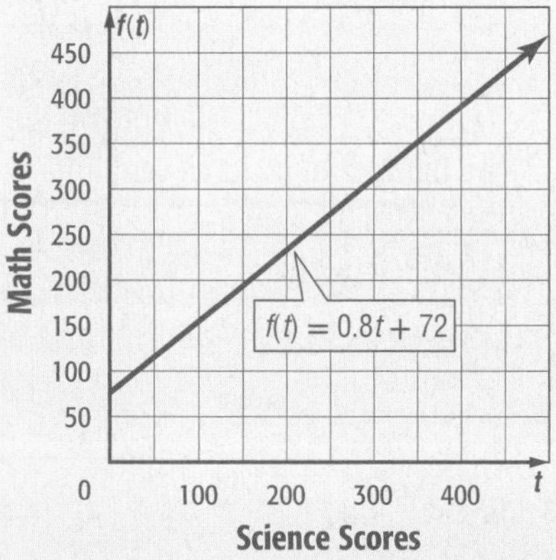

Practice and Problem Solving

● = **Step-by-Step Solutions** begin on page R12.
Extra Practice begins on page 815.

Example 1 p. 45

Determine whether each relation is a function. Explain.

20.

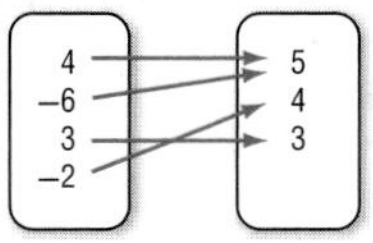

21.

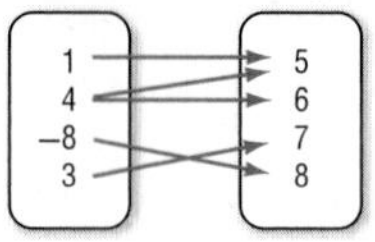

22.

Domain	Range
4	6
−5	3
6	−3
−5	5

23.

Domain	Range
−4	2
3	−5
4	2
9	−7
−3	−5

24.

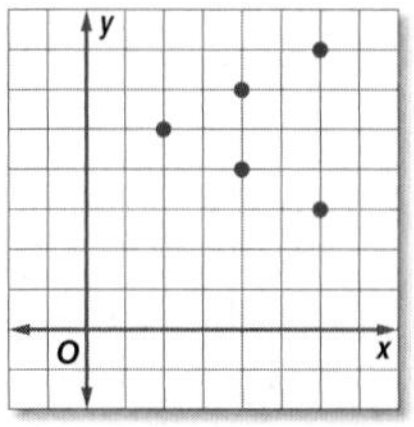

25.

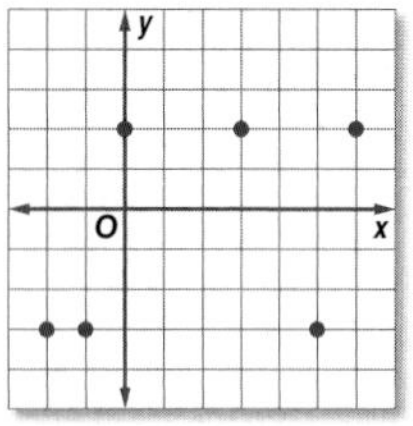

20. Yes; for each input there is exactly one output.
21. No; the domain value 4 is paired with both 5 and 6.
22. No; the domain value −5 is paired with both 3 and 5.
23. Yes; for each input there is exactly one output.
24. No; when $x = 4$, $y = 4$ and $y = 6$.
25. Yes; the graph passes the vertical line test.

Example 2 p. 46

26. HOME VALUE The table shows the median home prices in Raleigh, North Carolina, from 2004 to 2006.

Year	Median Home Price
2004	\$169,900
2005	\$194,900
2006	\$207,700

a. Write a set of ordered pairs representing the data in the table. **a. {(2004, 169,900), (2005, 194,900), (2006, 207,700)}**

b. Draw a graph showing the relationship between the year and price. **See margin.**

c. What is the domain and range for this data? **c. The domain is the year. The range is the median home price.**

Example 3 p. 47

Determine whether each relation is a function.

27. $\{(5, -7), (6, -7), (-8, -1), (0, -1)\}$ **yes**

28. $\{(4, 5), (3, -2), (-2, 5), (4, 7)\}$ **no**

29. $y = -8$ **yes**

30. $x = 15$ **no**

31. $y = 3x - 2$ **yes**

32. $y = 3x + 2y$ **yes**

Examples 4 and 5 p. 48

If $f(x) = -2x - 3$ and $g(x) = x^2 + 5x$, find each value.

33. $f(-1)$ **−1**

34. $f(6)$ **−15**

35. $g(2)$ **14**

36. $g(-3)$ **−6**

37. $g(-2) + 2$ **−4**

38. $f(0) - 7$ **−10**

39. $f(4y)$ **$-8y - 3$**

40. $g(-6m)$ **$36m^2 - 30m$**

41. $f(c - 5)$ **$-2c + 7$**

42. $f(r + 2)$ **$-2r - 7$**

43. $5[f(d)]$ **$-10d - 15$**

44. $3[g(n)]$ **$3n^2 + 15n$**

B

45 EDUCATION The average national math test scores $f(t)$ for 17-year-olds can be represented as a function of the national science scores t by $f(t) = 0.8t + 72$.

a. Graph this function. **See margin.**

b. What is the science score that corresponds to a math score of 308? **295**

c. What is the domain and range of this function? **The domain is the set of science scores. The range is the set of math scores.**

Differentiated Homework Options

Level	Assignment		Two-Day Option	
AL Basic	20–44, 49–50, 52, 54–57	21–43, 56–59	20–44 even, 49–50, 52, 54–57
OL Core	21–47 odd, 48–50, 52, 54–75	20–44, 56–59	45–50, 52, 54–55, 60–75
BL Advanced	45–69, (optional: 70–75)		

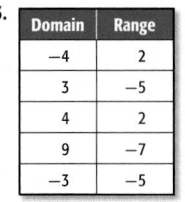

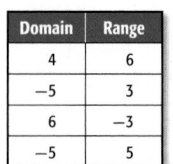

48b. Sample Answer:

h	$\$7.50h$
3	\$22.50
5	\$37.50
2	\$15
4	\$30
6	\$45

Real-World Link

Babysitters earn an average of \$6.04 per hour.

Source: Runzheimer International

52. Sample answer: Isn't a mapping another representation of a set of ordered pairs?

55. Sample answer: Functions can be used in traffic safety studies to determine the relationship between the speed of a car and the distance it takes to stop. This can help plan intersections and speed limits. This function can also help law enforcement officials to understand the cause of an accident.

Determine whether each relation is a function.

46.

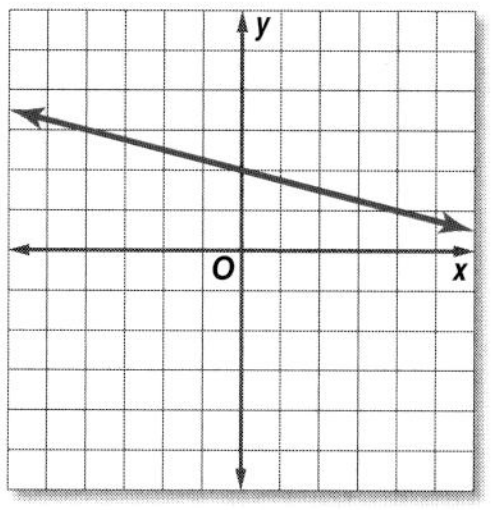

yes

47.

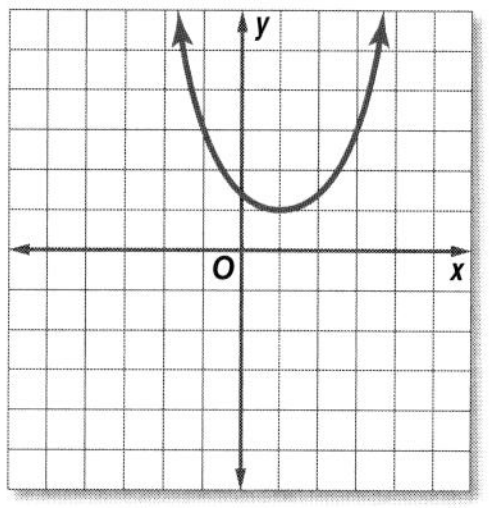

yes

48. **BABYSITTING** Christina earns \$7.50 an hour babysitting.

a. Write an algebraic expression to represent the money Christina will earn if she works h hours. **$\$7.50h$**

b. Choose five values for the number of hours Christina can babysit. Create a table with h and the amount of money she will make during that time.

c. Use the values in your table to create a graph. **See Ch. 1 Answer Appendix.**

d. Does it make sense to connect the points in your graph with a line? Why or why not? **Yes, because they could pay Christina for partial hours that she worked.**

H.O.T. Problems
Use Higher-Order Thinking Skills

49. **OPEN ENDED** Write a set of three ordered pairs that represent a function. Choose another display that represents this function. **See Ch. 1 Answer Appendix.**

50. **REASONING** The set of ordered pairs {(0, 1), (3, 2), (3, −5), (5, 4)} represents a relation between x and y. Graph the set of ordered pairs. Determine whether the relation is a function. Explain. **See Ch. 1 Answer Appendix.**

51. **CHALLENGE** Consider $f(x) = -4.3x - 2$. Write $f(g + 3.5)$ and simplify by combining like terms. **$f(g + 3.5) = -4.3g - 17.05$**

52. **WRITE A QUESTION** A classmate graphed a set of ordered pairs and used the vertical line test to determine whether it was a function. Write a question to help her decide if the same strategy can be applied to a mapping.

53. **CHALLENGE** If $f(3b - 1) = 9b - 1$, find one possible expression for $f(x)$. **53. Sample answer: $f(x) = 3x + 2$**

54. **FIND THE ERROR** Corazon and Maggie are analyzing the relation to determine whether it is a function. Is either of them correct? Explain your reasoning. **54. Neither; see Ch. 1 Answer Appendix for explanation.**

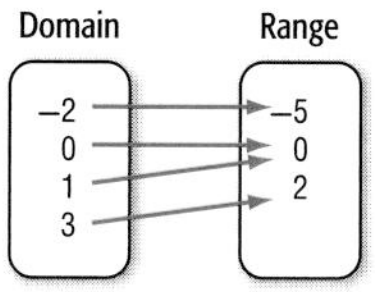

Corazon	Maggie
No, one member of the range is matched with two members of the domain.	No, each member of the domain is matched with one member of the range.

55. **WRITING IN MATH** Use the graph of stopping distances on page 45 to explain how graphs and functions can be used to model real-world situations.

Study Guide and Intervention
CRM pp. 43–44 AL OL ELL

NAME ______ DATE ______ PERIOD ______

1-7 Study Guide and Intervention

Representing Functions

Identify Functions Relations in which each element of the domain is paired with exactly one element of the range are called **functions**.

Example 1 **Determine whether the relation {(6, −3), (4, 1), (7, −2), (−3, 1)} is a function. Explain.**

Since each element of the domain is paired with exactly one element of the range, this relation is a function.

Example 2 **Determine whether $3x - y = 6$ is a function.**

Since the equation is in the form $Ax + By = C$, the graph of the equation will be a line, as shown at the right.

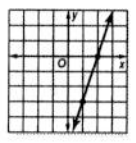

If you draw a vertical line through each value of x, the vertical line passes through just one point of the graph. Thus, the line represents a function.

Exercises

Determine whether each relation is a function.

1. 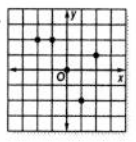 yes

2. 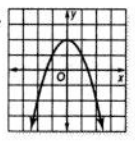 yes

3. 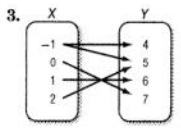 no

4. 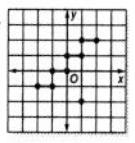 no

5. 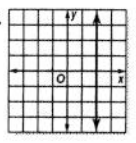 no

6. 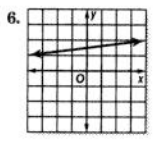 yes

7. {(4, 2), (2, 3), (6, 1)} **yes**

8. {(−3, −3), (−3, 4), (−2, 4)} **no**

9. {(−1, 0), (1, 0)} **yes**

10. $-2x + 4y = 0$ **yes**

11. $x^2 + y^2 = 8$ **no**

12. $x = -4$ **no**

Chapter 1 43 Glencoe Algebra 1

Lesson 1-7

Practice
CRM p. 46 AL OL BL ELL

NAME ______ DATE ______ PERIOD ______

1-7 Practice

Representing Functions

Determine whether each relation is a function. Explain.

1. 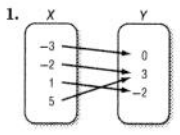 **yes**

2. **no**

X	Y
1	−5
−4	3
7	6
1	−2

3. 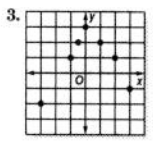 **yes**

4. {(1, 4), (2, −2), (3, −6), (−6, 3), (−3, 6)} **yes**

5. {(6, −4), (2, −4), (−4, 2), (4, 6), (2, 6)} **no**

6. $x = -2$ **no**

7. $y = 2$ **yes**

If $f(x) = 2x - 6$ and $g(x) = x - 2x^2$, find each value.

8. $f(2)$ **−2**

9. $f\left(-\frac{1}{2}\right)$ **−7**

10. $g(-1)$ **−3**

11. $g\left(-\frac{1}{3}\right)$ **$-\frac{5}{9}$**

12. $f(7) - 9$ **−1**

13. $g(-3) + 13$ **−8**

14. $f(h + 9)$ **$2h + 12$**

15. $g(3y)$ **$3y - 18y^2$**

16. $2[g(b) + 1]$ **$2b - 4b^2 + 2$**

17. **WAGES** Martin earns \$7.50 per hour proofreading ads at a local newspaper. His weekly wage w can be described by the equation $w = 7.5h$, where h is the number of hours worked.

a. Write the equation in functional notation. **$f(h) = 7.5h$**

b. Find $f(15)$, $f(20)$, and $f(25)$. **112.50, 150, 187.50**

18. **ELECTRICITY** The table shows the relationship between resistance R and current I in a circuit.

Resistance (ohms)	120	80	48	6	4
Current (amperes)	0.1	0.15	0.25	2	3

a. Is the relationship a function? Explain. **Yes; for each value in the domain, there is only one value in the range.**

b. If the relation can be represented by the equation $IR = 12$, rewrite the equation in functional notation so that the resistance R is a function of the current I. **$f(I) = \frac{12}{I}$**

c. What is the resistance in a circuit when the current is 0.5 ampere? **24 ohms**

Chapter 1 46 Glencoe Algebra 1

Word Problem Practice
CRM p. 47 AL OL BL ELL

NAME ______ DATE ______ PERIOD ______

1-7 Word Problem Pratice

Representing Functions

1. **TRANSPORTATION** The cost of riding in a cab is \$3.00 plus \$0.75 per mile. The equation that represents this relation is $y = 0.75x + 3$, where x is the number of miles traveled and y is the cost of the trip. Look at the graph of the equation and determine whether the relation is a function. **yes**

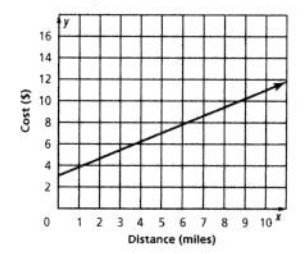

2. **TEXT MESSAGING** Many cell phones have a text messaging option in addition to regular cell phone service. The function for the monthly cost of text messaging service from Noline Wireless Company is $f(x) = 0.10x + 2$, where x is the number of text messages that are sent. Find $f(10)$ and $f(30)$, the cost of 10 text messages in a month and the cost of 30 text messages in a month.

$f(10) = \$3$; $f(30) = \$5$

3. **GEOMETRY** The area for any square is given by the function $y = x^2$, where x is the length of a side of the square and y is the area of the square. Write the equation in function notation and find the area of a square with a side length of 3.5 inches.

$f(x) = x^2$
$f(3.5) = (3.5)^2$
$= 12.25 \text{ in}^2$

4. **TRAVEL** The cost for cars entering President George Bush Turnpike at Beltline road is given by the relation $x = 0.75$, where x is the dollar amount for entrance to the toll road and y is the number of passengers. Determine if this relation is a function. Explain.

This relation is not a function. The graph would be a vertical line, which would not pass the vertical line test.

5. **CONSUMER CHOICES** Aisha just received a \$40 paycheck from her new job. She spends some of it buying music online and saves the rest in a bank account. Her savings is given by $f(x) = 40 - 1.25x$, where x is the number of songs she downloads at \$1.25 per song.

a. Graph the function.

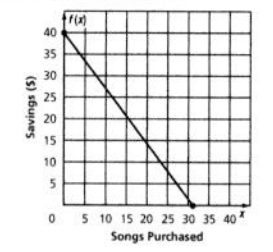

b. Find $f(3)$, $f(18)$, and $f(36)$. What do these values represent?

$f(3) = 36.25$; buys 3 songs, saves \$36.25
$f(18) = 17.50$; buys 18 songs, saves \$17.50
$f(36) = -5$; sample answer: if she wants to buy 36 songs, she needs \$5 extra

c. How many songs can Aisha buy if she wants to save \$30? **8 songs**

Chapter 1 47 Glencoe Algebra 1

Lesson 1-7

Enrichment
CRM p. 48 OL BL

NAME ______ DATE ______ PERIOD ______

1-7 Enrichment

Composite Functions

Three things are needed to have a function—a set called the domain, a set called the range, and a rule that matches each element in the domain with only one element in the range. Here is an example.

Rule: $f(x) = 2x + 1$

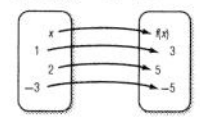

$f(x) = 2x + 1$
$f(1) = 2(1) + 1 = 2 + 1 = 3$
$f(2) = 2(2) + 1 = 4 + 1 = 5$
$f(-3) = 2(-3) + 1 = -6 + 1 = -5$

Suppose we have three sets A, B, and C and two functions described as shown below.

Rule: $f(x) = 2x + 1$ Rule: $g(y) = 3y - 4$

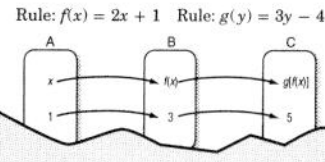

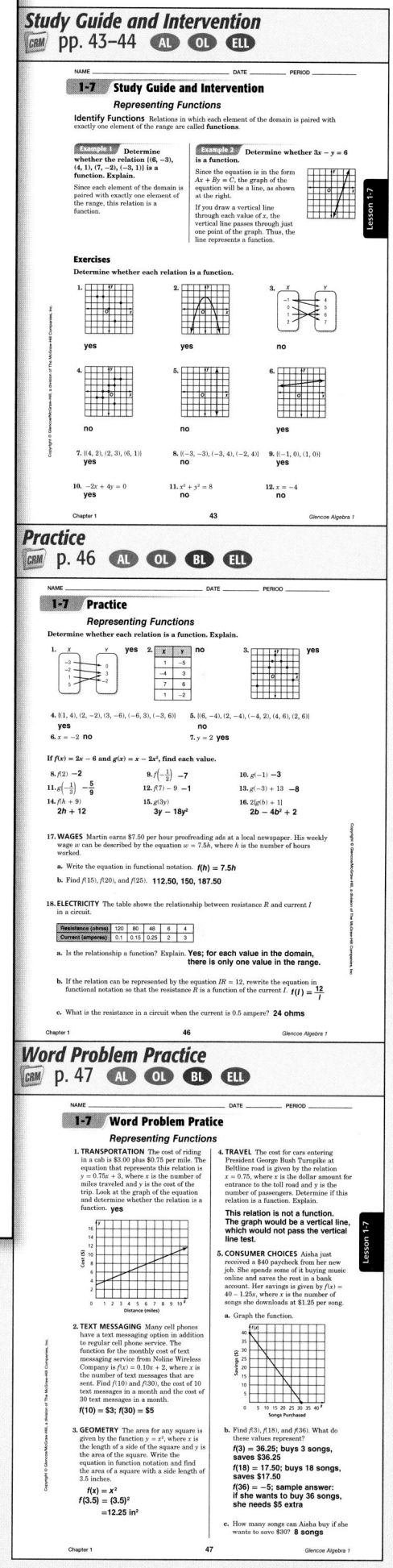

$g(y) = 3y - 4$
$g(3) = 3(3) - 4 = 5$

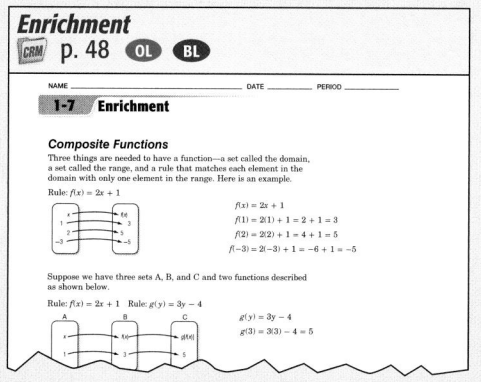

4 ASSESS

Crystal Ball Tell students that following this lesson is a graphing lab on representing functions. Ask them to write how they think what they have learned today about functions will connect with the lab.

Additional Answers

63. $4(1.99) + 10(0.25) + 4(1.85) = C$, where C is the cost of the items Tom needs. $C = 17.86$, so the cost is $17.86, which is not less than $10.

64. Sample answer: four times y plus two

65. Sample answer: two thirds times x

66. Sample answer: a squared times b plus 5

PSAE PRACTICE 6.11.01, 8.11.11, 9.11.12, 6.11.18

56. Which point on the number line represents a number whose square is less than itself? **B**

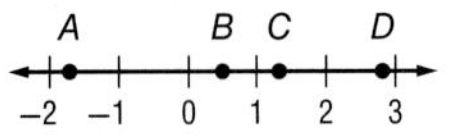

A A C C
B B D D

57. Determine which of the following relations is a function. **J**

F {(−3, 2), (4, 1), (−3, 5)}
G {(2, −1), (4, −1), (2, 6)}
H {(−3, −4), (−3, 6), (8, −2)}
J {(5, −1), (3, −2), (−2, −2)}

58. GEOMETRY What is the value of x? **A**

A 3 in.
B 4 in.
C 5 in.
D 6 in.

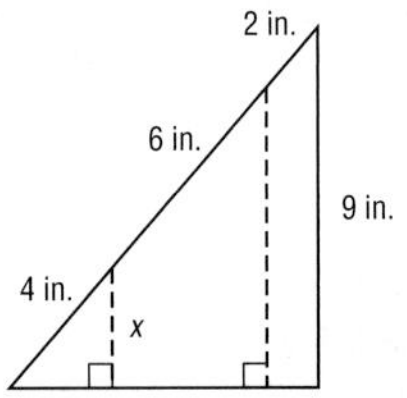

59. SHORT RESPONSE Camille made 16 out of 19 of her serves during her first volleyball game. She made 13 out of 16 of her serves during her second game. During which game did she make a greater percent of her serves? **her first game**

Spiral Review

Solve each equation. (Lesson 1-5)

60. $x = \frac{27 + 3}{10}$ **3**

61. $m = \frac{3^2 + 4}{7 - 5}$ $\frac{13}{2}$

62. $z = 32 + 4(-3)$ **20**

63. SCHOOL SUPPLIES The table shows the prices of some items Tom needs. If he needs 4 glue sticks, 10 pencils, and 4 notebooks, write and solve an equation to determine whether Tom can get them for under $10. Describe what the variables represent. (Lesson 1-6) **See margin.**

School Supplies Prices	
glue stick	$1.99
pencil	$0.25
notebook	$1.85

Write a verbal expression for each algebraic expression. (Lesson 1-1) **64–66. See margin.**

64. $4y + 2$

65. $\frac{2}{3}x$

66. $a^2b + 5$

Find the volume of each rectangular prism. (Lesson 0-9)

67.

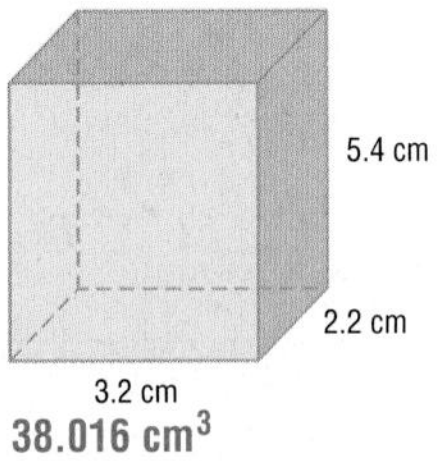

38.016 cm³

68.

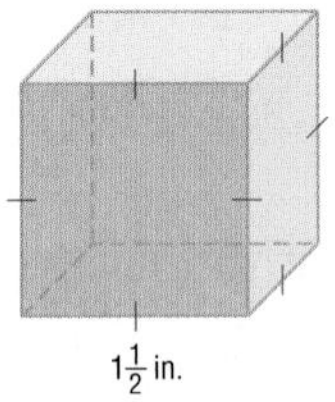

$3\frac{3}{8}$ in³

69.

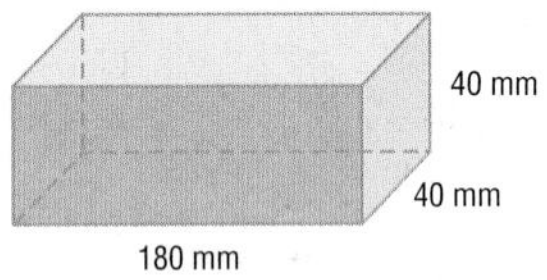

288,000 mm³

Skills Review

Evaluate each expression. (Lesson 1-2)

70. If $x = 3$, then $6x - 5 =$ __?__. **13**

71. If $n = -1$, then $2n + 1 =$ __?__. **−1**

72. If $p = 4$, then $3p + 4 =$ __?__. **16**

73. If $q = 7$, then $7q - 9 =$ __?__ **40**

74. If $k = -11$, then $4k + 6 =$ __?__ **−38**

75. If $y = 10$, then $8y - 15 =$ __?__ **65**

Differentiated Instruction BL

Extension Beyond-level students benefit from opportunities to learn independently. Students should be challenged to explain why the vertical line test can be used to tell whether a graph represents a function. In addition, students can pursue independent work to develop an understanding of how and why the *horizontal line* test is used in mathematics.

EXTEND 1-7

Graphing Technology Lab: Representing Functions

IL Math Online glencoe.com
- Other Calculator Keystrokes
- Graphing Technology Personal Tutor

IL Learning Standards **8.B.4a** Represent algebraic concepts with physical materials, words, diagrams, tables, graphs, equations and inequalities and use appropriate technology.

You can use TI-Nspire™ or TI-Nspire™ CAS technology to explore the different ways to represent a function.

ACTIVITY

Graph $f(x) = 2x + 3$ on the TI-Nspire graphing calculator.

Step 1 From the Home screen, select Graphs & Geometry.

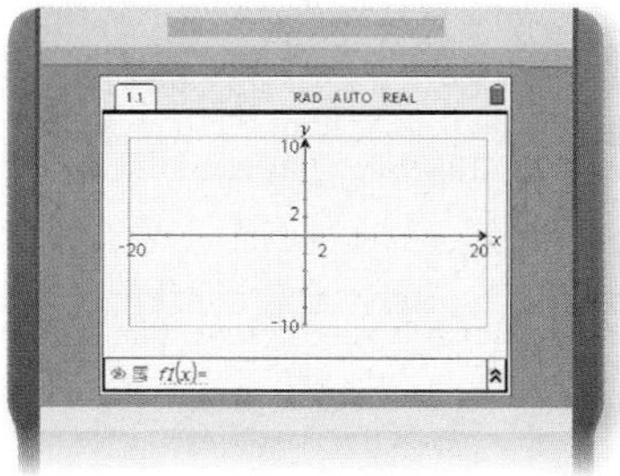

Step 2 Type $2x + 3$ (enter) in the entry line.

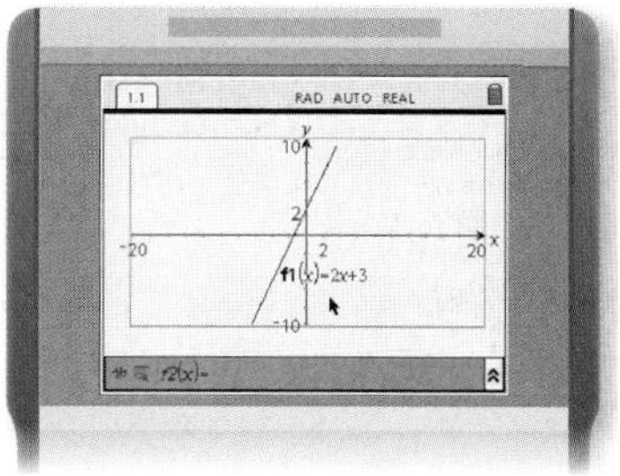

Represent the function as a table.

Step 3 Press (menu). Choose View, then Add Function Table. Then press (enter) or the click button.

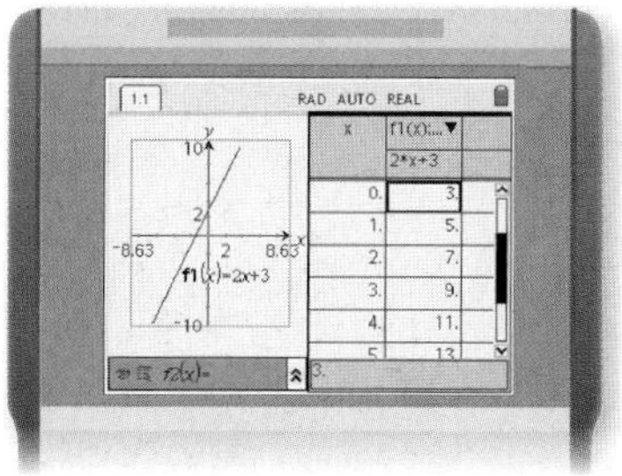

Step 4 Press (ctrl) + (tab) to toggle from the table to the graph. Press (tab) until an arrow appears on the graph. Use the click button to grab the line and move it. Notice how the values in the table change.

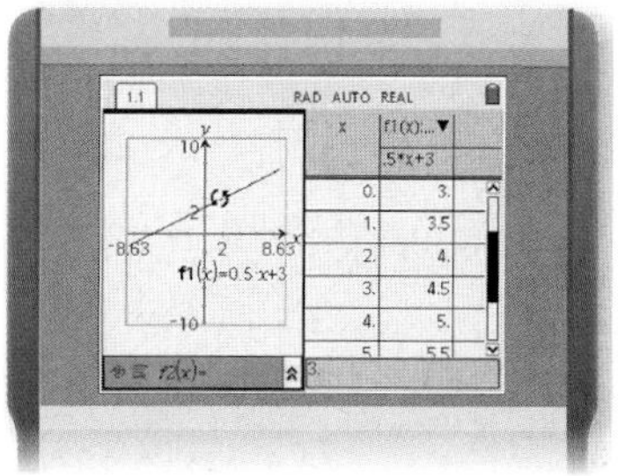

Analyze the Results

1–6. See Ch. 1 Answer Appendix.

Graph each function. Make a table of five ordered pairs that also represents the function.

1. $g(x) = -x - 3$

2. $h(x) = \frac{1}{3}x + 3$

3. $f(x) = -\frac{1}{2}x - 5$

4. $f(x) = 3x - \frac{1}{2}$

5. $g(x) = -2x + 5$

6. $h(x) = \frac{1}{5}x + 4$

EXTEND 1-7

Lesson Notes

1 FOCUS

Objective Use technology to represent a function as a graph and as a table.

Materials for Each Group

- TI-Nspire graphing calculator or software

Teaching Tip

The graphing calculator opens on the same screen as when it was turned off. Have students press the **Home** button to begin the lab.

2 TEACH

Working in Cooperative Groups

Have students of mixed abilities work in groups of two or three to complete the Activity and Exercises 1–2.

- For Step 3, students can also press (ctrl) T to add a function table.
- For Step 4, students may need to follow these steps to grab the line and move it. After toggling to the graph, press (tab) until the pointer appears on the screen. Move the pointer to the line until an icon appears. Use the click button to grab the line. Use the navigating arrows to move it. Note: If students grab the line near an end, rotating circles will appear, and they can rotate the line. If they grab the line near the middle, a cross with arrows will appear, and they can translate the line.
- For Exercises 1–6, students can add pages to the open document. Press (ctrl) I. Page 1.2 and so on will appear on the screen.

Practice Have students complete Exercises 3–6.

3 ASSESS

Formative Assessment

Use Exercise 5 to assess whether students know how to represent a function as a graph and as a table.

From Concrete to Abstract

Ask: How is the graph of a function related to the table of the function? Sample answer: The graph shows the direction and steepness of the line, while the table shows the coordinates of the points on the line for x and $f(x)$.

1 FOCUS

Vertical Alignment

Before Lesson 1-8
Apply properties of real numbers.

Lesson 1-8
Identify the hypothesis and conclusion in a conditional statement.
Use a counterexample to show that an assertion is false.

After Lesson 1-8
Analyze graphs of linear functions and draw conclusions.

2 TEACH

Scaffolding Questions

Have students read the *Why?* section of the lesson.

Ask:

- What is the purpose of the following sentence? *If an insect is a butterfly, then it was a caterpillar*. It tells you that a butterfly was once a caterpillar.
- Does it mean that other insects were not caterpillars? Explain. No; It refers to insects that are butterflies, not to other insects.
- What is an example of an insect that is not a butterfly, but was a caterpillar? moth

(continued on the next page)

1-8 Logical Reasoning and Counterexamples

Then
You applied the properties of real numbers. (Lesson 1-3)

Now
- Identify the hypothesis and conclusion in a conditional statement.
- Use a counterexample to show that an assertion is false.

IL Learning Standards
7.A.4b Apply formulas in a wide variety of theoretical and practical real-world measurement applications involving perimeter, area, volume, angle, time, temperature, mass, speed, distance, density and monetary values.

New Vocabulary
conditional statement
if-then statements
hypothesis
conclusion
deductive reasoning
counterexample

IL Math Online
glencoe.com
- Extra Examples
- Personal Tutor
- Self-Check Quiz
- Homework Help

Students can access online resources such as **Personal Tutor, Extra Examples, Self-Check Quizzes** and **Hot Math Homework Help** at glencoe.com.

Why?

The Butterfly Gardens is a conservatory in British Columbia, Canada, with over 50 species of butterflies. There is also an Emerging Room where you can see caterpillars change into butterflies.

Conditional Statements The statement *If an insect is a butterfly, then it was a caterpillar* is called a conditional statement. A **conditional statement** can be written in the form *If A, then B*. Statements in this form are called **if-then statements**.

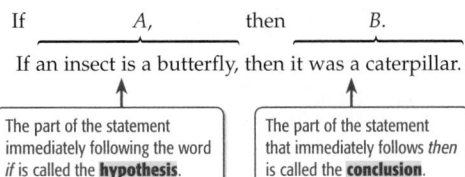

If *A*, then *B*.
If an insect is a butterfly, then it was a caterpillar.

The part of the statement immediately following the word *if* is called the **hypothesis**.

The part of the statement that immediately follows *then* is called the **conclusion**.

EXAMPLE 1 Identify Hypothesis and Conclusion

Identify the hypothesis and conclusion of each statement.

a. CELEBRATION **If it is the Fourth of July, then we will see fireworks.**
The hypothesis follows the word *if* and the conclusion follows the *then*.

Hypothesis: it is the 4th of July

Conclusion: we will see fireworks

b. If $2x - 10 = 0$, then $x = 5$.

Hypothesis: $2x - 10 = 0$

Conclusion: $x = 5$

Check Your Progress 1A. Hypothesis: we have enough sugar; Conclusion: we will make cookies

1A. If we have enough sugar, then we will make cookies.

1B. If $16z - 5 = 43$, then $z = 3$. Hypothesis: $16z - 5 = 43$; Conclusion: $z = 3$

Personal Tutor glencoe.com

Sometimes a conditional statement does not contain the words *if* and *then*. But a conditional statement can always be rewritten in if-then form.

Lesson 1-8 Resources

Resource	Approaching-Level	On-Level	Beyond-Level	English Learners
Teacher Edition	• Differentiated Instruction, p. 55	• Differentiated Instruction, pp. 55, 59	• Differentiated Instruction, p. 59	• Differentiated Instruction, p. 55
Chapter Resource Masters	• Study Guide and Intervention, pp. 49–50 • Skills Practice, p. 51 • Practice, p. 52 • Word Problem Practice, p. 53	• Study Guide and Intervention, pp. 49–50 • Skills Practice, p. 51 • Practice, p. 52 • Word Problem Practice, p. 53 • Enrichment, p. 54	• Practice, p. 52 • Word Problem Practice, p. 53 • Enrichment, p. 54	• Study Guide and Intervention, pp. 49–50 • Skills Practice, p. 51 • Practice, p. 52
Transparencies	• 5-Minute Check Transparency 1-8	• 5-Minute Check Transparency 1-8	• 5-Minute Check Transparency 1-8	• 5-Minute Check Transparency 1-8
Other	• Study Notebook	• Study Notebook	• Study Notebook	• Study Notebook

StudyTip

Conditional Statements If a conditional statement is true, the hypothesis need not always be true. For example, if Daniel plays air hockey, then he is at an arcade. But just because Daniel is at an arcade does not mean that he plays air hockey.

EXAMPLE 2 Write a Conditional in If-Then Form

Identify the hypothesis and conclusion of each statement. Then write each statement in if-then form.

a. Chen gets chocolate chip ice cream when she is at the ice cream parlor.

Hypothesis: Chen is at the ice cream parlor

Conclusion: she will get chocolate chip ice cream

If-Then Form: If Chen is at the ice cream parlor, then she will get chocolate chip ice cream.

b. For the equation $3y + 4 = 25$, $y = 7$.

Hypothesis: $3y + 4 = 25$

Conclusion: $y = 7$

If-Then Form: If $3y + 4 = 25$, then $y = 7$.

Check Your Progress

2A. Hypothesis: the store is open; Conclusion: the neon light is on; If the store is open, then the neon light is on.

2A. The neon light is on when the store is open.

2B. A circle with a radius of $w - 4$ has a circumference of $2\pi(w - 4)$.

2B. Hypothesis: the circle has a radius of $w - 4$; Conclusion: its circumference is $2\pi(w - 4)$; If the circle has a radius of $w - 4$, then its circumference is $2\pi(w - 4)$.

Personal Tutor glencoe.com

Deductive Reasoning and Counterexamples The process of using facts, rules, definitions, or properties to reach a valid conclusion is called **deductive reasoning**. If you know that the hypothesis of a true conditional is true for a given case, deductive reasoning allows you to say that the conclusion is true for that case.

ReadingMath

If-Then Statements Note that *if* is not part of the hypothesis, and *then* is not part of the conclusion.

EXAMPLE 3 Deductive Reasoning

Determine a valid conclusion that follows from the statement below for each condition. If a valid conclusion does not follow, write *no valid conclusion* and explain why.

If one number is odd and another is even, then their product must be even.

a. The numbers are 5 and 8.

5 is odd and 8 is even, so the hypothesis is true.

Their product is 40, which is even, so the conclusion is also true.

b. The product is 24.

The product is part of the conclusion. The product is even, so the conclusion is true.

The hypothesis is also true for numbers such as 3 and 8. However, for numbers such as 4 and 6 the hypothesis is not true. So, there is no valid conclusion.

Check Your Progress

Determine a valid conclusion that follows from the statement *If one number is negative and another is positive, then their product must be negative.* If a valid conclusion does not follow, write *no valid conclusion* and explain why.

3A. The numbers are -3 and 4. The product is negative.

3B. The product is 10. No valid conclusion; the product is not negative.

Personal Tutor glencoe.com

Conditional Statements

Example 1 shows how to identify the hypothesis and conclusion of conditional statements. **Example 2** shows how to write a statement in if-then form after identifying the hypothesis and conclusion of the statement.

Formative Assessment

Use the Check Your Progress exercises after each Example to determine students' understanding of concepts.

Additional Examples

1 Identify the hypothesis and conclusion of each statement.

a. SPORTS If it is raining, then Jon and Urzig will not play softball.
Hypothesis: It is raining.
Conclusion: Jon and Urzig will not play softball.

b. If $7y + 5 = 26$, then $y = 3$.
Hypothesis: $7y + 5 = 26$
Conclusion: $y = 3$

2 Identify the hypothesis and conclusion of each statement. Then write each statement in if-then form.

a. I eat light meals.
Hypothesis: I eat a meal.
Conclusion: It is light.
If I eat a meal, then it is light.

b. For the equation $8 + 5a = 43$, $a = 7$.
Hypothesis: $8 + 5a = 43$
Conclusion: $a = 7$
If $8 + 5a = 43$, then $a = 7$.

Additional Examples also in Interactive Classroom PowerPoint® Presentations

IWB INTERACTIVE WHITEBOARD READY

Differentiated Instruction

AL OL ELL

If students are having trouble with logic,

Then have students work together discussing examples in this lesson. You may also want them to complete some exercises cooperatively.

Deductive Reasoning and Counterexamples

Example 3 shows how to use deductive reasoning to determine whether a conclusion is valid. **Example 4** shows how to find a counterexample for a conditional statement.

Additional Examples

3 Determine a valid conclusion that follows from the statement below for each condition. If a valid conclusion does not follow, write *no valid conclusion* and explain why.

If one number is odd and another number is even, then their sum is odd.

a. The two numbers are 5 and 12. 5 is odd and 12 is even, and $5 + 12 = 17$. Conclusion: The sum of 5 and 12 is odd.

b. The two numbers are 8 and 26. 8 and 26 are even so the hypothesis is false. No valid conclusion.

4 Find a counterexample for each conditional statement.

a. If $x + y > xy$, then $x > y$. $x = 1, y = 2$

b. If Chloe is riding the Ferris wheel, then she is at the State Fair. Chloe could be riding a Ferris wheel at an amusement park.

TEACH with TECH

AUDIO RECORDING Break the class into groups, and give each group a list of conditional statements. Have them record a counterexample for each of these statements. Then have each group play back their recordings for the entire class.

To show that a conditional is false, we can use a counterexample. A **counterexample** is a specific case in which the hypothesis is true and the conclusion is false.

StudyTip

Counterexamples It takes only one counterexample to show that a statement is false.

EXAMPLE 4 Counterexamples

Find a counterexample for each conditional statement.

a. If $a + b > c$, then $b > c$.

One counterexample is when $a = 7$, $b = 3$, and $c = 9$. The hypothesis is true, $7 + 3 > 9$. However, the conclusion $3 > 9$ is false.

b. If the leaves on the tree are brown, then it is fall.

If the leaves are brown then the tree could have died. So, the conclusion is not necessarily true.

Check Your Progress

4A. If $ab > 0$, then a and b are greater than 0. $a = -1$ and $b = -2$

4B. If a clothing store is selling wool coats, then it must be December.

4B. The clothing store may sell wool coats before or after December.

Personal Tutor glencoe.com

Check Your Understanding

Example 1 p. 54

Identify the hypothesis and conclusion of each statement.

1. If the game is on Saturday, then Eduardo will play. H: the game is on Saturday; C: Eduardo will play
2. If the chicken burns, then it was left in the oven too long. H: the chicken burns; C: it was left in the oven too long
3. If $52 - 4x = 28$, then $x = 6$. H: $52 - 4x = 28$; C: $x = 6$

Example 2 p. 55

Identify the hypothesis and conclusion of each statement. Then write each statement in if-then form. 4–6. See margin.

4. Alisa plays with her dog in the yard when the weather is nice.
5. Two lines that are perpendicular form right angles.
6. A prime number is only divisible by one and itself.

Example 3 p. 55

Determine a valid conclusion that follows from the statement below for each given condition. If a valid conclusion does not follow, write *no valid conclusion* and explain why.

If a number is a multiple of 10, then the number is divisible by 5.

7. The number is divisible by 5. No valid conclusion; the last digit could be a 5.
8. The number is 5010. The number is divisible by 5.
9. The number is 955. No valid conclusion; the last digit is a 5.

Example 4 p. 56

Find a counterexample for each conditional statement.

10. If Jack is at the park, then he is flying a kite. Jack is playing baseball at the park.
11. If a teacher assigns a writing project, then it must be more than two pages long. A one-page paper is assigned.
12. If $|x| = 7$, then $x = 7$. $x = -7$
13. If a number y is multiplied by $\frac{1}{3}$, then $\frac{1}{3}y < y$. $y = -1$

Focus on Mathematical Content

Deductive Reasoning and Counterexamples You can use deductive reasoning to determine whether a valid conclusion follows from a conditional statement. You can show that a conditional statement is false by using a counterexample. Deductive reasoning uses facts, rules, definitions, or properties to show whether a conditional statement is valid. A counterexample is a specific case that shows a conditional statement is false. You need only one counterexample to show that a statement is false.

Practice and Problem Solving

= Step-by-Step Solutions begin on page R12.
Extra Practice begins on page 815.

Example 1 p. 54

Identify the hypothesis and conclusion of each statement.

14. If a team is playing at home, then they wear their white uniforms. H: team is playing at home; C: they wear their white uniforms

15. If you are in a grocery store, then you will buy food.

16. If $2n - 7 > 25$, then $n > 16$. H: $2n - 7 > 25$; C: $n > 16$

17. If x equals y and y equals z, then x equals z.

18. If it is not raining outside, we will walk the dogs. H: it is not raining outside; C: we will walk the dogs

19. If you play basketball, then you are tall. H: you play basketball; C: you are tall

15. H: you are in a grocery store; C: you will buy food

17. H: x equals y, and y equals z; C: x equals z

Example 2 p. 55

Identify the hypothesis and conclusion of each statement. Then write each statement in if-then form. 20–27. See Chapter 1 Answer Appendix.

20. Lamar's third-period class is art.

21. Joe will go to the mall after class.

22. For $x = 4$, $6x - 10 = 14$.

23. $5m - 8 < 52$ when $m < 12$.

24. A rectangle with sides of equal length is a square.

25. The sum of two even numbers is an even number.

26. August has 31 days.

27. Science teachers like to conduct experiments.

22. H: $x = 4$; C: $6x - 10 = 14$; If $x = 4$, then $6x - 10 = 14$.

23. H: $m < 12$; C: $5m - 8 < 52$; If $m < 12$, then $5m - 8 < 52$.

Example 3 p. 55

Determine whether a valid conclusion follows from the statement below for each given condition. If a valid conclusion does not follow, write *no valid conclusion* and explain why. 28–31. See Chapter 1 Answer Appendix.

If Belinda scores higher than 90% on the exam, then she will receive an A for the course.

28. Belinda scores a 91% on the exam.

29. Belinda scores an 89% on the exam.

30. Belinda receives an A for the course.

31. Belinda receives a B for the course.

Example 4 p. 56

Find a counterexample for each conditional statement. 33–34. See margin.

32. If you live in London, then you live in England. a person who lives in London, Ohio

33. If you attend the banquet, then you will eat the food.

34. If the four sides of a quadrilateral are congruent, then the shape is a square.

35. If a number is divisible by 3, then the number is odd. $6 \div 3 = 2$

36. If $3x + 17 \le 53$, then $x < 12$. $3(12) + 17 = 53$

37. If $x^2 = 1$, then x must equal 1. $(-1)^2 = 1$

38. If an animal has spots, then it is a Dalmatian. The animal is a leopard.

39. If a number is prime, then it is an odd number. The number is 2, an even number.

40. If an animal cannot fly, then the animal is not a bird. The animal is an ostrich.

Real-World Link

The Old Farmer's Almanac uses a formula devised in 1792 to predict weather patterns. It claims 80% accuracy in its forecasts.

41. RESEARCH Use the Internet or some other resource to research the weather predictions and actual weather for your region for the past five years. Summarize your data as examples and counterexamples. See students' work.

3 PRACTICE

Formative Assessment

Use Exercises 1–13 to check for understanding.

Use the chart at the bottom of the next page to customize assignments for your students.

Watch Out!

Common Error Caution students to read Exercise 36 carefully. Some students may fail to notice that one inequality symbol represents *less than or equal to* and the other represents *less than*. Such an oversight may result in the inability to find a counterexample.

Exercise Alert

Internet Exercise 41 requires the use of the Internet or other reference materials.

Additional Answers

4. H: the weather is nice; C: Alisa plays with her dog in the yard; If the weather is nice, then Alisa plays with her dog in the yard.

5. H: two lines are perpendicular; C: they form right angles; If two lines are perpendicular, then they form right angles.

6. H: a number is prime; C: it is only divisible by one and itself; If a number is prime, then it is only divisible by one and itself.

33. You attend the banquet, but do not eat because you are feeling ill.

34. a rhombus that is not a square

Differentiated Homework Options

Level	Assignment	Two-Day Option	
AL Basic	14–40, 47–67	15–39 odd, 51–54	14–40 even, 47–50, 55–67
OL Core	15–39 odd, 41–44, 47–67	14–40, 51, 54	41–44, 47–50, 55–67
BL Advanced	41–61, (optional: 62–67)		

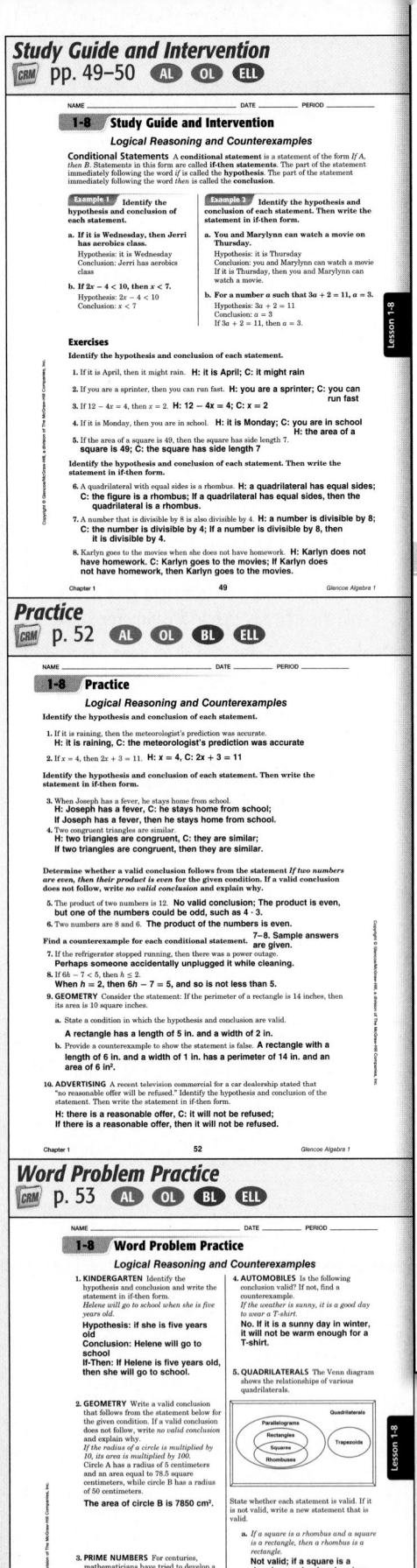

42. Determine whether a valid conclusion follows from the statement below for each given condition. If a valid conclusion does not follow, write *no valid conclusion* and explain why.

If the dimensions of rectangle ABCD are doubled, then the perimeter is doubled.

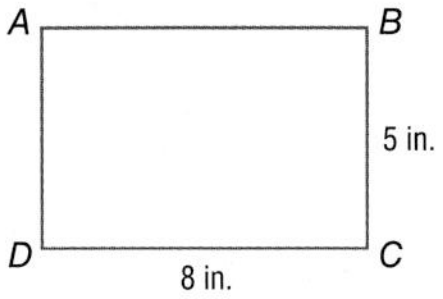

a. The new rectangle measures 16 inches by 10 inches. **The perimeter is doubled.**

b. The perimeter of the new rectangle is 52 inches. **See margin.**

43. **GEOMETRY** Use the following statement. **See margin.**

If there are three line segments $\overline{AB}$, $\overline{BC}$, and $\overline{CD}$, then they form a triangle.

a. Draw a diagram to provide an example for the conditional statement.

b. Draw a diagram to provide a counterexample for the conditional statement.

Real-World Link

Ground Hog's Day began with Pennsylvania's early settlers. They based it on the legend of Candlemas Day which states,"For as the sun shines on Candlemas Day, so far will the snow swirl in May…". The first official trek to Gobbler's Knob in Punxsutawney, Pennsylvania was on February 2, 1887.

Source: Punxsutawney Groundhog Club

44. **GROUNDHOG DAY** On Groundhog Day, some people say that if a groundhog sees its shadow, then there will be 6 more weeks of winter. If it does not see its shadow, then there will be an early spring.

a. The most famous groundhog, Punxsutawney Phil in Pennsylvania, sees his shadow 85% of the time. Write an algebraic expression to represent how many times he sees his shadow in y years. **$0.85y$**

b. The table lists each possible scenario. From the given conditional statement, determine whether this is *true* or *false*.

Sees His Shadow or Not	6 More Weeks of Winter or an Early Spring	True or False	
shadow	Winter	true	
shadow	Spring	?	**false**
no shadow	Winter	?	**false**
no shadow	Spring	?	**true**

c. Of the situations listed in the table, explain which situation could be considered a counterexample to the original statement.

c. The two cases that are counterexamples are when he sees his shadow and spring comes early and when he does not see his shadow and there are 6 more weeks of winter.

45. No; sample answer: Let $b = 4$ and $c = 5$; then $2 + (4 \cdot 5) \neq (2 + 4)(2 + 5)$.

H.O.T. Problems

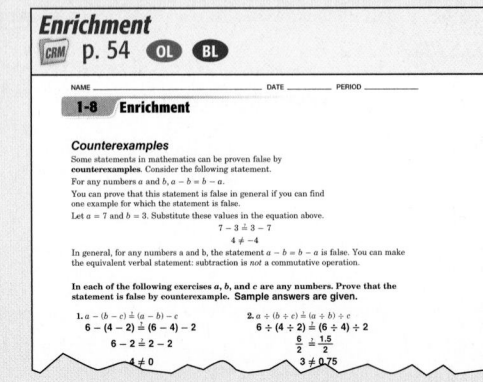

Use Higher-Order Thinking Skills

45. **CHALLENGE** Determine whether the following statement is always true. If not, provide a counterexample.

If $2(b + c) = 2b + 2c$, then $2 + (b \cdot c) = (2 + b)(2 + c)$.

46. **CHALLENGE** For what values of n is the opposite of n greater than n? For what values of n is the opposite of n less than n? For what values is n equal to its opposite? **See Chapter 1 Answer Appendix.**

47. **OPEN ENDED** Write a conditional statement. Label the hypothesis and conclusion.

48. **REASONING** Determine whether this statement is true or false. *If the length of a rectangle is doubled, then the area of the rectangle is doubled.* Justify your answer.

49. **OPEN ENDED** Write a conditional statement. Write a counterexample to the statement. Explain your reasoning. **See Chapter 1 Answer Appendix.**

50. **WRITING IN MATH** Explain how deductive reasoning is used to show that a conditional is true or false. **See Chapter 1 Answer Appendix.**

47. Sample answer: If you go swimming, then you get wet; H: you go swimming; C: you get wet.

48. True; if the length of the rectangle is ℓ and w is the width, then the area is ℓw. If ℓ is doubled, then the length is 2ℓ. The area of the new rectangle is $2\ell w$, which is double the original area.

Study Guide and Intervention

CRM pp. 49–50 AL OL ELL

NAME ______ DATE ______ PERIOD ______

1-8 Study Guide and Intervention

Logical Reasoning and Counterexamples

Conditional Statements A **conditional statement** is a statement of the form *If A, then B*. Statements in this form are called **if-then statements**. The part of the statement immediately following the word *if* is called the **hypothesis**. The part of the statement immediately following the word *then* is called the **conclusion**.

Example 1 **Identify the hypothesis and conclusion of each statement.**

a. If it is Wednesday, then Jerri has aerobics class.
Hypothesis: it is Wednesday
Conclusion: Jerri has aerobics class

b. If $2x - 4 < 10$, then $x < 7$.
Hypothesis: $2x - 4 < 10$
Conclusion: $x < 7$

Example 2 **Identify the hypothesis and conclusion of each statement. Then write the statement in if-then form.**

a. You and Marylynn can watch a movie on Thursday.
Hypothesis: it is Thursday
Conclusion: you and Marylynn can watch a movie
If it is Thursday, then you and Marylynn can watch a movie.

b. For a number a such that $3a + 2 = 11$, $a = 3$.
Hypothesis: $3a + 2 = 11$
Conclusion: $a = 3$
If $3a + 2 = 11$, then $a = 3$.

Lesson 1-8

Exercises

Identify the hypothesis and conclusion of each statement.

1. If it is April, then it might rain. **H: it is April; C: it might rain**
2. If you are a sprinter, then you can run fast. **H: you are a sprinter; C: you can run fast**
3. If $12 - 4x = 4$, then $x = 2$. **H: $12 - 4x = 4$; C: $x = 2$**
4. If it is Monday, then you are in school. **H: it is Monday; C: you are in school**
5. If the area of a square is 49, then the square has side length 7. **H: the area of a square is 49; C: the square has side length 7**

Identify the hypothesis and conclusion of each statement. Then write the statement in if-then form.

6. A quadrilateral with equal sides is a rhombus. **H: a quadrilateral has equal sides; C: the figure is a rhombus; If a quadrilateral has equal sides, then the quadrilateral is a rhombus.**
7. A number that is divisible by 8 is also divisible by 4. **H: a number is divisible by 8; C: the number is divisible by 4; If a number is divisible by 8, then it is divisible by 4.**
8. Karlyn goes to the movies when she does not have homework. **H: Karlyn does not have homework. C: Karlyn goes to the movies; If Karlyn does not have homework, then Karlyn goes to the movies.**

Chapter 1 49 Glencoe Algebra 1

Practice

CRM p. 52 AL OL BL ELL

NAME ______ DATE ______ PERIOD ______

1-8 Practice

Logical Reasoning and Counterexamples

Identify the hypothesis and conclusion of each statement.

1. If it is raining, then the meteorologist's prediction was accurate.
H: it is raining, C: the meteorologist's prediction was accurate
2. If $x = 4$, then $2x + 3 = 11$. **H: $x = 4$, C: $2x + 3 = 11$**

Identify the hypothesis and conclusion of each statement. Then write the statement in if-then form.

3. When Joseph has a fever, he stays home from school.
H: Joseph has a fever, C: he stays home from school;
If Joseph has a fever, then he stays home from school.
4. Two congruent triangles are similar.
H: two triangles are congruent, C: they are similar;
If two triangles are congruent, then they are similar.

Determine whether a valid conclusion follows from the statement *If two numbers are even, then their product is even* for the given condition. If a valid conclusion does not follow, write *no valid conclusion* and explain why.

5. The product of two numbers is 12. **No valid conclusion; The product is even, but one of the numbers could be odd, such as $4 \cdot 3$.**
6. Two numbers are 8 and 6. **The product of the numbers is even.**

Find a counterexample for each conditional statement. **7–8. Sample answers are given.**

7. If the refrigerator stopped running, then there was a power outage.
Perhaps someone accidentally unplugged it while cleaning.
8. If $6h - 7 < 5$, then $h \leq 2$.
When $h = 2$, then $6h - 7 = 5$, and so is not less than 5.
9. **GEOMETRY** Consider the statement: If the perimeter of a rectangle is 14 inches, then its area is 10 square inches.
a. State a condition in which the hypothesis and conclusion are valid.
A rectangle has a length of 5 in. and a width of 2 in.
b. Provide a counterexample to show the statement is false. **A rectangle with a length of 6 in. and a width of 1 in. has a perimeter of 14 in. and an area of 6 in².**
10. **ADVERTISING** A recent television commercial for a car dealership stated that "no reasonable offer will be refused." Identify the hypothesis and conclusion of the statement. Then write the statement in if-then form.
H: there is a reasonable offer, C: it will not be refused;
If there is a reasonable offer, then it will not be refused.

Chapter 1 52 Glencoe Algebra 1

Word Problem Practice

CRM p. 53 AL OL BL ELL

NAME ______ DATE ______ PERIOD ______

1-8 Word Problem Practice

Logical Reasoning and Counterexamples

1. **KINDERGARTEN** Identify the hypothesis and conclusion and write the statement in if-then form.
Helene will go to school when she is five years old.
Hypothesis: if she is five years old
Conclusion: Helene will go to school
If-Then: If Helene is five years old, then she will go to school.

2. **GEOMETRY** Write a valid conclusion that follows from the statement below for the given condition. If a valid conclusion does not follow, write *no valid conclusion* and explain why.
If the radius of a circle is multiplied by 10, its area is multiplied by 100.
Circle A has a radius of 5 centimeters and an area equal to 78.5 square centimeters, while circle B has a radius of 50 centimeters.
The area of circle B is 7850 cm².

3. **PRIME NUMBERS** For centuries, mathematicians have tried to develop a formula to generate prime numbers. Legendre and Euler each came up with a number of polynomial formulas that generate primes. Consider the following conditional statement and find a counterexample to show that it is not always true.
If n is a whole number, $2n^2 + 11$ is a prime number.
When $n = 11$, the expression yields 253, which is divisible by 11 (not prime).

4. **AUTOMOBILES** Is the following conclusion valid? If not, find a counterexample.
If the weather is sunny, it is a good day to wear a T-shirt.
No. If it is a sunny day in winter, it will not be warm enough for a T-shirt.

5. **QUADRILATERALS** The Venn diagram shows the relationships of various quadrilaterals.

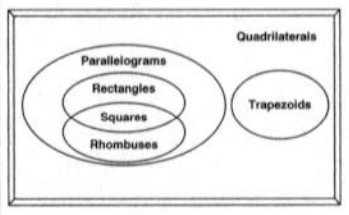

State whether each statement is valid. If it is not valid, write a new statement that is valid.

a. *If a square is a rhombus and a square is a rectangle, then a rhombus is a rectangle.*
Not valid; if a square is a rhombus and a rhombus is a parallelogram, then a square is a parallelogram.

b. *If a quadrilateral is not a parallelogram, it is a trapezoid.*
Not valid; if a quadrilateral is a parallelogram, it is not a trapezoid.

c. *If a quadrilateral is not a square, it is not a rhombus.* **valid**

Lesson 1-8

Chapter 1 53 Glencoe Algebra 1

Enrichment

CRM p. 54 OL BL

NAME ______ DATE ______ PERIOD ______

1-8 Enrichment

Counterexamples

Some statements in mathematics can be proven false by **counterexamples**. Consider the following statement.

For any numbers a and b, $a - b = b - a$.

You can prove that this statement is false in general if you can find one example for which the statement is false.

Let $a = 7$ and $b = 3$. Substitute these values in the equation above.

$$7 - 3 \stackrel{?}{=} 3 - 7$$
$$4 \neq -4$$

In general, for any numbers a and b, the statement $a - b = b - a$ is false. You can make the equivalent verbal statement: subtraction is *not* a commutative operation.

In each of the following exercises a, b, and c are any numbers. Prove that the statement is false by counterexample. **Sample answers are given.**

1. $a - (b - c) \stackrel{?}{=} (a - b) - c$
$6 - (4 - 2) \stackrel{?}{=} (6 - 4) - 2$
$6 - 2 \stackrel{?}{=} 2 - 2$
$4 \neq 0$

2. $a \div (b \div c) \stackrel{?}{=} (a \div b) \div c$
$6 \div (4 \div 2) \stackrel{?}{=} (6 \div 4) \div 2$
$\frac{6}{2} \stackrel{?}{=} \frac{1.5}{2}$
$3 \neq 0.75$

PSAE PRACTICE 9.11.18, 10.11.10, 8.11.21, 6.11.05

51. Which value of b serves as a counterexample to the statement $2b < 3b$? **A**

A -4 C $\frac{1}{2}$

B $\frac{1}{4}$ D 4

52. SHORT RESPONSE A deli serves boxed lunches with a sandwich, fruit, and a dessert. The sandwich choices are turkey, roast beef, or ham. The fruit choices are an orange or an apple. The dessert choices are a cookie or a brownie. How many different boxed lunches does the deli serve? **12**

53. Which illustrates the Transitive Property of Equality? **G**

F If $c = 1$, then $c \cdot \frac{1}{c} = 1$.

G If $c = d$ and $d = f$, then $c = f$.

H If $c = d$, then $d = c$.

J If $c = d$ and $d = c$, then $c = 1$.

54. Simplify the expression $5d(7 - 3) - 16d + 3 \cdot 2d$. **A**

A $10d$ C $21d$

B $14d$ D $25d$

Spiral Review

Determine whether each relation is a function. (Lesson 1-7)

55. **yes**

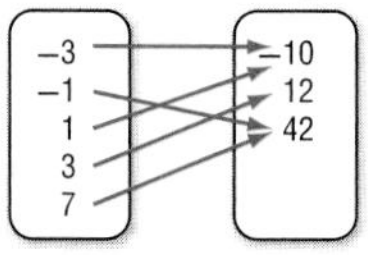

56. $\{(0, 2), (3, 5), (0, -1), (-2, 4)\}$ **no**

57. **yes**

x	y
17	6
18	6
19	5
20	4

58. **{(1, 3), (2, 6), (3, 9), (4, 12), (5, 15), (6, 18)}, Domain: {1, 2, 3, 4, 5, 6} Range: {3, 6, 9, 12, 15, 18}**

58. GEOMETRY Express the relation in the graph as a set of ordered pairs and describe the domain and range. (Lesson 1-6)

Perimeter of Equilateral Triangles

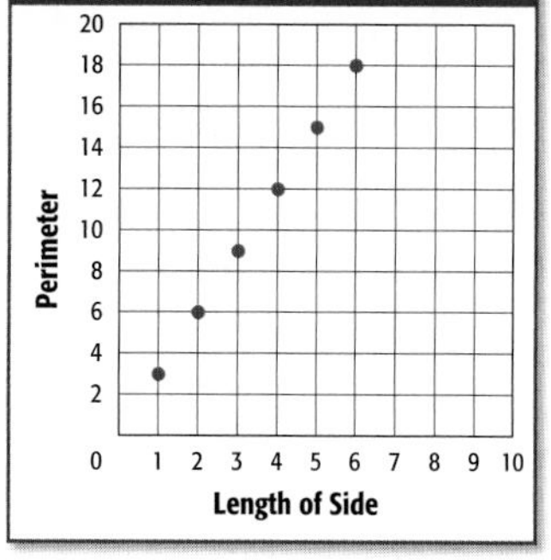

59. CLOTHING Robert has 30 socks in his sock drawer. 16 of the socks are white, 6 are black, 2 are red, and 6 are yellow. What is the probability that he randomly pulls out a black sock? (Lesson 0-9) $\frac{1}{5}$

Find the perimeter of each figure. (Lesson 0-7)

60. **20 in.**

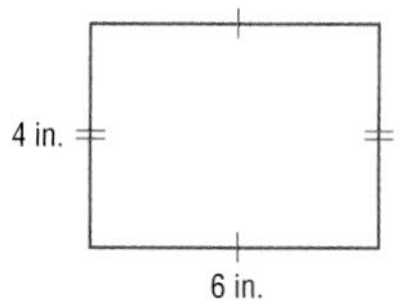

61. **38 cm**

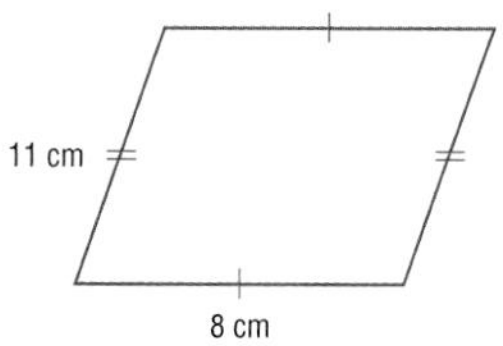

Skills Review

Evaluate each expression. (Lesson 1-2)

62. 7^2 **49**

63. $(-9)^2$ **81**

64. 2.7^2 **7.29**

65. $(-12.25)^2$ **150.0625**

66. 5^2 **25**

67. 25^2 **625**

4 ASSESS

Name the Math Have students work with partners. Ask them to explain to their partners when they would use deductive reasoning or a counterexample to show that a conditional statement is true or false.

Formative Assessment

Check for student understanding of Lessons 1-6 and 1-7.

CRM Quiz 4, p. 58

Tips for New Teachers

Student Questions Some students may question the value of learning the concepts in this lesson. Remind students that reasoning questions appear on tests and that the ability to reason from facts, rules, definitions, and properties provides a foundation for drawing valid conclusions in their daily lives.

Additional Answers

42b. No valid conclusion; the new rectangle could be 20 inches by 6 inches.

43a.

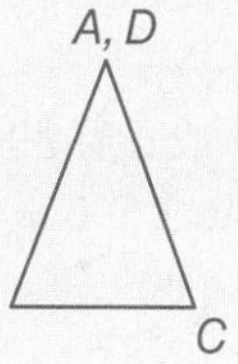

43b.

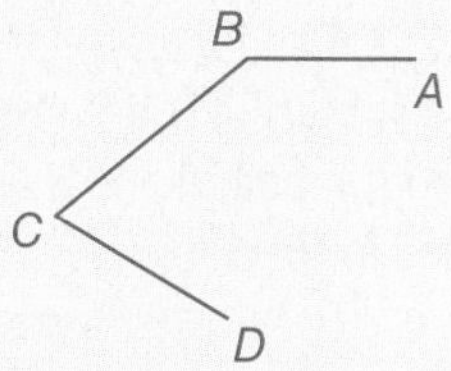

Differentiated Instruction OL BL

Extension A *paradox* is a statement that contradicts itself. The statement below is a paradox.

I am not telling the truth.

Have students write paradoxical statements and share their statements with the class.

Lesson 1-8 Logical Reasoning and Counterexamples 59

1 FOCUS

Objective Identify and write descriptions of specified subsets of a set of shapes.

Materials for Each Group

- paper (1 sheet)
- scissors
- string (4 pieces, with one long enough to encircle all of the shapes)
- colored pencils (blue, green, and yellow)

Teaching Tip

Students will need to cut 8 additional slips of paper to label the sets in the two activities. Stress that it is important to color the shapes as shown in the diagram, since color is one of the attributes used to identify the members or elements of a set.

2 TEACH

Working in Cooperative Groups

Have students work in groups of two or three to complete Steps 1–5 in Activity 1, Exercises 1–3, and Steps 1–6 in Activity 2.

- In Activity 1, make sure students understand that A and B are sets, and that both are subsets of U because all of the elements in both A and B are also contained in U.

Ask:

- Can U be a subset of A? Explain. No; the circles and triangles in U are not contained in A, so U cannot be a subset of A.
- Do subsets always contain fewer elements than the set? Explain. No; since U is a subset of U, the subset contains the same number of elements as the set.

IL Math Online glencoe.com
Math *in Motion*, Animation

IL Learning Standards 8.B.4a Represent algebraic concepts with physical materials, words, diagrams, tables, graphs, equations and inequalities and use appropriate technology.

A **set** is any collection of objects. The set that contains all objects is called the **universal set**, or the **universe**, usually labeled U. Each object is called a **member** or **element** of the set.

ACTIVITY 1

Step 1 Cut 6 pieces of paper for each color shown. Draw the shapes shown at the right.

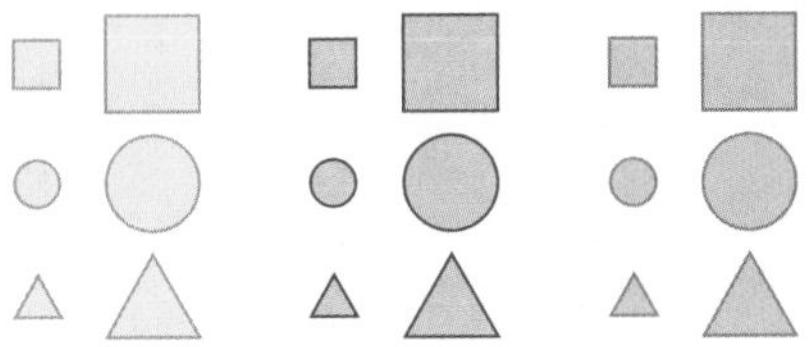

Step 2 Place the shapes inside a loop of string. Label the space inside of the loop U.

Step 3 Arrange the shapes and string as shown. Call the set of squares A.

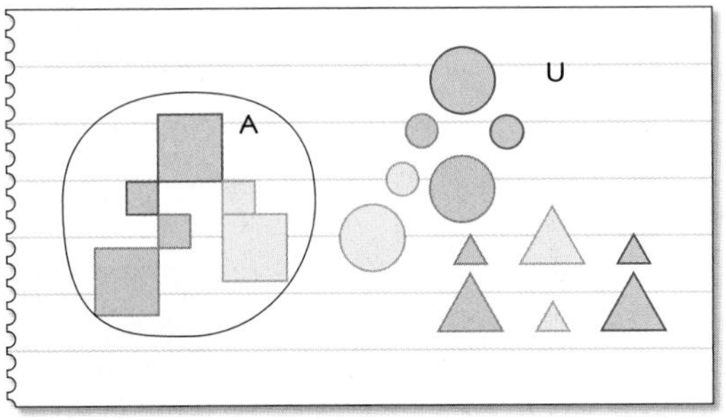

The set of squares is a **subset** of U. The **empty set**, denoted by { } or ∅, is a set with no objects. It is a subset of any set. A set is also a subset of itself. In math notation, we can write $A \subseteq U$, $A \subseteq A$, and $\varnothing \subseteq U$.

Step 4 We can identify a set by writing a description in brackets, such as {squares}. Put a loop around B = {circles}. Label it B. Notice that $B \subseteq U$.

Step 5 If A = {squares}, then the **complement** of A, written $\overline{A}$, is every object in U that is not in A. $\overline{A}$ = {circles and triangles}, or {nonsquares}. Draw the elements in $\overline{B}$. Write a description of $\overline{B}$ in brackets.

Model and Analyze

1. Let C = {triangles}. Write a description of the complement of set C in brackets. $\overline{C}$ = {squares and circles}
2. Let R = {yellow shapes}. Write a description of the complement of set R in brackets. Sample answer: $\overline{R}$ = {non-yellow squares, circles, and triangles}
3. Let U = {squares}. Subsets of U can have 0, 1, 2, 3, 4, 5, or 6 elements. How many subsets of U have exactly two elements? How many subsets are there total? There are 15 subsets with two elements. There are 64 subsets total.

ACTIVITY 2

You can perform operations on two or more numbers, such as addition, subtraction, multiplication, and division. Finding the complement of a set is an operation on one set. You can also perform operations on two or more sets at a time.

Step 1 Use U from Step 2 in Activity 1. Arrange the shapes as shown. Label the sets.

Write a description of L in brackets. Write a description of Q in brackets.

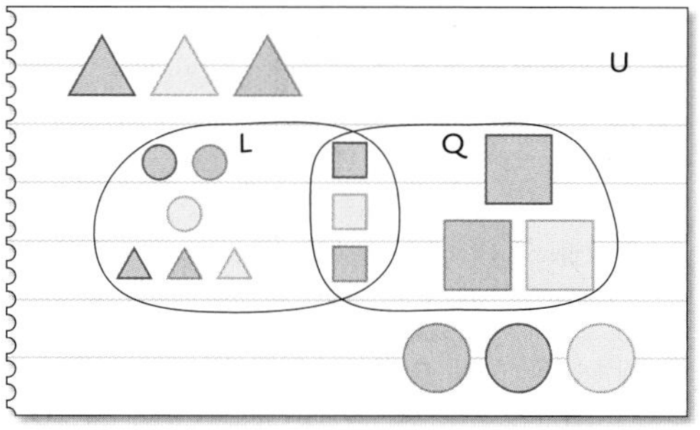

Step 2 In the diagram in Step 1, the region where L and Q overlap is shaded. Describe the shapes in the shaded region.

Step 3 The **intersection** of two sets is the set of elements common to both. The symbol for this operation is $\cap$. Intersection means that an element is in L and Q. Draw the elements in $L \cap Q$.

Step 4 The **union** of two sets is the set of elements in one set or the other set. The symbol for this operation is $\cup$. You might think of this operation as *adding up* or *combining* all elements in two or more sets. Draw the elements in the set $L \cup Q$.

Step 5 Recall that finding the complement is an operation on only one set. Draw the elements in $\overline{L \cap Q}$.

Step 6 Draw the elements in $\overline{L \cup Q}$.

Exercises

Refer to the Venn diagram shown at the right. Write a description of the shapes in each set.

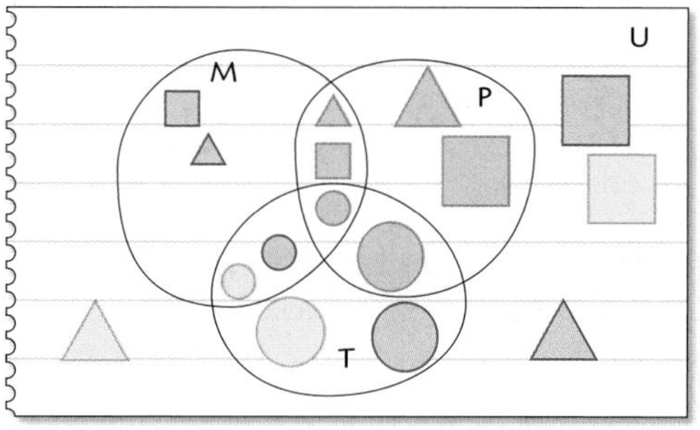

4. M $M =$ {small shapes}

5. P $P =$ {green shapes}

6. T $T =$ {circles}

7. $M \cap P$ $M \cap P =$ {small green shapes}

8. $M \cap T$

9. $P \cap T$

10. $M \cup P$

11. $M \cup T$

12. $P \cup T$

13. $M \cap P \cap T$

14. $M \cup P \cup T$

15. $\overline{M \cup P \cup T}$

16. CHALLENGE Use U from Step 2, Activity 1. Find two sets W and Z such that $W \cap Z = \emptyset$. Draw a diagram with W, Z, and U labeled and all shapes shown. Write a description of W, Z, and $\overline{W \cup Z}$ in brackets. See Chapter 1 Answer Appendix.

8. $M \cap T =$ {small circles}
9. $P \cap T =$ {green circles}
10. $M \cup P =$ {small or green shapes}
11. $M \cup T =$ {small shapes or circles}
12. $P \cup T =$ {green shapes or circles}
13. $M \cap P \cap T =$ {small green circle}
14. $M \cup P \cup T =$ {non-large yellow or blue triangles or squares}
15. $\overline{M \cup P \cup T} =$ {large yellow or blue triangles or squares}

- In Activity 2, remind students that U is the universal set, so it contains all of the elements in L and Q, as well as the three large circles and 3 large triangles.

Ask:

- How many elements are in $L \cup Q$? 12 How many elements are in $(L \cup Q)'$? 6 What is the relationship between the number of elements in $L \cup Q$, its complement $(L \cup Q)'$, and U? The number of elements in $L \cup Q$ + the number of elements in $(L \cup Q)'$ = the number of elements in U.
- How can you use the relationship between the number of elements in a set, its complement, and U to check your drawings for Steps 5 and 6? The number of elements in Step 5 should be $18 - 3$ or 15, and in Step 6 should be $18 - 12$ or 6.

Practice Have students complete Exercises 4–15. Suggest that students work in groups of two or three to complete Exercise 16.

3 ASSESS

Formative Assessment

- Use Exercise 5 to assess whether students understand how to use brackets to write a description of a set.
- Use Exercise 12 to assess whether students understand the difference between the union of two sets and the intersection of two sets.

From Concrete to Abstract

Ask: Using all of the students in your classroom as the universal set, U, find two sets A and B and then write a description of A, B, $A \cup B$, and $A \cap B$. Sample answer: $A =$ {males}, $B =$ {females}, $A \cup B =$ {males or females}, $A \cap B = \emptyset$

CHAPTER 1 Study Guide and Review

Formative Assessment

Key Vocabulary The page reference after each word denotes where that term was first introduced. If students have difficulty answering questions 1–7, remind them that they can use these page references to refresh their memories about the vocabulary terms.

Summative Assessment

CRM Vocabulary Test, p. 60

IL Math Online glencoe.com

Vocabulary PuzzleMaker improves students' mathematics vocabulary using four puzzle formats–crossword, scramble, word search using a word list, and word search using clues. Students can work online or from a printed worksheet.

CHAPTER 1 Study Guide and Review

IL Math Online glencoe.com
- STUDY TO GO
- Vocabulary Review

Chapter Summary

Key Concepts

Order of Operations (Lesson 1-2)
- Evalute expressions inside grouping symbols.
- Evaluate all powers.
- Multiply and/or divide in order from left to right.
- Add or subtract in order from left to right.

Properties of Equality (Lessons 1-3 and 1-4)
- For any numbers a, b, and c:

Reflexive: $a = a$
Symmetric: If $a = b$, then $b = a$.
Transitive: If $a = b$ and $b = c$, then $a = c$.
Substitution: If $a = b$, then a may be replaced by b in any expression.
Distributive: $a(b + c) = ab + ac$ and $a(b - c) = ab - ac$
Commutative: $a + b = b + a$ and $ab = ba$
Associative: $(a + b) + c = a + (b + c)$ and $(ab)c = a(bc)$

Solving Equations (Lesson 1-5)
- Apply order of operations and the properties of real numbers to solve equations.

Relations (Lesson 1-6)
- Relations can be represent by ordered pairs, a table, a mapping, or a graph.

Functions (Lesson 1-7)
- Use the vertical line test to determine if a relation is a function.

Conditional Statements (Lesson 1-8)
- An if-then statement has a hypothesis and a conclusion.

FOLDABLES® Study Organizer

Be sure the Key Concepts are noted in your Foldable.

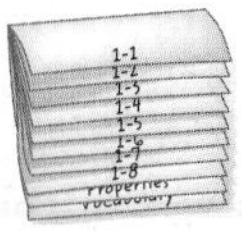

Key Vocabulary

algebraic expression (p. 5)
base (p. 5)
coefficient (p. 26)
conclusion (p. 54)
conditional statement (p. 54)
coordinate system (p. 38)
counterexample (p. 56)
deductive reasoning (p. 55)
dependent variable (p. 40)
domain (p. 38)
equation (p. 31)
exponent (p. 5)
function (p. 45)
hypothesis (p. 54)
independent variable (p. 40)
like terms (p. 25)
mapping (p. 38)
ordered pair (p. 38)
order of operations (p. 10)
origin (p. 38)
power (p. 5)
range (p. 38)
reciprocal (p. 17)
relation (p. 38)
replacement set (p. 31)
simplest form (p. 25)
solution (p. 31)
term (p. 5)
variables (p. 5)
vertical line test (p. 47)

Vocabulary Check

State whether each sentence is *true* or *false*. If *false*, replace the underlined term to make a true sentence.

1. A coordinate system is formed by two intersecting number lines. **true**
2. An exponent indicates the number of times the base is to be used as a factor. **true**
3. An expression is in simplest form when it contains like terms and parentheses. **false; not in simplest form**
4. In an expression involving multiplication, the quantities being multiplied are called factors. **true**
5. In a function, there is exactly one output for each input. **true**
6. Order of operations tells us to perform multiplication before subtraction. **true**
7. Since the product of any number and 1 is equal to the number, 1 is called the multiplicative inverse. **false; multiplicative identity**

FOLDABLES® Study Organizer

Dinah Zike's Foldables®

Have students look through the chapter to make sure they have included examples in their Foldables for each lesson of the chapter.

Suggest that students keep their Foldables handy while completing the Study Guide and Review pages. Point out that their Foldables can serve as a quick review when studying for the chapter test.

Lesson-by-Lesson Review

1-1 Variables and Expressions (pp. 5–9)

7.A.4b, 8.A.4b

Write a verbal expression for each algebraic expression. 8–10. See margin.

8. $h - 7$ **9.** $3x^2$ **10.** $5 + 6m^3$

Write an algebraic expression for each verbal expression.

11. a number increased by 9 $x + 9$

12. two thirds of a number d to the third power $\frac{2}{3}d^3$

13. 5 less than four times a number $4x - 5$

Evaluate each expression.

14. 2^5 32 **15.** 6^3 216 **16.** 4^4 256

17. **BOWLING** Fantastic Pins Bowling Alley charges $2.50 for shoe rental plus $3.25 for each game. Write an expression representing the cost to rent shoes and bowl g games. $2.50 + 3.25g$

EXAMPLE 1

Write a verbal expression for $4x + 9$.

nine more than four times a number x

EXAMPLE 2

Write an algebraic expression for *the difference of twelve and two times a number cubed.*

Variable Let x represent the number.

Expression $12 - 2x^3$

EXAMPLE 3

Evaluate 3^4.

The base is 3 and the exponent is 4.

$3^4 = 3 \cdot 3 \cdot 3 \cdot 3$ Use 3 as a factor 4 times.

$= 81$ Multiply.

1-2 Order of Operations (pp. 10–15)

7.A.4b

Evaluate each expression.

18. $24 - 4 \cdot 5$ 4 **19.** $15 + 3^2 - 6$ 18

20. $7 + 2(9 - 3)$ 19 **21.** $8 \cdot 4 - 6 \cdot 5$ 2

22. $[(2^5 - 5) \div 9]11$ 33 **23.** $\frac{11 + 4^2}{5^2 - 4^2}$ 3

Evaluate each expression if $a = 4$, $b = 3$, and $c = 9$.

24. $c + 3a$ 21

25. $5b^2 \div c$ 5

26. $(a^2 + 2bc) \div 7$ 10

27. **ICE CREAM** The cost of a one-scoop sundae is $2.75, and the cost of a two-scoop sundae is $4.25. Write and evaluate an expression to find the total cost of 3 one-scoop sundaes and 2 two-scoop sundaes. 2.75(3) + 4.25(2); $16.75

EXAMPLE 4

Evaluate the expression $3(9 - 5)^2 \div 8$.

$3(9 - 5)^2 \div 8 = 3(4)^2 \div 8$ Work inside parentheses.

$= 3(16) \div 8$ Evaluate 4^2.

$= 48 \div 8$ Multiply.

$= 6$ Divide.

EXAMPLE 5

Evaluate the expression $(5m - 2n) \div p^2$ if $m = 8$, $n = 4$, $p = 2$.

$(5m - 2n) \div p^2$

$= (5 \cdot 8 - 2 \cdot 4) \div 2^2$ Replace m with 8, n with 4, and p with 2.

$= (40 - 8) \div 2^2$ Multiply.

$= 32 \div 2^2$ Subtract.

$= 32 \div 4$ Evaluate 2^2.

$= 8$ Divide.

Lesson-by-Lesson Review

Intervention If the given examples are not sufficient to review the topics covered by the questions, remind students that the page references tell them where to review that topic in their textbooks.

Two-Day Option Have students complete the Lesson-by-Lesson Review on pp. 63–66. Then you can use ExamView® Assessment Suite to customize another review worksheet that practices all the objectives of this chapter or only the objectives on which your students need more help.

Differentiated Instruction

Super DVD: MindJogger Videoquizzes Use this DVD as an alternative format of review for the test.

Additional Answers

8. the difference between h and 7

9. the product of 3 and x squared

10. five more than the product of six and m cubed

CHAPTER 1 Study Guide and Review

1-3 Properties of Numbers (pp. 16–22)

6.A.4, 7.A.4b

Evaluate each expression using properties of numbers. Name the property used in each step. **28–35. See margin.**

28. $18 \cdot 3(1 \div 3)$

29. $[5 \div (8 - 6)]\frac{2}{5}$

30. $(16 - 4^2) + 9$

31. $2 \cdot \frac{1}{2} + 4(4 \cdot 2 - 7)$

32. $18 + 41 + 32 + 9$

33. $7\frac{2}{5} + 5 + 2\frac{3}{5}$

34. $8 \cdot 0.5 \cdot 5$

35. $5.3 + 2.8 + 3.7 + 6.2$

36. SCHOOL SUPPLIES Monica needs to purchase a binder, a textbook, a calculator, and a workbook for her algebra class. The binder costs $9.25, the textbook $32.50, the calculator $18.75, and the workbook $15.00. Find the total cost for Monica's algebra supplies. **$75.50**

EXAMPLE 6

Evaluate $6(4 \cdot 2 - 7) + 5 \cdot \frac{1}{5}$. Name the property used in each step.

$6(4 \cdot 2 - 7) + 5 \cdot \frac{1}{5}$

$= 6(8 - 7) + 5 \cdot \frac{1}{5}$ — **Substitution**

$= 6(1) + 5 \cdot \frac{1}{5}$ — **Substitution**

$= 6 + 5 \cdot \frac{1}{5}$ — **Multiplicative Identity**

$= 6 + 1$ — **Multiplicative Inverse**

$= 7$ — **Substitution**

1-4 The Distributive Property (pp. 23–29)

6.A.4

Use the Distributive Property to rewrite each expression. Then evaluate. **37–42. See margin.**

37. $(2 + 3)6$

38. $5(18 + 12)$

39. $8(6 - 2)$

40. $(11 - 4)3$

41. $-2(5 - 3)$

42. $(8 - 3)4$

Rewrite each expression using the Distributive Property. Then simplify. **43–48. See margin.**

43. $3(x + 2)$

44. $(m + 8)4$

45. $6(d - 3)$

46. $-4(5 - 2t)$

47. $(9y - 6)(-3)$

48. $-6(4z + 3)$

49. TUTORING Write and evaluate an expression for the number of tutoring lessons Mrs. Green gives in 4 weeks. **4(3 + 5 + 4); 48**

Tutoring Schedule	
Day	**Students**
Monday	3
Tuesday	5
Wednesday	4

EXAMPLE 7

Use the Distributive Property to rewrite the expression 5(3 + 8). Then evaluate.

$5(3 + 8) = 5(3) + 5(8)$ — **Distributive Property**

$= 15 + 40$ — **Multiply.**

$= 55$ — **Simplify.**

EXAMPLE 8

Rewrite the expression $6(x + 4)$ using the Distributive Property. Then simplify.

$6(x + 4) = 6 \cdot x + 6 \cdot 4$ — **Distributive Property**

$= 6x + 24$ — **Simplify.**

EXAMPLE 9

Rewrite the expression $(3x - 2)(-5)$ using the Distributive Property. Then simplify.

$(3x - 2)(-5)$

$= (3x)(-5) - (2)(-5)$ — **Distributive Property**

$= -15x + 10$ — **Simplify.**

Additional Answers

28. $18 \cdot 3(1 \div 3)$
$= 18 \cdot (3)\frac{1}{3}$ Substitution
$= 18 \cdot 1$ Multiplicative Inverse
$= 18$ Multiplicative Identity

29. $[5 \div (8 - 6)]\frac{2}{5}$
$= [5 \div 2]\frac{2}{5}$ Substitution
$= \frac{5}{2} \cdot \frac{2}{5}$ Substitution
$= 1$ Multiplicative Inverse

30. $(16 - 4^2) + 9$
$= 16 - 16 + 9$ Substitution
$= 0 + 9$ Additive Inverse
$= 9$ Additive Identity

31. $2 \cdot \frac{1}{2} + 4(4 \cdot 2 - 7)$
$= 2 \cdot \frac{1}{2} + 4(8 - 7)$ Substitution
$= 2 \cdot \frac{1}{2} + 4(1)$ Substitution
$= 1 + 4(1)$ Multiplicative Inverse
$= 1 + 4$ Multiplicative Identity
$= 5$ Substitution

32. $18 + 41 + 32 + 9$
$= 18 + 32 + 41 + 9$ Commutative (+)
$= (18 + 32) + (41 + 9)$ Associative (+)
$= 50 + 50$ Substitution
$= 100$ Substitution

33. $7\frac{2}{5} + 5 + 2\frac{3}{5}$
$= 7\frac{2}{5} + 2\frac{3}{5} + 5$ Commutative (+)
$= \left(7\frac{2}{5} + 2\frac{3}{5}\right) + 5$ Associative (+)
$= 10 + 5$ Substitution
$= 15$ Substitution

34. $8 \cdot 0.5 \cdot 5$
$= 8 \cdot 5 \cdot 0.5$ Commutative (×)
$= (8 \cdot 5) \cdot 0.5$ Associative (×)
$= 40 \cdot 0.5$ Substitution
$= 20$ Substitution

35. $5.3 + 2.8 + 3.7 + 6.2$
$= 5.3 + 3.7 + 2.8 + 6.2$ Commutative (+)
$= (5.3 + 3.7) + (2.8 + 6.2)$ Associative (+)
$= 9 + 9$ Substitution
$= 18$ Substitution

37. $2(6) + 3(6); 30$

38. $5(18) + 5(12); 150$

39. $8(6) - 8(2); 32$

40. $11(3) - 4(3); 21$

41. $-2(5) - (-2)(3); -4$

42. $8(4) - 3(4); 20$

43. $3(x) + 3(2); 3x + 6$

44. $m(4) + 8(4); 4m + 32$

45. $6(d) - 6(3); 6d - 18$

46. $-4(5) - (-4)(2t); -20 + 8t$

47. $(9y)(-3) - (6)(-3); -27y + 18$

48. $-6(4z) + (-6)(3); -24z - 18$

64 Chapter 1 Expressions, Equations, and Functions

1-5 Equations (pp. 31–37)

8.B.4a

Find the solution of each equation if the replacement sets are x: {1, 3, 5, 7, 9} and y: {6, 8, 10, 12, 14}

50. $y - 9 = 3$ 12

51. $14 + x = 21$ 7

52. $4y = 32$ 8

53. $3x - 11 = 16$ 9

54. $\frac{42}{y} = 7$ 6

55. $2(x - 1) = 8$ 5

Solve each equation.

56. $a = 24 - 7(3)$ 3

57. $z = 63 \div (3^2 - 2)$ 9

58. AGE Shandra's age is four more than three times Sherita's age. Write an equation for Shandra's age. Solve if Sherita is 3 years old. $3K + 4 = E$; 13

EXAMPLE 10

Solve the equation $5w - 19 = 11$ if the replacement set is w: {2, 4, 6, 8, 10}.

Replace w in $5w - 19 = 11$ with each value in the replacement set.

w	$5w - 19 = 11$	True or False?
2	$5(2) - 19 = 11$	False
4	$5(4) - 19 = 11$	False
6	$5(6) - 19 = 11$	True
8	$5(8) - 19 = 11$	False
10	$5(10) - 19 = 11$	False

Since the equation is true when $w = 6$, the solution of $5w - 19 = 11$ is $w = 6$.

1-6 Representing Relations (pp. 38–44)

8.B.4a

Express each relation as a table, a graph, and a mapping. Then determine the domain and range. 59–61. See Ch. 1 Answer Appendix.

59. {(1, 3), (2, 4), (3, 5), (4, 6)}

60. {(−1, 1), (0, −2), (3, 1), (4, −1)}

61. {(−2, 4), (−1, 3), (0, 2), (−1, 2)}

Express the relation shown in each table, mapping, or graph as a set of ordered pairs.

62.

x	y
5	3
3	−1
1	2
−1	0

{(5, 3), (3, −1), (1, 2), (−1, 0)}

63. {(−2, −2), (0, −3), (2, −2), (2, 0), (4, −1)}

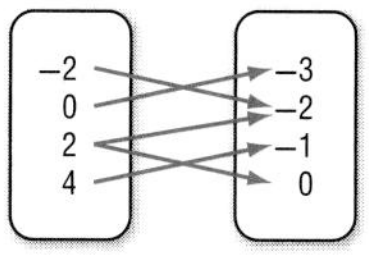

64. GARDENING On average, 7 plants grow for every 10 seeds of a certain type planted. Make a table to show the relation between seeds planted and plants growing for 50, 100, 150, and 200 seeds. Then state the domain and range and graph the relation. See margin.

EXAMPLE 11

Express the relation {(−3, 4), (1, −2), (0, 1), (3, −1)} as a table, a graph, and a mapping.

Table

Place the x-coordinates into the first column. Place the corresponding y-coordinates in the second column.

x	y
−3	4
1	−2
0	1
3	−1

Graph

Graph each ordered pair on a coordinate plane.

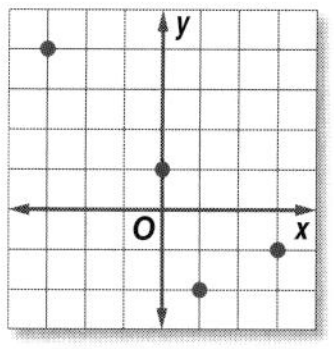

Mapping

List the x-values in the domain and the y-values in the range. Draw arrows from the x-values in set X to the corresponding y-values in set Y.

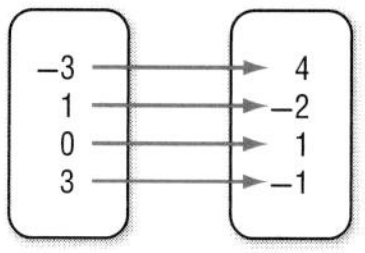

Additional Answer

64.

Planted	Growing
50	35
100	70
150	105
200	140

D = {50, 100, 150, 200}
R = {35, 70, 105, 140}

Seeds Growing Into Plants

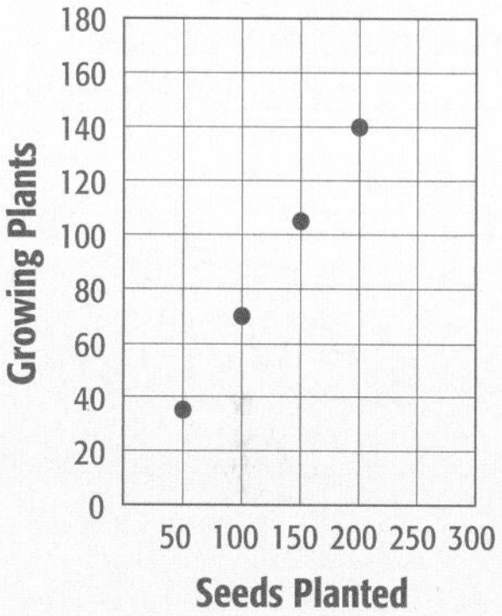

Problem Solving Review

For additional practice in problem solving for Chapter 1, see the Mixed Problem Solving Appendix, p. 845, in the Student Handbook section.

Anticipation Guide

Have students complete the Chapter 1 Anticipation Guide and discuss how their responses have changed now that they have completed Chapter 1.

Additional Answers

75. **Studying**

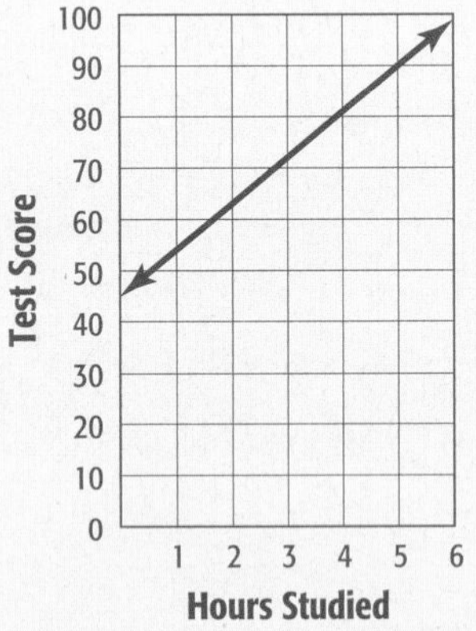

76. hypothesis: Orlando practices the piano; conclusion: he will perform well at his recital

78. If you don't go outside when it is raining, you won't get wet.

CHAPTER 1 Study Guide and Review

1-7 Representing Functions (pp. 45–52)

8.C.4b

Determine whether each relation is a function.

65.

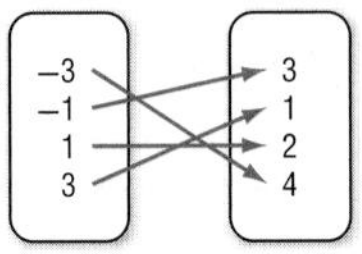

function

66.

x	y
−4	3
2	0
1	−2
2	1

not a function

67.

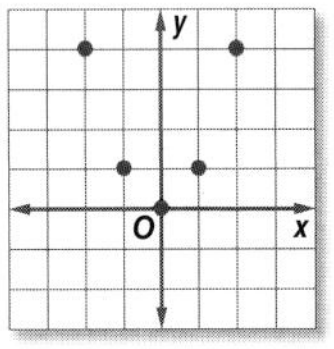

function

68. $\{(8, 4), (6, 3), (4, 2), (2, 1), (0, 0)\}$ function

If $f(x) = 2x + 4$ and $g(x) = x^2 - 3$, find each value.

69. $f(-3)$ -2 **70.** $g(2)$ 1 **71.** $f(0)$ 4

72. $g(-4)$ 13 **73.** $f(m + 2)$ $2m + 8$ **74.** $g(3p)$ $9p^2 - 3$

75. GRADES A teacher claims that the relationship between number of hours studied for a test and test score can be described by $g(x) = 45 + 9x$, where x represents the number of hours studied. Graph this function. See margin.

EXAMPLE 12

Determine whether the relation shown below is a function.

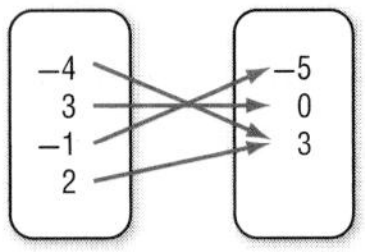

For each member of the domain, there is only one member of the range that corresponds to it. So this mapping represents a function. It does not matter that more than one element of the domain is paired with one element of the range.

EXAMPLE 13

Determine whether $2x - y = 1$ represents a function.

First make a table of values. Then graph the equation.

x	y
−1	−3
0	−1
1	1
2	3
3	5

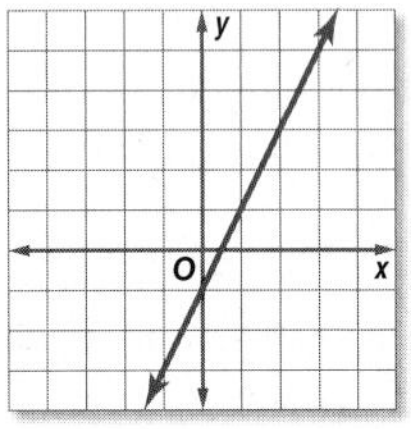

Using the vertical line test, it can be shown that $2x - y = 1$ does represent a function.

1-8 Logical Reasoning and Counterexamples (pp. 54–59)

7.A.4b

Identify the hypothesis and conclusion of each statement.

76. If Orlando practices the piano, then he will perform well at his recital. See margin.

77. If $2x + 7 > 31$, then $x > 12$.
Hypothesis: $2x + 7 > 31$ Conclusion: $x > 12$

Find a counterexample for each conditional statement. See margin.

78. If it is raining outside, then you will get wet.

79. If $4x - 11 = 53$, then $x < 16$. $x = 16$

EXAMPLE 14

Identify the hypothesis and the conclusion for the statement "If the football team wins their last game, then they will win the championship."

The hypothesis follows the word *if*, and the conclusion follows the word *then*.

Hypothesis: the football team wins their last game

Conclusion: they will win the championship

66 Chapter 1 Expressions, Equations, and Functions

IL Math Online glencoe.com
Chapter Test

Write an algebraic expression for each verbal expression.

1. six more than a number $n + 6$

2. twelve less than the product of three and a number $3n - 12$

3. four divided by the difference between a number and seven $\frac{4}{n-7}$

Evaluate each expression.

4. $32 \div 4 + 2^3 - 3$ 13

5. $\frac{(2 \cdot 4)^2}{7 + 3^2}$ 4

6. **MULTIPLE CHOICE** Find the value of the expression $a^2 + 2ab + b^2$ if $a = 6$ and $b = 4$. C

A 68

B 92

C 100

D 121

Evaluate each expression. Name the property used in each step. 7–9. See margin.

7. $13 + (16 - 4^2)$

8. $\frac{2}{9}[9 \div (7 - 5)]$

9. $37 + 29 + 13 + 21$

Rewrite each expression using the Distributive Property. Then simplify. 10–11. See margin.

10. $4(x + 3)$

11. $(5p - 2)(-3)$

12. **MOVIE TICKETS** A company operates three movie theaters. The chart shows the typical number of tickets sold each week at the three locations. Write and evaluate an expression for the total typical number of tickets sold by all three locations in four weeks.

$4(438 + 374 + 512)$; 5296

Location	Tickets Sold
A	438
B	374
C	512

Find the solution of each equation if the replacement sets are x: {1, 3, 5, 7, 9} and y: {2, 4, 6, 8, 10}.

13. $3x - 9 = 12$ 7

14. $y^2 - 5y - 11 = 13$ 8

15. **CELL PHONES** The ABC Cell Phone Company offers a plan that includes a flat fee of \$29 per month plus a \$0.12 charge per minute. Write an equation to find C, the total monthly cost for m minutes. Then solve the equation for $m = 50$. $C = 29 + 0.12m$; \$35

Express the relation shown in each table, mapping, or graph as a set of ordered pairs.

16.

x	y
−2	4
1	2
3	0
4	−2

{(−2, 4), (1, 2), (3, 0), (4, −2)}

17.

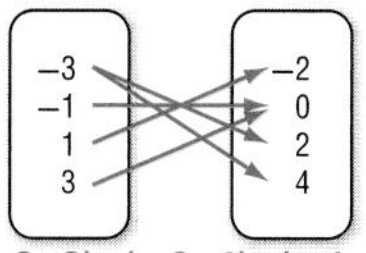

{(−3, 2), (−3, 4), (−1, 0), (1, −2), (3, 0)}

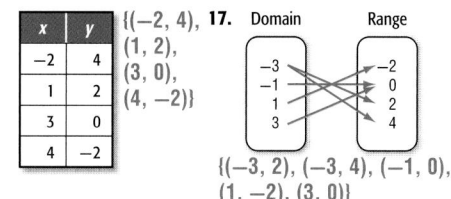

18. **MULTIPLE CHOICE** Determine the domain and range for the relation {(2, 5), (−1, 3), (0, −1), (3, 3), (−4, −2)}. F

F D: {2, −1, 0, 3, −4}, R: {5, 3, −1, 3, −2}

G D: {5, 3, −1, 3, −2}, R: {2, −1, 0, 3, 4}

H D: {0, 1, 2, 3, 4}, R: {−4, −3, −2, −1, 0}

J D: {2, −1, 0, 3, −4}, R: {2, −1, 0, 3, 4}

19. Determine whether the relation {(2, 3), (−1, 3), (0, 4), (3, 2), (−2, 3)} is a function. yes

If $f(x) = 5 - 2x$ and $g(x) = x^2 + 7x$, find each value.

20. $g(3)$ 30

21. $f(-6y)$ $5 + 12y$

Identify the hypothesis and conclusion of each statement.

22. If the temperature goes below 32°F, it will snow outside. H: the temperature goes below 32°F C: it will snow outside

23. If Ivan breaks his arm, he will need to go to the hospital. H: Ivan breaks his arm C: he will need to go to the hospital

Find a counterexample for each conditional statement. 24. You can go to the pool but not go in the water.

24. If you go to the pool, you will get wet.

25. If a quadrilateral has one pair of sides that are parallel, then it is a square. The quadrilateral could be a trapezoid.

CHAPTER 1 Practice Test

ExamView Assessment Suite Customize and create multiple versions of your chapter tests and their answer keys. All of the questions from the leveled chapter tests in the *Chapter 1 Resource Masters* are also available on ExamView® Assessment Suite.

Additional Answers

7. $13 + (16 - 4^2)$
$= 13 + (16 - 16)$ Substitution
$= 13 + 0$ Additive Inverse
$= 13$ Additive Identity

8. $\frac{2}{9}[9 \div (7 - 5)]$
$= \frac{2}{9}[9 \div 2]$ Substitution
$= \frac{2}{9} \cdot \frac{9}{2}$ Substitution
$= 1$ Multiplicative Inverse

9. $37 + 29 + 13 + 21$
$= 37 + 13 + 29 + 21$ Commutative Property (+)
$= (37 + 13) + (29 + 21)$ Associative Property (+)
$= 50 + 50$ Substitution
$= 100$

10. $4(x + 3)$
$= 4(x) + 4(3)$
$= 4x + 12$

11. $(5p - 2)(-3)$
$= (5p)(-3) - (2)(-3)$
$= -15p + 6$

Intervention Planner

Tier 1 On Level	Tier 2 Strategic Intervention approaching grade level	Tier 3 Intensive Intervention 2 or more grades below level
If students miss about 25% of the exercises or less,	**If** students miss about 50% of the exercises,	**If** students miss about 75% of the exercises,
Then choose a resource: SE Lessons 1-1, 1-2, 1-3, 1-4, 1-5, 1-6, 1-7 and 1-8; CRM Skills Practice, pp. 7, 13, 20, 26, 32, 39, 45, and 51; TE Chapter Project, p. 2; IL Math Online Self-Check Quiz	**Then** choose a resource: CRM Study Guide and Intervention, Chapter 1 pp. 5, 11, 18, 24, 30, 37, 43, and 49; *Quick Review Math Handbook*; IL Math Online Extra Examples, Personal Tutor, Homework Help	**Then** use *Math Triumphs Alg. 1*, Ch. 1, 2, 3, 5, and 6; IL Math Online Extra Examples, Personal Tutor, Homework Help, Review Vocabulary

1 FOCUS

Objective Use the strategy of eliminating unreasonable answers to solve standardized test problems.

2 TEACH

Scaffolding Questions

Ask:

- Have you ever thought that someone gave an unreasonable explanation for something that occurred? In general, what made you think the explanation was unreasonable? Sample answer: The explanation did not fit the circumstances or was unusual.
- In general, how would a reasonable explanation differ from an unreasonable explanation? Sample answer: A reasonable explanation would fit the facts or details of the situation, whereas the unreasonable explanation would not.

CHAPTER 1 Preparing for Standardized Tests

Eliminate Unreasonable Answers

You can eliminate unreasonable answers to help you find the correct one when solving multiple choice test items. Doing so will save you time by narrowing down the list of possible correct answers.

Strategies for Eliminating Unreasonable Answers

Step 1

Read the problem statement carefully to determine exactly what you are being asked to find.

Ask yourself:

- What am I being asked to solve?
- What format (i.e., fraction, number, decimal, percent, type of graph) will the correct answer be?
- What units (if any) will the correct answer have?

Step 2

Carefully look over each possible answer choice and evaluate for reasonableness.

- Identify any answer choices that are clearly incorrect and eliminate them.
- Eliminate any answer choices that are not in the proper format.
- Eliminate any answer choices that do not have the correct units.

Step 3

Solve the problem and choose the correct answer from those remaining. Check your answer.

EXAMPLE

Read each problem. Eliminate any unreasonable answers. Then use the information in the problem to solve.

Jason earns 8.5% commission on his weekly sales at an electronics retail store. Last week he had \$4200 in sales. What was his commission for the week?

A \$332 **C** \$425

B \$357 **D** \$441

68 Chapter 1 Expressions, Equations, and Functions

Using mental math, you know that 10% of $4200 is $420. Since 8.5% is less than 10%, you know that Jason earned less than $420 in commission for his weekly sales. So, answer choices C and D can be eliminated because they are greater than $420. The correct answer is either A or B.

$4200 × 0.085 = $357

So, the correct answer is B.

Exercises

Read each problem. Eliminate any unreasonable answers. Then use the information in the problem to solve.

1. Coach Roberts expects 35% of the student body to turn out for a pep rally. If there are 560 students, how many does Coach Roberts expect to attend the pep rally? B

A 184

B 196

C 214

D 390

2. Jorge and Sally leave school at the same time. Jorge walks 300 yards north and then 400 yards east. Sally rides her bike 600 yards south and then 800 yards west. What is the distance between the two students? J

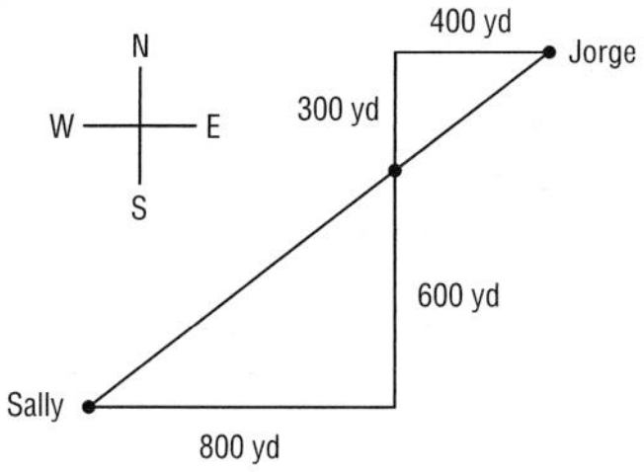

F 500 yd

G 750 yd

H 1,200 yd

J 1,500 yd

3. What is the range of the relation below? C

{(1, 2), (3, 4), (5, 6), (7, 8)}

A all real numbers

B all even numbers

C {2, 4, 6, 8}

D {1, 3, 5, 7}

4. The expression $3n + 1$ gives the total number of squares needed to make each figure of the pattern where n is the figure number. How many squares will be needed to make Figure 9? F

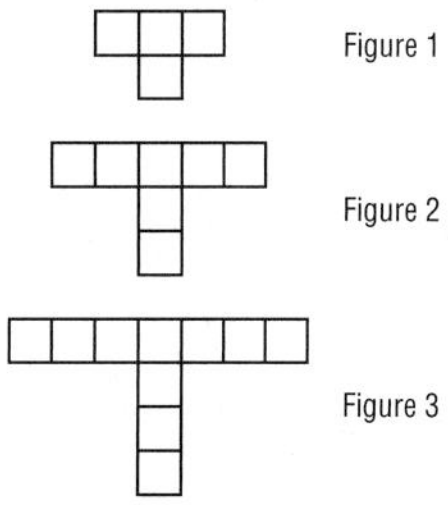

F 28 squares

G 32.5 squares

H 56 squares

J 88.5 squares

5. The expression $3x - (2x + 4x - 6)$ is equivalent to B

A $-3x - 6$

B $-3x + 6$

C $3x + 6$

D $3x - 6$

Additional Example

In a poll on favorite exercise activities, 22.5% of the students in the survey voted for weight lifting. If 1200 students participated in the poll, how many voted for weight lifting? B

A 246

B 270

C 318

D 390

3 ASSESS

Use Exercises 1–5 to assess students' understanding.

Chapter 1 Preparing for Standardized Tests 69

Diagnose Student Errors

Survey students' responses for each item. Class trends may indicate common errors and misconceptions.

1. A multiplied exponent times base
B found 2^5 instead of 2^6
C found 6^2 instead of 2^6
D correct
E found 2^7 instead of 2^6

2. F misunderstood concept of counterexample
G misunderstood concept of counterexample
H confused hypothesis and conclusion
J found example
K correct

3. A misunderstood relationship between feet and yards
B misunderstood relationship between feet and yards
C correct
D misunderstood relationship between feet and yards
E misunderstood relationship between feet and yards

4. F confused domain and range
G correct
H does not understand difference between domain and range
J guess
K selected numbers in middle

5. A underestimate
B correct
C overestimate
D overestimate
E overestimate

6. F guess
G guess
H guess
J correct
K 24 on wrong side of =

Multiple Choice

Read each question. Then fill in the correct answer on the answer document provided by your teacher or on a sheet of paper.

1. Evaluate the expression 2^6. D

A 12
B 32
C 36
D 64
E 128

2. Monica claims: *If you are in the drama club, then you are also on the academic team.* Which student is a counterexample to this statement? J

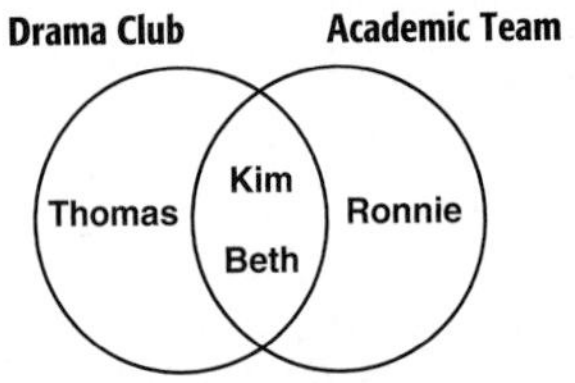

F Beth
G Kim
H Ronnie
J Thomas
K Kim and Beth

3. Let y represent the number of yards. Which algebraic expression represents the number of feet in y? C

A $y - 3$
B $y + 3$
C $3y$
D $\frac{3}{y}$
E $\frac{y}{3}$

4. What is the domain of the following relation? G

$$\{(1, 3), (-6, 4), (8, 5)\}$$

F $\{3, 4, 5\}$
G $\{-6, 1, 8\}$
H $\{-6, 1, 3, 4, 5, 8\}$
J $\{1, 3, 4, 5, 8\}$
K $\{-6, 4\}$

5. The table shows the number of some of the items sold at the concession stand at the first day of a soccer tournament. Estimate how many items were sold from the concession stand. B

Concession Sales Day 1 Results	
Item	**Number Sold**
Popcorn	78
Hot Dogs	80
Chip	48
Sodas	51
Bottled Water	92

A 330 items
B 350 items
C 400 items
D 450 items
E 500 items

6. There are 24 more cars than twice the number of trucks for sale at a dealership. If there are 100 cars for sale, how many trucks are there for sale at the dealership? J

F 28
G 32
H 34
J 38
K 62

7. Refer to the relation in the table below. Which of the following values would result in the relation *not* being a function? B

x	−6	−2	0	?	3	5
y	−1	8	3	−3	4	0

A −1
B 3
C 7
D 8
E 9

Test-TakingTip

Question 2 A *counterexample* is a specific case in which the hypothesis of a conditional statement is true, but the conclusion is false.

7. A does not understand concept of function
B correct
C does not understand concept of function
D does not understand concept of function
E does not understand concept of function

Short Response/Gridded Response

Record your answers on the answer sheet provided by your teacher or on a sheet of paper.

8. The edge of each box below is 1 unit long.

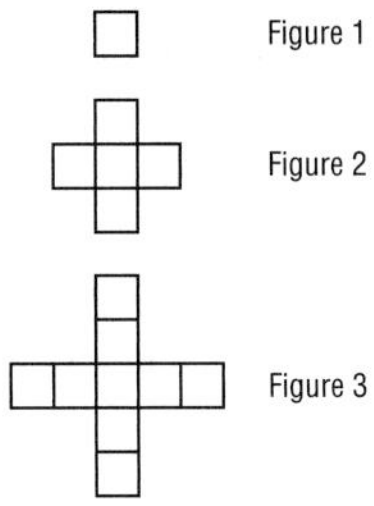

a. Make a table showing the perimeters of the first 3 figures in the pattern. 4 units, 12 units, 20 units

b. Look for a pattern in the perimeters of the shapes. Write an algebraic expression for the perimeter of Figure *n*. $4 + 8(n - 1)$ or $8n - 4$

c. What would be the perimeter of Figure 10 in the pattern? 76 units

9. The table shows the costs of certain items at a corner hardware store.

Item	Cost
box of nails	\$3.80
box of screws	\$5.25
claw hammer	\$12.95
electric drill	\$42.50

a. Write two expressions to represent the total cost of 3 boxes of nails, 2 boxes of screws, 2 hammers, and 1 electric drill. See margin.

b. What is the total cost of the items purchased? \$90.30

10. GRIDDED RESPONSE Evaluate the expression below. 20

$$\frac{5^3 \cdot 4^2 - 5^2 \cdot 4^3}{5 \cdot 4}$$

11. Use the equation $y = 2(4 + x)$ to answer each question. b–c. See margin.

a. Complete the table for each value of *x*.

x	*y*
1	10
2	12
3	14
4	16
5	18
6	20

b. Plot the points from the table on a coordinate grid. What do you notice about the points?

c. Make a conjecture about the relationship between the change in *x* and the change in *y*.

Extended Response

Record your answers on a sheet of paper. Show your work.

12. The volume of a sphere is four-thirds the product of π and the radius cubed.

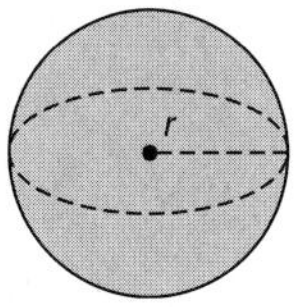

a. Write an expression for the volume of a sphere with radius *r*. $\left(\frac{4}{3}\right)\pi r^3$

b. Find the volume of a sphere with a radius of 6 centimeters. Explain your answer. See margin.

Need Extra Help?												
If you missed Question...	1	2	3	4	5	6	7	8	9	10	11	12
Go to Lesson or Page...	1-1	1-7	1-2	1-6	1-4	1-5	1-7	1-5	1-3	1-2	1-4	1-1
IL Assessment Objectives	6.11.18	9.11.01	8.11.11	8.11.11	6.11.13	6.11.13	8.11.11	8.11.04	6.11.13	8.11.01	8.11.12	8.11.06

Formative Assessment

You can use these two pages to benchmark student progress.

CRM Standardized Test Practice, pp. 74–76

Answer Sheet Practice

Have students simulate taking a standardized test by recording their answers on a practice recording sheet.

CRM Student Recording Sheet, p. 55

Chapter Resource Master
CRM p. 55

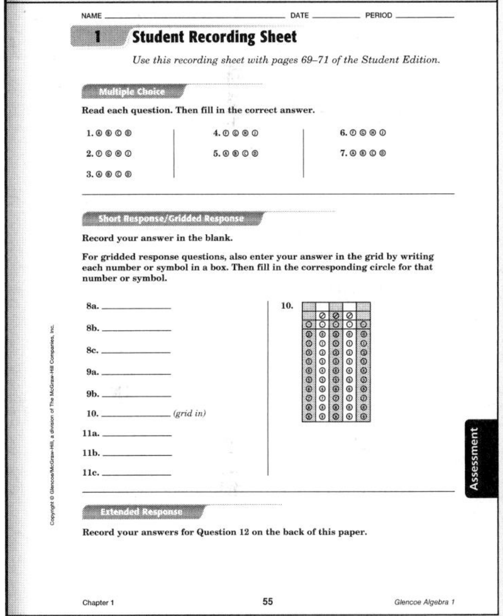

ExamView Assessment Suite Create practice worksheets or tests that align to your state's standards, as well as TIMSS and NAEP tests.

Additional Answers

9a. Sample answer: $3(3.80) + 2(5.25) + 2(12.95) + 42.50$; $3(3.80) + 2(5.25 + 12.95) + 42.50$

11b. See students' graphs. Sample answer: The points lie in a straight line.

11c. Sample answer: When *x* increases by 1, *y* increases by 2.

12b. 288π cm^3; Sample answer: Substitute 6 for *r* in the expression. Take 6 to the third power. Multiply by 4, then divide by 3. Pi is irrational so it appears in the answer.

Homework Option

Get Ready for Chapter 2 Assign students the exercises on p. 73 as homework to assess whether they possess the prerequisite skills needed for the next chapter.

Page 9, Lesson 1-1

47.

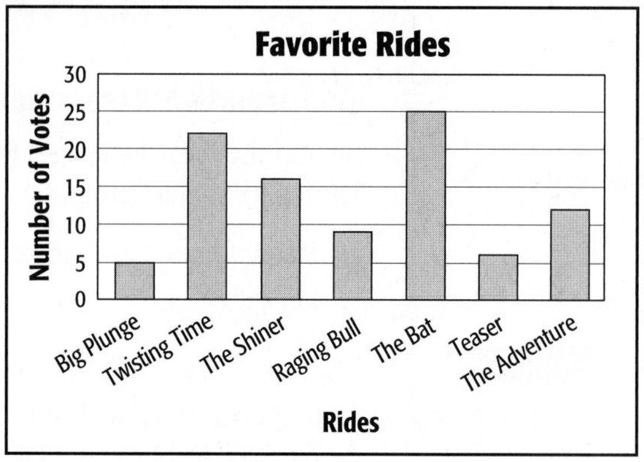

Pages 19–21, Lesson 1-3

1. $(1 \div 5)5 \cdot 14$
$= \frac{1}{5} \cdot 5 \cdot 14$ Substitution
$= (1) \cdot 14$ Multiplicative Inverse
$= 14$ Multiplicative Identity

2. $6 + 4(19 - 15)$
$= 6 + 4(4)$ Substitution
$= 6 + 16$ Substitution
$= 22$ Substitution

3. $5(14 - 5) + 6(3 + 7)$
$= 5(9) + 6(10)$ Substitution
$= 45 + 60$ Substitution
$= 105$ Substitution

4. $9(25) + 4(10) + 7(5) + 2$
$= 225 + 40 + 35 + 2$ Substitution
$= 302$ Substitution
Carolyn has 302¢ or $3.02.

5. $23 + 42 + 37$
$= 23 + 37 + 42$ Commutative (+)
$= (23 + 37) + 42$ Associative (+)
$= 60 + 42$ Substitution
$= 102$ Substitution

6. $2.75 + 3.5 + 4.25 + 1.5$
$= 2.75 + 4.25 + 3.5 + 1.5$ Commutative (+)
$= (2.75 + 4.25) + (3.5 + 1.5)$ Associative (+)
$= 7 + 5$ Substitution
$= 12$ Substitution

7. $3 \cdot 7 \cdot 10 \cdot 2$
$= 3 \cdot 2 \cdot 7 \cdot 10$ Commutative (×)
$= (3 \cdot 2) \cdot (7 \cdot 10)$ Associative (×)
$= 6 \cdot 70$ Substitution
$= 420$ Substitution

8. $\frac{1}{4} \cdot 24 \cdot \frac{2}{3}$
$= \frac{1}{4} \cdot \left(24 \cdot \frac{2}{3}\right)$ Associative (×)
$= \frac{1}{4} \cdot 16$ Substitution
$= 4$ Substitution

9. $3(22 - 3 \cdot 7)$
$= 3(22 - 21)$ Substitution
$= 3(1)$ Substitution
$= 3$ Multiplicative Identity

10. $7 + (9 - 3^2)$
$= 7 + (9 - 9)$ Substitution
$= 7 + 0$ Additive Inverse
$= 7$ Additive Identity

11. $\frac{3}{4}[4 \div (7 - 4)]$
$= \frac{3}{4}[4 \div 3]$ Substitution
$= \frac{3}{4} \cdot \frac{4}{3}$ Substitution
$= 1$ Multiplicative Inverse

12. $[3 \div (2 \cdot 1)]\frac{2}{3}$
$= [3 \div 2]\frac{2}{3}$ Multiplicative Identity
$= \frac{3}{2} \cdot \frac{2}{3}$ Substitution
$= 1$ Multiplicative Inverse

13. $2(3 \cdot 2 - 5) + 3 \cdot \frac{1}{3}$
$= 2(6 - 5) + 3 \cdot \frac{1}{3}$ Substitution
$= 2(1) + 3 \cdot \frac{1}{3}$ Substitution
$= 2 + 3 \cdot \frac{1}{3}$ Multiplicative Identity
$= 2 + 1$ Multiplicative Inverse
$= 3$ Substitution

14. $6 \cdot \frac{1}{6} + 5(12 \div 4 - 3)$
$= 6 \cdot \frac{1}{6} + 5(3 - 3)$ Substitution
$= 6 \cdot \frac{1}{6} + 5(0)$ Additive Inverse
$= 6 \cdot \frac{1}{6} + 0$ Multiplicative Property of Zero
$= 1 + 0$ Multiplicative Inverse
$= 1$ Additive Identity

15. $2 \cdot \frac{22}{7} \cdot 14^2 + 2 \cdot \frac{22}{7} \cdot 14 \cdot 7$
$= 2 \cdot \frac{22}{7} \cdot 196 + 2 \cdot \frac{22}{7} \cdot 14 \cdot 7$ Substitution
$= \frac{44}{7} \cdot 196 + \frac{44}{7} \cdot 14 \cdot 7$ Substitution
$= 1232 + 616$ Substitution
$= 1848$ Substitution
The surface area is 1848 in^2.

17. $25 + 14 + 15 + 36 = 25 + 15 + 14 + 36$ Commutative (+)
$= (25 + 15) + (14 + 36)$ Associative (+)
$= 40 + 50$ Substitution
$= 90$ Substitution

18. $11 + 7 + 5 + 13 = 11 + 5 + 7 + 13$ Commutative(+)
$= (11 + 5) + (7 + 13)$ Associative (+)
$= 16 + 20$ Substitution
$= 36$ Substitution

19. $3\frac{2}{3} + 4 + 5\frac{1}{3} = 3\frac{2}{3} + 5\frac{1}{3} + 4$ Commutative (+)
$= \left(3\frac{2}{3} + 5\frac{1}{3}\right) + 4$ Associative (+)
$= 9 + 4$ Substitution
$= 13$ Substitution

20. $4\frac{4}{9} + 7\frac{2}{9} = 4 + \frac{4}{9} + 7 + \frac{2}{9}$ Substitution
$= 4 + 7 + \frac{4}{9} + \frac{2}{9}$ Commutative (+)
$= (4 + 7) + \left(\frac{4}{9} + \frac{2}{9}\right)$ Associative (+)
$= 11 + \frac{6}{9}$ Substitution
$= 11\frac{2}{3}$ Substitution

21. $4.3 + 2.4 + 3.6 + 9.7$
$= 4.3 + 9.7 + 2.4 + 3.6$ Commutative (+)
$= (4.3 + 9.7) + (2.4 + 3.6)$ Associative (+)
$= 14 + 6$ Substitution
$= 20$ Substitution

22. $3.25 + 2.2 + 5.4 + 10.75$
$= 3.25 + 10.75 + 2.2 + 5.4$ Commutative (+)
$= (3.25 + 10.75) + (2.2 + 5.4)$ Associative (+)
$= 14 + 7.6$ Substitution
$= 21.6$ Substitution

23. $12 \cdot 2 \cdot 6 \cdot 5 = 12 \cdot 6 \cdot 2 \cdot 5$ Commutative (×)
$= (12 \cdot 6) \cdot (2 \cdot 5)$ Associative (×)
$= 72 \cdot 10$ Substitution
$= 720$ Substitution

24. $2 \cdot 8 \cdot 10 \cdot 2 = (2 \cdot 8) \cdot (10 \cdot 2)$ Associative (×)
$= 16 \cdot 20$ Substitution
$= 320$ Substitution

25. $0.2 \cdot 4.6 \cdot 5 = (0.2 \cdot 4.6) \cdot 5$ Associative (×)
$= 0.92 \cdot 5$ Substitution
$= 4.6$ Substitution

26. $3.5 \cdot 3 \cdot 6 = 3.5 \cdot (3 \cdot 6)$ Associative (×)
$= 3.5 \cdot 18$ Substitution
$= 63$ Substitution

27. $1\frac{5}{6} \cdot 24 \cdot 3\frac{1}{11}$
$= 1\frac{5}{6}\left(24 \cdot 3\frac{1}{11}\right)$ Associative (×)
$= 1\frac{5}{6} \cdot \frac{816}{11}$ Substitution
$= 136$ Substitution

28. $2\frac{3}{4} \cdot 1\frac{1}{8} \cdot 32$
$= \left(2\frac{3}{4} \cdot 1\frac{1}{8}\right) \cdot 32$ Associative (×)
$= \frac{99}{32} \cdot 32$ Substitution
$= 99$ Substitution

Page 30, Mid-Chapter Quiz

13. $(8 - 2^3) + 21$
$= (8 - 8) + 21$ Substitution
$= 0 + 21$ Additive Inverse
$= 21$ Additive Identity

14. $3(1 \div 3) \cdot 9$
$= 3 \cdot \frac{1}{3} \cdot 9$ Substitution
$= 1 \cdot 9$ Multiplicative Inverse
$= 9$ Multiplicative Identity

15. $[5 \div (3 \cdot 1)]\frac{3}{5}$
$= [5 \div 3]\frac{3}{5}$ Multiplicative Identity
$= \frac{5}{3} \times \frac{3}{5}$ Substitution
$= 1$ Multiplicative Inverse

16. $18 + 35 + 32 + 15$
$= 18 + 32 + 35 + 15$ Commutative Property (+)
$= (18 + 32) + (35 + 15)$ Associative Property (+)
$= 50 + 50$ Substitution
$= 100$ Substitution

17. $0.25 \cdot 7 \cdot 4$
$= 0.25 \cdot (7 \cdot 4)$ Associative Property (×)
$= 0.25 \cdot 28$ Substitution
$= 7$ Substitution

Page 34, Lesson 1-5

57.

x	$3x + 5$	y
−2	3(−2) + 5	−1
−1	3(−1) + 5	2
0	3(0) + 5	5
1	3(1) + 5	8
2	3(2) + 5	11

58.

x	$-2x - 3$	y
−2	−2(−2) − 3	1
−1	−2(−1) − 3	−1
0	−2(0) − 3	−3
1	−2(1) − 3	−5
2	−2(2) − 3	−7

59.

x	$\frac{1}{2}x + 2$	y
−2	$\frac{1}{2}(-2) + 2$	1
−1	$\frac{1}{2}(-1) + 2$	1.5
0	$\frac{1}{2}(0) + 2$	2
1	$\frac{1}{2}(1) + 2$	2.5
2	$\frac{1}{2}(2) + 2$	3

60.

x	$4.2x - 1.6$	y
−2	4.2(−2) − 1.6	−10
−1	4.2(−1) − 1.6	−5.8
0	4.2(0) − 1.6	−1.6
1	4.2(1) − 1.6	2.6
2	4.2(2) − 1.6	6.8

Page 41, Lesson 1-6

9.

x	y
0	0
−3	2
6	4
−1	1

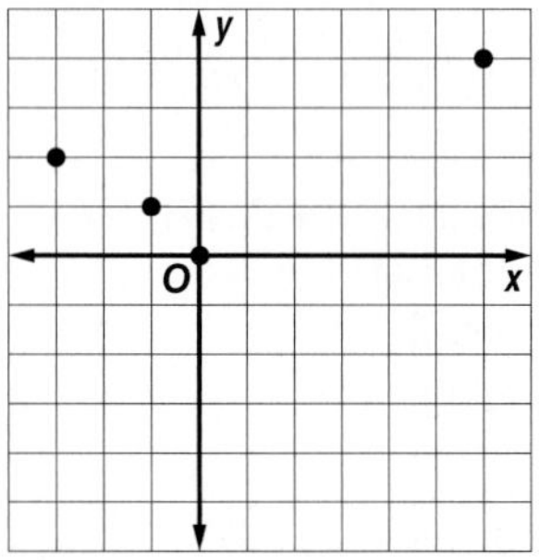

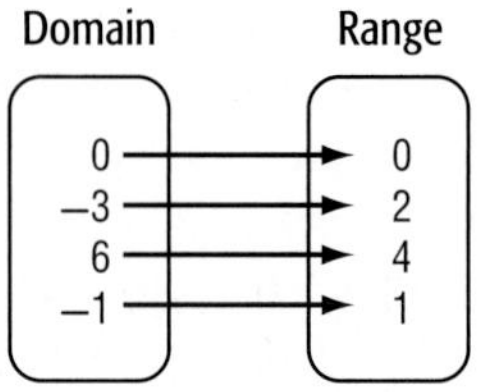

D = {0, −3, 6, −1}; R = {0, 2, 4, 1}

10.

x	y
5	2
5	6
3	−2
0	−2

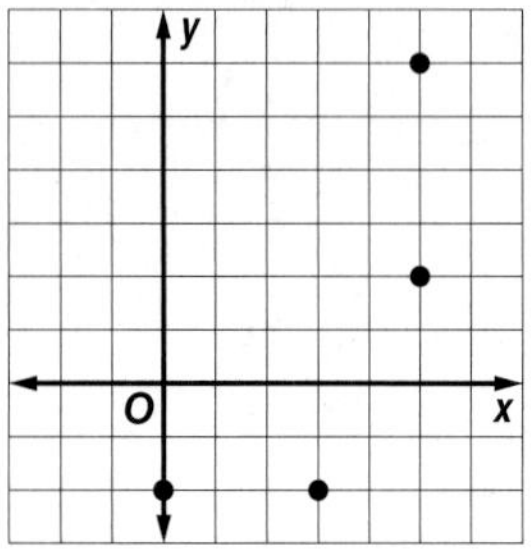

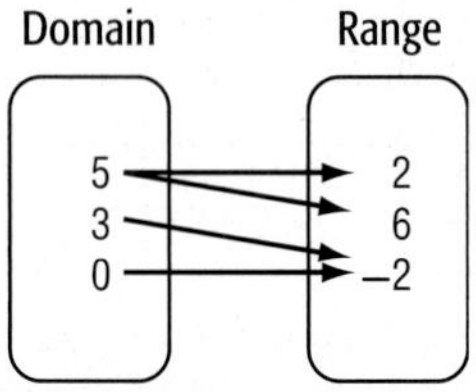

D = {0, 3, 5}; R = {−2, 2, 6}

11.

x	y
6	1
4	−3
3	2
−1	−3

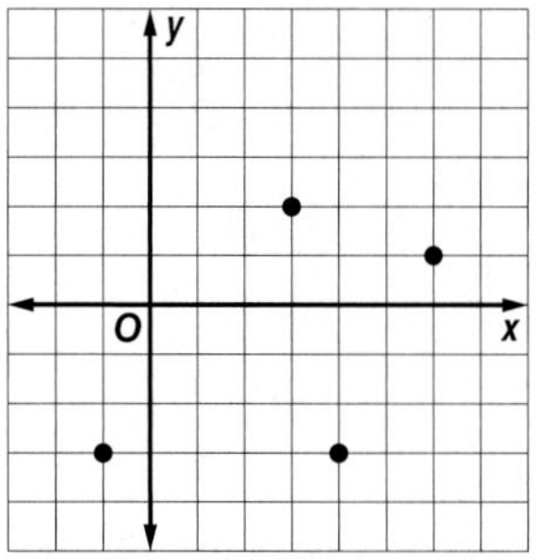

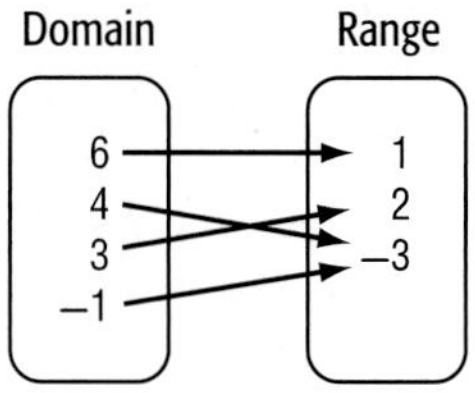

D = {6, 4, 3, −1}; R = {1, −3, 2}

12.

x	y
−1	3
3	−6
−1	−8
−3	−7

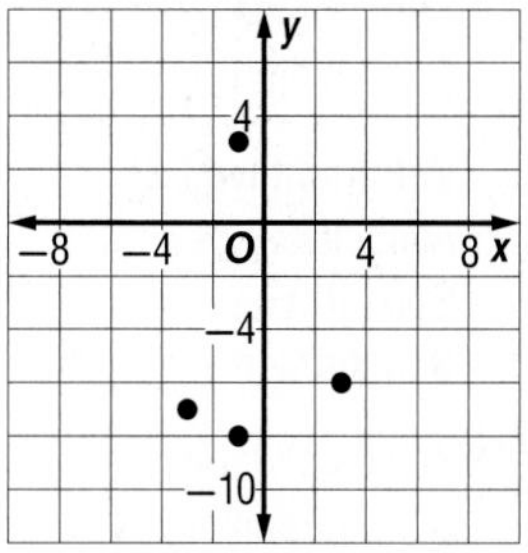

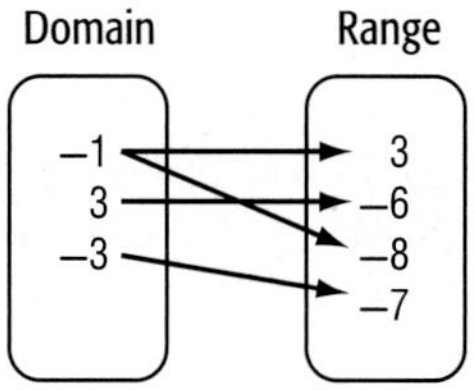

D = {−3, −1, 3}; R = {−8, −7, −6, 3}

13.

x	y
6	7
3	−2
8	8
−6	2
2	−6

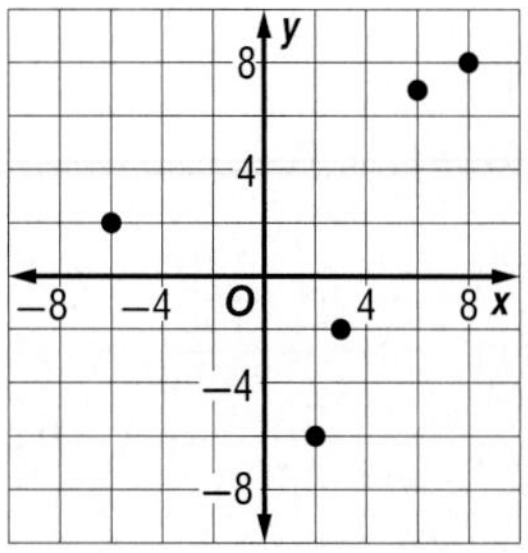

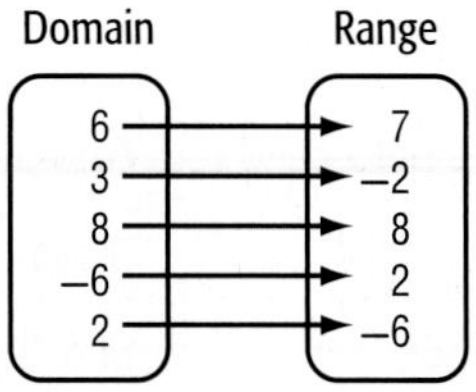

D = {−6, 2, 3, 6, 8}; R = {−6, −2, 2, 7, 8}

14.

x	y
4	−3
1	3
7	−2
2	−2
1	5

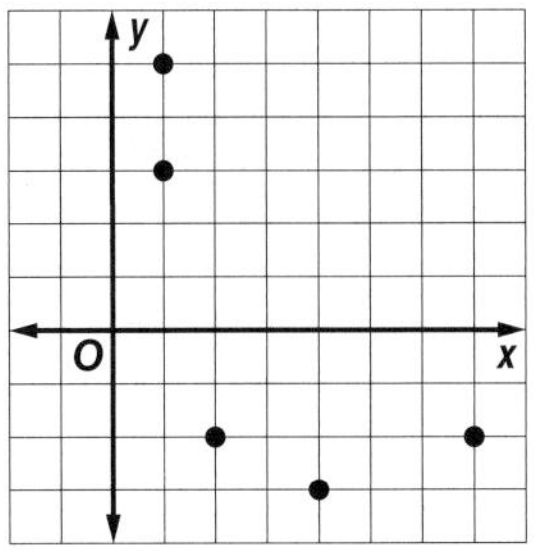

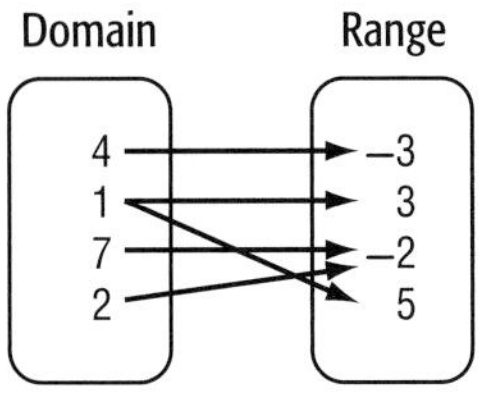

D = {1, 2, 4, 7}; R = {−3, −2, 3, 5}

15. I: the number of students who attend the fiesta; D: the amount of food that there will be at the fiesta

16. I: the speed of the car; D: the length of time it takes to stop the car

17. The bungee jumper starts at the maximum height then jumps. After the initial jump, the jumper bounces up and down until coming to a rest.

18. The sales of lawn mowers are high for part of the year, but low or decreasing for the rest of the time.

37a.

Body Weight (lb)	100	105	110	115	120	125	130
Water Weight (lb)	66.7	70	73.3	76.7	80	83.3	86.7

37b. The independent variable is *b*, the dependent variable is *w*.

37c. D = {100, 105, 110, 115, 120, 125, 130};
R = {66.7, 70, 73.3, 76.7, 80, 83.3, 86.7}

Water Weight Per Body Weight

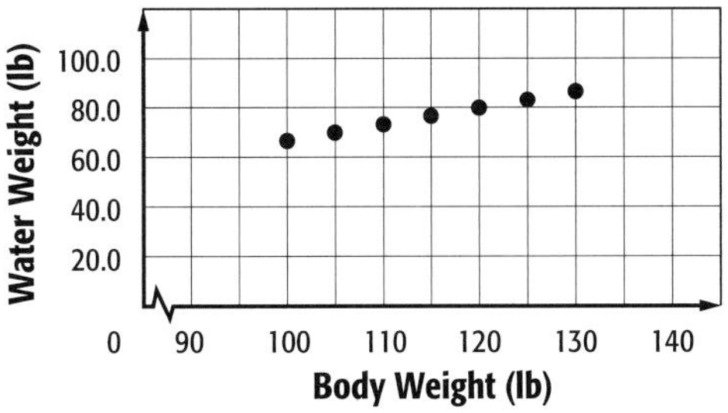

37d.

Body Weight Per Water Weight

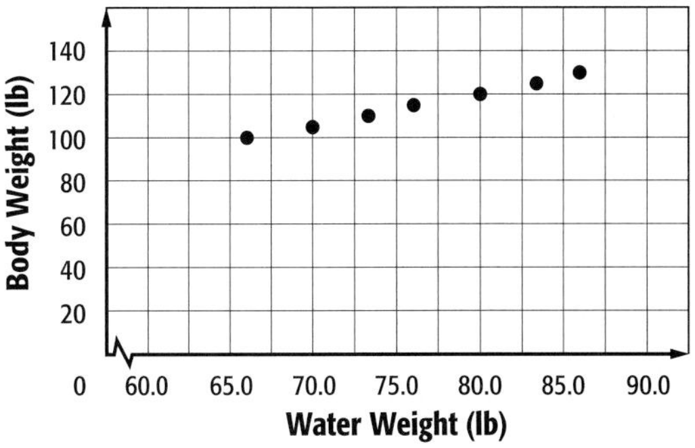

The body weight is dependent on the water weight. As the water weight increases, the body weight also increases.

38. Sample answer: The number of movie tickets bought and the total cost of the tickets can be represented using a relation. The total cost depends on the number of tickets bought. {(0, 0), (1, 9), (2, 18), (3, 27)}

Number of Tickets	Total Cost
0	$0.00
1	$9.00
2	$18.00
3	$27.00

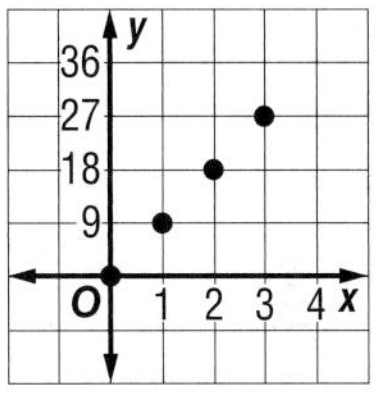

41. Reversing the coordinates gives (1, 0), (3, 1), (5, 2), and (7, 3).

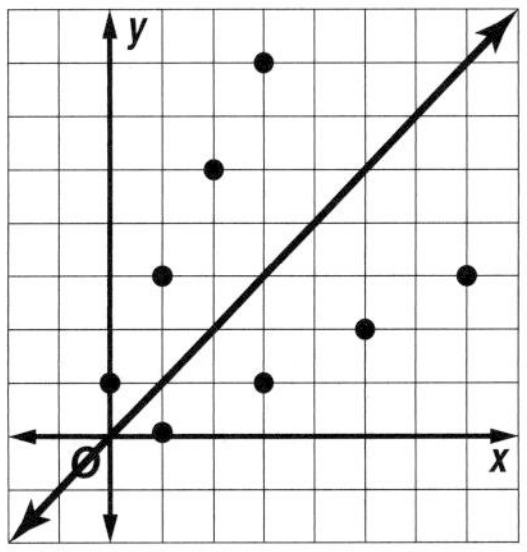

Each point in the original relation is the same distance from the line as the corresponding point of the reverse relation. The graphs are symmetric about the line $y = x$.

Page 46, Lesson 1-7, Check Your Progress

2A.

Amount of Seed (qt)	0	1	2	3
Weight (lb)	2.3	6	9.7	13.4

2B. The domain is the set of possible amounts of seed (0 to 3 quarts), and the range is the set of total weights possible (2.3 to 13.4 pounds).

2C. {(0, 2.3), (1, 6), (2, 9.7), (3, 13.4)};

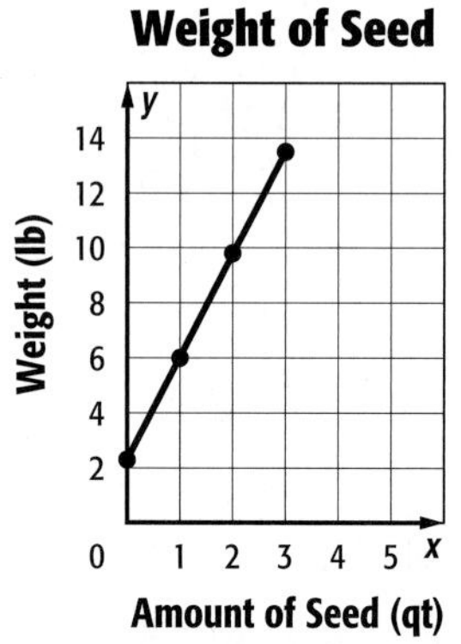

2D. Continuous; sample answer: Because the amount of both variables can be any amount up until the feeder is full, we can connect the points on the graph.

Page 51, Lesson 1-7

48c. Sample answer:

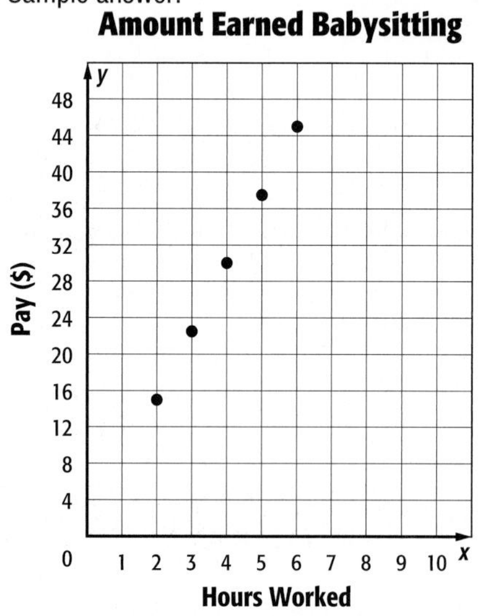

48d. Yes, because they could pay Christina for partial hours that she worked.

49. Sample answer: {(−2, 3), (0, 3), (2, 5)}

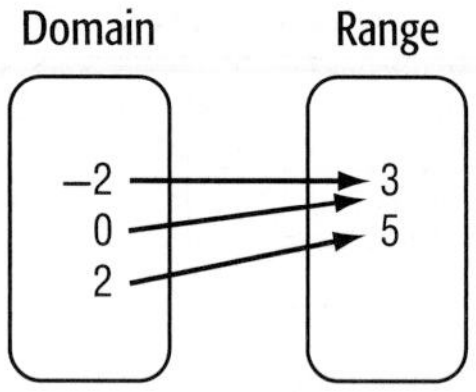

50.

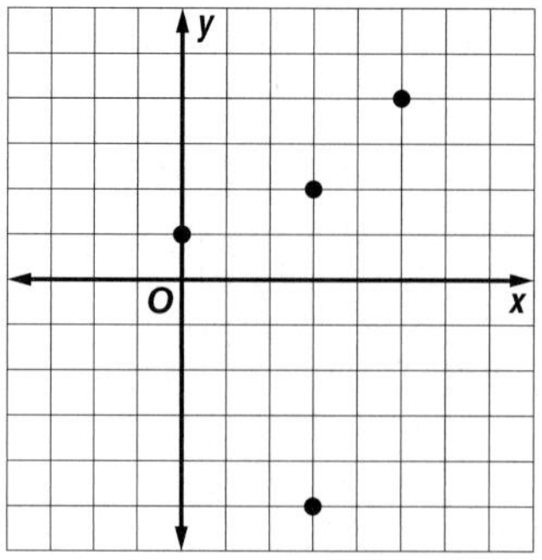

Not a function; one member of the domain, 3, is paired with two different members of the range, −5 and 2.

54. Neither; a relation is a function if each member of the domain is paired with exactly one member of the range. Members of the domain can be paired with the same member of the range.

Page 53, Extend 1-7

1.

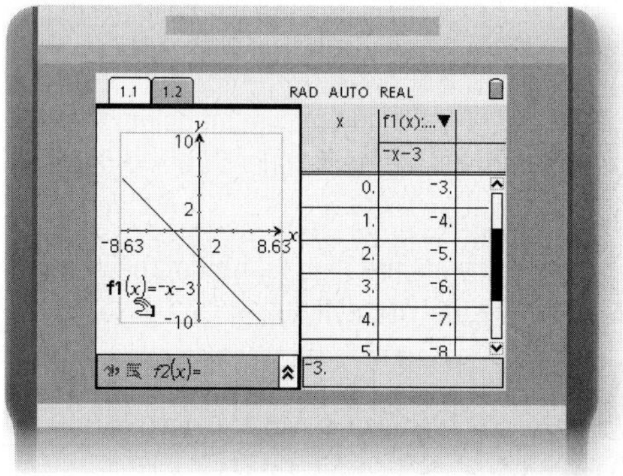

2.

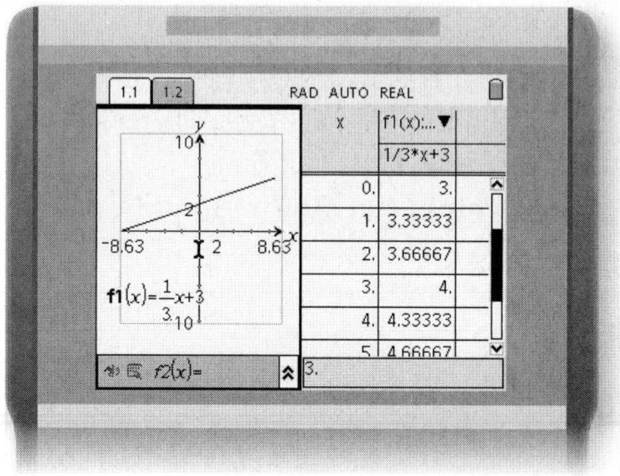

3.

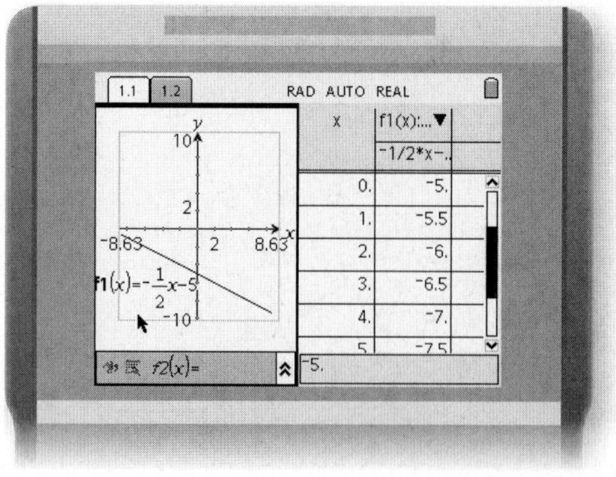

Chapter 1 Answer Appendix

4.

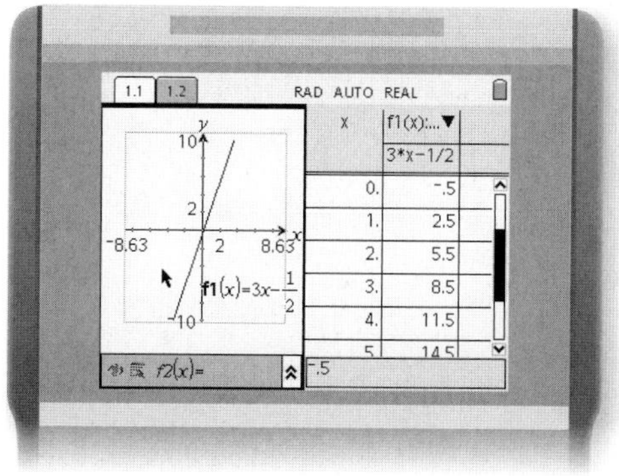

5.

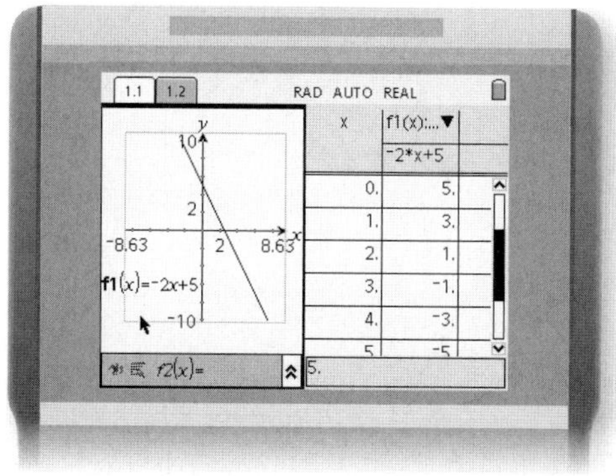

6.

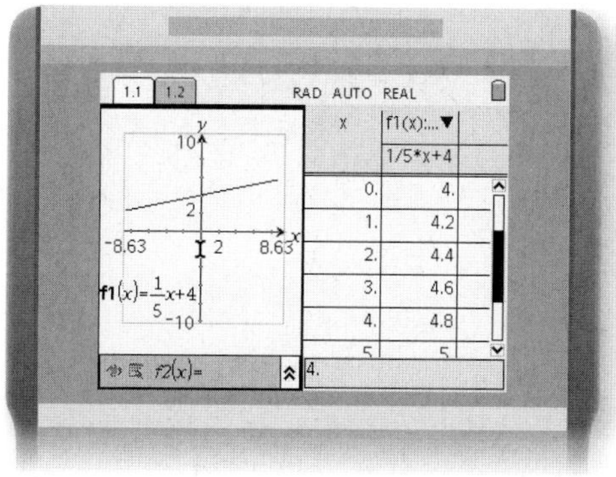

Pages 57–59, Lesson 1-8

20. H: it is Lamar's third period class; C: the class is art; If it is Lamar's third period class, then the class is art.

21. H: it is after class; C: Joe will go to the mall; If it is after class, then Joe will go to the mall.

22. H: $x = 4$; C: $6x - 10 = 14$; If $x = 4$, then $6x - 10 = 14$.

23. H: $m < 12$; C: $5m - 8 < 52$; If $m < 12$, then $5m - 8 < 52$.

24. H: a rectangle has sides of equal length; C: it is square; If the sides of a rectangle are equal in length, then it is a square.

25. H: two numbers are even; C: their sum is an even number; If two numbers are even, then their sum is an even number.

26. H: it is August; C: there are 31 days in the month; If it is August, then there are 31 days in the month.

27. H: you are a science teacher; C: you like to conduct experiments; If you are a science teacher, then you like to conduct experiments.

28. Belinda receives an A for the course.

29. No valid conclusion; the statement does not say that Belinda will not receive an A in the course if she scores lower than a 90% on the exam.

30. No valid conclusion; the statement does not tell us that scoring higher than 90% on the exam is the only way to earn an A.

31. Belinda did not score higher than 90% on the exam.

46. When n is negative, its opposite is greater than n. When n is positive, its opposite is less than n. Zero and its opposite are equal.

49. Sample answer: If you live in Ohio, then you live in Columbus. You do not have to live in Columbus, you could live in Canton.

50. Sample answer: You can use deductive reasoning to determine whether a hypothesis and its conclusion are both true or whether one or both are false.

Page 61, Extend 1-8

16. Sample answer: W = {green shapes}, Z = {yellow shapes}, $\overline{W \cup Z}$ = {blue shapes}

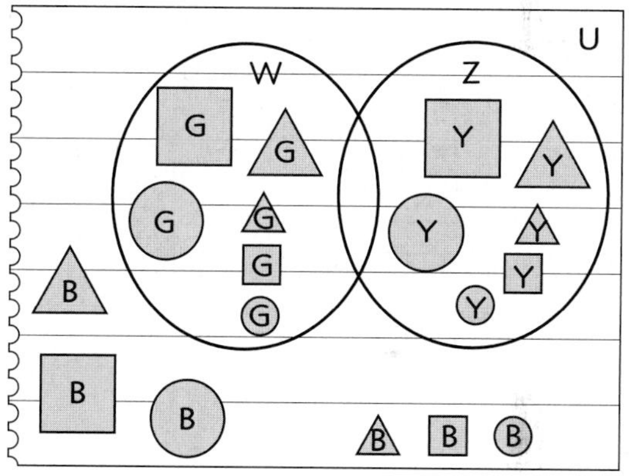

Page 65, Study Guide and Review

59.

x	y
1	3
2	4
3	5
4	6

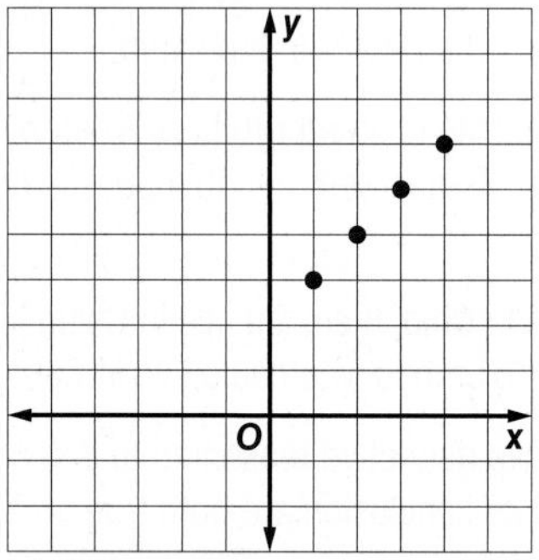

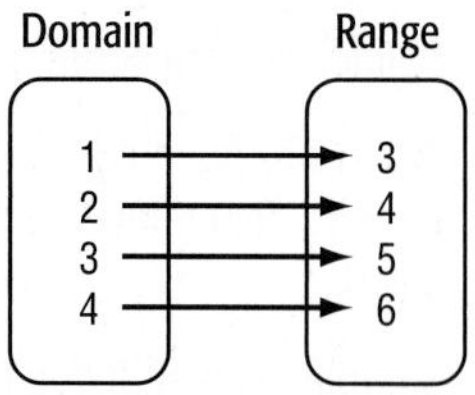

D = {1, 2, 3, 4}; R = {3, 4, 5, 6}

60.

x	y
−1	1
0	−2
3	1
4	−1

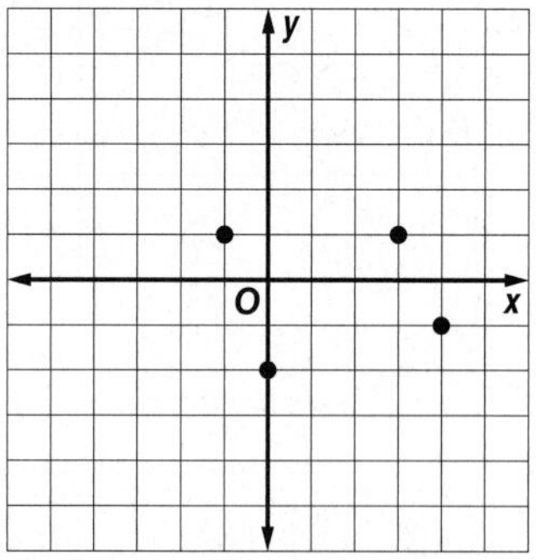

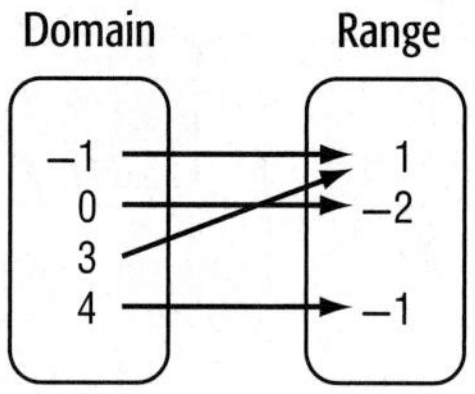

D = {−1, 0, 3, 4}; R = {−2, −1, 1}

61.

x	y
−2	4
−1	3
0	2
−1	2

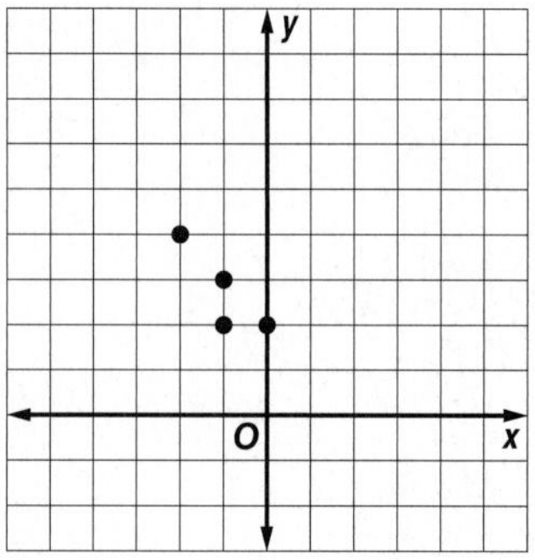

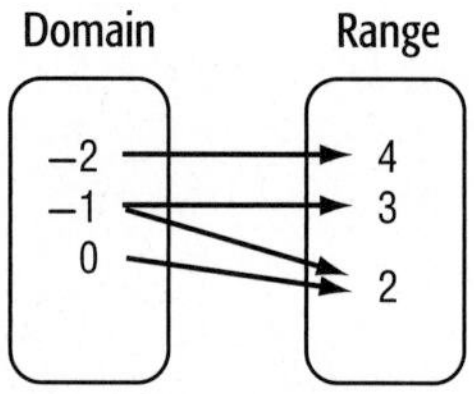

D = {−2, −1, 0}; R = {2, 3, 4}

NOTES

Chapter Planner

Diagnostic Assessment
Quick Check, p. 73

	Lesson 2-1 Pacing: 1 day	Explore 2-2 Pacing: 0.5 day	Lesson 2-2 Pacing: 1 day
Title	**Writing Equations**	**Algebra Lab: Solving Equations**	**Solving One-Step Equations**
Objectives	• Translate sentences into equations. • Translate equations into sentences.	• Use algebra tiles to solve addition, subtraction, and multiplication equations.	• Solve equations by using addition or subtraction. • Solve equations by using multiplication and division.
Key Vocabulary	formula		solve an equation equivalent equations
ILS	8.B.4a, B.D.4	8.D.4	8.B.4a, 8.D.4
Multiple Representations	p. 79		
Lesson Resources	**Chapter 2 Resource Masters** • Study Guide and Intervention, pp. 5–6 AL OL ELL • Skills Practice, p. 7 AL OL ELL • Practice, p. 8 AL OL BL ELL • Word Problem Practice, p. 9 AL OL BL ELL • Enrichment, p. 10 OL BL • Quiz 1, p. 63 AL OL BL ELL **Transparencies** • 5-Minute Check Transparency 2-1 AL OL BL ELL **Additional Print Resources** • *Study Notebook* AL OL BL ELL	**Additional Print Resources** • *Teaching Algebra with Manipulatives*, pp. 10–11, 16, 46 AL OL ELL	**Chapter 2 Resource Masters** • Study Guide and Intervention, pp. 11–12 AL OL ELL • Skills Practice, p. 13 AL OL ELL • Practice, p. 14 AL OL BL ELL • Word Problem Practice, p. 15 AL OL BL ELL • Enrichment, p. 16 OL BL • Quiz 1, p. 63 AL OL BL ELL **Transparencies** • 5-Minute Check Transparency 2-2 AL OL BL ELL **Additional Print Resources** • *Study Notebook* AL OL BL ELL • *Teaching Algebra with Manipulatives*, pp. 47–53 AL OL ELL
Technology for Every Lesson	**IL Math Online** glencoe.com • Extra Examples • Self-Check Quizzes • Personal Tutor • Homework Help	**CD/DVD Resources** IWB INTERACTIVE WHITEBOARD READY IWB StudentWorks Plus IWB Interactive Classroom IWB Diagnostic and Assessment Planner	• TeacherWorks Plus • eSolutions Manual Plus • ExamView Assessment Suite
Math in Motion		Animation	
Differentiated Instruction	pp. 77, 80		pp. 87, 89

KEY: AL Approaching Level OL On Level BL Beyond Level ELL English Learners

Suggested Pacing			
Time Periods	Instruction	Review & Assessment	Total
45-minute	11	2	13
90-minute	9	1	10

Explore 2-3 Pacing: 0.5 day	Lesson 2-3 Pacing: 1 day	Lesson 2-4 Pacing: 1 day	Lesson 2-5 Pacing: 1 day
Algebra Lab: Solving Multi-Step Equations	**Solving Multi-Step Equations**	**Solving Equations with the Variable on Each Side**	**Solving Equations Involving Absolute Value**
• Use algebra tiles to solve multi-step equations.	• Solve equations involving more than one operation. • Solve equations involving consecutive integers.	• Solve equations with the variable on each side. • Solve equations involving grouping symbols.	• Evaluate absolute value expressions. • Solve absolute value equations.
	multi-step equation consecutive integers number theory	identity	
8.D.4	8.B.4a, 8.D.4	8.B.4a, 8.D.4	8.B.4a
		p. 101	
Additional Print Resources • *Teaching Algebra with Manipulatives*, pp. 10–11, 16, 54 AL OL ELL	**Chapter 2 Resource Masters** • Study Guide and Intervention, pp. 17–18 AL OL ELL • Skills Practice, p. 19 AL OL ELL • Practice, p. 20 AL OL BL ELL • Word Problem Practice, p. 21 AL OL BL ELL • Enrichment, p. 22 OL BL • Quiz 1, p. 63 AL OL BL ELL **Transparencies** • 5-Minute Check Transparency 2-3 AL OL BL ELL **Additional Print Resources** • *Study Notebook* AL OL BL ELL • *Teaching Algebra with Manipulatives*, pp. 55–58 AL OL ELL	**Chapter 2 Resource Masters** • Study Guide and Intervention, pp. 23–24 AL OL ELL • Skills Practice, p. 25 AL OL ELL • Practice, p. 26 AL OL BL ELL • Word Problem Practice, p. 27 AL OL BL ELL • Enrichment, p. 28 OL BL • Quiz 2, p. 63 AL OL BL ELL **Transparencies** • 5-Minute Check Transparency 2-4 AL OL BL ELL **Additional Print Resources** • *Study Notebook* AL OL BL ELL • *Teaching Algebra with Manipulatives*, p. 59 AL OL ELL	**Chapter 2 Resource Masters** • Study Guide and Intervention, pp. 30–31 AL OL ELL • Skills Practice, p. 32 AL OL ELL • Practice, p. 33 AL OL BL ELL • Word Problem Practice, p. 34 AL OL BL ELL • Enrichment, p. 35 OL BL • Quiz 1, p. 63 AL OL BL ELL **Transparencies** • 5-Minute Check Transparency 2-5 AL OL BL ELL **Additional Print Resources** • *Study Notebook* AL OL BL ELL
	IL Math Online glencoe.com • Extra Examples • Self-Check Quizzes • Personal Tutor • Homework Help	**CD/DVD Resources** IWB INTERACTIVE WHITEBOARD READY IWB StudentWorks Plus IWB Interactive Classroom IWB Diagnostic and Assessment Planner	• TeacherWorks Plus • eSolutions Manual Plus • ExamView Assessment Suite
Animation		BrainPOP	
	pp. 92, 93, 96	pp. 98, 102	pp. 104, 109

Formative Assessment
Mid-Chapter Quiz, p. 110

CHAPTER 2 Chapter Planner

	Lesson 2-6 Pacing: 1 day	Extend 2-6 Pacing: 0.5 day	Lesson 2-7 Pacing: 1 day
Title	**Ratios and Proportions**	**Spreadsheet Lab: Financial Ratios**	**Percent of Change**
Objectives	• Compare ratios. • Solve proportions.	• Use a spreadsheet to investigate debt-to-income ratios.	• Find the percent of change. • Solve problems involving percent of change.
Key Vocabulary	ratio proportion means extremes rate unit rate scale scale model		percent of change percent of increase percent of decrease
ILS	7.C.4b, 9.A.4b	6.D.4	6.D.4, 8.A.4b
Multiple Representations	p. 116		p. 123
Lesson Resources	**Chapter 2 Resource Masters** • Study Guide and Intervention, pp. 36–37 AL OL ELL • Skills Practice, p. 38 AL OL ELL • Practice, p. 39 AL OL BL ELL • Word Problem Practice, p. 40 AL OL BL ELL • Enrichment, p. 41 OL BL • Quiz 3, p. 64 AL OL BL ELL **Transparencies** • 5-Minute Check Transparency 2-6 AL OL BL ELL **Additional Print Resources** • *Study Notebook* AL OL BL ELL • *Teaching Algebra with Manipulatives*, p. 61 AL OL ELL		**Chapter 2 Resource Masters** • Study Guide and Intervention, pp. 42–43 AL OL ELL • Skills Practice, p. 44 AL OL ELL • Practice, p. 45 AL OL BL ELL • Word Problem Practice, p. 46 AL OL BL ELL • Enrichment, p. 47 OL BL • Quiz 3, p. 64 AL OL BL ELL **Transparencies** • 5-Minute Check Transparency 2-7 AL OL BL ELL **Additional Print Resources** • *Study Notebook* AL OL BL ELL • *Teaching Algebra with Manipulatives*, pp. 62–64 AL OL ELL
Technology for Every Lesson	IL Math Online **glencoe.com** • Extra Examples • Self-Check Quizzes • Personal Tutor • Homework Help	**CD/DVD Resources** IWB INTERACTIVE WHITEBOARD READY IWB StudentWorks Plus IWB Interactive Classroom IWB Diagnostic and Assessment Planner	• TeacherWorks Plus • eSolutions Manual Plus • ExamView Assessment Suite
Math in Motion	Interactive Lab		
Differentiated Instruction	pp. 113, 114, 117		pp. 121, 124

KEY: AL Approaching Level OL On Level BL Beyond Level ELL English Learners

Extend 2-7 Pacing: 0.5 day	Lesson 2-8 Pacing: 1 day	Lesson 2-9 Pacing: 1 day
Algebra Lab: Percentiles	**Literal Equations and Dimensional Analysis**	**Weighted Averages**
• Find the percentile rank of a data item in a set of scores.	• Solve equations for given variables. • Use formulas to solve real-world problems.	• Solve mixture problems. • Solve uniform motion problems.
	literal equation dimensional analysis unit analysis	weighted average mixture problem uniform motion problem rate problem
10.A.4b	7.A.4b, 8.B.4a	6.C.4, 7.A.4b
	p. 130	
Additional Print Resources • *Teaching Algebra with Manipulatives,* p. 66 AL OL ELL	**Chapter 2 Resource Masters** • Study Guide and Intervention, pp. 49–50 AL OL ELL • Skills Practice, p. 51 AL OL ELL • Practice, p. 52 AL OL BL ELL • Word Problem Practice, p. 53 AL OL BL ELL • Enrichment, p. 54 OL BL • Quiz 4, p. 64 AL OL BL ELL **Transparencies** • 5-Minute Check Transparency 2-8 AL OL BL ELL **Additional Print Resources** • *Study Notebook* AL OL BL ELL	**Chapter 2 Resource Masters** • Study Guide and Intervention, pp. 55–56 AL OL ELL • Skills Practice, p. 57 AL OL ELL • Practice, p. 58 AL OL BL ELL • Word Problem Practice, p. 59 AL OL BL ELL • Enrichment, p. 60 OL BL • Quiz 4, p. 64 AL OL BL ELL **Transparencies** • 5-Minute Check Transparency 2-9 AL OL BL ELL **Additional Print Resources** • *Study Notebook* AL OL BL ELL • *Teaching Algebra with Manipulatives,* p. 67 AL OL ELL
	pp. 127, 131	pp. 134, 138

IL Math Online glencoe.com
- Extra Examples
- Self-Check Quizzes
- Personal Tutor
- Homework Help

CD/DVD Resources IWB INTERACTIVE WHITEBOARD READY
- IWB StudentWorks Plus
- IWB Interactive Classroom
- IWB Diagnostic and Assessment Planner
- TeacherWorks Plus
- eSolutions Manual Plus
- ExamView Assessment Suite

Summative Assessment
- Study Guide and Review, pp. 139–144
- Practice Test, p. 145

CHAPTER 2

Assessment and Intervention

SE = Student Edition, **TE** = Teacher Edition, **CRM** = Chapter Resource Masters

	Diagnosis	Prescription
Diagnostic Assessment	**Beginning Chapter 2**	
	Get Ready for Chapter 2 **SE**, p. 73	Intervention **TE**, p. 73
	Beginning Every Lesson	
	Then, Now, Why? **SE** 5-Minute Check Transparencies	Chapter 0 **SE**, pp. P1 through P45 Concepts and Skills Bank **SE**, pp. 857–867 *Quick Review Math Handbook*
Formative Assessment	**During/After Every Lesson**	
	Check Your Progress **SE**, every example Check Your Understanding **SE** H.O.T. Problems **SE** Spiral Review **SE** Additional Examples **TE** Watch Out! **TE** Step 4, Assess **TE** Chapter 2 Quizzes **CRM**, pp. 63–64 Self-Check Quizzes glencoe.com	**Tier 1 Intervention** Concepts and Skills Bank **SE**, pp. 857–867 Skills Practice **CRM**, Ch. 1–2 glencoe.com **Tier 2 Intervention** Differentiated Instruction **TE** Differentiated Homework Options **TE** Study Guide and Intervention Masters **CRM**, Ch. 1–2 *Quick Review Math Handbook* **Tier 3 Intervention** *Math Triumphs, Alg. 1,* Ch. 1–5
	Mid-Chapter	
	Mid-Chapter Quiz **SE**, p. 110 Mid-Chapter Test **CRM**, p. 65 ExamView Assessment Suite	**Tier 1 Intervention** Concepts and Skills Bank **SE**, pp. 857–867 Skills Practice **CRM**, Ch. 1–2 glencoe.com **Tier 2 Intervention** Study Guide and Intervention Masters **CRM**, Ch. 1–2 *Quick Review Math Handbook* **Tier 3 Intervention** *Math Triumphs, Alg. 1,* Ch. 1–5
	Before Chapter Test	
	Chapter Study Guide and Review **SE**, pp. 139–144 Practice Test **SE**, p. 145 Standardized Test Practice **SE**, pp. 146–149 Chapter Test glencoe.com Standardized Test Practice glencoe.com Vocabulary Review glencoe.com ExamView Assessment Suite	**Tier 1 Intervention** Concepts and Skills Bank **SE**, pp. 857–867 Skills Practice **CRM**, Ch. 1–2 glencoe.com **Tier 2 Intervention** Study Guide and Intervention Masters **CRM**, Ch. 1–2 *Quick Review Math Handbook* **Tier 3 Intervention** *Math Triumphs, Alg. 1,* Ch. 1–5
Summative Assessment	**After Chapter 2**	
	Multiple-Choice Tests, Forms 1, 2A, 2B **CRM**, pp. 67–71 Free-Response Tests, Forms 2C, 2D, 3 **CRM**, pp. 73–77 Vocabulary Test **CRM**, p. 66 Extended Response Test **CRM**, p. 79 Standardized Test Practice **CRM**, pp. 80–82 ExamView Assessment Suite	Study Guide and Intervention Masters **CRM**, Ch. 1–2 *Quick Review Math Handbook* glencoe.com

CHAPTER 2

Differentiated Instruction

Option 1 Reaching All Learners AL OL BL ELL

AUDITORY/MUSICAL Have students clap twice each second for 5 seconds. Then have students clap twice each second for 10 seconds. Write the following on the board, leaving space between the equations:

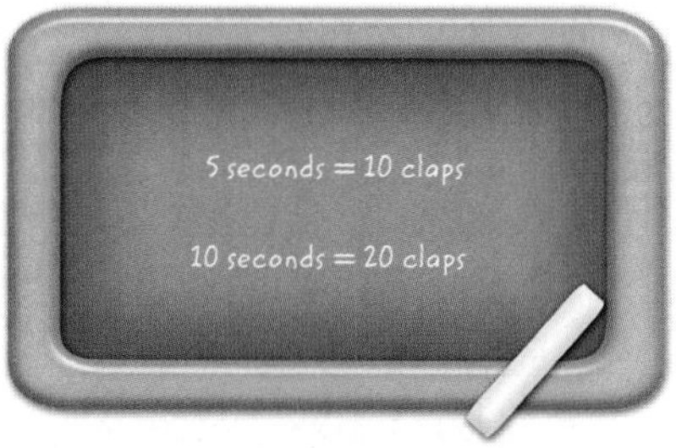

Point out that each value in the second equation is double the first, but the equation is still true. Write $\times$ 2 under each side of the first equation.

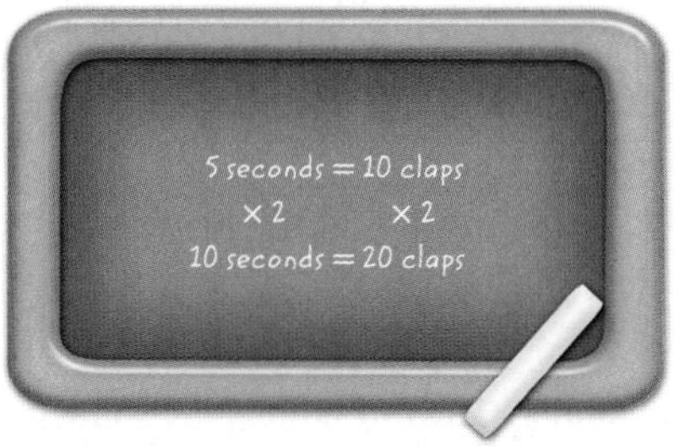

Explain that when you perform the same operation on each side of a true equation, the result is a true equation.

INTRAPERSONAL Have students make a list of four items and their prices. The items can be in the price range of their choosing. Then have students calculate the price of each item after a discount of 15%.

Option 2 Approaching Level AL

Explain to students that often class scores do not all carry the same weight toward the final grade. Tell students that homework counts 10%, quizzes count 30%, tests count 40%, and the final exam counts 20%. Have students compute the final grade for a homework average of 86%, quiz average of 89%, test average of 95%, and final exam of 98%. 0.929 or 92.9% Ask students to determine if this weighted average is greater than or less than the non-weighted average? greater than

Option 3 English Learners ELL

Have students make study cards for the key concepts in this chapter. On one side of the card, students write the name of the concept. On the flip side, students give an example of how the concept is used.

Option 4 Beyond Level BL

The study of number theory can be quite interesting for students. Ask pairs of students to write and solve their own consecutive integer problems, using Example 3 in Lesson 2-3 as a guide. Then have pairs “teach” the class how to solve their problem.

CHAPTER 2 Focus on Mathematical Content

Vertical Alignment

Before Chapter 2

Related Topics before Grade 8
- simplify numerical expressions involving order of operations
- find solutions to application problems involving percent

Related Topics from Grade 8
- make connections among various representations of a numerical relationship
- validate conclusions using mathematical properties
- use proportional relationships in similar figures to find missing measurements

Previous Topics from Algebra 1
- use the Distributive Property to simplify algebraic expressions

Chapter 2

Related Topics from Algebra 1
- describe functional relationships for given problem situations and write equations to answer questions arising from the situations
- represent relationships among quantities using diagrams, verbal descriptions, and equations
- find specific function values, and transform and solve equations in problem situations
- solve problems involving proportional change
- use the Commutative, Associative, and Distributive Properties to simplify expressions

After Chapter 2

Preparation for Algebra 2
- use the necessary algebraic skills required to simplify algebraic expressions and inequalities in problem situations
- use tools to simplify expressions and to transform and solve equations

Lesson-by-Lesson Preview

2-1 Writing Equations

Variables can be used to represent an unknown amount when writing equations from a verbal sentence.

- The ability to write an equation from a verbal sentence is needed when solving word problems.
- Following the four-step problem-solving plan can help solve any word problem.

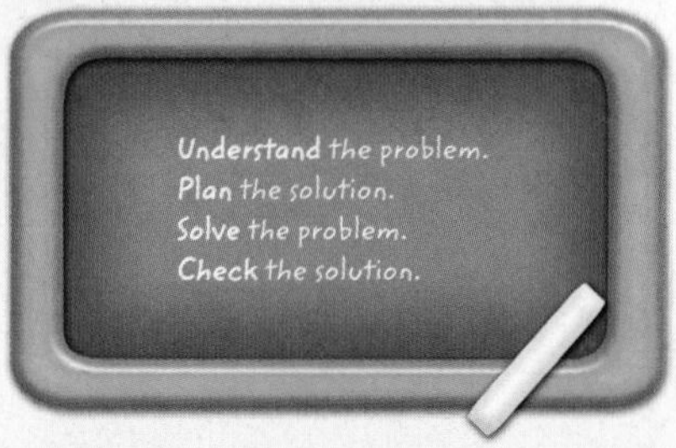

- When a verbal sentence can be translated into an equation that states a rule for the relationship between certain quantities, the equation is called a formula. It can be used to solve problems about those quantities.

2-2 Solving One-Step Equations

Solving an equation means finding the value of the variable in the equation that makes the equation true.

- To solve an equation, isolate the variable (with a coefficient of 1) on one side of the equation.
- Use the Properties of Equality to maintain equivalent equations in each step in this process.
- The Addition/Subtraction Property of Equality permits the same number to be added/subtracted to each side of an equation.
- The Multiplication/Division Property of Equality permits each side of an equation to be multiplied/divided by the same nonzero number.

2-3 Solving Multi-Step Equations

Multi-step equations involve more than one operation. These equations can be solved using the Properties of Equality and the strategy of undoing each operation by working backward.

In *number theory*, multi-step equations are written and solved to understand the relationship between numbers, such as consecutive integers.

2-4 Solving Equations with the Variable on Each Side

To solve equations with variables on each side:

- Simplify. Use the Distributive Property to remove any grouping symbols. Simplify again using the properties of equality.
- If all the variable terms are eliminated and the result, such as $3 = 5$, is not a true equation, there is no solution.
- If both sides of the equation are identical, the equation is an *identity*. All values are solutions for this equation.

2-5 Solving Equations Involving Absolute Value

The *absolute value* of a number is the distance the number is from zero on a number line. Open sentences involving an absolute value expression can be either an equation or an inequality.

- To solve an equation involving an absolute value, first isolate the absolute value on one side of the equation.
- Then, rewrite the equation as a compound sentence using the word *or*.
- The solution set of an absolute value equation can be graphed on a number line or written in set notation.

2-6 Ratios and Proportions

A ratio is a comparison of two numbers by division. A ratio is called a rate if the two numbers of a ratio represent measurements with different units, such as miles and hours.

A *proportion* is an equation stating that two ratios are equal.

2-7 Percent of Change

A *percent* is a ratio that compares a number to 100. The ratio of the change of an amount to the original amount is called a *percent of change*.

- If the new number is greater than the original number, the percent of change is a *percent of increase*.
- If the new number is less than the original number, the percent of change is a *percent of decrease*.

Percent of change can be found by solving for r in $\frac{\text{amount of change}}{\text{original number}} = \frac{r}{100}$. Finding sales tax and discounts are applications of percent of change.

2-8 Literal Equations and Dimensional Analysis

Some equations contain more than one variable. The processes for solving one-step or multi-step equations are used to solve these equations for one variable in terms of the other variable(s). A formula or equation with multiple variables is called a *literal equation*. Many formulas require using *dimensional analysis*, the process of carrying units of measure throughout a computation.

2-9 Weighted Averages

A *weighted average* is the sum of the product of the number of units in a set of data and the value per unit divided by the sum of the number of units. Mixture and uniform motion (rate) problems are applications of weighted averages.

Mc Graw Hill Professional Development

Targeted professional development has been articulated throughout *Algebra 1*. More quality, customized professional development is available from McGraw-Hill Professional Development. Visit glencoe.com for details on each product.

- **Online Lessons** emphasize the strategies and techniques used to teach Algebra 1. Includes streaming video, interactive pages, and online tools.
- **Video Workshops** allow mentors, coaches, or leadership personnel to facilitate on-site workshops on educational strategies in mathematics and mathematical concepts.
- **MHPD Online** (www.mhpdonline.com) offers online professional development with video clips of instructional strategies, links, student activities, and news and issues in education.
- **Teaching Today** (teachingtoday.glencoe.com) gives secondary teachers practical strategies and materials that inspire excellence and innovation in teaching.

CHAPTER 2 Notes

Chapter Project

Shopping on a Budget

Students use what they have learned about writing and solving equations, writing and solving proportions, and finding percent of change to work with concepts related to shopping on a budget.

- Divide students into groups of four. Ask each group member to list one item they would like to buy that costs less than \$100. Have groups find the prices for their list of items in ads or on-line. Have groups determine the sales tax rate in their community.
- Ask groups to circle the greatest price on their list of items. Tell groups that the amount of money they must budget to spend is four times the cost of this item, c, plus \$80. Have students write an equation for z, the amount they must budget for shopping. What is the value of z?
- If every \$20 in their budget represents 3 hours of after-school babysitting, how many hours of babysitting must each group do to earn money equal to their shopping budget?
- Ask groups to find the total cost of all the items on their shopping list, including sales tax. Then have groups determine the percent more or less the total cost is compared to the amount they budgeted.

CHAPTER 2 Linear Equations

Then

In Chapter 1 you learned to simplify algebraic expressions.

Now

In Chapter 2, you will:

- Solve equations by using the four basic operations.
- Solve equations by using multiple steps.
- Solve proportions.
- Use formulas to solve real-world problems.

IL Learning Standards

8.D.4 Formulate and solve linear equations.
6.D.4 Solve problems involving recipes or mixtures, financial calculations and geometric similarity using ratios, proportions and percents.

Why?

SHOPPING In recent years, the percent of change in sales per year at shopping malls in the U.S. averaged 5%. A store manager can use this data to set a sales goal for the upcoming year.

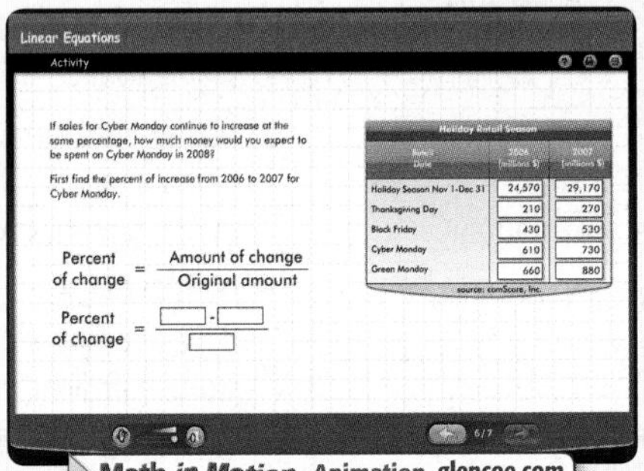

Math *in Motion*, Animation glencoe.com

Key Vocabulary Introduce the key vocabulary in the chapter using the routine below.

Define: A formula is an equation that states a rule for the relationship between certain quantities.

Example: The formula for the perimeter of a rectangle is $P = 2\ell + 2w$.

Ask: If $\ell = 4$ and $w = 7$, what does P equal? 22

Get Ready for Chapter 2

Diagnose Readiness You have two options for checking Prerequisite Skills.

Text Option Take the Quick Check below. Refer to the Quick Review for help.

*Quick*Check

(Used in Lessons 2-1 through 2-9)
Write an algebraic expression for each verbal expression. (Lesson 1-1)

1. four less than three times a number n $3n - 4$
2. a number d cubed less seven $d^3 - 7$
3. the difference between two times b and eleven $2b - 11$

(Used in Lessons 2-1 through 2-4)
Evaluate each expression. (Lesson 1-2)

4. $(9 - 4)^2 + 3$ 28
5. $\frac{3 \cdot 8 - 12 \div 2}{3^2}$ 2
6. $5(8 - 2) \div 3$ 10
7. $\frac{1}{3}(21) + \frac{1}{8}(32)$ 11
8. $72 \div 9 + 3 \cdot 2^3$ 32
9. $\frac{11 - 3}{2} + 7$ 11
10. $2[(5 - 3)^2 + 8] + (3 - 1) \div 2$ 25
11. **BAKERY** Sue buys 1 carrot cake for \$14, 6 large chocolate chip cookies for \$1.50 each, and a dozen doughnuts for \$0.45 each. How much money did Sue spend at the bakery? \$28.40

(Used in Lesson 2-7)
Find each percent. (Lesson 0-6)

12. What percent of 400 is 260? 65%
13. Twelve is what percent of 60? 20%
14. What percent of 25 is 75? 300%
15. **ICE CREAM** What percent of the people surveyed prefer strawberry ice cream? 21%

Favorite Flavor	Number of Responses
vanilla	82
chocolate	76
strawberry	42

*Quick*Review

EXAMPLE 1

Write an algebraic expression for the phrase *the product of eight and w increased by nine.*

the product of eight and w increased by nine

$8 \quad \cdot \quad w \quad + \quad 9$

The expression is $8w + 9$.

EXAMPLE 2

Evaluate $9 - \left[\frac{8 + 2^2}{2} - 2(5 \times 2 - 8)\right]$.

$9 - \left[\frac{8 + 2^2}{2} - 2(5 \times 2 - 8)\right]$	Original expression
$= 9 - \left[\frac{8 + 2^2}{2} - 2(2)\right]$	Evaluate inside the parentheses.
$= 9 - \left(\frac{8 + 2^2}{2} - 4\right)$	Multiply.
$= 9 - \left(\frac{8 + 4}{2} - 4\right)$	Evaluate the power.
$= 9 - (6 - 4)$	Add and then divide.
$= 7$	Simplify.

EXAMPLE 3

32 is what percent of 40?

$\frac{a}{b} = \frac{p}{100}$	Use the percent proportion.
$\frac{32}{40} = \frac{p}{100}$	Replace a with 32 and b with 40.
$32(100) = 40p$	Find the cross products.
$3200 = 40p$	Multiply.
$80 = p$	Divide each side by 40.

32 is 80% of 40.

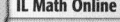

Online Option IL Math Online Take a self-check Chapter Readiness Quiz at glencoe.com.

Chapter 2 Get Ready for Chapter 2 **73**

Response to Intervention (RtI)

Use the *Quick Check* results and the Intervention Planner chart to help you determine your Response to Intervention. The If-Then statements in the chart below help you decide the appropriate tier of RtI and suggest intervention resources for each tier.

Intervention Planner

Tier 1 — On Level

If students miss about 25% of the exercises or less,

Then choose a resource:

SE Concepts and Skills Bank, p. 857
Lessons 1-1, 1-6, and 0-6

CRM Skills Practice, Chapter 2, p. 7

IL Math Online Self-Check Quiz

Tier 2 — Strategic Intervention approaching grade level

If students miss about 50% of the exercises,

Then choose a resource:

CRM Study Guide and Intervention, Chapter 2, p. 5

Quick Review Math Handbook

IL Math Online Extra Examples, Personal Tutor, Homework Help

Tier 3 — Intensive Intervention 2 or more grades below level

If students miss about 75% of the exercises,

Then use *Math Triumphs, Alg. 1*

IL Math Online Extra Examples, Personal Tutor, Homework Help, Review Vocabulary

CHAPTER 2 Notes

FOLDABLES® Study Organizer

Dinah Zike's Foldables®

Focus As students read and study this chapter, they should show examples and write notes about linear equations in their study booklets.

Teach Have students make and label their Foldables as illustrated. Have students fill in the appropriate pages of their booklets with study notes as they cover each lesson in this chapter. At the end of each lesson, ask students to use the booklets to take notes, write and solve equations, solve real-world problems, or to record and define vocabulary words and concepts.

When to Use It Encourage students to add to their Foldables as they work through the chapter and to use them to review for the chapter test.

Differentiated Instruction

CRM Student-Built Glossary, pp. 1–2 Students should complete the chart by providing the definition of each term and an example as they progress through Chapter 2. This study tool can also be used to review for the chapter test.

Get Started on Chapter 2

You will learn several new concepts, skills, and vocabulary terms as you study Chapter 2. To get ready, identify important terms and organize your resources. You may wish to refer to **Chapter 0** to review prerequisite skills.

FOLDABLES® Study Organizer

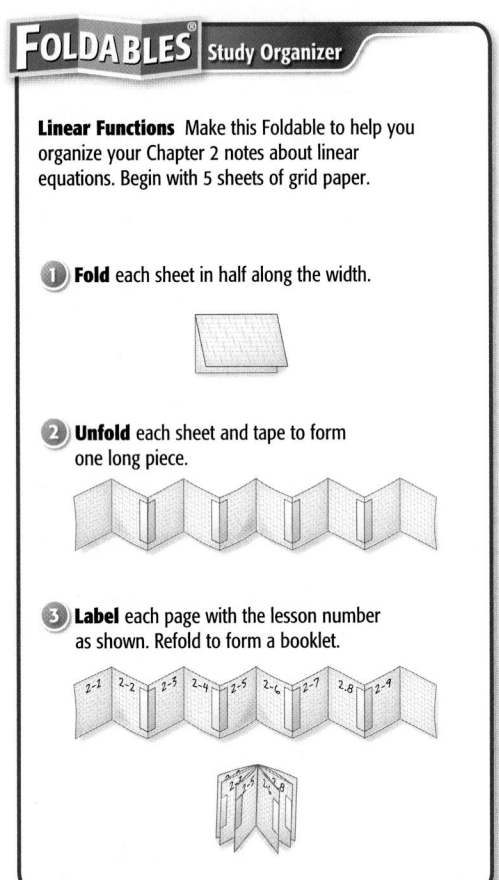

Linear Functions Make this Foldable to help you organize your Chapter 2 notes about linear equations. Begin with 5 sheets of grid paper.

1. **Fold** each sheet in half along the width.

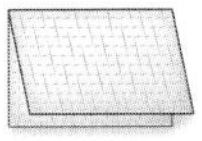

2. **Unfold** each sheet and tape to form one long piece.

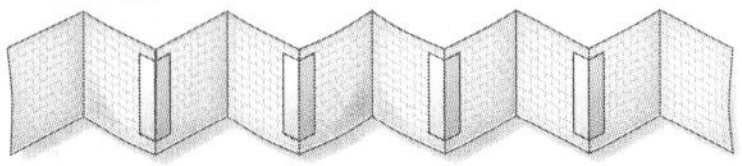

3. **Label** each page with the lesson number as shown. Refold to form a booklet.

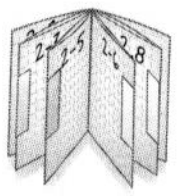

IL Math Online glencoe.com

- Study the chapter online
- Explore **Math in Motion**
- Get extra help from your own **Personal Tutor**
- Use **Extra Examples** for additional help
- Take a **Self-Check Quiz**
- **Review Vocabulary** in fun ways

New Vocabulary

English		Español
formula	• p. 76 •	fórmula
solve an equation	• p. 83 •	resolver una ecuación
equivalent equations	• p. 83 •	ecuaciones equivalentes
multi-step equation	• p. 91 •	ecuación de varios pasos
identity	• p. 98 •	identidad
ratio	• p. 111 •	razón
proportion	• p. 111 •	proporción
rate	• p. 113 •	tasa
unit rate	• p. 113 •	tasa unitaria
scale model	• p. 114 •	modelo de escala
percent of change	• p. 119 •	porcentaje de cambio
literal equation	• p. 127 •	ecuación literal
dimensional analysis	• p. 128 •	análisis dimensional
weighted average	• p. 132 •	promedio ponderado

Review Vocabulary

algebraic expression • p. 5 • expresion algebraica
an expression consisting of one or more numbers and variables along with one or more arithmetic operations

coordinate system • p. 38 • sistema de coordenedas
the grid formed by the intersection of two number lines, the horizontal axis and the vertical axis

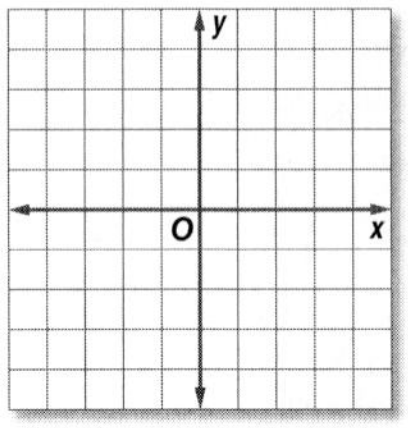

function • p. 45 • función
a relation in which each element of the domain is paired with exactly one element of the range

Multilingual eGlossary glencoe.com

2-1 Writing Equations

Why?

The Daytona 500 is widely considered to be the most important event of the NASCAR circuit. The distance around the track is 2.5 miles, and the race is a total of 500 miles. We can write an equation to determine how many laps it takes to finish the race.

Then
You evaluated and simplified algebraic expressions. (Lesson 1-2)

Now
- Translate sentences into equations.
- Translate equations into sentences.

IL Learning Standards
8.B.4a Represent algebraic concepts with physical materials, words, diagrams, tables, graphs, equations and inequalities and use appropriate technology.
8.D.4 Formulate and solve linear and quadratic **equations** and linear inequalities algebraically and investigate nonlinear inequalities using graphs, tables, calculators and computers. *Also addresses 7.A.4b.*

New Vocabulary
formula

IL Math Online
glencoe.com
- Extra Examples
- Personal Tutor
- Self-Check Quiz
- Homework Help

Write Verbal Expressions To write an equation, identify the unknown for which you are looking and assign a variable to it. Then, write the sentence as an equation. Look for key words such as *is, is as much as, is the same as,* or *is identical to* that indicate where you should place the equals sign.

Consider the Daytona 500 example above.

Words	The length of each lap times the number of laps is the length of the race.
Variable	Let ℓ represent the number of laps in the race.
Equation	$2.5 \times \ell = 500$

EXAMPLE 1 Translate Sentences into Equations

Translate each sentence into an equation.

a. Seven times a number squared is five times the difference of k and m.

Seven	times	n squared	is	five	times	the difference of k and m.
7	$\cdot$	n^2	=	5	$\cdot$	$(k - m)$

The equation is $7n^2 = 5(k - m)$.

b. Fifteen times a number subtracted from 80 is 25.

You can rewrite the verbal sentence so it is easier to translate. *Fifteen times a number subtracted from 80* is the same as *80 minus 15 times a number is 25.* Let n represent the number.

80	minus	15	times	a number	is	25.
80	−	15	$\cdot$	n	=	25

The equation is $80 - 15n = 25$.

Check Your Progress

1A. Two plus the quotient of a number and 8 is the same as 16. $2 + \frac{n}{8} = 16$

1B. Twenty-seven times k is h squared decreased by 9. $27k = h^2 - 9$

Personal Tutor glencoe.com

2-1 Lesson Notes

1 FOCUS

Vertical Alignment

Before Lesson 2-1
Evaluate and simplify algebraic expressions.

Lesson 2-1
Translate sentences into equations.
Translate equations into sentences.

After Lesson 2-1
Transform and solve equations.

2 TEACH

Scaffolding Questions

Have students read the *Why?* section of the lesson.

Ask:
- What is the length of the race? 500 miles
- What is the unknown that you want to find? the number of laps that equals 500 miles
- What do you know about the length of a lap? a lap is 2.5 miles
- What operation can you perform on the number of laps to equal the length of the race? Multiply the length of a lap, 2.5 miles, times the number of laps.

Lesson 2-1 Resources

Resource	Approaching-Level	On-Level	Beyond-Level	English Learners
Teacher Edition	• Differentiated Instruction, p. 77	• Differentiated Instruction, p. 77	• Differentiated Instruction, pp. 77, 80	• Differentiated Instruction, p. 77
Chapter Resource Masters	• Study Guide and Intervention, pp. 5–6 • Skills Practice, p. 7 • Practice, p. 8 • Word Problem Practice, p. 9	• Study Guide and Intervention, pp. 5–6 • Skills Practice, p. 7 • Practice, p. 8 • Word Problem Practice, p. 9 • Enrichment, p. 10	• Practice, p. 8 • Word Problem Practice, p. 9 • Enrichment, p. 10	• Study Guide and Intervention, pp. 5–6 • Skills Practice, p. 7 • Practice, p. 8
Transparencies	• 5-Minute Check Transparency 2-1	• 5-Minute Check Transparency 2-1	• 5-Minute Check Transparency 2-1	• 5-Minute Check Transparency 2-1
Other	• Study Notebook	• Study Notebook	• Study Notebook	• Study Notebook

Write Equations

Example 1 shows how to translate sentences into equations. **Example 2** shows how the four-step problem-solving plan is used to solve a real-world problem. **Example 3** shows how to write a formula by translating a sentence.

Formative Assessment

Use the Check Your Progress exercises after each Example to determine students' understanding of concepts.

Additional Examples

1 Translate each sentence into an equation.

a. A number b divided by three is six less than c.
$\frac{b}{3} = c - 6$

b. Fifteen more than z times 6 is 11 less than y times 2.
$15 + 6z = 2y - 11$

2 **JELLY BEANS** A jelly bean manufacturer produces 1,250,000 jelly beans per hour. How many hours does it take to produce 10,000,000 jelly beans? 8 hours

3 **GEOMETRY** Translate the sentence into a formula.

The perimeter of a square equals four times the length of a side.
$P = 4s$

Additional Examples also in Interactive Classroom PowerPoint® Presentations

IWB INTERACTIVE WHITEBOARD READY

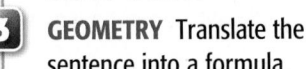

Real-World Link

In 1919, Britain and France offered a flight that carried two passengers at a time. Now there are approximately 45,000 flights each day in the U.S., carrying hundreds of passengers on each flight.

Source: *Flightaware*

Translating sentences to algebraic expressions and equations is a valuable skill in solving real-world problems.

Real-World EXAMPLE 2 Use the Four-Step Problem-Solving Plan

AIR TRAVEL Refer to the information at the left. In how many days will 180,000 flights have occurred in the United States?

Understand The information given in the problem is that there are approximately 45,000 flights per day in the United States. We are asked to find how many days it will take for 180,000 flights to have occurred.

Plan Write an equation. Let d represent the number of days needed.

45,000	times	the number of days	equals	180,000.
45,000	$\cdot$	d	=	180,000

Solve $45{,}000d = 180{,}000$ **Find d by asking, "What number times 45,000 is 180,000?"**

$d = 4$

Check Check your answer by substituting 4 for d in the equation.

$45{,}000(4) \stackrel{?}{=} 180{,}000$ **Substitute 4 for d.**

$180{,}000 = 180{,}000$ ✓ **Multiply.**

The answer makes sense and works for the original problem.

Check Your Progress

2. GOVERNMENT There are 50 members in the North Carolina Senate. This is 70 fewer than the number in the North Carolina House of Representatives. How many members are in the North Carolina House of Representatives?
$50 = r - 70$; 120

Personal Tutor glencoe.com

A rule for the relationship between certain quantities is called a **formula**. These equations use variables to represent numbers and form general rules.

EXAMPLE 3 Write a Formula

GEOMETRY Translate the sentence into a formula.

The area of a triangle equals the product of $\frac{1}{2}$ the length of the base and the height.

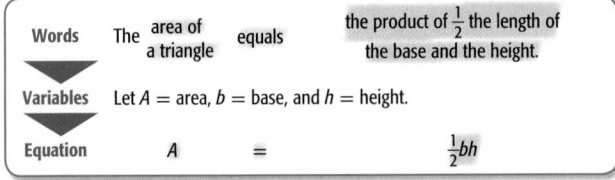

Words	The area of a triangle	equals	the product of $\frac{1}{2}$ the length of the base and the height.
Variables	Let A = area, b = base, and h = height.		
Equation	A	=	$\frac{1}{2}bh$

The formula for the area of a triangle is $A = \frac{1}{2}bh$.

Check Your Progress

3. GEOMETRY Translate the sentence into a formula.
In a right triangle, the square of the measure of the hypotenuse c is equal to the sum of the squares of the measures of the legs, a and b. $c^2 = a^2 + b^2$

Personal Tutor glencoe.com

Focus on Mathematical Content

Algebraic Expressions Algebraic expressions have one or more variables and usually contain some numbers and one or more operations. When writing an algebraic expression, variables are used to represent unknown numbers or measures.

TEACH with TECH

AUDIO RECORDING Make an audio recording of reading several equations out loud. Play the recording for students and have them write the equations algebraically. You could post these audio recordings on your secure classroom Web site and have students complete this as homework.

Tips for New Teachers

Translating Tell students that when translating between sentences and equations, there is usually more than one way to write the result. The equation in Example 2 could also be written as $180{,}000 \div d = 45{,}000$.

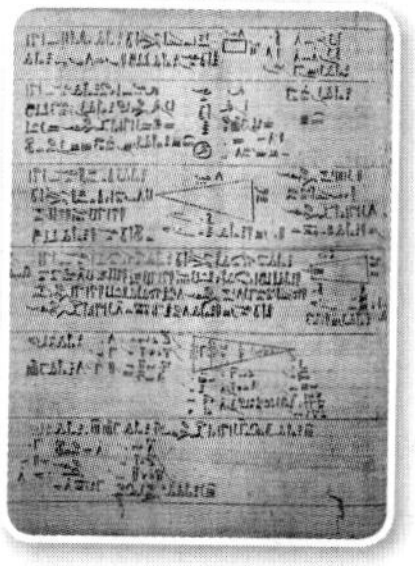

Math History Link

Ahmes (about 1680–1620 B.C.) Ahmes was the Egyptian mathematician and scribe who copied the Rhind Mathematical Papyrus. The papyrus contains 87 algebra problems of the same type. The first set of problems asks how to divide n loaves of bread between 10 people.

Write Sentences from Equations If you are given an equation, you can write a sentence or create your own word problem.

EXAMPLE 4 Translate Equations into Sentences

Translate each equation into a sentence.

a. $6z - 15 = 45$

$6z$	$-$	15	$=$	45
Six times z	minus	fifteen	equals	forty-five.

b. $y^2 + 3x = w$

y^2	$+$	$3x$	$=$	w
The sum of y squared and		three times x	is	w.

Check Your Progress

4A. $15 = 25u^2 + 2$

4B. $\frac{3}{2}r - t^3 = 132$

4A. Sample answer: Fifteen is equal to the product of 25 and u squared plus two.
4B. Sample answer: Three halves times r minus t cubed is the same as one hundred thirty-two.

Personal Tutor glencoe.com

When given a set of information, you can create a problem that relates a story.

EXAMPLE 5 Write a Problem

Write a problem based on the given information.

t = the time that Maxine drove; $t + 4$ = the time that Tia drove; $2t + (t + 4) = 28$

Sample problem:

Maxine and Tia went on a trip, and they took turns driving. During her turn, Tia drove 4 hours more than Maxine. Maxine took 2 turns, and Tia took 1 turn. Together they drove for 28 hours. How many hours did Maxine drive?

Check Your Progress

5. p = Beth's salary; $0.1p$ = bonus; $p + 0.1p = 525$

5. Beth gets paid at her job by both salary and a bonus. Her bonus is 10% of her salary. Her paycheck was \$525. How much is Beth's salary?

Personal Tutor glencoe.com

Check Your Understanding

Example 1 p. 75

Translate each sentence into an equation.

1. Three times r less than 15 equals 6. $15 - 3r = 6$
2. The sum of q and four times t is equal to 29. $q + 4t = 29$
3. A number n squared plus 12 is the same as the quotient of p and 4. $n^2 + 12 = p \div 4$
4. Half of j minus 5 is the sum of k and 13. $\frac{1}{2}j - 5 = k + 13$
5. The sum of 8 and three times k equals the difference of 5 times k and 3. $8 + 3k = 5k - 3$
6. Three fourths of w plus 5 is one half of w increased by nine. $\frac{3}{4}w + 5 = \frac{1}{2}w + 9$
7. The quotient of 25 and t plus 6 is the same as twice t plus 1. $\frac{25}{t} + 6 = 2t + 1$
8. Thirty-two divided by y is equal to the product of three and y minus four.

8. $\frac{32}{y} = 3y - 4$

Write Sentences from Equations

Example 4 shows how to translate equations into verbal sentences. **Example 5** shows how to write a verbal problem from information given in equations.

Additional Example

4 Translate each equation into a sentence.

a. $12 - 2x = -5$ Sample answer: Twelve minus two times x equals negative five.

b. $a^2 + 3b = \frac{c}{6}$ Sample answer: a squared plus three times b equals c divided by 6.

5 Write a problem based on the given information.

f = cost of fries
$f + 1.50$ = cost of burger
$4(f + 1.50) - f = 8.25$

Sample answer: The cost of a burger is \$1.50 more than the cost of fries. Four times the cost of a burger minus the cost of fries equals \$8.25. How much do fries cost?

Tips for New Teachers

Sense-Making Remind students that there is often more than one way to translate an equation into a verbal sentence. For example, $y^2 + 3x = w$ could also be translated as, "y squared plus 3 times x equals w."

Differentiated Instruction

AL OL BL ELL

If some students are having trouble translating sentences into equations,

Then pair those students with students who are able to translate sentences into equations easily. Have the pairs work through several problems in Check Your Understanding.

3 PRACTICE

Formative Assessment

Use Exercises 1–20 to check for understanding.

Use the chart at the bottom of this page to customize assignments for your students.

Watch Out!

Preventing Errors Explain that π is not a variable. The symbol π always represents the same nonterminating, nonrepeating decimal number.

Additional Answers

15. Sample answer: The product of seven and *m* minus *q* is equal to 23.

16. Sample answer: Six plus the product of nine and *k* plus the product 5 and *j* is fifty-four.

17. Sample answer: Three times the sum of *g* and eight is the same as 4 times *h* minus 10.

18. Sample answer: Six times *d* squared minus the product of seven and *f* is identical to eight times *d* plus *f* squared.

19. Sample answer: A team of gymnasts competed in a regional meet. Each member of the team won 3 medals. There were a total of 45 medals won by the team. How many team members were there?

20. A store receives a shipment of notebooks that costs the store *c* dollars. To sell the notebooks, the store marks them up by 25%. If the store charges \$3.75 for each notebook, what was the original cost of the notebook?

Example 2 p. 76

9. FINANCIAL LITERACY Samuel has \$1900 in the bank. He wishes to increase his account to a total of \$2500 by depositing \$30 per week from his paycheck. Write and solve an equation to find how many weeks he needs to reach his goal. $1900 + 30w = 2500$; 20

10. PAINTING Miguel is earning extra money by painting houses. He charges a \$200 fee plus \$12 per can of paint needed to complete the job. Write and use an equation to find how many cans of paint he needs for a \$260 job. $12c + 200 = 260$; 5

Example 3 p. 76

Translate each sentence into a formula.

11. The perimeter of a regular pentagon is 5 times the length of each side. $P = 5s$

12. The area of a circle is the product of π and the radius *r* squared. $A = \pi r^2$

13. Four times π times the radius squared is the surface area of a sphere. $4\pi r^2 = S$

14. One third the product of the length of the side squared and the height is the volume of a pyramid with a square base. $\frac{1}{3}s^2h = V$

Example 4 p. 77

Translate each equation into a sentence. 15–18. See margin.

15. $7m - q = 23$ **16.** $6 + 9k + 5j = 54$

17. $3(g + 8) = 4h - 10$ **18.** $6d^2 - 7f = 8d + f^2$

Example 5 p. 77

Write a problem based on the given information. 19–20. See margin.

19. g = gymnasts on a team; $3g = 45$

20. c = cost of a notebook; $0.25c$ = markup; $c + 0.25c = 3.75$

Practice and Problem Solving

● = Step-by-Step Solutions begin on page R12.
Extra Practice begins on page 815.

Example 1 p. 75

Translate each sentence into an equation.

21. The difference of *f* and five times *g* is the same as 25 minus *f*. $f - 5g = 25 - f$

22. Three times *b* less than 100 is equal to the product of 6 and *b*. $100 - 3b = 6b$

23. Four times the sum of 14 and *c* is *a* squared. $4(14 + c) = a^2$

Example 2 p. 76

24. MUSIC A piano has 52 white keys. Write and use an equation to find the number of octaves on a piano keyboard. $8k = 52$ or $52 \div 8 = k$; $6\frac{1}{2}$ octaves

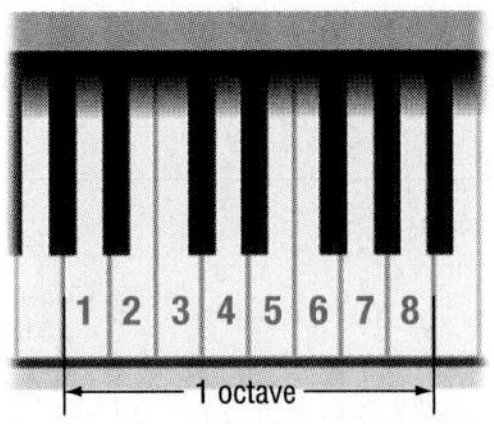

25. GARDENING A flat of plants contains 12 plants. Yoshi wants a garden that has three rows with 10 plants per row. Write and solve an equation for the number of flats Yoshi should buy. $3 \cdot 10 = 12f$; $2\frac{1}{2}$ flats

Example 3 p. 76

Translate each sentence into a formula.

26. The perimeter of a rectangle is equal to 2 times the length plus twice the width. $P = 2\ell + 2w$

27. Celsius temperature *C* is five ninths times the difference of the Fahrenheit temperature *F* and 32. $C = \frac{5}{9}(F - 32)$

28. The density of an object is the quotient of its mass and its volume. $D = \frac{m}{V}$

29. Simple interest is computed by finding the product of the principal amount *p*, the interest rate *r*, and the time *t*. $I = prt$

Example 4 p. 77

Translate each equation into a sentence. 30–35. See Ch. 2 Answer Appendix.

30. $j + 16 = 35$ **31.** $4m = 52$ **32.** $7(p + 23) = 102$

33. $r^2 - 15 = t + 19$ **34.** $\frac{2}{5}v + \frac{3}{4} = \frac{2}{3}x^2$ **35.** $\frac{1}{3} - \frac{4}{5}z = \frac{4}{3}y^3$

Differentiated Homework Options

Level	Assignment	Two-Day Option	
AL Basic	21–39, 47–48, 50–63	21–39 odd, 51–54	22–38 even, 47–48, 50, 55–63
OL Core	21–39 odd, 40–48, 50–63	21–39, 51–54	40–48, 50, 55–63
BL Advanced	40–59, (optional: 60–63)		

78 Chapter 2 Linear Equations

Example 5 p. 77

Write a problem based on the given information. **36–39. See Ch. 2 Answer Appendix.**

36. q = quarts of strawberries; $2.50q = 10$

37. p = the principal amount; $0.12p$ = the interest charged; $p + 0.12p = 224$

38. m = number of movies rented; $10 + 1.50m = 14.50$

39. p = the number of players in the game; $5p + 7$ = number of cards in a deck

B

For Exercises 40–43, match each sentence with an equation.

A. $g^2 = 2(g - 10)$ **C.** $g^3 = 24g + 4$

B. $\frac{1}{2}g + 32 = 15 + 6g$ **D.** $3g^2 = 30 + 9g$

40. One half of g plus thirty-two is as much as the sum of fifteen and six times g. **B**

41. A number g to the third power is the same as the product of 24 and g plus 4. **C**

42. The square of g is the same as two times the difference of g and 10. **A**

43. The product of 3 and the square of g equals the sum of thirty and the product of nine and g. **D**

44. FINANCIAL LITERACY Tim's bank contains quarters, dimes, and nickels. He has three more dimes than quarters and 6 fewer nickels than quarters. If he has 63 coins, write and solve an equation to find how many quarters Tim has. $q + (3 + q) + (q - 6) = 63$ **or** $3q - 3 = 63$; **22**

45. SHOPPING Pilar bought 17 items for her camping trip, including tent stakes, packets of drink mix, and bottles of water. She bought 3 times as many packets of drink mix as tent stakes. She also bought 2 more bottles of water than tent stakes. Write and solve an equation to discover how many tent stakes she bought. $17 = t + 3t + (t + 2)$ **or** $17 = 5t + 2$; **3**

Real-World Link

There are more than 16,000 commercial and public campgrounds nationwide. Camping is the number one outdoor vacation activity in America.

Source: Travel Industry Association of America

46. MULTIPLE REPRESENTATIONS In this problem, you will explore how to translate relations with powers.

C

x	2	3	4	5	6
y	5	10	17	26	37

a. VERBAL Write a sentence to describe the relationship between x and y in the table. **The value of y is equal to the square of the x-value plus 1.**

b. ALGEBRAIC Write an equation that represents the data in the table. $y = x^2 + 1$

c. GRAPHICAL Graph each ordered pair and draw the function. Describe the graph as discrete or continuous. **See Ch. 2 Answer Appendix.**

H.O.T. Problems

Use Higher-Order Thinking Skills

47. OPEN ENDED Write a problem about your favorite television show that uses the equation $x + 8 = 30$. **See Ch. 2 Answer Appendix.**

48. REASONING The surface area of a three-dimensional object is the sum of the areas of the faces. If ℓ represents the length of the side of a cube, write a formula for the surface area of the cube. $S = 6\ell^2$

49. CHALLENGE Given the perimeter P and width w of a rectangle, write a formula to find the length ℓ. $\ell = \frac{P - 2w}{2}$

50. WRITING IN MATH Explain how to translate a verbal sentence into an algebraic equation. Include any tips that you may have for your fellow students. **See Ch. 2 Answer Appendix.**

Multiple Representations In Exercise 46, students use a table of values, an equation, and a graph in the coordinate plane to illustrate the nature of a quadratic function.

Study Guide and Intervention

CRM pp. 5–6 AL OL ELL

NAME ______ DATE ______ PERIOD ______

2-1 Study Guide and Intervention

Writing Equations

Write Equations Writing equations is one strategy for solving problems. You can use a variable to represent an unspecified number or measure referred to in a problem. Then you can write a verbal expression as an algebraic expression.

Example 1 **Translate each sentence into an equation or a formula.**

a. Ten times a number x is equal to 2.8 times the difference y minus z.
$10 \times x = 2.8 \times (y - z)$
The equation is $10x = 2.8(y - z)$.

b. A number m minus 8 is the same as a number n divided by 2.
$m - 8 = n \div 2$
The equation is $m - 8 = \frac{n}{2}$.

c. The area of a rectangle equals the length times the width. Translate this sentence into a formula.
Let A = area, ℓ = length, and w = width.
Formula: *Area equals length times width.*
$A = \ell \times w$
The formula for the area of a rectangle is $A = \ell w$.

Example 2 **Use the Four-Step Problem-Solving Plan.**

POPULATION The population of the United States in July 2007 was about 301,000,000, and the land area of the United States is about 3,500,000 square miles. Find the average number of people per square mile in the United States.

Step 1 *Explore* You know that there are 301,000,000 people. You want to know the number of people per square mile.

Step 2 *Plan* Write an equation to represent the situation. Let p represent the number of people per square mile.
$3,500,000 \times p = 301,000,000$

Step 3 *Solve* $3,500,000 \times p = 301,000,000$.
$3,500,000p = 301,000,000$ Divide each side by 3,500,000.
$p = 86$
There are 86 people per square mile.

Step 4 *Check* If there are 86 people per square mile and there are 3,500,000 square miles, $86 \times 3,500,000 = 301,000,000$. The answer makes sense.

Lesson 2-1

Exercises

Translate each sentence into an equation or formula.

1. Three times a number t minus twelve equals forty. $3t - 12 = 40$

2. One-half of the difference of a and b is 54. $\frac{1}{2}(a - b) = 54$

3. Three times the sum of d and 4 is 32. $3(d + 4) = 32$

4. The area A of a circle is the product of π and the radius r squared. $A = \pi r^2$

5. **WEIGHT LOSS** Lou wants to lose weight to audition for a part in a play. He weighs 160 pounds now. He wants to weigh 150 pounds.

a. If p represents the number of pounds he wants to lose, write an equation to represent this situation. $160 - p = 150$

b. How many pounds does he need to lose to reach his goal? **10 lb**

Chapter 2 5 Glencoe Algebra 1

Practice

CRM p. 8 AL OL BL ELL

NAME ______ DATE ______ PERIOD ______

2-1 Practice

Writing Equations

Translate each sentence into an equation.

1. Fifty-three plus four times b is as much as 21. $53 + 4b = 21$

2. The sum of five times h and twice g is equal to 23. $5h + 2g = 23$

3. One fourth the sum of r and ten is identical to r minus 4. $\frac{1}{4}(r + 10) = r - 4$

4. Three plus the sum of the squares of w and x is 32. $3 + (w^2 + x^2) = 32$

Translate each sentence into a formula.

5. Degrees Kelvin K equals 273 plus degrees Celsius C. $K = 273 + C$

6. The total cost C of gas is the price p per gallon times the number of gallons g. $C = pg$

7. The sum S of the measures of the angles of a polygon is equal to 180 times the difference of the number of sides n and 2. $S = 180(n - 2)$

Translate each equation into a sentence.

8. $r - (4 + p) = \frac{1}{3}r$ **r minus the sum of 4 and p equals $\frac{1}{3}$ times r.**

9. $\frac{3}{5}t + 2 = t$ **Two more than $\frac{3}{5}$ of t equals t.**

10. $9(y^2 + x) = 18$ **9 times the sum of y squared and x is 18.**

11. $2(m - n) = x + 7$ **Twice the quantity m minus n is x plus 7.**

Write a problem based on the given information.

12. a = cost of one adult's ticket to zoo
$a - 4$ = cost of one children's ticket to zoo
$2a + 4(a - 4) = 38$
Sample answer: The cost of two adult's tickets and 4 children's tickets to the zoo is $38. How much is an adult's ticket?

13. c = regular cost of one airline ticket
$0.20c$ = amount of 20% promotional discount
$3(c - 0.20c) = 330$
Sample answer: The cost of three airline tickets that are discounted 20% is $330. What is the regular cost of a ticket?

14. **GEOGRAPHY** About 15% of all federally-owned land in the 48 contiguous states of the United States is in Nevada. If F represents the area of federally-owned land in these states, and N represents the portion in Nevada, write an equation for this situation. $0.15F = N$

15. **FITNESS** Deanna and Pietra each go for walks around a lake a few times per week. Last week, Deanna walked 7 miles more than Pietra.

a. If p represents the number of miles Pietra walked, write an equation that represents the total number of miles T the two girls walked. $T = p + (p + 7)$

b. If Pietra walked 9 miles during the week, how many miles did Deanna walk? **16 mi**

c. If Pietra walked 11 miles during the week, how many miles did the two girls walk together? **29 mi**

Chapter 2 8 Glencoe Algebra 1

Word Problem Practice

CRM p. 9 AL OL BL ELL

NAME ______ DATE ______ PERIOD ______

2-1 Word Problem Practice

Writing Equations

1. **HOUSES** The area of the Hartstein's kitchen is 182 square feet. This is 20% of the area of the first floor of their house. Let F represent the area of the first floor. Write an equation to represent the situation.
$182 = 0.2F$

2. **FAMILY** Katie is twice as old as her sister Mara. The sum of their ages is 24. Write a one-variable equation to represent the situation.
$m + 2m = 24$ or $3m = 24$

3. **GEOMETRY** The formula $F + V = E + 2$ shows the relationship between the number of faces F, edges E, and vertices V of a polyhedron, such as a pyramid. Write the formula in words.

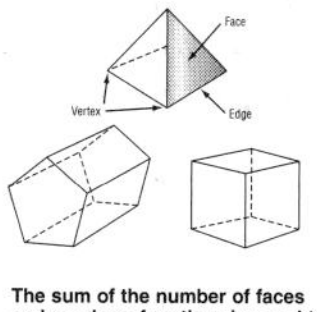

The sum of the number of faces and number of vertices is equal to the sum of two and the number of edges.

4. **WIRELESS PHONE** Spinfrog wireless phone company bills on a monthly basis. Each bill includes a $29.95 service fee for 1000 minutes plus a $2.95 federal communication tax. Additionally, there is a charge of $0.05 for each minute used over 1000. Let m represent the number of minutes over 1000 used during the month. Write an equation to describe the cost p of the wireless phone service per month.
$p = 32.90 + 0.05m$

5. **TEMPERATURE** The table below shows the temperature in Fahrenheit for some corresponding temperatures in Celsius.

Celsius	Fahrenheit
−20°	−4°
−10°	14°
0°	32°
10°	50°
20°	68°
30°	86°

a. Write a formula for converting Celsius temperatures to Fahrenheit temperatures.
$F = 1.8C + 32$

b. Find the Fahrenheit equivalents for 25°C and 35°C. **77°F and 95°F**

Lesson 2-1

Chapter 2 9 Glencoe Algebra 1

Enrichment

CRM p. 10 OL BL

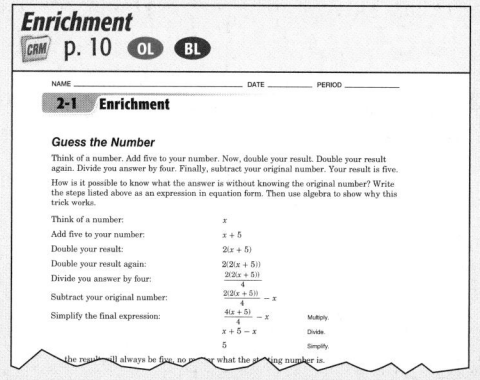

NAME ______ DATE ______ PERIOD ______

2-1 Enrichment

Guess the Number

Think of a number. Add five to your number. Now, double your result. Double your result again. Divide you answer by four. Finally, subtract your original number. Your result is five.

How is it possible to know what the answer is without knowing the original number? Write the steps listed above as an expression in equation form. Then use algebra to show why this trick works.

Think of a number:	x	
Add five to your number:	$x + 5$	
Double your result:	$2(x + 5)$	
Double your result again:	$2(2(x + 5))$	
Divide you answer by four:	$\frac{2(2(x + 5))}{4}$	
Subtract your original number:	$\frac{2(2(x + 5))}{4} - x$	
Simplify the final expression:	$\frac{4(x + 5)}{4} - x$	Multiply.
	$x + 5 - x$	Divide.
	5	Simplify.

the result will always be five, no matter what the starting number is.

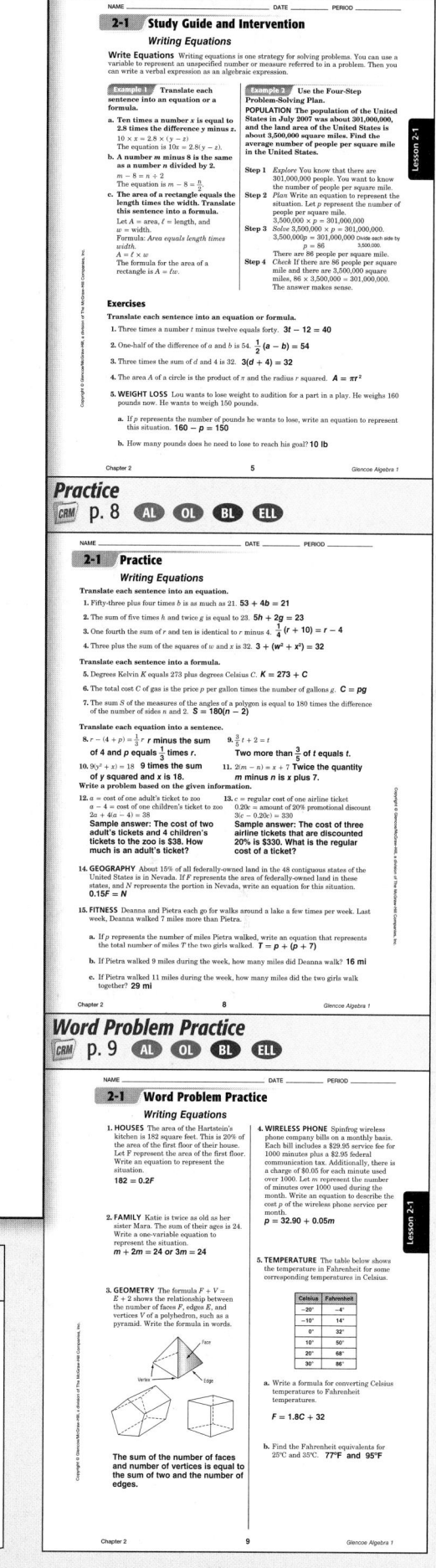

4 ASSESS

Ticket Out the Door Make several copies of five different equations. Give one equation to each student. As students leave, ask them to give a verbal sentence for the equation.

Additional Answers

58a.

Pairs of earrings	1	2	3	4	5
Total Cost	29	58	58	87	116

58b. {(1, 29), (2, 58), (3, 58), (4, 87), (5, 116)}

58c.

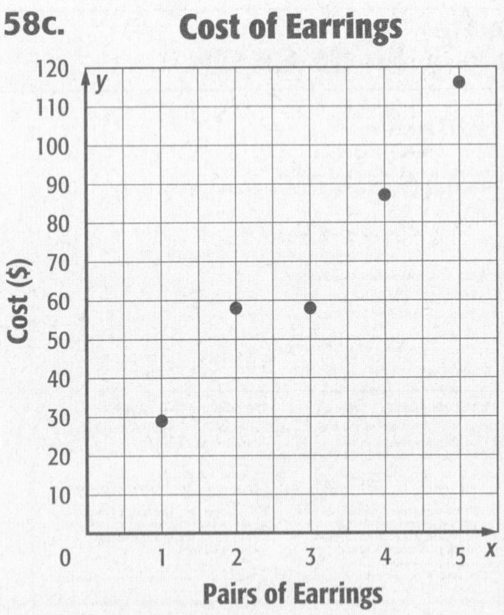

PSAE PRACTICE 8.11.07, 6.11.17, 7.11.04, 10.11.05

51. Which equation *best* represents the relationship between the number of hours an electrician works h and the total charges c? **C**

Cost of Electrician	
Emergency House Call	\$30 one time fee
Rate	\$55/hour

A $c = 30 + 55$
B $c = 30h + 55$
C $c = 30 + 55h$
D $c = 30h + 55h$

52. A car traveled at 55 miles per hour for 2.5 hours and then at 65 miles per hour for 3 hours. How far did the car travel in all? **J**

F 300.5 mi H 330 mi
G 305 mi J 332.5 mi

53. SHORT RESPONSE Suppose each dimension of rectangle *ABCD* is doubled. What is the perimeter of the new *ABCD*? **180 m**

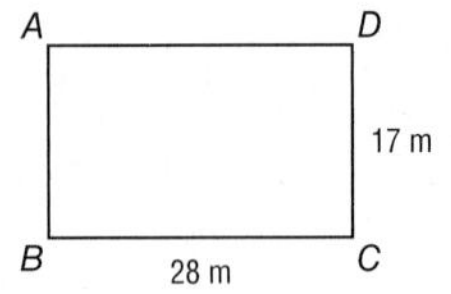

54. STATISTICS Stacy's first five science test scores were 95, 86, 83, 95, and 99. Which of the following is a true statement? **A**

A The mode is the same as the median.
B The median is the same as the mean.
C The range is the same as the mode.
D The mode is the same as the mean.

Spiral Review

Write a counterexample for each conditional statement. (Lesson 1-8)

55. If you were born in Florida, then you live in Florida. **I could have been born in Florida, moved to Kentucky, and still live in Kentucky.**

56. If the product of two numbers is an even number, then both factors must be even numbers. **$3 \cdot 2 = 6$; six is even, three is odd, two is even.**

57. If a number is divisible by 2, then it is divisible by 4. **10 is divisible by 2, but not by 4.**

58. SHOPPING Cuties is having a sale on earrings (Lesson 1-7) **a–c. See margin.**

a. Make a table that shows the cost of buying 1 to 5 pairs of earrings.
b. Write the data as a set of ordered pairs.
c. Graph the data.

59. GEOMETRY Refer to the table below. (Lesson 1-6)

Polygon	triangle	quadrilateral	pentagon	hexagon	heptagon
Number of Sides	3	4	5	6	7
Interior Angle Sum	180	360	540	720	900

a. Identify the independent and dependent variables.
b. Identify the domain and range for this situation.
c. State whether the function is *discrete* or *continuous*. Explain. **Discrete; sample answer: There cannot be a polygon with 3.5 sides, so the function cannot be continuous.**

59a. independent: number of sides; dependent: interior angle sum
59b. Domain: all integers greater than or equal to 3; Range: all positive integer multiples of 180

Skills Review

Evaluate each expression. (Lesson 1-1)

60. 9^2 **81** **61.** 10^6 **1,000,000** **62.** 3^5 **243** **63.** 5^3 **125**

Differentiated Instruction BL

Extension A pair of numbers that are in order and differ by 2, such as 4 and 6, are called *consecutive even numbers.*

a. Write an equation for three consecutive even numbers with a sum of 60 if x is the least of the three numbers. $x + (x + 2) + (x + 4) = 60$

b. Write an equation for three consecutive even numbers with a sum of 108 if x is the least of the three numbers. $x + (x + 2) + (x + 4) = 108$

Solving Equations

IL Math Online > glencoe.com
Math *in Motion*, Animation

IL Learning Standards — **8.D.4** Formulate and **solve linear** and quadratic **equations** and linear inequalities algebraically and investigate nonlinear inequalities using graphs, tables, calculators and computers. *Also addresses 8.B.4a.*

You can use **algebra tiles** to model solving equations. To **solve an equation** means to find the value of the variable that makes the equation true. An x tile represents the variable x. The 1 tile represents a positive 1. The −1 tile represents a negative 1. And, the −x tile represents the variable negative x. The goal is to get the x-tile by itself on one side of the mat by using the rules stated below.

Rules for Equation Models When Adding or Subtracting	
You can remove or add the same number of identical algebra tiles to each side of the mat without changing the equation.	
One positive tile and one negative tile of the same unit are called a zero pair. Since $1 + (-1) = 0$, you can remove or add zero pairs to either side of the equation mat without changing the equation.	

ACTIVITY 1 Addition Equation

Use an equation model to solve $x + 3 = -4$.

Step 1 Model the equation. Place 1 x-tile and 3 positive 1-tiles on one side of the mat. Place 4 negative 1-tiles on the other side of the mat.

Step 2 Isolate the x-term. Add 3 negative 1-tiles to each side. The resulting equation is $x = -7$.

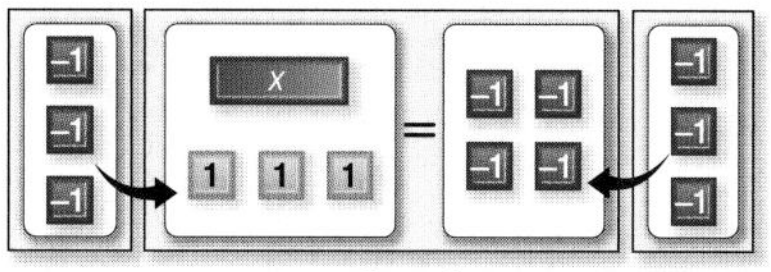

$x + 3 = -4$
$x + 3 + (-3) = -4 + (-3)$
$x = -7$

ACTIVITY 2 Subtraction Equation

Use an equation model to solve $x - 2 = 1$.

Step 1

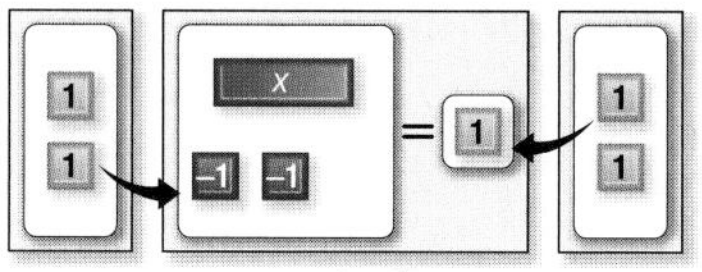

$x - 2 = 1$
$x - 2 + 2 = 1 + 2$

Place 1 x-tile and 2 negative 1-tiles on one side of the mat. Place 1 positive 1-tile on the other side of the mat. Then add 2 positive 1-tiles to each side.

Step 2

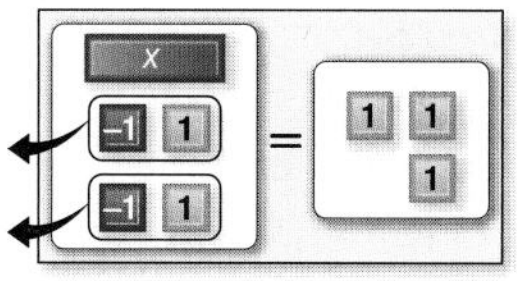

$x = 3$

Group the tiles to form zero pairs. Then remove all the zero pairs. The resulting equation is $x = 3$.

(continued on the next page)

EXPLORE 2-2 Lesson Notes

1 FOCUS

Objective Use algebra tiles to solve addition, subtraction, and multiplication equations.

Materials for Each Group

- equation mats
- algebra tiles (x-tiles, 1-tiles)

Easy to Make Manipulatives

Teaching Algebra with Manipulatives

templates for:
- algebra tiles, pp. 10–11
- equation mat, p. 16

Teaching Tip

Make sure students understand that zero pairs can be formed only after adding the same number of positive or negative tiles to each side of the equation mat. Point out that the number of positive or negative 1-tiles added to each side of the equation mat depends upon the 1-tiles on the side of the equation mat with the x-tile.

2 TEACH

Working in Cooperative Groups

Put students in groups of two or three, mixing abilities to complete the Activities.

Ask:

In Activity 1,

- What does the x-tile represent? an unknown number that when added to 3 equals −4
- Is it possible to remove identical 1-tiles from each side of the equation mat? Explain. No; the 1-tiles on the left side are negative and the 1-tiles on the right side are positive, so there are no identical algebra tiles that can be removed from each side.
- Why do you add 3 negative 1-tiles to each side of the equation? You need 3 negative 1-tiles to form 3 zero pairs on the left side of the equation mat.
- What do you do after you form zero pairs? Remove the zero pairs so that the x-tile is by itself.

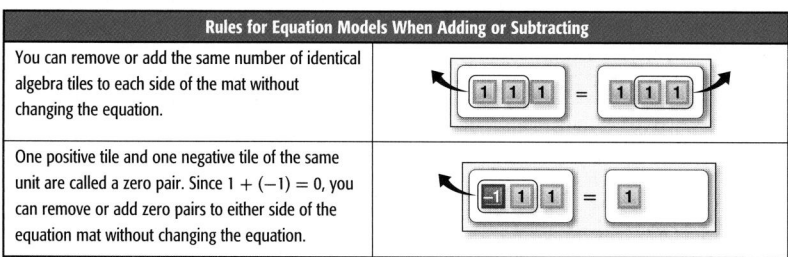

In Activity 2, remind students that when modeling subtraction with algebra tiles, they must add negative tiles.

Ask:

- Why do you add positive 1-tiles to each side of the equation mat? You need positive 1-tiles to form zero pairs with the negative 1-tiles on the left side of the equation mat.

In Activity 3, point out to students that what they do on one side of the equation mat, they must do on the other side. If they form one group of x-tiles on one side, they must form one group of 1-tiles on the other side and so on. If there is more than one x-tile, the number of 1-tiles paired with each x-tile must be the same for each group of 1-tiles.

Practice Have students complete Exercises 1–4 and 6–9.

3 ASSESS

Formative Assessment

Use Exercise 3 to assess whether students comprehend how to form zero-pairs in order to isolate the x-tile.

From Concrete to Abstract

Exercise 5 provides a symbolic representation for the addition and subtraction properties used in Examples 1 and 2. In Exercise 10, students should apply what they have learned to new situations.

Model and Analyze

Use algebra tiles to solve each equation.

1. $x + 4 = 9$ **5**
2. $x + (-3) = -4$ **−1**
3. $x + 7 = -2$ **−9**
4. $x + (-2) = 11$ **13**
5. **WRITING IN MATH** If $a = b$, what can you say about $a + c$ and $b + c$? about $a - c$ and $b - c$? $a + c = b + c$; $a - c = b - c$

When solving multiplication equations, the goal is still to get the x-tile by itself on one side of the mat by using the rules for dividing.

Rules for the Equation Models When Dividing	
You can group the tiles on each side of the equation mat into an equal number of groups without changing the equation.	
You can place an equal grouping on each side of the equation mat without changing the equation.	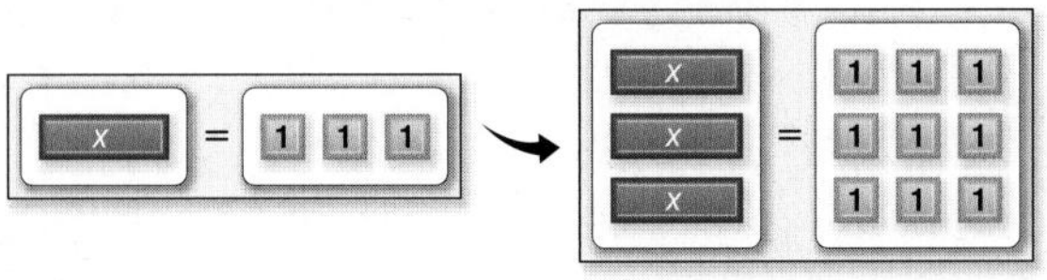

ACTIVITY 3 Multiplication Equation

Use an equation model to solve $3x = 12$.

Step 1 Model the equation. Place 3 x-tiles on one side of the mat. Place 12 positive 1-tiles on the other side of the mat.

Step 2 Isolate the x-term. Separate the tiles into 3 equal groups to match the 3 x-tiles. Each x-tile is paired with 4 positive 1-tiles. The resulting equation is $x = 4$.

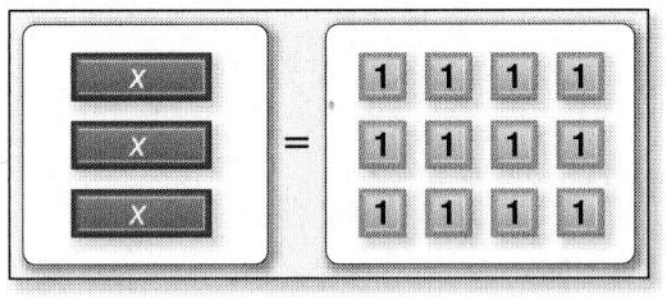

$3x = 12$

$\frac{3x}{3} = \frac{12}{3}$

$x = 4$

10. Sample answer: Since there is no $\frac{x}{4}$-tile, the equation cannot be solved using algebra tiles. To solve algebraically, multiply each side by 4.

Model and Analyze

Use algebra tiles to solve each equation.

6. $5x = -15$ **−3**
7. $-3x = -9$ **3**
8. $4x = 8$ **2**
9. $-6x = 18$ **−3**
10. **MAKE A CONJECTURE** How would you use algebra tiles to solve $\frac{x}{4} = 5$? Discuss the steps you would take to solve this equation algebraically.

Extending the Concept

Ask students how to use algebra tiles to solve $2x - 4 = 2$. Sample answer: After isolating the two x-tiles, separate the 1-tiles into 2 equal groups to correspond with each x-tile. The number of 1-tiles corresponding to one x-tile gives the solution. In this case, there should be three 1-tiles for each x-tile.

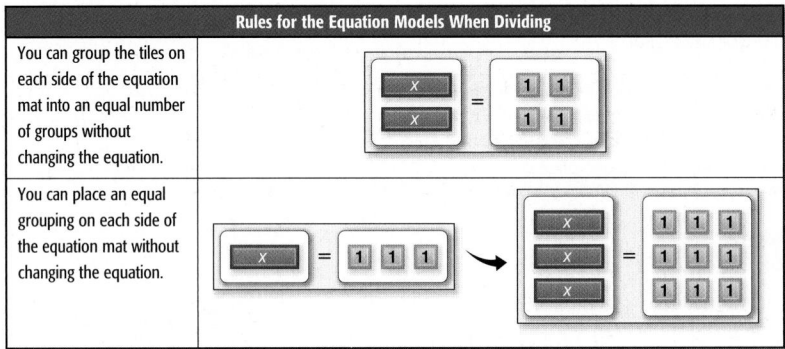

2-2 Solving One-Step Equations

Then
You translated sentences into equations. (Lesson 2-1)

Now
- Solve equations by using addition and subtraction.
- Solve equations by using multiplication and division.

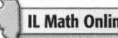

IL Learning Standards

8.B.4a Represent algebraic concepts with physical materials, words, diagrams, tables, graphs, equations and inequalities and use appropriate technology. **8.D.4 Formulate and solve linear** and quadratic **equations** and linear inequalities algebraically and investigate nonlinear inequalities using graphs, tables, calculators and computers. *Also addresses 6.B.4.*

New Vocabulary

solve an equation
equivalent equations

IL Math Online

glencoe.com
- Extra Examples
- Personal Tutor
- Self-Check Quiz
- Homework Help

Why?

A record for the most snow angels made at one time was set in Michigan when 3784 people participated. North Dakota had 8910 people register to break the record. To determine how many more people North Dakota had than Michigan, solve the equation $3784 + x = 8910$.

Solve Equations Using Addition or Subtraction In an equation, the variable represents the number that satisfies the equation. To **solve an equation** means to find the value of the variable that makes the equation true.

The process of solving an equation involves isolating the variable (with a coefficient of 1) on one side of the equation. Each step in this process results in equivalent equations. **Equivalent equations** have the same solution.

Key Concept — Addition Property of Equality *For Your FOLDABLE*

Words If an equation is true and the same number is added to each side of the equation, the resulting equivalent equation is also true.

Symbols For any real numbers a, b, and c, if $a = b$, then $a + c = b + c$.

Examples

$$14 = 14 \qquad\qquad -3 = -3$$
$$14 + 3 = 14 + 3 \qquad\qquad +9 = +9$$
$$17 = 17 \qquad\qquad 6 = 6$$

EXAMPLE 1 Solve by Adding

Solve $c - 22 = 54$.

Horizontal Method

$c - 22 = 54$	**Original equation**
$c - 22 + 22 = 54 + 22$	**Add 22 to each side.**
$c = 76$	**Simplify.**

Vertical Method

$$c - 22 = 54$$
$$+22 = +22$$
$$c = 76$$

To check that 76 is the solution, substitute 76 for c in the original equation.

CHECK $c - 22 = 54$	**Original equation**
$76 - 22 \stackrel{?}{=} 54$	**Substitute 76 for *c*.**
$54 = 54$ ✓	**Subtract.**

Check Your Progress Solve each equation.

1A. $113 = g - 25$ 138

1B. $j - 87 = -3$ 84

Personal Tutor glencoe.com

2-2 Lesson Notes

1 FOCUS

Vertical Alignment

Before Lesson 2-2
Translate sentences into equations.

Lesson 2-2
Solve equations by using addition and subtraction.
Solve equations by multiplication and division.

After Lesson 2-2
Solve multi-step equations.

2 TEACH

Scaffolding Questions

Have students read the *Why?* section of the lesson.

Ask:
- What is the Guinness World Record for the greatest number of snow angels made at one time? 8910
- What is the unknown quantity represented by x in the equation? how many more snow angels North Dakota made than Michigan at one time
- Is the value of x greater than or less than 8910? Explain. less than 8910 because $x + 3748$ is equal to 8910

Lesson 2-2 Resources

Resource	Approaching-Level	On-Level	Beyond-Level	English Learners
Teacher Edition	• Differentiated Instruction, p. 87	• Differentiated Instruction, pp. 87, 89	• Differentiated Instruction, p. 89	
Chapter Resource Masters	• Study Guide and Intervention, pp. 11–12 • Skills Practice, p. 13 • Practice, p. 14 • Word Problem Practice, p. 15	• Study Guide and Intervention, pp. 11–12 • Skills Practice, p. 13 • Practice, p. 14 • Word Problem Practice, p. 15 • Enrichment, p. 16	• Practice, p. 14 • Word Problem Practice, p. 15 • Enrichment, p. 16	• Study Guide and Intervention, pp. 11–12 • Skills Practice, p. 13 • Practice, p. 14
Transparencies	• 5-Minute Check Transparency 2-2	• 5-Minute Check Transparency 2-2	• 5-Minute Check Transparency 2-2	• 5-Minute Check Transparency 2-2
Other	• Study Notebook • Teaching Algebra with Manipulatives	• Study Notebook • Teaching Algebra with Manipulatives	• Study Notebook	• Study Notebook • Teaching Algebra with Manipulatives

Solve Equations Using Addition or Subtraction

Example 1 shows how to solve an equation by adding. **Example 2** shows how to solve an equation by subtracting.

Formative Assessment

Use the Check Your Progress exercises after each Example to determine students' understanding of concepts.

Additional Examples

1. Solve $h - 12 = -27$ -15
2. Solve $c + 102 = 36$ -66

Additional Examples also in Interactive Classroom PowerPoint® Presentations

IWB INTERACTIVE WHITEBOARD READY

Watch Out!

Preventing Errors Students may try to skip a step and solve the problem without first writing the equation. Tell students that they will make fewer mistakes in solving equations if they translate the sentence and write the equation before solving it.

Similar to the Addition Property of Equality, the **Subtraction Property of Equality** can also be used to solve equations.

StudyTip

Subtraction Subtracting a value is equivalent to adding the opposite of the value.

Key Concept — Subtraction Property of Equality (For Your FOLDABLE)

Words If an equation is true and the same number is subtracted from each side of the equation, the resulting equivalent equation is also true.

Symbols For any real numbers a, b, and c, if $a = b$, then $a - c = b - c$.

Examples

$$87 = 87$$
$$87 - 17 = 87 - 17$$
$$70 = 70$$

$$\begin{array}{r} 13 = 13 \\ -28 = -28 \\ \hline -15 = -15 \end{array}$$

StudyTip

Solving an Equation When solving equations you can use either the horizontal method or the vertical method. Both methods will produce the same result.

EXAMPLE 2 Solve by Subtracting

Solve $63 + m = 79$.

Horizontal Method

$63 + m = 79$	Original equation
$63 - 63 + m = 79 - 63$	Subtract 63 from each side.
$m = 16$	Simplify.

Vertical Method

$$\begin{array}{rcr} 63 + m &=& 79 \\ -63 & & =-63 \\ \hline m &=& 16 \end{array}$$

To check that 16 is the solution, replace m with 16 in the original equation.

CHECK $63 + m = 79$	Original equation
$63 + 16 \stackrel{?}{=} 79$	Substitution, $m = 16$
$79 = 79$ ✓	Simplify.

Check Your Progress Solve each equation.

2A. $27 + k = 30$ 3

2B. $-12 = p + 16$ -28

Personal Tutor glencoe.com

Solve Equations Using Multiplication or Division In the equation $\frac{x}{3} = 9$, the variable x is divided by 3. To solve for x, undo the division by multiplying each side by 3. This is an example of the **Multiplication Property of Equality**.

Key Concept — Multiplication Property of Equality (For Your FOLDABLE)

Words If an equation is true and each side is multiplied by the same nonzero number, the resulting equation is equivalent.

Symbols For any real numbers a, b, and c, $c \neq 0$, if $a = b$, then $ac = bc$.

Example If $x = 5$, then $3x = 15$.

Division Property of Equality

Words If an equation is true and each side is divided by the same nonzero number, the resulting equation is equivalent.

Symbols For any real numbers a, b, and c, $c \neq 0$, if $a = b$, then $\frac{a}{c} = \frac{b}{c}$.

Example If $x = -20$, then $\frac{x}{5} = \frac{-20}{5}$ or -4.

Focus on Mathematical Content

Solving Equations The Subtraction Property of Equality may be used to isolate the variable when solving an equation. When the same number is subtracted from each side of a true equation, the resulting equation will also be true.

The reciprocal of a number can be used to solve equations.

Review Vocabulary

reciprocal the multiplicative inverse of a number (Lesson 1-3)

EXAMPLE 3 **Solve by Multiplying and Dividing**

Solve each equation.

a. $\frac{2}{3}q = \frac{1}{2}$

$\frac{2}{3}q = \frac{1}{2}$ — Original equation

$\frac{3}{2}\left(\frac{2}{3}\right)q = \frac{3}{2}\left(\frac{1}{2}\right)$ — Multiply each side by $\frac{3}{2}$, the reciprocal of $\frac{2}{3}$.

$q = \frac{3}{4}$ — Check the result.

b. $39 = -3r$

$39 = -3r$ — Original equation

$\frac{39}{-3} = \frac{-3r}{-3}$ — Divide each side by -3.

$-13 = r$ — Check the result.

Check Your Progress

3A. $\frac{3}{5}k = 6$ **10**

3B. $-\frac{1}{4} = \frac{2}{3}b$ $-\frac{3}{8}$

Personal Tutor glencoe.com

We can also use reciprocals and properties of equality to solve real-world problems.

Real-World Link

Almost half of 10- to 18-year-olds in the U.S. use a cell phone. Of those, 53% play games on their phones, more than 33% download games, 52% use the calendar/organizer, and nearly all teens with camera phones snap pictures.

Source: Lexdon Business Library

Real-World EXAMPLE 4 **Solve by Multiplying**

SURVEYS Of a group of 13- to 15-year-old girls surveyed, 225, or about $\frac{9}{20}$ said they talk on the telephone while they watch television. About how many girls were surveyed?

Words	Nine twentieths times those surveyed	is	225.
Variable	Let g = the number of girls surveyed.		
Equation	$\frac{9}{20}g$	=	225

$\frac{9}{20}g = 225$ — Original equation

$\left(\frac{20}{9}\right)\frac{9}{20}g = \left(\frac{20}{9}\right)225$ — Multiply each side by $\frac{20}{9}$.

$g = \frac{4500}{9}$ — $\left(\frac{20}{9}\right)\left(\frac{9}{20}\right) = 1$

$g = 500$ — Simplify.

About 500 girls were surveyed.

Check Your Progress

4. STAINED GLASS Allison is making a stained glass window. Her pattern requires that one fifth of the glass should be blue. She has 288 square inches of blue glass. If she intends to use all of her blue glass, how much glass will she need for the entire project? **1440 square inches of glass**

Personal Tutor glencoe.com

Solve Equations Using Multiplication or Division

Example 3 shows how to solve an equation by multiplying or dividing each side by the same number. **Example 4** shows how to write and solve an equation for a real-world problem.

Additional Examples

3 Solve each equation.

a. $-1\frac{3}{8}k = \frac{2}{3}$ $-\frac{16}{33}$

b. $-75 = -15b$ 5

4 **TRAVEL** Ricardo is driving 780 miles to Memphis. He drove about $\frac{3}{5}$ of the distance on the first day. About how many miles did Ricardo drive? about 468 miles

Focus on Mathematical Content

Properties of Equality The Multiplication Property may be used to isolate the variable when solving an equation. When each side of a true equation is multiplied by the same nonzero number, the resulting equation will also be true. The Division Property may be used to isolate the variable when solving an equation. When each side of a true equation is divided by the same nonzero number, the resulting equation will also be true.

TEACH with TECH

BLOG On you secure classroom blog have students create a blog entry to summarize how to solve one-step equations. Make sure that students use the idea of inverse operations in their explanations.

3 PRACTICE

Formative Assessment

Use Exercises 1–17 to check for understanding.

Use the chart at the bottom of this page to customize assignments for your students.

Tips for New Teachers

Coefficients Students are sometimes confused about what to do with a variable in an equation such as $-x = 27$. Point out that the variable actually has a coefficient of -1. Remembering that the product of two negative numbers is a positive, you can multiply each side of the equation by -1. $(-1)(-x) = (-1)27$; $x = -27$

Check Your Understanding

Examples 1 and 3 pp. 83–85

Solve each equation. Check your solution.

1. $g + 5 = 33$ **28**
2. $104 = y - 67$ **171**
3. $\frac{2}{3} + w = 1\frac{1}{2}$ $\frac{5}{6}$
4. $-4 + t = -7$ **−3**
5. $a + 26 = 35$ **9**
6. $-6 + c = 32$ **38**
7. $1.5 = y - (-5.6)$ **−4.1**
8. $3 + g = \frac{1}{4}$ $-2\frac{3}{4}$
9. $x + 4 = \frac{3}{4}$ $-3\frac{1}{4}$
10. $\frac{t}{7} = -5$ **−35**
11. $\frac{a}{36} = \frac{4}{9}$ **16**
12. $\frac{2}{3}n = 10$ **15**
13. $\frac{8}{9} = \frac{4}{5}k$ $\frac{10}{9}$ or $1\frac{1}{9}$
14. $12 = \frac{x}{-3}$ **−36**
15. $-\frac{r}{4} = \frac{1}{7}$ $-\frac{4}{7}$

Example 4 p. 85

16. **FUNDRAISING** The television show "Idol Gives Back" raised money for relief organizations. During this show, viewers could call in and vote for their favorite performer. The parent company contributed \$5 million for the 50 million votes cast. What did they pay for each vote? **\$0.10**

17. **SHOPPING** Hana decides to buy her cat a bed from an online fund that gives $\frac{7}{8}$ of her purchase to shelters that care for animals. How much of Hana's money went to the animal shelter? **\$22.75**

Practice and Problem Solving

● = Step-by-Step Solutions begin on page R12. Extra Practice begins on page 815.

Examples 1 and 3 pp. 83–85

Solve each equation. Check your solution.

18. $v - 9 = 14$ **23**
19. $44 = t - 72$ **116**
20. $-61 = d + (-18)$ **−43**
21. $18 + z = 40$ **22**
22. $-4a = 48$ **−12**
23. $12t = -132$ **−11**
24. $18 - (-f) = 91$ **73**
25. $-16 - (-t) = -45$ **−29**
26. $\frac{1}{3}v = -5$ **−15**
27. $\frac{u}{8} = -4$ **−32**
28. $\frac{a}{6} = -9$ **−54**
29. $-\frac{k}{5} = \frac{7}{5}$ **−7**
30. $\frac{3}{4} = w + \frac{2}{5}$ $\frac{7}{20}$
31. $-\frac{1}{2} + a = \frac{5}{8}$ $1\frac{1}{8}$
32. $-\frac{t}{7} = \frac{1}{15}$ $-\frac{7}{15}$
33. $-\frac{5}{7} = y - 2$ $1\frac{2}{7}$
34. $v + 914 = -23$ **−937**
35. $447 + x = -261$ **−708**
36. $-\frac{1}{7}c = 21$ **−147**
37. $-\frac{2}{3}h = -22$ **33**
38. $\frac{3}{5}q = -15$ **−25**
39. $\frac{n}{8} = -\frac{1}{4}$ **−2**
40. $\frac{c}{4} = -\frac{9}{8}$ $-\frac{9}{2}$
41. $\frac{2}{3} + r = -\frac{4}{9}$ $-1\frac{1}{9}$

Example 4 p. 85

42. **CATS** A domestic cat can run at speeds of 27.5 miles per hour when chasing prey. A cheetah can run 42.5 miles per hour faster when chasing prey. How fast can the cheetah go? **70 mph**

43. **CARS** The average time t it takes to manufacture a car in the United States is 24.9 hours. This is 8.1 hours longer than the average time it takes to manufacture a car in Japan. Write and solve an equation to find the average time in Japan. **24.9 = 8.1 + t; 16.8 hours**

Differentiated Homework Options

Level	Assignment	Two-Day Option	
AL Basic	18–43, 72–74, 76, 78–91	19–43 odd, 79–82	18–42 even, 72–74, 76, 78, 83–91
OL Core	19–61 odd, 62–64, 76, 78–91	18–43, 79–82	44–74, 76, 78, 83–91
BL Advanced	44–90, (optional: 91)		

B **Solve each equation. Check your solution.**

44. $\frac{x}{9} = 10$ **90**

45. $\frac{b}{7} = -11$ **−77**

46. $\frac{3}{4} = \frac{c}{24}$ **18**

47. $\frac{2}{3} = \frac{1}{8}y$ **$\frac{16}{3}$**

48. $\frac{2}{3}n = 14$ **21**

49. $\frac{3}{5}g = -6$ **−10**

50. $4\frac{1}{5} = 3p$ **$\frac{7}{5}$ or $1\frac{2}{5}$**

51. $-5 = 3\frac{1}{2}x$ **$-\frac{10}{7}$ or $-1\frac{3}{7}$**

52. $6 = -\frac{1}{2}n$ **−12**

53. $-\frac{2}{5} = -\frac{z}{45}$ **18**

54. $-\frac{g}{24} = \frac{5}{12}$ **−10**

55. $-\frac{v}{5} = -45$ **225**

Write an equation for each sentence. Then solve the equation.

56. Six times a number is 132. **$6n = 132$; 22**

57. Two thirds equals negative eight times a number.

58. Five elevenths times a number is 55.

59. Four fifths is equal to ten sixteenths of a number.

60. Three and two thirds times a number equals two ninths.

61. Four and four fifths times a number is one and one fifth.

57. $\frac{2}{3} = -8n$; $-\frac{1}{12}$

58. $\frac{5}{11}n = 55$; 121

59. $\frac{4}{5} = \frac{10}{16}n$; $\frac{32}{25}$

60. $3\frac{2}{3}n = \frac{2}{9}$; $\frac{2}{33}$

61. $4\frac{4}{5}n = 1\frac{1}{5}$; $\frac{1}{4}$

62c. Super Power bar; each bar is \$1.45, while Feel Great bars are \$1.50 each.

62. SHOPPING Adelina is comparing prices for two brands of health and energy bars at the local grocery store. She wants to get the best price for each bar.

a. Write an equation to find the price for each bar of the Feel Great brand. **$12p = 18$**

b. Write an equation to find the price of each bar for the Super Power brand. **$15p = 21.75$**

c. Which bar should Adelina buy? Explain.

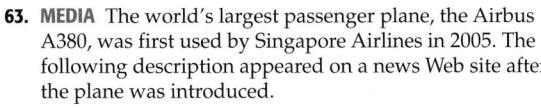

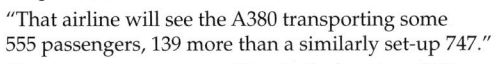

63. MEDIA The world's largest passenger plane, the Airbus A380, was first used by Singapore Airlines in 2005. The following description appeared on a news Web site after the plane was introduced.

"That airline will see the A380 transporting some 555 passengers, 139 more than a similarly set-up 747."

How many passengers will a similarly set-up 747 transport? **$555 = 139 + p$; 416**

64. FUEL In 2004, approximately 5 million cars and trucks were classified as flex-fuel, which means they could run on gasoline or ethanol. In 2006, that number increased to 7.5 million. How many more cars and trucks were flex-fuel in 2006? **$5 + c = 7.5$; 2.5 million**

65. CHEERLEADING At a certain cheerleading competition, the maximum time per team, including the set up, is 3 minutes. The Ridgeview High School squad's performance time is 2 minutes and 34 seconds. How much time does the squad have left for their set up? **$180 = t + 154$; 26 s**

66. COMIC BOOKS An X-Men #1 comic book in mint condition recently sold for \$45,000. An Action Comics #63 (Mile High), also in mint condition, sold for \$15,000. How much more did the X-Men comic book sell for than the Action Comics book? **$45{,}000 = 15{,}000 + t$; \$30,000**

67. MOVIES A certain movie made \$1.6 million in ticket sales. Its sequel made \$0.8 million in ticket sales. How much more did the first movie make than the sequel? **$1.6 - m = 0.8$; \$0.8 million**

68. CAMERAS An electronics store sells a certain digital camera for \$126. This is $\frac{2}{3}$ of the price that a photography store charges. What is the cost of the camera at the photography store? **$126 = \frac{2}{3}c$; \$189**

Real-World Link

Ethanol is produced from corn and is considered energy efficient because it yields 25% more energy than the process to create it.

Source: U.S. Department of Energy

Watch Out!

Preventing Errors Remind students that the product of a fraction and its reciprocal is 1.

Tips for New Teachers

Isolating Variables Explain that when isolating a variable, it does not matter whether the variable ends up on the left or right side of an equation. For example, the solution of $8 = 15 + z$ is still -7, even though the final step may be $-7 = z$.

Differentiated Instruction

AL OL

If students are having trouble solving equations by addition or subtraction,

Then write x and two numbers on the board. Give students the operation symbols + and −. Tell them to use both of the numbers, x, and the operation symbols to write two equations for which the value of x is the same. Have students solve for x in both equations. For example, suppose the two numbers were 23 and 45. Students could write $x + 23 = 45$ and $x = 45 - 23$. For both equations, the solution is 22.

Study Guide and Intervention
CRM pp. 11–12 AL OL ELL

NAME ______ DATE ______ PERIOD ______

2-2 Study Guide and Intervention
Solving One-Step Equations

Solve Equations Using Addition and Subtraction If the same number is added to each side of an equation, the resulting equation is equivalent to the original one. In general if the original equation involves subtraction, this property will help you solve the equation. Similarly, if the same number is subtracted from each side of an equation, the resulting equation is equivalent to the original one. This property will help you solve equations involving addition.

Addition Property of Equality	For any numbers a, b, and c, if $a = b$, then $a + c = b + c$.
Subtraction Property of Equality	For any numbers a, b, and c, if $a = b$, then $a - c = b - c$.

Example 1 Solve $m - 32 = 18$.

$m - 32 = 18$	Original equation
$m - 32 + 32 = 18 + 32$	Add 32 to each side.
$m = 50$	Simplify.

The solution is 50.

Example 2 Solve $22 + p = -12$.

$22 + p = -12$	Original equation
$22 + p - 22 = -12 - 22$	Subtract 22 from each side.
$p = -34$	Simplify.

The solution is −34.

Exercises

Solve each equation. Check your solution.

1. $h - 3 = -2$ **1**
2. $m - 8 = -12$ **−4**
3. $p - 5 = 15$ **20**
4. $20 = y - 8$ **28**
5. $k - 0.5 = 2.3$ **2.8**
6. $w - \frac{1}{2} = \frac{5}{8}$ $\mathbf{1\frac{1}{8}}$
7. $h - 18 = -17$ **1**
8. $-12 = -24 + k$ **12**
9. $j - 0.2 = 1.8$ **2**
10. $b - 40 = -40$ **0**
11. $m - (-12) = 10$ **−2**
12. $w - \frac{3}{2} = \frac{1}{4}$ $\mathbf{\frac{7}{4}}$
13. $x + 12 = 6$ **−6**
14. $w + 2 = -13$ **−15**
15. $-17 = b + 4$ **−21**
16. $k + (-9) = 7$ **16**
17. $-3.2 = \ell + (-0.2)$ **−3**
18. $-\frac{3}{8} + x = \frac{5}{8}$ **1**
19. $19 + h = -4$ **−23**
20. $-12 = k + 24$ **−36**
21. $j + 1.2 = 2.8$ **1.6**
22. $b + 80 = -80$ **−160**
23. $m + (-8) = 2$ **10**
24. $w + \frac{3}{2} = \frac{5}{8}$ $\mathbf{-\frac{7}{8}}$

Lesson 2-2

Chapter 2 11 *Glencoe Algebra 1*

Practice
CRM p. 14 AL OL BL ELL

NAME ______ DATE ______ PERIOD ______

2-2 Practice
Solving One-Step Equations

Solve each equation. Check your solution.

1. $d - 8 = 17$ **25**
2. $v + 12 = -5$ **−17**
3. $b - 2 = -11$ **−9**
4. $-16 = m + 71$ **−87**
5. $29 = a - 76$ **105**
6. $-14 + y = -2$ **12**
7. $8 - (-n) = 1$ **−7**
8. $78 + r = -15$ **−93**
9. $f + (-3) = -9$ **−6**
10. $8j = 96$ **12**
11. $-13z = -39$ **3**
12. $-180 = 15m$ **−12**
13. $243 = 27r$ **9**
14. $\frac{y}{9} = -8$ **−72**
15. $-\frac{j}{12} = -8$ **96**
16. $\frac{a}{15} = \frac{4}{5}$ **12**
17. $\frac{g}{27} = \frac{2}{9}$ **6**
18. $\frac{q}{24} = \frac{1}{6}$ **4**

Write an equation for each sentence. Then solve the equation.

19. Negative nine times a number equals −117. $\mathbf{-9n = -117; 13}$
20. Negative one eighth of a number is $-\frac{3}{4}$. $\mathbf{-\frac{1}{8}n = -\frac{3}{4}; 6}$
21. Five sixths of a number is $-\frac{5}{9}$. $\mathbf{\frac{5}{6}n = -\frac{5}{9}; -\frac{2}{3}}$
22. 2.7 times a number equals 8.37. $\mathbf{2.7n = 8.37; 3.1}$
23. **HURRICANES** The day after a hurricane, the barometric pressure in a coastal town has risen to 29.7 inches of mercury, which is 2.9 inches of mercury higher than the pressure when the eye of the hurricane passed over.
    a. Write an addition equation to represent the situation. $\mathbf{b + 2.9 = 29.7}$
    b. What was the barometric pressure when the eye passed over? **26.8 in. of mercury**
24. **ROLLER COASTERS** *Kingda Ka* in New Jersey is the tallest and fastest roller coaster in the world. Riders travel at an average speed of 61 feet per second for 3118 feet. They reach a maximum speed of 187 feet per second.
    a. If x represents the total time that the roller coaster is in motion for each ride, write an expression to represent the sitation. (*Hint:* Use the distance formula $d = rt$.) $\mathbf{61x = 3118}$
    b. How long is the roller coaster in motion? **51.1 seconds**

Chapter 2 14 *Glencoe Algebra 1*

Word Problem Practice
CRM p. 15 AL OL BL ELL

NAME ______ DATE ______ PERIOD ______

2-2 Word Problem Practice
Solving One-Step Equations

1. **SUPREME COURT** Chief Justice William Rehnquist served on the Supreme Court for 33 years until his death in 2005. Write and solve an equation to determine the year he was confirmed as a justice on the Supreme Court.
   2005 − x = 33; x = 1972
2. **SALARY** In 2007, the annual salary of the Governor of New York was $179,000. During the same year, the annual salary of the Governor of Tennessee was $94,000 less. Write and solve an equation it to find the annual salary of the Governor of Tennessee in 2007.
   179,000 − 94,000 = s or
   179,000 − s = 94,000;
   s = $85,000
3. **WEATHER** On a cold January day, Mavis noticed that the temperature dropped 21 degrees over the course of the day to −9°C. Write and solve an equation to determine what the temperature was at the beginning of the day.
   x − 21 = −9; x = 12°C
4. **FARMING** Mr. Hill's farm is 126 acres. Mr. Hill's farm is $\frac{1}{4}$ the size of Mr. Miller's farm. How many acres is Mr. Miller's farm?
   504 acres
5. **NAUTICAL** On the sea, distances are measured in nautical miles rather than miles.

   1 nautical mile = 6080 feet
   1 knot = $\frac{\text{1 nautical mile}}{\text{hour}}$

   a. If a boat travels 16 knots in 1 hour, how far will it have traveled in feet? Write and solve an equation.
   6080 × 16 = x;
   x = 97,280 ft
   b. About how fast was the boat traveling in miles per hour? Round your answer to the nearest hundredth.
   97,280 ÷ 5280 = 18.42 mph

Lesson 2-2

Chapter 2 15 *Glencoe Algebra 1*

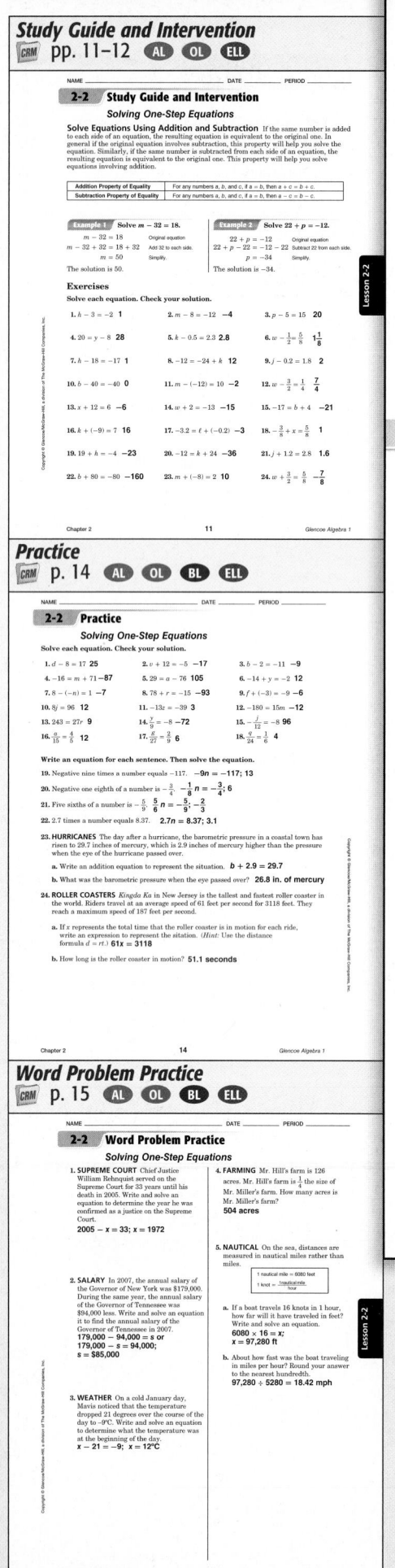

72. $n - 16 = 29$ doesn't belong because for the other three, $n = 13$, and for this one, $n = 45$.

Real-World Link

Schools have begun using an online voting system that allows students to log in and vote for homecoming king and queen.

Source: NewBay Media

73. Sample answer: $12 + n = 25$; subtract 12 from each side or add −12 to each side.

77. Sample answer: If we multiply each side of the first equation by 3, the result is the second equation. So, they have the same solution even though they have different variables.

78. Sample answer: Dividing by a nonzero number is the same as multiplying by its reciprocal, so the same rules would apply.

69. **BLOGS** In 2006, 57 million American adults read online blogs. However, 45 million fewer American adults say that they maintain their own blog. How many American adults maintain a blog? **12 million**

70. **SCIENCE CAREERS** According to the Bureau of Labor and Statistics, approximately 65,000,000 women were employed in the United States in 2004. **a–b. See margin.**
    a. The number of women in the computer science fields times 26 is the number of working women. Write an equation to represent the number of women employed in the computer sciences in 2004. Then solve the equation.
    b. The number of women in natural science fields is 2,266,000 less than the number of women in computer science fields. How many women are in natural science fields?

71. **DANCES** Student Council has a budget of $1000 for the homecoming dance. So far, they have spent $350 dollars for music. **a–c. See margin.**
    a. Write an equation to represent the amount of money left to spend. Then solve the equation.
    b. They then spent $225 on decorations. Write an equation to represent the amount of money left.
    c. If the Student Council spent their entire budget, write an equation to represent how many $6 tickets they must sell to make a profit.

H.O.T. Problems
Use Higher-Order Thinking Skills

72. **WHICH ONE DOESN'T BELONG?** Identify the equation that does not belong with the other three. Explain your reasoning.

    $n + 14 = 27$ | $12 + n = 25$ | $n - 16 = 29$ | $n - 4 = 9$

73. **OPEN ENDED** Write an equation involving addition and demonstrate two ways to solve it.

74. **REASONING** For which triangle is the height not $4\frac{1}{2}b$, where b is the length of the base? **△RST**

Triangle	Base (cm)	Height (cm)
△ABC	3.8	17.1
△MQP	5.4	24.3
△RST	6.3	28.5
△TRW	1.6	7.2

75. **CHALLENGE** Determine whether each sentence is *sometimes*, *always*, or *never true*. Explain your reasoning.
    a. $x + x = x$ **Sometimes; 0 + 0 = 0 but 2 + 2 ≠ 2.**
    b. $x + 0 = x$ **Always; this is the Additive Identity Property.**

76. **REASONING** Determine the value for each statement below.
    a. If $x - 7 = 14$, what is the value of $x - 2$? **19**
    b. If $t + 8 = -12$, what is the value of $t + 1$? **−19**

77. **CHALLENGE** Discuss why $\frac{2}{3}b = 16$ and $48 = 2c$ have the same solution.

78. **WRITING IN MATH** Consider the Multiplication Property of Equality and the Division Property of Equality. Explain why they can be considered the same property. Which one do you think is easier to use?

88 Chapter 2 Linear Equations

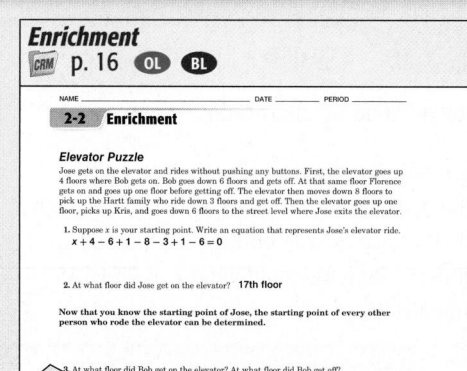

Enrichment
CRM p. 16 OL BL

NAME ______ DATE ______ PERIOD ______

2-2 Enrichment

Elevator Puzzle

Jose gets on the elevator and rides without pushing any buttons. First, the elevator goes up 4 floors where Bob gets on. Bob goes down 6 floors and gets off. At that same floor Florence gets on and goes up one floor before getting off. The elevator then moves down 8 floors to pick up the Hartt family who ride down 3 floors and get off. Then the elevator goes up one floor, picks up Kris, and goes down 6 floors to the street level where Jose exits the elevator.

1. Suppose x is your starting point. Write an equation that represents Jose's elevator ride.
   x + 4 − 6 + 1 − 8 − 3 + 1 − 6 = 0
2. At what floor did Jose get on the elevator? **17th floor**

Now that you know the starting point of Jose, the starting point of every other person who rode the elevator can be determined.

3. At what floor did Bob get on the elevator? At what floor did Bob get off?

Additional Answers

70a. $26w = 65{,}000{,}000$; 2,500,000

70b. $2{,}500{,}000 = n + 2{,}266{,}000$; 234,000

71a. $350 + m = 1000$; $650

71b. $350 + 225 + m = 1000$; $425

71c. $6t = 1000$; 167

PSAE PRACTICE 6.11.13, 6.11.17, 9.11.08

79. Which of the following best represents the equation $w - 15 = 33$? **C**

A Jake added w ounces of water to his bottle, which originally contained 33 ounces of water. How much water did he add?

B Jake added 15 ounces of water to his bottle, for a total of 33 ounces. How much water w was originally in the bottle?

C Jake drank 15 ounces of water from his bottle and 33 ounces were left. How much water w was originally in the bottle?

D Jake drank 15 ounces of water from his water bottle, which originally contained 33 ounces. How much water w was left?

80. **SHORT RESPONSE** Charlie's company pays him for every mile that he drives on his trip. When he drives 50 miles, he is paid \$30. To the nearest tenth, how many miles did he drive if he was paid \$275? **458.3**

81. The table shows the results of a survey given to 500 international travelers. Based on the data, which statement is true? **F**

Vacation Plans

Destination	Percent
The Tropics	37
Europe	19
Asia	17
Other	17
No Vacation	10

F Fifty have no vacation plans.
G Fifteen are going to Asia.
H One third are going to the tropics.
J One hundred are going to Europe.

82. **GEOMETRY** The amount of water needed to fill a pool represents the pool's ____. **A**

A volume
B surface area
C circumference
D perimeter

Spiral Review

Translate each sentence into an equation. (Lesson 2-1)

83. The sum of twice r and three times k is identical to thirteen. $2r + 3k = 13$

84. The quotient of t and forty is the same as twelve minus half of u. $\frac{t}{40} = 12 - \frac{1}{2}u$

85. The square of m minus the cube of p is sixteen. $m^2 - p^3 = 16$

86. Two times z is equal to two times the sum of v and x. $2z = 2(v + x)$

Write each statement in if-then form. (Lesson 1-8)

87. The trash is picked up on Monday. **Sample answer: If it is Monday, then the trash is picked up.**

88. Vito will call after school. **If it is after school, then Vito will call.**

89. For $x = 8$, $x^2 - 3x = 40$. **If $x^2 - 3x = 40$, then $x = 8$.**

90. $4q + 6 > 42$ when $q > 9$. **If $q > 9$, then $4q + 6 > 42$.**

Skills Review

91. **COMMUNICATION** Sato communicates with his friends for a math project. In a week, he averages 5 hours using e-mail, 18 hours on the phone, and 12 hours meeting with them in person. Write and evaluate an expression to predict how many hours he will spend communicating with his friends over the next 12 weeks. (Lesson 1-4) **$12(5 + 18 + 12)$; 420 hours**

92. **PETS** The Poochie Pet Supply Store has the following items on sale. Write and evaluate an expression to find the total cost of purchasing 1 collar, 2 T-shirts, 3 kerchiefs, 1 leash, and 4 flying disks. (Lesson 1-4)
$4.50 + 2(6.25) + 3(3.00) + 5.50 + 4(3.25)$; \$44.50

Item	Cost (\$)
studded collar	4.50
kerchief	3.00
doggy T-shirt	6.25
leash	5.50
flying disk	3.25

4 ASSESS

Name the Math Write an equation involving multiplication or division on the board. Have students identify the operation in the equation. Based on the operation they identify, have students suggest the operation that might be used to solve the equation.

Differentiated Instruction OL BL

Extension Write $\frac{30}{x} = 6$ on the board. Have students solve for x in two ways. Sample answers: Using mental math, think: 30 divided by what number is 6? Multiply each side by x, so $30 = 6x$; the solution is 5.

EXPLORE **2-3** Lesson Notes

1 FOCUS

Objective Use algebra tiles to solve multi-step equations.

Materials for Each Group

- equation mats
- algebra tiles (*x*-tiles, 1-tiles)

Easy to Make Manipulatives

Teaching Algebra with Manipulatives templates for:

- algebra tiles, pp. 10–11
- equation mat, p. 16

Teaching Tip

You may need to review the method of forming zero pairs before beginning the activity.

2 TEACH

Working in Cooperative Groups

Put students in groups of two or three, mixing abilities. Have groups complete the Activity and Exercises 1–4.

Point out that, in Step 4, separating the *x*-tiles and 1-tiles into 4 equivalent groups is a pictorial representation of dividing each side of the equation by 4.

Practice Have students complete Exercises 5–10.

From Concrete to Abstract

Ask students to discuss how the steps for solving an equation are similar to or different from the order of operations. Sample answer: When solving a multi-step equation, addition and subtraction are usually done before multiplication and division. This is the reverse of the order of operations.

EXPLORE **2-3** Algebra Lab

Solving Multi-Step Equations

IL Math Online glencoe.com
Math *in Motion,* Animation

IL Learning Standards **8.D.4** Formulate and **solve linear** and quadratic **equations** and linear inequalities algebraically and investigate nonlinear inequalities using graphs, tables, calculators and computers. *Also addresses 8.B.4a.*

You can use algebra tiles to model solving multi-step equations.

ACTIVITY **Use an equation model to solve $4x + 3 = -5$.**

Step 1 Model the equation.

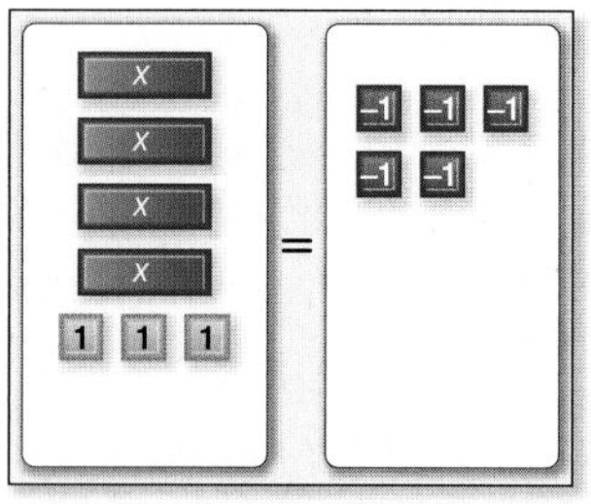

$4x + 3 = -5$

Place 4 *x*-tiles and 3 positive 1-tiles on one side of the mat. Place 5 negative 1-tiles on the other side.

Step 2 Isolate the *x*-term.

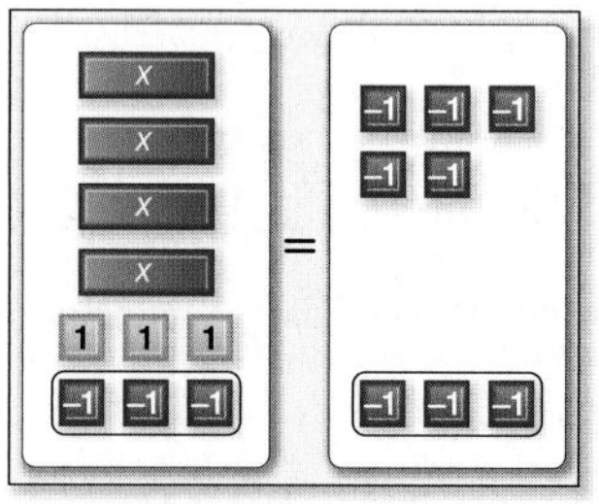

$4x + 3 - 3 = -5 - 3$

Since there are 3 positive 1-tiles with the *x*-tiles, add 3 negative 1-tiles to each side to form zero pairs.

Step 3 Remove zero pairs.

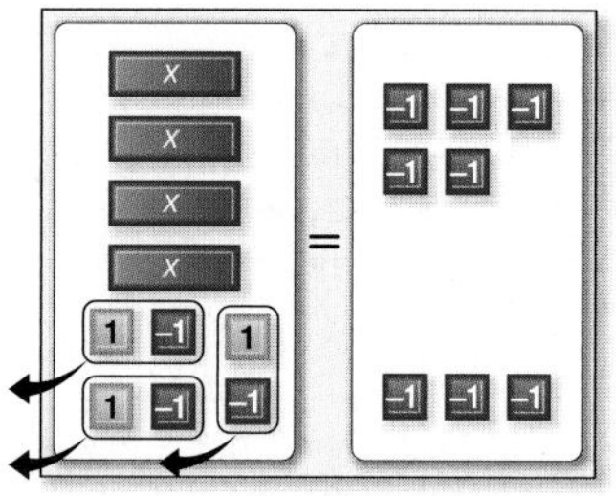

$4x = -8$

Group the tiles to form zero pairs and remove the zero pairs.

Step 4 Group the tiles.

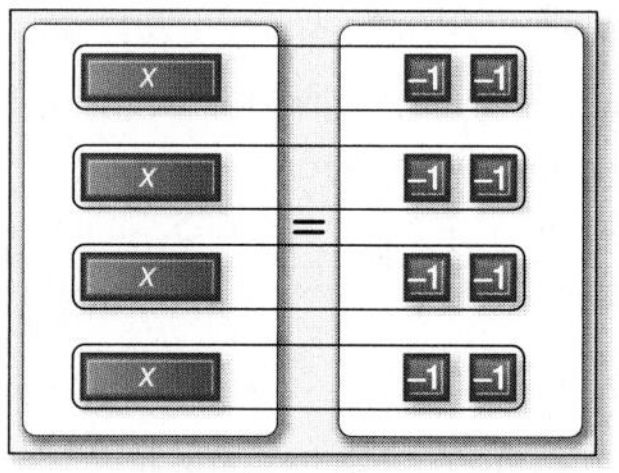

$\frac{4x}{4} = \frac{-8}{4}$

$x = -2$

Separate the remaining tiles into 4 equal groups to match the 4 *x*-tiles. Each *x*-tile is paired with 2 negative 1-tiles. The resulting equation is $x = -2$.

Model **Use algebra tiles to solve each equation.**

1. $3x - 7 = -10$ **−1**
2. $2x + 5 = 9$ **2**
3. $5x - 7 = 8$ **3**
4. $-7 = 3x + 8$ **−5**
5. $5 + 4x = -11$ **−4**
6. $3x + 1 = 7$ **2**
7. $11 = 2x - 5$ **8**
8. $7 + 6x = -11$ **−3**
9. What would be your first step in solving $8x - 29 = 67$? **Add 29 to each side.**
10. What steps would you use to solve $9x + 14 = -49$? **First subtract 14 from each side, and then divide each side by 9.**

3 ASSESS

Formative Assessment

Use Exercises 4 and 8 to assess whether students comprehend how to discover which side of the equation directs the method of solution.

Use Exercise 10 to assess whether students comprehend that addition and subtraction are done before multiplication and division when isolating the variable.

Solving Multi-Step Equations

Then

You solved single-step equations. (Lesson 2-2)

Now

- Solve equations involving more than one operation.
- Solve equations involving consecutive integers.

IL Learning Standards

8.B.4a Represent algebraic concepts with physical materials, words, diagrams, tables, graphs, equations and inequalities and use appropriate technology.
8.D.4 Formulate and **solve linear** and quadratic **equations** and linear inequalities algebraically and investigate nonlinear inequalities using graphs, tables, calculators and computers. *Also addresses 6.B.4.*

New Vocabulary

multi-step equation
consecutive integers
number theory

IL Math Online

glencoe.com

- Extra Examples
- Personal Tutor
- Self-Check Quiz
- Homework Help

Why?

The Tour de France is the premier cycling event in the world. The map shows the 2007 Tour de France course. If the length of the shortest portion of the race can be represented by k, the expression $4k + 20$ is the length of the longest stage or 236 kilometers.

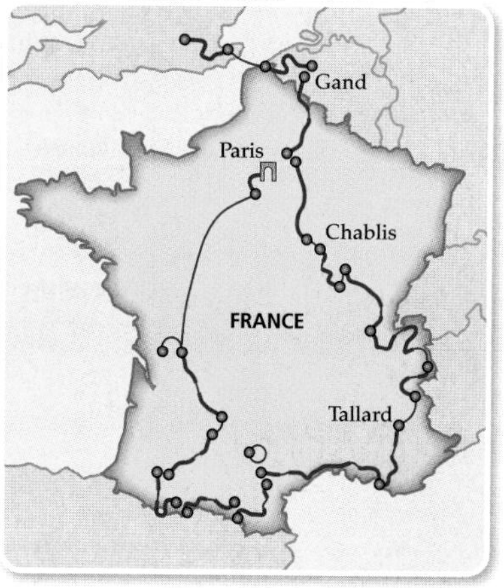

Solve Multi-Step Equations The situation above can be described by the equation $4k + 20 = 236$. Because this equation requires more than one step to solve, it is called a **multi-step equation**. To solve this equation, we must undo each operation by working backward.

EXAMPLE 1 Solve Multi-Step Equations

Solve each equation.

a. $11x - 4 = 29$

$11x - 4 = 29$	**Original equation**
$11x - 4 + 4 = 29 + 4$	**Add 4 to each side.**
$11x = 33$	**Simplify.**
$\frac{11x}{11} = \frac{33}{11}$	**Divide each side by 11.**
$x = 3$	**Simplify.**

b. $\frac{a+7}{8} = 5$

$\frac{a+7}{8} = 5$	**Original equation**
$8\left(\frac{a+7}{8}\right) = 8(5)$	**Multiply each side by 8.**
$a + 7 = 40$	**Simplify.**
$-7 = -7$	**Subtract 7 from each side.**
$a = 33$	**Simplify.**

You can check your solutions by substituting the results back into the original equations.

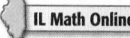

Check Your Progress

Solve each equation. Check your solution.

1A. $2a - 6 = 4$ **5**

1B. $\frac{n+1}{-2} = 15$ **−31**

Personal Tutor glencoe.com

Lesson 2-3 Solving Multi-Step Equations 91

2-3 Lesson Notes

1 FOCUS

Vertical Alignment

Before Lesson 2-3
Solve single-step equations.

Lesson 2-3
Solve equations involving more than one operation.
Solve equations involving consecutive integers.

After Lesson 2-3
Solve problems involving grouping symbols.

2 TEACH

Scaffolding Questions

Have students read the *Why?* section of the lesson.

Ask:

- In the expression $4k + 20$, what does $4k$ represent? the number 4 represents how many times longer the longest portion of the race is than the shortest; k represents the number of kilometers in the shortest portion of the race
- What does the number 20 in the expression $4k + 20$ represent? an additional 20 kilometers in the longest portion of the race
- What is the expression $4k + 20$ equal to? 236 kilometers How do you write this as an equation? $4k + 20 = 236$

(continued on the next page)

Lesson 2-3 Resources

Resource	Approaching-Level	On-Level	Beyond-Level	English Learners
Teacher Edition	• Differentiated Instruction, pp. 92, 93	• Differentiated Instruction, pp. 93, 96	• Differentiated Instruction, pp. 93, 96	• Differentiated Instruction, p. 93
Chapter Resource Masters	• Study Guide and Intervention, pp. 17–18 • Skills Practice, p. 19 • Practice, p. 20 • Word Problem Practice, p. 21	• Study Guide and Intervention, pp. 17–18 • Skills Practice, p. 19 • Practice, p. 20 • Word Problem Practice, p. 21 • Enrichment, p. 22	• Practice, p. 20 • Word Problem Practice, p. 21 • Enrichment, p. 22	• Study Guide and Intervention, pp. 17–18 • Skills Practice, p. 19 • Practice, p. 20
Transparencies	• 5-Minute Check Transparency 2-3	• 5-Minute Check Transparency 2-3	• 5-Minute Check Transparency 2-3	• 5-Minute Check Transparency 2-3
Other	• Study Notebook • Teaching Algebra with Manipulatives	• Study Notebook • Teaching Algebra with Manipulatives	• Study Notebook	• Study Notebook • Teaching Algebra with Manipulatives

- What operations do you need to perform to isolate the variable in the equation? subtraction and division

Solve Multi-Step Equations

Example 1 shows how to undo operations to solve multi-step problems. **Example 2** shows how to write and solve a multi-step equation.

Formative Assessment

Use the Check Your Progress exercises after each Example to determine students' understanding of concepts.

Additional Examples

1 Solve each equation. Check your solution.

a. $2q + 11 = 3$ -4

b. $\frac{k+9}{12} = -2$ -33

2 **SHOPPING** Susan had a $10 coupon for the purchase of any item. She bought a coat that was on sale for $\frac{1}{2}$ its original price. After using the coupon, Susan paid $125 for the coat before taxes. What was the original price of the coat? Write an equation for the problem. Then solve the equation. $\frac{1}{2}p - 10 = 125$; $p = 270$, so the original price of the coat was $270.

Additional Examples also in Interactive Classroom PowerPoint® Presentations

IWB INTERACTIVE WHITEBOARD READY

Real-World EXAMPLE 2 Write and Solve a Multi-Step Equation

SHOPPING **Hiroshi is buying a pair of water skis that are on sale for $\frac{2}{3}$ of the original price. After he uses a $25 gift certificate, the total cost before taxes is $115. What was the original price of the skis? Write an equation for the problem. Then solve the equation.**

Words	Two thirds	of	the price	minus	25	is	115.
Variable	Let p = original price of the skis.						
Equation	$\frac{2}{3}$	$\cdot$	p	$-$	25	$=$	115

$\frac{2}{3}p - 25 = 115$ **Original equation**

$\frac{2}{3}p - 25 + 25 = 115 + 25$ **Add 25 to each side.**

$\frac{2}{3}p = 140$ **Simplify.**

$\frac{3}{2}\left(\frac{2}{3}p\right) = \frac{3}{2}(140)$ **Multiply each side by $\frac{3}{2}$.**

$p = 210$ **Simplify.**

The original price of the skis was $210.

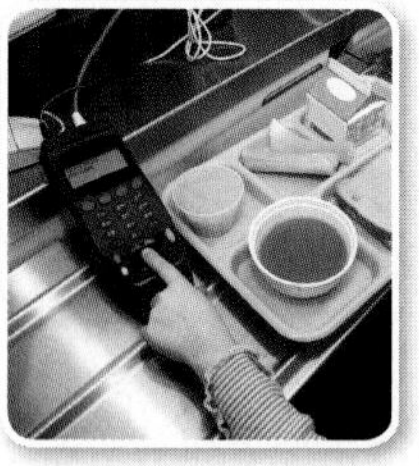

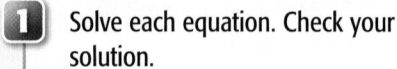

Real-World Link

Shoppers in Shanghai, China, can pay for purchased items at a terminal that can match the buyers' fingerprints with their bank accounts.

Source: *Shanghai Daily*

Check Your Progress

2A. RETAIL A music store has sold $\frac{3}{5}$ of their hip-hop CDs, but 10 were returned. Now the store has 62 hip-hop CDs. How many were there originally? 130

2B. READING Len read $\frac{3}{4}$ of a graphic novel over the weekend. Monday, he read 22 more pages. If he has read 220 pages, how many pages does the book have? 264

Personal Tutor glencoe.com

Solve Consecutive Integer Problems **Consecutive integers** are integers in counting order, such as 4, 5, and 6 or n, $n + 1$, and $n + 2$. Counting by two will result in *consecutive even integers* if the starting integer n is even and *consecutive odd integers* if the starting integer n is odd.

Concept Summary — Consecutive Integers

For Your FOLDABLE

Type	Words	Symbols	Example
Consecutive Integers	Integers that come in counting order.	$n, n + 1, n + 2, \ldots$	$\ldots, -2, -1, 0, 1, 2, \ldots$
Consecutive Even Integers	Even integer followed by the next even integer.	$n, n + 2, n + 4, \ldots$	$\ldots, -2, 0, 2, 4, \ldots$
Consective Odd Integers	Odd integer followed by the next even integer.	$n, n + 2, n + 4, \ldots$	$\ldots, -1, 1, -3, 5, \ldots$

Number theory is the study of numbers and the relationships between them.

TEACH with TECH

STUDENT RESPONSE SYSTEM Show students several different multi-step equations. Have a student state what operation should be done first, or next. Have students vote as to whether they agree or disagree. Save the results to track understanding.

Differentiated Instruction

AL

If in Example 1b, some students do not understand why both sides of the equation are multiplied by 8 before subtracting 7 from each side,

Then use an example, such as $\frac{23-7}{8}$. Have a volunteer tell the steps used to simplify this expression. Explain that Example 1b is solved using the reverse of the steps used to simplify $\frac{23-7}{8}$. Then have students discuss the steps they would use to solve $\frac{b-3}{-4} = 6$.

EXAMPLE 3 Solve a Consecutive Integer Problem

NUMBER THEORY **Write an equation for the following problem. Then solve the equation and answer the problem.**

Find three consecutive odd integers with a sum of −51.

Let n = the least odd integer.

Then $n + 2$ = the next greater odd integer, and $n + 4$ = the greatest of the three integers.

Words	The sum of three consecutive odd integers	is	−51.
Equation	$n + (n + 2) + (n + 4)$	=	−51

$n + (n + 2) + (n + 4) = -51$ **Original equation**

$3n + 6 = -51$ **Simplify.**

$-6 = -6$ **Subtract 6 from each side.**

$3n = -57$ **Simplify.**

$\frac{3n}{3} = \frac{-57}{3}$ **Divide each side by 3.**

$n = -19$ **Simplify.**

$n + 2 = -19 + 2$ or -17 $\quad n + 4 = -19 + 4$ or -15

The consecutive odd integers are −19, −17, and −15.

CHECK −19, −17, and −15 are consecutive odd integers.
$-19 + (-17) + (-15) = -51$ ✓

StudyTip

Representing Consecutive Integers You can use the same expressions to represent either consecutive even integers or consecutive odd integers. It is the value of n (odd or even) that differs between the two expressions.

Check Your Progress

3. Write an equation for the following problem. Then solve the equation and answer the problem. $n + (n + 1) + (n + 2) = 21$; 6, 7, 8

Find three consecutive integers with a sum of 21.

Personal Tutor glencoe.com

Check Your Understanding

Example 1 p. 91 — **Solve each equation. Check your solution.**

1. $3m + 4 = -11$ **−5**

2. $12 = -7f - 9$ **−3**

3. $-3 = 2 + \frac{a}{11}$ **−55**

4. $\frac{3}{2}a - 8 = 11$ $12\frac{2}{3}$

5. $8 = \frac{x - 5}{7}$ **61**

6. $\frac{c + 1}{-3} = -21$ **62**

Example 2 p. 92

7. NUMBER THEORY Twelve decreased by twice a number equals −34. Write an equation for this situation and then find the number. $12 - 2n = -34$; 23

8. BASEBALL Among the career home run leaders for Major League Baseball, Hank Aaron has 175 fewer than twice the number that Dave Winfield has. Hank Aaron hit 755 home runs. Write an equation for this situation. How many home runs did Dave Winfield hit in his career? $2h - 175 = 755$; 465 home runs

Example 3 p. 93 — **Write an equation and solve each problem.**

9. Find three consecutive odd integers with a sum of 75. $n + (n + 2) + (n + 4) = 75$; 23, 25, 27

10. Find three consecutive integers with a sum of −36. $n + (n + 1) + (n + 2) = -36$; −13, −12, −11

Focus on Mathematical Content

Multi-Step Equations Multi-step equations include two or more operations. To solve a multi-step equation, "undo" the operations in reverse of the order of operations.

Solve Consecutive Integer Problems

Example 3 introduces students to number theory by showing how to solve a consecutive integer problem.

Additional Example

3 **NUMBER THEORY** Write an equation for the following problem. Then solve the equation and answer the problem.
Find three consecutive odd integers with a sum of 57.
$n + (n + 2) + (n + 4) = 57$, or $3n + 6 = 57$. The consecutive integers are 17, 19, and 21.

Watch Out!

Preventing Errors Ask students to explain why an equation to find consecutive odd integers looks like an equation to find consecutive even integers. Students should note that both odds and evens are calculated by adding 2 to the previous odd or even.

Differentiated Instruction

AL OL BL ELL

Extension Hold a creativity competition for students. Each week, give students an equation and ask them to provide a context for the equation. Increase the difficulty level with each successive week and reward creativity for problems that accurately reflect the operations and variables in the equation. (Optional: Provide a prize for the winner each week.)

3 PRACTICE

Formative Assessment

Use Exercises 1–10 to check for understanding.

Use the chart at the bottom of this page to customize assignments for your students.

Additional Answer

51b.

Visits	Cost for Members	Cost for Nonmembers
3	290	90
6	305	180
9	320	270
12	335	360
15	350	450

51c.

Park Costs

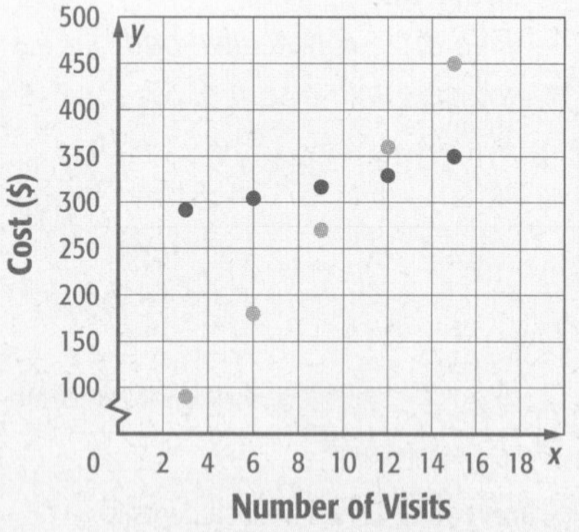

Both functions are linear. If a person is going to visit the park fewer than 11 times, it will be cheaper to be a nonmember.

Practice and Problem Solving

● = Step-by-Step Solutions begin on page R12.
Extra Practice begins on page 815.

Example 1 p. 91

Solve each equation. Check your solution.

11. $3t + 7 = -8$ **−5**
12. $8 = 16 + 8n$ **−1**
13. $-34 = 6m - 4$ **−5**
14. $9x + 27 = -72$ **−11**
15. $\frac{y}{5} - 6 = 8$ **70**
16. $\frac{f}{-7} - 8 = 2$ **−70**
17. $1 + \frac{r}{9} = 4$ **27**
18. $\frac{k}{3} + 4 = -16$ **−60**
19. $\frac{n-2}{7} = 2$ **16**
20. $14 = \frac{6+z}{-2}$ **−34**
21. $-11 = \frac{a-5}{6}$ **−61**
22. $\frac{22-w}{3} = -7$ **43**

Example 2 p. 92

23. **FINANCIAL LITERACY** The Cell+ Cellular Phone store offers the plans shown in the table. Raul chose the business plan and has budgeted $100 per month. Write an equation for this situation, and determine how many minutes per month he can use the phone and stay within budget.
$0.15m + 49.99 = 100$; $m \approx 333$; $650 + 333 = 983$ min

Plan	Flat Monthly Fee	Anytime Minutes	Cost per Minute After Anytime Minutes
personal	$29.99	250	$0.20
business	$49.99	650	$0.15
executive	$59.99	1200	$0.10

Example 3 p. 93

Write an equation and solve each problem.

24. Fourteen less than three fourths of a number is negative eight. Find the number.
25. Seventeen is thirteen subtracted from six times a number. What is the number?
26. Find three consecutive even integers with the sum of −84.
27. Find three consecutive odd integers with the sum of 141.
28. Find four consecutive integers with the sum of 54.
29. Find four consecutive integers with the sum of −142.

24. $\frac{3}{4}n - 14 = -8$; 8
25. $17 = 6x - 13$; 5
26. $n + (n + 2) + (n + 4) = -84$, −30, −28, −26
27. $n + (n + 2) + (n + 4) = 141$; 45, 47, 49
28. $n + (n + 1) + (n + 2) + (n + 3) = 54$; 12, 13, 14, 15
29. $n + (n + 1) + (n + 2) + (n + 3) = -142$; −37, −36, −35, −34

B **Solve each equation. Check your solution.**

30. $-6m - 8 = 24$ **$-5\frac{1}{3}$**
31. $45 = 7 - 5n$ **$-7\frac{3}{5}$**
32. $\frac{2b}{3} + 6 = 24$ **27**
33. $\frac{5x}{9} - 11 = -51$ **−72**
34. $65 = \frac{3}{4}c - 7$ **96**
35. $9 + \frac{2}{3}x = 81$ **108**
36. $-\frac{5}{2} = \frac{3}{4}z + \frac{1}{2}$ **−4**
37. $\frac{5}{6}k + \frac{2}{3} = \frac{4}{3}$ **$\frac{4}{5}$**
38. $-\frac{1}{5} - \frac{4}{9}a = \frac{2}{15}$ **$\frac{-3}{4}$**
39. $-\frac{3}{7} = \frac{3}{4} - \frac{b}{2}$ **$\frac{33}{14}$**

Write an equation and solve each problem.

40. **FAMILY** The ages of three brothers are consecutive integers with the sum of 96. How old are the brothers? **$n + n + 1 + n + 2 = 96$; 31, 32, and 33**

41. **VOLCANOES** Moving lava can build up and form beaches at the coast of an island. The growth of an island in a seaward direction may be modeled as $8y + 2$ centimeters, where y represents the number of years that the lava flows. An island has expanded 60 centimeters seaward. How long has the lava flowed? **$7\frac{1}{4}$ yr or 7 yr 3 mo**

Differentiated Homework Options

Level	Assignment	Two-Day Option	
AL Basic	11–29, 53–54, 57–78	11–29 odd, 58–61	12–28 even, 53, 54, 57, 62–78
OL Core	11–39 odd, 40–41, 43–51 odd, 52–54, 57–78	11–29, 58–61	30–54, 57, 62–78
BL Advanced	30–74, (optional: 75–78)		

C

Solve each equation. Check your solution.

42. $-5x - 4.8 = 6.7$ **−2.3**

43. $3.7q + 26.2 = 111.67$ **23.1**

44. $0.6a + 9 = 14.4$ **9**

45. $\frac{c}{2} - 4.3 = 11.5$ **31.6**

46. $9 = \frac{-6p - (-3)}{-8}$ **12.5**

47. $3.6 - 2.4m = 12$ **−3.5**

48. If $7m - 3 = 53$, what is the value of $11m + 2$? **90**

49. If $13y + 25 = 64$, what is the value of $4y - 7$? **5**

50. If $-5c + 6 = -69$, what is the value of $6c - 15$? **75**

Real-World Link

The top amusement parks in the world for attendance are:

1. Magic Kingdom – Orlando, FL
2. Disneyland – Anaheim, CA
3. Tokyo Disneyland – Urayasu, Chiba, Japan
4. Tokyo Disney Sea – Urayasu, Chiba, Japan
5. Disneyland Paris – Cedex, Marne La Valle, France

51. AMUSEMENT PARKS An amusement park offers a yearly membership of $275 that allows for free parking and admission to the park. Members can also use the water park for an additional $5 per day. Nonmembers pay $6 for parking, $15 for admission, and $9 for the water park.

a. Write and solve an equation to find the number of visits it would take for the total cost to be the same for a member and a nonmember if they both use the water park at each visit. **$5x + 275 = x(6 + 15 + 9)$; 11 visits**

b. Make a table for the costs of members and nonmembers after 3, 6, 9, 12, and 15 visits to the park. **See margin.**

c. Plot these points on a coordinate graph and describe things you notice from the graph. **See margin.**

52. SHOPPING At The Family Farm, you can pick your own fruits and vegetables.

The Family Farm	
Fruit	**Price ($)**
Apples	6.99/bag
Pumpkins	5.00 each
Blueberries	2.99/qt
Winter squash	2.99 each

a. The cost of a bag of potatoes is $1.50 less than $\frac{1}{2}$ of the price of apples. Write and solve an equation to find the cost of potatoes. **$p = \frac{1}{2}a - 1.50$; $2.00**

b. The price of each zucchini is 3 times the price of winter squash minus $7. Write and solve an equation to find the cost of zucchini. **$z = 3w - 7$; $1.97**

c. Write an equation to represent the cost of a pumpkin using the cost of the blueberries. **Sample answer: $p = 2b - 0.98$.**

H.O.T. Problems

Use Higher-Order Thinking Skills

53. OPEN ENDED Write a problem that can be modeled by the equation $2x + 40 = 60$. Then solve the equation and explain the solution in the context of the problem.

54. REASONING Describe the steps you can use to solve $\frac{w + 3}{5} - 4 = 6$.

55. CHALLENGE To find the measure of an interior angle of a regular polygon, you can use the formula $m = \frac{180(n - 2)}{n}$, where m represents the measure of each angle and n represents the number of sides in the polygon. If $m = 156$, how many sides does the polygon have? **15 sides**

56. CHALLENGE Determine whether the following statement is *sometimes*, *always*, or *never* true. Explain your reasoning. **Never; whenever three odd integers are added together, the sum is always odd.**

The sum of three consecutive odd integers equals an even integer.

57. WRITING IN MATH Write a paragraph explaining the order of the steps that you would take to solve a multi-step equation.

53. Sample answer: A pair of designer jeans costs $60. This is $40 more than twice the cost of a T-shirt. How much is the T-shirt? The T-shirt costs $10.

54. (1) Add 4 to each side. (2) Multiply each side by 5. (3) Subtract 3 from each side.

57. Sample answer: In order to solve the equation $4k + 20 = 236$, you would first subtract 20 from each side and then divide each side by 4.

Study Guide and Intervention

CRM pp. 17–18 AL OL ELL

NAME ______ DATE ______ PERIOD ______

2-3 Study Guide and Intervention

Solving Multi-Step Equations

Work Backward **Working backward** is one of many problem-solving strategies that you can use to solve problems. To work backward, start with the result given at the end of a problem and undo each step to arrive at the beginning number.

Example 1 **A number is divided by 2, and then 8 is subtracted from the quotient. The result is 16. What is the number?**

Solve the problem by working backward.

The final number is 16. Undo subtracting 8 by adding 8 to get 24. To undo dividing 24 by 2, multiply 24 by 2 to get 48.

The original number is 48.

Example 2 **A bacteria culture doubles each half hour. After 3 hours, there are 6400 bacteria. How many bacteria were there to begin with?**

Solve the problem by working backward.

The bacteria have grown for 3 hours. Since there are 2 one-half hour periods in one hour, in 3 hours there are 6 one-half hour periods. Since the bacteria culture has grown for 6 time periods, it has doubled 6 times. Undo the doubling by halving the number of bacteria 6 times.

$$6400 \times \frac{1}{2} \times \frac{1}{2} \times \frac{1}{2} \times \frac{1}{2} \times \frac{1}{2} \times \frac{1}{2} = 6400 \times \frac{1}{64} = 100$$

There were 100 bacteria to begin with.

Exercises

Solve each problem by working backward.

1. A number is divided by 3, and then 4 is added to the quotient. The result is 8. Find the number. **12**
2. A number is multiplied by 5, and then 3 is subtracted from the product. The result is 12. Find the number. **3**
3. Eight is subtracted from a number, and then the difference is multiplied by 2. The result is 24. Find the number. **20**
4. Three times a number plus 3 is 24. Find the number. **7**
5. **CAR RENTAL** Angela rented a car for $29.99 a day plus a one-time insurance cost of $5.00. Her bill was $124.96. For how many days did she rent the car? **4 days**
6. **MONEY** Mike withdrew an amount of money from his bank account. He spent one fourth for gasoline and had $90 left. How much money did he withdraw? **$120**

Lesson 2-3

Chapter 2 17 Glencoe Algebra 1

Practice

CRM p. 20 AL OL BL ELL

NAME ______ DATE ______ PERIOD ______

2-3 Practice

Solving Multi-Step Equations

Solve each problem by working backward.

1. Three is added to a number, and then the sum is multiplied by 4. The result is 16. Find the number. **1**
2. A number is divided by 4, and the quotient is added to 3. The result is 24. What is the number? **84**
3. Two is subtracted from a number, and then the difference is multiplied by 5. The result is 30. Find the number. **8**
4. **BIRD WATCHING** While Michelle sat observing birds at a bird feeder, one fourth of the birds flew away when they were startled by a noise. Two birds left the feeder to go to another stationed a few feet away. Three more birds flew into the branches of a nearby tree. Four birds remained at the feeder. How many birds were at the feeder initially? **12**

Solve each equation. Check your solution.

5. $-12n - 19 = 77$ **−8**
6. $17 + 3f = 14$ **−1**
7. $15t + 4 = 49$ **3**
8. $\frac{u}{5} + 6 = 2$ **−20**
9. $\frac{d}{-4} + 3 = 15$ **−48**
10. $\frac{b}{3} - 6 = -2$ **12**
11. $\frac{1}{2}y - \frac{1}{8} = \frac{7}{8}$ **2**
12. $-32 - \frac{3}{5}f = -17$ **−25**
13. $8 - \frac{3}{8}k = -4$ **32**
14. $\frac{r + 13}{12} = 1$ **−1**
15. $\frac{15 - a}{3} = -9$ **42**
16. $\frac{3k - 7}{5} = 16$ **29**
17. $\frac{x}{7} - 0.5 = 2.5$ **21**
18. $2.5g + 0.45 = 0.95$ **0.2**
19. $0.4m - 0.7 = 0.22$ **2.3**

Write an equation and solve each problem.

20. Seven less than four times a number equals 13. What is the number? **$4n - 7 = 13$; 5**
21. Find two consecutive odd integers whose sum is 116. **$n + (n + 2) = 116$; 57, 59**
22. Find two consecutive even integers whose sum is 126. **$n + (n + 2) = 126$; 62, 64**
23. Find three consecutive odd integers whose sum is 117. **$n + (n + 2) + (n + 4) = 117$; 37, 39, 41**
24. **COIN COLLECTING** Jung has a total of 92 coins in his coin collection. This is 8 more than three times the number of quarters in the collection. How many quarters does Jung have in his collection? **28**

Chapter 2 20 Glencoe Algebra 1

Word Problem Practice

CRM p. 21 AL OL BL ELL

NAME ______ DATE ______ PERIOD ______

2-3 Word Problem Practice

Solving Multi-Step Equations

1. **TEMPERATURE** The formula for converting a Fahrenheit temperature to a Celsius temperature is $C = \frac{F - 32°}{1.8}$. Find the equivalent Celsius temperature for 68°F.
   20°C

2. **HUMAN HEIGHT** It is a commonly used guideline that for the average American child, their maximum adult height will be about twice their height at age 2. Suppose that Micah's adult height fits the following equation $a = 2c - 1$, where a represents his adult height and c represents his height at age 2. At age 2 Micah was 35 inches tall. What is Micah's adult height? Write and solve an equation.
   $a = 2c - 1$; $c = 69$ inches

3. **CHEMISTRY** The half-life of a radioactive substance is the time required for half of a sample to undergo radioactive decay, or for the quantity to fall to half its original amount. Carbon 14 has a half-life of 5730 years. Suppose given samples of carbon 14 weigh $\frac{5}{8}$ of a pound and $\frac{7}{8}$ of a pound. What was the total weight of the samples 11,460 years ago?
   $w = \left(\frac{5}{8} + \frac{7}{8}\right) \times 2 \times 2$
   $w = 6$ pounds

4. **NUMBER THEORY** Write and solve an equation to find three consecutive odd integers whose sum is 3.
   $n + (n + 2) + (n + 4) = 3$
   $3n + 6 = 3$
   $3n = -3$
   $n = -1$
   $n + 2 = 1$
   $n + 4 = 3$

5. **GEOMETRY** A rectangular swimming pool is surrounded by a concrete sidewalk that is 3 feet wide. The dimensions of the rectangle created by the sidewalk are 21 feet by 31 feet.

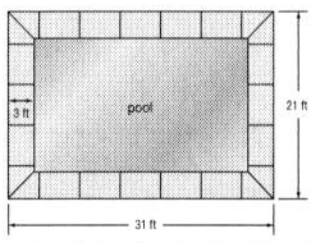

   a. Find the length and width of the pool.
   $\ell = 21 - 3 - 3$ $w = 31 - 3 - 3$
   $\ell = 15$ feet $w = 25$ feet

   b. Find the area of the pool.
   $A = \ell \cdot w$
   $A = 15 \cdot 25$
   $A = 375$ square feet

   c. Write and solve an equation to find the area of the sidewalk in square feet.
   $A = \ell \cdot w - 375$
   $A = (21 \cdot 31) - 375$
   $A = 651 - 375$
   $A = 276$ square feet

Lesson 2-3

Chapter 2 21 Glencoe Algebra 1

Enrichment

CRM p. 22 OL BL

NAME ______ DATE ______ PERIOD ______

2-3 Enrichment

Consecutive Integer Problems

Many types of problems and puzzles involve the idea of consecutive integers. Knowing how to represent these integers algebraically can help to solve the problem.

Example **Find four consecutive odd integers whose sum is −80.**

An odd integer can be written as $2n + 1$, where n is any integer.

If $2n + 1$ is the first odd integer, then add 2 to get the next largest odd integer, and so on.

Now write an equation to solve this problem.

$(2n + 1) + (2n + 3) + (2n + 5) + (2n + 7) = -80$

Exercises

Write an equation for each problem. Then solve.

1. Complete the solution to the problem in the example.
   −23, −21, −19, −17

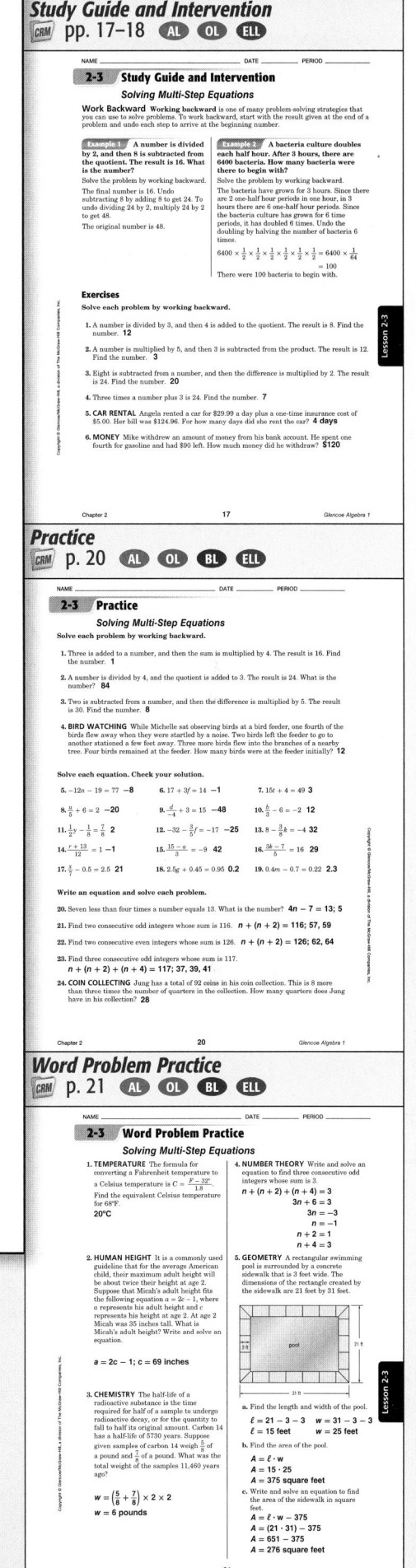

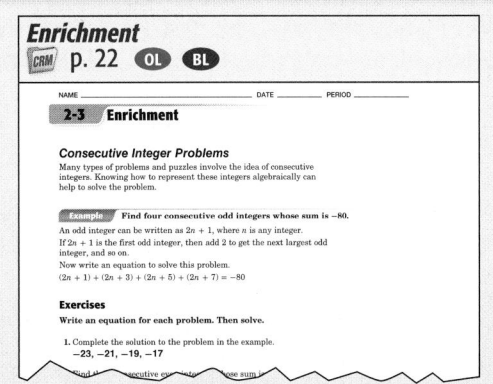

4 ASSESS

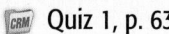

Yesterday's News Have students write how yesterday's lesson helped them with today's new material.

Formative Assessment

Check for student understanding of Lessons 2-1 through 2-3.

CRM Quiz 1, p. 63

Additional Answers

64. A number f minus 15 is 6.
65. Three times a number h is increased by 7 to equal 20.
66. A number k is squared and added to 18 to equal 54 decreased by m.
67. Three multiplied by a number p is the same as the difference of 8 times p and r.
68. Three fifths of t added to $\frac{1}{3}$ is t.
69. The product of $\frac{1}{2}$ and v is equal to the product of $\frac{2}{3}$ and v plus 4.

PSAE PRACTICE 6.11.09, 7.11.06, 7.11.01, 10.11.01

58. Which is the best estimate for the number of minutes on the calling card advertised below? **D**

A 10 min C 50 min
B 20 min D 200 min

59. GRIDDED RESPONSE The scale factor for two similar triangles is 2 : 3. The perimeter of the smaller triangle is 56 cm. What is the perimeter of the larger triangle in centimeters? **84**

60. Mr. Morrison is draining his cylindrical pool. The pool has a radius of 10 feet and a standard height of 4.5 feet. If the pool water is pumped out at a constant rate of 5 gallons per minute, about how long will it take to drain the pool? (1 ft^3 = 7.5 gal) **J**

F 37.8 min H 25.4 h
G 7 h J 35.3 h

61. STATISTICS Look at the golf scores for the five players in the table.

Player	1	2	3	4	5
Score	80	91	103	79	78

Which of these is the range of the golf scores? **B**

A 10 C 35
B 25 D 40

Spiral Review

62. GAS MILEAGE A midsize car with a 4-cylinder engine travels 34 miles on a gallon of gas. This is 10 miles more than a luxury car with an 8-cylinder engine travels on a gallon of gas. How many miles does a luxury car travel on a gallon of gas? (Lesson 2-2) **24 mi**

63. DEER In a recent year, 1286 female deer were born in Clark County. That is 93 fewer than the number of male deer born. How many male deer were born that year? (Lesson 2-2) **1379**

Translate each equation into a verbal sentence. (Lesson 2-1) **64–69. See margin.**

64. $f - 15 = 6$ **65.** $3h + 7 = 20$ **66.** $k^2 + 18 = 54 - m$

67. $3p = 8p - r$ **68.** $\frac{3}{5}t + \frac{1}{3} = t$ **69.** $\frac{1}{2}v = \frac{2}{3}v + 4$

70. GEOGRAPHY The Pacific Ocean covers about 46% of Earth. If P represents the surface area of the Pacific Ocean and E represents the surface area of Earth, write an equation for this situation. (Lesson 2-1) $P = 0.46E$

Find the value of n in each equation. Then name the property that is used. (Lesson 1-3)

71. $1.5 + n = 1.5$ **0; Additive Identity** **72.** $8n = 1$ **$\frac{1}{8}$; Multiplicative Inverse**

73. $4 - n = 0$ **4; Additive Inverse** **74.** $1 = 2n$ **$\frac{1}{2}$; Multiplicative Inverse**

Skills Review

Evaluate each expression. (Lesson 1-2)

75. $5 + 3(4^2)$ **53** **76.** $\frac{38 - 12}{2 \cdot 13}$ **1** **77.** $[5(1 + 1)]^3$ **1000** **78.** $[8(2) - 4^2] + 7(4)$ **28**

Differentiated Instruction OL BL

Extension Write $\frac{x}{10} + 3.2 = 4.7$ on the board. Ask students what would happen if each side of the equation were multiplied by 10. The result is an equivalent equation.

Ask a volunteer to explain why this might be a helpful first step in solving this type of equation. Multiplying by 10 changes all of the numbers in the equation to integers, and it might be easier to work with integers than with decimals and fractions.

Ask students to solve the equation both ways and confirm which way was easier. 15

2-4 Solving Equations with the Variable on Each Side

Then
You solved multi-step equations. (Lesson 2-3)

Now
- Solve equations with the variable on each side.
- Solve equations involving grouping symbols.

IL Learning Standards

8.B.4a Represent algebraic concepts with physical materials, words, diagrams, tables, graphs, equations and inequalities and use appropriate technology.
8.D.4 Formulate and solve linear and quadratic **equations** and linear inequalities algebraically and investigate nonlinear inequalities using graphs, tables, calculators and computers.

New Vocabulary
identity

IL Math Online

glencoe.com
- Extra Examples
- Personal Tutor
- Self-Check Quiz
- Homework Help
- Math in Motion

Why?

The equation $y = 1.3x + 19$ represents the number of times Americans eat in their cars each year, where x is the number of years since 1985, and y is the number of times that they eat in their car. The equation $y = -1.3x + 93$ represents the number of times Americans eat in restaurants each year, where x is the number of years since 1985, and y is the number of times that they eat in a restaurant.

The equation $1.3x + 19 = -1.3x + 93$ represents the year when the number of times Americans eat in their cars will equal the number of times Americans eat in restaurants.

Variables on Each Side To solve an equation that has variables on each side, use the Addition or Subtraction Property of Equality to write an equivalent equation with the variable terms on one side.

EXAMPLE 1 Solve an Equation with Variables on Each Side

Solve $2 + 5k = 3k - 6$. Check your solution.

$2 + 5k = 3k - 6$	Original equation
$-3k = -3k$	Subtract $3k$ from each side.
$2 + 2k = -6$	Simplify.
$-2 = -2$	Subtract 2 from each side.
$2k = -8$	Simplify.
$\frac{2k}{2} = \frac{-8}{2}$	Divide each side by 2.
$k = -4$	Simplify.
CHECK $2 + 5k = 3k - 6$	Original equation
$2 + 5(-4) \stackrel{?}{=} 3(-4) - 6$	Substitution, $k = -4$
$2 + -20 \stackrel{?}{=} -12 - 6$	Multiply.
$-18 = -18$ ✓	Simplify.

Check Your Progress

Solve each equation. Check your solution.

1A. $3w + 2 = 7w$ $\frac{1}{2}$

1B. $5a + 2 = 6 - 7a$ $\frac{1}{3}$

1C. $\frac{x}{2} + 1 = \frac{1}{4}x - 6$ -28

1D. $1.3c = 3.3c + 2.8$ -1.4

Personal Tutor glencoe.com

2-4 Lesson Notes

1 FOCUS

Vertical Alignment

Before Lesson 2-4
Solve multi-step equations.

Lesson 2-4
Solve equations with the variable on each side.
Solve equations involving grouping symbols.

After Lesson 2-4
Solve problems involving proportional change.

2 TEACH

Scaffolding Questions

Have students read the *Why?* section of the lesson.

Ask:
- What does x represent in each equation? the number of years since 1985
- What is the value of x in the year 1985? 0
- If $x = 28$, what year would that be? 2013

Lesson 2-4 Resources

Resource	Approaching-Level	On-Level	Beyond-Level	English Learners
Teacher Edition	• Differentiated Instruction, p. 98		• Differentiated Instruction, p. 102	
Chapter Resource Masters	• Study Guide and Intervention, pp. 23–24 • Skills Practice, p. 25 • Practice, p. 26 • Word Problem Practice, p. 27	• Study Guide and Intervention, pp. 23–24 • Skills Practice, p. 25 • Practice, p. 26 • Word Problem Practice, p. 27 • Enrichment, p. 28	• Practice, p. 26 • Word Problem Practice, p. 27 • Enrichment, p. 28	• Study Guide and Intervention, pp. 23–24 • Skills Practice, p. 25 • Practice, p. 26
Transparencies	• 5-Minute Check Transparency 2-4	• 5-Minute Check Transparency 2-4	• 5-Minute Check Transparency 2-4	• 5-Minute Check Transparency 2-4
Other	• Study Notebook • Teaching Algebra with Manipulatives	• Study Notebook • Teaching Algebra with Manipulatives	• Study Notebook	• Study Notebook • Teaching Algebra with Manipulatives

Lesson 2-4 Solving Equations with the Variable on Each Side 97

Variables on Each Side

Example 1 shows how to solve an equation with variables on each side.

Formative Assessment

Use the Check Your Progress exercises after each Example to determine students' understanding of concepts.

Additional Example

1 Solve $8 + 5c = 7c - 2$. Check your solution. 5

Additional Examples also in Interactive Classroom PowerPoint® Presentations

IWB INTERACTIVE WHITEBOARD READY

Grouping Symbols

Example 2 shows how to use the Distributive Property to solve an equation containing grouping symbols. **Example 3** shows how to determine when an equation with the variable on each side has no solution and when it is an identity. **Example 4** shows how to write an equation to represent a situation.

Additional Examples

2 Solve $\frac{1}{3}(18 + 12q) = 6(2q - 7)$. Check your solution. 6

3 Solve each equation.

a. $8(5c - 2) = 10(32 + 4c)$ no solution

b. $4(t + 20) = \frac{1}{5}(20t + 400)$ all numbers

TEACH with TECH

VIDEO RECORDING Create a video showing how to solve equations with variables on each side. Post the video on a video sharing Web site so that your students have an additional reference outside of class.

Grouping Symbols If equations contain grouping symbols such as parentheses or brackets, use the Distributive Property first to remove the grouping symbols.

StudyTip

Solving an Equation You may want to eliminate the terms with a variable from one side before eliminating a constant.

EXAMPLE 2 Solve an Equation with Grouping Symbols

Solve $6(5m - 3) = \frac{1}{3}(24m + 12)$.

$6(5m - 3) = \frac{1}{3}(24m + 12)$	Original equation
$30m - 18 = 8m + 4$	Distributive Property
$30m - 18 - 8m = 8m + 4 - 8m$	Subtract $8m$ from each side.
$22m - 18 = 4$	Simplify.
$22m - 18 + 18 = 4 + 18$	Add 18 to each side.
$22m = 22$	Simplify.
$\frac{22m}{22} = \frac{22}{22}$	Divide each side by 22.
$m = 1$	Simplify.

Check Your Progress

Solve each equation. Check your solution.

2A. $8s - 10 = 3(6 - 2s)$ 2

2B. $7(n - 1) = -2(3 + n)$ $\frac{1}{9}$

Personal Tutor glencoe.com

Some equations may have no solution. That is, there is no value of the variable that will result in a true equation. Some equations are true for all values of the variables. These are called **identities**.

ReadingMath

No Solution The symbol that represents no solution is Ø.

EXAMPLE 3 Find Special Solutions

Solve each equation.

a. $5x + 5 = 3(5x - 4) - 10x$

$5x + 5 = 3(5x - 4) - 10x$	Original equation
$5x + 5 = 15x - 12 - 10x$	Distributive Property
$5x + 5 = 5x - 12$	Simplify.
$-5x \quad = -5x$	Subtract $5x$ from each side.
$5 \neq -12$	

Since $5 \neq -12$, this equation has no solution.

b. $3(2b - 1) - 7 = 6b - 10$

$3(2b - 1) - 7 = 6b - 10$	Original equation
$6b - 3 - 7 = 6b - 10$	Distributive Property
$6b - 10 = 6b - 10$	Simplify.
$0 = 0$	Subtract $6b - 10$ from each side.

Since the expressions on each side of the equation are the same, this equation is an identity. It is true for all values of b.

Check Your Progress

3A. $7x + 5(x - 1) = -5 + 12x$ all numbers

3B. $6(y - 5) = 2(10 + 3y)$ no solution

Personal Tutor glencoe.com

Differentiated Instruction AL

If some students are having trouble solving equations with a variable on each side,

Then those students may benefit from using an equation mat and algebra tiles. Have students model the equation, and then get them started by asking what they must do to remove the x-tiles from one side of the equation mat. Use questions to focus their attention on isolating the variable. Have them write out the steps they used after they solve for x.

The steps for solving an equation can be summarized as follows.

Concept Summary — **Steps for Solving Equations** — For Your FOLDABLE

Step 1 Simplify the expressions on each side. Use the Distributive Property as needed.

Step 2 Use the Addition and/or Subtraction Properties of Equality to get the variables on one side and the numbers without variables on the other side. Simplify.

Step 3 Use the Multiplication or Division Property of Equality to solve.

Math *in Motion*, BrainPOP® glencoe.com

There are many situations in which variables are on both sides of the equation.

PSAE EXAMPLE 4 7.11.03

Find the value of x so that the figures have the same area.

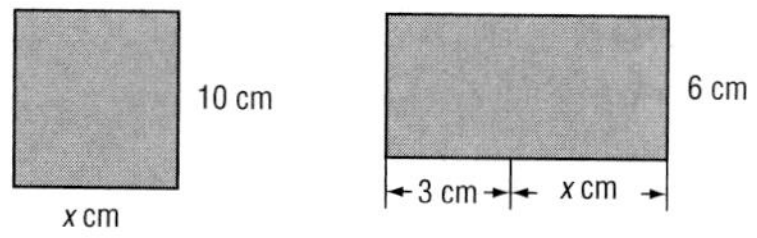

A 3 C 6.5

B 4.5 D 7

Read the Test Item

The area of the first rectangle is $10x$, and the area of the second is $6(3 + x)$. The equation $10x = 6(3 + x)$ represents this situation.

Solve the Test Item

A $10x = 6(3 + x)$

$10(3) \stackrel{?}{=} 6(3 + 3)$

$30 \stackrel{?}{=} 6(6)$

$30 \neq 36$ ✗

B $10x = 6(3 + x)$

$10(4.5) \stackrel{?}{=} 6(3 + 4.5)$

$45 \stackrel{?}{=} 6(7.5)$

$45 = 45$ ✓

Since the value 4.5 results in a true statement, you do not need to check 6.5 and 7. The answer is B.

Check Your Progress

4. Find the value of x so that the figures have the same perimeter. G

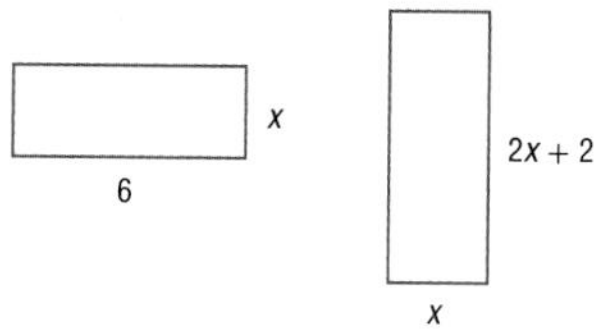

F 1.5 G 2 H 3.2 J 4

Personal Tutor glencoe.com

Test-Taking Tip

Choose a Method There is often more than one way to solve a problem. In this example, you can write an algebraic equation and solve for x. Or you can substitute each answer choice into the formulas to find the correct answer.

Tips for New Teachers

Eliminating the Variable Emphasize that there are only two possible outcomes under which the variable can be eliminated from an equation: either the equation has no solution (false statement) or the equation is an identity (true statement).

Focus on Mathematical Content

Grouping Symbols The Distributive Property may be used to simplify expressions with grouping symbols. When the expressions on each side of an equation are identical, the equation is true for every value of the variable. When the expressions simplify to a false statement, there are no solutions.

Additional Example

4 **STANDARDIZED TEST PRACTICE** Find the value of h so that the figures have the same area. D

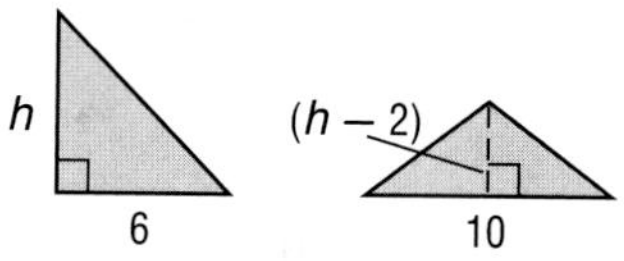

A 1 **C** 4

B 3 **D** 5

Watch Out!

Preventing Errors Caution students to be careful when checking possible answers on multiple-choice test items. Often, some of the incorrect possible answers are similar to the correct answer. A substitution or arithmetic error when checking possible answers could lead them to inadvertently choose the incorrect answer.

3 PRACTICE

Formative Assessment

Use Exercises 1–9 to check for understanding.

Use the chart at the bottom of this page to customize assignments for your students.

Additional Answers

41a. Sample answer: $y = 2x + 4$

x	−2	−1	0	1	2
y	0	2	4	6	8

$y = -x - 2$

x	−2	−1	0	1	2
y	0	−1	−2	−3	−4

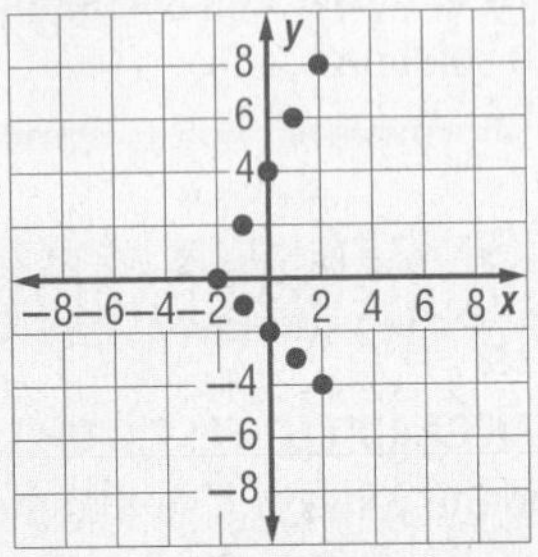

42. $t = 2 - 2[2t - 3(1 - t)]$ Original equation
$t = 2 - 2[2t - 3 + 3t]$ Distributive Property
$t = 2 - 4t + 6 - 6t$ Distributive Property
$t = 8 - 10t$ Substitution
$11t = 8$ Add $10t$ to each side.
$t = \frac{8}{11}$ Divide each side by 11.

45a. Incorrect; the 2 must be distributed over both g and 5; 6.

45b. correct

45c. Incorrect; to eliminate $-6z$ on the left side of the equals sign, $6z$ must be added to each side of the equation; 1.

Check Your Understanding

Examples 1–3 pp. 97–98

Solve each equation. Check your solution.

1. $13x + 2 = 4x + 38$ **4**
2. $\frac{2}{3} + \frac{1}{6}q = \frac{5}{6}q + \frac{1}{3}$ **$\frac{1}{2}$**
3. $6(n + 4) = -18$ **−7**
4. $7 = -11 + 3(b + 5)$ **1**
5. $5 + 2(n + 1) = 2n$ **no solution**
6. $7 - 3r = r - 4(2 + r)$ **no solution**
7. $14v + 6 = 2(5 + 7v) - 4$ **all numbers**
8. $5h - 7 = 5(h - 2) + 3$ **all numbers**

Example 4 p. 99

9. **MULTIPLE CHOICE** Find the value of x so that the figures have the same perimeter. **A**

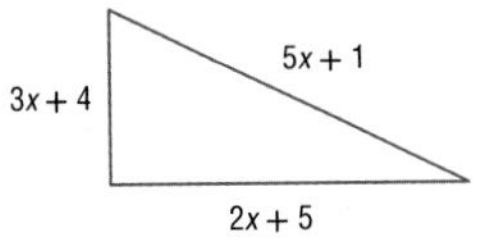

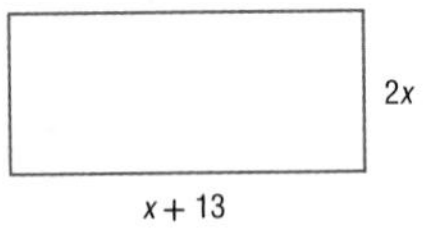

A 4　　B 5　　C 6　　D 7

Practice and Problem Solving

= Step-by-Step Solutions begin on page R12.
Extra Practice begins on page 815.

Examples 1–3 pp. 97–98

Solve each equation. Check your solution.

10. $7c + 12 = -4c + 78$ **6**
11. $2m - 13 = -8m + 27$ **4**
12. $9x - 4 = 2x + 3$ **1**
13. $6 + 3t = 8t - 14$ **4**
14. $\frac{b - 4}{6} = \frac{b}{2}$ **−2**
15. $\frac{5v - 4}{10} = \frac{4}{5}$ **$2\frac{2}{5}$**
16. $8 = 4(r + 4)$ **−2**
17. $6(n + 5) = 66$ **6**
18. $5(g + 8) - 7 = 103$ **14**
19. $12 - \frac{4}{5}(x + 15) = 4$ **−5**
20. $3(3m - 2) = 2(3m + 3)$ **4**
21. $6(3a + 1) - 30 = 3(2a - 4)$ **1**

Example 4 p. 99

22. **GEOMETRY** Find the value of x so the rectangles have the same area. **8**

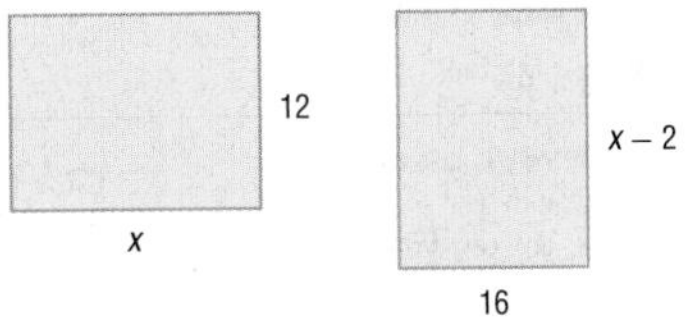

23. **NUMBER THEORY** Four times the lesser of two consecutive even integers is 12 less than twice the greater number. Find the integers. **−4, −2**
24. **NUMBER THEORY** Two times the least of three consecutive odd integers exceeds three times the greatest by 15. What are the integers? **−27, −25, −23**

B Solve each equation. Check your solution.

25. $2x = 2(x - 3)$ **no solution**
26. $\frac{2}{5}h - 7 = \frac{12}{5}h - 2h + 3$ **no solution**
27. $-5(3 - q) + 4 = 5q - 11$ **all numbers**
28. $2(4r + 6) = \frac{2}{3}(12r + 18)$ **all numbers**
29. $\frac{3}{5}f + 24 = 4 - \frac{1}{5}f$ **−25**
30. $\frac{1}{12} + \frac{3}{8}y = \frac{5}{12} + \frac{5}{8}y$ **$-\frac{4}{3}$**
31. $\frac{2m}{5} = \frac{1}{3}(2m - 12)$ **15**
32. $\frac{1}{8}(3d - 2) = \frac{1}{4}(d + 5)$ **12**
33. $6.78j - 5.2 = 4.33j + 2.15$ **3**
34. $14.2t - 25.2 = 3.8t + 26.8$ **5**
35. $3.2k - 4.3 = 12.6k + 14.5$ **−2**
36. $5[2p - 4(p + 5)] = 25$ **−12.5**

Differentiated Homework Options

Level	Assignment	Two-Day Option	
AL Basic	10–24, 42, 44–45, 47–74	11–23 odd, 48–51	10–24 even, 42, 44–45, 47, 52–74
OL Core	11–37 odd, 38–42, 44–45, 47–74	10–24, 48–51	25–42, 44–45, 47–74
BL Advanced	25–65, (optional: 66–74)		

Real-World Link

About 25% of American adults have Internet access and give time or money to charity. Of those, 56% have never visited the Web site of a charity, and only 7% say they have given online.

Source: Craver, Mathews, Smith & Co.

37. **NUMBER THEORY** Three times the lesser of two consecutive even integers is 6 less than six times the greater number. Find the integers. **−2, 0**

38. **MONEY** Chris has saved twice the number of quarters that Nora saved plus 6. The number of quarters Chris saved is also five times the difference of the number of quarters and 3 that Nora has saved. Write and solve an equation to find the number of quarters they each have saved.

39. **DVD** A company that replicates DVDs spends $1500 per day in building overhead plus $0.80 per DVD in supplies and labor. If the DVDs sell for $1.59 per disk, how many DVDs must the company sell each day before it makes a profit? **1899 DVDs/day**

40. **INTERNET ACCESS** The table shows the percent of households that have broadband Internet access and the average growth rates for two age groups. How long will it take for the percents to be the same? **2.7 years**

Age Group	Percent with Broadband in Their Homes in 2006	Growth Rate Percentage per Year
18–49	52.5	42
50+	25.5	52

Source: Pew Internet & American Life Project

41. **MULTIPLE REPRESENTATIONS** In this problem, you will explore $2x + 4 = -x - 2$.
    a. **GRAPHICAL** Make a table of values with five points for $y = 2x + 4$ and $y = -x - 2$. Graph the points from the tables. **See margin.**
    b. **ALGEBRAIC** Solve $2x + 4 = -x - 2$. **−2**
    c. **VERBAL** Explain how the solution you found in part **b** is related to the intersection point of the graphs in part **a**. **Sample answer: The solution in part b is the *x*-coordinate for the point of intersection on the graph.**

H.O.T. Problems

Use Higher-Order Thinking Skills

42. **REASONING** Solve the equation below. Describe each step.
$$t = 2 - 2[2t - 3(1 - t)]$$ **See margin.**

43. **CHALLENGE** Write an equation with the variable on each side of the equals sign, at least one fractional coefficient, and a solution of −6. Discuss the steps you used.

44. **OPEN ENDED** Create an equation with at least two grouping symbols for which there is no solution. **Sample answer: $2(3x + 6) = 3(2x + 5)$**

45. **REASONING** Determine whether each solution is correct. If the solution is not correct, describe the error and give the correct solution. **a–c. See margin.**

a.	b.	c.
$2(g + 5) = 22$	$5d = 2d - 18$	$-6z + 13 = 7z$
$2g + 5 = 22$	$5d - 2d = 2d - 18 - 2d$	$-6z + 13 - 6z = 7z - 6z$
$2g + 5 - 5 = 22$	$3d = -18$	$13 = z$
$2g = 17$	$d = -6$	
$2g = 8.5$		

46. **CHALLENGE** Find the value of k for which each equation is an identity.
    a. $k(3x - 2) = 4 - 6x$ **−2**
    b. $15y - 10 + k = 2(ky - 1) - y$ **8**

47. **WRITING IN MATH** Compare and contrast solving equations with variables on both sides of the equation to solving one-step or multi-step equations with a variable on one side of the equation.

38. $2q + 6 = 5(q - 3)$; Nora saved 7 quarters, and Chris saved 20 quarters.

43. Sample answer: $2x + 1 = \frac{3}{2}x - 2$; First I chose $\frac{3}{2}$ as the fractional coefficient. Then I chose 2 for the coefficient for the variable on the other side of the equation. After substituting −6 in for x on both sides, 1 must be added to the left and 2 must be subtracted from the right to balance the equation.

47. Sample answer: If the equation has variables on both sides of the equation, you must add or subtract so that the variable only appears on one side of the equation. Then, solving the equations uses the same steps.

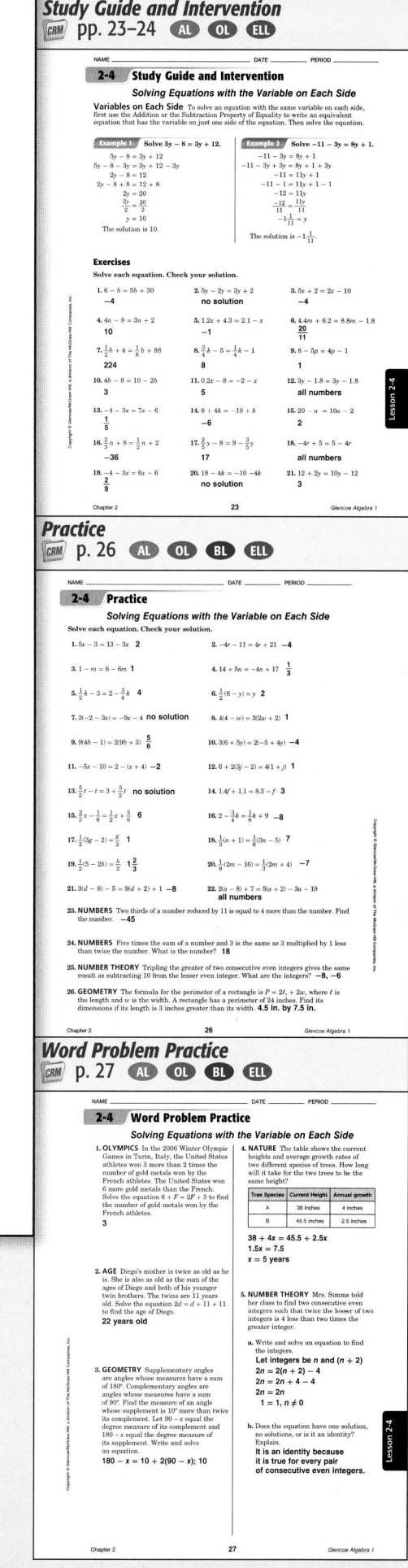

Multiple Representations In Exercise 41, students use a table of values and a graph in the coordinate plane to illustrate the solution of two simultaneous equations.

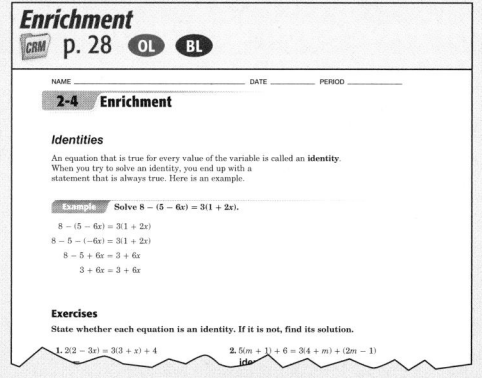

Study Guide and Intervention
CRM pp. 23–24 AL OL ELL

NAME ______ DATE ______ PERIOD ______

2-4 Study Guide and Intervention

Solving Equations with the Variable on Each Side

Variables on Each Side To solve an equation with the same variable on each side, first use the Addition or the Subtraction Property of Equality to write an equivalent equation that has the variable on just one side of the equation. Then solve the equation.

Example 1 Solve $5y - 8 = 3y + 12$.

$5y - 8 = 3y + 12$
$5y - 8 - 3y = 3y + 12 - 3y$
$2y - 8 = 12$
$2y - 8 + 8 = 12 + 8$
$2y = 20$
$\frac{2y}{2} = \frac{20}{2}$
$y = 10$

The solution is 10.

Example 2 Solve $-11 - 3y = 8y + 1$.

$-11 - 3y = 8y + 1$
$-11 - 3y + 3y = 8y + 1 + 3y$
$-11 = 11y + 1$
$-11 - 1 = 11y + 1 - 1$
$-12 = 11y$
$\frac{-12}{11} = \frac{11y}{11}$
$-1\frac{1}{11} = y$

The solution is $-1\frac{1}{11}$.

Exercises

Solve each equation. Check your solution.

1. $6 - b = 5b + 30$ **−4**
2. $5y - 2y = 3y + 2$ **no solution**
3. $5x + 2 = 2x - 10$ **−4**
4. $4n - 8 = 3n + 2$ **10**
5. $1.2x + 4.3 = 2.1 - x$ **−1**
6. $4.4m + 6.2 = 8.8m - 1.8$ **$\frac{20}{11}$**
7. $\frac{1}{2}b + 4 = \frac{1}{8}b + 88$ **224**
8. $\frac{3}{4}k - 5 = \frac{1}{4}k - 1$ **8**
9. $8 - 5p = 4p - 1$ **1**
10. $4b - 8 = 10 - 2b$ **3**
11. $0.2x - 8 = -2 - x$ **5**
12. $3y - 1.8 = 3y - 1.8$ **all numbers**
13. $-4 - 3x = 7x - 6$ **$\frac{1}{5}$**
14. $8 + 4k = -10 + k$ **−6**
15. $20 - a = 10a - 2$ **2**
16. $\frac{2}{3}n + 8 = \frac{1}{2}n + 2$ **−36**
17. $\frac{2}{5}y - 8 = 9 - \frac{3}{5}y$ **17**
18. $-4r + 5 = 5 - 4r$ **all numbers**
19. $-4 - 3x = 6x - 6$ **$\frac{2}{9}$**
20. $18 - 4k = -10 - 4k$ **no solution**
21. $12 + 2y = 10y - 12$ **3**

Lesson 2-4

Practice
CRM p. 26 AL OL BL ELL

NAME ______ DATE ______ PERIOD ______

2-4 Practice

Solving Equations with the Variable on Each Side

Solve each equation. Check your solution.

1. $5x - 3 = 13 - 3x$ **2**
2. $-4r - 11 = 4r + 21$ **−4**
3. $1 - m = 6 - 6m$ **1**
4. $14 + 5n = -4n + 17$ **$\frac{1}{3}$**
5. $\frac{1}{2}k - 3 = 2 - \frac{3}{4}k$ **4**
6. $\frac{1}{2}(6 - y) = y$ **2**
7. $3(-2 - 3x) = -9x - 4$ **no solution**
8. $4(4 - w) = 3(2w + 2)$ **1**
9. $9(4b - 1) = 2(9b + 3)$ **$\frac{5}{6}$**
10. $3(6 + 5y) = 2(-5 + 4y)$ **−4**
11. $-5x - 10 = 2 - (x + 4)$ **−2**
12. $6 + 2(3j - 2) = 4(1 + j)$ **1**
13. $\frac{5}{2}t - t = 3 + \frac{3}{2}t$ **no solution**
14. $1.4f + 1.1 = 8.3 - f$ **3**
15. $\frac{2}{3}x - \frac{1}{6} = \frac{1}{2}x + \frac{5}{6}$ **6**
16. $2 - \frac{3}{4}k = \frac{1}{8}k + 9$ **−8**
17. $\frac{1}{2}(3g - 2) = \frac{g}{2}$ **1**
18. $\frac{1}{3}(n + 1) = \frac{1}{6}(3n - 5)$ **7**
19. $\frac{1}{2}(5 - 2h) = \frac{h}{2}$ **$1\frac{2}{3}$**
20. $\frac{1}{9}(2m - 16) = \frac{1}{3}(2m + 4)$ **−7**
21. $3(d - 8) - 5 = 9(d + 2) + 1$ **−8**
22. $2(a - 8) + 7 = 5(a + 2) - 3a - 19$ **all numbers**
23. **NUMBERS** Two thirds of a number reduced by 11 is equal to 4 more than the number. Find the number. **−45**
24. **NUMBERS** Five times the sum of a number and 3 is the same as 3 multiplied by 1 less than twice the number. What is the number? **18**
25. **NUMBER THEORY** Tripling the greater of two consecutive even integers gives the same result as subtracting 10 from the lesser even integer. What are the integers? **−8, −6**
26. **GEOMETRY** The formula for the perimeter of a rectangle is $P = 2\ell, + 2w$, where ℓ is the length and w is the width. A rectangle has a perimeter of 24 inches. Find its dimensions if its length is 3 inches greater than its width. **4.5 in. by 7.5 in.**

Word Problem Practice
CRM p. 27 AL OL BL ELL

NAME ______ DATE ______ PERIOD ______

2-4 Word Problem Practice

Solving Equations with the Variable on Each Side

1. **OLYMPICS** In the 2006 Winter Olympic Games in Turin, Italy, the United States athletes won 3 more than 2 times the number of gold metals won by the French athletes. The United States won 6 more gold metals than the French. Solve the equation $6 + F = 2F + 3$ to find the number of gold metals won by the French athletes.
3

2. **AGE** Diego's mother is twice as old as he is. She is also as old as the sum of the ages of Diego and both of his younger twin brothers. The twins are 11 years old. Solve the equation $2d = d + 11 + 11$ to find the age of Diego.
22 years old

3. **GEOMETRY** Supplementary angles are angles whose measures have a sum of 180°. Complementary angles are angles whose measures have a sum of 90°. Find the measure of an angle whose supplement is 10° more than twice its complement. Let $90 - x$ equal the degree measure of its complement and $180 - x$ equal the degree measure of its supplement. Write and solve an equation.
180 − x = 10 + 2(90 − x); 10

4. **NATURE** The table shows the current heights and average growth rates of two different species of trees. How long will it take for the two trees to be the same height?

Tree Species	Current Height	Annual growth
A	38 inches	4 inches
B	45.5 inches	2.5 inches

38 + 4x = 45.5 + 2.5x
1.5x = 7.5
x = 5 years

5. **NUMBER THEORY** Mrs. Simms told her class to find two consecutive even integers such that twice the lesser of two integers is 4 less than two times the greater integer.
    a. Write and solve an equation to find the integers.
    Let integers be *n* and (*n* + 2)
    2n = 2(n + 2) − 4
    2n = 2n + 4 − 4
    2n = 2n
    1 = 1, n ≠ 0
    b. Does the equation have one solution, no solutions, or is it an identity? Explain.
    It is an identity because it is true for every pair of consecutive even integers.

Lesson 2-4

Enrichment
CRM p. 28 OL BL

NAME ______ DATE ______ PERIOD ______

2-4 Enrichment

Identities

An equation that is true for every value of the variable is called an **identity**. When you try to solve an identity, you end up with a statement that is always true. Here is an example.

Example Solve $8 - (5 - 6x) = 3(1 + 2x)$.

$8 - (5 - 6x) = 3(1 + 2x)$
$8 - 5 - (-6x) = 3(1 + 2x)$
$8 - 5 + 6x = 3 + 6x$
$3 + 6x = 3 + 6x$

Exercises

State whether each equation is an identity. If it is not, find its solution.

1. $2(2 - 3x) = 3(3 + x) + 4$
2. $5(m + 1) + 6 = 3(4 + m) + (2m - 1)$ ide

4 ASSESS

Name the Math On index cards, have students solve $3(x + 2) = 5(x - 8)$. Beside each step, have students write one or two sentences explaining and justifying their methods.

Additional Answers

60. 1; Multiplicative Identity

61. 2; Multiplicative Identity

62. 6; Reflexive Property

63. $\frac{2}{3}$; Additive Identity

64. 1; Multiplicative Inverse

65. 7; Transitive Property

PSAE PRACTICE 8.11.02, 7.11.03, 6.11.18, 6.11.13

48. A hang glider 25 meters above the ground starts to descend at a constant rate of 2 meters per second. Which equation shows the height h after t seconds of descent? **D**

A $h = 25t + 2t$

B $h = -25t + 2$

C $h = 2t + 25$

D $h = -2t + 25$

49. GEOMETRY Two rectangular walls each with a length of 12 feet and a width of 23 feet need to be painted. It costs $0.08 per square foot for paint. How much will it cost to paint the walls? **J**

F $22.08 H $34.50

G $23.04 J $44.16

50. SHORT RESPONSE Maddie works at Game Exchange. They are having a sale as shown.

Item	Price	Special
video games	$20	Buy 2 get 1 Free
DVDs	$15	Buy 1 get 1 Free

She purchases four video games and uses her employee discount of 15%. If sales tax is 7.25%, how much does she spend on the games? **$54.70**

51. Solve $\frac{4}{5}x + 7 = \frac{3}{15}x - 3$. **A**

A $-16\frac{2}{3}$ C $-6\frac{2}{3}$

B $-14\frac{4}{9}$ D -10

Spiral Review

Solve each equation. Check your solution. (Lesson 2-3)

52. $5n + 6 = -4$ **−2**

53. $-1 = 7 + 3c$ **$-2\frac{2}{3}$**

54. $\frac{1}{2}z + 7 = 16 - \frac{3}{5}z$ **$8\frac{2}{11}$**

55. $\frac{2}{5}x + 6 = \frac{2}{3}x + 10$ **−15**

56. $\frac{a}{7} - 3 = -2$ **7**

57. $9 + \frac{y}{5} = 6$ **−15**

58. WORLD RECORDS In 1998, Winchell's House of Donuts in Pasadena, California, made the world's largest donut. It weighed 5000 pounds and had a circumference of 298.3 feet. What was the donut's diameter to the nearest tenth? (*Hint:* $C = \pi d$) (Lesson 2-2) **95.0 ft**

59. ZOO At a zoo, the cost of admission is posted on the sign. Find the cost of admission for two adults and two children. (Lesson 1-3) **$34**

Find the value of n. Then name the property used in each step. (Lesson 1-3) **60–65. See margin.**

60. $25n = 25$

61. $n \cdot 1 = 2$

62. $12 \cdot n = 12 \cdot 6$

63. $n + 0 = \frac{2}{3}$

64. $4 \cdot \frac{1}{4} = n$

65. $(10 - 8)(7) = 2(n)$

Skills Review

Translate each sentence into an equation. (Lesson 2-1)

66. Twice a number t decreased by eight equals seventy. **$2t - 8 = 70$**

67. Five times the sum of m and k is the same as seven times k. **$5(m + k) = 7k$**

68. Half of p is the same as p minus 3. **$\frac{1}{2}p = p - 3$**

Evaluate each expression. (Lesson 0-3)

69. $-9 - (-14)$ **5**

70. $-10 + (20)$ **10**

71. $-15 - 9$ **−24**

72. $5(14)$ **70**

73. $-55 \div (-5)$ **11**

74. $-25(-5)$ **125**

Differentiated Instruction BL

Extension Remind students that they have learned that an equation can have 1, 0, or an endless number of solutions. Ask students to write an equation in which there are exactly two solutions for the variable. For example, in $|x| = 25$, $x = 25$ or -25 or $x^2 = 25$, $x = 5$ or -5.

2-5 Solving Equations Involving Absolute Value

Then

You solved equations with the variable on each side. (Lesson 2-5)

Now

- Evaluate absolute value expressions.
- Solve absolute value equations.

IL Learning Standards

8.B.4a Represent algebraic concepts with physical materials, words, diagrams, tables, graphs, equations and inequalities and use appropriate technology.

IL Math Online

glencoe.com

- Extra Examples
- Personal Tutor
- Self-Check Quiz
- Homework Help

Why?

In 2007, a telephone poll was conducted to determine the reading habits of Americans. People in this survey were allowed to select more than one type of book.

The survey had a margin of error of 3 percentage points. This means that the results could be three points higher or lower. So, the percent of people who read religious material could be as high as 69% or as low as 63%.

Source: CNN

Absolute Value Expressions Expressions with absolute values define an upper and lower range in which a value must lie. Expressions involving absolute value can be evaluated using the given value for the variable.

EXAMPLE 1 Expressions with Absolute Value

Evaluate $|m + 6| - 14$ if $m = 4$.

$\|m + 6\| - 14$	$= \|4 + 6\| - 14$	Replace m with 4.
	$= \|10\| - 14$	$4 + 6 = 10$
	$= 10 - 14$	$\|10\| = 10$
	$= -4$	Simplify.

Check Your Progress

1. Evaluate $23 - |3 - 4x|$ if $x = 2$. 18

Personal Tutor glencoe.com

Absolute Value Equations Looking at the example at the top of the page, we notice that the margin of error in the bar graph is an example of absolute value. The distance between 66 and 69 on a number line is the same as the distance between 63 and 66.

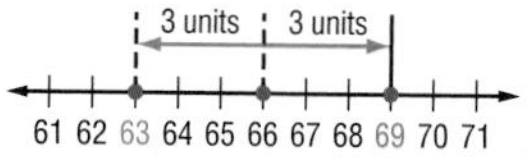

There are three types of open sentences involving absolute value, $|x| = n$, $|x| < n$, and $|x| > n$. In this lesson, we will consider only the first type. Look at the equation $|x| = 4$. This means that the distance between 0 and x is 4.

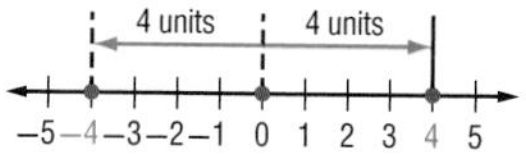

If $|x| = 4$, then $x = -4$ or $x = 4$. Thus, the solution set is $\{-4, 4\}$.

For each absolute value equation, we must consider both cases. To solve an absolute value equation, first isolate the absolute value on one side of the equals sign if it is not already by itself.

2-5 Lesson Notes

1 FOCUS

Vertical Alignment

Before Lesson 2-5
Solve equations with the variable on each side.

Lesson 2-5
Evaluate absolute value expressions.
Solve absolute value equations.

After Lesson 2-5
Solve inequalities involving absolute value.

2 TEACH

Scaffolding Questions

Have students read the *Why?* section of the lesson.

Ask:

- Which type of book in the survey is the least popular? Romance
- With a 3-point margin of error, the number of people who chose popular fiction could be as high as what percent? as low as what percent? 53%; 47%
- How would you represent with an absolute value equation the margin of error in the percent of people who chose religious books? $|x - 66| = 3$

Lesson 2-5 Resources

Resource	Approaching-Level	On-Level	Beyond-Level	English Learners
Teacher Edition	• Differentiated Instruction, p. 104	• Differentiated Instruction, p. 104	• Differentiated Instruction, p. 109	
Chapter Resource Masters	• Study Guide and Intervention, pp. 30–31 • Skills Practice, p. 32 • Practice, p. 33 • Word Problem Practice, p. 34	• Study Guide and Intervention, pp. 30–31 • Skills Practice, p. 32 • Practice, p. 33 • Word Problem Practice, p. 34 • Enrichment, p. 35	• Practice, p. 33 • Word Problem Practice, p. 34 • Enrichment, p. 35	• Study Guide and Intervention, pp. 30–31 • Skills Practice, p. 32 • Practice, p. 33
Transparencies	• 5-Minute Check Transparency 2-5	• 5-Minute Check Transparency 2-5	• 5-Minute Check Transparency 2-5	• 5-Minute Check Transparency 2-5
Other	• Study Notebook	• Study Notebook	• Study Notebook	• Study Notebook

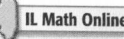

Absolute Value Expressions

Example 1 shows how to evaluate an absolute value expression using a given value for the variable.

Formative Assessment

Use the Check Your Progress exercises after each Example to determine students' understanding of concepts.

Additional Example

1 Evaluate $|a - 7| + 15$ if $a = 5$. 17

Additional Examples also in Interactive Classroom PowerPoint® Presentations

IWB INTERACTIVE WHITEBOARD READY

Absolute Value Equations

Example 2 shows how to solve an absolute value equation and graph the solution set and how to recognize when the solution set is the empty set. **Example 3** shows how to use two different methods to solve an absolute value equation involving a real-world situation. **Example 4** shows how to write an equation involving absolute value for a given graph.

Additional Example

2 Solve each equation. Then graph the solution set.

a. $|2x - 1| = 7$ $\{-3, 4\}$

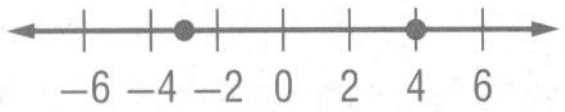

b. $|p + 6| = -5$ $\varnothing$

TEACH with TECH

INTERACTIVE WHITEBOARD On the board, work through several examples solving absolute value equations. Save your work to a file and send it to your students so they can use it as an additional reference.

ReadingMath

Absolute Values The expression $|f + 5|$ is read the *absolute value of the quantity f plus 5.*

Key Concept — Absolute Value Equations (For Your FOLDABLE)

Words When solving equations that involve absolute values, there are two cases to consider.

Case 1: The expression inside the absolute value symbol is positive or zero.

Case 2: The expression inside the absolute value symbol is negative.

Symbols For any real numbers a and b, if $|a| = b$, then $a = b$ or $a = -b$.

Example $|d| = 10$, so $d = 10$ or $d = -10$.

EXAMPLE 2 Solve Absolute Value Equations

Solve each equation. Then graph the solution set.

a. $|f + 5| = 17$

$|f + 5| = 17$ **Original equation**

Case 1

$f + 5 = 17$

$f + 5 - 5 = 17 - 5$ **Subtract 5 from each side.**

$f = 12$ **Simplify.**

Case 2

$f + 5 = -17$

$f + 5 - 5 = -17 - 5$

$f = -22$

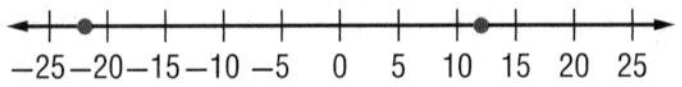

b. $|b - 1| = -3$

$|b - 1| = -3$ means the distance between b and 1 is −3. Since distance cannot be negative, the solution is the empty set $\varnothing$.

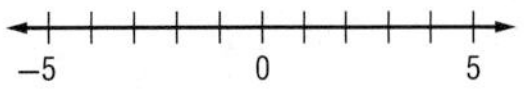

Check Your Progress

2A. $|y + 2| = 4$ $\{-6, 2\}$

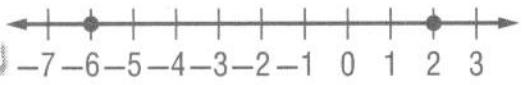

2B. $|3n - 4| = -1$ $\varnothing$

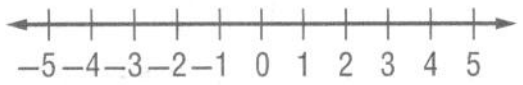

Personal Tutor glencoe.com

Absolute value equations occur in real-world situations that describe a range within which a value must lie.

Real-World Link

In 2001, the number of households in the U.S. that had either a turtle, snake, lizard, or other reptile as a pet was 1,678,000.

Source: American Veterinary Medical Association

Real-World EXAMPLE 3 Solve an Absolute Value Equation

SNAKES The temperature of an enclosure for a pet snake should be about 80°F, give or take 5°. Find the maximum and minimum temperatures.

You can use a number line to solve.

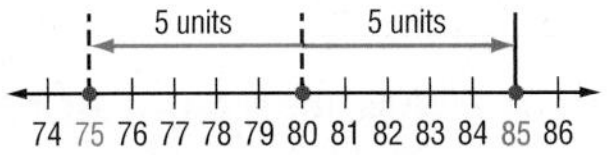

The distance from 80 to 75 is 5 units.
The distance from 80 to 85 is 5 units.

The solution set is {75, 85}. The maximum and minimum temperatures are 85° and 75°.

Differentiated Instruction (AL OL)

If some students are having trouble rewriting absolute value equations,

Then have students apply the two situations (positive and negative) to the expression within the absolute value symbols. For example, $|x| = 4$ can be written as $x = 4$ or as $-x = 4$, which yields $x = -4$.

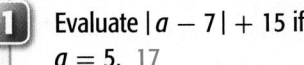

Check Your Progress

3. ICE CREAM Ice cream should be stored at 5°F with an allowance for 5°. Write and solve an equation to find the maximum and minimum temperatures at which the ice cream should be stored. $|t - 5| = 5$; 10°F and 0°F

Personal Tutor glencoe.com

When given two points on a graph, you can write an absolute value equation for the graph.

StudyTip

Find the Midpoint To find the point midway between two points, add the values together and divide by 2. For Example 4, $11 + 19 = 30$, $30 \div 2 = 15$. So 15 is the point halfway between 11 and 19.

EXAMPLE 4 Write an Absolute Value Equation

Write an equation involving absolute value for the graph.

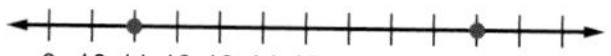

Find the point that is the same distance from 11 and from 19. This is the midpoint between 11 and 19, which is 15.

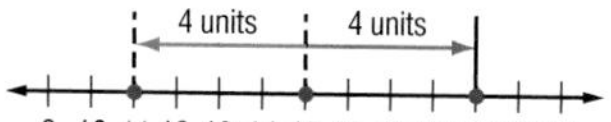

The distance from 15 to 11 is 4 units.
The distance from 15 to 19 is 4 units.

So an equation is $|x - 15| = 4$.

Check Your Progress

4. Write an equation involving absolute value for the graph. $|c - 22| = 5$

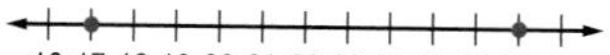

Personal Tutor glencoe.com

Check Your Understanding

Example 1 p. 103 — **Evaluate each expression if $f = 3$, $g = -4$, and $h = 5$.**

1. $|3 - h| + 13$ 15 **2.** $16 - |g + 9|$ 11 **3.** $|f + g| - h$ −4

Example 2 p. 104 — **Solve each equation. Then graph the solution set.** 4–9. See margin for graphs.

4. $|n + 7| = 5$ {−2, −12} **5.** $|3z - 3| = 9$ {4, −2} **6.** $|4n - 1| = -6$ ∅

7. $|b + 4| = 2$ {−6, −2} **8.** $|2t - 4| = 8$ {−2, 6} **9.** $|5h + 2| = -8$ ∅

Example 3 p. 104

10. FINANCIAL LITERACY For a company to invest in a product, they must believe they will receive a 12% return on investment (ROI) plus or minus 3%. Write an equation to find the least and the greatest ROI they believe they will receive. $|x - 12| = 3$; {9, 15}

Example 4 p. 105 — **Write an equation involving absolute value for each graph.**

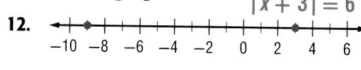

11.

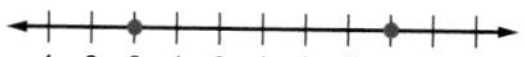

$|x - 1| = 3$

12. $|x + 3| = 6$

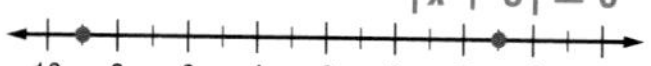

Focus on Mathematical Content

Absolute Value Equations
Solve absolute value equations by graphing them on a number line or by writing a compound sentence and then solving it algebraically. Consider two cases: the expression inside the symbol is positive and the expression inside the symbol is negative.

Additional Examples

3 **WEATHER** The average January temperature in a northern Canadian city is 1°F. The actual January temperature for that city may be about 5°F warmer or colder. Write and solve an equation to find the maximum and minimum temperatures. $|t - 1| = 5$; {−4, 6}; the maximum and minimum temperatures are −4° and 6°.

4 Write an equation involving absolute value for the graph.

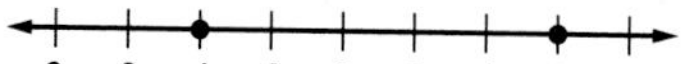

$|y - 1| = 5$

3 PRACTICE

Formative Assessment

Use Exercises 1–12 to check for understanding.

Use the chart at the bottom of the next page to customize assignments for your students.

Additional Answers

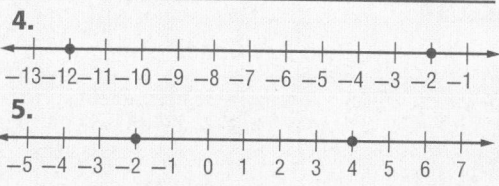

4.

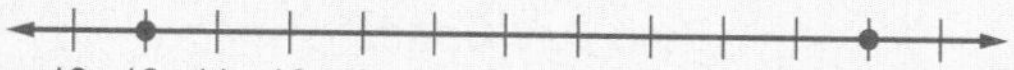

5.

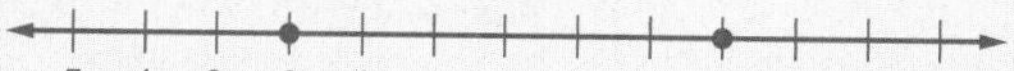

6.

7.

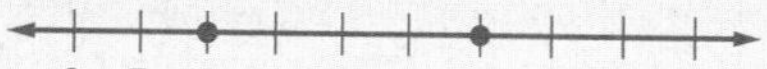

8.

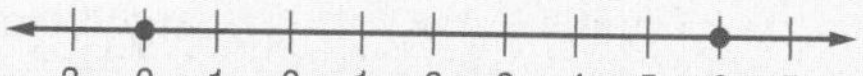

9.

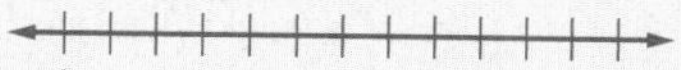

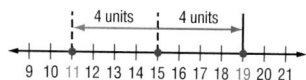

Additional Answers

22. 

23. 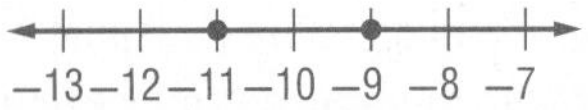

24. 

25. 

26. 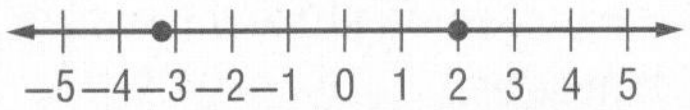

27. 

28. 

29. 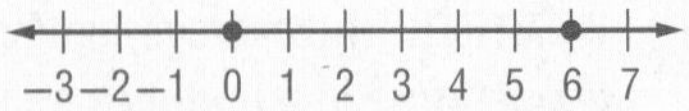

30. 

37. 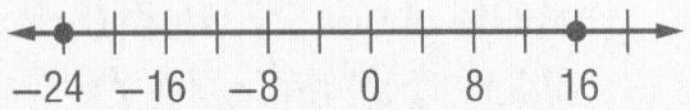

38. 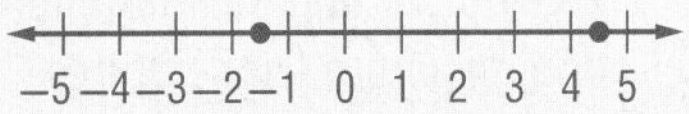

39. 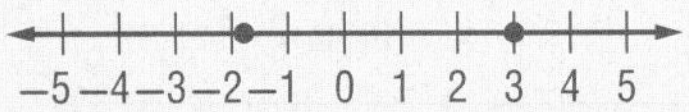

40. 

41. 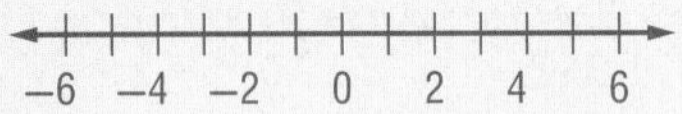

42. 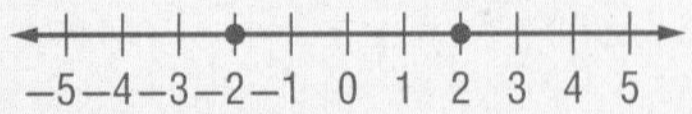

44a. $|t - 20| = 2$

44b. 18 in. to 22 in.

44c. No; the difference in heights of the models is greater than the difference in hem length of the skirt.

Practice and Problem Solving

● = **Step-by-Step Solutions** begin on page R12. **Extra Practice** begins on page 815.

Example 1 p. 103

Evaluate each expression if $a = -2$, $b = -3$, $c = 2$, $x = 2.1$, $y = 3$, and $z = -4.2$.

13. $|2x + z| + 2y$ **6**
14. $4a - |3b + 2c|$ **−13**
15. $-|5a + c| + |3y + 2z|$ **−7.4**
16. $-a + |2x - a|$ **8.2**
17. $|y - 2z| - 3$ **8.4**
18. $3|3b - 8c| - 3$ **72**
19. $|2x - z| + 6b$ **−9.6**
20. $-3|z| + 2(a + y)$ **−10.6**
21. $-4|c - 3| + 2|z - a|$ **0.4**

Example 2 p. 104

Solve each equation. Then graph the solution set. 22–30. See margin for graphs.

22. $|n - 3| = 5$ **{8, −2}**
23. $|f + 10| = 1$ **{−11, −9}**
24. $|v - 2| = -5$ **∅**
25. $|4t - 8| = 20$ **{7, −3}**
26. $|8w + 5| = 21$ **{2, −3.25}**
27. $|6y - 7| = -1$ **∅**
28. $\left|\frac{1}{2}x + 5\right| = -3$ **∅**
29. $|-2y + 6| = 6$ **{0, 6}**
30. $\left|\frac{3}{4}a - 3\right| = 9$ **{16, −8}**

Example 3 p. 104

31. SURVEY The circle graph at the right shows the results of a survey that asked, "How likely is it that you will be rich some day?" If the margin of error is ±4%, what is the range of the percent of teens who say it is very likely that they will be rich? **11% to 19%**

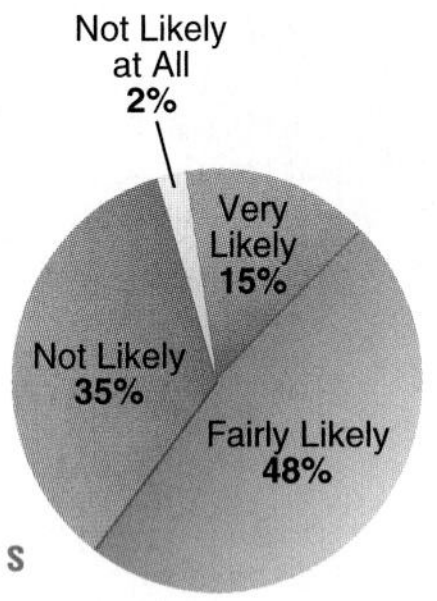

32. CHEERLEADING For competition, the cheerleading team is preparing a dance routine that must last 4 minutes, with a variation of ±5 seconds.

a. Find the least and greatest possible times for the routine in minutes and seconds. **4 min 5 s, 3 min 55 s**

b. Find the least and greatest possible times in seconds. **235 s, 245 s**

Example 4 p. 105

Write an equation involving absolute value for each graph. **33–36. Sample answers given.**

33. 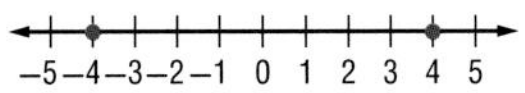 **|x| = 4**

34. 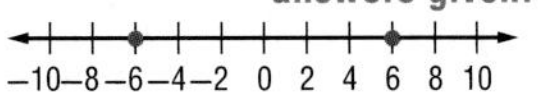 **|x| = 6**

35. 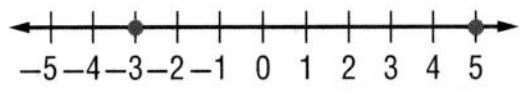 **|x − 1| = 4**

36. 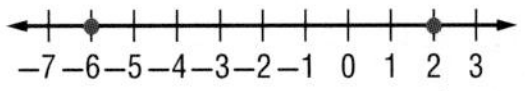 **|x + 2| = 4**

B **Solve each equation. Then graph the solution set. 37–42. See margin for graphs.**

37. $\left|-\frac{1}{2}b - 2\right| = 10$ **{−24, 16}**
38. $|-4d + 6| = 12$ $\left\{-\frac{3}{2}, \frac{9}{2}\right\}$
39. $|5f - 3| = 12$ $\left\{3, -\frac{9}{5}\right\}$
40. $2|h| - 3 = 8$ **{5.5, −5.5}**
41. $4 - 3|q| = 10$ **no solution**
42. $\frac{4}{|p|} + 12 = 14$ **{2, −2}**

43. TRACK The 4×400 relay is a race where 4 runners take turns running 400 meters, or one lap around the track.

a. If a runner runs the first leg in 52 seconds plus or minus 2 seconds, write an equation to find the fastest and slowest times. **|x − 52| = 2; {50, 54}**

b. If the runners of the second and third legs run their laps in 53 seconds plus or minus 1 second, write an equation to find the fastest and slowest times. **|x − 53| = 1; {52, 54}**

c. Suppose the runner of the fourth leg is the fastest on the team. If he runs an average of 50.5 seconds plus or minus 1.5 seconds, what are the team's fastest and slowest times? **203 seconds and 214 seconds**

Differentiated Homework Options

Level	Assignment	Two-Day Option	
AL Basic	13–36, 56–61, 63–75	13–35 odd, 65–68	14–36 even, 56–61, 63–64, 69–75
OL Core	13–41 odd, 43–45, 47–51 odd, 52–61, 63–75	13–36, 65–68	37–61, 63–64, 69–75
BL Advanced	37–71, (optional: 72–75)		

Real-World Link

An increasing number of fashion designers are using computer-aided design (CAD). CAD allows designers to view designs on virtual models.

Source: Bureau of Labor Statistics

44. FASHION To allow for a model's height, a designer is willing to use models that require him to change hems either up or down 2 inches. The length of the skirts is 20 inches. **a–c. See margin.**

a. Write an absolute value equation that represents the length of the skirts.

b. What is the range of the lengths of the skirts?

c. If a 20-inch skirt was fitted for a model that is 5 feet 9 inches tall, will the designer use a 6-foot-tall model?

45. CARS Speedometer accuracy can be affected by many details such as tire diameter and axle ratio. For example, there is variation of ±3 miles per hour when calibrated at 50 miles per hour.

a. What is the range of actual speeds of the car if calibrated at 50 miles per hour?

b. A speedometer calibrated at 45 miles per hour has an accepted variation of ±1 mile per hour. What can we conclude from this?

45a. 47 to 53 mph

45b. The slower the speed that the speedometer is calibrated at the more accurate the setting.

Write an equation involving absolute value for each graph. **46–51. Sample answers given.**

46.  $\left|x - \frac{1}{4}\right| = 4$

47. 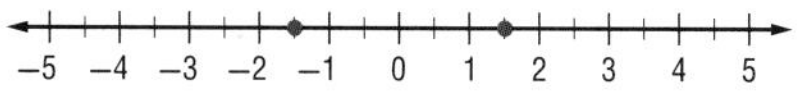 $|x| = 1\frac{1}{2}$

48. 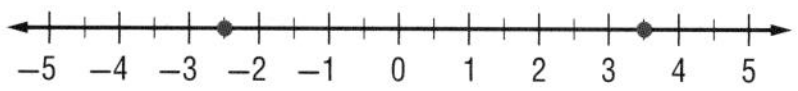 $\left|x - \frac{1}{2}\right| = 3$

49.  $\left|x - \frac{1}{4}\right| = \frac{1}{4}$

50.  $\left|x - \frac{2}{3}\right| = \frac{2}{3}$

51. 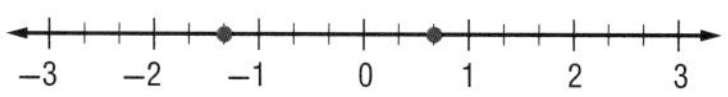 $\left|x + \frac{1}{3}\right| = 1$

52. MUSIC A CD will record an hour and a half of music plus or minus 3 minutes for time to change tracks.

a. Write an absolute value equation that represents the recording time. **$|t - 90| = 3$**

b. What is the range of time in minutes that the CD could run? **87 to 93 minutes**

c. Graph the possible times on a number line. **See Ch. 2 Answer Appendix.**

53. ACOUSTICS The Red Rocks Amphitheater located in the Red Rock Park near Denver, Colorado, is the only naturally occurring amphitheater. The acoustic qualities here are such that a maximum of 20,000 people, plus or minus 1000, can hear natural voices clearly.

a. Write an equation involving an absolute value that represents the number of people that can hear natural voices at Red Rocks Amphitheater.

b. Find the maximum and minimum number of people that can hear natural voices clearly in the amphitheater. **21,000; 19,000**

c. What is the range of people in part **b**? **19,000 to 21,000**

53a. Let h = the number of people that can clearly hear voices, $|h - 20{,}000| = 1000$.

Study Guide and Intervention

CRM pp. 30–31 AL OL ELL

NAME ______________________ DATE __________ PERIOD __________

2-5 Study Guide and Intervention

Solving Equations Involving Absolute Value

Absolute Value Expressions Expressions with absolute values define an upper and lower range in which a value must lie. Expressions involving absolute value can be evaluated using the given value for the variable.

Example Evaluate $|t - 5| - 7$ if $t = 3$.

$\|t - 5\| - 7 = \|3 - 5\| - 7$	Replace t with 3.
$= \|-2\| - 7$	$3 - 5 = -2$
$= 2 - 7$	$\|-2\| = 2$
$= -5$	Simplify.

Exercises

Evaluate each expression if $r = -2$, $n = -3$, and $t = 3$.

1. $|8 - t| + 3$ **8**
2. $|t - 3| - 7$ **−7**
3. $5 + |3 - n|$ **11**
4. $|r + n| - 7$ **−2**
5. $|n - t| + 4$ **10**
6. $-|r + n + t|$ **−2**

Evaluate each expression if $n = 2$, $q = -1.5$, $r = -3$, $v = -8$, $w = 4.5$, and $x = 4$.

7. $|2q + r|$ **6**
8. $10 - |2n + v|$ **6**
9. $|3x - 2w| - q$ **4.5**
10. $v - |3n + x|$ **−18**
11. $1 + |5q - w|$ **13**
12. $2\,|3r - v|$ **2**
13. $|-2x + 5n| + (n - x)$ **0**
14. $4w - |2r + v|$ **4**
15. $3|w - n| - 5|q - r|$ **0**

Practice

CRM p. 33 AL OL BL ELL

NAME ______________________ DATE __________ PERIOD __________

2-5 Practice

Solving Equations Involving Absolute Value

Evaluate each expression if $x = -1$, $y = 3$, and $z = -4$.

1. $16 - |2z + 1|$ **9**
2. $|x - y| + 4$ **8**
3. $|-3y + z| - x$ **14**
4. $3\,|z - x| + |2 - y|$ **10**

Solve each equation. Then graph the solution set.

5. $|2z - 9| = 1$ **{4, 5}** 
6. $|3 - 2r| = 7$ **{−2, 5}** 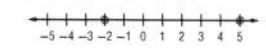
7. $|3t + 6| = 9$ **{−5, 1}** 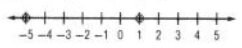
8. $|2g - 5| = 9$ **{−2, 7}** 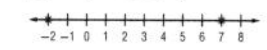

Write an equation involving absolute value for each graph.

9.  $|x - 6| = 5$
10. 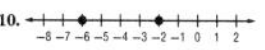 $|x + 4| = 2$
11. 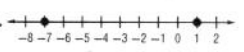 $|x + 3| = 4$
12.  $|x - 2| = 4$

13. **FITNESS** Taisha uses the elliptical cross-trainer at the gym. Her general goal is to burn 280 Calories per workout, but she varies by as much as 25 Calories from this amount on any given day. Write and solve an equation to find the maximum and minimum number of Calories Taisha burns on the cross-trainer.

{|c − 280| = 25; min = 255; max = 305}

14. **TEMPERATURE** A thermometer is guaranteed to give a temperature no more than 1.2°F from the actual temperature. If the thermometer reads 28°F, write and solve an equation to find the maximum and minimum temperatures it could be.

{|t − 28| = 1.2; min = 26.8°F; max = 29.2°F}

Lesson 2-5

Word Problem Practice

CRM p. 34 AL OL BL ELL

NAME ______________________ DATE __________ PERIOD __________

2-5 Word Problem Practice

Solving Open Sentences Involving Absolute Value

1. **ENGINEERING** Tolerance in engineering is an allowance made for imperfections in a manufactured object. The manufacturer of an oven specifies a temperature tolerance of ±15°F. This means that the temperature inside the oven will be within 15°F of the temperature that it is set on. Write an absolute value expression to represent the maximum and minimum temperatures inside the oven when the thermostat is set on 400°F.

$|t - 400| = 15$

2. **AVIATION** The circle graph shows the results of a survey that asked 4300 students ages 7 to 18 what they thought would be the most important benefit of air travel in the future. There are about 40 million students in the United States. If the margin of error is ±3%, what is the range of the number of students ages 7 to 18 who would likely say that "finding new resources for Earth" is the most important benefit of future flight?

The Next Frontier for Flight

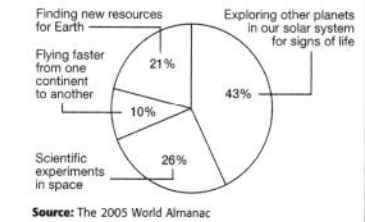

Source: The 2005 World Almanac

between 7,200,000 and 9,600,000

3. **COLLEGE** A certain scholarship and student loan fund uses a formula to determine whether or not a student qualifies for college funding. The formula is $|3k + 6| = 15$, where k is a need score determined by an interview. What are the possible need scores?

{−7; 3}

4. **STATISTICS** The most familiar statistical measure is the arithmetic mean, or average. A second important statistical measure is the standard deviation, which is a measure of how far the individual scores are from the mean. For example, the mean score on the Wechsler IQ test is 100 and the standard deviation is 15. This means that people within one deviation of the mean have IQ scores that are 15 points higher or lower than the mean.

a. Write an absolute value equation to find the maximum and minimum test scores within one standard deviation if the mean was 80 and the standard deviation was 12.

$|t - 80| = 12$

b. What is the range of Wechsler IQ test scores ±3 standard deviations from the mean?

55 to 145

Enrichment

CRM p. 35 OL BL

NAME ______________________ DATE __________ PERIOD __________

2-5 Enrichment

Precision of Measurement

The precision of a measurement depends both on your accuracy in measuring and the number of divisions on the ruler you use. Suppose you measured a length of wood to the nearest one-eighth of an inch and got a length of $6\frac{5}{8}$ in.

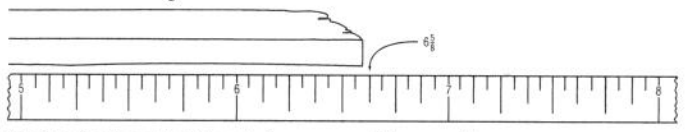

The drawing shows that the actual measurement lies somewhere between $6\frac{9}{16}$ in. and $6\frac{11}{16}$ in. This measurement can be written using the symbol ±, which is read *plus or minus.*

$$6\frac{5}{8} \pm \frac{1}{16} \text{ in.}$$

In this example, $\frac{1}{16}$ in. is the absolute error. The absolute error is one-half the smallest unit used in a measurement.

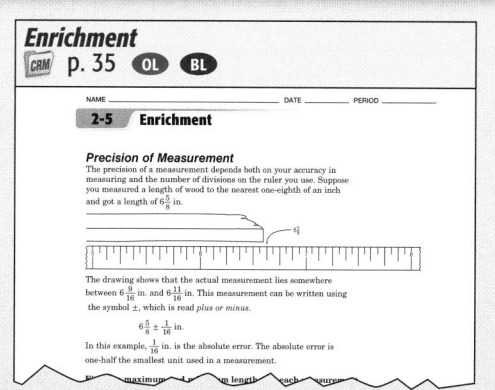

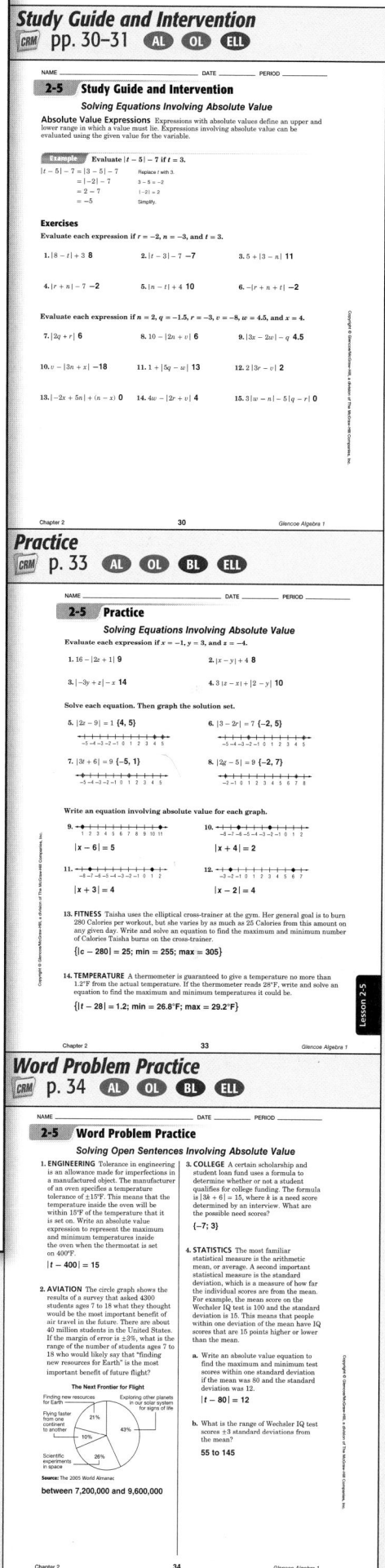

Watch Out!

Find the Error In Exercise 63, suggest that students consider why Wesley thinks the solution set is the empty set. Students should see that the absolute value is equal to a negative number. Since absolute value represents the distance from zero on a number line and distance cannot be a negative number, there is no solution.

Additional Answers

55b. Sample answer:

Number of questions correct	Points
0	0
1	10
2	20
3	30
4	40
5	50

63. Wesley; the absolute value of a number cannot be a negative number.

64. Sample answer: There are two solutions when the absolute value is equal to a positive number. There is one solution if the equation indicates that the absolute value is equal to zero. There are no solutions if the absolute value is equal to a negative number. Absolute values are distances which can never be negative numbers. Two solutions: $|x| = 10$, because $|10| = 10$ and $|-10| = 10$. One solution: $|x| = 0$, because $|0| = 0$. No solution: $|x| = -10$, because the distance a number x is from 0 cannot be negative.

Real-World Link

Each spring since 1997, Gallaudet University holds its National Academic Bowl for Deaf and Hard of Hearing High School Students. Here, teams of high school students compete in local, regional, and national events throughout the U.S.

Source: Galluadet University

54. BOOK CLUB The members of a book club agree to read within ten pages of the last page of the chapter. The chapter ends on page 203.

a. Write an absolute value equation that represents the pages where club members could stop reading. $|p - 203| = 10$

b. Write the range of the pages where the club members could stop reading. **193 to 213**

55. SCHOOL Washington High School and McKinley High School are competing in an academic challenge. The team with a correct response is awarded 10 points. An incorrect response has a point value of −10. There are 5 mathematics questions.

a. Write an equation that represents the scoring for the challenge.

b. Make a table of values for the possible points that a school could receive during the mathematics portion of the challenge. **See margin.**

c. Write about how absolute values can be used in classes other than math. **Sample answer: In science class, absolute values can be used for tolerance ranges of pollution on plants.**

H.O.T. Problems — Use Higher-Order Thinking Skills

56. OPEN ENDED Describe a real-world situation that could be represented by the absolute value equation $|x - 4| = 10$.

REASONING Determine whether the following statements are *sometimes*, *always*, or *never* true, if c is an integer. Explain your reasoning.

57. The value of $|x + 1|$ is greater than zero. **Sometimes; when $x = -1$, the value is 0.**

58. The solution of $|x + c| = 0$ is greater than 0.

59. The inequality $|x| + c < 0$ has no solution.

60. The value of $|x + c| + c$ is greater than zero.

61. REASONING Explain why an absolute value can never be negative.

61. An absolute value represents a distance from zero on a number line. A distance can never be a negative number.

62. CHALLENGE Use the sentence $x = 7 \pm 4.6$.

a. Describe the values of x that make the sentence true. **2.4, 11.6**

b. Translate the sentence into an equation involving absolute value. $|x - 7| = 4.6$

63. ERROR ANALYSIS Alex and Wesley are solving $|x + 5| = -3$. Is either of them correct? Explain your reasoning. **See margin.**

Alex		Wesley
$\|x + 5\| = 3$ or	$\|x + 5\| = -3$	$\|x + 5\| = -3$
$x + 5 = 3$	$x + 5 = -3$	The solution is $\emptyset$.
$-5 \quad -5$	$-5 \quad -5$	
$x = -2$	$x = -8$	

64. WRITING IN MATH Explain why there are either two, one, or no solutions for absolute value equations. Demonstrate an example of each possibility. **See margin.**

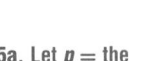

55a. Let p = the number of points awarded for each question; $|p| = 10$.

56. Sample answer: Let x = the time in minutes to run one mile. Then the time to run one mile is 4 ± 10.

58. Sometimes; when c is a negative value, x is a positive value.

59. Sometimes; when c is a negative value, the inequality is true.

60. Sometimes; when $c = 1$, $x > -2$.

PSAE PRACTICE 8.11.22, 7.11.03, 6.11.18, 8.11.04

65. Which equation represents the second step of the solution process? D

Step 1: $4(2x + 7) - 6 = 3x$
Step 2: ____________
Step 3: $5x + 28 - 6 = 0$
Step 4: $5x = -22$
Step 5: $x = -4.4$

A $4(2x - 6) + 7 = 3x$
B $4(2x + 1) = 3x$
C $8x + 7 - 6 = 3x$
D $8x + 28 - 6 = 3x$

66. GEOMETRY The area of a circle is 25π square centimeters. What is the circumference? J

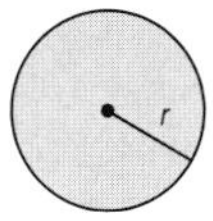

F 625π cm
G 50π cm
H 5π cm
J 10π cm

67. Tanya makes \$5 an hour and 15% commission of the total dollar value on cosmetics she sells. Suppose Tanya's commission is increased to 17%. How much money will she make if she sells \$300 worth of product and works 30 hours? A

A \$201
B \$226
C \$255
D \$283

68. EXTENDED RESPONSE John's mother has agreed to take him driving every day for two weeks. On the first day, John drives for 20 minutes. Each day after that, John drives 5 minutes more than the day before. See margin.

a. Write an expression for the nth term. Explain how you found the expression.

b. For how many minutes will John drive on the last day? Show your work.

c. John's driver's education teacher requires that each student drive for 30 hours with an adult outside of class. Will John's sessions with his mother fulfill this requirement?

Spiral Review

Write and solve an equation for each sentence. (Lesson 2-4)

69. One half of a number increased by 16 is four less than two thirds of the number. $\frac{1}{2}n + 16 = \frac{2}{3}n - 4$; 120

70. The sum of one half of a number and 6 equals one third of the number. $\frac{1}{2}n + 6 = \frac{1}{3}n$; −36

71. SHOE If ℓ represents the length of a man's foot in inches, the expression $2\ell - 12$ can be used to estimate his shoe size. What is the approximate length of a man's foot if he wears a size 8? (Lesson 2-3) 10 in.

Skills Review

Write an equation for each problem. Then solve the equation. (Lesson 2-2)

72. Seven times a number equals −84. What is the number? $7n = -84$; −12

73. Two fifths of a number equals −24. Find the number. $\frac{2}{5}n = -24$; −60

74. Negative 117 is nine times a number. Find the number. $-117 = 9n$; −13

75. Twelve is one fifth of a number. What is the number? $12 = \frac{1}{5}n$; 60

4 ASSESS

Yesterday's News Ask students to write how yesterday's lesson on solving equations with variables on each side helped them with today's lesson on solving equations involving absolute value.

Formative Assessment

Check for student understanding of Lessons 2-4 and 2-5.

CRM Quiz 2, p. 63

Additional Answers

68a. $15 + 5(n)$ where n represents the number of days, because John will drive 20 minutes on the first day and then an additional 5 minutes for each day after that.

68b. 85 min; $15 + 5(14) = 85$

68c. No; 30 hours is 1800 minutes. John only drove 85 minutes with his mother.

Differentiated Instruction BL

Extension Have students solve the absolute value equation $|4b - 3| = 2b + 9$. Remind them to check the solutions. If necessary, give this hint: Use the opposite of the quantity of $2b + 9$ to solve for Case 2. $\{-1, 6\}$

Lesson 2-5 Solving Equations Involving Absolute Value 109

Formative Assessment

Use the Mid-Chapter Quiz to assess students' progress in the first half of the chapter.

For problems answered incorrectly, have students review the lessons indicated in parentheses.

ExamView Assessment Suite — Customize and create multiple versions of your Mid-Chapter Quiz and their answer keys.

FOLDABLES Follow-Up

Before students complete the Mid-Chapter Quiz, encourage them to review the information for Lessons 2-1 through 2-5 in their Foldables.

CHAPTER 2 Mid-Chapter Quiz

Lessons 2-1 through 2-5

IL Learning Standards: 8.B.4a, 8.D.4

Translate each sentence into an equation. (Lesson 2-1)

1. The sum of three times a and four is the same as five times a. $3a + 4 = 5a$
2. One fourth of m minus six is equal to two times the sum of m and 9. $\frac{1}{4}m - 6 = 2(m + 9)$
3. The product of five and w is the same as w to the third power. $5w = w^3$
4. **MARBLES** Drew has 50 red, green, and blue marbles. He has six more red marbles than blue marbles and four fewer green marbles than blue marbles. Write and solve an equation to determine how many blue marbles Drew has. (Lesson 2-1) $3b + 2 = 50$; 16

Solve each equation. Check your solution. (Lesson 2-2)

5. $p + 8 = 13$ 5
6. $-26 = b - 3$ -23
7. $\frac{t}{6} = 3$ 18
8. **MULTIPLE CHOICE** Solve the equation $\frac{3}{5}a = \frac{1}{4}$. (Lesson 2-2) C
   - A $\frac{3}{20}$
   - B 2
   - C $\frac{5}{12}$
   - D -3

Solve each equation. Check your solution. (Lesson 2-3)

9. $2x + 5 = 13$ 4
10. $-21 = 7 - 4y$ 7
11. $\frac{m}{6} - 3 = 8$ 66
12. $-4 = \frac{d + 3}{5}$ -23
13. **FISH** The average length of a yellow-banded angelfish is 12 inches. This is 4.8 times as long as an average common goldfish. (Lesson 2-3)
    a. Write an equation you could use to find the length of the average common goldfish. $12 = 4.8g$
    b. What is the length of an average common goldfish? 2.5 in.

Write an equation and solve each problem. (Lesson 2-3)

14. Three less than three fourths of a number is negative 9. Find the number. $\frac{3}{4}n - 3 = -9$; -8
15. Thirty is twelve added to six times a number. What is the number? $30 = 12 + 6n$; 3
16. Find four consecutive integers with a sum of 106. $n + (n + 1) + (n + 2) + (n + 3) = 106$; 25, 26, 27, 28

Solve each equation. Check your solution. (Lesson 2-4)

17. $8p + 3 = 5p + 9$ 2
18. $\frac{3}{4}w + 6 = 9 - \frac{1}{4}w$ 3
19. $\frac{z + 6}{3} = \frac{2z}{4}$ 12
20. **PERIMETER** Find the value of x so that the triangles have the same perimeter. (Lesson 2-4) 20

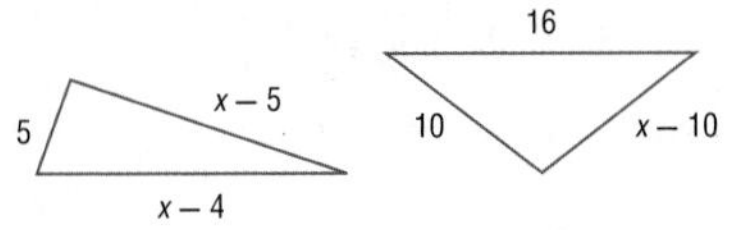

21. **PRODUCTION** ABC Sporting Goods Company produces baseball gloves. Their fixed monthly production cost is \$8000 with a per glove cost of \$5. XYZ Sporting Goods Company also produces baseball gloves. Their fixed monthly production cost is \$10,000 with a per glove cost of \$3. Find the value of x, the number of gloves produced monthly, so that the total monthly production cost is the same for both companies. (Lesson 2-4) 1000

Evaluate each expression if $x = -4$, $y = 7$, and $z = -9$. (Lesson 2-5)

22. $|3x - 2| + 2y$ 28
23. $|-4y + 2z| - 7z$ 109
24. **MULTIPLE CHOICE** Solve $|6m - 3| = 9$. (Lesson 2-5) G
    - F $\{2\}$
    - G $\{-1, 2\}$
    - H $\{-3, 6\}$
    - J $\{-3, 3\}$
25. **COFFEE** Some say to brew an excellent cup of coffee, you must have a brewing temperature of 200° F, plus or minus 5 degrees. Write and solve an equation describing the maximum and minimum brewing temperatures for an excellent cup of coffee. $|t - 200| = 5$; {205°, 195°}

110 Chapter 2 Linear Equations

Intervention Planner

Tier 1 On Level	Tier 2 Strategic Intervention approaching grade level	Tier 3 Intensive Intervention 2 or more grades below level
If students miss about 25% of the exercises or less,	**If** students miss about 50% of the exercises,	**If** students miss about 75% of the exercises,
Then choose a resource: **SE** Lessons 2-1, 2-2, 2-3, 2-4, and 2-5 **CRM** Skills Practice, pp. 7, 13, 19, 25 and 32 **TE** Chapter Project, p. 72 IL Math Online Self-Check Quiz	**Then** choose a resource: **CRM** Study Guide and Intervention, Chapter 2, pp. 5, 11, 17, 23, and 30 *Quick Review Math Handbook* IL Math Online Extra Examples, Personal Tutor, Homework Help	**Then** use *Math Triumphs, Alg. 1*, Ch. 1–5 IL Math Online Extra Examples, Personal Tutor, Homework Help, Review Vocabulary

2-6 Ratios and Proportions

Then

You evaluated percents by using a proportion. (Lesson 0-5)

Now

- Compare ratios.
- Solve proportions.

IL Learning Standards

7.C.4b Interpret scale drawings and models using maps and blueprints. **9.A.4b Make perspective drawings, tessellations and scale drawings, with and without the use of technology.** *Also addresses 6.D.4, 7.A.4a, and 7.C.4a.*

New Vocabulary

ratio
proportion
means
extremes
rate
unit rate
scale
scale model

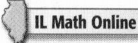

IL Math Online

glencoe.com

- Extra Examples
- Personal Tutor
- Self-Check Quiz
- Homework Help
- Math in Motion

Why?

Ratios allow us to compare many items by using a common reference. The table below shows the number of a certain popular fast food restaurants, per 10,000 people, in the United States as well as other countries. This allows us to compare the number of these restaurants using an equal reference.

Countries	United States	New Zealand	Canada	Australia	Japan	Singapore
Number of Restaurants per 10,000 People	0.433	0.369	0.352	0.349	0.282	0.273

Ratios and Proportions The comparison between the number of restaurants and the number of people is a ratio. A **ratio** is a comparison of two numbers by division. The ratio of x to y can be expressed in the following ways.

$$x \text{ to } y \qquad x{:}y \qquad \frac{x}{y}$$

Suppose you wanted to determine the number of restaurants per 100,000 people in Australia. Notice that this ratio is equal to the original ratio.

× 10

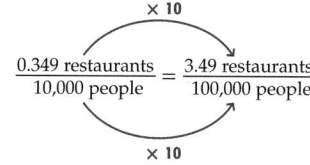

$$\frac{0.349 \text{ restaurants}}{10{,}000 \text{ people}} = \frac{3.49 \text{ restaurants}}{100{,}000 \text{ people}}$$

× 10

An equation stating that two ratios are equal is called a **proportion**. So, we can state that $\frac{0.349}{10{,}000} = \frac{3.49}{100{,}000}$ is a proportion.

EXAMPLE 1 Determine Whether Ratios Are Equivalent

Determine whether $\frac{2}{3}$ and $\frac{16}{24}$ are equivalent ratios. Write *yes* or *no*. Justify your answer.

÷ 1 $\qquad$ ÷ 8

$$\frac{2}{3} = \frac{2}{3} \qquad \frac{16}{24} = \frac{2}{3}$$

÷ 1 $\qquad$ ÷ 8

When expressed in simplest form, the ratios are equivalent.

Check Your Progress

Determine whether each pair of ratios are equivalent ratios. Write *yes* or *no*. Justify your answer.

1A. $\frac{6}{10}, \frac{2}{5}$ no; $\frac{3}{5} \neq \frac{2}{5}$

1B. $\frac{1}{6}, \frac{5}{30}$ yes; $\frac{1}{6} = \frac{1}{6}$

Personal Tutor glencoe.com

2-6 Lesson Notes

1 FOCUS

Vertical Alignment

Before Lesson 2-6
Evaluate percents by using a proportion.

Lesson 2-6
Compare ratios.
Solve proportions.

After Lesson 2-6
Describe functional relationships for given problem situations.

2 TEACH

Scaffolding Questions

Have students read the *Why?* section of the lesson.

Ask:

- How can you use the information in the table to determine the number of fast food restaurants per 1,000,000 people? Multiply the number of fast food restaurants and the number of people by 100.
- Suppose you want to know the number of restaurants per 500,000 people. How can you determine this number? Multiply the number of restaurants and the number of people by 50.
- Which country has 1.41 fast food restaurants per 50,000 people? Japan

Lesson 2-6 Resources

Resource	Approaching-Level	On-Level	Beyond-Level	English Learners
Teacher Edition	• Differentiated Instruction, p. 113	• Differentiated Instruction, pp. 113, 114	• Differentiated Instruction, pp. 114, 117	
Chapter Resource Masters	• Study Guide and Intervention, pp. 36–37 • Skills Practice, p. 38 • Practice, p. 39 • Word Problem Practice, p. 40	• Study Guide and Intervention, pp. 36–37 • Skills Practice, p. 38 • Practice, p. 39 • Word Problem Practice, p. 40 • Enrichment, p. 41	• Practice, p. 39 • Word Problem Practice, p. 40 • Enrichment, p. 41	• Study Guide and Intervention, pp. 36–37 • Skills Practice, p. 38 • Practice, p. 39
Transparencies	• 5-Minute Check Transparency 2-6	• 5-Minute Check Transparency 2-6	• 5-Minute Check Transparency 2-6	• 5-Minute Check Transparency 2-6
Other	• Study Notebook • Teaching Algebra with Manipulatives	• Study Notebook • Teaching Algebra with Manipulatives	• Study Notebook	• Study Notebook • Teaching Algebra with Manipulatives

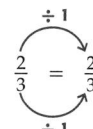

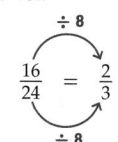

Ratios and Proportions

Example 1 shows how to determine whether ratios are equivalent.

Example 2 shows how to determine whether ratios form a proportion using cross products.

Formative Assessment

Use the Check Your Progress exercises after each Example to determine students' understanding of concepts.

Additional Examples

1 Determine whether $\frac{7}{8}$ and $\frac{49}{56}$ are equivalent ratios. Write *yes* or *no*. Justify your answer. Yes; the ratios are equivalent when expressed in simplest form.

2 Use cross products to determine whether each pair of ratios forms a proportion.

a. $\frac{0.25}{0.6}, \frac{1.25}{2}$ not a proportion

b. $\frac{2}{2.5}, \frac{16}{20}$ a proportion

Additional Examples also in Interactive Classroom PowerPoint® Presentations

IWB INTERACTIVE WHITEBOARD READY

Focus on Mathematical Content

Proportions One way to determine if two ratios form a proportion is to use cross products. In a proportion, the product of the extremes is equal to the product of the means.

TEACH with TECH

INTERACTIVE WHITEBOARD Write two ratios on the board and show students how to determine if they form a proportion. Drag the numerators and denominators to show how to form the cross products and then simplify.

StudyTip

Means and Extremes To solve a proportion using cross products, write an equation that sets the product of the extremes equal to the product of the means.

There are special names for the terms in a proportion.

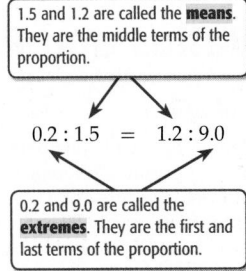

1.5 and 1.2 are called the **means**. They are the middle terms of the proportion.

$0.2 : 1.5 = 1.2 : 9.0$

0.2 and 9.0 are called the **extremes**. They are the first and last terms of the proportion.

Key Concept — For Your FOLDABLE

Means-Extremes Property of Proportion

Words In a proportion, the product of the extremes is equal to the product of the means.

Symbols If $\frac{a}{b} = \frac{c}{d}$ and $b, d \neq 0$, then $ad = bc$.

Example Since $\frac{2}{4} = \frac{1}{2}$, $2(2) = 4(1)$ or $4 = 4$.

Another way to determine whether two ratios form a proportion is to use cross products. If the cross products are equal, then the ratios form a proportion.

This is the same as multiplying the means, and multiplying the extremes.

EXAMPLE 2 Cross Products

Use cross products to determine whether each pair of ratios forms a proportion.

a. $\frac{2}{3.5}, \frac{8}{14}$

$\frac{2}{3.5} \stackrel{?}{=} \frac{8}{14}$	Original proportion
$2(14) \stackrel{?}{=} 3.5(8)$	Cross products
$28 = 28$ ✓	Simplify.

The cross products are equal, so the ratios form a proportion.

b. $\frac{0.3}{1.5}, \frac{0.5}{2.0}$

$\frac{0.3}{1.5} \stackrel{?}{=} \frac{0.5}{2.0}$	Original proportion
$0.3(2.0) \stackrel{?}{=} 1.5(0.5)$	Cross products
$0.6 \neq 0.75$ ✗	Simplify.

The cross products are not equal, so the ratios do not form a proportion.

Check Your Progress

2A. $\frac{0.2}{1.8}, \frac{1}{0.9}$ no

2B. $\frac{15}{36}, \frac{35}{42}$ no

Personal Tutor glencoe.com

Watch Out!

Preventing Errors Point out that the definitions of extremes and means are not arbitrary. In the proportion $\frac{a}{b} = \frac{c}{d}$, *a* and *d* are the extremes, and *b* and *c* are the means. Remind students that the ratios can be written in the form *x*:*y*. If the proportions above are rewritten in this form, they are *a*:*b* = *c*:*d*. Looking at this proportion, *a* and *d* are the extremes because they are on the outside, and *extreme* is a synonym for outside. Similarly, *b* and *c* are the means because they are in the middle, and *mean* is often a synonym for middle.

112 Chapter 2 Linear Equations

StudyTip

Cross Products When you find cross products, you are said to be *cross multiplying*.

Solve Proportions

Solve Proportions To solve proportions, use cross products.

EXAMPLE 3 Solve a Proportion

Solve each proportion. If necessary, round to the nearest hundredth.

a. $\frac{x}{10} = \frac{3}{5}$

$\frac{x}{10} = \frac{3}{5}$	Original proportion
$x(5) = 10(3)$	Find the cross products.
$5x = 30$	Simplify.
$\frac{5x}{5} = \frac{30}{5}$	Divide each side by 5.
$x = 6$	Simplify.

Math *in Motion*, BrainPOP® glencoe.com

b. $\frac{x-2}{14} = \frac{2}{7}$

$\frac{x-2}{14} = \frac{2}{7}$	Original proportion
$(x-2)7 = 14(2)$	Find the cross products.
$7x - 14 = 28$	Simplify.
$7x = 42$	Add 14 to each side.
$x = 6$	Divide each side by 7.

Check Your Progress

3A. $\frac{r}{8} = \frac{25}{40}$ 5

3B. $\frac{x+4}{5} = \frac{3}{8}$ −2.13

Personal Tutor glencoe.com

The ratio of two measurements having different units of measure is called a **rate**. For example, a price of $9.99 per 10 songs is a rate. A rate that tells how many of one item is being compared to 1 of another item is called a **unit rate**.

Real-World Career

Retail Buyer
A retail buyer purchases goods for stores, primarily from wholesalers, for resale to the general public. Buyers use math to determine the amount of each product to order. A bachelor's degree with an emphasis on business studies is usually required.

Real-World EXAMPLE 4 Rate of Growth

RETAIL In the past two years, a retailer has opened 232 stores. If the rate of growth remains constant, how many stores will the retailer open in the next 3 years?

Understand Let r represent the number of retail stores.

Plan Write a proportion for the problem.

$$\frac{232 \text{ retail stores}}{2 \text{ years}} = \frac{r \text{ retail stores}}{3 \text{ years}}$$

Solve

$\frac{232}{2} = \frac{r}{3}$	Original proportion
$232(3) = 2r$	Find the cross products.
$696 = 2r$	Simplify.
$\frac{696}{2} = \frac{2r}{2}$	Divide each side by 2.
$348 = r$	Simplify.

It will open 348 stores in 3 years.

Check If the clothing retailer continues to open 232 stores every 2 years, then in the next 3 years, it will open 348 stores.

Solve Proportions

Example 3 shows how to solve a proportion involving a variable. **Example 4** shows how to write and solve a proportion for a problem involving rates (the ratio of two measurements having different units of measure). **Example 5** shows how to write and solve a problem using a ratio or rate called a scale.

Additional Examples

3 Solve each proportion. If necessary, round to the nearest hundredth.

a. $\frac{n}{12} = \frac{3}{8}$ $n = 4.5$

b. $\frac{x+4}{12} = \frac{3}{4}$ $x = 5$

4 **BICYCLING** The gear on a bicycle is 8:5. This means that for every 8 turns of the pedals, the wheel turns 5 times. Suppose the bicycle wheel turns about 2435 times during a trip. How many times would you have to crank the pedals during the trip? about 3896 times

Tips for New Teachers

Cross Products Point out to students that the cross products must be equal regardless of the location of the x in the proportion.

Differentiated Instruction

AL OL

If you have any doubt that your students have mastered the concept of proportions,

Then place students in small groups to work through the Check Your Understanding problems. Have a student from each group report on that group's progress and areas in which the group may need assistance. It is important for students to have a good understanding of writing and solving proportions before studying the next few lessons.

Lesson 2-6 Ratios and Proportions 113

Additional Example

5 **MAP** In a road atlas, the scale for the map of Connecticut is 5 inches = 41 miles. What is the distance in miles represented by $2\frac{1}{2}$ inches on the map? $20\frac{1}{2}$ mi

3 PRACTICE

Formative Assessment

Use Exercises 1–8 to check for understanding.

Use the chart at the bottom of the next page to customize assignments for your students.

Check Your Progress

4. EXERCISE It takes 7 minutes for Isabella to walk around the gym track twice. At this rate, how many times can Isabella walk around the track in a half hour? **about 8.6 times**

Personal Tutor glencoe.com

A **scale** is used when making a model of something that is too large or too small to be convenient at actual size. The scale compares the model to the actual size of the object using a proportion. A **scale model** is a three-dimensional reproduction of an item that has been reduced or increased in size proportionally.

Real-World Link

The Great Smoky Mountains National Park in Tennessee is home to several waterfalls. The Ramsey Cascades is 100 feet tall. It is the tallest in the park.

Source: National Park Service

Math *in Motion*, Interactive Lab glencoe.com

Real-World EXAMPLE 5 Scale and Scale Models

MOUNTAIN TRAIL The scale on a map of the Great Smoky Mountains National Park is 3 inches = 10 miles. The length of the Ramsey Cascades Trail is about $1\frac{1}{8}$ inches on the map. What is the actual length of the trail?

Let ℓ represent the actual length.

scale → / actual → $\frac{3}{10} = \frac{1\frac{1}{8}}{\ell}$ ← scale / ← actual

$3(\ell) = 1\frac{1}{8}(10)$ **Find the cross products.**

$3\ell = \frac{45}{4}$ **Simplify.**

$3\ell \div 3 = \frac{45}{4} \div 3$ **Divide each side by 3.**

$\ell = \frac{15}{4}$ or $3\frac{3}{4}$ **Simplify.**

The actual length is about $3\frac{3}{4}$ miles.

Check Your Progress

5. AIRPLANES On a model airplane, the scale is 5 centimeters = 2 meters. If the wingspan of the scale model is 28.5 centimeters, what is the actual wingspan? **11.4 m**

Personal Tutor glencoe.com

Check Your Understanding

Examples 1 and 2 pp. 111–112

Determine whether each pair of ratios are equivalent ratios. Write *yes* or *no*.

1. $\frac{3}{7}, \frac{9}{14}$ **no**　**2.** $\frac{7}{8}, \frac{42}{48}$ **yes**　**3.** $\frac{2.8}{4.4}, \frac{1.4}{2.1}$ **no**

Examples 3 p. 113

Solve each proportion. If necessary, round to nearest hundredth.

4. $\frac{n}{9} = \frac{6}{27}$ **2**　**5.** $\frac{4}{u} = \frac{28}{35}$ **5**　**6.** $\frac{3}{8} = \frac{b}{10}$ **3.75**

Example 4 p. 113

7. RACE Jennie ran the first 6 miles of a marathon in 58 minutes. If she is able to maintain the same pace, how long will it take her to finish the 26.2 miles? **≈ 253.3 min or ≈ 4 h 13.3 min**

Example 5 p. 114

8. MAPS On a map of North Carolina, Raleigh and Asheville are about 8 inches apart. If the scale is 1 inch = 12 miles, how far apart are the cities? **about 96 mi**

Differentiated Instruction OL BL

Extension The development of proportional reasoning is crucial to future success in mathematics. While students typically find success with the process of cross multiplication, they rarely take the time to figure out why this procedure works. Engage mathematically talented students in other methods of solving proportions, such as multiplying the numerator and denominator by a common factor (focusing on non-integer factors).

Practice and Problem Solving

= Step-by-Step Solutions begin on page R12. Extra Practice begins on page 815.

Examples 1 and 2 pp. 111–112

Determine whether each pair of ratios are equivalent ratios. Write *yes* or *no*.

9. $\frac{9}{11}, \frac{81}{99}$ yes
10. $\frac{3}{7}, \frac{18}{42}$ yes
11. $\frac{8.4}{9.2}, \frac{8.8}{9.6}$ no
12. $\frac{4}{3}, \frac{6}{8}$ no
13. $\frac{29.2}{10.4}, \frac{7.3}{2.6}$ yes
14. $\frac{39.68}{60.14}, \frac{6.4}{9.7}$ yes

Example 3 p. 113

Solve each proportion. If necessary, round to the nearest hundredth.

15. $\frac{3}{8} = \frac{15}{a}$ 40
16. $\frac{t}{2} = \frac{6}{12}$ 1
17. $\frac{4}{9} = \frac{13}{q}$ 29.25
18. $\frac{15}{35} = \frac{g}{7}$ 3
19. $\frac{7}{10} = \frac{m}{14}$ 9.8
20. $\frac{8}{13} = \frac{v}{21}$ 12.92
21. $\frac{w}{2} = \frac{4.5}{6.8}$ 1.32
22. $\frac{1}{0.19} = \frac{12}{n}$ 2.28
23. $\frac{2}{0.21} = \frac{8}{n}$ 0.84
24. $\frac{2.4}{3.6} = \frac{k}{1.8}$ 1.2
25. $\frac{t}{0.3} = \frac{1.7}{0.9}$ 0.57
26. $\frac{7}{1.066} = \frac{z}{9.65}$ 63.37
27. $\frac{x-3}{5} = \frac{6}{10}$ 6
28. $\frac{7}{x+9} = \frac{21}{36}$ 3
29. $\frac{10}{15} = \frac{4}{x-5}$ 11

Example 4 p. 113

30. **CAR WASH** The B-Clean Car Wash washed 128 cars in 3 hours. At that rate, how many cars can they wash in 8 hours? about 341 cars

Example 5 p. 114

31. **MENU** On Monday, a restaurant made \$545 from selling 110 hamburgers. If they sold 53 hamburgers on Tuesday, how much did they make? about \$262.59

32. **MODELS** An artist used interlocking building blocks to build a scale model of Kennedy Space Center, Florida. In the model, 1 inch equals 1.67 feet of an actual space shuttle. The model is 110.3 inches tall. How tall is the actual space shuttle? Round to the nearest tenth. 184.2 ft

33. **GEOGRAPHY** On a map of Florida, the distance between Jacksonville and Tallahassee is 7.5 centimeters. If 2 centimeters = 40 miles, what is the distance between the two cities? 150 mi

B **Solve each proportion. If necessary, round to the nearest hundredth.**

34. $\frac{6}{14} = \frac{7}{x-3}$ 19.33
35. $\frac{7}{4} = \frac{f-4}{8}$ 18
36. $\frac{3-y}{4} = \frac{1}{9}$ 2.56
37. $\frac{4v+7}{15} = \frac{6v+2}{10}$ 0.8
38. $\frac{9b-3}{9} = \frac{5b+5}{3}$ −3
39. $\frac{2n-4}{5} = \frac{3n+3}{10}$ 11

40. **ATHLETES** At Piedmont High School, 3 out of every 8 students are athletes. If there are 1280 students at the school, how many are not athletes? 800 students

41. **BRACES** Two out of five students in the ninth grade have braces. If there are 325 students in the ninth grade, how many have braces? 130 students

42. **PAINT** Joel used a half gallon of paint to cover 84 square feet of wall. He has 932 square feet of wall to paint. How many gallons of paint should he purchase? 6 gal

Tips for New Teachers

Reasoning Remind the students that while ratios often appear as fractions, a ratio is a comparison of two quantities. This means that if the quantities have units, the numerator and denominator should have the same units, and in some cases, a conversion factor may be needed.

Differentiated Homework Options

Level	Assignment	Two-Day Option	
AL Basic	9–33, 46–47, 49–70	9–33 odd, 51–54	10–32 even, 46–47, 49–50, 55–70
OL Core	9–39 odd, 40–47, 49–70	9–33, 51–54	34–47, 49–50, 55–70
BL Advanced	34–67, (optional: 68–70)		

43 **MOVIE THEATERS** Use the table at the right. **a–b. See margin.**

a. Write a ratio of the number of indoor theaters to the total number of theaters for each year.

b. Do any two of the ratios you wrote for part a form a proportion? If so, explain the real-world meaning of the proportion.

Year	Indoor	Drive-In	Total
2000	35,567	683	36,250
2001	34,490	683	35,173
2002	35,170	666	35,836
2003	35,361	634	35,995
2004	36,012	640	36,652
2005	37,092	648	37,740
2006	37,776	649	38,425

Source: North American Theater Owners

44. DIARIES In a survey, 36% of the students said that they kept an electronic diary. There were 900 students who kept an electronic diary. How many students were in the survey? **2500**

Real-World Link

At a drive-in theater, the film is projected onto a large outdoor screen while the moviegoers sit in their cars. The sound for the film is broadcast on a radio station. In 1987, there were over 2000 drive-in theaters. By 1989, half of them had closed.

Source: North American Theater Owners

45. MULTIPLE REPRESENTATIONS In this problem, you will explore how changing the lengths of the sides of a shape by a factor changes the perimeter of that shape.

a. GEOMETRIC Draw a square *ABCD*. Measure and label the sides. Draw a second square *MNPQ* with sides twice as long as *ABCD*. Draw a third square *FGHJ* with sides half as long as *ABCD*. **See margin.**

b. TABULAR Complete the table below using the appropriate measures.

ABCD		*MNPQ*		*FGHJ*	
Side length	2	Side length	4	Side length	1
Perimeter	8	Perimeter	16	Perimeter	4

c. VERBAL Make a conjecture about the change in the perimeter of a square if the side length is increased or decreased by a factor. **See margin.**

H.O.T. Problems
Use Higher-Order Thinking Skills

46. OPEN ENDED Write a real-life example of a ratio.

47. REASONING Compare and contrast ratios and rates.

48. CHALLENGE If $\frac{a+1}{b-1} = \frac{5}{1}$ and $\frac{a-1}{b+1} = \frac{1}{1}$, find the value of $\frac{b}{a}$. (*Hint:* Choose different values of *a* and *b* for which the proportions are true and evaluate the expression $\frac{b}{a}$.) $\frac{2}{4}$ **or** $\frac{1}{2}$

49. FIND THE ERROR Tim and Aisha are solving the following problem. Is either of them correct? Explain.

Two years ago, 78 women were enrolled in a dance class, while 162 men were enrolled. This year 193 men enrolled, while the ratio of women to men did not change. How many women enrolled this year? **See Chapter 2 Answer Appendix.**

Tim

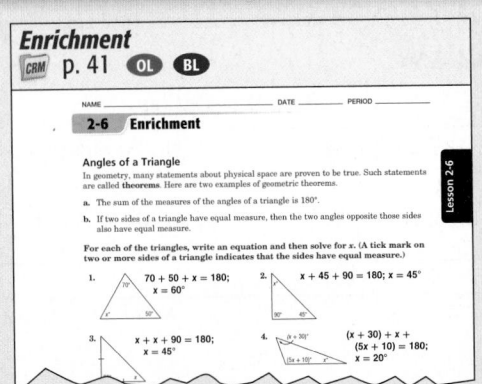

$\frac{78}{162} = \frac{193}{x}$

$78x = (162)(193)$

$78x = 31,266$

$x \approx 400.8$

Aisha

$\frac{162}{78} = \frac{x}{193}$

$162(193) = 78x$

$31,266 = 78x$

$x = 400.8$

50. WRITING IN MATH Describe how businesses can use ratios. Write about a real-world situation in which a business would use a ratio. **See Chapter 2 Answer Appendix.**

46. Sample answer: A basketball player makes one free throw shot for every 4 attempts. His ratio of points scored to points attempted on the free throw line is 1 : 4.

47. Ratios and rates each compare two numbers by using division. However, rates compare two measurements that involve different units of measure.

Multiple Representations In Exercise 45, students use a geometric sketch, a table of values, and verbal analysis to show how the perimeter of a square is affected by a change in dimensions.

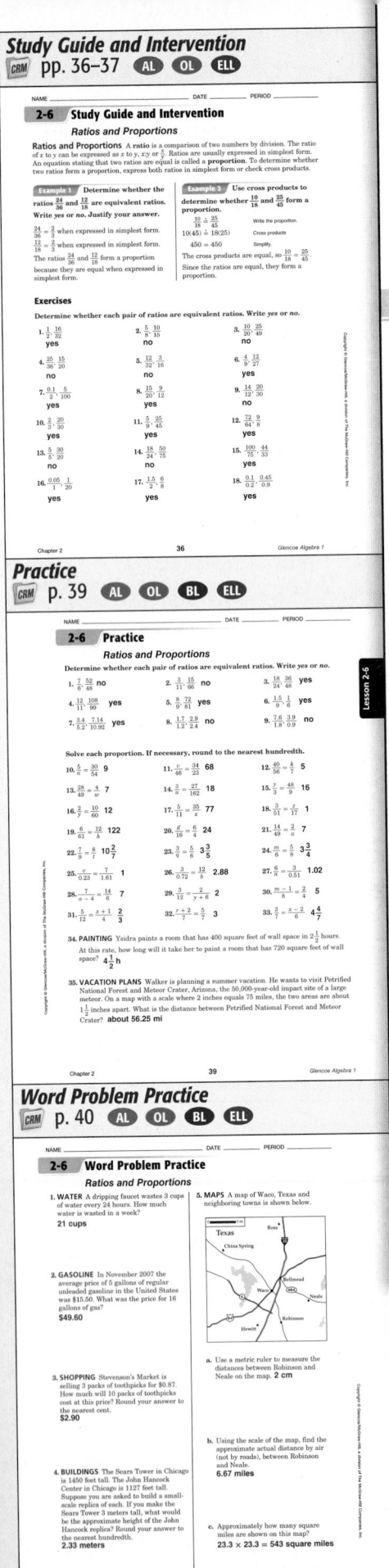

Study Guide and Intervention
CRM pp. 36–37 AL OL ELL

NAME ______ DATE ______ PERIOD ______

2-6 Study Guide and Intervention

Ratios and Proportions

Ratios and Proportions A **ratio** is a comparison of two numbers by division. The ratio of *x* to *y* can be expressed as *x* to *y*, *x*:*y* or $\frac{x}{y}$. Ratios are usually expressed in simplest form. An equation stating that two ratios are equal is called a **proportion**. To determine whether two ratios form a proportion, express both ratios in simplest form or check cross products.

Example 1 Determine whether the ratios $\frac{24}{36}$ and $\frac{12}{18}$ are equivalent ratios. Write *yes* or *no*. Justify your answer.

$\frac{24}{36} = \frac{2}{3}$ when expressed in simplest form.
$\frac{12}{18} = \frac{2}{3}$ when expressed in simplest form.
The ratios $\frac{24}{36}$ and $\frac{12}{18}$ form a proportion because they are equal when expressed in simplest form.

Example 2 Use cross products to determine whether $\frac{10}{18}$ and $\frac{25}{45}$ form a proportion.

$\frac{10}{18} \stackrel{?}{=} \frac{25}{45}$ Write the proportion.
$10(45) \stackrel{?}{=} 18(25)$ Cross products
$450 = 450$ Simplify.
The cross products are equal, so $\frac{10}{18} = \frac{25}{45}$. Since the ratios are equal, they form a proportion.

Exercises

Determine whether each pair of ratios are equivalent ratios. Write *yes* or *no*.

1. $\frac{1}{2}, \frac{16}{32}$ yes
2. $\frac{5}{8}, \frac{10}{15}$ no
3. $\frac{10}{20}, \frac{25}{49}$ no
4. $\frac{25}{36}, \frac{15}{20}$ no
5. $\frac{12}{32}, \frac{3}{16}$ no
6. $\frac{4}{9}, \frac{12}{27}$ yes
7. $\frac{0.1}{2}, \frac{5}{100}$ yes
8. $\frac{15}{20}, \frac{9}{12}$ yes
9. $\frac{14}{12}, \frac{20}{30}$ no
10. $\frac{2}{3}, \frac{20}{30}$ yes
11. $\frac{5}{9}, \frac{25}{45}$ yes
12. $\frac{72}{64}, \frac{9}{8}$ yes
13. $\frac{5}{5}, \frac{30}{20}$ no
14. $\frac{18}{24}, \frac{50}{75}$ no
15. $\frac{100}{75}, \frac{44}{33}$ yes
16. $\frac{0.05}{1}, \frac{1}{20}$ yes
17. $\frac{1.5}{2}, \frac{6}{8}$ yes
18. $\frac{0.1}{0.2}, \frac{0.45}{0.9}$ yes

Chapter 2 36 Glencoe Algebra 1

Practice
CRM p. 39 AL OL BL ELL

NAME ______ DATE ______ PERIOD ______

2-6 Practice

Ratios and Proportions

Determine whether each pair of ratios are equivalent ratios. Write *yes* or *no*.

1. $\frac{7}{6}, \frac{52}{48}$ no
2. $\frac{3}{11}, \frac{15}{66}$ no
3. $\frac{18}{24}, \frac{36}{48}$ yes
4. $\frac{12}{11}, \frac{108}{99}$ yes
5. $\frac{8}{9}, \frac{72}{81}$ yes
6. $\frac{1.5}{9}, \frac{1}{6}$ yes
7. $\frac{3.4}{5.2}, \frac{7.14}{10.92}$ yes
8. $\frac{1.7}{1.2}, \frac{2.9}{2.4}$ no
9. $\frac{7.6}{1.8}, \frac{3.9}{0.9}$ no

Solve each proportion. If necessary, round to the nearest hundredth.

10. $\frac{5}{a} = \frac{30}{54}$ 9
11. $\frac{v}{46} = \frac{34}{23}$ 68
12. $\frac{40}{56} = \frac{k}{7}$ 5
13. $\frac{28}{49} = \frac{4}{w}$ 7
14. $\frac{3}{a} = \frac{27}{162}$ 18
15. $\frac{7}{3} = \frac{48}{9}$ 16
16. $\frac{2}{r} = \frac{10}{60}$ 12
17. $\frac{5}{11} = \frac{35}{x}$ 77
18. $\frac{3}{51} = \frac{z}{17}$ 1
19. $\frac{6}{61} = \frac{12}{b}$ 122
20. $\frac{d}{16} = \frac{6}{4}$ 24
21. $\frac{14}{49} = \frac{2}{u}$ 7
22. $\frac{7}{9} = \frac{8}{d}$ $10\frac{2}{7}$
23. $\frac{3}{q} = \frac{5}{6}$ $3\frac{3}{5}$
24. $\frac{m}{6} = \frac{5}{8}$ $3\frac{3}{4}$
25. $\frac{v}{0.23} = \frac{7}{1.61}$ 1
26. $\frac{3}{0.72} = \frac{12}{b}$ 2.88
27. $\frac{6}{n} = \frac{3}{0.51}$ 1.02
28. $\frac{7}{a-4} = \frac{14}{6}$ 7
29. $\frac{3}{12} = \frac{2}{y+6}$ 2
30. $\frac{m-1}{8} = \frac{2}{4}$ 5
31. $\frac{5}{12} = \frac{x+1}{4}$ $\frac{2}{3}$
32. $\frac{r+2}{7} = \frac{5}{7}$ 3
33. $\frac{3}{5} = \frac{x-2}{4}$ $4\frac{4}{5}$

34. **PAINTING** Ysidra paints a room that has 400 square feet of wall space in $2\frac{1}{2}$ hours. At this rate, how long will it take her to paint a room that has 720 square feet of wall space? $4\frac{1}{2}$ h

35. **VACATION PLANS** Walker is planning a summer vacation. He wants to visit Petrified National Forest and Meteor Crater, Arizona, the 50,000-year-old impact site of a large meteor. On a map with a scale where 2 inches equals 75 miles, the two areas are about $1\frac{1}{2}$ inches apart. What is the distance between Petrified National Forest and Meteor Crater? about 56.25 mi

Chapter 2 39 Glencoe Algebra 1

Word Problem Practice
CRM p. 40 AL OL BL ELL

NAME ______ DATE ______ PERIOD ______

2-6 Word Problem Practice

Ratios and Proportions

1. **WATER** A dripping faucet wastes 3 cups of water every 24 hours. How much water is wasted in a week? 21 cups

2. **GASOLINE** In November 2007 the average price of 5 gallons of regular unleaded gasoline in the United States was $15.50. What was the price for 16 gallons of gas? $49.60

3. **SHOPPING** Stevenson's Market is selling 3 packs of toothpicks for $0.87. How much will 10 packs of toothpicks cost at this price? Round your answer to the nearest cent. $2.90

4. **BUILDINGS** The Sears Tower in Chicago is 1450 feet tall. The John Hancock Center in Chicago is 1127 feet tall. Suppose you are asked to build a small-scale replica of each. If you make the Sears Tower 3 meters tall, what would be the approximate height of the John Hancock replica? Round your answer to the nearest hundredth. 2.33 meters

5. **MAPS** A map of Waco, Texas and neighboring towns is shown below.

a. Use a metric ruler to measure the distances between Robinson and Neale on the map. 2 cm

b. Using the scale of the map, find the approximate actual distance by air (not by roads), between Robinson and Neale. 6.67 miles

c. Approximately how many square miles are shown on this map? 23.3 × 23.3 = 543 square miles

Chapter 2 40 Glencoe Algebra 1

Enrichment
CRM p. 41 OL BL

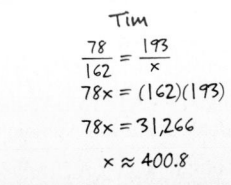

NAME ______ DATE ______ PERIOD ______

2-6 Enrichment

Angles of a Triangle

In geometry, many statements about physical space are proven to be true. Such statements are called **theorems**. Here are two examples of geometric theorems.

a. The sum of the measures of the angles of a triangle is 180°.

b. If two sides of a triangle have equal measure, then the two angles opposite those sides also have equal measure.

For each of the triangles, write an equation and then solve for *x*. (A tick mark on two or more sides of a triangle indicates that the sides have equal measure.)

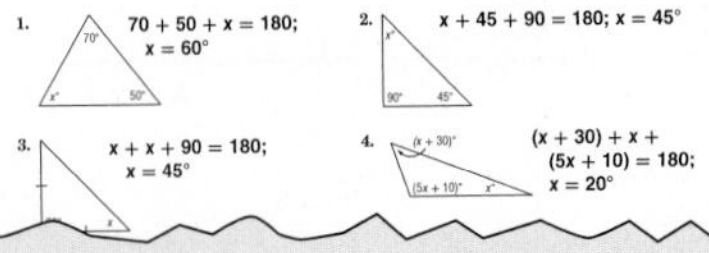

1. 70 + 50 + x = 180; x = 60°
2. x + 45 + 90 = 180; x = 45°
3. x + x + 90 = 180; x = 45°
4. (x + 30) + x + (5x + 10) = 180; x = 20°

PSAE PRACTICE 6.11.17, 10.11.05, 7.11.05, 8.11.21

51. In the figure, $x : y = 2 : 3$ and $y : z = 3 : 5$. If $x = 10$, find the value of z. **C**

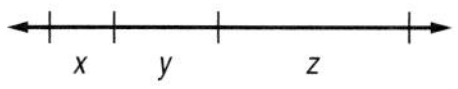

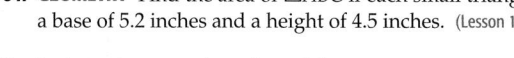

A 15
B 20
C 25
D 30

52. GRIDDED RESPONSE A race car driver records the finishing times for recent practice trials.

Trial	Time (seconds)
1	5.09
2	5.10
3	4.95
4	4.91
5	5.05

What is the mean time, in seconds, for the trials? **5.02**

53. GEOMETRY If $\angle LMN$ is similar to $\angle LPO$, what is z? **G**

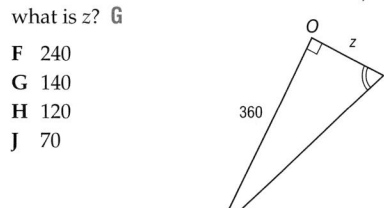

F 240
G 140
H 120
J 70

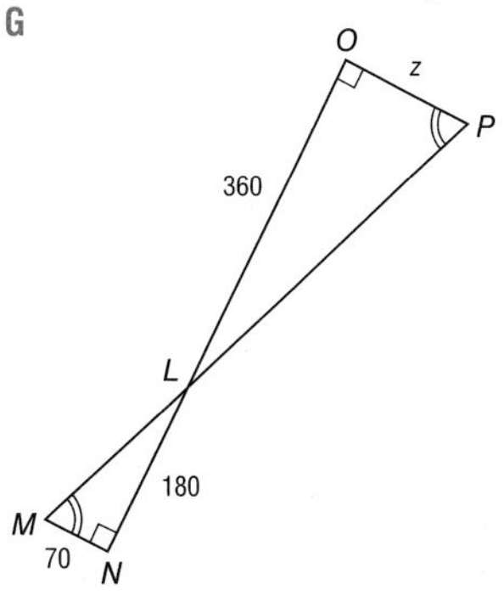

54. Which equation below illustrates the Commutative Property? **C**

A $(3x + 4y) + 2z = 3x + (4y + 2z)$
B $7(x + y) = 7x + 7y$
C $xyz = yxz$
D $x + 0 = x$

Spiral Review

Solve each equation. (Lesson 2-5)

55. $|x + 5| = -8$ $\varnothing$

56. $|b + 9| = 2$ $\{-7, -11\}$

57. $|2p - 3| = 17$ $\{10, -7\}$

58. $|5c - 8| = 12$ $\left\{4, -\frac{4}{5}\right\}$

59. HEALTH When exercising, a person's pulse rate should not exceed a certain limit. This maximum rate is represented by the expression $0.8(220 - a)$, where a is age in years. Find the age of a person whose maximum pulse rate is 152. (Lesson 2-4) **30 years**

Solve each equation. Check your solution. (Lesson 2-3)

60. $15 = 4a - 5$ **5**

61. $7g - 14 = -63$ **−7**

62. $9 + \frac{y}{5} = 6$ **−15**

63. $\frac{t}{8} - 6 = -12$ **−48**

64. GEOMETRY Find the area of $\triangle ABC$ if each small triangle has a base of 5.2 inches and a height of 4.5 inches. (Lesson 1-3) **46.8 in^2**

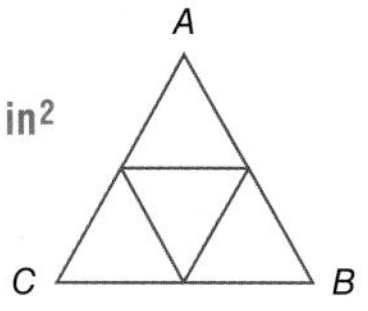

Evaluate each expression. (Lesson 1-2)

65. $3 + 16 \div 8 \cdot 5$ **13**

66. $4^2 \cdot 3 - 5(6 + 3)$ **3**

Skills Review

Solve each equation. (Lesson 2-2)

67. $4p = 22$ **5.5**

68. $5h = 33$ **6.6**

69. $1.25y = 4.375$ **3.5**

70. $9.8m = 30.87$ **3.15**

Exercise Alert

Ruler For Exercise 45, students need a ruler to draw and measure the sides of three squares.

Watch Out!

Find the Error In Exercise 49, help students sort out the four elements of the proportions. The first ratio in Tim's solution compares women to men. Tim's second ratio does not compare women to men. It compares men to women. Aisha's first ratio compares men to women and her second compares women to men.

4 ASSESS

Crystal Ball Have students write a sentence on how they think today's lesson will connect with tomorrow's lesson on finding the percent of change.

Additional Answers

43a. 2000: $\frac{35{,}567}{36{,}250}$, 2001: $\frac{34{,}490}{35{,}173}$; 2002: $\frac{35{,}170}{35{,}836}$; 2003: $\frac{35{,}361}{35{,}995}$; 2004: $\frac{36{,}012}{36{,}652}$; 2005: $\frac{37{,}092}{37{,}740}$; 2006: $\frac{37{,}776}{38{,}425}$

43b. None of the ratios form a proportion.

45a.

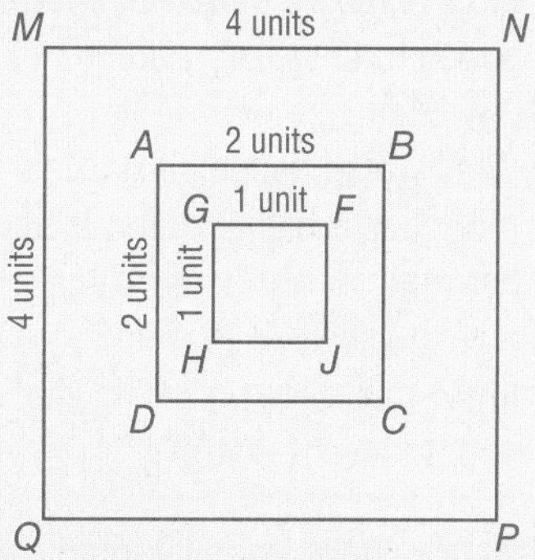

45c. If the length of a side is increased by a factor, the perimeter is also increased by that factor. If the length of the sides are decreased by a factor, the perimeter is also decreased by the same factor.

Differentiated Instruction BL

Extension Present students with the following problem: Kala made a scale drawing of a 12 m × 15 m room. The scale drawing is 9.6 cm × 12 cm. What scale did she use? Explain. Justify your answer. 1 cm = 1.25 m; Sample answer: To find the scale, simplify 9.6/12. Then use the scale to check that the length and width of the scale drawing and the original room are proportional: $\frac{1}{1.25} = \frac{9.6}{12}$, $12 = 12$ and $\frac{1}{1.25} = \frac{12}{15}$; $15 = 15$; since the cross products are equal, the scale is correct.

EXTEND 2-6

Lesson Notes

1 FOCUS

Objective Use a spreadsheet to investigate debt-to-income ratios.

Materials for Each Student

- computer
- spreadsheet software

Teaching Tip

You may want to explain that lending institutions use the debt-to-income ratio to determine their risk in lending money to an individual. Debt-to-income ratios are also used for car loans and other major purchases.

2 TEACH

Working in Cooperative Groups

Have students work in pairs to complete the Activity.

Ask:

- What would happen to the debt-to-income ratio if more items were added to the expenses column? It would increase.
- What would happen to the debt-to-income ratio if more items were added to the salary column? It would decrease.
- What would happen if Dorrie's mortgage is higher or lower than her rent? A higher mortgage means a greater debt-to-income ratio; a lower mortgage means a lower debt-to-income ratio.

Practice Have students complete Exercises 1–4.

EXTEND 2-6

Spreadsheet Lab
Financial Ratios

IL Math Online glencoe.com
Graphing Calculator Personal Tutor

IL Learning Standards **6.D.4 Solve problems involving recipes or mixtures, financial calculations and geometric similarity using ratios, proportions and percents.** *Also addresses 6.B.4 and 8.B.4a.*

You can use a spreadsheet to investigate the debt-to-income ratio in mortgage lending.

ACTIVITY

Dorrie is thinking about buying a house. She has the following expenses: rent of $650, credit card monthly bills of $320, a car payment of $410, and a student loan payment of $115. Dorrie has a yearly salary of $46,500. You can use a spreadsheet to find Dorrie's debt-to-income ratio.

Step 1 Enter Dorrie's debts in column B.

Step 2 Add her debts using a function in cell B6. Go to Insert and then Function. Then choose Sum. The resulting sum of 1495 should appear in B6.

Step 3 Now insert Dorrie's salary in column C. Remember to find her monthly salary by dividing the yearly salary by 12.

A mortgage company will use her debt-to-income ratio in part to determine if Dorrie qualifies for a mortgage loan. The **debt-to-income ratio** is calculated as *how much she owes per month* divided by *how much she earns each month.*

Step 4 Enter a formula to find the debt-to-income ratio in cell C6. In the formula bar, enter =B6/C2.

The ratio of about 0.39 appears. An ideal ratio would be 0.36 or less. A ratio higher than 0.36 would cause an increased interest rate or may require a higher down payment.

The spreadsheet shows a debt-to-income ratio of about 0.39. Dorrie should try to eliminate or reduce some debts or try to earn more money in order to lower her debt-to-income ratio.

Lab 2-6 B Spreadsheet.xls

◇	A	B	C
1	Type of Debt	Expenses	Salary
2	Rent	650	3875
3	Credit Cards	320	
4	Car Payment	410	
5	Student Loan	115	
6		1495	0.385806
7			

Sheet 1 / Sheet 2 / Sheet 3

Exercises

1. If Dorrie waits until she pays off her credit card bills to buy a house, what would be her new debt-to-income ratio? **about 0.30**
2. Dorrie decides to reduce her monthly credit card payments to $160 per month, and she sells her car. How would her debt-to-income ratio change? **Her ratio would be lowered to about 0.24.**
3. How could Dorrie improve her debt-to-income ratio? **Sample answer: Reduce or eliminate credit card debt, reduce or eliminate car payments, or earn a higher salary.**
4. How would your spreadsheet be different if Dorrie had income other than her monthly salary? **Sample answer: Column C would have other entries and then a cell with the sum of assets.**

3 ASSESS

Formative Assessment

Use Exercise 2 to assess whether students understand how the ratio of debt-to-income is affected by the amount of debt.

From Concrete to Abstract

Use Exercise 4 to assess whether students understand how to set up and use a spreadsheet to determine debt-to-income ratios.

2-7 Percent of Change

Then
You solved proportions. (Lesson 2-6)

Now
- Find the percent of change.
- Solve problems involving percent of change.

IL Learning Standards

6.D.4 Solve problems involving recipes or mixtures, financial calculations and geometric similarity using ratios, proportions and percents. **8.A.4b** Represent mathematical patterns and describe their properties using variables and mathematical symbols.

New Vocabulary
percent of change
percent of increase
percent of decrease

IL Math Online

glencoe.com
- Extra Examples
- Personal Tutor
- Self-Check Quiz
- Homework Help

Why?

Every year, millions of people volunteer their time to improve their community. The difference in the number of volunteers from one year to the next can be used to determine a percent to represent the increase or decrease in volunteers.

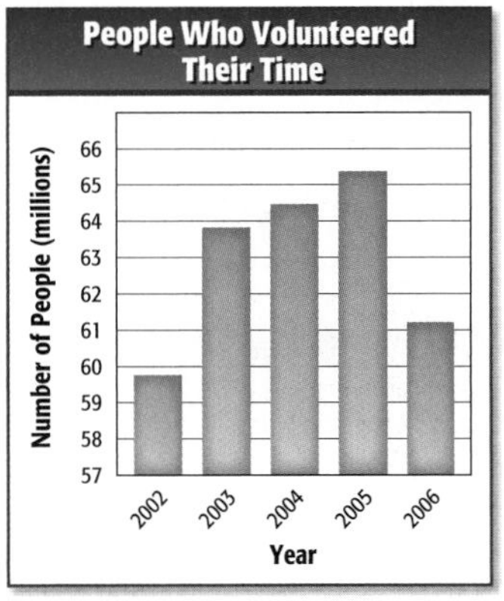

Source: Bureau of Labor and Statistics

Percent of Change **Percent of change** is the ratio of the change in an amount to the original amount expressed as a percent. If the new number is greater than the original number, the percent of change is a **percent of increase.** If the new number is less than the original number, the percent of change is a **percent of decrease.**

EXAMPLE 1 Percent of Change

Determine whether each percent of change is a percent of *increase* or a percent of *decrease*. Then find the percent of change.

a. original: 20
final: 23

Subtract the original amount from the final amount to find the amount of change: 23 − 20 = 3.

Since the new amount is greater than the original, this is a percent of increase.

Use the original number, 20, as the base.

change → , original amount → $\frac{3}{20} = \frac{r}{100}$

$3(100) = r(20)$

$300 = 20r$

$\frac{300}{20} = \frac{20r}{20}$

$15 = r$

The percent of increase is 15%.

b. original: 25
final: 17

Subtract the original amount from the final amount to find the amount of change: 17 − 25 = −8.

Since the new amount is less than the original, this is a percent of decrease.

Use the original number, 25, as the base.

change → , original amount → $\frac{-8}{25} = \frac{r}{100}$

$-8(100) = r(25)$

$-800 = 25r$

$\frac{-800}{25} = \frac{25r}{25}$

$-32 = r$

The percent of decrease is 32%.

Check Your Progress

1A. original: 66
new: 30 dec.; about 55%

1B. original: 9.8
new: 12.1 inc.; about 23.5%

1C. original: 24
new: 40 inc.; about 66.7%

1D. original: 500
new: 131 dec.; 73.8%

Personal Tutor glencoe.com

2-7 Lesson Notes

1 FOCUS

Vertical Alignment

Before Lesson 2-7
Solve proportions.

Lesson 2-7
Find the percent of change.
Solve problems involving percent of change.

After Lesson 2-7
Develop the concept of slope as rate of change.

2 TEACH

Scaffolding Questions

Have students read the *Why?* section of the lesson.

Ask:
- Which year(s) do you think will show a percent of increase? 2003, 2004, 2005
- Which year(s) will show a percent of decrease? 2006
- About how many more people volunteered in 2003 than in 2002? about 4 million more

Lesson 2-7 Resources

Resource	Approaching-Level	On-Level	Beyond-Level	English Learners
Teacher Edition	• Differentiated Instruction, p. 121	• Differentiated Instruction, p. 121	• Differentiated Instruction, p. 124	
Chapter Resource Masters	• Study Guide and Intervention, pp. 42–43 • Skills Practice, p. 44 • Practice, p. 45 • Word Problem Practice, p. 46	• Study Guide and Intervention, pp. 42–43 • Skills Practice, p. 44 • Practice, p. 45 • Word Problem Practice, p. 46 • Enrichment, p. 47	• Practice, p. 45 • Word Problem Practice, p. 46 • Enrichment, p. 47	• Study Guide and Intervention, pp. 42–43 • Skills Practice, p. 44 • Practice, p. 45
Transparencies	• 5-Minute Check Transparency 2-7	• 5-Minute Check Transparency 2-7	• 5-Minute Check Transparency 2-7	• 5-Minute Check Transparency 2-7
Other	• Study Notebook • Teaching Algebra with Manipulatives	• Study Notebook • Teaching Algebra with Manipulatives	• Study Notebook	• Study Notebook • Teaching Algebra with Manipulatives

Percent of Change

Example 1 shows how to determine if a percent of change is a percent of increase or a percent of decrease and how to find the percent of change.
Example 2 shows how to write a percent of change proportion and use it to solve a real-world problem.

Formative Assessment

Use the Check Your Progress exercises after each Example to determine students' understanding of concepts.

Additional Examples

1 Determine whether each percent of change is a percent of *increase* or a percent of *decrease*. Then find the percent of change.

a. original: 32
new: 40
percent of increase; 25%

b. original: 20
new: 4
percent of decrease; 80%

2 **SALES** The price a used-book store pays to buy a book is \$5. The store sells the book for 28% above the price that it pays for the book. What is the selling price of the book? \$6.40

Additional Examples also in Interactive Classroom PowerPoint® Presentations

IWB INTERACTIVE WHITEBOARD READY

Real-World Link

Over 11.8 million people around the world went on a cruise in 2006.

Source: M&L Research, Inc.

Real-World EXAMPLE 2 Percent of Change

CRUISE The number of cruise ships in North America increased 18% from 2000 to 2005. If there were 192 ships in 2005, how many were there in 2000?

Let c = the number of cruise ships in 2000. Since 18% is a percent of increase, the number of cruise ships in 2000 is less than the number of ships in 2005.

change → / original amount →	$\frac{192 - c}{c} = \frac{18}{100}$	Percent proportion
	$(192 - c)100 = 18c$	Find the cross products.
	$19{,}200 - 100c = 18c$	Distibutive Property
	$19{,}200 - 100c + 100c = 18c + 100c$	Add $100c$ to each side.
	$19{,}200 = 118c$	Simplify.
	$\frac{19{,}200}{118} = \frac{118c}{118}$	Divide each side by 118.
	$163 \approx c$	Simplify.

There were approximately 163 cruise ships in 2000.

Check Your Progress

2. TUITION A recent percent of increase in tuition at Northwestern University, in Evanston, Illinois, was 5.4%. If the new cost is \$33,408 per year, find the original cost per year. **\$31,696.39**

Personal Tutor glencoe.com

Solve Problems Two applications of percent of change are sales tax and discounts. Sales tax is an example of a percent of increase. Discount is an example of a percent of decrease.

EXAMPLE 3 Sales Tax

SHOPPING Marta is purchasing wire and beads to make jewelry. Her merchandise is \$28.62 before tax. If the tax is 7.25% of the total sales, what is the final cost?

Step 1 Find the tax.

The tax is 7.25% of the price of the merchandise.

7.25% of \$28.62 = 0.0725×28.62	7.25% = 0.0725
= 2.07495	Use a calculator.

Step 2 Find the cost with tax.

Round \$2.07495 to \$2.07 since tax is always rounded to the nearest cent. Add this amount to the original price: \$28.62 + \$2.07 = \$30.69.

The total cost of Marta's jewelry supplies is \$30.69.

Check Your Progress

3. SHOPPING A new DVD costs \$24.99. If the sales tax is 6.85%, what is the total cost? **\$26.70**

Personal Tutor glencoe.com

To find a discounted amount, you will follow similar steps to those for sales tax.

Focus on Mathematical Content

Changing Percents to Decimals When changing a percent to a decimal, move the decimal point two places to the left and drop the percent sign.

Tips for New Teachers

Percent of Change Tell students to remember that the percent of change is relative to the original amount. So, the change in value is divided by the original amount.

StudyTip

Key Words When translating a problem from word sentences to math sentences, the word "is" translates to =, and the word "of" translates to ×.

EXAMPLE 4 Discounts

DISCOUNT Since Tyrell has earned good grades in school, he qualifies for the Good Student Discount on his car insurance. His monthly payment without the discount is $85. If the discount is 20%, what will he pay each month?

Step 1 Find the discount.

The discount is 20% of the original payment.

20% of $85 = 0.20 × 85 — **20% = 0.20**

= 17 — **Use a calculator.**

Step 2 Find the cost after discount.

Subtract $17 from the original payment: $85 − $17 = $68.

With the Good Student Discount, Tyrell will pay $68 per month.

Check Your Progress

4. **SALES** A picture frame originally priced at $14.89 is on sale for 40% off. What is the discounted price? **$8.93**

Personal Tutor glencoe.com

Check Your Understanding

Example 1 p. 119

State whether each percent of change is a percent of *increase* or a percent of *decrease*. Then find the percent of change. Round to the nearest whole percent.

1. original: 78
   new: 125 **inc.;60%**
2. original: 41
   new: 24 **dec.;41%**
3. original: 6 candles
   new: 8 candles **inc.;33%**
4. original: 35 computers
   new: 32 computers **dec.;9%**

Example 2 p. 120

5. **GEOGRAPHY** The distance from Phoenix to Tucson is 120 miles. The distance from Phoenix to Flagstaff is about 21.7% longer. To the nearest mile, what is the distance from Phoenix to Flagstaff? **146 mi**

Example 3 p. 120

Find the total price of each item.

6. dress: $22.50
   sales tax: 7.5% **$24.19**
7. video game: $35.99
   sales tax: 6.75% **$38.42**
8. **PROM** A limo costs $85 to rent for 3 hours plus a 7% sales tax. What is the total cost to rent a limo for 6 hours? **$181.90**
9. **GAMES** A computer game costs $49.95 plus a 6.25% sales tax. What is the total cost of the game? **$53.07**

Example 4 p. 121

Find the discounted price of each item.

10. guitar: $95.00
    discount: 15% **$80.75**
11. DVD: $22.95
    discount: 25% **$17.21**
12. **SKATEBOARD** A skateboard costs $99.99. If you have a coupon for 20% off, how much will you save? **$20**
13. **TICKETS** Tickets to the county fair are $8 for an adult and $5 for a child. If you have a 15% discount card, how much will 2 adult tickets and 2 child tickets cost? **$22.10**

Differentiated Instruction AL OL

If students have difficulty recognizing patterns that involve percents,

Then pair these students with those who are able to recognize and work with patterns. After they complete Exercise 44, have them use the table in the exercise as a model to explore patterns using other numbers, such as 1% of 200 is 2, and so on.

Solve Problems

Example 3 shows how to solve real-world problems that deal with a percent of increase, such as sales tax. **Example 4** shows how to solve real-world problems that deal with a percent of decrease, such as a discounted price.

TEACH with TECH

WEB SEARCH Ask students to research populations of different cities and states from the U.S. Census Bureau Web site. Have them calculate the percent of change in population over different time periods.

Additional Examples

3. **SALES TAX** A meal for two at a restaurant costs $32.75. If the sales tax is 5%, what is the total price of the meal? $34.39
4. **DISCOUNT** A dog toy is on sale for 20% off the original price. If the original price of the toy is $3.80, what is the discounted price? $3.04

3 PRACTICE

Formative Assessment

Use Exercises 1–13 to check for understanding.

Use the chart at the bottom of the next page to customize assignments for your students.

Watch Out!

Find the Error In Exercise 47, the only difference between Maddie's and Xavier's work is the number in the denominator of the first ratio in the proportion. Maddie has 28, which is the new amount in the problem, and Xavier has 25, which is the original amount in the problem. Suggest that students review Examples 1 and 2. Remind them that the ratio to use is the amount of change to the original amount.

Additional Answers

44c. 16% of 31.25 is 5.
6.25% of 320 is 20.
400% of 5 is 20.

48. Sometimes; the percent of change can be greater than 100%. If the original amount was 20 and the new amount was 40, then the percent of change is 100%.

49. Sample answer: To determine whether a percent of change is a percent of increase or decrease, compare the new amount with the old amount. If the new amount is greater, the change is an increase. If the new amount is less, then the change is a decrease. To find the percent of change, subtract the original from the new amount. Then write a proportion, comparing the change to the original amount. The answer should be written as a percent.

Practice and Problem Solving

● = Step-by-Step Solutions begin on page R12.
Extra Practice begins on page 815.

Example 1 p. 119

State whether each percent of change is a percent of *increase* or a percent of *decrease*. Then find the percent of change. Round to the nearest whole percent.

14. original: 35
new: 40 **inc.; 14%**

15. original: 16
new: 10 **dec.; 38%**

16. original: 27
new: 73 **inc.; 170%**

17. original: 92
new: 21 **dec.; 77%**

18. original: 21.2 grams
new: 10.8 grams **dec.; 49%**

19. original: 11 feet
new: 25 feet **inc.; 127%**

20. original: $68
new: $76 **inc.; 12%**

21. original: 21 hours
new: 40 hours **inc.; 90%**

Example 2 p. 120

22. **GASOLINE** The average cost of regular gasoline in North Carolina increased by 73% from 2006 to 2007. If the average cost of a gallon of gas in 2006 was $2.069, what was the average cost in 2007? Round to the nearest cent. **$3.58**

23. **CARS** Beng is shopping for a car. The cost of a new car is $15,500. This is 25% greater than the cost of a used car. What is the cost of the used car? **$12,400**

Example 3 p. 120

Find the total price of each item.

24. messenger bag: $28.00
tax: 7.25% **$30.03**

25. software: $45.00
tax: 5.5% **$47.48**

26. vase: $5.50
tax: 6.25% **$5.84**

27. book: $25.95
tax: 5.25% **$27.31**

28. magazine: $3.50
tax: 5.75% **$3.70**

29. pillow: $9.99
tax: 6.75% **$10.66**

Example 4 p. 121

Find the discounted price of each item.

30. computer: $1099.00
discount: 25% **$824.25**

31. CD player: $89.99
discount: 15% **$76.49**

32. athletic shoes: $59.99
discount: 40% **$35.99**

33. jeans: $24.50
discount: 33% **$16.42**

34. jacket: $125.00
discount: 25% **$93.75**

35. belt: $14.99
discount: 20% **$11.99**

B **Find the final price of each item.**

36. sweater: $14.99
discount: 12%
tax: 6.25% **$14.02**

37. printer: $60.00
discount: 25%
tax: 6.75% **$48.04**

38. board game: $25.00
discount: 15%
tax: 7.5% **$22.84**

39. **CONSUMER PRICE INDEX** An *index* measures the percent change of a value from a base year. An index of 115 means that there was a 15% increase from the base year. In 2000, the consumer price index of dairy products was 160.7. In 2005, it was 182.4. Determine the percent of change. **about 13.5% increase**

40. **FINANCIAL LITERACY** The current price of each share of a technology company is $135. If this represents a 16.2% increase over the past year, what was the price per share a year ago? **$116.18**

Real-World Link

Softball became an Olympic event in 1996. The American women, winning the gold medal in 2004, capped a 79-game winning streak.

Source: *USA TODAY*

41. **SHOPPING** A group of girls are shopping for dresses to wear to the spring dance. One finds a dress priced $75 with a 20% discount. A second girl finds a dress priced $85 with a 30% discount.

a. Find the amount of discount for each dress. **first girl's dress = $15; second girl's dress = $25.50**

b. Which girl is getting the better price for the dress? **the second girl by $0.50**

42. **RECREATIONAL SPORTS** In 1995, there were 73,567 youth softball teams. By 2007, there were 86,049. Determine the percent of increase. **about 17%**

Differentiated Homework Options

Level	Assignment	Two-Day Option	
AL Basic	14–35, 45–47, 49–73	15–35 odd, 50–53	14–34 even, 45–47, 49, 54–73
OL Core	15–35 odd, 36–47, 49–73	14–35, 50–53	36–47, 49, 54–73
BL Advanced	36–67, (optional: 68–73)		

44b. Sample answer: In the second column, as the percent doubles the amount is cut in half. In the fifth column, as the percent is cut in half the amount doubles.

45. Sample answer: A CD is on sale for $9.99. If tax is 6.5%, what will the CD cost?

46. 25%;60%; The percentage of the number and the decrease add to 100%; Yes

43. **GROCERIES** Which grocery item had the greatest percent increase in cost from 2000 to 2005? **ground beef**

Average Retail Prices of Selected Grocery Items

Grocery Item	Cost in 2000 ($ per pound)	Cost in 2005 ($ per pound)
milk (gallon)	2.79	3.24
eggs (dozen)	0.96	1.35
chicken (whole)	1.08	1.06
ground beef	1.63	2.30
apples	0.82	0.97
iceberg lettuce	0.85	0.85
peanut butter	1.96	1.70

Source: Statistical Abstract of the United States

44. **MULTIPLE REPRESENTATIONS** In this problem, you will explore patterns in percentages.

a. **TABULAR** Copy and complete the following table.

1% of	500	is 5.	100% of	20	is 20.	25	% of 80 is 20.
2% of	250	is 5.	50% of	40	is 20.	50	% of 40 is 20.
4% of	125	is 5.	25% of	80	is 20.	100	% of 20 is 20.
8% of	62.5	is 5.	12.5% of	160	is 20.	200	% of 10 is 20.

b. **VERBAL** Describe the patterns in the second and fifth columns.

c. **ANALYTICAL** Use the patterns to write the fifth row of the table. **See margin.**

Real-World Link

In a recent year, the amount of sales tax varied across the United States from 0% to 7.25%.

Source: Federation of Tax Administrators

H.O.T. Problems Use Higher-Order Thinking Skills

45. **OPEN ENDED** Write a real-world problem to find the total price of an item including sales tax.

46. **REASONING** If you have 75% of a number *n*, what percent of decrease is it from the number *n*? If you have 40% of a number *a*, what percent of decrease do you have from the number *a*? What pattern do you notice? Is this always true?

47. **FIND THE ERROR** Maddie and Xavier are solving for the percent change if the original amount was $25 and the new amount is $28. Is either of them correct? Explain your reasoning. **Xavier; Maddie divided by the new amount instead of the original amount.**

Maddie	Xavier
$\frac{3}{28} = \frac{r}{100}$	$\frac{3}{25} = \frac{r}{100}$
$3(100) = 28r$	$3(100) = 25r$
$300 = 28r$	$300 = 25r$
$10.7 = r$	$12 = r$

48. **CHALLENGE** Determine whether the following statement is *sometimes*, *always*, or *never* true. *The percent of change is less than 100%.* **See margin.**

49. **WRITING IN MATH** Explain how to find a percent of change between two values and how to determine whether the change is a percent of increase or decrease. **See margin.**

Multiple Representations In Exercise 44, students use a table of values and verbal analysis to show patterns of percentages.

Study Guide and Intervention
CRM pp. 42–43 AL OL ELL

NAME ______ DATE ______ PERIOD ______

2-7 Study Guide and Intervention

Percent of Change

Percent of Change When an increase or decrease in an amount is expressed as a percent, the percent is called the **percent of change**. If the new number is greater than the original number, the percent of change is a **percent of increase**. If the new number is less than the original number, the percent of change is the **percent of decrease.**

Example 1 Find the percent of increase.
original: 48
new: 60

First, subtract to find the amount of increase. The amount of increase is $60 - 48 = 12$.
Then find the percent of increase by using the original number, 48, as the base.

$\frac{12}{48} = \frac{r}{100}$ Percent proportion
$12(100) = 48(r)$ Cross products
$1200 = 48r$ Simplify.
$\frac{1200}{48} = \frac{48r}{48}$ Divide each side by 48.
$25 = r$ Simplify.

The percent of increase is 25%.

Example 2 Find the percent of decrease.
original: 30
new: 22

First, subtract to find the amount of decrease. The amount of decrease is $30 - 22 = 8$.
Then find the percent of decrease by using the original number, 30, as the base.

$\frac{8}{30} = \frac{r}{100}$ Percent proportion
$8(100) = 30(r)$ Cross products
$800 = 30r$ Simplify.
$\frac{800}{30} = \frac{30r}{30}$ Divide each side by 30.
$26\frac{2}{3} = r$ Simplify.

The percent of decrease is $26\frac{2}{3}$%, or about 27%.

Exercises

State whether each percent of change is a percent of *increase* or a percent of *decrease*. Then find each percent of change. Round to the nearest whole percent.

1. original: 50, new: 80 **increase; 60%**
2. original: 90, new: 100 **increase; 11%**
3. original: 45, new: 20 **decrease; 56%**
4. original: 77.5, new: 62 **decrease; 20%**
5. original: 140, new: 150 **increase; 7%**
6. original: 135, new: 90 **decrease; 33%**
7. original: 120, new: 180 **increase; 50%**
8. original: 90, new: 270 **increase; 200%**
9. original: 27.5, new: 25 **decrease; 9%**
10. original: 84, new: 98 **increase; 17%**
11. original: 12.5, new: 10 **decrease; 20%**
12. original: 250, new: 500 **increase; 100%**

Chapter 2 42 Glencoe Algebra 1

Practice
CRM p. 45 AL OL BL ELL

NAME ______ DATE ______ PERIOD ______

2-7 Practice

Percent of Change

State whether each percent of change is a percent of *increase* or a percent of *decrease*. Then find each percent of change. Round to the nearest whole percent.

1. original: 18, new: 10 **decrease; 44%**
2. original: 140, new: 160 **increase; 14%**
3. original: 200, new: 320 **increase; 60%**
4. original: 10, new: 25 **increase; 150%**
5. original: 76, new: 60 **decrease; 21%**
6. original: 128, new: 120 **decrease; 6%**
7. original: 15, new: 35.5 **increase; 137%**
8. original: 98.6, new: 64 **decrease; 35%**
9. original: 58.8, new: 65.7 **increase; 12%**

Find the total price of each item.

10. concrete blocks: $95.00, tax: 6% **$100.70**
11. crib: $240.00, tax: 6.5% **$255.60**
12. jacket: $125.00, tax: 5.5% **$131.88**
13. class ring: $325.00, tax: 6% **$344.50**
14. blanket: $24.99, tax: 7% **$26.74**
15. kite: $18.90, tax: 5% **$19.85**

Find the discounted price of each item.

16. dry cleaning: $25.00, discount: 15% **$21.25**
17. computer game: $49.99, discount: 25% **$37.49**
18. luggage: $185.00, discount: 30% **$129.50**
19. stationery: $12.95, discount: 10% **$11.66**
20. prescription glasses: $149, discount: 20% **$119.20**
21. pair of shorts: $24.99, discount: 45% **$13.74**

Find the final price of each item.

22. television: $375.00, discount: 25%, tax: 6% **$298.13**
23. DVD player: $269.00, discount: 20%, tax: 7% **$230.26**
24. printer: $255.00, discount: 30%, tax: 5.5% **$188.32**

25. **INVESTMENTS** The price per share of a stock decreased from $90 per share to $36 per share early in 2009. By what percent did the price of the stock decrease? **60%**

26. **HEATING COSTS** Customers of a utility company received notices in their monthly bills that heating costs for the average customer had increased 125% over last year because of an unusually severe winter. In January of last year, the Garcia's paid $120 for heating. What should they expect to pay this January if their bill increased by 125%? **$270**

Chapter 2 45 Glencoe Algebra 1

Lesson 2-7

Word Problem Practice
CRM p. 46 AL OL BL ELL

NAME ______ DATE ______ PERIOD ______

2-7 Word Problem Practice

Percent of Change

1. **SPORTS** A regulation girls' fast pitch softball diamond has bases that are 60 feet apart. A regulation professional baseball diamond has bases that are 50% farther apart. Label the distance between the bases on the regulation baseball diamond diagram.

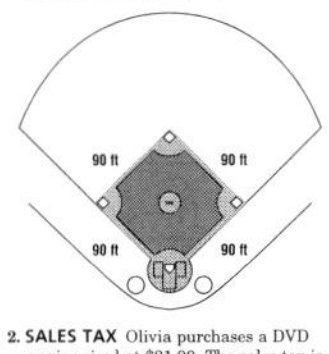

2. **SALES TAX** Olivia purchases a DVD movie priced at $21.99. The sales tax is 6.5%. What is the total price of the movie, including tax? **$23.42**

3. **EDUCATION** The ACT is a college entrance exam taken by high school students. The maximum score that can be earned is 36. The average score in the United States was 21.2 during the 2007 school year. The average score for Vermont students was 7.5% higher than the national average. What was the average ACT score for Vermont students? Round your answer to the nearest tenth. **22.8**

4. **CARS** Mr. Thompson plans to purchase a used car priced at $8400. He will receive a 15% employee discount and then will have to pay a 5.5% sales tax. What will be the final price of the car? **$7532.70**

5. **MUSIC** The table below shows the total number of CDs, downloaded singles, and music videos sold from 2004 to 2006.

Sales of Recorded Music and Music Videos (millions of units)

Format	2004	2005	2006
CD	767.0	705.4	614.9
Downloaded	139.4	366.9	586.4
Video	32.8	33.8	23.1

Source: Recording Industry Association of America

a. Find the percent of change in the number of units sold between 2004 and 2005 and between 2005 and 2006 for each format. Round your answers to the nearest tenth.
CD 8.0%; 12.8%
Downloaded 163.2%; 59.8%
Video 3.0%; 31.7%

b. Tell whether each percent of change in Exercise a is a percent of increase or a percent of decrease.
CD decrease; decrease
Downloaded increase; increase
DVD video increase; decrease

c. Did these trends change from 2005 to 2006? Explain.
Only the video sales trends changed. First they increased and then they decreased. The CD sales decreased both years and downloaded sales increased both years.

Chapter 2 46 Glencoe Algebra 1

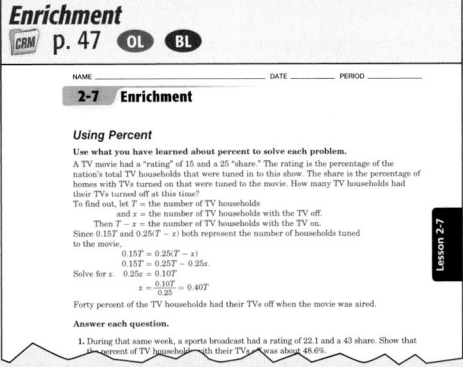

Enrichment
CRM p. 47 OL BL

NAME ______ DATE ______ PERIOD ______

2-7 Enrichment

Using Percent

Use what you have learned about percent to solve each problem.

A TV movie had a "rating" of 15 and a 25 "share." The rating is the percentage of the nation's total TV households that were tuned in to this show. The share is the percentage of homes with TVs turned on that were tuned to the movie. How many TV households had their TVs turned off at this time?

To find out, let T = the number of TV households
and x = the number of TV households with the TV off.
Then $T - x$ = the number of TV households with the TV on.

Since $0.15T$ and $0.25(T - x)$ both represent the number of households tuned to the movie,

$0.15T = 0.25(T - x)$
$0.15T = 0.25T - 0.25x$.

Solve for x. $0.25x = 0.10T$

$x = \frac{0.10T}{0.25} = 0.40T$

Forty percent of the TV households had their TVs off when the movie was aired.

Answer each question.

1. During that same week, a sports broadcast had a rating of 22.1 and a 43 share. Show that the percent of TV households with their TVs off was about 48.6%.

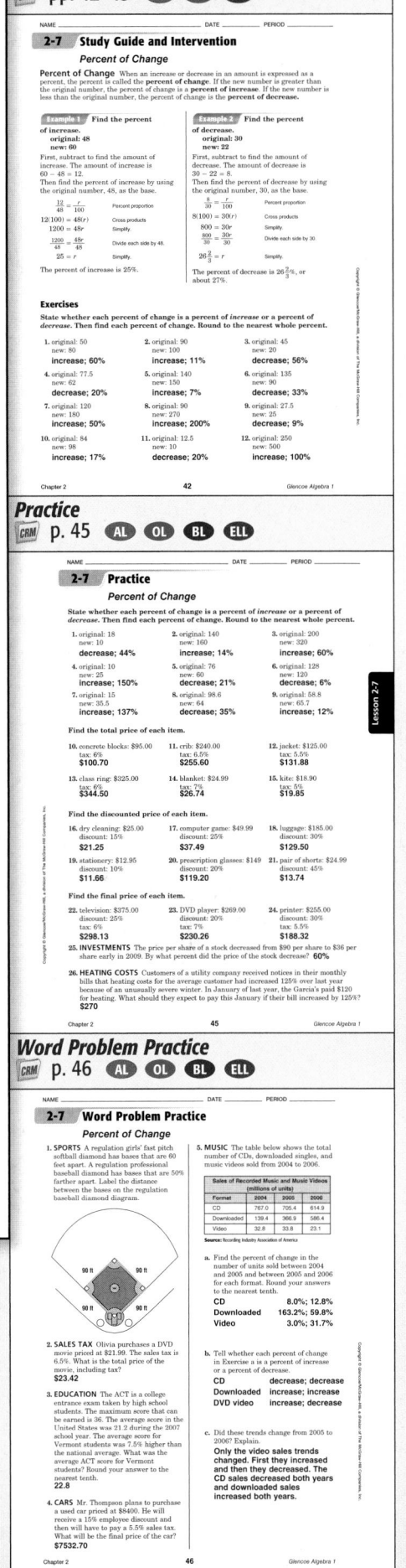

Lesson 2-7

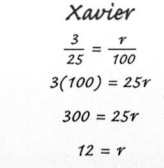

4 ASSESS

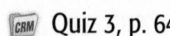

Yesterday's News Have students write how yesterday's lesson on ratio and proportions has helped them with today's new material.

Formative Assessment

Check for student understanding of Lessons 2-6 and 2-7.

CRM Quiz 3, p. 64

Additional Answers

68. Sample answer: A number *d* minus fourteen is five.

69. Sample answer: Six more than twice a number *f* equals nineteen.

70. Sample answer: Twelve less than *y* is the same as eight more than *y*.

71. Sample answer: The product of three and a number *a* when added to 5 is equal to the difference of 27 and two times *a*.

72. Sample answer: Negative six times a number *c* squared minus four times *c* is the same as twenty-five.

73. Sample answer: The fourth power of a number *d* increased by sixty-four is three times that number *d* to the third power plus seventy-seven.

PSAE PRACTICE 8.11.02, 7.11.03, 6.11.02, 10.11.07

50. GEOMETRY The rectangle has a perimeter of *P* centimeters. Which equation could be used to find the length ℓ of the rectangle? **D**

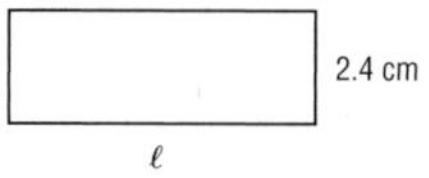

A $P = 2.4\ell$ C $P = 2.4 + 2\ell$
B $P = 4.8 + \ell$ D $P = 4.8 + 2\ell$

51. SHORT RESPONSE Henry is painting a room with four walls that are 12 feet by 14 feet. A gallon of paint costs $18 and covers 350 square feet. If he uses two coats of paint, how much will it cost him to paint the room? **$72**

52. The number of students at Franklin High School increased from 840 to 910 over a 5-year period. What was the percent of increase? **F**

F 8.3%
G 14.0%
H 18.5%
J 92.3%

53. PROBABILITY Two dice are rolled. What is the probability that the sum is 10? **C**

A $\frac{1}{6}$ B $\frac{1}{3}$ C $\frac{1}{12}$ D $\frac{1}{36}$

Spiral Review

54. TRAVEL The Chan's minivan requires 5 gallons of gasoline to travel 120 miles. How many gallons of gasoline will they need to travel 360 miles? (Lesson 2-6) **15 gal**

Evaluate each expression if $x = -2$, $y = 6$, and $z = 4$. (Lesson 2-5)

55. $|3 - x| + 7$ **12**
56. $12 - |z + 9|$ **−1**
57. $|y + x| - z + 4$ **4**

Solve each equation. Round to the nearest hundredth. Check your solution. (Lesson 2-4)

58. $1.03p - 4 = -2.15p + 8.72$ **4**
59. $18 - 3.8t = 7.36 - 1.9t$ **5.6**
60. $5.4w + 8.2 = 9.8w - 2.8$ **2.5**
61. $2[d + 3(d - 1)] = 18$ **3**

Solve each equation. Check your solution. (Lesson 2-3)

62. $5n + 6 = -4$ **−2**
63. $-11 = 7 + 3c$ **−6**
64. $15 = 4a - 5$ **5**
65. $-14 + 7g = -63$ **−7**

66. RIVERS The Congo River in Africa is 2900 miles long. That is 310 miles longer than the Niger River, which is also in Africa. (Lesson 2-2)

a. Write an equation you could use to find the length of the Niger River. $n + 310 = 2900$

b. What is the length of the Niger River? **2590 mi**

67. GEOMETRY Two perpendicular lines meet to form four right angles. Write two different if-then statements for this definition. (Lesson 1-8) **If two lines are perpendicular, then they meet to form four right angles. If two lines meet to form four right angles, then they are perpendicular.**

Skills Review

Translate each equation into a sentence. (Lesson 2-1) **68–73. See margin.**

68. $d - 14 = 5$
69. $2f + 6 = 19$
70. $y - 12 = y + 8$
71. $3a + 5 = 27 - 2a$
72. $-6c^2 - 4c = 25$
73. $d^4 + 64 = 3d^3 + 77$

Differentiated Instruction BL

Extension A DVD with an original price of $10 is in the 20% off bin. If another reduction of 50% is taken at the cash register, is the total reduction 70%? If not, find the actual reduction. No, the reduction is not 70%, it is an actual reduction of 60% off.

Algebra Lab: Percentiles

Objective
Use percentiles to represent data.

IL Learning Standards

10.A.4b Analyze data using mean, median, mode, range, variance and standard deviation of a data set, with and without the use of technology.

A **percentile** is a measure that is often used to report test data, such as standardized test scores. It tells us what percent of the total scores were below a given score.

- Percentiles measure rank from the bottom.
- There is no 0 percentile rank. The lowest score is at the 1st percentile.
- There is no 100th percentile rank. The highest score is at the 99th percentile.

ACTIVITY

A talent show was held for the fifteen finalists in the Teen Idol contest. Each performer received a score from 0 through 30 with 30 being the highest.

Name	Score	Name	Score
Arnold	17	Malik	10
Benito	9	Natalie	26
Carmen	21	Pearl	4
Delia	29	Twyla	6
Fernando	15	Victor	28
Horatio	5	Warren	22
Ingrid	11	Yolanda	18
Ishi	27		

Step 1 Write one score on each of 15 slips of paper.

Step 2 Arrange the slips vertically from greatest to least score.

Step 3 Find Victor's percentile rank.

Victor had a score of 28. There are 13 scores below his score. To find his percentile rank, use the following formula:

$$\frac{\text{number of scores below 28}}{\text{total number of scores}} \cdot 100 = \frac{13}{15} \cdot 100 \text{ or about } 87.$$

Victor scored at the 87th percentile in the contest.

Analyze the Results

1. Find the median, lower quartile, and upper quartile of the scores. **17, 9, 26**
2. Which performer was at the 50th percentile? Which performer was at the 25th percentile? the 75th percentile? **Arnold, Benito, Natalie**
3. Compare and contrast the values for the median, lower quartile, and upper quartile and the scores for the 25th, 50th, and 75th percentiles. **See Ch. 2 Answer Appendix.**
4. While Victor scored at the 87th percentile, what percent of the 30 possible points did he score? **about 93%**
5. Compare and contrast the percentile rank and the percent score. **See Ch. 2 Answer Appendix.**
6. Are there any outliers in the data that could alter the results of our computations? **There are no outliers.**

EXTEND 2-7 Lesson Notes

1 FOCUS

Objective Find the percentile rank of a data item in a set of scores.

Materials for Each Student

- paper (1 sheet)
- scissors

Teaching Tip

You may want to discuss the differences between percent and percentile. For example, a score at the 65th percentile means that 65% of the scores are either the same as the score at the 65th percentile or less than the score at that rank. It does not mean that the contestant scored 65% of the possible points.

2 TEACH

Working in Cooperative Groups

Have students work in groups of three or four, mixing abilities, to complete Steps 1–3 in the Activity and Exercises 1–3.

Ask:

- What is the purpose of arranging the scores vertically from greatest to least score? to see the number of scores at or below a particular score
- What is the least score? 4 At what percentile rank is the least score? 1st percentile What is the score at the 99th percentile? 29

Teaching Tip

Review how to find the median, lower quartile, and upper quartile of a set of numbers for Exercise 1.

Practice Have students complete Exercises 1–6.

3 ASSESS

Formative Assessment

Use Exercise 5 to assess whether students understand the difference between percentile and percent.

From Concrete to Abstract

Exercise 6 asks students to consider factors that might affect the percentile ranking of a set of scores.

2-8 Lesson Notes

1 FOCUS

Vertical Alignment

Before Lesson 2-8
Solve equations with variables on each side.

Lesson 2-8
Solve equations for given variables. Use formulas to solve real-world problems.

After Lesson 2-8
Solve systems of equations.

2 TEACH

Scaffolding Questions

Have students read the *Why?* section of the lesson.

Ask:

- In the formula $A = P(1 + r)$, what operation do you perform to find A? Multiply P times $(1 + r)$.
- Suppose you know the quantities for A and r, but not P. How would you solve for P? Divide both sides of the equation by $(1 + r)$.
- Why solve a formula for a specific variable before you substitute quantities for the known variables? It makes it easier to solve the formula since you only need to perform operations on one side of the equation.

2-8 Literal Equations and Dimensional Analysis

Then
You solved equations with variables on each side. (Lesson 2-4)

Now
- Solve equations for given variables.
- Use formulas to solve real-world problems.

IL Learning Standards

7.A.4b Apply formulas in a wide variety of theoretical and practical real-world measurement applications involving perimeter, area, volume, angle, time, temperature, mass, speed, distance, density and monetary values.
8.B.4a Represent algebraic concepts with physical materials, words, diagrams, tables, graphs, equations and inequalities and use appropriate technology. *Also addresses 6.C.4 and 7.B.4.*

New Vocabulary
literal equation
dimensional analysis
unit analysis

IL Math Online
glencoe.com
- Extra Examples
- Personal Tutor
- Self-Check Quiz
- Homework Help

Why?

Each year, more people use credit cards to make everyday purchases. If the entire balance is not paid by the due date, compound interest is applied. The formula for computing the balance of an account with compound interest added annually is $A = P(1 + r)$.

- A represents the amount of money in the account including the interest,
- P is the amount in the account before interest is added,
- r is the interest rate written as a decimal.

Solve for a Specific Variable Some equations such as the one above contain more than one variable. At times, you will need to solve these equations for one of the variables.

EXAMPLE 1 Solve for a Specific Variable

Solve $4m - 3n = 8$ for m.

$4m - 3n = 8$	Original equation
$4m - 3n + 3n = 8 + 3n$	Add $3n$ to each side.
$4m = 8 + 3n$	Simplify.
$\frac{4m}{4} = \frac{8 + 3n}{4}$	Divide each side by 4.
$m = \frac{8}{4} + \frac{3}{4}n$	Simplify.
$m = 2 + \frac{3}{4}n$	Simplify.

Check Your Progress

Solve each equation for the variable indicated.

1A. $15 = 3n + 6p$, for n $5 - 2p$

1B. $\frac{k - 2}{5} = 11j$, for k $55j + 2$

1C. $28 = t(r + 4)$, for t $\frac{28}{r + 4}$

1D. $a(q - 8) = 23$, for q $\frac{23}{a} + 8$

Personal Tutor glencoe.com

Sometimes we need to solve equations for a variable that is on both sides of the equation. When this happens, you must get all terms with that variable onto one side of the equation. It is then helpful to use the Distributive Property to isolate the variable for which you are solving.

Lesson 2-8 Resources

Resource	Approaching-Level	On-Level	Beyond-Level	English Learners
Teacher Edition	• Differentiated Instruction, p. 127	• Differentiated Instruction, p. 127	• Differentiated Instruction, p. 131	
Chapter Resource Masters	• Study Guide and Intervention, pp. 49–50 • Skills Practice, p. 51 • Practice, p. 52 • Word Problem Practice, p. 53	• Study Guide and Intervention, pp. 49–50 • Skills Practice, p. 51 • Practice, p. 52 • Word Problem Practice, p. 53 • Enrichment, p. 54	• Practice, p. 52 • Word Problem Practice, p. 53 • Enrichment, p. 54	• Study Guide and Intervention, pp. 49–50 • Skills Practice, p. 51 • Practice, p. 52
Transparencies	• 5-Minute Check Transparency 2-8	• 5-Minute Check Transparency 2-8	• 5-Minute Check Transparency 2-8	• 5-Minute Check Transparency 2-8
Other	• Study Notebook	• Study Notebook	• Study Notebook	• Study Notebook

StudyTip

Solving for a Specific Variable When an equation has more than one variable, it can be helpful to highlight the variable for which you are solving on your paper.

EXAMPLE 2 Solve for a Specific Variable

Solve $3x - 2y = xz + 5$ for x.

$3x - 2y = xz + 5$	**Original equation**
$3x - 2y + 2y = xz + 5 + 2y$	**Add $2y$ to each side.**
$3x - xz = xz - xz + 5 + 2y$	**Subtract xz from each side.**
$3x - xz = 5 + 2y$	**Simplify.**
$x(3 - z) = 5 + 2y$	**Distributive Property**
$\frac{x(3 - z)}{3 - z} = \frac{5 + 2y}{3 - z}$	**Divide each side by $3 - z$.**
$x = \frac{5 + 2y}{3 - z}$	**Simplify.**

Since division by 0 is undefined, $3 - z \neq 0$ so $z \neq 3$.

Check Your Progress

Solve each equation for the variable indicated.

2A. $d + 5c = 3d - 1$, for d $\frac{5c + 1}{2}$ **2B.** $6q - 18 = qr + t$, for q $\frac{18 + t}{6 - r}$

Personal Tutor glencoe.com

Use Formulas A formula or equation that involves several variables is called a **literal equation**. To solve a literal equation, apply the process of solving for a specific variable.

Real-World Link

The largest yo-yo in the world is 32.7 feet in circumference. It was launched by crane from a height of 189 feet.

Source: *Guinness Book of World Records*

Real-World EXAMPLE 3 Use Literal Equations

YO-YOS Use the information about the largest yo-yo at the left. The formula for the circumference of a circle is $C = 2\pi r$, where C represents circumference and r represents radius.

a. Solve the formula for r.

$C = 2\pi r$	**Formula for circumference**
$\frac{C}{2\pi} = \frac{2\pi r}{2\pi}$	**Divide each side by 2π.**
$\frac{C}{2\pi} = r$	**Simplify.**

b. Find the radius of the yo-yo.

$\frac{C}{2\pi} = r$	**Formula for radius**
$\frac{32.7}{2\pi} = r$	**$C = 32.7$**
$5.2 \approx r$	**Use a calculator.**

The yo-yo has a radius of about 5.2 feet.

Check Your Progress

3. GEOMETRY The formula for the volume of a rectangular prism is $V = \ell wh$, where ℓ is the length, w is the width, and h is the height.

A. Solve the formula for w. $\frac{V}{\ell h} = w$

B. Find the width of a rectangular prism that has a volume of 79.04 cubic centimeters, a length of 5.2 centimeters, and a height of 4 centimeters. **3.8 cm**

Personal Tutor glencoe.com

Solve for a Specific Variable

Example 1 shows how to solve an equation with more than one variable for a specific variable. **Example 2** shows how the Distributive Property can be used to isolate the variable for which you are solving an equation or formula.

Formative Assessment

Use the Check Your Progress exercises after each Example to determine students' understanding of concepts.

Additional Examples

1 Solve $5b + 12c = 9$ for b. $b = \frac{9 - 12c}{5}$

2 Solve $7x - 2z = 4 - xy$ for x. $x = \frac{4 + 2z}{7 + y}$

Additional Examples also in Interactive Classroom PowerPoint® Presentations

IWB INTERACTIVE WHITEBOARD READY

TEACH with TECH

INTERACTIVE WHITEBOARD Give students an equation that has several variables. Break the class into groups, and have each group solve the equation for a different variable. Then have one member from each group present and explain their work to the rest of the class on the board.

Use Formulas

Example 3 shows how to solve for a specific variable in a formula when solving a real-world problem. **Example 4** shows how to use dimensional analysis to convert units in a real-world problem.

Differentiated Instruction

AL OL

If students are confused by equations with more than one variable and with variables on both sides of the equation, such as Example 2,

Then have students work in pairs to analyze, discuss, and write out the steps necessary for solving the equation. They can then refer to and mark off the steps as they work through the solution.

Additional Example

3 **FUEL ECONOMY** A car's fuel economy E (miles per gallon) is given by the formula $E = \frac{m}{g}$, where m is the number of miles driven and g is the number of gallons of fuel used.

a. Solve the formula for m.
$m = Eg$

b. If Quanah's car has an average fuel consumption of 30 miles per gallon and she used 9.5 gallons, how far did she drive? 285 mi

Additional Example

4 **CHIMPANZEES** The average weight of the chimpanzees at a zoo is 52 kilograms. If 1 gram ≈ 0.0353 ounce, use dimensional analysis to find the average weight of the chimpanzees in pounds. (**Hint:** 1 lb = 16 oz)
≈115 lb

Watch Out!

Preventing Errors Encourage students to write the units for values they are substituting into an equation. Writing the units will help them to determine the reasonableness of an answer. If the problem asks for "miles" and they have "hours," they will know something is wrong.

When using formulas, you may want to use dimensional analysis. **Dimensional analysis** or **unit analysis** is the process of carrying units throughout a computation.

StudyTip

Rewriting Equations with Exponents When rewriting an equation to solve for a specific variable, the exponents of a variable are moved with that variable. They are not separated.

EXAMPLE 4 Use Dimensional Analysis

RUNNING A 10K run is 10 kilometers long. If 1 meter = 1.094 yards, use dimensional analysis to find the length of the race in miles. (*Hint*: 1 mi = 1760 yd)

Since the given conversion relates meters to yards, first convert 10 kilometers to meters. Then multiply by the conversion factor such that the unit meters are divided out. To convert from yards to miles, multiply by $\frac{1 \text{ mi}}{1760 \text{ yd}}$.

length of run	×	kilometers to meters	×	meters to yards	×	yards to miles
10 km	×	$\frac{1000 \text{ m}}{1 \text{ km}}$	×	$\frac{1.094 \text{ yd}}{1 \text{ m}}$	×	$\frac{1 \text{ mi}}{1760 \text{ yd}}$

Notice how the units cancel, leaving the unit to which you are converting.

$$10 \cancel{\text{km}} \times \frac{1000 \cancel{\text{m}}}{1 \cancel{\text{km}}} \times \frac{1.094 \cancel{\text{yd}}}{1 \cancel{\text{m}}} \times \frac{1 \text{ mi}}{1760 \cancel{\text{yd}}} = \frac{10940}{1760} \text{ mi}$$
$$= \frac{10,940}{1760}$$
$$\approx 6.2 \text{ mi}$$

A 10K race is approximately 6.2 miles.

Check Your Progress

4. A car travels a distance of 100 feet in about 2.8 seconds. What is the velocity of the car in miles per hour? Round to the nearest whole number. 24 mph

Personal Tutor glencoe.com

Check Your Understanding

Examples 1 and 2 pp. 126–127

Solve each equation or formula for the variable indicated.

1. $5a + c = -8a$, for a $a = -\frac{c}{13}$

2. $7h + f = 2h + g$, for g $5h + f = g$

3. $\frac{k + m}{-7} = n$, for k $k = -7n - m$

4. $q = p(r + s)$, for p $p = \frac{q}{r + s}$

Example 3 p. 127

5. PACKAGING A soap company wants to use a cylindrical container to hold their new liquid soap.

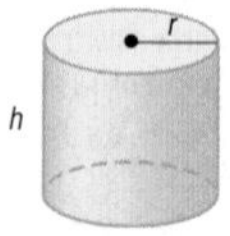

$V = \pi r^2 h$

a. Solve the formula for h. $h = \frac{V}{\pi r^2}$

b. What is the height of a container if the volume is 56.52 cubic inches and the radius is 1.5 inches? Round to the nearest tenth. 8 in.

Example 4 p. 128

6. SHOPPING Scott found a rare video game on an online auction site priced at 35 Australian dollars. If the exchange rate is \$1 U.S. = \$1.24 Australian, find the cost of the game in United States dollars. Round to the nearest cent. \$28.23

7. PHOTOGRAPHY A fisheye lens has a minimum focus range of 13.5 centimeters. If 1 centimeter is equal in length to about 0.39 inches, what is the minimum focus range of the lens in feet? about 0.43875 ft

3 PRACTICE

Formative Assessment

Use Exercises 1–7 to check for understanding.

Use the chart at the bottom of the next page to customize assignments for your students.

Focus on Mathematical Content

Using Formulas Many real-world problems require the use of formulas. Solving a formula for a specific variable may help to solve the problem.

Practice and Problem Solving

● = **Step-by-Step Solutions** begin on page R12.
Extra Practice begins on page 815.

Examples 1 and 2 pp. 126–127

Solve each equation or formula for the variable indicated.

8. $u = vw + z$, for v $v = \frac{u - z}{w}$

9. $x = b - cd$, for c $c = \frac{x - b}{-d}$

10. $fg - 9h = 10j$, for g $g = \frac{10j + 9h}{f}$

11. $10m - p = -n$, for m $m = \frac{-n + p}{10}$

12. $r = \frac{2}{3}t + v$, for t $t = \frac{3}{2}(r - v)$

13. $\frac{5}{9}v + w = z$, for v $v = \frac{9}{5}(z - w)$

14. $\frac{10ac - x}{11} = -3$, for a $a = \frac{-33 + x}{10c}$

15. $\frac{df + 10}{6} = g$, for f $f = \frac{6g - 10}{d}$

Example 3 p. 127

16. FITNESS The formula to compute a person's body mass index is $B = 703 \cdot \frac{w}{h^2}$. B represents the body mass index, w is the person's weight in pounds, and h represents the person's height in inches.

a. Solve the formula for w. $W = \frac{Bh^2}{703}$

b. What is the weight to the nearest pound of a person who is 64 inches tall and has a body mass index of 21.45? **125 lb**

17. PHYSICS Acceleration is the measure of how fast a velocity is changing. The formula for acceleration is $a = \frac{v_f - v_i}{t}$. a represents the acceleration rate, v_f is the final velocity, v_i is the initial velocity, and t represents the time in seconds.

a. Solve the formula for v_f. $V_f = at + V_i$

b. What is the final velocity of a runner who is accelerating at 2 feet per second squared for 3 seconds with an initial velocity of 4 feet per second? **10 ft/s²**

Example 4 p. 128

18. SWIMMING If each lap in a pool is 100 meters long, how many laps equal one mile? Round to the nearest tenth. (*Hint*: 1 foot ≈ 0.3048 meter) **16.1 laps**

19. GASOLINE How many liters of gasoline are needed to fill a 13.2-gallon tank? There are about 1.06 quarts per 1 liter. Round to the nearest tenth. **49.8 L**

Solve each equation or formula for the variable indicated.

20. $-14n + q = rt - 4n$, for n $n = \frac{rt - q}{-10}$

21. $18t + 11v = w - 13t$, for t $t = \frac{w - 11v}{31}$

22. $ax + z = aw - y$, for a $a = \frac{-y - z}{x - w}$

23. $10c - f = -13 + cd$, for c $c = \frac{-13 + f}{10 - d}$

B **Select an appropriate unit from the choices below and convert the rate to that unit.**

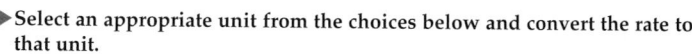

ft/s	mph	mm/s	km/s

24. a car traveling at 36 ft/s **about 24.5 mph**

25. a snail moving at 3.6 m/h **1.0 mm/s**

26. a person walking at 3.4 mph **about 5.0 ft/s**

27. a satellite moving at 234,000 m/min **3.9 km/s**

28. DANCING The formula $P = \frac{1.2W}{H^2}$ represents the amount of pressure exerted on the floor by a ballroom dancer's heel. In this formula, P is the pressure in pounds per square inch, W is the weight of a person wearing the shoe in pounds, and H is the width of the heel of the shoe in inches.

a. Solve the formula for W. $W = \frac{H^2P}{1.2}$

b. Find the weight of the dancer if the heel is 3 inches wide and the pressure exerted is 30 pounds per square inch. **225 lb**

Real-World Link

In most dance competitions, dancers compete as couples, or formation teams. At "Jack & Jill" competitions, individuals are paired by random draw.

Source: USA Dance

Differentiated Homework Options

Level	Assignment	Two-Day Option	
AL Basic	8–23, 36–38, 40–61	9–23 odd, 41–44	8–22 even, 36–38, 40, 45–61
OL Core	9–23 odd, 24–34, 36–38, 40–61	8–23, 41–44	24–34, 36–38, 40, 45–61
BL Advanced	24–55, (optional: 56–61)		

Study Guide and Intervention
CRM pp. 49–50 AL OL ELL

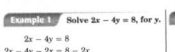

NAME ________ DATE ________ PERIOD ________

2-8 Study Guide and Intervention

Literal Equations and Dimensional Analysis

Solve for Variables Sometimes you may want to solve an equation such as $V = lwh$ for one of its variables. For example, if you know the values of V, w, and h, then the equation $\ell = \frac{V}{wh}$ is more useful for finding the value of ℓ. If an equation that contains more than one variable is to be solved for a specific variable, use the properties of equality to isolate the specified variable on one side of the equation.

Example 1 Solve $2x - 4y = 8$, for y.

$2x - 4y = 8$
$2x - 4y - 2x = 8 - 2x$
$-4y = 8 - 2x$
$\frac{-4y}{-4} = \frac{8 - 2x}{-4}$
$y = \frac{8 - 2x}{-4}$ or $\frac{2x - 8}{4}$

The value of y is $\frac{2x - 8}{4}$.

Example 2 Solve $3m - n = km - 8$, for m.

$3m - n = km - 8$
$3m - n - km = km - 8 - km$
$3m - n - km = -8$
$3m - n - km + n = -8 + n$
$3m - km = -8 + n$
$m(3 - k) = -8 + n$
$\frac{m(3 - k)}{3 - k} = \frac{-8 + n}{3 - k}$
$m = \frac{-8 + n}{3 - k}$, or $\frac{n - 8}{3 - k}$

The value of m is $\frac{n - 8}{3 - k}$. Since division by 0 is undefined, $3 - k \neq 0$, or $k \neq 3$.

Lesson 2-8

Exercises

Solve each equation or formula for the variable indicated.

1. $ax - b = c$, for x **$x = \frac{c + b}{a}, a \neq 0$**
2. $15x + 1 = y$, for x **$x = \frac{y - 1}{15}$**
3. $(x + f) + 2 = j$, for x **$x = j - 2 - f$**
4. $xy + w = 9$, for y **$y = \frac{9 - w}{x}, x \neq 0$**
5. $x(4 - k) = p$, for k **$k = 4 - \frac{p}{x}, x \neq 0$**
6. $7x + 3y = m$, for y **$y = \frac{m - 7x}{3}$**
7. $4(r + 3) = t$, for r **$r = \frac{t}{4} - 3$**
8. $2x + b = w$, for x **$x = \frac{w - b}{2}$**
9. $x(1 + y) = z$, for x **$x = \frac{z}{1 + y}, y \neq -1$**
10. $16w + 4x = y$, for x **$x = \frac{y - 16w}{4}$**
11. $d = rt$, for r **$r = \frac{d}{t}, t \neq 0$**
12. $A = \frac{h(a + b)}{2}$, for h **$h = \frac{2A}{a + b}, a \neq -b$**
13. $C = \frac{5}{9}(F - 32)$, for F **$F = \frac{9}{5}C + 32$**
14. $P = 2\ell + 2w$, for w **$W = \frac{p - 2\ell}{2}$**
15. $A = \ell w$, for ℓ **$\ell = \frac{A}{w}, w \neq 0$**

Chapter 2 49 Glencoe Algebra 1

Practice
CRM p. 52 AL OL BL ELL

NAME ________ DATE ________ PERIOD ________

2-8 Practice

Literal Equations and Dimensional Analysis

Solve each equation or formula for the variable indicated.

1. $d = rt$, for r **$r = \frac{d}{t}$**
2. $6w - y = 2z$, for w **$w = \frac{2z + y}{6}$**
3. $mx + 4y = 3t$, for x **$x = \frac{3t - 4y}{m}$**
4. $9s - 5g = -4u$, for s **$s = \frac{-4u + 5g}{9}$**
5. $ab + 3c = 2x$, for b **$b = \frac{2x - 3c}{a}$**
6. $2p = kx - t$, for x **$x = \frac{2p + t}{k}$**
7. $\frac{2}{3}m + a = a + r$, for m **$m = \frac{3}{2}r$**
8. $\frac{2}{5}h + g = d$, for h **$h = \frac{5}{2}(d - g)$**
9. $\frac{2}{3}y + v = x$, for y **$y = \frac{3}{2}(x - v)$**
10. $\frac{3}{4}a - q = k$, for a **$a = \frac{4}{3}(k + q)$**
11. $\frac{rx + 9}{5} = h$, for x **$x = \frac{5n - 9}{r}$**
12. $\frac{3b - 4}{2} = c$, for b **$b = \frac{2c + 4}{3}$**
13. $2w - y = 7w - 2$, for w **$w = \frac{2 - y}{5}$**
14. $3\ell + y = 5 + 5\ell$, for ℓ **$\ell = \frac{y - 5}{2}$**

15. **ELECTRICITY** The formula for Ohm's Law is $E = IR$, where E represents voltage measured in volts, I represents current measured in amperes, and R represents resistance measured in ohms.
    a. Solve the formula for R. **$R = \frac{E}{I}$**
    b. Suppose a current of 0.25 ampere flows through a resistor connected to a 12-volt battery. What is the resistance in the circuit? **48 ohms**

16. **MOTION** In *uniform circular motion*, the speed v of a point on the edge of a spinning disk is $v = \frac{2\pi}{t}r$, where r is the radius of the disk and t is the time it takes the point to travel once around the circle.
    a. Solve the formula for r. **$r = \frac{tv}{2\pi}$**
    b. Suppose a merry-go-round is spinning once every 3 seconds. If a point on the outside edge has a speed of 12.56 feet per second, what is the radius of the merry-go-round? (Use 3.14 for π.) **6 ft**

17. **HIGHWAYS** Interstate 90 is the longest interstate highway in the United States, connecting the cities of Seattle, Washington and Boston, Massachusetts. The interstate is 4,987,000 meters in length. If 1 mile = 1.609 kilometers, how many miles long is Interstate 90? **3099 mi**

Chapter 2 52 Glencoe Algebra 1

Word Problem Practice
CRM p. 53 AL OL BL ELL

NAME ________ DATE ________ PERIOD ________

2-8 Word Problem Practice

Literal Equations and Dimensional Analysis

1. **INTEREST** Simple interest that you may earn on money in a savings account can be calculated with the formula $I = prt$. I is the amount of interest earned, p is the principal or initial amount invested, r is the interest rate, and t is the amount of time the money is invested for. Solve the formula for p.
   $p = \frac{I}{rt}$

2. **DISTANCE** The distance d a car can travel is found by multiplying its rate of speed r by the amount of time t that it took to travel the distance. If a car has already traveled 5 miles, the total distance d is found by the formula $d = rt + 5$. Solve the formula for r.
   $r = \frac{d - 5}{t}$

3. **ENVIRONMENT** The United States released 5.877 billion metric tons of carbon dioxide into the environment through the burning of fossil fuels in 2006. If 1 trillion pounds = 0.4536 billion metric tons, how many trillions of pounds of carbon dioxide did the United States release in 2006?
   ≈12.96

4. **PHYSICS** The pressure exerted on an object is calculated by the formula $P = \frac{F}{A}$, where P is the pressure, F is the force, and A is the surface area of the object. Water shooting from a hose has a pressure of 75 pounds per square inch (psi). Suppose the surface area covered by the direct hose spray is 0.442 square inches. Solve the equation for F and find the force of the spray.
   33.15 pounds

5. **GEOMETRY** The regular octagon is divided into 8 congruent triangles. Each triangle has an area of 21.7 square centimeters. The perimeter of the octagon is 48 centimeters.

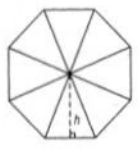

   a. What is the length of each side of the octagon?
   6 centimeters
   b. Solve the area of a triangle formula for h.
   $h = \frac{2A}{b}$
   c. What is the height of each triangle? Round to the nearest tenth.
   7.2 centimeters

Lesson 2-8

Chapter 2 53 Glencoe Algebra 1

34a. $h = \frac{S - 2\pi r^2}{2\pi r}$; $h = \frac{2500 - 6.28r^2}{6.28r}$

34b.

r	h
20	−0.10
15	11.54
10	29.81
5	74.62
0	undefined

36. Sample answer: No; since the rate of a car is faster than a caterpillar, the rate of a car is best described by miles per hour and the caterpillar by inches per second.

38. Sample answer for a triangle: $A = \frac{1}{2}bh$; $b = \frac{2A}{h}$

Write an equation and solve for the variable indicated.

29. Seven less than a number t equals another number r plus 6. Solve for t. **$t - 7 = r + 6$; $t = r + 13$**

30. Ten plus eight times a number a equals eleven times another number d minus six. Solve for a. **$10 + 8a = 11d - 6$; $a = \frac{11d - 16}{8}$**

31. Nine tenths of a number g is the same as seven plus two thirds of another number k. Solve for k. **$\frac{9}{10}g = 7 + \frac{2}{3}k$; $k = \frac{3}{2}\left[\frac{9}{10}g - 7\right]$**

32. Three fourths of a number p less two is five sixths of another number r plus five. Solve for r. **$\frac{3}{4}p - 2 = \frac{5}{6}r + 5$; $r = \frac{6}{5}\left[\frac{3}{4}p - 7\right]$**

33. **GIFTS** Ashley has 214 square inches of paper to wrap a gift box. The surface area S of the box can be found by using the formula $S = 2w(\ell + h) + 2\ell h$, where w is the width of the box, ℓ is the length of the box, and h is the height. If the length of the box is 7 inches and the width is 6 inches, how tall can Ashley's box be? **5 in.**

34. **MULTIPLE REPRESENTATIONS** In this problem, you will investigate cylinders. The surface area of cylinder can be found by the formula $S = 2\pi rh + 2\pi r^2$.
    a. **ALGEBRAIC** Solve for h. Rewrite the solution using 3.14 for π and 2500 for S.
    b. **TABULAR** Make a table of values using your new formula to find h if $r = 20$, 15, 10, 5, and 0. Round to the nearest hundredth.
    c. **VERBAL** What do we know about the domain (possible values of r)? **r must be greater than 0 and less than 20.**

H.O.T. Problems Use Higher-Order Thinking Skills

35. **CHALLENGE** The circumference of an NCAA women's basketball is 29 inches, and the rubber coating is $\frac{3}{16}$ inch thick. Use the formula $v = \frac{4}{3}\pi r^3$, where v represents the volume and r is the radius of the inside of the ball, to determine the volume of the air inside the ball. Round to the nearest whole number. **about 396 in^3**

Real-World Link

In 2007, Louisiana State University lost to the University of Connecticut by a score of 71 to 72, ending a 43-game winning streak, an NCAA Women's Basketball record.

Source: National Collegiate Athletic Association

36. **REASONING** Select an appropriate unit to describe the highway speed of a car and the speed of a caterpillar crawling on a tree. Can the same unit be used for both situations? Explain.

37. **FIND THE ERROR** Sandrea and Fernando are solving $4a - 5b = 7$ for b. Is either of them correct? Explain.

Sandrea; she performed each step correctly; Fernando omitted the negative sign from $-5b$.

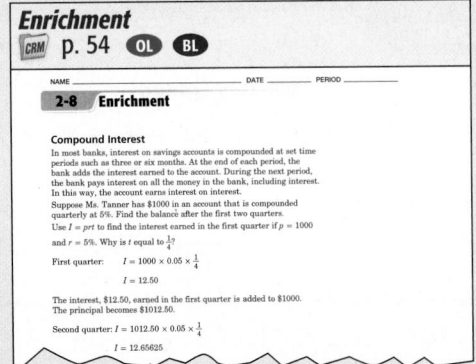

Sandrea	Fernando
$4a - 5b = 7$	$4a - 5b = 7$
$-5b = 7 - 4a$	$5b = 7 - 4a$
$\frac{-5b}{-5} = \frac{7 - 4a}{-5}$	$\frac{5b}{5} = \frac{7 - 4a}{5}$
$b = \frac{7 - 4a}{-5}$	$b = \frac{7 - 4a}{5}$

38. **OPEN ENDED** Write a formula for A, the area of a geometric figure such as a triangle or rectangle. Then solve the formula for a variable other than A.

39. **CHALLENGE** Solve each equation or formula for the variable indicated. **39a–b. See margin.**
    a. $n = \frac{x + y - 1}{xy}$ for x
    b. $\frac{x + y}{x - y} = \frac{1}{2}$ for y

40. **WRITING IN MATH** Explain what a literal equation is and how to solve one. **See margin.**

Enrichment
CRM p. 54 OL BL

NAME ________ DATE ________ PERIOD ________

2-8 Enrichment

Compound Interest

In most banks, interest on savings accounts is compounded at set time periods such as three or six months. At the end of each period, the bank adds the interest earned to the account. During the next period, the bank pays interest on all the money in the bank, including interest. In this way, the account earns interest on interest.

Suppose Ms. Tanner has \$1000 in an account that is compounded quarterly at 5%. Find the balance after the first two quarters.

Use $I = prt$ to find the interest earned in the first quarter if $p = 1000$ and $r = 5\%$. Why is t equal to $\frac{1}{4}$?

First quarter: $I = 1000 \times 0.05 \times \frac{1}{4}$

$I = 12.50$

The interest, \$12.50, earned in the first quarter is added to \$1000. The principal becomes \$1012.50.

Second quarter: $I = 1012.50 \times 0.05 \times \frac{1}{4}$

$I = 12.65625$

Multiple Representations In Exercise 34, students use algebra, a table of values, and mathematical analysis to rewrite a formula for the surface area of a cylinder to give the height when the surface area is known.

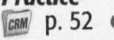

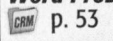

PSAE PRACTICE 6.11.18, 6.11.17, 6.11.13, 9.11.05

41. Eula is investing \$6000, part at 4.5% interest and the rest at 6% interest. If d represents the amount invested at 4.5%, which expression represents the amount of interest earned in one year by the amount paying 6%? **D**

A $0.06d$
B $0.06(d - 6000)$
C $0.06(d + 6000)$
D $0.06(6000 - d)$

42. Todd drove from Boston to Cleveland, a distance of 616 miles. His breaks, gasoline, and food stops took 2 hours. If his trip took 16 hours altogether, what was Todd's average speed? **H**

F 38.5 mph
G 40 mph
H 44 mph
J 47.5 mph

43. SHORT RESPONSE Brian has 3 more books than Erika. Jasmine has triple the number of books that Brian has. Altogether Brian, Erika, and Jasmine have 22 books. How many books does Jasmine have? **15**

44. GEOMETRY Which of the following best describes a plane? **B**

A a location having neither size nor shape
B a flat surface made up of points having no depth
C made up of points and has no thickness or width
D a boundless, three-dimensional set of all points

Spiral Review

Find the final price of each item. (Lesson 2-7)

45. lamp: \$120.00 **\$101.76**
discount: 20%
tax: 6%

46. dress: \$70.00 **\$52.43**
discount: 30%
tax: 7%

47. camera: \$58.00 **\$46.33**
discount: 25%
tax: 6.5%

48. jacket: \$82.00 **\$73.88**
discount: 15%
tax: 6%

49. comforter: \$67.00 **\$56.95**
discount: 20%
tax: 6.25%

50. lawnmower: \$720.00 **\$500.76**
discount: 35%
tax: 7%

Solve each proportion. If necessary, round to the nearest hundredth. (Lesson 2-6)

51. $\frac{3}{4.5} = \frac{x}{2.5}$ **1.67**

52. $\frac{2}{0.36} = \frac{7}{p}$ **1.26**

53. $\frac{m}{9} = \frac{2.8}{4.9}$ **5.14**

54. JOBS Laurie mows lawns to earn extra money. She can mow at most 30 lawns in one week. She profits \$15 on each lawn she mows. Identify a reasonable domain and range for this situation and draw a graph. (Lesson 1-6) **See margin.**

55. ENTERTAINMENT Each member of the pit orchestra is selling tickets for the school musical. The trombone section sold 50 floor tickets and 90 balcony tickets. Write and evaluate an expression to find how much money the trombone section collected. (Lesson 1-2) **50(7.50)+90(5.00); \$825**

Skills Review

Solve each equation. (Lesson 2-5)

56. $8k + 9 = 7k + 6$ **−3**

57. $3 - 4q = 10q + 10$ **−0.5**

58. $\frac{3}{4}n + 16 = 2 - \frac{1}{8}n$ **−16**

59. $\frac{1}{4} - \frac{2}{3}y = \frac{3}{4} - \frac{1}{3}y$ **−1.5**

60. $4(2a - 1) = -10(a - 5)$ **3**

61. $2(w - 3) + 5 = 3(w - 1)$ **2**

Differentiated Instruction BL

Extension Write $\frac{1}{R} = \frac{1}{a} + \frac{1}{b}$ on the board. Tell students that the total resistance R in an electrical circuit consisting of two resistances of a ohms and b ohms connected in parallel is given by this equation. Ask students to explain how to solve this formula for R.
Multiply each side by R. $R\left(\frac{1}{R}\right) = \left(\frac{1}{a} + \frac{1}{b}\right)R$. Divide each side by $\frac{1}{a} + \frac{1}{b}$. $R = \frac{1}{\frac{1}{a} + \frac{1}{b}}$ or $\frac{ab}{b + a}$

Watch Out!

Find the Error For Exercise 37, suggest that students work backward from the solution of the equation to discover whether Sandrea or Fernando made the error in solving the equation for the variable b. In doing so, they should discover that the only difference in the solutions is the negative sign for 5 and that Fernando overlooked it when solving for b. Tell students this is a common error they should check for when solving equations.

4 ASSESS

Ticket Out the Door Have students pick a formula that was not used in this lesson, perhaps from science class, and explain the variables in the formula and what the formula is used to find. Have students solve the formula for a different variable.

Additional Answers

39a. $x = \frac{y - 1}{yn - 1}$

39b. $y = -\frac{1}{3}x$

40. Sample answer: A literal equation is an equation or formula that involves different variables. To solve a literal equation, isolate the variable that is required by applying the process of solving for a specific variable.

54. D = whole numbers from 0 to 30; R = whole-number multiples of 15 from 0 to 450

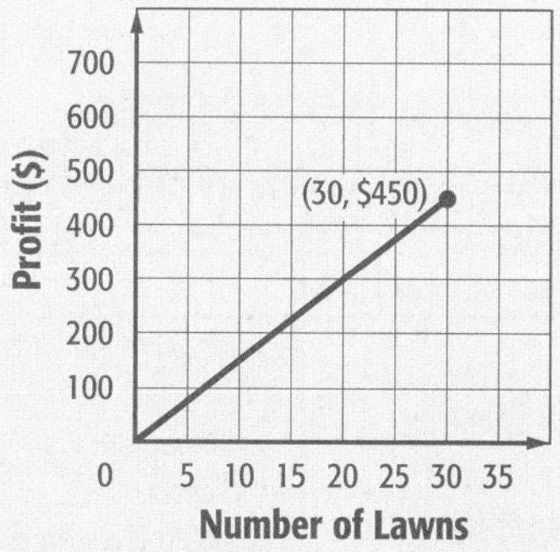

2-9 Lesson Notes

1 FOCUS

Vertical Alignment

Before Lesson 2-9
Translate sentences into equations.

Lesson 2-9
Solve mixture problems.
Solve uniform motion problems.

After Lesson 2-9
Formulate linear equations to solve problems.

2 TEACH

Scaffolding Questions

Have students read the *Why?* section of the lesson.

Ask:

- How is the slugging average weighted? The number of times a hitter gets to first base is counted once, to second base is counted twice, to third base is counted three times, and to home is counted four times.
- How would you calculate a slugging average that is not weighted? The number of times a hitter gets to each of the bases would be counted once and then divided by the number of times at bat.

(continued on the next page)

2-9 Weighted Averages

Then
You translated sentences into equations.
(Lesson 2-1)

Now
- Solve mixture problems.
- Solve uniform motion problems.

IL Learning Standards

6.C.4 Determine whether exact values or approximations are appropriate.
7.A.4b Apply formulas in a wide variety of theoretical and practical real-world measurement applications involving perimeter, area, volume, angle, time, temperature, mass, speed, distance, density and monetary values.

New Vocabulary
weighted average
mixture problem
uniform motion problem
rate problem

IL Math Online
glencoe.com
- Extra Examples
- Personal Tutor
- Self-Check Quiz
- Homework Help

Why?

Baseball players' performance is measured in large part by statistics. Slugging average (SLG) is a weighted average that measures the power of a hitter. The slugging average is calculated by using the following formula.

$$\text{SLG} = \frac{1B + (2 \times 2B) + (3 \times 3B) + (4 \times HR)}{\text{at bats}}$$

Weighted Averages The batter's slugging percentage is an example of a weighted average. The **weighted average** M of a set of data is the sum of the product of the number of units and the value per unit divided by the sum of the number of units.

Mixture problems are problems in which two or more parts are combined into a whole. They are solved using weighted averages. In a mixture problem, the units are usually the number of gallons or pounds and the value is the cost, value, or concentration per unit.

Real-World EXAMPLE 1 Mixture Problem

RETAIL A tea company sells blended tea for \$25 per pound. To make blackberry tea, dried blackberries that cost \$10.50 per pound are blended with black tea that costs \$35 per pound. How many pounds of black tea should be added to 5 pounds of dried blackberries to make blackberry tea?

Step 1 Let w be the weight of the black tea. Make a table to organize the information.

	Number of Units (lb)	Price per Unit (\$)	Total Price (price)(units)
Dried Blackberries	5	10.50	10.50(5)
Black Tea	w	35	$35w$
Blackberry Tea	$5 + w$	25	$25(5 + w)$

Write an equation using the information in the table.

Price of blackberries	plus	price of tea	equals	price of blackberry tea.
10.50(5)	+	$35w$	=	$25(5 + w)$

Step 2 Solve the equation.

$10.50(5) + 35w = 25(5 + w)$	**Original equation**
$52.5 + 35w = 125 + 25w$	**Distributive Property**
$52.5 + 35w - 25w = 125 + 25w - 25w$	**Subtract $25w$ from each side.**
$52.5 + 10w = 125$	**Simplify.**
$52.5 - 52.5 + 10w = 125 - 52.5$	**Subtract 52.5 from each side.**
$10w = 72.5$	**Simplify.**
$w = 7.25$	**Divide each side by 10.**

Lesson 2-9 Resources

Resource	Approaching-Level	On-Level	Beyond-Level	English Learners
Teacher Edition			• Differentiated Instruction, pp. 134, 138	
Chapter Resource Masters	• Study Guide and Intervention, pp. 55–56 • Skills Practice, p. 57 • Practice, p. 58 • Word Problem Practice, p. 59	• Study Guide and Intervention, pp. 55–56 • Skills Practice, p. 57 • Practice, p. 58 • Word Problem Practice, p. 59 • Enrichment, p. 60	• Practice, p. 58 • Word Problem Practice, p. 59 • Enrichment, p. 60	• Study Guide and Intervention, pp. 55–56 • Skills Practice, p. 57 • Practice, p. 58
Transparencies	• 5-Minute Check Transparency 2-9	• 5-Minute Check Transparency 2-9	• 5-Minute Check Transparency 2-9	• 5-Minute Check Transparency 2-9
Other	• Study Notebook • Teaching Algebra with Manipulatives	• Study Notebook • Teaching Algebra with Manipulatives	• Study Notebook	• Study Notebook • Teaching Algebra with Manipulatives

StudyTip

Mixture Problems When you organize the information in mixture problems, remember that the final mixture must contain the sum of the parts in the correct quantities and at the correct percents.

Problem-SolvingTip

Make a Table Using a table is a great way to organize the given information. It also helps you understand how to write an equation to solve for the missing value.

To make the blackberry tea, 7.25 pounds of black tea will need to be added to the dried blackberries.

Check Your Progress

1. COFFEE How many pounds of Premium coffee beans should be mixed with 2 pounds of Supreme coffee to make the Blend coffee? **7 lb**

Personal Tutor glencoe.com

Sometimes mixture problems are expressed in terms of percents.

Real-World EXAMPLE 2 Percent Mixture Problem

FRUIT PUNCH Mrs. Matthews has 16 cups of punch that is 3% pineapple juice. She also has a punch that is 33% pineapple juice. How many cups of the 33% punch will she need to add to the 3% punch to obtain a punch that is 20% pineapple juice?

Step 1 Let x = the amount of 33% solution to be added. Make a table.

	Amount of Punch (cups)	Amount of Pineapple Juice
3% Punch	16	0.03(16)
33% Punch	x	$0.33x$
20% Punch	$16 + x$	$0.20(16 + x)$

Write an equation using the information in the table.

Amount of pineapple juice in 3% punch	plus	amount of pineapple juice in 33% punch	equals	amount of pineapple juice in 20% punch.
0.03(16)	+	$0.33x$	=	$0.20(16 + x)$

Step 2 Solve the equation.

$0.03(16) + 0.33x = 0.20(16 + x)$ **Original equation**

$0.48 + 0.33x = 3.2 + 0.20x$ **Simplify.**

$0.48 + 0.33x - 0.20x = 3.2 + 0.20x - 0.20x$ **Subtract 0.20x from each side.**

$0.48 + 0.13x = 3.2$ **Simplify.**

$0.48 - 0.48 + 0.13x = 3.2 - 0.48$ **Subtract 0.48 from each side.**

$0.13x = 2.72$ **Simplify.**

$\frac{0.13x}{0.13} = \frac{2.72}{0.13}$ **Divide each side by 0.13.**

$x \approx 20.9$ **Round to the nearest tenth.**

Mrs. Matthews should add about 20.9 cups of the 33% punch to the 16 cups of the 3% punch.

Check Your Progress

2. ANTIFREEZE One type of antifreeze is 40% glycol, and another type of antifreeze is 60% glycol. How much of each kind should be used to make 100 gallons of antifreeze that is 48% glycol? **60 gal of 40% glycol, 40 gal of 60% glycol**

Personal Tutor glencoe.com

- Why is the slugging average weighted? The more powerful the hit, the more bases a hitter can get to, so the weighted average assigns a greater value to each subsequent base the hitter reaches.

Weighted Averages

Example 1 shows how to solve a real-world mixture problem using weighted averages. **Example 2** shows how to solve a real-world mixture problem expressed in terms of percents using weighted averages.

Formative Assessment

Use the Check Your Progress exercises after each Example to determine students' understanding of concepts.

Additional Examples

1 **PETS** Mandisha feeds her cat gourmet cat food that costs $1.75 per pound. She combines it with cheaper food that costs $0.50 per pound. How many pounds of cheaper food should Mandisha buy to go with 5 pounds of gourmet food, if she wants the average price to be $1.00 per pound? 7.5 lb of cheaper food

2 **AUTO MAINTENANCE** A car's radiator should contain a solution of 50% antifreeze. Bae has 2 gallons of 35% antifreeze. How many gallons of 100% antifreeze should he add to his solution to produce a solution of 50% antifreeze? 0.6 gal of 100% antifreeze

Additional Examples also in Interactive Classroom PowerPoint® Presentations

IWB INTERACTIVE WHITEBOARD READY

Tips for New Teachers

Making a Connection Once students have learned the concept of weighted average, challenge them to describe a weighted average in terms of weights on a balance. How do the weights help to "tip" the balance?

TEACH with TECH

WIKI Have groups of students create a wiki page about weighted averages. Tell students to include a description of weighted averages, and to use the page to keep a running list of examples of weighted averages. Have students maintain and update this page as they learn and think of additional examples.

Uniform Motion Problems

Example 3 shows how to solve a real-world, uniform-motion problem using weighted averages. **Example 4** shows how to solve a real-world, uniform motion problem using weighted averages and making a table.

Additional Example

3 **AIR TRAVEL** Nita took a non-stop flight to visit her grandmother. The 750-mile trip took three hours and 45 minutes. Because of bad weather, the return trip took four hours and 45 minutes. What was her average speed for the round trip? The average speed for the round trip was about 176 mph.

Focus on Mathematical Content

Uniform Motion If an object moves without changing its speed, it is said to be in uniform motion. Uniform motion problems are solved using this formula:

Distance = rate × time

$d = r \times t$

Uniform Motion Problems **Uniform motion problems** or **rate problems** are problems in which an object moves at a certain speed or rate. The formula $d = rt$ is used to solve these problems. In the formula, d represents distance, r represents rate, and t represents time.

Real-World Link

In-line skating is the fourth most popular recreational activity in the U.S.

Source: *Statistical Abstract of the United States*

Real-World EXAMPLE 3 Speed of One Vehicle

INLINE SKATING It took Travis and Tony 40 minutes to skate 5 miles. The return trip took them 30 minutes. What was their average speed for the trip?

Understand We know that the boys did not travel the same amount of time on each portion of their trip. So, we will need to find the weighted average of their speeds. We are asked to find their average speed for both portions of the trip.

Plan First find the rate of the going portion, and then the return portion of the trip. Because the rate is in miles per hour we convert 40 minutes to about 0.667 hours and 30 minutes to 0.5 hours.

Going

$r = \frac{d}{t}$ — Formula for rate

$\approx \frac{5 \text{ miles}}{0.667 \text{ hour}}$ or about 7.5 miles per hour — Substitution $d = 5$ mi, $t = 0.667$ h

Return

$r = \frac{d}{t}$ — Formula for rate

$= \frac{5 \text{ miles}}{0.5 \text{ hour}}$ or 10 miles per hour — Substitution $d = 5$ mi, $t = 0.5$ h

Because we are looking for a weighted average we cannot just average their speeds. We need to find the weighted average for the round trip.

Solve $M = \frac{(\text{rate of going})(\text{time of going}) + (\text{rate of return})(\text{time of return})}{\text{time of going} + \text{time of return}}$

$\approx \frac{(7.5)(0.667) + (10)(0.5)}{0.667 + 0.5}$ — Substitution

$\approx \frac{10.0025}{1.167}$ or about 8.6 — Simplify.

Their average speed was about 8.6 miles per hour.

Check Our solution of 8.6 miles per hour is between the going portion rate, 7.5 miles per hour, and the return rate, 10 miles per hour. So, we know that our answer is reasonable.

Check Your Progress

3. EXERCISE Austin jogged 2.5 miles in 16 minutes and then walked 1 mile in 10 minutes. What was his average speed? about 0.13 mi/min

Personal Tutor glencoe.com

Math *in Motion*, Animation glencoe.com

The formula $d = rt$ can also be used to solve real-world problems involving two vehicles in motion.

Differentiated Instruction BL

Logical Some students will appreciate the way in which weighted averages can be used to manipulate data. Challenge these students to create additional example problems using weighted averages. Share these problems with the class.

134 Chapter 2 Linear Equations

StudyTip

Draw a Diagram Drawing a diagram is not just for geometry problems. You can use diagrams to visualize many problem situations that can be represented by equations.

Real-World EXAMPLE 4 Speeds of Two Vehicles

FREIGHT TRAINS Two trains are 550 miles apart heading toward each other on parallel tracks. Train A is traveling east at 35 miles per hour, while Train B travels west at 45 miles per hour. When will the trains pass each other?

Step 1 Draw a diagram.

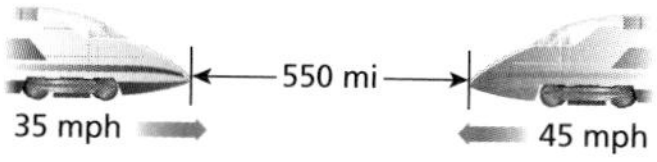

Step 2 Let t = the number of hours until the trains pass each other. Make a table.

	r	t	$d = rt$
Train A	35	t	$35t$
Train B	45	t	$45t$

Step 3 Write and solve an equation.

Distance traveled by Train A	plus	distance traveled by Train B	equals	550 miles.
$35t$	$+$	$45t$	$=$	550

$35t + 45t = 550$ **Original equation**

$80t = 550$ **Simplify.**

$\frac{80t}{80} = \frac{550}{80}$ **Divide each side by 80.**

$t = 6.875$ **Simplify.**

The trains will pass each other in about 6.875 hours.

Check Your Progress

4. CYCLING Two cyclists begin traveling in opposite directions on a circular bike trail that is 5 miles long. One cyclist travels 12 miles per hour, and the other travels 18 miles per hour. How long will it be before they meet? $\frac{1}{6}$ **hour or 10 min**

Personal Tutor glencoe.com

Check Your Understanding

Example 1 p. 132

1. FOOD Tasha ordered soup and salad for lunch. If Tasha ordered 10 ounces of soup for lunch and the total cost was \$3.30, how many ounces of salad did Tasha order? **9 oz**

Example 2 p. 133

2. CHEMISTRY Margo has 40 milliliters of 25% solution. How many milliliters of 60% solution should she add to obtain the required 30% solution? **about 6.67 mL**

Example 3 p. 134

3. TRAVEL A boat travels 16 miles due north in 2 hours and 24 miles due west in 2 hours. What is the average speed of the boat? **10 mph**

4. EXERCISE Felisa jogged 3 miles in 25 minutes and then jogged 3 more miles in 30 minutes. What was her average speed in miles per minute? **about 0.11 mi/min**

Example 4 p. 135

5. CYCLING A cyclist begins traveling 18 miles per hour. At the same time and at the same starting point, an inline skater follows the cyclist's path and begins traveling 6 miles per hour. After how much time will they be 24 miles apart? **2 hours**

Additional Example

4 RESCUE A railroad switching operator has discovered that two trains are heading toward each other on the same track. Currently, the trains are 53 miles apart. One train is traveling at 75 miles per hour and the other 40 miles per hour. The faster train will require 5 miles to stop safely, and the slower train will require 3 miles to stop safely. About how many minutes does the operator have to warn the train engineers to stop their trains? about 23 min

3 PRACTICE

Formative Assessment

Use Exercises 1–5 to check for understanding.

Use the chart at the bottom of the next page to customize assignments for your students.

Additional Answers

16. 3.67

17. about 10.89 mph

18. 3.8 min

19a. 390 mi

19b. about 9.62 hours

26. Sample answer: Multiply the 1 gallon times 0.25. Then multiply the unknown amount by 0.10. Add these results together. This should equal the total amount times 0.15.

Practice and Problem Solving

= Step-by-Step Solutions begin on page R12.
Extra Practice begins on page 815.

Example 1 p. 132

6. **CANDY** A candy store wants to create a mix using two hard candies. One is priced at \$5.45 per pound, and the other is priced at \$7.33 per pound. How many pounds of the \$7.33 candy should be mixed with 11 pounds of the \$5.45 candy to sell the mixture for \$6.14 per pound? **about 6.38 lb**

7. **BUSINESS** Party Supplies Inc. sells metallic balloons for \$2 each and helium balloons for \$3.50 per bunch. Yesterday, they sold 36 more metallic balloons than the number of bunches of helium balloons. The total sales for both types of balloons were \$281. Let b represent the number of metallic balloons sold.

a. Copy and complete the table representing the problem.

	Number	Price	Total Price
Metallic Balloons	b	\$2.00	$2.00b$
Bunches of Helium Balloons	$b - 36$	\$3.50	$3.50(b - 36)$

b. Write an equation to represent the problem. $2.00b + 3.50(b - 36) = 281.00$

c. How many metallic balloons were sold? **74**

d. How many bunches of helium balloons were sold? **38**

8. **FINANCIAL LITERACY** Lakeisha spent \$4.57 on color and black-and-white copies for her project. She made 7 more black-and-white copies than color copies. How many color copies did she make? **8 color copies**

Type of Copy	Cost per Page
color	\$0.44
black-and-white	\$0.07

Example 2 p. 133

9. **FISH** Rosamaria is setting up a 20-gallon saltwater fish tank that needs to have a salt content of 3.5%. If Rosamaria has water that has 2.5% salt and water that has 3.7% salt, how many gallons of the water with 3.7% salt content should Rosamaria use? **about 16.67 gal**

10. 64 mL of the 25% solution and 96 mL of the 50% solution

10. **CHEMISTRY** Hector is performing a chemistry experiment that requires 160 milliliters of 40% sulfuric acid solution. He has a 25% sulfuric acid solution and a 50% sulfuric acid solution. How many millimeters of each solution should he mix to obtain the needed solution?

Example 3 p. 134

11. **TRAVEL** A boat travels 36 miles in 1.5 hours and then 14 miles in 0.75 hour. What is the average speed of the boat? **about 22.2 mph**

12. **RUNNING** A runner ran 1.5 miles in 28 minutes and then 1.2 more miles in 10 minutes. What was the average speed in miles per minute? **about 0.07 mi/min**

13. **AIRLINERS** Two airliners are 1600 miles apart and heading toward each other at different altitudes. The first plane is traveling north at 620 miles per hour, while the second is traveling south at 780 miles per hour. When will the planes pass each other? **$1\frac{1}{7}$ hours or 1 h 8 min 34 s**

Example 4 p. 135

14. **SAILING** A ship is sailing due east at 20 miles per hour when it passes the lighthouse. At the same time a ship is sailing due west at 15 miles per hour when it passes a point. The lighthouse and the point are 175 miles apart. When will these ships pass each other? **5 hours**

15. **CHEMISTRY** A lab technician has 40 gallons of a 15% iodine solution. How many gallons of a 40% iodine solution must he add to make a 20% iodine solution? **10 gal**

Differentiated Homework Options

Level	Assignment	Two-Day Option	
AL Basic	6–15, 22–23, 26–47	7–15 odd, 27–30	6–14 even, 22–23, 26, 31–47
OL Core	7–15 odd, 16–23, 26–47	6–15, 27–30	16–23, 26, 31–47
BL Advanced	16–39, (optional: 40–47)		

Real-World Link

Different countries have individual grading scales. For example, French schools give number grades ranging from 0 to 20, rather than letter grades like those in the U.S.

Source: Morris

16. GRADES At Westbridge High School, a student's grade point average (GPA) is based on the student's grade and the class credit rating. Brittany's grades for this quarter are shown. Find Brittany's GPA if a grade of A equals 4 and a B equals 3. **See margin.**

Class	Credit Rating	Grade
Algebra 1	1	A
Science	1	A
English	1	B
Spanish	1	A
Music	$\frac{1}{2}$	B

17. SPORTS In a triathlon, Steve swam 0.5 mile in 15 minutes, biked 20 miles in 90 minutes, and ran 4 miles in 30 minutes. What was Steve's average speed for the triathlon in miles per hour? **See margin.**

18. MUSIC Amalia has 10 songs on her MP3 player. If 3 songs are 5 minutes long, 3 are 4 minutes long, 2 are 2 minutes long, and 2 are 3.5 minutes long, what is the average length of the songs? **See margin.**

19. DISTANCE Garcia is driving to Florida for vacation. The trip is a total of 625 miles.

a. How far can he drive in 6 hours at 65 miles per hour?

b. If Garcia maintains a speed of 65 miles per hour, how long will it take him to drive to Florida? **a–b. See margin.**

20. TRAVEL Two buses leave Smithville at the same time, one traveling north and the other traveling south. The northbound bus travels at 50 miles per hour, and the southbound bus travels at 65 miles per hour. Let t represent the amount of time since their departure.

a. Copy and complete the table representing the situation.

	r	t	$d = rt$
Northbound bus	50 ?	t ?	$50t$?
Southbound bus	65 ?	t ?	$65t$?

b. Write an equation to find when the buses will be 345 miles apart. $50t + 65t = 345$

c. Solve the equation. Explain how you found your answer. **3 hours**

21. TRAVEL A subway travels 60 miles per hour from Glendale to Midtown. Another subway, traveling at 45 miles per hour, takes 11 minutes longer for the same trip. How far apart are Glendale and Midtown? **33 mi**

H.O.T. Problems

Use Higher-Order Thinking Skills

22. OPEN ENDED Write a problem that depicts motion in opposite directions.

23. REASONING Describe the conditions so that adding a 50% solution to a 100% solution would produce a 75% solution.

24. CHALLENGE Find five consecutive odd integers from least to greatest in which the sum of the first and the fifth is one less than three times the fourth. $-9, -7, -5, -3, -1$

25. CHALLENGE Describe a situation involving mixtures that could be represented by $1.00x + 0.15(36) = 0.50(x + 36)$.

26. WRITING IN MATH Describe how a gallon of 25% solution is added to an unknown amount of 10% solution to get a 15% solution. **See margin.**

22. Sample answer: Miles and Tara live 15 miles apart. If Tara rides her bike towards Miles's house at 10 miles per hour and Miles rides his bike at 12 miles per hour towards her, when will they meet?

23. Sample answer: For a 50% solution being added to a 100% solution to produce a 75% resulting solution, the quantity of each must be the same.

25. Sample answer: How many grams of salt must be added to 36 grams of a 15% salt solution to obtain a 50% salt solution?

Study Guide and Intervention

CRM pp. 55–56 AL OL ELL

NAME ______ DATE ______ PERIOD ______

2-9 Study Guide and Intervention

Weighted Averages

Mixture Problems **Mixture Problems** are problems where two or more parts are combined into a whole. They involve weighted averages. In a mixture problem, the weight is usually a price or a percent of something.

Weighted Average	The weighted average M of a set of data is the sum of the product of each number in the set and its weight divided by the sum of all the weights.

Example **COOKIES Delectable Cookie Company sells chocolate chip cookies for \$6.95 per pound and white chocolate cookies for \$5.95 per pound. How many pounds of chocolate chip cookies should be mixed with 4 pounds of white chocolate cookies to obtain a mixture that sells for \$6.75 per pound.**

Let w = the number of pounds of chocolate chip cookies

	Number of Pounds	Price per Pound	Total Price
Chocolate Chip	w	6.95	$6.95w$
White Chocolate	4	5.95	4(5.95)
Mixture	$w + 4$	6.75	$6.75(w + 4)$

Equation: $6.95w + 4(5.95) = 6.75(w + 4)$

Solve the equation.

$6.95w + 4(5.95) = 6.75(w + 4)$ Original equation

$6.95w + 23.80 = 6.75w + 27$ Simplify.

$6.95w + 23.80 - 6.75w = 6.75w + 27 - 6.75w$ Subtract 6.75w from each side.

$0.2w + 23.80 = 27$ Simplify.

$0.2w + 23.80 - 23.80 = 27 - 23.80$ Subtract 23.80 from each side.

$0.2w = 3.2$ Simplify.

$w = 16$ Simplify.

16 pounds of chocolate chip cookies should be mixed with 4 pounds of white chocolate cookies.

Exercises

1. **SOLUTIONS** How many grams of sugar must be added to 60 grams of a solution that is 32% sugar to obtain a solution that is 50% sugar? **21.6 g**

2. **NUTS** The Quik Mart has two kinds of nuts. Pecans sell for \$1.55 per pound and walnuts sell for \$1.95 per pound. How many pounds of walnuts must be added to 15 pounds of pecans to make a mixture that sells for \$1.75 per pound? **15 lb**

3. **INVESTMENTS** Alice Gleason invested a portion of \$32,000 at 9% interest and the balance at 11% interest. How much did she invest at each rate if her total income from both investments was \$3,200. **\$16,000 at 9% and \$16,000 at 11%**

4. **MILK** Whole milk is 4% butterfat. How much skim milk with 0% butterfat should be added to 32 ounces of whole milk to obtain a mixture that is 2.5% butterfat? **19.2 oz**

Lesson 2-9

Chapter 2 55 Glencoe Algebra 1

Practice

CRM p. 58 AL OL BL ELL

NAME ______ DATE ______ PERIOD ______

2-9 Practice

Weighted Averages

1. **GRASS SEED** A nursery sells Kentucky Blue Grass seed for \$5.75 per pound and Tall Fescue seed for \$4.50 per pound. The nursery sells a mixture of the two kinds of seed for \$5.25 per pound. Let k represent the amount of Kentucky Blue Grass seed the nursery uses in 5 pounds of the mixture.

   a. Complete the table representing the problem.

	Number of Pounds	Price per Pound	Cost
Kentucky Blue Grass	k	\$5.75	$5.75k$
Tall Fescue	$5 - k$	\$4.50	$4.50(5 - k)$
Mixture	5	\$5.25	5.25(5)

   b. Write an equation to represent the problem. $5.75k + 4.50(5 - k) = 5.25(5)$

   c. How much Kentucky Blue Grass does the nursery use in 5 pounds of the mixture? **3 lb**

   d. How much Tall Fescue does the nursery use in 5 pounds of the mixture? **2 lb**

2. **TRAVEL** Two commuter trains carry passengers between two cities, one traveling east, and the other west, on different tracks. Their respective stations are 150 miles apart. Both trains leave at the same time, one traveling at an average speed of 55 miles per hour and the other at an average speed of 65 miles per hour. Let t represent the time until the trains pass each other.

   a. Copy and complete the table representing the problem.

	r	t	$d = rt$
First Train	55	t	$55t$
Second Train	65	t	$65t$

   b. Write an equation using t that describes the distances traveled. $55t + 65t = 150$

   c. How long after departing will the trains pass each other? **1.25 h**

3. **TRAVEL** Two trains leave Raleigh at the same time, one traveling north, and the other south. The first train travels at 50 miles per hour and the second at 60 miles per hour. In how many hours will the trains be 275 miles apart? **2.5 h**

4. **JUICE** A pineapple drink contains 15% pineapple juice. How much pure pineapple juice should be added to 8 quarts of the pineapple drink to obtain a mixture containing 50% pineapple juice? **5.6 qt**

Chapter 2 58 Glencoe Algebra 1

Word Problem Practice

CRM p. 59 AL OL BL ELL

NAME ______ DATE ______ PERIOD ______

2-9 Word Problem Practice

Weighted Averages

1. **DRIVING** The drive from New York City to Boston is about 240 miles. It took Samir 5 hours to drive one way, but due to severe weather it took him 6.5 hours for the return trip. What was his average speed round trip? Round the answer to the nearest hundredth.
   41.74 miles per hour

2. **GRADES** In math classes at Gorbine High School, all tests are given double the weight of a quiz or homework score when calculating grades. Use Donna's grade record sheet to determine her average grade so far this term.

Assignment	Grade
Homework chapter 1	95
Quiz chapter 1	80
Test chapter 1	92
Homework chapter 2	93
Quiz chapter 2	96
Test chapter 2	81

   88.75

3. **MIXTURE** Keith wants to create a drink that is 40% juice. How much of a 10% juice solution should he add to 100 milliliters of 100% grape juice to obtain the 40% mixture?
   200 mL

4. **BUSINESS** Mrs. Winship sells chocolate fudge for \$7.50 per pound and peanut butter fudge for \$7.00 per pound. The total number of pounds sold on Saturday was 146 and the total amount of money collected was \$1065. How many pounds of each type of fudge were sold?
   86 pounds of chocolate and 60 pounds of peanut butter

5. **TRAINS** Two trains are 5000 feet apart, heading toward each other, but on separate parallel straight tracks, Train A is traveling at 45 miles per hour and Train B is traveling at 24 miles per hour.

   a. Change 45 miles per hour and 24 miles per hour into feet per second.
   Train A: 66 feet per second
   Train B: 35.2 feet per second

   b. About how far will each train travel before they meet? Round your answers to the nearest hundredth.
   Train A: 3260.87 feet
   Train B: 1739.13 feet

   c. In how many seconds will Train A and Train B meet?
   49.4 seconds

Lesson 2-9

Chapter 2 59 Glencoe Algebra 1

Enrichment

CRM p. 60 OL BL

NAME ______ DATE ______ PERIOD ______

2-9 Enrichment

Expected Value

Expected value is the average return of an event over repeated trial. Expected value is also a form of weighted average and can be used to determine whether or not you should play a game based on what the expected value of your winnings is. It can also be used to determine the expected length of a game.

Example **You are rolling a number cube to determine the number of candy bars you will win at a school fair. If you roll a one, you get 12 candy bars. If you roll a two or a three, you get 3 candy bars. If you roll a four, five or six, you get 2 candy bars.**

Since there are six possibilities for what you can roll:

- $\frac{1}{6}$ of the time, you will win 12 candy bars.
- $\frac{2}{6}$ or $\frac{1}{3}$ of the time, you will win 3 candy bars.
- $\frac{3}{6}$ or $\frac{1}{2}$ of the time, you will win 2 candy bars.

The expected value is $\frac{1}{6}(12) + \frac{1}{3}(3) + \frac{1}{2}(2)$ or 4 candy bars.

Therefore, if you played the game 100 times, you could expect to win about 4 candy bars each time.

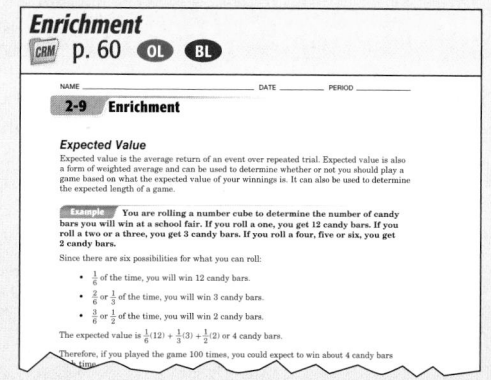

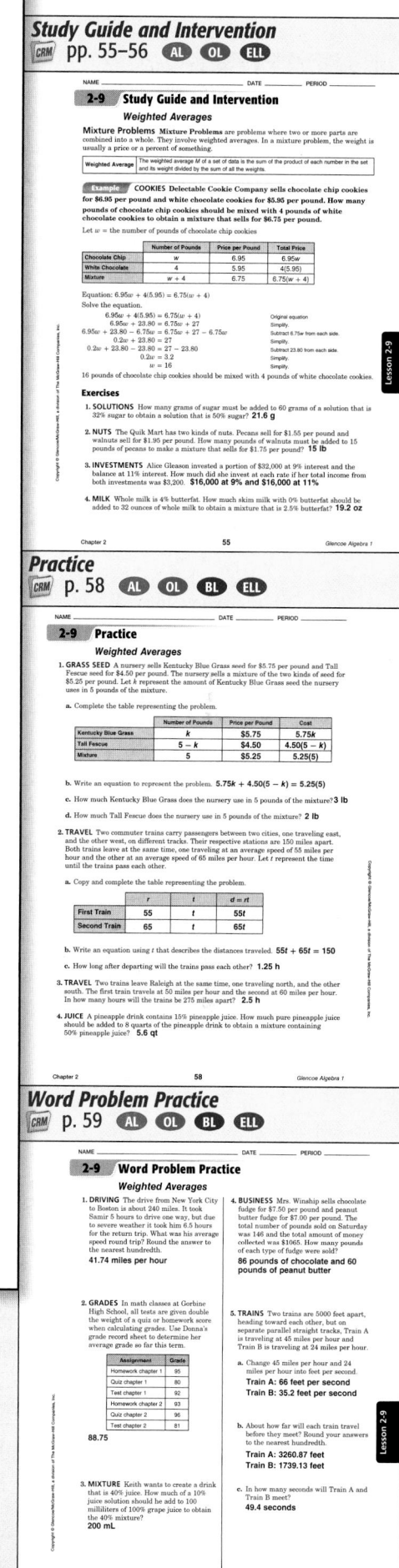

4 ASSESS

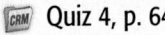

Name the Math Have students tell what mathematical procedures they would use to solve Exercise 7.

Formative Assessment

Check for student understanding of Lessons 2-8 and 2-9.

CRM Quiz 4, p. 64

Additional Answers

35. Sample answer: The quotient of n and -6 is the same as the sum of two times n and one.

36. Sample answer: Eighteen decreased by five times h is the same as thirteen times h.

37. Sample answer: The sum of three and twice x squared is equal to twenty-one.

PSAE PRACTICE 6.11.13, 8.11.01, 7.11.03, 6.11.18

27. If $2x + y = 5$, what is the value of $4x$? **B**

A $10 - y$
B $10 - 2y$
C $\frac{5 - y}{2}$
D $\frac{10 - y}{2}$

28. Which expression is equivalent to $7x^2 3x^{-4}$? **J**

F $21x^{-8}$
G $21x^2$
H $21x^{-6}$
J $21x^{-2}$

29. GEOMETRY What is the base of the triangle if the area is 56 square meters? **C**

A 4 m
B 8 m
C 16 m
D 28 m

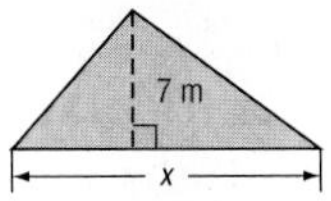

30. SHORT RESPONSE Brianne makes blankets for a baby store. She works on the blankets 30 hours per week. The store pays her $9.50 per hour plus 30% of the profit. If her hourly rate is increased by $0.75 and her commission is raised to 40%, how much will she earn for a $300 profit? **$427.50**

Spiral Review

Solve each equation or formula for x. (Lesson 2-8)

31. $2bx - b = -5$ $\frac{-5 + b}{2b}$

32. $3x - r = r(-3 + x)$ $\frac{-2r}{3 - r}$

33. $A = 2\pi r^2 + 2\pi rx$ $\frac{A}{2\pi r} - r$

34. SKIING Yuji is registering for ski camp. The cost of the camp is $1254, but there is a sales tax of 7%. What is the total cost of the camp including tax? (Lesson 2-7) **$1341.78**

Translate each equation into a sentence. (Lesson 2-1) **35–37. See margin.**

35. $\frac{n}{-6} = 2n + 1$

36. $18 - 5h = 13h$

37. $2x^2 + 3 = 21$

Refer to the graph.

38. Name the ordered pair at point A and explain what it represents. (Lesson 1-6)

39. Name the ordered pair at point B and explain what it represents. (Lesson 1-6)

40. Identify the independent and dependent variables for the function. (Lesson 1-6) **I: number of cars washed; D: amount earned**

Touchdown Club Car Wash

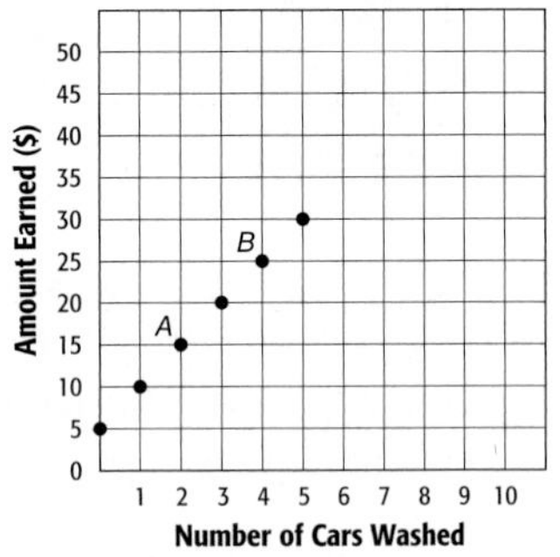

41. BASEBALL Tickets to a baseball game cost $18.95, $12.95, or $9.95. A hot dog and soda combo costs $5.50. The Madison family is having a reunion. They buy 10 tickets in each price category and plan to buy 30 combos. What is the total cost for the tickets and meals? (Lesson 1-3) **$583.50**

38. (2, 15); Sample answer: If two cars are washed, $15 is earned.
39. (4, 25); Sample answer: If four cars are washed, $25 is earned.

Skills Review

Solve each equation. (Lesson 2-4)

42. $a - 8 = 15$ **23**

43. $9m - 11 = -29$ **−2**

44. $18 - 2k = 24$ **−3**

45. $5 - 8y = 61$ **−7**

46. $7 = \frac{h}{2} + 3$ **8**

47. $\frac{n}{6} + 1 = 5$ **24**

Differentiated Instruction BL

Extension In many high schools, a special weight is assigned to the grades received in Advanced Placement classes when a student's GPA is calculated (A = 5 points; B = 4 points; C = 3 points). Have students pretend that one of their classes is an Advanced Placement class with a grade having special weight assigned to it. Have them use their current grades to calculate their GPAs. Ask students to explain how the class chosen as an Advanced Placement class made their GPA higher.

IL Math Online glencoe.com
- STUDY TO GO
- Vocabulary Review

Chapter Summary

Key Concepts

Writing Equations (Lesson 2-1)

- Identify the unknown you are looking for and assign a variable to it. Then, write the sentence as an equation.

Solving Equations (Lessons 2-2 to 2-4)

- Addition and Subtraction Properties of Equality: If an equation is true and the same number is added to or subtracted from each side, the resulting equation is true.
- Multiplication and Division Properties of Equality: If an equation is true and each side is multiplied or divided by the same nonzero number, the resulting equation is true.
- Steps for Solving Equations:

  Step 1 Simplify the expression on each side. Use the Distributive Property as needed.

  Step 2 Use the Addition and/or Subtraction Properties of Equality to get the variables on one side and the numbers without variables on the other side.

  Step 3 Use the Multiplication or Division Property of Equality to solve.

Absolute Value Equations (Lesson 2-5)

- For any real numbers a and b, if $|a| = b$, then $a = b$ or $a = -b$.

Ratios and Proportions (Lesson 2-6)

- The Means-Extremes Property of Proportion states that in a proportion, the product of the extremes is equal to the product of the means.

FOLDABLES® Study Organizer

Be sure the Key Concepts are noted in your Foldable.

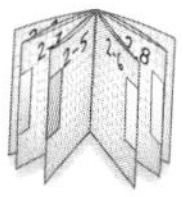

Key Vocabulary

consecutive integers (p. 92)
dimensional analysis (p. 128)
equivalent equations (p. 83)
extremes (p. 112)
formula (p. 76)
identity (p. 98)
literal equation (p. 127)
means (p. 112)
multi-step equations (p. 91)
number theory (p. 92)
percent of change (p. 119)
percent of decrease (p. 119)
percent of increase (p. 119)
proportion (p. 111)
rate (p. 113)
ratio (p. 111)
scale (p. 114)
scale model (p. 114)
solve an equation (p. 83)
unit analysis (p. 128)
unit rate (p. 113)
weighted average (p. 132)

Vocabulary Check

State whether each sentence is *true* or *false*. If *false*, replace the underlined term to make a true sentence.

1. In order to write an equation to solve a problem, identify the unknown for which you are looking and assign a(n) <u>number</u> to it. **false, variable**
2. To <u>solve an equation</u> means to find the value of the variable that makes the equation true. **true**
3. The numbers 10, 12, and 14 are an example of <u>consecutive even integers</u>. **true**
4. The <u>absolute value</u> of any number is simply the distance the number is away from zero on a number line. **true**
5. A(n) <u>equation</u> is a comparison of two numbers by division. **false, ratio**
6. An equation stating that two ratios are equal is called a(n) <u>proportion</u>. **true**
7. If the new number is less than the original number, the percent of change is a percent of <u>increase</u>. **false, decrease**
8. The <u>weighted average</u> of a set of data is the sum of the product of the number of units and the value per unit divided by the sum of the number of units. **true**

CHAPTER 2 Study Guide and Review

Formative Assessment

Key Vocabulary The page reference after each word denotes where that term was first introduced. If students have difficulty answering questions 1–8, remind them that they can use these page references to refresh their memories about the vocabulary terms.

Summative Assessment

CRM Vocabulary Test, p. 66

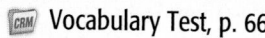

IL Math Online glencoe.com

Vocabulary PuzzleMaker improves students' mathematics vocabulary using four puzzle formats–crossword, scramble, word search using a word list, and word search using clues. Students can work online or from a printed worksheet.

FOLDABLES® Study Organizer

Dinah Zike's Foldables®

Have students look through the chapter to make sure they have included examples in their Foldables for each lesson of the chapter.

Suggest that students keep their Foldables handy while completing the Study Guide and Review pages. Point out that their Foldables can serve as a quick review when studying for the chapter test.

Lesson-by-Lesson Review

Intervention If the given examples are not sufficient to review the topics covered by the questions, remind students that the page references tell them where to review that topic in their textbooks.

Two-Day Option Have students complete the Lesson-by-Lesson Review on pp. 140–144. Then you can use ExamView® Assessment Suite to customize another review worksheet that practices all the objectives of this chapter or only the objectives on which your students need more help.

Differentiated Instruction

Super DVD: MindJogger Videoquizzes Use this DVD as an alternative format of review for the test.

Lesson-by-Lesson Review

2-1 Writing Equations (pp. 75–80)

8.B.4a, 8.D.4

Translate each sentence into an equation.

9. The sum of five times a number x and three is the same as fifteen. **$5x + 3 = 15$**
10. Four times the difference of b and six is equal to b squared. **$4(b - 6) = b^2$**
11. One half of m cubed is the same as four times m minus nine. **$\frac{1}{2}m^3 = 4m - 9$**

Translate each equation into a sentence.

12. $3p + 8 = 20$
13. $h^2 - 5h + 6 = 0$
14. $\frac{3}{4}w^2 + \frac{2}{3}w - \frac{1}{5} = 2$

15. **FENCING** Adrianne wants to create an outdoor rectangular kennel. The length will be three feet more than twice the width. Write and use an equation to find the length and the width of the kennel if Adrianne has 54 feet of fencing. **width: 8 ft, length: 19 ft**

EXAMPLE 1

Translate the following sentence into an equation.

Six times the sum of a number n and four is the same as the difference between two times n to the second power and ten.

$6(n + 4) = 2n^2 - 10$

EXAMPLE 2

Translate $3d^2 - 9d + 8 = 4(d + 2)$ into a sentence.

Three times a number d squared minus nine times d increased by eight is equal to four times the sum of d and two.

12. The sum of three times p and eight is the same as twenty.
13. h squared minus five times h plus six is equal to zero.
14. Three-fourths w squared plus two-thirds w minus one fifth is equal to two.

2-2 Solving One-Step Equations (pp. 83–89)

8.B.4a, 8.D.4

Solve each equation. Check your solution.

16. $x - 9 = 4$ **13**
17. $-6 + g = -11$ **−5**
18. $\frac{5}{9} + w = \frac{7}{9}$ **$\frac{2}{9}$**
19. $3.8 = m + 1.7$ **2.1**
20. $\frac{a}{12} = 5$ **60**
21. $8y = 48$ **6**
22. $\frac{2}{5}b = -4$ **−10**
23. $-\frac{t}{16} = -\frac{7}{8}$ **14**

24. **AGE** Max is four years younger than his sister Brenda. The total of their ages is 16. Write and solve an equation to find their ages. **$x + (x - 4) = 16$; Max: 6, Brenda: 10**

EXAMPLE 3

Solve $x - 13 = 9$. Check your solution.

$x - 13 = 9$	**Original equation**
$x - 13 + 13 = 9 + 13$	**Add 13 to each side.**
$x = 22$	**$-13 + 13 = 0$ and $9 + 13 = 22$**

To check that 22 is the solution, substitute 22 for x in the original equation.

CHECK	$x - 13 = 9$	**Original equation**
	$22 - 13 \stackrel{?}{=} 9$	**Substitute 22 for x.**
	$9 = 9$ ✓	**Subtract.**

2-3 Solving Multi-Step Equations (pp. 91–96)

8.B.4a, 8.D.4

Solve each equation. Check your solution.

25. $2d - 4 = 8$ **6**
26. $-9 = 3t + 6$ **−5**
27. $14 = -8 - 2k$ **−11**
28. $\frac{n}{4} - 7 = -2$ **20**
29. $\frac{r+4}{3} = 7$ **17**
30. $-18 = \frac{9-a}{2}$ **45**
31. $6g - 3.5 = 8.5$ **2**
32. $0.2c + 4 = 6$ **10**
33. $\frac{f}{3} - 9.2 = 3.5$ **38.1**
34. $4 = \frac{-3u - (-7)}{-8}$ **13**
35. **CONSECUTIVE INTEGERS** Find three consecutive odd integers with a sum of 63. **19, 21, 23**
36. **CONSECUTIVE INTEGERS** Find three consecutive integers with a sum of −39. **−12, −13, −14**

EXAMPLE 4

Solve $7y - 9 = 33$. Check your solution.

$7y - 9 = 33$	Original equation
$7y - 9 + 9 = 33 + 9$	Add 9 to each side.
$7y = 42$	Simplify.
$\frac{7y}{7} = \frac{42}{7}$	Divide each side by 7.
$y = 6$	Simplify.
CHECK $7y - 9 = 33$	Original equation
$7(6) - 9 \stackrel{?}{=} 33$	Substitute 6 for *y*.
$42 - 9 \stackrel{?}{=} 33$	Multiply.
$33 = 33$ ✓	Subtract.

2-4 Solving Equations with the Variable on Each Side (pp. 97–102)

8.B.4a, 8.D.4

Solve each equation. Check your solution.

37. $8m + 7 = 5m + 16$ **3**
38. $2h - 14 = -5h$ **2**
39. $21 + 3j = 9 - 3j$ **−2**
40. $\frac{x-3}{4} = \frac{x}{2}$ **−3**
41. $\frac{6r-7}{10} = \frac{r}{4}$ **2**
42. $3(p + 4) = 33$ **7**
43. $-2(b - 3) - 4 = 18$ **−8**
44. $4(3w - 2) = 8(2w + 3)$ **−8**

Write an equation and solve each problem.

45. Find the sum of three consecutive odd integers if the sum of the first two integers is equal to twenty-four less than four times the third integer. **21**
46. **TRAVEL** Mr. Jones drove 480 miles to a business meeting. His travel time to the meeting was 8 hours and from the meeting was 7.5 hours. Find his rate of travel for each leg of the trip.

EXAMPLE 5

Solve $9w - 24 = 6w + 18$.

$9w - 24 = 6w + 18$	Original equation
$9w - 24 - 6w = 6w + 18 - 6w$	Subtract 6*w* from each side.
$3w - 24 = 18$	Simplify.
$3w - 24 + 24 = 18 + 24$	Add 24 to each side.
$3w = 42$	Simplify.
$\frac{3w}{3} = \frac{42}{3}$	Divide each side by 3.
$w = 14$	Simplify.

EXAMPLE 6

Write an equation to find three consecutive integers such that three times the sum of the first two integers is the same as thirteen more than four times the third integer.

Let x, $x + 1$, and $x + 2$ represent the three consecutive integers.

$3(x + x + 1) = 4(x + 2) + 13$

46. to meeting: 60 mph; from meeting: 64 mph

Chapter 2 Study Guide and Review 141

Additional Answers

51. $\{-5, 17\}$

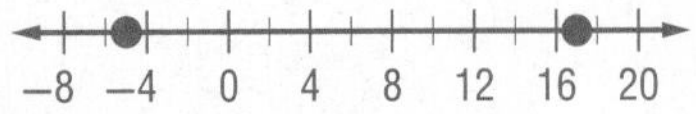

52. $\{-3, 4\}$

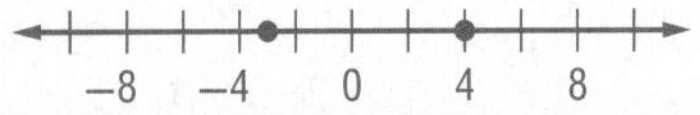

53. $\{-27, 63\}$

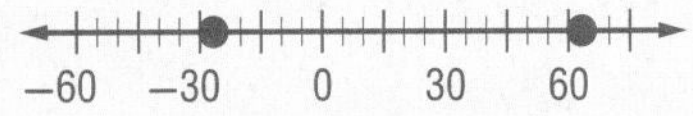

54. $\{18, -42\}$;

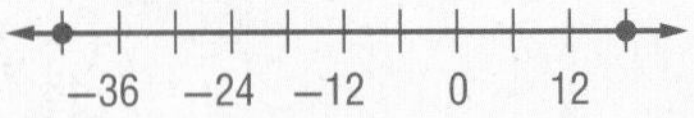

CHAPTER 2 Study Guide and Review

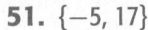

2-5 Solving Equations Involving Absolute Value (pp. 103–109)

8.B.4a

Evaluate each expression if $m = -8$, $n = 4$, and $p = -12$.

47. $|3m - n|$ 28

48. $|-2p + m| - 3n$ 4

49. $-3|6n - 2p|$ −144

50. $4|7m + 3p| + 4n$ 384

Solve each equation. Then graph the solution set. 51–54. See margin.

51. $|x - 6| = 11$

52. $|-4w + 2| = 14$

53. $\left|\frac{1}{3}d - 6\right| = 15$

54. $\left|\frac{2b}{3} + 8\right| = 20$

EXAMPLE 7

Solve $|y - 9| = 16$. Then graph the solution set.

Case 1

$y - 9 = 16$	Original equation
$y - 9 + 9 = 16 + 9$	Add 9 to each side.
$y = 25$	Simplify.

Case 2

$y - 9 = -16$	Original equation
$y - 9 + 9 = -16 + 9$	Add 9 to each side.
$y = -7$	Simplify.

The solution set is $\{-7, 25\}$.

Graph the points on a number line.

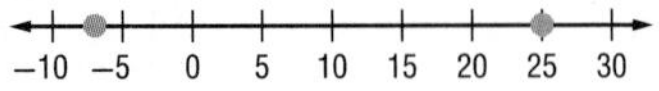

2-6 Ratios and Proportions (pp. 111–117)

7.C.4b, 9.A.4b

Determine whether each pair of ratios are equivalent ratios. Write *yes* or *no*.

55. $\frac{27}{45}, \frac{3}{5}$ yes

56. $\frac{18}{32}, \frac{3}{4}$ no

Solve each proportion. If necessary, round to the nearest hundredth.

57. $\frac{4}{9} = \frac{a}{45}$ 20

58. $\frac{3}{8} = \frac{21}{t}$ 56

59. $\frac{9}{12} = \frac{g}{16}$ 12

60. **CONSTRUCTION** A new gym is being built at Greenfield Middle School. The length of the gym as shown on the builder's blueprints is 12 inches. Find the actual length of the new gym. 80 ft

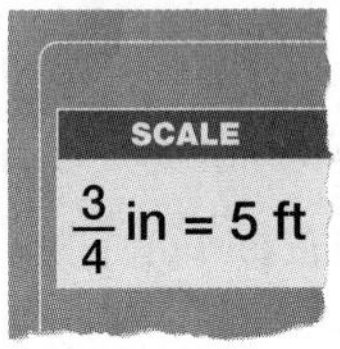

EXAMPLE 8

Determine whether $\frac{7}{9}$ and $\frac{42}{54}$ are equivalent ratios. Write *yes* or *no*. Justify your answer.

First, simplify each ratio. $\frac{7}{9}$ is already in simplest form.

$$\frac{42}{54} = \frac{42 \div 6}{54 \div 6} = \frac{7}{9}$$

When expressed in simplest form, the ratios are equivalent. The answer is yes.

EXAMPLE 9

Solve $\frac{r}{8} = \frac{3}{4}$. If necessary, round to the nearest hundredth.

$\frac{r}{8} = \frac{3}{4}$	Original equation
$r(4) = 3(8)$	Find the cross products.
$4r = 24$	Simplify.
$\frac{4r}{4} = \frac{24}{4}$	Divide each side by 4.
$r = 6$	Simplify.

MIXED PROBLEM SOLVING
For mixed problem-solving practice, see page 846.

2-7 Percent of Change (pp. 119–124)

6.D.4, 8.A.4b

State whether each percent of change is a percent of *increase* or a percent of *decrease*. Then find the percent of change. Round to the nearest whole percent.

61. original: 40, new: 50 increase, 25%

62. original: 36, new: 24 decrease, 33%

63. original: \$72, new: \$60 decrease, 17%

Find the total price of each item.

64. boots: \$64, tax: 7% \$68.48

65. video game: \$49, tax: 6.5% \$52.19

66. hockey skates: \$199, tax: 5.25% \$209.45

Find the discounted price of each item.

67. MP3 player: \$69.00, discount: 20% \$55.20

68. jacket: \$129, discount: 15% \$109.65

69. backpack: \$45, discount: 25% \$33.75

70. ATTENDANCE An amusement park recorded attendance of 825,000 one year. The next year, the attendance increased to 975,000. Determine the percent of increase in attendance. about 18.2%

EXAMPLE 10

State whether the percent of change is a percent of *increase* or a percent of *decrease*. Then find the percent of change. Round to the nearest whole percent.

original: 80
new: 60

Since the new amount is less than the original, this is a percent of decrease. Subtract to find the amount of change: $80 - 60 = 20$.

Use the original number, 80, as the base.

$$\frac{\text{change}}{\text{original amount}} \rightarrow \frac{20}{80} = \frac{r}{100}$$

$$20(100) = r(80)$$

$$2000 = 80r$$

$$\frac{2000}{80} = \frac{80r}{80}$$

$$25 = r$$

The percent of decrease is 25%.

2-8 Literal Equations and Dimensional Analysis (pp. 126–131)

7.A.4b, 8.B.4a

Solve each equation or formula for the variable indicated.

71. $3x + 2y = 9$, for y $y = \frac{9 - 3x}{2}$

72. $P = 2\ell + 2w$, for ℓ $\ell = \frac{P - 2w}{2}$

73. $-5m + 9n = 15$, for m $m = \frac{15 - 9n}{-5}$

74. $14w + 15x = y - 21w$, for w $w = \frac{y - 15x}{35}$

75. $m = \frac{2}{5}y + n$, for y $y = \frac{5}{2}(m - n)$

76. $7d - 3c = f + 2d$, for d $d = \frac{f + 3c}{5}$

77. GEOMETRY The formula for the area of a trapezoid is $A = \frac{1}{2}h(a + b)$, where h represents the height and a and b represent the lengths of the bases. Solve for h. $h = \frac{2A}{a + b}$

EXAMPLE 11

Solve $6p - 8n = 12$ for p.

$6p - 8n = 12$	Original equation
$6p - 8n + 8n = 12 + 8n$	Add $8n$ to each side.
$6p = 12 + 8n$	Simplify.
$\frac{6p}{6} = \frac{12 + 8n}{6}$	Divide each side by 6.
$\frac{6p}{6} = \frac{12}{6} + \frac{8}{6}n$	Simplify.
$p = 2 + \frac{4}{3}n$	Simplify.

Chapter 2 Study Guide and Review 143

CHAPTER 2 Study Guide and Review

Problem Solving Review

For additional practice in problem solving for Chapter 2, see the Mixed Problem Solving Appendix, p. 846, in the Student Handbook section.

Anticipation Guide

Have students complete the Chapter 2 Anticipation Guide and discuss how their responses have changed now that they have completed Chapter 2.

CHAPTER 2 Study Guide and Review

2-9 Weighted Averages (pp. 132–138)

6.C.4, 7.A.4b

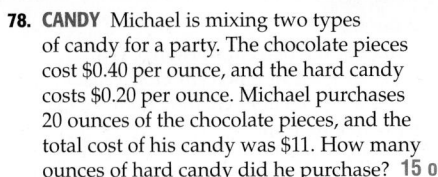

78. CANDY Michael is mixing two types of candy for a party. The chocolate pieces cost \$0.40 per ounce, and the hard candy costs \$0.20 per ounce. Michael purchases 20 ounces of the chocolate pieces, and the total cost of his candy was \$11. How many ounces of hard candy did he purchase? **15 oz**

79. TRAVEL A car travels 100 miles east in 2 hours and 30 miles north in half an hour. What is the average speed of the car? **52 mph**

80. FINANCIAL LITERACY A candle supply store sells votive wax and low-shrink wax. How many pounds of low-shrink wax should be mixed with 8 pounds of votive wax to obtain a blend that sells for \$0.98 a pound? $10\frac{2}{3}$ **lb**

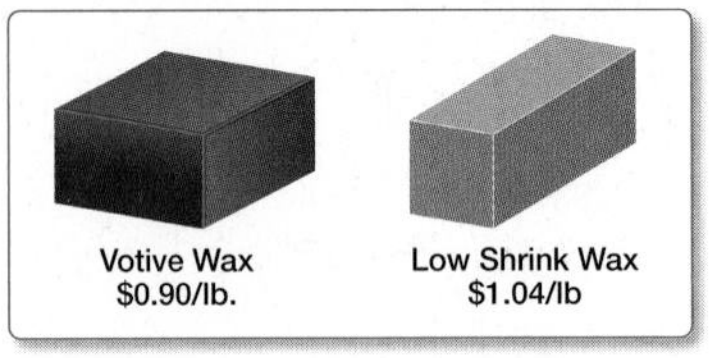

EXAMPLE 12

METALS An alloy of metals is 25% copper. Another alloy is 50% copper. How much of each should be used to make 1000 grams of an alloy that is 45% copper?

Let x = the amount of the 25% copper alloy. Write and solve an equation.

$0.25x + 0.50(1000 - x) = 0.45(1000)$	Original Equation
$0.25x + 500 - 0.50x = 450$	Distributive Property
$-0.25x + 500 = 450$	Simplify.
$-0.25x + 500 - 500 = 450 - 500$	Subtract 500 from each side.
$-0.25x = -50$	Simplify.
$\frac{-0.25x}{-0.25} = \frac{-50}{-0.25}$	Divide each side by −0.25.
$x = 200$	Simplify.

200 grams of the 25% alloy and 800 grams of the 50% alloy should be used.

IL Math Online > glencoe.com
Chapter Test

Translate each sentence into an equation.

1. The sum of six and four times d is the same as d minus nine. $6 + 4d = d - 9$
2. Three times the difference of two times m and five is equal to eight times m to the second power increased by four. $3(2m - 5) = 8m^2 + 4$

Solve each equation. Check your solutions.

3. $x - 5 = -11$ -6
4. $\frac{2}{3} = w + \frac{1}{4}$ $\frac{5}{12}$
5. $\frac{t}{6} = -3$ -18

Solve each equation. Check your solution.

6. $2a - 5 = 13$ 9
7. $\frac{p}{4} - 3 = 9$ 48
8. **MULTIPLE CHOICE** At Mama Mia Pizza, the price of a large pizza is determined by $P = 9 + 1.5x$, where x represents the number of toppings added to a cheese pizza. Daniel spent $13.50 on a large pizza. How many toppings did he get? C

   A 0

   B 1

   C 3

   D 5

Solve each equation. Check your solution.

9. $5y - 4 = 9y + 8$ -3
10. $3(2k - 2) = -2(4k - 11)$ 2
11. **GEOMETRY** Find the value of x so that the figures have the same perimeter. 7

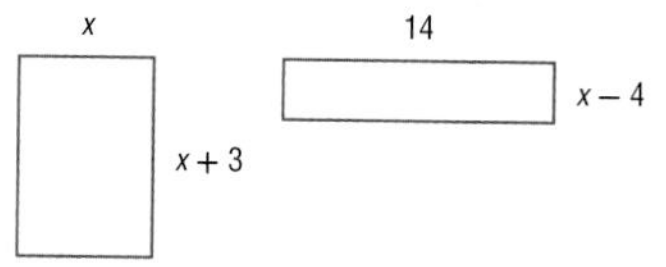

12. Evaluate the expression $|3t - 2u| + 5v$ if $t = 2$, $u = -5$, and $v = -3$. 1

Solve each equation. Then graph the solution set.

13. $|p - 4| = 6$ $\{-2, 10\}$
14. $|2b + 5| = 9$ $\{-7, 2\}$

13–14. See margin for graphs.

Solve each proportion. If necessary, round to the nearest hundredth.

15. $\frac{a}{3} = \frac{16}{24}$ 2
16. $\frac{9}{k + 3} = \frac{3}{5}$ 12
17. **MULTIPLE CHOICE** Akiko uses 2 feet of thread for every three squares that she sews for her quilt. How many squares can she sew if she has 38 feet of thread? G

    F 19

    G 57

    H 76

    J 228

18. State whether the percent of change is a percent of *increase* or a percent of *decrease*. Then find the percent of change. Round to the nearest whole percent. decrease; 17%

    original: 54 new: 45
19. Find the total price of a sweatshirt that is priced at $48 and taxed at 6.5%. $51.12
20. **SHOPPING** Kirk wants to purchase a wide-screen TV. He sees an advertisement for a TV that was originally priced at $3200 and is 20% off. Find the discounted price of the TV. $2560
21. Solve $5x - 3y = 9$ for y. $y = \frac{5}{3}x - 3$
22. Solve $A = \frac{1}{2}bh$ for h. $h = \frac{2A}{b}$
23. **CHEMISTRY** Deon has 12 milliliters of a 5% solution. He also has a solution that has a concentration of 30%. How many milliliters of the 30% solution does Deon need to add to the 5% solution to obtain a 20% solution? 18 mL
24. **BICYCLING** Shanee bikes 5 miles to the park in 30 minutes and 3 miles to the library in 45 minutes. What was her average speed? 6.4 mph
25. **MAPS** On a map of North Carolina, the distance between Charlotte and Wilmington is 14.75 inches. If 2 inches equals 24 miles, what is the approximate distance between the two cities? 177 mi

CHAPTER 2 Practice Test

ExamView Assessment Suite Customize and create multiple versions of your chapter tests and their answer keys. All of the questions from the leveled chapter tests in the *Chapter 2 Resource Masters* are also available on ExamView Assessment Suite.

Additional Answers

13.

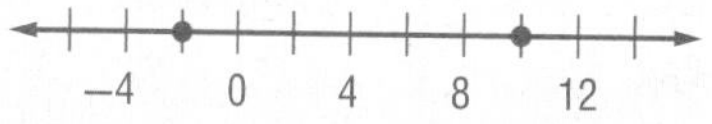

14.

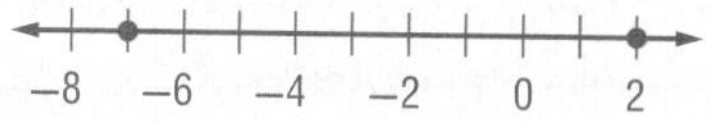

Intervention Planner

Tier 1 On Level	Tier 2 Strategic Intervention approaching grade level	Tier 3 Intensive Intervention 2 or more grades below level
If students miss about 25% of the exercises or less,	**If** students miss about 50% of the exercises,	**If** students miss about 75% of the exercises,
Then choose a resource:	**Then** choose a resource:	**Then** use *Math Triumphs, Alg. 1*
SE Lessons 2-1, 2-2, 2-3, 2-4, 2-5, 2-6, 2-7, 2-8 and 2-9 **CRM** Skills Practice, pp. 7, 13, 19, 25, 32, 38, 44, 51, and 57 **TE** Chapter Project, p. 72 IL Math Online > Self-Check Quiz	**CRM** Study Guide and Intervention, Chapter 2, pp. 5, 11, 17, 23, 30, 36, 42, 49, and 55 *Quick Review Math Handbook* IL Math Online > Extra Examples, Personal Tutor, Homework Help	IL Math Online > Extra Examples, Personal Tutor, Homework Help, Review Vocabulary

1 FOCUS

Objective Use strategies for gridded response standardized test problems.

2 TEACH

Scaffolding Questions

Ask:

- For what subjects have you filled in grids when taking a test? Answers will vary.
- What was most confusing about filling in the grids? Answers will vary.
- What can you do to avoid confusion when filling in grids? Sample answer: Make sure you understand the directions before filling in the grids.

CHAPTER 2 Preparing for Standardized Tests

Gridded Response Questions

In addition to multiple-choice, short-answer, and extended-response questions, you will likely encounter gridded-response questions on standardized tests. For gridded-response questions, you must print your answer on an answer sheet and mark in the correct circles on the grid to match your answer.

Strategies for Solving Gridded Response Questions

Step 1

Read the problem carefully.

- **Ask yourself:** "What information is given?" "What do I need to find?" "How do I solve this type of problem?"
- **Solve the Problem:** Use the information given in the problem to solve.
- **Check your answer:** If time permits, check your answer to make sure you have solved the problem correctly.

Step 2

Write your answer in the answer boxes.

- Print only one digit or symbol in each answer box.
- Do not write any digits or symbols outside the answer boxes.
- You may write your answer with the first digit in the left answer box, or with the last digit in the right answer box. You may leave blank any boxes you do not need on the right or the left side of your answer.

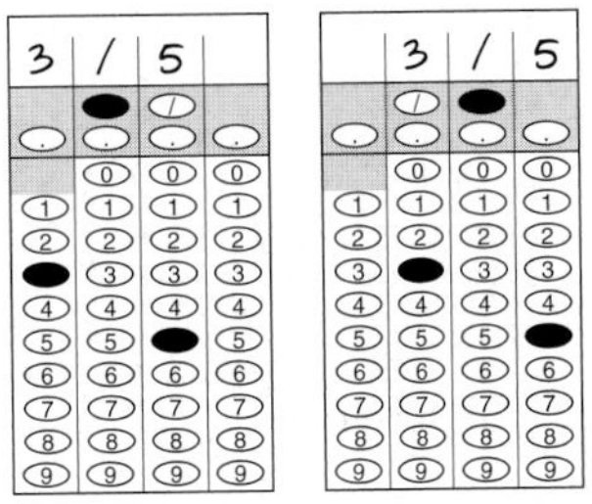

Step 3

Fill in the grid.

- Fill in only one bubble for every answer box that you have written in. Be sure not to fill in a bubble under a blank answer box.
- Fill in each bubble completely and clearly.

EXAMPLE

Read the problem. Identify what you need to know. Then use the information in the problem to solve.

> **GRIDDED RESPONSE** Ashley is 3 years older than her sister, Tina. Combined, the sum of their ages is 27 years. How old is Ashley?

146 Chapter 2 Linear Equations

Read the problem carefully. You are told that Ashley is 3 years older than her sister and that their ages combined equal 27 years. You need to find Ashley's age.

Solve the Problem

Words Ashley's age plus Tina's age is equal to 27 years.

Variable Let a represent Ashley's age. Then Tina's age is $a - 3$, since she is 3 years younger than Ashley.

Equation $a \quad + \quad (a - 3) \quad = \quad 27$

Fill in the Grid

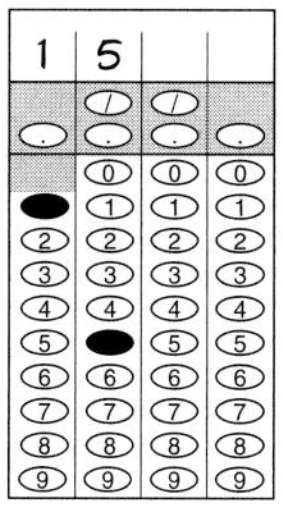

Solve the equation for a.

$a + (a - 3) = 27$	**Original equation.**
$2a - 3 = 27$	**Add like terms.**
$2a = 30$	**Add 3 to each side.**
$a = 15$	**Divide each side by 2.**

Since we let a represent Ashley's age, we know that she is 15 years old.

Exercises

Read each problem. Identify what you need to know. Then use the information in the problem to solve. Copy and complete an answer grid on your paper.

1. Orlando has $1350 in the bank. He wants to increase his balance to a total of $2550 by depositing $40 each week from his paycheck. How many weeks will he need to save in order to reach his goal? **30**

2. Fourteen less than three times a number is equal to 40. Find the number. **18**

3. The table shows the regular prices and sale prices of certain items at a department store this week. What is the percent of discount during the sale? **20**

Item	Regular Price ($)	Sale Price ($)
pillows	25	20
sweaters	30	24
entertainment center	125	100

4. Maureen is driving from Raleigh, North Carolina, to Charlotte, North Carolina, to visit her brother at college. If she averages 65 miles per hour on the trip, then the equation $\frac{d}{2.65} = 65$ can be solved for the distance d. What is the distance to the nearest mile from Raleigh to Charlotte? **172**

5. Find the value of x so that the figures below have the same area. **5**

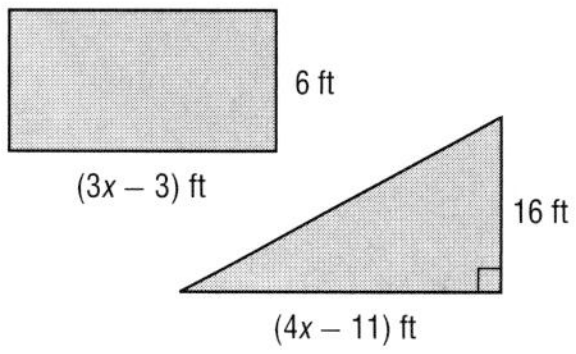

6. The sum of three consecutive whole numbers is 18. What is the greatest of the numbers? **7**

Additional Example

GRIDDED RESPONSE Derek and Tamara mailed a total of 86 invitations for the upcoming environmental fair. If Derek mailed 18 more invitations than Tamara did, how many invitations did Tamara mail?

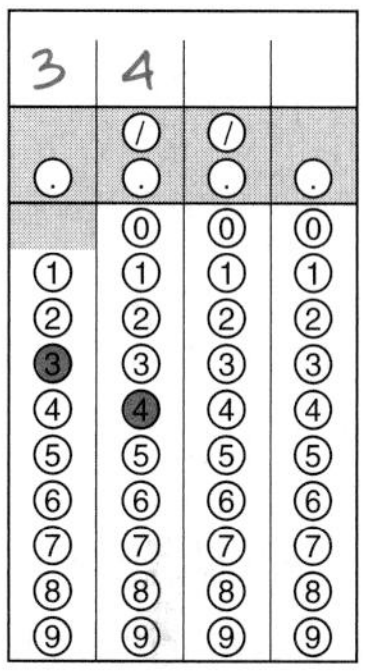

3 ASSESS

Use Exercises 1–6 to assess students' understanding.

CHAPTER 2 PSAE Practice

Cumulative, Chapters 1 through 2

Multiple Choice

Read each question. Then fill in the correct answer on the answer document provided by your teacher or on a sheet of paper.

1. Which point on the number line best represents the position of $\sqrt{8}$? **C**

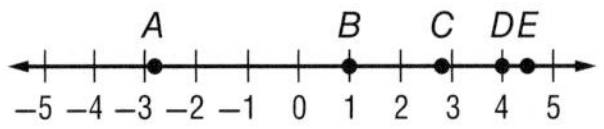

A -2.8
B 1
C 2.8
D 4
E 4.5

2. Find the value of x so that the figures have the same area. **J**

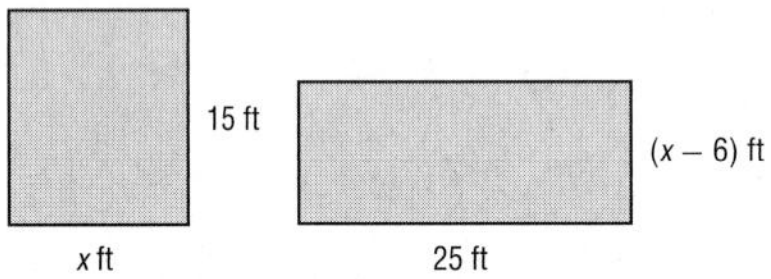

F 10
G 12
H 13
J 15
K 17

3. The elevation of Black Mountain is 27 feet more than 16 times the lowest point in the state. If the elevation of the lowest point in the state is 257 feet, what is the elevation of Black Mountain? **C**

A 4,085 feet
B 4,103 feet
C 4,139 feet
D 4,139 feet
E 4,215 feet

4. The expression $(3x^2 + 5x - 12) - 2(x^2 + 4x + 9)$ is equivalent to which of the following? **F**

F $x^2 - 3x - 30$
G $x^2 + 13x + 6$
H $5x^2 + x - 18$
J $x^2 + 3x - 21$
K $x^2 + 9x - 3$

5. The amount of soda dispensed from a machine must satisfy the equation $|a - 20| = 0.4$. Which graph shows the acceptable minimum and maximum amounts that can be dispensed? **A**

A 

B 

C 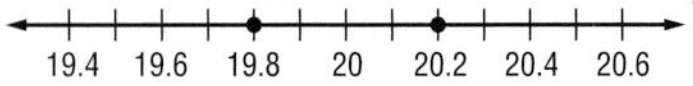

D 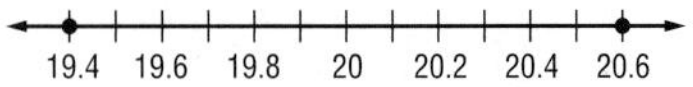

E 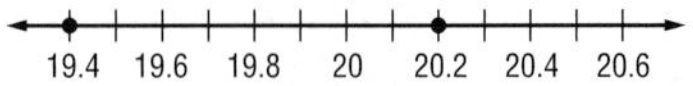

6. If a and b represent integers, $ab = ba$ is an example of which property? **G**

F Associative Property
G Commutative Property
H Distributive Property
J Closure Property
K Reflexive Property

7. The sum of one fifth of a number and three is equal to half of the number. What is the number? **B**

A 5
B 10
C 15
D 20
E 30

8. Aaron charges \$15 to mow the lawn and \$10 per hour for other gardening work. Which expression represents his earnings? **K**

F $10h$
G $15h$
H $15h + 10$
J $25h$
K $15 + 10h$

Test-TakingTip

Question 2 Use the figures and the formula for area to set up an equation. The product of the length and width of each figure should be equal.

Diagnose Student Errors

Survey students' responses for each item. Class trends may indicate common errors and misconceptions.

1. A mistakenly chose estimate of the negative instead of positive square root
B misunderstood concept of estimating square roots
C correct
D misunderstood concept of estimating square roots
E misunderstood estimation

2. F calculation error
G calculation error
H calculation error
J correct
K combined all numbers

3. A subtracted instead of added 27
B guess
C correct
D guess
E guess

4. F correct
G calculation error: added $5x + 8x$ instead of $5x + (-8x)$ and $-12 + 18$ instead of $-12 + (-18)$
H multiple calculation errors
J calculation error: added $-12 + (-9)$
K did not distribute completely

5. A correct
B guess or calculation error
C guess or calculation error
D guess or calculation error
E guess or calculation error

6. F confused Associative and Commutative Properties
G correct
H confused Associative and Distributive Properties
J confused Associative Property with Closure Property
K confused properties

7. A guess or calculation error: divided by $\frac{1}{10}$
B correct
C guess or calculation error: divided by $\frac{1}{5}$
D guess
E guess

8. F wrote expression for hours only
G does not understand how to write expressions
H transposed hours and fee to mow lawns
J combined fixed and variable cost
K correct

Short Response/Gridded Response

Record your answers on the answer sheet provided by your teacher or on a sheet of paper.

9. The formula for the lateral area of a cylinder is $A = 2\pi rh$, where r is the radius and h is the height. Solve the equation for h. $h = \frac{A}{2\pi r}$

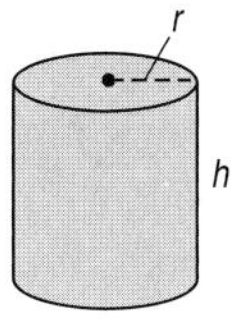

10. GRIDDED RESPONSE Solve the proportion $\frac{x}{18} = \frac{7}{21}$. 6

11. GRIDDED RESPONSE The table shows the cost of renting a moving van. If Miguel budgeted $75, how many miles could he drive the van and maintain his budget? 425

Moving Van Rentals	
Flat Fee	$50 for up to 300 miles
Variable Fee	$0.20 per mile over 300

12. Find the height of a soup can if the area of the label is 302 square centimeters and the radius of the can is 4 centimeters. Round to the nearest whole number. 12 cm

13. GRIDDED RESPONSE Lara's car needed a particular part that costs $75. The mechanic charges $50 per hour to install the part. If the total cost was $350, how many hours did it take to install the part? 5.5

14. Lucinda is buying a set of patio furniture that is on sale for $\frac{4}{5}$ of the original price. After she uses a $50 gift certificate, the total cost before sales tax is $222. What was the original price of the patio furniture? $340

Extended Response

Record your answers on a sheet of paper. Show your work.

15. The city zoo offers a yearly membership that costs $120. A yearly membership includes free parking. Members can also purchase a ride pass for an additional $2 per day that allows them unlimited access to the rides in the park. Nonmembers pay $12 for admission to the park, $5 for parking, and $5 for a ride pass.

a. Write an equation that could be solved for the number of visits it would take for the total cost to be the same for a member and a nonmember if they both purchase a ride pass each day. Solve the equation.

b. What would the total cost be for members and nonmembers after this number of visits? $132

c. Georgena is deciding whether or not to purchase a yearly membership. Explain how she could use the results above to help make her decision. Sample answer: If she will go more than 6 times, she should buy the membership. Otherwise, she should simply pay the daily fees.

15a. $120 + 2x = (12 + 5 + 5)x$ or $120 + 2x = 22x$; $x = 6$ visits

Need Extra Help?															
If you missed Question...	1	2	3	4	5	6	7	8	9	10	11	12	13	14	15
Go to Lesson or Page...	0-2	2-5	2-2	1-4	2-5	1-3	2-4	1-1	2-8	2-6	2-3	2-8	2-3	2-3	2-4
IL Assessment Objectives	6.11.01	8.11.01	6.11.13	8.11.01	8.11.19	6.11.05	6.11.13	8.11.02	8.11.06	6.11.17	6.11.13	7.11.03	6.11.13	6.11.13	6.11.13

Chapters 1–2 PSAE Practice 149

Formative Assessment

You can use these two pages to benchmark student progress.

CRM Standardized Test Practice, pp. 80–82

Answer Sheet Practice

Have students simulate taking a standardized test by recording their answers on a practice recording sheet.

CRM Student Recording Sheet, p. 61

Chapter Resource Master

CRM p. 61

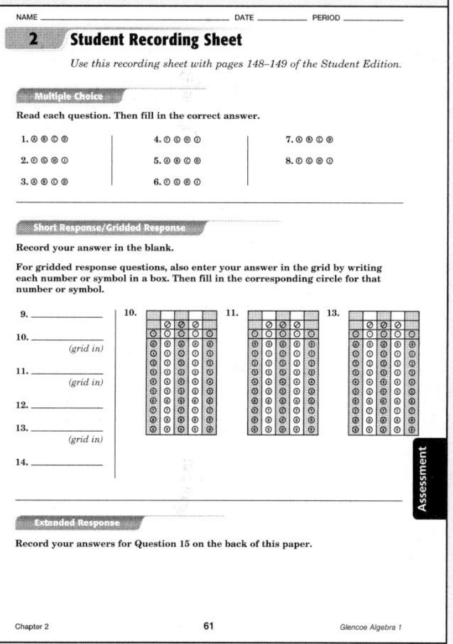
NAME ______ DATE ______ PERIOD ______

2 Student Recording Sheet

Use this recording sheet with pages 148–149 of the Student Edition.

Multiple Choice

Read each question. Then fill in the correct answer.

1.–8.

Short Response/Gridded Response

Record your answer in the blank.

For gridded response questions, also enter your answer in the grid by writing each number or symbol in a box. Then fill in the corresponding circle for that number or symbol.

9. ______
10. ______ (grid in)
11. ______ (grid in)
12. ______
13. ______ (grid in)
14. ______

Extended Response

Record your answers for Question 15 on the back of this paper.

Chapter 2 61 Glencoe Algebra 1

Assessment

ExamView Assessment Suite: Create practice worksheets or tests that align to your state's standards, as well as TIMSS and NAEP tests.

Homework Option

Get Ready for Chapter 3 Assign students the exercises on p. 151 as homework to assess whether they possess the prerequisite skills needed for the next chapter.

Page 78, Lesson 2-1

30. Sample answer: The sum of *j* and sixteen is thirty-five.
31. Sample answer: Four times *m* is equal to fifty-two.
32. Sample answer: Seven times the sum of *p* and twenty-three is the same as one hundred two.
33. Sample answer: Fifteen less than the square of *r* equals the sum of *t* and nineteen.
34. Sample answer: Two fifths of *v* plus three fourths is identical to two thirds of *x* squared.
35. Sample answer: One third minus four fifths of *z* is four thirds of *y* cubed.
36. Sample answer: Allison is going to the market to buy some strawberries. She has \$10. The strawberries cost \$2.50 for each quart. How many quarts can Allison buy?
37. Sample answer: Ashley has a credit card that charges 12% interest on the principal balance. If Ashley's payment was \$224, what was the principal balance on the credit card?
38. Sample answer: Barbara first joined a video club that charged a one-time membership fee of \$10. She then paid \$1.50 for each movie that she rented. If Barbara's first bill came to \$14.50, how many movies did she rent?
39. Sample answer: Fred was teaching his friends a new card game. Each player gets 5 cards, and 7 cards are placed in the center of the table. Since there are 52 cards in a deck, find how many players are in the game.

46c.

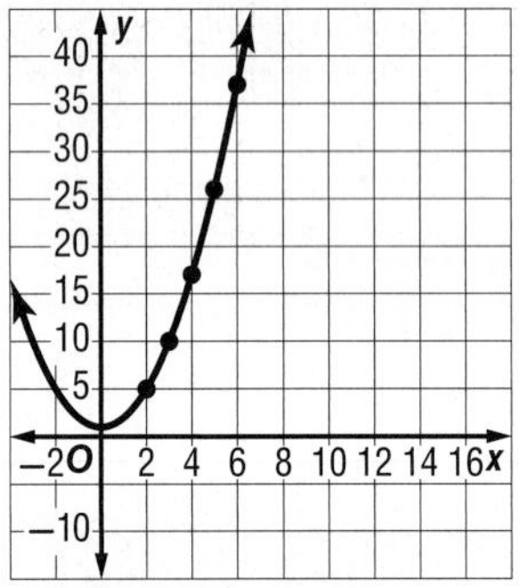

continuous

47. Sample answer: My favorite television show has 30 new episodes each year. So far eight have aired. How many new episodes are left?
50. Sample answer: I would translate using key words to rewrite a sentence into an equation. Don't forget that the word "of" with a fraction or decimal means to multiply.

Page 107, Lesson 2-5

52c.

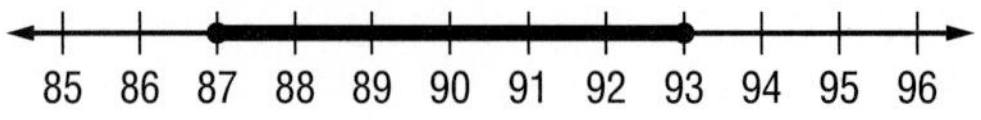

Page 117, Lesson 2-6

49. Neither; Tim inverted the woman-to-man comparison when he wrote the second ratio. Aisha wrote a proportion that is equivalent to Tim's incorrect proportion.
50. Sample answer: A business can use ratios to compare how many of the potential customers in an area use their business. Using ratios, a pizza business can find the number of potential customers in their area and compare them to how many they have. They can do the same with their competitors.

Page 125, Extend 2-7

3. If you estimate the percentiles, then the quartiles and the percentiles correspond. If you calculate the percentiles, Arnold is at the 47th percentile, Benito is at the 20th percentile, and Natalie is at the 73rd percentile.
5. The percentile rank tells where a score ranks among the rest of the scores. The percent is a comparison of a score to the highest score possible.

NOTES

CHAPTER 3

Chapter Planner

Diagnostic Assessment
Quick Check, p. 151

	Lesson 3-1 Pacing: 1 day	Lesson 3-2 Pacing: 1 day	Extend 3-2 Pacing: 0.5 day	Explore 3-3 Pacing: 0.5 day
Title	**Graphing Linear Equations**	**Solving Linear Equations by Graphing**	**Graphing Technology Lab: Graphing Linear Equations**	**Algebra Lab: Rate of Change of a Linear Function**
Objectives	• Identify linear equations, intercepts, and zeros. • Graph linear equations.	• Solve equations by graphing. • Estimate solutions to an equation by graphing.	• Change the viewing window so that a complete graph of a linear function can be displayed.	• Investigate the steepness of a line using concrete models.
Key Vocabulary	linear equation *x*-intercept *y*-intercept	linear function root zeros		
ILS	8.B.4b, 8.C.4b	8.B.4b, 8.C.4b	8.B.4b	7.B.4
Multiple Representations	p. 159			
Lesson Resources	**Chapter 3 Resource Masters** • Study Guide and Intervention, pp. 5–6 AL OL ELL • Skills Practice, Practice, pp. 7–8 AL OL BL ELL • Word Problem Practice, p. 9 AL OL BL ELL • Enrichment, p. 10 OL BL • Spreadsheet Activity, p. 11 OL **Transparencies** • 5-Minute Check Transparency 3-1 AL OL BL ELL **Additional Print Resources** • *Study Notebook* AL OL BL ELL • *Teaching Algebra with Manipulatives,* p. 71 AL OL ELL	**Chapter 3 Resource Masters** • Study Guide and Intervention, pp. 12–13 AL OL ELL • Skills Practice, p. 14 AL OL ELL • Practice, p. 15 AL OL BL ELL • Word Problem Practice, p. 16 AL OL BL ELL • Enrichment, p. 17 OL BL • Quiz 1, p. 45 **Transparencies** • 5-Minute Check Transparency 3-2 AL OL BL ELL **Additional Print Resources** • *Study Notebook* AL OL BL ELL	**Materials** • TI-83/84 Plus or other graphing calculator	**Additional Print Resources** • *Teaching Algebra with Manipulatives,* pp. 1, 72 AL OL ELL **Materials** • 2 rulers • 5 books • tape • grid paper
Technology for Every Lesson	IL Math Online glencoe.com • Extra Examples • Self-Check Quizzes • Personal Tutor • Homework Help	**CD/DVD Resources** IWB INTERACTIVE WHITEBOARD READY IWB StudentWorks Plus IWB Interactive Classroom IWB Diagnostic and Assessment Planner	• TeacherWorks Plus • eSolutions Manual Plus • ExamView Assessment Suite	
Math in Motion	Animation			
Differentiated Instruction	pp. 156, 160	pp. 162, 166		

KEY: AL Approaching Level OL On Level BL Beyond Level ELL English Learners

Suggested Pacing

Time Periods	Instruction	Review & Assessment	Total
45-minute	9	2	11
90-minute	5	1	6

Lesson 3-3 Pacing: 1 day	Lesson 3-4 Pacing: 1 day	Lesson 3-5 Pacing: 2 days	Extend 3-5 Pacing: 0.5 day	Lesson 3-6 Pacing: 1.5 days
Rate of Change and Slope	**Direct Variation**	**Arithmetic Sequences as Linear Functions**	**Algebra Lab: Inductive and Deductive Reasoning**	**Proportional and Nonproportional Relationships**
• Use rate of change to solve problems. • Find the slope of a line.	• Write and graph direct variation equations. • Solve problems involving direct variation.	• Recognize arithmetic sequences. • Relate arithmetic sequences to linear functions.	• Investigate inductive and deductive reasoning.	• Write an equation for a proportional relationship. • Write an equation for a nonproportional relationship.
rate of change slope	direct variation constant of variation constant of proportionality	sequence terms arithmetic sequence		inductive reasoning
7.B.4	7.A.4a, 7.A.4b	8.A.4b, 8.C.4b	8.A.4b	8.A.4b
	p. 185	p. 192		
Chapter 3 Resource Masters • Study Guide and Intervention, pp. 18–19 AL OL ELL • Skills Practice, Practice, pp. 20–21 AL OL BL ELL • Word Problem Practice, p. 22 AL OL BL ELL • Enrichment, p. 23 OL BL • Quiz 2, p. 45 **Transparencies** • 5-Minute Check Transparency 3-3 AL OL BL ELL **Additional Print Resources** • *Study Notebook* AL OL BL ELL • *Teaching Algebra with Manipulatives,* pp. 73–74 AL OL ELL	**Chapter 3 Resource Masters** • Study Guide and Intervention, pp. 24–25 AL OL ELL • Skills Practice, p. 26 AL OL ELL • Practice, p. 27 AL OL BL ELL • Word Problem Practice, p. 28 AL OL BL ELL • Enrichment, p. 29 OL BL **Transparencies** • 5-Minute Check Transparency 3-4 AL OL BL ELL **Additional Print Resources** • *Study Notebook* AL OL BL ELL	**Chapter 3 Resource Masters** • Study Guide and Intervention, pp. 30–31 AL OL ELL • Skills Practice, Practice, pp. 32–33 AL OL BL ELL • Word Problem Practice, p. 34 AL OL BL ELL • Enrichment, p. 35 OL BL • Quiz 3, p. 46 AL OL BL ELL **Transparencies** • 5-Minute Check Transparency 3-5 AL OL BL ELL **Additional Print Resources** • *Study Notebook* AL OL BL ELL	**Additional Print Resources** • *Teaching Algebra with Manipulatives,* p. 75 AL OL ELL	**Chapter 3 Resource Masters** • Study Guide and Intervention, pp. 37–38 AL OL ELL • Skills Practice, Practice, pp. 39–40 AL OL BL ELL • Word Problem Practice, p. 41 AL OL BL ELL • Enrichment, p. 42 OL BL • Quiz 4, p. 46 AL OL BL ELL **Transparencies** • 5-Minute Check Transparency 3-6 AL OL BL ELL **Additional Print Resources** • *Study Notebook* AL OL BL ELL

IL Math Online glencoe.com
- Extra Examples
- Self-Check Quizzes
- Personal Tutor
- Homework Help

CD/DVD Resources IWB INTERACTIVE WHITEBOARD READY
- IWB StudentWorks Plus
- IWB Interactive Classroom
- IWB Diagnostic and Assessment Planner
- TeacherWorks Plus
- eSolutions Manual Plus
- ExamView Assessment Suite

	Animation			
pp. 173, 178	pp. 183, 186	pp. 188, 190, 193		pp. 197, 200

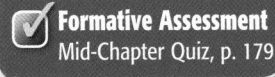

Formative Assessment
Mid-Chapter Quiz, p. 179

Summative Assessment
- Study Guide and Review, pp. 201–204
- Practice Test, p. 205

CHAPTER 3

Assessment and Intervention

SE = Student Edition, **TE** = Teacher Edition, **CRM** = Chapter Resource Masters

	Diagnosis	Prescription
Diagnostic Assessment	**Beginning Chapter 3**	
	Get Ready for Chapter 3 **SE**, p. 151	Response to Intervention **TE**, p. 151
	Beginning Every Lesson	
	Then, Now, Why? **SE** 5-Minute Check Transparencies	Chapter 0 **SE**, pp. P1–P45 Concepts and Skills Bank **SE**, pp. 857–867 *Quick Review Math Handbook*
Formative Assessment	**During/After Every Lesson**	
	Check Your Progress **SE**, every example Check Your Understanding **SE** H.O.T. Problems **SE** Spiral Review **SE** Additional Examples **TE** Watch Out! **TE** Step 4, Assess **TE** Chapter 3 Quizzes **CRM**, pp. 45–46 Self-Check Quizzes glencoe.com	**Tier 1 Intervention** Concepts and Skills Bank **SE**, pp. 857–867 Skills Practice **CRM**, Ch. 1–3 glencoe.com **Tier 2 Intervention** Differentiated Instruction **TE** Differentiated Homework Options **TE** Study Guide and Intervention Masters **CRM**, Ch. 1–3 *Quick Review Math Handbook* **Tier 3 Intervention** *Math Triumphs, Alg. 1, Ch. 3*
	Mid-Chapter	
	Mid-Chapter Quiz **SE**, p. 179 Mid-Chapter Test **CRM**, p. 47 ExamView Assessment Suite	**Tier 1 Intervention** Concepts and Skills Bank **SE**, pp. 857–867 Skills Practice **CRM**, Ch. 1–3 glencoe.com **Tier 2 Intervention** Study Guide and Intervention Masters **CRM**, Ch. 1–3 *Quick Review Math Handbook* **Tier 3 Intervention** *Math Triumphs, Alg. 1, Ch. 3*
	Before Chapter Test	
	Chapter Study Guide and Review **SE**, pp. 201–204 Practice Test **SE**, p. 205 Standardized Test Practice **SE**, pp. 206–209 Chapter Test glencoe.com Standardized Test Practice glencoe.com Vocabulary Review glencoe.com ExamView Assessment Suite	**Tier 1 Intervention** Concepts and Skills Bank **SE**, pp. 857–867 Skills Practice **CRM**, Ch. 1–3 glencoe.com **Tier 2 Intervention** Study Guide and Intervention Masters **CRM**, Ch. 1–3 *Quick Review Math Handbook* **Tier 3 Intervention** *Math Triumphs, Alg. 1, Ch. 3*
Summative Assessment	**After Chapter 3**	
	Multiple-Choice Tests, Forms 1, 2A, 2B **CRM**, pp. 49–53 Free-Response Tests, Forms 2C, 2D, 3 **CRM**, pp. 55–59 Vocabulary Test **CRM**, p. 48 Extended Response Test **CRM**, p. 61 Standardized Test Practice **CRM**, pp. 62–64 ExamView Assessment Suite	Study Guide and Intervention Masters **CRM**, Ch. 1–3 *Quick Review Math Handbook* glencoe.com

CHAPTER 3 Differentiated Instruction

Option 1 Reaching All Learners AL OL BL ELL

VISUAL/SPATIAL Provide students with four pipe-cleaners, glue, poster board, and grid paper. Ask students to glue the pipe-cleaners on the grids on their poster to demonstrates positive slope, negative slope, no slope, and zero slope. Have students find two points on each line and calculate the slope of each line.

KINESTHETIC On the board write the following sentences, drawing three rectangles in each sentence as shown.

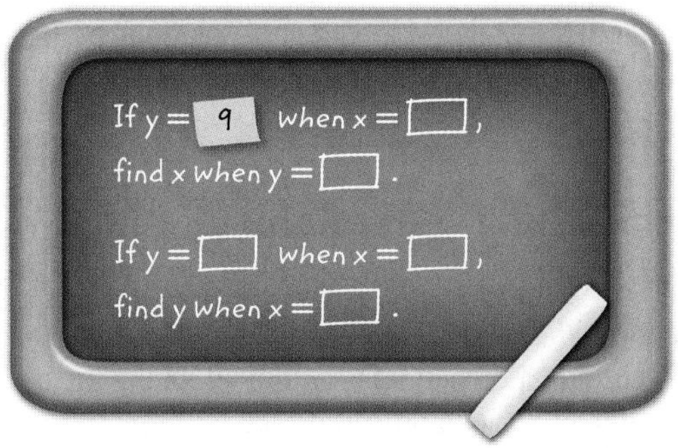

On self-sticking notes, write the digits 1–9. Ask one student to stick 1- or 2-digit numbers in the rectangles of one of the sentences. Then as a class, write a direct variation equation that relates x and y; then solve for either x or y.

Option 2 Approaching Level AL

Put students into groups of three. One student should write down a starting number (the first term of the sequence) and a value for d, the common difference. Ask the second student to use a calculator to add the common difference six times, making sure to proceed slowly enough so that the third student can record each sum showing on the calculator's screen. Then ask the group to write a formula that can be used to find the nth term of their sequence. Ask students to trade roles and then repeat this activity.

Option 3 English Learners ELL

Use floor tiles as a grid or use masking tape on the floor to create a grid. Have students walk the path from one point to another on the floor, allowing only one horizontal and vertical path. Ask them to describe their trip in terms of positive and negative movement and the number of squares traveled in each direction. Then have them write the description of their movement as the slope of the line connecting these two points.

Option 4 Beyond Level BL

Have small groups of students use a triple-beam balance and 4 stacks of identical washers. Each stack should contain a different number of washers tied together so that students cannot weigh just one washer. Record the number of washers, n, in each stack. Have students weigh one stack and then predict the weights, W, of the other stacks. How do they think this relates to the equation $W = kn$? See students' work. What does k represent? the weight of each washer

Focus on Mathematical Content

Vertical Alignment

Before Chapter 3

- locate and name points on a coordinate plane using ordered pairs
- simplify numeric expressions
- represent relationships among quantities using graphs

Related Topics before Grade 8

- use operations to solve problems involving rational numbers

Related Topics from Grade 8

- solve linear equations

Chapter 3

Related Topics from Algebra 1

- use, translate, and make connections among algebraic, tabular, graphical, or verbal descriptions of linear functions
- interpret the meaning of intercepts in situations using data, symbolic representation, or graphs
- determine the intercepts of the graphs of linear functions and zeros of linear functions from graphs, tables, and algebraic representations
- look for patterns and represent generalizations algebraically
- develop the concept of slope as rate of change and determine the slope from graphs, tables, and algebraic representations
- interpret the meaning of slope in situations using data, symbolic representations, or graphs
- relate direct variation to linear functions and solve problems involving proportional change

After Chapter 3

Preparation for Algebra 2

- use properties and attributes of functions and apply functions to problem situations
- identify mathematical domains and ranges and determine reasonable domain and range values for given situations, both continuous and discrete
- solve systems of equations
- use functions to model and make predictions involving direct variation

Lesson-by-Lesson Preview

3-1 Graphing Linear Equations

Linear equations can be written in the form $Ax + By = C$, the standard form of a linear equation. An equation is linear if the Properties of Equality can be applied to rewrite it in standard form. The graph of a linear function has at most one x-intercept (where the graph crosses the x-axis) and one y-intercept (where the graph crosses the y-axis). The intercepts can be found by alternately replacing x and y with 0. If these two points are graphed and then a line that connects them is drawn, all of the ordered pairs that lie on the line are solutions of the equation. Values of x for which $y = 0$ are called zeros. A zero is an x-intercept.

3-2 Solving Linear Equations by Graphing

The solution or root of an equation is any value that makes the equation true. A linear equation has none or one root. The root of a linear equation can be found by graphing the equation's related function.

- To find the related function, get all nonzero terms on one side of the equation and 0 on the other side. Then replace 0 with $f(x)$. For example, for $3x + 4 = 0$, the related function is $3x + 4 = f(x)$.
- To graph the function, make a table of values.
- When the graph is a line (horizontal) that does not intersect the x-axis, there is no solution.
- When the graph is a line that intersects the x-axis, there is one solution, the value of the x-intercept. This value is also called the *zero* of the function.
- When the x-intercept is not a whole number, an estimate can be made and checked using algebra.

3-3 Rate of Change and Slope

Rate of change is a ratio that describes, on average, how one quantity changes with respect to a change in another quantity. Slope can be used to describe rate of change.

The slope of a line is the ratio of the vertical change in the line to the horizontal change in the line. The slope can be expressed in several ways.

- slope $= \frac{\text{rise}}{\text{run}}$

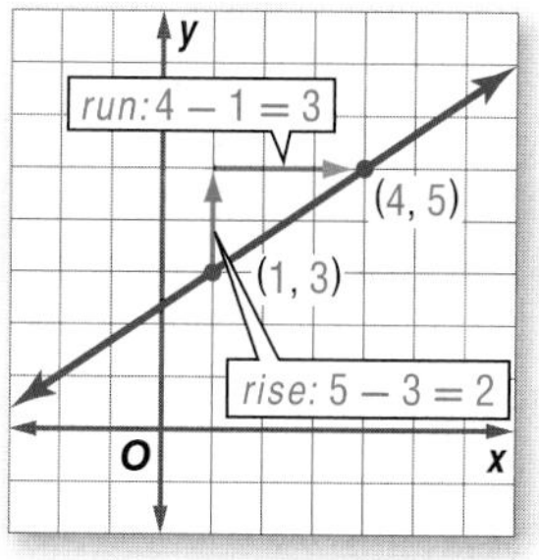

This can be observed from graphed lines, and it works well for whole number increments for the rise and run.

- $m = \frac{y_2 - y_1}{x_2 - x_1}$

This algebraic formula represents slope m using the coordinates of two points on a line (x_1, y_1) and (x_2, y_2). You can use this formula to determine the slope of a line without a graph if you know two points on the line.

3-4 Direct Variation

The concept of direct variation grows from the meaning of ratio (Lesson 2-6). If the ratio of two variables is a constant, then direct variation is the way of expressing the relationship between the two variables. That is, $\frac{y}{x} = k$, where y and x are variables and k is the constant (number) of variation. Multiply each side of the equation by x and you get $y = kx$. This represents an equation of a line. The k has the same value as the slope of the line. So, when you graph a direct variation, you are graphing lines with slope k. All of these lines pass through the origin. In real-world applications, most direct variation graphs are found in the first quadrant.

3-5 Arithmetic Sequences as Linear Functions

A sequence is a set of numbers in a specific order. The numbers in a sequence are called terms.

- If the terms of a sequence increase or decrease at a constant rate, it is called an arithmetic sequence.
- The difference between successive terms of an arithmetic sequence is called the common difference d.
- Any term of an arithmetic sequence can be found by adding the common difference to the preceding term.

The formula that can be used to find a specific term in an arithmetic sequence is $a_n = a_1 + (n - 1)d$. This means to find a specific term a_n find the sum of the first term a_1 and the product of the common difference, times one less than n, the number of the specific term.

3-6 Proportional and Nonproportional Relationships

When you solve a problem by making a conclusion based on a pattern, you are using inductive reasoning. Often patterns in sequences of figures or numbers can be found. Sometimes these patterns can lead to a general rule for the pattern. If the relationship between the domain and range of the relation is linear, a linear equation can be used to describe the relationship. Some linear relationships are proportional and can be modeled with an equation of the form $y = kx$. Other linear relationships are nonproportional.

To write an equation for a pattern that exhibits a linear relationship and is made up of a set of data with two variables (x and y) follow these steps:

- Use a ratio to compare the common difference of the range values to the common difference of the domain values. This ratio should be a constant ratio.
- Then, write the equation as this: dependant variable = constant ratio × independent variable. That is, y = (constant ratio)x.
- Check to be sure this equation works for the set of data. If it does not, then check to see if the difference between the value obtained for the y using your equation and the given value of y is the same for each pair of x- and y-values in the pattern. If so, add that difference to one side of the equation to correctly describe the relation.

Professional Development

Targeted professional development has been articulated throughout *Algebra 1.* More quality, customized professional development is available from McGraw-Hill Professional Development. Visit glencoe.com for details on each product.

- **Online Lessons** emphasize the strategies and techniques used to teach Algebra 1. Includes streaming video, interactive pages, and online tools.
- **Video Workshops** allow mentors, coaches, or leadership personnel to facilitate on-site workshops on educational strategies in mathematics and mathematical concepts.
- **MHPD Online** (www.mhpdonline.com) offers online professional development with video clips of instructional strategies, links, student activities, and news and issues in education.
- **Teaching Today** (teachingtoday.glencoe.com) gives secondary teachers practical strategies and materials that inspire excellence and innovation in teaching.

CHAPTER 3 Notes

Chapter Project

Amusing Admission Costs

Students use what they have learned about linear equations, rates of change, and arithmetic sequences to work with the cost of admission to amusement parks.

- Ask each student to name his or her favorite amusement park. Ask them to research the admission costs for their park for this year, 5 years ago, and 10 years ago.
- Divide students into groups. Then ask them to write an equation for each park that shows the relationship between the cost to enter this year y and the number of guests x entering the park. Have students graph each equation by making a table of values. What will it cost for everyone in the group to enter each park?
- Ask each group to write ratios that describe a rate of change for admission costs from 5 years ago to this year and from 10 years ago to 5 years ago. Has the rate of change for admission to each park over the last 10 years been linear? How do they know?
- Have each group choose one of the parks from their group and write an arithmetic sequence to relate the number of rides they might ride to the number of minutes or hours that pass. Then have them write an equation for the nth term of their sequence.

CHAPTER 3 Linear Functions

Then

In Chapter 2, you solved linear equations algebraically.

Now

In Chapter 3, you will:

- Identify linear equations, intercepts, and zeros.
- Graph and write linear equations.
- Use rate of change to solve problems.

IL Learning Standards

8.A.4b Represent mathematical patterns and describe their properties using variables and mathematical symbols.
8.C.4b Apply algebraic properties and procedures with functions and sequences using data found in business, industry and consumer situations.

Why?

AMUSEMENT PARKS The Magic Kingdom in Orlando, Florida, is one of the most popular amusement parks in the world. Yearly attendance figures increase steadily each year. Quantities like populations that change with respect to time can be described using rate of change. Often you can represent these situations with linear functions.

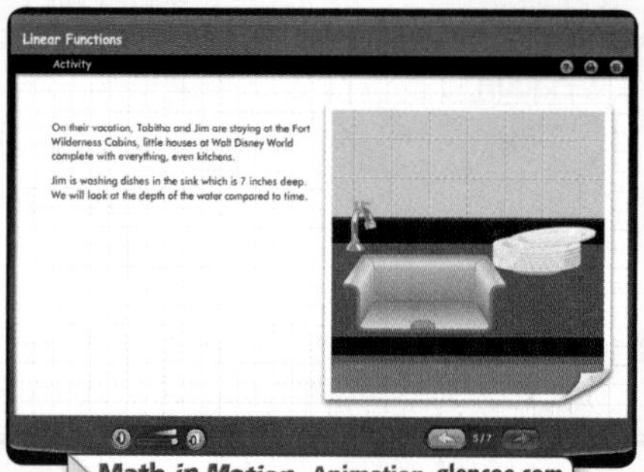

Linear Functions
Activity
On their vacation, Tabitha and Jim are staying at the Fort Wilderness Cabins, little houses at Walt Disney World complete with everything, even kitchens.
Jim is washing dishes in the sink which is 7 inches deep. We will look at the depth of the water compared to time.
5/7

Math *in Motion*, Animation glencoe.com

Key Vocabulary Introduce the key vocabulary in the chapter using the routine below.

Define: A term is a number, or variable, or a product or quotient of numbers and variables.

Example: $2x^2 + 6x + 5$, where each part of the expression, containing numbers or numbers and variables between operation signs, is called a term.

Ask: How many different terms are in this expression? three

Get Ready for Chapter 3

Diagnose Readiness You have two options for checking Prerequisite Skills.

Text Option

Take the Quick Check below. Refer to the Quick Review for help.

QuickCheck

(Used in Lessons 3-1 through 3-3)

Graph each ordered pair on a coordinate grid. (Lesson 1-6) **1–6. See Chapter 3 Answer Appendix.**

1. $(-3, 3)$ **2.** $(-2, 1)$ **3.** $(3, 0)$

4. $(-5, 5)$ **5.** $(0, 6)$ **6.** $(2, -1)$

Write the ordered pair for each point.

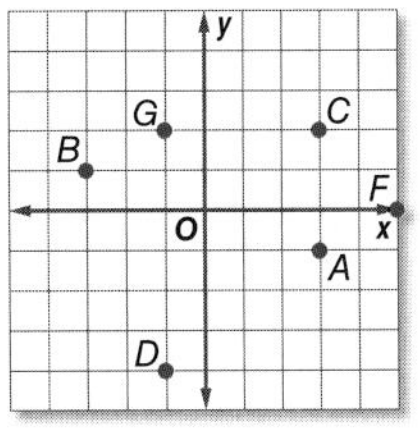

7. A **8.** B

9. C **10.** D

11. F **12.** G

7. (3, −1) 8. (−3, 1)
9. (3, 2) 10. (−1, −4)

(Used in Lesson 3-1 through 3-5)

Solve each equation for y. (Lesson 2-8)

13. $3x + y = 1$ **14.** $8 - y = x$

15. $5x - 2y = 12$ **16.** $3x + 4y = 10$

17. $3 - \frac{1}{2}y = 5x$ **18.** $\frac{y + 1}{3} = x + 2$

13. $y = -3x + 1$ **14.** $y = -x + 8$
15. $y = \frac{5}{2}x - 6$ **16.** $y = \frac{-3}{4}x + \frac{5}{2}$
17. $y = -10x + 6$ **18.** $y = 3x + 5$

(Used in Lesson 3-4)

Evaluate $\frac{a - b}{c - d}$ for each set of values. (Lesson 1-2)

19. $a = 7, b = 6, c = 9, d = 5$ $\frac{1}{4}$

20. $a = -3, b = 0, c = 3, d = -1$ $-\frac{3}{4}$

21. $a = -5, b = -5, c = 5, d = 8$ **0**

22. $a = -6, b = 3, c = 8, d = 2$ $\frac{-3}{2}$

23. **MOVIES** A movie made $297.2 million in 22 weeks. How much did the movie make on average each week? (Lesson 1-3) **about $13.5 million**

QuickReview

EXAMPLE 1

Graph (3, −2) on a coordinate grid.

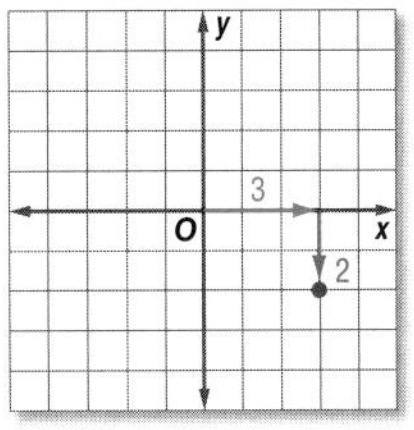

11. (5, 0)
12. (−1, 2)

EXAMPLE 2

Solve $x - 2y = 8$ for y.

$x - 2y = 8$	Original equation
$x - x - 2y = 8 - x$	Subtract x from each side.
$-2y = 8 - x$	Simplify.
$\frac{-2y}{-2} = \frac{8 - x}{-2}$	Divide each side by −2.
$y = \frac{1}{2}x - 4$	Simplify.

EXAMPLE 3

Evaluate $\frac{a - b}{c - d}$ for $a = 3, b = 5, c = -2$, and $d = -6$.

$\frac{a - b}{c - d}$	Original expression
$= \frac{3 - 5}{-2 - (-6)}$	Substitute 3 for a, 5 for b, −2 for c, and −6 for d.
$= \frac{-2}{4}$	Simplify.
$= \frac{-2 \div 2}{4 \div 2}$	Divide −2 and 4 by their GCF, 2.
$= \frac{-1}{2}$ or $-\frac{1}{2}$	Simplify. The signs are different so the quotient is negative.

Online Option

IL Math Online Take a self-check Chapter Readiness Quiz at glencoe.com.

Response to Intervention (RtI)

Use the *Quick Check* results and the Intervention Planner chart to help you determine your Response to Intervention. The If-Then statements in the chart below help you decide the appropriate tier of RtI and suggest intervention resources for each tier.

Intervention Planner

Tier 1 — On Level

If students miss about 25% of the exercises or less,

Then choose a resource:

SE Lessons 1-2, 1-6, and 2-8

CRM Skills Practice, Chapter 1, pp. 13, 39, Chapter 2, p. 51

IL Math Online Self-Check Quiz

Tier 2 — Strategic Intervention approaching grade level

If students miss about 50% of the exercises,

Then choose a resource:

CRM Study Guide and Intervention, Chapter 1, pp. 11, 37, Chapter 2, p. 49

Quick Review Math Handbook

IL Math Online Extra Examples, Personal Tutor, Homework Help

Tier 3 — Intensive Intervention 2 or more grades below level

If students miss about 75% of the exercises,

Then use *Math Triumps, Alg. 1, Ch. 3*

IL Math Online Extra Examples, Personal Tutor, Homework Help, Review Vocabulary

CHAPTER 3 Notes

FOLDABLES® Study Organizer

Dinah Zike's Foldables®

Focus Students write about linear functions as these concepts are presented in the lessons of this chapter.

Teach Have students make and label their Foldables as illustrated. Have students make notes under the appropriate tab as they cover each lesson in this chapter. Point out that the seventh tab should be used to list the Key Concepts in the chapter. The eighth tab should be used to note any Study Tips that are found in the chapter. Encourage students to write short descriptive paragraphs about each lesson and graph examples.

When to Use It Encourage students to add to their Foldables as they work through the chapter and to use them to review for the chapter test.

Differentiated Instruction

CRM Student-Built Glossary, pp. 1–2 Students should complete the chart by providing the definition of each term and an example as they progress through Chapter 3. This study tool can also be used to review for the chapter test.

Get Started on Chapter 3

You will learn several new concepts, skills, and vocabulary terms as you study Chapter 3. To get ready, identify important terms and organize your resources. You may wish to refer to **Chapter 0** to review prerequisite skills.

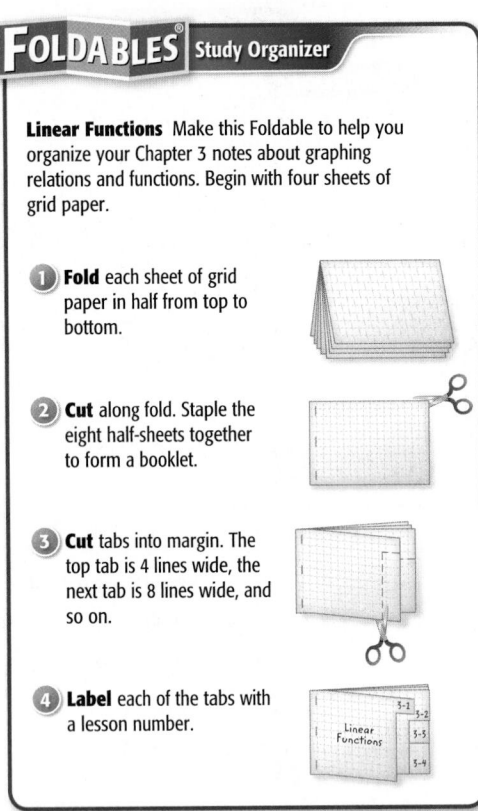

FOLDABLES® Study Organizer

Linear Functions Make this Foldable to help you organize your Chapter 3 notes about graphing relations and functions. Begin with four sheets of grid paper.

1. **Fold** each sheet of grid paper in half from top to bottom.

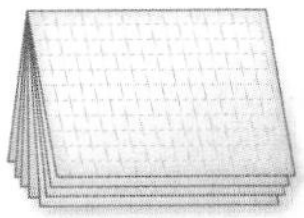

2. **Cut** along fold. Staple the eight half-sheets together to form a booklet.

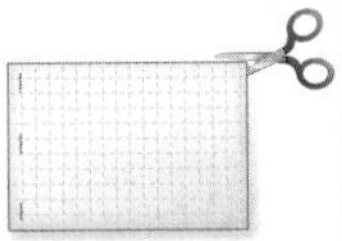

3. **Cut** tabs into margin. The top tab is 4 lines wide, the next tab is 8 lines wide, and so on.

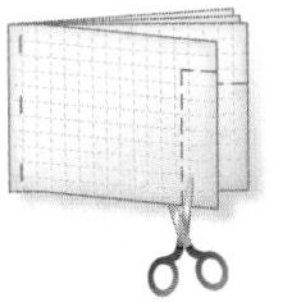

4. **Label** each of the tabs with a lesson number.

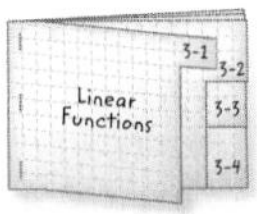

IL Math Online glencoe.com

- Study the chapter online
- Explore **Math in Motion**
- Get extra help from your own **Personal Tutor**
- Use **Extra Examples** for additional help
- Take a **Self-Check Quiz**
- **Review Vocabulary** in fun ways

New Vocabulary

English		Español
linear equation	p. 153	ecuación lineal
standard form	p. 153	forma estándar
constant	p. 153	constante
x-intercept	p. 154	intersección *x*
y-intercept	p. 154	intersección *y*
linear function	p. 161	función lineal
parent function	p. 161	críe la functión
family of graphs	p. 161	la familia de gráficas
root	p. 161	raiz
rate of change	p. 170	tasa de cambio
slope	p. 172	pendiente
direct variation	p. 180	variación directa
constant of variation	p. 180	constante de variación
arithmetic sequence	p. 187	sucesión arithmética
inductive reasoning	p. 195	razonamiento inductivo

Review Vocabulary

origin • p. 697 • origen the point where the two axes in a coordinate plane intersect with coordinates (0, 0)

x-axis • p. 697 • eje *x* the horizontal number line on a coordinate plane

y-axis • p. 697 • eje *y* the vertical number line on a coordinate plane

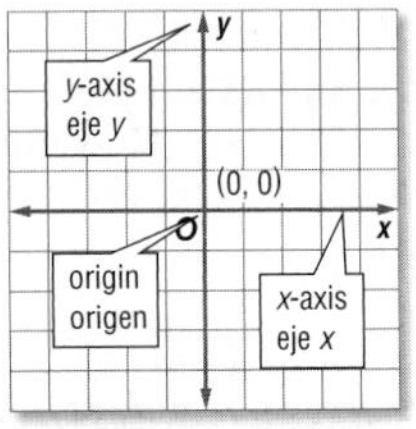

Multilingual eGlossary glencoe.com

3-1 Graphing Linear Equations

Why?

Recycling one ton of waste paper saves an average of 17 trees, 7000 gallons of water, 3 barrels of oil, and about 3.3 cubic yards of landfill space.

The relationship between the amount of paper recycled and the number of trees saved can be expressed with the equation $y = 17x$, where y represents the number of trees and x represents the tons of paper recycled.

Then
You represented relationships among quantities using equations. (Lesson 2-1)

Now
- Identify linear equations, intercepts, and zeros.
- Graph linear equations.

IL Learning Standards
8.B.4b Use the basic functions of absolute value, square root, **linear**, quadratic and step **to describe numerical relationships.**
8.C.4b Apply algebraic properties and procedures with matrices, vectors, functions and sequences using data found in business, industry and consumer situations. *Also addresses 7.A.4b.*

New Vocabulary
linear equation
standard form
constant
x-intercept
y-intercept

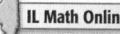

IL Math Online
glencoe.com
- Extra Examples
- Personal Tutor
- Self-Check Quiz
- Homework Help
- Math in Motion

Linear Equations and Intercepts A **linear equation** is an equation that forms a line when it is graphed. Linear equations are often written in the form $Ax + By = C$. This is called the **standard form** of a linear equation. In this equation, C is called a **constant**, or a number. Ax and By are variable terms.

Key Concept — Standard Form of a Linear Equation (For Your FOLDABLE)

Words The standard form of a linear equation is $Ax + By = C$, where $A \geq 0$, A and B are not both zero, and A, B, and C are integers with a greatest common factor of 1.

Examples In $3x + 2y = 5$, $A = 3$, $B = 2$, and $C = 5$.
In $x = -7$, $A = 1$, $B = 0$, and $C = -7$.

EXAMPLE 1 Identify Linear Equations

Determine whether each equation is a linear equation. Write the equation in standard form.

a. $y = 4 - 3x$
Rewrite the equation so that it appears in standard form.

$y = 4 - 3x$ **Original equation**
$y + 3x = 4 - 3x + 3x$ **Add 3x to each side.**
$3x + y = 4$ **Simplify.**

The equation is now in standard form where $A = 3$, $B = 1$, and $C = 4$. This is a linear equation.

b. $6x - xy = 4$
Since the term xy has two variables, the equation cannot be written in the form $Ax + By = C$. Therefore, this is not a linear equation.

Check Your Progress

1A. $\frac{1}{3}y = -1$ yes; $y = -3$ **1B.** $y = x^2 - 4$ no

Personal Tutor glencoe.com

3-1 Lesson Notes

1 FOCUS

Vertical Alignment

Before Lesson 3-1
Represent relationships among quantities using equations.

Lesson 3-1
Identify linear equations, intercepts, and zeros.
Graph linear equations.

After Lesson 3-1
Solve linear equations by graphing.

2 TEACH

Scaffolding Questions
Have students read the *Why?* section of the lesson.

Ask:
- If a community recycles 6 tons of waste paper per year, how many trees are saved? about 102 trees
- What is the coefficient of x in the equation $y = 17x$? 17 What is the coefficient of y? 1
- How can you write $y = 17x$ so that the coefficient of y is -1? $17x - y = 0$

Lesson 3-1 Resources

Resource	Approaching-Level	On-Level	Beyond-Level	English Learners
Teacher Edition		• Differentiated Instruction, p. 156	• Differentiated Instruction, pp. 156, 160	
Chapter Resource Masters	• Study Guide and Intervention, pp. 5–6 • Skills Practice, p. 7 • Practice, p. 8 • Word Problem Practice, p. 9 • Spreadsheet Activity, p. 11	• Study Guide and Intervention, pp. 5–6 • Skills Practice and Practice, pp. 7–8 • Word Problem Practice, p. 9 • Enrichment, p. 10 • Spreadsheet Activity, p. 11	• Practice, p. 8 • Word Problem Practice, p. 9 • Enrichment, p. 10 • Spreadsheet Activity, p. 11	• Study Guide and Intervention, pp. 5–6 • Skills Practice, p. 7 • Practice, p. 8 • Spreadsheet Activity, p. 11
Transparencies	• 5-Minute Check Transparency 3-1	• 5-Minute Check Transparency 3-1	• 5-Minute Check Transparency 3-1	• 5-Minute Check Transparency 3-1
Other	• Study Notebook • Teaching Algebra with Manipulatives	• Study Notebook • Teaching Algebra with Manipulatives	• Study Notebook	• Study Notebook • Teaching Algebra with Manipulatives

Identify Linear Equations and Intercepts

Example 1 shows how to identify a linear equation and write it in standard form. **Example 2** shows how to determine the *x*- and *y*-intercepts. **Example 3** shows how to determine and interpret the intercepts for real-world problems and describe what the intercepts mean in terms of the situation.

Formative Assessment

Use the Check Your Progress exercises after each Example to determine students' understanding of concepts.

Additional Examples

1 Determine whether each equation is a linear equation. Write the equation in standard form.

a. $5x + 3 = xy + 2$ not linear

b. $\frac{3}{4}x = y + 8$ linear; $3x - 4y = 32$

2 **STANDARDIZED TEST PRACTICE** Find the *x*- and *y*-intercepts of the segment graphed below. B

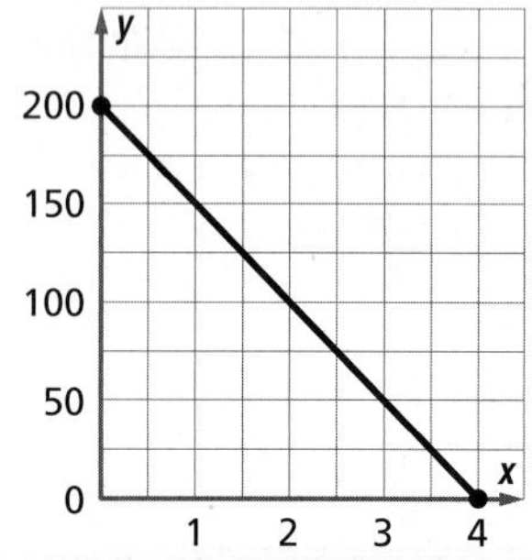

A *x*-intercept is 200; *y*-intercept is 4

B *x*-intercept is 4; *y*-intercept is 200

C *x*-intercept is 2; *y*-intercept is 100

D *x*-intercept is 4; *y*-intercept is 0

Additional Examples also in Interactive Classroom PowerPoint® Presentations

IWB INTERACTIVE WHITEBOARD READY

A linear equation can be represented on a coordinate graph. The *x*-coordinate of the point at which the graph of an equation crosses the *x*-axis is an **x-intercept**. The *y*-coordinate of the point at which the graph crosses the *y*-axis is called a **y-intercept**.

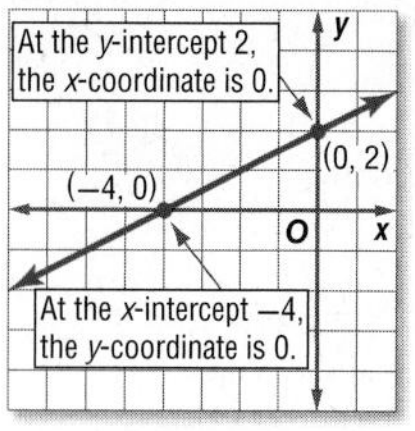

The graph of a linear equation has at most one *x*-intercept and one *y*-intercept, unless it is the equation $x = 0$ or $y = 0$, in which case every number is a *y*-intercept or an *x*-intercept, respectively.

PSAE EXAMPLE 2 — 8.11.13

Find the *x*- and *y*-intercepts of the line graphed at the right.

A *x*-intercept is 0; *y*-intercept is 30.

B *x*-intercept is 20; *y*-intercept is 30.

C *x*-intercept is 20; *y*-intercept is 0.

D *x*-intercept is 30; *y*-intercept is 20.

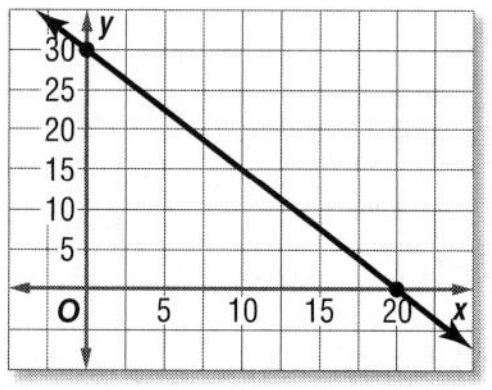

ReadingMath

Intercepts Usually, the individual coordinates are called the *x*-intercept and the *y*-intercept. The *x*-intercept 20 is located at (20, 0). The *y*-intercept 60 is located at (0, 60).

Read the Test Item

We need to determine the *x*- and *y*-intercepts of the line in the graph.

Solve the Test Item

Step 1 Find the *x*-intercept. Look for the point where the line crosses the *x*-axis.

The line crosses at (20, 0). The *x*-intercept is 20 because it is the *x*-coordinate of the point where the line crosses the *x*-axis.

Step 2 Find the *y*-intercept. Look for the point where the line crosses the *y*-axis.

The line crosses the *y*-axis at (0, 30). The *y*-intercept is 30 because it is the *y*-coordinate of the point where the line crosses the *y*-axis.

Thus, the answer is B.

Check Your Progress

2. HEALTH Find the *x*- and *y*-intercepts of the graph. J

F *x*-intercept is 0; *y*-intercept is 150.

G *x*-intercept is 150; *y*-intercept is 0.

H *x*-intercept is 150; no *y*-intercept.

J No *x*-intercept; *y*-intercept is 150.

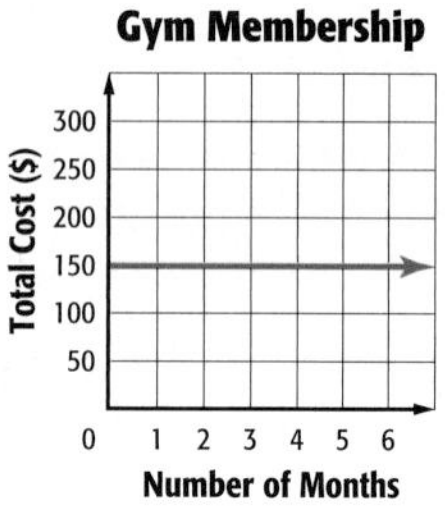

Personal Tutor glencoe.com

When equations represent a real-world situation, the *x*- and *y*-intercepts have a real-world meaning.

Watch Out!

Standard Form Students may assume that the standard form implies that linear equations must have positive coefficients on *x* and *y*. Point out that there are no restrictions on the value of *B*. This means that *B* could be negative. So, an equation like $3x - 4y = 7$ is a linear equation.

Focus on Mathematical Content

Linear Equations The standard form of a linear equation is $Ax + By = C$. If the properties of equality can be applied to an equation to rewrite it in standard form, then the equation is linear.

StudyTip

Defining Variables In Example 3, time is the *independent* variable, and volume of water is the *dependent* variable.

Real-World EXAMPLE 3 Find Intercepts

SWIMMING POOL **A swimming pool is being drained at a rate of 720 gallons per hour. The table shows the function relating the volume of water in a pool and the time in hours that the pool has been draining.**

Draining a Pool	
Time (h) x	Volume (gal) y
0	10,080
2	8640
6	5760
10	2880
12	1440
14	0

a. Find the x- and y-intercepts of the graph of the function.

x-intercept = 14 — **14 is the value of x when $y = 0$.**

y-intercept = 10,080 — **10,080 is the value of y when $x = 0$.**

b. Describe what the intercepts mean in this situation.

The x-intercept 14 means that after 14 hours, the water has a volume of 0 gallons, or the pool is completely drained.

The y-intercept 10,080 means that the pool contained 10,080 gallons of water at time 0, or before it started to drain. This is shown in the graph.

Draining a Pool

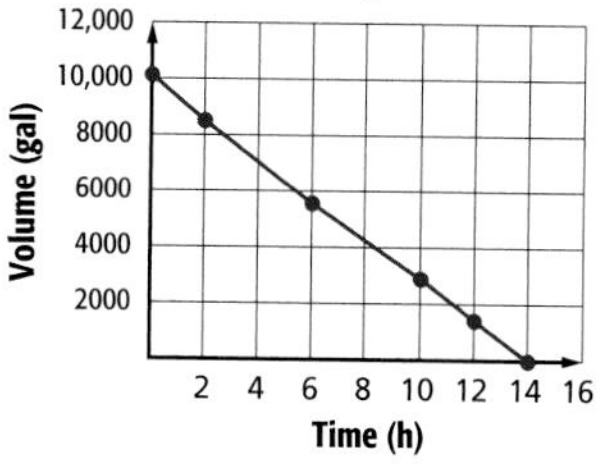

3. The x-intercept 4 means the Torrez family arrived at the amusement park after 4 hours of driving. The y-intercept 248 means their house is 248 mi away from the amusement park.

Check Your Progress

3. DRIVING The table shows the function relating the distance to an amusement park in miles and the time in hours the Torres family has driven. Find the x- and y-intercepts. Describe what the intercepts mean in this situation.

Time (h)	Distance (mi)
0	248
1	186
2	124
3	62
4	0

Personal Tutor glencoe.com

StudyTip

Equivalent Equations Rewriting equations by solving for y may make it easier to find values for y. $4x + y = -3$ → $y = -4x - 3$

Graph Linear Equations By first finding the x- and y-intercepts, you have two ordered pairs of two points through which the graph of the linear equation passes. This information can be used to graph the line because only two points are needed to graph a line.

EXAMPLE 4 Graph by Using Intercepts

Graph $2x + 4y = 16$ by using the x- and y-intercepts.

To find the x-intercept, let $y = 0$.

$2x + 4y = 16$	**Original equation**
$2x + 4(0) = 16$	**Replace y with 0.**
$2x = 16$	**Simplify.**
$x = 8$	**Divide each side by 2.**

The x-intercept is 8. This means that the graph intersects the x-axis at (8, 0).

(continued on the next page)

Additional Example

3 **ANALYZE TABLES** A box of peanuts is poured into bags at the rate of 4 ounces per second. The table shows the function relating the weight of peanuts in the box and the time in seconds the peanuts have been pouring out of the box.

Pouring Peanuts	
Time (s) x	Weight (oz) y
0	2000
125	1500
250	1000
375	500
500	0

a. Find the x- and y-intercepts of the graph of the function.

Pouring Peanuts

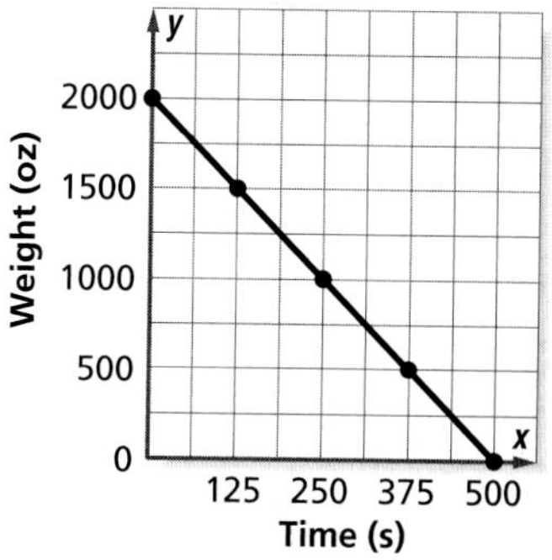

500; 2000

b. Describe what the intercepts mean in terms of this situation. x-intercept: 0 oz after 500 s; y-intercept: 2000 oz before pouring began

Graph Linear Equations

Example 4 shows how to graph a linear equation using the x- and y-intercepts. **Example 5** shows how to graph an equation by making a table.

Tips for New Teachers

Interpreting Graphs When discussing Example 3, take the opportunity to discuss what the points on the line with coordinates that are not part of the original data set represent.

TEACH with TECH

INTERACTIVE WHITEBOARD Drag a coordinate grid onto the board. Use this as a template as you plot points and draw graphs for your class.

Additional Examples

4 Graph $4x - y = 4$ by using the x- and y-intercepts.

x-intercept: 1; y-intercept: -4

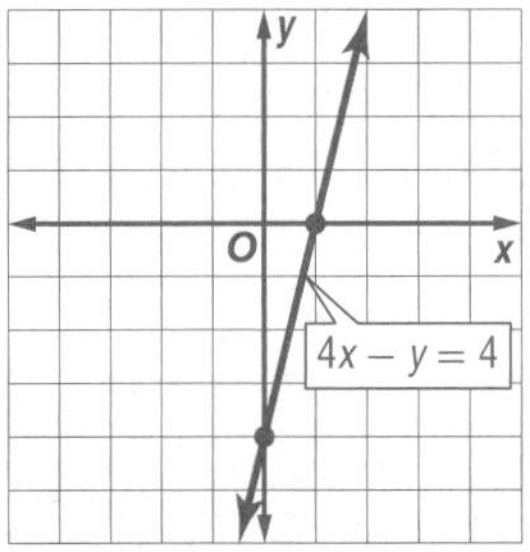

5 Graph $y = 2x + 2$.

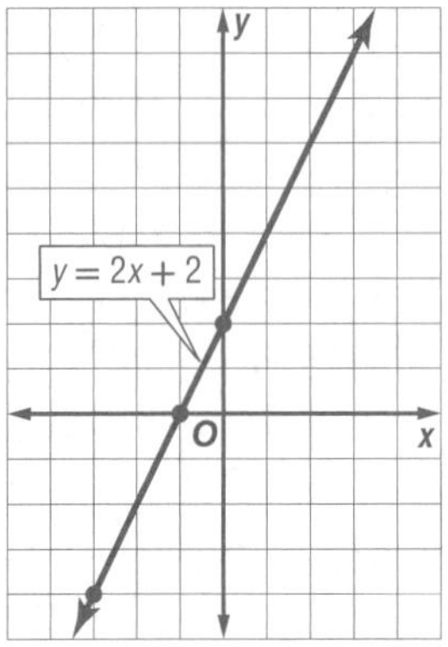

Additional Answers (Check Your Progress)

4A.

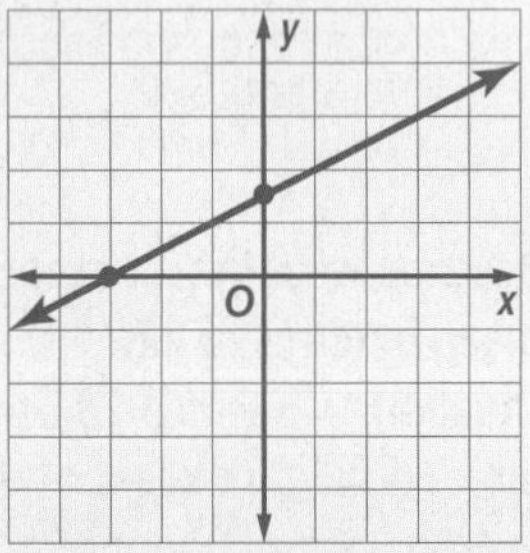

4B.

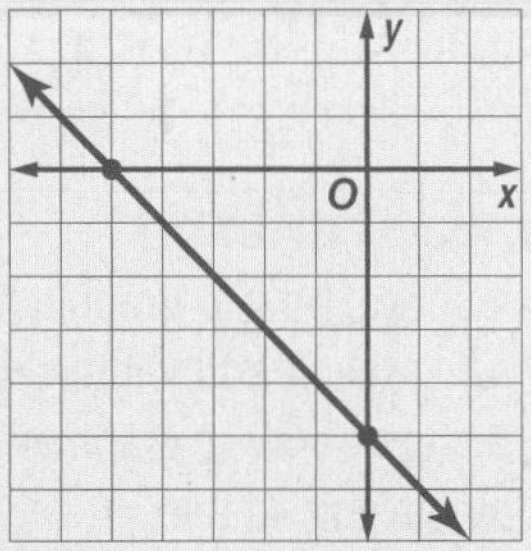

StudyTip

Intercepts The x-intercept is where the graph crosses the x-axis. So the y-value is always 0. The y-intercept is where the graph crosses the y-axis. So, the x-value is always 0.

To find the y-intercept, let $x = 0$.

$2x + 4y = 16$		**Original equation**
$2(0) + 4y = 16$		**Replace x with 0.**
$4y = 16$		**Simplify.**
$y = 4$		**Divide each side by 4.**

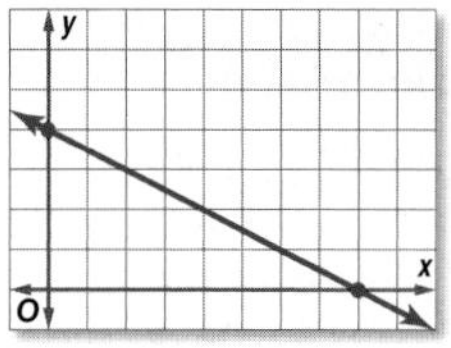

The y-intercept is 4. This means the graph intersects the y-axis at (0, 4).

Plot these two points and then draw a line through them.

Check Your Progress **4A–4B. See margin.**

Graph each equation by using the x- and y-intercepts.

4A. $-x + 2y = 3$ **4B.** $y = -x - 5$

Personal Tutor glencoe.com

Note that the equation in Example 4 has both an x- and a y-intercept. Some lines have an x-intercept and no y-intercept or vice versa. The graph of $y = b$ is a horizontal line that only has a y-intercept (unless $b = 0$). The intercept occurs at $(0, b)$. The graph of $x = a$ is a vertical line that only has an x-intercept (unless $a = 0$). The intercept occurs at $(a, 0)$.

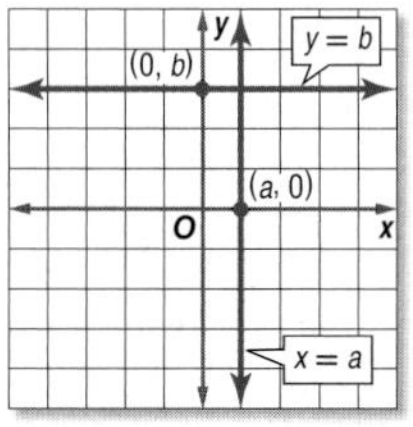

Every ordered pair that makes an equation true represents a point on the graph. So, the graph of an equation represents all of its solutions. Any ordered pair that does not make the equation true represents a point that is not on the line.

EXAMPLE 5 Graph by Making a Table

Graph $y = \frac{1}{3}x + 2$.

The domain is all real numbers. Select values from the domain and make a table. When the x-coefficient is a fraction, select a number from the domain that is a multiple of the denominator. Create ordered pairs and graph them.

x	$\frac{1}{3}x + 2$	y	(x, y)
-3	$\frac{1}{3}(-3) + 2$	1	$(-3, 1)$
0	$\frac{1}{3}(0) + 2$	2	$(0, 2)$
3	$\frac{1}{3}(3) + 2$	3	$(3, 3)$
6	$\frac{1}{3}(6) + 2$	4	$(6, 4)$

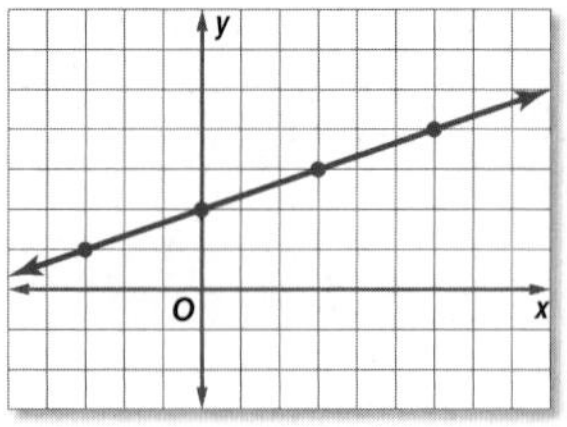

Math *in Motion,* Animation glencoe.com

Check Your Progress

Graph each equation by making a table. **5A–5C. See margin.**

5A. $2x - y = 2$ **5B.** $x = 3$ **5C.** $y = -2$

Personal Tutor glencoe.com

Differentiated Instruction

OL BL

If students have mastered graphing with whole-number intercepts,

Then give students an equation with at least one of the intercepts of the graph not a whole number. Have students suggest an easier way to graph the equation.

Check Your Understanding

Example 1 p. 153

Determine whether each equation is a linear equation. Write *yes* or *no*. If yes, write the equation in standard form.

1. $x = y - 5$ yes; $x - y = -5$
2. $-2x - 3 = y$ yes; $2x + y = -3$
3. $-4y + 6 = 2$ yes; $y = 1$
4. $\frac{2}{3}x - \frac{1}{3}y = 2$ yes; $2x - y = 6$

Examples 2 and 3 pp. 154–155

Find the x- and y-intercepts of the graph of each linear function. Describe what the intercepts mean.

5. **Increasing Temperature**

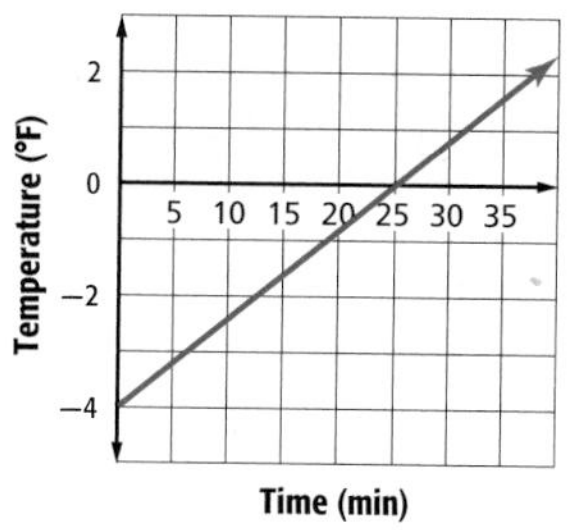

5. 25, −4; The x-intercept 25 means that after 25 minutes, the temperature is 0°F. The y-intercept −4 means that at time 0, the temperature is −4°F.

6. **Position of Scuba Diver**

Time (s)	Depth (m)
x	y
0	−24
3	−18
6	−12
9	−6
12	0

6. 12, −24; The x-intercept 12 means that after 12 seconds, the scuba diver is at a depth of 0 meters, or at the surface. The y-intercept −24 means that at time 0, the scuba diver is at a depth of −24 meters, or 24 meters below sea level.

Example 4 p. 155

Graph each equation by using the x- and y-intercepts.

7. $y = 4 + x$
8. $2x - 5y = 1$

7–8. See Ch. 3 Answer Appendix.

Example 5 p. 156

Graph each equation by making a table. 9–11. See Ch. 3 Answer Appendix.

9. $x + 2y = 4$
10. $-3 + 2y = -5$
11. $y = 3$

12. **RODEOS** The equation $5x + 10y = 60$ represents the number of children x and adults y who can attend the rodeo for $60.

   a. Use the x- and y-intercepts to graph the equation.

   b. Describe what these values mean.

The x-intercept means that 12 children and 0 adults can attend for $60. The y-intercept means that 0 children and 6 adults can attend for $60.

12a.

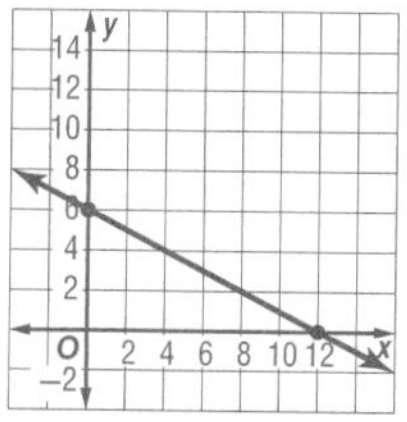

Practice and Problem Solving

● = Step-by-Step Solutions begin on page R12. Extra Practice begins on page 815.

Example 1 p. 153

Determine whether each equation is a linear equation. Write *yes* or *no*. If yes, write the equation in standard form.

13. $5x + y^2 = 25$ no
14. $8 + y = 4x$ yes; $4x - y = 8$
15. $9xy - 6x = 7$ no
16. $4y^2 + 9 = -4$ no
17. $12x = 7y - 10y$ yes; $4x + y = 0$
18. $y = 4x + x$ yes; $5x - y = 0$

Examples 2 and 3 pp. 154–155

Find the x- and y-intercepts of the graph of each linear function.

19.

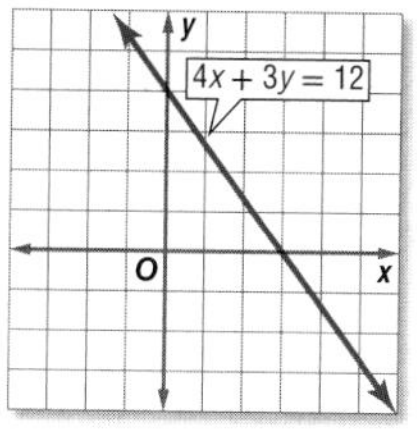

3, 4

20.

x	y
−3	−1
−2	0
−1	1
0	2
1	3

−2, 2

3 PRACTICE

Formative Assessment

Use Exercises 1–12 to check for understanding.

Use the chart at the bottom of this page to customize assignments for your students.

Additional Answers (Check Your Progress)

5A.

x	y
−2	−6
−1	−4
0	−2
1	0
2	2

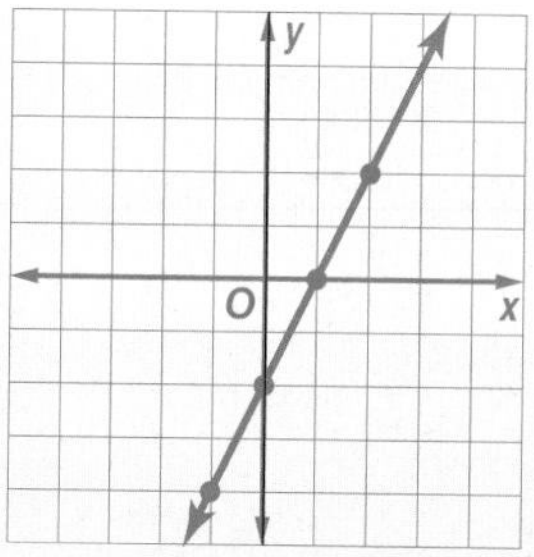

5B.

x	y
3	−2
3	−1
3	0
3	1
3	2

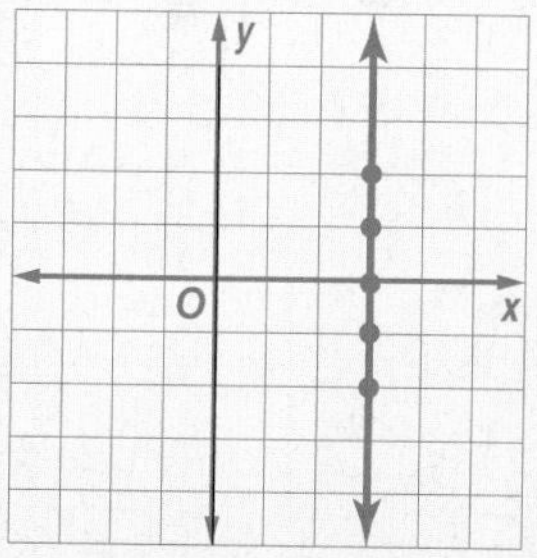

5C.

x	y
−2	−2
−1	−2
0	−2
1	−2
2	−2

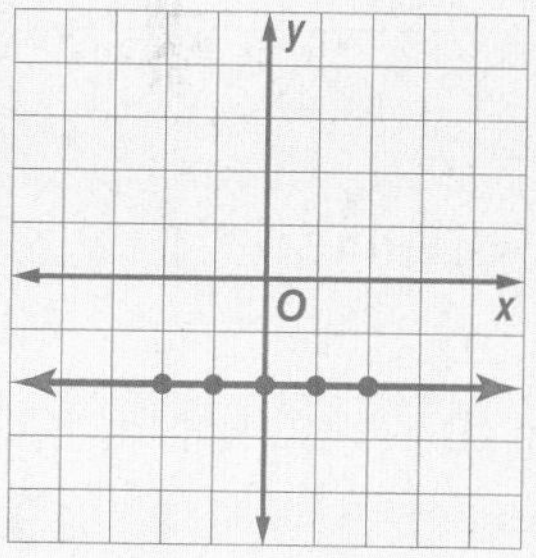

Differentiated Homework Options

Level	Assignment	Two-Day Option	
AL Basic	13–35, 60–77	13–35 odd, 65–68	14–34 even, 60–64, 69–77
OL Core	13–49 odd, 42, 50, 51–57 odd, 58, 60–77	13–35, 65–68	36–58, 60–64, 69–77
BL Advanced	36–73, (optional: 74–77)		

Exercise Alert

Grid Paper For Exercises 42–48, 50, 57, 58, and 61–63, students will need grid paper.

Straightedge For Exercise 58, students will need a straightedge.

Additional Answers

23.

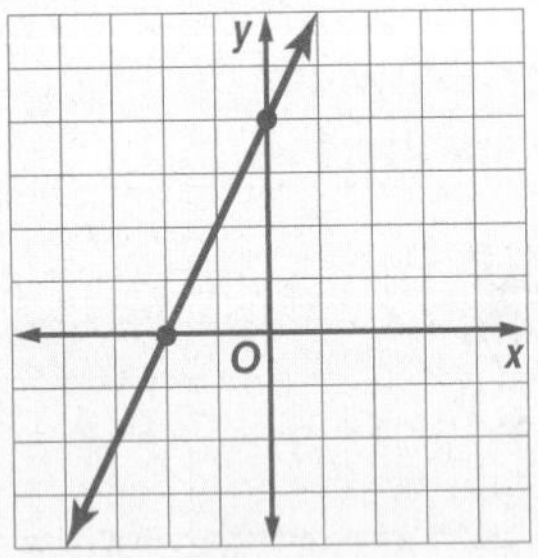

24.

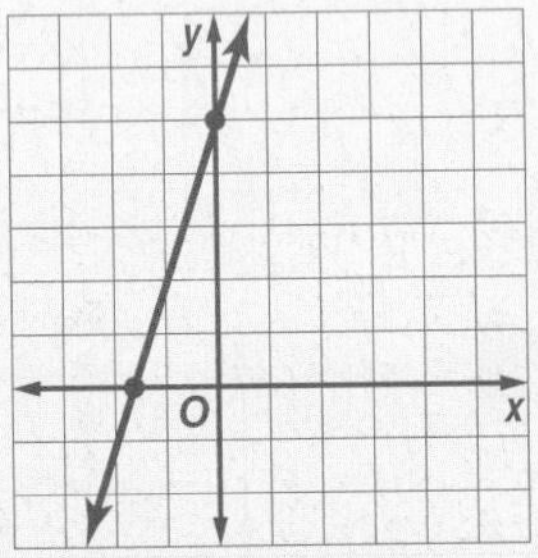

25.

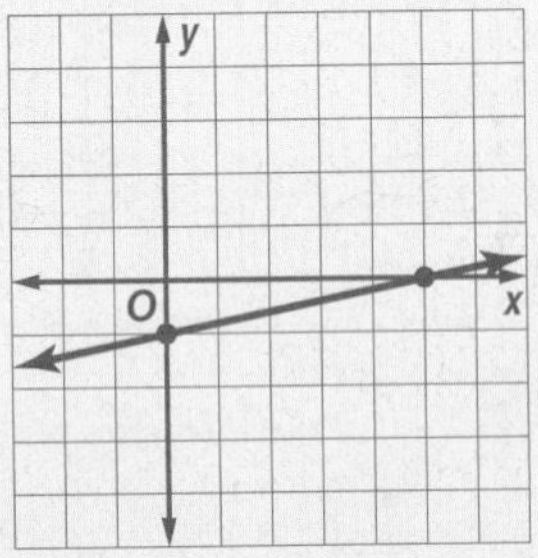

26.

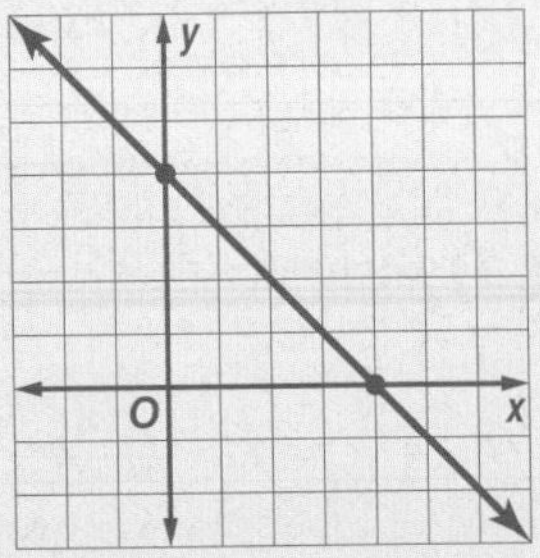

27.

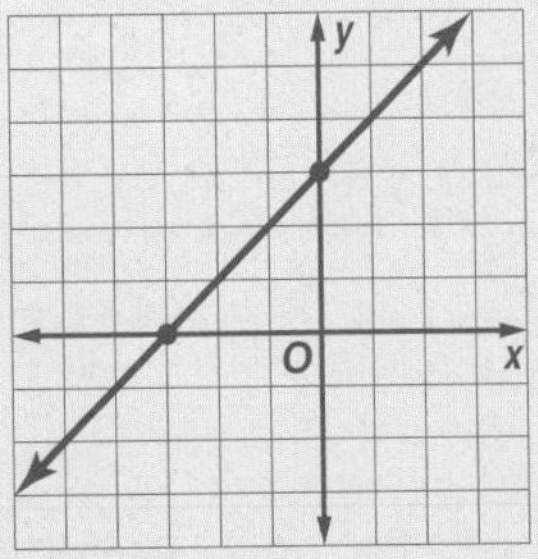

28.

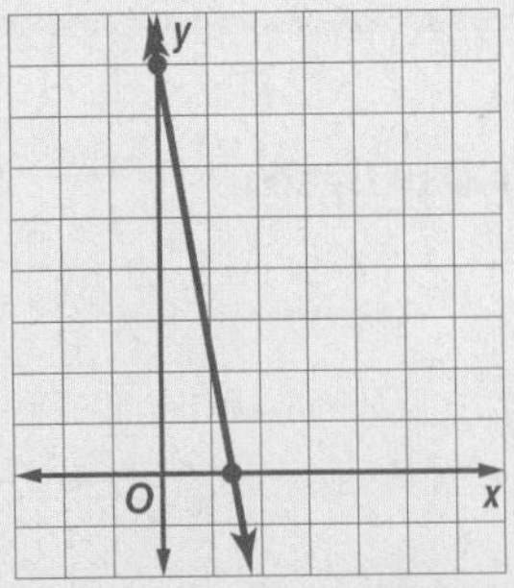

59. Sample answer: Table 1: Yes; we used the formula $P = 4s$, which is linear. Table 2: No; we used the formula $A = s^2$, which is not linear. Table 3: No; we used the formula $V = s^3$, which is not linear.

Examples 2 and 3 pp. 154–155

Find the x- and y-intercepts of each linear function. Describe what the intercepts mean.

21. 6, 20; The x-intercept represents the number of seconds that it takes the eagle to land. The y-intercept represents the initial height of the eagle.

21. Descent of Eagle

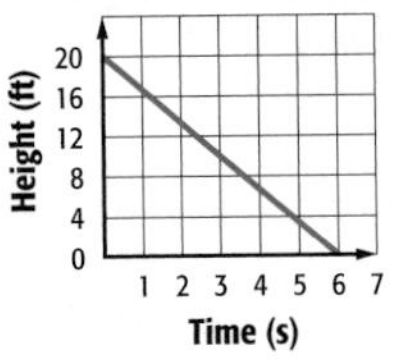

22.

Eva's Distance from Home	
Time (min)	Distance (mi)
x	y
0	4
2	3
4	2
6	1
8	0

8, 4; The x-intercept 8 means that it took Eva 8 minutes to get home. The y-intercept 4 means that Eva was initially 4 miles from home.

Example 4 p. 155

Graph each equation by using the x- and y-intercepts. 23–28. See margin.

23. $y = 4 + 2x$ **24.** $5 - y = -3x$ **25.** $x = 5y + 5$

26. $x + y = 4$ **27.** $x - y = -3$ **28.** $y = 8 - 6x$

Example 5 p. 156

Graph each equation by making a table. 29–34. See Chapter 3 Answer Appendix.

29. $x = -2$ **30.** $y = -4$ **31.** $y = -8x$

32. $3x = y$ **33.** $y - 8 = -x$ **34.** $x = 10 - y$

Real-World Link

In a recent survey, the top five uses for a DVR were: to skip commercials easily (53%); to be able to watch one show while recording another (47%); to pause live TV (32%); to use the on-screen program guide (31%); to record all the episodes of a given show (31%).

Source: MIT

35. TV RATINGS The number of people who watch a singing competition can be given by $p = 0.15v$, where p represents the number of people in millions who saw the show and v is the number of potential viewers in millions.

a. Make a table of values for the points (v, p). 35a–b. See Chapter 3 Answer Appendix.

b. Graph the equation.

c. Use the graph to estimate the number of people who saw the show if there are 14 million potential viewers. ≈2.1 million

d. Explain why it would not make sense for v to be a negative number. There cannot be fewer than 0 viewers.

Determine whether each equation is a linear equation. Write *yes* or *no*. If yes, write the equation in standard form.

B **36.** $x + \frac{1}{y} = 7$ no **37.** $\frac{x}{2} = 10 + \frac{2y}{3}$ yes; $3x - 4y = 60$

38. $7n - 8m = 4 - 2m$ 38. yes; $6m - 7n = -4$ **39.** $3a + b - 2 = b$ yes; $3a = 2$

40. $2r - 3rt + 5t = 1$ no **41.** $\frac{3m}{4} = \frac{2n}{3} - 5$ yes, $9m - 8n = -60$

42. FINANCIAL LITERACY James earns a monthly salary of $1200 and a commission of $125 for each car he sells.

a. Graph an equation that represents how much James earns in a month in which he sells x cars. See Chapter 3 Answer Appendix.

b. Use the graph to estimate the number of cars James needs to sell in order to earn $5000. about 30 cars

Graph each equation. 43–48. See Chapter 3 Answer Appendix.

43. $2.5x - 4 = y$ **44.** $1.25x + 7.5 = y$ **45.** $y + \frac{1}{5}x = 3$

46. $\frac{2}{3}x + y = -7$ **47.** $2x - 3 = 4y + 6$ **48.** $3y - 7 = 4x + 1$

49. No; sample answer: The rental car would cost $176. Mrs. Johnson only has $160 to spend.

49. VACATION Mrs. Johnson is renting a car for vacation and plans to drive a total of 800 miles. A rental car company charges $153 for the week including 700 miles and $0.23 for each additional mile. If Mrs. Johnson has only $160 to spend on the rental car, can she afford to rent a car? Explain your reasoning.

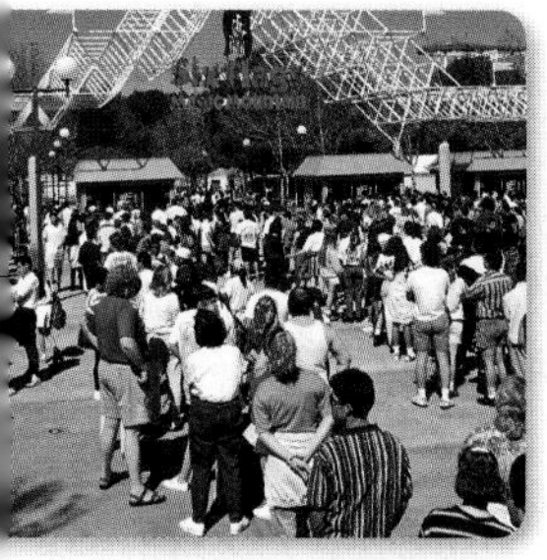

Real-World Link

Attendance at America's theme parks outnumber attendance to all NHL, NFL, NBA, and MLB games combined each year.

Source: *Pricewater Coopers*

50. AMUSEMENT PARKS An amusement park charges \$50 for admission before 6 P.M. and \$20 for admission after 6 P.M. On Saturday, the park took in a total of \$20,000.

a. Write an equation that represents the number of admissions that may have been sold. Let x represent the admissions sold before 6 P.M., and let y represent the admissions sold after 6 P.M. **$20{,}000 = 50x + 20y$**

b. Graph the equation. **b–c. See Chapter 3 Answer Appendix.**

c. Find the x- and y-intercepts of the graph. What does each intercept represent?

Find the x-intercept and y-intercept of the graph of each equation.

51. $5x + 3y = 15$ **3; 5** **52.** $2x - 7y = 14$ **7; −2** **53.** $2x - 3y = 5$ **$2\frac{1}{2}$; $-1\frac{2}{3}$**

54. $6x + 2y = 8$ **$1\frac{1}{3}$; 4** **55.** $y = \frac{1}{4}x - 3$ **12; −3** **56.** $y = \frac{2}{3}x + 1$ **$-1\frac{1}{2}$; 1**

57. ONLINE GAMES The percent of teens who play online games can be modeled by $p = \frac{15}{4}t + 66$. p is the percent of students and t represents time in years since 2000.

a. Graph the equation. **See Chapter 3 Answer Appendix.**

b. Use the graph to estimate the percent of students playing the games in 2008. **96%**

58. MULTIPLE REPRESENTATIONS In this problem, you will explore x- and y-intercepts of graphs of linear equations.

a. **GRAPHICAL** If possible, use a straightedge to draw a line on a coordinate plane with each of the following characteristics. **See Chapter 3 Answer Appendix.**

x- and y-intercept	x-intercept, no y-intercept	exactly 2 x-intercepts	no x-intercept, y-intercept	exactly 2 y-intercepts

b. **ANALYTICAL** For which characteristics were you able to create a line and for which characteristics were you unable to create a line? Explain.

c. **VERBAL** What must be true of the x- and y-intercepts of a line? **Lines that are neither vertical or horizontal cannot have more than one x- and/or y-intercept.**

58b. Sample answer: I was able to draw a line with an x- and a y-intercept, an x-intercept and no y-intercept, and no x-intercept and a y-intercept. I was unable to draw a line with 2 x-intercepts or 2 y-intercepts

60. Sample answer: The first graph is a set of points that are not connected. The second graph is of a line. The points of the first graph are points on the line in the second graph.

61. Sample answer: $y = 8$; horizontal line

62. Sample answer: $x = 5$; vertical line

63. Sample answer: $x - y = 0$; line through (0, 0)

H.O.T. Problems

Use Higher-Order Thinking Skills

59. CHALLENGE Copy and complete each table. State whether any of the tables show a linear relationship. Explain. **See margin for explanation.**

Perimeter of a Square

Side Length	Perimeter
1	4
2	8
3	12
4	16

Area of a Square

Side Length	Area
1	1
2	4
3	9
4	16

Volume of a Cube

Side Length	Volume
1	1
2	8
3	27
4	64

60. REASONING Compare and contrast the graphs of $y = 2x + 1$ with the domain {1, 2, 3, 4} and $y = 2x + 1$ with the domain of all real numbers.

OPEN ENDED Give an example of a linear equation of the form $Ax + By = C$ for each condition. Then describe the graph of the equation.

61. $A = 0$ **62.** $B = 0$ **63.** $C = 0$

64. WRITING IN MATH Explain how to find the x-intercept and y-intercept of a graph and summarize how to graph a linear equation. **See Chapter 3 Answer Appendix.**

Multiple Representations In Exercise 58, students use a straightedge to graph lines with different types of intercepts. They will discover what types of intercepts are possible for the graph of a linear equation.

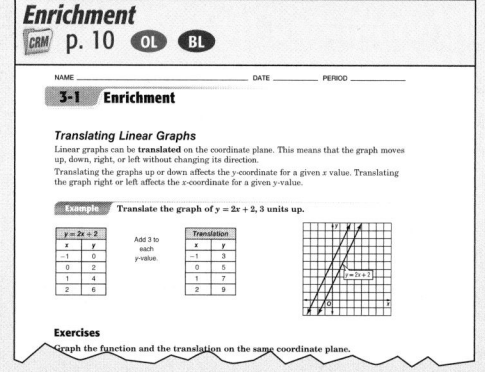

Study Guide and Intervention

CRM pp. 5–6 AL OL ELL

NAME ______ DATE ______ PERIOD ______

3-1 Study Guide and Intervention

Graphing Linear Equations

Identify Linear Equations and Intercepts A **linear equation** is an equation that can be written in the form $Ax + By = C$. This is called the **standard form** of a linear equation.

Standard Form of a Linear Equation	$Ax + By = C$, where $A \ge 0$, A and B are not both zero, and A, B, and C are integers with GCF of 1.

Example 1 Determine whether $y = 6 - 3x$ is a linear equation. Write the equation in standard form.

First rewrite the equation so both variables are on the same side of the equation.

$y = 6 - 3x$ Original equation.
$y + 3x = 6 - 3x + 3x$ Add 3x to each side.
$3x + y = 6$ Simplify.

The equation is now in standard form, with $A = 3$, $B = 1$ and $C = 6$. This is a linear equation.

Example 2 Determine whether $3xy + y = 4 + 2x$ is a linear equation. Write the equation in standard form.

Since the term $3xy$ has two variables, the equation cannot be written in the form $Ax + By = C$. Therefore, this is not a linear equation.

Exercises

Determine whether each equation is a linear equation. Write yes or no. If yes, write the equation in standard form.

1. $2x = 4y$ yes; $2x - 4y = 0$
2. $6 + y = 8$ yes; $y = 2$
3. $4x - 2y = -1$ yes; $4x - 2y = -1$
4. $3xy + 8 = 4y$ no
5. $3x - 4 = 12$ yes; $3x = 16$
6. $y = x^2 + 7$ no
7. $y - 4x = 9$ yes; $4x - y = -9$
8. $x + 8 = 0$ yes; $x = -8$
9. $-2x + 3 = 4y$ yes; $2x + 4y = 3$
10. $2 + \frac{1}{2}x = y$ yes; $x - 2y = -4$
11. $\frac{1}{4}y = 12 - 4x$ yes; $16x + y = 48$
12. $3xy - y = 8$ no
13. $6x + 4y - 3 = 0$ yes; $6x + 4y = 3$
14. $yx - 2 = 8$ no
15. $6x - 2y = 8 + y$ yes; $6x - 3y = 8$
16. $\frac{1}{4}x - 12y = 1$ yes; $x - 48y = 4$
17. $3 + x + x^2 = 0$ no
18. $x^2 = 2xy$ no

Chapter 3 5 Glencoe Algebra 1

Practice

CRM p. 8 AL OL BL ELL

NAME ______ DATE ______ PERIOD ______

3-1 Practice

Graphing Linear Equations

Determine whether each equation is a linear equation. Write yes or no. If yes, write the equation in standard form and determine the x- and y-intercepts.

1. $4xy + 2y = 9$ no
2. $8x - 3y = 6 - 4x$ yes; $4x - y = 2$; x: $\frac{1}{2}$; y: −2
3. $7x + y + 3 = y$ yes; $7x = -3$; x: $\frac{-3}{7}$; y: none
4. $5 - 2y = 3x$ yes; $3x + 2y = 5$; x: $\frac{5}{3}$; y: $\frac{5}{2}$
5. $\frac{x}{4} - \frac{y}{3} = 1$ yes; $3x - 4y = 12$; x: 4; y: −3
6. $\frac{5}{x} - \frac{2}{y} = 7$ no

Graph each equation.

7. $\frac{1}{2}x - y = 2$ 8. $5x - 2y = 7$ 9. $1.5x + 3y = 9$

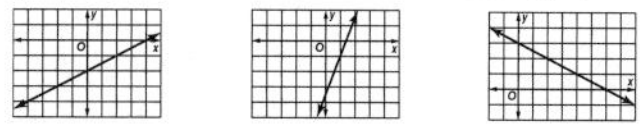

10. COMMUNICATIONS A telephone company charges \$4.95 per month for long distance calls plus \$0.05 per minute. The monthly cost c of long distance calls can be described by the equation $c = 0.05m + 4.95$, where m is the number of minutes.
a. Find the y-intercept of the graph of the equation. (0, 4.95)
b. Graph the equation.
c. If you talk 140 minutes, what is the monthly cost? \$11.95

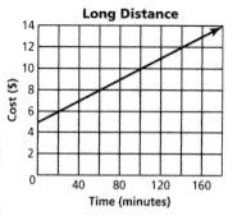

11. MARINE BIOLOGY Killer whales usually swim at a rate of 3.2–9.7 kilometers per hour, though they can travel up to 48.4 kilometers per hour. Suppose a migrating killer whale is swimming at an average rate of 4.5 kilometers per hour. The distance d the whale has traveled in t hours can be predicted by the equation $d = 4.5t$.
a. Graph the equation.
b. Use the graph to predict the time it takes the killer whale to travel 30 kilometers. between 6 h and 7 h

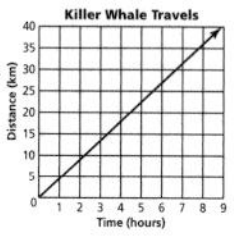

Chapter 3 8 Glencoe Algebra 1

Word Problem Practice

CRM p. 9 AL OL BL ELL

NAME ______ DATE ______ PERIOD ______

3-1 Word Problem Practice

Graphing Linear Equations

1. FOOTBALL One football season, the Carolina Panthers won 4 more games than they lost. This can be represented by $y = x + 4$, where x is the number of games lost and y is the number of games won. Write this linear equation in standard form. $x - y = -4$

2. TOWING Pick-M-Up Towing Company charges \$40 to hook a car and \$1.70 for each mile that it is towed. The equation $y = 1.7x + 40$ represents the total cost y for x miles towed. Determine the y-intercept. Describe what the value means in this context. The y-intercept is 40, which is the fee to hook the car.

3. SHIPPING The *OOCL Shenzhen*, one of the world's largest container ships, carries 8063 TEUs (1280 cubic feet containers). Workers can unload a ship at a rate of a TEU every minute. Using this rate, write and graph an equation to determine how many hours it will take the workers to unload half of the containers from the *Shenzhen*. $y = 8063 - 60x$; about 67.4 hours, or 67 hours and 21.5 minutes

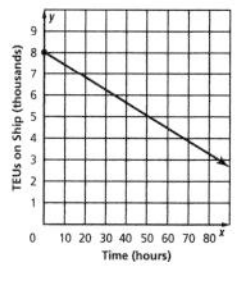

4. BUSINESS The equation $y = 1000x - 5000$ represents the monthly profits of a start-up dry cleaning company. Time in months is x and profit in dollars is y. The first date of operation is when time is zero. However, preparation for opening the business began 3 months earlier with the purchase of equipment and supplies. Graph the linear function for x-values from −3 to 8.

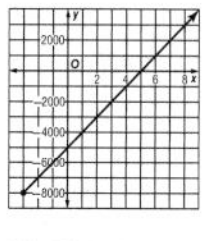

5. BONE GROWTH The height of a woman can be predicted by the equation $h = 81.2 + 3.34r$, where h is her height in centimeters and r is the length of her radius bone in centimeters.
a. Is this is a linear function? Explain. yes; the equation can be written in standard form where $A = 1$, $B = -3.34$, and $C = -81.2$.
b. What are the r- and h-intercepts of the equation? Do they make sense in the situation? Explain. y-intercept = 81.2; x-intercept ≈ −24.3; no – we would expect a woman 81.2 cm tall to have arms, and a negative radius length has no real meaning.
c. Use the function to find the approximate height of a woman whose radius bone is 25 centimeters long. 165 cm

Chapter 3 9 Glencoe Algebra 1

Enrichment

CRM p. 10 OL BL

NAME ______ DATE ______ PERIOD ______

3-1 Enrichment

Translating Linear Graphs

Linear graphs can be **translated** on the coordinate plane. This means that the graph moves up, down, right, or left without changing its direction.

Translating the graphs up or down affects the y-coordinate for a given x value. Translating the graph right or left affects the x-coordinate for a given y-value.

Example Translate the graph of $y = 2x + 2$, 3 units up.

x	y
−1	0
0	2
1	4
2	6

Add 3 to each y-value.

Translation

x	y
−1	3
0	5
1	7
2	9

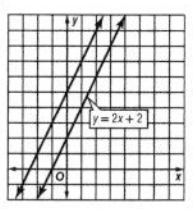

Exercises

Graph the function and the translation on the same coordinate plane.

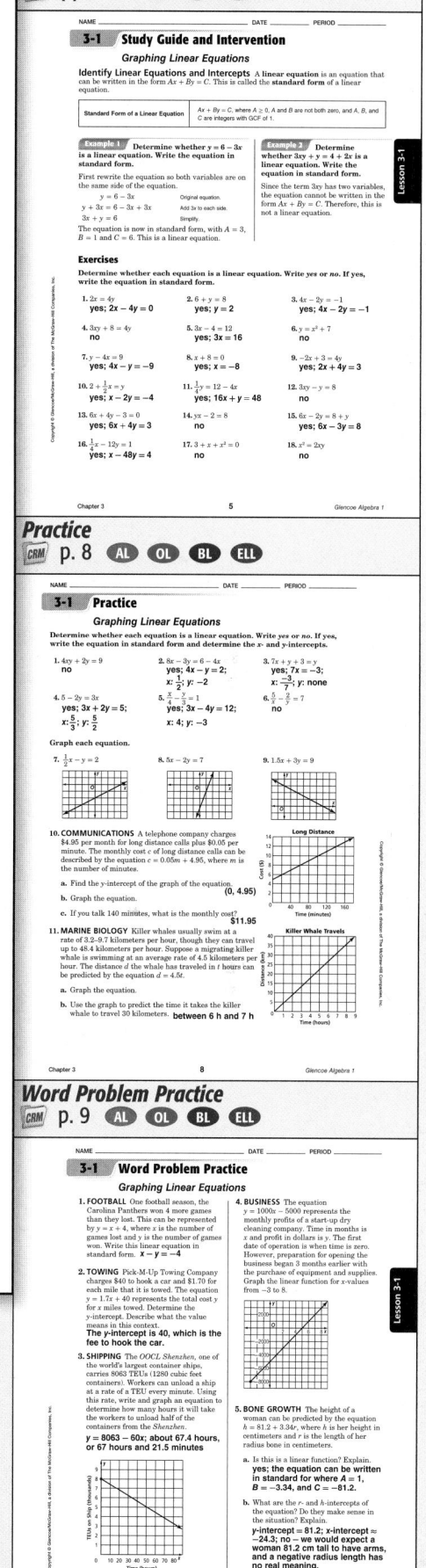

4 ASSESS

Ticket Out the Door Make several copies of five different linear equations. Give one equation to each student. As students leave the room, ask them to identify the x- and y-intercepts.

PSAE PRACTICE 8.11.13, 6.11.17, 8.11.14

65. Sancho can ride 8 miles on his bicycle in 30 minutes. At this rate, about how long would it take him to ride 30 miles? **D**

A 8 hours
B 6 hours 32 minutes
C 2 hours
D 1 hour 53 minutes

66. GEOMETRY Which is a true statement about the relation graphed? **H**

Surface Area of Cube

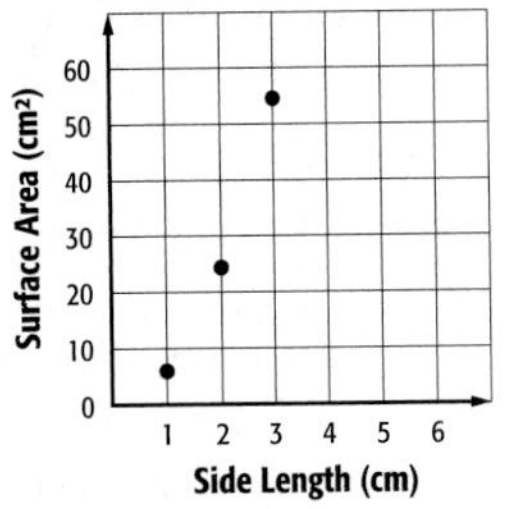

F The relation is not a function.
G Surface area is the independent quantity.
H The surface area of a cube is a function of the side length.
J As the side length of a cube increases, the surface area decreases.

67. SHORT RESPONSE Selena deposited \$2000 into a savings account that pays 1.5% interest compounded annually. If she does not deposit any more money into her account, how much will she earn in interest at the end of one year? **\$30**

68. A candle burns as shown in the graph.

Candle Height

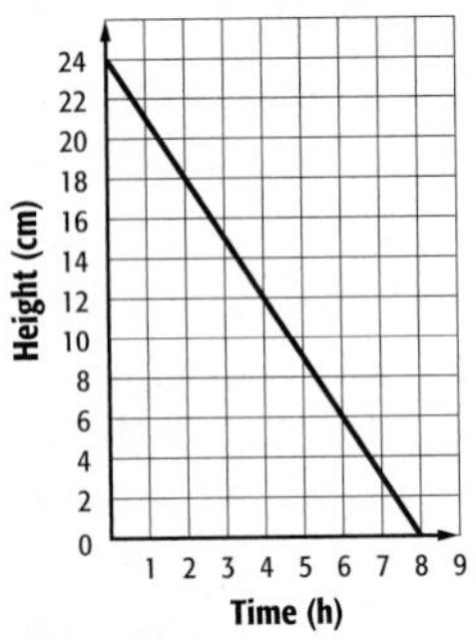

If the height of the candle is 8 centimeters, approximately how long has the candle been burning? **D**

A 0 hours
B 24 minutes
C 64 minutes
D $5\frac{1}{2}$ hours

Spiral Review

69. FUNDRAISING The Madison High School Marching Band sold solid-color gift wrap for \$4 and print gift wrap for \$6 per roll. The total number of rolls sold was 480, and the total amount of money collected was \$2,340. How many rolls of each kind of gift wrap were sold? (Lesson 2-9) **270 rolls of solid wrap, 210 rolls of print wrap**

Solve each equation or formula for the variable specified. (Lesson 2-8)

70. $S = \frac{n}{2}(A + t)$, for A $A = \frac{2S - nt}{n}$

71. $2g - m = 5 - gh$, for g $g = \frac{5 + m}{2 + h}$

72. $\frac{y + a}{3} = c$, for y $y = 3c - a$

73. $4z + b = 2z + c$, for z $z = \frac{c - b}{2}$

Skills Review

Evaluate each expression if $x = 2$, $y = 5$, and $z = 7$. (Lesson 1-2)

74. $3x^2 - 4y$ -8

75. $\frac{x - y^2}{2z}$ $-\frac{23}{14}$

76. $\left(\frac{y}{z}\right)^2 + \frac{xy}{2}$ $\frac{270}{49}$

77. $z^2 - y^3 + 5x^2$ -56

Differentiated Instruction BL

Extension Explain to students that the graph of a linear equation is called a *continuous graph*. It represents all solutions of the linear equation. Every ordered pair on a continuous line satisfies the equation. When the variables in an equation must be whole numbers, the points cannot be connected with a line. This type of graph is a *discrete graph*. Ask students to think of an example of when a discrete graph would be used. Sample answer: if x stood for the number of boys in a class and y stood for the number of girls in a class

160 Chapter 3 Linear Functions

3-2 Solving Linear Equations by Graphing

Why?

The cost of braces can vary widely. The graph shows the balance of the cost of treatments as payments are made. This is modeled by the function $b = -85p + 5100$, where p represents the number of \$85 payments made, and b is the remaining balance.

Orthodontic Payments

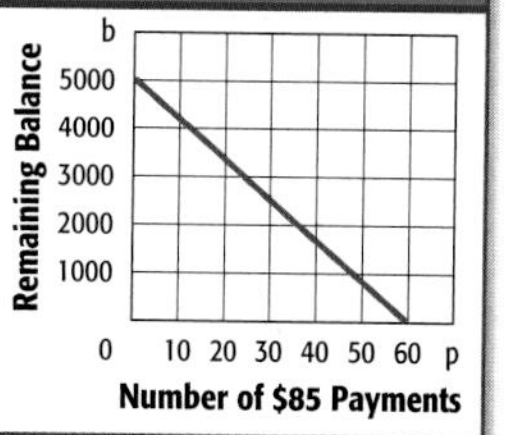

Then
You graphed linear equations by using tables and finding roots, zeros, and intercepts. (Lesson 3-1)

Now
- Solve linear equations by graphing.
- Estimate solutions to a linear equation by graphing.

IL Learning Standards
8.B.4b Use the basic functions of absolute value, square root, **linear**, quadratic and step **to describe numerical relationships.**
8.C.4b Apply algebraic properties and procedures with matrices, vectors, functions and sequences using data found in business, industry and consumer situations.

New Vocabulary
linear function
parent function
family of graphs
root
zeros

IL Math Online
glencoe.com
- Extra Examples
- Personal Tutor
- Self-Check Quiz
- Homework Help

Solve by Graphing A **linear function** is a function for which the graph is a line. The simplest linear function is $f(x) = x$ and is called the **parent function** of the family of linear functions. A **family of graphs** is a group of graphs with one or more similar characteristics.

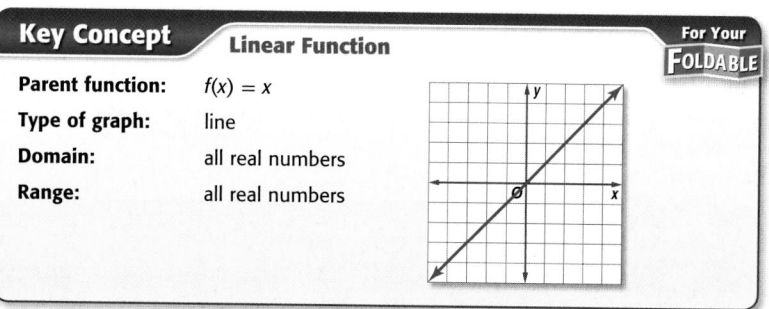

Key Concept — Linear Function
For Your FOLDABLE

Parent function: $f(x) = x$
Type of graph: line
Domain: all real numbers
Range: all real numbers

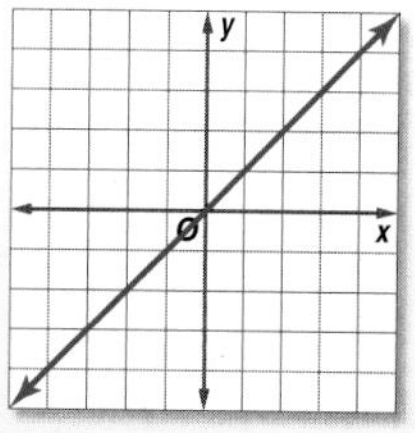

The solution or **root** of an equation is any value that makes the equation true. A linear equation has at most one root. You can find the root of an equation by graphing its related function. To write the related function for an equation, replace 0 with $f(x)$.

Linear Equation	Related Function
$2x - 8 = 0$	$f(x) = 2x - 8$ or $y = 2x - 8$

Values of x for which $f(x) = 0$ are called **zeros** of the function f. The zero of a function is located at the x-intercept of the function. The root of an equation is the value of the x-intercept. So:

- 4 is the x-intercept of $2x - 8 = 0$.
- 4 is the solution of $2x - 8 = 0$.
- 4 is the root of $2x - 8 = 0$.
- 4 is the zero of $f(x) = 2x - 8$.

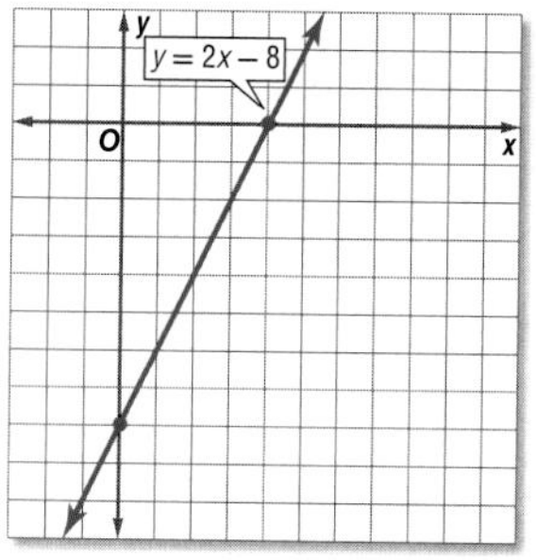

3-2 Lesson Notes

1 FOCUS

Vertical Alignment

Before Lesson 3-2
Graph linear equations by using tables and finding roots, zeros, and intercepts.

Lesson 3-2
Solve equations by graphing. Estimate solutions to an equation by graphing.

After Lesson 3-2
Determine slope of a line.

2 TEACH

Scaffolding Questions
Have students read the *Why?* section of the lesson.

Ask:
- If a parent has made 20 payments on her teenager's braces, what is the remaining balance to be paid? \$3400
- How can you use the graph to answer the question? Find 20 on the p-axis. Look to where the vertical line through 20 meets the line. Move to the b-axis to read the value.
- How can a parent use the graph to find how many payments there will be in all? Find where the graph meets the p-axis. The graph meets it at 60, so there will be a total of 60 payments.

Lesson 3-2 Resources

Resource	Approaching-Level	On-Level	Beyond-Level	English Learners
Teacher Edition	• Differentiated Instruction, p. 162	• Differentiated Instruction, pp. 162, 166	• Differentiated Instruction, p 166	
Chapter Resource Masters	• Study Guide and Intervention, pp. 12–13 • Skills Practice, p. 14 • Practice, p. 15 • Word Problem Practice, p. 16	• Study Guide and Intervention, pp. 12–13 • Skills Practice, p. 14 • Practice, p. 15 • Word Problem Practice, p. 16 • Enrichment, p. 17	• Practice, p. 15 • Word Problem Practice, p. 16 • Enrichment, p. 17	• Study Guide and Intervention, pp. 12–13 • Skills Practice, p. 14 • Practice, p. 15
Transparencies	• 5-Minute Check Transparency 3-2	• 5-Minute Check Transparency 3-2	• 5-Minute Check Transparency 3-2	• 5-Minute Check Transparency 3-2
Other	• Study Notebook	• Study Notebook	• Study Notebook	• Study Notebook

Solve by Graphing

Example 1 shows how to solve an equation with one root algebraically and by graphing. **Example 2** shows how to solve an equation that has no solution algebraically and by graphing.

Formative Assessment

Use the Check Your Progress exercises after each example to determine students' understanding of concepts.

Additional Examples

1 Solve each equation.

a. $0 = \frac{1}{2}x + 3$ -6

b. $2 = \frac{1}{3}x + 3$ -3

2 Solve each equation.

a. $2x + 5 = 2x + 3$ no solution

b. $5x - 7 = 5x + 2$ no solution

Additional Examples also in Interactive Classroom PowerPoint® Presentations

IWB INTERACTIVE WHITEBOARD READY

Focus on Mathematical Content

Identity Equations A linear equation in one variable has at most one root. There are equations with one variable that have infinitely many roots, but they are not linear equations. For example, $2x - 8 = 2(x - 4)$ when simplified becomes $2x - 8 = 2x - 8$ or $0 = 0$. This means any value chosen for x is a solution.

Tips for New Teachers

Function Notation Explain to students that $f(x)$ is a special notation, and is not "f" times "x."

EXAMPLE 1 Solve an Equation with One Root

Solve each equation.

a. $0 = \frac{1}{3}x - 2$

Method 1 Solve algebraically.

$0 = \frac{1}{3}x - 2$	**Original equation**
$0 + 2 = \frac{1}{3}x - 2 + 2$	**Add 2 to each side.**
$3(2) = 3\left(\frac{1}{3}x\right)$	**Multiply each side by 3.**
$6 = x$	**Solve.**

The solution is 6.

b. $3x + 1 = -2$

Method 2 Solve by graphing.

Find the related function. Rewrite the equation with 0 on the right side.

$3x + 1 = -2$	**Original equation**
$3x + 1 + 2 = -2 + 2$	**Add 2 to each side.**
$3x + 3 = 0$	**Simplify.**

The related function is $f(x) = 3x + 3$. To graph the function, make a table.

x	$f(x) = 3x + 3$	$f(x)$	$(x, f(x))$
-2	$f(-2) = 3(-2) + 3$	-3	$(-2, -3)$
1	$f(1) = 3(1) + 3$	6	$(1, 6)$

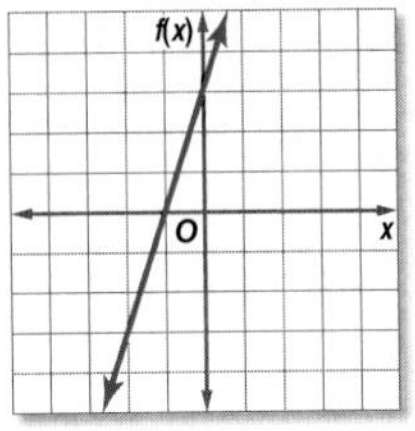

The graph intersects the x-axis at -1. So, the solution is -1.

StudyTip

Zeros from tables The zero is located at the x-intercept, so the value of y will equal 0. When looking at a table, the zero is the x-value when $y = 0$.

Check Your Progress

1A. $0 = \frac{2}{5}x + 6$ -15

1B. $-1.25x + 3 = 0$ 2.4 or $\frac{12}{5}$

Personal Tutor glencoe.com

For equations with the same variable on each side of the equation, use addition or subtraction to get the terms with variables on one side. Then solve.

EXAMPLE 2 Solve an Equation with No Solution

Solve each equation.

a. $3x + 7 = 3x + 1$

Method 1 Solve algebraically.

$3x + 7 = 3x + 1$	**Original equation**
$3x + 7 - 1 = 3x + 1 - 1$	**Subtract 1 from each side.**
$3x + 6 = 3x$	**Simplify.**
$3x - 3x + 6 = 3x - 3x$	**Subtract 3x from each side.**
$6 = 0$	**Simplify.**

The related function is $f(x) = 6$. The root of a linear equation is the value of x when $f(x) = 0$. Since $f(x)$ is always equal to 6, this equation has no solution.

Differentiated Instruction

AL OL

If students have difficulty graphing equations,

Then consider having them work in small groups to work on problems like Example 1b. Make a large coordinate grid on a tiled floor. Assign one or two group members to make a table of values. Then have students stand on the grid on the ordered pairs and hold a string between them, close to the floor, to model the line. Have a student locate where the string crosses the x-axis.

b. $2x - 4 = 2x - 6$

Method 2 Solve by graphing.

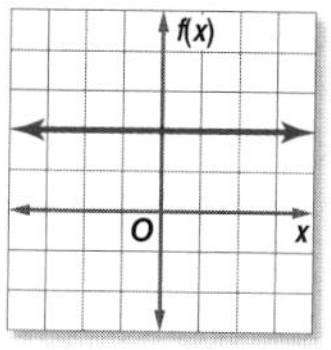

$2x - 4 = 2x - 6$	**Original equation**
$2x - 4 + 6 = 2x - 6 + 6$	**Add 6 to each side.**
$2x + 2 = 2x$	**Simplify.**
$2x - 2x + 2 = 2x - 2x$	**Subtract 2x from each side.**
$2 = 0$	**Simplify.**

Graph the related function, which is $f(x) = 2$. The graph does not intersect the x-axis. Thus, there is no solution.

Check Your Progress

2A. $4x + 3 = 4x - 5$ no solution

2B. $2 - 3x = 6 - 3x$ no solution

Personal Tutor glencoe.com

Estimate Solutions by Graphing Graphing may provide only an estimate. In these cases, solve algebraically to find the exact solution.

Real-World Career

Entertainment Manager
An entertainment manager supervises tech tests, calls show cues, schedules performances and performers, coaches employees and guest talent, and manages expenses. Entertainment managers need a college degree in a field such as communication or theater.

Real-World EXAMPLE 3 Estimate by Graphing

AMUSEMENT PARKS Emily is going to a local carnival. The function $m = 20 - 0.75r$ represents the amount of money m she has left after r rides. Find the zero of this function. Describe what this value means in this context.

Make a table of values.

r	$m = 20 - 0.75r$	m	(r, m)
0	$m = 20 - 0.75(0)$	20	(0, 20)
5	$m = 20 - 0.75(5)$	16.25	(5, 16.25)

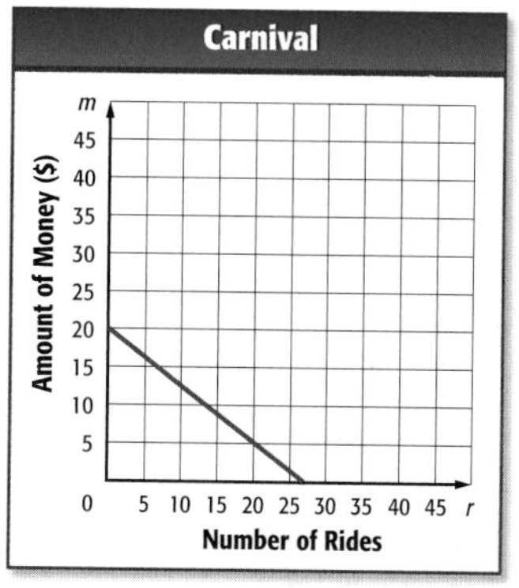

The graph appears to intersect the r-axis at 27.

Next, solve algebraically to check.

$m = 20 - 0.75r$	**Original equation**
$0 = 20 - 0.75r$	**Replace m with 0.**
$0 + 0.75r = 20 - 0.75r + 0.75r$	**Add 0.75r to each side.**
$0.75r = 20$	**Simplify.**
$\frac{0.75r}{0.75} = \frac{20}{0.75}$	**Divide each side by 0.75.**
$r \approx 26.67$	**Simplify and round to the nearest hundredth.**

The zero of this function is about 26.67. Since Emily cannot ride part of a ride, she can ride 26 rides before she will run out of money.

Check Your Progress

3. Antoine's class must sell 30 candy bars before they make a profit.

3. FINANCIAL LITERACY Antoine's class is selling candy to raise money for a class trip. They paid \$45 for the candy, and they are selling each candy bar for \$1.50. The function $y = 1.50x - 45$ represents their profit y when they sell x candy bars. Find the zero and describe what it means in the context of this situation.

Personal Tutor glencoe.com

Estimate Solutions by Graphing

Example 3 shows how to estimate the zero of a function by graphing the function.

Additional Example

3 **FUNDRAISING** Kendra's class is selling greeting cards to raise money for new soccer equipment. They paid \$115 for the cards, and they are selling each card for \$1.75. The function $y = 1.75x - 115$ represents their profit y for selling x greeting cards. Find the zero of this function. Describe what this value means in this context. About 65.71; they must sell 66 cards to make a profit.

Tips for New Teachers

Reasoning Advise students to look for key words that describe situations in which it may be necessary to round an estimate up or down. For example, if you do not want to have *too few*, you need to round up. If you do not want to have *too much*, you round down.

TEACH with TECH

VIDEO RECORDING Have students work in groups to explain how to solve linear equations by graphing. Have them check their answers by solving the equations algebraically.

3 PRACTICE

Formative Assessment

Use Exercises 1–9 to check for understanding.

Use the chart at the bottom of this page to customize assignments for your students.

Exercise Alert

Grid Paper Exercises 38–44 require the use of grid paper.

Watch Out!

Find the Error For Exercise 46, students should see that Clarissa did not simplify $x + 5 = 4$ correctly.

Additional Answers

22. 160; The text message is full after Sean has typed 160 characters.

36. $d = 1.67$; The water level in New Orleans has reached sea level after 1.67 days of rain.

48. Sample answer: It is better to solve an equation algebraically if an exact answer is needed. It is better to solve graphically if an exact answer is not needed.

Check Your Understanding

Examples 1 and 2 pp. 162–163

Solve each equation.

1. $-2x + 6 = 0$ **3**
2. $-x - 3 = 0$ **−3**
3. $4x - 2 = 0$ $\frac{1}{2}$
4. $9x + 3 = 0$ $-\frac{1}{3}$
5. $2x - 5 = 2x + 8$ **no solution**
6. $4x + 11 = 4x - 24$ **no solution**
7. $3x - 5 = 3x - 10$ **no solution**
8. $-6x + 3 = -6x + 5$ **no solution**

Example 3 p. 163

9. **NEWSPAPERS** The function $w = 30 - \frac{3}{4}n$ represents the weight w in pounds of the papers in Tyrone's newspaper delivery bag after he delivers n newspapers. Find the zero and explain what it means in the context of this situation.
Tyrone must deliver 40 newspapers for the papers in his bag to weigh 0 pounds.

12. no solution
13. no solution
15. $-\frac{10}{7}$ or $-1\frac{3}{7}$

Practice and Problem Solving

● = Step-by-Step Solutions begin on page R12.
Extra Practice begins on page 815

Examples 1 and 2 pp. 162–163

17. no solution
18. no solution

Solve each equation. **19.** no solution **21.** no solution

10. $0 = x - 5$ **5**
11. $0 = x + 3$ **−3**
12. $5 - 8x = 16 - 8x$
13. $3x - 10 = 21 + 3x$
14. $4x - 36 = 0$ **9**
15. $0 = 7x + 10$
16. $2x + 22 = 0$ **−11**
17. $5x - 5 = 5x + 2$
18. $-7x + 35 = 20 - 7x$
19. $-4x - 28 = 3 - 4x$
20. $0 = 6x - 8$ $\frac{4}{3}$ or $1\frac{1}{3}$
21. $12x + 132 = 12x - 100$

Example 3 p. 163

22. **TEXT MESSAGING** Sean is sending text messages to his friends. The function $y = 160 - x$ represents the number of characters y the message can hold after he has typed x characters. Find the zero and explain what it means in the context of this situation. **See margin.**

23. **GIFT CARDS** For her birthday Kwan receives a \$50 gift card to download songs. The function $m = -0.50d + 50$ represents the amount of money m that remains on the card after a number of songs d are downloaded. Find the zero and explain what it means in the context of this situation. **100; She can download a total of 100 songs before the gift card is completely used.**

Real-World Link

In 2006, 158 billion text messages were sent nationwide, nearly double the amount in 2005.

Source: The Wireless Association

B Solve each equation. **29.** $-\frac{34}{13}$ or $-2\frac{8}{13}$

24. $-7 = 4x + 1$ **−2**
25. $4 - 2x = 20$ **−8**
26. $2 - 5x = -23$ **5**
27. $10 - 3x = 0$ $\frac{10}{3}$ or $3\frac{1}{3}$
28. $15 + 6x = 0$ $-\frac{5}{2}$ or $-2\frac{1}{2}$
29. $0 = 13x + 34$
30. $0 = 22x - 10$ $\frac{5}{11}$
31. $25x - 17 = 0$ $\frac{17}{25}$
32. $0 = \frac{1}{2} + \frac{2}{3}x$ $-\frac{3}{4}$
33. $0 = \frac{3}{4} - \frac{2}{5}x$ $\frac{15}{8}$ or $1\frac{7}{8}$
34. $13x + 117 = 0$ **−9**
35. $24x - 72 = 0$ **3**

36. **SEA LEVEL** Parts of New Orleans lie 0.5 meter below sea level. After d days of rain the equation $w = 0.3d - 0.5$ represents the water level w in meters. Find the zero, and explain what it means in the context of this situation. **See margin.**

37. **ICE SCULPTURE** An artist completed an ice sculpture when the temperature was −10°C. The equation $t = 1.25h - 10$ shows the temperature h hours after the sculpture's completion. If the artist completed the sculpture at 8:00 A.M., at what time will it begin to melt? **4:00 P.M.**

Solve each equation by graphing. Verify your answer algebraically. **38–43. See Chapter 3 Answer Appendix for graphs.**

38. $7 - 3x = 8 - 4x$ **1**
39. $19 + 3x = 13 + x$ **−3**
40. $16x + 6 = 14x + 10$ **2**
41. $15x - 30 = 5x - 50$ **−2**
42. $\frac{1}{2}x - 5 = 3x - 10$ **2**
43. $3x - 11 = \frac{1}{3}x - 8$ $\frac{9}{8}$ or $1\frac{1}{8}$

Differentiated Homework Options

Level	Assignment	Two-Day Option	
AL Basic	10–23, 46, 48–67	11–23 odd, 51–54	10–22 even, 46, 48–50, 55–67
OL Core	11–43 odd, 36, 44–46, 48–67	10–23, 51–54	24–46, 48–50, 55–67
BL Advanced	24–60, (optional: 61–67)		

44c. The solution must remain on the hair for 8 minutes to be completely effective.

StudyTip

Zero of a Function The zero of a function is also called the root or x-intercept.

49. Sample answer: $3 + 4x = 0$; $y = 3 + 4x$ or $f(x) = 3 + 4x$

50. Sample answer: To solve a linear equation algebraically, solve the equation for x. To solve a linear equation graphically, find the related function by setting the equation equal to zero. Then, make a table and choose different values for x and find the corresponding y-coordinate. Determine where the graph intersects the x-axis. This is the solution. If the graph does not intersect the x-axis, there is no solution.

44. HAIR PRODUCTS Chemical hair straightening makes curly hair straight and smooth. The percent of the process left to complete is modeled by $p = -12.5t + 100$, where t is the time in minutes that the solution is left on the hair, and p represents the percent of the process left to complete.

a. Find the zero of this function. 8

b. Make a graph of this situation. See Chapter 3 Answer Appendix.

c. Explain what the zero represents in this context.

d. State the possible domain and range of this function. d. D: $\{t \mid 0 \leq t \leq 8\}$, R: $\{p \mid 0 \leq p \leq 100\}$

45 C **MUSIC DOWNLOADS** In this problem, you will investigate the change between two quantities.

a. Copy and complete the table. Sample answers given.

Number of Songs Downloaded	Total Cost ($)	Total Cost / Number of Songs Downloaded
2	4	2
4	8	2
6	12	2
8	16	2
10	20	2

b. As the number of songs downloaded increases, how does the total cost change? increases by 4 for each 2 songs downloaded

c. Interpret the value of the total cost divided by the number of songs downloaded. It costs $2 per song to download.

46. Koko; Clarissa did not subtract the 5 from each side of the equation

H.O.T. Problems
Use Higher-Order Thinking Skills

46. FIND THE ERROR Clarissa and Koko solve $3x + 5 = 2x + 4$ by graphing the related function. Is either of them correct? Explain your reasoning.

Clarissa

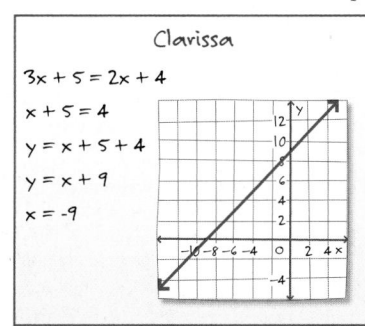

$3x + 5 = 2x + 4$
$x + 5 = 4$
$y = x + 5 + 4$
$y = x + 9$
$x = -9$

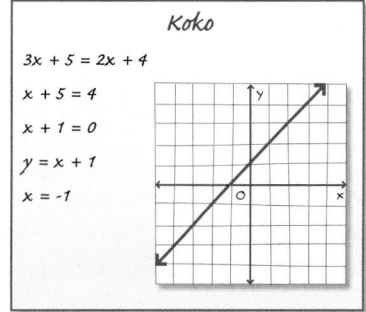

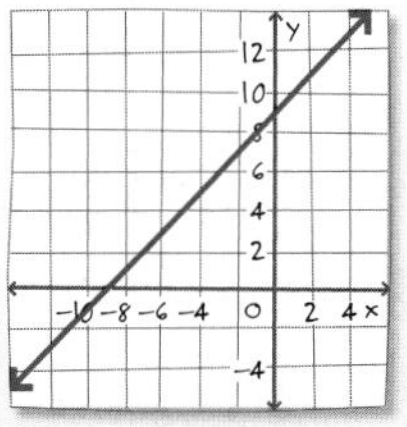

Koko

$3x + 5 = 2x + 4$
$x + 5 = 4$
$x + 1 = 0$
$y = x + 1$
$x = -1$

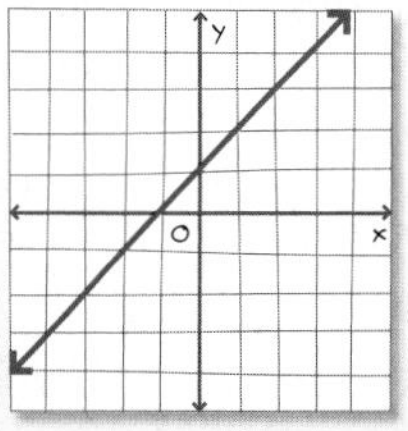

47. CHALLENGE Use a graphing calculator to find the solution of $\frac{2}{3}(x + 3) = \frac{1}{2}(x + 5)$. Verify your solution algebraically. 3

48. REASONING Explain when it is better to solve an equation using algebraic methods and when it is better to solve by graphing. See margin.

49. OPEN ENDED Write a linear equation that has a root of $-\frac{3}{4}$. Write its related function.

50. WRITING IN MATH Summarize how to solve a linear equation algebraically and graphically.

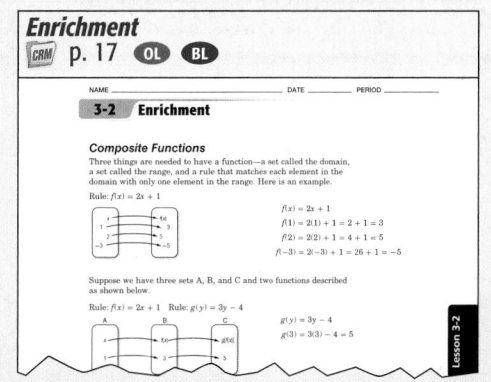

Study Guide and Intervention CRM pp. 12–13 AL OL ELL

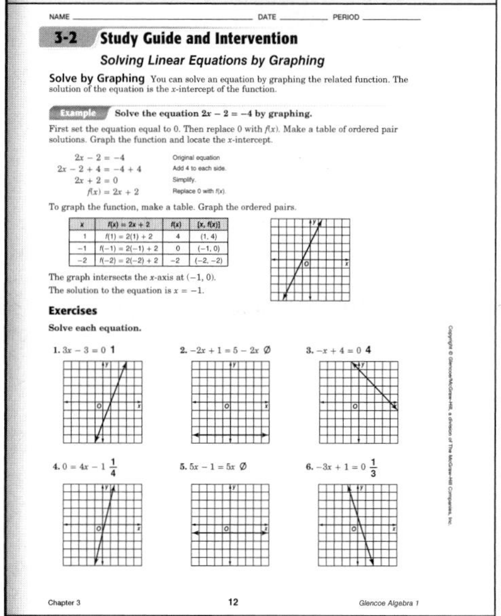
NAME DATE PERIOD

3-2 Study Guide and Intervention

Solving Linear Equations by Graphing

Solve by Graphing You can solve an equation by graphing the related function. The solution of the equation is the x-intercept of the function.

Example Solve the equation $2x - 2 = -4$ by graphing.

First set the equation equal to 0. Then replace 0 with $f(x)$. Make a table of ordered pair solutions. Graph the function and locate the x-intercept.

$2x - 2 = -4$ Original equation
$2x - 2 + 4 = -4 + 4$ Add 4 to each side.
$2x + 2 = 0$ Simplify.
$f(x) = 2x + 2$ Replace 0 with $f(x)$.

To graph the function, make a table. Graph the ordered pairs.

x	$f(x) = 2x + 2$	$f(x)$	$[x, f(x)]$
1	$f(1) = 2(1) + 2$	4	(1, 4)
−1	$f(-1) = 2(-1) + 2$	0	(−1, 0)
−2	$f(-2) = 2(-2) + 2$	−2	(−2, −2)

The graph intersects the x-axis at (−1, 0). The solution to the equation is $x = -1$.

Exercises

Solve each equation.

1. $3x - 3 = 0$ 1
2. $-2x + 1 = 5 - 2x$ Ø
3. $-x + 4 = 0$ 4
4. $0 = 4x - 1$ $\frac{1}{4}$
5. $5x - 1 = 5x$ Ø
6. $-3x + 1 = 0$ $\frac{1}{3}$

Chapter 3 12 Glencoe Algebra 1

Practice CRM p. 15 AL OL BL ELL

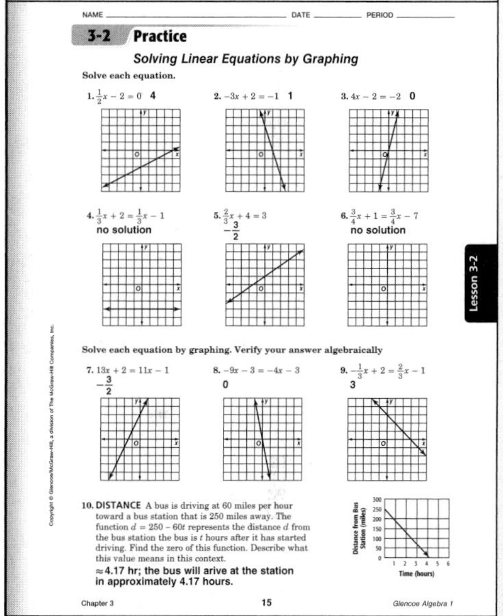
NAME DATE PERIOD

3-2 Practice

Solving Linear Equations by Graphing

Solve each equation.

1. $\frac{1}{2}x - 2 = 0$ 4
2. $-3x + 2 = -1$ 1
3. $4x - 2 = -2$ 0
4. $\frac{1}{3}x + 2 = \frac{1}{3}x - 1$ no solution
5. $\frac{2}{3}x + 4 = 3$ $-\frac{3}{2}$
6. $\frac{3}{4}x + 1 = \frac{3}{4}x - 7$ no solution

Solve each equation by graphing. Verify your answer algebraically.

7. $13x + 2 = 11x - 1$ $-\frac{3}{2}$
8. $-9x - 3 = -4x - 3$ 0
9. $-\frac{1}{3}x + 2 = \frac{2}{3}x - 1$ 3

10. DISTANCE A bus is driving at 60 miles per hour toward a bus station that is 250 miles away. The function $d = 250 - 60t$ represents the distance d from the bus station the bus is t hours after it has started driving. Find the zero of this function. Describe what this value means in this context.
≈4.17 hr; the bus will arrive at the station in approximately 4.17 hours.

Chapter 3 15 Glencoe Algebra 1

Word Problem Practice CRM p. 16 AL OL BL ELL

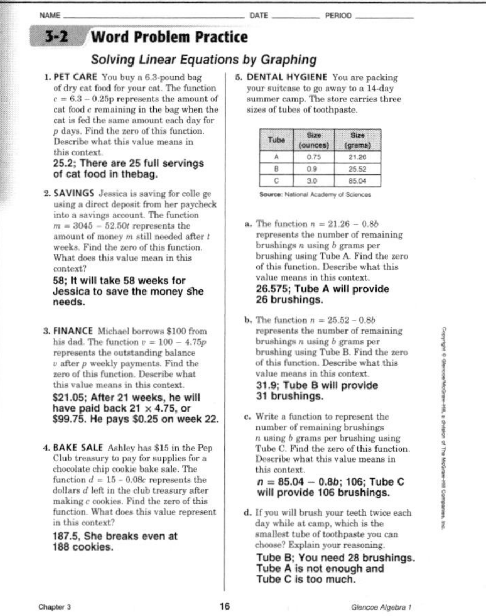
NAME DATE PERIOD

3-2 Word Problem Practice

Solving Linear Equations by Graphing

1. PET CARE You buy a 6.3-pound bag of dry cat food for your cat. The function $c = 6.3 - 0.25p$ represents the amount of cat food c remaining in the bag when the cat is fed the same amount each day for p days. Find the zero of this function. Describe what this value means in this context.
25.2; There are 25 full servings of cat food in the bag.

2. SAVINGS Jessica is saving for college using a direct deposit from her paycheck into a savings account. The function $m = 3045 - 52.50t$ represents the amount of money m still needed after t weeks. Find the zero of this function. What does this value mean in this context?
58; It will take 58 weeks for Jessica to save the money she needs.

3. FINANCE Michael borrows $100 from his dad. The function $v = 100 - 4.75p$ represents the outstanding balance v after p weekly payments. Find the zero of this function. Describe what this value means in this context.
$21.05; After 21 weeks, he will have paid back 21 × 4.75, or $99.75. He pays $0.25 on week 22.

4. BAKE SALE Ashley has $15 in the Pep Club treasury to pay for supplies for a chocolate chip cookie bake sale. The function $d = 15 - 0.08c$ represents the dollars d left in the club treasury after making c cookies. Find the zero of this function. What does this value represent in this context?
187.5, She breaks even at 188 cookies.

5. DENTAL HYGIENE You are packing your suitcase to go away to a 14-day summer camp. The store carries three sizes of tubes of toothpaste.

Tube	Size (ounces)	Size (grams)
A	0.75	21.26
B	0.9	25.52
C	3.0	85.04

Source: National Academy of Sciences

a. The function $n = 21.26 - 0.8b$ represents the number of remaining brushings n using b grams per brushing using Tube A. Find the zero of this function. Describe what this value means in this context.
26.575; Tube A will provide 26 brushings.

b. The function $n = 25.52 - 0.8b$ represents the number of remaining brushings n using b grams per brushing using Tube B. Find the zero of this function. Describe what this value means in this context.
31.9; Tube B will provide 31 brushings.

c. Write a function to represent the number of remaining brushings n using b grams per brushing using Tube C. Find the zero of this function. Describe what this value means in this context.
$n = 85.04 - 0.8b$; 106; Tube C will provide 106 brushings.

d. If you will brush your teeth twice each day while at camp, which is the smallest tube of toothpaste you can choose? Explain your reasoning.
Tube B; You need 28 brushings. Tube A is not enough and Tube C is too much.

Chapter 3 16 Glencoe Algebra 1

Enrichment CRM p. 17 OL BL

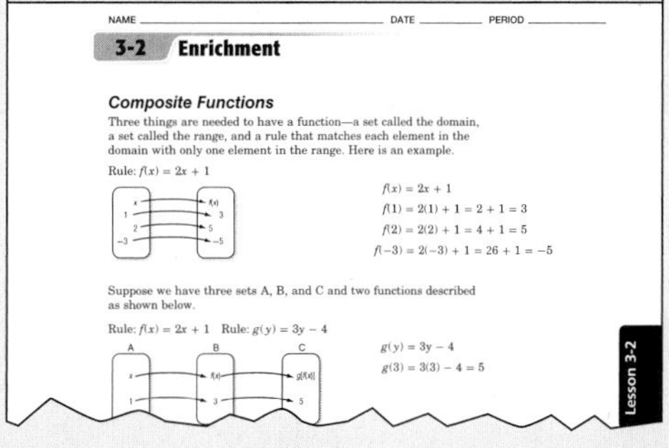
NAME DATE PERIOD

3-2 Enrichment

Composite Functions

Three things are needed to have a function—a set called the domain, a set called the range, and a rule that matches each element in the domain with only one element in the range. Here is an example.

Rule: $f(x) = 2x + 1$

$f(x) = 2x + 1$
$f(1) = 2(1) + 1 = 2 + 1 = 3$
$f(2) = 2(2) + 1 = 4 + 1 = 5$
$f(-3) = 2(-3) + 1 = -6 + 1 = -5$

Suppose we have three sets A, B, and C and two functions described as shown below.

Rule: $f(x) = 2x + 1$ Rule: $g(y) = 3y - 4$

$g(y) = 3y - 4$
$g(3) = 3(3) - 4 = 5$

Lesson 3-2

4 ASSESS

Yesterday's News Ask students to write how yesterday's lesson on graphing linear equations helped them with today's new material.

Formative Assessment

Check for student understanding of Lessons 3-1 and 3-2.

CRM Quiz 1, p. 45

PSAE PRACTICE 8.11.07, 8.11.11, 7.11.03

51. What are the x- and y-intercepts of the graph of the function? A

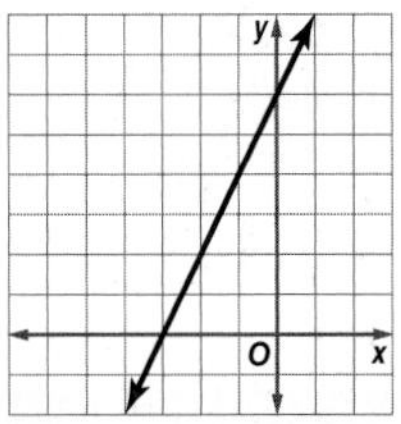

A $-3, 6$ C $3, -6$
B $6, -3$ D $-6, 3$

52. The table shows the cost C of renting a pontoon boat for h hours.

Hours	1	2	3
Cost ($)	7.25	14.5	21.75

Which equation best represents the data? F

F $C = 7.25h$ H $C = 21.75 - 7.25h$
G $C = h + 7.25$ J $C = 7.25h + 21.75$

53. Which is the best estimate for the x-intercept of the graph of the linear function represented in the table? B

x	y
0	5
1	3
2	1
3	−1
4	−3

A between 0 and 1
B between 2 and 3
C between 1 and 2
D between 3 and 4

54. EXTENDED RESPONSE Mr. Kauffmann has the following options for a backyard pool.

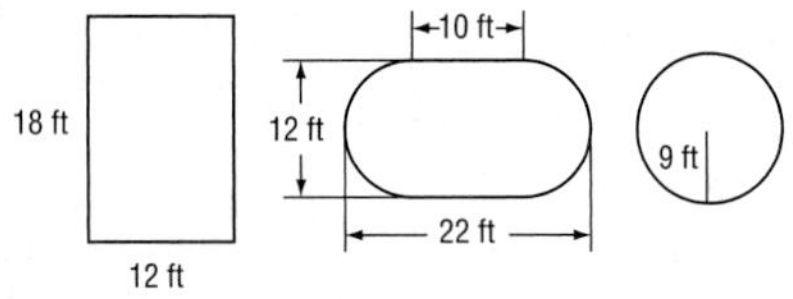

Which pool would give the greatest area to swim? Explain your reasoning.
Circular pool; circular pool has an area ≈ 254.5 ft^2, which is greater than the rectangular pool with area $= 216$ ft^2 and the rounded pool with area ≈ 233 ft^2.

Spiral Review

Find the x- and y-intercepts of the graph of each linear equation. (Lesson 3-1)

55. $y = 2x + 10$ $-5, 10$ **56.** $3y = 6x - 9$ $\frac{3}{2}, -3$ **57.** $4x - 14y = 28$ $7, -2$

58. FOOD If 2% milk contains 2% butterfat and whipping cream contains 9% butterfat, how much whipping cream and 2% milk should be mixed to obtain 35 gallons of milk with 4% butterfat? (Lesson 2-9) 10 gal of cream, 25 gal of 2% milk

Identify the hypothesis and conclusion of each statement. Then write each statement in if-then form. (Lesson 1-8)

59. A number that is divisible by 10 is also divisible by 5.

60. A rectangle is a quadrilateral with four right angles.

59. H: a number is divisible by 10; C: it is divisible by 5; If a number is divisible by 10, then it is divisible by 5.
60. H: a figure is a rectangle; C: it is a quadrilateral with four right angles; If a figure is a rectangle, then it is a quadrilateral with four right angles.

Skills Review

Simplify. (Lesson 0-3)

61. $\frac{25}{10}$ $\frac{5}{2}$ **62.** $\frac{-4}{-12}$ $\frac{1}{3}$ **63.** $\frac{6}{-12}$ $-\frac{1}{2}$ **64.** $\frac{-36}{8}$ $-\frac{9}{2}$

Evaluate $\frac{a-b}{c-d}$ for the given values. (Lesson 1-2)

65. $a = 6, b = 2, c = 9, d = 3$ $\frac{2}{3}$ **66.** $a = -8, b = 4, c = 5, d = -3$ $-\frac{3}{2}$ **67.** $a = 4, b = -7, c = -1, d = -2$ 11

Differentiated Instruction OL BL

Extension Solve $0 > \frac{1}{3}x - 1$. $3 > x$

Graphing Technology Lab
Graphing Linear Functions

IL Math Online glencoe.com
- Other Calculator Keystrokes
- Graphing Technology Personal Tutor

IL Learning Standards **8.B.4b Use the basic functions of** absolute value, square root, **linear**, quadratic and step **to describe numerical relationships.**

The power of a graphing calculator is the ability to graph different types of equations accurately and quickly. By entering one or more equations in the calculator you can view features of a graph, such as the x-intercept, y-intercept, the origin, intersections, and the coordinates of specific points.

Often linear equations are graphed in the **standard viewing window**, which is [−10, 10] by [−10, 10] with a scale of 1 on each axis. To quickly choose the standard viewing window on a TI-83/84 Plus, press [Zoom] 6.

ACTIVITY 1 Graph a Linear Equation

Graph $3x - y = 4$.

Step 1 Enter the equation in the Y= list.

- The Y= list shows the equation or equations that you will graph.
- Equations must be entered with the y isolated on one side of the equation. Solve the equation for y, then enter it into the calculator.

$3x - y = 4$	**Original equation**
$3x - y - 3x = 4 - 3x$	**Subtract $3x$ from each side.**
$-y = -3x + 4$	**Simplify.**
$y = 3x - 4$	**Multiply each side by −1.**

KEYSTROKES: [Y=] 3 [X,T,θ,n] [−] 4

The equals sign appears shaded for graphs that are selected to be displayed.

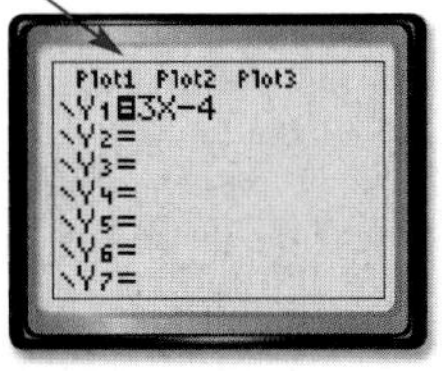

Step 2 Graph the equation in the standard viewing window.

- Graph the selected equation.

KEYSTROKES: [Zoom] 6

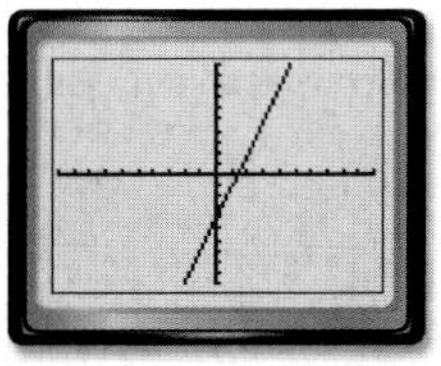

[−10, 10] scl: 1 by [−10, 10] scl: 1

Sometimes a complete graph is not displayed using the standard viewing window. A **complete graph** includes all of the important characteristics of the graph on the screen including the origin and the x- and y-intercepts. Note that the graph above is a complete graph because all of these points are visible.

When a complete graph is not displayed using the standard viewing window, you will need to change the viewing window to accommodate these important features. Use what you have learned about intercepts to help you choose an appropriate viewing window.

(continued on the next page)

1 FOCUS

Objective Change the viewing window so that a complete graph of a linear function can be displayed.

Materials for Each Group

- T1–83/84 Plus or other graphing calculator

Teaching Tip

- The graphing calculator has the ability to make graphs appear differently on the screen. The symbol before each Y= entry shows how the line will appear. Highlight the symbol and press [ENTER] repeatedly until the line type you want appears.
- The standard viewing window is selected by pressing [Zoom] **6**. This is a [−10, 10] by [−10, 10] screen with scales, Xscl and Yscl, of 1.
- You can keep an equation in the Y= list and have it not appear on the graphing screen by highlighting the = sign and pressing [ENTER].

2 TEACH

Working in Cooperative Groups

Put students in groups of three or four, mixing abilities. Have groups help each other to complete Activities 1–2.

Make sure students have cleared or suppressed any equation in the Y= list other than those they wish to graph.

Ask:

- In what form must the equation be written to be entered into the calculator? with the y isolated on one side.
- How do you know you have a complete graph displayed in your window? The origin and the x- and y-intercepts are seen on the screen.

Practice Have students complete Exercises 1–15.

3 ASSESS

Formative Assessment

- Use Exercise 4 to assess whether students understand how to rewrite the equation with the y isolated on one side of the equation and enter it into their calculators.
- Use Exercise 10 to assess whether students understand how to modify the viewing window on their calculators.

From Concrete to Abstract

Ask:

How can the function $y = 3x + 15$ help you choose a viewing window for its graph? Sample answer: Since b is the y-intercept of the graph, you know that the window must at least include $y = 15$.

ACTIVITY 2 Graph a Complete Graph

Graph $y = 5x - 14$.

Step 1 Enter the equation in the Y= list and graph in the standard viewing window.

- Clear the previous equation from the Y= list. Then enter the new equation and graph.

KEYSTROKES: [Y=] [CLEAR] 5 [X,T,θ,n] [–] 14 [Zoom] 6

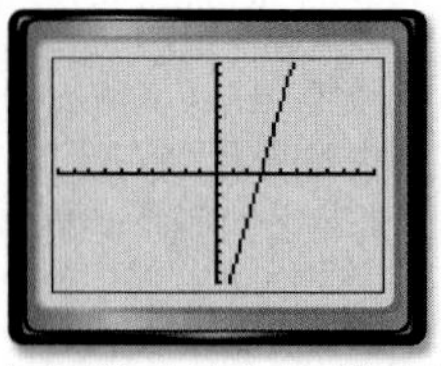

[−10, 10] scl: 1 by [−10, 10] scl: 1

Step 2 Modify the viewing window and graph again.

- The origin and the x-intercept are displayed in the standard viewing window. But notice that the y-intercept is outside of the viewing window.

Find the y-intercept.

$y = 5x - 14$	**Original equation**
$= 5(0) - 14$	**Replace x with 0.**
$= -14$	**Simplify.**

Since the y-intercept is -14, choose a viewing window that includes a number less than -14. The window $[-10, 10]$ by $[-20, 5]$ with a scale of 1 on each axis is a good choice.

KEYSTROKES: [WINDOW] -10 [ENTER] 10 [ENTER] 1 [ENTER] -20 [ENTER] 5 [ENTER] 1 [GRAPH]

This window allows the complete graph, including the y-intercept, to be displayed.

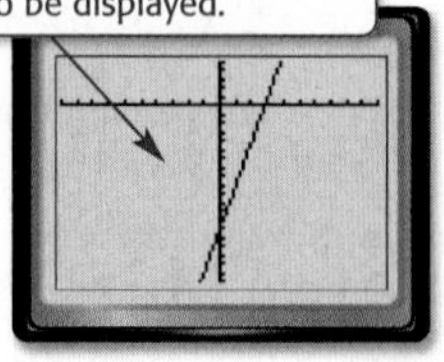

[−10, 10] scl: 1 by [−20, 5] scl: 1

Exercises

Use a graphing calculator to graph each equation in the standard viewing window. Sketch the result. 1–6. See Ch. 3 Answer Appendix.

1. $y = x + 5$ **2.** $y = 5x + 6$ **3.** $y = 9 - 4x$

4. $3x + y = 5$ **5.** $x + y = -4$ **6.** $x - 3y = 6$

Graph each equation in the standard viewing window. Determine whether the graph is complete. If the graph is not complete, adjust the viewing window and graph the equation again. 7–12. See Ch. 3 Answer Appendix.

7. $y = 4x + 7$ **8.** $y = 9x - 5$ **9.** $y = 2x - 11$

10. $4x - y = 16$ **11.** $6x + 2y = 23$ **12.** $x + 4y = -36$

Consider the linear equation $y = 3x + b$.

13. Choose several different positive and negative values for b. Graph each equation in the standard viewing window. See students' work.

14. For which values of b is the complete graph in the standard viewing window? $-10 \leq b \leq 10$

15. How is the value of b related to the y-intercept of the graph of $y = 3x + b$? b is the y-intercept of the graph.

168 Chapter 3 Linear Functions

Algebra Lab: Rate of Change of a Linear Function

IL Math Online glencoe.com
Math *in Motion*, Animation

Objective
Investigate the steepness of a line using concrete models.

IL Learning Standards
7.B.4 Estimate and measure the magnitude and directions of physical quantities using rulers, protractors and other scientific instruments including timers, calculators and computers.

In mathematics, you can measure the steepness of a line using a ratio.

Set Up the Lab

- Stack three books on your desk.
- Lean a ruler on the books to create a ramp.
- Tape the ruler to the desk.
- Measure the **rise** and the **run**. Record your data in a table like the one at the right.
- Calculate and record the ratio $\frac{\text{rise}}{\text{run}}$.

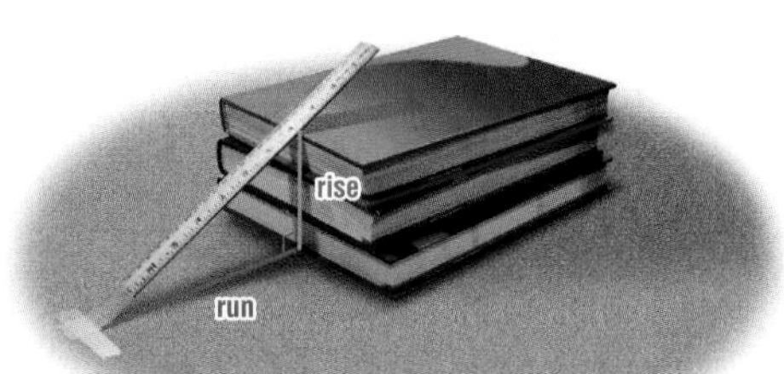

rise	run	$\frac{\text{rise}}{\text{run}}$

ACTIVITY

Step 1

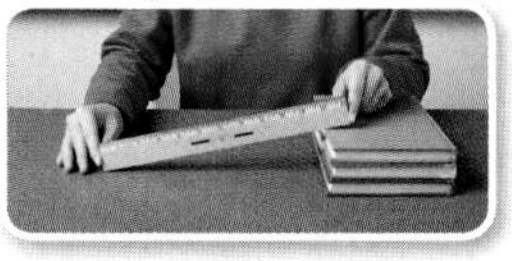

Move the books to make the ramp steeper. Measure and record the **rise** and the **run**. Calculate and record $\frac{\text{rise}}{\text{run}}$.

Step 2

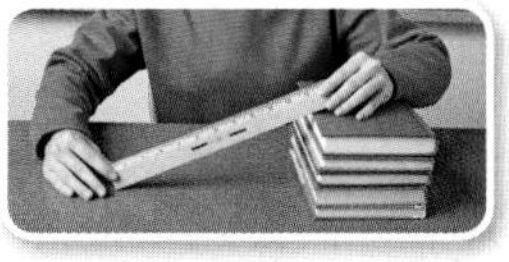

Add books to the stack to make the ramp even steeper. Measure, calculate, and record your data in the table.

Analyze the Results

1. Examine the ratios you recorded. How did they change as the ramp became steeper? **The ratios increased.**

2. **MAKE A PREDICTION** Suppose you want to construct a skateboard ramp that is not as steep as the one shown at the left. List three different sets of $\frac{\text{rise}}{\text{run}}$ measurements that will result in a less steep ramp. Verify your predictions by calculating the ratio $\frac{\text{rise}}{\text{run}}$ for each ramp. **Answers will vary.**

$m = \frac{18}{24} = \frac{3}{4}$

3. Copy the coordinate graph and draw a line through the origin with a $\frac{\text{rise}}{\text{run}}$ ratio greater than the original line. Then draw a line through the origin with a ratio less than that of the original line. Explain using the words *rise* and *run* why the lines you drew have a ratio greater or less than the original line. **Answers will vary.**

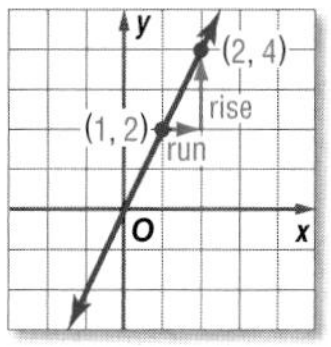

4. We have seen what happens on the graph as the $\frac{\text{rise}}{\text{run}}$ ratio gets closer to zero. What would you predict will happen when the ratio is zero? Explain your reasoning. Give an example to support your prediction.

4. **Sample answer: If the ratio is zero, the rise must be zero. So, the line does not rise and would be horizontal. The line through (0, 2) and (2, 2) has a ratio of 0 and is horizontal.**

Lesson Notes

1 FOCUS

Objective Investigate the steepness of a line using concrete materials.

Materials for Each Group

- 2 rulers
- 5 books
- a large piece of tape
- grid paper

Easy to Make Manipulatives

Teaching Algebra with Manipulatives

Template for grid paper, p. 1

2 TEACH

Working in Cooperative Groups

Put students in groups of three or four, mixing abilities. Have groups complete the Activity and Exercise 1.

Ask:

- Which measurement, rise or run, changes as you move the books? run
- In Step 2, which measurement changes when you add books? rise

Practice Have students complete Exercises 2 and 3.

3 ASSESS

Formative Assessment

Use Exercise 4 to assess whether students comprehend how to find slope from a coordinate graph.

From Concrete to Abstract

Give students a piece of uncooked spaghetti and a coordinate grid. Have them place the spaghetti on the grid and record the slope of the represented line. Repeat this activity five times.

Extending the Concept

Ask:

- If the run is not zero, is the $\frac{\text{rise}}{\text{run}}$ always a fraction? $\frac{\text{rise}}{\text{run}}$ can always be expressed as a fraction, even if it appears to be an integer.
- If the run is not zero, can $\frac{\text{rise}}{\text{run}}$ be negative? When? Yes; the $\frac{\text{rise}}{\text{run}}$ is negative when the line slopes down from left to right.

3-3 Lesson Notes

1 FOCUS

Vertical Alignment

Before Lesson 3-3
Graph ordered pairs in the coordinate plane.

Lesson 3-3
Use rate of change to solve problems.
Find the slope of a line.

After Lesson 3-3
Write, graph, and solve direct variation equations.

2 TEACH

Scaffolding Questions

Have students read the *Why?* section of the lesson.

Ask:

- How can you write the rate of change of the ride? $\frac{\text{change in distance}}{\text{change in time}}$
- What might the ratio be for a ride with a rate of change of 2? Sample answers: $\frac{10}{5}, \frac{6}{3}, \frac{2}{1}$
- Which has a steeper waterchute, a ride with a rate of change of $\frac{1}{2}$ or a ride with a rate of change of $\frac{5}{2}$? Why? $\frac{5}{2}$, because the change in distance is greater than in $\frac{1}{2}$ and both have the same change in time.

3-3 Rate of Change and Slope

Then
You graphed ordered pairs in the coordinate plane. (Lesson 1-6)

Now
- Use rate of change to solve problems.
- Find the slope of a line.

IL Learning Standards
7.B.4 Estimate and measure the magnitude and directions of physical quantities using rulers, protractors and other scientific instruments including timers, calculators and computers.

New Vocabulary
rate of change
slope

IL Math Online
glencoe.com
- Extra Examples
- Personal Tutor
- Self-Check Quiz
- Homework Help

Why?

The Daredevil Drop at Wet 'n Wild Emerald Pointe in Greensboro, North Carolina, is a thrilling ride that drops you 76 feet down a steep water chute. The *rate of change* of the ride describes how far a rider goes over the course of time on the ride.

Rate of Change **Rate of change** is a ratio that describes, on average, how much one quantity changes with respect to a change in another quantity.

Key Concept Rate of Change — For Your FOLDABLE

If x is the independent variable and y is the dependent variable, then

$$\text{rate of change} = \frac{\text{change in } y}{\text{change in } x}.$$

Real-World EXAMPLE 1 Find Rate of Change

ENTERTAINMENT **Use the table to find the rate of change. Then explain its meaning.**

Number of Computer Games	Total Cost ($)
x	y
2	78
4	156
6	234

$$\begin{aligned}\text{rate of change} &= \frac{\text{change in } y}{\text{change in } x} \begin{matrix}\leftarrow \textbf{dollars}\\ \leftarrow \textbf{games}\end{matrix}\\ &= \frac{\text{change in cost}}{\text{change in number of games}}\\ &= \frac{156-78}{4-2}\\ &= \frac{78}{2} \text{ or } \frac{39}{1}\end{aligned}$$

The rate of change is $\frac{39}{1}$. This means that each game costs $39.

Check Your Progress

1. **REMODELING** The table shows how the tiled surface area changes with the number of floor tiles.
   A. Find the rate of change. 16
   B. Explain the meaning of the rate of change. 16 in^2 of surface is tiled for each floor tile that is used.

Number of Floor Tiles	Area of Tiled Surface (in^2)
x	y
3	48
6	96
9	144

Personal Tutor glencoe.com

Lesson 3-3 Resources

Resource	Approaching-Level	On-Level	Beyond-Level	English Learners
Teacher Edition	• Differentiated Instruction, pp. 173	• Differentiated Instruction, pp. 173, 174, 178	• Differentiated Instruction, pp. 173, 174, 178	
Chapter Resource Masters	• Study Guide and Intervention, pp. 18–19 • Skills Practice and Practice, pp. 20–21 • Word Problem Practice, p. 22	• Study Guide and Intervention, pp. 18–19 • Skills Practice and Practice, pp. 20–21 • Word Problem Practice, p. 22 • Enrichment, p. 23	• Practice, p. 21 • Word Problem Practice, p. 22 • Enrichment, p. 23	• Study Guide and Intervention, pp. 18–19 • Skills Practice, p. 20 • Practice, p. 21
Transparencies	• 5-Minute Check Transparency 3-3	• 5-Minute Check Transparency 3-3	• 5-Minute Check Transparency 3-3	• 5-Minute Check Transparency 3-3
Other	• Study Notebook • Teaching Algebra with Manipulatives	• Study Notebook • Teaching Algebra with Manipulatives	• Study Notebook	• Study Notebook • Teaching Algebra with Manipulatives

StudyTip

Rate A positive rate of change indicates an increase over time. A negative rate of change indicates that a quantity is decreasing.

So far, you have seen rates of change that are *constant*. Many real-world situations involve rates of change that are not constant.

Real-World EXAMPLE 2 Variable Rate of Change

AMUSEMENT PARKS The graph shows the number of people who visited U.S. theme parks in recent years.

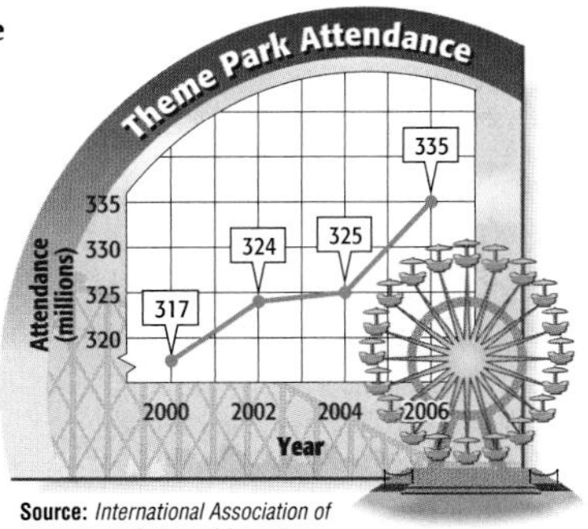

Source: *International Association of Amusement Parks and Attractions*

a. Find the rates of change for 2000–2002 and 2002–2004.

2000–2002:

$\frac{\text{change in attendance}}{\text{change in time}} = \frac{324 - 317}{2002 - 2000}$ ← people ← years **Substitute.**

$= \frac{7}{2}$ or 3.5 **Simplify.**

Over this 2-year period, attendance increased by 7 million, for a rate of change of 3.5 million per year.

2002–2004:

$\frac{\text{change in attendance}}{\text{change in time}} = \frac{328 - 324}{2004 - 2002}$ **Substitute.**

$= \frac{4}{2}$ or 2 **Simplify.**

Over this 2-year period, attendance increased by 4 million, for a rate of change of 2 million per year.

b. Explain the meaning of the rate of change in each case.

For 2000–2002, on average, 3.5 million more people went to a theme park each year than the last.

For 2002–2004, on average, 2 million more people attended theme parks each year than the last.

c. How are the different rates of change shown on the graph?

There is a greater vertical change for 2000–2002 than for 2002–2004. Therefore, the section of the graph for 2000–2002 is steeper.

Check Your Progress 2002–2004; Attendance increased by 2 million per year.

2. Refer to the graph above. Without calculating, find the 2-year period that has the least rate of change. Then calculate to verify your answer.

Personal Tutor glencoe.com

A rate of change is constant for a function when the rate of change is the same between any pair of points on the graph of the function. Linear functions have a constant rate of change.

Rate of Change

Example 1 shows how to find the rate of change given a table of values for a real-world situation. **Example 2** shows how to describe the rate of change for a real-world problem in which the difference between two *y*-values divided by the difference between their corresponding *x*-values is not constant. **Example 3** shows how to determine whether a function is linear or nonlinear.

Formative Assessment

Use the Check Your Progress exercises after each Example to determine students' understanding of concepts.

Additional Example

1 **DRIVING TIME** Use the table to find the rate of change. Then explain its meaning.

Time Driving (h)	Distance Traveled (mi)
x	*y*
2	76
4	152
6	228

$\frac{38}{1}$; this means the car is traveling at a rate of 38 miles per hour.

Additional Examples also in Interactive Classroom PowerPoint® Presentations

IWB INTERACTIVE WHITEBOARD READY

Tips for New Teachers

Sense-Making Explain to students that linear functions have a constant rate of change or slope, regardless of which pair of points is used in the calculation, due to the properties of similar triangles. Demonstrate the idea by calculating the slopes of the sides of two triangles that can be formed from a line. Assure students that they will learn about similar triangles in Lesson 10-7.

Additional Examples

2 **TRAVEL** The graph below shows the number of U.S. passports issued in 2002, 2004, and 2006.

U.S. Passports Issued

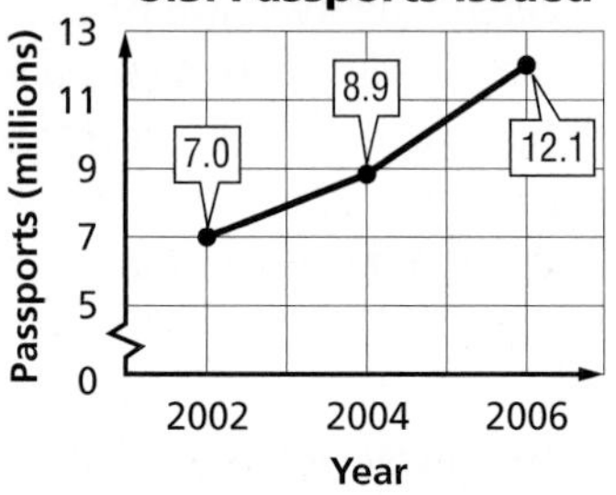

a. Find the rates of change for 2002–2004 and 2004–2006. 950,000/yr; 1,600,000/yr

b. Explain the meaning of the rate of change in each case. For 2002–2004, there was an average annual increase of 950,000 passports issued. Between 2004 and 2006, there was an average yearly increase of 1,600,000 passports issued.

c. How are the different rates of change shown on the graph? There is a greater vertical change for 2004–2006 than for 2002–2004. Therefore, the section of the graph for 2004–2006 is steeper.

3 Determine whether each function is linear. Explain.

a.

x	y
1	6
2	12
3	18
4	24

Yes; the rate of change is constant.

b.

x	y
−10	5
−2	1
6	−4
14	−10

No; the rate of change is not constant.

StudyTip

Linear or Nonlinear Function? Notice that the changes in x and y are not the same. For the rate of change to be linear, the change in x-values must be constant and the change in y-values must be constant.

EXAMPLE 3 Constant Rates of Change

Determine whether each function is linear. Explain.

a.

x	y
1	−6
4	−8
7	−10
10	−12
13	−14

x	y	rate of change
1	−6	
4	−8	$\frac{-8-(-6)}{4-1}$ or $-\frac{2}{3}$
7	−10	$\frac{-10-(-8)}{7-4}$ or $-\frac{2}{3}$
10	−12	$\frac{-12-(-10)}{10-7}$ or $-\frac{2}{3}$
13	−14	$\frac{-14-(-12)}{13-10}$ or $-\frac{2}{3}$

The rate of change is constant. Thus, the function is linear.

b.

x	y
−3	10
−1	12
1	16
3	18
5	22

x	y	rate of change
−3	10	
−1	12	$\frac{12-10}{-1-(-3)}$ or 1
1	16	$\frac{16-12}{1-(-1)}$ or 2
3	18	$\frac{18-16}{3-1}$ or 1
5	22	$\frac{22-18}{5-3}$ or 2

This rate of change is not constant. Thus, the function is not linear.

Check Your Progress

3A.

x	y
−3	11
−2	15
−1	19
1	23
2	27

No; there is not a constant rate of change.

3B.

x	y
12	−4
9	1
6	6
3	11
0	16

Yes; the rate of change is constant.

Personal Tutor glencoe.com

Find Slope The **slope** of a nonvertical line is the ratio of the change in the y-coordinates (rise) to the change in the x-coordinates (run) as you move from one point to another.

It can be used to describe a rate of change. Slope describes how steep a line is. The greater the absolute value of the slope, the steeper the line.

The graph shows a line that passes through (−1, 3) and (2, −2).

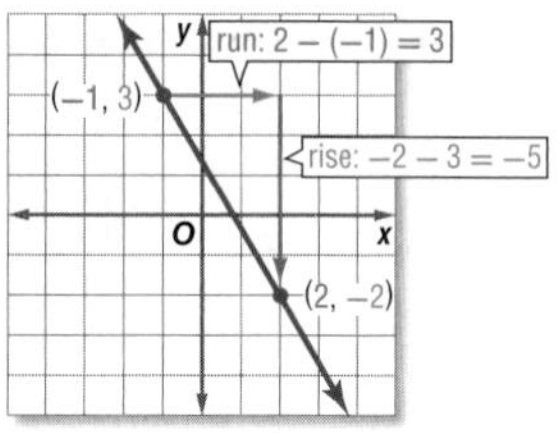

$$\text{slope} = \frac{\text{rise}}{\text{run}}$$

$$= \frac{\text{change in } y\text{-coordinates}}{\text{change in } x\text{-coordinates}}$$

$$= \frac{-2-3}{2-(-1)} \text{ or } -\frac{5}{3}$$

So, the slope of the line is $-\frac{5}{3}$.

Because a linear function has a constant rate of change, any two points on a nonvertical line can be used to determine its slope.

172 **Chapter 3** Linear Functions

ReadingMath

Subscripts y_1 is read as *y sub one* and x_2 is read as *x sub two*. The 1 and 2 are subscripts and refer to the first and second point to which the *x*- and *y*-values correspond.

Key Concept — Slope

For Your FOLDABLE

Words The slope of a nonvertical line is the ratio of the rise to the run.

Symbols The slope m of a nonvertical line through any two points, (x_1, y_1) and (x_2, y_2), can be found as follows.

$$m = \frac{y_2 - y_1}{x_2 - x_1} \begin{array}{l} \leftarrow \text{change in } y \\ \leftarrow \text{change in } x \end{array}$$

Graph

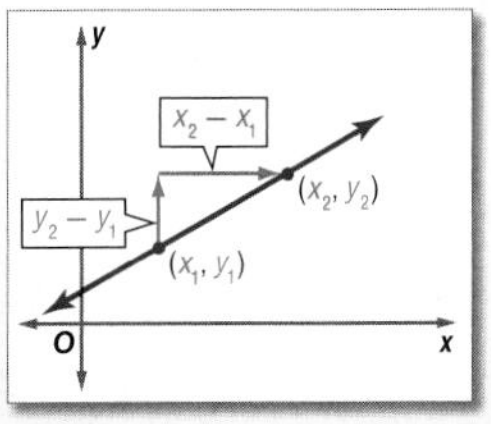

The slope of a line can be positive, negative, zero, or undefined. If the line is not horizontal or vertical, then the slope is either positive or negative.

EXAMPLE 4 Positive, Negative, and Zero Slope

Find the slope of a line that passes through each pair of points.

a. (−2, 0) and (1, 5)

$m = \frac{y_2 - y_1}{x_2 - x_1}$ **rise/run**

$= \frac{5 - 0}{1 - (-2)}$ **$(-2, 0) = (x_1, y_1)$ and $(1, 5) = (x_2, y_2)$**

$= \frac{5}{3}$ **Simplify.**

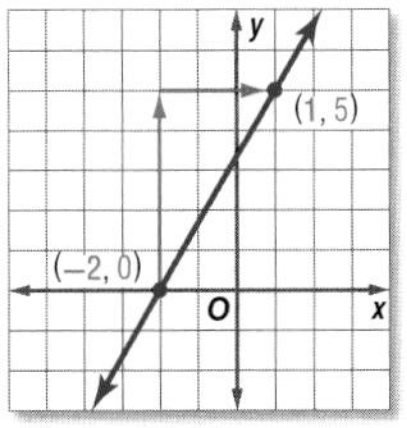

b. (−3, 4) and (2, −3)

$m = \frac{y_2 - y_1}{x_2 - x_1}$ **rise/run**

$= \frac{-3 - 4}{2 - (-3)}$ **$(-3, 4) = (x_1, y_1)$ and $(2, -3) = (x_2, y_2)$**

$= \frac{-7}{5}$ or $-\frac{7}{5}$ **Simplify.**

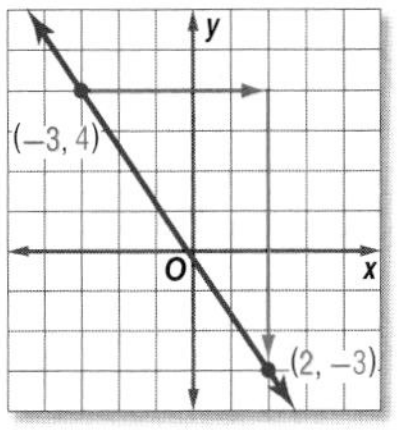

c. (−3, −1) and (2, −1)

$m = \frac{y_2 - y_1}{x_2 - x_1}$ **rise/run**

$= \frac{-1 - (-1)}{2 - (-3)}$ **Substitute.**

$= \frac{0}{2}$ or 0 **Simplify.**

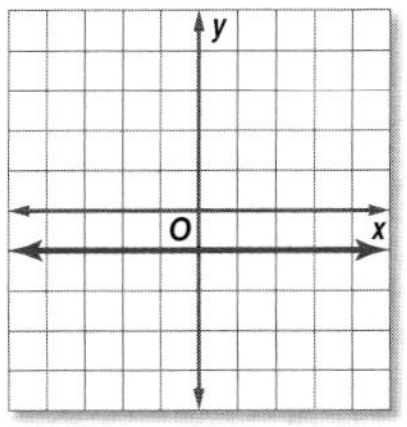

Watch Out!

Order Be careful not to transpose the order of the *x*-values or the *y*-values.

Check Your Progress

Find the slope of the line that passes through each pair of points.

4A. (3, 6), (4, 8) 2 **4B.** (−4, −2), (0, −2) 0 **4C.** (−4, 2), (−2, 10) 4

4D. (6, 7), (−2, 7) 0 **4E.** (−2, 2), (−6, 4) $-\frac{1}{2}$ **4F.** (4, 3), (−1, 11) $-\frac{8}{5}$

Personal Tutor glencoe.com

Differentiated Instruction

AL OL BL

If students automatically assume that the left-most point has to be (x_1, y_1) and the point farther right is (x_2, y_2),

Then explain that the designation of (x_1, y_1) and (x_2, y_2) is arbitrary. Write pairs of points on index cards. Give one card to each student. Have them find the slope both ways. Then ask which way made the subtraction easier.

Find Slope

Examples 4 and 5 show the four types possible when we try to find the slope of a line. **Example 6** shows how to use algebraic manipulation to find a missing coordinate when the slope is known.

Focus on Mathematical Content

Zero Slope A slope of 0 does not mean there is no slope. It means that the line has no steepness—that is, the line is horizontal.

Additional Example

4 Find the slope of the line that passes through each pair of points.

a. (−3, 2) and (5, 5) $\frac{3}{8}$

b. (−3, −4) and (−2, −8) −4

c. (−3, 4) and (4, 4) 0

Tips for New Teachers

Horizontal Lines After reviewing Example 4c, ask students how they would determine whether two points lie on a horizontal line without graphing the points.

Focus on Mathematical Content

Slope and Improper Fractions Slope is usually expressed as a fraction or an integer because it gives information about the direction of the line. A mixed number may not easily reveal that information.

TEACH with TECH

AUDIO RECORDING Have students work in groups. Give each group graphs of several lines, without labels. Have students verbally describe real-world situations that could be shown by each graph.

Focus on Mathematical Content

Undefined Slope Undefined slope is not the same as slope of 0. The slope of a vertical line is undefined because the formula yields an expression with 0 as the denominator, and division by zero is undefined.

Additional Examples

5 Find the slope of the line that passes through (−2, −4) and (−2, 3). undefined

6 Find the value of *r* so that the line through (6, 3) and (*r*, 2) has a slope of $\frac{1}{2}$. 4

Watch Out!

Preventing Errors As students work through Example 6, watch for those who try to find the cross product mentally and forget to multiply both *r* and −4 by 3.

StudyTip

Zero and Undefined Slopes If the change in *y*-values is 0, then the graph of the line is horizontal. If the change in *x*-values is 0, then the slope is undefined. This graph is a vertical line.

EXAMPLE 5 Undefined Slope

Find the slope of the line that passes through (−2, 4) and (−2, −3).

$m = \frac{y_2 - y_1}{x_2 - x_1}$ **$\frac{\text{rise}}{\text{run}}$**

$= \frac{-3 - 4}{-2 - (-2)}$ **Substitute.**

$= \frac{-7}{0}$ or undefined **Simplify.**

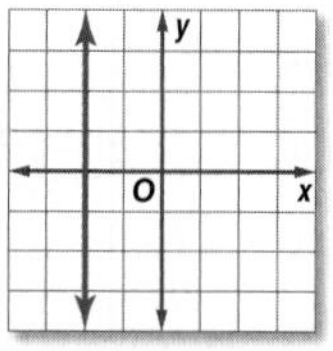

Check Your Progress

Find the slope of the line that passes through each pair of points.

5A. (6, 3), (6, 7) undefined

5B. (−3, 2), (−3, −1) undefined

Personal Tutor glencoe.com

The graphs of lines with different slopes are summarized below.

Concept Summary Slope

For Your FOLDABLE

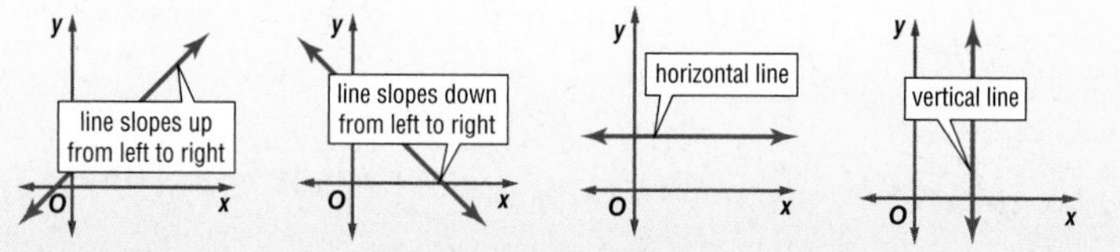

Sometimes you are given the slope and must find a missing coordinate.

EXAMPLE 6 Find Coordinates Given the Slope

Find the value of *r* so that the line through (1, 4) and (−5, *r*) has a slope of $\frac{1}{3}$.

$m = \frac{y_2 - y_1}{x_2 - x_1}$ **Slope Formula**

$\frac{1}{3} = \frac{r - 4}{-5 - 1}$ **Let (1, 4) = (x_1, y_1) and (−5, *r*) = (x_2, y_2).**

$\frac{1}{3} = \frac{r - 4}{-6}$ **Subtract.**

$3(r - 4) = 1(-6)$ **Find the cross products.**

$3r - 12 = -6$ **Distributive Property.**

$3r = 6$ **Add 12 to each side and simplify.**

$r = 2$ **Divide each side by 3 and simplify.**

So, the line goes through (−5, 2).

Check Your Progress

Find the value of *r* so the line that passes through each pair of points has the given slope.

6A. (−2, 6), (*r*, −4); $m = -5$ 0

6B. (*r*, −6), (5, −8); $m = -8$ 4.75

Personal Tutor glencoe.com

Differentiated Instruction OL BL

Extension Provide students with opportunities to analyze slope by giving contexts to graphs where the slope varies from point to point. Students can explore why graphs increase or decrease rapidly, steadily or slowly.

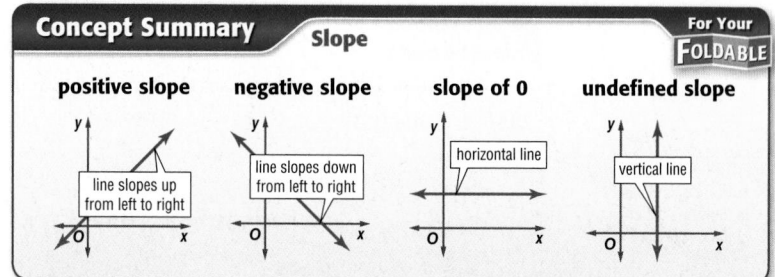

Check Your Understanding

Example 1 p. 170

Find the rate of change represented in each table or graph.

1. 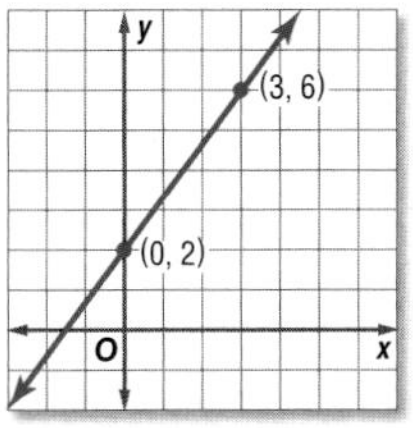

$\frac{4}{3}$

2. 4

x	y
3	−6
5	2
7	10
9	18
11	26

Example 2 p. 171

3. **SPORTS** Refer to the graph at the right.

a. Find the rate of change of prices from 2002 to 2004. Explain the meaning of the rate of change.

b. Without calculating, find a two-year period that had a greater rate of change than 2002–2004. Explain.

c. Between which years would you guess the new stadium was built? Explain your reasoning. Sample answer: 1998–2000; Ticket prices show a sharp increase.

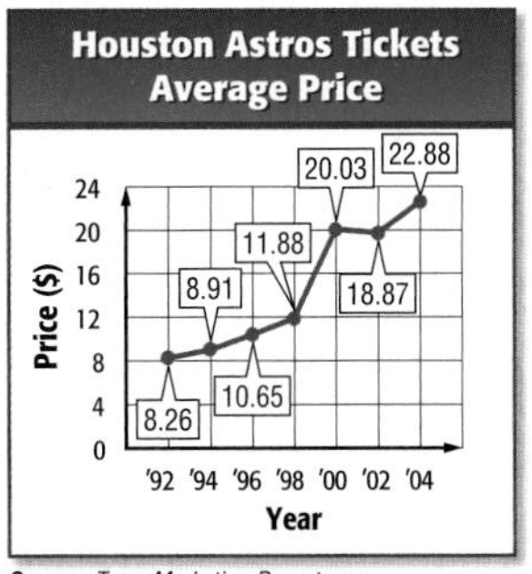

Source: *Team Marketing Report*

3a. 2.005; There was an average increase in ticket price of $2.005 per year.
3b. Sample answer: 1998–2000; A steeper segment means a greater rate of change.
4. Yes; as the *x*-values increase by a constant amount, so do the corresponding *y*-values.

Example 3 p. 172

Determine whether each function is linear. Write *yes* or *no*. Explain.

4.

x	−7	−4	−1	2	5
y	5	4	3	2	1

5.

x	8	12	16	20	24
y	7	5	3	0	−2

No; the *y*-values do not decrease by a constant amount.

Examples 4 and 5 pp. 173–174

Find the slope of the line that passes through each pair of points.

6. (5, 3), (6, 9) 6
7. (−4, 3), (−2, 1) −1
8. (6, −2), (8, 3) $\frac{5}{2}$
9. (1, 10), (−8, 3) $\frac{7}{9}$
10. (−3, 7), (−3, 4) undefined
11. (5, 2), (−6, 2) 0

Example 6 p. 174

Find the value of *r* so the line that passes through each pair of points has the given slope.

12. $(-4, r), (-8, 3), m = -5$ −17
13. $(5, 2), (-7, r), m = \frac{5}{6}$ −8

Practice and Problem Solving

● = **Step-by-Step Solutions** begin on page R12. **Extra Practice** begins on page 815.

Example 1 p. 170

Find the rate of change represented in each table or graph.

14. $\frac{1}{5}$

x	y
5	2
10	3
15	4
20	5

15. −6

x	y
1	15
2	9
3	3
4	−3

3 PRACTICE

Formative Assessment

Use Exercises 1–13 to check for understanding.

Use the chart at the bottom of this page to customize assignments for your students.

Tips for New Teachers

Pacing Because slope is an important concept throughout this chapter, students should have a good understanding of it. If you are uncertain that your students have mastered the concept of slope, consider spending an extra day on this lesson.

Exercise Alert

Grid Paper For Exercises 46, 47, and 57–59, students will need grid paper.

Differentiated Homework Options

Level	Assignment	Two-Day Option	
AL Basic	14–39, 48–49, 51–68	15–39 odd, 53–56	14–38 even, 48, 49, 51–68
OL Core	15–39 odd, 40–49, 51–68	14–39, 53–56	40–49, 51–52, 57–68
BL Advanced	40–62, (optional: 63–68)		

Lesson 3-3 Rate of Change and Slope 175

Watch Out!

Find the Error For Exercise 52, if students have difficulty substituting the correct coordinates into the slope formula, show them the following diagram.

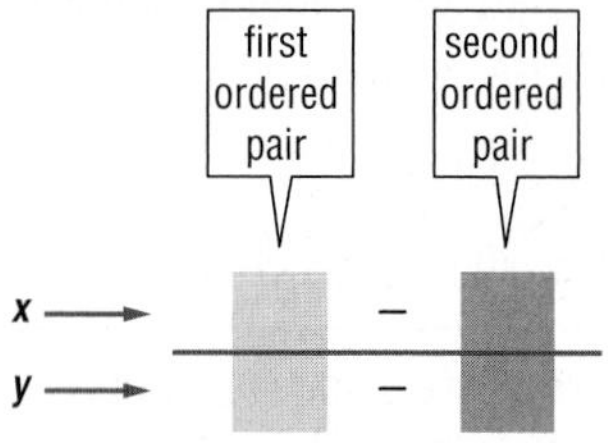

Additional Answers

46a.

Time (months)	Hair Length (in.)
0	8
3	9
6	10

46b. May's Hair

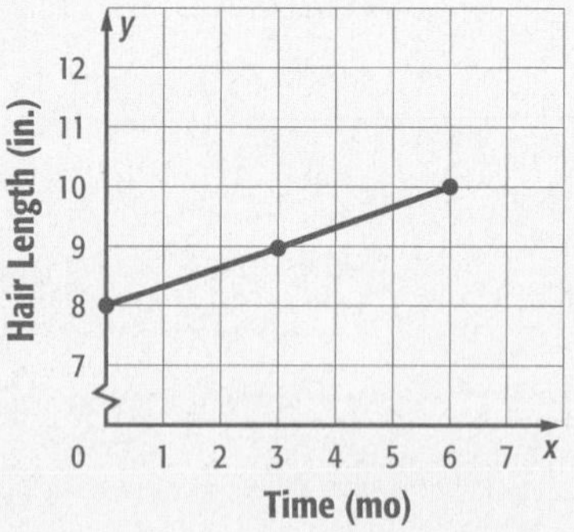

46c. $\frac{1}{3}$; a rate of growth of 1 inch every 3 months or $\frac{1}{3}$ inch per month

47a. Michael Redd's PPG

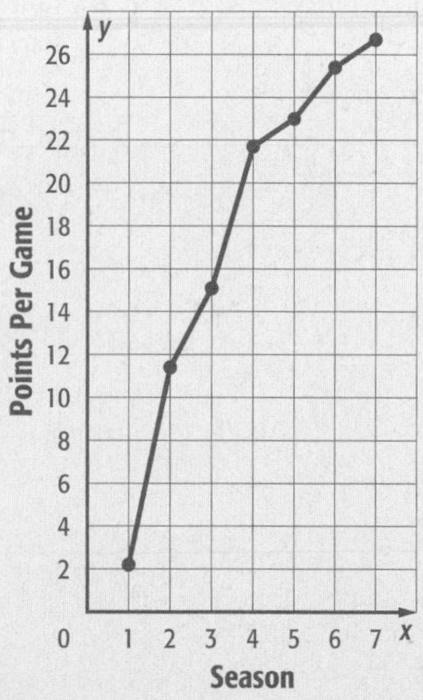

Example 1 p. 170

18. 1812.5; There was an average increase of 1812.5 women per year competing in triathlons.

19a. Sample answer: $p = -1811.67t + 19548.30$

Find the rate of change represented in each table or graph.

16. $-\frac{4}{3}$

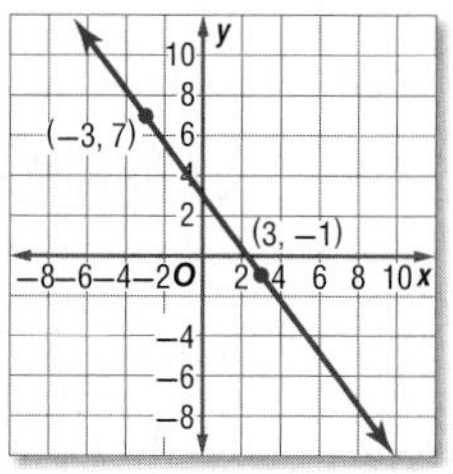

17. $\frac{1}{2}$

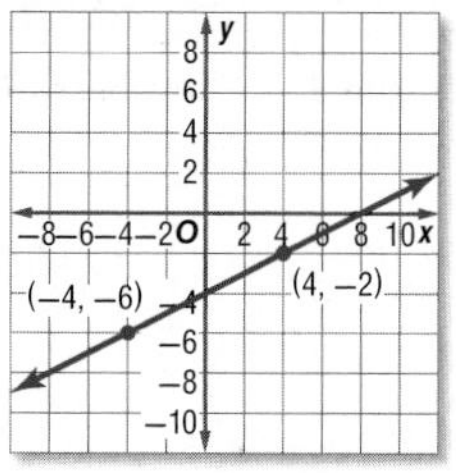

Example 2 p. 171

19b. The car value depreciates by $1811.67 each year.

18. SPORTS What was the annual rate of change from 1995 to 2003 for women competing in triathlons? Explain the meaning of the rate of change.

Year	Number of Women
1995	4600
2003	19,100

20. Yes; both the *x*-values and the *y*-values change at a constant rate.

21. No; the *x*-values do not increase at a constant rate.

19. RETAIL The average retail price in the spring of 2008 for a used car is shown in the table at the right.

Age (years)	Value ($)
2	15,924.96
3	14,113.29

a. Write a linear function to model the price of the car with respect to age.

b. Interpret the meaning of the slope of the line.

c. Assuming a constant rate of change predict the average retail price for a 7-year-old car. **$6866.61**

Example 3 p. 172

22. No; the *y*-values do not decrease at a constant rate.

23. Yes; both the *x*-values and the *y*-values increase at a constant rate.

Determine whether each function is linear. Write *yes* or *no*. Explain.

20.

x	4	2	0	−2	−4
y	−1	1	3	5	7

21.

x	−7	−5	−3	−1	0
y	11	14	17	20	23

22.

x	−0.2	0	0.2	0.4	0.6
y	0.7	0.4	0.1	0.3	0.6

23.

x	$\frac{1}{2}$	$\frac{3}{2}$	$\frac{5}{2}$	$\frac{7}{2}$	$\frac{9}{2}$
y	$\frac{1}{2}$	1	$\frac{3}{2}$	2	$\frac{5}{2}$

Examples 4 and 5 pp. 173–174

27. undefined

33. undefined

34. $-\frac{14}{15}$

Find the slope of the line that passes through each pair of points.

24. (4, 3), (−1, 6) $-\frac{3}{5}$

25. (8, −2), (1, 1) $-\frac{3}{7}$

26. (2, 2), (−2, −2) **1**

27. (6, −10), (6, 14)

28. (5, −4), (9, −4) **0**

29. (11, 7), (−6, 2) $\frac{5}{17}$

30. (−3, 5), (3, 6) $\frac{1}{6}$

31. (−3, 2), (7, 2) **0**

32. (8, 10), (−4, −6) $\frac{4}{3}$

33. (−8, 6), (−8, 4)

34. (−12, 15), (18, −13)

35. (−8, −15), (−2, 5) $\frac{10}{3}$

Example 6 p. 174

Find the value of *r* so the line that passes through each pair of points has the given slope.

36. (12, 10), (−2, *r*), $m = -4$ **66**

37. (*r*, −5), (3, 13), $m = 8$ $\frac{3}{4}$

38. (3, 5), (−3, *r*), $m = \frac{3}{4}$ $\frac{1}{2}$

39. (−2, 8), (*r*, 4), $m = -\frac{1}{2}$ **6**

B **ESTIMATION** Use a ruler to estimate the slope of each object.

40.

Sample answer: about −0.5

41.

Sample answer: about 0.5

47b. Season 1 to Season 2; It is the steepest part of the graph.

47c. The rate of change was much more dramatic or steeper in the first four years, whereas it leveled off in the last few years.

48. The difference in the *x*-values is always 0, and division by 0 is undefined.

42. **DRIVING** When driving up a certain hill, you rise 15 feet for every 1000 feet you drive forward. What is the slope of the road? $\frac{3}{200}$

Find the slope of the line that passes through each pair of points.

43. $\frac{15}{4}$

x	y
4.5	−1
5.3	2

44. undefined

x	y
0.75	1
0.75	−1

45. $-\frac{2}{3}$

x	y
$2\frac{1}{2}$	$-1\frac{1}{2}$
$-\frac{1}{2}$	$\frac{1}{2}$

46. **GROWTH RATE** May's hair was 8 inches long. In three months, it grew another inch at a steady rate. Assume that her hair growth continues at the same rate.
   a. Make a table that shows May's hair length for each of the three months and for the next three months. **a–c. See margin.**
   b. Draw a graph showing the relationship between May's hair length and time in months.
   c. What is the slope of the graph? What does it represent?

Real-World Link

You have about 100,000 hairs on your head. Often hair grows faster in warm weather.

Source: HairBoutique

47. **BASKETBALL** The table shown below shows the average points per game (PPG) Michael Redd, of the NBA's Milwaukee Bucks, has scored each season of his career.

Season	2000–01	2001–02	2002–03	2003–04	2004–05	2005–06	2006–07
PPG	2.2	11.4	15.1	21.7	23.0	25.4	26.7

   a. Make a graph of the data. Connect each pair of adjacent points with a line. **See margin.**
   b. Use the graph to determine in which period Michael Redd's PPG increased the fastest. Explain your reasoning. **See margin.**
   c. Discuss the difference in the rate of change from the 2000–01 through the 2003–04 seasons and from the 2003–04 through the 2006–07 seasons. **See margin.**

H.O.T. Problems
Use Higher-Order Thinking Skills

48. **REASONING** Why does the Slope Formula not work for vertical lines? Explain. **See margin.**

49. **OPEN ENDED** Use what you know about rate of change to describe the function represented by the table.

Time (wk)	Height of Plant (in.)
4	9.0
6	13.5
8	18.0

50. **CHALLENGE** Find the value of d so the line that passes through (a, b) and (c, d) has a slope of $\frac{1}{2}$. $\frac{c - a + 2b}{2}$

51. **WRITING IN MATH** Explain how the rate of change and slope are related and how to find the slope of a line.

52. **FIND THE ERROR** Kyle and Luna are finding the value of x so the line that passes through $(10, x)$ and $(-2, 8)$ has a slope of $\frac{1}{4}$. Is either of them correct? Explain.

Kyle	Luna
$\frac{-2-10}{8-x} = \frac{1}{4}$	$\frac{8-x}{-2-10} = \frac{1}{4}$
$1(8-x) = 4(-12)$	$4(8-x) = 1(-12)$
$8 - x = -48$	$32 - 4x = -12$
$x = 56$	$x = 11$

49. See students' work. The rate of change is $2\frac{1}{4}$ inches of growth per week.

51. Sample answer: Slope can be used to describe a rate of change. Rate of change is a ratio that describes how much one quantity changes with respect to a change in another quantity. The slope of a line is also a ratio and it is the ratio of the change in the y-coordinates to the change in the x-coordinates.

52. Luna; Kyle divided the change in x by the change in y.

Study Guide and Intervention
CRM pp. 18–19 AL OL ELL

NAME ________ DATE ________ PERIOD ________

3-3 Study Guide and Intervention
Rate of Change and Slope

Rate of Change The **rate of change** tells, on average, how a quantity is changing over time.

Example POPULATION **The graph shows the population growth in China.**

a. **Find the rates of change for 1950–1975 and for 2000–2025.**

1950–1975: $\frac{\text{change in population}}{\text{change in time}} = \frac{0.93 - 0.55}{1975 - 1950} = \frac{0.38}{25}$ or 0.0152

2000–2025: $\frac{\text{change in population}}{\text{change in time}} = \frac{1.45 - 1.27}{2025 - 2000} = \frac{0.18}{25}$ or 0.0072

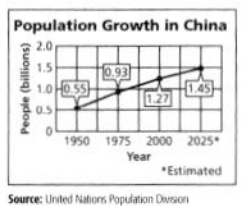

Source: United Nations Population Division

b. **Explain the meaning of the rate of change in each case.**
From 1950–1975, the growth was 0.0152 billion per year, or 15.2 million per year. From 2000–2025, the growth is expected to be 0.0072 billion per year, or 7.2 million per year.

c. **How are the different rates of change shown on the graph?**
There is a greater vertical change for 1950–1975 than for 2000–2025. Therefore, the section of the graph for 1950–1975 has a steeper slope.

Exercises

1. **LONGEVITY** The graph shows the predicted life expectancy for men and women born in a given year.
   a. Find the rates of change for women from 2000–2025 and 2025–2050. **0.16/yr, 0.12/yr**
   b. Find the rates of change for men from 2000–2025 and 2025–2050. **0.16/yr, 0.12/yr**
   c. Explain the meaning of your results in Exercises 1 and 2. **Both men and women increased their life expectancy at the same rates.**
   d. What pattern do you see in the increase with each 25-year period? **While life expectancy increases, it does not increase at a constant rate.**
   e. Make a prediction for the life expectancy for 2050–2075. Explain how you arrived at your prediction. **Sample answer: 89 for women and 83 for men; the decrease in rate from 2000–2025 to 2025–2050 is 0.04/yr. If the decrease in the rate remains the same, the change of rate for 2050–2075 might be 0.08/yr and 25(0.08) = 2 years of increase over the 25-year span.**

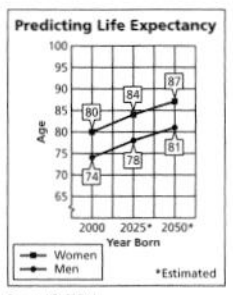

Source: USA TODAY

Practice
CRM p. 21 AL OL BL ELL

NAME ________ DATE ________ PERIOD ________

3-3 Practice
Rate of Change and Slope

Find the slope of the line that passes through each pair of points.

1. 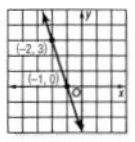

−3

2. 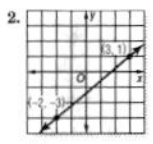

$\frac{4}{5}$

3. 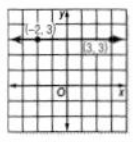

0

4. (6, 3), (7, −4) **−7**
5. (−9, −3), (−7, −5) **−1**
6. (6, −2), (5, −4) **2**
7. (7, −4), (4, 8) **−4**
8. (−7, 8), (−7, 5) **undefined**
9. (5, 9), (3, 9) **0**
10. (15, 2), (−6, 5) $-\frac{1}{7}$
11. (3, 9), (−2, 8) $\frac{1}{5}$
12. (−2, −5), (7, 8) $\frac{13}{9}$
13. (12, 10), (12, 5) **undefined**
14. (0.2, −0.9), (0.5, −0.9) **0**
15. $\left(\frac{7}{3}, \frac{4}{3}\right), \left(-\frac{1}{3}, \frac{2}{3}\right)$ $\frac{1}{4}$

Find the value of r so the line that passes through each pair of points has the given slope.

16. $(-2, r), (6, 7), m = \frac{1}{2}$ **3**
17. $(-4, 3), (r, 5), m = \frac{1}{4}$ **4**
18. $(-3, -4), (-5, r), m = -\frac{9}{2}$ **5**
19. $(-5, r), (1, 3), m = \frac{7}{6}$ **−4**
20. $(1, 4), (r, 5)$, m undefined **1**
21. $(-7, 2), (-8, r), m = -5$ **7**
22. $(r, 7), (11, 8), m = -\frac{1}{5}$ **16**
23. $(r, 2), (5, r), m = 0$ **2**

24. **ROOFING** The *pitch* of a roof is the number of feet the roof rises for each 12 feet horizontally. If a roof has a pitch of 8, what is its slope expressed as a positive number? $\frac{2}{3}$

25. **SALES** A daily newspaper had 12,125 subscribers when it began publication. Five years later it had 10,100 subscribers. What is the average yearly rate of change in the number of subscribers for the five-year period? **−405 subscribers per year**

Lesson 3-3

Word Problem Practice
CRM p. 22 AL OL BL ELL

NAME ________ DATE ________ PERIOD ________

3-3 Word Problem Practice
Rate of Change and Slope

1. **HIGHWAYS** Roadway signs such as the one below are used to warn drivers of an upcoming steep down grade that could lead to a dangerous situation. What is the grade, or slope, of the hill described on the sign? $\frac{2}{25}$

2. **AMUSEMENT PARKS** The SheiKra roller coaster at Busch Gardens in Tampa, Florida, features a 138-foot vertical drop. What is the slope of the coaster track at this part of the ride? Explain.
The slope is undefined because the drop is vertical.

3. **CENSUS** The table shows the population density for the state of Texas in various years. Find the average annual rate of change in the population density from 2000 to 2006.

Population Density	
Year	People Per Square Mile
1930	22.1
1960	36.4
1980	54.3
2000	79.6
2006	87.5

Source: Bureau of the Census, U.S. Dept. of Commerce

increased about 1.32 people per square mile

4. **REAL ESTATE** The median price of an existing single-family home in the United States was $195,200 in 2004. The median price had risen to $221,900 by 2006. Find the average annual rate of change in median home price from 2004 to 2006. **$13,350**

5. **COAL EXPORTS** The graph shows the annual coal exports from U.S. mines in millions of short tons.

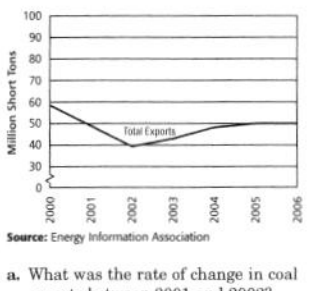

Source: Energy Information Association

   a. What was the rate of change in coal exports between 2001 and 2002?
   −9 million tons per year or $-\frac{9}{1}$
   b. How does the rate of change in coal exports from 2005 to 2006 compare to that of 2001 to 2002?
   In 2005–2006, the rate was 0 compared to $-\frac{9}{1}$ in 2001–2002.
   c. Explain the meaning of the part of the graph with a slope of zero.
   The slope indicates that there was no change in the amount of coal exported between 2005 and 2006.

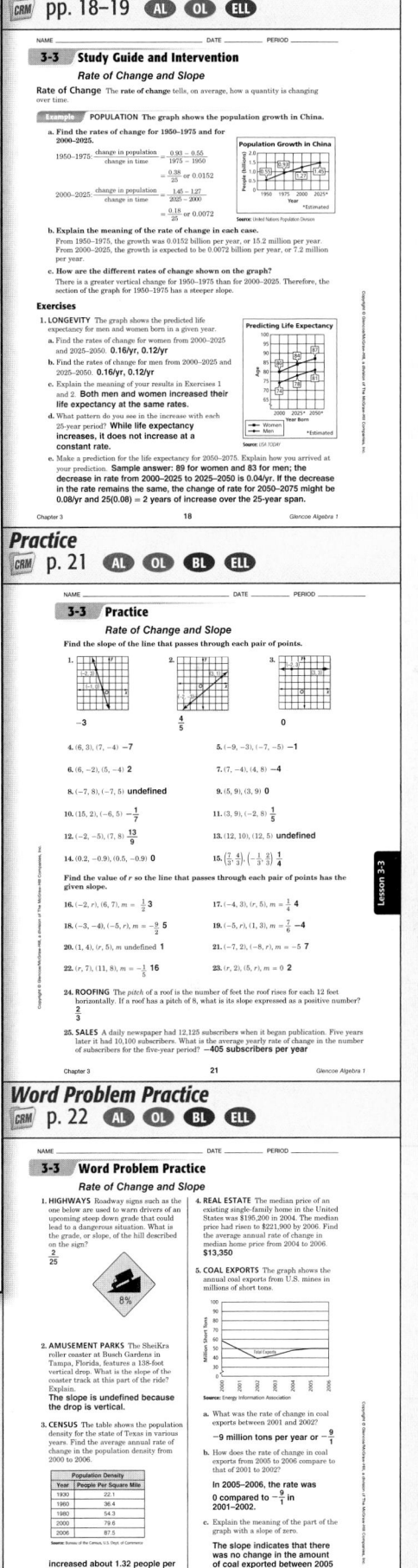

Enrichment
CRM p. 23 OL BL

NAME ________ DATE ________ PERIOD ________

3-3 Enrichment

Treasure Hunt with Slopes

Using the definition of slope, draw segments with the slopes listed below in order. A correct solution will trace the route to the treasure.

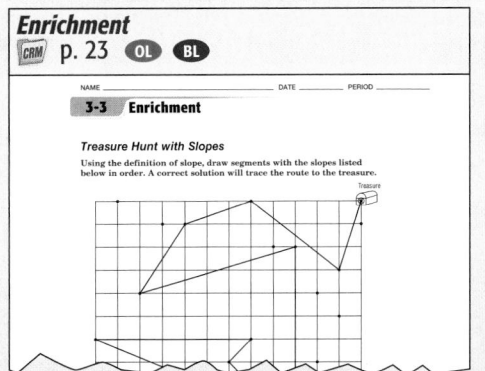

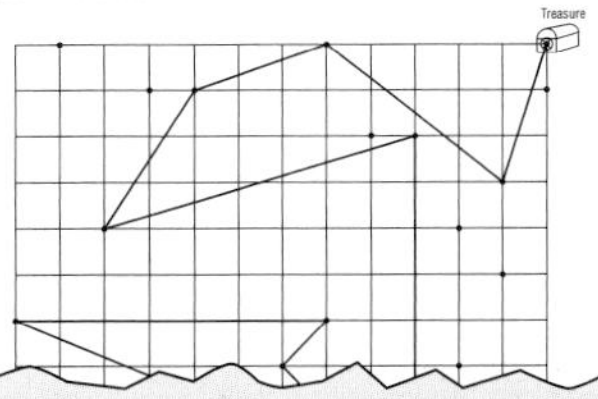

4 ASSESS

Ticket Out the Door Make several copies of five different lines graphed on a coordinate plane. Give one graph to each student. As the students leave the room, ask them to tell you the slopes of the lines they possess.

Formative Assessment

Check for student understanding of Lesson 3-3.

CRM Quiz 2, p. 45

Additional Answers (Mid-Chapter Quiz)

4.

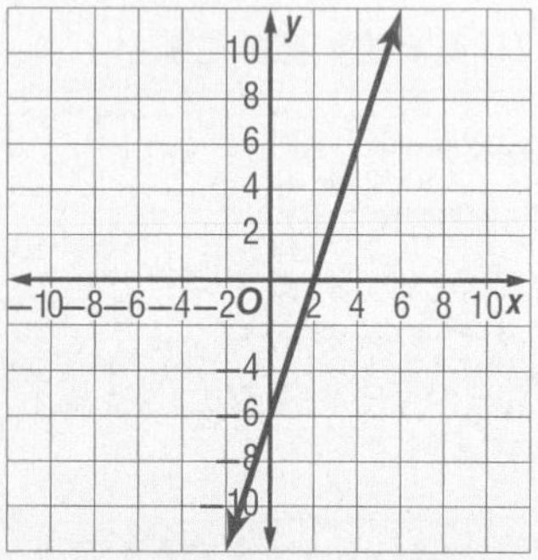

5.

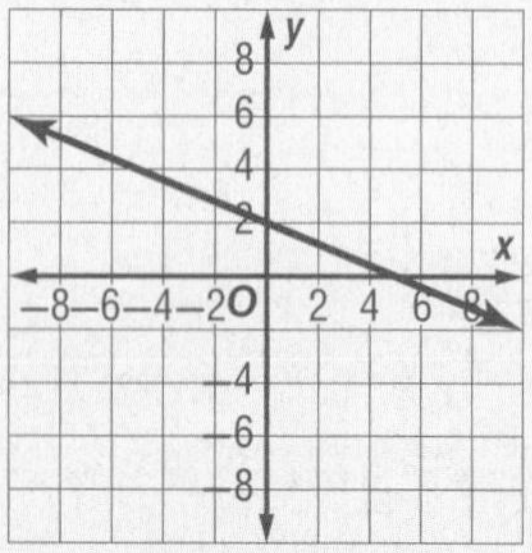

6.

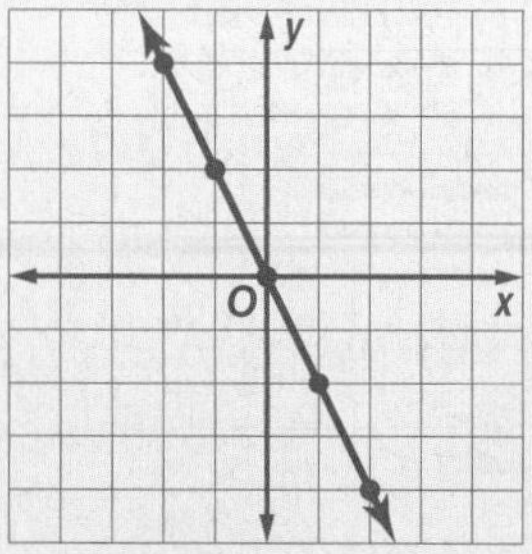

7.

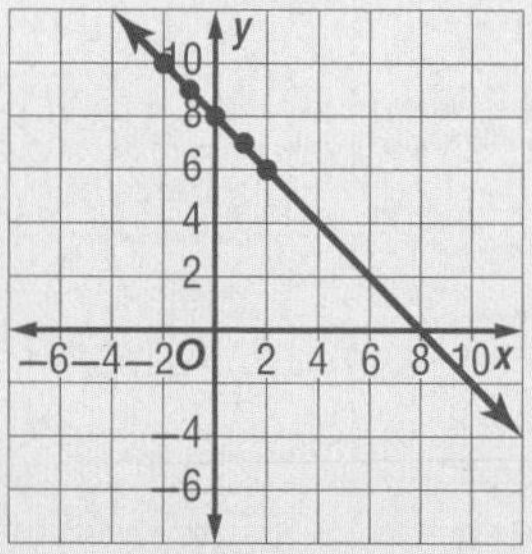

PSAE PRACTICE 8.11.09, 8.11.17, 8.11.08, 10.11.07

53. The cost of prints from an online photo processor is given by $C(p) = 29.99 + 0.13p$. \$29.99 is the cost of the membership, and p is the number of 4-inch by 6-inch prints. What does the slope represent? **A**

A cost per print
B cost of the membership
C cost of the membership and 1 print
D number of prints

54. Danita bought a computer for \$1200 and its value depreciated linearly. After 2 years, the value was \$250. What was the amount of yearly depreciation? **G**

F \$950
G \$475
H \$250
J \$225

55. SHORT RESPONSE The graph represents how much the Wright Brothers National Monument charges visitors. How much does the park charge each visitor? **\$4**

Wright Brothers National Monument

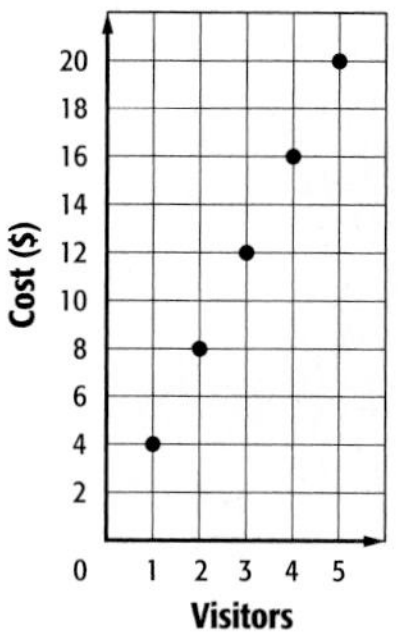

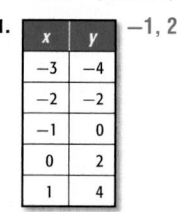

56. PROBABILITY At a gymnastics camp, 1 gymnast is chosen at random from each team. The Flipstars Gymnastics Team consists of 5 eleven-year-olds, 7 twelve-year-olds, 10 thirteen-year-olds, and 8 fourteen-year-olds. What is the probability that the age of the gymnast chosen is an odd number? **C**

A $\frac{1}{30}$ B $\frac{1}{15}$ C $\frac{1}{2}$ D $\frac{3}{5}$

Spiral Review

Solve each equation by graphing. (Lesson 3-2)

57. $3x + 18 = 0$ **−6** **58.** $8x - 32 = 0$ **4** **59.** $0 = 12x - 48$ **4**

Find the x- and y-intercepts of the graph of each linear function. (Lesson 3-1)

60.

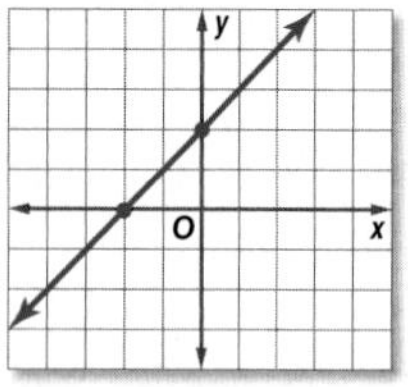

−2, 2

61. **−1, 2**

x	y
−3	−4
−2	−2
−1	0
0	2
1	4

62. HOMECOMING Dance tickets are \$9 for one person and \$15 for two people. If a group of seven students wishes to go to the dance, write and solve an equation that would represent the least expensive price p of their tickets. (Lesson 1-3) **$p = 15(3) + 9(1)$; \$54**

Skills Review

Find each quotient. (Lesson 0-5)

63. $8 \div \frac{2}{3}$ **12** **64.** $\frac{3}{8} \div \frac{1}{4}$ **$\frac{3}{2}$** **65.** $\frac{5}{8} \div 2$ **$\frac{5}{16}$** **66.** $\frac{12 \cdot 6}{9}$ **8** **67.** $\frac{2 \cdot 15}{6}$ **5** **68.** $\frac{18 \cdot 5}{15}$ **6**

Differentiated Instruction OL BL

Extension The road sign on a hill says 5% grade. The elevation of the road at that point is 1200 feet. Make a drawing of this situation. What would be the elevation of the road at an additional 2000 horizontal feet from the road sign? 1300 ft

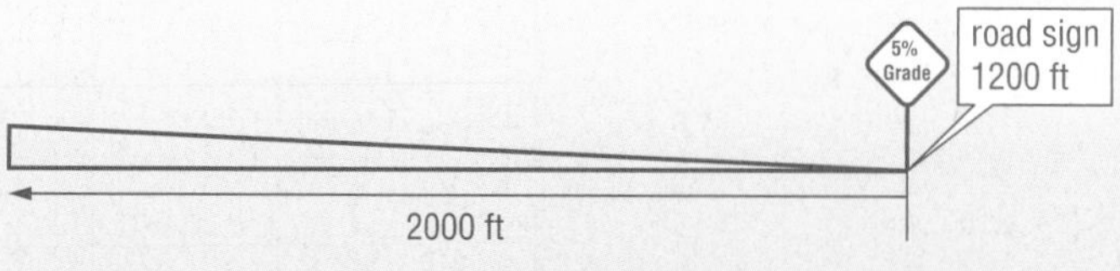

IL Learning Standards
8.B.4a, 8.B.4b

Determine whether each equation is a linear equation. Write *yes* or *no*. If yes, write the equation in standard form. (Lesson 3-1)

1. $y = -4x + 3$ **yes, $4x + y = 3$**
2. $x^2 + 3y = 8$ **no**
3. $\frac{1}{4}x - \frac{3}{4}y = -1$ **yes, $x - 3y = -4$**

Graph each equation using the *x*- and *y*-intercepts. (Lesson 3-1) **4–5. See margin.**

4. $y = 3x - 6$
5. $2x + 5y = 10$

Graph each equation by making a table. (Lesson 3-1)

6. $y = -2x$
7. $x = 8 - y$

6–7. See margin.

8. **BOOK SALES** The equation $5x + 12y = 240$ describes the total amount of money collected when selling x paperback books at \$5 per book and y hardback books at \$12 per book. Graph the equation using the x- and y-intercepts. (Lesson 3-1) **See margin.**

Find the root of each equation. (Lesson 3-2)

9. $x + 8 = 0$ **-8**
10. $4x - 24 = 0$ **6**
11. $18 + 8x = 0$ **$-\frac{9}{4}$**
12. $\frac{3}{5}x - \frac{1}{2} = 0$ **$\frac{5}{6}$**

Solve each equation by graphing. (Lesson 3-2)

13. $-5x + 35 = 0$ **7**
14. $14x - 84 = 0$ **6**
15. $118 + 11x = -3$ **-11**

16. **MULTIPLE CHOICE** The function $y = -15 + 3x$ represents the outside temperature, in degrees Fahrenheit, in a small Alaskan town where x represents the number of hours after midnight. The function is accurate for x values representing midnight through 4:00 P.M. Find the zero of this function. (Lesson 3-2) **C**

A 0
C 5
B 3
D -15

17. Find the rate of change represented in the table. (Lesson 3-3) **$\frac{4}{3}$**

x	y
1	2
4	6
7	10
10	14

Find the slope of the line that passes through each pair of points. (Lesson 3-3)

18. (2, 6), (4, 12) **3**
19. (1, 5), (3, 8) **$\frac{3}{2}$**
20. $(-3, 4)$, $(2, -6)$ **-2**
21. $\left(\frac{1}{3}, \frac{3}{4}\right)$, $\left(\frac{2}{3}, \frac{1}{4}\right)$ **$-\frac{3}{2}$**

22. **MULTIPLE CHOICE** Find the value of r so the line that passes through the pair of points has the given slope. (Lesson 3-3) **G**

$$(-4, 8), (r, 12), m = \frac{4}{3}$$

F -4
G -1
H 0
J 3

23. Find the slope of the line that passes through the pair of points. (Lesson 3-3) **12**

x	y
2.6	−2
3.1	4

24. **POPULATION GROWTH** The graph shows the population growth in Leesburg, Florida, since 2000. (Lesson 3-3)

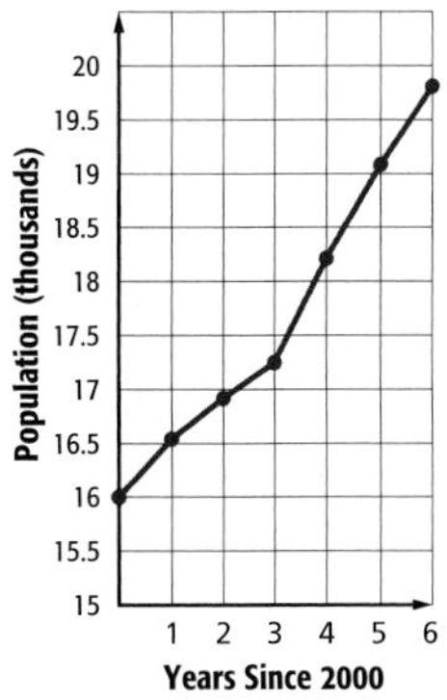

a. For which time period is the rate of change the greatest? **2003–2004**

b. Explain the meaning of the slope from 2000 to 2006. **See margin.**

CHAPTER 3 Mid-Chapter Quiz

Formative Assessment

Use the Mid-Chapter Quiz to assess students' progress in the first half of the chapter.

For problems answered incorrectly, have students review the lessons indicated in parentheses.

ExamView Assessment Suite Customize and create multiple versions of your Mid-Chapter Test and their answer keys.

FOLDABLES Follow-Up

Before students complete the Mid-Chapter Quiz, encourage them to review the information for Lessons 3-1 through 3-3 in their Foldables.

Additional Answers

8.

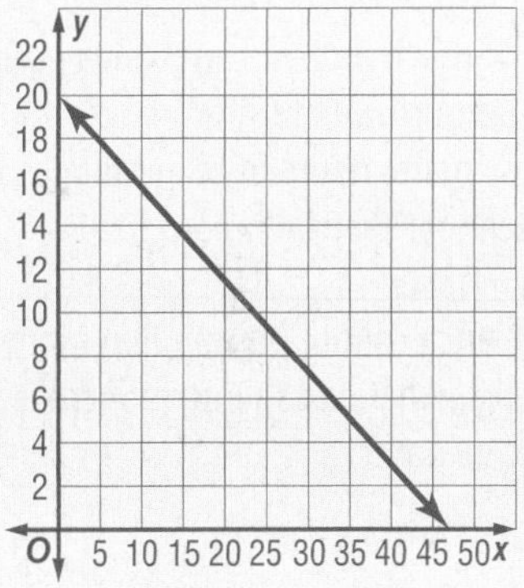

24b. The population of Leesburg has increased by about 630 per year.

Intervention Planner

Tier 1 On Level	Tier 2 Strategic Intervention approaching grade level	Tier 3 Intensive Intervention 2 or more grades below level
If students miss about 25% of the exercises or less,	**If** students miss about 50% of the exercises,	**If** students miss about 75% of the exercises,
Then choose a resource: **SE** Lessons 3-1, 3-2, and 3-3 **CRM** Skills Practice, pp. 7, 14, and 20 **TE** Chapter Project, p. 150 **IL Math Online** Self-Check Quiz	**Then** choose a resource: **CRM** Study Guide and Intervention, Chapter 3, pp. 5, 12, and 18 *Quick Review Math Handbook* **IL Math Online** Extra Examples, Personal Tutor, Homework Help	**Then** use *Math Triumphs, Alg. 1, Ch. 3* **IL Math Online** Extra Examples, Personal Tutor, Homework Help, Review Vocabulary

3-4 Lesson Notes

1 FOCUS

Vertical Alignment

Before Lesson 3-4
Find rates of change of linear functions.

Lesson 3-4
Write and graph direct variation equations.
Solve problems involving direct variation.

After Lesson 3-4
Write an equation for a proportional relationship.

2 TEACH

Scaffolding Questions

Have students read the *Why?* section of the lesson.

Ask:

- How much money can Bianca earn in 5 hours of babysitting? $62.50
- How many hours of babysitting will it take for Bianca to earn $295? 23.6 hours
- If Bianca cannot babysit that many hours, what can she do to increase her income? She can charge more per hour.

3-4 Direct Variation

Then
You found rates of change of linear functions. (Lesson 3-3)

Now
- Write and graph direct variation equations.
- Solve problems involving direct variation.

IL Learning Standards

7.A.4a Apply units and scales to describe and compare numerical data and physical objects.
7.A.4b Apply formulas in a wide variety of theoretical and practical real-world measurement applications involving perimeter, area, volume, angle, time, temperature, mass, speed, distance, density and monetary values.

New Vocabulary
direct variation
constant of variation
constant of proportionality

IL Math Online
glencoe.com
- Extra Examples
- Personal Tutor
- Self-Check Quiz
- Homework Help

Why?

Bianca is saving her money to buy a designer purse that costs $295. To help raise the money, she charges $12.50 per hour to babysit her neighbors' two children. The slope of the line that represents the amount of money Bianca earns is 12.5, and the rate of change is constant.

Direct Variation Equations A **direct variation** is described by an equation of the form $y = kx$, where $k \neq 0$. The equation $y = kx$ illustrates a constant rate of change, and k is the **constant of variation**, also called the **constant of proportionality**.

EXAMPLE 1 Slope and Constant of Variation

Name the constant of variation for each equation. Then find the slope of the line that passes through each pair of points.

a.

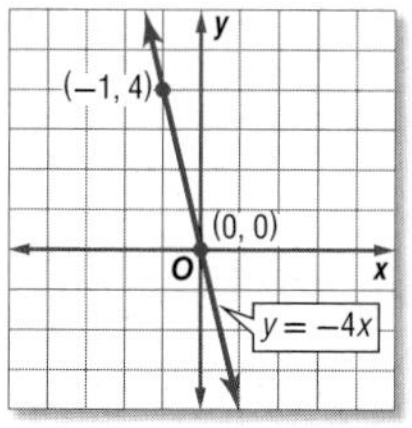

The constant of variation is −4.

$m = \frac{y_2 - y_1}{x_2 - x_1}$ Slope Formula

$= \frac{4 - 0}{-1 - 0}$ $(x_1, y_1) = (0, 0)$, $(x_2, y_2) = (-1, 4)$

$= -4$ The slope is −4.

b.

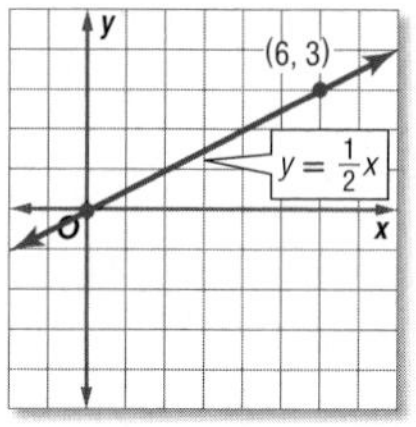

The constant of variation is $\frac{1}{2}$.

$m = \frac{y_2 - y_1}{x_2 - x_1}$ Slope Formula

$= \frac{3 - 0}{6 - 0}$ $(x_1, y_1) = (0, 0)$, $(x_2, y_2) = (6, 3)$

$= \frac{1}{2}$ The slope is $\frac{1}{2}$.

Check Your Progress

1A. Name the constant of variation for $y = \frac{1}{4}x$. Then find the slope of the line that passes through (0, 0) and (4, 1), two points on the line. $\frac{1}{4}$; $\frac{1}{4}$

1B. Name the constant of variation for $y = -2x$. Then find the slope of the line that passes through (0, 0) and (1, −2), two points on the line. −2; −2

Personal Tutor glencoe.com

The slope of the graph of $y = kx$ is k. Since $0 = k(0)$, the graph of $y = kx$ always passes through the origin. Therefore the x- and y-intercepts are zero.

Lesson 3-4 Resources

Resource	Approaching-Level	On-Level	Beyond-Level	English Learners
Teacher Edition	• Differentiated Instruction, p. 183		• Differentiated Instruction, p. 186	• Differentiated Instruction, p. 183
Chapter Resource Masters	• Study Guide and Intervention, pp. 24–25 • Skills Practice, p. 26 • Practice, p. 27 • Word Problem Practice, p. 28	• Study Guide and Intervention, pp. 24–25 • Skills Practice, p. 26 • Practice, p. 27 • Word Problem Practice, p. 28 • Enrichment, p. 29	• Practice, p. 27 • Word Problem Practice, p. 28 • Enrichment, p. 29	• Study Guide and Intervention, pp. 24–25 • Skills Practice, p. 26 • Practice, p. 27
Transparencies	• 5-Minute Check Transparency 3-4	• 5-Minute Check Transparency 3-4	• 5-Minute Check Transparency 3-4	• 5-Minute Check Transparency 3-4
Other	• Study Notebook	• Study Notebook	• Study Notebook	• Study Notebook

StudyTip

Constant of Variation A line with a positive constant of variation will go up from left to right and a line with a negative constant of variation will go down from left to right.

EXAMPLE 2 Graph a Direct Variation

Graph $y = -6x$.

Step 1 Write the slope as a ratio.

$-6 = \frac{-6}{1}$ $\frac{\text{rise}}{\text{run}}$

Step 2 Graph (0, 0).

Step 3 From the point (0, 0), move down 6 units and right 1 unit. Draw a dot.

Step 4 Draw a line containing the points.

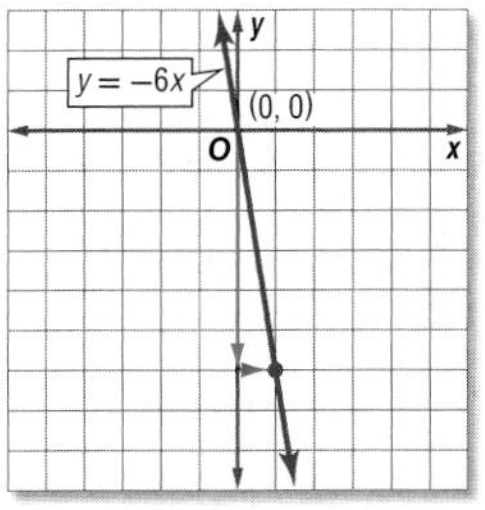

Check Your Progress 2A–2D. See Chapter 3 Answer Appendix.

2A. $y = 6x$ **2B.** $y = \frac{2}{3}x$ **2C.** $y = -5x$ **2D.** $y = -\frac{3}{4}x$

Personal Tutor glencoe.com

The graphs of all direct variation equations share some common characteristics.

Concept Summary Direct Variation Graphs

For Your FOLDABLE

- Direct variation equations are of the form $y = kx$, where $k \neq 0$.
- The graph of $y = kx$ always passes through the origin.
- The slope is positive if $k > 0$.

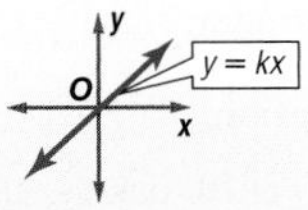

- The slope is negative if $k < 0$.

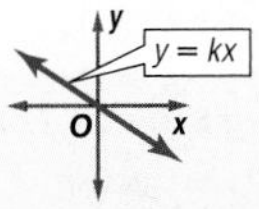

Math *in Motion*, Animation glencoe.com

If the relationship between the values of y and x can be described by a direct variation equation, then we say that y varies directly as x.

EXAMPLE 3 Write and Solve a Direct Variation Equation

Suppose y varies directly as x, and $y = 72$ when $x = 8$.

a. Write a direct variation equation that relates x and y.

$y = kx$	**Direct variation formula**
$72 = k(8)$	**Replace y with 72 and x with 8.**
$9 = k$	**Divide each side by 8.**

Therefore, the direct variation equation is $y = 9x$.

b. Use the direct variation equation to find x when $y = 63$.

$y = 9x$	**Direct variation formula**
$63 = 9x$	**Replace y with 63.**
$7 = x$	**Divide each side by 9.**

Therefore, $x = 7$ when $y = 63$.

Check Your Progress

3. Suppose y varies directly as x, and $y = 98$ when $x = 14$. Write a direct variation equation that relates x and y. Then find y when $x = -4$. $y = 7x; -28$

Personal Tutor glencoe.com

Direct Variation Equations

Example 1 shows how the constant of variation for an equation is related to the slope of the line. **Example 2** shows how to graph an equation of the form $y = kx$, for $k > 0$ or $k < 0$, by graphing (0, 0) and using the rise and run to find another point on the graph. **Example 3** shows how to use the definition of direct variation to write and solve direct variation equations.

Formative Assessment

Use the Check Your Progress exercises after each Example to determine students' understanding of concepts.

Additional Examples

1 Name the constant of variation for each equation. Then find the slope of the line that passes through each pair of points.

a.

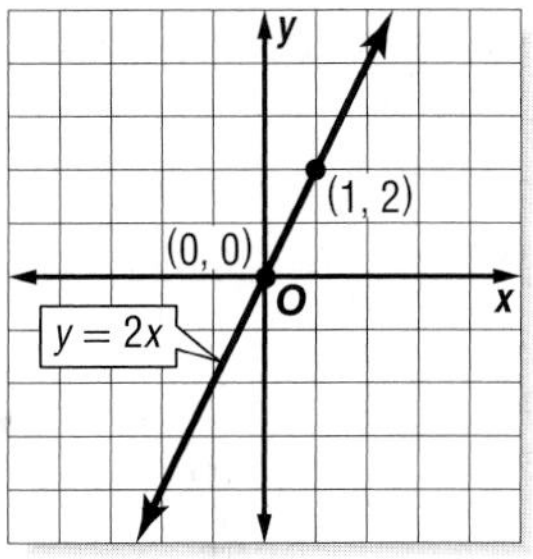

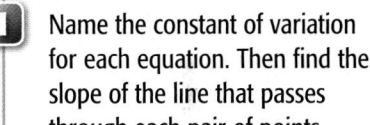

constant of variation: 2; slope: 2

b.

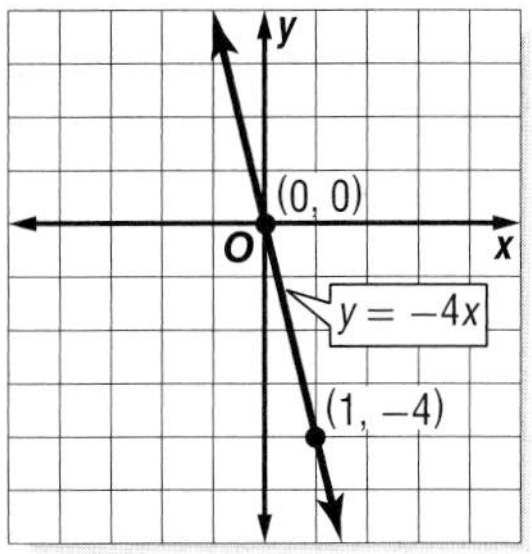

constant of variation: −4; slope: −4

2 Graph $y = -\frac{3}{2}x$. See bottom margin.

Additional Examples are also in Interactive Classroom PowerPoint® Presentations

IWB INTERACTIVE WHITEBOARD READY

Additional Answer (Additional Examples)

2.

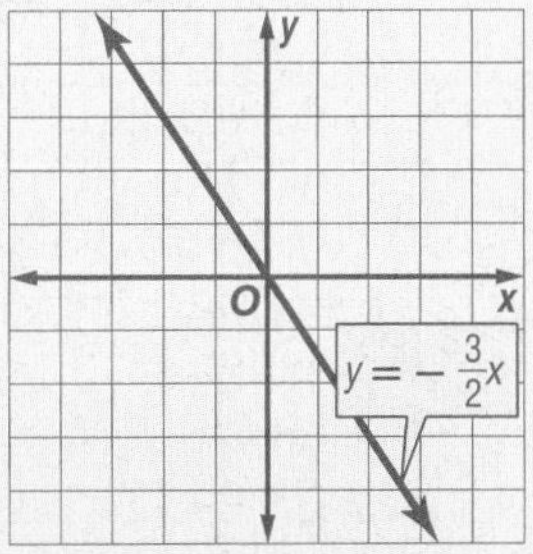

Additional Example

3 Suppose y varies directly as x, and $y = 9$ when $x = -3$.

a. Write a direct variation equation that relates x and y. $y = -3x$

b. Use the direct variation equation to find x when $y = 15$. -5

Direct Variation Problems

Example 4 shows how to use a direct variation equation to solve a real-world problem.

Additional Example

4 **TRAVEL** The Ramirez family is driving cross-country on vacation. They drive 330 miles in 5.5 hours.

a. Write a direct variation equation to find the distance d driven in time t. $d = 60t$

b. Graph the equation.

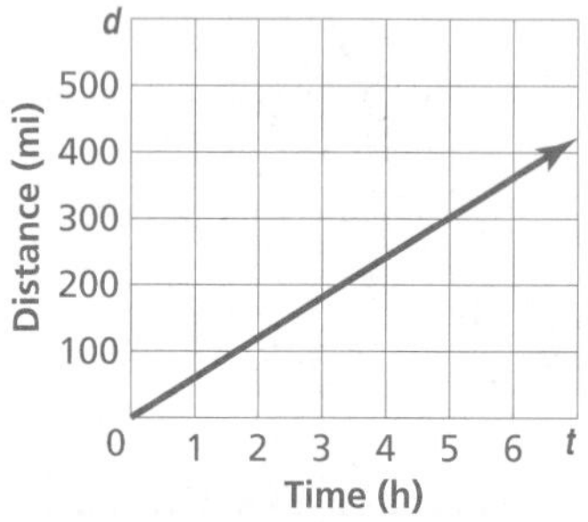

c. Estimate how many hours it would take to drive 500 miles. about 8.3 h

TEACH with TECH

INTERACTIVE WHITEBOARD Choose a student to work through an example in front of the class. Give him or her an x-value and a y-value, and have the student find the constant of variation given that y varies directly with x.

Direct Variation Problems One of the most common applications of direct variation is the formula $d = rt$. Distance d varies directly as time t, and the rate r is the constant of variation.

Real-World Link

In 2006, domestic airlines transported over 660 million passengers an average distance of 724 miles per flight.

Source: Bureau of Transportation Statistics

Real-World EXAMPLE 4 Estimate Using Direct Variation

TRAVEL **The distance a jet travels varies directly as the number of hours it flies. A jet traveled 3420 miles in 6 hours.**

a. Write a direct variation equation for the distance d flown in time t.

Words	Distance	equals	rate	times	time.
Variable	Let r = rate.				
Equation	3420	=	r	×	6

Solve for the rate.

$3420 = r(6)$ **Original equation**

$\frac{3420}{6} = \frac{r(6)}{6}$ **Divide each side by 6.**

$570 = r$ **Simplify.**

Therefore, the direct variation equation is $d = 570t$. The airliner flew at a rate of 570 miles per hour.

Problem-Solving Tip

Write an Equation Sometimes the best way to solve a problem is to write an equation from the given information and solve.

b. Graph the equation.

The graph of $d = 570t$ passes through the origin with slope 570.

$m = \frac{570}{1}$ $\frac{\text{rise}}{\text{run}}$

Distance Flown

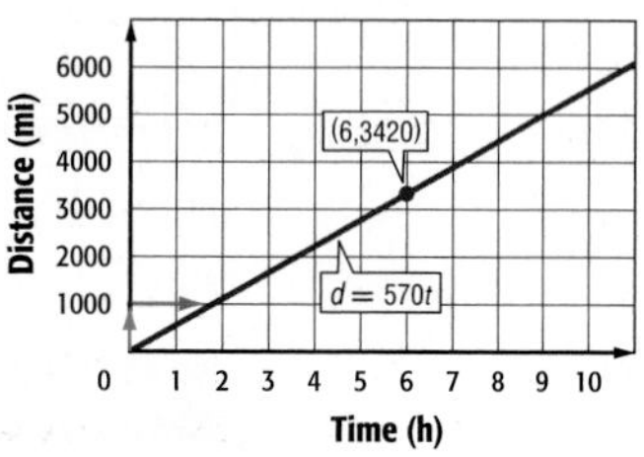

c. Estimate how many hours it will take for an airliner to fly 6500 miles.

$d = 570t$ **Original equation**

$6500 = 570t$ **Replace d with 6500.**

$\frac{6500}{570} = \frac{570t}{570}$ **Divide each side by 570.**

$t \approx 11.4$ **Simplify.**

It would take the airliner approximately 11.4 hours to fly 6500 miles.

Check Your Progress

4. HOT-AIR BALLOONS A hot-air balloon's height varies directly as the balloon's ascent time in minutes.

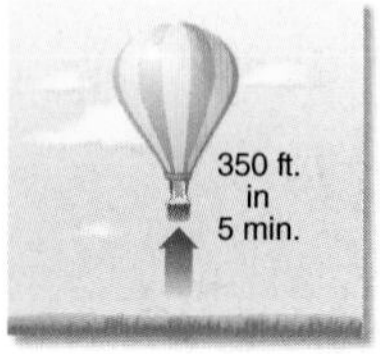

A. Write a direct variation for the distance d ascended in time t. $d = 70t$

B. Graph the equation. See Chapter 3 Answer Appendix.

C. Estimate how many minutes it would take to ascend 2100 feet. 30 min.

D. About how many minutes would it take to ascend 3500 feet? 50 min.

Personal Tutor glencoe.com

Additional Answers

3.

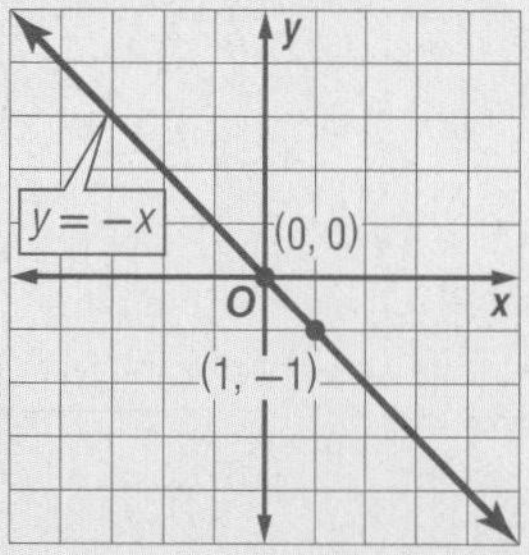

4.

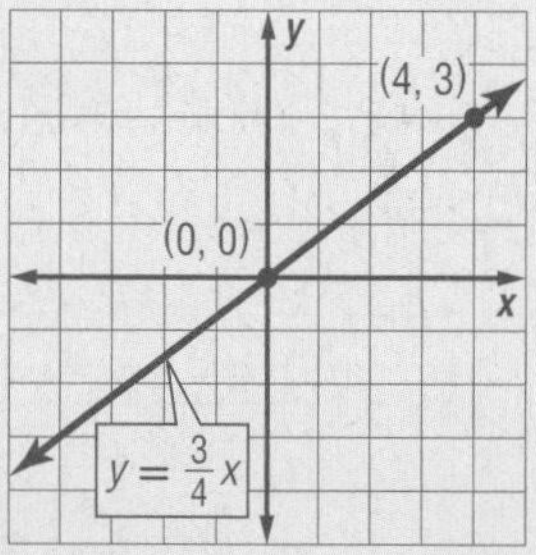

5.

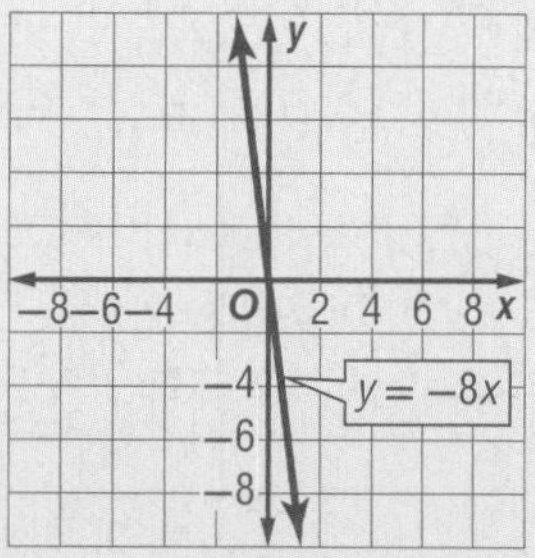

182 Chapter 3 Linear Functions

Check Your Understanding

Example 1 p. 180 — **Name the constant of variation for each equation. Then find the slope of the line that passes through each pair of points.**

1. $-\frac{4}{5}; -\frac{4}{5}$

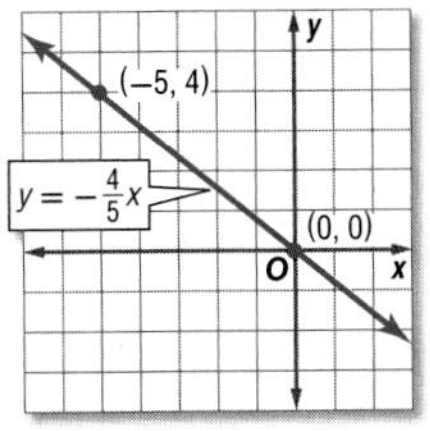

2. 2; 2

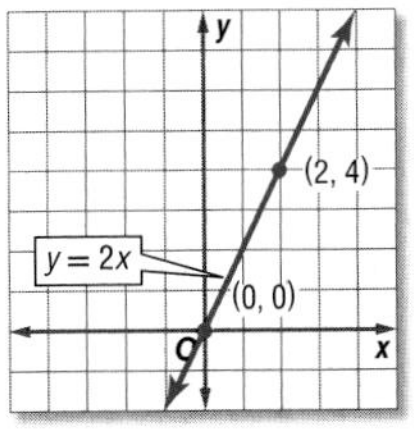

Example 2 p. 181 — **Graph each equation.** 3–6. See margin.

3. $y = -x$ **4.** $y = \frac{3}{4}x$ **5.** $y = -8x$ **6.** $y = -\frac{8}{5}x$

Example 3 p. 181 — **Suppose y varies directly as x. Write a direct variation equation that relates x and y. Then solve.**

7. If $y = 15$ when $x = 12$, find y when $x = 32$. $y = \frac{5}{4}x$; 40

8. If $y = -11$ when $x = 6$, find x when $y = 44$. $y = -\frac{11}{6}x$; −24

Example 4 p. 182

9. **MESSAGE BOARDS** You find that the number of messages you receive on your message board varies directly as the number of messages you post. When you post 5 messages, you receive 12 messages in return.

a. Write a direct variation equation relating your posts to the messages received. Then graph the equation. $y = \frac{12}{5}x$ See margin for graph.

b. Find the number of messages you need to post to receive 96 messages. 40

Practice and Problem Solving

● = **Step-by-Step Solutions** begin on page R12.
Extra Practice begins on page 815.

Example 1 p. 180 — **Name the constant of variation for each equation. Then find the slope of the line that passes through each pair of points.** 10–15. See margin.

10.

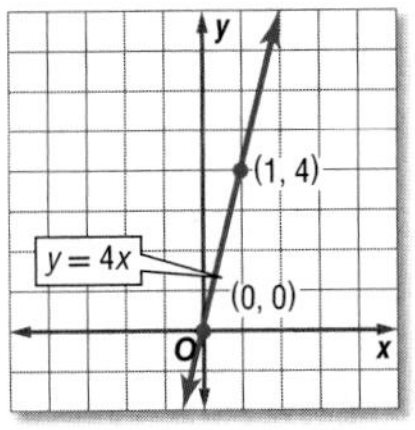

11.

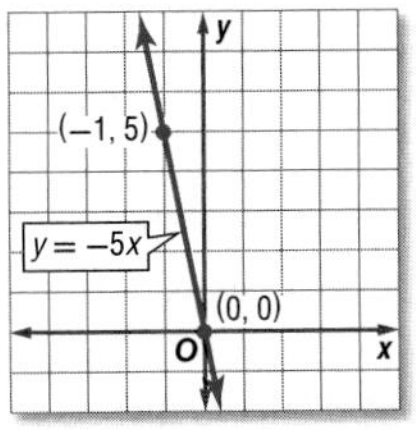

12.

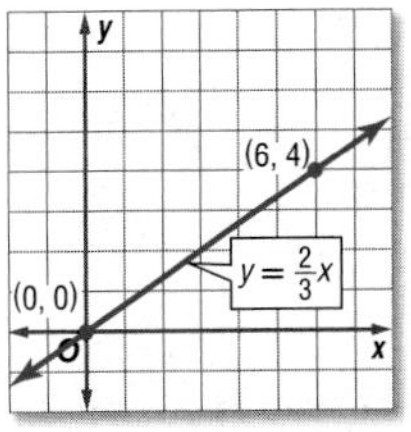

13.

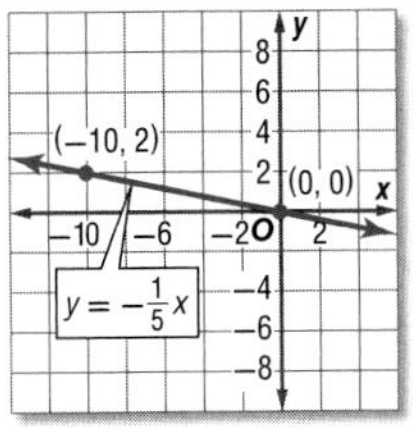

14.

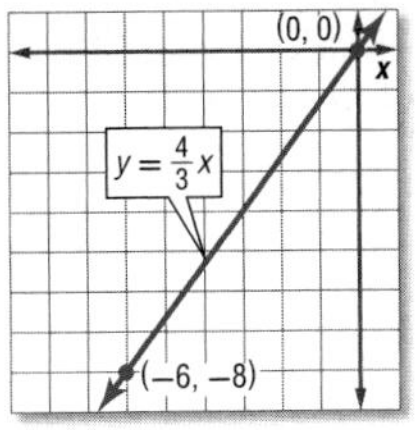

15.

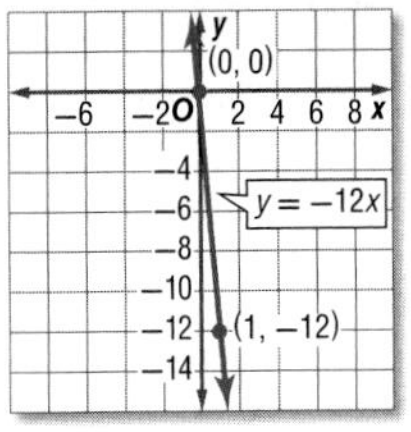

Differentiated Instruction

AL ELL

If students have trouble with direct variation equations,

Then give students one function at a time. Have them read the function aloud, then tell if the function is a direct variation. If it is, ask them to tell the constant of variation.

Watch Out!

Preventing Errors Be sure students do not interchange the values of x and y when substituting them into an equation.

Exercise Alert

Grid Paper Students will need grid paper to answer Exercises 3–6, 9, 16–23, 28, 38–41, 47, and 53–58.

3 PRACTICE

Formative Assessment

Use Exercises 1–9 to check for understanding.

Use the chart at the bottom of the next page to customize assignments for your students.

Additional Answers

6.

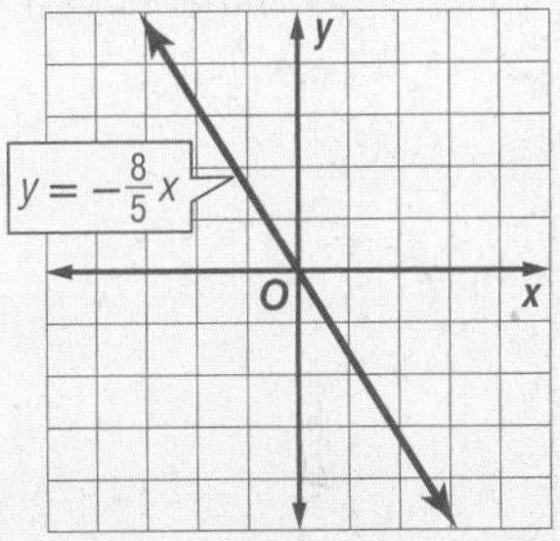

9a.

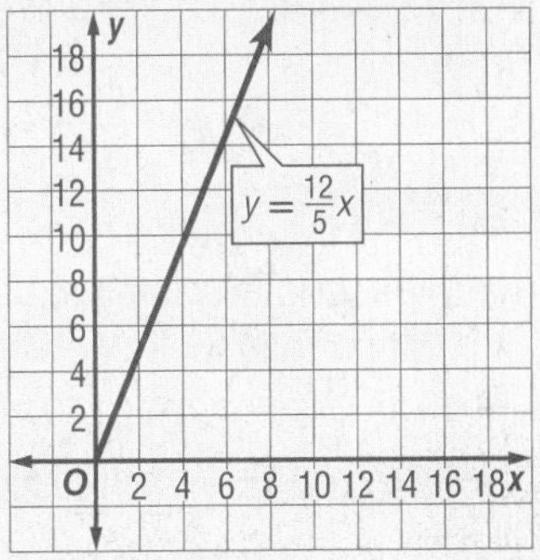

10. 4; 4

11. −5; −5

12. $\frac{2}{3}; \frac{2}{3}$

13. $-\frac{1}{5}; -\frac{1}{5}$

14. $\frac{4}{3}; \frac{4}{3}$

15. −12; −12

Multiple Representations In Exercise 41, students use graphs and equations to investigate the relationship between the constant of variation and the slope of the line and the rate of change of the graph.

Additional Answer

38.

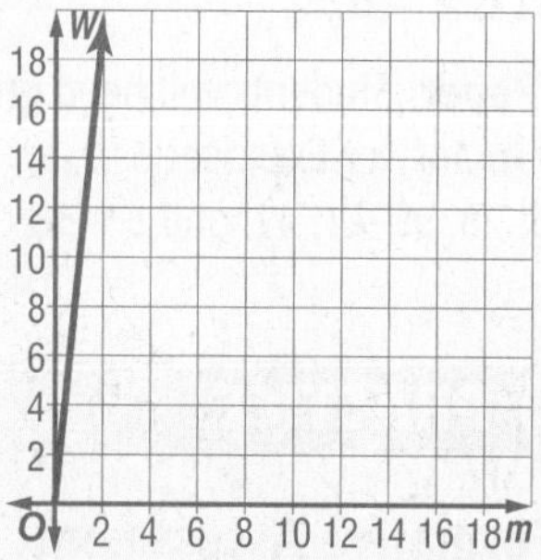

39.

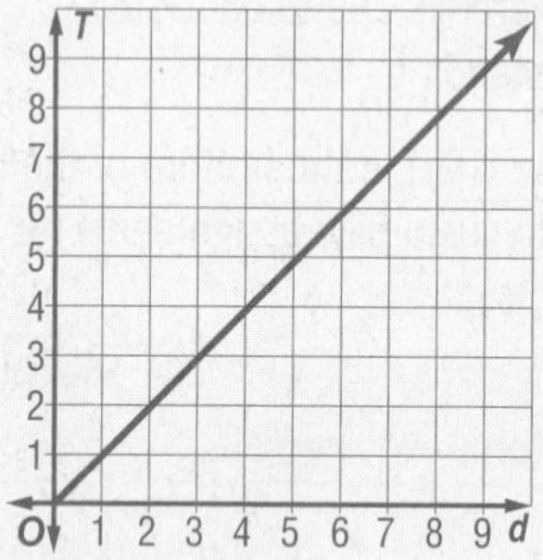

40.

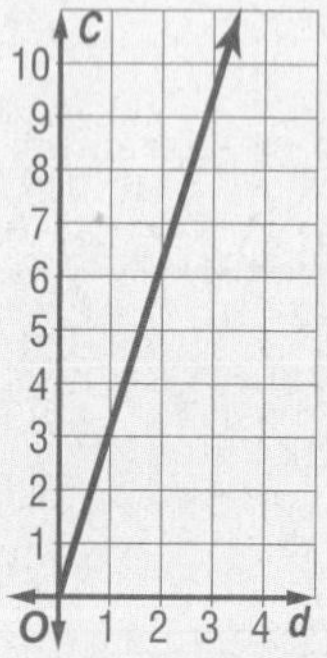

48. Always; if the equation is $y = kx$ $(k \neq 0)$, then the value of y when $x = a$ is ka, and the value of y when $x = 2a$ is $k(2a)$ or $2(ka)$.

49. Neither; the slope is constant, and it is k.

50. Sample answer: The graph of a direct variation equation $y = kx$ always passes through the origin. The graph has a positive slope if k is positive and the graph has a negative slope if k is negative.

Example 2 p. 181

Graph each equation. 16–23. See Chapter 3 Answer Appendix.

16. $y = 10x$ **17.** $y = -7x$ **18.** $y = x$ **19.** $y = \frac{7}{6}x$

20. $y = \frac{1}{6}x$ **21.** $y = \frac{2}{9}x$ **22.** $y = \frac{6}{5}x$ **23.** $y = -\frac{5}{4}x$

Example 3 p. 181

Suppose y varies directly as x. Write a direct variation equation that relates x and y. Then solve.

24. If $y = 6$ when $x = 10$, find x when $y = 18$. $y = \frac{3}{5}x$; 30

25 If $y = 22$ when $x = 8$, find y when $x = -16$. $y = \frac{11}{4}x$; -44

26. If $y = 4\frac{1}{4}$ when $x = \frac{3}{4}$, find y when $x = 4\frac{1}{2}$. $y = 5\frac{2}{3}x$; $25\frac{1}{2}$

27. If $y = 12$ when $x = \frac{6}{7}$, find x when $y = 16$. $y = 14x$; $1\frac{1}{7}$

Example 4 p. 182

28. SPORTS The distance a golf ball travels at an altitude of 7000 feet varies directly with the distance the ball travels at sea level, as shown.

Hitting a Golf Ball		
Altitude (ft)	0 (sea level)	7000
Distance (yd)	200	210

a. Write and graph an equation that relates the distance a golf ball travels at an altitude of 7000 feet y with the distance at sea level x. $y = 1.05x$ See Chapter 3 Answer Appendix for graph.

b. What would be a person's average driving distance at 7000 feet if his average driving distance at sea level is 180 yards? 189 yd

29. FINANCIAL LITERACY Depreciation is the decline in a car's value over the course of time. The table below shows the values of a car with an average depreciation.

Age of Car (years)	1	2	3	4	5
Value (dollars)	12,000	10,200	8400	6600	4800

a. Write an equation that relates the age x of the car to the value y that it lost after each year. $y = 1800x$

b. Find the age of the car if the value is \$300. 7 yr 6 mo

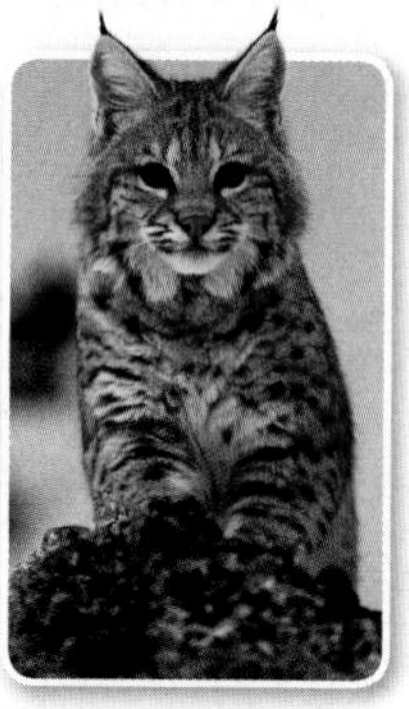

Real-World Link

The name Lynx comes from the Greek word "to shine." It may be in reference to the reflective ability of the cat's eyes.

Source: Lions, Tigers, and Bears

Suppose y varies directly as x. Write a direct variation equation that relates x and y. Then solve.

30. If $y = 3.2$ when $x = 1.6$, find y when $x = 19$. $y = 2x$; 38

31. If $y = 15$ when $x = \frac{3}{4}$, find x when $y = 25$. $y = 20x$; $\frac{5}{4}$

32. If $y = 4.5$ when $x = 2.5$, find y when $x = 12$. $y = 1.8x$; 21.6

33. If $y = -6$ when $x = 1.6$, find y when $x = 8$. $y = -3.75x$; -30

B

ENDANGERED SPECIES **Certain endangered species experience cycles in their populations as shown in the graph at the right. Match each animal below to one of the colored lines in the graph.**

34. red grouse, 8 years per cycle red

35. voles, 3 years per cycle dark green

36. lemmings, 4 years per cycle blue

37. lynx, 10 years per cycle. lime green

Population Cycles of Endangered Species

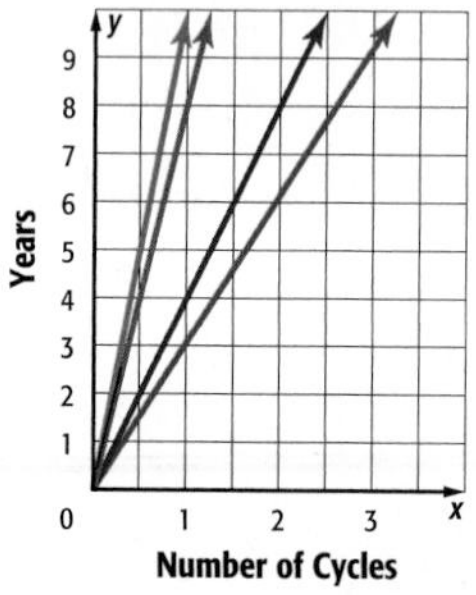

Differentiated Homework Options

Level	Assignment	Two-Day Option	
AL Basic	10–33, 45–47, 49–73	11–33 odd, 51–54	10–32 even, 45–47, 49–50, 55–73
OL Core	11–33 odd, 35, 37–47, 49–73	10–33, 51–54	34–47, 49–50, 55–73
BL Advanced	34–67, (optional: 68–73)		

184 Chapter 3 Linear Functions

41b. Sample answer: The constant of variation, slope, and rate of change of a graph all have the same value.

41c. Sample answer: Find the absolute value of k in each equation. The one with the greater value of $|k|$ has the steeper graph.

42. 55.8 miles

45. $z = \frac{1}{9}x$; It is the only equation that is a direct variation.

Real-World Link

More than 41 million fans attended Minor League Baseball games in 2006. Minor League Baseball draws more fans than the NBA or NFL.

Source: Minor League Basebal

46. They are equal; In $y = kx$, the constant of variation is k. The graph passes through (0, 0) and (1, k), so its slope is k.

47. Sample answer: $y = 0.50x$ represents the cost of x apples. The rate of change, 0.50, is the cost per apple. See Ch. 3 Answer Appendix for graph.

In Exercises 38–40, write and graph a direct variation equation that relates the variables.

38. PHYSICAL SCIENCE The weight W of an object is 9.8 m/s^2 times the mass of the object m. $W = 9.8m$ **38–40. See margin for graphs.**

39. MUSIC Music downloads are \$0.99 per song. The total cost of d songs is T. $T = 0.99d$

40. GEOMETRY The circumference of a circle C is approximately 3.14 times the diameter d. $C = 3.14d$

41. MULTIPLE REPRESENTATIONS In this problem, you will investigate the family of direct variation functions. **See Chapter 3 Answer Appendix.**

a. **GRAPHICAL** Graph $y = x$, $y = 3x$, and $y = 5x$ on the same coordinate plane.

b. **ALGEBRAIC** Describe the relationship among the constant of variation, the slope of the line, and the rate of change of the graph.

c. **VERBAL** Make a conjecture about how you can determine without graphing which of two direct variation equations has the steeper graph.

42. TRAVEL A map of North Carolina is scaled so that 3 inches represents 93 miles. How far apart are Raleigh and Charlotte if they are 1.8 inches apart on the map?

43. INTERNET A company will design and maintain a Web site for your company for \$9.95 per month. Write a direct variation equation to find the total cost C for having a Web page for n months. $C = 9.95n$

44. BASEBALL Before their first game, high school student Todd McCormick warmed all 5200 seats in a new minor league stadium. He started at 11:50 A.M. and finished around 3 P.M.

44a. $y = 27.3684t$; Every minute Todd warms about 27 additional seats.

a. Write a direct variation equation relating the number of seats to time. What is the meaning of the constant of variation in this situation?

b. About how many seats had Todd sat in by 1:00 P.M.? **about 1915 seats**

c. How long would you expect it to take Todd to sit in all of the seats at a major league stadium with more than 40,000 seats? **about 1461 min or 24 h and 21 min**

H.O.T. Problems

Use Higher-Order Thinking Skills

45. WHICH ONE DOESN'T BELONG? Identify the equation that does not belong. Explain.

$9 = rt$	$9a = 0$	$z = \frac{1}{9}x$	$w = \frac{9}{t}$

46. REASONING How are the constant of variation and the slope related in a direct variation equation? Explain your reasoning.

47. OPEN ENDED Model a real-world situation using a direct variation equation. Graph the equation and describe the rate of change. **See margin.**

48. CHALLENGE Suppose y varies directly as x. If the value of x is doubled, then the value of y is also *always, sometimes* or *never* doubled. Explain your reasoning.

49. FIND THE ERROR Eddy says the slope between any two points on the graph of a direct variation equation $y = kx$ is $\frac{1}{k}$. Adelle says the slope depends on the points chosen. Is either of them correct? Explain. **See margin.**

50. WRITING IN MATH Describe the graph of a direct variation equation. **See margin.**

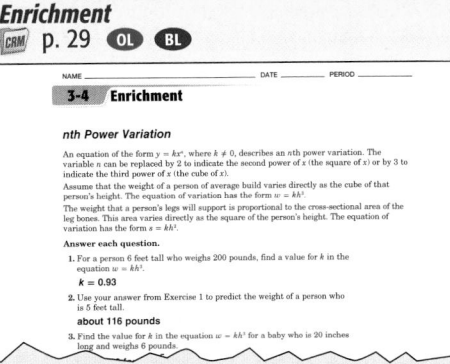

Study Guide and Intervention

CRM pp. 24–25 AL OL ELL

NAME ______ DATE ______ PERIOD ______

3-4 Study Guide and Intervention

Direct Variation

Direct Variation Equations A direct variation is described by an equation of the form $y = kx$, where $k \neq 0$. We say that y *varies directly* as x. In the equation $y = kx$, k is the constant of variation.

Example 1 Name the constant of variation for the equation. Then find the slope of the line that passes through the pair of points.

For $y = \frac{1}{2}x$, the constant of variation is $\frac{1}{2}$.

$m = \frac{y_2 - y_1}{x_2 - x_1}$ Slope formula

$= \frac{1 - 0}{2 - 0}$ $(x_1, y_1) = (0, 0), (x_2, y_2) = (2, 1)$

$= \frac{1}{2}$ Simplify.

The slope is $\frac{1}{2}$.

Example 2 Suppose y varies directly as x, and $y = 30$ when $x = 5$.

a. Write a direct variation equation that relates x and y.

Find the value of k.

$y = kx$ Direct variation equation

$30 = k(5)$ Replace y with 30 and x with 5.

$6 = k$ Divide each side by 5.

Therefore, the equation is $y = 6x$.

b. Use the direct variation equation to find x when $y = 18$.

$y = 6x$ Direct variation equation

$18 = 6x$ Replace y with 18.

$3 = x$ Divide each side by 6.

Therefore, $x = 3$ when $y = 18$.

Exercises

Name the constant of variation for each equation. Then determine the slope of the line that passes through each pair of points.

1. -2; -2 2. 3; 3 3. $\frac{3}{2}$; $\frac{3}{2}$

Suppose y varies directly as x. Write a direct variation equation that relates x to y. Then solve.

4. If $y = 4$ when $x = 2$, find y when $x = 16$. $y = 2x$; 32

5. If $y = 9$ when $x = -3$, find x when $y = 6$. $y = -3x$; -2

6. If $y = -4.8$ when $x = -1.6$, find x when $y = -24$. $y = 3x$; -8

7. If $y = \frac{1}{4}$ when $x = \frac{1}{8}$, find x when $y = \frac{3}{16}$. $y = 2x$; $\frac{3}{32}$

Chapter 3 24 Glencoe Algebra 1

Practice

CRM p. 27 AL OL BL ELL

NAME ______ DATE ______ PERIOD ______

3-4 Practice

Direct Variation

Name the constant of variation for each equation. Then determine the slope of the line that passes through each pair of points.

1. $\frac{3}{4}$; $\frac{3}{4}$ 2. $\frac{4}{3}$; $\frac{4}{3}$ 3. $-\frac{5}{2}$; $-\frac{5}{2}$

Graph each equation.

4. $y = -2x$ 5. $y = \frac{6}{5}x$ 6. $y = -\frac{5}{2}x$

Suppose y varies directly as x. Write a direct variation equation that relates x and y. Then solve.

7. If $y = 7.5$ when $x = 0.5$, find y when $x = -0.3$. $y = 15x$; -4.5

8. If $y = 80$ when $x = 32$, find x when $y = 100$. $y = 2.5x$; 40

9. If $y = \frac{3}{4}$ when $x = 24$, find y when $x = 12$. $y = \frac{1}{32}x$; $\frac{3}{8}$

Write a direct variation equation that relates the variables. Then graph the equation.

10. MEASURE The width W of a rectangle is two thirds of the length ℓ. $W = \frac{2}{3}\ell$

11. TICKETS The total cost C of tickets is \$4.50 times the number of tickets t. $C = 4.50t$

12. PRODUCE The cost of bananas varies directly with their weight. Miguel bought $3\frac{1}{2}$ pounds of bananas for \$1.12. Write an equation that relates the cost of the bananas to their weight. Then find the cost of $4\frac{1}{4}$ pounds of bananas. $C = 0.32p$; \$1.36

Chapter 3 27 Glencoe Algebra 1

Lesson 3-4

Word Problem Practice

CRM p. 28 AL OL BL ELL

NAME ______ DATE ______ PERIOD ______

3-4 Word Problem Practice

Direct Variation

1. ENGINES The engine of a chainsaw requires a mixture of engine oil and gasoline. According to the directions, oil and gasoline should be mixed as shown in the graph below. What is the constant of variation for the line graphed? 2.5

2. RACING In 2007, English driver Lewis Hamilton won the United States Grand Prix at the Indianapolis Motor Speedway. His speed during the race averaged 125.145 miles per hour. Write a direct variation equation for the distance d that Hamilton drove in h hours at that speed. $d = 125.145h$

3. CURRENCY The exchange rate from U.S. dollars to British pound sterling (£) was approximately \$2.07 to £1 in 2007. Write and solve a direct variation equation to determine how many pounds sterling you would receive in exchange for \$90 of U.S. currency. $u = 2.07b$; about £43.48

4. SALARY Henry started a new job in which he is paid \$9.50 an hour. Write and solve an equation to determine Henry's gross salary for a 40-hour work week. $p = 9.5h$; \$380

5. SALES TAX Amelia received a gift card to a local music shop for her birthday. She plans to use the gift card to buy some new CDs.

a. Amelia chose 3 CDs that each cost \$16. The sales tax on the three CDs is \$3.96. Write a direct variation equation relating sales tax to the price. $T = 0.0825P$

b. Graph the equation you wrote in part a.

c. What is the sales tax rate that Amelia is paying on the CDs? 8.25%

Chapter 3 28 Glencoe Algebra 1

Watch Out!

Find the Error For Exercise 49, suggest that students substitute different values for k, graph the equations, and then find the slopes.

Enrichment

CRM p. 29 OL BL

NAME ______ DATE ______ PERIOD ______

3-4 Enrichment

nth Power Variation

An equation of the form $y = kx^n$, where $k \neq 0$, describes an nth power variation. The variable n can be replaced by 2 to indicate the second power of x (the square of x) or by 3 to indicate the third power of x (the cube of x).

Assume that the weight of a person of average build varies directly as the cube of that person's height. The equation of variation has the form $w = kh^3$.

The weight that a person's legs will support is proportional to the cross-sectional area of the leg bones. This area varies directly as the square of the person's height. The equation of variation has the form $s = kh^2$.

Answer each question.

1. For a person 6 feet tall who weighs 200 pounds, find a value for k in the equation $w = kh^3$. $k = 0.93$

2. Use your answer from Exercise 1 to predict the weight of a person who is 5 feet tall. about 116 pounds

3. Find the value for k in the equation $w = kh^3$ for a baby who is 20 inches long and weighs 6 pounds.

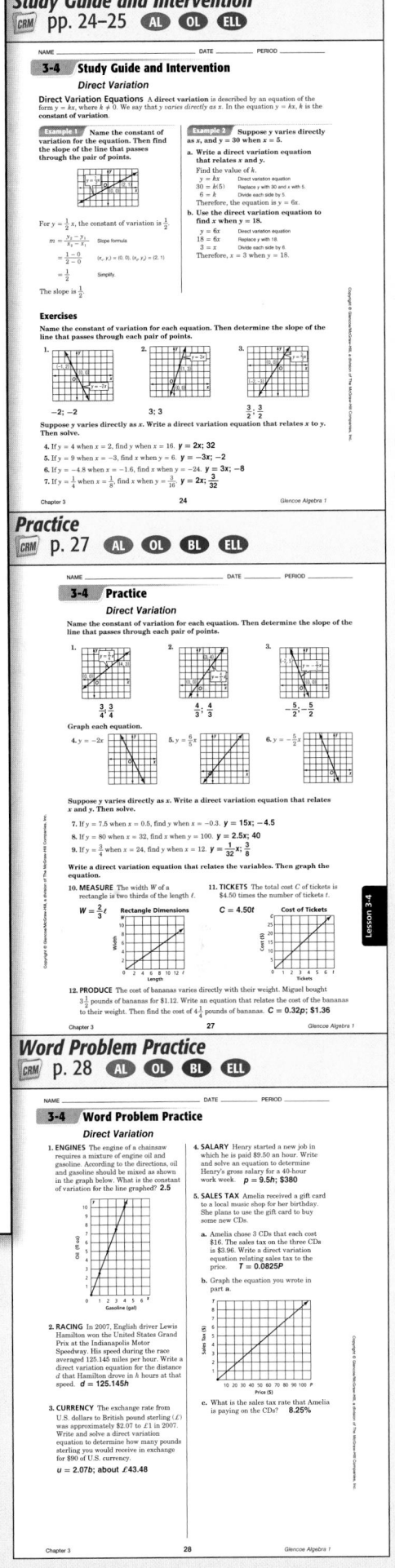

4 ASSESS

Crystal Ball Tell students that the next lesson they will study is about relating arithmetic sequences to linear functions. Ask them to write how they think today's lesson on the equation for direct variation will connect with the next lesson they study.

PSAE PRACTICE 8.11.14, 6.11.19, 8.11.13, 8.11.06

51. Patricia pays \$1.19 each to download songs to her MP3 player. If n is the number of downloaded songs, which equation represents the cost C in dollars? **A**

A $C = 1.19n$
B $n = 1.19C$
C $C = 1.19 \div n$
D $C = n + 1.19$

52. Suppose that y varies directly as x, and $y = 8$ when $x = 6$. What is the value of y when $x = 8$? **H**

F 6
G 12
H $10\frac{2}{3}$
J 16

53. What is the relationship between the input (x) and output (y)? **D**

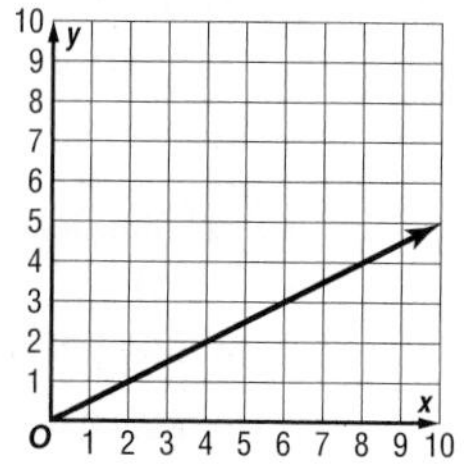

A The output is two more than the input.
B The output is two less than the input.
C The output is twice the input.
D The output is half the input.

54. SHORT RESPONSE A telephone company charges \$40 per month plus \$0.07 per minute. How much would a month of service cost a customer if the customer talked for 200 minutes? **\$54**

Spiral Review

55. TELEVISION The graph shows the average number of television channels American households receive. What was the annual rate of change from 2004 to 2006? Explain the meaning of the rate of change. (Lesson 3-3)
5.8; There was an average increase of 5.8 channels per year.

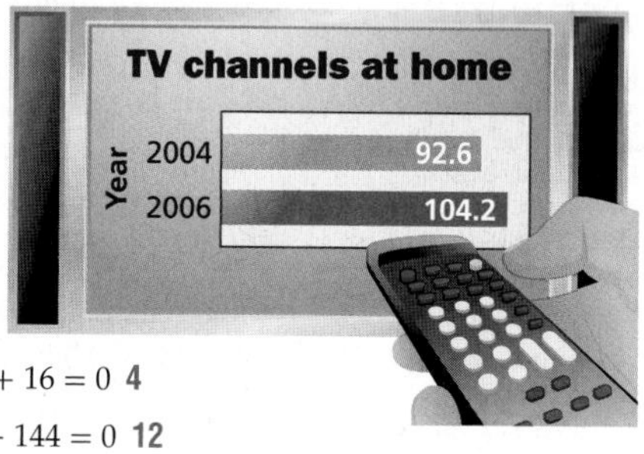

Solve each equation by graphing. (Lesson 3-2)

56. $0 = 18 - 9x$ **2**
57. $2x + 14 = 0$ **−7**
58. $-4x + 16 = 0$ **4**
59. $-5x - 20 = 0$ **−4**
60. $8x - 24 = 0$ **3**
61. $12x - 144 = 0$ **12**

Evaluate each expression if $a = 4$, $b = -2$, and $c = -4$. (Lesson 2-5)

62. $|2a + c| + 1$ **5**
63. $4a - |3b + 2|$ **12**
64. $-|a + 1| + |3c|$ **7**
65. $-a + |2 - a|$ **−2**
66. $|c - 2b| - 3$ **−3**
67. $-2|3b - 8|$ **−28**

Skills Review

Find each difference. (Lesson 0-3)

68. $13 - (-1)$ **14**
69. $4 - 16$ **−12**
70. $-3 - 3$ **−6**
71. $-8 - (-2)$ **−6**
72. $16 - (-10)$ **26**
73. $-8 - 4$ **−12**

Differentiated Instruction BL

Extension Write $y = kx^2$ on the board. Tell students that y varies directly as the *square* of x, and $y = 48$ when $x = 4$. Ask students to find y when $x = 10$. Since $k = 3$, $y = 300$.

186 Chapter 3 Linear Functions

3-5

Arithmetic Sequences as Linear Functions

Then
You indentified linear functions. (Lesson 3-1)

Now
- Recognize arithmetic sequences.
- Relate arithmetic sequences to linear functions.

IL Learning Standards

8.A.4b Represent mathematical patterns and describe their properties using variables and mathematical symbols. 8.C.4b Apply algebraic properties and procedures with matrices, vectors, functions and sequences using data found in business, industry and consumer situations. *Also addresses 8.B.4b.*

New Vocabulary
sequence
terms of the sequence
arithmetic sequence
common difference

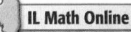

IL Math Online
glencoe.com
- Extra Examples
- Personal Tutor
- Self-Check Quiz
- Homework Help

Why?

During a 2000-meter race, the coach of a women's crew team recorded the team's times at several intervals.

- At 400 meters, the time was 1 minute 32 seconds.
- At 800 meters, it was 3 minutes 4 seconds.
- At 1200 meters, it was 4 minutes 36 seconds.
- At 1600 meters, it was 6 minutes 8 seconds.

They completed the race with a time of 7 minutes 40 seconds.

Recognize Arithmetic Sequences You can relate the pattern of team times to linear functions. A **sequence** is a set of numbers, called the **terms of the sequence**, in a specific order. Look for a pattern in the information given for the women's crew team. Make a table to analyze the data.

Distance (m)	400	800	1200	1600	2000
Time (min : sec)	1:32	3:04	4:36	6:08	7:40

+ 1:32 + 1:32 + 1:32 + 1:32

As the distance increases in regular intervals, the time increases by 1 minute 32 seconds. Since the difference between successive terms is constant, this is an **arithmetic sequence**. The difference between the terms is called the **common difference** d.

Key Concept Arithmetic Sequence — For Your FOLDABLE

Words An arithmetic sequence is a numerical pattern that increases or decreases at a constant rate called the *common difference.*

Examples 3, 5, 7, 9, 11, . . . (+2 +2 +2 +2) $d = 2$ 33, 29, 25, 21, 17, . . . (−4 −4 −4 −4) $d = -4$

The three dots used with sequences are called an *ellipsis*. The ellipsis indicates that there are more terms in the sequence that are not listed.

3-5 Lesson Notes

1 FOCUS

Vertical Alignment

Before Lesson 3-5
Identify linear functions.

Lesson 3-5
Recognize arithmetic sequences. Relate arithmetic sequences to linear functions.

After Lesson 3-5
Write equations in slope intercept form.

2 TEACH

Scaffolding Questions

Have students read the *Why?* section of the lesson.

Ask:
- What pattern do you see in the distances? The distances increase in regular intervals of 400 meters.
- What pattern do you see in the team's times? Each time is 1 minute 32 seconds more than the time before it.
- How could you find the team's time at 2000 meters? 6:08 + 1:32 = 7:40

Lesson 3-5 Resources

Resource	Approaching-Level	On-Level	Beyond-Level	English Learners
Teacher Edition	• Differentiated Instruction, p. 190	• Differentiated Instruction, pp. 188, 190	• Differentiated Instruction, pp. 188, 190, 193	
Chapter Resource Masters	• Study Guide and Intervention, pp. 30–31 • Skills Practice, p. 32 • Practice, p. 33 • Word Problem Practice, p. 34	• Study Guide and Intervention, pp. 30–31 • Skills Practice, p. 32 • Practice, p. 33 • Word Problem Practice, p. 34 • Enrichment, p. 35	• Practice, p. 33 • Word Problem Practice, p. 34 • Enrichment, p. 35	• Study Guide and Intervention, pp. 30–31 • Skills Practice, p. 32 • Practice, p. 33
Transparencies	• 5-Minute Check Transparency 3-5	• 5-Minute Check Transparency 3-5	• 5-Minute Check Transparency 3-5	• 5-Minute Check Transparency 3-5
Other	• Study Notebook	• Study Notebook	• Study Notebook	• Study Notebook

Recognize Arithmetic Sequences

Example 1 shows how to determine whether a sequence is arithmetic. **Example 2** shows how to find the next term in an arithmetic sequence. **Example 3** shows how to write an equation for the *n*th term of an arithmetic sequence to find any term in the sequence or to find the term number of the term in the sequence.

Formative Assessment

Use the Check Your Progress exercises after each Example to determine students' understanding of concepts.

Additional Examples

1 Determine whether each sequence is an arithmetic sequence. Explain.

a. $-15, -13, -11, -9, \ldots$ Yes; there is a common difference of 2.

b. $\frac{7}{8}, \frac{5}{8}, \frac{1}{8}, -\frac{5}{8}, \ldots$ No; there is no common difference.

2 Find the next three terms of the arithmetic sequence $-8, -11, -14, -17 \ldots$. $-20, -23, -26$

Additional Examples also in Interactive Classroom PowerPoint® Presentations

IWB INTERACTIVE WHITEBOARD READY

Tips for New Teachers

Building on Prior Knowledge Ask a volunteer to count from zero by twos. Ask another to count from zero by threes. Ask a third to count from zero by fives. Explain to students that when they count by a certain number, whether 1, 2, 3, 5, or $\frac{1}{8}$, they are using an arithmetic sequence because there is a common difference.

StudyTip

Common Difference If the terms of an arithmetic sequence are increasing, the common difference is positive. If the terms are decreasing, the common difference is negative.

EXAMPLE 1 Identify Arithmetic Sequences

Determine whether each sequence is an arithmetic sequence. Explain.

a. $-4, -2, 0, 2, \ldots$

$-4 \quad -2 \quad 0 \quad 2$

$+2 \quad +2 \quad +2$

The difference between terms in the sequence is constant. Therefore, this sequence is arithmetic.

b. $\frac{1}{2}, \frac{5}{8}, \frac{3}{4}, \frac{13}{16}, \ldots$

$\frac{1}{2} \quad \frac{5}{8} \quad \frac{3}{4} \quad \frac{13}{16}$

$+\frac{1}{8} \quad +\frac{1}{8} \quad +\frac{1}{16}$

This is not an arithmetic sequence. The difference between terms is not constant.

Check Your Progress 1B. No; the sequence does not have a common difference.

1A. $-26, -22, -18, -14, \ldots$ Yes; the sequence has a common difference of 4.

1B. $1, 4, 9, 25, \ldots$

Personal Tutor glencoe.com

You can use the common difference of an arithmetic sequence to find the next term in the sequence.

EXAMPLE 2 Find the Next Term

Find the next three terms of the arithmetic sequence 15, 9, 3, −3, … .

Step 1 Find the common difference by subtracting successive terms.

$15 \quad 9 \quad 3 \quad -3$

$-6 \quad -6 \quad -6$

The common difference is −6.

Step 2 Add −6 to the last term of the sequence to get the next term.

$-3 \quad -9 \quad -15 \quad -21$

$-6 \quad -6 \quad -6$

The next three terms in the sequence are −9, −15, and −21.

Check Your Progress 2. 15.5, 17.0, 18.5, 20.0

2. Find the next four terms of the arithmetic sequence 9.5, 11.0, 12.5, 14.0, … .

Personal Tutor glencoe.com

Math History Link

Mina Rees (1902–1997) Rees received the first award for Distinguished Service to Mathematics from the Mathematical Association of America. Her work in analyzing patterns is still inspiring young women to study mathematics today.

Each term in an arithmetic sequence can be expressed in terms of the first term a_1 and the common difference d.

Term	Symbol	In Terms of a_1 and d	Numbers
first term	a_1	a_1	8
second term	a_2	$a_1 + d$	$8 + 1(3) = 11$
third term	a_3	$a_1 + 2d$	$8 + 2(3) = 14$
fourth term	a_4	$a_1 + 3d$	$8 + 3(3) = 17$
⋮	⋮	⋮	⋮
*n*th term	a_n	$a_1 + (n - 1)d$	$8 + (n - 1)(3)$

Key Concept *n*th Term of an Arithmetic Sequence — For Your FOLDABLE

The *n*th term of an arithmetic sequence with first term a_1 and common difference d is given by $a_n = a_1 + (n - 1)d$, where n is a positive integer.

Differentiated Instruction OL BL

Extension Arithmetic sequences can be programmed in graphing calculators and results displayed in lists. A good option for advanced learners or those who enjoy using technology might be locating a set of directions for programming a sequence and developing a lesson for their classmates on analyzing sequences using the calculator.

StudyTip

***n*th Terms** Since n represents the number of the term, the inputs for n are the counting numbers.

EXAMPLE 3 Find the *n*th Term

a. Write an equation for the *n*th term of the arithmetic sequence −12, −8, −4, 0, … .

Step 1 Find the common difference.

$$-12 \quad -8 \quad -4 \quad 0$$
$$+4 \quad +4 \quad +4$$

The common difference is 4.

Step 2 Write an equation.

$a_n = a_1 + (n - 1)d$	**Formula for the *n*th term**
$= -12 + (n - 1)4$	$a_1 = -12$ **and** $d = 4$
$= -12 + 4n - 4$	**Distributive Property**
$= 4n - 16$	**Simplify.**

b. Find the 9th term of the sequence.

Substitute 9 for n in the formula for the nth term.

$a_n = 4n - 16$	**Formula for the *n*th term**
$a_9 = 4(9) - 16$	$n = 9$
$a_9 = 36 - 16$	**Multiply.**
$a_9 = 20$	**Simplify.**

c. Graph the first five terms of the sequence.

n	$4n - 16$	a_n	(n, a_n)
1	4(1) − 16	−12	(1, −12)
2	4(2) − 16	−8	(2, −8)
3	4(3) − 16	−4	(3, −4)
4	4(4) − 16	0	(4, 0)
5	4(5) − 16	4	(5, 4)

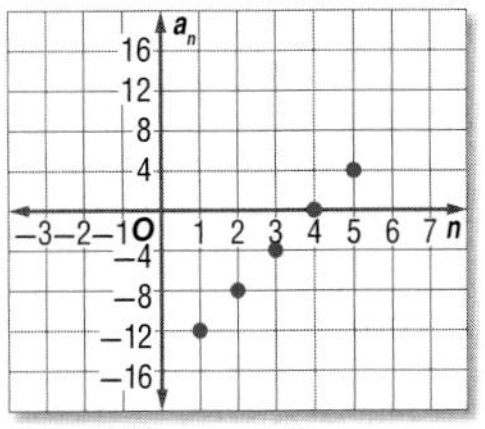

d. Which term of the sequence is 32?

In the formula for the nth term, substitute 32 for a_n.

$a_n = 4n - 16$	**Formula for the *n*th term**
$32 = 4n - 16$	$a_n = 32$
$32 + 16 = 4n - 16 + 16$	**Add 16 to each side.**
$48 = 4n$	**Simplify.**
$12 = n$	**Divide each side by 4.**

Check Your Progress

Consider the arithmetic sequence 3, −10, −23, −36, … .

3A. Write an equation for the nth term of the sequence. $a_n = -13n + 16$

3B. Find the 15th term in the sequence. −179

3C. Graph the first five terms of the sequence. See margin.

3D. Which term of the sequence is −114? 10

Personal Tutor glencoe.com

Additional Example

3

a. Write an equation for the nth term of the arithmetic sequence 1, 10, 19, 28,…. $a_n = 9n - 8$

b. Find the 12th term of the sequence. $a_{12} = 100$

c. Graph the first five terms of the sequence.

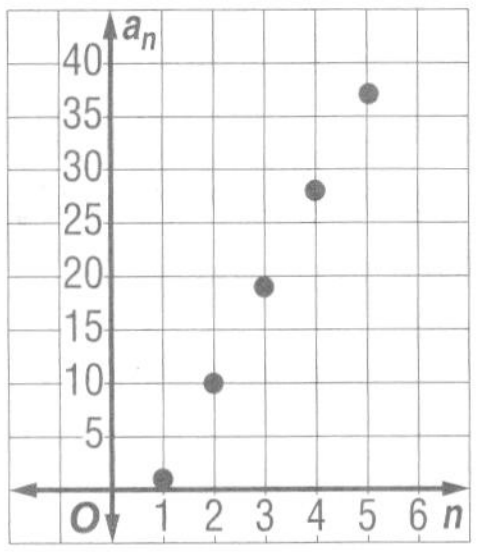

d. Which term of the sequence is 172? 20th term

Focus on Mathematical Content

Arithmetic Sequences After the first term, each term of an arithmetic sequence can be found by adding the common difference. The nth term of an arithmetic sequence with first term a_1 and a common difference d is given by $a_n = a_1 + (n - 1)d$, where n is a positive integer.

TEACH with TECH

BLOG On your secure classroom blog have students enter how to find a specific term of an arithmetic sequence. Make sure that students use the formula for finding the nth term of the sequence. Have each class select the best explanation to represent them and be posted on the classroom Web site for reference.

Additional Answer (Check Your Progress)

3C.

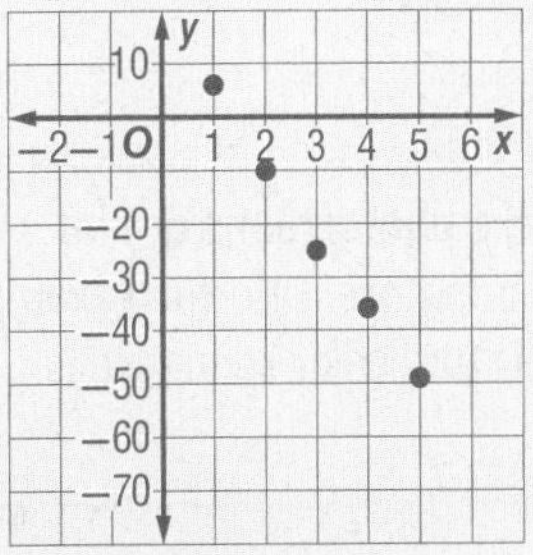

Watch Out!

Preventing Errors Make sure students carefully keep track of the variables in the function $a_n = a_1 + (n - 1)d$ as it is easy to substitute for the wrong variable when using this function.

Arithmetic Sequences and Functions

Example 4 shows how to solve a real-world problem by writing and graphing a function to represent an arithmetic sequence.

Additional Example

4 **NEWSPAPERS** The arithmetic sequence 12, 23, 34, 45 … represents the total number in ounces that a bag weighs after each additional newspaper is added.

a. Write a function to represent this sequence. $a_n = 11n + 1$

b. Graph the function and determine the domain.

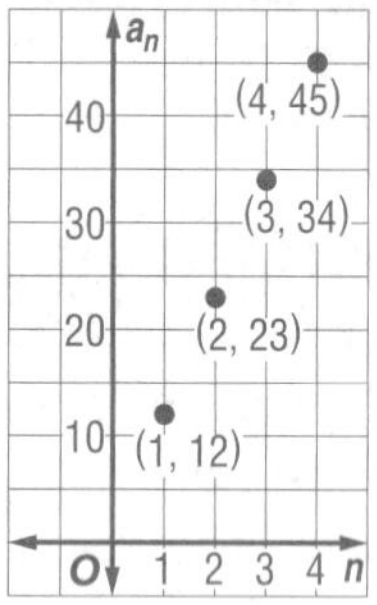

D = 0, 1, 2, 3, ...

Additional Answer (Check Your Progress)

4B.

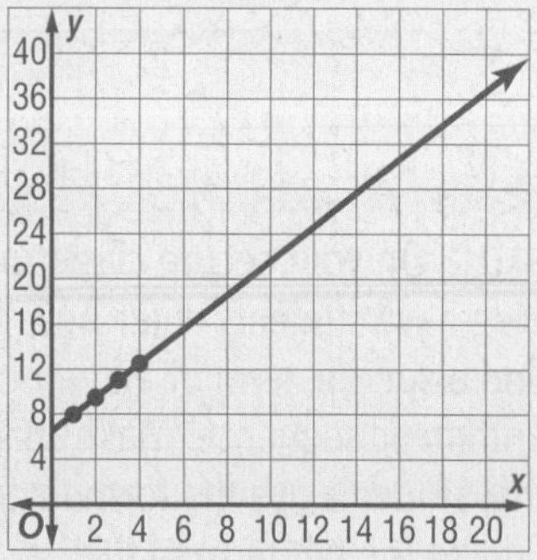

Arithmetic Sequences and Functions As you can see from Example 3, the graph of the first five terms of the arithmetic sequence lie on a line. An arithmetic sequence is a linear function in which n is the independent variable, a_n is the dependent variable, and d is the slope. The formula can be rewritten as the function $f(n) = (n - 1)d + a_1$, where n is a counting number.

While the domain of most linear functions are all real numbers, in Example 3 the domain of the function is the set of counting numbers and the range of the function is the set of integers on the line.

Real-World Link

When a Latina turns 15, her family may host a quinceañera for her birthday. The quinceañera is a traditional Hispanic ceremony and reception that signifies the transition from childhood to adulthood.

Source: Quince Girl

Real-World EXAMPLE 4 Arithmetic Sequences as Functions

INVITATIONS Marisol is mailing invitations to her quinceañera. The arithmetic sequence \$0.42, \$0.84, \$1.26, \$1.68, … represents the cost of postage.

a. Write a function to represent this sequence.

The first term, a_1, is 0.42. Find the common difference.

0.42 0.84 1.26 1.68

+0.42 +0.42 +0.42

The common difference is 0.41.

$a_n = a_1 + (n - 1)d$	**Formula for the *n*th term**
$= 0.42 + (n - 1)0.42$	**$a_1 = 0.42$ and $d = 0.42$**
$= 0.42 + 0.42n - 0.42$	**Distributive Property**
$= 0.42n$	**Simplify.**

The function is $f(n) = 0.42n$.

b. Graph the function and determine the domain.

The rate of change of the function is 0.42. Make a table and plot points.

n	$f(n)$
1	0.42
2	0.84
3	1.26
4	1.68
5	2.10

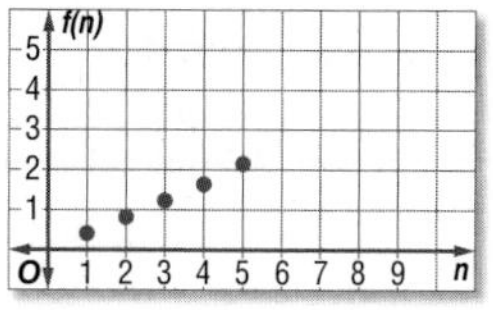

The domain of a function is the number of invitations Marisol mails. So, the domain is {0, 1, 2, 3, …}.

Check Your Progress

4. TRACK The chart below shows the length of Martin's long jumps.

Jump	1	2	3	4
Length (ft)	8	9.5	11	12.5

A. Write a function to represent this arithmetic sequence. $g(n) = 1.5n + 6.5$

B. Then graph the function. See margin.

Personal Tutor glencoe.com

Differentiated Instruction

AL OL BL

If students have an interest in nature,

Then share that sequences are often visible in nature. Have students take photographs or find pictures in magazines or on calendars of examples of sequences in nature. One such example is the sequence found in the arrangement of seeds in a daisy. This particular sequence is called the Fibonacci sequence.

Check Your Understanding

Example 1 p. 188 — **Determine whether each sequence is an arithmetic sequence. Write *yes* or *no*. Explain.**

1. 18, 16, 15, 13, … No; there is no common difference.

2. 4, 9, 14, 19, … Yes; the common difference is 5.

Example 2 p. 188 — **Find the next three terms of each arithmetic sequence.**

3. 12, 9, 6, 3, … 0, −3, −6

4. −2, 2, 6, 10, … 14, 18, 22

Example 3 p. 189 — **Write an equation for the *n*th term of each arithmetic sequence. Then graph the first five terms of the sequence.** 5–6. See margin for graphs.

5. 15, 13, 11, 9, … $a_n = 17 - 2n$

6. −1, −0.5, 0, 0.5, … $a_n = 0.5n - 1.5$

Example 4 p. 190

7. **SAVINGS** Kaia has $525 in a savings account. After one month she has $580 in the account. The next month the balance is $635. The balance after the third month is $690. Write a function to represent the arithmetic sequence. Then graph the function. $f(n) = 55n + 525$; See margin for graph.

Practice and Problem Solving

● = **Step-by-Step Solutions** begin on page R12. **Extra Practice** begins on page 815.

Example 1 p. 188 — **Determine whether each sequence is an arithmetic sequence. Write *yes* or *no*. Explain.**

8. −3, 1, 5, 9, … Yes; the common difference is 4.

9. $\frac{1}{2}, \frac{3}{4}, \frac{5}{8}, \frac{7}{16}, \ldots$ No; there is no common difference.

10. −10, −7, −4, 1, … No; there is no common difference.

11. −12.3, −9.7, −7.1, −4.5, … Yes; the common difference is 2.6.

Example 2 p. 188 — **Find the next three terms of each arithmetic sequence.**

12. 0.02, 1.08, 2.14, 3.2, … 4.26, 5.32, 6.38

13. 6, 12, 18, 24, … 30, 36, 42

14. 21, 19, 17, 15, … 13, 11, 9

15. $-\frac{1}{2}, 0, \frac{1}{2}, 1, \ldots$ $1\frac{1}{2}, 2, 2\frac{1}{2}$

16. $2\frac{1}{3}, 2\frac{2}{3}, 3, 3\frac{1}{3}, \ldots$ $3\frac{2}{3}, 4, 4\frac{1}{3}$

17. $\frac{7}{12}, 1\frac{1}{3}, 2\frac{1}{12}, 2\frac{5}{6}, \ldots$ $3\frac{7}{12}, 4\frac{1}{3}, 5\frac{1}{12}$

Example 3 p. 189 — **Write an equation for the *n*th term of the arithmetic sequence. Then graph the first five terms in the sequence.** See Ch. 3 Answer Appendix for graphs.

18. −3, −8, −13, −18, … $a_n = -5n + 2$

19. −2, 3, 8, 13, … $a_n = 5n - 7$

20. −11, −15, −19, −23, … $a_n = -4n - 7$

21. −0.75, −0.5, −0.25, 0, … $a_n = 0.25n - 1$

Example 4 p. 190

22. **AMUSEMENT PARKS** Shiloh and her friends spent the day at an amusement park. In the first hour, they rode two rides. After 2 hours, they had ridden 4 rides. They had ridden 6 rides after 3 hours.

a. Write a function to represent the arithmetic sequence. $f(n) = 2n$

b. Graph the function and determine the domain. See Ch. 3 Answer Appendix.

23. **JOBS** The table shows how Ryan is paid at his lumber yard job.

Linear Feet of 2×4 Planks Cut	10	20	30	40	50	60	70
Amount Paid in Commission ($)	8	16	24	32	40	48	56

a. Write a function to represent Ryan's commission. $f(n) = 0.80n$

b. Graph the function and determine the domain. See Ch. 3 Answer Appendix.

Differentiated Homework Options

Level	Assignment	Two-Day Option	
AL Basic	8–23, 32, 34, 36–55	9–23 odd, 37–40	8–22 even, 32, 34, 36, 41–55
OL Core	9–23 odd, 24–32, 34, 36–55	8–23, 37–40	24–32, 34, 36, 41–55
BL Advanced	24–49, (optional: 50–55)		

3 PRACTICE

Formative Assessment

Use Exercises 1–7 to check for understanding.

Use the chart at the bottom of this page to customize assignments for your students.

Exercise Alert

Grid Paper Students will need grid paper to answer Exercises 5–7, 18–21, 22–23, and 50–55.

Additional Answers

5.

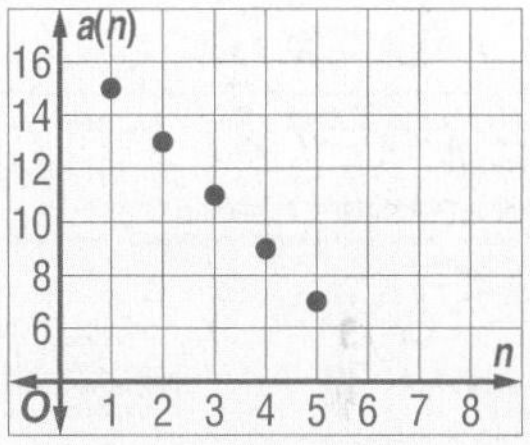

6.

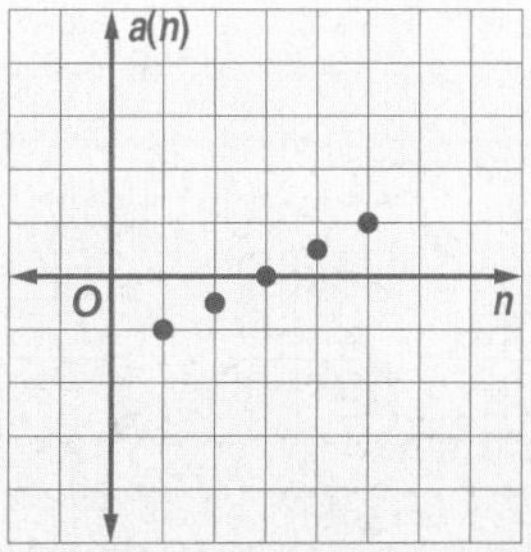

7.

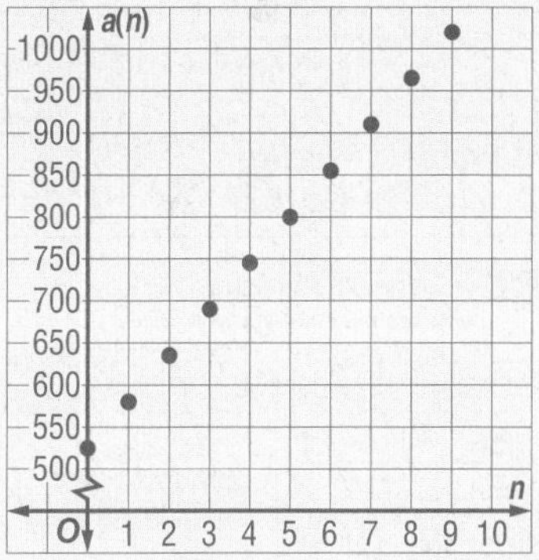

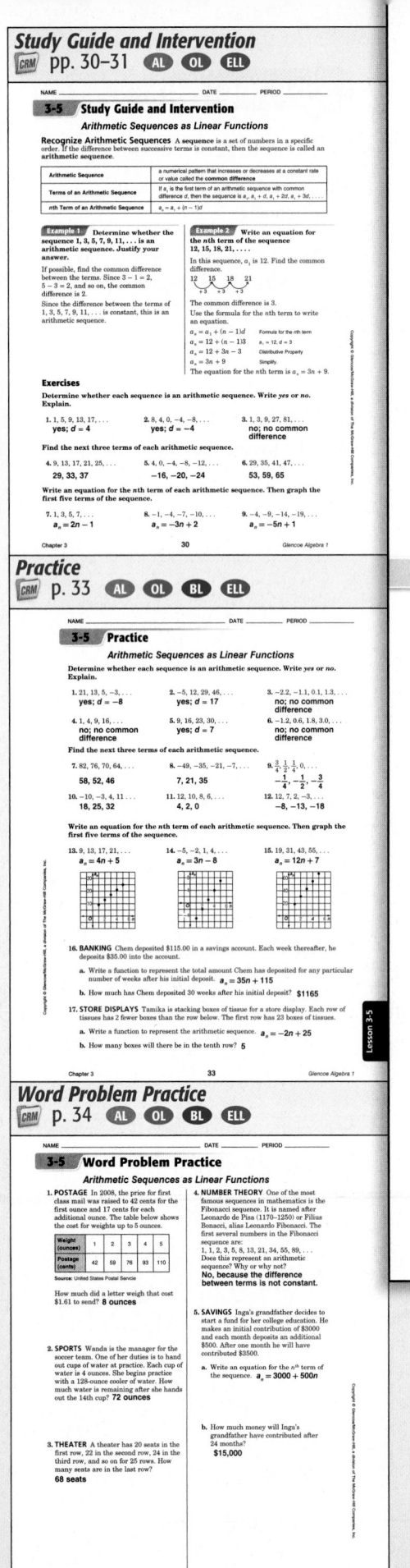

Study Guide and Intervention
CRM pp. 30–31 AL OL ELL

NAME ______ DATE ______ PERIOD ______

3-5 Study Guide and Intervention
Arithmetic Sequences as Linear Functions

Recognize Arithmetic Sequences A **sequence** is a set of numbers in a specific order. If the difference between successive terms is constant, then the sequence is called an **arithmetic sequence**.

Arithmetic Sequence	a numerical pattern that increases or decreases at a constant rate or value called the **common difference**
Terms of an Arithmetic Sequence	If a_1 is the first term of an arithmetic sequence with common difference d, then the sequence is $a_1, a_1 + d, a_1 + 2d, a_1 + 3d, \ldots$
nth Term of an Arithmetic Sequence	$a_n = a_1 + (n - 1)d$

Example 1 **Determine whether the sequence 1, 3, 5, 7, 9, 11, . . . is an arithmetic sequence. Justify your answer.**

If possible, find the common difference between the terms. Since $3 - 1 = 2$, $5 - 3 = 2$, and so on, the common difference is 2.

Since the difference between the terms of 1, 3, 5, 7, 9, 11, . . . is constant, this is an arithmetic sequence.

Example 2 **Write an equation for the nth term of the sequence 12, 15, 18, 21, ...**

In this sequence, a_1 is 12. Find the common difference.

12 15 18 21 (+3 +3 +3)

The common difference is 3.

Use the formula for the nth term to write an equation.

$a_n = a_1 + (n - 1)d$ Formula for the nth term
$a_n = 12 + (n - 1)3$ $a_1 = 12, d = 3$
$a_n = 12 + 3n - 3$ Distributive Property
$a_n = 3n + 9$ Simplify.

The equation for the nth term is $a_n = 3n + 9$.

Exercises

Determine whether each sequence is an arithmetic sequence. Write *yes* or *no*. Explain.

1. 1, 5, 9, 13, 17, . . . **yes; $d = 4$**
2. 8, 4, 0, −4, −8, . . . **yes; $d = -4$**
3. 1, 3, 9, 27, 81, . . . **no; no common difference**

Find the next three terms of each arithmetic sequence.

4. 9, 13, 17, 21, 25, . . . **29, 33, 37**
5. 4, 0, −4, −8, −12, . . . **−16, −20, −24**
6. 29, 35, 41, 47, . . . **53, 59, 65**

Write an equation for the nth term of each arithmetic sequence. Then graph the first five terms of the sequence.

7. 1, 3, 5, 7, . . . **$a_n = 2n - 1$**
8. −1, −4, −7, −10, . . . **$a_n = -3n + 2$**
9. −4, −9, −14, −19, . . . **$a_n = -5n + 1$**

Chapter 3 30 Glencoe Algebra 1

Practice
CRM p. 33 AL OL BL ELL

NAME ______ DATE ______ PERIOD ______

3-5 Practice
Arithmetic Sequences as Linear Functions

Determine whether each sequence is an arithmetic sequence. Write *yes* or *no*. Explain.

1. 21, 13, 5, −3, . . . **yes; $d = -8$**
2. −5, 12, 29, 46, . . . **yes; $d = 17$**
3. −2.2, −1.1, 0.1, 1.3, . . . **no; no common difference**
4. 1, 4, 9, 16, . . . **no; no common difference**
5. 9, 16, 23, 30, . . . **yes; $d = 7$**
6. −1.2, 0.6, 1.8, 3.0, . . . **no; no common difference**

Find the next three terms of each arithmetic sequence.

7. 82, 76, 70, 64, . . . **58, 52, 46**
8. −49, −35, −21, −7, . . . **7, 21, 35**
9. $\frac{3}{4}, \frac{1}{2}, \frac{1}{4}, 0, \ldots$ **$-\frac{1}{4}, -\frac{1}{2}, -\frac{3}{4}$**
10. −10, −3, 4, 11 . . . **18, 25, 32**
11. 12, 10, 8, 6, . . . **4, 2, 0**
12. 12, 7, 2, −3, . . . **−8, −13, −18**

Write an equation for the nth term of each arithmetic sequence. Then graph the first five terms of the sequence.

13. 9, 13, 17, 21, . . . **$a_n = 4n + 5$**

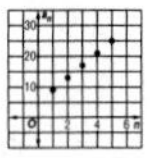

14. −5, −2, 1, 4, . . . **$a_n = 3n - 8$**

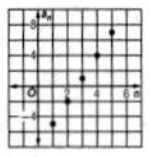

15. 19, 31, 43, 55, . . . **$a_n = 12n + 7$**

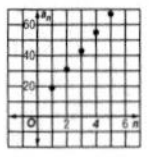

16. **BANKING** Chem deposited $115.00 in a savings account. Each week thereafter, he deposits $35.00 into the account.
   a. Write a function to represent the total amount Chem has deposited for any particular number of weeks after his initial deposit. **$a_n = 35n + 115$**
   b. How much has Chem deposited 30 weeks after his initial deposit? **$1165**

17. **STORE DISPLAYS** Tamika is stacking boxes of tissue for a store display. Each row of tissues has 2 fewer boxes than the row below. The first row has 23 boxes of tissues.
   a. Write a function to represent the arithmetic sequence. **$a_n = -2n + 25$**
   b. How many boxes will there be in the tenth row? **5**

Chapter 3 33 Glencoe Algebra 1

Lesson 3-5

Word Problem Practice
CRM p. 34 AL OL BL ELL

NAME ______ DATE ______ PERIOD ______

3-5 Word Problem Practice
Arithmetic Sequences as Linear Functions

1. **POSTAGE** In 2008, the price for first class mail was raised to 42 cents for the first ounce and 17 cents for each additional ounce. The table below shows the cost for weights up to 5 ounces.

Weight (ounces)	1	2	3	4	5
Postage (cents)	42	59	76	93	110

Source: United States Postal Servcie

How much did a letter weigh that cost $1.61 to send? **8 ounces**

2. **SPORTS** Wanda is the manager for the soccer team. One of her duties is to hand out cups of water at practice. Each cup of water is 4 ounces. She begins practice with a 128-ounce cooler of water. How much water is remaining after she hands out the 14th cup? **72 ounces**

3. **THEATER** A theater has 20 seats in the first row, 22 in the second row, 24 in the third row, and so on for 25 rows. How many seats are in the last row? **68 seats**

4. **NUMBER THEORY** One of the most famous sequences in mathematics is the Fibonacci sequence. It is named after Leonardo de Pisa (1170–1250) or Filius Bonacci, alias Leonardo Fibonacci. The first several numbers in the Fibonacci sequence are:
1, 1, 2, 3, 5, 8, 13, 21, 34, 55, 89, . . .
Does this represent an arithmetic sequence? Why or why not?
No, because the difference between terms is not constant.

5. **SAVINGS** Inga's grandfather decides to start a fund for her college education. He makes an initial contribution of $3000 and each month deposits an additional $500. After one month he will have contributed $3500.
   a. Write an equation for the nth term of the sequence. **$a_n = 3000 + 500n$**
   b. How much money will Inga's grandfather have contributed after 24 months? **$15,000**

Chapter 3 34 Glencoe Algebra 1

31a. Sample answer: The first two terms are 1. Starting with the third term, the two previous terms are added together to get the next term; 5, 8, 13, 21, 34.

31d. There is no common difference.

Real-World Link

The first high school yearbook, called *The Evergreen,* was published in 1845 in Waterville, New York.

Source: Brownielocks

34. Sample answer: The domain of the function described by $Ax + By = C$ is the set of all real numbers, and the range is either the set of all real numbers or a set of just one number when the graph is a horizontal line. For an arithmetic sequence, the domain is the set of all counting numbers. The range will be an infinite discrete set of real numbers if $d \neq 0$. If $d \neq 0$, then the range will be $\{a_1\}$.

B

24. The graph is a representation of an arithmetic sequence.

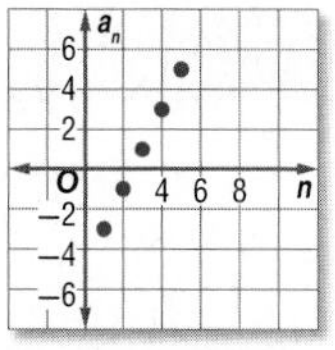

   a. List the first five terms. **−3, −1, 1, 3, 5**
   b. Write the formula for the nth term. **$a_n = 2n - 5$**
   c. Write the function. **$f(n) = 2n - 5$**

25. **NEWSPAPERS** A local newspaper charges by the number of words for advertising. Write a function to represent the advertising costs. **$f(n) = 0.25n + 5$**

DAILY NEWS ADVERTISING	
10 words $7.50	20 words $10.00
15 words $8.75	25 words $11.25

26. The fourth term of an arithmetic sequence is 8. If the common difference is 2, what is the first term? **2**

27. The common difference of an arithmetic sequence is −5. If a_{12} is 22, what is a_1? **77**

28. The first four terms of an arithmetic sequence are 28, 20, 12, and 4. Which term of the sequence is −36? **9**

29. **CARS** Jamal's odometer of his car reads 24,521. If Jamal drives 45 miles every day, what will the odometer reading be in 25 days? **25,646**

30. **YEARBOOKS** The yearbook staff is unpacking a box of school yearbooks. The arithmetic sequence 281, 270, 259, 248 … represents the total number of ounces that the box weighs as each yearbook is taken out of the box.
   a. Write a function to represent this sequence. **$f(n) = -11n + 292$**
   b. Determine the weight of each yearbook. **11 oz**
   c. If the box weighs at least 11 ounces empty and 292 ounces when it is full, how many yearbooks were in the box? **25**

C

31. **MULTIPLE REPRESENTATIONS** The Fibonacci sequence can be defined by a recursive formula. This means each term after the first two terms comes from one or more previous terms. The first six terms are 1, 1, 2, 3, 5, 8 … .
   a. **LOGICAL** Determine the relationship between the terms of the sequence. What are the next five terms in the sequence?
   b. **ALGEBRAIC** Write a formula for the nth term if $n \geq 3$. **$a_n = a_{n-2} + a_{n-1}$**
   c. **ALGEBRAIC** Find the 15th term. **610**
   d. **ANALYTICAL** Explain why the Fibonacci sequence is not an arithmetic sequence.

H.O.T. Problems
Use Higher-Order Thinking Skills

32. Sample answer: 2, −8, −18, −28, …

32. **OPEN ENDED** Create an arithmetic sequence with a common difference of −10.

33. **CHALLENGE** Find the value of x that makes $x + 8$, $4x + 6$, and $3x$ the first three terms of an arithmetic sequence. **−1**

34. **REASONING** Compare and contrast the domain and range of the linear functions described by $Ax + By = C$ and $a_n = a_1 + (n - 1)d$.

35. **CHALLENGE** Determine whether each sequence is an arithmetic sequence. Write *yes* or *no*. Explain. If yes, find the common difference and the next three terms.
   a. $2x + 1, 3x + 1, 4x + 1\ldots$ **See margin.** b. $2x, 4x, 8x, \ldots$ **See margin.**

36. **WRITING IN MATH** Explain how to find a certain term of an arithmetic sequence and how an arithmetic sequence is related to a linear function. **See margin.**

Enrichment
CRM p. 35 OL BL

NAME ______ DATE ______ PERIOD ______

3-5 Enrichment

Arithmetic Series

An arithmetic series is a series in which each term after the first may be found by adding the same number to the preceding term. Let S stand for the following series in which each term is 3 more than the preceding one.

$S = 2 + 5 + 8 + 11 + 14 + 17 + 20$

The series remains the same if we reverse the order of all the terms. So let us reverse the order of the terms and add one series to the other, term by term. This is shown at the right.

$S = 2 + 5 + 8 + 11 + 14 + 17 + 20$
$S = 20 + 17 + 14 + 11 + 8 + 5 + 2$
$2S = 22 + 22 + 22 + 22 + 22 + 22 + 22$
$2S = 7(22)$
$S = \frac{7(22)}{2} = 7(11) = 77$

Let a represent the first term of the series.

Let ℓ represent the last term of the series.

Let n represent the number of terms in the series.

In the preceding example, a = 2, l = 20, and $n = 7$. Notice that when you add the two series, term by term, the sum of each pair of terms is 22. That sum can be found by adding the first and last terms, $2 + 20$ or $a + \ell$. Notice also that there are 7, or n, such sums. Therefore, the value of $2S$ is 7(22), or $n(a + \ell)$ in the general case. Since this is twice the sum of the series, you can use the formula $S = \frac{n(a + \ell)}{2}$ to find the sum of any arithmetic series.

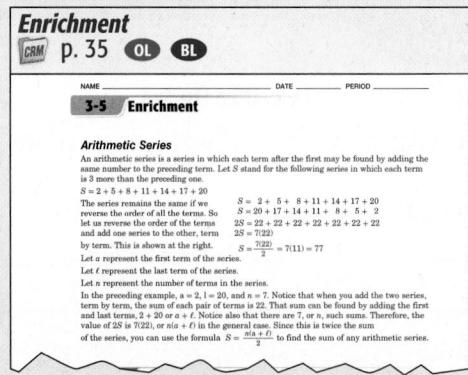

Multiple Representations In Exercise 31, students use logic, analysis, and algebra to explore the Fibonacci sequence and find terms as needed.

PSAE PRACTICE 8.11.16, 8.11.11, 8.11.04, 10.11.05

37. GRIDDED RESPONSE The population of Westerville is about 35,000. Each year the population increases by about 400. This can be represented by the following equation, where n represents the number of years from now and p represents the population.

$$p = 35{,}000 + 400n$$

In how many years will the Westerville population be about 38,200? **8**

38. Which relation is a function? **D**

A $\{(-5, 6), (4, -3), (2, -1), (4, 2)\}$
B $\{(3, -1), (3, -5), (3, 4), (3, 6)\}$
C $\{(-2, 3), (0, 3), (-2, -1), (-1, 2)\}$
D $\{(-5, 6), (4, -3), (2, -1), (0, 2)\}$

39. Find the formula for the nth term of the arithmetic sequence. **H**

$$-7, -4, -1, 2, \dots$$

F $a_n = 3n - 4$
G $a_n = -7n + 10$
H $a_n = 3n - 10$
J $a_n = -7n + 4$

40. STATISTICS A class received the following scores on the ACT. What is the difference between the median and the mode in the scores? **D**

18, 26, 20, 30, 25, 21, 32, 19, 22, 29, 29, 27, 24

A 1 C 3
B 2 D 4

Spiral Review

Name the constant of variation for each direct variation. Then find the slope of the line that passes through each pair of points. (Lesson 3-4)

41.

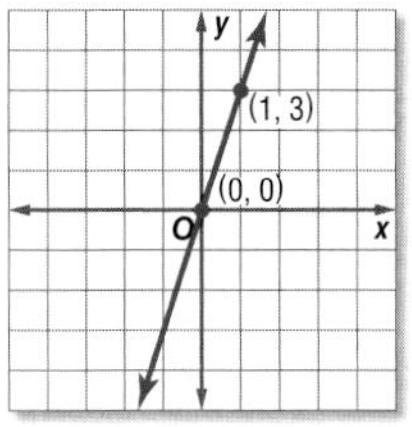

3, 3

42.

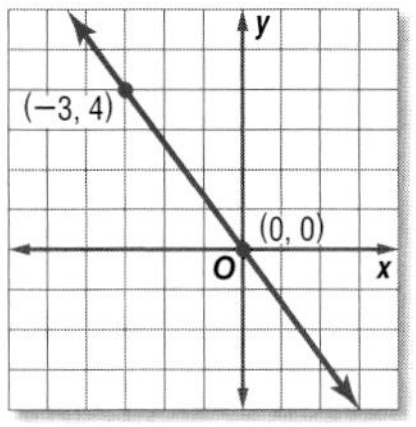

$\frac{-4}{3}, \frac{-4}{3}$

Find the slope of the line that passes through each pair of points. (Lesson 3-3)

43. $(5, 3), (-2, 6)$ $-\frac{3}{7}$

44. $(9, 2), (-3, -1)$ $\frac{1}{4}$

45. $(2, 8), (-2, -4)$ **3**

Solve each equation. Check your solution. (Lesson 2-4)

46. $5x + 7 = -8$ **−3**

47. $8 = 2 + 3n$ **2**

48. $12 = \frac{c - 6}{2}$ **30**

49. SPORTS The most popular sports for high school girls are basketball and softball. Write and use an equation to find how many more girls play on basketball teams than on softball teams. (Lesson 2-1)
Sample answer: $453{,}000 - d = 369{,}000$; 84,000

Basketball
453,000 girls

Softball
369,000 girls

Skills Review

Graph each point on the same coordinate plane. **50–55. See margin.**

50. $A(2, 5)$

51. $B(-2, 1)$

52. $C(-3, -1)$

53. $D(0, 4)$

54. $F(5, -3)$

55. $G(-5, 0)$

4 ASSESS

Name the Math Have students explain how they would find the 15th term of the arithmetic sequence −3, −1, 1, 1, −3 …

Formative Assessment

Check for student understanding of Lesson 3-4 and 3-5.

CRM Quiz 3, p. 46

Additional Answers

35a. Yes; there is a common difference; x; $5x + 1$, $6x + 1$, $7x + 1$.

35b. No; unless $x = 0$, there is no common difference.

36. Sample answer: First, find the common difference of the given sequence. Then use the formula $a_n = a_1 + (n - 1)d$, substituting for n the number of whichever term is needed. An arithmetic sequence is basically a linear function in which d represents the slope, n is the independent variable, and a_n is the dependent variable.

50–55.

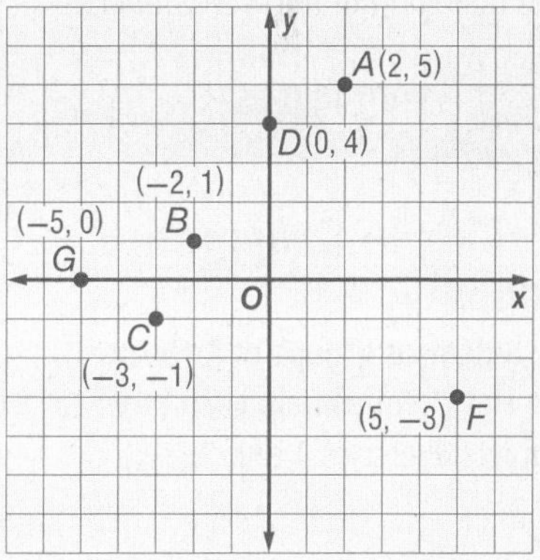

Differentiated Instruction BL

Extension Tell students that you applied a procedure that determines an arithmetic sequence in which the 4th term is 27 and the 8th term is 59. Ask students to find the starting number and the common difference. (Hint: Let the 4th term temporarily be the 1st term, which in turn makes the 8th term the 5th term.) $a_1 = 3, d = 8$

Lesson 3-5 Arithmetic Sequences as Linear Functions 193

EXTEND
3-5 Lesson Notes

1 FOCUS

Objective Investigate inductive and deductive reasoning.

Teaching Tip

- Ask students to explain the types of thoughts they have when they solve a problem. If students have trouble coming up with ideas, give them a situation. Ask them how they would solve the problem of opening a locked door if they had a key ring with 100 keys on it.
- Explain to students that the root of inductive is *induce.* Induce is a verb that means *to call forth or bring about by influence*, or *to cause the formation of.* After students read the description of inductive reasoning, have them relate the principle of inductive reasoning to the definition of the word *induce.*
- Explain to students that the root of deductive is *deduce.* Deduce is a verb that means *to infer from a general principle*. Ask students to relate the principle of deductive reasoning to the definition of the word *deduce.*

2 TEACH

Working in Cooperative Groups

Put students is groups of three or four. Have groups help each other to complete Exercises 1 and 2.

Ask:

- What is a conjecture? a guess based on incomplete information

Practice Have students complete Exercises 3–5.

EXTEND
3-5 Algebra Lab: Inductive and Deductive Reasoning

Objective
Investigate inductive and deductive reasoning.

IL Learning Standards
8.A.4b Represent mathematical patterns and describe their properties using variables and mathematical symbols.

If Jolene is not feeling well, she may go to a doctor. The doctor will ask her questions about how she is feeling and possibly run other tests. Based on her symptoms, the doctor can diagnose Jolene's illness. This is an example of inductive reasoning. **Inductive reasoning** is used to derive a general rule after observing many events.

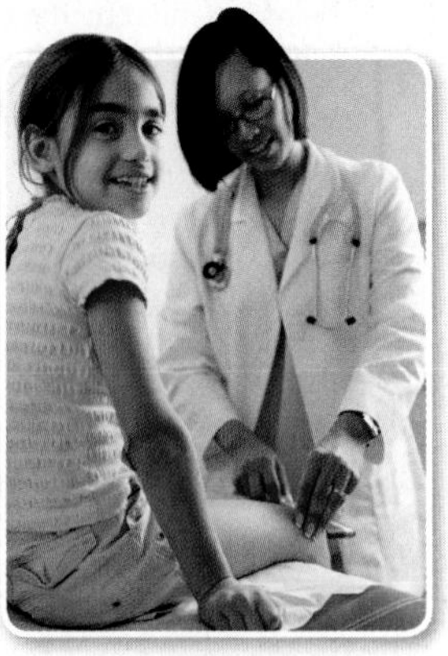

To use inductive reasoning:

Step 1 Observe many examples.

Step 2 Look for a pattern.

Step 3 Make a conjecture.

Step 4 Check the conjecture.

Step 5 Discover a likely conclusion.

With **deductive reasoning**, you come to a conclusion by accepting facts. The results of the tests ordered by the doctor may support the original diagnosis or lead to a different conclusion. This is an example of deductive reasoning. There is no conjecturing involved. Consider the two statements below.

1) If the strep test is positive, then the patient has strep throat.

2) Jolene tested positive for strep.

If these two statements are accepted as facts, then the obvious conclusion is that Jolene has strep throat. This is an example of deductive reasoning.

Exercises 1–4. See Chapter 3 Answer Appendix.

1. Explain the difference between *inductive* and *deductive* reasoning. Then give an example of each.
2. When a detective reaches a conclusion about the height of a suspect from the distance between footprints, what kind of reasoning is being used? Explain.
3. When you examine a finite number of terms in a sequence of numbers and decide that it is an arithmetic sequence, what kind of reasoning are you using? Explain.
4. Suppose you have found the common difference for an arithmetic sequence based on analyzing a finite number of terms, what kind of reasoning do you use to find the 100th term in the sequence?
5. **a.** Copy and complete the table.

3^1	3^2	3^3	3^4	3^5	3^6	3^7	3^8	3^9
3	9	27	81	243	729	2187	6561	19,683

3, 9, 7, 1, 3, 9, 7, 1, 3, … **b.** Write the sequence of numbers representing the numbers in the ones place.

c. Find the number in the ones place for the value of 3^{100}. Explain your reasoning. State the type of reasoning that you used. See Chapter 3 Answer Appendix.

3 ASSESS

Formative Assessment

Ask students whether predicting the next term on a sequence of numbers is done by trial and error, or by interpreting given information with a set of rules.

From Concrete to Abstract

Use Exercises 3 and 4 to bridge the gap between using inductive and deductive reasoning in specific events and using this type of reasoning to solve problems concerning algebraic sequences.

Proportional and Nonproportional Relationships

Then

You recognized arithmetic sequences and related them to linear functions. (Lesson 3-5)

Now

- Write an equation for a proportional relationship.
- Write an equation for a nonproportional relationship.

IL Learning Standards

8.A.4b Represent mathematical patterns and describe their properties using variables and mathematical symbols.

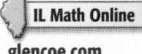

IL Math Online

glencoe.com

- Extra Examples
- Personal Tutor
- Self-Check Quiz
- Homework Help

Why?

Heather is planting flats of flowers. The table shows the number of flowers that she has planted and the amount of time that she has been working in the garden.

Number of flowers planted (*p*)	1	6	12	18
Number of minutes working (*t*)	5	30	60	90

The relationship between the flowers planted and the time that Heather worked in minutes can be graphed. Let *p* represent the number of flowers planted. Let *t* represent the number of minutes that Heather has worked.

When the ordered pairs are graphed, they form a linear pattern. This pattern can be described by an equation.

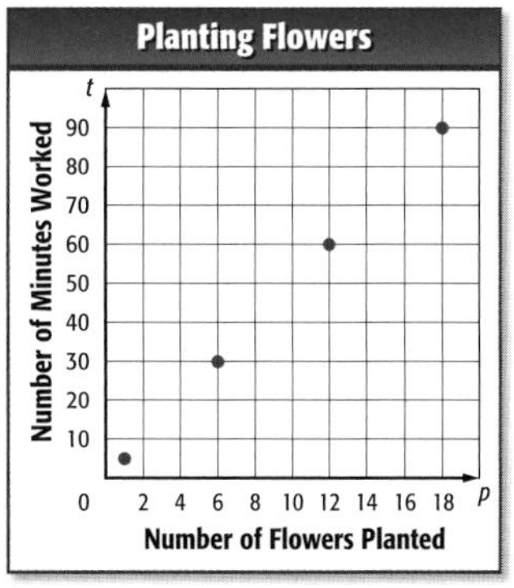

Proportional Relationships If the relationship between the domain and range of a relation is linear, the relationship can be described by a linear equation. If the equation is of the form $y = kx$, then the relationship is proportional. In a proportional relationship, the graph will pass through (0, 0). So, direct variations are proportional relationships.

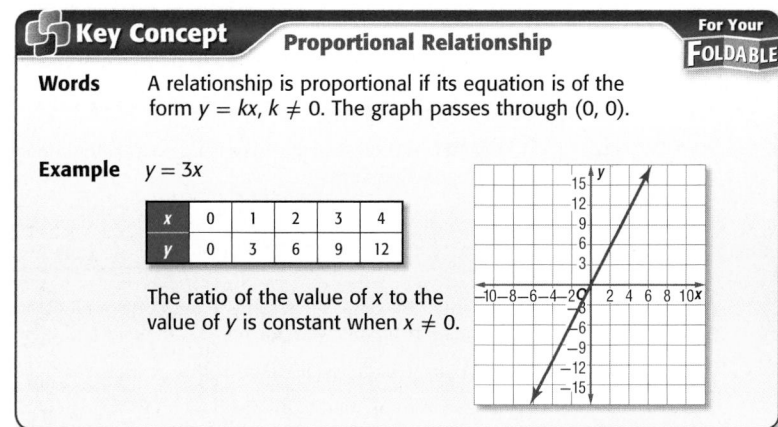

Key Concept — Proportional Relationship

For Your FOLDABLE

Words A relationship is proportional if its equation is of the form $y = kx$, $k \neq 0$. The graph passes through (0, 0).

Example $y = 3x$

x	0	1	2	3	4
y	0	3	6	9	12

The ratio of the value of *x* to the value of *y* is constant when $x \neq 0$.

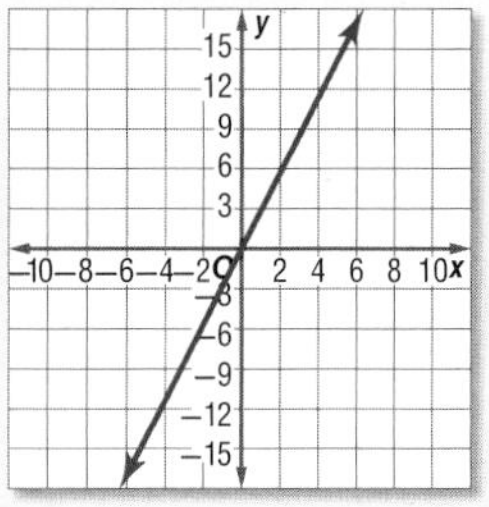

3-6 Lesson Notes

1 FOCUS

Vertical Alignment

Before Lesson 3-6
Recognize arithmetic sequences and relate them to linear functions.

Lesson 3-6
Write an equation for a proportional relationship.
Write an equation for a nonproportional relationship.

After Lesson 3-6
Write and graph linear functions in various forms.

2 TEACH

Scaffolding Questions

Have students read the *Why?* section of the lesson.

Ask:

- If the linear pattern is extended, is (0, 0) part of the pattern? yes
- Is there an equation of the form $t = kp$ that describes the relationship? Yes, $t = 5p$.

(continued on the next page)

Lesson 3-6 Resources

Resource	Approaching-Level	On-Level	Beyond-Level	English Learners
Teacher Edition	• Differentiated Instruction, p. 197	• Differentiated Instruction, p. 197	• Differentiated Instruction, p. 200	• Differentiated Instruction, p. 197
Chapter Resource Masters	• Study Guide and Intervention, pp. 37–38 • Skills Practice, p. 39 • Practice, p. 40 • Word Problem Practice, p. 41	• Study Guide and Intervention, pp. 37–38 • Skills Practice, p. 39 • Practice, p. 40 • Word Problem Practice, p. 41 • Enrichment, p. 42	• Practice, p. 40 • Word Problem Practice, p. 41 • Enrichment, p. 42	• Study Guide and Intervention, pp. 37–38 • Skills Practice, p. 39 • Practice, p. 40
Transparencies	• 5-Minute Check Transparency 3-6	• 5-Minute Check Transparency 3-6	• 5-Minute Check Transparency 3-6	• 5-Minute Check Transparency 3-6
Other	• Study Notebook • Teaching Algebra with Manipulatives	• Study Notebook • Teaching Algebra with Manipulatives	• Study Notebook	• Study Notebook • Teaching Algebra with Manipulatives

Scaffolding Questions continued

- Based on your answer to the previous question, do you think there might be a way to predict the number of minutes it will take to plant 65 flowers? Yes, substitute 65 into the equation $t = 5p$ to get $t = 5(65)$. It will take 325 minutes.

Formative Assessment

Use the Check Your Progress exercises after each Example to determine students' understanding of concepts.

Proportional Relationships

Example 1 shows how to write an equation for a real-world problem, given a table of data.

Additional Example

1 **ENERGY** The table shows the number of miles driven for each hour of driving.

Hours	1	2	3	4
Miles	50	100	150	200

a. Graph the data. What can you deduce from the pattern about the relationship between the number of hours of driving h and the number of miles driven m?

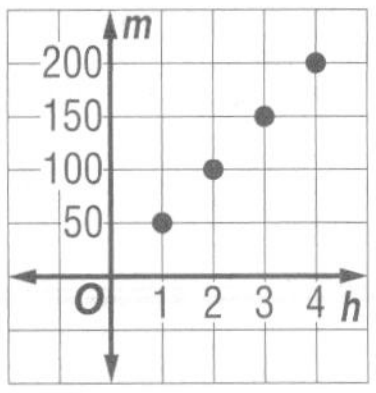

There is a linear relationship between hours of driving and miles driven.

b. Write an equation to describe this relationship. $m = 50h$

c. Use this equation to predict the number of miles driven in 8 hours of driving. 400 miles

Real-World Link

Attendance at fitness clubs has steadily grown over the past fifteen years. Members' ages are expanding to a range of 15–34 on average.

Source: International Health, Raquet, and Sportsclub Association

Real-World EXAMPLE 1 Proportional Relationships

BONUS PAY **Marcos is a personal trainer at a gym. In addition to his salary, he receives a bonus for each client he sees.**

Number of Clients	1	2	3	4	5
Bonus Pay ($)	45	90	135	180	225

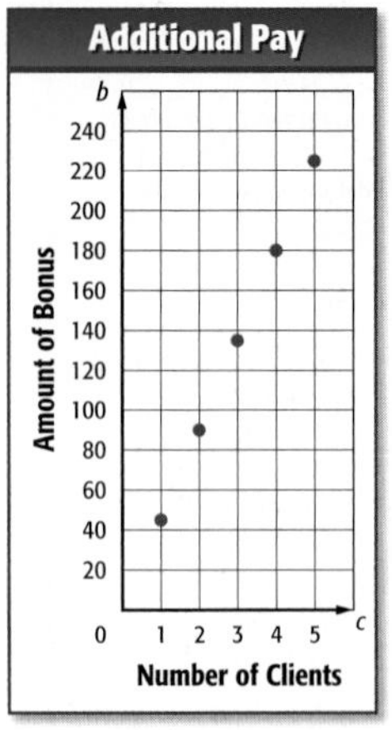

a. Graph the data. What can you deduce from the pattern about the relationship between the number of clients and the bonus pay?

The graph demonstrates a linear relationship between the number of clients and the bonus pay.

The graph also passes through the point (0, 0) because when Marcos sees 0 clients, he does not receive any bonus money. Therefore, the relationship is proportional.

b. Write an equation to describe this relationship.

Look for a pattern that can be described in an equation.

+1 +1 +1 +1

Number of Clients	1	2	3	4	5
Bonus Pay ($)	45	90	135	180	225

+45 +45 +45 +45

StudyTip

Patterns Look for a pattern that shows a constant rate of change between the terms.

The difference between the values for the number of clients c is 1. The difference in the values for the bonus pay b is 45. This suggests that the k-value is $\frac{45}{1}$ or 45. So the equation is $b = 45c$. You can check this equation by substituting values for c into the equation.

CHECK If $c = 1$, then $b = 45(1)$ or 45. ✓
If $c = 5$, then $b = 45(5)$ or 225. ✓

c. Use this equation to predict the amount of Marcos' bonus if he sees 8 clients.

$b = 45c$ **Original equation**
$= 45(8)$ or 360 **$c = 8$**

Marcos will receive a bonus of $360 if he sees 8 clients.

Check Your Progress

1. CHARITY A professional soccer team is donating money to a local charity for each goal they score.

Number of Goals	1	2	3	4	5
Donation ($)	75	150	225	300	375

A. Graph the data. What can you deduce from the pattern about the relationship between the number of goals and the money donated? See margin.

B. Write an equation to describe this relationship. $d = 75g$

C. Use this equation to predict how much money will be donated for 12 goals. $900

Personal Tutor glencoe.com

Additional Answer (Check Your Progress)

1A.

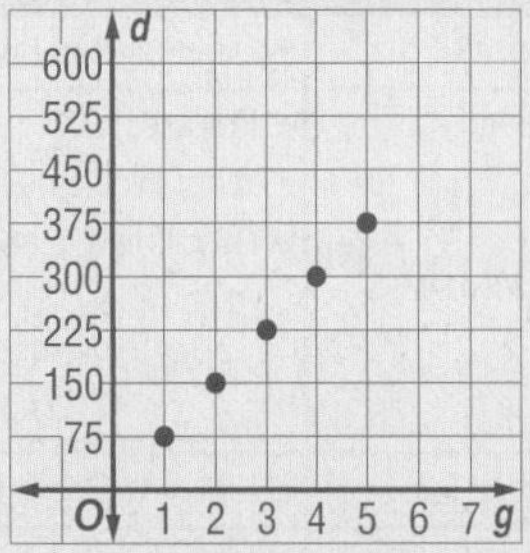

The graph demonstrates a linear pattern and passes through (0, 0). The relationship is proportional.

196 Chapter 3 Linear Functions

StudyTip

A value added to or subtracted from one side of the equation $y = ax$ will cause a shift along the y-axis for the graph of the line.

Nonproportional Relationships Some linear equations can represent a nonproportional relationship. If the ratio of the value of x to the value of y is different for select ordered pairs that are on the line, the equation is nonproportional and the graph will not pass through (0, 0).

EXAMPLE 2 Nonproportional Relationships

Write an equation in function notation for the graph.

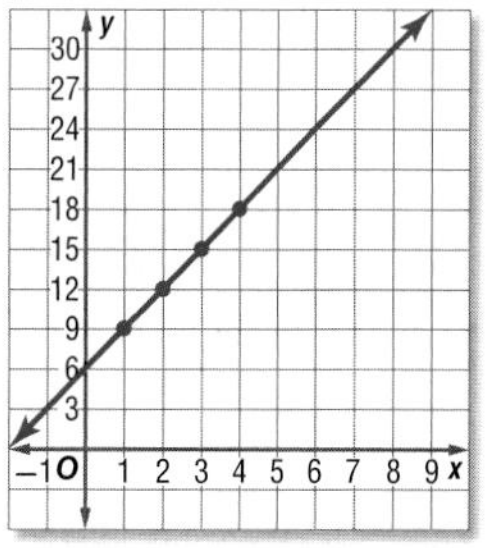

Understand You are asked to write an equation of the relation that is graphed in function notation.

Plan Find the difference between the x-values and the difference between the y-values.

Solve Select points from the graph and place them in a table.

+1 +1 +1

x	1	2	3	4
y	9	12	15	18

+3 +3 +3

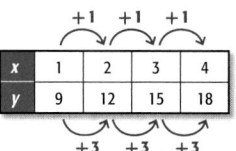

Notice that $\frac{1}{9} \neq \frac{2}{12} \neq \frac{3}{15} \neq \frac{4}{18}$.

The difference between the x-values is 1, while the difference between the y-values is 3. This suggests that $y = 3x$ or $f(x) = 3x + 6$.

If $x = 1$, then $y = 3(1)$ or 3. But the y-value for $x = 1$ is 9. Let's try some other values and see if we can detect a pattern.

x	1	2	3	4
$3x$	3	6	9	12
y	9	12	15	18

y is always 6 more than $3x$.

This pattern shows that 6 should be added to one side of the equation. Thus, the equation is $y = 3x + 6$ or $f(x) = 3x + 6$.

Check Compare the ordered pairs from the table to the graph. The points correspond. ✓

Check Your Progress

2. Write an equation in function notation for the relation shown in the table.

A.

x	1	2	3	4
y	3	2	1	0

$y = -x + 4$ or $f(x) = -x + 4$

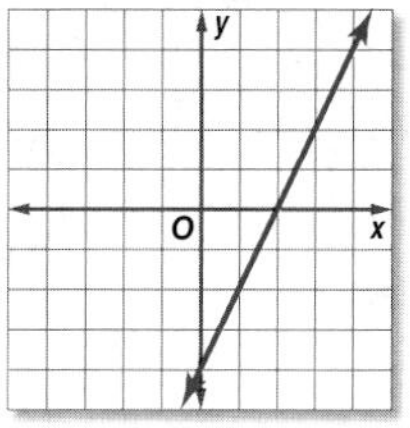

B. Write an equation in function notation for the graph. $y = 2x - 4$; $f(x) = 2x - 4$

Personal Tutor glencoe.com

Nonproportional Relationships

Example 2 shows how to write an equation in function notation, given a graph of a relation.

Additional Example

2 Write an equation in function notation for the graph.

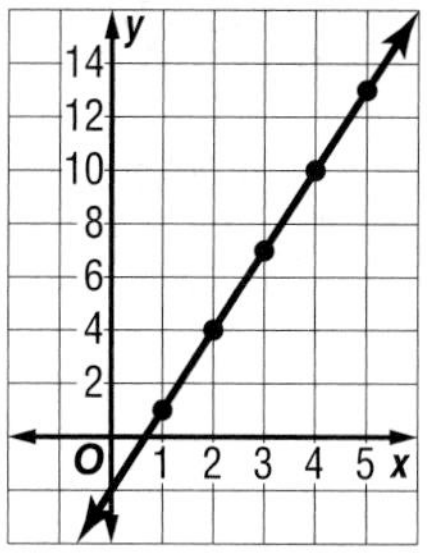

$f(x) = 3x - 2$

Additional Examples also in Interactive Classroom PowerPoint® Presentations

IWB INTERACTIVE WHITEBOARD READY

Focus on Mathematical Content

Graphs The graph of a relation represented by $y = ax$ will be parallel to the graph of relations represented by $y = ax + b$ and $y = ax - b$.

TEACH with TECH

STUDENT RESPONSE SYSTEM Create a quiz that presents students with several relationships and ask them if each is a proportional or a non-proportional relationship. Have students respond with 1 for proportional or 2 for non-proportional.

Differentiated Instruction

AL OL ELL

If students need a concrete representation,

Then provide groups with posterboard. Have groups draw a large 10 × 10 coordinate grid on their posterboard. Then have half the groups draw a graph of a proportional relationship and the other half draw a graph of a nonproportional relationship. Then have groups explain which type of graph their example represents.

3 PRACTICE

Formative Assessment

Use Exercises 1–3 to check for understanding.

Use the chart at the bottom of this page to customize assignments for your students.

Exercise Alert

Grid Paper Students will need grid paper to graph equations in Exercises 1, 4, 13, and 33–35.

Watch Out!

Find the Error For Exercise 14, suggest students think of the equation in the form $y = kx$, then substitute values in to determine the value of k.

Additional Answers

1a.

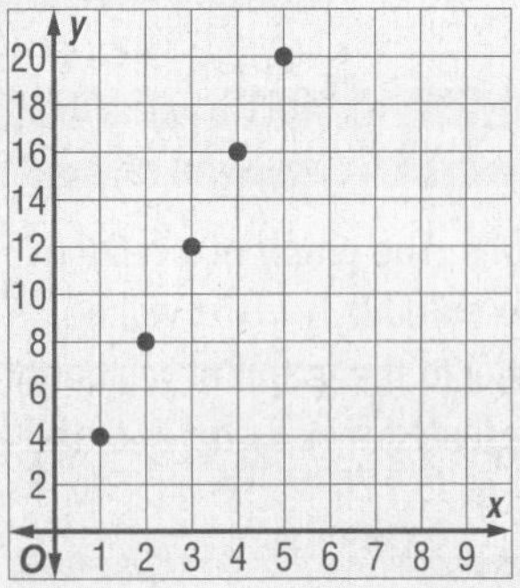

4a.

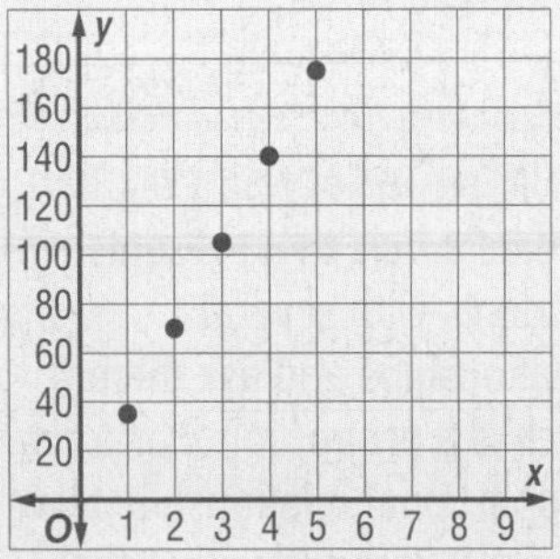

17. $f(n) = 3n + 2$ is the related function for the arithmetic sequence 5, 8, 11, 14, …, but it is not proportional. The line through (1, 5) and (2, 8) does not pass through (0, 0).

Check Your Understanding

Example 1 p. 196

1. GEOMETRY The table shows the perimeter of a square with sides of a given length.

Side Length (in.)	1	2	3	4	5
Perimeter (in.)	4	8	12	16	20

a. Graph the data. **See margin.**

b. Write an equation to describe the relationship. $y = 4x$

c. What conclusion can you make regarding the relationship between the side and the perimeter? **The perimeter is 4 times the length of the side.**

Example 2 p. 197

Write an equation in function notation for each relation.

2. 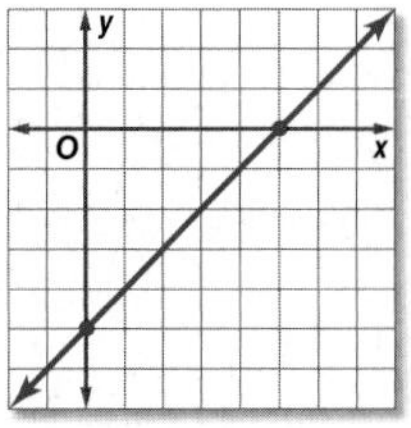 $f(x) = x - 5$

3. 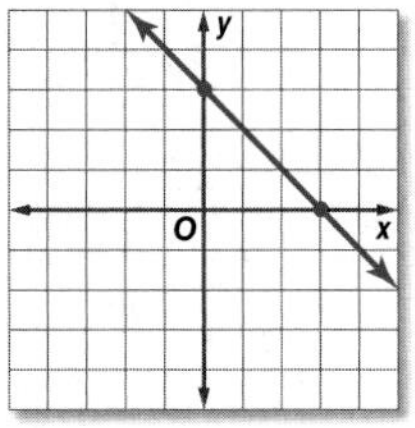 $f(x) = -x + 3$

Practice and Problem Solving

= **Step-by-Step Solutions** begin on page R12. **Extra Practice** begins on page 815.

Example 1 p. 196

4. The table shows the pages of comic books read.

Books Read	1	2	3	4	5
Pages Read	35	70	105	140	175

a. Graph the data. **See margin.**

b. Write an equation to describe the relationship. $y = 35x$

c. Find the number of pages read if 8 comic books were read. **280**

Example 2 p. 197

Write an equation in function notation for each relation.

5. 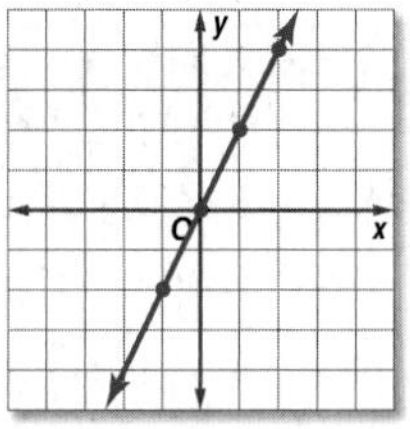 $f(x) = 2x$

6. 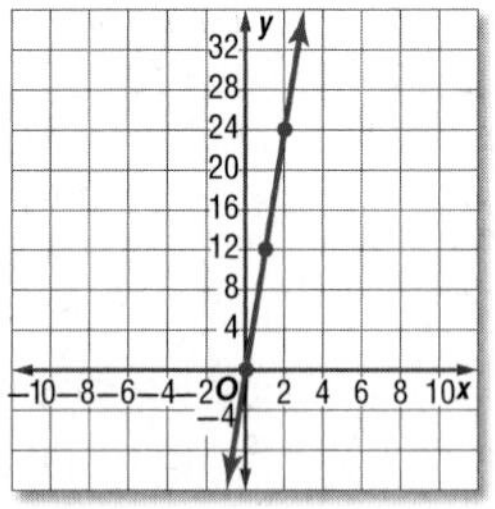 $f(x) = 12x$

7. 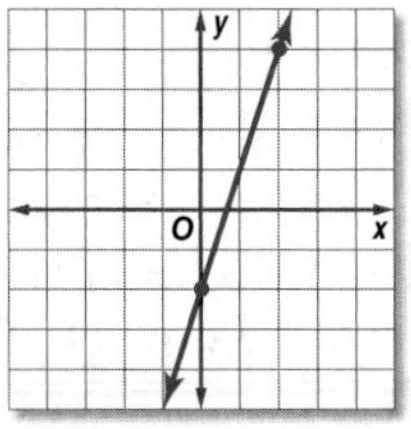 $f(x) = 3x - 2$

8. 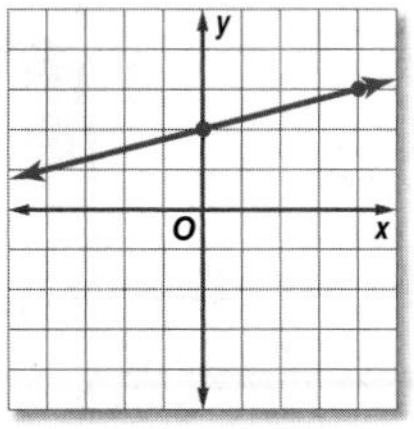 $f(x) = \frac{1}{4}x + 2$

Differentiated Homework Options

Level	Assignment		Two-Day Option	
AL Basic	4–8, 14–15, 17–35	5, 7, 19–22	4–8 even, 14, 15, 17–18, 23–35
OL Core	5, 7, 9–15, 17–35	4–8, 19–22	9–15, 17–18, 23–35
BL Advanced	9–29, (optional: 30–35)		

B For each arithmetic sequence, determine the related function. Then determine if the function is *proportional* or *nonproportional*. Explain.

9. 0, 3, 6, … **10.** −4, 0, 4, …

11. PHOTOGRAPH Marielle wants to enlarge a picture of her family. The store charges $2.50 to develop the picture, and the table shows the list of prices for enlarging photographs. Write an equation to represent the total price y of the photograph with an enlargement of x size. $y = 2.25x + 2.50$

Size	Price ($)
3 × 5	2.25
4 × 6	4.50
5 × 7	6.75
8 × 10	9

12. SNOWFALL The total snowfall each hour of a winter snowstorm is shown in the table below.

Hour	1	2	3	4
Inches of Snowfall	1.65	3.30	4.95	6.60

a. Write an equation to fit the data in the table. $a_n = 1.65n$

b. Describe the relationship between the hour and inches of snowfall. The relation is proportional.

13. FUNDRAISER The Cougar Pep Squad wants to sell T-shirts in the bookstore for the spring dance. The cost in dollars to order T-shirts in their school colors is represented by the equation $C = 2t + 3$.

a. Make a table of values that represents this relationship. See Chapter 3 Answer Appendix.

b. Rewrite the equation in function notation. $C(t) = 2t + 3$

c. Graph the function. See Chapter 3 Answer Appendix.

d. Describe the relationship between the number of T-shirts and the cost. This relation is nonproportional.

H.O.T. Problems Use Higher-Order Thinking Skills

C 14. ERROR ANALYSIS Quentin and Claudia are writing an equation to describe the following relationship. Is either of them correct? Explain.

x	y
2	1
4	2
6	3

Quentin

Since the difference in the y-values is half as much as the difference in the x-values, the equation is $y = \frac{1}{2}x$.

Claudia

Since the difference in the x-values is half as much as the difference in the y-values, the equation is $y = 2x$.

15. OPEN ENDED Create an arithmetic sequence in which the first term is 4. Explain the pattern that you used. Write an equation that represents your sequence.

16. CHALLENGE Describe how inductive reasoning can be used to write an equation from a pattern.

17. REASONING Provide a counterexample to the following statement. *The related function of an arithmetic sequence is always proportional.* Explain why the counterexample is true. See margin.

18. WRITING IN MATH Compare and contrast proportional relationships with nonproportional relationships. See margin.

Real-World Link

The ski resort town of Mt. Baker, Washington, set the world record for the most snowfall in one year at 93 feet 8 inches.

Source: *USA TODAY*

9. $f(n) = 3n - 3$; nonproportional; the function does not describe a direct variation.
10. $f(n) = 4n$; proportional; the graph of the line passes through (0, 0).
14. Quentin; he correctly interpreted the relationship between the change in the x-values and the change in the y-values.
15. Sample answer: 4, 7, 10, 13; add a common difference of 3; $a_n = 3n + 1$.
16. Sample answer: Once you recognize a pattern, you can find a general rule that can be written as an algebraic expression.

18. Sample answer: In a proportional relationship, the ratio of $\frac{y}{x}$ is the same for each ordered pair in the line for which $x \neq 0$. However, this is not the case in a nonproportional relationship. Both can be represented by a linear equation.

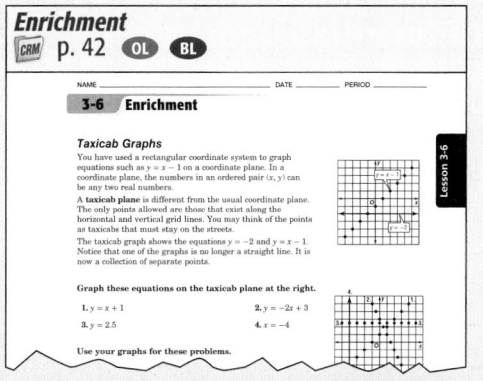

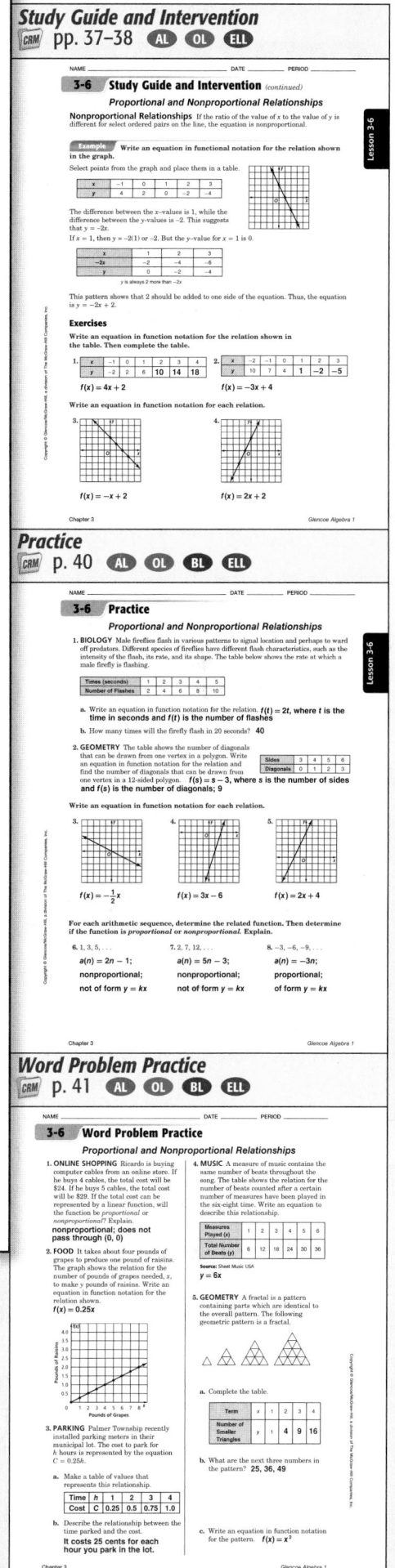

Study Guide and Intervention
CRM pp. 37–38 AL OL ELL

NAME ______ DATE ______ PERIOD ______

3-6 Study Guide and Intervention *(continued)*

Proportional and Nonproportional Relationships

Nonproportional Relationships If the ratio of the value of x to the value of y is different for select ordered pairs on the line, the equation is nonproportional.

Example Write an equation in functional notation for the relation shown in the graph.

Select points from the graph and place them in a table.

x	−1	0	1	2	3
y	4	2	0	−2	−4

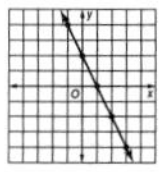

The difference between the x-values is 1, while the difference between the y-values is −2. This suggests that $y = -2x$.

If $x = 1$, then $y = -2(1)$ or −2. But the y-value for $x = 1$ is 0.

x	1	2	3
−2x	−2	−4	−6
y	0	−2	−4

y is always 2 more than −2x

This pattern shows that 2 should be added to one side of the equation. Thus, the equation is $y = -2x + 2$.

Exercises

Write an equation in function notation for the relation shown in the table. Then complete the table.

1.

x	−1	0	1	2	3	4
y	−2	2	6	10	14	18

$f(x) = 4x + 2$

2.

x	−2	−1	0	1	2	3
y	10	7	4	1	−2	−5

$f(x) = -3x + 4$

Write an equation in function notation for each relation.

3. 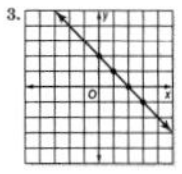

$f(x) = -x + 2$

4. 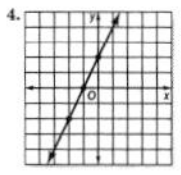

$f(x) = 2x + 2$

Chapter 3 *Glencoe Algebra 1*

Practice
CRM p. 40 AL OL BL ELL

NAME ______ DATE ______ PERIOD ______

3-6 Practice

Proportional and Nonproportional Relationships

1. **BIOLOGY** Male fireflies flash in various patterns to signal location and perhaps to ward off predators. Different species of fireflies have different flash characteristics, such as the intensity of the flash, its rate, and its shape. The table below shows the rate at which a male firefly is flashing.

Times (seconds)	1	2	3	4	5
Number of Flashes	2	4	6	8	10

a. Write an equation in function notation for the relation. $f(t) = 2t$, where t is the time in seconds and $f(t)$ is the number of flashes

b. How many times will the firefly flash in 20 seconds? 40

2. **GEOMETRY** The table shows the number of diagonals that can be drawn from one vertex in a polygon. Write an equation in function notation for the relation and find the number of diagonals that can be drawn from one vertex in a 12-sided polygon. $f(s) = s - 3$, where s is the number of sides and $f(s)$ is the number of diagonals; 9

Sides	3	4	5	6
Diagonals	0	1	2	3

Write an equation in function notation for each relation.

3. 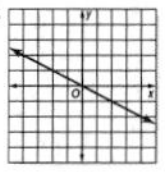

$f(x) = -\frac{1}{2}x$

4. 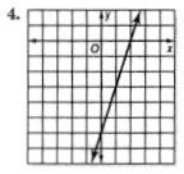

$f(x) = 3x - 6$

5. 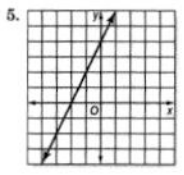

$f(x) = 2x + 4$

For each arithmetic sequence, determine the related function. Then determine if the function is *proportional* or *nonproportional*. Explain.

6. 1, 3, 5, . . . $a(n) = 2n - 1$; nonproportional; not of form $y = kx$

7. 2, 7, 12, . . . $a(n) = 5n - 3$; nonproportional; not of form $y = kx$

8. −3, −6, −9, . . . $a(n) = -3n$; proportional; of form $y = kx$

Chapter 3 *Glencoe Algebra 1*

Word Problem Practice
CRM p. 41 AL OL BL ELL

NAME ______ DATE ______ PERIOD ______

3-6 Word Problem Practice

Proportional and Nonproportional Relationships

1. **ONLINE SHOPPING** Ricardo is buying computer cables from an online store. If he buys 4 cables, the total cost will be $24. If he buys 5 cables, the total cost will be $29. If the total cost can be represented by a linear function, will the function be *proportional* or *nonproportional*? Explain. nonproportional; does not pass through (0, 0)

2. **FOOD** It takes about four pounds of grapes to produce one pound of raisins. The graph shows the relation for the number of pounds of grapes needed, x, to make y pounds of raisins. Write an equation in function notation for the relation shown. $f(x) = 0.25x$

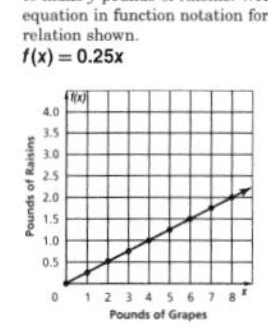

3. **PARKING** Palmer Township recently installed parking meters in their municipal lot. The cost to park for h hours is represented by the equation $C = 0.25h$.

a. Make a table of values that represents this relationship.

Time	h	1	2	3	4
Cost	C	0.25	0.5	0.75	1.0

b. Describe the relationship between the time parked and the cost. It costs 25 cents for each hour you park in the lot.

4. **MUSIC** A measure of music contains the same number of beats throughout the song. The table shows the relation for the number of beats counted after a certain number of measures have been played in the six-eight time. Write an equation to describe this relationship.

Measures Played (x)	1	2	3	4	5	6
Total Number of Beats (y)	6	12	18	24	30	36

Source: Sheet Music USA

$y = 6x$

5. **GEOMETRY** A fractal is a pattern containing parts which are identical to the overall pattern. The following geometric pattern is a fractal.

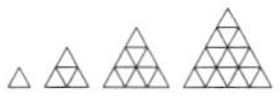

a. Complete the table.

Term	x	1	2	3	4
Number of Smaller Triangles	y	1	4	9	16

b. What are the next three numbers in the pattern? 25, 36, 49

c. Write an equation in function notation for the pattern. $f(x) = x^2$

Chapter 3 *Glencoe Algebra 1*

Enrichment
CRM p. 42 OL BL

NAME ______ DATE ______ PERIOD ______

3-6 Enrichment

Taxicab Graphs

You have used a rectangular coordinate system to graph equations such as $y = x - 1$ on a coordinate plane. In a coordinate plane, the numbers in an ordered pair (x, y) can be any two real numbers.

A **taxicab plane** is different from the usual coordinate plane. The only points allowed are those that exist along the horizontal and vertical grid lines. You may think of the points as taxicabs that must stay on the streets.

The taxicab graph shows the equations $y = -2$ and $y = x - 1$. Notice that one of the graphs is no longer a straight line. It is now a collection of separate points.

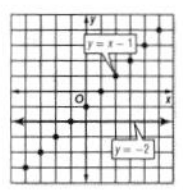

Graph these equations on the taxicab plane at the right.

1. $y = x + 1$ 2. $y = -2x + 3$

3. $y = 2.5$ 4. $x = -4$

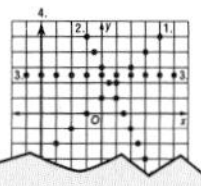

Use your graphs for these problems.

4 ASSESS

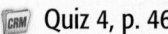

Ticket Out the Door On a 10×10 coordinate grid, have students draw a line that has whole number x- and y-intercepts. Have them write an equation in function notation for the relation.

Formative Assessment

Check for student understanding of concepts in Lesson 3-6.

CRM Quiz 4, p. 46

Additional Answers

33.

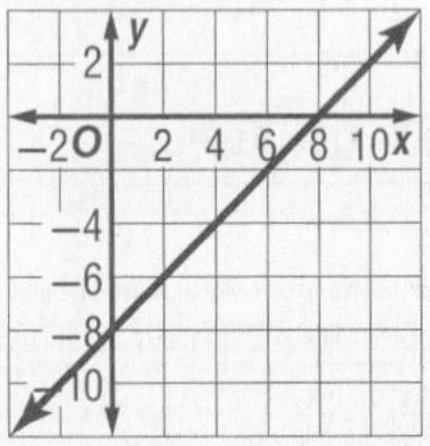

34.

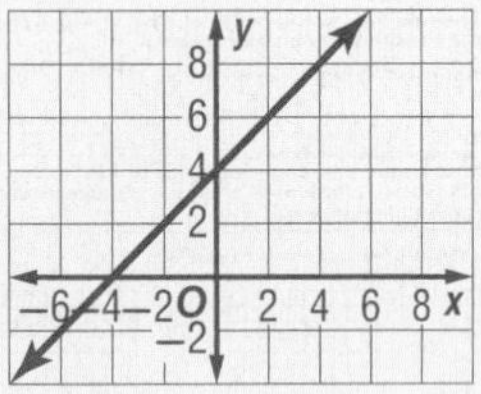

35.

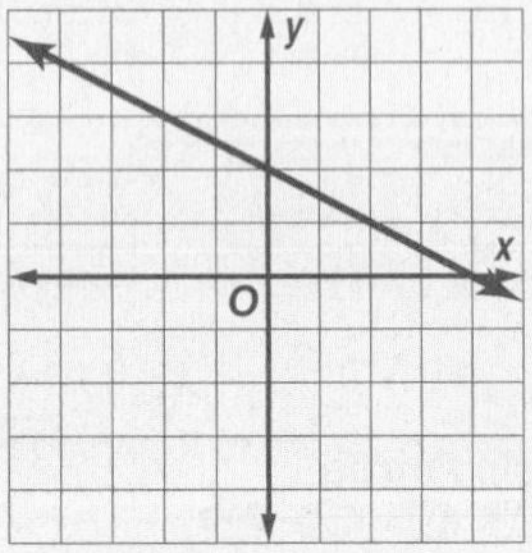

PSAE PRACTICE 8.11.07, 9.11.05, 8.11.16, 9.11.01

19. What is the slope of a line that contains the point $(1, -5)$ and has the same y-intercept as $2x - y = 9$? **D**

A -9 C 2
B -7 D 4

20. SHORT RESPONSE $\triangle FGR$ is an isosceles triangle. What is the measure of $\angle G$? **41°**

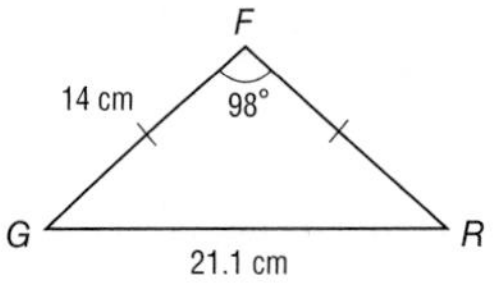

21. Luis deposits \$25 each week into a savings account from his part-time job. If he has \$350 in savings now, how much will he have in 12 weeks? **H**

F \$600 H \$650
G \$625 J \$675

22. GEOMETRY Omar and Mackenzie want to build a zip-line by attaching one end of a rope to their 8-foot-tall tree house and anchoring the other end to the ground 28 feet away from the base of the tree house. How long, to the nearest foot, does the piece of rope need to be? **D**

A 26 ft C 28 ft
B 27 ft D 29 ft

Spiral Review

Find the next three terms in each sequence. (Lesson 3-5)

23. 3, 13, 23, 33, … **43, 53, 63**

24. $-2, -1.4, -0.8, -0.2, \ldots$ **0.4, 1, 1.6**

25. $\frac{3}{4}, \frac{7}{8}, 1, \frac{9}{8}, \ldots$ **$\frac{5}{4}, \frac{11}{8}, \frac{3}{2}$**

Suppose y varies directly as x. Write a direct variation equation that relates x and y. Then solve. (Lesson 3-4)

26. If $y = 45$ when $x = 9$, find y when $x = 7$. **$y = 5x$; 35**

27. If $y = -7$ when $x = -1$, find x when $y = -84$. **$y = 7x$; −12**

28. GENETICS About $\frac{2}{25}$ of the male population in the world cannot distinguish red from green. If there are 14 boys in the ninth grade who cannot distinguish red from green, about how many ninth-grade boys are there in all? Write and solve an equation to find the answer. (Lesson 2-3) **$14 = \frac{2}{25}b$; 175 boys**

29. GEOMETRY The volume V of a cone equals one third times the product of π, the square of the radius r of the base, and the height h. (Lesson 2-1)

a. Write the formula for the volume of a cone. **$V = \frac{1}{3}\pi r^2 h$**

b. Find the volume of a cone if r is 10 centimeters and h is 30 centimeters. **about 3142 cm^3**

Skills Review

Solve each equation for y. (Lesson 2-8)

30. $3x = y + 7$ **$y = 3x - 7$**

31. $2y = 6x - 10$ **$y = 3x - 5$**

32. $9y + 2x = 12$ **$y = -\frac{2}{9}x + \frac{4}{3}$**

Graph each equation. (Lesson 3-1) **33–35. See margin.**

33. $y = x - 8$

34. $x - y = -4$

35. $2x + 4y = 8$

Differentiated Instruction BL

Extension Write 1, 2, 3, 4, 5, 6, 7, 8, 9, 10 on the board. Ask students to find the sum of the first 10 integers and then use inductive reasoning to find the sum of the first 100 positive integers. (Hint: sum = 10 + (9 + 1) + (8 + 2) + (7 + 3) + (6 + 4) + 5) 55; 5050

CHAPTER 3
Study Guide and Review

IL Math Online glencoe.com
- STUDY TO GO
- Vocabulary Review

Chapter Summary

Key Concepts

Graphing Linear Equations (Lesson 3-1)

- The standard form of a linear equation is $Ax + By = C$, where $A \geq 0$, A and B are not both zero, and A, B, and C are integers whose greatest common factor is 1.

Solving Linear Equations by Graphing (Lesson 3-2)

- Values of x for which $f(x) = 0$ are called zeros of the function f. A zero of a function is located at an x-intercept of the graph of the function.

Rate of Change and Slope (Lesson 3-3)

- If x is the independent variable and y is the dependent variable, then rate of change equals

$$\frac{\text{change in } y}{\text{change in } x}.$$

- The slope of a line is the ratio of the rise to the run.

$$m = \frac{y_2 - y_1}{x_2 - x_1}$$

Direct Variation (Lesson 3-4)

- A direct variation is described by an equation of the form $y = kx$, where $k \neq 0$.

Arithmetic Sequences (Lesson 3-5)

- The nth term a_n of an arithmetic sequence with first term a_1 and common difference d is given by $a_n = a_1 + (n - 1)d$, where n is a positive integer.

Proportional and Nonproportional Relationships (Lesson 3-6)

- In a proportional relationship, the graph will pass through (0, 0).
- In a nonproportional relationship, the graph will *not* pass through (0, 0).

FOLDABLES® Study Organizer

Be sure the Key Concepts are noted in your Foldable.

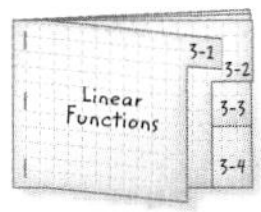

Key Vocabulary

arithmetic sequence (p. 187)
common difference (p. 187)
constant (p. 153)
constant of variation (p. 180)
direct variation (p. 180)
inductive reasoning (p. 194)
linear equation (p. 153)
linear function (p. 161)
rate of change (p. 170)
root (p. 161)
sequence (p. 187)
slope (p. 172)
standard form (p. 153)
terms of the sequence (p. 187)
***x*-intercept** (p. 154)
***y*-intercept** (p. 154)
zero of a function (p. 161)

Vocabulary Check

State whether each sentence is *true* or *false*. If *false*, replace the underlined word or number to make a true sentence.

1. The x-coordinate of the point at which the graph of an equation crosses the x-axis is an <u>x-intercept</u>. **true**
2. A <u>linear equation</u> is an equation of a line. **true**
3. The difference between successive terms of an arithmetic sequence is the <u>constant of variation</u>. **false; common difference**
4. The <u>regular form</u> of a linear equation is $Ax + By = C$. **false; standard form**
5. Values of x for which $f(x) = 0$ are called <u>zeros</u> of the function f. **true**
6. Any two points on a nonvertical line can be used to determine the <u>slope</u>. **true**
7. The slope of the line $y = 5$ is <u>5</u>. **false; 0**
8. The graph of any direct variation equation passes through <u>(0, 1)</u>. **false; (0, 0)**
9. A ratio that describes, on average, how much one quantity changes with respect to a change in another quantity is a <u>rate of change</u>. **true**
10. In the linear equation $4x + 3y = 12$, the constant term is <u>12</u>. **true**

CHAPTER 3
Study Guide and Review

Formative Assessment

Key Vocabulary The page reference after each word denotes where that term was first introduced. If students have difficulty answering questions 1–10, remind them that they can use these page references to refresh their memories about the vocabulary terms.

Summative Assessment

CRM Vocabulary Test, p. 48

IL Math Online glencoe.com

Vocabulary PuzzleMaker improves students' mathematics vocabulary using four puzzle formats–crossword, scramble, word search using a word list, and word search using clues. Students can work online or from a printed worksheet.

FOLDABLES® Study Organizer

Dinah Zike's Foldables®

Have students look through the chapter to make sure they have included examples in their Foldables for each lesson of the chapter.

Suggest that students keep their Foldables handy while completing the Study Guide and Review pages. Point out that their Foldables can serve as a quick review when studying for the Chapter Test.

Lesson-by-Lesson Review

Intervention If the given examples are not sufficient to review the topics covered by the questions, remind students that the page references tell them where to review that topic in their textbooks.

Two-Day Option Have students complete the Lesson-by-Lesson Review on pp. 202–204. Then you can use ExamView® Assessment Suite to customize another review worksheet that practices all the objectives of this chapter or only the objectives on which your students need more help.

Differentiated Instruction

Super DVD: MindJogger Videoquizzes Use this DVD as an alternative format of review for the test.

CHAPTER 3 Study Guide and Review

Lesson-by-Lesson Review

3-1 Graphing Linear Equations (pp. 153–160)

8.B.4b, 8.C.4b

Find the x- intercept and y- intercept of the graph of each linear function.

11. −8, 6

x	y
−8	0
−4	3
0	6
4	9
8	12

12. 3, −2

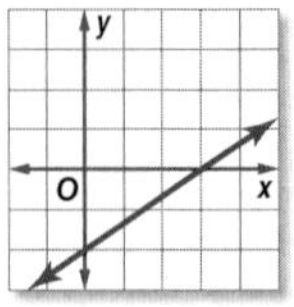

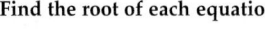

Graph each equation. 13–16. See margin.

13. $y = -x + 2$

14. $x + 5y = 4$

15. $2x - 3y = 6$

16. $5x + 2y = 10$

17. SOUND The distance d in kilometers that sound waves travel through water is given by $d = 1.6t$, where t is the time in seconds.

a. Make a table of values and graph the equation. See margin.

b. Use the graph to estimate how far sound can travel through water in 7 seconds. about 11 km

EXAMPLE 1

Graph $3x - y = 4$ by using the x- and y-intercepts.

Find the x-intercept.

$3x - y = 4$

$3x - 0 = 4$ **Let $y = 0$.**

$3x = 4$

$x = \frac{4}{3}$

Find the y-intercept.

$3x - y = 4$

$3(0) - y = 4$ **Let $x = 0$.**

$-y = 4$

$y = -4$

x-intercept: $\frac{4}{3}$

y-intercept: -4

The graph intersects the x-axis at $\left(\frac{4}{3}, 0\right)$ and the y-axis at $(0, -4)$. Plot these points. Then draw the line through them.

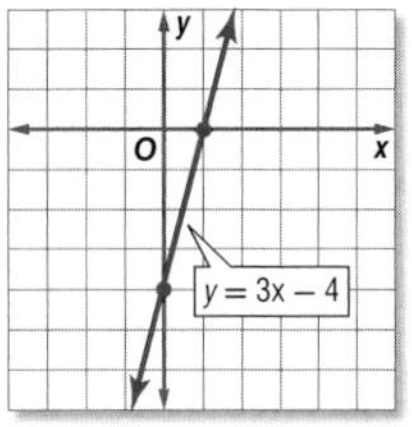

3-2 Solving Linear Equations by Graphing (pp. 161–168)

8.B.4b

Find the root of each equation.

18. $0 = 2x + 8$ −4

19. $0 = 4x - 24$ 6

20. $3x - 5 = 0$ $\frac{5}{3}$ or $1\frac{2}{3}$

21. $6x + 3 = 0$ $-\frac{1}{2}$

Solve each equation by graphing.

22. $0 = 16 - 8x$ 2

23. $0 = 21 + 3x$ −7

24. $-4x - 28 = 0$ −7

25. $25x - 225 = 0$ 9

26. FUNDRAISING Sean's class is selling boxes of popcorn to raise money for a class trip. Sean's class paid \$85 for the popcorn, and they are selling each box for \$1. The function $y = x - 85$ represents their profit y for each box of popcorn sold x. Find the zero and describe what it means in this situation. See margin.

EXAMPLE 2

Solve $3x + 1 = -2$ by graphing.

The first step is to find the related function.

$3x + 1 = -2$ **Original equation**

$3x + 1 + 2 = -2 + 2$ **Add 2 to each side.**

$3x + 3 = 0$ **Simplify.**

The related function is $y = 3x + 3$.

The graph intersects the x-axis at −1. So, the solution is −1.

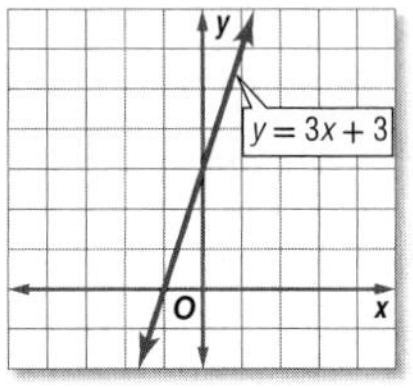

Additional Answers

13.

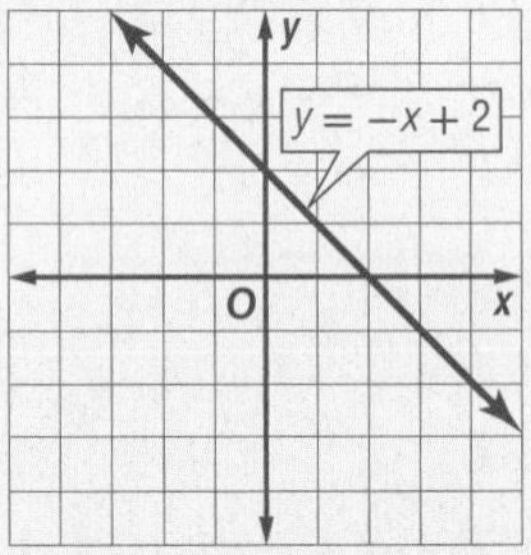

14.

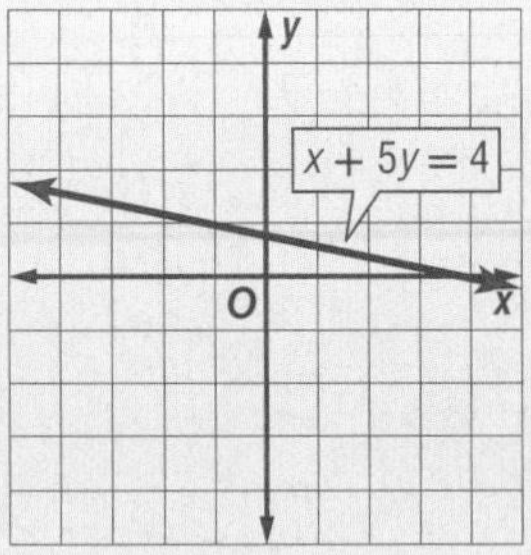

15.

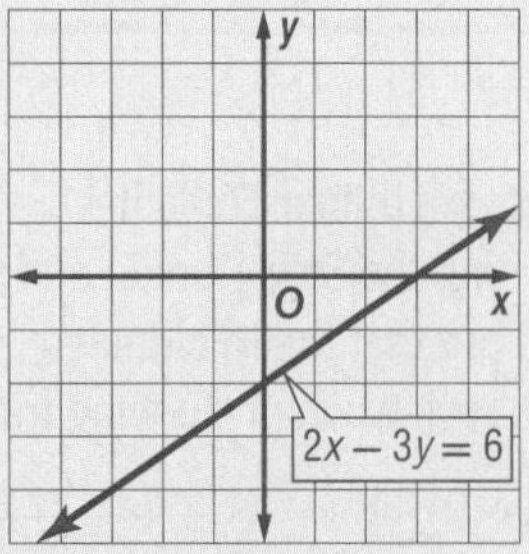

16.

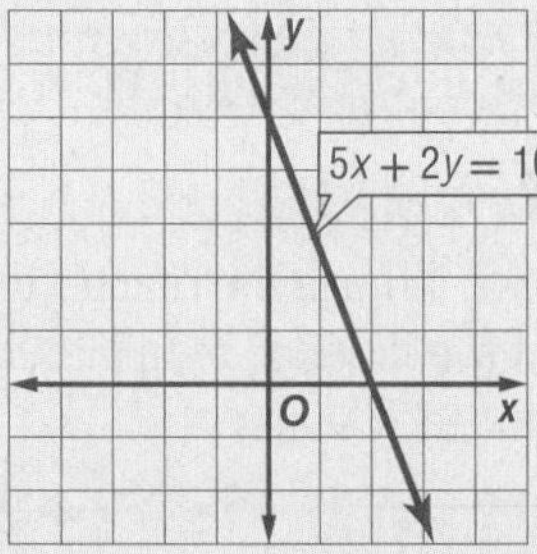

3-3 Rate of Change and Slope (pp. 169–178)

7.B.4

Find the rate of change represented in each table or graph.

27.

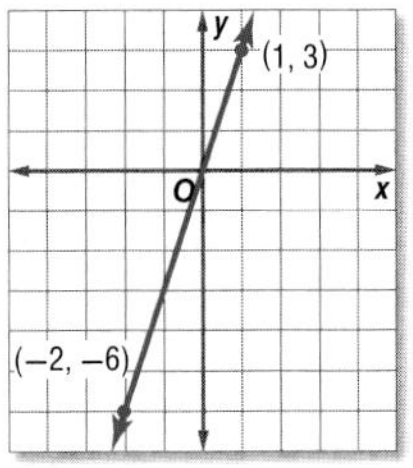

3

28. 0

x	y
−2	−3
0	−3
4	−3
12	−3

Find the slope of the line that passes through each pair of points.

29. (0, 5), (6, 2) $-\frac{1}{2}$ **30.** (−6, 4), (−6, −2) undefined

31. PHOTOS The average cost of online photos decreased from \$0.50 per print to \$0.27 per print between 2002 and 2007. Find the average rate of change in the cost. Explain what it means.

EXAMPLE 3

Find the slope of the line that passes through (0, −4) and (3, 2).

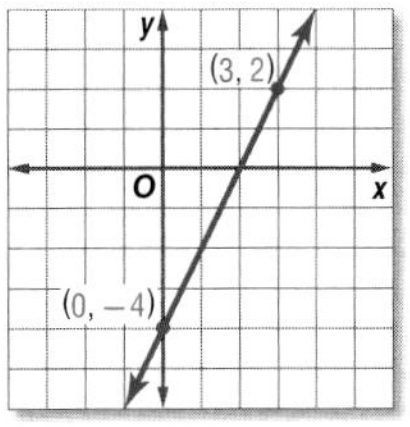

Let (0, −4) = (x_1, y_1) and (3, 2) = (x_2, y_2).

$m = \frac{y_2 - y_1}{x_2 - x_1}$ **Slope formula**

$= \frac{2 - (-4)}{3 - 0}$ **$x_1 = 0, x_2 = 3, y_1 = -4, y_2 = 2$**

$= \frac{6}{3}$ or 2 **Simplify.**

31. −0.046; an average decrease in cost of \$0.046 per year

3-4 Direct Variation (pp. 180–186)

7.A.4a, 7.A.4b

Graph each equation. 32–34. See margin.

32. $y = x$ **33.** $y = \frac{4}{3}x$ **34.** $y = -2x$

Suppose y varies directly as x. Write a direct variation equation that relates x and y. Then solve.

35. $y = 7.5x$; $y = 60$

35. If $y = 15$ when $x = 2$, find y when $x = 8$.

36. If $y = -6$ when $x = 9$, find x when $y = -3$.

37. If $y = 4$ when $x = -4$, find y when $x = 7$.

38. JOBS Suppose you earn \$127 for working 20 hours.

a. Write a direct variation equation relating your earnings to the number of hours worked. $y = 6.35x$

b. How much would you earn for working 35 hours? \$222.25

36. $y = -\frac{2}{3}x$; $x = 4\frac{1}{2}$ 37. $y = -x$; $y = -7$

EXAMPLE 4

Suppose y varies directly as x, and $y = -24$ when $x = 8$.

a. Write a direct variation equation that relates x and y.

$y = kx$ **Direct variation equation**

$-24 = k(8)$ **Substitute −24 for y and 8 for x.**

$\frac{-24}{8} = \frac{k(8)}{8}$ **Divide each side by 8.**

$-3 = k$ **Simplify.**

So, the direct variation equation is $y = -3x$.

b. Use the direct variation equation to find x when $y = -18$.

$y = -3x$ **Direct variation equation**

$-18 = -3x$ **Replace y with −18.**

$\frac{-18}{-3} = \frac{-3x}{-3}$ **Divide each side by −3.**

$6 = x$ **Simplify.**

Therefore, $x = 6$ when $y = -18$.

Additional Answers

17a.

t	d
0	0
1	1.6
2	3.2
3	4.8
4	6.4
5	8

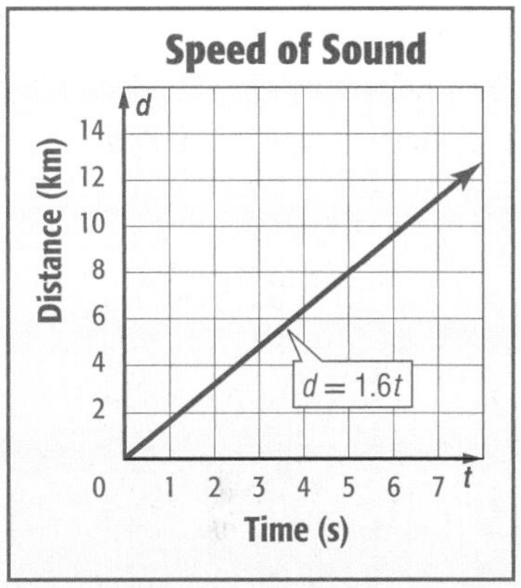

26. 85; Once they have sold 85 boxes of popcorn they will have earned back their initial investment.

32.

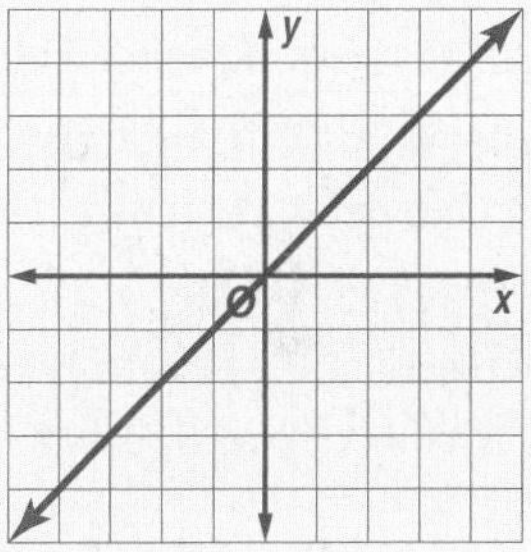

33.

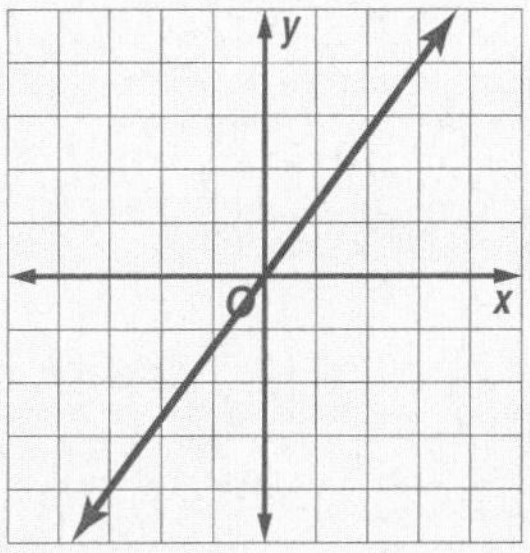

34.

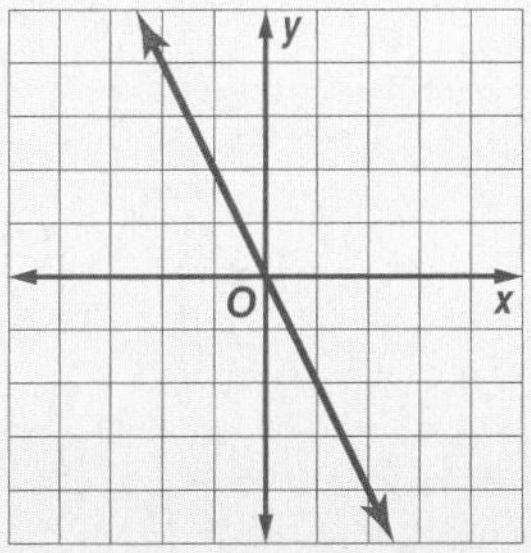

Problem Solving Review

For additional practice in problem solving for Chapter 3, see the Mixed Problem Solving Appendix, p. 847, in the Student Handbook section.

Anticipation Guide

Have students complete the Chapter 4 Anticipation Guide and discuss how their responses have changed now that they have completed Chapter 3.

Additional Answers

45a.

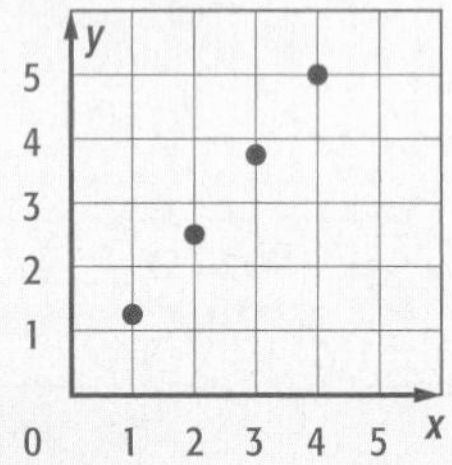

45b. $f(x) = 1.25x$

45c. $7.50

Additional Answers (Practice Test)

1a. Independent: *C*, dependent: *K*; Kelvin temperature depends on Celsius temperature.

1b. *C*-int: (−273, 0); −273°C is equal to 0°K; *K*-int: (0, 273); 0°C is equal to 273°K.

CHAPTER 3 Study Guide and Review

3-5 Arithmetic Sequences as Linear Functions (pp. 187–194)

8.A.4b, 8.C.4b

Find the next three terms of each arithmetic sequence.

39. 6, 11, 16, 21, … **26, 31, 36**

40. 1.4, 1.2, 1.0, … **0.8, 0.6, 0.4**

Write an equation for the *n*th term of each arithmetic sequence.

41. $a_1 = 6, d = 5$ $a_n = 5n + 1$

42. 28, 25, 22, 19, … $a_n = -3n + 31$

43. SCIENCE The table shows the distance traveled by sound in water. Write an equation for this sequence. Then find the time for sound to travel 72,300 feet. **43.** $a_n = 4820n$; **15 s**

Time (s)	1	2	3	4
Distance (ft)	4820	9640	14,460	19,280

EXAMPLE 5

Find the next three terms of the arithmetic sequence 10, 23, 36, 49, … .

Find the common difference.

10 23 36 49
+13 +13 +13

So, $d = 13$.

Add 13 to the last term of the sequence. Continue adding 13 until the next three terms are found.

49 62 75 88
+13 +13 +13

The next three terms are 62, 75, and 88.

3-6 Proportional and Nonproportional Relationships (pp. 195–200)

8.A.4b

44. Write an equation in function notation for this relation. $f(x) = 3x$

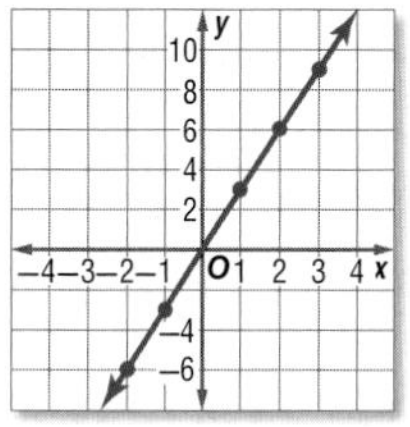

45. ANALYZE TABLES The table shows the cost of picking your own strawberries at a farm.

Number of Pounds	1	2	3	4
Total Cost ($)	1.25	2.50	3.75	5.00

a. Graph the data. **a–c. See margin.**

b. Write an equation in function notation to describe this relationship.

c. How much would it cost to pick 6 pounds of strawberries?

EXAMPLE 6

Write an equation in function notation for this relation.

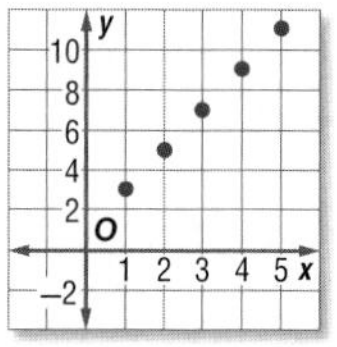

Make a table of ordered pairs for several points on the graph.

x	1	2	3	4	5
y	3	5	7	9	11

The difference in *y*-values is twice the difference of *x* values. This suggests that $y = 2x$. However, $3 \neq 2(1)$. Compare the values of *y* to the values of $2x$.

x	1	2	3	4	5
2x	2	4	6	8	10
y	3	5	7	9	11

The difference between *y* and $2x$ is always 1. So the equation is $y = 2x + 1$. Since this relation is also a function, it can be written as $f(x) = 2x + 1$.

2.

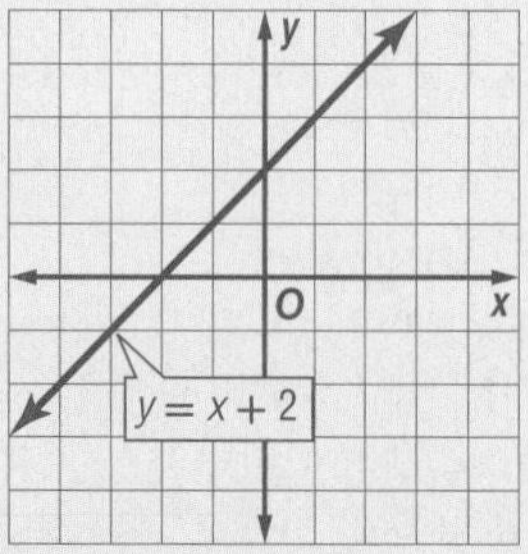

3.

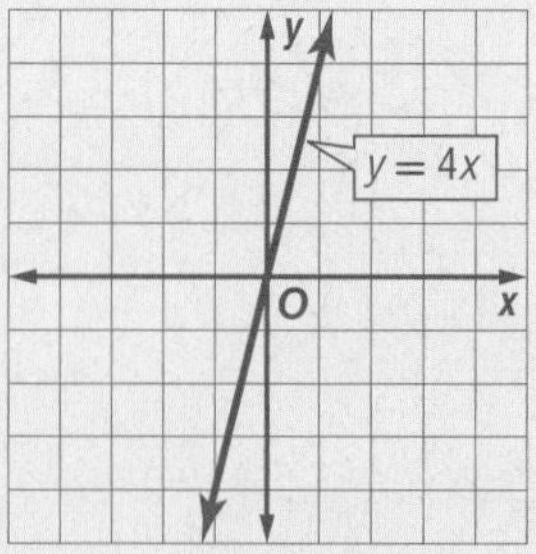

IL Math Online glencoe.com
Chapter Test

1. **TEMPERATURE** The equation to convert Celsius temperature C to Kelvin temperature K is shown.

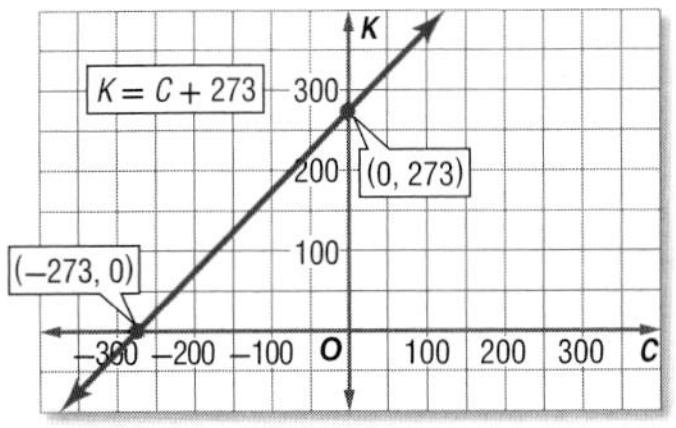

a. State the independent and dependent variables. Explain. **See margin.**

b. Determine the C- and K-intercepts and describe what the intercepts mean in this situation. **See margin.**

Graph each equation. 2–5. See margin.

2. $y = x + 2$
3. $y = 4x$
4. $x + 2y = -1$
5. $-3x = 5 - y$

Solve each equation by graphing.

6. $4x + 2 = 0$ $-\frac{1}{2}$
7. $0 = 6 - 3x$ **2**
8. $5x + 2 = -3$ **−1**
9. $12x = 4x + 16$ **2**

Find the slope of the line that passes through each pair of points.

10. $(5, 8), (-3, 7)$ $\frac{1}{8}$
11. $(5, -2), (3, -2)$ **0**
12. $(-4, 7), (8, -1)$ $-\frac{2}{3}$
13. $(6, -3), (6, 4)$ **undefined**

14. **MULTIPLE CHOICE** Which is the slope of the linear function shown in the graph? **B**

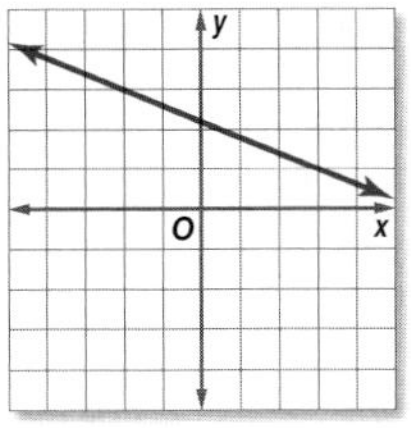

A $-\frac{5}{2}$
C $\frac{5}{2}$
B $-\frac{2}{5}$
D $\frac{2}{5}$

Suppose y varies directly as x. Write a direct variation equation that relates x and y. Then solve.

15. If $y = 6$ when $x = 9$, find x when $y = 12$.
16. When $y = -8$, $x = 8$. What is x when $y = -6$?
17. If $y = -5$ when $x = -2$, what is y when $x = 14$?
18. If $y = 2$ when $x = -12$, find y when $x = -4$.

15–18. See margin.

19. **BIOLOGY** The number of pints of blood in a human body varies directly with the person's weight. A person who weighs 120 pounds has about 8.4 pints of blood in his or her body.

a. Write and graph an equation relating weight and amount of blood in a person's body.

b. Predict the weight of a person whose body holds 12 pints of blood. **171 lbs**

19. $y = 0.07w$; See Chapter 3 Answer Appendix for graph.

Find the next three terms in each sequence.

20. 5, −10, 15, −20, 25, … **−30, 35, −40**
21. 5, 5, 6, 8, 11, 15, … **20, 26, 33**

Determine whether each sequence is an arithmetic sequence. If it is, state the common difference.

22. −40, −32, −24, −16, … **yes; 8**
23. 0.75, 1.5, 3, 6, 12, … **no**
24. 5, 17, 29, 41, … **yes; 12**

25. **MULTIPLE CHOICE** In each figure, only one side of each regular pentagon is shared with another pentagon. Each side of each pentagon is 1 centimeter. If the pattern continues, what is the perimeter of a figure that has 6 pentagons? **H**

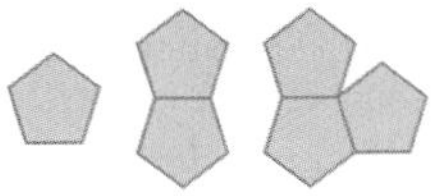

F 15 cm
H 20 cm
G 25 cm
J 30 cm

CHAPTER 3 Practice Test

ExamView Assessment Suite Customize and create multiple versions of your chapter test and their answer keys. All of the questions from the leveled chapter tests in the *Chapter 3 Resource Masters* are also available on ExamView® Assessment Suite.

Additional Answers

4.

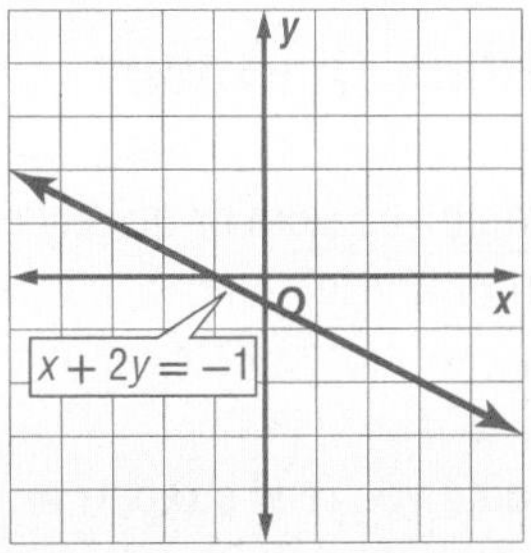

5.

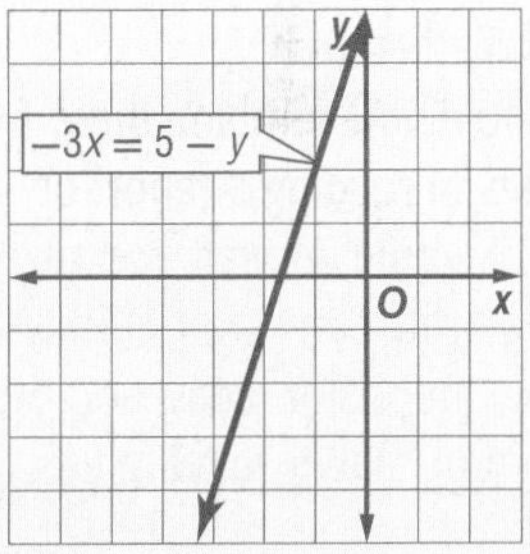

15. $y = \frac{2}{3}x; x = 18$

16. $y = -x; x = 6$

17. $y = \frac{5}{2}x; y = 35$

18. $y = -\frac{1}{6}x; y = \frac{2}{3}$

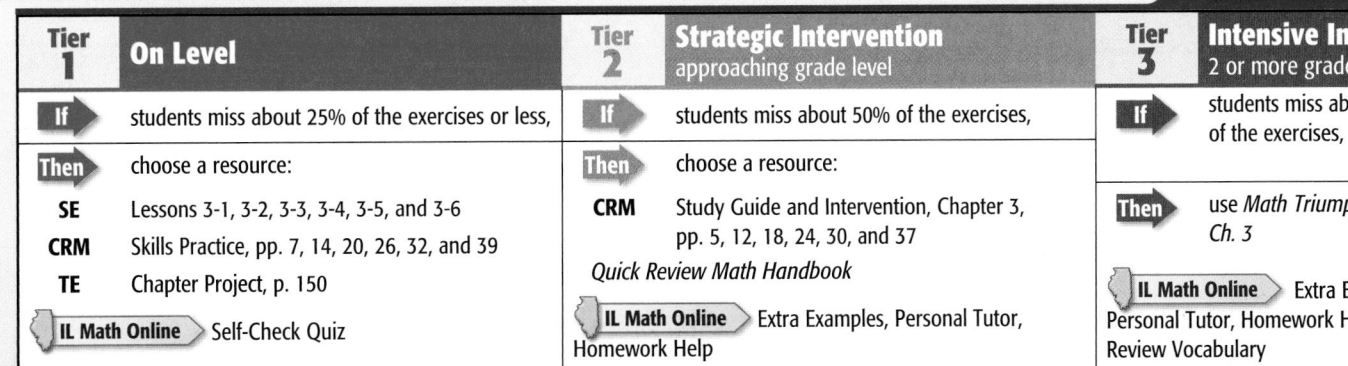

Intervention Planner

Tier 1 On Level	Tier 2 Strategic Intervention approaching grade level	Tier 3 Intensive Intervention 2 or more grades below level
If students miss about 25% of the exercises or less,	**If** students miss about 50% of the exercises,	**If** students miss about 75% of the exercises,
Then choose a resource:	**Then** choose a resource:	**Then** use *Math Triumphs, Alg. 1, Ch. 3*
SE Lessons 3-1, 3-2, 3-3, 3-4, 3-5, and 3-6	**CRM** Study Guide and Intervention, Chapter 3, pp. 5, 12, 18, 24, 30, and 37	IL Math Online Extra Examples, Personal Tutor, Homework Help, Review Vocabulary
CRM Skills Practice, pp. 7, 14, 20, 26, 32, and 39	*Quick Review Math Handbook*	
TE Chapter Project, p. 150	IL Math Online Extra Examples, Personal Tutor, Homework Help	
IL Math Online Self-Check Quiz		

1 FOCUS

Objective Use the strategy of reading the problem to solve standardized test problems.

2 TEACH

Scaffolding Questions

Ask:

- Why would you skim or quickly read a report or article? Sample answer: To get an idea of what the report or article is about.
- Why would you read a report or article more slowly? Sample answer: To find the details.
- How would you combine these two strategies in reading a report or article? Sample answer: You might read the article or report quickly to jot down the major ideas, and then read it more slowly to fill in the details.

CHAPTER 3 Preparing for Standardized Tests

Reading Math Problems

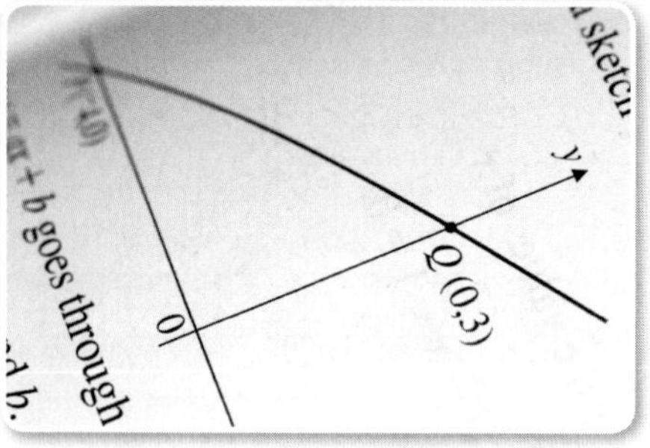

The first step to solving any math problem is to read the problem. When reading a math problem to get the information you need to solve, it is helpful to use special reading strategies.

Strategies for Reading Math Problems

Step 1

Read the problem quickly to gain a general understanding of it.

- **Ask yourself:** "What do I know?" "What do I need to find out?"
- **Think:** "Is there enough information to solve the problem? Is there extra information?"
- **Highlight:** If you are allowed to write in your test booklet, underline or highlight important information. Cross out any information you don't need.

Step 2

Reread the problem to identify relevant facts.

- **Analyze:** Determine how the facts are related.
- **Key Words:** Look for keywords to solve the problem.
- **Vocabulary:** Identify mathematical terms. Think about the concepts and how they are related.
- **Plan:** Make a plan to solve the problem.
- **Estimate:** Quickly estimate the answer.

Step 3

Identify any obvious wrong answers.

- **Eliminate:** Eliminate any choices that are very different from your estimate.
- **Units of Measure:** Identify choices that are possible answers based on the units of measure in the question. For example, if the question asks for area, only answers in square units will work.

Step 4

Look back after solving the problem.

Check: Make sure you have answered the question.

EXAMPLE

Read the problem. Identify what you need to know. Then use the information in the problem to solve.

Jamal, Gina, Lisa, and Renaldo are renting a car for a road trip. The cost of renting the car is given by the function $C = 12.5 + 21d$, where C is the total cost for renting the car for d days. What does the slope of the function represent?

A number of people

B cost per day

C number of days

D miles per gallon

Read the problem carefully. The number of people going on the trip is not needed information. You need to know what the slope of the function represents.

Slope is a ratio. The word "per" in answers B and D imply that they are both ratios. Since choices A and C are not ratios, eliminate them.

The problem says that C represents the cost of renting the car. So the slope cannot represent the miles per gallon of the car. The slope must represent the cost per day.

The correct answer is B.

Exercises

Read each problem. Identify what you need to know. Then use the information in the problem to solve.

1. What does the x-intercept mean in the context of the situation given below? A

Draining a Bathtub

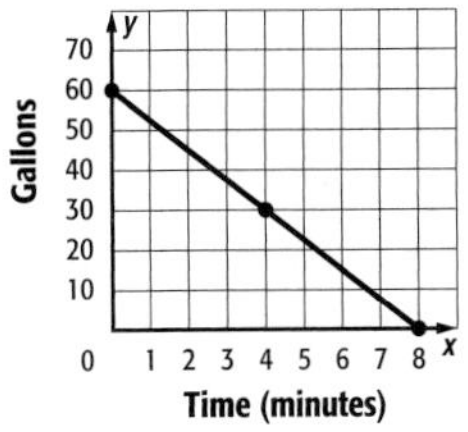

A amount of time needed to drain the bathtub

B number of gallons in the tub when the drain plug is pulled

C number of gallons in the tub after x minutes

D amount of water drained each minute

2. The amount of money raised by a charity carwash varies directly as the number of cars washed. When 11 cars are washed, \$79.75 is raised. How many cars must be washed to raise \$174.00? J

F 10 cars

G 16 cars

H 22 cars

J 24 cars

3. The function $C = 25 + 0.45(x - 450)$ represents the cost of a monthly cell phone bill, when x minutes are used. Which statement best represents the formula for the cost of the bill? C

A The cost consists of a flat fee of \$0.45 and \$25 for each minute used over 450.

B The cost consists of a flat fee of \$450 and \$0.45 for each minute used over 25.

C The cost consists of a flat fee of \$25 and \$0.45 for each minute used over 450.

D The cost consists of a flat fee of \$25 and \$0.45 for each minute used.

Additional Example

Manuel is filling an aquarium with water. The amount of water in the aquarium is given by the formula $G(t) = 2.5 + 3t$, where $G(t)$ is the total number of gallons of water in the aquarium and t is time in minutes. What does the slope of the function represent? C

A total number of gallons of water

B number of gallons of water after 3 minutes

C number of gallons per minute

D number of minutes per gallon

3 ASSESS

Use Exercises 1–3 to assess students' understanding.

Diagnose Student Errors

Survey students' responses for each item. Class trends may indicate common errors and misconceptions.

1. A guess
B guess
C correct
D guess
E guess

2. F guess
G guess
H guess
J correct
K added 2^5 instead of subtracted

3. A did not read test-taking tip and does not understand the concept of slope
B guess or calculation error
C correct
D calculated change in x-coordinates to change in y-coordinates instead of change in y-coordinates to change in x-coordinates
E only counted run

4. F subtracted 11.00 – 5.50 incorrectly
G correct
H interpreted change as decrease instead of increase
J subtracted incorrectly and misinterpreted increase as decrease
K subtracted 5.50 from 22.00; forgot to divide by 4 hours

5. A guess
B guess
C guess
D correct
E guess

6. F guess
G guess
H guess
J correct
K double the number

7. A correct
B misunderstood how to write the function
C solved for 1 hour only
D misunderstood how to write the function
E wrong slope and y-intercept

8. F correct
G guess
H guess
J guess or calculation error
K guess

9. A correct
B interchanged n and h
C found wrong rate of change
D found wrong rate of change
E found wrong rate of change

Multiple Choice

Read each question. Then fill in the correct answer on the answer document provided by your teacher or on a sheet of paper.

1. Horatio is buying a cable for \$15.49. If the sales tax rate is 5.25%, what is the total cost? **C**

A \$24.62
B \$16.42
C \$16.30
D \$15.73
E \$15.62

2. What is the value of $3^2 + 5^3 - 2^5$? **J**

F 11
G 14
H 34
J 102
K 166

3. What is the slope of the line graphed below? **C**

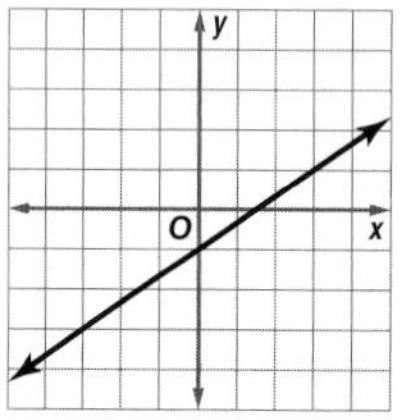

A $-\frac{1}{3}$
B $\frac{1}{2}$
C $\frac{2}{3}$
D $\frac{3}{2}$
E 3

4. Find the rate of change for the linear function represented in the table. **G**

Hours Worked	1	2	3	4
Money Earned (\$)	5.50	11.00	16.50	22.00

F increase \$6.50/h
G increase \$5.50/h
H decrease \$5.50/h
J decrease \$6.50/h
K increase \$16.50/h

5. Suppose that y varies directly as x, and $y = 14$ when $x = 4$. What is the value of y when $x = 9$? **D**

A 25.5
B 27.5
C 29.5
D 31.5
E 47

6. Write an equation for the nth term of the arithmetic sequence shown below. **J**

$-2, 1, 4, 7, 10, 13, \ldots$

F $a_n = 2n - 1$
G $a_n = 2n + 4$
H $a_n = 3n + 2$
J $a_n = 3n - 5$
K $a_n = 2n$

7. The table shows the labor charges of an electrician for jobs of different lengths.

Number of Hours (n)	Labor Charges (C)
1	\$60
2	\$85
3	\$110
4	\$135

Which function represents the situation? **A**

A $C(n) = 25n + 35$
B $C(n) = 25n + 30$
C $C(n) = 35n + 25$
D $C(n) = 35n + 40$
E $C(n) = 30n + 30$

8. Find the value of x so that the figures have the same area. **F**

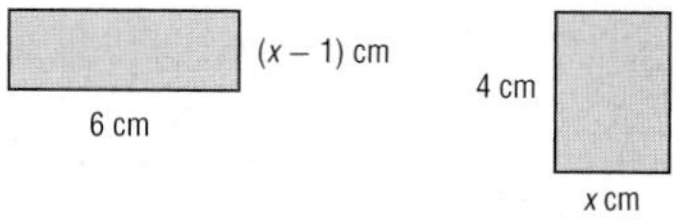

F 3 G 4 H 5 J 6 K 7

9. The table shows the total amount of rain during a storm. Write a formula to find out how much rain will fall after a given hour. **B**

Hour (h)	1	2	3	4
Inches (n)	0.45	0.9	1.35	1.8

A $h = 0.45n$
B $n = 0.45h$
C $h = 0.9n$
D $h = 1.8n$
E $n = 1.35h$

Test-Taking Tip

Question 3 You can *eliminate unreasonable answers* to multiple choice items. The line slopes up from left to right, so the slope is positive. Answer choice A can be eliminated.

Short Response/Gridded Response

Record your answers on the answer sheet provided by your teacher or on a sheet of paper.

10. The scale on a map is 1.5 inches = 6 miles. If two cities are 4 inches apart on the map, what is the actual distance between the cities? **16 miles**

11. Write a direct variation equation to represent the graph below. $y = 2x$

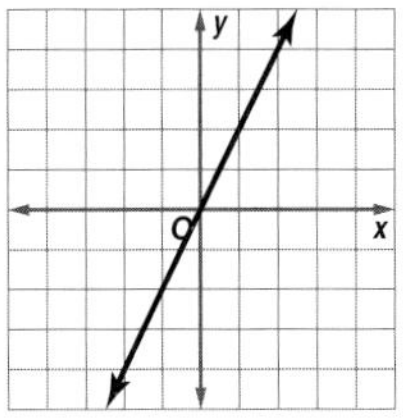

12. Justine bought a car for $18,500 and its value depreciated linearly. After 3 years, the value was $14,150. What is the amount of yearly depreciation? **$1450**

13. GRIDDED RESPONSE Use the graph to determine the solution to the equation $-\frac{1}{3}x + 1 = 0$? **3**

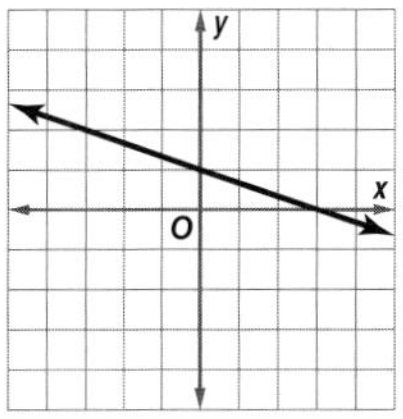

14. Write an expression that represents the total surface area (including the top and bottom) of a tower of n cubes each having a side length of s. (Do not include faces that cover each other.) $(4n + 2)s^2$

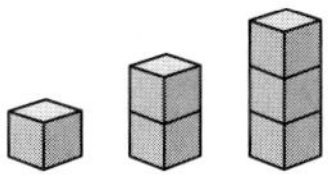

$n = 1$ $n = 2$ $n = 3$

15. GRIDDED RESPONSE There are 120 members in the North Carolina House of Representatives. This is 70 more than the number of members in the North Carolina Senate. How many members are in the North Carolina Senate? **50**

Extended Response

Record your answers on a sheet of paper. Show your work.

16. A hot air balloon was at a height of 60 feet above the ground when it began to ascend. The balloon climbed at a rate of 15 feet per minute.

a. Make a table that shows the height of the hot air balloon after climbing for 1, 2, 3, and 4 minutes. **75 ft, 90 ft, 105 ft, 120 ft**

b. Let t represent the time in minutes since the balloon began climbing. Write an algebraic equation for a sequence that can be used to find the height, h, of the balloon after t minutes. $h = 60 + 15t$

c. Use your equation from part b to find the height, in feet, of the hot air balloon after climbing for 8 minutes. **180 ft**

Need Extra Help?																
If you missed Question...	1	2	3	4	5	6	7	8	9	10	11	12	13	14	15	16
Go to Lesson or Page...	2-7	1-2	3-3	3-3	3-4	3-5	2-1	0-8	3-5	2-8	3-4	3-3	3-2	0-10	2-1	3-5
IL Assessment Objectives	6.11.18	6.11.10	8.11.09	8.11.10	6.11.19	8.11.04	8.11.07	7.11.05	8.11.07	6.11.17	6.11.19	8.11.16	9.11.11	8.11.04	6.11.13	8.11.12

Formative Assessment

You can use these two pages to benchmark student progress.

CRM Standardized Test Practice, pp. 62–64

Answer Sheet Practice

Have students simulate taking a standardized test by recording their answers on a practice recording sheet.

CRM Student Recording Sheet, p. 43

Chapter Resource Master
CRM p. 43

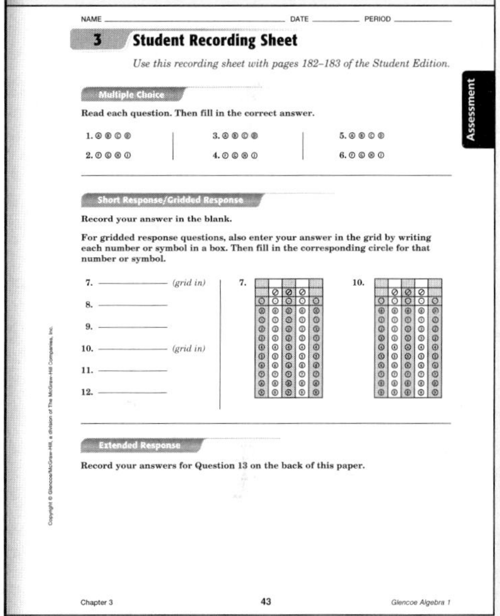

NAME DATE PERIOD

3 **Student Recording Sheet**

Use this recording sheet with pages 182–183 of the Student Edition.

Multiple Choice

Read each question. Then fill in the correct answer.

Short Response/Gridded Response

Record your answer in the blank.

For gridded response questions, also enter your answer in the grid by writing each number or symbol in a box. Then fill in the corresponding circle for that number or symbol.

Extended Response

Record your answers for Question 13 on the back of this paper.

Chapter 3 43 Glencoe Algebra 1

ExamView Assessment Suite Create practice worksheets or tests that align to your state's standards, as well as TIMSS and NAEP tests.

Homework Option

Get Ready for Chapter 4 Assign students the exercises on p. 211 as homework to assess whether they possess the prerequisite skills needed for the next chapter.

Page 151, Get Ready for Chapter 3

1.

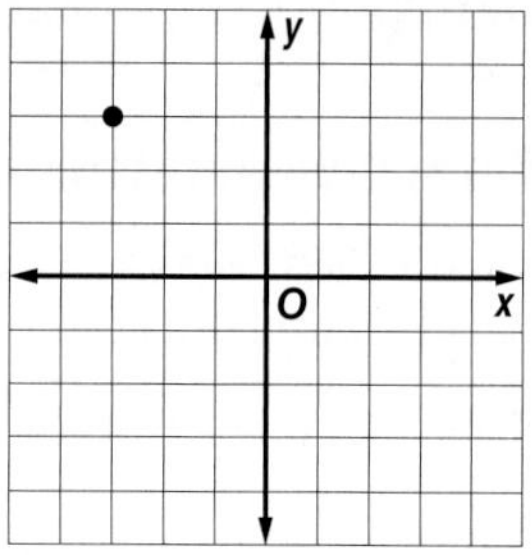

2.

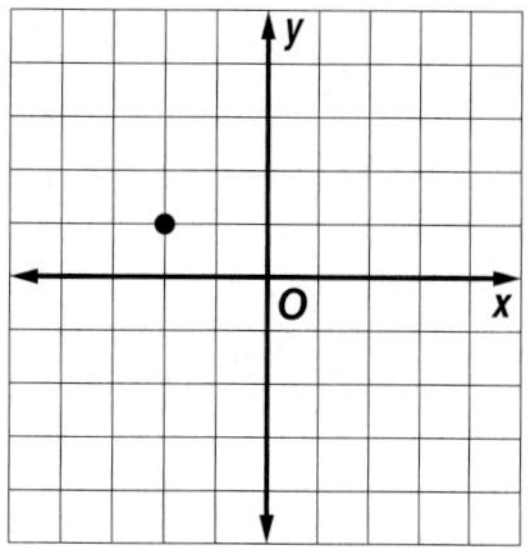

3.

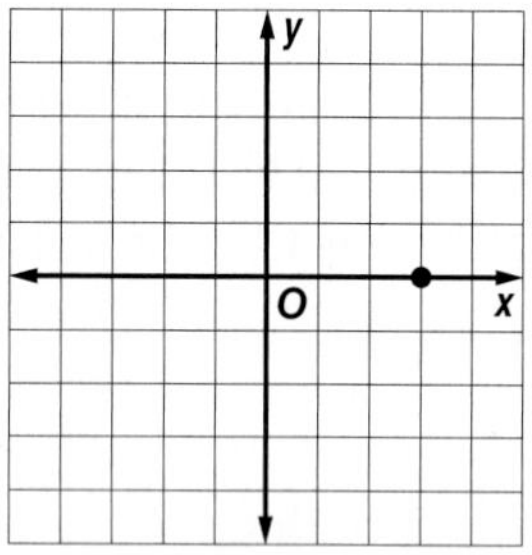

4.

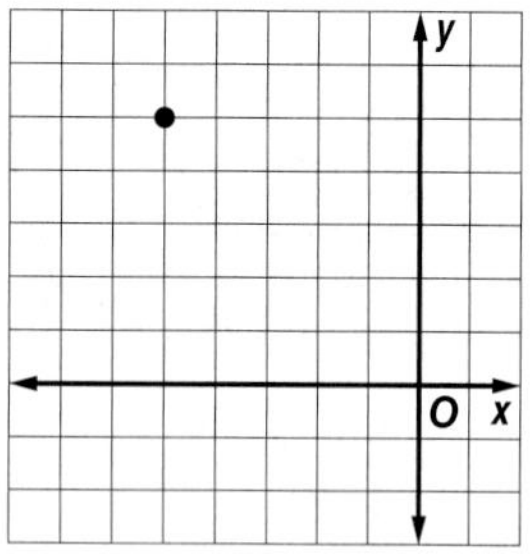

5.

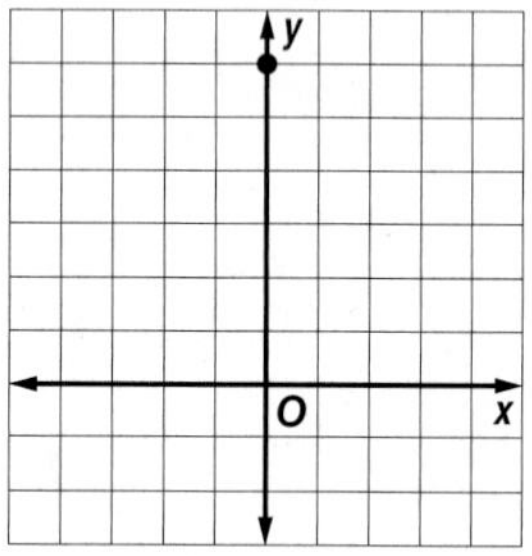

6.

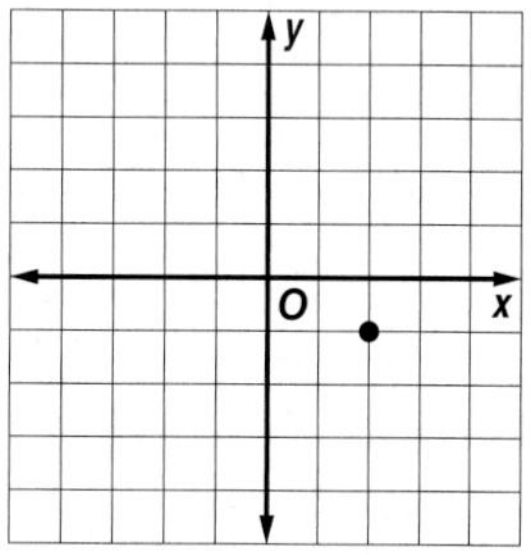

Pages 157–159, Lesson 3-1

7.

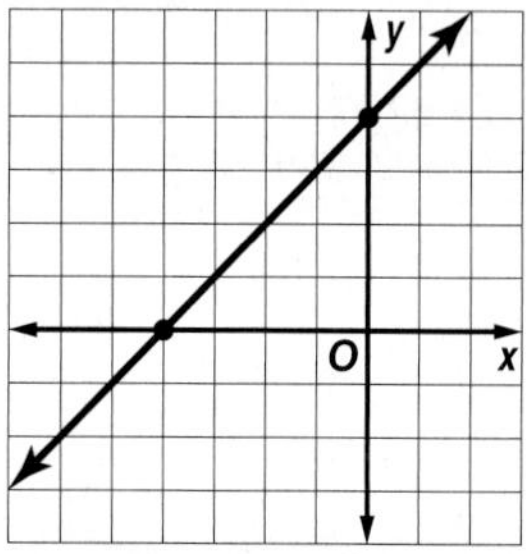

8.

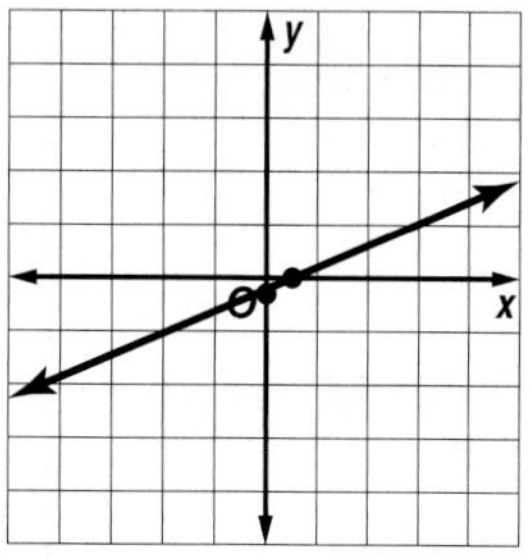

9.

x	$x + 2y = 4$	y	(x, y)
−4	$(-4) + 2y = 4$	4	(−4, 4)
−2	$(-2) + 2y = 4$	3	(−2, 3)
0	$0 + 2y = 4$	2	(0, 2)
2	$2 + 2y = 4$	1	(2, 1)
4	$4 + 2y = 4$	0	(4, 0)

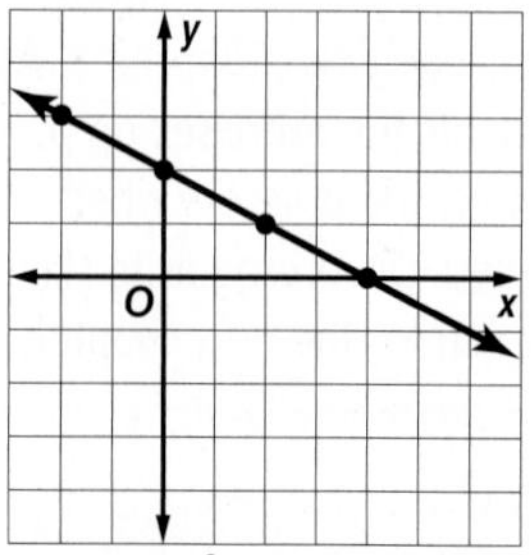

10.

x	$-3 + 2y = -5$	y	(x, y)
−2	$-3 + 2y = -5$	−1	(−2, −1)
−1	$-3 + 2y = -5$	−1	(−1, −1)
0	$-3 + 2y = -5$	−1	(0, −1)
1	$-3 + 2y = -5$	−1	(1, −1)
2	$-3 + 2y = -5$	−1	(2, −1)

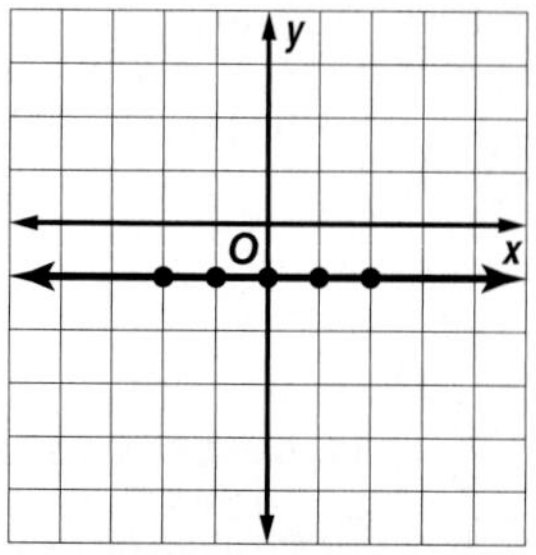

11.

x	$y = 3$	y	(x, y)
−2	$y = 3$	3	(−2, 3)
−1	$y = 3$	3	(−1, 3)
0	$y = 3$	3	(0, 3)
1	$y = 3$	3	(1, 3)
2	$y = 3$	3	(2, 3)

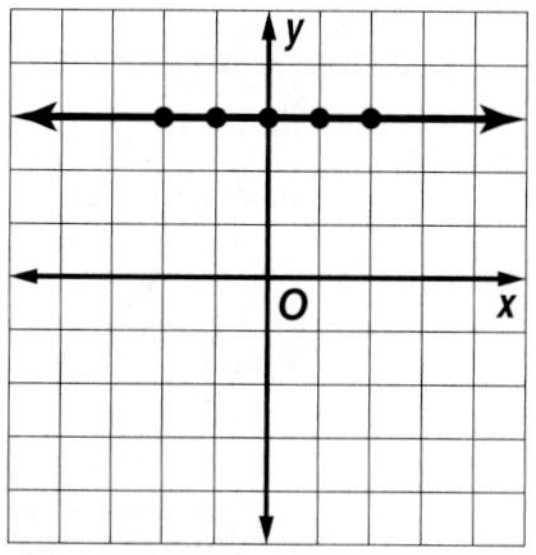

29.

x	y
−2	0
−2	1
−2	2

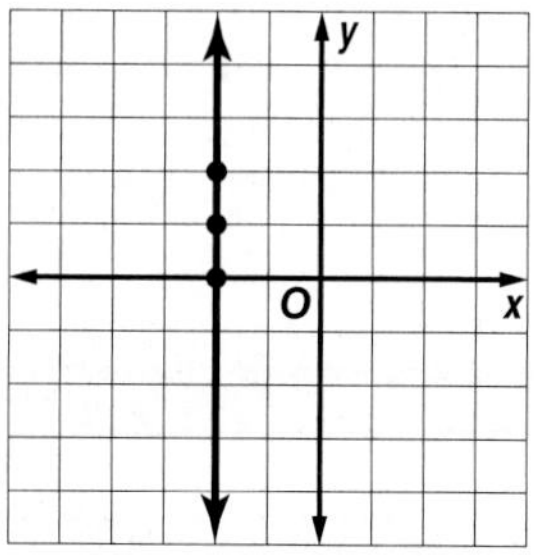

30.

x	y
0	−4
1	−4
2	−4

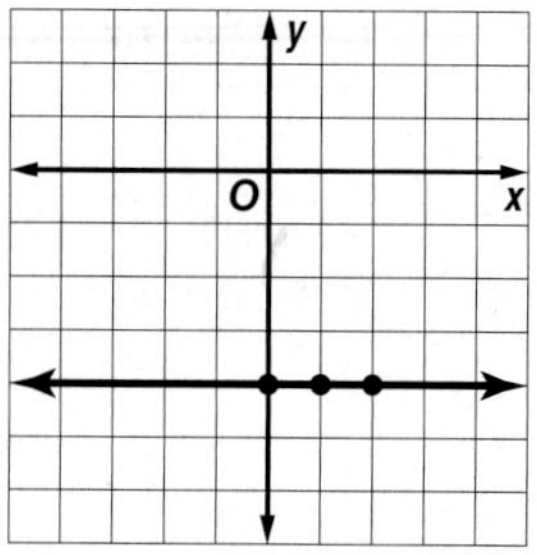

31.

x	y
−1	8
0	0
1	−8

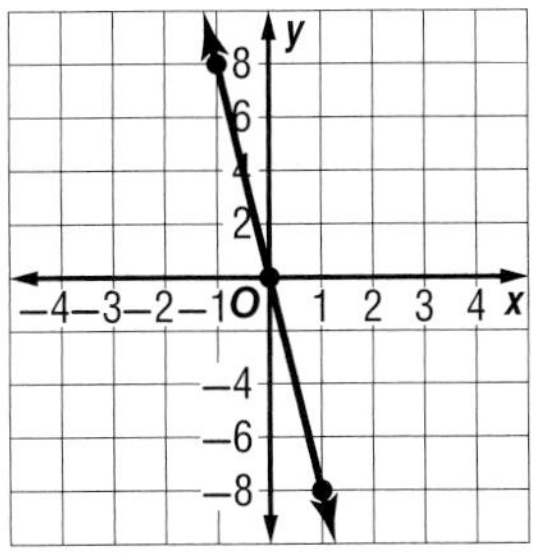

32.

x	y
0	0
1	3
2	6

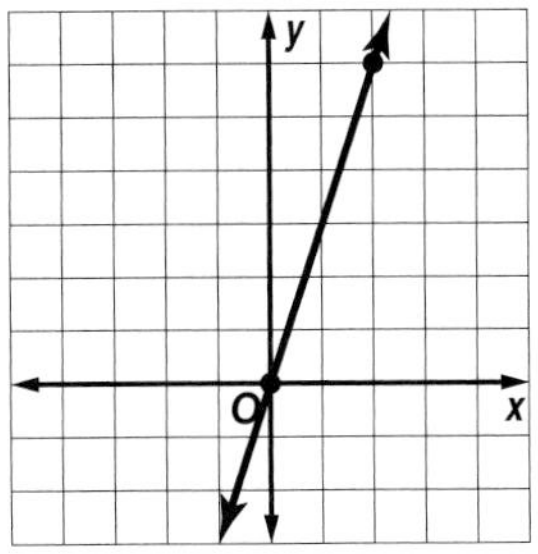

33.

x	y
0	8
1	7
2	6

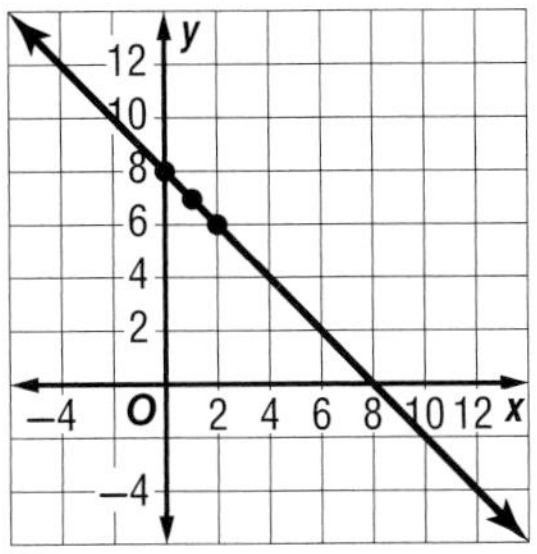

34.

x	y
0	10
1	9
2	8

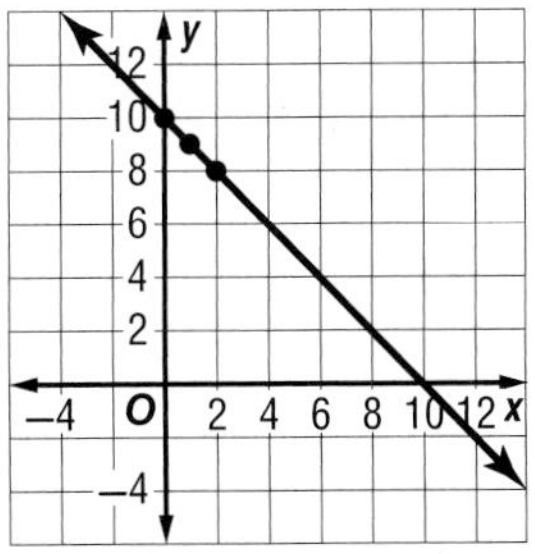

35a.

v	p = 0.15v	p	(v, p)
0	$p = 0.15(0)$	0	(0, 0)
2	$p = 0.15(2)$	0.3	(2, 0.3)
4	$p = 0.15(4)$	0.6	(4, 0.6)
6	$p = 0.15(6)$	0.9	(6, 0.9)
8	$p = 0.15(8)$	1.2	(8, 1.2)
10	$p = 0.15(10)$	1.5	(10, 1.5)

35b.

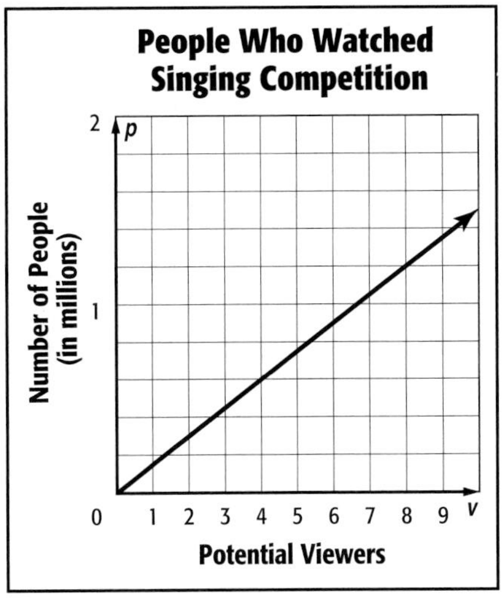

42a.

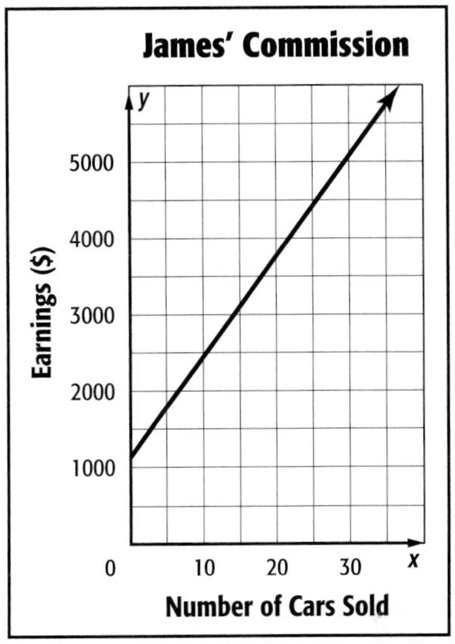

43.

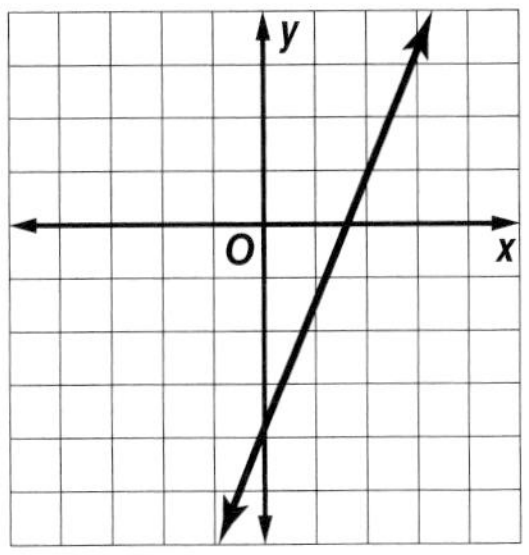

44.

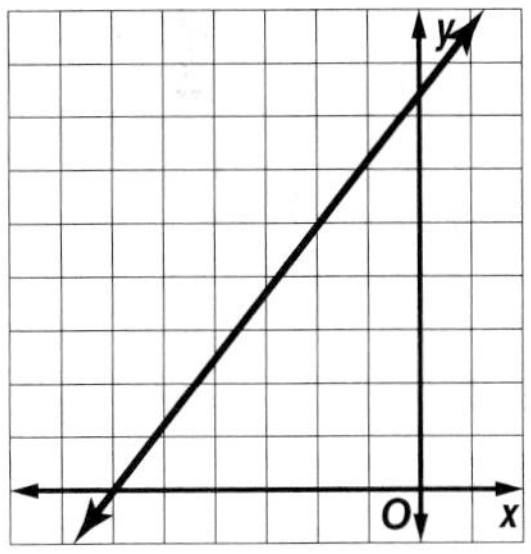

45.

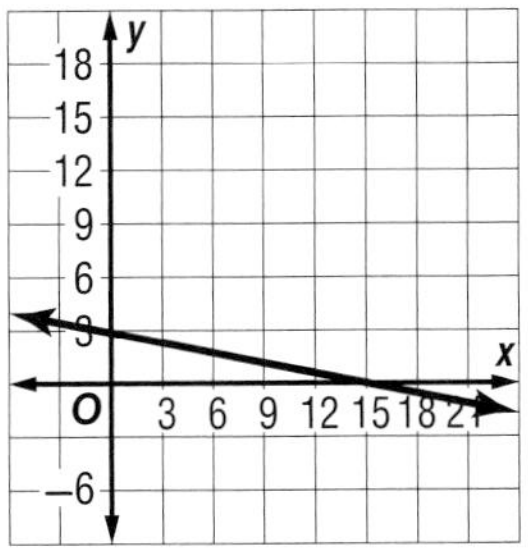

46.

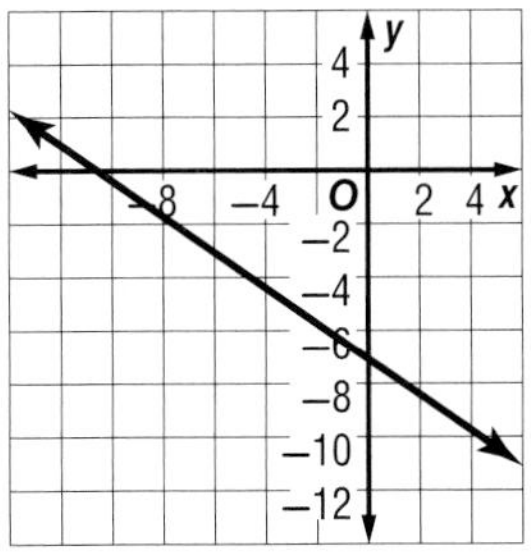

47.

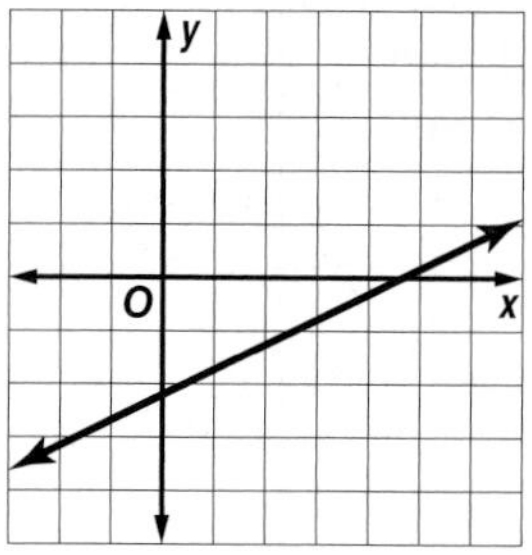

48.

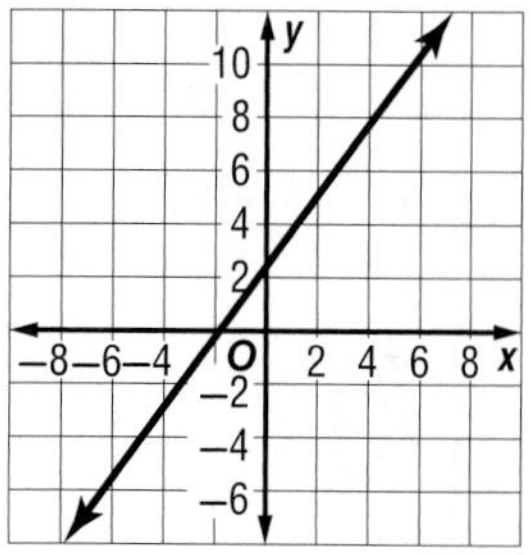

50b.

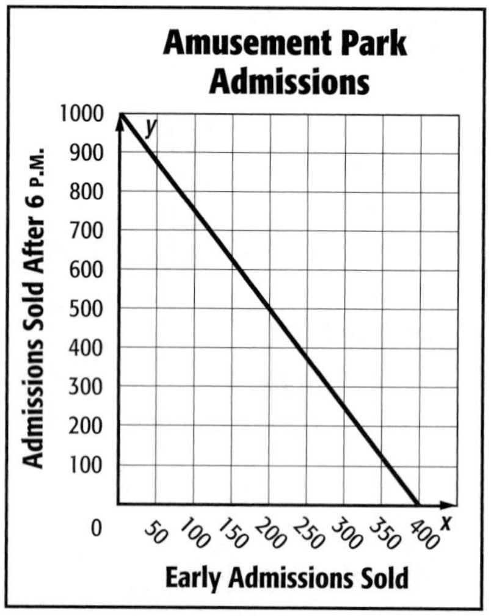

50c. 400; 1000; The *x*-intercept represents the number of admissions sold before 6 P.M. when no admissions are sold after 6 P.M. The *y*-intercept represents the number of admissions sold after 6 P.M. when no admissions are sold before 6 P.M.

57a.

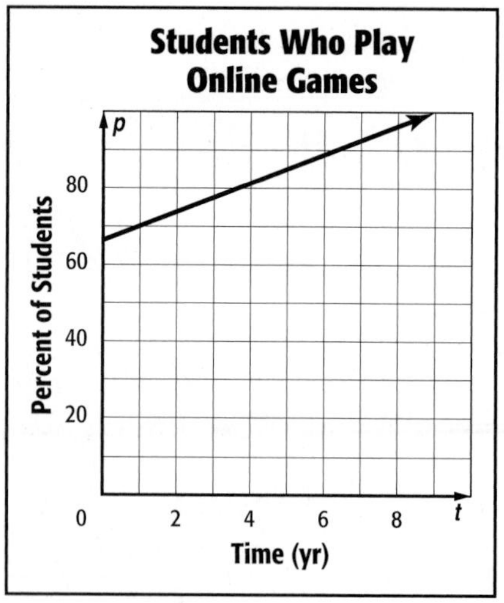

58a. Sample answer:

x- and *y*-intercept

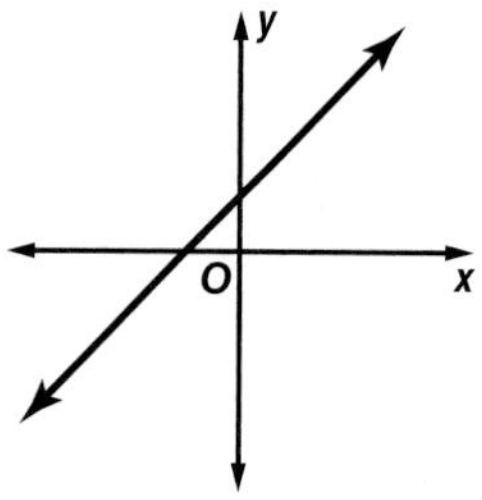

x-intercept, no *y*-intercept

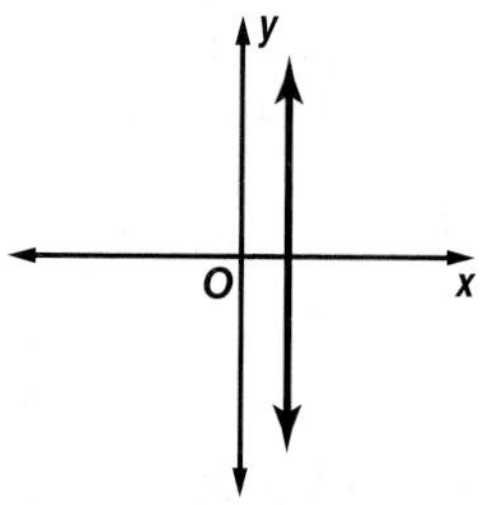

no *x*-intercept, *y*-intercept

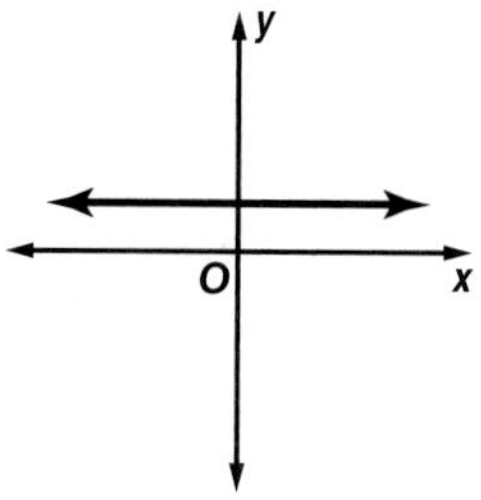

cannot draw lines with 2 *x*-intercepts or with 2 *y*-intercepts

64. Sample answer: To find an *x*-intercept, let $y = 0$ and solve the equation for *x*. To find a *y*-intercept, let $x = 0$ and solve the equation for *y*. To graph most linear equations, plot the *x*-intercept and *y*-intercept and connect the points to form a line. Another way to graph an equation is to choose any value in the domain and create ordered pairs. Plot the ordered pairs and connect the points to form a line.

Pages 164–165, Lesson 3-2

38.

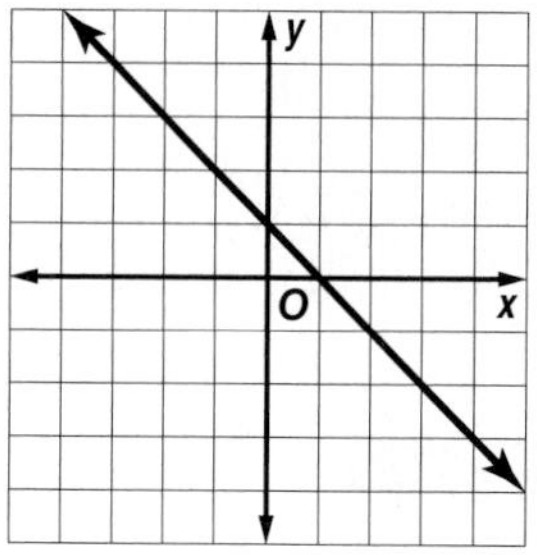

39.

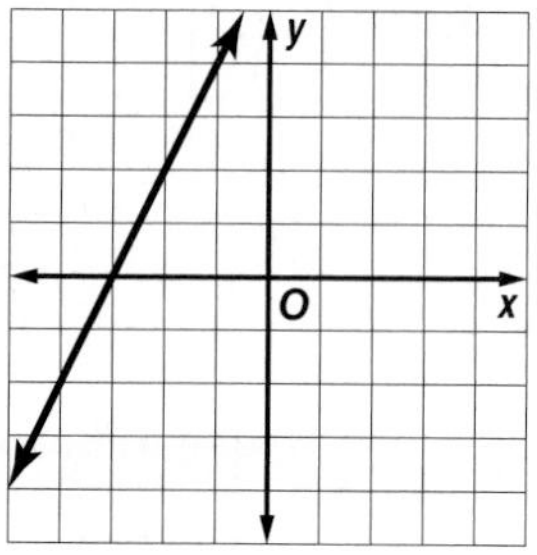

40.

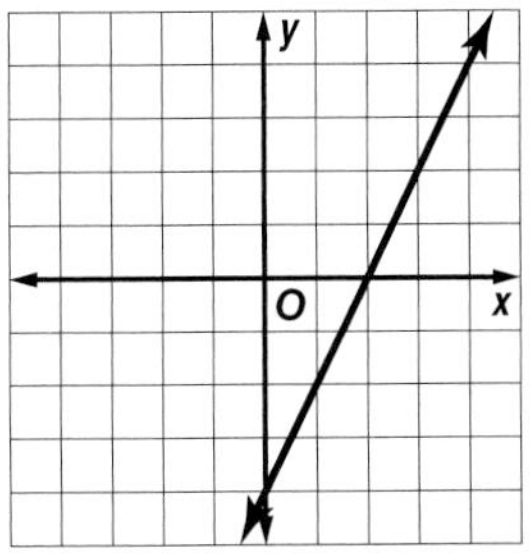

41.

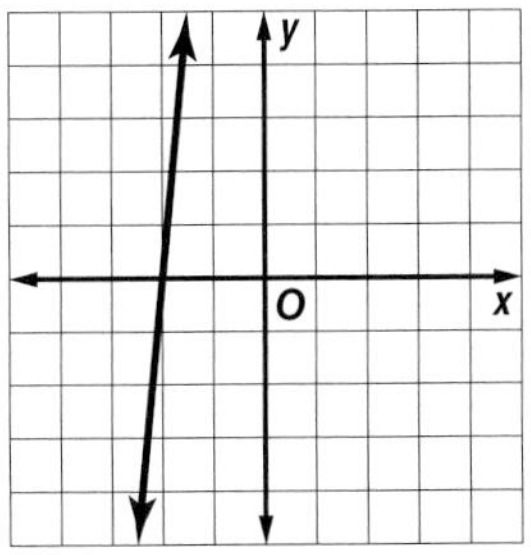

42.

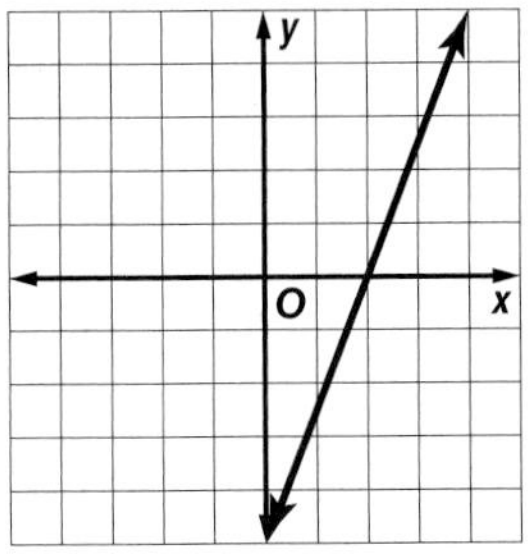

43.

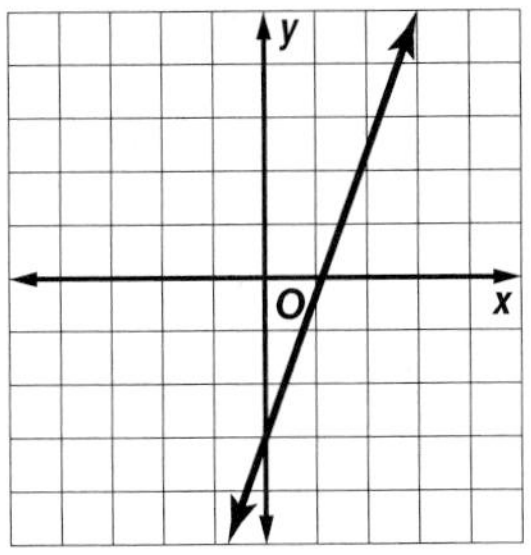

44b.

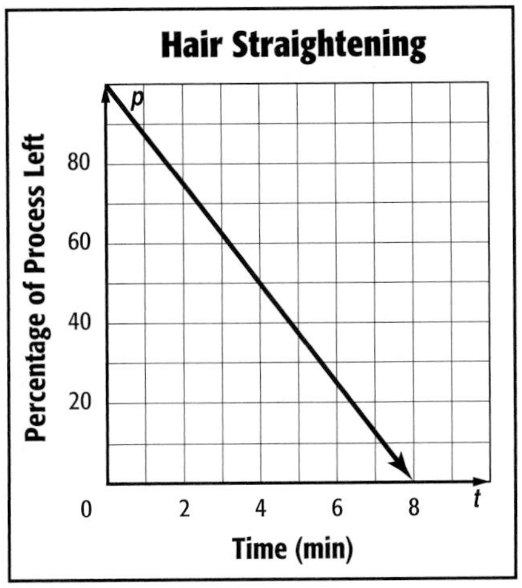

Page 168, Extend 3-2

1.

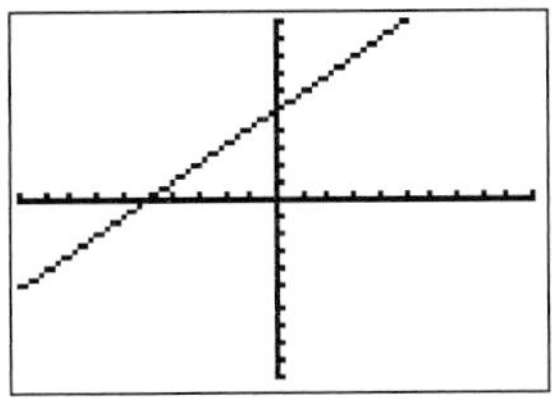

[−10, 10] scl: 1 by
[−10, 10] scl: 1

2.

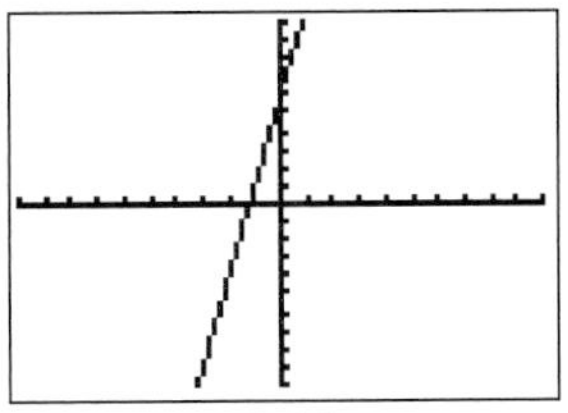

[−10, 10] scl: 1 by
[−10, 10] scl: 1

3.

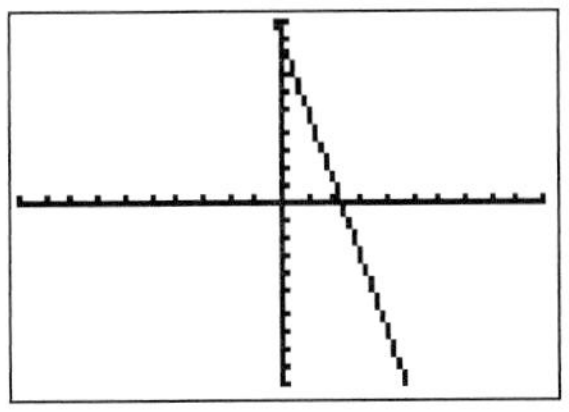

[−10, 10] scl: 1 by
[−10, 10] scl: 1

4.

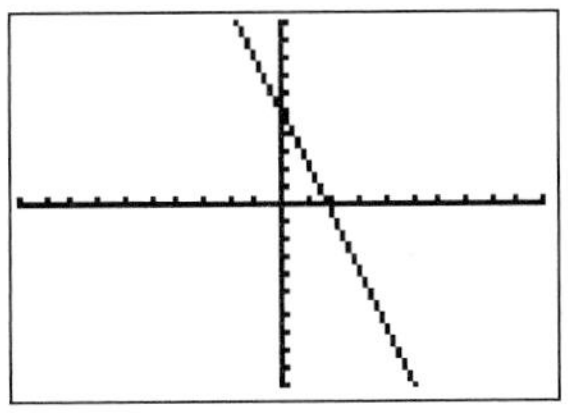

[−10, 10] scl: 1 by
[−10, 10] scl: 1

5.

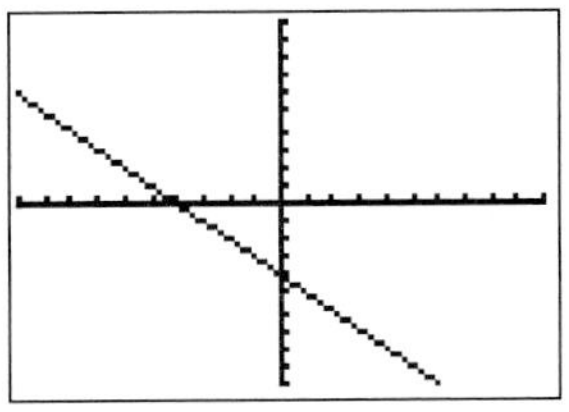

[−10, 10] scl: 1 by
[−10, 10] scl: 1

6.

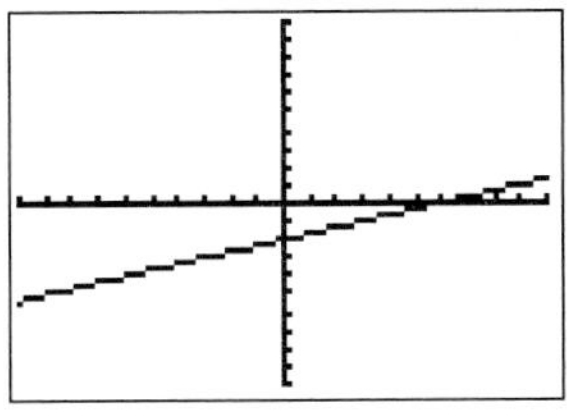

[−10, 10] scl: 1 by
[−10, 10] scl: 1

7.

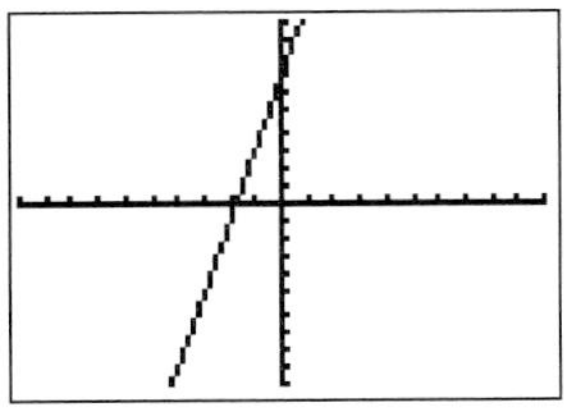

[−10, 10] scl: 1 by
[−10, 10] scl: 1

8.

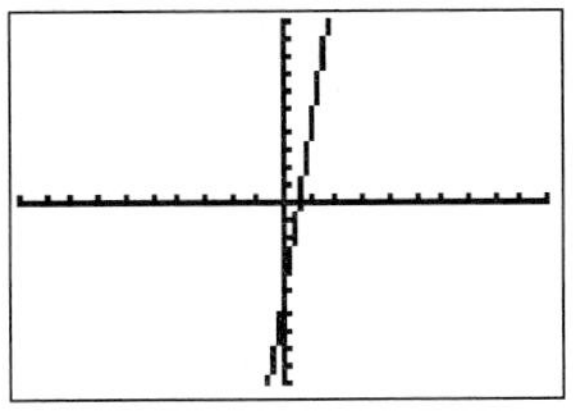

[−10, 10] scl: 1 by
[−10, 10] scl: 1

9.

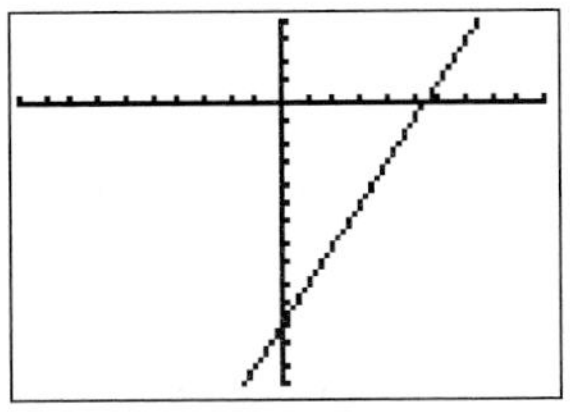

[−10, 10] scl: 1 by
[−10, 10] scl: 1

10.

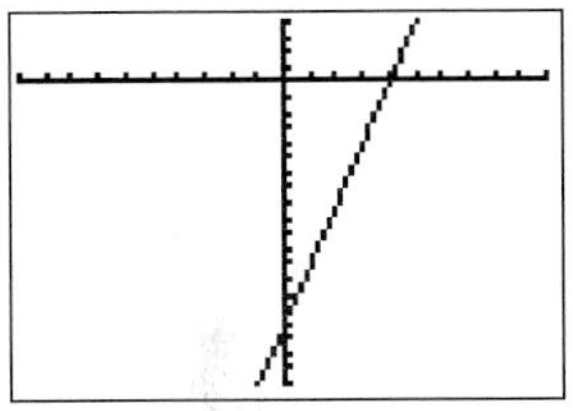

[−10, 10] scl: 1 by
[−10, 10] scl: 1

11.

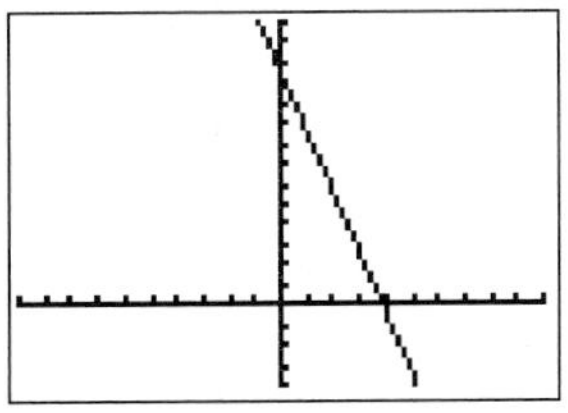

[−10, 10] scl: 1 by
[−10, 10] scl: 1

12.

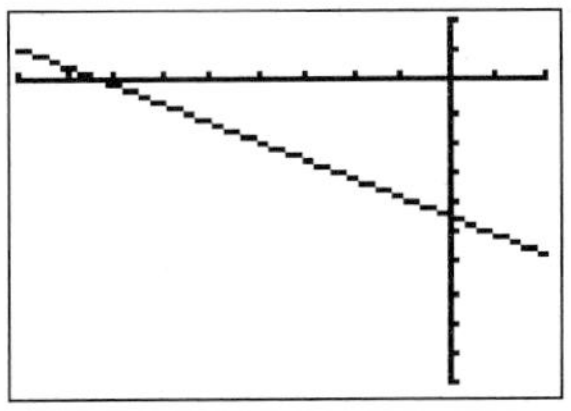

[−10, 10] scl: 1 by
[−10, 10] scl: 1

Pages 181–182, Lesson 3-4, Check Your Progress

2A.

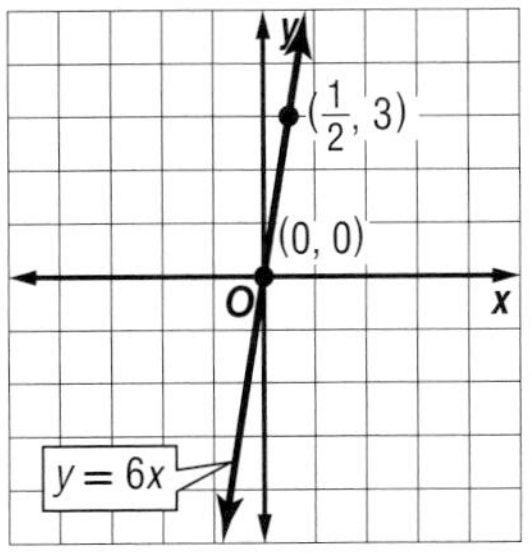

2B.

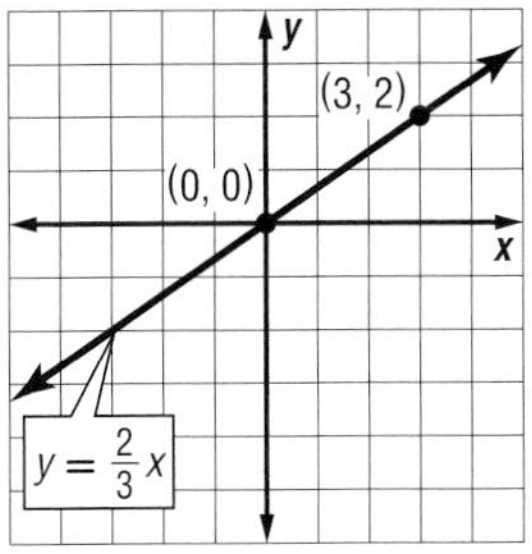

2C.

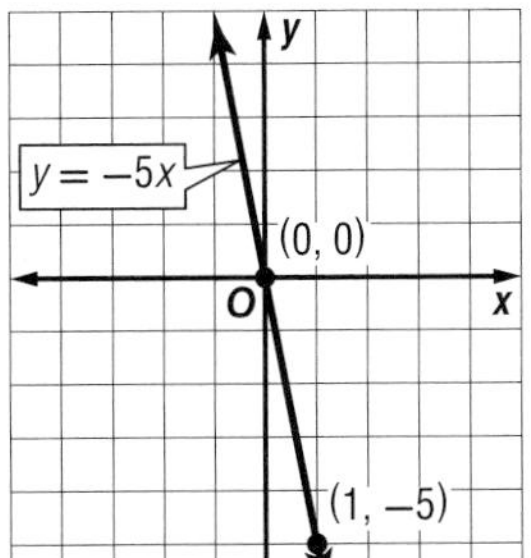

2D.

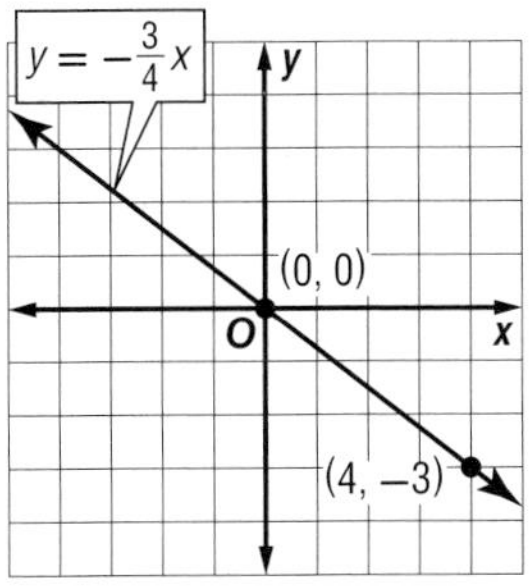

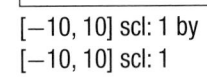

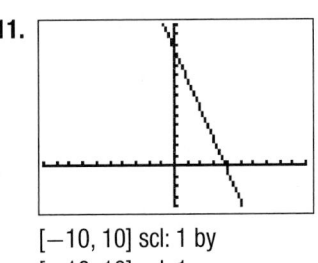

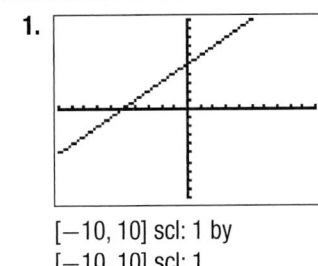

4B.

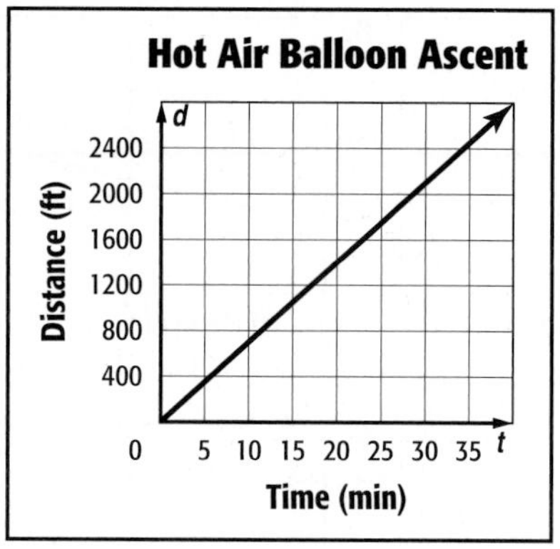

28a.

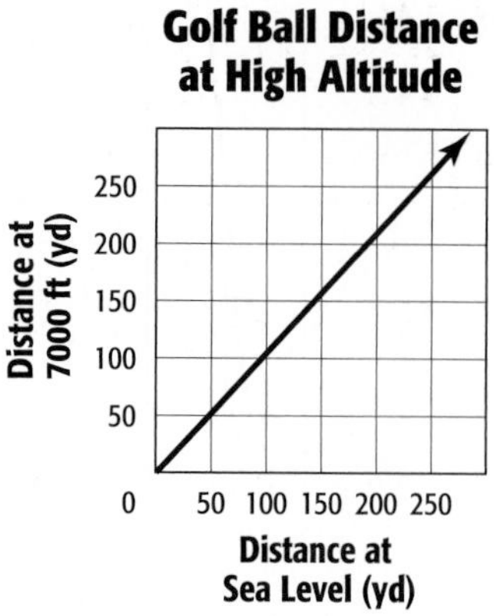

Page 184, Lesson 3-4

16.

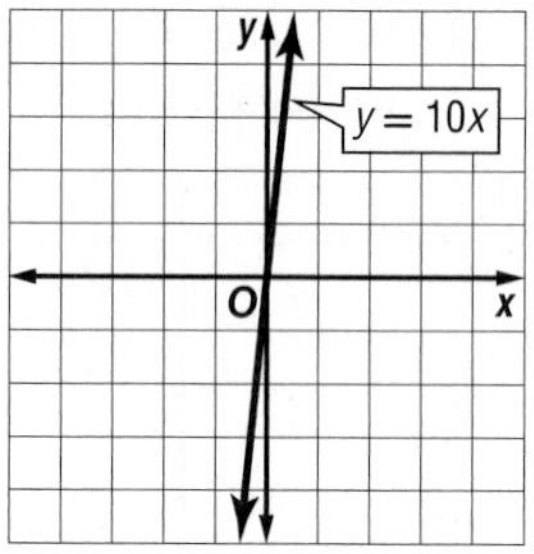

17.

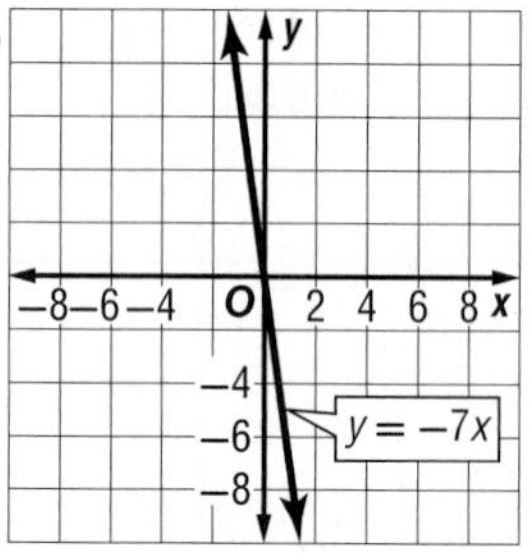

18.

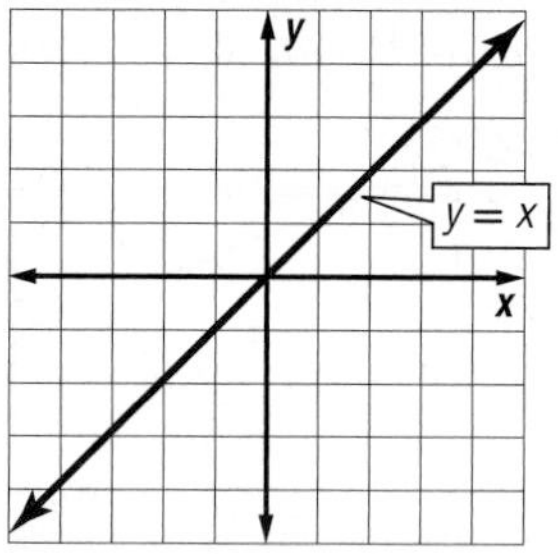

19.

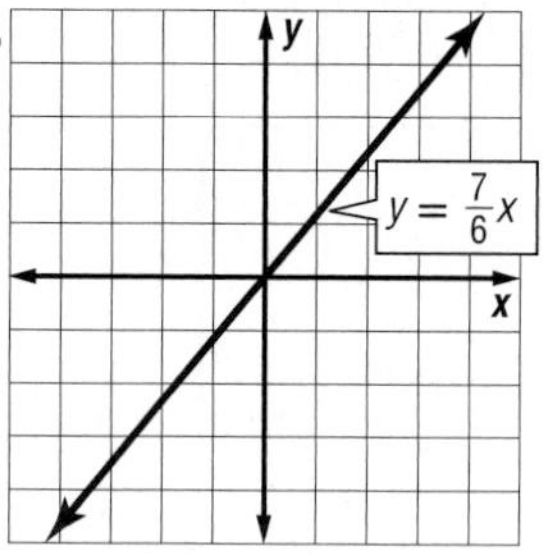

20.

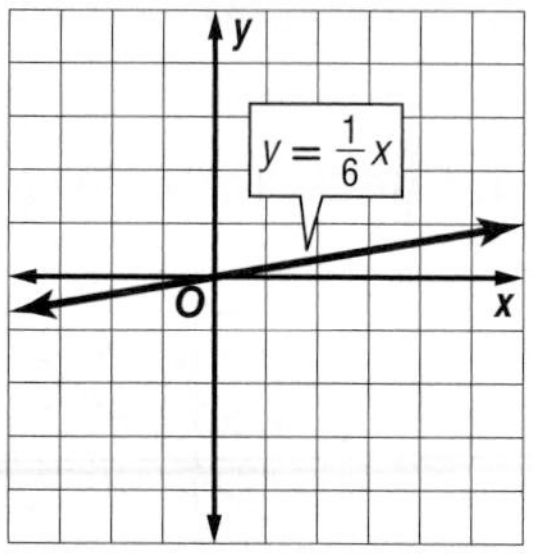

21.

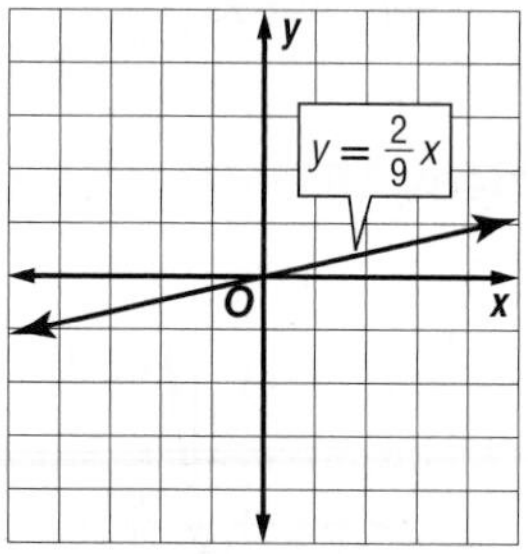

22.

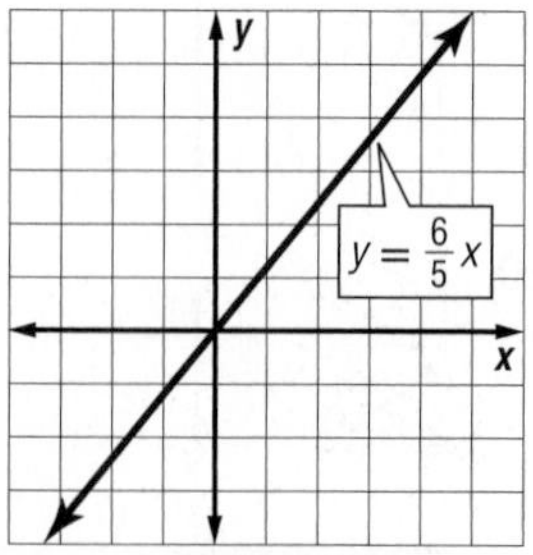

23.

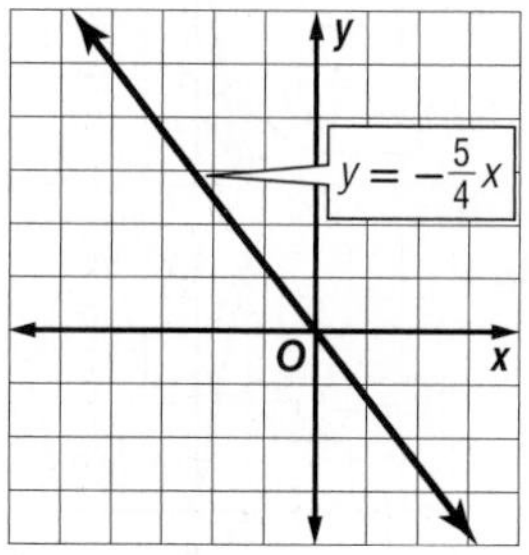

41a.

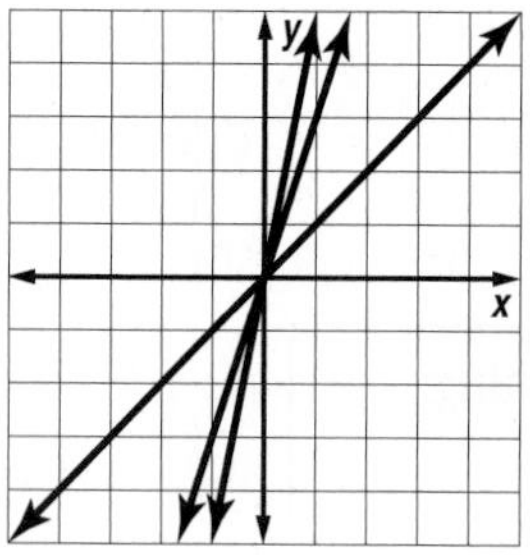

47.

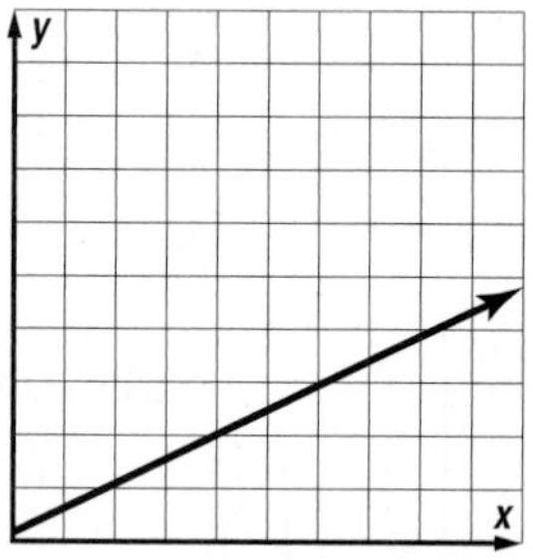

Page 191, Lesson 3-5

18.

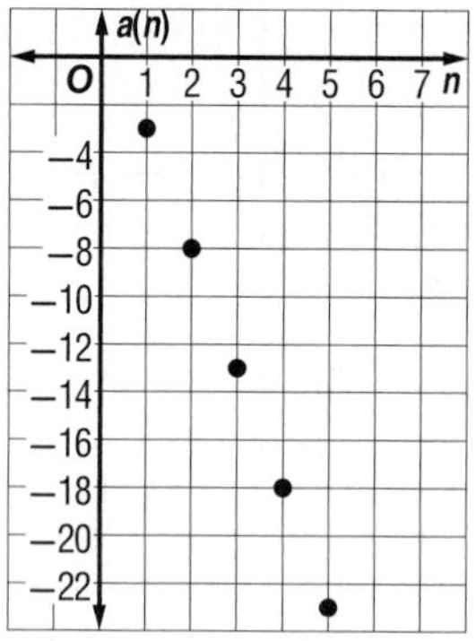

19.

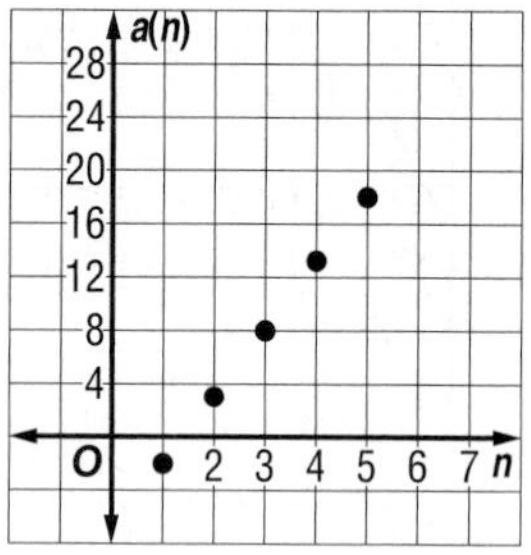

20.

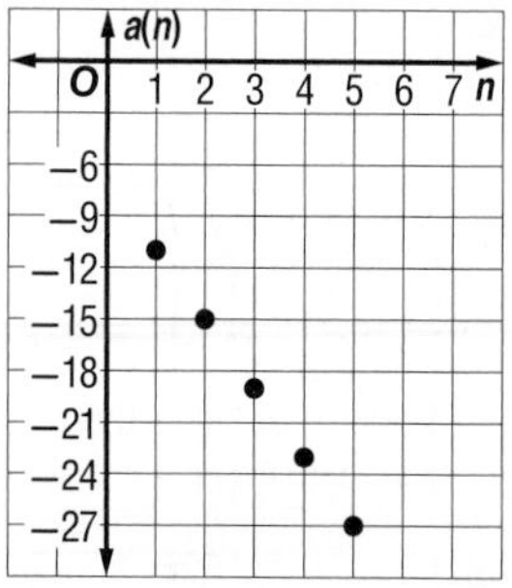

21.

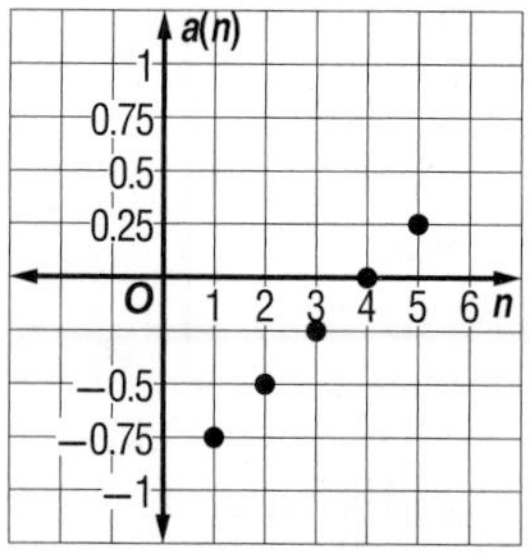

22b.

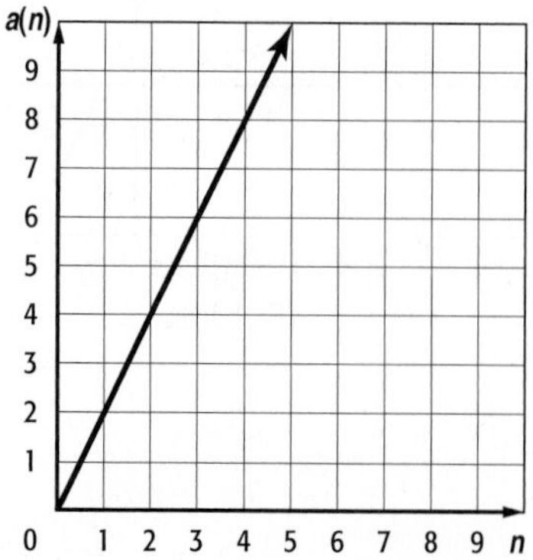

23b.

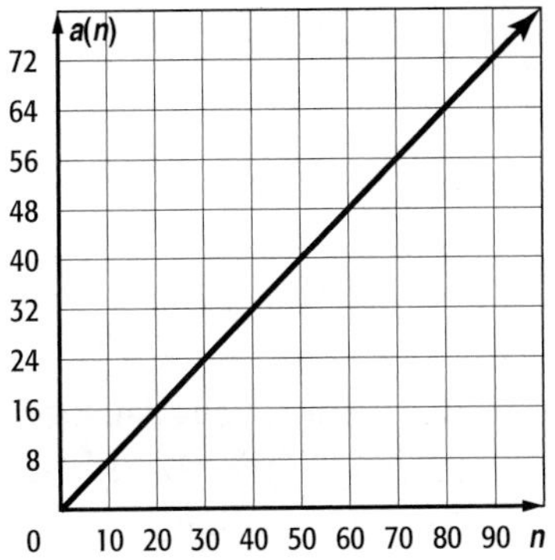

D = {10, 20, 30, 40, ...}

Page 194, Extend 3-5

1. Sample answer: Inductive reasoning uses examples or past experience to make conclusions; deductive reasoning uses rules to make conclusions. Looking at a pattern of numbers to decide the next number is an example of inductive reasoning. Using the formula $A = \ell w$ and the length and width of a rectangle to find the area of a rectangle is an example of deductive reasoning.

2. Deductive reasoning; the detective is applying a general rule about height to a specific case.

3. Inductive reasoning; you are observing specific pairs of terms and discovering a common difference, and you conclude that the common difference applies to the sequence in general.

4. Deductive reasoning; you are using the general formula for the *n*th term and applying it to a particular term of a particular sequence.

5c. 1; 100 is divisible by 4. According to the pattern, all powers with exponents divisible by 4 have 1 in the ones place; inductive reasoning.

Page 199, Lesson 3-6

13a. Sample answer:

Number of T-Shirts Ordered	5	10	15	20	25
Cost ($)	13	23	33	43	53

13c.

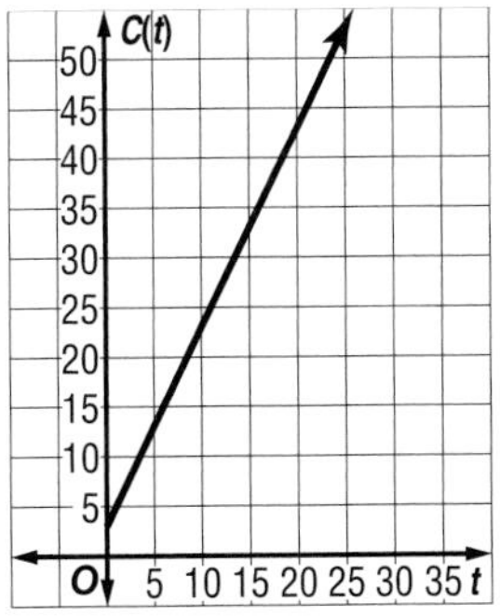

Page 205, Practice Test

19a.

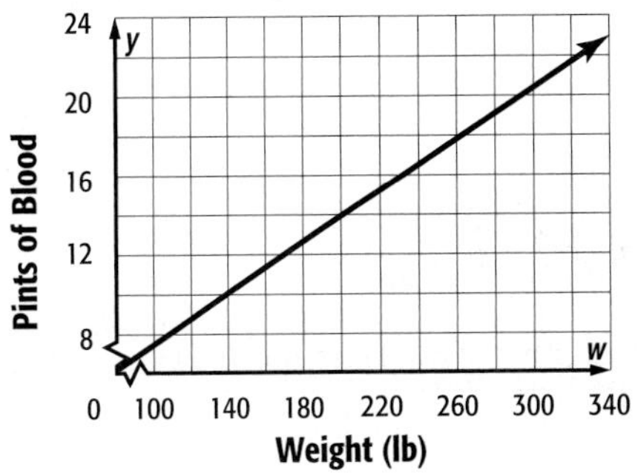

Chapter 3 Answer Appendix

CHAPTER 4

Chapter Planner

Diagnostic Assessment
Quick Check, p. 211

	Explore 4-1 Pacing: 0.5 day	Lesson 4-1 Pacing: 1 day	Extend 4-1 Pacing: 0.5 day
Title	**Graphing Technology Lab: Investigating Slope-Intercept Form**	**Graphing Equations in Slope-Intercept Form**	**Graphing Technology Lab: The Family of Linear Graphs**
Objectives	• Use a graphing calculator to collect data and investigate slope-intercept form.	• Write and graph linear equations in slope-intercept form. • Model real-world data with equations in slope-intercept form.	• Use a graphing calculator to investigate families of linear functions.
Key Vocabulary		slope-intercept form	
ILS	7.B.4	8.C.4b	8.C.4a
Multiple Representations			
Lesson Resources	**Materials** • T1–83/84 Plus or other graphing calculator • CBL or other data collection device and force sensor • plastic sandwich bag • washers	**Chapter 4 Resource Masters** • Study Guide and Intervention, pp. 5–6 AL OL ELL • Skills Practice, p. 7 AL OL ELL • Practice, p. 8 AL OL BL ELL • Word Problem Practice, p. 9 AL OL BL ELL • Enrichment, p. 10 OL BL **Transparencies** • 5-Minute Check Transparency 4-1 AL OL BL ELL **Additional Print Resources** • *Study Notebook* AL OL BL ELL	**Materials** • TI–83/84 Plus or other graphing calculator
Technology for Every Lesson	**IL Math Online** glencoe.com • Extra Examples • Self-Check Quizzes • Personal Tutor • Homework Help	**CD/DVD Resources** IWB INTERACTIVE WHITEBOARD READY IWB StudentWorks Plus IWB Interactive Classroom IWB Diagnostic and Assessment Planner	• TeacherWorks Plus • eSolutions Manual Plus • ExamView Assessment Suite
Math in Motion		BrainPOP	
Differentiated Instruction		pp. 217, 219	

KEY: AL Approaching Level OL On Level BL Beyond Level ELL English Learners

Suggested Pacing			
Time Periods	Instruction	Review & Assessment	Total
45-minute	10	2	12
90-minute	7	1	8

Linear Functions and Relations

Lesson 4-2 Pacing: 1 day	Lesson 4-3 Pacing: 1 day	Lesson 4-4 Pacing: 1 day	Lesson 4-5 Pacing: 1 day
Writing Equations in Slope-Intercept Form	**Writing Equations in Point-Slope Form**	**Parallel and Perpendicular Lines**	**Scatter Plots and Lines of Fit**
• Write an equation of a line in slope-intercept form given the slope and one point. • Write an equation of a line in slope-intercept form given two points.	• Write equations of lines in point-slope form. • Write linear equations in different forms.	• Write an equation of the line that passes through a given point, parallel to a given line. • Write an equation of the line that passes through a given point, perpendicular to a given line.	• Investigate relationships between quantities by using points on scatter plots. • Use lines of fit to make and evaluate predictions.
linear extrapolation	point-slope form	parallel lines perpendicular lines	bivariate data scatter plot line of fit linear interpolation
8.C.4b	8.C.4b	8.B.4b	8.A.4b, 10.A.4c
p. 228		p. 242	
Chapter 4 Resource Masters • Study Guide and Intervention, pp. 11–12 AL OL ELL • Skills Practice, p. 13 AL OL ELL • Practice, p. 14 AL OL BL ELL • Word Problem Practice, p. 15 AL OL BL ELL • Enrichment, p. 16 OL BL • Quiz 1, p. 51 AL OL BL ELL **Transparencies** • 5-Minute Check Transparency 4-2 AL OL BL ELL **Additional Print Resources** • *Study Notebook* AL OL BL ELL • *Teaching Algebra with Manipulatives,* p. 78 AL OL ELL	**Chapter 4 Resource Masters** • Study Guide and Intervention, pp. 17–18 AL OL ELL • Skills Practice, p. 19 AL OL ELL • Practice, p. 20 AL OL BL ELL • Word Problem Practice, p. 21 AL OL BL ELL • Enrichment, p. 22 OL BL • Graphing Calculator Activity, p. 23 OL **Transparencies** • 5-Minute Check Transparency 4-3 AL OL BL ELL **Additional Print Resources** • *Study Notebook* AL OL BL ELL • *Teaching Algebra with Manipulatives,* p. 30 AL OL ELL	**Chapter 4 Resource Masters** • Study Guide and Intervention, pp. 24–25 AL OL ELL • Skills Practice, p. 26 AL OL ELL • Practice, p. 27 AL OL BL ELL • Word Problem Practice, p. 28 AL OL BL ELL • Enrichment, p. 29 OL BL • Quiz 2, p. 51 AL OL BL ELL **Transparencies** • 5-Minute Check Transparency 4-4 AL OL BL ELL **Additional Print Resources** • *Study Notebook* AL OL BL ELL • *Teaching Algebra with Manipulatives,* pp. 82–83 AL OL ELL	**Chapter 4 Resource Masters** • Study Guide and Intervention, pp. 30–31 AL OL ELL • Skills Practice, p. 32 AL OL ELL • Practice, p. 33 AL OL BL ELL • Word Problem Practice, p. 34 AL OL BL ELL • Enrichment, p. 35 OL BL • Spreadsheet Activity, p. 36 OL **Transparencies** • 5-Minute Check Transparency 4-5 AL OL BL ELL **Additional Print Resources** • *Study Notebook* AL OL BL ELL • *Teaching Algebra with Manipulatives,* p. 84 AL OL ELL
	IL Math Online glencoe.com • Extra Examples • Self-Check Quizzes • Personal Tutor • Homework Help	**CD/DVD Resources** IWB INTERACTIVE WHITEBOARD READY IWB StudentWorks Plus IWB Interactive Classroom IWB Diagnostic and Assessment Planner	• TeacherWorks Plus • eSolutions Manual Plus • ExamView Assessment Suite
			Interactive Lab
pp. 226, 230	pp. 233, 236	pp. 239, 243	pp. 246, 249

Formative Assessment
Mid-Chapter Quiz, p. 244

CHAPTER 4

Chapter Planner

	Extend 4-5 Pacing: 0.5 day	Lesson 4-6 Pacing: 1.5 days	Lesson 4-7 Pacing: 1.5 days	Extend 4-7 Pacing: 0.5 day
Title	**Algebra Lab: Correlation and Causation**	**Regression and Median-Fit Lines**	**Special Functions**	**Graphing Technology Lab: Piecewise-Linear Functions**
Objectives	• Explore the difference between correlation and causation.	• Write equations of best-fit lines using linear regression. • Write equations of median-fit lines.	• Identify and graph step functions. • Identify and graph absolute value and piecewise-defined functions.	• Use a graphing calculator to investigate piecewise-linear functions.
Key Vocabulary		best-fit line linear regression correlation coefficient median-fit line	step function piecewise-linear function greatest integer function absolute value function piecewise-defined function	
ILS		10.A.4c	8.B.4b, 8.C.4b	8.B.4b
Multiple Representations			p. 267	
Lesson Resources	**Materials** • grid paper **Additional Print Resources** • *Teaching Algebra with Manipulatives,* pp. 1, 85 AL OL ELL	**Chapter 4 Resource Masters** • Study Guide and Intervention, pp. 37–38 AL OL ELL • Skills Practice, p. 39 AL OL ELL • Practice, p. 40 AL OL BL ELL • Word Problem Practice, p. 41 AL OL BL ELL • Enrichment, p. 42 OL BL • Quiz 3, p. 52 AL OL BL ELL **Transparencies** • 5-Minute Check Transparency 4-6 AL OL BL ELL **Additional Print Resources** • *Study Notebook* AL OL BL ELL • *Teaching Algebra with Manipulatives,* p. 81 AL OL ELL	**Chapter 4 Resource Masters** • Study Guide and Intervention, pp. 43–44 AL OL ELL • Skills Practice, p. 45 AL OL ELL • Practice, p. 46 AL OL BL ELL • Word Problem Practice, p. 47 AL OL BL ELL • Enrichment, p. 48 OL BL • Quiz 4, p. 52 AL OL BL ELL **Transparencies** • 5-Minute Check Transparency 4-7 AL OL BL ELL **Additional Print Resources** • *Study Notebook* AL OL BL ELL	**Materials** • TI–83/84 Plus or other graphing calculator
Technology for Every Lesson	IL Math Online glencoe.com • Extra Examples • Self-Check Quizzes • Personal Tutor • Homework Help	**CD/DVD Resources** IWB INTERACTIVE WHITEBOARD READY IWB StudentWorks Plus IWB Interactive Classroom IWB Diagnostic and Assessment Planner	• TeacherWorks Plus • eSolutions Manual Plus • ExamView Assessment Suite	
Math in Motion	Animation			
Differentiated Instruction		pp. 255, 258	pp. 265, 266	

Summative Assessment
- Study Guide and Review, pp. 270–274
- Practice Test, p. 275

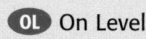

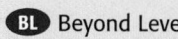

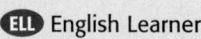

KEY: AL Approaching Level OL On Level BL Beyond Level ELL English Learners

Quick Review Math Handbook*

is Glencoe's mathematical handbook for students and parents.

Hot Words includes a glossary of terms.

Hot Topics consists of two parts:

- explanations of key mathematical concepts
- exercises to check students' understanding.

Lesson	Hot Topics Section	Lesson	Hot Topics Section
4-1	6.7, 6.8	4-5	4.2
4-2	6.8	4-6	4.3
4-3	6.8	4-7	6.8
4-4	6.7, 6.8		

**Also available in Spanish*

What the Research Says...

Good questioning includes challenging students to think about the main ideas in the lesson and go beyond simple recall or parroting of what has just been said. Questioning also increases student-to-student interaction so that students' ideas, expressed in their terminology are shared with the class. (Hiebert et al, 1997)

- Stress that the concept of slope is one that is used widely in mathematics through calculus.
- Understanding what slope represents will help students easily master skills in this chapter.

[Source: Heibert, J., Carpenter, T.P., Fennema, E., Fuson, K.C., Murray, H., Olivier, A., Human, P., and Wearner, D. (1997) *Making Sense: Teaching and Learning Mathematics with Understanding*, Portsmouth, New Hampshire, Heinemann.]

Project CRISS STUDY SKILL

A point-by-point format and example can be used to help students better understand the steps of many mathematical processes. In order to explain a process, they must understand how to perform a step as well as the reasoning behind each step.

Provide students with the description at the right as an example of using point-by-point format to explain how to write an equation of a line when two points are given. After reading Lesson 4-2, have students write a description of how to write an equation of a line when a point and slope are given.

Main Idea:	Point-by-Point Steps	Example for the Points: (1, 5), (−1, 1)
Find an equation of a line when two points on the line are given.	Step 1 Find the slope of the line containing the points.	$m = \frac{y_2 - y_1}{x_2 - x_1}$ $m = \frac{1 - 5}{-1 - 1}$ $m = \frac{-4}{-2}$ or 2
	Step 2 Choose one of the points and find the y-intercept	$y = mx + b$ $1 = 2(-1) + b$ $3 = b$
	Step 3 Write the slope-intercept form of the equation using the slope and y-intercept.	Using $m = 2$ and $b = 3$, $y = mx + b$ $y = 2x + 3$

Creating Independence through Student-owned Strategies

CHAPTER 4

Assessment and Intervention

SE = Student Edition, **TE** = Teacher Edition, **CRM** = Chapter Resource Masters

	Diagnosis	Prescription
Diagnostic Assessment	**Beginning Chapter 4**	
	Get Ready for Chapter 4 **SE**, p. 211	Response to Intervention **TE**, p. 211
	Beginning Every Lesson	
	Then, Now, Why? **SE** 5-Minute Check Transparencies	Chapter 0 **SE**, pp. P1–P45 Concepts and Skills Bank **SE**, pp. 845–867 *Quick Review Math Handbook*
Formative Assessment	**During/After Every Lesson**	
	Check Your Progress **SE**, every example Check Your Understanding **SE** H.O.T. Problems **SE** Spiral Review **SE** Additional Examples **TE** Watch Out! **TE** Step 4, Assess **TE** Chapter 4 Quizzes **CRM**, pp. 51–52 Self-Check Quizzes glencoe.com	**Tier 1 Intervention** Concepts and Skills Bank **SE**, pp. 845–867 Skills Practice **CRM**, Ch. 1–4 glencoe.com **Tier 2 Intervention** Differentiated Instruction **TE** Differentiated Homework Options **TE** Study Guide and Intervention Masters **CRM**, Ch. 1–4 *Quick Review Math Handbook* **Tier 3 Intervention** *Math Triumphs, Alg. 1,* Ch. 4
	Mid-Chapter	
	Mid-Chapter Quiz **SE**, p. 244 Mid-Chapter Test **CRM**, p. 53 ExamView Assessment Suite	**Tier 1 Intervention** Concepts and Skills Bank **SE**, pp. 845–867 Skills Practice **CRM**, Ch. 1–4 glencoe.com **Tier 2 Intervention** Study Guide and Intervention Masters **CRM**, Ch. 1–4 *Quick Review Math Handbook* **Tier 3 Intervention** *Math Triumphs, Alg. 1,* Ch. 4
	Before Chapter Test	
	Chapter Study Guide and Review **SE**, pp. 270–274 Practice Test **SE**, p. 275 Standardized Test Practice **SE**, pp. 276–279 Chapter Test glencoe.com Standardized Test Practice glencoe.com Vocabulary Review glencoe.com ExamView Assessment Suite	**Tier 1 Intervention** Concepts and Skills Bank **SE**, pp. 845–867 Skills Practice **CRM**, Ch. 1–4 glencoe.com **Tier 2 Intervention** Study Guide and Intervention Masters **CRM**, Ch. 1–4 *Quick Review Math Handbook* **Tier 3 Intervention** *Math Triumphs, Alg. 1,* Ch. 4
Summative Assessment	**After Chapter 4**	
	Multiple-Choice Tests, Forms 1, 2A, 2B **CRM**, pp. 55–60 Free-Response Tests, Forms 2C, 2D, 3 **CRM**, pp. 61–66 Vocabulary Test **CRM**, p. 54 Extended Response Test **CRM**, p. 67 Standardized Test Practice **CRM**, pp. 68–70 ExamView Assessment Suite	Study Guide and Intervention Masters **CRM**, Ch. 1–4 *Quick Review Math Handbook* glencoe.com

Differentiated Instruction

Option 1 Reaching All Learners AL OL BL ELL

INTERPERSONAL Place students in teams of three or four. Since there are several tasks involved in writing and graphing an equation in slope-intercept form, have the team members decide which tasks each will perform. For example, one member can be responsible for writing an equation given the slope and *y*-intercept, another can rewrite a given equation into slope-intercept form, and the remaining members can use the *y*-intercept and the slope to graph the equation.

SOCIAL Have each student plot (2, 1) on a coordinate grid. Then ask them to use a straightedge to draw a line through this point and crossing the *y*-axis. Then have students compare their lines. Discuss why so many different lines are drawn. Ask students what you would have had to give them, along with the original point, so that they would all have drawn the same line. slope or another point As a class, graph and write equations for the lines through (2, 1) with a slope of 3, and through (2, 1) and (1, 3).

Option 2 Approaching Level AL

Provide students with four equations in slope-intercept form that all have the same slope. Ask students to graph each equation, extending the lines so that each crosses the *y*-axis. Then have students write the equation for each line on the line itself. Discuss with students the relationships between the graph of the line and its equation, that is, the slope and the coefficient of *x* and the *y*-intercept and the value for *b*.

Option 3 English Learners ELL

Give students several exercises that ask them to write a particular type of equation. Have them describe or write how they would solve each type of problem. Then have them summarize the technique they think works best for each given situation (point and slope, two points, rewriting equations in various forms).

Option 4 Beyond Level BL

Have students research Galileo's Tower of Pisa experiment. Then have students conduct a similar experiment to determine if there is a correlation between the weight of an object and the speed at which it falls. Caution students to keep the distance the objects fall a constant, the size of the objects similar, but the mass of the objects different.

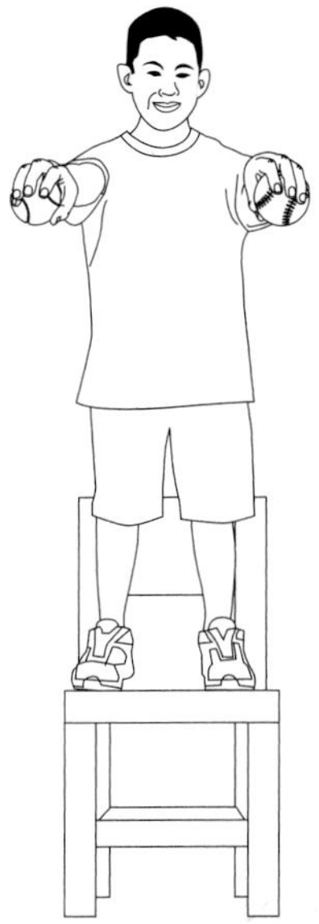

CHAPTER 4

Focus on Mathematical Content

Vertical Alignment

Before Chapter 4

Related Topics before Grade 8
- represent relationships among quantities using graphs

Related Topics from Grade 8
- use operations to solve problems involving rational numbers
- make predictions by analyzing trends in scatter plots

Previous Topics From Algebra 1
- transform and solve linear equations
- develop the concept of slope as rate of change and determine the slope from graphs, tables, and algebraic representations
- interpret the meaning of slope in situations using data, symbolic representations, or graphs
- relate direct variation to linear functions and solve problems involving proportional change

Chapter 4

Related Topics from Algebra 1
- write equations of lines given specific characteristics
- interpret and predict the effects of changing the slope and *y*-intercept in applied situations
- interpret and make decisions, predictions, and critical judgments from functional relationships
- collect and organize data, make and interpret scatter plots, and model, predict, and make decisions and critical judgments in problem situations

After Chapter 4

Preparation for Algebra 2
- make and interpret scatter plots, fit the graph of a function to the data, and make predictions based on the function
- solve systems of equations
- use functions to model and make predictions

Lesson-by-Lesson Preview

4-1 Graphing Equations in Slope-Intercept Form

An equation of the form $y = mx + b$, in which m is the slope and b is the y-value where the graph of the equation crosses the y-axis, is said to be in slope-intercept form. The slope-intercept form of an equation offers two ways to graph a line.

- Select any two values for x, substitute the values into the equation, and then calculate the corresponding values of y to create two ordered pairs that can be graphed. Draw the line that contains these two points.
- Graph the y-intercept, use it as a starting point, and then use the slope to determine the distance and direction to move up/down and right/left to find another point on the line. Then draw the line.

4-2 Writing Equations in Slope-Intercept Form

The general equation for slope-intercept form is $y = mx + b$. This is the starting point for creating an equation from different types of information given.

- Given the slope m and one point (x, y)

Step 1: Substitute the values of m, x, and y into the slope-intercept form and solve for b.

Step 2: Write the slope-intercept form by substituting the values of m and b into $y = mx + b$.

- Given two points

Step 1: Use the two points to find m, the slope.

Step 2: Choose one of the two points to use.

Step 2: Follow the steps for writing an equation given the slope, m, and one point (x, y).

4-3 Writing Equations in Point-Slope Form

Point-slope form is derived from the definition of slope using the coordinates of two points on a line. Suppose the two points on a line are given as (x, y) and (x_1, y_1). Using the definition of the slope, $m = \frac{y - y_1}{x - x_1}$. If each side of the equation is multiplied by $(x - x_1)$, the result is $y - y_1 = m(x - x_1)$, the point-slope form of a linear equation.

Linear Functions and Relations

4-4 Parallel and Perpendicular Lines

In coordinate geometry, graphing and properties of graphs are used to prove lines parallel or perpendicular.

- When two distinct lines lie in the same plane and have the same slope, they are parallel.
- When two lines do not have the same slope, they intersect. If two oblique lines intersect at right angles, forming perpendicular lines, the slopes of the two lines are negative reciprocals of each other, and the product of their slopes is -1.

4-5 Scatter Plots and Lines of Fit

A scatter plot consists of graphs of ordered pairs (x, y) that belong to a set in which the x-coordinate represents one real-world measurement and the y-coordinate represents another.

If a set of data exhibits a linear trend, a line of fit can be drawn to summarize the data. Once the line is drawn, an equation for the line can be written.

4-6 Regression and Median-Fit Lines

An equation for a best-fit line can be written for any set of data. The equation is only useful if the data exhibits a linear trend or pattern.

- The graphing calculator function LinReg$(ax + b)$ uses a least-squares fit method to determine the values for a, the slope, and b, the y-intercept. Once a and b are calculated, the equation for the line can be written.
- The values for a and b will be displayed in the calculator's window along with the value for the correlation coefficient. The closer the correlation coefficient is to 1 or -1, the more closely the equation for the best-fit line models the data inputted.
- Points on the best-fit line are used to estimate values that are not in the data set.

4-7 Special Functions

Other functions closely related to linear functions are the piecewise functions. These include the following functions.

Piecewise-defined function

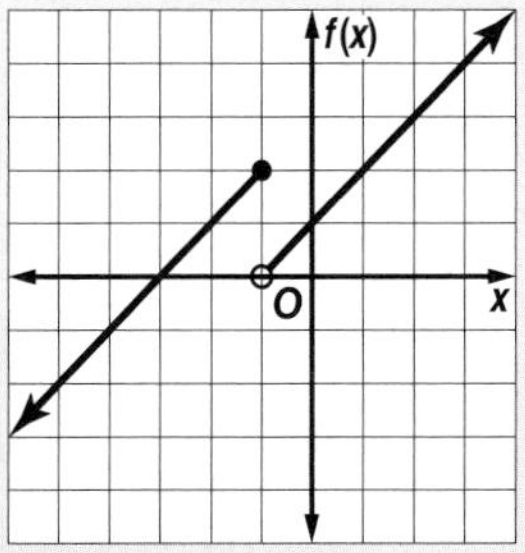

- These functions are defined by two or more equations. For example,

$$f(x) = \begin{cases} x + 1 \text{ if } x > -1 \\ x + 3 \text{ if } x \leq -1 \end{cases}$$

Greatest integer function (step function)

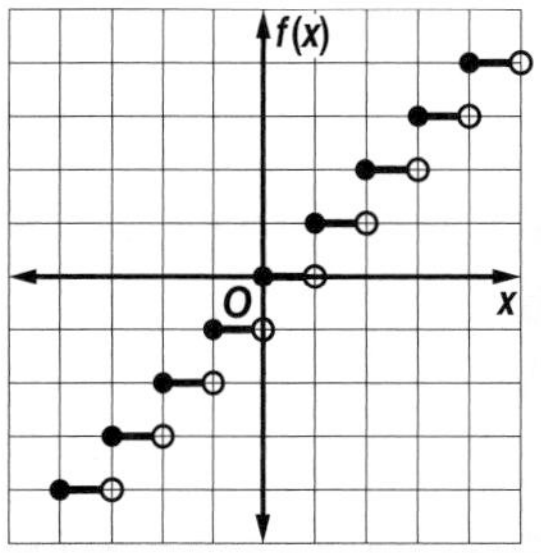

- $f(x) = [\![x]\!]$ means the greatest integer less than or equal to x. For example, if $x = 3.25$, then $[\![x]\!] = 3$. The graph of a greatest integer function is made up of disjointed line segments that look like a set of steps.

Absolute value function

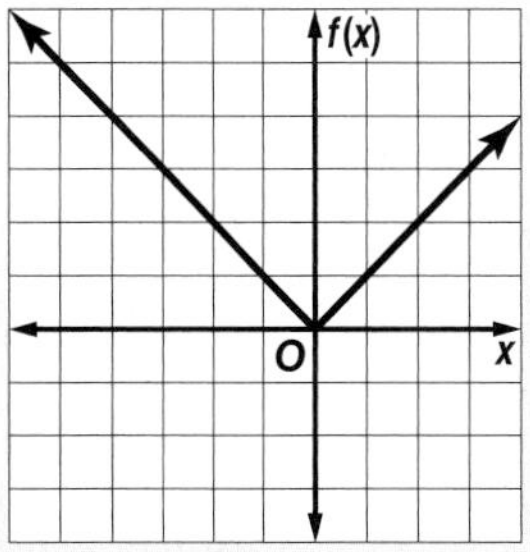

- $f(x) = |x|$ means that when $x \geq 0$, the graph of the function is like $y = x$, but when finding $x < 0$, the graph of the function is like $y = -x$. The graph of an absolute value function has a V-shape.

Professional Development

Targeted professional development has been articulated throughout *Algebra 1.* More quality, customized professional development is available from McGraw-Hill Professional Development. Visit glencoe.com for details on each product.

- **Online Lessons** emphasize the strategies and techniques used to teach Algebra 1. Includes streaming video, interactive pages, and online tools.
- **Video Workshops** allow mentors, coaches, or leadership personnel to facilitate on-site workshops on educational strategies in mathematics and mathematical concepts.
- **MHPD Online** (www.mhpdonline.com) offers online professional development with video clips of instructional strategies, links, student activities, and news and issues in education.
- **Teaching Today** (teachingtoday.glencoe.com) gives secondary teachers practical strategies and materials that inspire excellence and innovation in teaching.

CHAPTER 4 Notes

Chapter Project

Destined to Travel

Students use what they have learned about writing and graphing linear equations and median-fit lines to work with the distance and cost to travel to a vacation destination.

- Ask students to determine a vacation destination in their state. Then ask students to determine the distance x to the nearest mile to their destination.
- Ask students to write and graph an equation in slope-intercept form for the cost y to take a taxicab that charges \$6 per mile plus an additional \$25. Then have students use the equation and graph to find the cost of taking a cab to each of their destinations.
- Tell students that another taxi service charges \$3 per mile plus an additional \$50. Ask students to write an equation for this service. Then have them graph their equation on the same coordinate system as they graphed the first equation. Which service would be cheaper for traveling to their destination?
- As a class, compile a table of values for B, the birth month, and N, the number of miles to each student's destination. Use 1 for January, 2 for February, etc. Plot those ordered pairs on a coordinate grid. Is there a correlation between a person's birth month and the distance they would travel? If not, eliminate points as necessary from the plot so that there appears to be a correlation. Find the equation of the median-fit line. Graph this equation. How far would you predict people in Algebra 1 at your school might travel in your state if they were born in October?

CHAPTER 4 Linear Functions and Relations

Then

In Chapter 3, you graphed linear functions.

Now

In Chapter 4, you will:

- Write and graph linear equations in various forms.
- Use scatter plots and lines of fit, and write equations of best-fit lines using linear regression.
- Identify and graph special functions.

IL Learning Standards

8.A.4b Represent mathematical patterns and describe their properties using variables and mathematical symbols.
10.A.4c Predict from data using interpolation, extrapolation and trend lines, with and without the use of technology.

Why?

TRAVEL The number of trips people take changes from year to year. From the yearly data, patterns emerge. Rate of change can be applied to these data to determine a linear model. This can be used to predict the number of trips taken in future years.

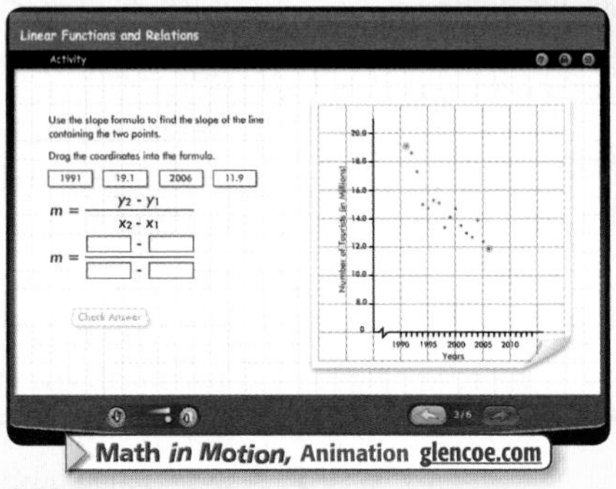

Math *in Motion*, Animation glencoe.com

Key Vocabulary Introduce the key vocabulary in the chapter using the routine below.

Define: Slope-intercept form is an equation of the form $y = mx + b$, where m is the slope and b is the y-intercept.

Example: $y = 3x + 5$ has a slope of 3 and a y-intercept of 5.

Ask: Is the slope on the right side or the left side of the equation? right side

Get Ready for Chapter 4

Diagnose Readiness You have two options for checking Prerequisite Skills.

Text Option

Take the Quick Check below. Refer to the Quick Review for help.

QuickCheck

(Used in Lessons 4-1 through 4-7)

Evaluate $3a^2 - 2ab + c$ for the values given. (Lesson 1-5)

1. $a = 2, b = 1, c = 5$ **13**
2. $a = -3, b = -2, c = 3$ **18**
3. $a = -1, b = 0, c = 11$ **14**
4. $a = 5, b = -3, c = -9$ **96**
5. **CAR RENTAL** The cost of renting a car is given by $49x + 0.3y$. Let x represent the number of days rented, and let y represent the number of miles driven. Find the cost for a five-day rental over 125 miles. **$282.50**

(Used in Lessons 4-1 through 4-3)

Solve each equation for the given variable. (Lesson 2-8)

6. $x + y = 5$ for y **$y = 5 - x$**
7. $2x - 4y = 6$ for x **$x = 3 + 2y$**
8. $y - 2 = x + 3$ for y **$y = x + 5$**
9. $4x - 3y = 12$ for x **$x = \frac{3}{4}y + 3$**
10. **GEOMETRY** The formula for the perimeter of a rectangle is $P = 2w + 2\ell$, where w represents width and ℓ represents length. Solve for w. **$w = \frac{P}{2} - \ell$**

Write the ordered pair for each point. (Lesson 1-6) (Used in Lessons 4-1 through 4-7)

11. A **(4, 2)**
12. B **(0, 3)**
13. C **(2, −4)**
14. D **(0, 0)**
15. E **(−3, −3)**
16. F **(−5, 2)**

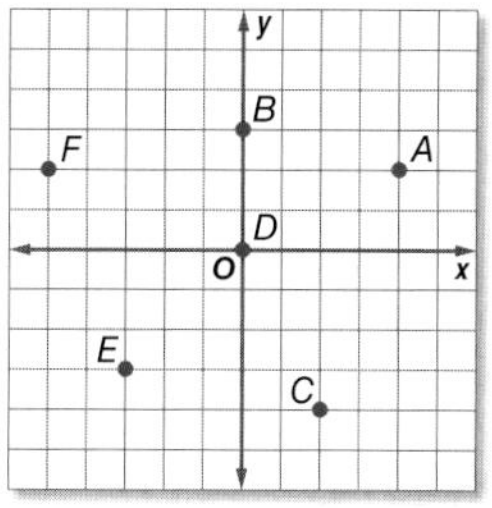

QuickReview

EXAMPLE 1

Evaluate $2(m - n)^2 + 3p$ for $m = 5$, $n = 2$, and $p = -3$.

$2(m - n)^2 + 3p$	Original expression
$= 2(5 - 2)^2 + 3(-3)$	Substitute.
$= 2(3)^2 + 3(-3)$	Subtract.
$= 2(9) + 3(-3)$	Evaluate power.
$= 18 + (-9)$	Multiply.
$= 9$	Add.

EXAMPLE 2

Solve $5x + 15y = 9$ for x.

$5x + 15y = 9$	Original equation
$5x + 15y - 15y = 9 - 15y$	Subtract $15y$ from each side.
$5x = 9 - 15y$	Simplify.
$\frac{5x}{5} = \frac{9 - 15y}{5}$	Divide each side by 5.
$x = \frac{9}{5} - 3y$	Simplify.

EXAMPLE 3

Write the ordered pair for A.

Step 1 Begin at point A.

Step 2 Follow along a vertical line to the x-axis. The x-coordinate is -4.

Step 3 Follow along a horizontal line to the y-axis. The y-coordinate is 2.

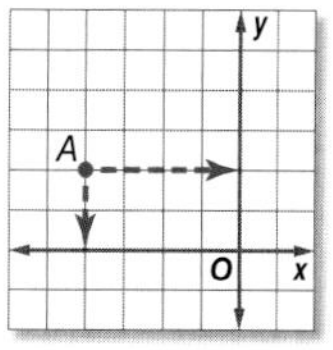

The ordered pair for point A is $(-4, 2)$.

Online Option

IL Math Online Take a self-check Chapter Readiness Quiz at glencoe.com.

Get Ready for Chapter 4

Response to Intervention (RtI)

Use the *Quick Check* results and the Intervention Planner to help you determine your Response to Intervention. The If-Then statements in the chart below help you decide the appropriate tier of RtI and suggest intervention resources for each tier.

Intervention Planner

Tier 1 — On Level

If students miss about 25% of the exercises or less,

Then choose a resource:

SE Concepts and Skills Bank, p. 859; Lessons 1-5, 1-6, and 2-8

CRM Skills Practice, Chapter 1, pp. 32 and 39, Chapter 2, p. 51

IL Math Online Self-Check Quiz

Tier 2 — Strategic Intervention approaching grade level

If students miss about 50% of the exercises,

Then choose a resource:

CRM Study Guide and Intervention, Chapter 1, pp. 30 and 37, Chapter 2, p. 49

Quick Review Math Handbook

IL Math Online Extra Examples, Personal Tutor, Homework Help

Tier 3 — Intensive Intervention 2 or more grades below level

If students miss about 75% of the exercises,

Then use *Math Triumphs, Alg. 1*, Ch. 4

IL Math Online Extra Examples, Personal Tutor, Homework Help, Review Vocabulary

CHAPTER 4 Notes

FOLDABLES® Study Organizer

Dinah Zike's Foldables®

Focus As students read and study this chapter, they should show examples and write notes about linear functions and relations.

Teach Have students make and label their Foldables as illustrated. Students should label the first three pockets with two lesson titles each. The fourth pocket should be labeled with the last lesson title. Students should list the vocabulary words on one index card per lesson. On the reverse of each card, students write the definitions of the vocabulary words. The cards are then placed in the appropriate pocket. The index cards can be used as flash cards for students to quiz each other.

When to Use It Encourage students to add to their Foldables as they work through the chapter and to use them to review for the chapter test.

Differentiated Instruction

CRM Student-Built Glossary, pp. 1–2 Students should complete the chart by providing a definition of each term and an example as they progress through Chapter 4. This study tool can also be used to review for the chapter test.

Get Started on Chapter 4

You will learn several new concepts, skills, and vocabulary terms as you study Chapter 4. To get ready, identify important terms and organize your resources. You may wish to refer to **Chapter 0** to review prerequisite skills.

FOLDABLES® Study Organizer

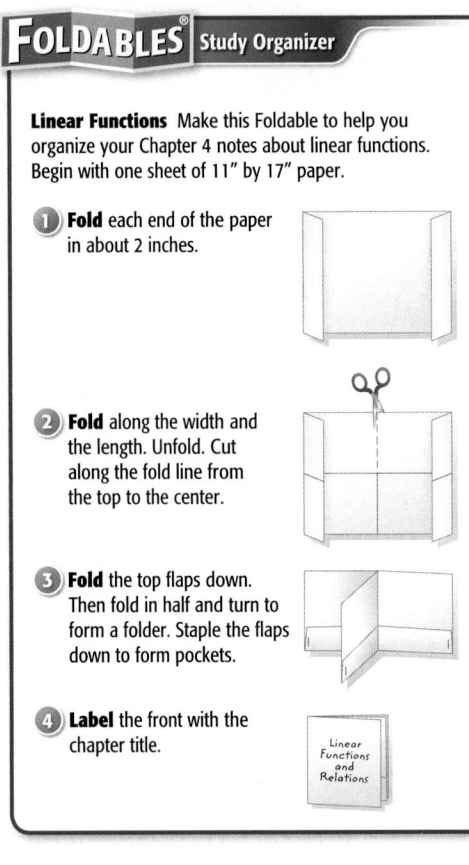

Linear Functions Make this Foldable to help you organize your Chapter 4 notes about linear functions. Begin with one sheet of 11″ by 17″ paper.

1 **Fold** each end of the paper in about 2 inches.

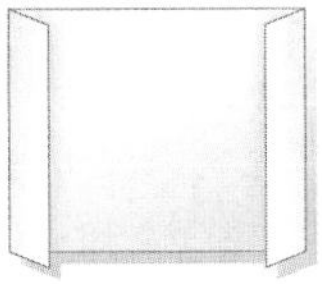

2 **Fold** along the width and the length. Unfold. Cut along the fold line from the top to the center.

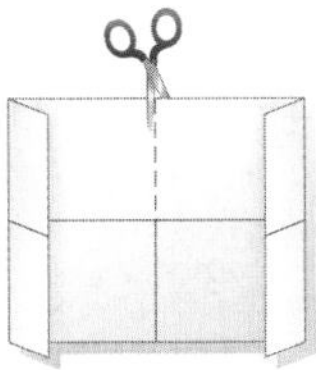

3 **Fold** the top flaps down. Then fold in half and turn to form a folder. Staple the flaps down to form pockets.

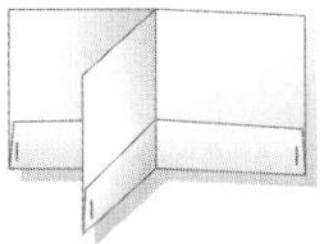

4 **Label** the front with the chapter title.

IL Math Online glencoe.com

- Study the chapter online
- Explore **Math in Motion**
- Get extra help from your own **Personal Tutor**
- Use **Extra Examples** for additional help
- Take a **Self-Check Quiz**
- **Review Vocabulary** in fun ways

New Vocabulary

English		Español
slope-intercept form	• p. 214 •	forma pendiente-intersección
linear extrapolation	• p. 226 •	extrapolación lineal
point-slope form	• p. 231 •	forma punto-pendiente
parallel lines	• p. 237 •	rectas paralelas
perpendicular lines	• p. 238 •	rectas perpendiculares
scatter plot	• p. 245 •	gráfica de dispersión
line of fit	• p. 246 •	recta de ajuste
linear interpolation	• p. 247 •	interpolación lineal
best-fit line	• p. 253 •	recta de ajuste óptimo
linear regression	• p. 253 •	retroceso lineal
correlation coefficient	• p. 253 •	coeficiente de correlación
median-fit line	• p. 255 •	línea de mediana-ataque
step function	• p. 261 •	función etapa
piecewise function	• p. 261 •	función a intervalos
greatest integer function	• p. 261 •	función del máximo entero

Review Vocabulary

coefficient • p. 26 • coeficiente the numerical factor of a term

function • p. 45 • función a relation in which each element of the domain is paired with exactly one element of the range

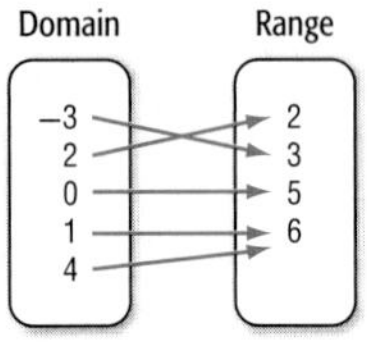

ratio • p. 111 • razon a comparison of two numbers by division

Multilingual eGlossary glencoe.com

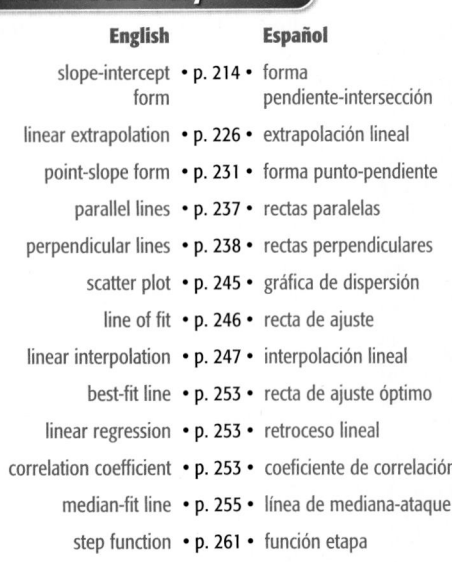

EXPLORE 4-1

Graphing Technology Lab
Investigating Slope-Intercept Form

Objective
Use a graphing calculator to collect data and investigate slope-intercept form.

IL Learning Standards

7.B.4 Estimate and measure the magnitude and directions of physical quantities using rulers, protractors and other scientific instruments including timers, calculators and computers.

Set Up the Lab

- Cut a small hole in a top corner of a plastic sandwich bag. Hang the bag from the end of the force sensor.
- Connect the force sensor to your data collection device.

ACTIVITY

Step 1 Use the sensor to collect the weight with 0 washers in the bag. Record the data pair in the calculator.

Step 2 Place one washer in the plastic bag. Wait for the bag to stop swinging, then measure and record the weight.

Step 3 Repeat the experiment, adding different numbers of washers to the bag. Each time, record the number of washers and the weight.

Analyze the Results

1. The domain contains values of the independent variable, number of washers. The range contains values of the dependent variable, weight. Use the graphing calculator to create a scatter plot using the ordered pairs (washers, weight). **See students' work.**
2. Write a sentence that describes the points on the graph. **Sample answer: It is a linear pattern.**
3. Describe the position of the point on the graph that represents the trial with no washers in the bag. **It is the y-intercept.**
4. The rate of change can be found by using the formula for slope. **See students' work. Sample answer: 0.025**

   $$\frac{\text{rise}}{\text{run}} = \frac{\text{change in weight}}{\text{change in number of washers}}$$

   Find the rate of change in the weight as more washers are added.
5. Explain how the rate of change is shown on the graph. **The slope represents the rate of change.**

Make a Conjecture

The graph shows sample data from a washer experiment. Describe the graph for each situation.

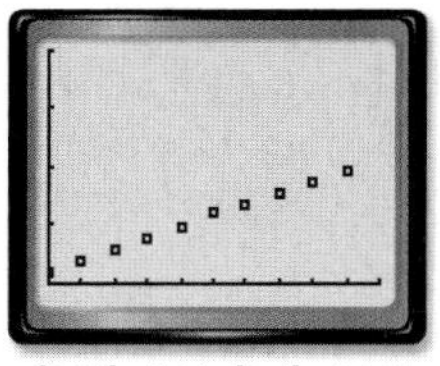

[0, 20] scl: 2 by [0, 1] scl: 0.25

6. a bag that hangs weighs 0.8 N when empty and increases in weight at the rate of the sample
7. a bag that has the same weight when empty as the sample and increases in weight at a faster rate
8. a bag that has the same weight when empty as the sample and increases in weight at a slower rate

6. Sample answer: The graph is the same as the one shown, shifted upward so that the y-intercept is at (0, 0.8).
7. Sample answer: The graph has the same y-intercept, but the rate of change is greater.
8. Sample answer: The graph has the same y-intercept, but the rate of change is less.

From Concrete to Abstract

- Ask students what they think the graph would look like if a bag had the same weight when empty as the sample and increased in weight at a slower and slower rate. Sample answer: the same y-intercept but the rate of change would be less and less
- Ask what the graph would look like if the slope were close to 0. Sample answer: a linear pattern that is close to horizontal

EXPLORE 4-1

Lesson Notes

1 FOCUS

Objective Use a graphing calculator to collect data and investigate slope-intercept form.

Materials for Each Group

- T1–83/84 Plus or other graphing calculator
- CBL or other data collection device and force sensor
- plastic sandwich bag
- washers

Teaching Tip

Point out to students the features of the data collection device and show them how to weigh the washers. Urge students to record their data carefully. One careless recording will prevent students from seeing a pattern.

2 TEACH

Working in Cooperative Groups

Have students work in groups of two or three, mixing abilities. Have groups complete the Activity and Exercises 1–5. In Step 1 of the Activity, suggest that students enter the number of washers in L1 and the corresponding weights in L2. In Exercise 3, point out that the weight with no washers is the weight of the bag.

Practice Have students complete Exercises 6–8.

3 ASSESS

Formative Assessment

Use Exercise 4 to assess whether students can calculate the rate of change correctly. Use Exercise 7 to assess whether students understand that the rate of change is the slope of the line connecting the points.

4-1 Lesson Notes

1 FOCUS

Vertical Alignment

Before Lesson 4-1
Find rates of change and slopes.

Lesson 4-1
Write and graph linear equations in slope-intercept form.
Model real-world data with equations in slope-intercept form.

After Lesson 4-1
Write an equation of a line given two points or a point and the slope in slope-intercept form.

2 TEACH

Scaffolding Questions

Have students read the *Why?* section of the lesson.

Ask:

- How many songs could Jamil have on his MP3 player after two months? 560
- How many songs could he have after four months? 620
- Would a graph of the equation $y = 30x + 500$ have a positive or negative slope? positive

4-1 Graphing Equations in Slope-Intercept Form

Then
You found rates of change and slopes. (Lesson 3-3)

Now
- Write and graph linear equations in slope-intercept from.
- Model real-world data with equations in slope-intercept form.

IL Learning Standards
8.C.4b Apply algebraic properties and procedures with matrices, vectors, functions and sequences using data found in business, industry and consumer situations.

New Vocabulary
slope-intercept form

IL Math Online
glencoe.com
- Extra Examples
- Personal Tutor
- Self-Check Quiz
- Homework Help
- Math in Motion

Why?

Jamil has 500 songs on his MP3 player. He joins a music club that lets him download 30 songs per month for a monthly fee. The number of songs that Jamil could eventually have in his player if he does not delete any songs is represented by $y = 30x + 500$.

Slope-Intercept Form An equation of the form $y = mx + b$, where m is the slope and b is the y-intercept, is in **slope-intercept form**. The variables m and b are called *parameters* of the equation. Changing either value changes the equation's graph.

Key Concept — Slope-Intercept Form (For Your FOLDABLE)

Words The slope-intercept form of a linear equation is $y = mx + b$, where m is the slope and b is the y-intercept.

Example $y = mx + b$

$y = 2x + 6$ (2: slope; 6: y-intercept)

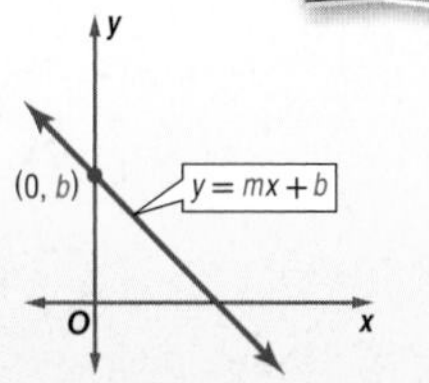

Math *in Motion*, BrainPOP® glencoe.com

EXAMPLE 1 Write and Graph an Equation

Write an equation in slope-intercept form for the line with a slope of $\frac{3}{4}$ and a y-intercept of -2. Then graph the equation.

$y = mx + b$ — Slope-intercept form

$y = \frac{3}{4}x + (-2)$ — Replace m with $\frac{3}{4}$ and b with -2.

$y = \frac{3}{4}x - 2$ — Simplify.

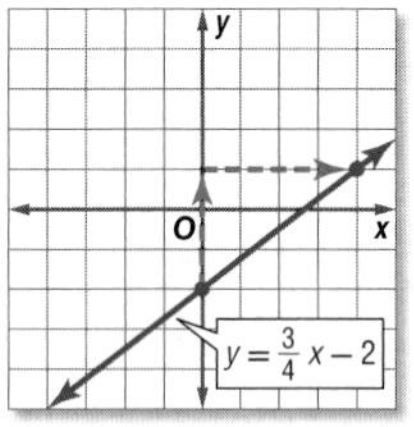

Now graph the equation.

Step 1 Plot the y-intercept $(0, -2)$.

Step 2 The slope is $\frac{\text{rise}}{\text{run}} = \frac{3}{4}$. From $(0, -2)$, move up 3 units and right 4 units. Plot the point.

Step 3 Draw a line through the two points.

Check Your Progress

Write an equation of a line in slope intercept form with the given slope and y-intercept. Then graph the equation. 1A–1B. See Ch. 4 Answer Appendix for graphs.

1A. slope: $-\frac{1}{2}$, y-intercept: 3 $y = -\frac{1}{2}x + 3$ **1B.** slope: -3, y-intercept: -8 $y = -3x - 8$

Personal Tutor glencoe.com

Lesson 4-1 Resources

Resource	Approaching-Level	On-Level	Beyond-Level	English Learners
Teacher Edition	• Differentiated Instruction, p. 217	• Differentiated Instruction, p. 219	• Differentiated Instruction, p. 219	• Differentiated Instruction, p. 217
Chapter Resource Masters	• Study Guide and Intervention, pp. 5–6 • Skills Practice, p. 7 • Practice, p. 8 • Word Problem Practice, p. 9	• Study Guide and Intervention, pp. 5–6 • Skills Practice, p. 7 • Practice, p. 8 • Word Problem Practice, p. 9 • Enrichment, p. 10	• Practice, p. 8 • Word Problem Practice, p. 9 • Enrichment, p. 10	• Study Guide and Intervention, pp. 5–6 • Skills Practice, p. 7 • Practice, p. 8
Transparencies	• 5-Minute Check Transparency 4-1	• 5-Minute Check Transparency 4-1	• 5-Minute Check Transparency 4-1	• 5-Minute Check Transparency 4-1
Other	• Study Notebook	• Study Notebook	• Study Notebook	• Study Notebook

When an equation is not written in slope-intercept form, it may be easier to rewrite it before graphing.

StudyTip

Dependent Variables *y* is the *dependent* variable because it *depends* on changes in *x*.

EXAMPLE 2 Graph Linear Equations

Graph $3x + 2y = 6$.

Rewrite the equation in slope-intercept form.

$3x + 2y = 6$	**Original equation**
$3x + 2y - 3x = 6 - 3x$	**Subtract 3x from each side.**
$2y = 6 - 3x$	**Simplify.**
$2y = -3x + 6$	**$6 - 3x = 6 + (-3x)$ or $-3x + 6$**
$\frac{2y}{2} = \frac{-3x + 6}{2}$	**Divide each side by 2.**
$y = -\frac{3}{2}x + 3$	**Slope-intercept form**

Now graph the equation. The slope is $-\frac{3}{2}$, and the *y*-intercept is 3.

Step 1 Plot the *y*-intercept (0, 3).

Step 2 The slope is $\frac{\text{rise}}{\text{run}} = -\frac{3}{2}$. From (0, 3), move down 3 units and right 2 units. Plot the point.

Step 3 Draw a line through the two points.

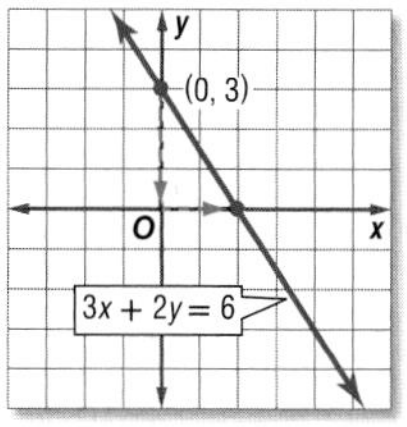

StudyTip

Counting and Direction When counting rise and run, a negative sign may be associated with the value in the numerator or denominator. If with the numerator, begin by counting down for the rise. If with the denominator, count left when counting the run. The resulting line will be the same.

Check Your Progress

Graph each equation. **2A–2B. See Ch. 4 Answer Appendix.**

2A. $3x - 4y = 12$ **2B.** $-2x + 5y = 10$

Personal Tutor glencoe.com

Horizontal lines have a slope of 0. So, equations of horizontal lines can be written in slope intercept form as $y = 0x + b$ or $y = b$. Vertical lines have no slope. So, equations of vertical lines cannot be written in slope-intercept form.

EXAMPLE 3 Graph Linear Equations

Graph $y = -3$.

Step 1 Plot the *y*-intercept (0, −3).

Step 2 The slope is 0. Draw a line through the points with *y*-coordinate −3.

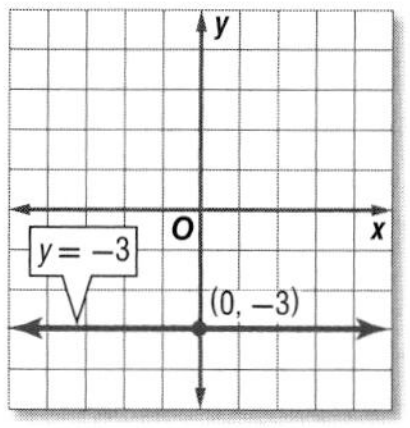

Check Your Progress

Graph each equation. **3A–3B. See Ch. 4 Answer Appendix.**

3A. $y = 5$ **3B.** $2y = 1$

Personal Tutor glencoe.com

Notice that the equations of horizontal lines do not have an *x* variable. The graph of a horizontal line does not cross the *x*-axis. The equation $y = 0$ lies on the *x*-axis.

Slope-Intercept Form

Example 1 shows how to write and graph a linear equation given the slope and *y*-intercept. **Example 2** shows how to rewrite a linear equation in slope-intercept form in order to graph it. **Example 3** shows how to graph a linear equation with a slope of 0. **Example 4** shows how to write an equation in slope-intercept form for a line on a graph.

Formative Assessment

Use the Check Your Progress exercises after each Example to determine students' understanding of concepts.

Additional Examples

1 Write an equation in slope-intercept form of the line with a slope of $\frac{1}{4}$ and a *y*-intercept of −1. Then graph the equation.

$y = \frac{1}{4}x - 1$

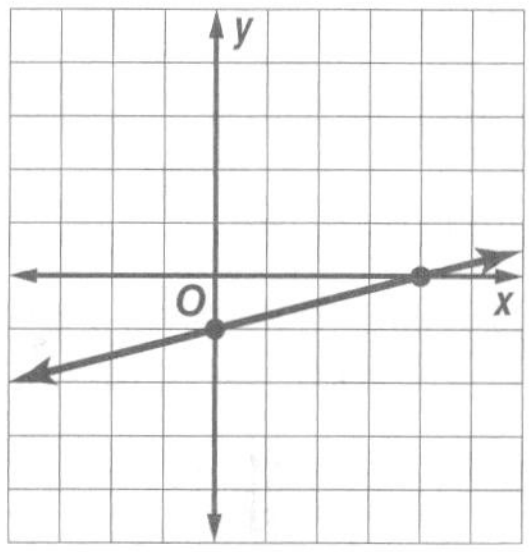

2 Graph $5x + 4y = 8$. (See bottom margin for graph.)

3 Graph $y = -7$. (See bottom margin for graph.)

Additional Examples also in Interactive Classroom PowerPoint® Presentations

IWB INTERACTIVE WHITEBOARD READY

Watch Out!

Preventing Errors Remind students that *b* can be negative, so equations may not always have positive constants.

Additional Answers (Additional Examples)

2.

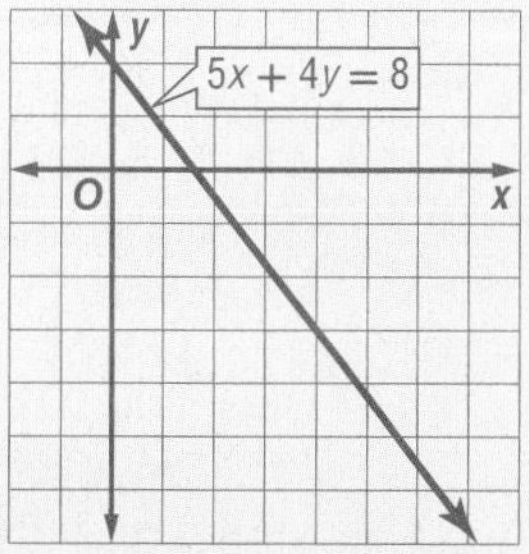

3.

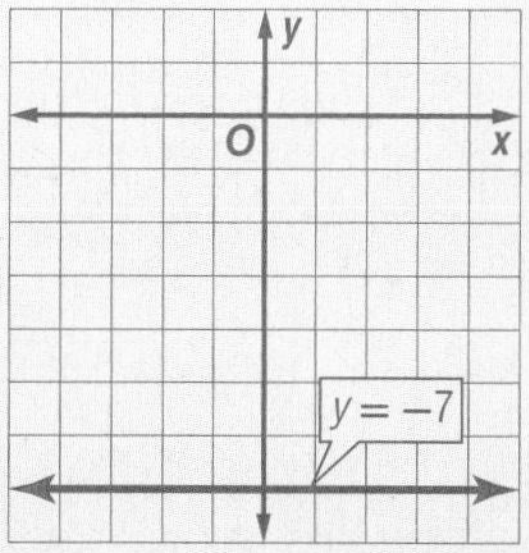

Additional Example

4 **Standardized Test Practice** Which of the following is an equation in slope-intercept form for the line shown in the graph? B

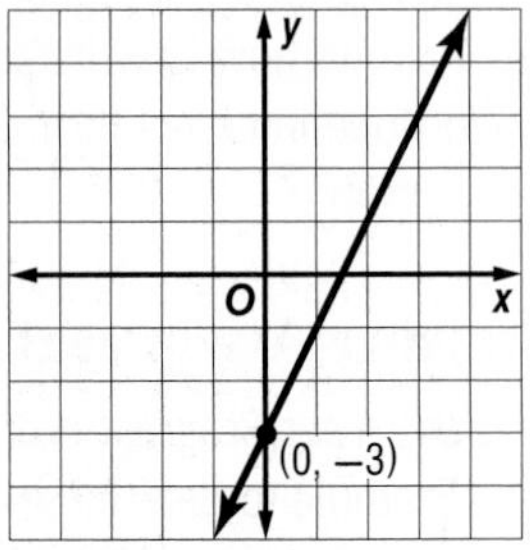

A $y = \frac{1}{2}x + 3$
B $y = 2x - 3$
C $y = \frac{1}{2}x + 3$
D $y = -2x - 3$

Focus on Mathematical Content

Slope-Intercept Form The slope-intercept form of a linear equation is $y = mx + b$. The b in this form represents the y-intercept of the graph, the y-coordinate of the point where the line crosses the y-axis. The m represents the slope of the line.

Modeling Real-World Data

Example 5 shows how to model real-world data with an equation in slope-intercept form and then use that equation to solve a problem.

TEACH with TECH

INTERACTIVE WHITEBOARD Drag a coordinate grid on the board. Draw a line on the grid, and have students write the equation of the line in slope-intercept form. Then drag more line from other locations on the board and again have students write the equation of the line. Discuss how the equations are similar and different.

There are times when you will need to write an equation when given a graph. To do this, locate the y-intercept and use the rise and run to find another point on the graph. Then write the equation in slope-intercept form.

Test-Taking Tip

Eliminating Choices Analyze the graph to determine the slope and the y-intercept. Then you can save time by eliminating answer choices that do not match the graph.

PSAE EXAMPLE 4 8.11.07

Which of the following is an equation in slope-intercept form for the line shown?

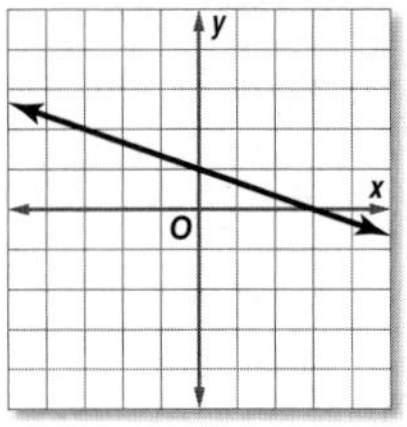

A $y = -3x + 1$
B $y = -3x + 3$
C $y = -\frac{1}{3}x + 1$
D $y = -\frac{1}{3}x + 3$

Read the Test Item

You need to find the slope and y-intercept of the line to write the equation.

Solve the Test Item

Step 1 The line crosses the y-axis at (0, 1), so the y-intercept is 1. The answer is either A or C.

Step 2 To get from (0, 1) to (3, 0), go down 1 unit and 3 units to the right. The slope is $-\frac{1}{3}$.

Step 3 Write the equation.

$y = mx + b$

$y = -\frac{1}{3}x + 1$

CHECK The graph also passes through (−3, 2). If the equation is correct, this should be a solution.

$y = -\frac{1}{3}x + 1$

$2 \stackrel{?}{=} -\frac{1}{3}(-3) + 1$

$2 \stackrel{?}{=} 1 + 1$

$2 = 2$ ✓ The answer is C.

Check Your Progress

4. Which of the following is an equation in slope-intercept form for the line shown? F

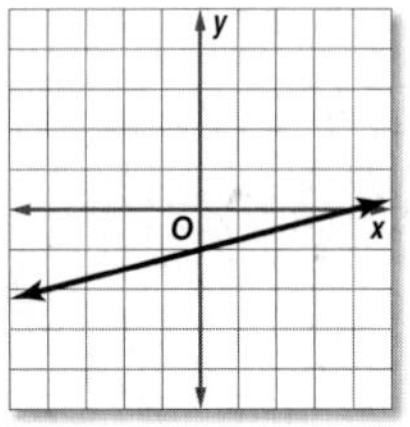

F $y = \frac{1}{4}x - 1$
G $y = \frac{1}{4}x + 4$
H $y = 4x - 1$
J $y = 4x + 4$

Personal Tutor glencoe.com

Modeling Real-World Data Real-world data can be modeled by a linear equation if there is a constant rate of change. The rate of change represents the slope. The y-intercept is the point where the value of the independent variable is 0.

216 Chapter 4 Linear Functions and Relations

Real-World Link

In 1997, about 2.6 million girls competed in high school sports. The number of girls competing in high school sports has increased by an average of 0.06 million per year since 1997.

Source: National Federation of High School Associations

Real-World EXAMPLE 5 Write and Graph a Linear Equation

SPORTS Use the information at the left about high school sports.

a. Write a linear equation to find the number of girls in high school sports after 1997.

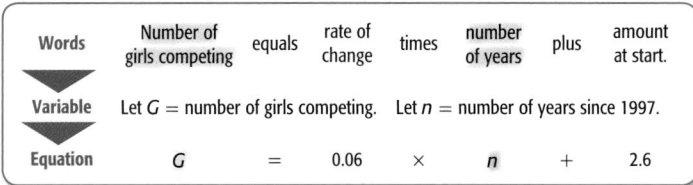

Words	Number of girls competing	equals	rate of change	times	number of years	plus	amount at start.
Variable	Let G = number of girls competing.				Let n = number of years since 1997.		
Equation	G	$=$	0.06	$\times$	n	$+$	2.6

The equation is $G = 0.06n + 2.6$.

b. Graph the equation.

The y-intercept is where the data begins. So, the graph passes through (0, 2.6).

The rate of change is the slope, so the slope is 0.06.

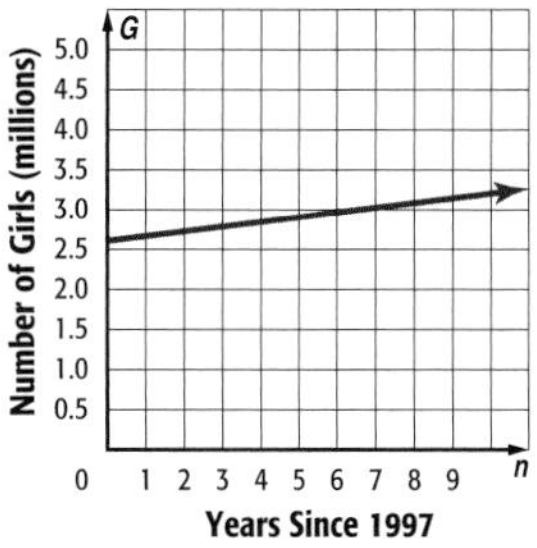

c. Estimate the number of girls competing in 2017.

The year 2017 is 20 years after 1997.

$G = 0.06n + 2.6$ **Write the equation.**

$= 0.06(20) + 2.6$ **Replace n with 20.**

$= 3.8$ **Simplify.**

There will be about 3.8 million girls competing in high school sports in 2017.

Check Your Progress

5. FUNDRAISERS The band boosters are selling subs for \$5 each. They bought \$1160 in ingredients.

A. Write an equation for the profit P made on n sandwiches. $P = 5n - 1160$

B. Graph the equation. See margin.

C. Find the total profit if 1400 sandwiches are sold. \$5840

Personal Tutor glencoe.com

Check Your Understanding

Example 1 p. 214

Write an equation of a line in slope-intercept form with the given slope and y-intercept. Then graph the equation. 1–4. See Ch. 4 Answer Appendix.

1. slope: 2, y-intercept: 4

2. slope: -5, y-intercept: 3

3. slope: $\frac{3}{4}$, y-intercept: -1

4. slope: $-\frac{5}{7}$, y-intercept: $-\frac{2}{3}$

Examples 2 and 3 p. 215

Graph each equation. 5–10. See Ch. 4 Answer Appendix.

5. $-4x + y = 2$

6. $2x + y = -6$

7. $-3x + 7y = 21$

8. $6x - 4y = 16$

9. $y = -1$

10. $15y = 3$

Additional Example

5 **HEALTH** The ideal maximum heart rate for a 25-year-old exercising to burn fat is 117 beats per minute. For every five years older than 25, that ideal rate drops three beats per minute.

a. Write a linear equation to find the ideal maximum heart rate for anyone over 25 who is exercising to burn fat. $R = -\frac{3}{5}a + 117$, where R is the ideal maximum heart rate for a 25-year-old and a is the number of years older than 25

b. Graph the equation.

Ideal Heart Rates

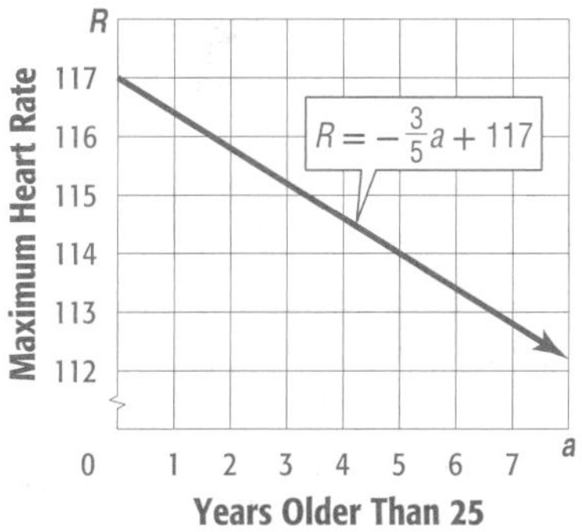

c. Find the ideal maximum heart rate for a 55-year-old person exercising to burn fat. 99 beats per minute

Additional Answer (Check Your Progress)

5B.

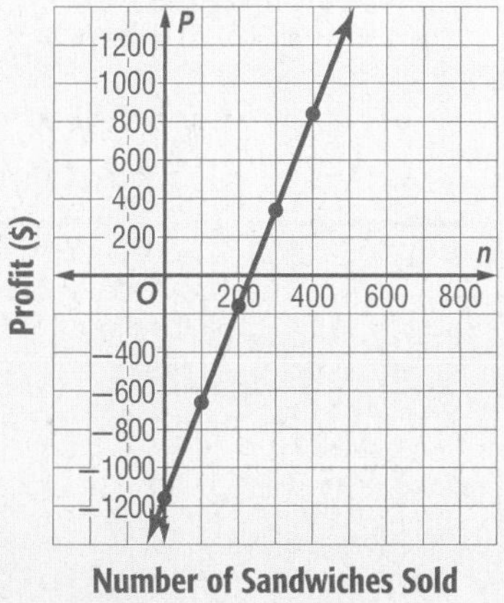

Differentiated Instruction AL ELL

If some students have difficulty with word problems because they cannot picture what the problem is trying to communicate,

Then sometimes it is easier for those students to graph or draw a picture of the given information before writing the equation. For Additional Example 5, you may wish to have students do part **b** first by using the starting point and the rate of change to determine other points on the graph. Then have students write the equation that describes the line formed.

3 PRACTICE

Formative Assessment

Use Exercises 1–16 to check for understanding.

Use the chart at the bottom of the next page to customize assignments for your students.

Additional Answers

15b.

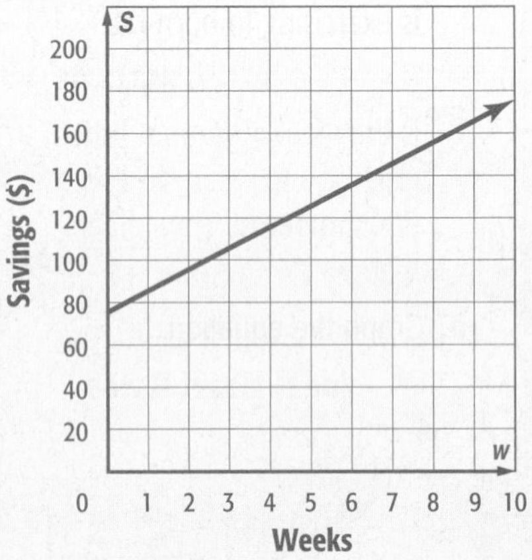

16b.

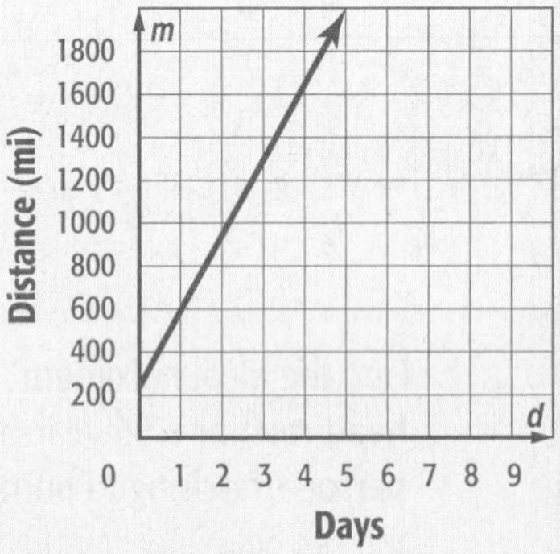

Example 4 p. 216

Write an equation in slope-intercept form for each graph shown.

11. 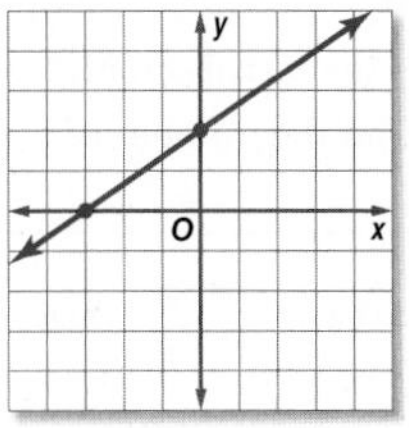 $y = \frac{2}{3}x + 2$

12. 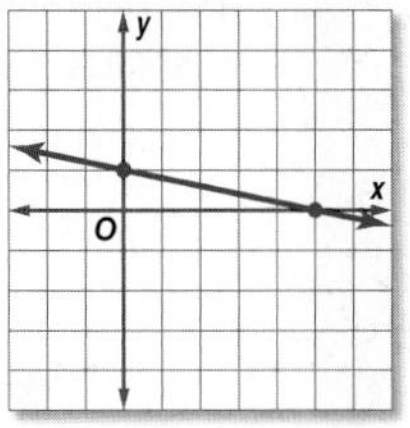 $y = -\frac{1}{5}x + 1$

13. 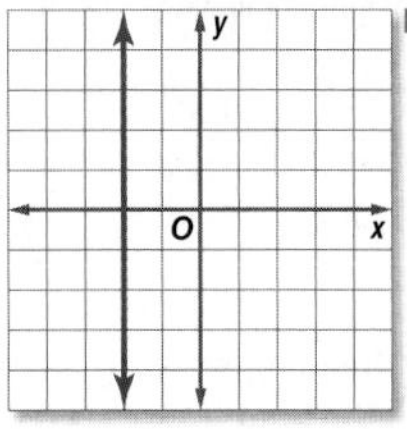 not possible

14. 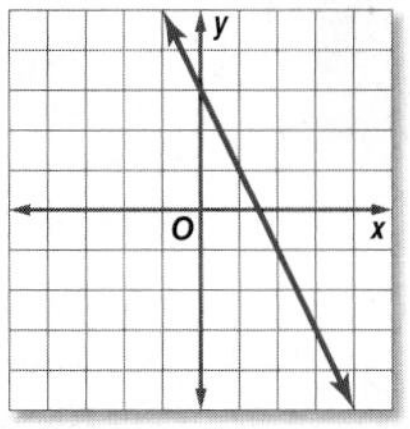 $y = -2x + 3$

Example 5 p. 217

15. FINANCIAL LITERACY Rondell is buying a new stereo system for his car using a layaway plan.

a. Write an equation for the total amount S that he has paid after w weeks. $S = 10w + 75$

b. Graph the equation. See margin.

c. Find out how much Rondell will have saved after 8 weeks. $155

16. TRAVEL Ana is driving from her home in Miami, Florida, to her grandmother's house in New York City. On the first day, she will travel 240 miles to Orlando, Florida, to pick up her cousin. Then they will travel 350 miles each day.

a. Write an equation for the total number of miles m that Ana has traveled after d days. $m = 350d + 240$

b. Graph the equation. See margin.

c. It is 1293 miles from Miami to New York City. How long will the drive take? about 4 days

Practice and Problem Solving

= **Step-by-Step Solutions** begin on page R12. **Extra Practice** begins on page 815.

Example 1 p. 214

Write an equation of a line in slope-intercept form with the given slope and y-intercept. Then graph the equation. 17–22. See Ch. 4 Answer Appendix.

17. slope: 5, y-intercept: 8
18. slope: 3, y-intercept: 10
19. slope: −4, y-intercept: 6
20. slope: −2, y-intercept: 8
21. slope: 3, y-intercept: −4
22. slope: 4, y-intercept: −6

Examples 2 and 3 p. 215

Graph each equation. 23–32. See Ch. 4 Answer Appendix.

23. $-3x + y = 6$
24. $-5x + y = 1$
25. $-2x + y = -4$
26. $y = 8x - 7$
27. $5x + 2y = 8$
28. $4x + 9y = 27$
29. $y = 7$
30. $y = -\frac{2}{3}$
31. $21 = 7y$
32. $3y - 6 = 2x$

Differentiated Homework Options

Level	Assignment	Two-Day Option	
AL Basic	17–37, 62–63, 65–83	17–37 odd, 67–70	18–36 even, 62–63, 65–66, 71–83
OL Core	17–49 odd, 50–51, 53–57 odd, 58–63, 65–83	17–37, 67–70	38–63, 65–66, 71–83
BL Advanced	38–79, (optional: 80–83)		

Example 4 p. 216 Write an equation in slope-intercept form for each graph shown.

33.

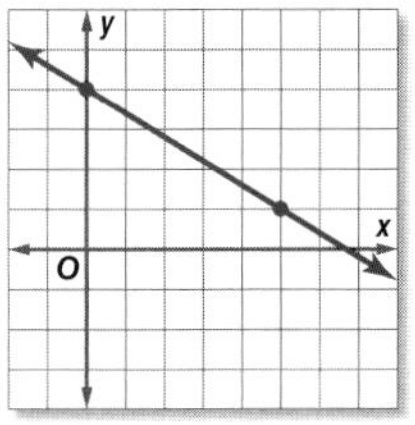

$y = -\frac{3}{5}x + 4$

34.

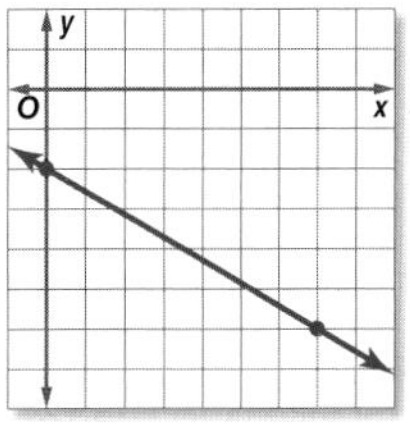

$y = -\frac{4}{7}x - 2$

35.

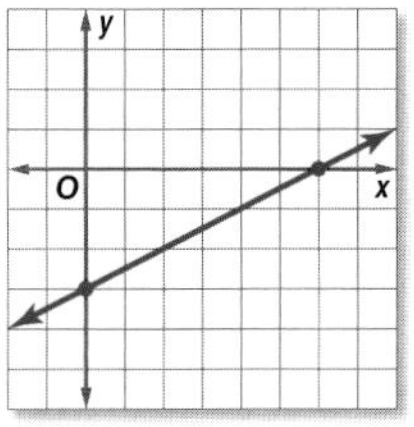

$y = \frac{1}{2}x - 3$

36.

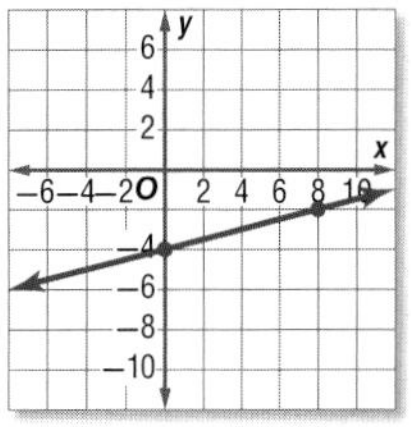

$y = \frac{1}{4}x - 4$

Example 5 p. 217 **37** **MANATEES** In 1991, 1267 manatees inhabited Florida's waters. The manatee population has increased at a rate of 123 manatees per year.

a. Write an equation for the manatee population, P, t years since 1991. $P = 1267 + 123t$

b. Graph this equation. **See margin.**

c. In 2006, the manatee was removed from Florida's endangered species list. What was the manatee population in 2006? **3112 manatees**

B **Write an equation of a line in slope-intercept form with the given slope and y-intercept. 38–43. See margin.**

38. slope: $\frac{1}{2}$, y-intercept: -3

39. slope: $\frac{2}{3}$, y-intercept: -5

40. slope: $-\frac{5}{6}$, y-intercept: 5

41. slope: $-\frac{3}{7}$, y-intercept: 2

42. slope: 1, y-intercept: 4

43. slope: 0, y-intercept: 5

Graph each equation. 44–49. See Ch. 4 Answer Appendix.

44. $y = \frac{3}{4}x - 2$

45. $y = \frac{5}{3}x + 4$

46. $3x + 8y = 32$

47. $5x - 6y = 36$

48. $-4x + \frac{1}{2}y = -1$

49. $3x - \frac{1}{4}y = 2$

50. **TRAVEL** A rental company charges \$8 per hour for a mountain bike plus a \$5 fee for a helmet.

a. Write an equation in slope-intercept form for the total rental cost C for a helmet and a bicycle for t hours. $C = 8t + 5$

b. Graph the equation. **See margin.**

c. What would the cost be for 2 helmets and 2 bicycles for 8 hours? **\$138**

Real-World Link

More than 3 million teens participate in mountain biking each year.

Source: *Statistical Abstract of the United States*

51. **COLLEGE TUITION** For Illinois residents, the average tuition at Chicago State University is \$157 per credit hour. Fees cost \$218 per year.

a. Write an equation in slope-intercept form for the tuition T for c credit hours. $T = 157c + 218$

b. Find the cost for a student who is taking 32 credit hours. **\$5242**

Exercise Alert

Grid Paper Exercises 1–10, 15–32, 37–50, 58, 61, and 62 require the use of grid paper.

Additional Answers

37b.

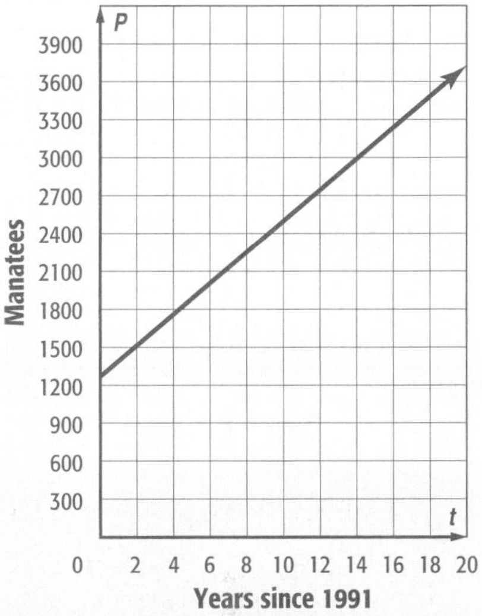

38. $y = \frac{1}{2}x - 3$

39. $y = \frac{2}{3}x - 5$

40. $y = -\frac{5}{6}x + 5$

41. $y = -\frac{3}{7}x + 2$

42. $y = x + 4$

43. $y = 5$

50b.

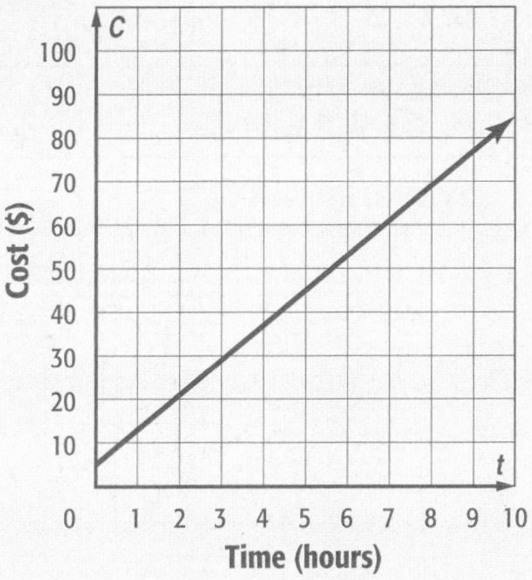

Differentiated Instruction

OL BL

Extension Write $3x + 2y = 8$ and $-3x + 2y = 8$ on the board. Remind students that these equations are in the standard form for the equation of a line. Ask students to tell how the equations are alike and how they are different. Then, ask students to tell how the graphs of these two equations are alike and how they are different. The coefficients of x are additive inverses; the coefficients of y are the same, and the constant after the equals sign in each equation is the same. The slopes, $-\frac{3}{2}$ and $\frac{3}{2}$, are additive inverses of each other; they both have the same y-intercept, 4.

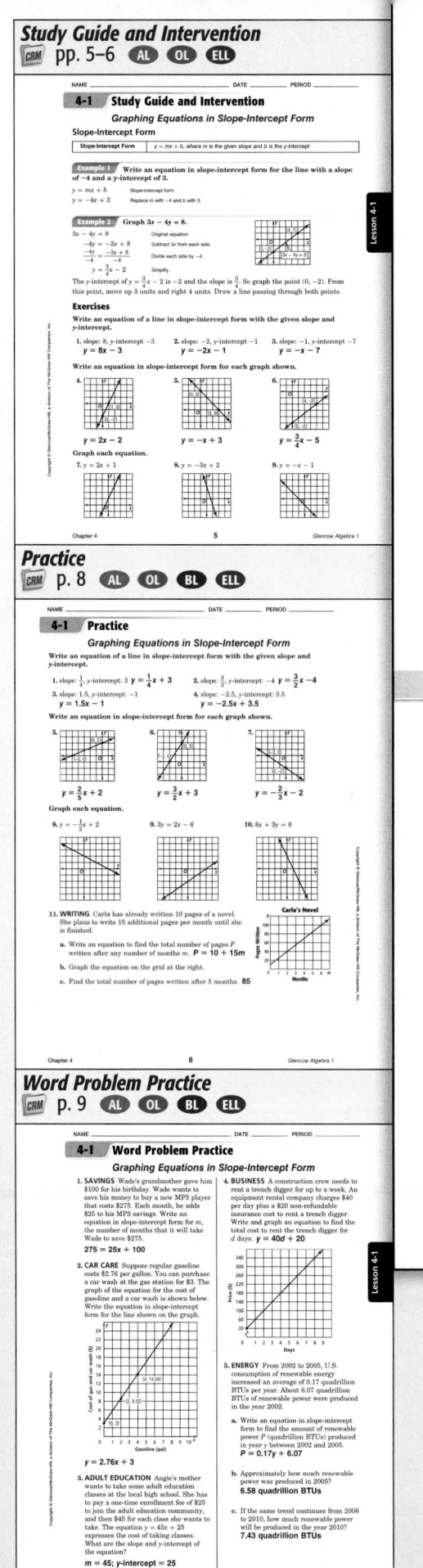

Study Guide and Intervention
CRM pp. 5–6 AL OL ELL

NAME ______ DATE ______ PERIOD ______

4-1 Study Guide and Intervention

Graphing Equations in Slope-Intercept Form

Slope-Intercept Form

Slope-Intercept Form	$y = mx + b$, where m is the given slope and b is the y-intercept

Example 1 Write an equation in slope-intercept form for the line with a slope of −4 and a y-intercept of 3.

$y = mx + b$ Slope-intercept form
$y = -4x + 3$ Replace m with −4 and b with 3.

Example 2 Graph $3x - 4y = 8$.

$3x - 4y = 8$ Original equation
$-4y = -3x + 8$ Subtract 3x from each side.
$\frac{-4y}{-4} = \frac{-3x + 8}{-4}$ Divide each side by −4.
$y = \frac{3}{4}x - 2$ Simplify.

The y-intercept of $y = \frac{3}{4}x - 2$ is −2 and the slope is $\frac{3}{4}$. So graph the point (0, −2). From this point, move up 3 units and right 4 units. Draw a line passing through both points.

Exercises

Write an equation of a line in slope-intercept form with the given slope and y-intercept.

1. slope: 8, y-intercept −3 **$y = 8x - 3$**
2. slope: −2, y-intercept −1 **$y = -2x - 1$**
3. slope: −1, y-intercept −7 **$y = -x - 7$**

Write an equation in slope-intercept form for each graph shown.

4. **$y = 2x - 2$**
5. **$y = -x + 3$**
6. **$y = \frac{3}{4}x - 5$**

Graph each equation.

7. $y = 2x + 1$
8. $y = -3x + 2$
9. $y = -x - 1$

Practice
CRM p. 8 AL OL BL ELL

NAME ______ DATE ______ PERIOD ______

4-1 Practice

Graphing Equations in Slope-Intercept Form

Write an equation of a line in slope-intercept form with the given slope and y-intercept.

1. slope: $\frac{1}{4}$, y-intercept: 3 **$y = \frac{1}{4}x + 3$**
2. slope: $\frac{3}{2}$, y-intercept: −4 **$y = \frac{3}{2}x - 4$**
3. slope: 1.5, y-intercept: −1 **$y = 1.5x - 1$**
4. slope: −2.5, y-intercept: 3.5 **$y = -2.5x + 3.5$**

Write an equation in slope-intercept form for each graph shown.

5. **$y = \frac{2}{5}x + 2$**
6. **$y = \frac{3}{2}x + 3$**
7. **$y = -\frac{2}{3}x - 2$**

Graph each equation.

8. $y = -\frac{1}{2}x + 2$
9. $3y = 2x - 6$
10. $6x + 3y = 6$

11. **WRITING** Carla has already written 10 pages of a novel. She plans to write 15 additional pages per month until she is finished.
a. Write an equation to find the total number of pages P written after any number of months m. **$P = 10 + 15m$**
b. Graph the equation on the grid at the right.
c. Find the total number of pages written after 5 months. **85**

Word Problem Practice
CRM p. 9 AL OL BL ELL

NAME ______ DATE ______ PERIOD ______

4-1 Word Problem Practice

Graphing Equations in Slope-Intercept Form

1. **SAVINGS** Wade's grandmother gave him $100 for his birthday. Wade wants to save his money to buy a new MP3 player that costs $275. Each month, he adds $25 to his MP3 savings. Write an equation in slope-intercept form for m, the number of months that it will take Wade to save $275. **$275 = 25x + 100$**

2. **CAR CARE** Suppose regular gasoline costs $2.76 per gallon. You can purchase a car wash at the gas station for $3. The graph of the equation for the cost of gasoline and a car wash is shown below. Write the equation in slope-intercept form for the line shown on the graph. **$y = 2.76x + 3$**

3. **ADULT EDUCATION** Angie's mother wants to take some adult education classes at the local high school. She has to pay a one-time enrollment fee of $25 to join the adult education community, and then $45 for each class she wants to take. The equation $y = 45x + 25$ expresses the cost of taking classes. What are the slope and y-intercept of the equation? **$m = 45$; y-intercept = 25**

4. **BUSINESS** A construction crew needs to rent a trench digger for up to a week. An equipment rental company charges $40 per day plus a $20 non-refundable insurance cost to rent a trench digger. Write and graph an equation to find the total cost to rent the trench digger for d days. **$y = 40d + 20$**

5. **ENERGY** From 2002 to 2005, U.S. consumption of renewable energy increased an average of 0.17 quadrillion BTUs per year. About 6.07 quadrillion BTUs of renewable power were produced in the year 2002.
a. Write an equation in slope-intercept form to find the amount of renewable power P (quadrillion BTUs) produced in year y between 2002 and 2005. **$P = 0.17y + 6.07$**
b. Approximately how much renewable power was produced in 2005? **6.58 quadrillion BTUs**
c. If the same trend continues from 2006 to 2010, how much renewable power will be produced in the year 2010? **7.43 quadrillion BTUs**

Write an equation of a line in slope-intercept form with the given slope and y-intercept. **52–55. See margin.**

52. slope: −1, y-intercept: 0
53. slope: 0.5, y-intercept: 7.5
54. slope: 0, y-intercept: 7
55. slope: −1.5, y-intercept: −0.25
56. Write an equation of a horizontal line that crosses the y-axis at (0, −5). **$y = -5$**
57. Write an equation of a line that passes through the origin and has a slope of 3. **$y = 3x$**

58. TEMPERATURE The temperature dropped rapidly overnight. Starting at 80°F, the temperature dropped 3° per minute.
a. Draw a graph that represents this drop from 0 to 8 minutes. **See margin.**
b. Write an equation that describes this situation. Describe the meaning of each variable as well as the slope and y-intercept. **See margin.**

59b. the cost per month to maintain the membership
59c. the startup fee

59. FITNESS Refer to the information at the right.
a. Write an equation that represents the cost C of a membership for m months. **$C = 45m + 145$**
b. What does the slope represent?
c. What does the C-intercept represent?
d. What is the cost of a two-year membership? **$1225**

GET FIT GYM
startup fee **$145**
$45 monthly fee

Real-World Link
Seventeen magazine debuted in 1944, during World War II. Today, the magazine has a circulation of over 2,000,000.
Source: *Chicago-Sun Times*

60. MAGAZINES A teen magazine began with a circulation of 500,000 in its first year. Since then, the circulation has increased an average of 33,388 per year.
a. Write an equation that represents the circulation c after y years. **$c = 33,388y + 500,000$**
b. What does the slope represent? **the increase in circulation each year**
c. What does the y-intercept represent? **the circulation in the first year**
d. If the magazine began in 1944, and this trend continues, in what year will the circulation reach 3,000,000? **2019**

61. CELL PHONES In 2007, 3.25 billion customers worldwide used a cell phone, and 1000 new customers signed up each minute.
a. Write an equation for the number of cell phone customers in billions, C, t years since 2007. Graph this equation. **See margin.**
b. How many cell phone customers will there be in 2011? **5.3524 billion**
c. During what year will the number of customers reach 10 billion? **2019**

H.O.T. Problems
Use Higher-Order Thinking Skills

62. OPEN ENDED Draw a graph representing a real-world linear function and write an equation for the graph. Describe what the graph represents. **See Ch. 4 Answer Appendix.**

63. REASONING Determine whether the equation of a vertical line can be written in slope-intercept form. Explain your reasoning.

63. No; because a vertical line has no slope, it cannot be written in slope-intercept form.

64. CHALLENGE Summarize the characteristics that the graphs $y = 2x + 3$, $y = 4x + 3$, $y = -x + 3$, and $y = -10x + 3$ have in common.

64. Sample answer: All four graphs are lines that cross the y-axis at 3.

65. WRITING IN MATH If given an equation in standard form, explain how to determine the rate of change. **See margin.**

66. WRITING IN MATH Explain how you would use a given y-intercept and the slope to make predictions about what the y-value will be for a given x-value without graphing. **See margin.**

Enrichment
CRM p. 10 OL BL

NAME ______ DATE ______ PERIOD ______

4-1 Enrichment

Using Equations: Ideal Weight

You can find your ideal weight as follows.
A woman should weigh 100 pounds for the first 5 feet of height and 5 additional pounds for each inch over 5 feet (5 feet = 60 inches).
A man should weigh 106 pounds for the first 5 feet of height and 6 additional pounds for each inch over 5 feet. These formulas apply to people with normal bone structures.
To determine your bone structure, wrap your thumb and index finger around the wrist of your other hand. If the thumb and finger just touch, you have normal bone structure. If they overlap, you are small-boned. If they don't overlap, you are large-boned. Small-boned people should decrease their calculated ideal weight by 10%. Large-boned people should increase the value by 10%.

Calculate the ideal weights of these people.

1. woman, 5 ft 4 in., normal-boned **120 lb**
2. man, 5 ft 11 in., large-boned **189.2 lb**
3. man, 6 ft 5 in., small-boned **187.2 lb**
4. you, if you are at least 5 ft tall **Answers will vary.**

For Exercises 5–9, use the following information.

Additional Answers

52. $y = -x$
53. $y = 0.5x + 7.5$
54. $y = 7$
55. $y = -1.5x - 0.25$

PSAE PRACTICE 8.11.02, 10.11.07, 6.11.17

67. A music store has x CDs in stock. If 350 are sold and $3y$ are added to stock, which expression represents the number of CDs in stock? **B**

A $350 + 3y - x$
C $x + 350 + 3y$
B $x - 350 + 3y$
D $3y - 350 - x$

68. PROBABILITY The table shows the result of a survey of favorite activities. What is the probability that a student's favorite activity is sports or drama club? **H**

Extracurricular Activity	Students
art club	24
band	134
choir	37
drama club	46
mock trial	19
school paper	26
sports	314

F $\frac{3}{8}$ G $\frac{4}{9}$ H $\frac{3}{5}$ J $\frac{2}{3}$

69. A recipe for fruit punch calls for 2 ounces of orange juice for every 8 ounces of lemonade. If Jennifer uses 64 ounces of lemonade, which proportion can she use to find x, the number of ounces of orange juice needed? **C**

A $\frac{2}{x} = \frac{64}{6}$
C $\frac{2}{8} = \frac{x}{64}$
B $\frac{8}{x} = \frac{64}{2}$
D $\frac{6}{2} = \frac{x}{64}$

70. EXTENDED RESPONSE The table shows the results of a canned food drive. 1225 cans were collected, and the 12th-grade class collected 55 more cans than the 10th-grade class. How many cans each did the 10th- and 12th-grade classes collect? Show your work. **See margin.**

Grade	Cans
9	340
10	x
11	280
12	y

Spiral Review

For each arithmetic sequence, determine the related function. Then determine if the function is *proportional* or *nonproportional*. (Lesson 3-6) **71–74. See Ch. 4 Answer Appendix.**

71. 3, 7, 11, ...
72. 8, 6, 4, ...
73. 0, 3, 6, ...
74. 1, 2, 3, ...

75. GAME SHOWS Contestants on a game show win money by answering 10 questions. (Lesson 3-5)

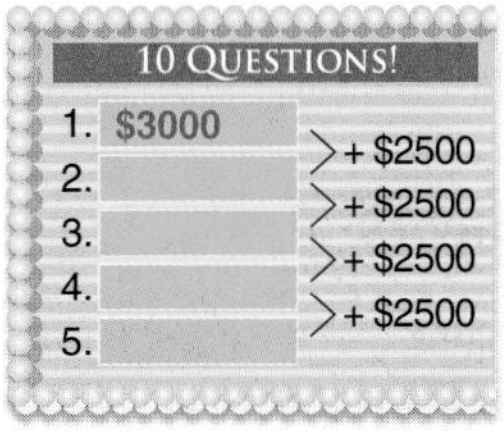

a. Find the value of the 10th question. **$25,500**

b. If all questions are answered correctly, how much are the winnings? **$142,500**

Suppose y varies directly as x. Write a direct variation equation that relates x and y. Then solve. (Lesson 3-4)

76. If $y = 10$ when $x = 5$, find y when $x = 6$. $y = 2x$; 12

77. If $y = -16$ when $x = 4$, find x when $y = 20$. $y = -4x$; -5

78. If $y = 6$ when $x = 18$, find y when $x = -12$. $y = \frac{1}{3}x$; -4

79. If $y = 12$ when $x = 15$, find x when $y = -6$. $y = 0.8x$; -7.5

Skills Review

Find the slope of the line that passes through each pair of points. (Lesson 3-3)

80. (2, 3), (9, 7) $\frac{4}{7}$
81. (−3, 6), (2, 4) $-\frac{2}{5}$
82. (2, 6), (−1, 3) 1
83. (−3, 3), (1, 3) 0

4 ASSESS

Name the Math Have students summarize how they can draw the graph of an equation without finding points that satisfy the equation.

Additional Answers

58a.

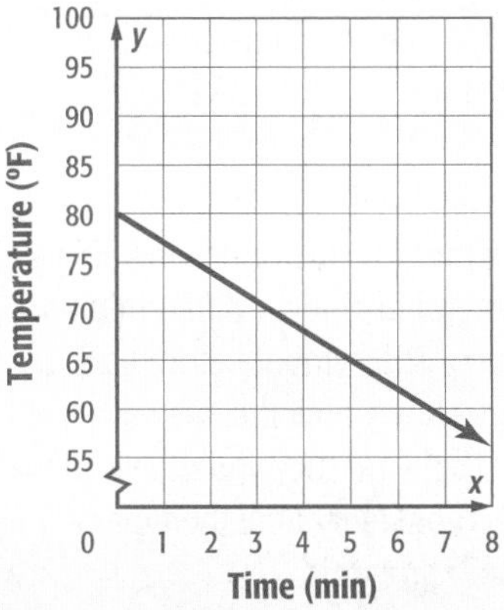

58b. $y = -3x + 80$; y represents the temperature, x represents the elapsed time, the slope represents the change in temperature per minute, and the y-intercept represents the temperature when the temperature started to drop.

61a. $C = 3.25 + 0.5256t$

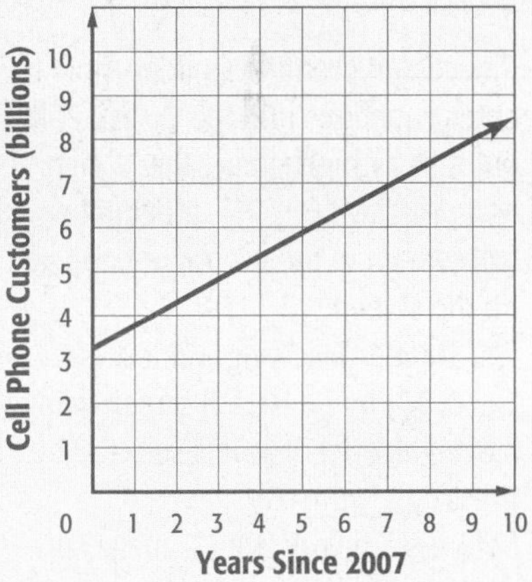

66. Sample answer: If the slope is m and the y-intercept is b, substitute the given x-value for x in $y = mx + b$. Then simplify.

70. The 10th grade class collected 275, and the 12th grade class collected 330. First I found that the total number of cans collected by the 10th and 12th grade classes is $1225 - (340 + 280)$ or 605. Then, if x is the number of cans the 10th grade class collected, then the 12th grade class collected $x + 55$ cans. The sum of these is 605.

10th $= x$, 12th $= x + 55$
$x + x + 55 = 605$
$x = 275$
10th $= 275$; 12th $= 330$

65. Sample answer: Assume that the coefficient of y is not 0. We would first have to rewrite the equation in slope-intercept form. The rate of change is also the slope so the coefficient for the x-variable is the rate of change. Assume that the coefficient of y is not 0.

1 FOCUS

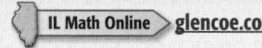

Objective Use a graphing calculator to investigate families of linear functions.

Materials for Each Student

- T1–83/84 Plus or other graphing calculator

Teaching Tip

The graphing calculator has the ability to make graphs appear differently on the screen. The symbol before each Y = entry shows how the line will appear. Highlight the symbol and press ENTER repeatedly until the type of line you want appears.

2 TEACH

Working in Cooperative Groups

Have students work in groups of two or three, mixing abilities. Have groups complete Activities 1-3 and Exercises 1-9.

- If necessary, remind students how to enter equations into the Y= list. Point out that by highlighting the = sign and pressing ENTER, an equation will remain in the list but not appear on the screen.
- The standard viewing window is a [−10, 10] by [−10, 10] screen with X Scl and Y Scl of 1. It is selected by pressing Zoom 6.
- Before starting Activity 1, make sure students have cleared or suppressed any equations in the Y= list other than those they wish to graph.

Practice Have students complete Exercises 10–16.

The Family of Linear Graphs

IL Math Online glencoe.com
- Other Calculator Keystrokes
- Graphing Technology Personal Tutor

IL Learning Standards **8.C.4a Analyze and report the effects of changing coefficients, exponents and other parameters on functions and their graphs.**

A family of people is related by birth, marriage, or adoption. Often people in families share characteristics. The graphs in a family share at least one characteristic. Graphs in the linear family are all lines, with the simplest graph in the family being that of the parent function $y = x$.

You can use a graphing calculator to investigate how changing the parameters m and b in $y = mx + b$ affects the graphs in the family of linear functions.

Parent Graph

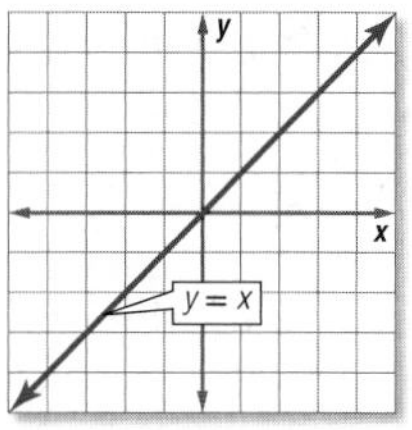

ACTIVITY 1 Changing b in $y = mx + b$

Graph $y = x$, $y = x + 4$, and $y = x - 2$ in the standard viewing window.

Enter the equations in the Y= list as Y1, Y2, and Y3. Then graph the equations.

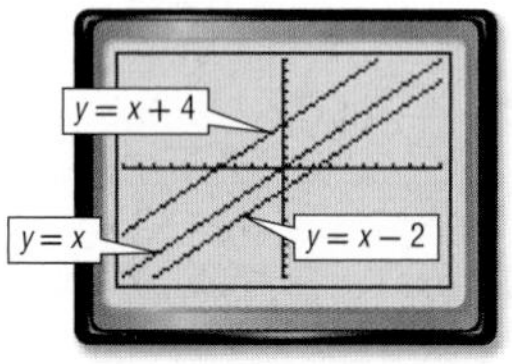

[−10, 10] scl: 1 by [−10, 10] scl: 1

KEYSTROKES: *Review graphing on pages 167 and 168.*

1A. How do the slopes of the graphs compare? **They have the same slope.**

1B. Compare the graph of $y = x + 4$ and the graph of $y = x$. How would you obtain the graph of $y = x + 4$ from the graph of $y = x$? **1B. Shift the graph of $y = x$ up 4 units.**

1C. How would you obtain the graph of $y = x - 2$ from the graph of $y = x$? **Shift the graph of $y = x$ down 2 units.**

Changing m in $y = mx + b$ affects the graphs in a different way than changing b. First, investigate positive values of m.

ACTIVITY 2 Changing m in $y = mx + b$, Positive Values

Graph $y = x$, $y = 2x$, and $y = \frac{1}{3}x$ in the standard viewing window.

Enter the equations in the Y= list and graph.

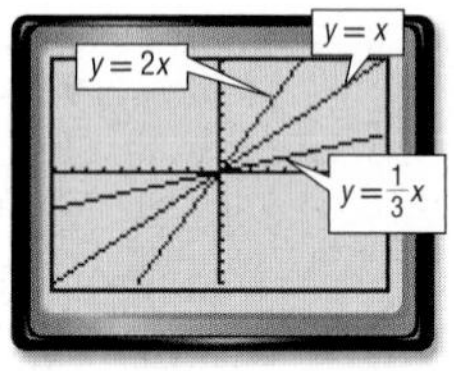

[−10, 10] scl: 1 by [−10, 10] scl: 1

2A. How do the y-intercepts of the graphs compare? **They have the same y-intercept.**

2B. Compare the graph of $y = 2x$ and the graph of $y = x$.

2C. Which is steeper, the graph of $y = \frac{1}{3}x$ or the graph of $y = x$? **The graph of $y = x$ is steeper.**

2B. The graph of $y = 2x$ is steeper than the graph of $y = x$.

Does changing m to a negative value affect the graph differently than changing it to a positive value?

Additional Answers

11. The value of m tells you how steep the graph should be compared to the graph of $y = x$ and the value of b tells you how many units higher or lower than $y = x$ the graph will be.

12. The graphs are all horizontal lines. They are all parallel. They intersect the y-axis at different points.

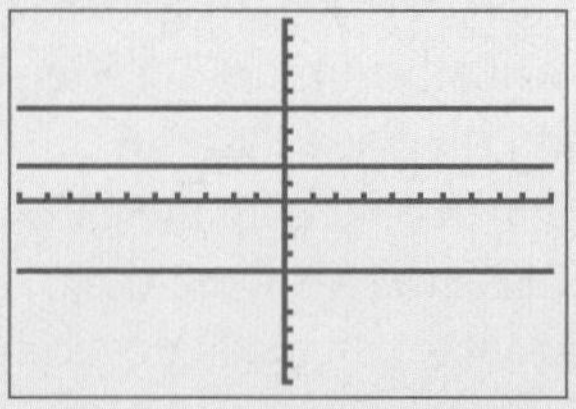

[−10, 10] scl: 1 by [−10, 10] scl: 1

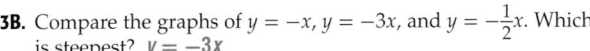

ACTIVITY 3 Changing m in $y = mx + b$, Negative Values

Graph $y = x$, $y = -x$, $y = -3x$, and $y = -\frac{1}{2}x$ in the standard viewing window.

Enter the equations in the Y= list and graph.

3A. How are the graphs with negative values of m different than graphs with a positive m?

3B. Compare the graphs of $y = -x$, $y = -3x$, and $y = -\frac{1}{2}x$. Which is steepest? $y = -3x$

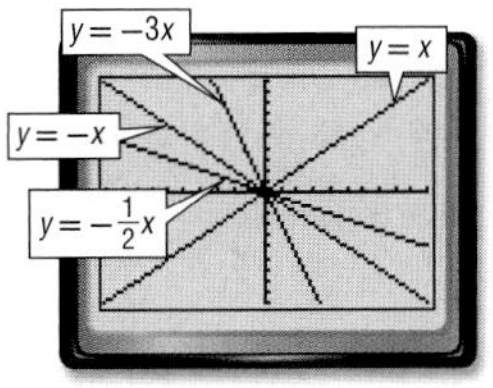

[−10, 10] scl: 1 by [−10, 10] scl: 1

3A. The graphs with negative values of m slope downward from left to right. Graphs with a positive m slope upward from left to right.

Analyze the Results

Graph each set of equations on the same screen. Describe the similarities or differences. 1–6. See Ch. 4 Answer Appendix.

1. $y = 2x$; $y = 2x + 3$; $y = 2x - 7$

2. $y = x + 1$; $y = 2x + 1$; $y = \frac{1}{4}x + 1$

3. $y = x + 4$; $y = 2x + 4$; $y = \frac{3}{4}x + 4$

4. $y = 0.5x + 2$; $y = 0.5x - 5$; $y = 0.5x + 4$

5. $y = -2x - 2$; $y = -4.2x - 2$; $y = -\frac{1}{3}x - 2$

6. $y = 3x$; $y = 3x + 6$; $y = 3x - 7$

7. Families of graphs have common characteristics. What do the graphs of all equations of the form $y = mx + b$ have in common? They all are nonvertical lines.

8. How does the value of b affect the graph of $y = mx + b$? The value of b determines the y-intercept.

9. What is the result of changing the value of m on the graph of $y = mx + b$ if m is positive?

10. How can you determine which graph is steepest by examining the following equations?
$y = 3x$, $y = -4x - 7$, $y = \frac{1}{2}x + 4$

11. Explain how knowing about the effects of m and b can help you sketch the graph of an equation. See margin.

12. The equation $y = k$ can also be a parent graph. Graph $y = 5$, $y = 2$, and $y = -4$ on the same screen. Describe the similarities or differences among the graphs. See margin.

9. Changing the value of m changes the slope of the graph. If m is positive, then the greater the value of m the steeper the graph.

10. The graph of $y = -4x - 7$ is steepest because the absolute value of m is greatest.

Extension

Nonlinear functions can also be defined in terms of a family of graphs. Graph each set of equations on the same screen. Describe the similarities or differences. 13–15. See margin.

13. $y = x^2$; $y = -3x^2$; $y = (-3x)^2$

14. $y = x^2$; $y = x^2 + 3$; $y = (x - 2)^2$

15. $y = x^2$; $y = 2x^2 + 4$; $y = (3x)^2 - 5$

16. Describe the similarities and differences in the classes of functions $f(x) = x^2 + c$ and $f(x) = (x + c)^2$, where c is any real number. See margin.

3 ASSESS

Formative Assessment

Ask students to summarize what belonging to a family of graphs means.

- Use Exercise 1 to assess whether students understand how changing b affects the graphs in a family of linear functions.
- Use Exercises 3 and 5 to assess whether students understand how changing m affects the graphs in a family of linear functions.

From Concrete to Abstract

Ask:

How can the graph of $y = mx + b$ be drawn from the graph of $y = mx$?

Sample answer: Shift the graph of $y = mx$ up b units if b is positive and down $|b|$ units if b is negative.

Additional Answers

13. The graphs have the same y-intercept, but different widths.

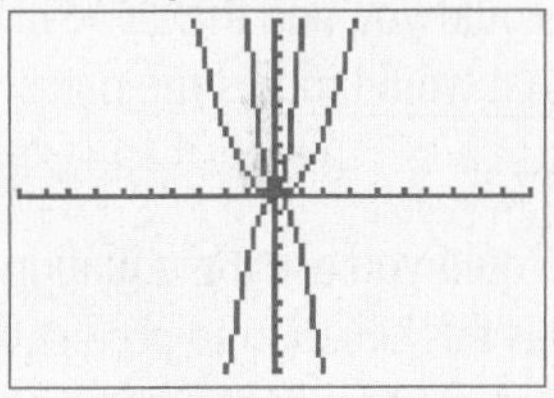

[−10, 10] scl: 1 by [−10, 10] scl: 1

14. The widths of each graph are the same, but each graph has different y-intercepts.

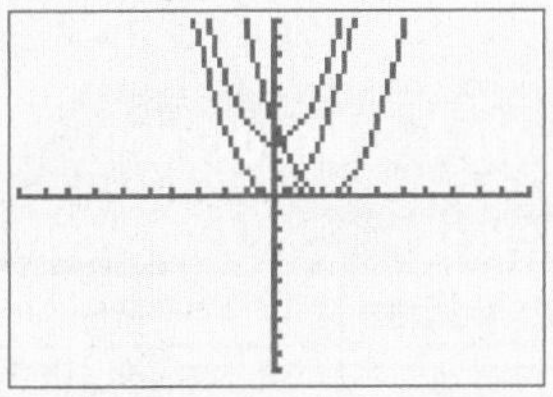

[−10, 10] scl: 1 by [−10, 10] scl: 1

15. The graphs have different widths and different y-intercepts.

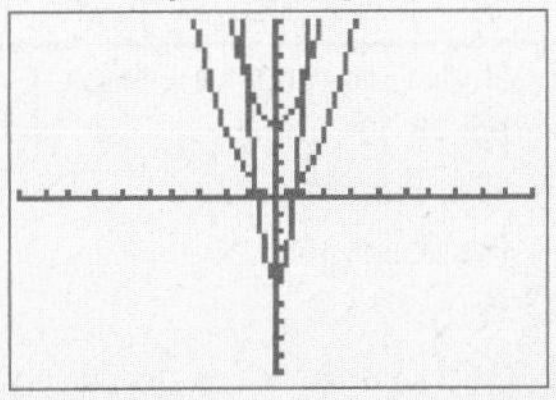

[−10, 10] scl: 1 by [−10, 10] scl: 1

16. In the graph of $f(x) = x^2 + c$, the graph is like $f(x) = x^2$, but shifted vertically $|c|$ units. In the graph of $f(x) = (x + c)^2$, the graph is like $f(x) = x^2$, but shifted horizontally $|c|$ units.

4-2 Lesson Notes

1 FOCUS

Vertical Alignment

Before Lesson 4-2
Graph lines given the slope and y-intercept.

Lesson 4-2
Write an equation of a line in slope-intercept form given the slope and one point or two points.

After Lesson 4-2
Write linear equations in point-slope form.

2 TEACH

Scaffolding Questions

Have students read the *Why?* section of the lesson.

Ask:

- What two points would be on the graph of the data? (2000, 337.1) and (2004, 375.4)
- How could you find the slope of a line that would model the data? $\frac{337.1 - 375.4}{2000 - 2004} = \frac{-38.3}{-4} = \frac{38.3}{4}$
- How could you use the equation that models this situation to predict the number of vacations taken at any given year? Substitute the year for x, then solve for y.

4-2 Writing Equations in Slope-Intercept Form

Then

You graphed lines given the slope and the y-intercept. (Lesson 4-1)

Now

- Write an equation of a line in slope-intercept form given the slope and one point.
- Write an equation of a line in slope-intercept form given two points.

IL Learning Standards

8.C.4b Apply algebraic properties and procedures with matrices, vectors, functions and sequences using data found in business, industry and consumer situations.

New Vocabulary

linear extrapolation

IL Math Online

glencoe.com

- Extra Examples
- Personal Tutor
- Self-Check Quiz
- Homework Help

Why?

In 2000, Americans took 337.1 million vacations. In 2004, Americans took 375.4 million vacations. You can find the average rate of change for these data. Then you can write an equation that would model the average number of vacations taken per year.

Write an Equation Given the Slope and a Point The next example shows how to write an equation of a line if you are given a slope and a point other than the y-intercept.

EXAMPLE 1 Write an Equation Given the Slope and a Point

Write an equation of the line that passes through (2, 1) with a slope of 3.

You are given the slope but not the y-intercept.

Step 1 Find the y-intercept.

$y = mx + b$	**Slope-intercept form**
$1 = 3(2) + b$	**Replace m with 3, y with 1, and x with 2.**
$1 = 6 + b$	**Simplify.**
$1 - 6 = 6 + b - 6$	**Subtract 6 from each side.**
$-5 = b$	**Simplify.**

Step 2 Write the equation in slope-intercept form.

$y = mx + b$	**Slope-intercept form**
$y = 3x - 5$	**Replace m with 3 and b with -5.**

Therefore, the equation of the line is $y = 3x - 5$.

Check Your Progress

Write an equation of a line that passes through the given point and has the given slope.

1A. $(-2, 5)$, slope 3 $y = 3x + 11$ **1B.** $(4, -7)$, slope -1 $y = -x - 3$

Personal Tutor glencoe.com

Write an Equation Given Two Points If you are given two points through which a line passes, you can use them to find the slope first. Then follow the steps in Example 1 to write the equation.

Lesson 4-2 Resources

Resource	Approaching-Level	On-Level	Beyond-Level	English Learners
Teacher Edition	• Differentiated Instruction, p. 226	• Differentiated Instruction, pp. 226, 230	• Differentiated Instruction, p. 230	
Chapter Resource Masters	• Study Guide and Intervention, pp. 11–12 • Skills Practice, p. 13 • Practice, p. 14 • Word Problem Practice, p. 15	• Study Guide and Intervention, pp. 11–12 • Skills Practice, p. 13 • Practice, p. 14 • Word Problem Practice, p. 15 • Enrichment, p. 16	• Practice, p. 14 • Word Problem Practice, p. 15 • Enrichment, p. 16	• Study Guide and Intervention, pp. 11–12 • Skills Practice, p. 13 • Practice, p. 14
Transparencies	• 5-Minute Check Transparency 4-2	• 5-Minute Check Transparency 4-2	• 5-Minute Check Transparency 4-2	• 5-Minute Check Transparency 4-2
Other	• Study Notebook • Teaching Algebra with Manipulatives	• Study Notebook • Teaching Algebra with Manipulatives	• Study Notebook	• Study Notebook • Teaching Algebra with Manipulatives

EXAMPLE 2 Write an Equation Given Two Points

Write an equation of the line that passes through each pair of points.

a. (3, 1) and (2, 4)

Step 1 Find the slope of the line containing the given points.

$m = \frac{y_2 - y_1}{x_2 - x_1}$	**Slope Formula**
$= \frac{4 - 1}{2 - 3}$	**$(x_1, y_1) = (3, 1)$ and $(x_2, y_2) = (2, 4)$**
$= \frac{3}{-1}$ or -3	**Simplify.**

Step 2 Use either point to find the y-intercept.

$y = mx + b$	**Slope-intercept form**
$4 = (-3)(2) + b$	**Replace m with -3, x with 2, and y with 4.**
$4 = -6 + b$	**Simplify.**
$4 - (-6) = -6 + b - (-6)$	**Subtract -6 from each side.**
$10 = b$	**Simplify.**

Step 3 Write the equation in slope-intercept form.

$y = mx + b$	**Slope-intercept form**
$y = -3x + 10$	**Replace m with -3 and b with 10.**

Therefore, the equation is $y = -3x + 10$.

b. (−4, −2) and (−5, −6)

Step 1 Find the slope of the line containing the given points.

$m = \frac{y_2 - y_1}{x_2 - x_1}$	**Slope Formula**
$= \frac{-6 - (-2)}{-5 - (-4)}$	**$(x_1, y_1) = (-4, -2)$ and $(x_2, y_2) = (-5, -6)$**
$= \frac{-4}{-1}$ or 4	**Simplify.**

Step 2 Use either point to find the y-intercept.

$y = mx + b$	**Slope-intercept form**
$-2 = 4(-4) + b$	**Replace m with 4, x with -4, and y with -2.**
$-2 = -16 + b$	**Simplify.**
$-2 - (-16) = -16 + b - (-16)$	**Subtract -16 from each side.**
$14 = b$	**Simplify.**

Step 3 Write the equation in slope-intercept form.

$y = mx + b$	**Slope-intercept form**
$y = 4x + 14$	**Replace m with 4 and b with 14.**

Therefore, the equation is $y = 4x + 14$.

Check Your Progress

Write an equation of the line that passes through each pair of points.

2A. (−1, 12), (4, −8) $y = -4x + 8$ **2B.** (5, −8), (−7, 0) $y = -\frac{2}{3}x - \frac{14}{3}$

Personal Tutor glencoe.com

StudyTip

Choosing a point Given two points on a line, you may select either point to be (x_1, y_1). Be sure to remain consistent throughout the problem.

StudyTip

Slope If the (x_1, y_1) coordinates are negative, be sure to account for both the negative signs and the subtraction symbols in the Slope Formula.

Write an Equation Given the Slope and a Point

Example 1 shows how to write an equation for a line given the slope and a point on the line.

Formative Assessment

Use the Check Your Progress exercises after each Example to determine students' understanding of concepts.

Additional Example

1 Write an equation of a line that passes through (2, −3) with a slope of $\frac{1}{2}$. $y = \frac{1}{2}x - 4$

Additional Examples also in Interactive Classroom PowerPoint® Presentations

IWB INTERACTIVE WHITEBOARD READY

Write an Equation Given Two Points

Example 2 shows how to write an equation for a line given any two points on the line. **Example 3** shows how to solve a real-world problem by writing an equation for a line given two points on the line. **Example 4** shows how to use a linear equation to predict values for a real-world problem.

Additional Example

2 Write an equation of the line that passes through each pair of points.

a. (−3, −4) and (−2, −8)
$y = -4x - 16$

b. (6, −2) and (3, 4)
$y = -2x + 10$

TEACH with TECH

AUDIO RECORDING Have students record an explanation what each number of an equation in slope intercept form represents in a real world situation. This recording can be replayed as review before beginning an assignment or a quiz.

Focus on Mathematical Content

Slope-Intercept Form When only the coordinates of two points on a line are known, use the two points to find the slope. Substitute the slope and the values of one of the points into $y = mx + b$ and solve for b, the y-intercept.

Additional Examples

3 **ECONOMY** During one year, Malik's cost for self-serve regular gasoline was \$3.20 on the first of June and \$3.42 on the first of July. Write a linear equation to predict Malik's cost of gasoline the first of any month during the year, using 1 to represent January. $y = 0.22x + 1.88$

4 **ECONOMY** On average, Malik uses 25 gallons of gasoline per month. He budgeted \$100 for gasoline in October. Use the prediction equation in Additional Example 3 to determine if Malik will have to add to his budget. Explain. If gasoline prices increase at the same rate, a gallon will cost \$4.08 in October. 25 gallons at this price is \$102, so Malik will have to add at least \$2 to his budget.

Watch Out!

Student Misconceptions Remind students that the x and y in an equation represent any pairs of x- and y-values that satisfy the equation. The coordinates of the given point are one pair of these values.

Make sure students understand that while two points can be used to write an equation, real-life prediction equations involve many more data points.

Real-World Career

Baggage Handler
Airline ground crew responsibilities include checking tickets, helping passengers with luggage, and making sure that baggage is secure. This job usually requires a high school diploma or GED.

Source: Airline Jobs

Real-World EXAMPLE 3 Use Slope-Intercept Form

AIR FARES The table shows the average fares for domestic flights in certain years. Write an equation that could be used to predict air fares if fares continue to increase at this rate.

Year	Cost (\$)
2004	354
2005	366
2006	378
2007	390

Understand You know the air fares for the years listed.

Plan Let x represent the number of years since 2000, and let y represent the air fare. Write an equation of the line that passes through (5, 366) and (6, 378).

Solve Find the slope.

$m = \frac{y_2 - y_1}{x_2 - x_1}$ **Slope Formula**

$= \frac{378 - 366}{6 - 5}$ **Let $(x_1, y_1) = (5, 366)$ and $(x_2, y_2) = (6, 378)$.**

$= \frac{12}{1}$ or 12 **Simplify.**

Choose (6, 378) and find the y-intercept of the line.

$y = mx + b$ **Slope-intercept form**

$378 = 12(6) + b$ **Replace m with 12, x with 6, and y with 378.**

$378 = 72 + b$ **Simplify.**

$306 = b$ **Subtract 72 from each side.**

Write the equation using $m = 12$ and $b = 306$.

$y = mx + b$ **Slope-intercept form**

$y = 12x + 306$ **Replace m with 12 and b with 306.**

Check Check your result by using the coordinates of the other point.

$y = 12x + 306$ **Original equation**

$366 \stackrel{?}{=} 12(5) + 306$ **Replace x with 5 and y with 366.**

$366 = 366$ ✓ **Simplify.**

Check Your Progress

3. FINANCIAL LITERACY In addition to his weekly salary, Ethan is paid \$16 per delivery. Last week, he made 5 deliveries, and his total pay was \$215. Write a linear equation to find Ethan's total weekly pay T if he makes d deliveries. $T = 16d + 135$

Personal Tutor glencoe.com

You can use a linear equation to make predictions about values that are beyond the range of the data. This process is called **linear extrapolation**.

Real-World EXAMPLE 4 Predict from Slope-Intercept Form

AIR FARES Use the equation from Example 3 to estimate the cost of airfares in 2010.

$y = 12x + 306$ **Original equation**

$= 12(10) + 306$ **Replace x with 10.**

$= 426$ An estimate of the average air fares is \$426.

Check Your Progress

4. MONEY Use the equation in Check Your Progress 3 to predict how much money Ethan will earn in a week if he makes 8 deliveries. \$263

Personal Tutor glencoe.com

Differentiated Instruction

AL OL

If students are confused by learning more than one way to write a linear equation,

Then have those students use the definition of slope to derive the slope-intercept form of an equation. This same approach can be used in Lesson 4-3 for the point-slope form of an equation. The logical learner does best when relating new concepts to concepts already learned.

Check Your Understanding

Example 1 p. 224

Write an equation of the line that passes through the given point and has the given slope.

1. (3, −3), slope 3 $y = 3x - 12$
2. (2, 4), slope 2 $y = 2x$
3. (1, 5), slope −1 $y = -x + 6$
4. (−4, 6), slope −2 $y = -2x - 2$

Example 2 p. 225

Write an equation of the line that passes through each pair of points.

5. (4, −3), (2, 3)
6. (−7, −3), (−3, 5)
7. (−1, 3), (0, 8)
8. (−2, 6), (0, 0)

Examples 3 and 4 p. 226

5. $y = -3x + 9$
6. $y = 2x + 11$
7. $y = 5x + 8$
8. $y = -3x$

9. **WHITEWATER RAFTING** Ten people from a local youth group went to Black Hills Whitewater Rafting Tour Company for a one-day rafting trip. The group paid $425.

a. Write an equation in slope-intercept form to find the total cost C for p people. $C = 35p + 75$

b. How much would it cost for 15 people? $600

Practice and Problem Solving

● = **Step-by-Step Solutions** begin on page R12. **Extra Practice** begins on page 815.

Example 1 p. 224

Write an equation of the line that passes through the given point and has the given slope.

10. (3, 1), slope 2 $y = 2x - 5$
11. (−1, 4), slope −1 $y = -x + 3$
12. (1, 0), slope 1 $y = x - 1$
13. (7, 1), slope 8 $y = 8x - 55$
14. (2, 5), slope −2 $y = -2x + 9$
15. (2, 6), slope 2 $y = 2x + 2$

Example 2 p. 225

Write an equation of the line that passes through each pair of points.

16. (9, −2), (4, 3) $y = -x + 7$
17. (−2, 5), (5, −2) $y = -x + 3$
18. (−5, 3), (0, −7) $y = -2x - 7$
19. (3, 5), (2, −2) $y = 7x - 16$
20. (−1, −3), (−2, 3) $y = -6x - 9$
21. (−2, −4), (2, 4) $y = 2x$

Examples 3 and 4 p. 226

22. **RC CAR** Greg is driving a remote control car at a constant speed. He starts the timer when the car is 5 feet away. After 2 seconds the car is 35 feet away.

a. Write a linear equation to find the distance d of the car from Greg. $d = 15t + 5$

b. Estimate the distance the car has traveled after 10 seconds. 155 ft

Problem-Solving Tip

Determine Reasonable Answers Deciding whether an answer is reasonable is useful when an exact answer is not neccessary.

23. **TRAVEL** Refer to the beginning of the lesson.

a. Write a linear equation to find the number of vacations (in millions) y after x years. Let x be the number of years since 2000. $y = 9.575x + 337.1$

b. Estimate the number of vacations that will be taken in 2012. 452 million

24. **BOOKS** In 1904, a dictionary cost 30¢. Since then the cost of a dictionary has risen an average of 6¢ per year.

a. Write a linear equation to find the cost C of a dictionary y years after 2004. $C = 30 + 6y$

b. If this trend continues, what will the cost of a dictionary be in 2020? $7.26

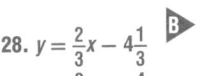

B Write an equation of the line that passes through the given point and has the given slope.

25. (4, 2), slope $\frac{1}{2}$ $y = \frac{1}{2}x$
26. (3, −2), slope $\frac{1}{3}$ $y = \frac{1}{3}x - 3$
27. (6, 4), slope $-\frac{3}{4}$ $y = -\frac{3}{4}x + 8\frac{1}{2}$
28. (2, −3), slope $\frac{2}{3}$
29. (2, −2), slope $\frac{2}{7}$
30. (−4, −2), slope $-\frac{3}{5}$

28. $y = \frac{2}{3}x - 4\frac{1}{3}$
29. $y = \frac{2}{7}x - 2\frac{4}{7}$
30. $y = -\frac{3}{5}x - 4\frac{2}{5}$

3 PRACTICE

Formative Assessment

Use Exercises 1–9 to check for understanding.

Use the chart at the bottom of this page to customize assignments for your students.

Tips for New Teachers

Sense-Making Remind students that the coefficient of x represents the slope only when the equation is in slope-intercept form. Demonstrate using an example with two equations, one that is not in slope-intercept form and one that is in slope-intercept form.

Differentiated Homework Options

Level	Assignment	Two-Day Option	
AL Basic	10–24, 47, 49–77	11–23 odd, 53–56	10–24 even, 47, 49–52, 57–77
OL Core	11–31 odd, 32, 33–39 odd, 40–47, 49–77	10–24, 53–56	25–47, 49–52, 57–77
BL Advanced	25–71, (optional: 72–77)		

Exercise Alerts

Grid Paper Students will need grid paper for Exercises 31, 44–46, 57–62, and 65.

Protractor and straightedge For Exercise 44, students will need a protractor and a straightedge.

Multiple Representations In Exercise 44, students use a coordinate graph and algebraic analysis to compare the slopes of perpendicular lines.

Additional Answers

31b.

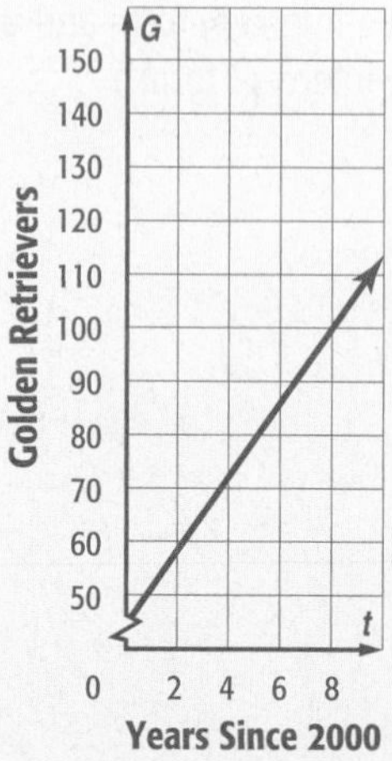

38. No; substituting 3 and −1 for x and y, respectively, results in an equation that is not true.

39. Yes; substituting 6 and −2 for x and y, respectively, results in and equation that is true.

44a.

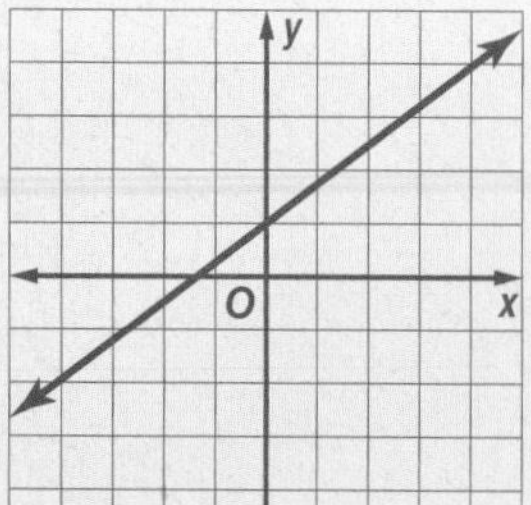

44b. Sample answer:

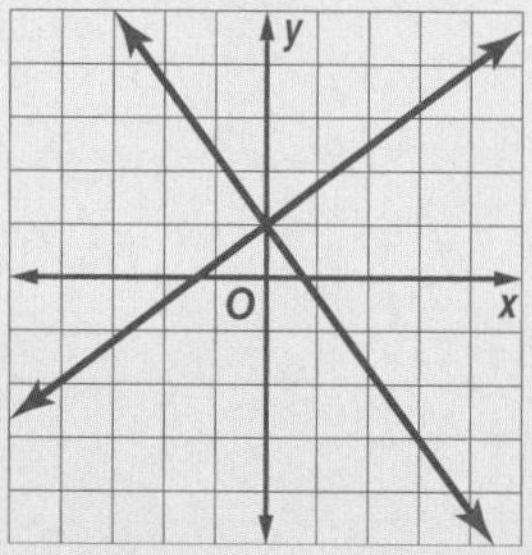

Real-World Link

There are approximately 73 million dogs kept as pets in the United States. Thirty-nine percent of households in the United States own at least one dog.

Source: The Humane Society of the United States

31. DOGS In 2001, there were about 56.1 thousand golden retrievers registered in the United States. In 2002, the number was 62.5 thousand.

a. Write a linear equation to find the number of golden retrievers G that will be registered in year t, where $t = 0$ is the year 2000. $G = 6.4t + 49.7$

b. Graph the equation. See margin.

c. Estimate the number of golden retrievers that will be registered in 2012. 126,500

32. GYM MEMBERSHIPS A local recreation center offers a yearly membership for \$265. The center offers aerobics classes for an additional \$5 per class.

a. Write an equation that represents the total cost of the membership. $y = 5x + 265$

b. Carly spent \$500 one year. How many aerobics classes did she take? 47 classes

33. SUBSCRIPTION A magazine offers an online subscription that allows you to view up to 25 archived articles free. To view 30 archived articles, you pay \$49.15. To view 33 archived articles, you pay \$57.40.

a. What is the cost of each archived article for which you pay a fee? \$2.75

b. What is the cost of the magazine subscription? \$35.40

C **Write an equation of the line that passes through the given points.**

34. (5, −2), (7, 1) **35.** (5, −3), (2, 5) **36.** $\left(\frac{5}{4}, 1\right), \left(-\frac{1}{4}, \frac{3}{4}\right)$ **37.** $\left(\frac{5}{12}, -1\right), \left(-\frac{3}{4}, \frac{1}{6}\right)$

Determine whether the given point is on the line. Explain why or why not.

38. $(3, -1); y = \frac{1}{3}x + 5$ **39.** $(6, -2); y = \frac{1}{2}x - 5$ 38–39. See margin.

For Exercises 40–42, determine which equation best represents each situation. Explain the meaning of each variable.

A $y = -\frac{1}{3}x + 72$	B $y = 2x + 225$	C $y = 8x + 4$

40. CONCERTS Tickets to a concert cost \$8 each plus a processing fee of \$4 per order.

41. FUNDRAISING The freshman class has \$225. They sell raffle tickets at \$2 each to raise money for a field trip.

42. POOLS The current water level of a swimming pool in Tucson, Arizona, is 6 feet. The rate of evaporation is $\frac{1}{3}$ inch per day.

43. ENVIRONMENT A manufacturer implemented a program to reduce waste. In 1998 they sent 946 tons of waste to landfills. Each year after that, they reduced their waste by an average 28.4 tons.

a. How many tons were sent to the landfill in 2010? 605.2

b. In what year will it become impossible for this trend to continue? Explain.

44. MULTIPLE REPRESENTATIONS In this problem, you will explore the slopes of perpendicular lines. a–d. See margin.

a. **GRAPHICAL** On a coordinate plane, graph $y = \frac{3}{4}x + 1$.

b. **PICTORIAL** Use a straightedge and a protractor to draw a line that is perpendicular to the line you graphed.

c. **ALGEBRAIC** Find the equation of the line that is perpendicular to the original line. Describe which method you used to write the equation.

d. **ANALYTICAL** Compare the slopes of the lines. Describe the relationship, if any, between the two values.

34. $y = 1\frac{1}{2}x - 9\frac{1}{2}$

35. $y = -2\frac{2}{3}x + 10\frac{1}{3}$

36. $y = \frac{1}{6}x + \frac{19}{24}$

37. $y = -x - \frac{7}{12}$

40. C; x represents the number of tickets per order and y represents the total cost of an order.

41. B; x represents the number of raffle tickets sold, y represents the total amount of money in the treasury.

42. A; x represents the number of days, y represents the total depth of water in inches of the pool.

43b. 2032; In that year the waste would be 0 tons. After that, the waste would be a negative amount, which is impossible.

44c. Sample answer: $y = -\frac{4}{3}x + 1$; the line passes through the points (0, 1) and (−3, 5). From these two points, I found that the slope of the line is $-\frac{4}{3}$. Since 1 is the y-intercept, I substituted 1 for b and $-\frac{4}{3}$ for m in the equation $y = mx + b$ to get $y = -\frac{4}{3}x + 1$.

44d. The slope of the original line is $\frac{3}{4}$ and the slope of the perpendicular line is $-\frac{4}{3}$. The slopes are opposite reciprocals of each other.

228 Chapter 4 Linear Functions and Relations

Real-World Link

55% of people who buy tickets for events use online ticket agents.

Source: Pew Internet & American Life Project

45. **CONCERT TICKETS** Jackson is ordering tickets for a concert online. There is a processing fee for each order, and the tickets are $52 each. Jackson ordered 5 tickets and the cost was $275. **b–c. See Ch. 4 Answer Appendix.**
   a. Determine the processing fee. Write a linear equation to represent the total cost C for t tickets. **$15; $C = 52t + 15$**
   b. Make a table of values for at least three other numbers of tickets.
   c. Graph this equation. Predict the cost of 8 tickets.

46. **MUSIC** A music store is offering a Frequent Buyers Club membership. The membership costs $22 per year, and then a member can buy CDs at a reduced price. If a member buys 17 CDs in one year, the cost is $111.25.
   a. Determine the cost of each CD for a member. **$5.25**
   b. Write a linear equation to represent the total cost y of a one year membership, if x CDs are purchased. **$y = 5.25x + 22$**
   c. Graph this equation. **See Ch. 4 Answer Appendix.**

H.O.T. Problems

Use Higher-Order Thinking Skills

47. **FIND THE ERROR** Tess and Jacinta are writing an equation of the line through (3, −2) and (6, 4). Is either of them correct? Explain your reasoning. **Jacinta; Tess switched the x- and y-coordinates on the point that she entered in step 3.**

Tess	Jacinta
$m = \frac{4-(-2)}{6-3} = \frac{6}{3}$ or 2	$m = \frac{4-(-2)}{6-3} = \frac{6}{3}$ or 2
$y = mx + b$	$y = mx + b$
$6 = 2(4) + b$	$-2 = 2(3) + b$
$6 = 8 + b$	$-2 = 6 + b$
$-2 = b$	$-8 = b$
$y = 2x - 2$	$y = 2x - 8$

48. 11; Use the first two points to find the equation of the line, then replace x and y with 9 and p, respectively, to solve for p.

48. **CHALLENGE** Consider three points, (3, 7), (−6, 1) and (9, p), on the same line. Find the value of p and explain your steps.

49. **REASONING** Consider the standard form of a linear equation, $Ax + By = C$.
   a. Rewrite the equation in slope-intercept form. **$y = -\frac{A}{B}x + \frac{C}{B}$**
   b. What is the slope? **slope $= -\frac{A}{B}$**
   c. What is the y-intercept? **y-intercept $= \frac{C}{B}$**
   d. Is this true for all real values of A, B, and C? **No, $B \neq 0$**

50. **OPEN ENDED** Create a real-world situation that fits the graph at the right. Define the two quantities and describe the functional relationship between them. Write an equation to represent this relationship and describe what the slope and y-intercept mean. **See Ch. 4 Answer Appendix.**

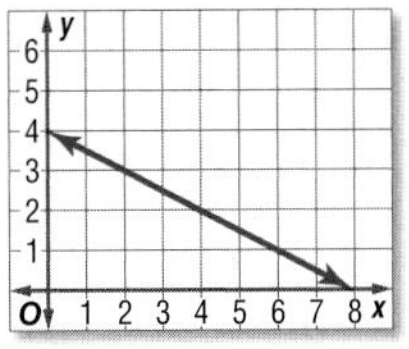

51. **WRITING IN MATH** Linear equations are useful in predicting future events. Describe some factors in real-world situations that might affect the reliability of the graph in making any predictions. **See Ch. 4 Answer Appendix.**

52. **WRITING IN MATH** What information is needed to write the equation of a line? Explain. **You need to know the slope and y-intercept of the line, the slope and the coordinates of another point on the line, or the coordinates of two points on the line.**

Watch Out!

Find the Error For Exercise 47, students should see that Teresa and Jacinta have done something different in the equation they wrote under $y = mx + b$. Explain to students that it is very important to keep the values for x and y correctly identified.

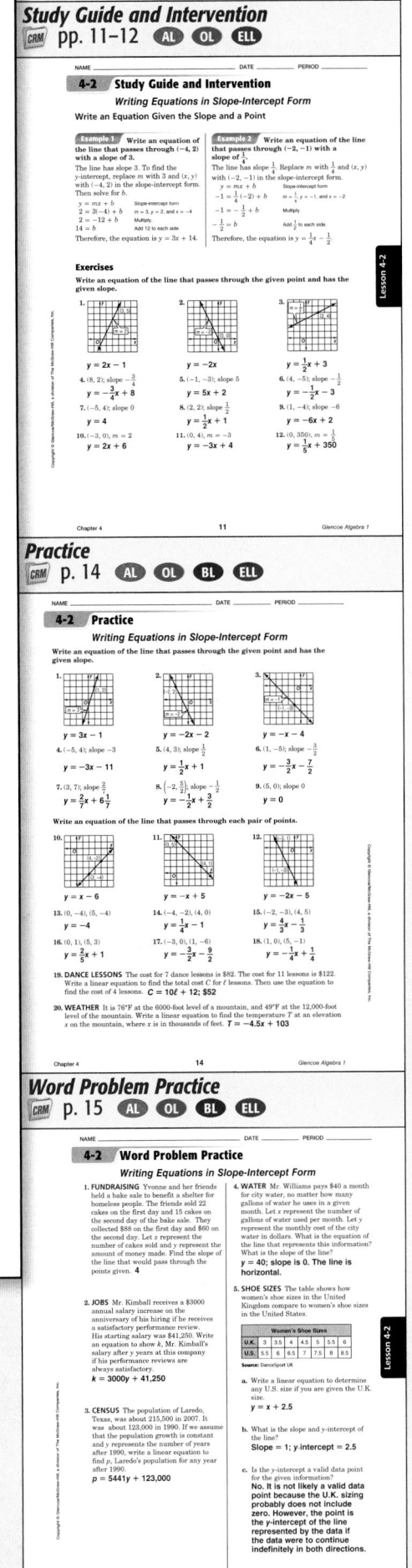

Study Guide and Intervention

CRM pp. 11–12 AL OL ELL

NAME ______ DATE ______ PERIOD ______

4-2 Study Guide and Intervention

Writing Equations in Slope-Intercept Form

Write an Equation Given the Slope and a Point

Example 1 Write an equation of the line that passes through (−4, 2) with a slope of 3.

The line has slope 3. To find the y-intercept, replace m with 3 and (x, y) with (−4, 2) in the slope-intercept form. Then solve for b.

$y = mx + b$ Slope-intercept form
$2 = 3(-4) + b$ $m = 3$, $y = 2$, and $x = -4$
$2 = -12 + b$ Multiply.
$14 = b$ Add 12 to each side.

Therefore, the equation is $y = 3x + 14$.

Example 2 Write an equation of the line that passes through (−2, −1) with a slope of $\frac{1}{4}$.

The line has slope $\frac{1}{4}$. Replace m with $\frac{1}{4}$ and (x, y) with (−2, −1) in the slope-intercept form.

$y = mx + b$ Slope-intercept form
$-1 = \frac{1}{4}(-2) + b$ $m = \frac{1}{4}$, $y = -1$, and $x = -2$
$-1 = -\frac{1}{2} + b$ Multiply.
$-\frac{1}{2} = b$ Add $\frac{1}{2}$ to each side.

Therefore, the equation is $y = \frac{1}{4}x - \frac{1}{2}$.

Exercises

Write an equation of the line that passes through the given point and has the given slope.

1. 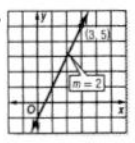 $y = 2x - 1$
2. 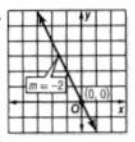 $y = -2x$
3. 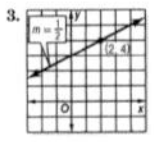 $y = \frac{1}{2}x + 3$
4. (8, 2); slope $-\frac{3}{4}$ $y = -\frac{3}{4}x + 8$
5. (−1, −3); slope 5 $y = 5x + 2$
6. (4, −5); slope $-\frac{1}{2}$ $y = -\frac{1}{2}x - 3$
7. (−5, 4); slope 0 $y = 4$
8. (2, 2); slope $\frac{1}{2}$ $y = \frac{1}{2}x + 1$
9. (1, −4); slope −6 $y = -6x + 2$
10. (−3, 0), $m = 2$ $y = 2x + 6$
11. (0, 4), $m = -3$ $y = -3x + 4$
12. (0, 350), $m = \frac{1}{5}$ $y = \frac{1}{5}x + 350$

Lesson 4-2

Chapter 4 11 Glencoe Algebra 1

Practice

CRM p. 14 AL OL BL ELL

NAME ______ DATE ______ PERIOD ______

4-2 Practice

Writing Equations in Slope-Intercept Form

Write an equation of the line that passes through the given point and has the given slope.

1. 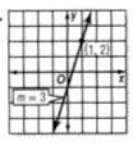 $y = 3x - 1$
2. 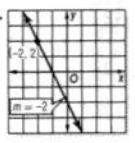 $y = -2x - 2$
3. 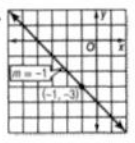 $y = -x - 4$
4. (−5, 4); slope −3 $y = -3x - 11$
5. (4, 3); slope $\frac{1}{2}$ $y = \frac{1}{2}x + 1$
6. (1, −5); slope $-\frac{3}{2}$ $y = -\frac{3}{2}x - \frac{7}{2}$
7. (3, 7); slope $\frac{2}{7}$ $y = \frac{2}{7}x + 6\frac{1}{7}$
8. $\left(-2, \frac{5}{2}\right)$; slope $-\frac{1}{2}$ $y = -\frac{1}{2}x + \frac{3}{2}$
9. (5, 0); slope 0 $y = 0$

Write an equation of the line that passes through each pair of points.

10. 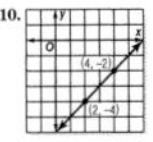 $y = x - 6$
11. 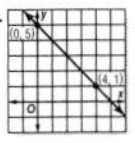 $y = -x + 5$
12. 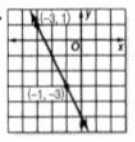 $y = -2x - 5$
13. (0, −4), (5, −4) $y = -4$
14. (−4, −2), (4, 0) $y = \frac{1}{4}x - 1$
15. (−2, −3), (4, 5) $y = \frac{4}{3}x - \frac{1}{3}$
16. (0, 1), (5, 3) $y = \frac{2}{5}x + 1$
17. (−3, 0), (1, −6) $y = -\frac{3}{2}x - \frac{9}{2}$
18. (1, 0), (5, −1) $y = -\frac{1}{4}x + \frac{1}{4}$
19. **DANCE LESSONS** The cost for 7 dance lessons is $82. The cost for 11 lessons is $122. Write a linear equation to find the total cost C for ℓ lessons. Then use the equation to find the cost of 4 lessons. **$C = 10\ell + 12$; $52**
20. **WEATHER** It is 76°F at the 6000-foot level of a mountain, and 49°F at the 12,000-foot level of the mountain. Write a linear equation to find the temperature T at an elevation x on the mountain, where x is in thousands of feet. **$T = -4.5x + 103$**

Chapter 4 14 Glencoe Algebra 1

Word Problem Practice

CRM p. 15 AL OL BL ELL

NAME ______ DATE ______ PERIOD ______

4-2 Word Problem Practice

Writing Equations in Slope-Intercept Form

1. **FUNDRAISING** Yvonne and her friends held a bake sale to benefit a shelter for homeless people. The friends sold 22 cakes on the first day and 15 cakes on the second day of the bake sale. They collected $88 on the first day and $60 on the second day. Let x represent the number of cakes sold and y represent the amount of money made. Find the slope of the line that would pass through the points given. **4**
2. **JOBS** Mr. Kimball receives a $3000 annual salary increase on the anniversary of his hiring if he receives a satisfactory performance review. His starting salary was $41,250. Write an equation to show k, Mr. Kimball's salary after y years at this company if his performance reviews are always satisfactory. **$k = 3000y + 41,250$**
3. **CENSUS** The population of Laredo, Texas, was about 215,500 in 2007. It was about 123,000 in 1990. If we assume that the population growth is constant and y represents the number of years after 1990, write a linear equation to find p, Laredo's population for any year after 1990. **$p = 5441y + 123,000$**
4. **WATER** Mr. Williams pays $40 a month for city water, no matter how many gallons of water he uses in a given month. Let x represent the number of gallons of water used per month. Let y represent the monthly cost of the city water in dollars. What is the equation of the line that represents this information? What is the slope of the line? **$y = 40$; slope is 0. The line is horizontal.**
5. **SHOE SIZES** The table shows how women's shoe sizes in the United Kingdom compare to women's shoe sizes in the United States.

Women's Shoe Sizes							
U.K.	3	3.5	4	4.5	5	5.5	6
U.S.	5.5	6	6.5	7	7.5	8	8.5

Source: DanceSport UK

   a. Write a linear equation to determine any U.S. size if you are given the U.K. size. **$y = x + 2.5$**
   b. What is the slope and y-intercept of the line? **Slope = 1; y-intercept = 2.5**
   c. Is the y-intercept a valid data point for the given information? **No. It is not likely a valid data point because the U.K. sizing probably does not include zero. However, the point is the y-intercept of the line represented by the data if the data were to continue indefinitely in both directions.**

Lesson 4-2

Chapter 4 15 Glencoe Algebra 1

Enrichment

CRM p. 16 OL BL

NAME ______ DATE ______ PERIOD ______

4-2 Enrichment

Tangent to a Curve

A tangent line is a line that intersects a curve at a point with the same rate of change, or slope, as the rate of change of the curve at that point.

For quadratic functions (functions of the form $ax^2 + bx + c$), the equation of the tangent line can be found. This is based on the fact that the slope through any two points on the curve is equal to the slope of the line tangent to the curve at the point whose x-value is halfway between the x-values of the other two points.

Example To find the equation of a tangent line to the curve $y = x^2 + 3x + 2$ through the point (2, 12), first find two points on the curve whose x-values are equidistant from the x-value of the point the tangent needs to go through.

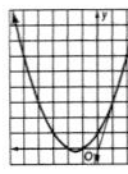

Step 1: Find two more points. Use $x = 1$ and $x = 3$.
When $x = 1$, $y = 1^2 + 3(1) + 2$ or 6.
When $x = 3$, $y = 3^2 + 3(3) + 2$ or 20.
So, the two ordered pairs are (1, 6) and (3, 20).

Step 2: Find the slope of the line that goes through these two points.

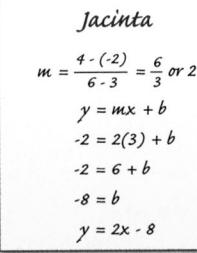

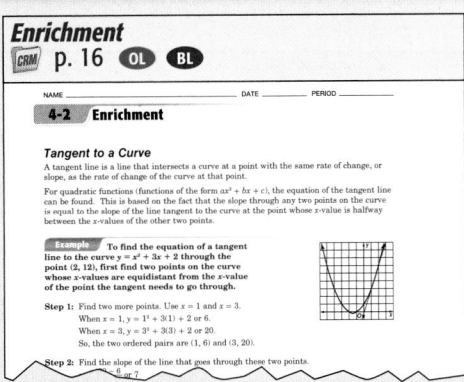

4 ASSESS

Yesterday's News Have students write how yesterday's lesson helped them with writing equations in slope-intercept form today.

Formative Assessment

Check for student understanding of concepts in Lessons 4-1 and 4-2.

CRM Quiz 1, p. 51

PSAE PRACTICE 8.11.07, 6.11.18, 9.11.01, 8.11.16

53. Which equation *best* represents the graph? **D**

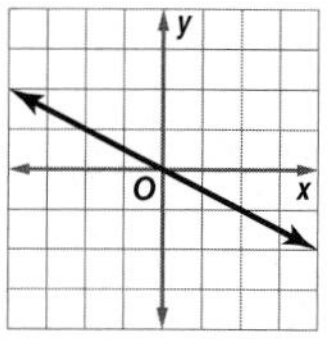

A $y = 2x$
B $y = -2x$
C $y = \frac{1}{2}x$
D $y = -\frac{1}{2}x$

54. Roberto receives an employee discount of 12%. If he buys a \$355 item at the store, what is his discount to the nearest dollar? **J**

F \$3　　H \$30
G \$4　　J \$43

55. GEOMETRY The midpoints of the sides of the large square are joined to form a smaller square. What is the area of the smaller square? **B**

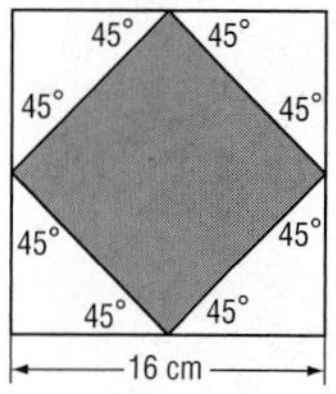

A 64 cm^2
B 128 cm^2
C 248 cm^2
D 256 cm^2

56. SHORT RESPONSE If $\frac{5(x+4)}{2} + 7 = 37$, what is the value of $3x - 9$? **15**

Spiral Review

Graph each equation. (Lesson 4-1) **57–62. See Ch. 4 Answer Appendix.**

57. $y = 3x + 2$　**58.** $y = -4x + 2$　**59.** $3y = 2x + 6$

60. $y = \frac{1}{2}x + 6$　**61.** $3x + y = -1$　**62.** $2x + 3y = 6$

Write an equation in function notation for each relation. (Lesson 3-6)

63.

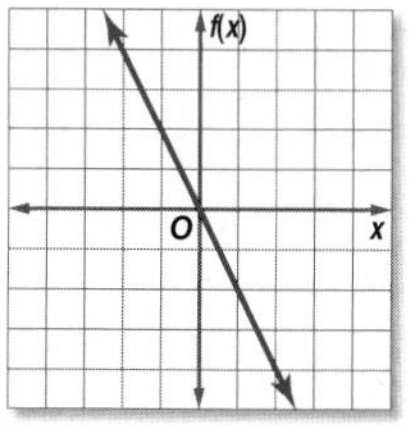

$f(x) = -2x$

64.

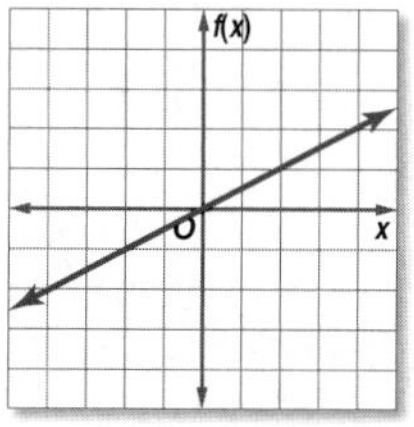

$f(x) = \frac{1}{2}x$

65a.

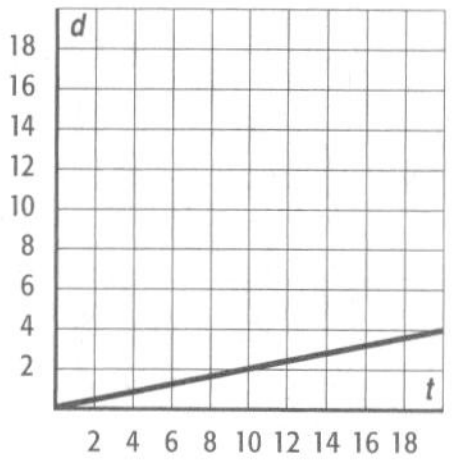

65. METEOROLOGY The distance d in miles that the sound of thunder travels in t seconds is given by the equation $d = 0.21t$. (Lesson 3-1)

a. Graph the equation.

b. Use the graph to estimate how long it will take you to hear thunder from a storm 3 miles away. **about 14 seconds**

Solve each equation. Check your solution. (Lesson 2-3)

66. $-5t - 2.2 = -2.9$ **0.14**　**67.** $-5.5a - 43.9 = 77.1$ **−22**　**68.** $4.2r + 7.14 = 12.6$ **1.3**

69. $-14 - \frac{n}{9} = 9$ **−207**　**70.** $\frac{-8b - (-9)}{-10} = 17$ **22.375**　**71.** $9.5x + 11 - 7.5x = 14$ **1.5**

Skills Review

Find the value of *r* so the line through each pair of points has the given slope. (Lesson 3-3)

72. $(6, -2), (r, -6), m = 4$ **5**　**73.** $(8, 10), (r, 4), m = 6$ **7**　**74.** $(7, -10), (r, 4), m = -3$ $2\frac{1}{3}$

75. $(6, 2), (9, r), m = -1$ **−1**　**76.** $(9, r), (6, 3), m = -\frac{1}{3}$ **2**　**77.** $(5, r), (2, -3), m = \frac{4}{3}$ **1**

Differentiated Instruction

OL BL

Extension Write (3, 4) and (5, 4) on the board. Ask students to find b, the y-intercept, for the line through these two points. After they have done this, write (3, 5) and (3, 4) on the board and ask students to find b for the line through these two points and have them explain. $b = 4$; there is no y-intercept because these two points are on a vertical line.

230 Chapter 4 Linear Functions and Relations

Writing Equations in Point-Slope Form

Then

You wrote linear equations given either one point and the slope or two points. (Lesson 4-2)

Now

- Write equations of lines in point-slope form.
- Write linear equations in different forms.

IL Learning Standards

8.C.4b Apply algebraic properties and procedures with matrices, vectors, functions and sequences using data found in business, industry and consumer situations.

New Vocabulary

point-slope form

IL Math Online

glencoe.com

- Extra Examples
- Personal Tutor
- Self-Check Quiz
- Homework Help

Why?

Most humane societies have foster homes for newborn puppies, kittens, and injured or ill animals. During the spring and summer, a large shelter can place 3000 animals in homes each month.

If a shelter had 200 animals in foster homes at the beginning of spring, the number of animals in foster homes at the end of the summer could be represented by $y = 3000x + 200$, where x is the number of months and y is the number of animals.

Point-Slope Form An equation of a line can be written in **point-slope form** when given the coordinates of one known point on a line and the slope of that line.

Key Concept Point-Slope Form — For Your FOLDABLE

Words The linear equation $y - y_1 = m(x - x_1)$ is written in point-slope form, where (x_1, y_1) is a given point on a nonvertical line and m is the slope of the line.

Symbols $y - y_1 = m(x - x_1)$

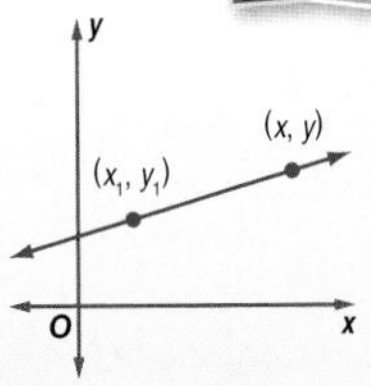

EXAMPLE 1 Write and Graph an Equation in Point-Slope Form

Write an equation in point-slope form for the line that passes through (3, −2) with a slope of $\frac{1}{4}$. Then graph the equation.

$y - y_1 = m(x - x_1)$ — **Point-slope form**

$y - (-2) = \frac{1}{4}(x - 3)$ — $(x_1, y_1) = (3, -2), m = \frac{1}{4}$

$y + 2 = \frac{1}{4}(x - 3)$ — **Simplify.**

Plot the point at (3, −2) and use the slope to find another point on the line. Draw a line through the two points.

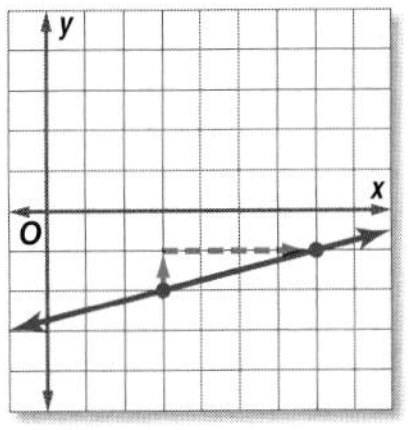

Check Your Progress See Ch. 4 Answer Appendix for graph.

1. Write an equation in point-slope form for the line that passes through (−2, 1) with a slope of −6. Then graph the equation. $y - 1 = -6(x + 2)$

Personal Tutor glencoe.com

1 FOCUS

Vertical Alignment

Before Lesson 4-3
Write linear equations given either one point and the slope or two points.

Lesson 4-3
Write equations of lines in point-slope form.
Write linear equations in different forms.

After Lesson 4-3
Use lines of fit on scatter plots to make and evaluate predictions.

2 TEACH

Scaffolding Questions

Have students read the *Why?* section of the lesson.

Ask:

- What is the slope of the graph of the equation $y = 3000x + 200$? 3000
- What is one point on the graph of this line? Sample answer: (0, 200)
- Write an equation that relates the slope, the point you gave, and any point (x, y) on the line. Sample answer: $\frac{y - 200}{x - 0} = 3000$

Lesson 4-3 Resources

Resource	Approaching-Level	On-Level	Beyond-Level	English Learners
Teacher Edition	• Differentiated Instruction, p. 233	• Differentiated Instruction, pp. 233, 236	• Differentiated Instruction, p. 236	• Differentiated Instruction, p. 233
Chapter Resource Masters	• Study Guide and Intervention, pp. 17–18 • Skills Practice, p. 19 • Practice, p. 20 • Word Problem Practice, p. 21 • Graphing Calculator, p. 23	• Study Guide and Intervention, pp. 17–18 • Skills Practice, p. 19 • Practice, p. 20 • Word Problem Practice, p. 21 • Enrichment, p. 22 • Graphing Calculator, p. 23	• Practice, p. 20 • Word Problem Practice, p. 21 • Enrichment, p. 22 • Graphing Calculator, p. 23	• Study Guide and Intervention, pp. 17–18 • Skills Practice, p. 19 • Practice, p. 20 • Graphing Calculator, p. 23
Transparencies	• 5-Minute Check Transparency 4-3	• 5-Minute Check Transparency 4-3	• 5-Minute Check Transparency 4-3	• 5-Minute Check Transparency 4-3
Other	• Study Notebook • Teaching Algebra with Manipulatives	• Study Notebook • Teaching Algebra with Manipulatives	• Study Notebook	• Study Notebook • Teaching Algebra with Manipulatives

Point-Slope Form

Example 1 shows how to write an equation in point-slope form when the slope and a point on the line are known.

Formative Assessment

Use the Check Your Progress exercises after each Example to determine students' understanding of concepts.

Additional Example

1 Write an equation in point-slope form for the line that passes through (−2, 0) with a slope of $-\frac{3}{2}$. Then graph the equation. $y = -\frac{3}{2}(x + 2)$

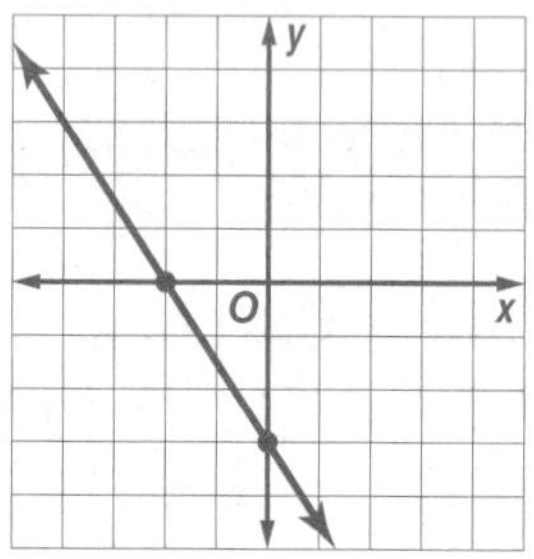

Forms of Linear Equations

Example 2 shows how to write an equation in standard form when given an equation in point-slope form. **Example 3** shows how to write an equation in slope-intercept form when given an equation in point-slope form. **Example 4** shows how to use the point-slope form to write an equation for the line making up a side of a geometric figure.

Additional Examples

2 Write $y = \frac{3}{4}x - 5$ in standard form. $3x - 4y = 20$

3 Write $y - 5 = \frac{4}{3}(x - 3)$ in slope-intercept form. $y = \frac{4}{3}x + 1$

Forms of Linear Equations If you are given the slope and the coordinates of one or two points, you can write the linear equation in the following ways.

StudyTip

Slope The slope of the line remains unchanged throughout the line. You can go in either direction along the line using the same rise over run and you will always end at a point on the line.

Concept Summary — Writing Equations

For Your FOLDABLE

Given the Slope and One Point	Given Two Points
Step 1 Substitute the value of m and let the x and y coordinates be (x_1, y_1). Or, substitute the values of m, x, and y into the slope-intercept form and solve for b.	**Step 1** Find the slope.
Step 2 Rewrite the equation in the needed form.	**Step 2** Choose one of the two points to use.
	Step 3 Follow the steps for writing an equation given the slope and one point.

Review Vocabulary

standard form of a linear equation $Ax + By = C$, where $A \geq 0$, A and B are not both zero, and A, B, and C are integers with a greatest common factor of 1 (Lesson 3-1)

EXAMPLE 2 Standard Form

Write $y - 1 = -\frac{2}{3}(x - 5)$ in standard form.

$y - 1 = -\frac{2}{3}(x - 5)$	Original equation
$3(y - 1) = 3\left(-\frac{2}{3}\right)(x - 5)$	Multiply each side by 3 to eliminate the fraction.
$3(y - 1) = -2(x - 5)$	Simplify.
$3y - 3 = -2x + 10$	Distributive Property
$3y = -2x + 13$	Add 3 to each side.
$2x + 3y = 13$	Add $2x$ to each side.

Check Your Progress

2. Write $y - 1 = 7(x + 5)$ in standard form. $7x - y = -36$

Personal Tutor glencoe.com

To find the y-intercept of an equation, rewrite the equation in slope-intercept form.

EXAMPLE 3 Slope-Intercept Form

Write $y + 3 = \frac{3}{2}(x + 1)$ in slope-intercept form.

$y + 3 = \frac{3}{2}(x + 1)$	Original equation
$y + 3 = \frac{3}{2}x + \frac{3}{2}$	Distributive Property
$y = \frac{3}{2}x - \frac{3}{2}$	Subtract 3 from each side.

Check Your Progress

3. Write $y + 6 = -3(x - 4)$ in slope-intercept form. $y = -3x + 6$

Personal Tutor glencoe.com

Watch Out!

Preventing Errors Emphasize that in standard form, A, B, and C are all integers. Example 2 is an exercise in algebraic manipulation.

Multiplication Facts Another way for students to write the equation in Example 3 in slope-intercept form is to identify the slope m of the line and let $x = 0$ to find the y-intercept. Solve for y. This value is the value of b for the equation in slope-intercept form.

TEACH with TECH

INTERACTIVE WHITEBOARD Drag a coordinate plane onto the whiteboard. Plot two points on the plane and ask students to find the equation of the line that goes through these two points. Then, drag the points to other locations on the plane and repeat.

232 Chapter 4 Linear Functions and Relations

Being able to use a variety of forms of linear equations can be useful in other subjects as well.

StudyTip

Slopes in Squares Nonvertical opposite sides of a square have equal slopes. If the coordinates for one of the vertices are unavailable, use the slope of the opposite side.

EXAMPLE 4 Point-Slope Form and Standard Form

GEOMETRY The figure shows square *RSTU*.

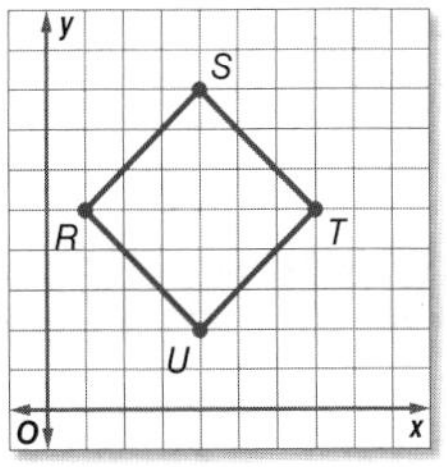

a. Write an equation in point-slope form for the line containing side $\overline{TU}$.

Step 1 Find the slope of $\overline{TU}$.

$m = \frac{y_2 - y_1}{x_2 - x_1}$ **Slope Formula**

$= \frac{5-2}{7-4}$ or 1 **$(x_1, y_1) = (4, 2)$ and $(x_2, y_2) = (7, 5)$**

Step 2 You can select either point for (x_1, y_1) in the point-slope form.

$y - y_1 = m(x - x_1)$ **Point-slope form**

$y - 2 = 1(x - 4)$ **$(x_1, y_1) = (4, 2)$**

$y - 5 = 1(x - 7)$ **$(x_1, y_1) = (7, 5)$**

b. Write an equation in standard form for the same line.

$y - 2 = 1(x - 4)$	**Original equation**	$y - 5 = 1(x - 7)$
$y - 2 = 1x - 4$	**Distributive Property**	$y - 5 = 1x - 7$
$y = 1x - 2$	**Add to each side.**	$y = 1x - 2$
$-1x + y = -2$	**Subtract 1x from each side.**	$-1x + y = -2$
$x - y = 2$	**Multiply each side by −1.**	$x - y = 2$

Check Your Progress

4A. Write an equation in point-slope form of the line containing side $\overline{ST}$. $y - 8 = -1(x - 4)$ or $y - 5 = -1(x - 7)$

4B. Write an equation in standard form of the line containing $\overline{ST}$. $x + y = 12$

Personal Tutor glencoe.com

Check Your Understanding

1–3. See Ch. 4 Answer Appendix.

Example 1 p. 231 Write an equation in point-slope form for the line that passes through the given point with the slope provided. Then graph the equation.

1. $(-2, 5)$, slope -6
2. $(-2, -8)$, slope $\frac{5}{6}$
3. $(4, 3)$, slope $-\frac{1}{2}$

Example 2 p. 232 Write each equation in standard form.

4. $y + 2 = \frac{7}{8}(x - 3)$ $7x - 8y = 37$
5. $y + 7 = -5(x + 3)$ $5x + y = -22$
6. $y + 2 = \frac{5}{3}(x + 6)$ $5x - 3y = -24$

Example 3 p. 232 Write each equation in slope-intercept form.

7. $y - 10 = 4(x + 6)$ $y = 4x + 34$
8. $y - 7 = -\frac{3}{4}(x + 5)$ 8. $y = -\frac{3}{4}x + \frac{13}{4}$
9. $y - 9 = x + 4$ $y = x + 13$

Focus on Mathematical Content

Point-Slope Form In general, if the point (x_1, y_1) is on a line with a slope of m, the definition of slope can be used to write an equation for all points (x, y). $m = \frac{y - y_1}{x - x_1}$ Multiply both sides of the equation by $(x - x_1)$. $y - y_1 = m(x - x_1)$ This form of the equation of a line is known as the point-slope form.

Additional Example

4 **GEOMETRY** The figure shows trapezoid *ABCD*, with bases $\overline{AB}$ and $\overline{CD}$.

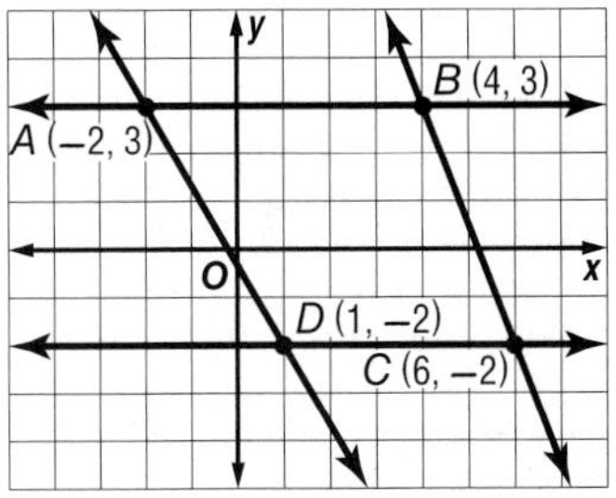

a. Write an equation in point-slope form for the line containing the side $\overline{BC}$.
$y - 3 = -\frac{5}{2}(x - 4)$ or
$y + 2 = -\frac{5}{2}(x - 6)$

b. Write an equation in standard form for the same line.
$5x + 2y = 26$

Additional Examples also in Interactive Classroom PowerPoint® Presentations

IWB INTERACTIVE WHITEBOARD READY

Differentiated Instruction

AL OL ELL

If students have trouble remembering whether a vertical line or a horizontal line has slope 0,

Then tell them the word *horizontal* has an *o* to remind them of 0. A horizontal line has slope **0**. Challenge students to create a catchy phrase to help them remember the different forms for a linear equation.

3 PRACTICE

Formative Assessment

Use Exercises 1–10 to check for understanding.

Use the chart at the bottom of the next page to customize assignments for your students.

Exercise Alert

Grid Paper Students will need grid paper for Exercises 1–3 and 11–16.

Watch Out!

Find the Error For Exercise 50, students should see that the slopes in the equations are different.

Additional Answers

11–16. See Ch. 4 Answer Appendix for graphs

11. $y - 3 = 7(x - 5)$

12. $y + 1 = -3(x - 2)$

13. $y + 3 = -1(x + 6)$

14. $y - 6 = 0$

15. $y - 11 = \frac{4}{3}(x + 2)$

16. $y + 8 = -\frac{3}{7}(x + 7)$

51. Sample answer: Jocari spent $14 to go to an amusement park and ride ponies. The price she paid included admission. The 5 pony rides cost $2 each; $y - 14 = 2(x - 5)$, $y = 2x + 4$.

52. $y = -\frac{15}{7}x - \frac{4}{7}$; $m = -\frac{15}{7}, -\frac{4}{15}, -\frac{4}{7}$

54. Write an equation by using the fraction from the definition of slope on the left side and the given slope on the right side. Use (x, y) as one point and (x_1, y_1) as the other. Then multiply each side by the denominator $(x - x_1)$ of the fraction on the left of the equals sign.

Example 4 p. 233

10. GEOMETRY Use right triangle FGH.

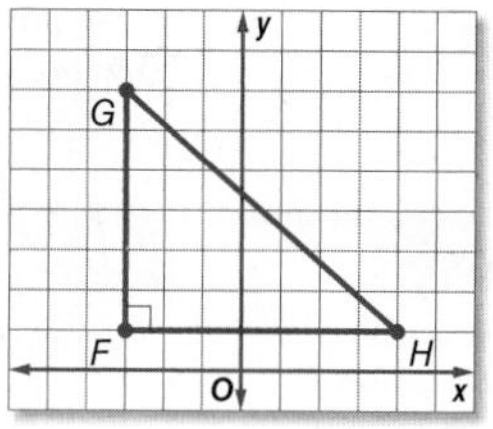

a. Write an equation in point-slope form for the line containing $\overline{GH}$. $y - 7 = -\frac{6}{7}(x + 3)$

b. Write the standard form of the line containing $\overline{GH}$. $6x + 7y = 31$

Practice and Problem Solving

= **Step-by-Step Solutions** begin on page R12. **Extra Practice** begins on page 815.

Example 1 p. 231

11–16. See margin for graphs.

Write an equation in point-slope form for the line that passes through each point with the given slope. Then graph the equation.

11. $(5, 3), m = 7$ **12.** $(2, -1), m = -3$ **13.** $(-6, -3), m = -1$

14. $(-7, 6), m = 0$ **15.** $(-2, 11), m = \frac{4}{3}$ **16.** $(-7, -8), m = -\frac{3}{7}$

17. Write an equation in point-slope form for a line that passes through $(-2, -9)$ with a slope of $-\frac{7}{5}$. $y + 9 = -\frac{7}{5}(x + 2)$

18. Write an equation in point-slope form for a horizontal line that passes through $(-6, 0)$. $y = 0$

Example 2 p. 232

Write each equation in standard form.

19. $y - 10 = 2(x - 8)$ $2x - y = 6$ **20.** $y - 6 = -3(x + 2)$ $3x + y = 0$

21. $y - 9 = -6(x + 9)$ $6x + y = -45$ **22.** $y + 4 = \frac{2}{3}(x + 7)$ $2x - 3y = -2$

23. $y + 7 = \frac{9}{10}(x + 3)$ $9x - 10y = 43$ **24.** $y + 7 = -\frac{3}{2}(x + 1)$ $3x + 2y = -17$

25. $2y + 3 = -\frac{1}{3}(x - 2)$ $x + 6y = -7$ **26.** $4y - 5x = 3(4x - 2y + 1)$ $17x - 10y = -3$

Example 3 p. 232

Write each equation in slope-intercept form.

27. $y - 6 = -2(x - 7)$ $y = -2x + 20$ **28.** $y - 11 = 3(x + 4)$ $y = 3x + 23$

29. $y + 5 = -6(x + 7)$ $y = -6x - 47$ **30.** $y - 1 = \frac{4}{5}(x + 5)$ $y = \frac{4}{5}x + 5$

31. $y + 2 = \frac{1}{6}(x - 4)$ $y = \frac{1}{6}x - \frac{8}{3}$ **32.** $y + 6 = -\frac{3}{4}(x + 8)$ $y = -\frac{3}{4}x - 12$

33. $y + 3 = -\frac{1}{3}(2x + 6)$ $y = -\frac{2}{3}x - 5$ **34.** $y + 4 = 3(3x + 3)$ $y = 9x + 5$

Example 4 p. 233

35 **MOVIE RENTALS** The number of copies of a movie rented at a video store decreased at a constant rate of 5 copies per week. The 6th week after the movie was released, 4 copies were rented. How many copies were rented during the second week? 24 copies

B

36. CABLE A company offers premium cable for $39.95 per month plus a one-time setup fee. The total cost for setup and 6 months of service is $264.70.

a. Write an equation in point-slope form to find the total price y for any number of months x. (*Hint*: The point (6, 264.70) is a solution to the equation.)

b. Write the equation in slope-intercept form. $y = 39.95x + 25$

c. What is the setup fee? $25

36a. $y - 264.70 = 39.95(x - 6)$
37. $11x + 12y = 58$
38. $5x - 2y = -11$
39. $14x - 10y = 91$

Write each equation in standard form.

37. $y + 8 = -\frac{11}{12}(x - 14)$ **38.** $y - 3 = 2.5(x + 1)$ **39.** $y + 2.1 = 1.4(x - 5)$

Differentiated Homework Options

Level	Assignment	Two-Day Option	
AL Basic	11–35, 49–52, 54–75	11–35 odd, 55–58	12–34 even, 49–52, 54, 59–75
OL Core	11–35 odd, 36, 37, 39, 40–52, 54–75	11–35, 55–58	36–52, 54, 59–75
BL Advanced	36–71, (optional: 72–75)		

C Write an equation in point-slope form for each line.

40.

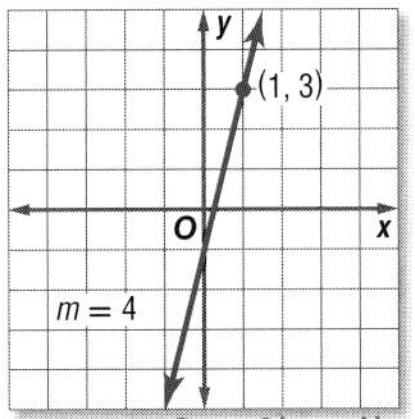

$y - 3 = 4(x - 1)$

41.

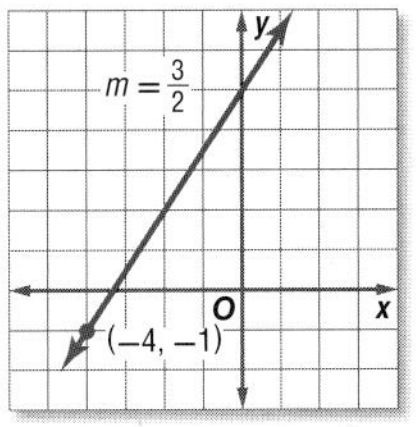

$y + 1 = \frac{3}{2}(x + 4)$

42. $y - 7 = -\frac{4}{3}(x + 3)$

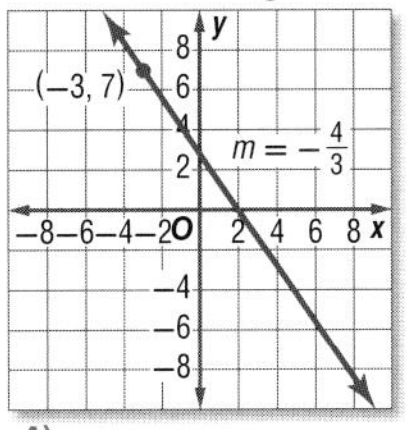

Write each equation in slope-intercept form.

43 $y + \frac{3}{5} = x - \frac{2}{5}$ $y = x - 1$

44. $y - \frac{7}{2} = \frac{1}{2}(x - 4)$

45. $y + \frac{1}{3} = \frac{5}{6}\left(x + \frac{2}{5}\right)$

46. Write an equation in point-slope form, slope-intercept form, and standard form for a line that passes through $(-2, 8)$ with slope $\frac{8}{5}$.

47. Line ℓ passes through $(-9, 4)$ with slope $\frac{4}{7}$. Write an equation in point-slope form, slope-intercept form, and standard form for line ℓ.

48. WEATHER Barometric pressure is a linear function of altitude. The barometric pressure is 598 millimeters of mercury (mmHg) at an altitude of 1.8 kilometers. The pressure is 577 millimeters of mercury at 2.1 kilometers.

a. Write a formula for the barometric pressure as a function of the altitude. $f(x) = -70x + 724$

b. What is the altitude if the pressure is 657 millimeters of mercury? **0.96 km**

H.O.T. Problems

Use **H**igher-**O**rder **T**hinking Skills

49. WHICH ONE DOESN'T BELONG? Identify the equation that does not belong. Explain your reasoning. **$y + 4 = 3(x + 1)$; The slope-intercept form is not $y = 3x + 2$.**

$y - 5 = 3(x - 1)$	$y + 1 = 3(x + 1)$	$y + 4 = 3(x + 1)$	$y - 8 = 3(x - 2)$

50. FIND THE ERROR Juana and Sabrina wrote an equation in point-slope form for the line that passes through $(3, -7)$ and $(-6, 4)$. Is either of them correct? Explain.

Juana	Sabrina
$y - 7 = -\frac{11}{9}(x + 3)$	$y - 4 = -\frac{9}{11}(x + 6)$

51. OPEN ENDED Describe a real-life scenario that has a constant rate of change and a value of y for a particular value of x. Represent this situation using an equation in point-slope form and an equation in slope-intercept form. **See margin.**

52. REASONING Write an equation for the line that passes through $(-4, 8)$ and $(3, -7)$. What is the slope? Where does the line intersect the x-axis? the y-axis? **See margin.**

53. CHALLENGE Write an equation in point-slope form for the line that passes through the points (f, g) and (h, j). **Sample answer: $y - g = \frac{j - g}{h - f}(x - f)$**

54. WRITING IN MATH Demonstrate how you can use the Slope Formula to write the point-slope form of an equation of a line. **See margin.**

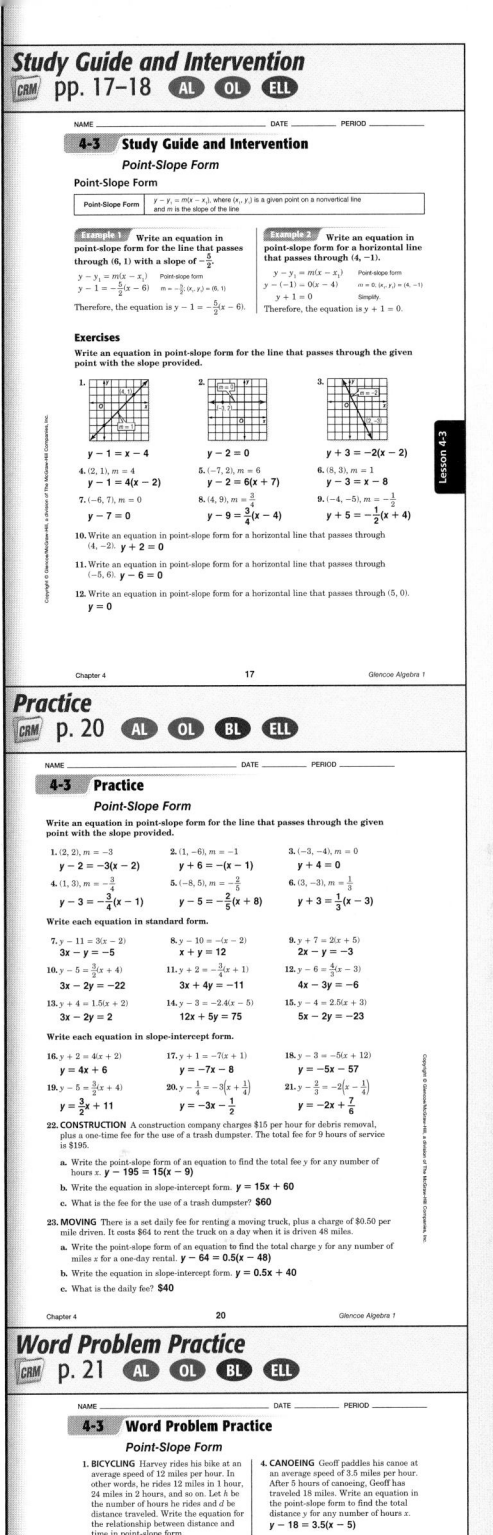

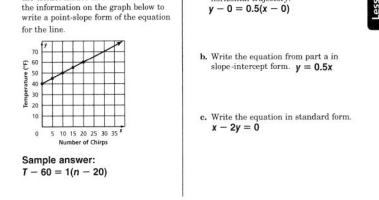

44. $y = \frac{1}{2}x + \frac{3}{2}$

45. $y = \frac{5}{6}x$

Real-World Link

At higher altitudes, air is at a lower pressure and contains less oxygen. Prolonged exposure to low air pressure causes altitude sickness. Experienced mountain climbers take precautions to prevent altitude sickness.

Source: Altitude Physiology Expeditions Charity

46. $y - 8 = \frac{8}{5}(x + 2)$; $y = \frac{8}{5}x + \frac{56}{5}$; $8x - 5y = -56$

47. $y - 4 = \frac{4}{7}(x + 9)$; $y = \frac{4}{7}x + \frac{64}{7}$; $4x - 7y = -64$

50. Neither; Juana used $(-3, 7)$ for the coordinates of the point instead of $(3, -7)$ and Sabrina used the change in x over the change in y for slope.

Study Guide and Intervention

CRM pp. 17–18 AL OL ELL

NAME ______ DATE ______ PERIOD ______

4-3 Study Guide and Intervention

Point-Slope Form

Point-Slope Form

Point-Slope Form	$y - y_1 = m(x - x_1)$, where (x_1, y_1) is a given point on a nonvertical line and m is the slope of the line

Example 1 Write an equation in point-slope form for the line that passes through (6, 1) with a slope of $-\frac{5}{2}$.

$y - y_1 = m(x - x_1)$ Point-slope form

$y - 1 = -\frac{5}{2}(x - 6)$ $m = -\frac{5}{2}$; $(x_1, y_1) = (6, 1)$

Therefore, the equation is $y - 1 = -\frac{5}{2}(x - 6)$.

Example 2 Write an equation in point-slope form for a horizontal line that passes through (4, −1).

$y - y_1 = m(x - x_1)$ Point-slope form

$y - (-1) = 0(x - 4)$ $m = 0$; $(x_1, y_1) = (4, -1)$

$y + 1 = 0$ Simplify.

Therefore, the equation is $y + 1 = 0$.

Exercises

Write an equation in point-slope form for the line that passes through the given point with the slope provided.

1.

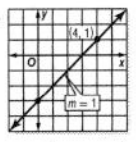

$y - 1 = x - 4$

2.

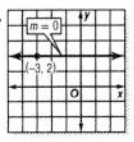

$y - 2 = 0$

3.

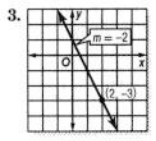

$y + 3 = -2(x - 2)$

4. $(2, 1)$, $m = 4$ **$y - 1 = 4(x - 2)$**

5. $(-7, 2)$, $m = 6$ **$y - 2 = 6(x + 7)$**

6. $(8, 3)$, $m = 1$ **$y - 3 = x - 8$**

7. $(-6, 7)$, $m = 0$ **$y - 7 = 0$**

8. $(4, 9)$, $m = \frac{3}{4}$ **$y - 9 = \frac{3}{4}(x - 4)$**

9. $(-4, -5)$, $m = -\frac{1}{2}$ **$y + 5 = -\frac{1}{2}(x + 4)$**

10. Write an equation in point-slope form for a horizontal line that passes through (4, −2). **$y + 2 = 0$**

11. Write an equation in point-slope form for a horizontal line that passes through (−5, 6). **$y - 6 = 0$**

12. Write an equation in point-slope form for a horizontal line that passes through (5, 0). **$y = 0$**

Lesson 4-3

Chapter 4 17 Glencoe Algebra 1

Practice

CRM p. 20 AL OL BL ELL

NAME ______ DATE ______ PERIOD ______

4-3 Practice

Point-Slope Form

Write an equation in point-slope form for the line that passes through the given point with the slope provided.

1. $(2, 2)$, $m = -3$ **$y - 2 = -3(x - 2)$**

2. $(1, -6)$, $m = -1$ **$y + 6 = -(x - 1)$**

3. $(-3, -4)$, $m = 0$ **$y + 4 = 0$**

4. $(1, 3)$, $m = -\frac{3}{4}$ **$y - 3 = -\frac{3}{4}(x - 1)$**

5. $(-8, 5)$, $m = -\frac{2}{5}$ **$y - 5 = -\frac{2}{5}(x + 8)$**

6. $(3, -3)$, $m = \frac{1}{3}$ **$y + 3 = \frac{1}{3}(x - 3)$**

Write each equation in standard form.

7. $y - 11 = 3(x - 2)$ **$3x - y = -5$**

8. $y - 10 = -(x - 2)$ **$x + y = 12$**

9. $y + 7 = 2(x + 5)$ **$2x - y = -3$**

10. $y - 5 = \frac{3}{2}(x + 4)$ **$3x - 2y = -22$**

11. $y + 2 = -\frac{3}{4}(x + 1)$ **$3x + 4y = -11$**

12. $y - 6 = \frac{4}{3}(x - 3)$ **$4x - 3y = -6$**

13. $y + 4 = 1.5(x + 2)$ **$3x - 2y = 2$**

14. $y - 3 = -2.4(x - 5)$ **$12x + 5y = 75$**

15. $y - 4 = 2.5(x + 3)$ **$5x - 2y = -23$**

Write each equation in slope-intercept form.

16. $y + 2 = 4(x + 2)$ **$y = 4x + 6$**

17. $y + 1 = -7(x + 1)$ **$y = -7x - 8$**

18. $y - 3 = -5(x + 12)$ **$y = -5x - 57$**

19. $y - 5 = \frac{3}{2}(x + 4)$ **$y = \frac{3}{2}x + 11$**

20. $y - \frac{1}{4} = -3\left(x + \frac{1}{4}\right)$ **$y = -3x - \frac{1}{2}$**

21. $y - \frac{2}{3} = -2\left(x - \frac{1}{4}\right)$ **$y = -2x + \frac{7}{6}$**

22. **CONSTRUCTION** A construction company charges $15 per hour for debris removal, plus a one-time fee for the use of a trash dumpster. The total fee for 9 hours of service is $195.

a. Write the point-slope form of an equation to find the total fee y for any number of hours x. **$y - 195 = 15(x - 9)$**

b. Write the equation in slope-intercept form. **$y = 15x + 60$**

c. What is the fee for the use of a trash dumpster? **$60**

23. **MOVING** There is a set daily fee for renting a moving truck, plus a charge of $0.50 per mile driven. It costs $64 to rent the truck on a day when it is driven 48 miles.

a. Write the point-slope form of an equation to find the total charge y for any number of miles x for a one-day rental. **$y - 64 = 0.5(x - 48)$**

b. Write the equation in slope-intercept form. **$y = 0.5x + 40$**

c. What is the daily fee? **$40**

Chapter 4 20 Glencoe Algebra 1

Word Problem Practice

CRM p. 21 AL OL BL ELL

NAME ______ DATE ______ PERIOD ______

4-3 Word Problem Practice

Point-Slope Form

1. **BICYCLING** Harvey rides his bike at an average speed of 12 miles per hour. In other words, he rides 12 miles in 1 hour, 24 miles in 2 hours, and so on. Let h be the number of hours he rides and d be distance traveled. Write the equation for the relationship between distance and time in point-slope form.
$d - 12 = 12(h - 1)$

2. **GEOMETRY** The perimeter of a square varies directly with the side length. The point-slope form of the equation for this function is $y - 4 = 4(x - 1)$. Write the equation in standard form.
$4x - y = 0$

3. **NATURE** In a near perfect linear relationship, the frequency of a male cricket's chirp matches the outdoor temperature. The relationship is expressed by the equation $T = n + 40$, where T is the temperature in degrees Fahrenheit and n is the number of chirps the cricket makes in 14 seconds. Use the information on the graph below to write a point-slope form of the equation for the line.

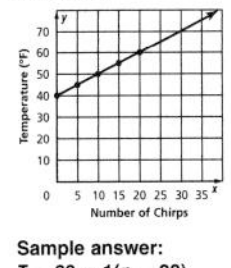

Sample answer:
$T - 60 = 1(n - 20)$

4. **CANOEING** Geoff paddles his canoe at an average speed of 3.5 miles per hour. After 5 hours of canoeing, Geoff has traveled 18 miles. Write an equation in the point-slope form to find the total distance y for any number of hours x.
$y - 18 = 3.5(x - 5)$

5. **AVIATION** A jet plane takes off and climbs consistently 20 feet for every 40 feet it moves horizontally. The graph shows the trajectory of the jet.

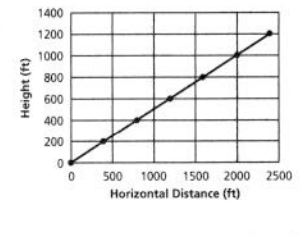

a. Write an equation in point-slope form for the line representing the jet's horizontal trajectory.
$y - 0 = 0.5(x - 0)$

b. Write the equation from part a in slope-intercept form. **$y = 0.5x$**

c. Write the equation in standard form.
$x - 2y = 0$

Lesson 4-3

Chapter 4 21 Glencoe Algebra 1

Enrichment

CRM p. 22 OL BL

NAME ______ DATE ______ PERIOD ______

4-3 Enrichment

Collinearity

You have learned how to find the slope between two points on a line. Does it matter which two points you use? How does your choice of points affect the slope-intercept form of the equation of the line?

1. Choose three different pairs of points from the graph at the right. Write the slope-intercept form of the line using each pair.
$y = x + 1$

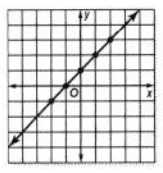

2. How are the equations related?
They are the same.

3. What conclusion can you draw from your answers to Exercises 1 and 2?
The equation of a line is the same no matter which two points you choose.

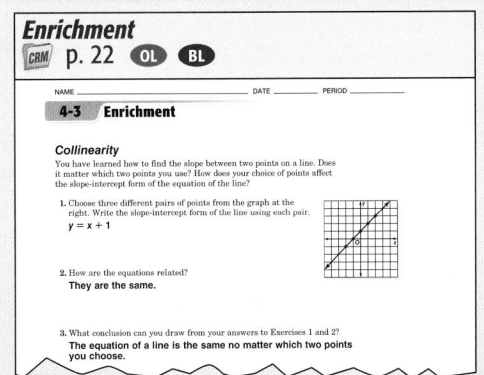

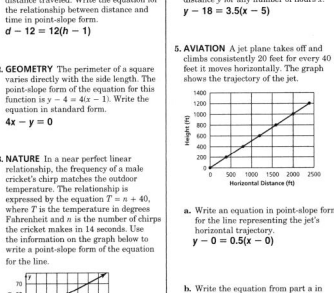

4 ASSESS

Name the Math Prepare two paper bags containing pieces of paper. One bag will contain a value for the slope on each slip of paper; the other will contain an ordered pair on each slip of paper. Have students select both a slope and an ordered pair or two ordered pairs. Ask students to write equations in the three forms discussed in this lesson.

PSAE PRACTICE 8.11.13, 6.11.17, 9.11.12, 10.11.03

55. Which statement is *most* strongly supported by the graph? **B**

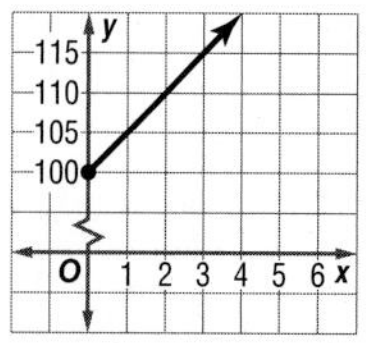

A You have \$100 and spend \$5 weekly.
B You have \$100 and save \$5 weekly.
C You need \$100 for a new CD player and save \$5 weekly.
D You need \$100 for a new CD player and spend \$5 weekly.

56. SHORT RESPONSE A store offers customers a \$5 gift certificate for every \$75 they spend. How much would a customer have to spend to earn \$35 worth of gift certificates? **\$525**

57. GEOMETRY Which triangle is similar to $\triangle ABC$? **J**

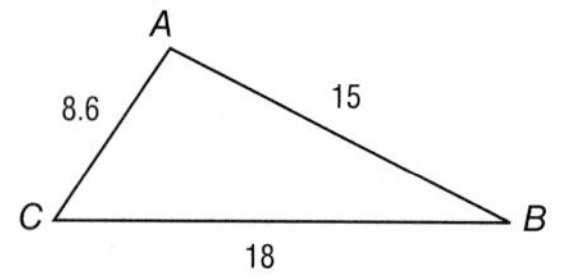

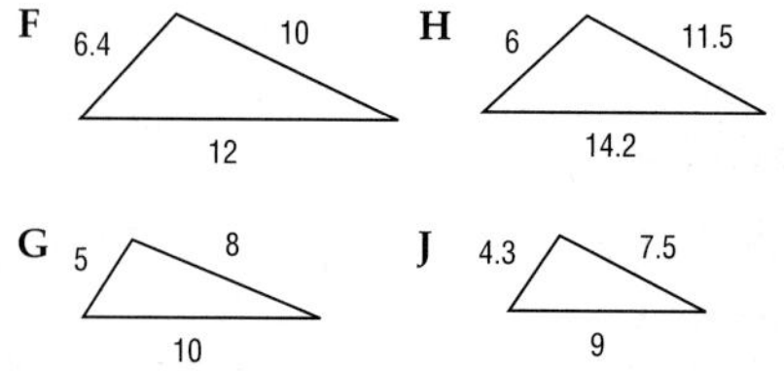

58. In a class of 25 students, 6 have blue eyes, 15 have brown hair, and 3 have blue eyes and brown hair. How many students have neither blue eyes nor brown hair? **B**

A 4
B 7
C 10
D 22

Spiral Review

Write an equation of the line that passes through each pair of points. (Lesson 4-2)

59. (4, 2), (−2, −4) $y = x - 2$
60. (3, −2), (6, 4) $y = 2x - 8$
61. (−1, 3), (2, −3) $y = -2x + 1$
62. (2, −2), (3, 2) $y = 4x - 10$
63. (7, −2), (−4, −2) $y = -2$
64. (0, 5), (−3, 5) $y = 5$

Write an equation in slope-intercept form of the line with the given slope and *y*-intercept. (Lesson 4-1)

65. slope: −2, *y*-intercept: 6 $y = -2x + 6$
66. slope: 3, *y*-intercept: −5 $y = 3x - 5$
67. slope: $\frac{1}{2}$, *y*-intercept: 3 $y = \frac{1}{2}x + 3$
68. slope: $-\frac{3}{5}$, *y*-intercept: 12 $y = -\frac{3}{5}x + 12$
69. slope: 0, *y*-intercept: 3 $y = 3$
70. slope: −1, *y*-intercept: 0 $y = -x$

71. THEATER The Coral Gables Actors' Playhouse has 7 rows of seats in the orchestra section. The number of seats in the rows forms an arithmetic sequence, as shown in the table. On opening night, 368 tickets were sold for the orchestra section. Was the section oversold? (Lesson 3-5) **Yes, there are only 364 seats.**

Rows	Number of Seats
7	76
6	68
5	60

Skills Review

Solve each equation or formula for the variable specified. (Lesson 2-7)

72. $y = mx + b$, for m $m = \frac{y - b}{x}$
73. $v = r + at$, for a $a = \frac{v - r}{t}$
74. $km + 5x = 6y$, for m $m = \frac{6y - 5x}{k}$
75. $4b - 5 = -t$, for b $b = \frac{-t + 5}{4}$

Differentiated Instruction OL BL

Extension Write $4x + 3y = 8$ on the board. Ask students to rewrite the equation in slope-intercept form. Have students name the slope and then draw a conclusion about the relationship between the slope and values of A and B when an equation is written in standard form, $Ax + By = C$. $y = -\frac{4}{3}x + \frac{8}{3}$; $-\frac{4}{3}$; The slope is $-\frac{4}{3}$; $m = -\frac{B}{A}$.

Then

You wrote equations in point-slope form. (Lesson 4-3)

Now

- Write an equation of the line that passes through a given point, parallel to a given line.
- Write an equation of the line that passes through a given point, perpendicular to a given line.

IL Learning Standards

8.B.4b Use the basic functions of absolute value, square root, linear, quadratic and step to describe numerical relationships.

New Vocabulary

parallel lines
perpendicular lines

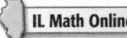

IL Math Online

glencoe.com

- Extra Examples
- Personal Tutor
- Self-Check Quiz
- Homework Help

4-4 Parallel and Perpendicular Lines

Why?

Notice the squares, rectangles and lines in the piece of art shown at the right. Some of the lines intersect forming right angles. Other lines do not intersect at all.

Parallel Lines Lines in the same plane that do not intersect are called **parallel lines**. Parallel lines have the same slope.

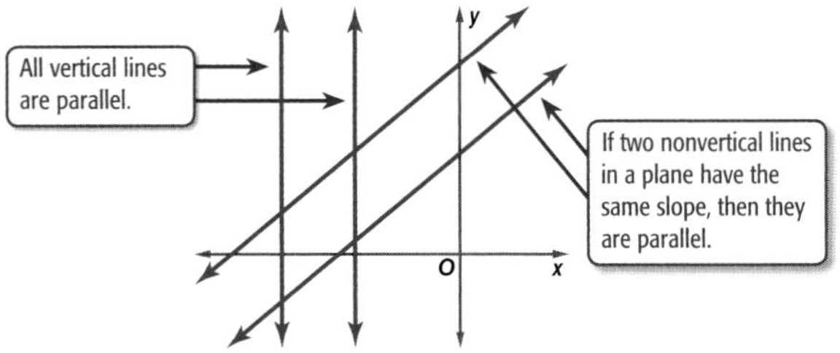

You can write an equation of a line parallel to a given line if you know a point on the line and an equation of the given line. First find the slope of the given line. Then, substitute the point provided and the slope from the given line into the point-slope form.

EXAMPLE 1 Parallel Line Through a Given Point

Write an equation in slope-intercept form for the line that passes through $(-3, 5)$ and is parallel to the graph of $y = 2x - 4$.

Step 1 The slope of the line with equation $y = 2x - 4$ is 2. The line parallel to $y = 2x - 4$ has the same slope, 2.

Step 2 Find the equation in slope-intercept form.

$y - y_1 = m(x - x_1)$	**Point-slope form**
$y - 5 = 2[x - (-3)]$	**Replace m with 2 and (x_1, y_1) with $(-3, 5)$.**
$y - 5 = 2(x + 3)$	**Simplify.**
$y - 5 = 2x + 6$	**Distributive Property**
$y - 5 + 5 = 2x + 6 + 5$	**Add 5 to each side.**
$y = 2x + 11$	**Write the equation in slope-intercept form.**

Check Your Progress

1. Write an equation in point-slope form for the line that passes through $(4, -1)$ and is parallel to the graph of $y = \frac{1}{4}x + 7$. $y + 1 = \frac{1}{4}(x - 4)$

Personal Tutor glencoe.com

4-4 Lesson Notes

1 FOCUS

Vertical Alignment

Before Lesson 4-4
Write equations in point-slope form.

Lesson 4-4
Write an equation of the line that passes through a given point, parallel to a given line.
Write an equation of the lines that pass through a given point, perpendicular to a given line.

After Lesson 4-4
Identify and graph absolute value and step functions.

2 TEACH

Scaffolding Questions

Have students read the *Why?* section of the lesson.

Ask:

- How would you describe the relationship between the vertical lines in the art shown? They are parallel to each other. They have no slope.
- How would you describe the relationship between the horizontal lines in the art? They are parallel to each other. They have the same slope.

Lesson 4-4 Resources

Resource	Approaching-Level	On-Level	Beyond-Level	English Learners
Teacher Edition	• Differentiated Instruction, p. 239	• Differentiated Instruction, p. 243	• Differentiated Instruction, p. 243	• Differentiated Instruction, p. 239
Chapter Resource Masters	• Study Guide and Intervention, pp. 24–25 • Skills Practice, p. 26 • Practice, p. 27 • Word Problem Practice, p. 28	• Study Guide and Intervention, pp. 24–25 • Skills Practice, p. 26 • Practice, p. 27 • Word Problem Practice, p. 28 • Enrichment, p. 29	• Practice, p. 27 • Word Problem Practice, p. 28 • Enrichment, p. 29	• Study Guide and Intervention, pp. 24–25 • Skills Practice, p. 26 • Practice, p. 27
Transparencies	• 5-Minute Check Transparency 4-4	• 5-Minute Check Transparency 4-4	• 5-Minute Check Transparency 4-4	• 5-Minute Check Transparency 4-4
Other	• Study Notebook • Teaching Algebra with Manipulatives	• Study Notebook • Teaching Algebra with Manipulatives	• Study Notebook	• Study Notebook • Teaching Algebra with Manipulatives

Parallel Lines

Example 1 shows how to write the slope-intercept form of an equation for a line that passes through a particular point and is parallel to a given line.

Formative Assessment

Use the Check Your Progress exercises after each Example to determine students' understanding of concepts.

Additional Example

1 Write an equation in slope-intercept form for the line that passes through (4, −2) and is parallel to the graph of $y = \frac{1}{2}x - 7$. $y = \frac{1}{2}x - 4$

Additional Examples also in Interactive Classroom PowerPoint® Presentations

IWB INTERACTIVE WHITEBOARD READY

Perpendicular Lines

Example 2 shows how to determine whether two line segments in a real-world situation are perpendicular or parallel. **Example 3** shows how to determine whether the graphs of given equations are parallel or perpendicular. **Example 4** shows how to write an equation in slope-intercept form for a line perpendicular to a given line if you know a point on the line and the equation of the given line.

TEACH with TECH

INTERACTIVE WHITEBOARD Give students an equation of a line and a point not on the line. Have one student show and explain how to find a line parallel to the given line that goes through that point. Have a second student show and explain how to find a line perpendicular to the given line that goes through that point.

Review Vocabulary

opposite reciprocals The opposite reciprocal of $\frac{a}{b}$ is $-\frac{b}{a}$. Their product is −1.

Perpendicular Lines Lines that intersect at right angles are called **perpendicular lines**. The slopes of perpendicular lines are opposite reciprocals. That is, if the slope of a line is 4, the slope of the line perpendicular to it is $-\frac{1}{4}$.

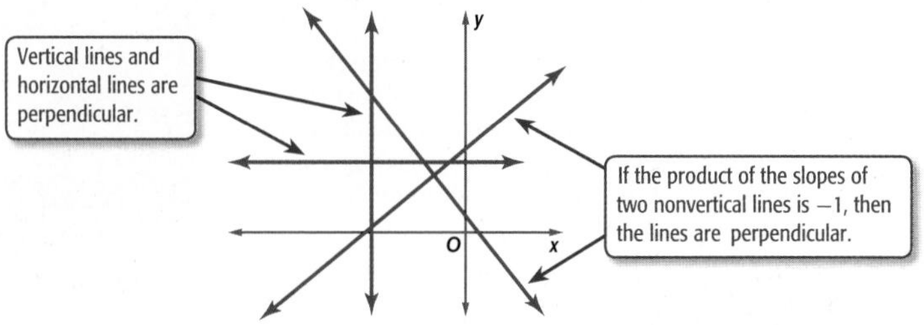

You can use slope to determine whether two lines are perpendicular.

Real-World EXAMPLE 2 Slopes of Perpendicular Lines

DESIGN The outline of a company's new logo is shown on a coordinate plane.

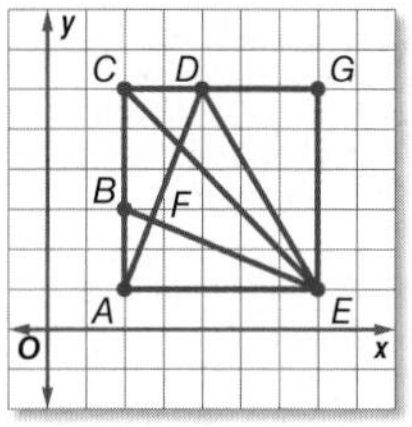

a. Is ∠DFE a right angle in the logo?

If $\overline{BE}$ and $\overline{AD}$ are perpendicular, then ∠DFE is a right angle. Find the slopes of $\overline{BE}$ and $\overline{AD}$.

slope of $\overline{BE}$: $m = \frac{1-3}{7-2}$ or $-\frac{2}{5}$

slope of $\overline{AD}$: $m = \frac{6-1}{4-2}$ or $\frac{5}{2}$

The line segments are perpendicular because $-\frac{2}{5} \times \frac{5}{2} = -1$. Therefore, ∠DFE is a right angle.

b. Is each pair of opposite sides parallel?

If a pair of opposite sides are parallel, then they have the same slope.

slope of $\overline{AC}$: $m = \frac{6-1}{2-2}$ or undefined

Since $\overline{AC}$ and $\overline{GE}$ are both parallel to the y-axis, they are vertical and are therefore parallel.

slope of $\overline{CG}$: $m = \frac{6-6}{7-2}$ or 0

Since $\overline{CG}$ and $\overline{AE}$ are both parallel to the x-axis, they are horizontal and are therefore parallel.

Check Your Progress

2. CONSTRUCTION On the plans for a treehouse, a beam represented by $\overline{QR}$ has endpoints $Q(-6, 2)$ and $R(-1, 8)$. A connecting beam represented by $\overline{ST}$ has endpoints $S(-3, 6)$ and $T(-8, 5)$. Are the beams perpendicular? Explain.

2. Slope of $\overline{QR} = \frac{6}{5}$; slope of $\overline{ST} = \frac{1}{5}$; the beams are not perpendicular since the product of their slopes is not −1.

Personal Tutor glencoe.com

Real-World Link

The oldest treehouse still in existence was built in England in the 1700s.

Source: The Treehouse Company

You can determine whether the graphs of two linear equations are parallel or perpendicular by comparing the slopes of the lines.

Focus on Mathematical Content

Parallel and Perpendicular Lines All vertical lines are parallel, and all horizontal lines are parallel. All vertical lines are perpendicular to all horizontal lines and therefore, all horizontal lines are perpendicular to all vertical lines. Two nonvertical lines are parallel if their slopes are the same. They are perpendicular if the product of their slopes is −1.

ReadingMath

Parallel and Perpendicular Lines The symbol for parallel is ∥. The symbol for perpendicular is ⊥.

EXAMPLE 3 Parallel or Perpendicular Lines

Determine whether the graphs of $y = 5$, $x = 3$, and $y = -2x + 1$ are *parallel* or *perpendicular*. Explain.

Graph each line on a coordinate plane.

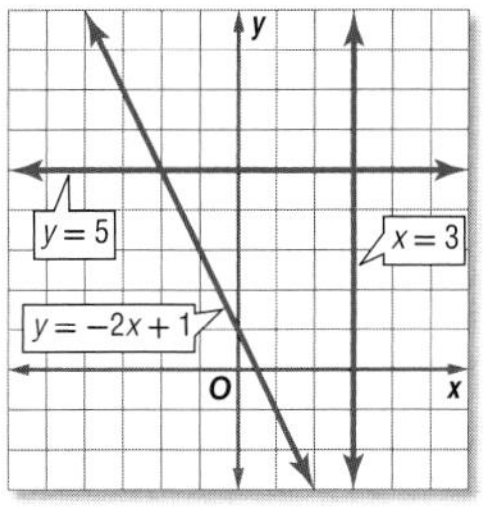

From the graph, you can see that $y = 5$ is parallel to the x-axis and $x = 3$ is parallel to the y-axis. Therefore, they are perpendicular. None of the lines are parallel.

Check Your Progress

3. Determine whether the graphs of $6x - 2y = -2$, $y = 3x - 4$, and $y = 4$ are *parallel* or *perpendicular*. Explain. $y = 3x - 4$ and $6x - 2y = -2$ are parallel since both have slope 3. None of the lines are perpendicular.

Personal Tutor glencoe.com

You can write the equation of a line perpendicular to a given line if you know a point on the line and the equation of the given line.

StudyTip

Visualize the Problem Graph the given equation on a coordinate grid and plot the given point. Using a ruler, draw a line perpendicular to the given line that passes through the point.

EXAMPLE 4 Perpendicular Line Through a Given Point

Write an equation in slope-intercept form for the line that passes through $(-4, 6)$ and is perpendicular to the graph of $2x + 3y = 12$.

Step 1 Find the slope of the given line by solving the equation for y.

$2x + 3y = 12$	Original equation
$2x - 2x + 3y = -2x + 12$	Subtract $2x$ from each side.
$3y = -2x + 12$	Simplify.
$\frac{3y}{3} = \frac{-2x + 12}{3}$	Divide each side by 3.
$y = -\frac{2}{3}x + 4$	Simplify.

The slope is $-\frac{2}{3}$.

Step 2 The slope of the perpendicular line is the opposite reciprocal of $-\frac{2}{3}$ or $\frac{3}{2}$. Find the equation of the perpendicular line.

$y - y_1 = m(x - x_1)$	Point-slope form
$y - 6 = \frac{3}{2}(x - (-4))$	$(x_1, y_1) = (-4, 6)$ and $m = \frac{3}{2}$
$y - 6 = \frac{3}{2}(x + 4)$	Simplify.
$y - 6 = \frac{3}{2}x + 6$	Distributive Property
$y - 6 + 6 = \frac{3}{2}x + 6 + 6$	Add 6 to each side.
$y = \frac{3}{2}x + 12$	Simplify.

Check Your Progress

4. Write an equation in slope-intercept form for the line that passes through $(4, 7)$ and is perpendicular to the graph of $y = \frac{2}{3}x - 1$. $y = -\frac{3}{2}x + 13$

Personal Tutor glencoe.com

Differentiated Instruction

AL ELL

Kinesthetic Students may be familiar with the terms *parallel* and *perpendicular*. However, before covering the examples, you may want students to use rulers to draw parallel and perpendicular lines on graph paper.

Additional Examples

2 **GEOMETRY** The height of a trapezoid is the length of a segment that is perpendicular to both bases. In trapezoid *ARTP*, $\overline{AP}$ and $\overline{RT}$ are bases.

a. Can $\overline{EZ}$ be used to measure the height of the trapezoid? Explain.

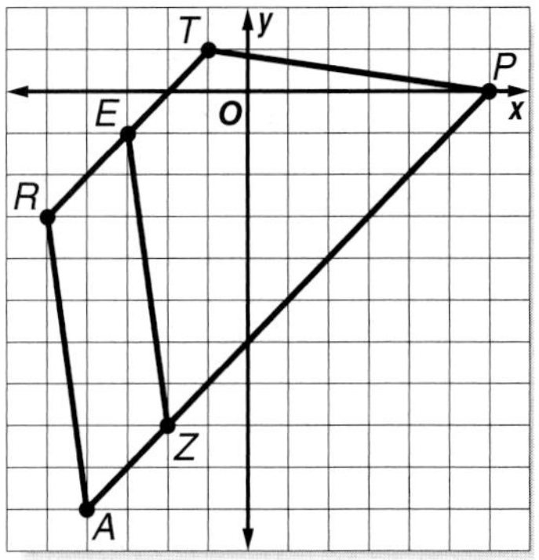

No, the slope of $\overline{RT}$ is 1, and the slope of $\overline{EZ}$ is -7. Since $1(-7) \neq -1$, $\overline{EZ}$ is not perpendicular to $\overline{RT}$. So, it cannot be used to measure the height of *ARTP*.

b. Are the bases parallel? Yes, both $\overline{RT}$ and $\overline{AP}$ have a slope of 1.

3 Determine whether the graphs of $3x + y = 12$, $y = \frac{1}{3}x + 2$, and $2x - 6y = -5$ are *parallel* or *perpendicular*. Explain.

$y = \frac{1}{3}x + 2$ is parallel to $2x - 6y = -5$ because they have equal slopes. $x + 3y = 12$ is perpendicular to them both because the product of their slopes, $\frac{1}{3}$ and -3, is -1.

4 Write an equation in slope-intercept form for the line that passes through $(4, -1)$ and is perpendicular to the graph of $7x - 2y = 3$. $y = -\frac{2}{7}x + \frac{1}{7}$

Watch Out!

Preventing Errors Encourage students to understand the process used instead of simply the mechanics. For example, what do they know from the given information? What do they know about perpendicular lines? What do they need to know to write a new equation?

Tips for New Teachers

Geometry Concept The fact that two nonvertical lines are perpendicular if and only if the product of their slopes is −1 depends on the considerations of similar triangles. This should be made clear to students, with the added assurance that they will learn the concept in geometry.

3 PRACTICE

Formative Assessment

Use Exercises 1–10 to check for understanding.

Use the chart at the bottom of the next page to customize assignments for your students.

Additional Answer

4. Since $\overline{EH}$ and $\overline{FG}$ are parallel to the y-axis, they are parallel. Since $\overline{EF}$ and $\overline{HG}$ are parallel to the x-axis they are parallel and $\overline{EH}$ is perpendicular to $\overline{EF}$ and $\overline{HG}$. Likewise, $\overline{FG}$ is perpendicular to $\overline{EF}$ and $\overline{HG}$. The slope of $\overline{EG}$ is −1 and the slope of $\overline{FH}$ is 1. Since the slopes are opposite reciprocals, $\overline{EG} \perp \overline{FH}$. The quadrilateral is a square.

Concept Summary — Parallel and Perpendicular Lines

For Your FOLDABLE

	Parallel Lines	Perpendicular Lines
Words	Two nonvertical lines are parallel if they have the same slope.	Two nonvertical lines are perpendicular if the product of their slopes is −1.
Symbols	$\overleftrightarrow{AB} \parallel \overleftrightarrow{CD}$	$\overleftrightarrow{EF} \perp \overleftrightarrow{GH}$
Models	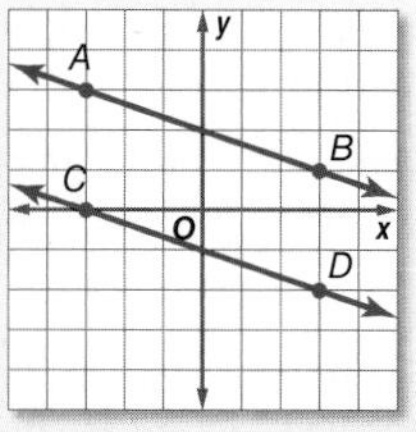	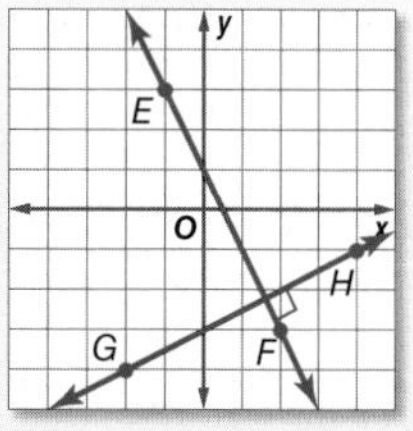

Check Your Understanding

Example 1 p. 237

Write an equation in slope-intercept form for the line that passes through the given point and is parallel to the graph of the given equation.

1. $(-1, 2), y = \frac{1}{2}x - 3$ $y = \frac{1}{2}x + 2\frac{1}{2}$
2. $(0, 4), y = -4x + 5$ $y = -4x + 4$

Example 2 p. 238

3. **GARDENS** A garden is in the shape of a quadrilateral with vertices $A(-2, 1)$, $B(3, -3)$, $C(5, 7)$, and $D(-3, 4)$. Two paths represented by $\overline{AC}$ and $\overline{BD}$ cut across the garden. Are the paths perpendicular? Explain.

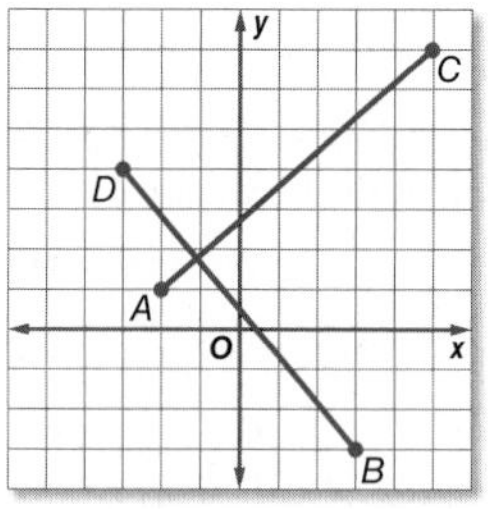

4. **GEOMETRY** A square is a quadrilateral that has opposite sides parallel, consecutive sides that are perpendicular, and diagonals that are perpendicular. Determine whether the quadrilateral is a square. Explain. **See margin.**

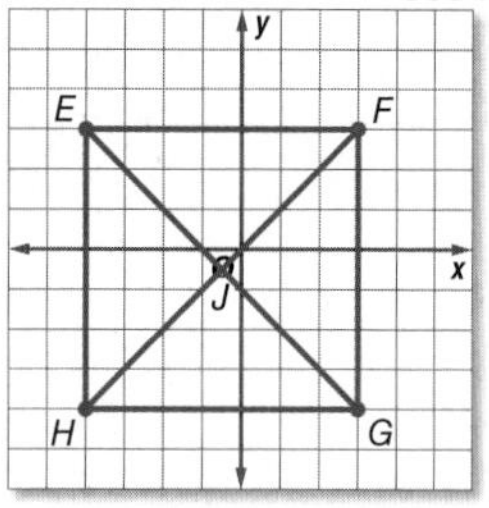

3. Slope of $\overline{AC} = \frac{1-7}{-2-5}$ or $\frac{6}{7}$; slope of $\overline{BD} = \frac{-3-4}{3-(-3)}$ or $-\frac{7}{6}$; the paths are perpendicular.
5. $y = -2x$ and the other two graphs are perpendicular; slopes are opposite reciprocals; $2y = x$ and $4y = 2x + 4$ are parallel; equal slopes.

Example 3 p. 239

Determine whether the graphs of the following equations are *parallel* or *perpendicular*. Explain.

5. $y = -2x, 2y = x, 4y = 2x + 4$
6. $y = \frac{1}{2}x, 3y = x, y = -\frac{1}{2}x$ None are parallel or perpendicular; none of the slopes are equal or opposite reciprocals.

Example 4 p. 239

Write an equation in slope-intercept form for the line that passes through the given point and is perpendicular to the graph of the equation.

7. $(-2, 3), y = -\frac{1}{2}x - 4$ $y = 2x + 7$
8. $(-1, 4), y = 3x + 5$ $y = -\frac{1}{3}x + 3\frac{2}{3}$
9. $(2, 3), 2x + 3y = 4$ $y = \frac{3}{2}x$
10. $(3, 6), 3x - 4y = -2$ $y = -\frac{4}{3}x + 10$

240 Chapter 4 Linear Functions and Relations

Practice and Problem Solving

● = **Step-by-Step Solutions** begin on page R12.
Extra Practice begins on page 815.

Example 1 p. 237

Write an equation in slope-intercept form for the line that passes through the given point and is parallel to the graph of the given equation.

11. $(3, -2), y = x + 4$ **12.** $(4, -3), y = 3x - 5$ **13.** $(0, 2), y = -5x + 8$

14. $(-4, 2), y = -\frac{1}{2}x + 6$ **15.** $(-2, 3), y = -\frac{3}{4}x + 4$ **16.** $(9, 12), y = 13x - 4$

Example 2 p. 238

17. GEOMETRY A trapezoid is a quadrilateral that has exactly one pair of parallel opposite sides. Is *ABCD* a trapezoid? Explain your reasoning.

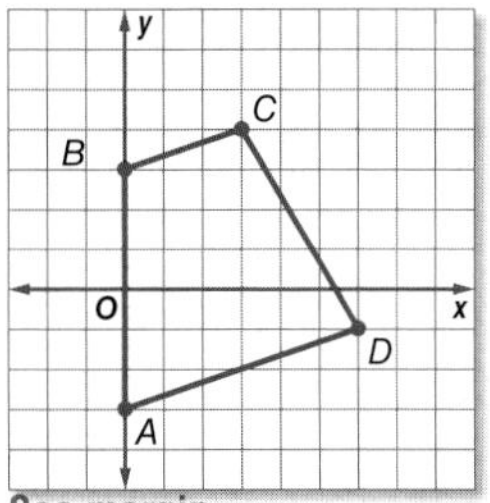

See margin.

18. GEOMETRY *CDEF* is a kite. Are the diagonals of the kite perpendicular? Explain your reasoning.

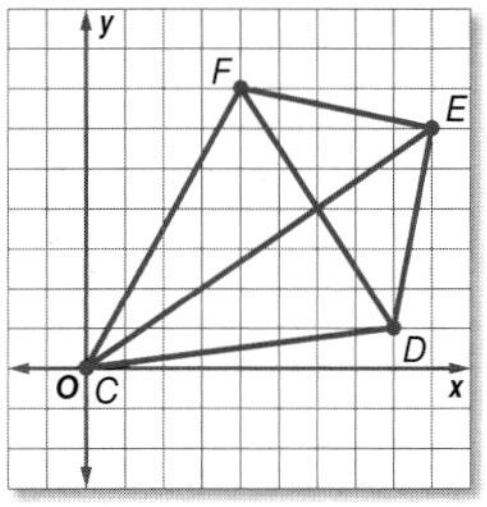

19. Determine whether the graphs of $y = -6x + 4$ and $y = \frac{1}{6}x$ are perpendicular. Explain.

20. MAPS On a map, Elmwood Drive passes through $R(4, -11)$ and $S(0, -9)$, and Taylor Road passes through $J(6, -2)$ and $K(4, -5)$. If they are straight lines, are the two streets perpendicular? Explain. No; the slopes are $-\frac{1}{2}$ and $\frac{3}{2}$.

Example 3 p. 239

Determine whether the graphs of the following equations are *parallel* or *perpendicular*. Explain.

21. $2x - 8y = -24, 4x + y = -2, x - 4y = 4$

22. $3x - 9y = 9, 3y = x + 12, 2x - 6y = 12$

21. $2x - 8y = -24$ and $4x + y = -2$ are perpendicular; $2x - 8y = -24$ and $x - 4y = 4$ are parallel.
22. All of the lines are parallel.

Example 4 p. 239

Write an equation in slope-intercept form for the line that passes through the given point and is perpendicular to the graph of the equation. 23–28. See margin.

23. $(-3, -2), y = -2x + 4$ **24.** $(-5, 2), y = \frac{1}{2}x - 3$ **25.** $(-4, 5), y = \frac{1}{3}x + 6$

26. $(2, 6), y = -\frac{1}{4}x + 3$ **27.** $(3, 8), y = 5x - 3$ **28.** $(4, -2), y = 3x + 5$

B **Write an equation in slope-intercept form for a line perpendicular to the graph of the equation that passes through the *x*-intercept of that line.** 29–31. See margin.

29. $y = -\frac{1}{2}x - 4$ **30.** $y = \frac{2}{3}x - 6$ **31.** $y = 5x + 3$

32. Write an equation in slope-intercept form for the line that is perpendicular to the graph of $3x + 2y = 8$ and passes through the *y*-intercept of that line. $y = \frac{2}{3}x + 4$

Determine whether the graphs of each pair of equations are *parallel*, *perpendicular*, or *neither*.

33. $y = 4x + 3$, $4x + y = 3$ neither

34. $y = -2x$, $2x + y = 3$ parallel

35. $3x + 5y = 10$, $5x - 3y = -6$ perpendicular

36. $-3x + 4y = 8$, $-4x + 3y = -6$ neither

37. $2x + 5y = 15$, $3x + 5y = 15$ neither

38. $2x + 7y = -35$, $4x + 14y = -42$ parallel

11. $y = x - 5$
12. $y = 3x - 15$
13. $y = -5x + 2$
14. $y = -\frac{1}{2}x$
15. $y = -\frac{3}{4}x + 1\frac{1}{2}$
16. $y = 13x - 105$
18. The slope of $\overline{CE}$ is $\frac{2}{3}$ and the slope of $\overline{DF}$ is $-\frac{3}{2}$. The diagonals are perpendicular because the slopes are opposite reciprocals.
19. Yes; the slopes are -6 and $\frac{1}{6}$.

Exercise Alert

Grid Paper For Exercises 42, 46 and 70–73, students will need grid paper.

Additional Answers

17. Yes; the line containing $\overline{AD}$ and the line containing $\overline{BC}$ have the same slope, $\frac{1}{3}$. Therefore, one pair of sides is parallel. The slope of $\overline{AB}$ is undefined and the slope of $\overline{CD}$ is $-\frac{5}{3}$.

23. $y = \frac{1}{2}x - \frac{1}{2}$

24. $y = -2x - 8$

25. $y = -3x - 7$

26. $y = 4x - 2$

27. $y = -\frac{1}{5}x + 8\frac{3}{5}$

28. $y = -\frac{1}{3}x - \frac{2}{3}$

29. $y = 2x + 16$

30. $y = -\frac{3}{2}x + \frac{27}{2}$

31. $y = -\frac{1}{5}x - \frac{3}{25}$

Differentiated Homework Options

Level	Assignment	Two-Day Option	
AL Basic	11–28, 45–73	11–27 odd, 49–52	12–28 even, 45–48, 53–73
OL Core	11–37 odd, 39–43, 45–73	11–28, 49–52	29–43, 45–48, 53–73
BL Advanced	33–69, (optional: 70–73)		

Real-World Career

Archaeologist
An archaeologist studies artifacts of ancient civilizations to piece together information about ancient societies. Archaeology is considered a branch of anthropology. Most archaeologists have a master's degree at least.

41. Yes; the slope of the line through the hair accessories and the pottery is $-\frac{7}{2}$. The slope of the line through the endpoints of the pole is $\frac{2}{7}$, so the lines are perpendicular.

39. Write an equation of the line that is parallel to the graph of $y = 7x - 3$ and passes through the origin. **$y = 7x$**

40. EXCAVATION Scientists excavating a dinosaur mapped the site on a coordinate plane. If one bone lies from $(-5, 8)$ to $(10, -1)$ and a second bone lies from $(-10, -3)$ to $(-5, -6)$, are the bones parallel? Explain. **Yes; both have a slope of $-\frac{3}{5}$.**

41. ARCHAEOLOGY In the ruins of an ancient civilization, an archaeologist found pottery at $(2, 6)$ and hair accessories at $(4, -1)$. A pole is found with one end at $(7, 10)$ and the other end at $(14, 12)$. Is the pole perpendicular to the line through the pottery and the hair accessories? Explain.

42. GRAPHICS To create a design on a computer, Andeana must enter the coordinates for points on the design. One line segment she drew has endpoints of $(-2, 1)$ and $(4, 3)$. The other coordinates that Andeana entered are $(2, -7)$ and $(8, -3)$. Could these points be the vertices of a rectangle? Explain. **See margin.**

43. MULTIPLE REPRESENTATIONS In this problem, you will explore parallel and perpendicular lines. **a–c. See Ch. 4 Answer Appendix.**

a. **GRAPHICAL** Graph the points $A(-3, 3)$, $B(3, 5)$, and $C(-4, 0)$ on a coordinate plane.

b. **ANALYTICAL** Determine the coordinates of a fourth point D that would form a parallelogram. Explain your reasoning.

c. **ANALYTICAL** What is the minimum number of points that could be moved to make the parallelogram a rectangle? Describe which points should be moved, and explain why.

H.O.T. Problems

Use **H**igher-**O**rder **T**hinking Skills

44. CHALLENGE If the line through $(-2, 4)$ and $(5, d)$ is parallel to the graph of $y = 3x + 4$, what is the value of d? **25**

45. REASONING Is a horizontal line perpendicular to a vertical line *sometimes*, *always*, or *never*? Explain your reasoning. **Always; horizontal lines and vertical lines intersect at right angles.**

46. OPEN ENDED Graph a line that is parallel and a line that is perpendicular to $y = 2x - 1$. **See margin.**

47. FIND THE ERROR Carmen and Chase are finding an equation of the line that is perpendicular to the graph of $y = \frac{1}{3}x + 2$ and passes through the point $(-3, 5)$. Is either of them correct? Explain your reasoning.

Carmen	Chase
$y - 5 = -3[x - (-3)]$	$y - 5 = 3[x - (-3)]$
$y - 5 = -3(x + 3)$	$y - 5 = 3(x + 3)$
$y = -3x - 9 + 5$	$y = 3x + 9 + 5$
$y = -3x - 4$	$y = -3x + 14$

47. Carmen is correct; she correctly determined the slope of the perpendicular line.

48. WRITING IN MATH Illustrate how you can determine whether two lines are parallel or perpendicular. Write an equation for the graph that is parallel and an equation for the graph that is perpendicular to the line shown. Explain your reasoning. **See Ch. 4 Answer Appendix.**

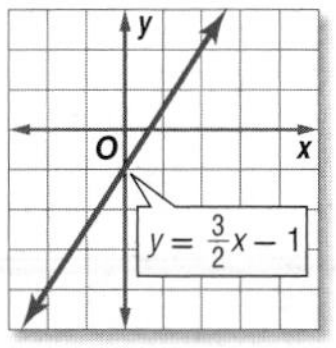

242 Chapter 4 Linear Functions and Relations

Study Guide and Intervention

CRM pp. 24–25 AL OL ELL

NAME ________ DATE ________ PERIOD ________

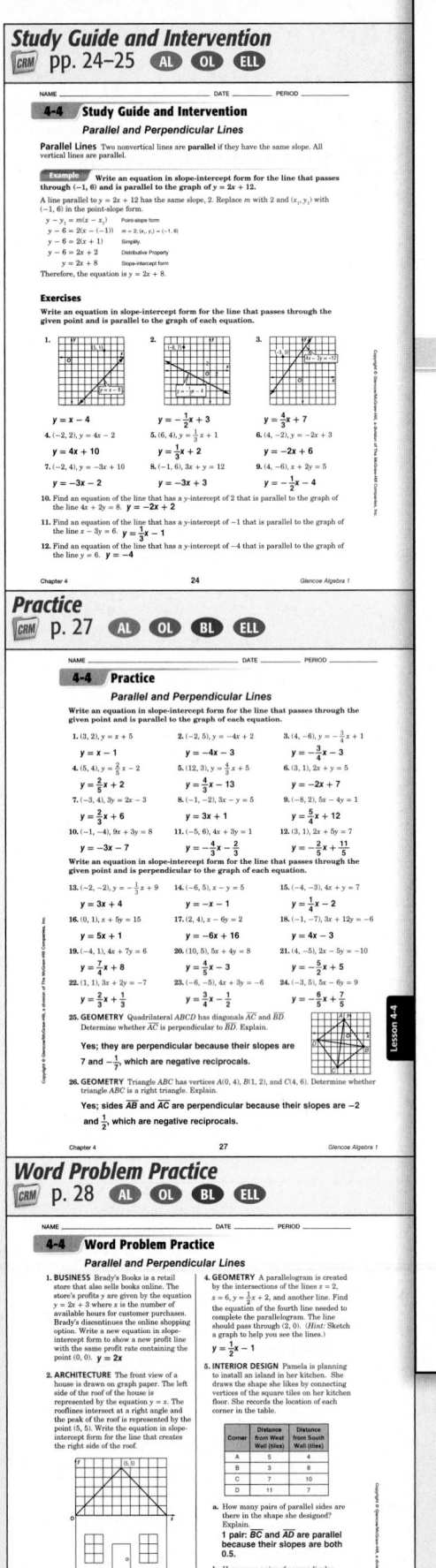

4-4 Study Guide and Intervention

Parallel and Perpendicular Lines

Parallel Lines Two nonvertical lines are **parallel** if they have the same slope. All vertical lines are parallel.

Example **Write an equation in slope-intercept form for the line that passes through $(-1, 6)$ and is parallel to the graph of $y = 2x + 12$.**

A line parallel to $y = 2x + 12$ has the same slope, 2. Replace m with 2 and (x_1, y_1) with $(-1, 6)$ in the point-slope form.

$y - y_1 = m(x - x_1)$	Point-slope form
$y - 6 = 2(x - (-1))$	$m = 2$; $(x_1, y_1) = (-1, 6)$
$y - 6 = 2(x + 1)$	Simplify.
$y - 6 = 2x + 2$	Distributive Property
$y = 2x + 8$	Slope-intercept form

Therefore, the equation is $y = 2x + 8$.

Exercises

Write an equation in slope-intercept form for the line that passes through the given point and is parallel to the graph of each equation.

1. 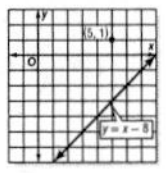

$y = x - 4$

2. 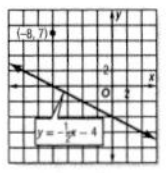

$y = -\frac{1}{2}x + 3$

3. 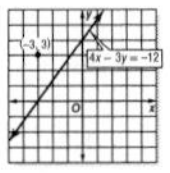

$y = \frac{4}{3}x + 7$

4. $(-2, 2)$, $y = 4x - 2$ **$y = 4x + 10$**
5. $(6, 4)$, $y = \frac{1}{3}x + 1$ **$y = \frac{1}{3}x + 2$**
6. $(4, -2)$, $y = -2x + 3$ **$y = -2x + 6$**
7. $(-2, 4)$, $y = -3x + 10$ **$y = -3x - 2$**
8. $(-1, 6)$, $3x + y = 12$ **$y = -3x + 3$**
9. $(4, -6)$, $x + 2y = 5$ **$y = -\frac{1}{2}x - 4$**
10. Find an equation of the line that has a y-intercept of 2 that is parallel to the graph of the line $4x + 2y = 8$. **$y = -2x + 2$**
11. Find an equation of the line that has a y-intercept of -1 that is parallel to the graph of the line $x - 3y = 6$. **$y = \frac{1}{3}x - 1$**
12. Find an equation of the line that has a y-intercept of -4 that is parallel to the graph of the line $y = 6$. **$y = -4$**

Chapter 4 24 Glencoe Algebra 1

Practice

CRM p. 27 AL OL BL ELL

NAME ________ DATE ________ PERIOD ________

4-4 Practice

Parallel and Perpendicular Lines

Write an equation in slope-intercept form for the line that passes through the given point and is parallel to the graph of each equation.

1. $(3, 2)$, $y = x + 5$ **$y = x - 1$**
2. $(-2, 5)$, $y = -4x + 2$ **$y = -4x - 3$**
3. $(4, -6)$, $y = -\frac{3}{4}x + 1$ **$y = -\frac{3}{4}x - 3$**
4. $(5, 4)$, $y = \frac{2}{5}x - 2$ **$y = \frac{2}{5}x + 2$**
5. $(12, 3)$, $y = \frac{4}{3}x + 5$ **$y = \frac{4}{3}x - 13$**
6. $(3, 1)$, $2x + y = 5$ **$y = -2x + 7$**
7. $(-3, 4)$, $3y = 2x - 3$ **$y = \frac{2}{3}x + 6$**
8. $(-1, -2)$, $3x - y = 5$ **$y = 3x + 1$**
9. $(-8, 2)$, $5x - 4y = 1$ **$y = \frac{5}{4}x + 12$**
10. $(-1, -4)$, $9x + 3y = 8$ **$y = -3x - 7$**
11. $(-5, 6)$, $4x + 3y = 1$ **$y = -\frac{4}{3}x - \frac{2}{3}$**
12. $(3, 1)$, $2x + 5y = 7$ **$y = -\frac{2}{5}x + \frac{11}{5}$**

Write an equation in slope-intercept form for the line that passes through the given point and is perpendicular to the graph of each equation.

13. $(-2, -2)$, $y = -\frac{1}{3}x + 9$ **$y = 3x + 4$**
14. $(-6, 5)$, $x - y = 5$ **$y = -x - 1$**
15. $(-4, -3)$, $4x + y = 7$ **$y = \frac{1}{4}x - 2$**
16. $(0, 1)$, $x + 5y = 15$ **$y = 5x + 1$**
17. $(2, 4)$, $x - 6y = 2$ **$y = -6x + 16$**
18. $(-1, -7)$, $3x + 12y = -6$ **$y = 4x - 3$**
19. $(-4, 1)$, $4x + 7y = 6$ **$y = \frac{7}{4}x + 8$**
20. $(10, 5)$, $5x + 4y = 8$ **$y = \frac{4}{5}x - 3$**
21. $(4, -5)$, $2x - 5y = -10$ **$y = -\frac{5}{2}x + 5$**
22. $(1, 1)$, $3x + 2y = -7$ **$y = \frac{2}{3}x + \frac{1}{3}$**
23. $(-6, -5)$, $4x + 3y = -6$ **$y = \frac{3}{4}x - \frac{1}{2}$**
24. $(-3, 5)$, $5x - 6y = 9$ **$y = -\frac{6}{5}x + \frac{7}{5}$**

25. **GEOMETRY** Quadrilateral $ABCD$ has diagonals $\overline{AC}$ and $\overline{BD}$. Determine whether $\overline{AC}$ is perpendicular to $\overline{BD}$. Explain.

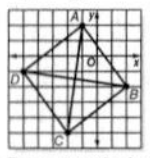

Yes; they are perpendicular because their slopes are 7 and $-\frac{1}{7}$, which are negative reciprocals.

26. **GEOMETRY** Triangle ABC has vertices $A(0, 4)$, $B(1, 2)$, and $C(4, 6)$. Determine whether triangle ABC is a right triangle. Explain.

Yes; sides $\overline{AB}$ and $\overline{AC}$ are perpendicular because their slopes are -2 and $\frac{1}{2}$, which are negative reciprocals.

Lesson 4-4

Chapter 4 27 Glencoe Algebra 1

Word Problem Practice

CRM p. 28 AL OL BL ELL

NAME ________ DATE ________ PERIOD ________

4-4 Word Problem Practice

Parallel and Perpendicular Lines

1. **BUSINESS** Brady's Books is a retail store that also sells books online. The store's profits y are given by the equation $y = 2x + 3$ where x is the number of available hours for customer purchases. Brady's discontinues the online shopping option. Write a new equation in slope-intercept form to show a new profit line with the same profit rate containing the point $(0, 0)$. **$y = 2x$**

2. **ARCHITECTURE** The front view of a house is drawn on graph paper. The left side of the roof of the house is represented by the equation $y = x$. The rooflines intersect at a right angle and the peak of the roof is represented by the point $(5, 5)$. Write the equation in slope-intercept form for the line that creates the right side of the roof.

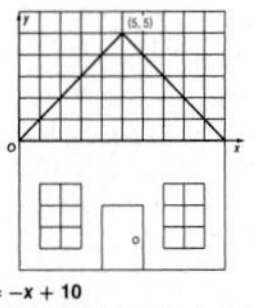

$y = -x + 10$

3. **ARCHAEOLOGY** An archaeologist is comparing the location of a jeweled box she just found to the location of a brick wall. The wall can be represented by the equation $y = -\frac{5}{3}x + 13$. The box is located at the point $(10, 9)$. Write an equation representing a line that is perpendicular to the wall and that passes through the location of the box. **$y = \frac{3}{5}x + 3$**

4. **GEOMETRY** A parallelogram is created by the intersections of the lines $x = 2$, $x = 6$, $y = \frac{1}{2}x + 2$, and another line. Find the equation of the fourth line needed to complete the parallelogram. The line should pass through $(2, 0)$. (*Hint:* Sketch a graph to help you see the lines.) **$y = \frac{1}{2}x - 1$**

5. **INTERIOR DESIGN** Pamela is planning to install an island in her kitchen. She draws the shape she likes by connecting vertices of the square tiles on her kitchen floor. She records the location of each corner in the table.

Corner	Distance from West Wall (tiles)	Distance from South Wall (tiles)
A	5	4
B	3	8
C	7	10
D	11	7

a. How many pairs of parallel sides are there in the shape she designed? Explain.
1 pair: $\overline{BC}$ and $\overline{AD}$ are parallel because their slopes are both 0.5.

b. How many pairs of perpendicular sides are there in the shape she designed? Explain.
2 pairs: $\overline{BC} \perp \overline{AB}$ and $\overline{AB} \perp \overline{AD}$ because $\overline{AB}$ has a slope of -2, which is the opposite reciprocal of the slopes of $\overline{BC}$ and $\overline{AD}$, 0.5.

c. What is the shape of her new island?
a trapezoid

Chapter 4 28 Glencoe Algebra 1

Enrichment

CRM p. 29 OL BL

NAME ________ DATE ________ PERIOD ________

4-4 Enrichment

Pencils of Lines

All of the lines that pass through a single point in the same plane are called a **pencil of lines**.

All lines with the same slope, but different intercepts, are also called a "pencil," a **pencil of parallel lines**.

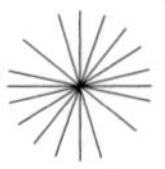

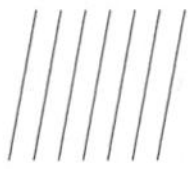

Graph some of the lines in each pencil.

1. A pencil of lines through the point $(1, 3)$

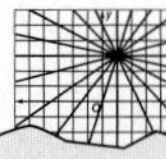

2. A pencil of lines described by $y - 4 = m(x - 2)$, where m is any real number

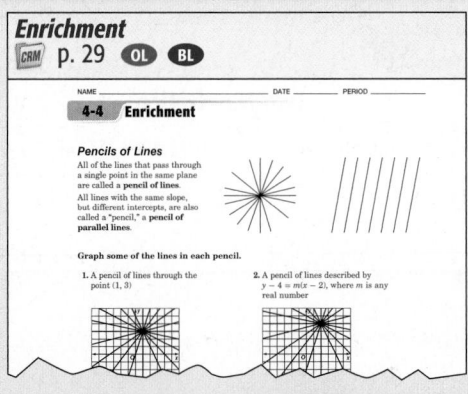

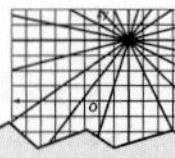

Multiple Representations In Exercise 43, students use a graph in the coordinate plane and analysis to compare parallelograms and rectangles.

PSAE PRACTICE 8.11.02, 8.11.07, 6.11.17

49. Which of the following is an algebraic translation of the following phrase? **B**

5 less than the quotient of a number and 8

A $5 - \frac{n}{8}$ **C** $5 - \frac{8}{n}$

B $\frac{n}{8} - 5$ **D** $\frac{8}{n} - 5$

50. A line through which two points would be parallel to a line with a slope of $\frac{3}{4}$? **F**

F (0, 5) and (−4, 2) **H** (0, 0) and (0, −2)

G (0, 2) and (−4, 1) **J** (0, −2) and (−4, −2)

51. Which equation best fits the data in the table? **B**

x	y
1	5
2	7
3	9
4	11

A $y = x + 4$
B $y = 2x + 3$
C $y = 7$
D $y = 4x - 5$

52. SHORT RESPONSE Tyler is filling his 6000-gallon pool at a constant rate. After 4 hours, the pool contained 800 gal. How many total hours will it take to completely fill the pool? **30 hours**

Spiral Review

53. $4x - y = -5$ **54.** $2x + y = 1$ **55.** $5x + y = -8$ **56.** $x - 2y = 12$ **57.** $5x - 6y = 14$ **58.** $2x + 5y = 26$

Write each equation in standard form. (Lesson 4-3)

53. $y - 13 = 4(x - 2)$ **54.** $y - 5 = -2(x + 2)$ **55.** $y + 3 = -5(x + 1)$

56. $y + 7 = \frac{1}{2}(x + 2)$ **57.** $y - 1 = \frac{5}{6}(x - 4)$ **58.** $y - 2 = -\frac{2}{5}(x - 8)$

59. CANOE RENTAL Latanya and her friends rented a canoe for 3 hours and paid a total of \$45. (Lesson 4-2)

a. Write a linear equation to find the total cost C of renting the canoe for h hours. $C = 10h + 15$

b. How much would it cost to rent the canoe for 8 hours? **\$95**

Write an equation of the line that passes through each point with the given slope. (Lesson 4-2)

60. $(5, -2), m = 3$ $y = 3x - 17$ **61.** $(-5, 4), m = -5$ $y = -5x - 21$ **62.** $(3, 0), m = -2$ $y = -2x + 6$

63. $(3, 5), m = 2$ $y = 2x - 1$ **64.** $(-3, -1), m = -3$ $y = -3x - 10$ **65.** $(-2, 4), m = -5$ $y = -5x - 6$

Simplify each expression. If not possible, write *simplified*. (Lesson 1-4)

66. $13m + m$ **14m** **67.** $14a^2 + 13b^2 + 27$ **simplified** **68.** $3(x + 2x)$ **9x**

69. FINANCIAL LITERACY At a Farmers' Market, merchants can rent a small table for \$5.00 and a large table for \$8.50. One time, 25 small and 10 large tables were rented. Another time, 35 small and 12 large were rented. (Lesson 1-2)

a. Write an expression to show the total amount of money collected. **25(5) + 10(8.5) + 35(5) + 12(8.5)**

b. Evaluate the expression. **\$487**

Skills Review

70–73. See Ch. 4 Answer Appendix.

Express each relation as a graph. Then determine the domain and range. (Lesson 1-6)

70. {(3, 8), (3, 7), (2, −9), (1, −9), (−5, −3)} **71.** {(3, 4), (4, 3), (2, 2), (5, −4), (−4, 5)}

72. {(0, 2), (−5, 1), (0, 6), (−1, 9), (−4, −5)} **73.** {(7, 6), (3, 4), (4, 5), (−2, 6), (−3, 2)}

Watch Out!

Find the Error For Exercise 47, students should see that Carmen and Chase have used different slopes in the first equation. Explain to students that once they have identified a difference, it is that difference that they need to investigate.

4 ASSESS

Ticket Out the Door Ask students to write and graph a line whose equation is of the form $Ax + By = C$. Have students draw two lines parallel to this line and describe the characteristics of those lines in terms of A, B, and C.

Formative Assessment

Check for student understanding of concepts in Lessons 4-3 and 4-4.

CRM Quiz 2, p. 51

Additional Answers

42. No; The segment from (−2, 1) to (4, 3) is not perpendicular to the segment from (4, 3) to (8, −3).

46. Sample answer:

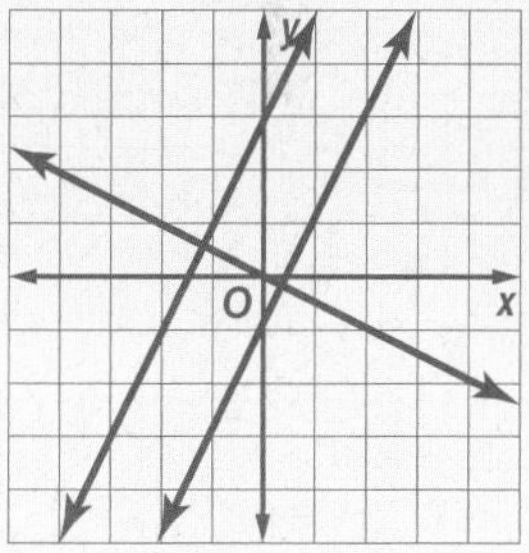

Differentiated Instruction OL BL

Extension Write $A(-4, -1)$, $B(1, 4)$, $C(4, 1)$, and $D(-1, -4)$ on the board. Ask students to determine what geometric figure is made if they were to connect these points to get a polygon. Ask students to justify their answer. Rectangle; the slope of $\overline{AB}$ is 1. The slope of $\overline{CD}$ is 1. So $\overline{AB}$ is parallel to $\overline{CD}$. The slope of $\overline{AD}$ is −1. The slope of $\overline{BC}$ is −1. So $\overline{AD}$ is parallel to $\overline{BC}$. This makes the figure a parallelogram. Since the slopes of $\overline{AB}$ and $\overline{BC}$ are negative reciprocals of each other, $\overline{AB}$ and $\overline{BC}$ are perpendicular. This makes the figure a rectangle. Since the four sides are not of equal length, the figure is not a square.

CHAPTER 4 Mid-Chapter Quiz

Formative Assessment

Use the Mid-Chapter Quiz to assess students' progress in the first half of the chapter.

For problems answered incorrectly, have students review the lessons indicated in parentheses.

ExamView Assessment Suite Customize and create multiple versions of your Mid-Chapter Test and their answer keys.

FOLDABLES® Follow-Up

Before students complete the Mid-Chapter Quiz, encourage them to review the information for Lessons 4-1 through 4-4 in their Foldables.

CHAPTER 4 Mid-Chapter Quiz

Lessons 4-1 through 4-4

IL Learning Standards 8.B.4b, 8.C.4b

Write an equation in slope-intercept form for each graph shown. (Lesson 4-1)

1. 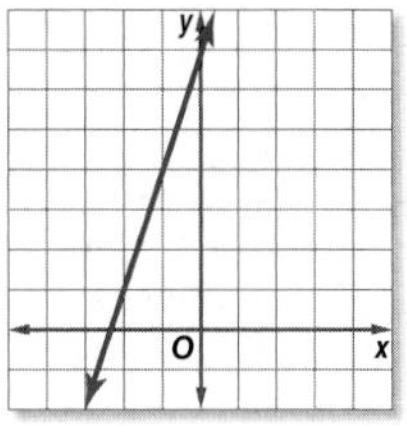 $y = 3x + 7$

2. 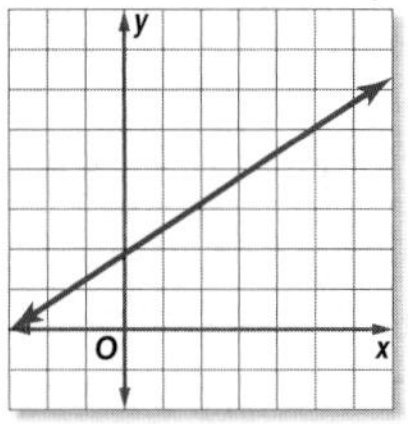 $y = \frac{3}{5}x + 2$

Graph each equation. (Lesson 4-1) **3–4. See Ch. 4 Answer Appendix.**

3. $y = 2x + 3$
4. $y = \frac{1}{3}x - 2$

5. **BOATS** Write an equation in slope-intercept form for the total rental cost C for a pontoon boat used for t hours. (Lesson 4-1) $C = 60t + 20$

Write an equation of the line with the given conditions. (Lesson 4-2)

6. (2, 5); slope 3 $y = 3x - 1$
7. (−3, −1), slope $\frac{1}{2}$ $y = \frac{1}{2}x + \frac{1}{2}$
8. (−3, 4), (1, 12) $y = 2x + 10$
9. (−1, 6), (2, 4) $y = -\frac{2}{3}x + \frac{16}{3}$
10. (2, 1), slope 0 $y = 1$

11. **MULTIPLE CHOICE** Write an equation of the line that passes through the point (0, 0) and has slope −4. (Lesson 4-2) **C**
    - A $y = x - 4$
    - B $y = x + 4$
    - C $y = -4x$
    - D $y = 4 - x$

Write an equation in point-slope form for the line that passes through each point with the given slope. (Lesson 4-3)

12. (1, 4), $m = 6$ $y - 4 = 6(x - 1)$
13. (−2, −1), $m = -3$ $y + 1 = -3(x + 2)$
14. Write an equation in point-slope form for the line that passes through the point (8, 3), $m = -2$. (Lesson 4-3) $y - 3 = -2(x - 8)$
15. Write $y + 3 = \frac{1}{2}(x - 5)$ in standard form. (Lesson 4-3) $x - 2y = 11$
16. Write $y + 4 = -7(x - 3)$ in slope-intercept form. (Lesson 4-3) $y = -7x + 17$

Write each equation in standard form. (Lesson 4-3)

17. $y - 5 = -2(x - 3)$ $2x + y = 11$
18. $y + 4 = \frac{2}{3}(x - 3)$ $2x - 3y = 18$

Write each equation in slope-intercept form. (Lesson 4-3)

19. $y - 3 = 4(x + 3)$ $y = 4x + 15$
20. $y + 1 = \frac{1}{2}(x - 8)$ $y = \frac{1}{2}x - 5$

21. **MULTIPLE CHOICE** Determine whether the graphs of the pair of equations are *parallel*, *perpendicular*, or *neither*. (Lesson 4-4) **F**

$$y = -6x + 8$$
$$3x + \frac{1}{2}y = -3$$

- F parallel
- G perpendicular
- H neither
- J not enough information

Write an equation in slope-intercept form for the line that passes through the given point and is perpendicular to the graph of the equation. (Lesson 4-4)

22. (3, −4); $y = -\frac{1}{3}x - 5$ $y = 3x - 13$
23. (0, −3); $y = -2x + 4$ $y = \frac{1}{2}x - 3$
24. (−4, −5); $-4x + 5y = -6$ $y = -\frac{5}{4}x - 10$
25. (−1, −4); $-x - 2y = 0$ $y = 2x - 2$

Intervention Planner

Tier 1 On Level	Tier 2 Strategic Intervention approaching grade level	Tier 3 Intensive Intervention 2 or more grades below level
If students miss about 25% of the exercises or less,	**If** students miss about 50% of the exercises,	**If** students miss about 75% of the exercises,
Then choose a resource:	**Then** choose a resource:	**Then** use *Math Triumphs, Alg. 1,* Ch. 4
SE Lessons 4-1, 4-2, 4-3, and 4-4 **CRM** Skills Practice, pp. 7, 13, 19, and 26 **TE** Chapter Project, p. 210 **IL Math Online** Self-Check Quiz	**CRM** Study Guide and Intervention, Chapter 4, pp. 5, 11, 17, and 24 *Quick Review Math Handbook* **IL Math Online** Extra Examples, Personal Tutor, Homework Help	**IL Math Online** Extra Examples, Personal Tutor, Homework Help, Review Vocabulary

Scatter Plots and Lines of Fit

Why?

The graph shows the number of people from the United States who travel to other countries. The points do not all lie on the same line; however, you may be able to draw a line that is close to all of the points. That line would show a linear relationship between the year x and the number of travelers each year y. Generally, international travel has increased.

International Travel

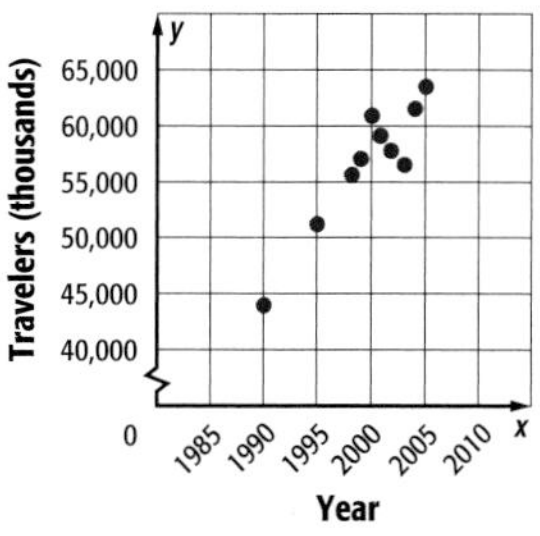

Source: *Statistical Abstract of the United States*

Then

You wrote linear equations given a point and the slope. (Lesson 4-3)

Now

- Investigate relationships between quantities by using points on scatter plots.
- Use lines of fit to make and evaluate predictions.

IL Learning Standards

8.A.4b Represent mathematical patterns and describe their properties using variables and mathematical symbols.
10.A.4c Predict from data using interpolation, extrapolation and trend lines, with and without the use of technology.

New Vocabulary

bivariate data
scatter plot
line of fit
linear interpolation

IL Math Online

glencoe.com

- Extra Examples
- Personal Tutor
- Self-Check Quiz
- Homework Help
- Math in Motion

Investigate Relationships Using Scatter Plots Data with two variables are called **bivariate data**. A **scatter plot** is a graph in which two sets of data are plotted as ordered pairs in a coordinate plane. Scatter plots are used to investigate a relationship between two quantities.

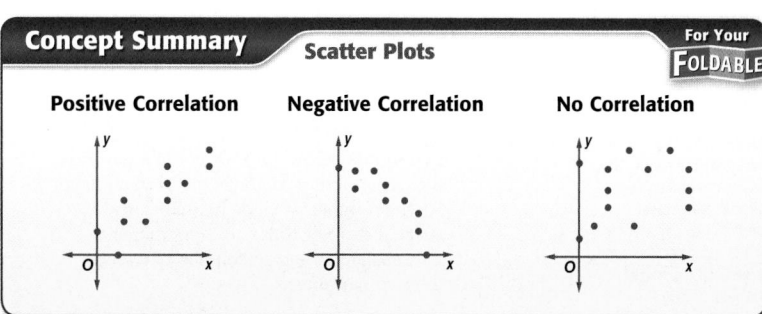

Concept Summary Scatter Plots — For Your FOLDABLE

Positive Correlation

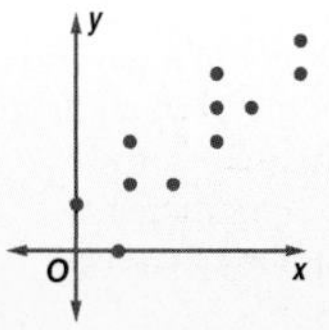

Negative Correlation

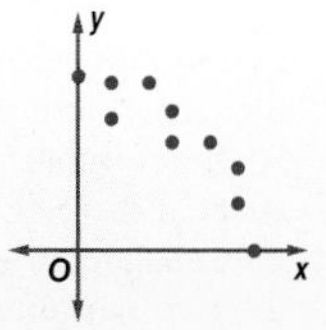

No Correlation

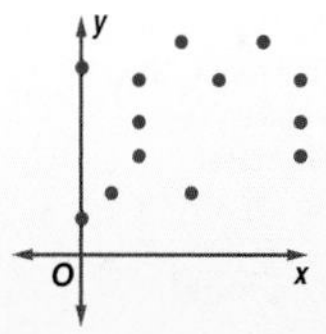

Real-World EXAMPLE 1 Evaluate a Correlation

WAGES Determine whether the graph shows a *positive*, *negative*, or *no* correlation. If there is a positive or negative correlation, describe its meaning in the situation.

Wages

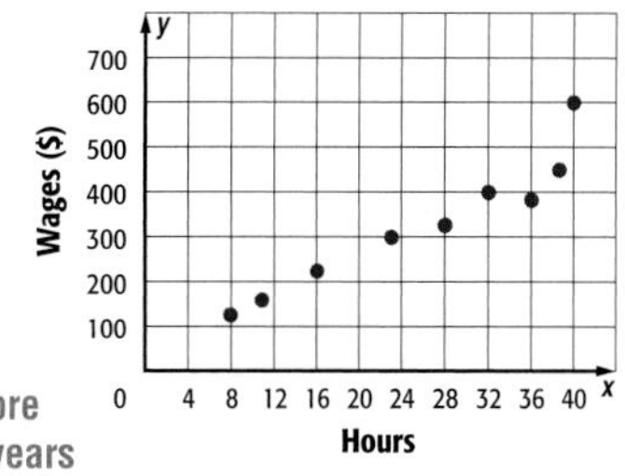

The graph shows a positive correlation. As the number of hours worked increases, the wages usually increase.

1. Positive, there are more travelers in the later years than in the early years.

Check Your Progress

1. Refer to the graph on international travel. Determine whether the graph shows a *positive*, *negative*, or *no* correlation. If there is a positive or negative correlation, describe its meaning.

Personal Tutor glencoe.com

1 FOCUS

Vertical Alignment

Before Lesson 4-5
Write linear equations given a point and the slope.

Lesson 4-5
Investigate relationships between quantities by using points on scatter plots.
Use lines of fit to make and evaluate predictions.

After Lesson 4-5
Write equations of best-fit lines and median-fit lines using linear regression.

2 TEACH

Scaffolding Questions

Have students read the *Why?* section of the lesson.

Ask:

- Would a line that is close to all of the points have a positive or negative slope? positive
- What would you do to find the equation of that line? Use two points on the line to write the equation.
- What type of graph would show that the relationship between the year and the number of travelers who travel to another country is decreasing? a line with a negative slope

Lesson 4-5 Resources

Resource	Approaching-Level	On-Level	Beyond-Level	English Learners
Teacher Edition	• Differentiated Instruction, p. 246	• Differentiated Instruction, pp. 246, 249	• Differentiated Instruction, p. 249	
Chapter Resource Masters	• Study Guide and Intervention, pp. 30–31 • Skills Practice, p. 32 • Practice, p. 33 • Word Problem Practice, p. 34 • Spreadsheet Activity, p. 36	• Study Guide and Intervention, pp. 30–31 • Skills Practice, p. 32 • Practice, p. 33 • Word Problem Practice, p. 34 • Enrichment, p. 35 • Spreadsheet Activity, p. 36	• Practice, p. 33 • Word Problem Practice, p. 34 • Enrichment, p. 35 • Spreadsheet Activity, p. 36	• Study Guide and Intervention, pp. 30–31 • Skills Practice, p. 32 • Practice, p. 33 • Spreadsheet Activity, p. 36
Transparencies	• 5-Minute Check Transparency 4-5	• 5-Minute Check Transparency 4-5	• 5-Minute Check Transparency 4-5	• 5-Minute Check Transparency 4-5
Other	• Study Notebook • Teaching Algebra with Manipulatives	• Study Notebook • Teaching Algebra with Manipulatives	• Study Notebook	• Study Notebook • Teaching Algebra with Manipulatives

Investigate Relationships Using Scatter Plots

Example 1 shows how to determine whether the graph of real-world data shows a *positive correlation*, a *negative correlation*, or *no correlation*.

Formative Assessment

Use the Check Your Progress exercises after each Example to determine students' understanding of concepts.

Additional Example

1 **TECHNOLOGY** The graph shows the average number of students per computer in Maria's school. Determine whether the graph shows a *positive correlation*, a *negative correlation*, or *no correlation*. If there is a positive or negative correlation, describe its meaning in the situation.

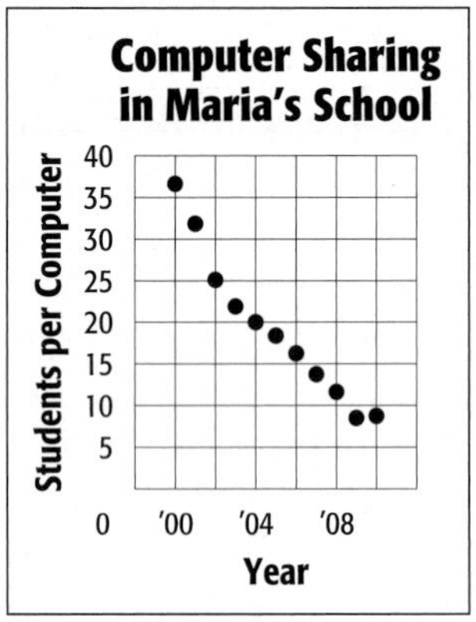

Negative correlation; sample answer: Each year, Maria's school has more computers, making the students-per-computer rate smaller.

Additional Examples also in Interactive Classroom PowerPoint® Presentations

IWB INTERACTIVE WHITEBOARD READY

StudyTip

Correlations
positive: as *x* increases, *y* increases
negative: as *x* increases, *y* decreases
no correlation: no relationship between *x* and *y*

Use Lines of Fit Scatter plots can show whether there is a trend in a set of data. When the data points all lie close to a line, a **line of fit** or *trend line* can model the trend.

Key Concept — Using a Linear Function to Model Data

For Your FOLDABLE

Step 1 Make a scatter plot. Determine whether any relationship exists in the data.

Step 2 Draw a line that seems to pass close to most of the data points.

Step 3 Use two points on the line of fit to write an equation for the line.

Step 4 Use the line of fit to make predictions.

Math *in Motion*, Interactive Lab glencoe.com

Real-World Link

The Kingda Ka roller coaster at Six Flags Great Adventure in Jackson, New Jersey, has broken three records: tallest roller coaster at 456 feet, fastest at 128 miles per hour, and largest vertical drop of 418 feet.

Source: Ultimate Roller Coaster

Real-World EXAMPLE 2 Write a Line of Fit

ROLLER COASTERS The table shows the largest vertical drops of nine roller coasters in the United States and the number of years after 1988 that they were opened. Identify the independent and the dependant variables. Is there a relationship in the data? If so, predict the vertical drop in a roller coaster built 25 years after 1988.

Years Since 1988	1	3	5	8	12	12	12	13	15
Vertical Drop (ft)	151	155	225	230	306	300	255	255	400

Source: Ultimate Roller Coaster

Step 1 Make a scatter plot.

The independent variable is the year, and the dependent variable is the vertical drop. As the number of years increases, the vertical drop of roller coasters increases. There is a positive correlation between the two variables.

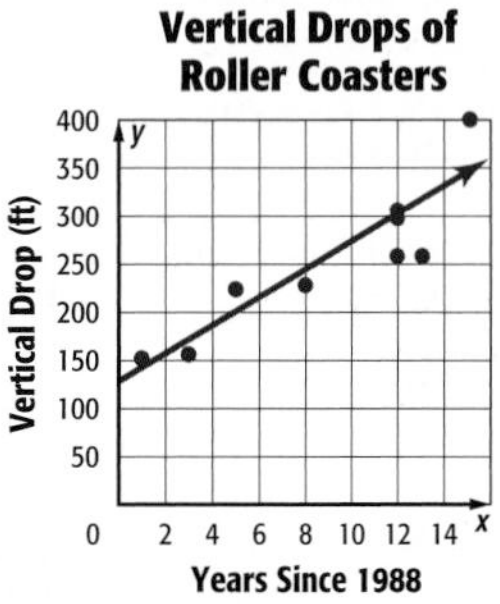

Step 2 Draw a line of fit.

No one line will pass through all of the data points. Draw a line that passes close to the points. A line of fit is shown.

Step 3 Write the slope-intercept form of an equation for the line of fit.

The line of fit passes close to (2, 150) and the data point (12, 300).

Find the slope.

$m = \frac{y_2 - y_1}{x_2 - x_1}$ $\quad (x_1, y_1) = (2, 150), (x_2, y_2) = (12, 300)$

$= \frac{300 - 150}{12 - 2}$

$= \frac{150}{10}$ or 15

Use $m = 15$ and either the point-slope form or the slope-intercept form to write the equation of the line of fit.

$y - y_1 = m(x - x_1)$

$y - 150 = 15(x - 2)$

$y - 150 = 15x - 30$

$y = 15x + 120$

A slope of 15 means that the vertical drops increased an average of 15 feet per year. To predict the vertical drop of a roller coaster built 25 years after 1988, substitute 25 for x in the equation. The vertical drop is $15(25) + 120$ or 495 feet.

Differentiated Instruction

AL OL

If students need more practice making and interpreting scatter plots,

Then have them make a scatter plot of their height (*x*-values) and age (*y*-values) for the first ten years of their life. Students estimate their heights as needed, but check to be sure estimates are reasonable. Ask them to draw a line of fit and write the slope-intercept form of an equation for the line. Then ask students to compare their current height with that derived from their equation.

Check Your Progress

See Ch. 4 Answer Appendix.

2. MUSIC The table shows the dollar value in millions for the sales of CDs for the year. Make a scatter plot and determine what relationship exists, if any.

Year	2000	2001	2002	2003	2004	2005
Sales	13,215	12,909	12,044	11,233	11,447	10,520

Personal Tutor glencoe.com

ReadingMath

Interpolation and Extrapolation The Latin prefix *inter-* means between, and the Latin prefix *extra-* means beyond.

In Lesson 4-2, you learned that linear extrapolation is used to predict values *outside* the range of the data. You can also use a linear equation to predict values *inside* the range of the data. This is called **linear interpolation**.

Real-World EXAMPLE 3 Use Interpolation or Extrapolation

TRAVEL Use the scatter plot to find the approximate number of United States travelers to international countries in 1996.

International Travel

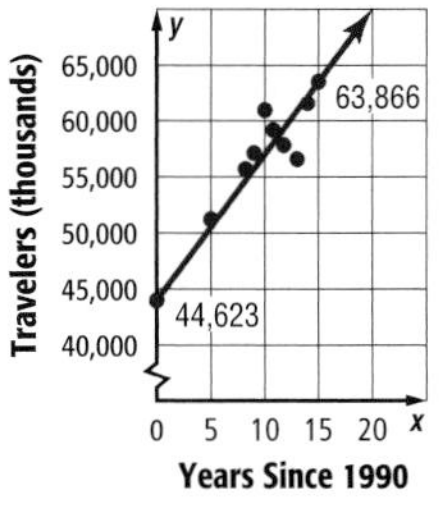

Source: *Statistical Abstract of the United States*

Step 1 Draw a line of fit. The line should be as close to as many points as possible.

Step 2 Write the slope-intercept form of the equation. The line of fit passes through (0, 44,623) and (15, 63,866).

Find the slope.

$m = \frac{y_2 - y_1}{x_2 - x_1}$ **Slope Formula**

$= \frac{63,866 - 44,623}{15 - 0}$ **$(x_1, y_1) = (0, 44,623)$, $(x_2, y_2) = (15, 63,866)$**

$= \frac{19,243}{15}$ **Simplify.**

Use $m = \frac{19,243}{15}$ and either the point-slope form or the slope-intercept form to write the equation of the line of fit.

$$y - y_1 = m(x - x_1)$$
$$y - 44,623 = \frac{19,243}{15}(x - 0)$$
$$y - 44,623 = \frac{19,243}{15}x$$
$$y = \frac{19,243}{15}x + 44,623$$

Step 3 Evaluate the function for $x = 1996 - 1990$ or 6.

$y = \frac{19,243}{15}x + 44,623$ **Equation of best-fit line**

$= \frac{19,243}{15}(6) + 44,623$ **$x = 6$**

$= 7697\frac{1}{5} + 44,623$ or $52,320\frac{1}{5}$ **Add.**

In 1996, there were approximately 52,320 thousand or 52,320,000 people who traveled from the United States to international countries.

Check Your Progress

3. MUSIC Use the equation for the line of fit in Check Your Progress 2 to estimate CD sales in 2015. $5715 million

Personal Tutor glencoe.com

Use Lines of Fit

Example 2 shows how to draw a scatter plot for real-world data, draw a line of fit, and then write the slope-intercept form of an equation for the line of fit. **Example 3** shows how to use the equation for the line of fit to predict values inside the range of the data for a real-world situation.

Additional Examples

2 **POPULATION** The table shows the growth of the world population. Identify the independent and dependent variables.

Make a scatter plot and determine what relationship, if any, exists in the data.

Year	Populations (millions)
1650	500
1850	1000
1930	2000
1975	4000
2004	6400

independent variable: year; dependent variable: population; positive correlation; sample answer: $y = 35.1x - 63,870$

World Population

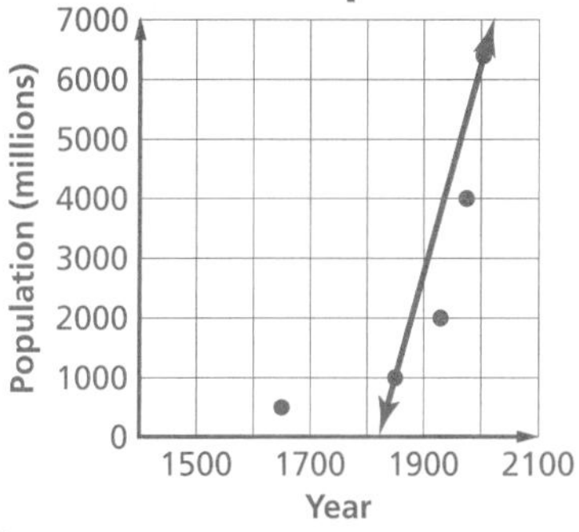

3 Use the equation for the line of fit in Additional Example 2 to predict the world's population in 2025. 7207.5 million

Focus on Mathematical Content

Scatter Plot A scatter plot has points unconnected by a line. These points can show trends in the relationship between two sets of data. If the points show a linear trend, you can draw a line of fit to model that trend. Once a line is drawn, you can find an equation of the line and use that equation to make predictions.

TEACH with TECH

INTERACTIVE WHITEBOARD Show a scatter plot on the board. Choose several students to draw lines that they believe fit the data. Have students explain why they chose to draw those particular lines.

Watch Out!

Student Misconceptions Remind students that predictions are only as valid as the equations used to find them. Therefore, there are as many predictions as there are equations that can be written from pairs of points.

3 PRACTICE

Formative Assessment

Use Exercises 1–3 to check for understanding.

Use the chart at the bottom of this page to customize assignments for your students.

Exercise Alert

Grid Paper For Exercises 3, 10–12, 17, 32–34, 42–43 students will need grid paper.

Additional Answers

3a–b. Median Age of Females When First Married

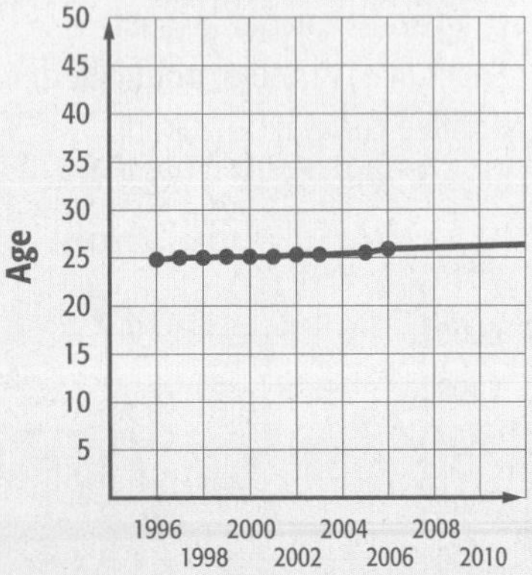

Positive; independent variable is the year and dependent variable is the median age of females when they were first married.

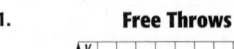

Check Your Understanding

Example 1 p. 245

Determine whether each graph shows a *positive*, *negative*, or *no* correlation. If there is a positive or negative correlation, describe its meaning in the situation.

1. Positive; the longer you practice free throws, the more free throws you will make.
2. Positive; the warmer the temperature, the more lemonade you sell.

1. **Free Throws**

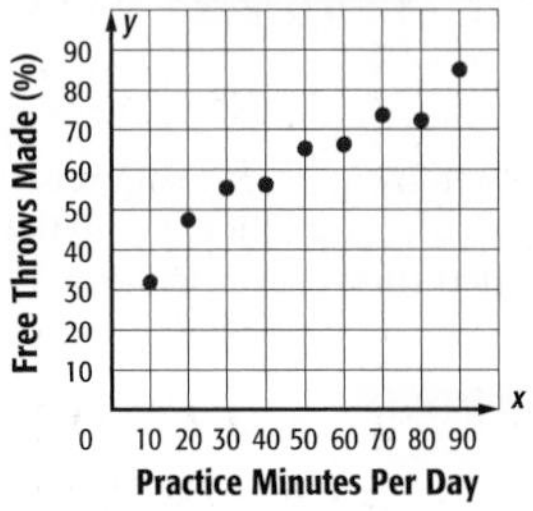

2. **Lemonade Sales**

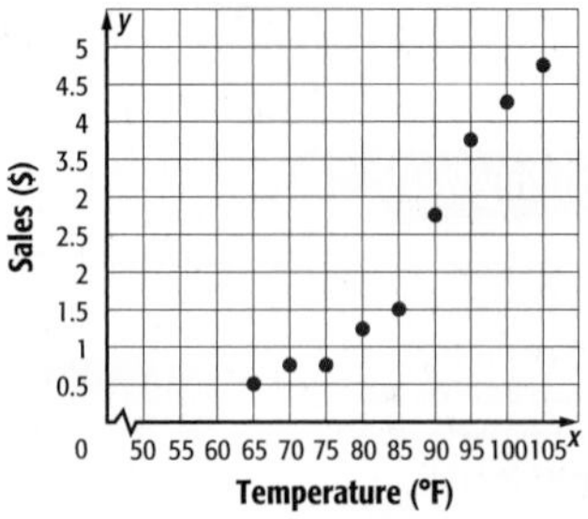

Example 2 p. 246

3. MARRIAGE The table shows the median age of females when they were first married.

a. Make a scatter plot and determine what relationship exists, if any, in the data. Identify the independent and the dependant variables. **a–b. See margin.**

b. Draw a line of fit for the scatter plot.

c. Write an equation in slope-intercept form for the line of fit.

3c. Sample answer: Using (1996, 24.8) and (2006, 25.9) and rounding, $y = 0.11x - 194.8$

Example 3 p. 247

d. Predict what the median age of females when they are first married will be in 2016. **Sample answer: 27.0**

e. Do you think the equation can give a reasonable estimate for the year 2056? Explain.
Yes, according to the equation, the median age would be 31.4, which is likely.

Year	Age
1996	24.8
1997	25.0
1998	25.0
1999	25.1
2000	25.1
2001	25.1
2002	25.3
2003	25.3
2005	25.5
2006	25.9

Source: U.S. Bureau of Census

Practice and Problem Solving

● = Step-by-Step Solutions begin on page R12.
Extra Practice begins on page 815.

Example 1 p. 245

Determine whether each graph shows a *positive*, *negative*, or *no* correlation. If there is a positive or negative correlation, describe its meaning in the situation.

4. Positive; the more tickets you buy, the more game prizes you will win.
5. Negative; the taller the NBA player, the lower his 3-point shooting percentage.

4. **Game Tickets at the Fair**

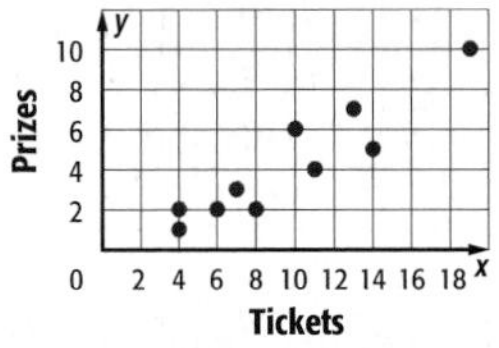

5 **NBA 3-Point Percentage**

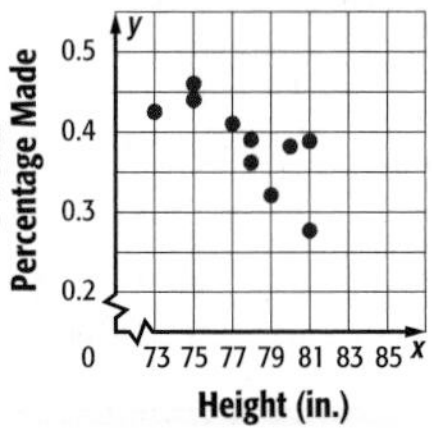

Differentiated Homework Options

Level	Assignment	Two-Day Option	
AL Basic	4–9, 13–14, 16–43	5–7, 18–21	4–8 even, 13–14, 16–17, 22–43
OL Core	5, 7, 9–14, 16–43	4–9, 18–21	9–14, 16–17, 22–43
BL Advanced	9–41, (optional: 42–43)		

6. Positive; the more years of formal education you receive, the higher your salary will be.
7. No; various vehicles give too many varying results for there to be a correlation.

6. Salaries

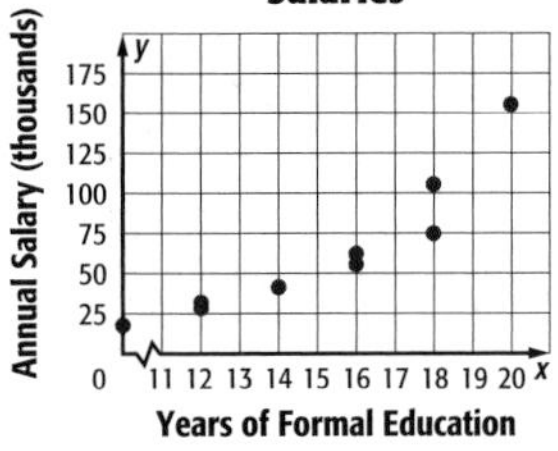

7 Gas Mileage of Various Vehicles

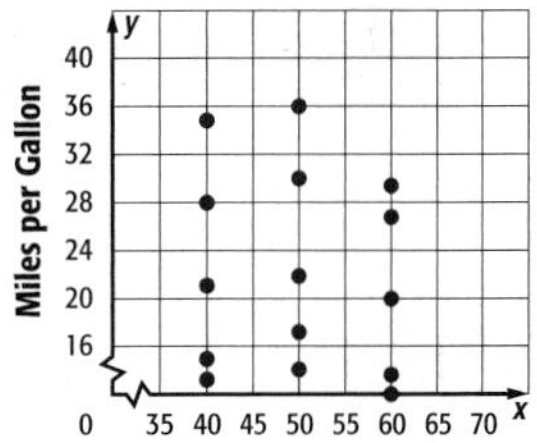

Examples 2 and 3
pp. 246-247

8. MILK Refer to the scatter plot of gallons of milk consumption per person for selected years.

Consumption of Milk in Gallons

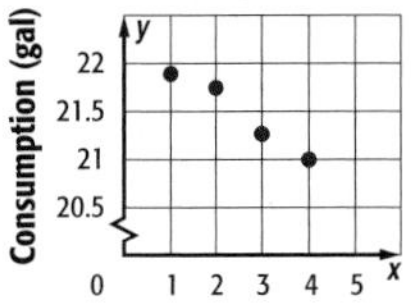

a. Use the points (2, 21.75) and (4, 21) to write the slope-intercept form of an equation for the line of fit. $y = -0.375x + 22.5$

b. Predict the milk consumption in 2015. about 16.875 gal

c. Predict in what year milk consumption will be 10 gallons. 2033

d. Is it reasonable to use the equation to estimate the consumption of milk for any year? Explain.

Real-World Career

Camera Operator
A camera operator is responsible for physically operating a camera and framing a scene. This job requires on-the-job training, while the educational requirements range from a high school diploma to a college degree.

9. FOOTBALL Use the scatter plot.

Buffalo Bills Attendance

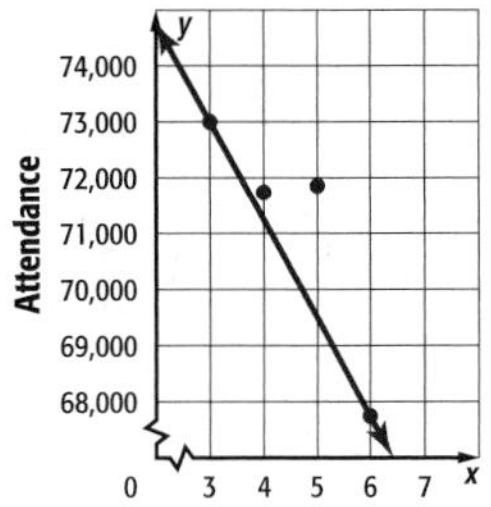

a. Use the points (3, 73,000) and (6, 67,650) to write the slope-intercept form of an equation for the line of fit shown in the scatter plot. $y \approx -1783x + 78{,}349$

b. Predict the average attendance at a game in 2012. 56,953

c. Can you use the equation to make a decision about the average attendance in any given year in the future? Explain.

B **10. WEIGHT** The Body Mass Index (BMI) is a measure of body fat using height and weight. The heights and weights of twelve men with normal BMI are given in the table at the right.

Height (in.)	Weight (lb)
62	115
63	124
65	120
67	134
67	140
68	138
68	144
68	152
69	147
72	155
73	168
73	166

a–b. See Ch. 4 Answer Appendix.

a. Make a scatter plot comparing the height in inches to the weight in pounds.

b. Draw a line of fit for the data.

c. Write the slope-intercept form of an equation for the line of fit. Sample answer: $y = 4.57x - 168.33$

d. Predict the normal weight for a man who is 84 inches tall. Sample answer: 215.6 lb

e. A man's weight is 188 pounds. Use the equation of the line of fit to predict the height of the man. Sample answer: about 78 in.

8d. Yes; if the current trend continues, the consumption of milk will continue to decrease.

9c. No; the average attendance will fluctuate with other variables such as how good the team is that year.

Tips for New Teachers

Reasoning Encourage students to think about why trends are occuring in the problems on which they are working. Then ask students how problems of this type could be important in other fields, such as engineering, marketing, and statistics.

Differentiated Instruction

OL BL

Extension Write (1, 10.1), (2, 9.8), (3, 10), (4, 10.5), (5, 10.4), (6, 10.8), and (7, 10.3) on the board. As a class, graph these data points on two separate graphs. Make the scale on the first graph such that the result is a scatter plot with no correlation. Make the scale on the second graph such that the result is a scatter plot with a positive correlation. Discuss how graphs can be manipulated to show different trends.

Study Guide and Intervention
CRM pp. 30–31 AL OL ELL

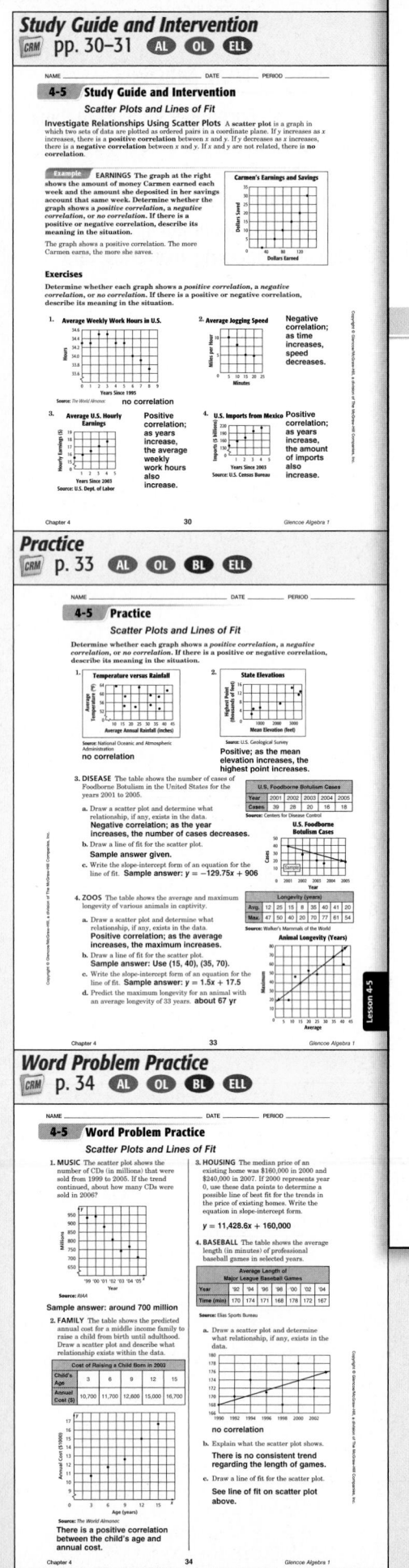

NAME ______ DATE ______ PERIOD ______

4-5 Study Guide and Intervention

Scatter Plots and Lines of Fit

Investigate Relationships Using Scatter Plots A **scatter plot** is a graph in which two sets of data are plotted as ordered pairs in a coordinate plane. If y increases as x increases, there is a **positive correlation** between x and y. If y decreases as x increases, there is a **negative correlation** between x and y. If x and y are not related, there is **no correlation**.

Example EARNINGS The graph at the right shows the amount of money Carmen earned each week and the amount she deposited in her savings account that same week. Determine whether the graph shows a *positive correlation*, a *negative correlation*, or *no correlation*. If there is a positive or negative correlation, describe its meaning in the situation.

The graph shows a positive correlation. The more Carmen earns, the more she saves.

Exercises

Determine whether each graph shows a *positive correlation*, a *negative correlation*, or *no correlation*. If there is a positive or negative correlation, describe its meaning in the situation.

1. Average Weekly Work Hours in U.S. — no correlation
2. Average Jogging Speed — Negative correlation; as time increases, speed decreases.
3. Average U.S. Hourly Earnings — Positive correlation; as years increase, the average weekly work hours also increase.
4. U.S. Imports from Mexico — Positive correlation; as years increase, the amount of imports also increase.

Chapter 4 30 Glencoe Algebra 1

Practice
CRM p. 33 AL OL BL ELL

NAME ______ DATE ______ PERIOD ______

4-5 Practice

Scatter Plots and Lines of Fit

Determine whether each graph shows a *positive correlation*, a *negative correlation*, or *no correlation*. If there is a positive or negative correlation, describe its meaning in the situation.

1. Temperature versus Rainfall — no correlation
2. State Elevations — Positive; as the mean elevation increases, the highest point increases.

3. DISEASE The table shows the number of cases of Foodborne Botulism in the United States for the years 2001 to 2005.

Year	2001	2002	2003	2004	2005
Cases	39	28	20	16	18

a. Draw a scatter plot and determine what relationship, if any, exists in the data. Negative correlation; as the year increases, the number of cases decreases.

b. Draw a line of fit for the scatter plot. Sample answer given.

c. Write the slope-intercept form of an equation for the line of fit. Sample answer: $y = -129.75x + 906$

4. ZOOS The table shows the average and maximum longevity of various animals in captivity.

Avg.	12	25	15	8	35	40	41	20
Max.	47	50	40	20	70	77	61	54

a. Draw a scatter plot and determine what relationship, if any, exists in the data. Positive correlation; as the average increases, the maximum increases.

b. Draw a line of fit for the scatter plot. Sample answer: Use (15, 40), (35, 70).

c. Write the slope-intercept form of an equation for the line of fit. Sample answer: $y = 1.5x + 17.5$

d. Predict the maximum longevity for an animal with an average longevity of 33 years. about 67 yr

Chapter 4 33 Glencoe Algebra 1

Word Problem Practice
CRM p. 34 AL OL BL ELL

NAME ______ DATE ______ PERIOD ______

4-5 Word Problem Practice

Scatter Plots and Lines of Fit

1. MUSIC The scatter plot shows the number of CDs (in millions) that were sold from 1999 to 2005. If the trend continued, about how many CDs were sold in 2006? Sample answer: around 700 million

2. FAMILY The table shows the predicted annual cost for a middle income family to raise a child from birth until adulthood. Draw a scatter plot and describe what relationship exists within the data.

Child's Age	3	6	9	12	15
Annual Cost ($)	10,700	11,700	12,600	15,000	16,700

There is a positive correlation between the child's age and annual cost.

3. HOUSING The median price of an existing home was \$160,000 in 2000 and \$240,000 in 2007. If 2000 represents year 0, use these data points to determine a possible line of best fit for the trends in the price of existing homes. Write the equation in slope-intercept form. $y = 11{,}428.6x + 160{,}000$

4. BASEBALL The table shows the average length (in minutes) of professional baseball games in selected years.

Year	'92	'94	'96	'98	'00	'02	'04
Time (min)	170	174	171	168	178	172	167

a. Draw a scatter plot and determine what relationship, if any, exists in the data. no correlation

b. Explain what the scatter plot shows. There is no consistent trend regarding the length of games.

c. Draw a line of fit for the scatter plot. See line of fit on scatter plot above.

Chapter 4 34 Glencoe Algebra 1

Real-World Link

Old Faithful is located in Yellowstone National Park. The Washburn Expedition of 1870 named the geyser because of its size and frequency.

Source: The Geyser Observation and Study Association

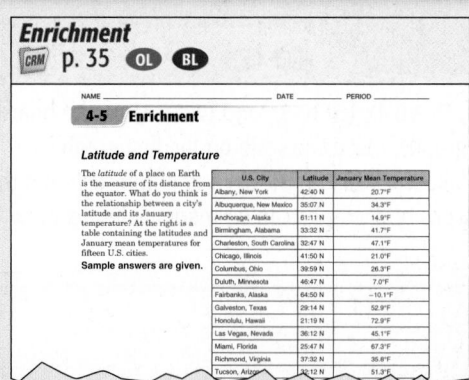

11a. The independent variable is the interval between eruptions and the dependent variable is the duration of the eruptions. There is a positive correlation between the independent and dependent variables. See Ch.4 Answer Appendix for graph.

11b. Sample answer using (2, 55) and (4, 82): $y = 13.5x + 28$; Sample answer: about 129.25 min

11c. Sample answer: The duration of an eruption is not dependent on the previous interval. Only the interval can be predicted by the length of the eruption.

11. **GEYSERS** The time to the next eruption of Old Faithful can be predicted by using the duration of the current eruption.

Duration (min)	1.5	2	2.5	3	3.5	4	4.5	5
Interval (min)	48	55	70	72	74	82	93	100

a. Identify the independent and the dependent variables. Make a scatter plot and determine what relationship, if any, exists in the data. Draw a line of fit for the scatter plot.

b. Let x represent the duration of the previous interval. Let y represent the time between eruptions. Write the slope-intercept form of the equation for the line of fit. Predict the interval after a 7.5-minute eruption.

c. Make a critical judgment about using the equation to predict the duration of the next eruption. Would the equation be a useful model?

12. **COLLECT DATA** Use a tape measure to measure both the foot size and the height in inches of ten individuals. **a–c. See students' work.**

a. Record your data in a table.

b. Make a scatter plot and draw a line of fit for the data.

c. Write an equation for the line of fit.

d. Make a conjecture about the relationship between foot size and height. **Sample answer: There seems to be a general trend that taller people have larger feet.**

H.O.T. Problems
Use Higher-Order Thinking Skills

13. **OPEN ENDED** Describe a real-life situation that can be modeled using a scatter plot. Decide whether there is a *positive*, *negative*, or *no* correlation. Explain what this correlation means. **See margin.**

14. **WHICH ONE DOESN'T BELONG?** Analyze the following situations and determine which one does not belong. **See margin.**

hours worked and amount of money earned	height of an athlete and favorite color
seedlings that grow an average of 2 centimeters each week	number of photos stored on a camera and capacity of camera

15. **CHALLENGE** Determine which line of fit is better for the scatter plot. Explain your reasoning. **See margin.**

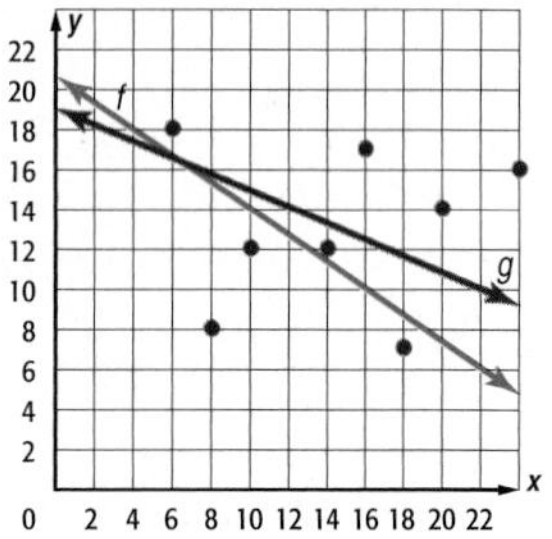

16. **REASONING** What can make a scatter plot and line of fit more useful for accurate predictions? Does an accurate line of fit always predict what will happen in the future? Explain. **See margin.**

17. **WRITING IN MATH** Make a scatter plot that shows the height of a person and age. Explain how you could use the scatter plot to predict the age of a person given his or her height. How can the information from a scatter plot be used to identify trends and make decisions? **See margin.**

Enrichment
CRM p. 35 OL BL

NAME ______ DATE ______ PERIOD ______

4-5 Enrichment

Latitude and Temperature

The *latitude* of a place on Earth is the measure of its distance from the equator. What do you think is the relationship between a city's latitude and its January temperature? At the right is a table containing the latitudes and January mean temperatures for fifteen U.S. cities.

Sample answers are given.

U.S. City	Latitude	January Mean Temperature
Albany, New York	42:40 N	20.7°F
Albuquerque, New Mexico	35:07 N	34.3°F
Anchorage, Alaska	61:11 N	14.9°F
Birmingham, Alabama	33:32 N	41.7°F
Charleston, South Carolina	32:47 N	47.1°F
Chicago, Illinois	41:50 N	21.0°F
Columbus, Ohio	39:59 N	26.3°F
Duluth, Minnesota	46:47 N	7.0°F
Fairbanks, Alaska	64:50 N	−10.1°F
Galveston, Texas	29:14 N	52.9°F
Honolulu, Hawaii	21:19 N	72.9°F
Las Vegas, Nevada	36:12 N	45.1°F
Miami, Florida	25:47 N	67.3°F
Richmond, Virginia	37:32 N	35.8°F
Tucson, Arizona	32:12 N	51.3°F

Exercise Alert

Tape Measure Exercise 12 requires the use of a tape measure to measure foot size and height.

PSAE PRACTICE 8.11.07, 10.11.01, 7.11.03, 8.11.16

18. Which equation best describes the relationship between the values of x and y in the table? **B**

A $y = x - 5$
B $y = 2x - 5$
C $y = 3x - 7$
D $y = 4x - 7$

x	y
−1	−7
0	−5
2	−1
4	3

19. STATISTICS Mr. Hernandez collected data on the heights and average stride lengths of a random sample of high school students. He then made a scatter plot. What kind of correlation did he most likely see? **F**

F positive
G constant
H negative
J no

20. GEOMETRY Mrs. Aguilar's rectangular bedroom measures 13 feet by 11 feet. She wants to purchase carpet for the bedroom that costs \$2.95 per square foot, including tax. How much will the carpet cost? **D**

A \$70.80
B \$141.60
C \$145.95
D \$421.85

21. SHORT RESPONSE Nikia bought a one-month membership to a fitness center for \$35. Each time she goes, she rents a locker for \$0.25. If she spent \$40.50 at the fitness center last month, how many days did she go? **22 days**

Spiral Review

Determine whether the graphs of each pair of equations are *parallel*, *perpendicular*, or *neither*. (Lesson 4-4)

22. $y = -2x + 11$, $y + 2x = 23$ **parallel**

23. $3y = 2x + 14$, $2x + 3y = 2$ **neither**

24. $y = -5x$, $y = 5x - 18$ **neither**

25. $y = 3x + 2$, $y = -\frac{1}{3}x - 2$ **perpendicular**

Write each equation in standard form. (Lesson 4-3)

26. $y - 13 = 4(x - 2)$
27. $y - 5 = -2(x + 2)$
28. $y + 3 = -5(x + 1)$
29. $y + 7 = \frac{1}{2}(x + 2)$
30. $y - 1 = \frac{5}{6}(x - 4)$
31. $y - 2 = -\frac{2}{5}(x - 8)$

26. $4x - y = -5$
27. $2x + y = 1$
28. $5x + y = -8$
29. $x - 2y = 12$
30. $5x - 6y = 14$
31. $2x + 5y = 26$

Graph each equation. (Lesson 4-1) **32–34. See margin.**

32. $y = 2x + 3$
33. $4x + y = -1$
34. $3x + 4y = 7$

Find the slope of the line that passes through each pair of points. (Lesson 3-3)

35. (3, 4), (10, 8) $\frac{4}{7}$
36. (−4, 7), (3, 5) $-\frac{2}{7}$
37. (3, 7), (−2, 4) $\frac{3}{5}$
38. (−3, 2), (−3, 4) **undefined**
39. (−2, −6), (−1, 10) **16**
40. (1, −5), (−3, −5) **0**

41. DRIVING Latisha drove 248 miles in 4 hours. At that rate, how long will it take her to drive an additional 93 miles? (Lesson 2-6) **1.5 h**

Skills Review

Express each relation as a graph. Then determine the domain and range. (Lesson 1-6) **42–43. See Ch. 4 Answer Appendix.**

42. {(4, 5), (5, 4), (−2, −2), (4, −5), (−5, 4)}
43. {(7, 6), (3, 4), (4, 5), (−2, 6), (−3, 2)}

32.

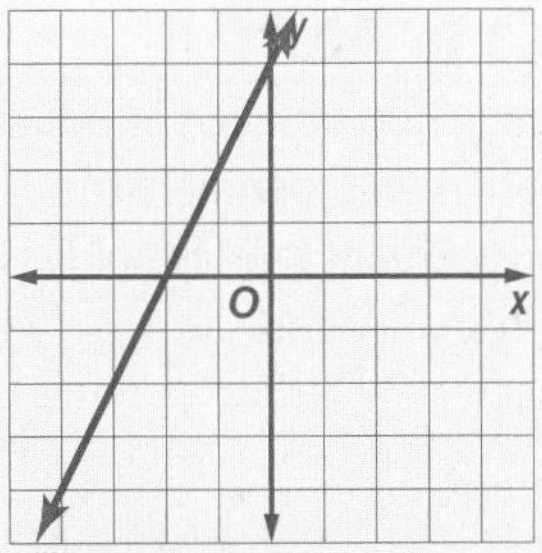

33.

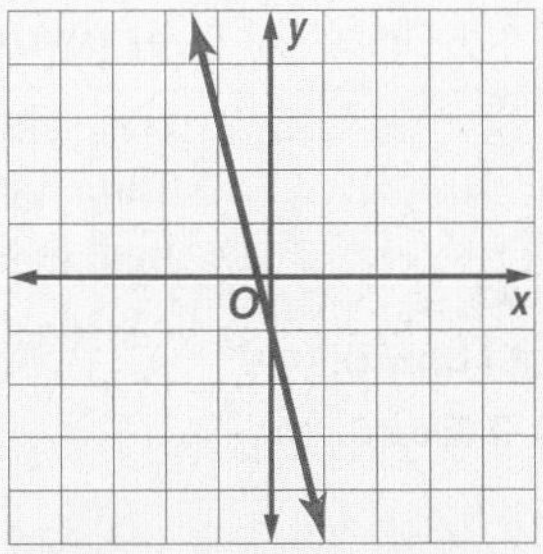

34.

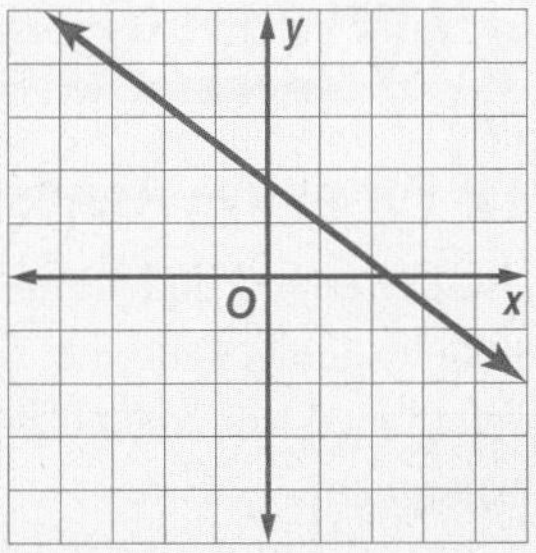

4 ASSESS

Crystal Ball Ask students to write how they think what they learned today about lines of fit will help them with tomorrow's lesson about finding the best-fit line for a set of data.

Additional Answers

13. Sample answer: The salary of an individual and the years of experience that they have; this would be a positive correlation because the more experience an individual has, the higher the salary would probably be.

14. Height and favorite color does not belong. The other situations have a positive correlation, this has no correlation.

15. Neither; line *g* has the same number of points above the line and below the line. Line *f* is close to 2 of the points; but for the rest of the data, there are 3 points above and 3 points below the line.

16. The more data you have, the more accurate the scatter plot and line of fit will be. No, trends can change and a line of fit assumes that the same pattern or trend will continue indefinitely.

17. Sample answer: You can visualize a line to determine whether the data has a positive or negative correlation. The graph below shows the ages and heights of people. To predict a person's age given his or her height, write a linear equation for the line of fit. Then substitute the person's height and solve for the corresponding age. You can use the pattern in the scatter plot to make decisions.

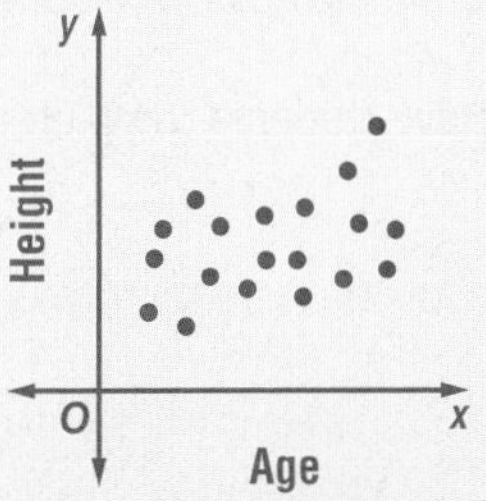

EXTEND 4-5

Lesson Notes

1 FOCUS

Objective Explore the difference between correlation and causation.

Materials for Each Student

- grid paper

Easy to Make Manipulatives

Teaching Algebra with Manipulatives

- grid paper, p. 1

Teaching Tip

Remind students that they have identified positive, negative, and no correlation between two variables. Some correlations may be purely coincidental, or they may have a common underlying cause. That is, the change in one variable may be the cause for the change in the other.

2 TEACH

Working in Cooperative Groups

Suggest that students work in groups of three or four to allow for an exchange of ideas when answering the questions posed in the Activity. However, for Step 1 of the Activity, ask each group member to make his or her own graph.

Ask:

- Can you think of another product that has had an increase in sales since 2001? Sample answers: computers, homes, gasoline, electricity
- Do you think it is possible that any one of those products might also be related to the increase in tuition? yes

Practice Have students complete Exercises 1–5.

EXTEND 4-5

Algebra Lab
Correlation and Causation

You may be considering attending a college or technical school in the future. What factors cause tuition to rise—increased building costs, higher employee salaries, or the amount of bottled water consumed?

Let's see how bottled water and college tuition are related. The table shows the average college tuition and fees for public colleges and the per person consumption of bottled water per year for 2001 through 2005.

Year	2001	2002	2003	2004	2005
Water Consumed (gallons)	18.8	20.9	22.4	24.0	26.1
Tuition ($)	3725	4081	4694	5132	5491

Source: *The New York Times Almanac*

ACTIVITY

Follow the steps to learn about correlation and causation.

Step 1 Graph the ordered pairs (gallons, tuition) to create a scatter plot. For example, one ordered pair is (18.8, 2562). Describe the graph.

Step 2 Is the correlation *positive* or *negative*? Explain.

Step 3 Do you think drinking more bottled water *causes* college tuition costs to rise? Explain.

Step 4 **Causation** occurs when a change in one variable produces a change in another variable. Correlation can be observed between many variables, but causation can only be determined from data collected from a controlled experiment. Describe an experiment that could illustrate causation.

Exercises

For each exercise, determine whether each situation illustrates *correlation* or *causation*. Explain your reasoning, including other factors that might be involved. 1–5. See Ch. 4 Answer Appendix.

1. A survey showed that sleeping with the light on was positively correlated to nearsightedness.
2. A controlled experiment showed a positive correlation between the number of cigarettes smoked and the probability of developing lung cancer.
3. A random sample of students found that owning a cell phone had a negative correlation with riding the bus to school.
4. A controlled experiment showed a positive correlation between the number of hours using headphones when listening to music and the level of hearing loss.
5. DeQuan read in the newspaper that shark attacks are positively correlated with monthly ice cream sales.

3 ASSESS

Formative Assessment

Use Exercises 3 and 4 to assess whether students understand that causation can only be determined from data collected from a controlled experiment.

From Concrete to Abstract

Have students examine the situation in Exercise 5. Then have them design an experiment that shows that an increase in ice cream sales is not likely to cause an increase in shark attacks.

Regression and Median-Fit Lines

Then

You used lines of fit and scatter plots to evaluate trends and make predictions. (Lesson 4-5)

Now

- Write equations of best-fit lines using linear regression.
- Write equations of median-fit lines.

IL Learning Standards

10.A.4c Predict from data using interpolation, extrapolation and trend lines, with and without the use of technology.

New Vocabulary

best-fit line
linear regression
correlation coefficient
median-fit line

IL Math Online

glencoe.com

- Extra Examples
- Personal Tutor
- Self-Check Quiz
- Homework Help

Why?

Spider-Man comics have been around since 1962. Since then Spider-Man has made appearances in magazines, books, and movies.

The table shows the number of comic books and appearances that he has made. We can estimate how many appearances he will make in 2012.

Spider-Man Comics and Appearances

Year	Number
1962	1
1972	39
1982	110
1992	164
2002	278
2012	?

Best-Fit Lines You have learned how to find and write equations for lines of fit by hand. Many calculators use complex algorithms that find a more precise line of fit called the **best-fit line**. One algorithm is called **linear regression**.

Your calculator may also compute a number called the **correlation coefficient**. This number will tell you if your correlation is positive or negative and how closely the equation is modeling the data. The closer the correlation coefficient is to 1 or −1, the more closely the equation models the data.

Real-World EXAMPLE 1 Best-Fit Line

MOVIES The table shows the amount of money made by movies in the United States. Use a graphing calculator to write an equation for the best-fit line for that data.

Year	2000	2001	2002	2003	2004	2005	2006
Income ($ billion)	7.66	8.41	9.52	9.49	9.54	8.99	9.49

Before you begin, make sure that your Diagnostic setting is on. You can find this under the CATALOG menu. Press D and then scroll down and click DiagnosticOn. Then press ENTER.

Step 1 Enter the data by pressing STAT and selecting the Edit option. Let the year 2000 be represented by 0. Enter the years since 2000 into List 1 (L_1). These will represent the x-values. Enter the income ($ billion) into List 2 (L_2). These will represent the y-values.

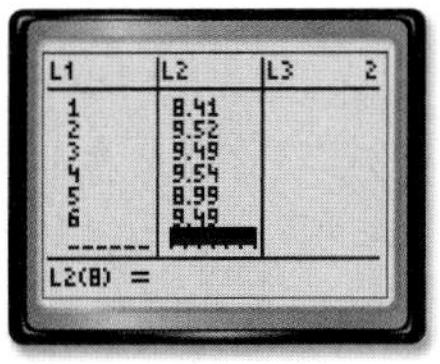

Step 2 Perform the regression by pressing STAT and selecting the CALC option. Scroll down to LinReg (ax+b) and press ENTER.

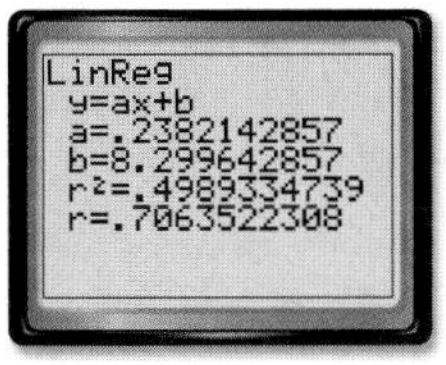

slope
y-intercept
correlation coefficient

4-6 Lesson Notes

1 FOCUS

Vertical Alignment

Before Lesson 4-6
Use lines of fit and scatter plots to evaluate trends and make predictions.

Lesson 4-6
Write equations of best-fit lines using linear regression.
Write equations of median-fit lines.

After Lesson 4-6
Find a curve of best-fit in the form of a polynomial function for data.

2 TEACH

Scaffolding Questions

Have students read the *Why?* section of the lesson.

Ask:

- What type of correlation does the data in the table have? positive
- How could you estimate the number of Spider-Man appearances in 2012? Make a scatter plot of the data in the table. Draw a line that seems to be close to all the points, then use two points on that line to write an equation. Finally, substitute 2012 into the equation for x and solve for y.
- Is this the only line of fit for the data? No, other lines could be drawn that fit.

Lesson 4-6 Resources

Resource	Approaching-Level	On-Level	Beyond-Level	English Learners
Teacher Edition	• Differentiated Instruction, p. 255	• Differentiated Instruction, pp. 255, 258	• Differentiated Instruction, p. 258	
Chapter Resource Masters	• Study Guide and Intervention, pp. 37–38 • Skills Practice, p. 39 • Practice, p. 40 • Word Problem Practice, p. 41	• Study Guide and Intervention, pp. 37–38 • Skills Practice, p. 39 • Practice, p. 40 • Word Problem Practice, p. 41 • Enrichment, p. 42	• Practice, p. 40 • Word Problem Practice, p. 41 • Enrichment, p. 42	• Study Guide and Intervention, pp. 37–38 • Skills Practice, p. 39 • Practice, p. 40
Transparencies	• 5-Minute Check Transparency 4-6	• 5-Minute Check Transparency 4-6	• 5-Minute Check Transparency 4-6	• 5-Minute Check Transparency 4-6
Other	• Study Notebook • Teaching Algebra with Manipulatives	• Study Notebook • Teaching Algebra with Manipulatives	• Study Notebook	• Study Notebook • Teaching Algebra with Manipulatives

Equations of Best-Fit Lines

Example 1 shows how to use a calculator to write an equation for a best-fit line for a set of data. **Example 2** shows how to use a calculator and an equation of the best-fit line for data, and then estimate a number outside of the range of the data.

Formative Assessment

Use the Check Your Progress exercises after each Example to determine students' understanding of concepts.

Additional Examples

1 **EARNINGS** The table below shows Ariana's hourly earnings for the years 2001–2007. Use a graphing calculator to write an equation for the best-fit line for that data. Name the correlation coefficient. Round to the nearest ten-thousandth. Let x be the number of years since 2000.

Year	Cost
2001	$10
2002	$10.50
2003	$11
2004	$13
2005	$15
2006	$15.75
2007	$16.50

$y = 1.21x + 8.25$; 0.9801

2 **BOWLING** The table below shows the points earned by the top ten bowlers in a tournament. How many points did the 15th-ranked bowler earn?

Rank	Score	Rank	Score
1	210	6	147
2	197	7	144
3	164	8	142
4	158	9	134
5	151	10	132

about 83

Additional Examples also in Interactive Classroom PowerPoint® Presentations

IWB INTERACTIVE WHITEBOARD READY

Real-World Link

In 1994, Minnesota became the first state to sanction girls' ice hockey as a high school varsity sport.

Source: ESPNET SportsZone

1A. For x as years since 2003, $y = 1.87x + 28.58$; 0.6142

1B. For x as years since 2003, $y = 5.95x + 50.17$; 0.8495

Step 3 Write the equation of the regression line by rounding the a and b values. The form that we chose was $ax + b$, so the equation is $y = 0.24x + 8.30$. The correlation coefficient is about 0.7064, which means that the equation models the data fairly well.

Check Your Progress

Write an equation of the best-fit line for the data in each table. Name the correlation coefficient. Round to the nearest ten-thousandth. Let x be the number of years since 2003.

1A. HOCKEY The table shows the number of goals of leading scorers.

Mustang Girls Hockey Leading Scorers								
Year	2003	2004	2005	2006	2007	2008	2009	2010
Goals	30	23	41	35	31	43	33	45

1B. HOCKEY The table gives the number of goals scored by the team each season.

Mustang Girls Hockey Team Goals								
Year	2003	2004	2005	2006	2007	2008	2009	2010
Goals	63	44	55	63	81	85	93	84

Personal Tutor glencoe.com

We can use points on the best-fit line to estimate values that are not in the data. Recall that when we estimate values that are between known values, this is called *linear interpolation*. When we estimate a number outside of the range of the data, it is called *linear extrapolation*.

Real-World EXAMPLE 2 Use Interpolation and Extrapolation

PAINTBALL The table shows the points received by the top ten paintball teams at a tournament. How many points did the 20th-ranked team receive?

Top Ten Teams										
Rank	1	2	3	4	5	6	7	8	9	10
Score	100	89	96	99	97	98	78	70	64	80

Write an equation of the best-fit line for the data. Then extrapolate to find the missing value.

Step 1 Enter the data from the table into the lists as you did before. Let the ranks be the x-values and the scores be the y-values. Then graph the scatter plot.

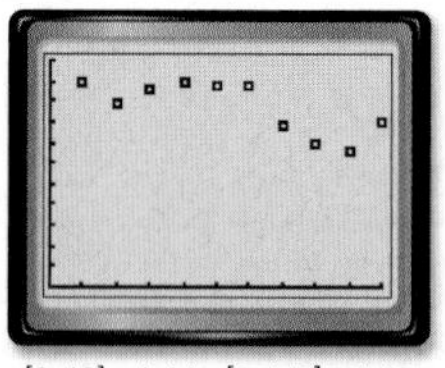

[0, 10] scl: 1 by [0, 110] scl: 10

Step 2 Perform the linear regression using the data in the lists. Find the equation of the best-fit line.

The equation is $y = -3.32x + 105.3$.

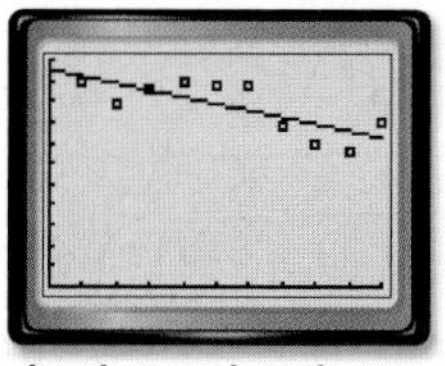

[0, 10] scl: 1 by [0, 110] scl: 10

Focus on Mathematical Content

Equation of a Best-Fit Line The TI-83/84 Plus graphing calculator has two methods to compute the equation of a best-fit line:

- LinReg($ax + b$) linear regression
- Med-Med median-fit line.

The linear regression method uses a least-squares fit method to determine the values for a and b. This utilizes calculus involving the distance each point is from the best-fit line. The median-fit method calculates the medians of the coordinates of the data points

254 Chapter 4 Linear Functions and Relations

StudyTip

Median-Fit Line The median-fit line is computed using a different algorithm than linear regression.

Step 3 Graph the best-fit line. Press [2nd] [CALC] [ENTER] to find that when $x = 20$, $y \approx 39$.

It is estimated that the 20th ranked team received 39 points.

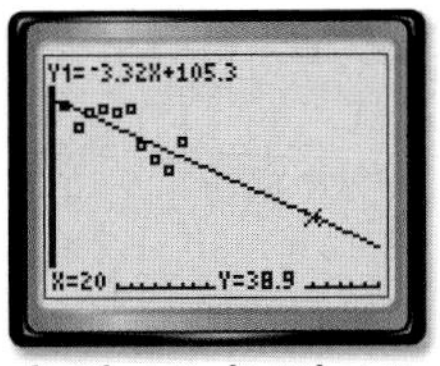

[0, 25] scl: 1 by [0, 125] scl: 10

Check Your Progress

ONLINE GAMES **Use linear interpolation to find the percent of Americans that play online games for the following ages.**

Percent of Americans Who Play Online Games

Age	15	20	30	40	50
Percent	81	54	37	29	25

Source: Pew Internet & American Life Survey

2A. 35 years ≈39%

2B. 18 years ≈64%

Personal Tutor glencoe.com

Median-Fit Lines A second type of fit line that can be found using a graphing calculator is a **median-fit line**. The equation of a median-fit line is calculated using the medians of the coordinates of the data points.

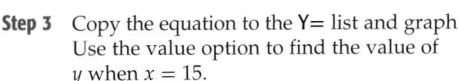

EXAMPLE 3 Median-Fit Line

PAINTBALL **Find and graph the equation of a median-fit line for the data in Example 2. Then predict the score of the 15th ranked team.**

Step 1 The data should be in the lists. Graph the scatter plot.

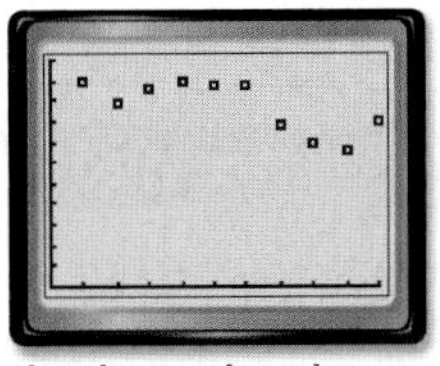

[0, 10] scl: 1 by [0, 110] scl: 10

Step 2 To find the median-fit equation, press the [STAT] key and select the CALC option. Scroll down to the Med-Med option and press [ENTER]. The value of a is the slope, and the value of b is the y-intercept.

The equation for the median-fit line is $y = -3.71x + 108.26$.

Step 3 Copy the equation to the Y= list and graph. Use the value option to find the value of y when $x = 15$.

The 15th place team scored about 53 points.

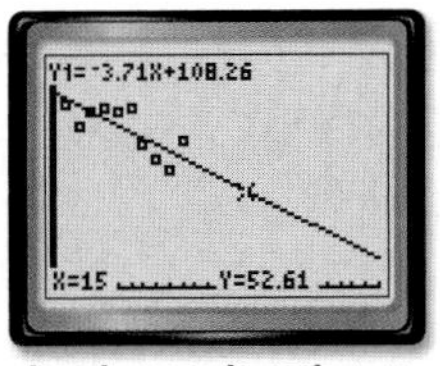

[0, 25] scl: 1 by [0, 125] scl: 10

Notice that the equations for the regression line and the median-fit line are very similar.

Check Your Progress

3. Use the data from Check Your Progress 2 and a median-fit line to estimate the numbers of 18- and 35-year-olds who play online games. Compare these values with the answers from the regression line.

3. ≈63%, ≈38%; These values are relatively close to those in Check Your Progress 2A and 2B.

Personal Tutor glencoe.com

Real-World Link

Paintball is more popular with 12- to 17-year-olds than any other age group. In 2002, 3,649,000 teenagers participated in paintball while 2,195,000 18- to 24-year-olds participated.

Source: *Statistical Abstract of the United States*

Tips for New Teachers

Graphing Calculator Make sure that students understand the keystrokes for the [STAT] menu. Make sure students have cleared the L1 and L2 lists before entering new data. If students enter their data into L3 and L4 instead of L1 and L2, they must type in "L3, L4" after "LinReg(ax+b)" and then press [ENTER].

Correlation Coefficient With DiagnosticOn, the calculator also displays values for r^2 and r. The closer the value for $|r|$ is to 1, the better the equation fits the data.

Equations of Median-Fit Lines

Example 3 shows how to calculate the equation of a median-fit line using a graphing calculator and then use the equation to predict a value.

Additional Example

3 Find and graph the equation of a median-fit line for the data on the bowling tournament in Additional Example 2. $y = -9x + 209.5$ Then predict the score of the 20th ranked bowler. about 30

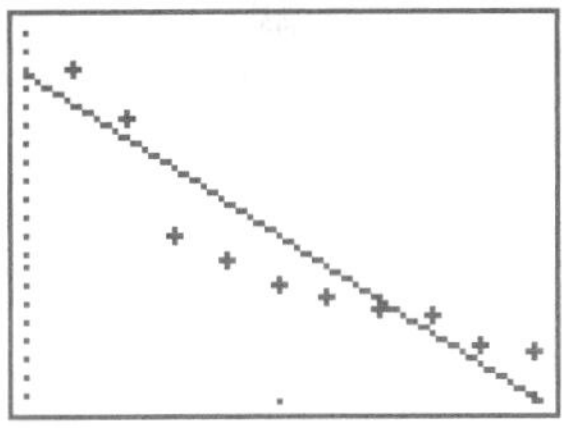

[0, 22] scl: 1 by [0, 225] scl: 5

Differentiated Instruction AL OL

If students have trouble remembering certain keystrokes on their graphing calculators,

Then have students make "recipe" cards for each calculator activity they study. For example, have them title a card "Best-fit Line" and then write the keystrokes for using their graphing calculator to find the best-fit line for data and correlation coefficient. Students can refer to these cards as needed until they commit the steps to memory. Be sure students include a card for how to clear all previous data lists using the following keystrokes: [2nd] [MEM] 4 [ENTER].

TEACH with TECH

VIDEO RECORDING Have students work in pairs to create a video showing how to find a regression equation or median-fit line. Share each group's videos with the class.

3 PRACTICE

Formative Assessment

Use Exercises 1–3 to check for understanding.

Use the chart at the bottom of this page to customize assignments for your students.

Additional Answer

3a.

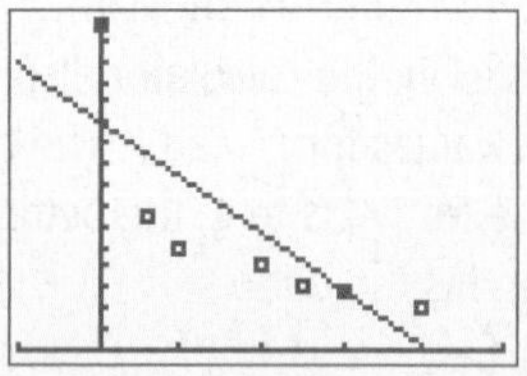

[−0.5, 2.5] scl: 1 by [0, 785] scl: 10

Check Your Understanding

Example 1 p. 253

1. **POTTERY** A local university is keeping track of the number of art students who use the pottery studio each day. Write an equation of the regression line and find the correlation coefficient.

Students Throwing Pottery							
Day	1	2	3	4	5	6	7
Students	10	15	18	15	13	19	20

$y = 1.18x + 11$; 0.7181

Example 2 p. 254

2. **COMPUTERS** The table below shows the percent of Americans with a broadband connection at home in a recent year. Use linear extrapolation and a regression equation to estimate the percentage of 60-year-olds with broadband at home. 29%

Percentage of Americans with Broadband At Home						
Age	25	30	35	40	45	50
Percent	40	42	36	35	36	32

Example 3 p. 255

3. **VACATION** The Smiths want to rent a house on the lake that sleeps eight people. The cost of the house per night is based on how close it is to the water.

Rental Properties							
Distance from Lake (mi)	0.0 (houseboat)	0.3	0.5	1.0	1.25	1.5	2.0
Price/Night ($)	785	325	250	200	150	140	100

a. Find and graph an equation for the median-fit line.

b. What would you estimate is the cost of a rental 1.75 miles from the lake? $78.69

a. $y = -271.88x + 554.48$; See margin for graph.

Practice and Problem Solving

● = Step-by-Step Solutions begin on page R12.
Extra Practice begins on page 815.

Examples 1 and 2 pp. 253–254

Write an equation of the regression line for the data in each table. Then find the correlation coefficient.

4. **SKYSCRAPERS** The table ranks the ten tallest buildings in the world. $y = -2.75x + 102.53$; −0.6071

Tallest Buildings and Stories										
Rank	1	2	3	4	5	6	7	8	9	10
Stories	101	88	110	88	88	80	69	102	78	70

5. **MUSIC** The table gives the number of annual violin auditions held by a youth symphony each year since 2000. Let x be the number of years since 2000.

5. $y = 3.54x + 19.68$; 0.9007

Youth Symphony Violin Auditions							
Year	2000	2001	2002	2003	2004	2005	2006
Auditions	22	19	25	37	32	35	42

6. **RETAIL** The table gives the sales of jeans at a clothing chain since 2004. Let x be the number of years since 2004.

6. $y = 3.04x + 5.66$; 0.9883

Jeans Sales By Year						
Year	2004	2005	2006	2007	2008	2009
Sales (Millions of Dollars)	6.84	7.6	10.9	15.4	17.6	21.2

Differentiated Homework Options

Level	Assignment	Two-Day Option	
AL Basic	4–7, 20–46	5, 7, 23–26	4–6 even, 20–22, 27–46
OL Core	5, 7, 9–18, 20–46	4–7, 23–26	8–18, 20–22, 27–46
BL Advanced	8–38, (optional: 39–46)		

Example 3 p. 255

7. **MARATHON** The number of entrants in the Boston Marathon every five years since 1975 is shown. Let x be the number of years since 1975.

Year	1975	1980	1985	1990	1995	2000	2005
Entrants	2395	5417	5594	9412	9416	17,813	20,453

Source: Boston Athletic Association

a. Find an equation for the median-fit line. $y = 609.08x + 1680.8$

b. According to the equation, how many entrants were there in 2003? about 18,735

B

8. **CAMPING** A campground keeps a record of the number of campsites rented the week of July 4 for several years. Let x be the number of years since 2000.

Campsites Rented July 4th Week						
Year	2002	2003	2004	2005	2006	2007
Sites Rented	34	45	42	53	58	47

a. Find an equation for the regression line. $y = 3.29x + 31.71$

b. Predict the number of campsites that will be rented in 2010. about 65 campsites

c. Predict the number of campsites that will be rented in 2020. about 98 campsites

9. **ICE CREAM** An ice cream company keeps a count of the tubs of cookie dough ice cream delivered to each of their stores in a particular area.

Store Delivery of Cookie Dough Ice Cream					
Store Size (ft^2)	2100	2225	3135	3569	4587
Tubs (hundreds)	110	102	215	312	265

a. Find an equation for the median-fit line. $y = 0.095x - 94.58$

b. Graph the points and the median-fit line. See margin.

c. How many tubs would be delivered to a 1500-square-foot store? a 5000-square-foot store? about 48 tubs; about 380 tubs

10. **COLLEGE TESTING** The ACT is an exam that evaluates students' readiness to perform college-level work. The table below shows the number of participants who took the test in the given years. Let x be the number of years since 1990.

Years	1990	1995	2000	2001	2002	2003	2004	2005	2006
Participants (thousands)	817	945	1065	1070	1116	1175	1171	1186	1206

Source: ACT

a. Find an equation for the regression line. $y = 24.91x + 817.72$

b. According to the equation, how many participants were there in 1998? 1017

c. How many students would you predict will participate in 2011? 1341

11. **FINANCIAL LITERACY** The prices of the eight top-selling brands of jeans at Jeanie's Jeans are given in the table below.

Sales Rank	1	2	3	4	5	6	7	8
Price ($)	43	44	50	61	64	135	108	78

a. Find the equation for the regression line. $y = 9.8x + 28.79$

b. According to the equation, what would be the price of a pair of the 12th best-selling brand? $146.39

c. Is this a reasonable prediction? Explain.

Real-World Link

The average American eats 20 quarts of ice cream per year.

Source: *Real Simple Magazine*

11c. Sample answer: Yes; the number is within a reasonable range of the other pairs of jeans.

Exercise Alert

Grid Paper For Exercises 12, 17, and 43–46, students will need grid paper.

Additional Answer

9b.

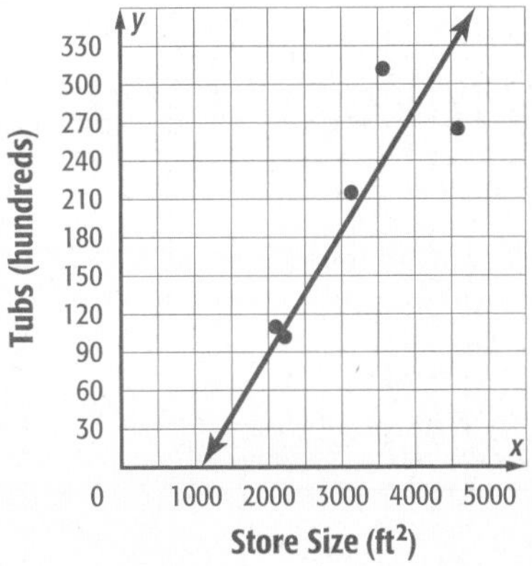

Additional Answers

12a.

Years Since 2000	Attendance (Thousands)
0	53.331
1	47.940
2	54.036
3	61.364
4	61.289
5	52.201

12b.

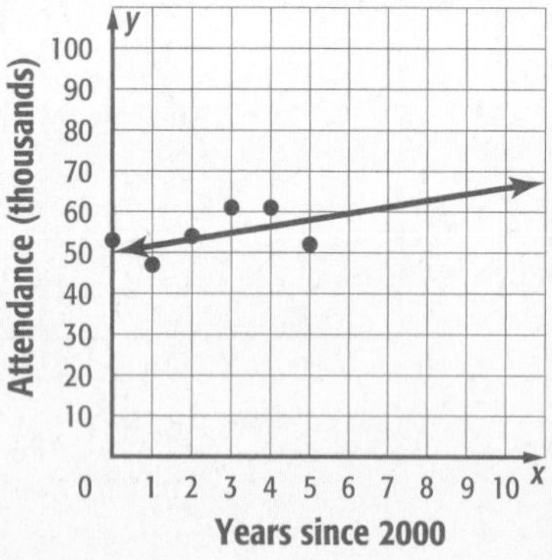

12c. 66,350

14a. $y = -841.42x + 223288$

14b.

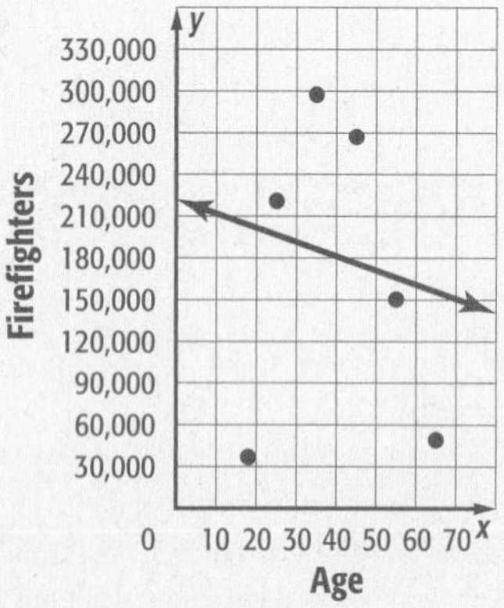

17b.

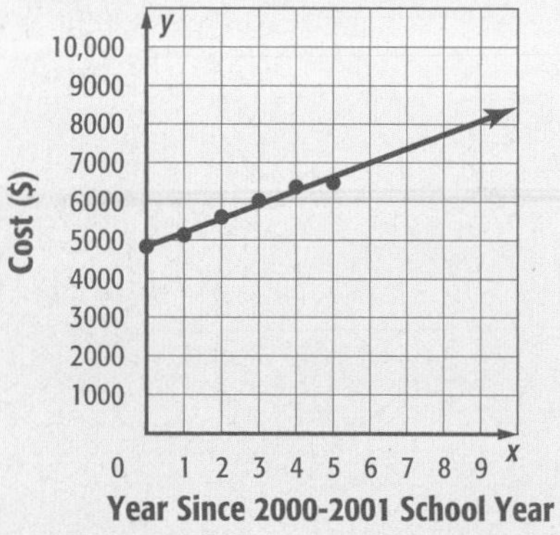

Math History Link

Florence Nightingale David (1909–1993)
A renowned statistician born in Ivington, England, Florence Nightingale David received the first Elizabeth L. Scott Award for her "efforts in opening the door to women in statistics; ... for research contributions to ... statistical methods ...; and her spirit as a lecturer and as a role model."

14c. No; sample answer: The points show no linear correlation; therefore a line cannot accurately portray the data.

16c. No, the correlation coefficient is 0.48, so the linear model is not a good fit for the data.

12. **STATE FAIRS** Opening day attendance at the North Carolina State Fair for 2000 was 53,331, for 2001 it was 47,940, for 2002 it was 54,036, for 2003 it was 61,364, for 2004 it was 61,289, and for 2005 it was 52,201. **a–c. See margin.**
    a. Construct a table for the given data.
    b. Graph the points and the regression line.
    c. Predict the attendance on opening day in 2012.

13. **MUSIC** For the following data, find the equation of the regression line and give the correlation coefficient to the nearest ten-thousandth place. **$y = 420.17x + 1682.22$; 0.9464**

Battle of the Bands Concessions

Year	1998	1999	2000	2001	2002	2003	2004	2005	2006
Amount Raised ($)	1236	1560	1423	1740	2230	2563	3215	4517	4219

14. **FIREFIGHTERS** The table shows statistics from the U.S. Fire Administration.
    a. Find an equation for the median-fit line. **See margin.**
    b. Graph the points and the median-fit line. **See margin.**
    c. Does the median-fit line give you an accurate picture of the number of firefighters? Explain.

Age	Number of Firefighters
18	40,919
25	245,516
35	330,516
45	296,665
55	167,087
65	54,559

15. **ATHLETICS** The table shows the number of participants in high school athletics.

Year Since 1970	1	10	20	30	35
Athletes	3,960,932	5,356,913	5,298,671	6,705,223	7,159,904

    a. Find an equation for the regression line. **$y = 87{,}390.5x + 4{,}018{,}431$**
    b. According to the equation, how many participated in 1988? **about 5,591,460**

16. **ART** A count was kept on the number of paintings sold at an auction by the year in which they were painted. Let x be the number of years since 1950.

Paintings Sorted by Year of Execution

Year Painted	1950	1955	1960	1965	1970	1975
Paintings Solds	8	5	25	21	9	22

    a. Find the equation for the linear regression line. **$y = 0.446x + 9.43$**
    b. How many paintings were sold that were painted in 1961? **about 14 paintings**
    c. Is the linear regression equation an accurate model of the data? Explain why or why not.

17. **SCHOOL** The table shows the average cost of a technical school between 2000 and 2006. Let x be 0 for the school year 2000–2001.

Average Cost of Public 2-Year Institution

Year	2000–2001	2001–2002	2002–2003	2003–2004	2004–2005	2005–2006
Cost ($)	4839	5137	5601	6020	6375	6492

Source: U.S. Department of Education

    a. Find the equation of the median-fit line. **$y = 361.38x + 4840.6$**
    b. Graph the points and the median-fit line. **See margin.**
    c. What would you estimate the cost to be in 2020–2021? **$12,068.20**

Differentiated Instruction

OL BL

Extension Remind students that outliers are points that are significantly distant from the other data points. Ask students to determine if removing the outlier in Exercise 3 affects the estimated cost of a rental 1.75 miles from the lake. Yes, the outlier (0.0, 785) causes the estimate to be lower than it currently is. Removing the outlier and using the median-fit line for the remaining data points results in a more realistic estimated cost of $112 per night for renting a house 1.75 miles from the lake.

258 Chapter 4 Linear Functions and Relations

18. SPACE EXPLORATION As of 2006, the names of the space shuttles launched each year since 1993 are given below. Let x be the year.

Space Shuttle Launches

Year	Launches
1993	STS-61, STS-58, STS-51, STS-57, STS-55, STS-56, STS-54
1994	STS-66, STS-68, STS-64, STS-65, STS-59, STS-62, STS-60
1995	STS-74, STS-73, STS-69, STS-70, STS-71, STS-67, STS-63
1996	STS-80, STS-79, STS-78, STS-77, STS-76, STS-75, TSTS-72
1997	STS-87, STS-86, STS-85, STS-94, STS-84, STS-83, STS-82, STS-81
1998	STS-88, STS-95, STS-91, STS-90, STS-89
1999	STS-103, STS-93, STS-96
2000	STS-97, STS-92, STS-106, STS-101, STS-99
2001	STS-108, STS-105, STS-104, STS-100, STS-102, STS-98
2002	STS-113, STS-112, STS-111, STS-110, STS-109
2003	STS-107
2004	
2005	STS-114
2006	STS-116, STS-115, STS-121

a. Construct a table of values for the data that could be used for graphing.

b. Find an equation for the regression line. $y = -0.5121x + 1028.5626$

c. Predict the number of launches there will be in 2015. Is your prediction reasonable? What influences might cause the actual number of flights to be different from your prediction? Explain.

18a. See Ch. 4 Answer Appendix.

18c. −3; No, it is not possible to have a negative number of shuttle launches. Funding for the space program affects the number of shuttle launches each year.

H.O.T. Problems — Use Higher-Order Thinking Skills

19. CHALLENGE Below are the results of the World Superpipe Championships in 2008.

Men	Score	Rank	Women	Score
Shaun White	93.00	1	Torah Bright	96.67
Mason Aguirre	90.33	2	Kelly Clark	93.00
Janne Korpi	85.33	3	Soko Yamaoka	85.00
Luke Mitrani	85.00	4	Ellery Hollingsworth	79.33
Keir Dillion	81.33	5	Sophie Rodriguez	71.00

See Ch. 4 Answer Appendix.

Find an equation of the regression line for each, and graph them on the same coordinate plane. Compare and contrast the men's and women's graphs.

Real-World Link

The World Superpipe Championship is held in Park City, Utah. This is home to one of the largest half-pipes in the world, with walls 22 feet high.

Source: Park City Mountain Resort

20. REASONING For a class project, the scores that 10 randomly selected students earned on the first 8 tests of the school year are given. Explain how to find a line of best fit. Could it be used to predict the scores of other students? Explain your reasoning. **See Ch. 4 Answer Appendix.**

21. OPEN ENDED For 10 different people, measure their heights and the lengths of their heads from chin to top. Use these data to generate a linear regression equation and a median-fit equation. Make a prediction using both of the equations. **See students' work.**

22. WRITING IN MATH Using the data at the beginning of the lesson, describe the steps you would take to determine the number of appearances Spiderman will make in 2012. **See Ch. 4 Answer Appendix.**

Study Guide and Intervention
CRM pp. 37–38 AL OL ELL

NAME ______ DATE ______ PERIOD ______

4-6 Study Guide and Intervention
Regression and Median-Fit Lines

Equations of Best-Fit Lines Many graphing calculators utilize an algorithm called **linear regression** to find a precise line of fit called the **best-fit line**. The calculator computes the data, writes an equation, and gives you the **correlation coefficent**, a measure of how closely the equation models the data.

Example GAS PRICES **The table shows the average price of a gallon of regular gasoline in Los Angeles, California.**

Year	2002	2003	2004	2005	2006	2007
Average Price	\$1.47	\$1.82	\$2.15	\$2.49	\$2.83	\$3.04

Source: U.S. Department of Energy

a. **Use a graphing calculator to write an equation for the best-fit line for that data.** Enter the data by pressing STAT and selecting the Edit option. Let the year 2002 be represented by 0. Enter the years since 2002 into List 1 (L_1). Enter the average price into List 2 (L_2).

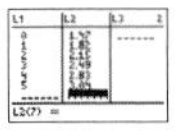

Then, perform the linear regression by pressing STAT and selecting the CALC option. Scroll down to LinReg (ax+b) and press ENTER. The best-fit equation for the regression is shown to be $y = 0.321x + 1.499$.

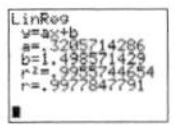

b. **Name the correlation coefficient.** The correlation coefficient is the value shown for r on the calculator screen. The correlation coefficient is about 0.998.

Exercises

Write an equation of the regression line for the data in each table below. Then find the correlation coefficient.

1. **OLYMPICS** Below is a table showing the number of gold medals won by the United States at the Winter Olympics during various years.

Year	1988	1992	1994	1998	2002	2006
Gold Medals	2	5	6	6	10	9

Source: International Olympic Committee

$y = 1.43x + 2.76$; $r = 0.930$

2. **INTEREST RATES** Below is a table showing the U.S. Federal Reserve's prime interest rate on January 1 of various years.

Year	2003	2004	2005	2006	2007
Prime Rate (percent)	4.25	4.00	5.25	7.25	8.25

Source: Federal Reserve Board

$y = 1.125x + 3.55$; $r = 0.949$

Chapter 4 — 37 — Glencoe Algebra 1

Lesson 4-6

Practice
CRM p. 40 AL OL BL ELL

NAME ______ DATE ______ PERIOD ______

4-6 Practice
Regression and Median-Fit Lines

Write an equation of the regression line for the data in each table below. Then find the correlation coefficient.

1. **TURTLES** The table shows the number of turtles hatched at a zoo each year since 2002.

Year	2003	2004	2005	2006	2007
Turtles Hatched	21	17	16	16	14

$y = -1.5x + 19.8$; $r = -0.916$

2. **SCHOOL LUNCHES** The table shows the percentage of students receiving free or reduced price school lunches in Marin County, California each year since 2003.

Year	2003	2004	2005	2006	2007
Percentage	14.4%	15.8%	18.3%	18.6%	20.9%

Source: KidsData

$y = 1.58x + 14.44$; $r = 0.983$

3. **SPORTS** Below is a table showing the number of students signed up to play lacrosse after school in each age group. $y = -1.5x + 34.1$; $r = -0.554$

Age	13	14	15	16	17
Lacrosse Players	17	14	6	9	12

4. **LANGUAGE** The State of California keeps track of how many millions of students are learning English as a second language each year.

Year	2003	2004	2005	2006	2007
English Learners	1.600	1.599	1.592	1.570	1.569

Source: California Department of Education

a. Find an equation for the median-fit line. $y = -0.01x + 1.607$

b. Predict the number of students who were learning English in California in 2001. **about 1,627,000 students**

c. Predict the number of students who will be learning English in California in 2010. **about 1,537,000 students**

5. **POPULATION** Detroit, Michigan, like a number of large cities, is losing population every year. Below is a table showing the population of Detroit each decade.

Year	1960	1970	1980	1990	2000
Population (millions)	1.67	1.51	1.20	1.03	0.95

Source: U.S. Census Bureau

a. Find an equation for the regression line. $y = -0.019x + 1.656$

b. Find the correlation coefficient and explain the meaning of its sign. **$r = -0.982$; The sign is negative, meaning that there is a negative correlation to the data.**

c. Estimate the population of Detroit in 2008. **about 734,000 people**

Chapter 4 — 40 — Glencoe Algebra 1

Word Problem Practice
CRM p. 41 AL OL BL ELL

NAME ______ DATE ______ PERIOD ______

4-6 Word Problem Practice
Regression and Median-Fit Lines

1. **FOOTBALL** Rutgers University running back Ray Rice ran for 1732 total yards in the 2007 regular season. The table below shows his cumulative total number of yards ran after select games.

Game Number	1	3	6	9	12
Cumulative Yards	184	431	818	1257	1732

Source: Rutgers University Athletics

Use a calculator to find an equation for the regression line showing the total yards y scored after x games. What is the real-world meaning of the value returned for a?

$y = 140.4x + 13.8$; a represents the number of yards Ray Rice can be expected to run per game.

2. **GOLD** Ounces of gold are traded by large investment banks in commodity exchanges much the same way that shares of stock are traded. The table below shows the cost of a single ounce of gold on the last day of trading in given years.

Year	2002	2003	2004	2005	2006
Price	\$346.70	\$414.80	\$438.10	\$517.20	\$636.30

Source: Global Financial Data

Use a calculator to find an equation for the regression line. Then predict the price of an ounce of gold on the last day of trading in 2009. Is this a reasonable prediction? Explain.

$y = 68.16x + 334.3$; \$811.42; The prediction may not be reasonable, because the value of an investment can fluctuate.

3. **GOLF SCORES** Emmanuel is practicing golf as part of his school's golf team. Each week he plays a full round of golf and records his total score. His scorecard after five weeks is below.

Week	1	2	3	4	5
Golf Score	112	107	108	104	98

Use a calculator to find an equation for the median-fit line. Then estimate how many games Emmanuel will have to play to get a score of 86.

$y = -2.83x + 114.67$; about 10 games

4. **STUDENT ELECTIONS** The vote totals for five of the candidates participating in Montvale High School's student council elections and the number of hours each candidate spent campaigning are shown in the table below.

Hours Campaigning	1	3	4	6	8
Votes Received	9	22	24	46	78

a. Use a calculator to find an equation for the median-fit line. **$y = 9.3x - 6.47$**

b. Plot the data points and draw the median-fit line on the graph below.

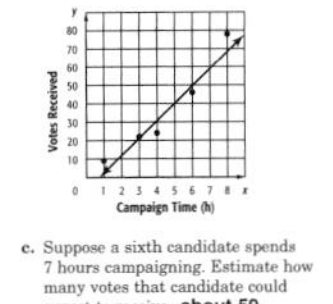

c. Suppose a sixth candidate spends 7 hours campaigning. Estimate how many votes that candidate could expect to receive. **about 59**

Chapter 4 — 41 — Glencoe Algebra 1

Lesson 4-6

Enrichment
CRM p. 42 OL BL

NAME ______ DATE ______ PERIOD ______

4-6 Enrichment
Quadratic Regression Parabolas

For some sets of data, a linear equation in the form $y = ax + b$ does not adequately describe the relationship between data points. The "QuadReg" function on a graphing calculator will output an equation in the form $y = ax^2 + bx + c$. The value of R^2, the **coefficient of determination** tells you how closely the parabola fits the data.

Example **The table shows the population of Atlanta in various years.**

Year	1970	1980	1990	2000	2005	2007
Population	497,000	425,000	394,017	416,474	470,688	498,109

Source: U.S. Census Bureau

a. **Find the equation of a quadratic-regression parabola for the data.**

Running a linear regression on the data provides an r value of 0.03, which indicates a poor fit. The data appears to be a good candidate for a quadratic regression.

Step 1 Enter the data by pressing STAT and selecting the Edit option. Enter the years since 1970 as your x-values (L_1) and enter the population figures as your y-values (L_2).

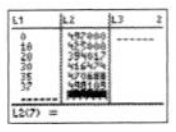

Step 2 Perform the quadratic regression by pressing STAT and selecting the CALC option. Scroll down to QuadReg and press ENTER.

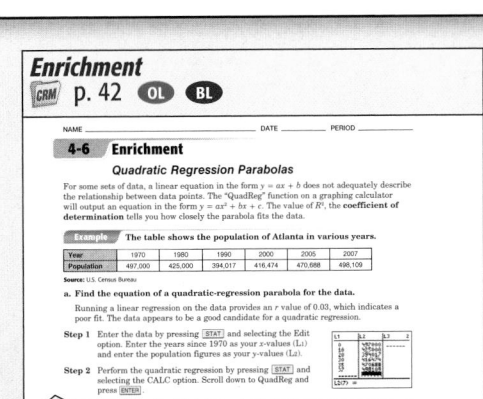

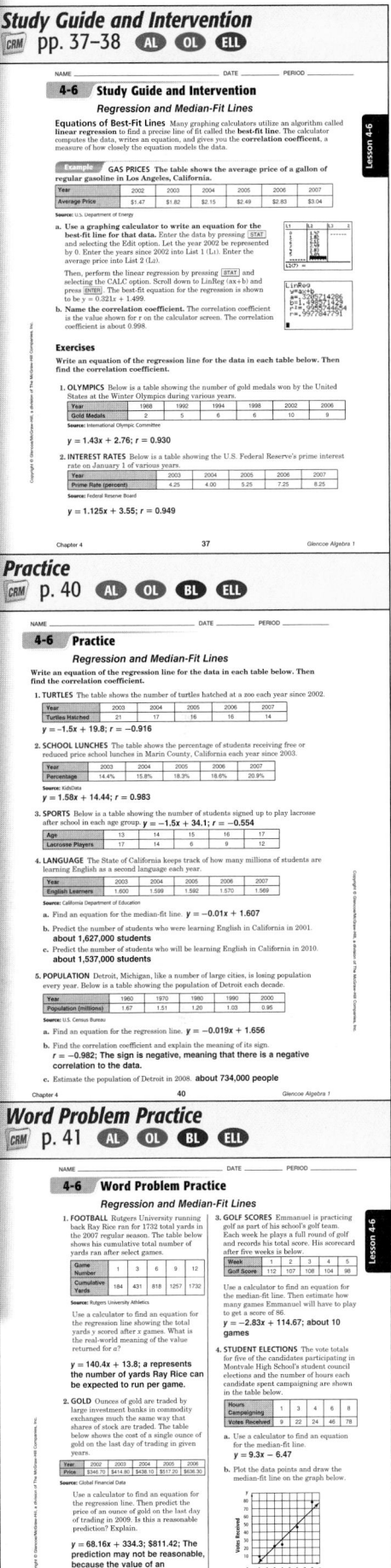

4 ASSESS

Yesterday's News Ask students to write how investigating relationships using scatter plots and lines of fit in yesterday's lesson helped them in today's new material.

Formative Assessment

Check for student understanding of Lessons 4-5 and 4-6.

CRM Quiz 3, p. 52

Additional Answers

28. Yes; opposite sides have the same slope, so they are parallel. Consecutive sides have slopes that are opposite reciprocals, so they are perpendicular.

43.

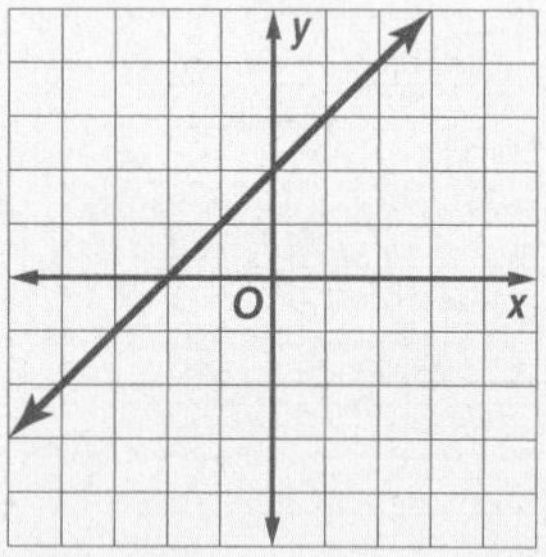

44.

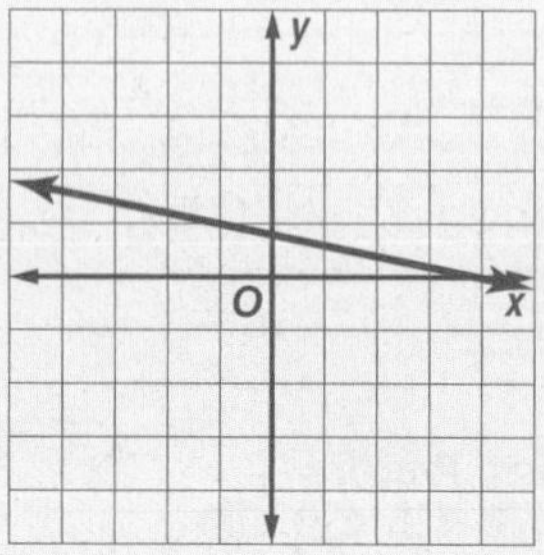

45.

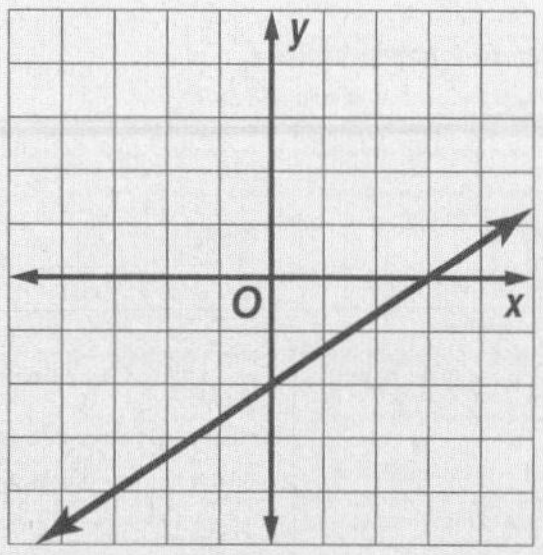

46.

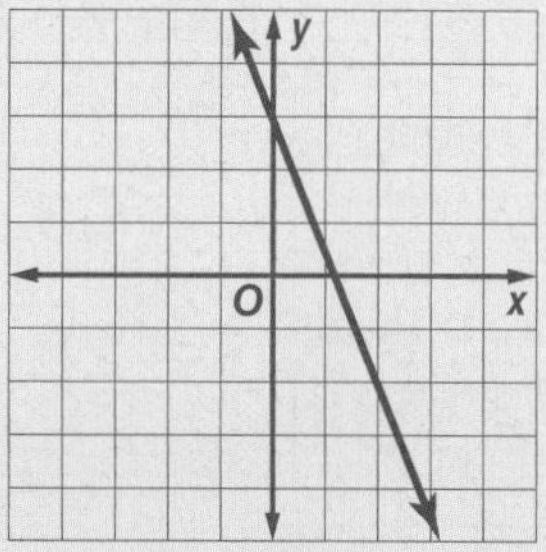

PSAE PRACTICE 8.11.02, 6.11.17, 8.11.07

23. GEOMETRY Sam is putting a border around a poster. x represents the poster's width, and y represents the poster's length. Which equation represents how much border Sam will use if he doubles the length and the width? **C**

A $4xy$ C $4(x + y)$
B $(x + y)^4$ D $16(x + y)$

24. SHORT RESPONSE Tatiana wants to run 5 miles at an average pace of 9 minutes per mile. After 4 miles, her average pace is 9 minutes 10 seconds. In how many minutes must she complete the final mile to reach her goal? **8 min 20 s**

25. What is the slope of the line that passes through (1, 3) and (−3, 1)? **H**

F −2 H $\frac{1}{2}$
G $-\frac{1}{2}$ J 2

26. What is an equation of the line that passes through (0, 1) and has a slope of 3? **D**

A $y = 3x - 1$
B $y = 3x - 2$
C $y = 3x + 4$
D $y = 3x + 1$

Spiral Review

27. USED CARS Gianna wants to buy a specific make and model of a used car. She researched prices from dealers and private sellers and made the graph shown. (Lesson 4-5)

a. Describe the relationship in the data. **negative correlation**

b. Use the line of fit to predict the price of a car that is 7 years old. **$3600**

c. Is it reasonable to use this line of fit to predict the price of a 10-year-old car? Explain. **No, according to the line of fit, the cost would be $0.**

Used Cars

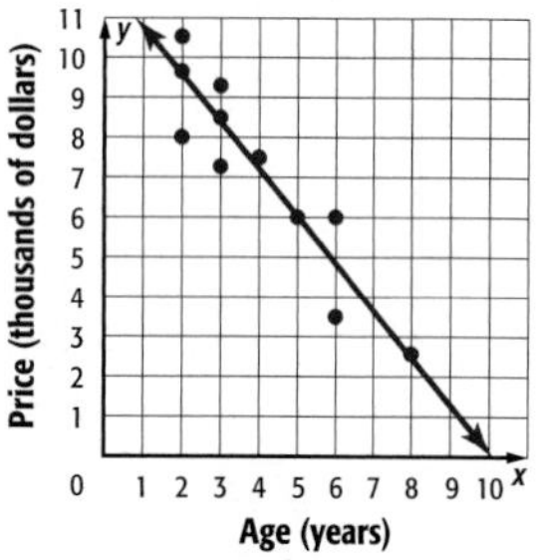

28. GEOMETRY A quadrilateral has sides with equations $y = -2x$, $2x + y = 6$, $y = \frac{1}{2}x + 6$, and $x - 2y = 9$. Is the figure a rectangle? Explain your reasoning. (Lesson 4-4) **See margin.**

Write each equation in standard form. (Lesson 4-3)

29. $y - 2 = 3(x - 1)$ $\mathbf{3x - y = 1}$

30. $y - 5 = 6(x + 1)$ $\mathbf{6x - y = -11}$

31. $y + 2 = -2(x - 5)$ $\mathbf{2x + y = 8}$

32. $y + 3 = \frac{1}{2}(x + 4)$ $\mathbf{x - 2y = 2}$

33. $y - 1 = \frac{2}{3}(x + 9)$ $\mathbf{2x - 3y = -21}$

34. $y + 3 = -\frac{1}{4}(x + 2)$ $\mathbf{x + 4y = -14}$

Find the slope of the line that passes through each pair of points. (Lesson 3-3)

35. (3, 4), (10, 8) $\frac{4}{7}$

36. (−4, 7), (3, 5) $-\frac{2}{7}$

37. (3, 7), (−2, 4) $\frac{3}{5}$

38. (−3, 2), (−3, 4) **undefined**

Skills Review

If $f(x) = x^2 - x + 1$, find each value. (Lesson 1-7)

39. $f(-1)$ **3**

40. $f(5) - 3$ **18**

41. $f(a)$ $\mathbf{a^2 - a + 1}$

42. $f(b + 2)$ $\mathbf{b^2 + 3b + 3}$

Graph each equation. (Lesson 3-1) **43–46. See margin.**

43. $y = x + 2$

44. $x + 5y = 4$

45. $2x - 3y = 6$

46. $5x + 2y = 6$

Additional Answer (p. 261, Check Your Progress)

1. D = {all real numbers}, R = {all even integers}

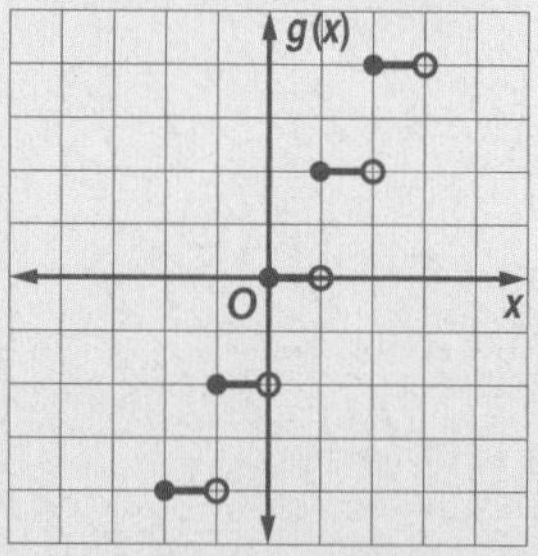

4-7 Special Functions

Then
You wrote equations of lines that pass through a particular point, either parallel or perpendicular to a given line. (Lesson 4-4)

Now
- Identify and graph step functions.
- Identify and graph absolute value and piecewise-defined functions.

IL Learning Standards

8.B.4b Use the basic functions of absolute value, square root, linear, quadratic **and step to describe numerical relationships.**
8.C.4b Apply algebraic properties and procedures with matrices, vectors, functions and sequences using data found in business, industry and consumer situations.

New Vocabulary
step function
piecewise-linear function
greatest integer function
absolute value function
piecewise-defined function

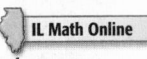

IL Math Online

glencoe.com
- Extra Examples
- Personal Tutor
- Self-Check Quiz
- Homework Help

Why?

Kim is ordering books online. The site charges for shipping based on the amount of the order. If the order is less than \$10, shipping costs \$3. If the order is more than \$10 but less than \$20, it will cost \$5 to ship it.

Step Functions The graph of a **step function** is a series of line segments. Because each part of a step function is linear, this type of function is called a **piecewise-linear function**.

One example of a step function is the **greatest integer function**, written as $f(x) = [\![x]\!]$, where $f(x)$ is the greatest integer not greater than x. For example, $[6.8] = 6$ because 6 is the greatest integer that is not greater than 6.8.

Key Concept — Greatest Integer Function (For Your FOLDABLE)

Parent function: $f(x) = [\![x]\!]$
Type of graph: disjointed line segments
Domain: all real numbers
Range: all integers

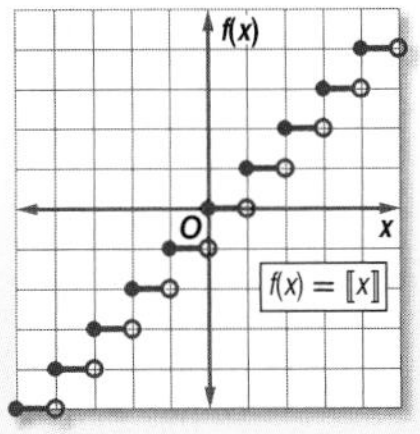

EXAMPLE 1 Greatest Integer Function

Graph $f(x) = [\![x + 2]\!]$. State the domain and range.

First, make a table. Select a few values between integers. On the graph, dots represent included points. Circles represent points not included.

x	$x + 2$	$[\![x + 2]\!]$
0	2	2
0.25	2.25	2
0.5	2.5	2
1	3	3
1.25	3.25	3
1.5	3.5	3
2	4	4
2.25	4.25	4

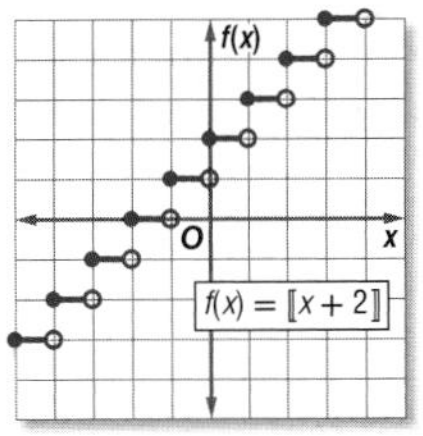

Note that this is the graph of $f(x) = [\![x]\!]$ shifted 2 units to the left.

Because the dots and circles overlap, the domain is all real numbers. The range is all integers.

Check Your Progress

1. Graph $g(x) = 2[\![x]\!]$. State the domain and range. **See margin.**

Personal Tutor glencoe.com

4-7 Lesson Notes

1 FOCUS

Vertical Alignment

Before Lesson 4-7
Write equations of lines that pass through a particular point, either parallel or perpendicular to a given line.

Lesson 4-7
Identify and graph step functions, absolute value functions, and piecewise-defined functions.

After Lesson 4-7
Solve inequalities by adding, subtracting, multiplying, dividing, and graphing.
Solve inequalities involving absolute value.

2 TEACH

Scaffolding Questions

Have students read the *Why?* section of the lesson.

Ask:
- For what order values will you pay \$3 for shipping? all values greater than \$0 and less than \$10
- If x is the cost of an order that is less than \$10 and y is the cost of the shipping, name three ordered pairs on the graph that represent this situation. Sample answer: (5, 3), (6, 3), (9, 3)
- How much would it cost to ship a \$10 item? \$5

Lesson 4-7 Resources

Resource	Approaching-Level	On-Level	Beyond-Level	English Learners
Teacher Edition	• Differentiated Instruction, p. 265	• Differentiated Instruction, pp. 265, 266	• Differentiated Instruction, p. 266	
Chapter Resource Masters	• Study Guide and Intervention, pp. 43–44 • Skills Practice, p. 45 • Practice, p. 46 • Word Problem Practice, p. 47	• Study Guide and Intervention, pp. 43–44 • Skills Practice, p. 45 • Practice, p. 46 • Word Problem Practice, p. 47 • Enrichment, p. 48	• Practice, p. 46 • Word Problem Practice, p. 47 • Enrichment, p. 48	• Study Guide and Intervention, pp. 43–44 • Skills Practice, p. 45 • Practice, p. 46
Transparencies	• 5-Minute Check Transparency 4-7	• 5-Minute Check Transparency 4-7	• 5-Minute Check Transparency 4-7	• 5-Minute Check Transparency 4-7
Other	• Study Notebook	• Study Notebook	• Study Notebook	• Study Notebook

Step Functions

Example 1 shows how to state the domain and range and draw the graph of a greatest integer function. **Example 2** shows how to represent a real-world situation with a step function graph.

✓ Formative Assessment

Use the Check Your Progress exercises after each Example to determine students' understanding of concepts.

Additional Examples

1 Graph $f(x) = [\![x - 2]\!]$. State the domain and range. D = {all real numbers} R = {all integers}

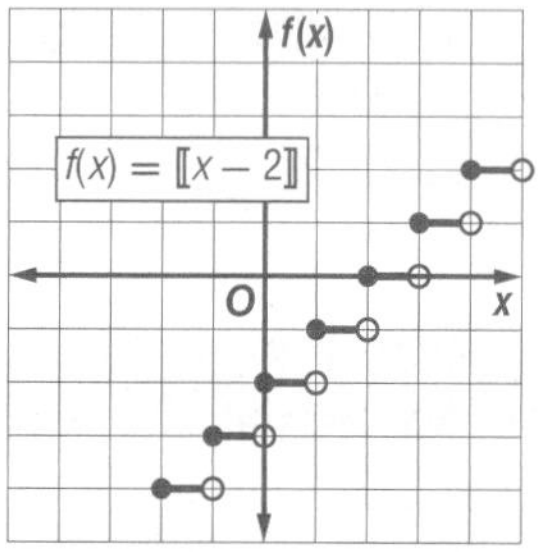

2 **TAXI** A taxi company charges a fee for waiting at a rate of \$0.75 per minute or any fraction thereof. Draw a graph that represents this situation.

Taxi Waiting Fee

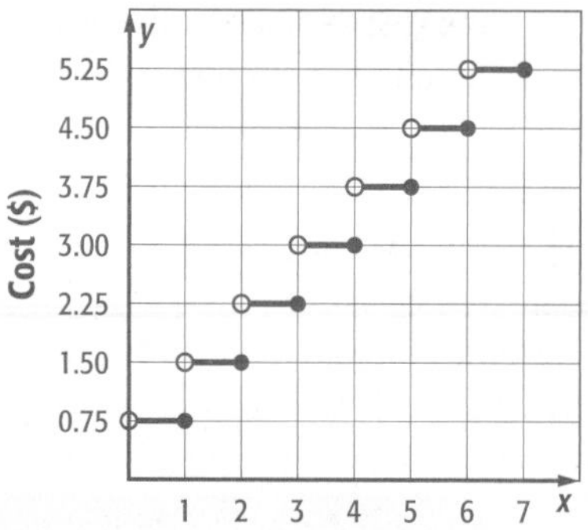

Additional Examples also in Interactive Classroom PowerPoint® Presentations

IWB INTERACTIVE WHITEBOARD READY

Step functions can be used to represent many real-world situations involving money.

Real-World Link

North Americans are the most likely to have cell phones with 93.2% of the population owning phones.

Source: IT Facts

Real-World EXAMPLE 2 Step Function

CELL PHONE PLANS **Cell phone companies charge by the minute, not by the second. A cell phone company charges \$0.45 per minute or any fraction thereof for exceeding the number of minutes allotted on each plan. Draw a graph that represents this situation.**

The total cost for the extra minutes will be a multiple of \$0.45, and the graph will be a step function. If the time is greater than 0 but less than or equal to 1 minute, the charge will be \$0.45. If the time is greater than 2 but is less than or equal to 3 minutes, you will be charged for 3 minutes or \$1.35.

x	$f(x)$
$0 < x \leq 1$	0.45
$1 < x \leq 2$	0.90
$2 < x \leq 3$	1.35
$3 < x \leq 4$	1.80
$4 < x \leq 5$	2.25
$5 < x \leq 6$	2.70
$6 < x \leq 7$	3.15

Cell Phone Overage

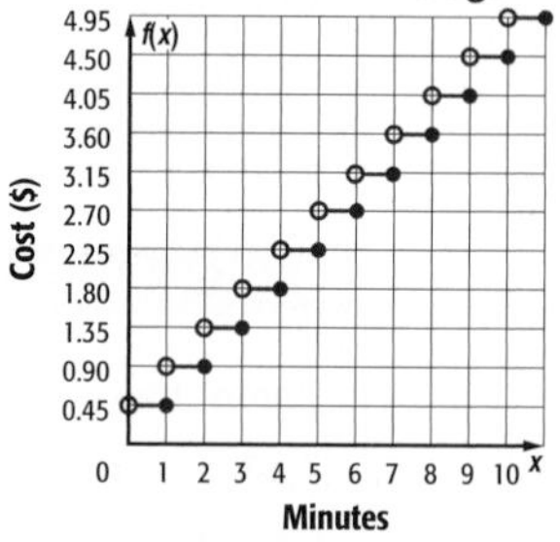

✓ Check Your Progress

2. **PARKING** A garage charges \$4 for the first hour and \$1 for each additional hour. Draw a graph that represents this situation. **See Ch. 4 Answer Appendix.**

Personal Tutor glencoe.com

Review Vocabulary

absolute value the distance a number is from zero on a number line; written $|n|$ (Lesson 2-5)

Absolute Value Functions Another type of piecewise-linear function is the **absolute value function**. Recall that the absolute value of a number is always nonnegative. So in the absolute value parent function, written as $f(x) = |x|$, all of the values of the range are nonnegative.

Key Concept — Absolute Value Function

For Your FOLDABLE

Parent function: $f(x) = |x|$, defined as

$$f(x) = \begin{cases} x \text{ if } x > 0 \\ 0 \text{ if } x = 0 \\ -x \text{ if } x < 0 \end{cases}$$

Type of graph: V-shaped

Domain: all real numbers

Range: all nonnegative real numbers

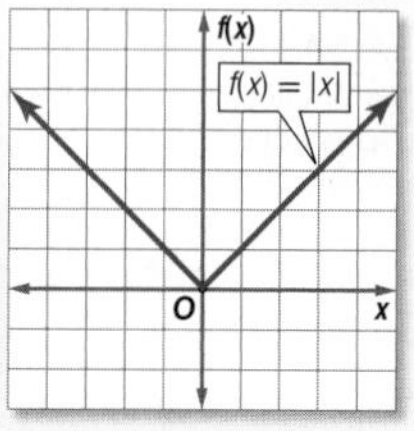

The absolute value function is called a **piecewise-defined function** because it is defined using two or more expressions.

TEACH with TECH

BLOG On your secure classroom blog give students a picture file of a graph of the greatest integer function. Have students write a blog entry explaining how to interpret the function and its graph.

Additional Answers (Check Your Progress)

3.

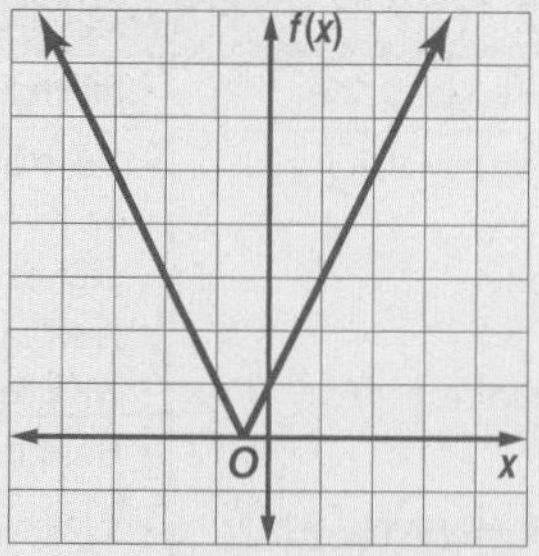

4.

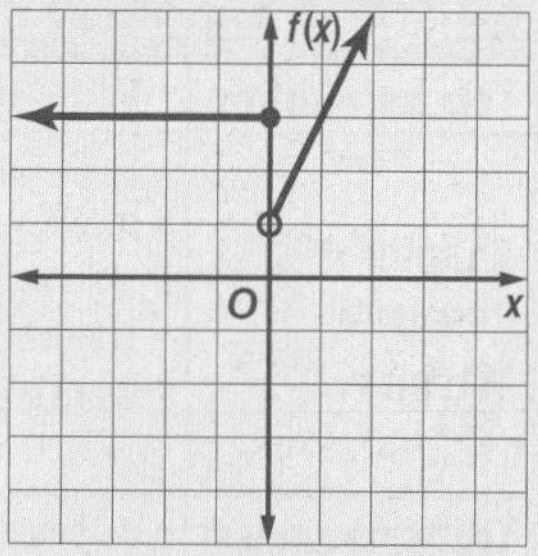

EXAMPLE 3 Absolute Value Function

Graph $f(x) = |x - 4|$. State the domain and range.

Since $f(x)$ cannot be negative, the minimum point of the graph is where $f(x) = 0$.

$f(x) = \|x - 4\|$	**Original function**
$0 = x - 4$	**Replace $f(x)$ with 0 and $\|x - 4\|$ with $x - 4$.**
$4 = x$	**Add 4 to each side.**

Next make a table of values. Include values for $x > 4$ and $x < 4$.

$f(x) = \|x - 4\|$	
x	$f(x)$
−2	6
0	4
2	2
4	0
5	1
6	2
7	3
8	4

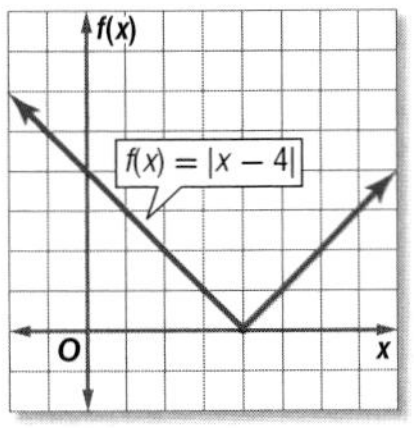

The domain is all real numbers. The range is all real numbers greater than or equal to 0. Note that this is the graph of $f(x) = |x|$ shifted 4 units to the right.

Check Your Progress

3. Graph $f(x) = |2x + 1|$. State the domain and range. **See margin.**

Personal Tutor glencoe.com

Not all piecewise-defined functions are absolute value functions. Step functions are also piecewise-defined functions. In fact, all piecewise-linear functions are piecewise-defined.

StudyTip

Piecewise Functions To graph a piecewise-defined function, graph each "piece" separately. There should be a dot or line that contains each member of the domain.

EXAMPLE 4 Piecewise-Defined Function

Graph $f(x) = \begin{cases} -2x \text{ if } x > 1 \\ x + 3 \text{ if } x \leq 1 \end{cases}$. State the domain and range.

Graph the first expression. Create a table of values for when $x > 1$, $f(x) = -2x$ and draw the graph. Since x is not equal to 1, place a circle at $(1, -2)$.

Next, graph the second expression. Create a table of values for when $x \leq 1$, $f(x) = x + 3$ and draw the graph. If $x = 1$, then $f(x) = 4$; place a dot at $(1, 4)$.

The domain is all real numbers. The range is $y \leq 4$.

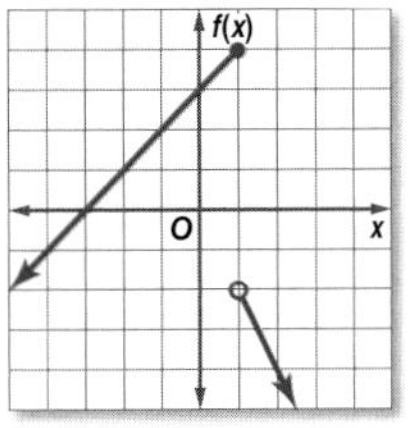

Check Your Progress

4. Graph $f(x) = \begin{cases} 2x + 1 \text{ if } x > 0 \\ 3 \text{ if } x \leq 0 \end{cases}$. State the domain and range. **See margin for graph; D = all real numbers, R = $f(x) > 1$.**

Personal Tutor glencoe.com

Absolute Value Function

Example 3 shows how to graph an absolute value function and determine the domain and range of the function. **Example 4** shows how to graph a piecewise-defined function that is not an absolute value function, and determine its domain and range.

Tips for New Teachers

Table of Values Students having difficulty with the absolute value function may benefit from making a table of values for the parent function $f(x) = |x|$ and then graphing it.

Additional Examples

3 Graph $f(x) = |2x + 2|$. State the domain and range.

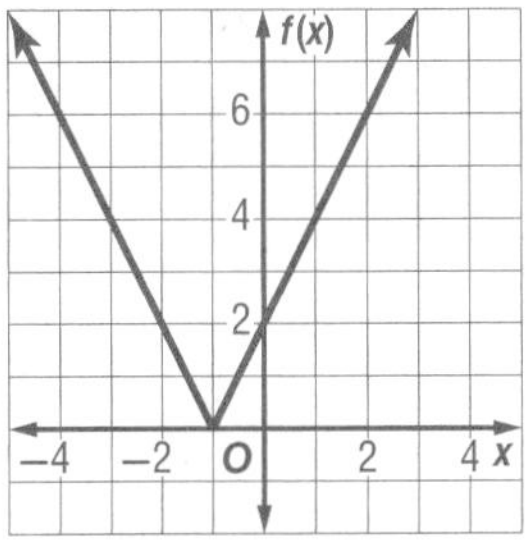

D = all real numbers;
R = all nonnegative numbers

4 Graph $f(x) = \begin{cases} -x \text{ if } x < 0 \\ -x + 2 \text{ if } x \geq 0 \end{cases}$.

State the domain and range.

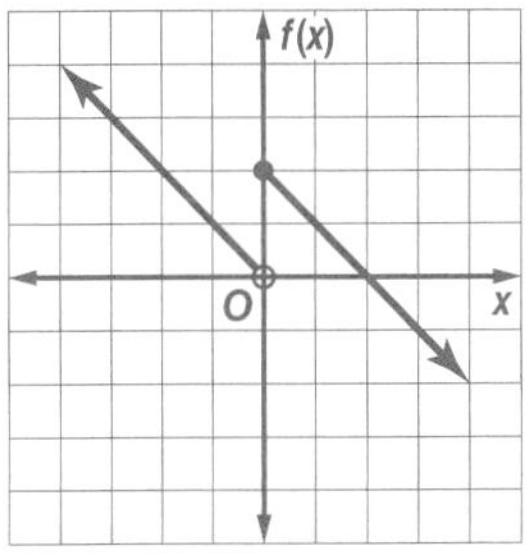

D = all real numbers;
R = all real numbers

Additional Examples also in Interactive Classroom PowerPoint® Presentations

IWB INTERACTIVE WHITEBOARD READY

Focus on Mathematical Content

Functions The vertical line test can be used to verify that an absolute value function, a greatest-integer function, and a piecewise-defined function are actually functions. Graph the functions and then draw vertical lines anywhere on the graph. If any of the lines intersect the graph in more than one point, it is not a graph of a function. A vertical line drawn on a step-function at the end of one step and the beginning of the next would appear to intersect at two points, however the circle on one end of a step in the graph represents a point not included on the graph.

3 PRACTICE

Formative Assessment

Use Exercises 1–8 to check for understanding.

Use the chart at the bottom of this page to customize assignments for your students.

Additional Answers

1. 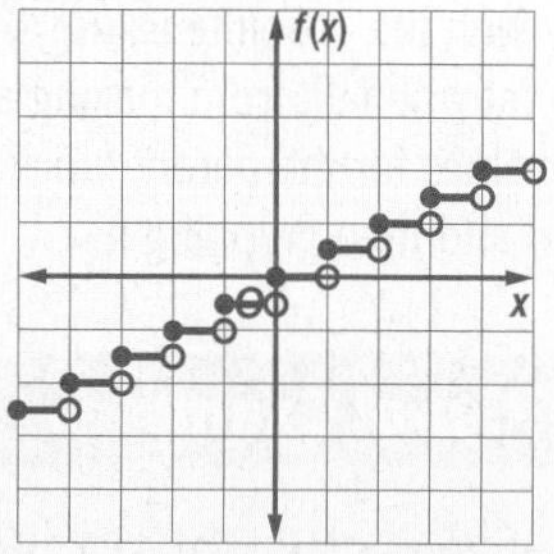

D = all real numbers;
R = all integer multiples of 0.5

2. 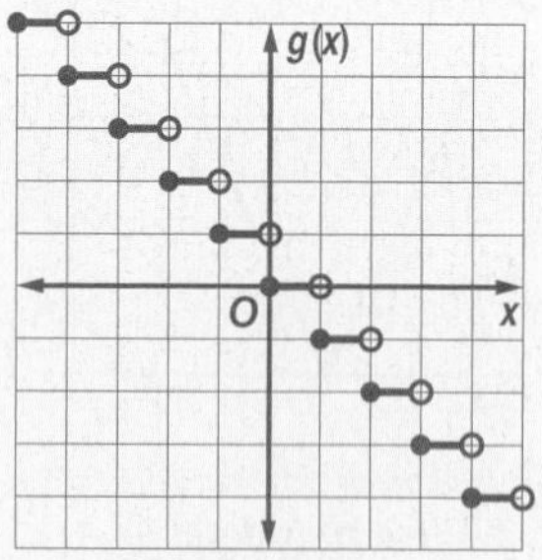

D = all real numbers;
R = all integers

3. 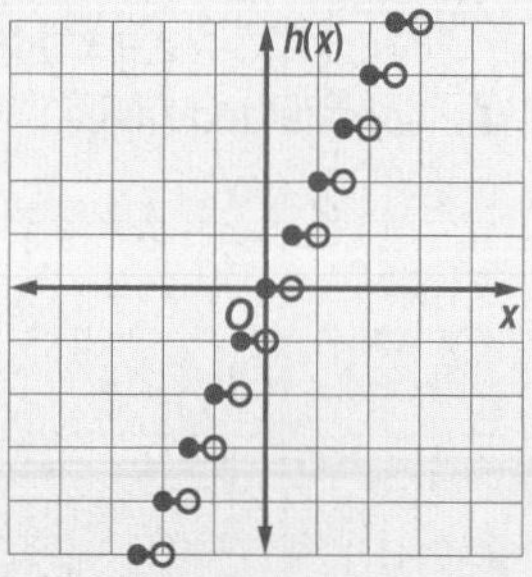

D = all real numbers;
R = all integers

4. 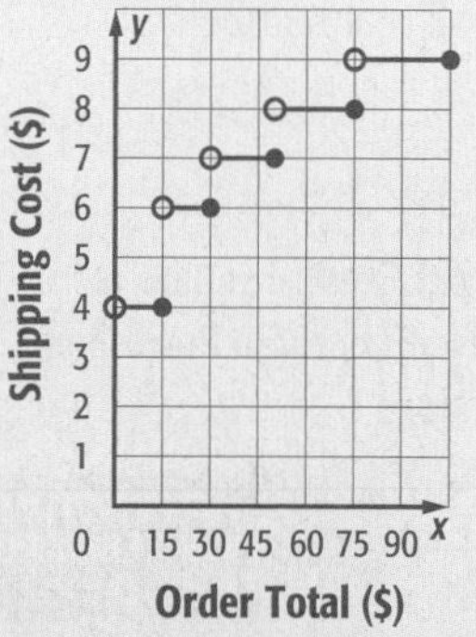

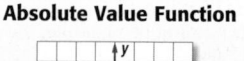

Concept Summary: Special Functions

For Your FOLDABLE

Step Function

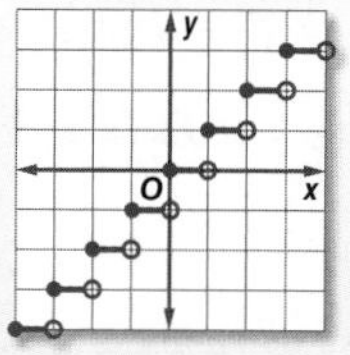

Absolute Value Function

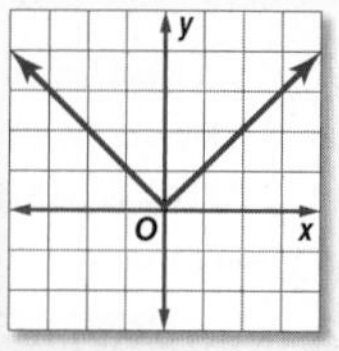

Piecewise-Defined Function

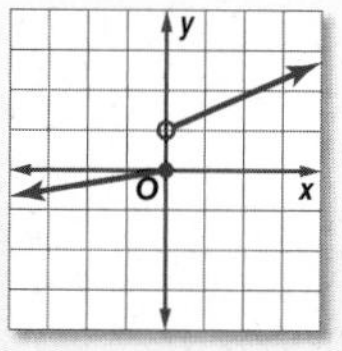

Check Your Understanding

1–3. See margin.

Example 1 p. 261

Graph each function. State the domain and range.

1. $f(x) = \frac{1}{2}[\![x]\!]$
2. $g(x) = -[\![x]\!]$
3. $h(x) = [\![2x]\!]$

Example 2 p. 262

4. **SHIPPING** Elan is ordering a gift for his dad online. The table shows the shipping rates. Graph the step function. See margin.

Order Total ($)	Shipping Cost ($)
0–15	3.99
15.01–30	5.99
30.01–50	6.99
50.01–75	7.99
75.01–100	8.99
Over $100	9.99

Examples 3 and 4 p. 263

Graph each function. State the domain and range. 5–8. See Ch. 4 Answer Appendix.

5. $f(x) = |x - 3|$
6. $g(x) = |2x + 4|$
7. $f(x) = \begin{cases} 2x - 1 \text{ if } x > -1 \\ -x \text{ if } x \leq -1 \end{cases}$
8. $g(x) = \begin{cases} -3x - 2 \text{ if } x > -2 \\ -x + 1 \text{ if } x \leq -2 \end{cases}$

Practice and Problem Solving

● = **Step-by-Step Solutions** begin on page R12.
Extra Practice begins on page 815.

Example 1 p. 261

Graph each function. State the domain and range. 9–14. See Ch. 4 Answer Appendix.

9. $f(x) = 3[\![x]\!]$
10. $f(x) = [\![-x]\!]$
11. $g(x) = -2[\![x]\!]$
12. $g(x) = [\![x]\!] + 3$
13. $h(x) = [\![x]\!] - 1$
14. $h(x) = \frac{1}{2}[\![x]\!] + 1$

Example 2 p. 262

15. **CAB FARES** Lauren wants to take a taxi from a hotel to a friend's house. The rate is $3 plus $1.50 per mile after the first mile. Every fraction of a mile is rounded up to the next mile.
    a. Draw a graph to represent the cost of using a taxi cab. See margin.
    b. What is the cost if the trip is 8.5 miles long? $15

16. **POSTAGE** The United States Postal Service increases the rate of postage periodically. The table shows the cost to mail a letter weighing 1 ounce or less from 1988 through 2007. Draw a step graph to represent the data. See margin.

Year	1988	1991	1995	1999	2001	2002	2006	2007
Cost ($)	0.25	0.29	0.32	0.33	0.34	0.37	0.39	0.41

Differentiated Homework Options

Level	Assignment	Two-Day Option	
AL Basic	9–30, 55, 59, 61–79	9–29 odd, 61–64	10–30 even, 55, 59, 65–79
OL Core	9–35 odd, 37–47, 49, 51, 53–55, 59, 61–79	9–30, 61–64	31–55, 59, 65–79
BL Advanced	31–73, (optional: 74–79)		

Examples 3 and 4 p. 263

Graph each function. State the domain and range. 17–30. See Ch. 4 Answer Appendix.

17. $f(x) = |2x - 1|$

18. $f(x) = |x + 5|$

19. $g(x) = |-3x - 5|$

20. $g(x) = |-x - 3|$

21. $f(x) = \left|\frac{1}{2}x - 2\right|$

22. $f(x) = \left|\frac{1}{3}x + 2\right|$

23. $g(x) = |x + 2| + 3$

24. $g(x) = |2x - 3| + 1$

25. $f(x) = \begin{cases} \frac{1}{2}x - 1 \text{ if } x > 3 \\ -2x + 3 \text{ if } x \le 3 \end{cases}$

26. $f(x) = \begin{cases} 2x - 5 \text{ if } x > 1 \\ 4x - 3 \text{ if } x \le 1 \end{cases}$

27. $f(x) = \begin{cases} 2x + 3 \text{ if } x \ge -3 \\ -\frac{1}{3}x + 1 \text{ if } x < -3 \end{cases}$

28. $f(x) = \begin{cases} 3x + 4 \text{ if } x \ge 1 \\ x + 3 \text{ if } x < 1 \end{cases}$

29. $f(x) = \begin{cases} 3x + 2 \text{ if } x > -1 \\ -\frac{1}{2}x - 3 \text{ if } x \le -1 \end{cases}$

30. $f(x) = \begin{cases} 2x + 1 \text{ if } x < -2 \\ -3x - 1 \text{ if } x \ge -2 \end{cases}$

B Determine the domain and range of each function.

31.

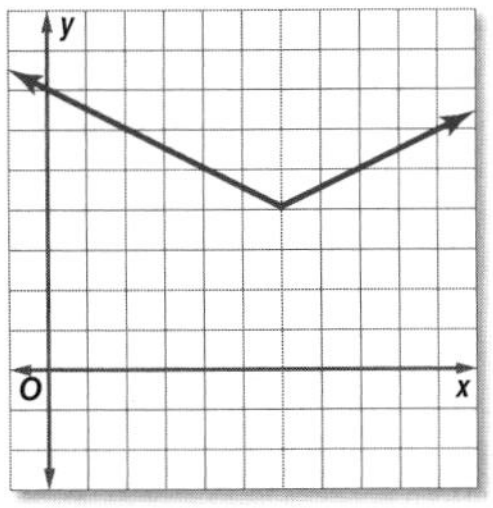

32.

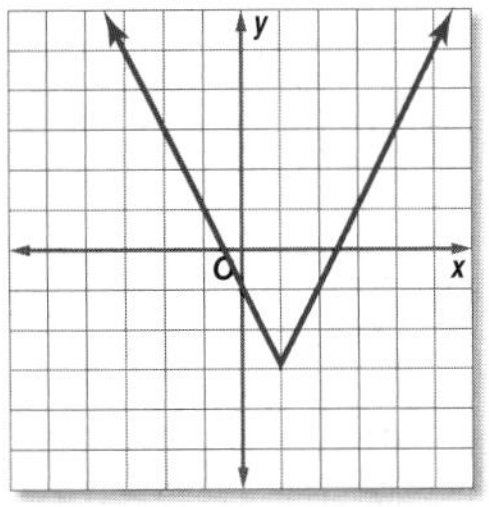

33.

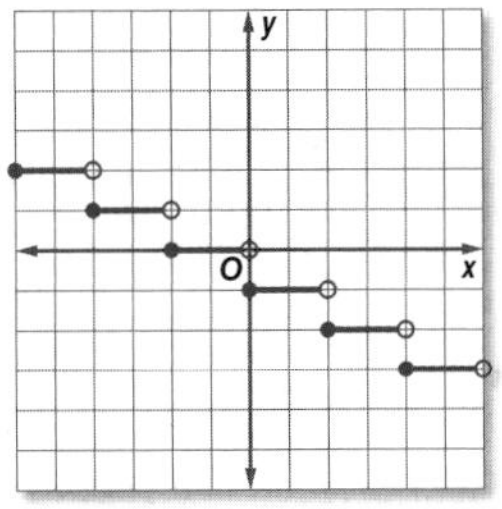

34.

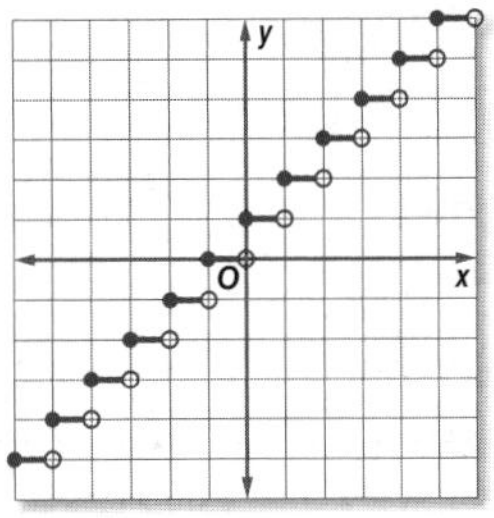

35.

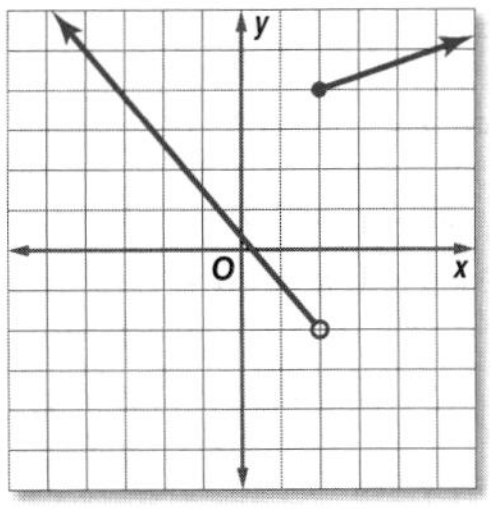

36.

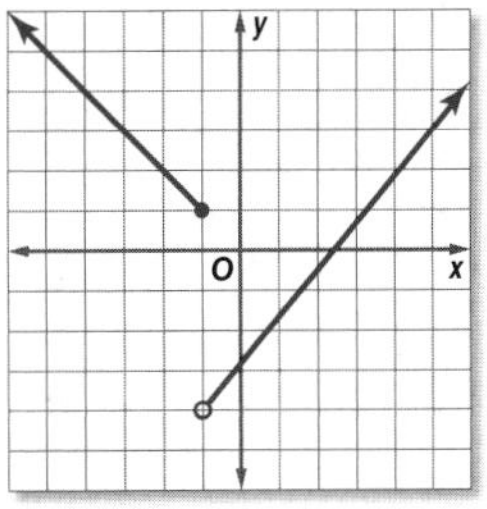

StudyTip

Nonlinear Functions The greatest integer function, absolute value function, and piecewise defined functions are examples of nonlinear functions.

31. D = all real numbers; R = $y \ge 4$
32. D = all real numbers; R = $y \ge -3$
33. D = all real numbers; R = all integers
34. D = all real numbers; R = all integers
35. D = all real numbers; R = $y > -2$
36. D = all real numbers; R = $y > -4$

37. BOATING According to Boat Minnesota, the maximum number of people that can safely ride in a boat is determined by the boat's length and width. The table shows some guidelines for the length of a boat that is 6 feet wide. Graph this relation. See margin.

Length of Boat (ft)	18–19	20–22	23–24
Number of People	7	8	9

Exercise Alert

Grid Paper For Exercises 1–30, 37, 42–54, and 60 students will need grid paper.

Additional Answers

15a.

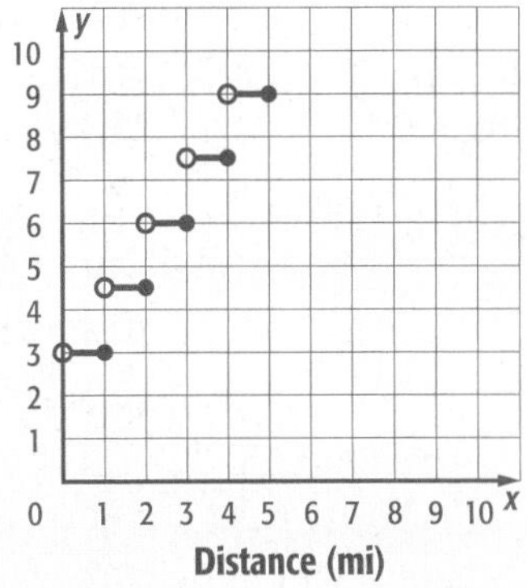

16.

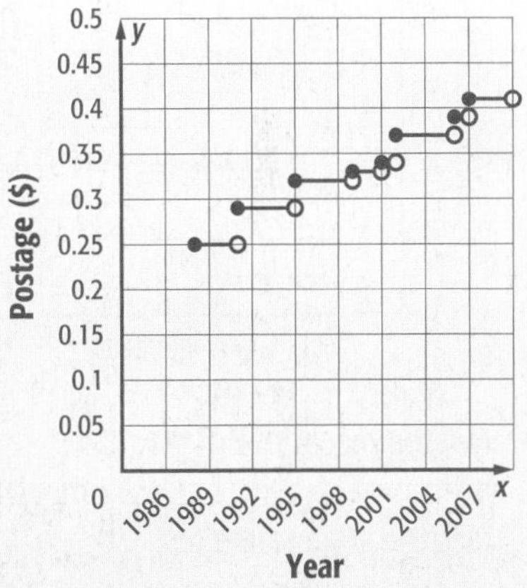

37.

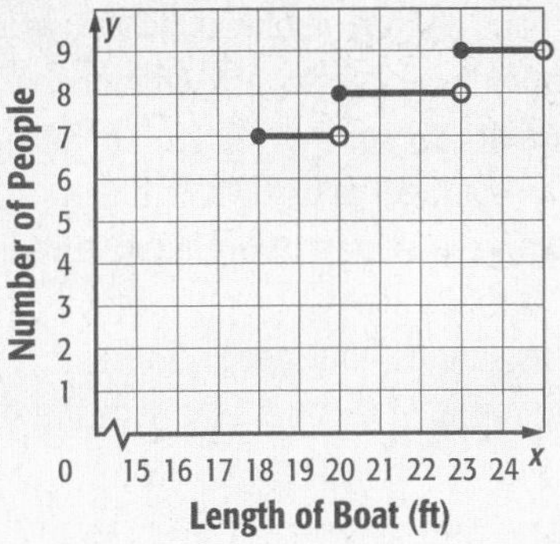

Differentiated Instruction

AL OL

If students have trouble picturing the graphs of special functions,

Then have students draw a large coordinate grid on three sheets of inch-grid paper. Students should use scissors, tape or glue, and straws to model the general shape of a step function, an absolute value function, and a piecewise-defined function. Have students label each type of graph.

Additional Answers

42.

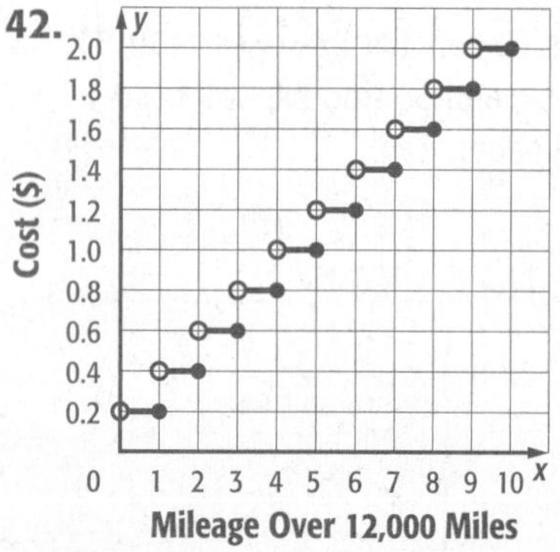

46.

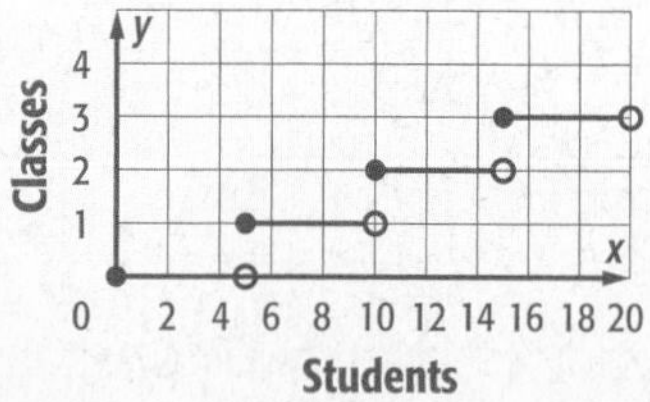

47.

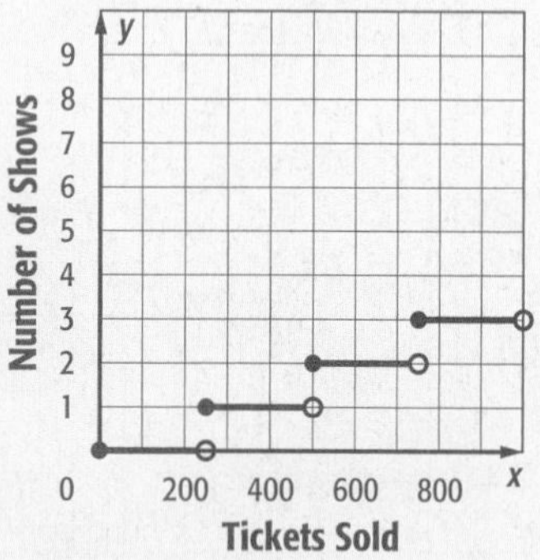

55. No; the pieces of the graph overlap vertically, so the graph fails the vertical line test.

59. Sample answer: The cost of exceeding the allotted minutes on your cell phone plan is billed per minute. So, if you are 2.5 minutes over, you are charged for 3 minutes of overage. The graph of this is called a step function because you cannot trace the graph without picking up your pencil. There is a range of x-values that have the same y-value on the graph.

For Exercises 38–41, match each graph to one of the following equations.

A	B	C	D
$y = 2x - 1$	$y = [\![2x]\!] - 1$	$y = \lvert 2x \rvert - 1$	$y = \begin{cases} 2x + 1 \text{ if } x > 0 \\ -2x + 1 \text{ if } x \leq 0 \end{cases}$

38.

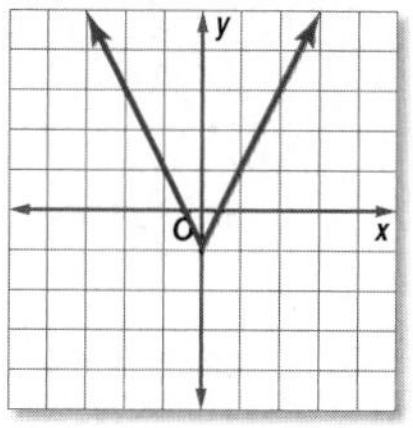

C

39.

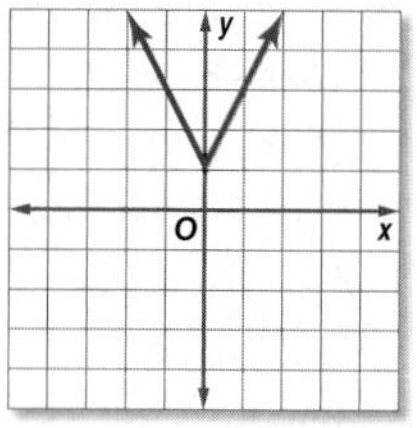

D

40.

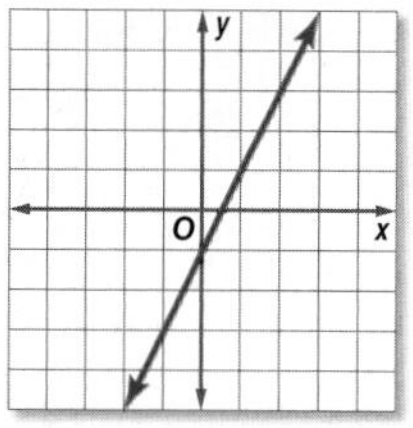

A

41.

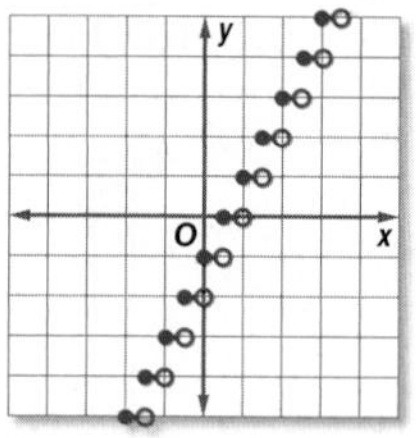

B

42. CAR LEASE As part of Marcus' leasing agreement, he will be charged \$0.20 per mile for each mile over 12,000. Any fraction of a mile is rounded up to the next mile. Make a step graph to represent the cost of going over the mileage. **See margin.**

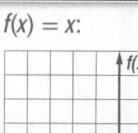

Real-World Link

Leasing a car differs from buying a car. When leasing a car, you may pay a lower monthly cost; however, you do not own the car at the end of the lease term. Most leasing agreements limit the number of miles you can drive the car before incurring additional costs.

Source: Federal Reserve

43. BASEBALL A baseball team is ordering T-shirts with the team logo on the front and the players' names on the back. A graphic design store charges \$10 to set up the artwork plus \$10 per shirt, \$4 each for the team logo, and \$2 to print the last name for an order of 10 shirts or less. For orders of 11–20 shirts, a 5% discount is given. For orders of more than 20 shirts, a 10% discount is given.

a. Organize the information into a table. Include a column showing the total order price for each size order. **See Ch. 4 Answer Appendix.**

b. Write an equation representing the total price for an order of x shirts.

c. Graph the piecewise relation. **c. See Ch. 4 Answer Appendix.**

b. $y = \begin{cases} 10 + 16x \text{ if } 1 \leq x \leq 10 \\ 9.50 + 15.20x \text{ if } 11 < x \leq 20 \\ 9 + 14.40x \text{ if } x > 20 \end{cases}$

44. Consider the function $f(x) = |2x + 3|$. **a–c. See Ch. 4 Answer Appendix.**

a. Make a table of values where x is all integers from -5 to 5, inclusive.

b. Plot the points on a coordinate grid.

c. Graph the function.

45. Consider the function $f(x) = |2x| + 3$. **a–d. See Ch. 4 Answer Appendix.**

a. Make a table of values where x is all integers from -5 to 5, inclusive.

b. Plot the points on a coordinate grid.

c. Graph the function.

d. Describe how this graph is different from the graph in Exercise 44.

Differentiated Instruction

OL BL

Extension Ask students to compare the graph of $f(x) = x$ to the graph of $f(x) = [\![x]\!]$ and the graph of $f(x) = |x|$ to the graph of $f(x) = |[\![x]\!]|$.

$f(x) = x$:

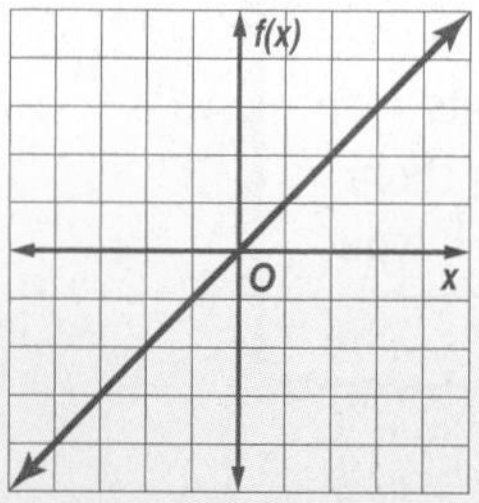

$f(x) = [\![x]\!]$:

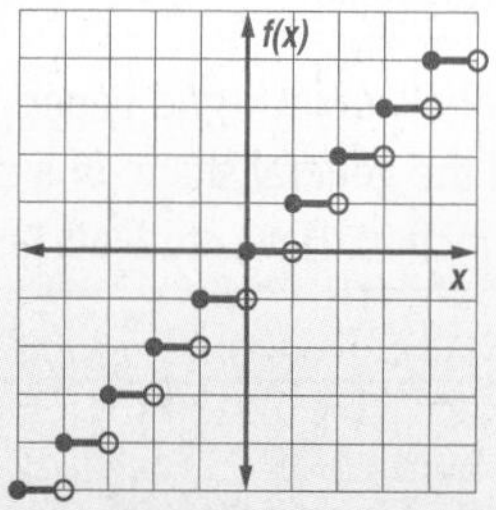

$f(x) = |x|$:

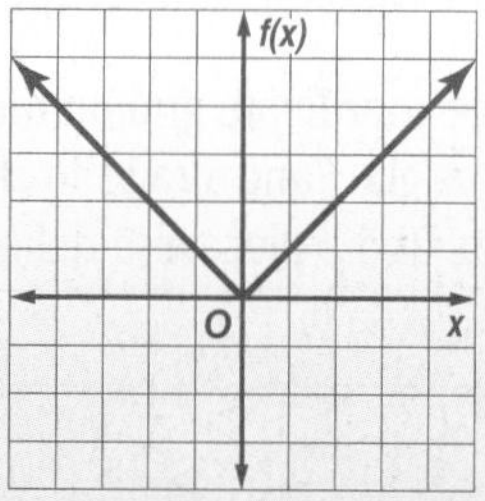

$f(x) = |[\![x]\!]|$:

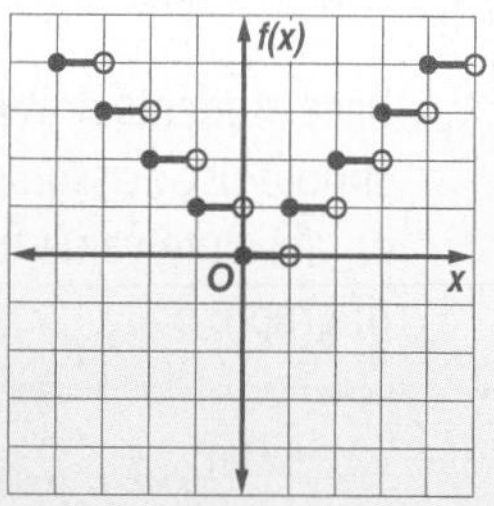

Real-World Link

In addition to traditional dance classes like ballet and tap, more studios are offering classes in hip-hop, jazz/hip-hip, and cardio dance.

Source: Ariel Dance Studio

46. **DANCE** A local studio must have at least 5 students enrolled in a class, or else the class will be canceled. Once 10 students are enrolled, a second class is started. Draw a graph for this situation. **See margin.**

47. **THEATERS** A certain theater will not have a show unless it has sold 50 tickets for that show. Once the capacity of 250 seats are sold, the theater begins selling tickets for the next show. Draw a graph that describes this situation. **See margin.**

C Graph each function. **48–53. See Ch. 4 Answer Appendix.**

48. $f(x) = \frac{1}{2}|x| + 2$
49. $g(x) = \frac{1}{3}|x| + 4$
50. $h(x) = -2|x - 3| + 2$
51. $f(x) = -4|x + 2| - 3$
52. $g(x) = -\frac{2}{3}|x + 6| - 1$
53. $h(x) = -\frac{3}{4}|x - 8| + 1$

54. **MULTIPLE REPRESENTATIONS** In this problem, you will explore piecewise-defined functions.

a. **TABULAR** Copy and complete the table of values for $f(x) = |[\![x]\!]|$ and $g(x) = [\![|x|]\!]$.

x	$[\![x]\!]$	$f(x) = \|[\![x]\!]\|$	$\|x\|$	$g(x) = [\![\|x\|]\!]$
−3	−3	3	3	3
−2.5	−3	3	2.5	2
−2	−2	2	2	2
0	0	0	0	0
0.5	0	0	0.5	0
1	1	1	1	1
1.5	1	1	1.5	1

b. **GRAPHICAL** Graph each function on a coordinate plane. **See Ch. 4 Answer Appendix.**

c. **ANALYTICAL** Compare and contrast the graphs of $f(x)$ and $g(x)$.

54c. When x is nonnegative, the graphs have the same y-values. The graphs have different y-values for the negative x-values.

H.O.T. Problems

Use Higher-Order Thinking Skills

55. **REASONING** Does the piecewise relation below represent a function? Why or why not? **See margin.**

$$y = \begin{cases} -2x + 4 \text{ if } x \geq 2 \\ -\frac{1}{2}x - 1 \text{ if } x \leq 4 \end{cases}$$

CHALLENGE Refer to the graph.

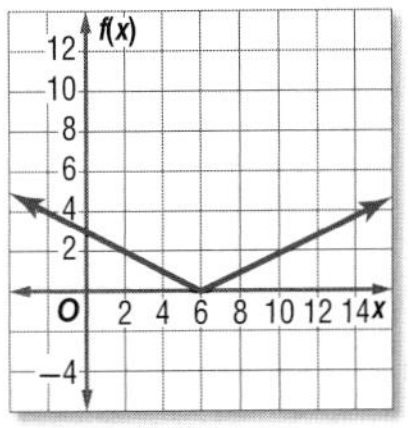

56. Write an absolute value function that represents the graph. $f(x) = \left|\frac{1}{2}x - 3\right|$

57. Write a piecewise function to represent the graph.

58. What are the domain and range?

57. $f(x) = \begin{cases} \frac{1}{2}x - 3 & x > 6 \\ -\frac{1}{2}x + 3 & x \leq 6 \end{cases}$

58. D = all real numbers; R = $f(x) \geq 0$

59. **WRITING IN MATH** Refer to the information on cell phone plans in Example 2. Explain why the graph of this description is called a *step graph*. **See margin.**

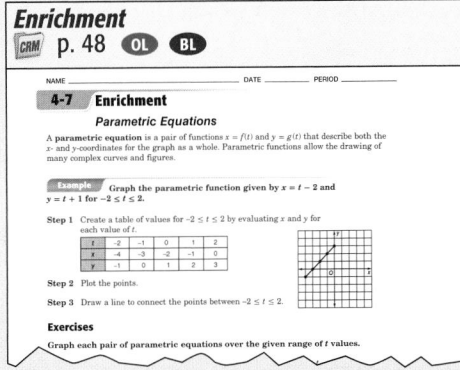

60. **CHALLENGE** A bicyclist travels up and down a hill. The hill has a vertical cross section that can be modeled by the equation $y = -\frac{1}{4}|x - 400| + 100$ where x and y are measured in feet.

a. If $0 \leq x \leq 800$, find the slope for the uphill portion of the trip and then the downhill portion of the trip. $\frac{1}{4}$ **going up;** $-\frac{1}{4}$ **going down**

b. Graph this function. **See Ch. 4 Answer Appendix.**

c. What are the domain and range of the graph? **D = ≤ x ≤ 800; R = ≤ y ≤ 100**

Multiple Representations In Exercise 54, students use a table of values and a graph in the coordinate plane to compare and contrast the graphs of two piecewise functions.

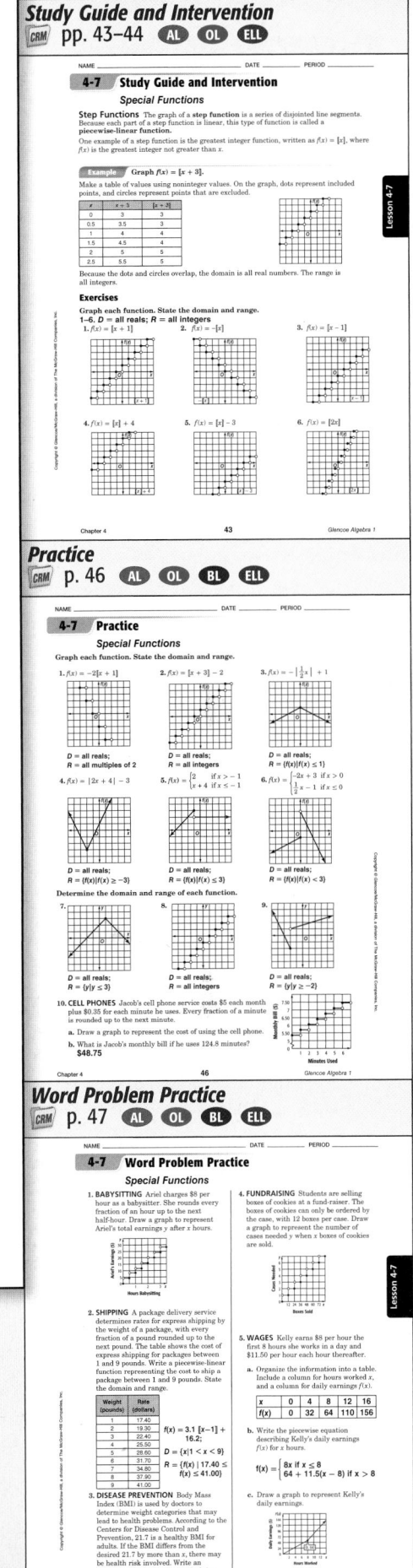

Study Guide and Intervention

CRM pp. 43–44 AL OL ELL

NAME ______ DATE ______ PERIOD ______

4-7 Study Guide and Intervention

Special Functions

Step Functions The graph of a **step function** is a series of disjointed line segments. Because each part of a step function is linear, this type of function is called a **piecewise-linear function.**

One example of a step function is the greatest integer function, written as $f(x) = [\![x]\!]$, where $f(x)$ is the greatest integer not greater than x.

Example Graph $f(x) = [\![x + 3]\!]$.

Make a table of values using noninteger values. On the graph, dots represent included points, and circles represent points that are excluded.

x	$x + 3$	$[\![x + 3]\!]$
0	3	3
0.5	3.5	3
1	4	4
1.5	4.5	4
2	5	5
2.5	5.5	5

Because the dots and circles overlap, the domain is all real numbers. The range is all integers.

Exercises

Graph each function. State the domain and range.
1–6. D = all reals; R = all integers

1. $f(x) = [\![x + 1]\!]$ 2. $f(x) = -[\![x]\!]$ 3. $f(x) = [\![x - 1]\!]$
4. $f(x) = [\![x]\!] + 4$ 5. $f(x) = [\![x]\!] - 3$ 6. $f(x) = [\![2x]\!]$

Chapter 4 43 Glencoe Algebra 1

Lesson 4-7

Practice

CRM p. 46 AL OL BL ELL

NAME ______ DATE ______ PERIOD ______

4-7 Practice

Special Functions

Graph each function. State the domain and range.

1. $f(x) = -2[\![x + 1]\!]$ — D = all reals; R = all multiples of 2
2. $f(x) = [\![x + 3]\!] - 2$ — D = all reals; R = all integers
3. $f(x) = -\left|\frac{1}{2}x\right| + 1$ — D = all reals; R = {f(x)|f(x) ≤ 1}
4. $f(x) = |2x + 4| - 3$ — D = all reals; R = {f(x)|f(x) ≥ −3}
5. $f(x) = \begin{cases} 2 & \text{if } x > -1 \\ x + 4 & \text{if } x \leq -1 \end{cases}$ — D = all reals; R = {f(x)|f(x) ≤ 3}
6. $f(x) = \begin{cases} -2x + 3 & \text{if } x > 0 \\ \frac{1}{2}x - 1 & \text{if } x \leq 0 \end{cases}$ — D = all reals; R = {f(x)|f(x) < 3}

Determine the domain and range of each function.

7. D = all reals; R = {y|y ≤ 3}
8. D = all reals; R = all integers
9. D = all reals; R = {y|y ≥ −2}

10. **CELL PHONES** Jacob's cell phone service costs $5 each month plus $0.35 for each minute he uses. Every fraction of a minute is rounded up to the next minute.

a. Draw a graph to represent the cost of using the cell phone.

b. What is Jacob's monthly bill if he uses 124.8 minutes? $48.75

Chapter 4 46 Glencoe Algebra 1

Word Problem Practice

CRM p. 47 AL OL BL ELL

NAME ______ DATE ______ PERIOD ______

4-7 Word Problem Practice

Special Functions

1. **BABYSITTING** Ariel charges $8 per hour as a babysitter. She rounds every fraction of an hour up to the next half-hour. Draw a graph to represent Ariel's total earnings y after x hours.

2. **SHIPPING** A package delivery service determines rates for express shipping by the weight of a package, with every fraction of a pound rounded up to the next pound. The table shows the cost of express shipping for packages between 1 and 9 pounds. Write a piecewise-linear function representing the cost to ship a package based on its weight. State the domain and range.

Weight (pounds)	Rate (dollars)
1	17.40
2	19.30
3	22.40
4	25.50
5	28.60
6	31.70
7	34.80
8	37.90
9	41.00

f(x) = 3.1 [x−1] + 16.2; D = {x|1 < x < 9}; R = {f(x) | 17.40 ≤ f(x) ≤ 41.00}

3. **DISEASE PREVENTION** Body Mass Index (BMI) is used by doctors to determine weight categories that may lead to health problems. According to the Centers for Disease Control and Prevention, 21.7 is a healthy BMI for adults. If the BMI differs from the desired 21.7 by more than x, there may be health risk involved. Write an equation that can be used to find the highest and lowest BMI for a healthy adult. Then solve if $x = 3.2$.
y = |x−21.7|; 18.5

4. **FUNDRAISING** Students are selling boxes of cookies at a fund-raiser. The boxes of cookies can only be ordered by the case, with 12 boxes per case. Draw a graph to represent the number of cases needed y when x boxes of cookies are sold.

5. **WAGES** Kelly earns $8 per hour for the first 8 hours she works in a day and $11.50 per hour each hour thereafter.

a. Organize the information into a table. Include a column for hours worked x, and a column for daily earnings $f(x)$.

x	0	4	8	12	16
f(x)	0	32	64	110	156

b. Write the piecewise equation describing Kelly's daily earnings $f(x)$ for x hours.

$f(x) = \begin{cases} 8x \text{ if } x \leq 8 \\ 64 + 11.5(x - 8) \text{ if } x > 8 \end{cases}$

c. Draw a graph to represent Kelly's daily earnings.

Chapter 4 47 Glencoe Algebra 1

Lesson 4-7

Enrichment

CRM p. 48 OL BL

NAME ______ DATE ______ PERIOD ______

4-7 Enrichment

Parametric Equations

A **parametric equation** is a pair of functions $x = f(t)$ and $y = g(t)$ that describe both the x- and y-coordinates for the graph as a whole. Parametric functions allow the drawing of many complex curves and figures.

Example Graph the parametric function given by $x = t - 2$ and $y = t + 1$ for $-2 \leq t \leq 2$.

Step 1 Create a table of values for $-2 \leq t \leq 2$ by evaluating x and y for each value of t.

t	−2	−1	0	1	2
x	−4	−3	−2	−1	0
y	−1	0	1	2	3

Step 2 Plot the points.

Step 3 Draw a line to connect the points between $-2 \leq t \leq 2$.

Exercises

Graph each pair of parametric equations over the given range of t values.

4 ASSESS

Ticket Out the Door Write the function $f(x) = 25[\![x]\!]$ on the board. As the students leave the room, ask them to tell you a real-world situation that could be described by the function. For example, a piano tuner charges $25 for every hour or fraction of an hour.

Formative Assessment

Check for student understanding of Lesson 4-7.

CRM Quiz 4, p. 52

Additional Answer

69. Positive; it means the more you study, the better your test score.

Additional Answers, Extend 4-7

2. This situation is modeled by an absolute value function because the graph will consist of segments joined at their endpoints.

4.

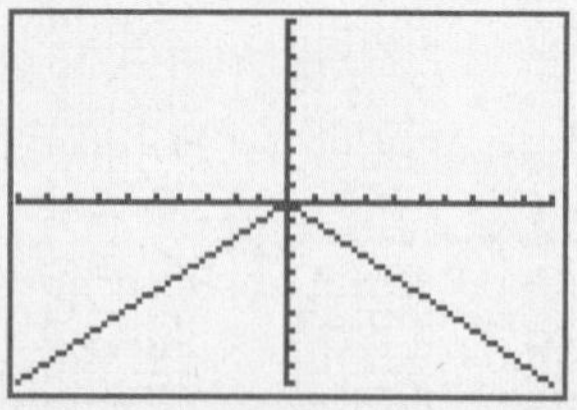

$[-10, 10]$ scl: 1 by $[-10, 10]$ scl: 1
The graph is the reflection of $y = |x|$ over the x-axis.

5. Sample answer: The graph of $y = |x + c|$ is the graph of $y = |x|$ shifted c units left if $c > 0$ and $|c|$ units right if $c < 0$.

PSAE PRACTICE 8.11.07, 6.11.17, 9.11.12, 8.11.06

61. Which equation represents a line that is perpendicular to the graph and passes through the point at (2, 0)? **C**

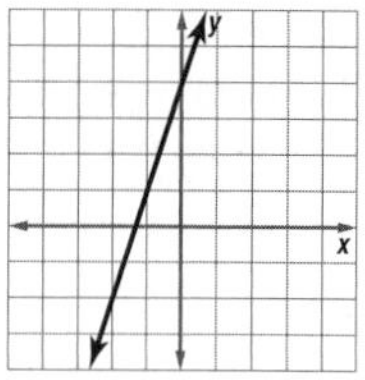

A $y = 3x - 6$
B $y = -3x + 6$
C $y = -\frac{1}{3}x + \frac{2}{3}$
D $y = \frac{1}{3}x - \frac{2}{3}$

62. A giant tortoise travels at a rate of 0.17 mile per hour. Which equation models the time t it would take the giant tortoise to travel 0.8 mile? **F**

F $t = \frac{0.8}{0.17}$ H $t = \frac{0.17}{0.8}$
G $t = (0.17)(0.8)$ J $0.8 = \frac{0.17}{t}$

63. GEOMETRY If $\triangle JKL$ is similar to $\triangle JNM$ what is the value a? **B**

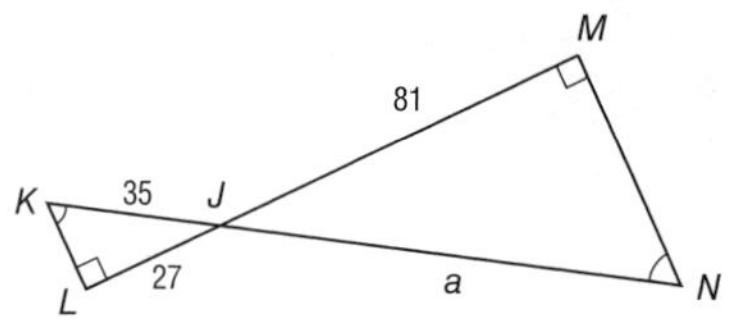

A 62.5
B 105
C 125
D 155.5

64. GRIDDED RESPONSE What is the difference in the value of $2.1(x + 3.2)$, when $x = 5$ and when $x = 3$? **4.2**

Spiral Review

Write an equation of the regression line for the data in each table. (Lesson 4-6)

65. $y = 2.3x + 1.5$

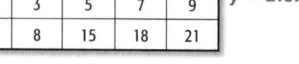

x	1	3	5	7	9
y	3	8	15	18	21

66. $y = 8.235x - 17.365$

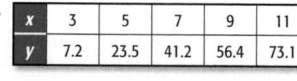

x	3	5	7	9	11
y	7.2	23.5	41.2	56.4	73.1

67. $y = 10.7x + 10.1$

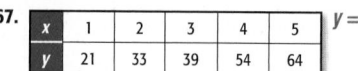

x	1	2	3	4	5
y	21	33	39	54	64

68. $y = 0.325x + 0.89$

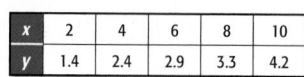

x	2	4	6	8	10
y	1.4	2.4	2.9	3.3	4.2

69. TESTS Determine whether the graph at the right shows a *positive*, *negative*, or *no* correlation. If there is a correlation, describe its meaning. (Lesson 4-5) **See margin.**

Test Scores

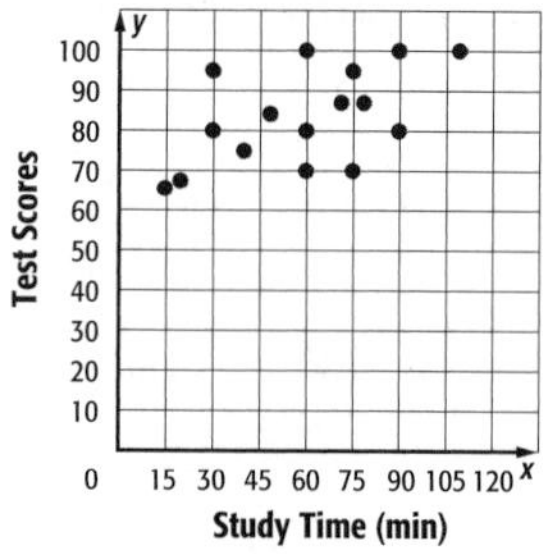

Suppose y varies directly as x. (Lesson 3-4)

70. If $y = 2.5$ when $x = 0.5$, find y when $x = 20$. **100**

71. If $y = -6.6$ when $x = 9.9$, find y when $x = 6.6$. **−4.4**

72. If $y = 2.6$ when $x = 0.25$, find y when $x = 1.125$. **11.7**

73. If $y = 6$ when $x = 0.6$, find x when $y = 12$. **1.2**

Skills Review

Solve each equation. (Lesson 2-2)

74. $104 = k - 67$ **171**

75. $-4 + x = -7$ **−3**

76. $\frac{m}{7} = -11$ **−77**

77. $\frac{2}{3}p = 14$ **21**

78. $-82 = n + 18$ **100**

79. $\frac{9}{t} = -27$ $-\frac{1}{3}$

Piecewise-Linear Functions

IL Math Online glencoe.com
- Other Calculator Keystrokes
- Graphing Technology Personal Tutor

IL Learning Standards — **8.B.4b Use the basic functions of absolute value,** square root, linear, quadratic and **step to describe numerical relationships.**

You can use a graphing calculator to graph and analyze various piecewise functions, including greatest integer functions and absolute value functions.

ACTIVITY 1 Greatest Integer Functions

Graph $f(x) = \llbracket x \rrbracket$ in the standard viewing window.

The calculator may need to be changed to dot mode for the function to graph correctly. Press [MODE] then use the arrow and [ENTER] keys to select DOT.

Enter the equation in the Y= list. Then graph the equation.

KEYSTROKES: [Y=] [MATH] [▶] 5 [X,T,θ,n] [ )] [Zoom] 6

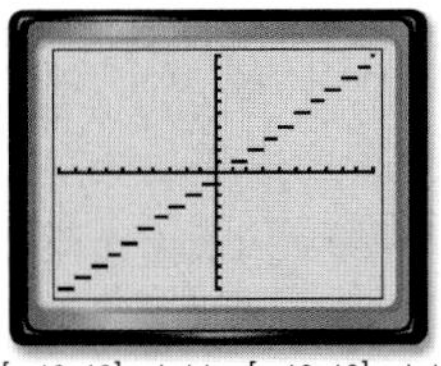

[−10, 10] scl: 1 by [−10, 10] scl: 1

1A. How does the graph of $f(x) = \llbracket x \rrbracket$ compare to the graph of $f(x) = x$?

1B. What are the domain and range of the function $f(x) = \llbracket x \rrbracket$? Explain. D = {all real numbers}; R = {all integers}

1A. The graph of $f(x) = x$ is a line that passes through the left endpoints of the segments that comprise the graph of $f(x) = \llbracket x \rrbracket$.

The graphs of piecewise functions are affected by changes in parameters.

ACTIVITY 2 Absolute Value Functions

Graph $y = |x| - 3$ and $y = |x| + 1$ in the standard viewing window.

Enter the equations in the Y= list. Then graph.

KEYSTROKES: [Y=] [MATH] [▶] 1 [X,T,θ,n] [ )] [−] 3 [ENTER] [MATH] [▶] 1 [X,T,θ,n] [ )] [+] 1 [Zoom] 6

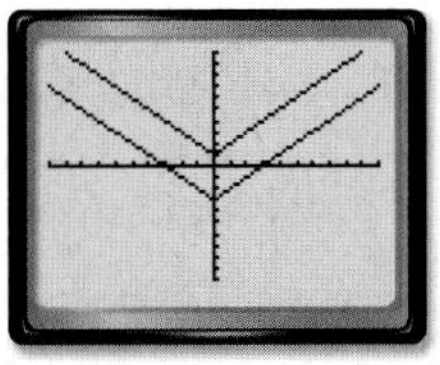

[−10, 10] scl: 1 by [−10, 10] scl: 1

2A. Compare and contrast the graphs to the graph of $y = |x|$.

2B. How does the value of c affect the graph of $y = |x| + c$?

2A. The graph of $y = |x| - 3$ is the graph of $y = |x|$, shifted 3 units down. The graph of $y = |x| + 1$ is the graph of $y = |x|$, shifted 1 unit up.

2B. Sample answer: The value of c shifts the graph up c units if $c > 0$ and down $|c|$ units if $c < 0$.

Analyze The Results

1. A parking garage charges $4 for every hour or fraction of an hour. Is this situation modeled by a *linear* function or a *step* function? Explain your reasoning.
2. A maintenance technician is testing an elevator system. The technician starts the elevator at the fifth floor. It is sent to the ground floor, then back to the fifth floor. Assume the elevator travels at a constant rate. Should the height of the elevator be modeled by a step function or an absolute value function? Explain. See margin.
3. **MAKE A CONJECTURE** Explain why the greatest integer function is sometimes called the *floor function*.
4. Graph $y = -|x|$ in the standard viewing window. How is this graph related to the graph of $y = |x|$? See margin.
5. **MAKE A CONJECTURE** Describe the transformation of the parent graph to $y = |x + c|$. Use a graphing calculator with different values of c to test your conjecture. See margin.

1. Step; the garage charges $4 for a portion of an hour.
3. Sample answer: The function returns the greatest integer value that is not greater than the given value. So the function value is always at or below the value of x, like a floor.

EXTEND 4-7 Lesson Notes

1 FOCUS

Objective Use a graphing calculator to investigate piecewise-linear functions.

Materials for Each Student

- TI–83/84 Plus or other graphing calculator

Teaching Tip

Students may be unfamiliar with how to select the dot mode and the correct viewing window for their calculators. Demonstrate the steps needed as students follow along on their own calculators.

2 TEACH

Working in Cooperative Groups

Put students in groups of two or three, mixing abilities. Have groups complete Activities 1 and 2.

Ask:

- What viewing window setting do you need for Activities 1 and 2? [−10, 10] scl: 1 by [−10, 10] scl:1
- In Activity 2, how does the y-intercept of the graph of a function in the form $y = |x| \pm c$ relate to the constant in each function? The y-intercept of a function's graph is the same as the c in each function.

Practice Have students complete Exercises 1–5.

3 ASSESS

Formative Assessment

Use Activity 1 to assess whether students understand the difference between a piecewise-linear function and a linear function.

From Concrete to Abstract

Have students write and graph an equation that would represent Exercise 1. Ask students how the equation would change if the parking garage charged $8 for every hour or fraction of an hour. The equations would be $f(x) = -4\llbracket -x \rrbracket$ and $g(x) = -8\llbracket -x \rrbracket$.

✓ Formative Assessment

Key Vocabulary The page reference after each word denotes where that term was first introduced. If students have difficulty answering questions 1–9, remind them that they can use these page references to refresh their memories about the vocabulary terms.

✓ Summative Assessment

CRM Vocabulary Test, p. 54

IL Math Online glencoe.com

Vocabulary PuzzleMaker improves students' mathematics vocabulary using four puzzle formats–crossword, scramble, word search using a word list, and word search using clues. Students can work online or from a printed worksheet.

Additional Answers

14.

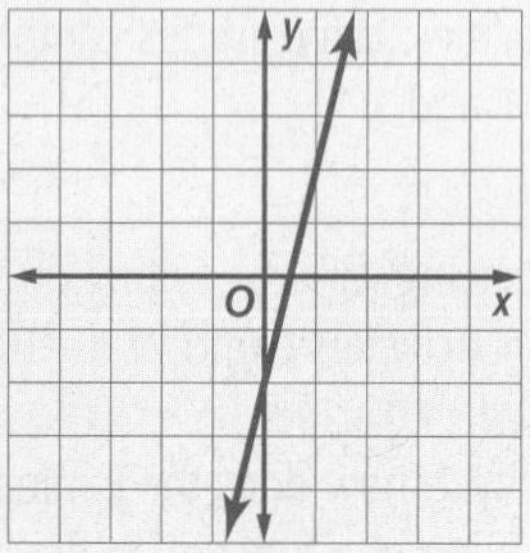

15.

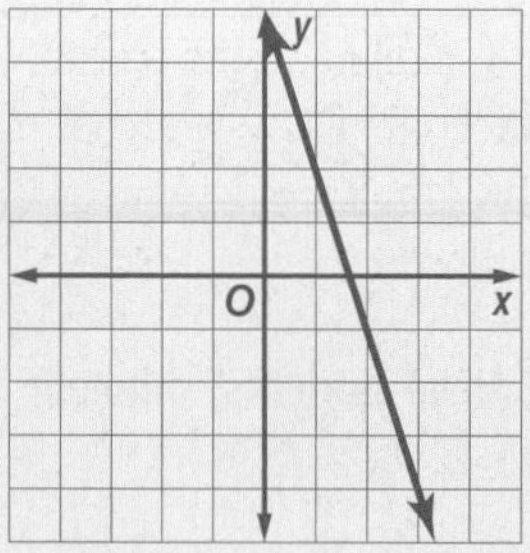

IL Math Online glencoe.com
- STUDY TO GO
- Vocabulary Review

Chapter Summary

Key Concepts

Slope-Intercept Form (Lessons 4-1 and 4-2)

- The slope-intercept form of a linear equation is $y = mx + b$, where m is the slope and b is the y-intercept.
- If you are given two points through which a line passes, use them to find the slope first.

Point-Slope Form (Lesson 4-3)

- The linear equation $y - y_1 = m(x - x_1)$ is written in point-slope form, where (x_1, y_1) is a given point on a nonvertical line and m is the slope of the line.

Parallel and Perpendicular Lines (Lesson 4-4)

- Nonvertical parallel lines have the same slope.
- Lines that intersect at right angles are called perpendicular lines. The slopes of perpendicular lines are opposite reciprocals.

Scatter Plots and Lines of Fit (Lesson 4-5)

- Data with two variables are called bivariate data.
- A scatter plot is a graph in which two sets of data are plotted as ordered pairs in a coordinate plane.

Regression and Median-Fit Lines (Lesson 4-6)

- A graphing calculator can be used to find regression lines and median-fit lines.

Special Functions (Lesson 4-7)

- The greatest integer function is written as $f(x) = [\![x]\!]$, where $f(x)$ is the greatest integer not greater than x.
- The absolute value function is written as $f(x) = |x|$, where $f(x)$ is the distance between x and 0 on a number line.

FOLDABLES® Study Organizer

Be sure the Key Concepts are noted in your Foldable.

Key Vocabulary

absolute value function (p. 262)
best-fit line (p. 253)
bivariate data (p. 245)
correlation coefficient (p. 253)
greatest integer function (p. 261)
linear extrapolation (p. 226)
linear interpolation (p. 247)
linear regression (p. 253)
line of fit (p. 246)
median-fit line (p. 255)
parallel lines (p. 237)
perpendicular lines (p. 238)
piecewise-defined function (p. 262)
piecewise-linear function (p. 261)
point-slope form (p. 231)
scatter plot (p. 245)
slope-intercept form (p. 214)
step function (p. 261)

Vocabulary Check

State whether each sentence is *true* or *false*. If *false*, replace the underlined term to make a true sentence.

1. The y-intercept is the y-coordinate of the point where the graph crosses the y-axis. **T**
2. The process of using a linear equation to make predictions about values that are beyond the range of the data is called linear regression. **F, linear extrapolation**
3. A graph in which two sets of data are plotted as ordered pairs in a coordinate plane is called a step function. **F, scatter plot**
4. The correlation coefficient describes whether the correlation between the variables is positive or negative and how closely the regression equation is modeling the data. **T**
5. Lines in the same plane that do not intersect are called parallel lines. **T**
6. Lines that intersect at acute angles are called perpendicular lines. **F, right**
7. A function that is defined differently for different parts of its domain is called a piecewise-defined function. **T**
8. The range of the greatest integer function is the set of all real numbers. **F, domain**
9. A piecewise-linear function is also called a step function. **F, greatest integer function**

FOLDABLES® Study Organizer

Dinah Zike's Foldables®

Have students look through the chapter to make sure they have included examples in their Foldables for each lesson of the chapter.

Suggest that students keep their Foldables handy while completing the Study Guide and Review pages. Point out that their Foldables can serve as a quick review when studying for the chapter test.

Lesson-by-Lesson Review

4-1 Graphing Equations in Slope-Intercept Form (pp. 214–221) 8.C.4b

Write an equation of a line in slope-intercept form with the given slope and y-intercept. Then graph the equation. **10–13. See margin for graphs.**

10. slope: 3, y-intercept: 5 $y = 3x + 5$

11. slope: -2, y-intercept: -9 $y = -2x - 9$

12. slope: $\frac{2}{3}$, y-intercept: 3 $y = \frac{2}{3}x + 3$

13. slope: $-\frac{5}{8}$, y-intercept: -2 $y = -\frac{5}{8}x - 2$

Graph each equation. **14–17. See margin.**

14. $y = 4x - 2$ **15.** $y = -3x + 5$

16. $y = \frac{1}{2}x + 1$ **17.** $3x + 4y = 8$

18. SKI RENTAL Write an equation in slope-intercept form for the total cost of skiing for h hours with one lift ticket. $y = 5h + 15$

EXAMPLE 1

Write an equation of a line in slope-intercept form with slope −5 and y-intercept −3. Then graph the equation.

$y = mx + b$	**Slope-intercept form**
$y = -5x + (-3)$	**$m = -5$ and $b = -3$**
$y = -5x - 3$	**Simplify.**

To graph the equation, plot the y-intercept $(0, -3)$. Then move up 5 units and left 1 unit. Plot the point. Draw a line through the two points.

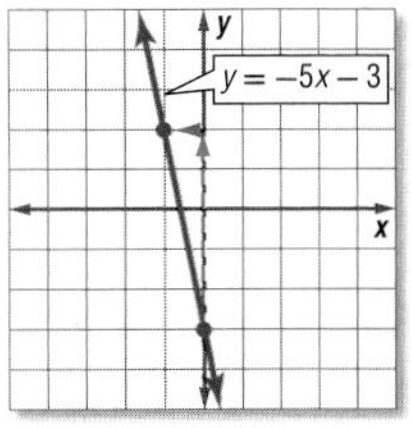

4-2 Writing Equations in Slope-Intercept Form (pp. 224–230) 8.C.4b

Write an equation of the line that passes through the given point and has the given slope. **19.** $y = 3x - 1$ **20.** $y = -4x + 2$

19. (1, 2), slope 3 **20.** (2, −6), slope −4

21. (−3, −1), slope $\frac{2}{5}$ $y = \frac{2}{5}x + \frac{1}{5}$ **22.** (5, −2), slope $-\frac{1}{3}$ $y = -\frac{1}{3}x - \frac{1}{3}$

Write an equation of the line that passes through the given points. **23–26. See margin.**

23. (2, −1), (5, 2) **24.** (−4, 3), (1, 13)

25. (3, 5), (5, 6) **26.** (2, 4), (7, 2)

27. CAMP In 2000, a camp had 450 campers. Five years later, the number of campers rose to 750. Write a linear equation that represents the number of campers that attend camp. $y = 60x + 450$

EXAMPLE 2

Write an equation of the line that passes through (3, 2) with a slope of 5.

Step 1 Find the y-intercept.

$y = mx + b$	**Slope-intercept form**
$2 = 5(3) + b$	**$m = 5$, $y = 2$, and $x = 3$**
$2 = 15 + b$	**Simplify.**
$-13 = b$	**Subtract 15 from each side.**

Step 2 Write the equation in slope-intercept form.

$y = mx + b$	**Slope-intercept form**
$y = 5x - 13$	**$m = 5$ and $b = -13$**

Lesson-by-Lesson Review

Intervention If the given examples are not sufficient to review the topics covered by the questions, remind students that the page references tell them where to review that topic in their textbooks.

Two-Day Option Have students complete the Lesson-by-Lesson Review on pp. 271–274. Then you can use ExamView® Assessment Suite to customize another review worksheet that practices all the objectives of this chapter or only the objectives on which your students need more help.

Differentiated Instruction

Super DVD: MindJogger Videoquizzes Use this DVD as an alternative format of review for the test.

Additional Answers

13.

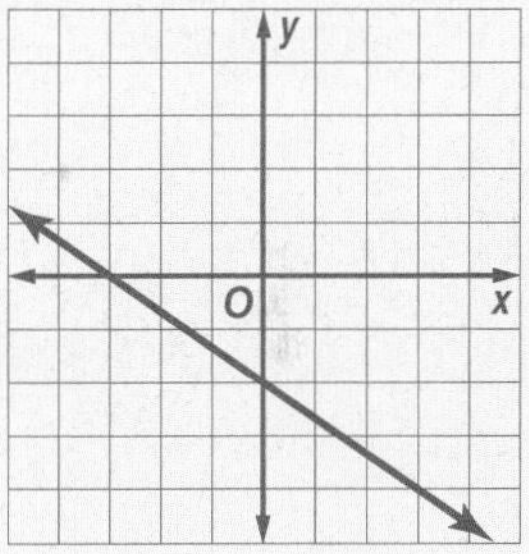

14.

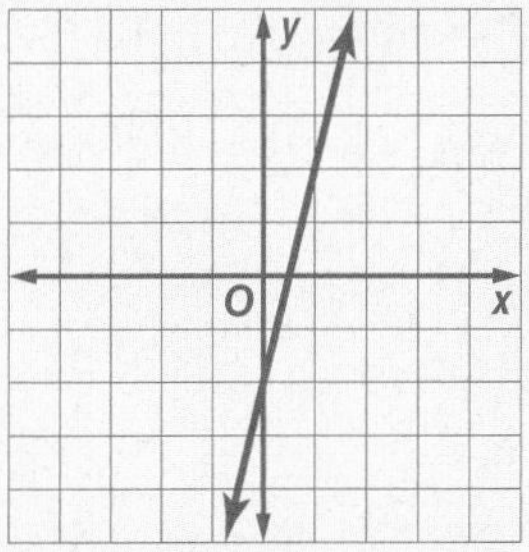

15.

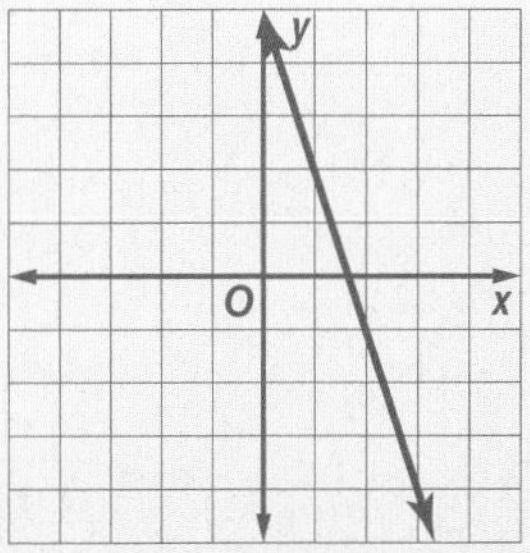

16.

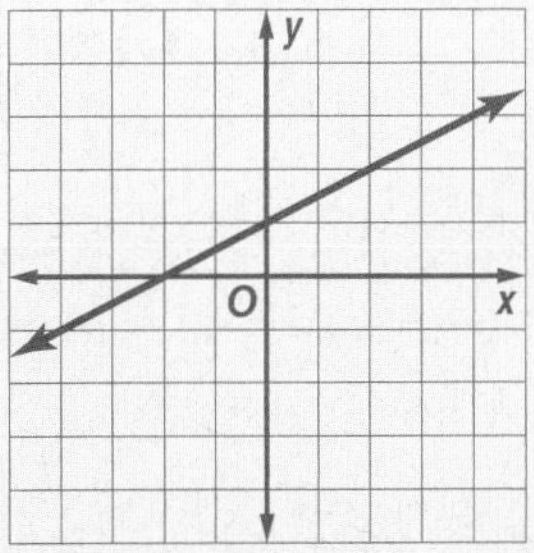

17.

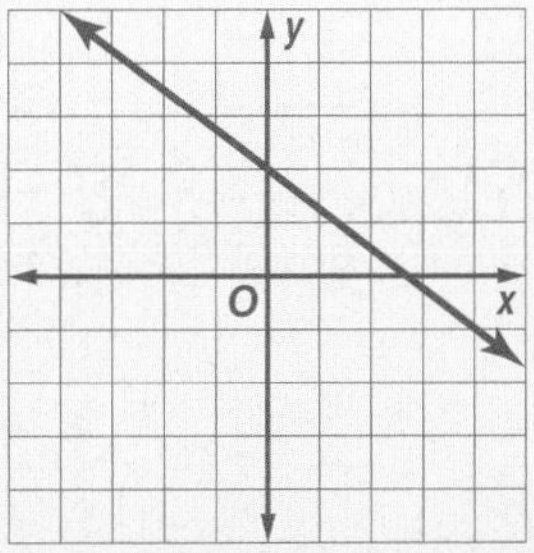

23. $y = x - 3$

24. $y = 2x + 11$

25. $y = \frac{1}{2}x + \frac{7}{2}$

26. $y = -\frac{2}{5}x + \frac{24}{5}$

CHAPTER 4 Study Guide and Review

4-3 Point-Slope Form (pp. 231–236)

8.C.4b

Write an equation in point-slope form for the line that passes through the given point with the slope provided.

28. (6, 3), slope 5 $y - 3 = 5(x - 6)$

29. (−2, 1), slope −3 $y - 1 = -3(x + 2)$

30. (−4, 2), slope 0 $y - 2 = 0$

Write each equation in standard form.

31. $y - 3 = 5(x - 2)$ $5x - y = 7$

32. $y - 7 = -3(x + 1)$ $3x + y = 4$

33. $y + 4 = \frac{1}{2}(x - 3)$ $x - 2y = 11$

34. $y - 9 = -\frac{4}{5}(x + 2)$ $4x + 5y = 37$

Write each equation in slope-intercept form.

35. $y - 2 = 3(x - 5)$ $y = 3x - 13$

36. $y - 12 = -2(x - 3)$ $y = -2x + 18$

37. $y + 3 = 5(x + 1)$ $y = 5x + 2$

38. $y - 4 = \frac{1}{2}(x + 2)$ $y = \frac{1}{2}x + 5$

EXAMPLE 3

Write an equation in point-slope form for the line that passes through (3, 4) with a slope of −2.

$y - y_1 = m(x - x_1)$	**Point-slope form**
$y - 4 = -2(x - 3)$	**Replace *m* with −2 and (x_1, y_1) with (3, 4).**

EXAMPLE 4

Write $y + 6 = -4(x - 3)$ in standard form.

$y + 6 = -4(x - 3)$	**Original equation**
$y + 6 = -4x + 12$	**Simplify.**
$4x + y + 6 = 12$	**Add 4*x* to each side.**
$4x + y = 6$	**Subtract 6 from each side.**

4-4 Parallel and Perpendicular Lines (pp. 237–243)

8.B.4b

Write an equation in slope-intercept form for the line that passes through the given point and is parallel to the graph of each equation.

39. (2, 5), $y = x - 3$ $y = x + 3$

40. (0, 3), $y = 3x + 5$ $y = 3x + 3$

41. (−4, 1), $y = -2x - 6$ $y = -2x - 7$

42. (−5, −2), $y = -\frac{1}{2}x + 4$ $y = -\frac{1}{2}x - \frac{9}{2}$

Write an equation in slope-intercept form for the line that passes through the given point and is perpendicular to the graph of the given equation.

43. (2, 4), $y = 3x + 1$ $y = -\frac{1}{3}x + \frac{14}{3}$

44. (1, 3), $y = -2x - 4$ $y = \frac{1}{2}x + \frac{5}{2}$

45. (−5, 2), $y = \frac{1}{3}x + 4$ $y = -3x - 13$

46. (3, 0), $y = -\frac{1}{2}x$ $y = 2x - 6$

EXAMPLE 5

Write an equation in slope-intercept form for the line that passes through (−2, 4) and is parallel to the graph of $y = 6x - 3$.

The slope of the line with equation $y = 6x - 3$ is 6. The line parallel to $y = 6x - 3$ has the same slope, 6.

$y - y_1 = m(x - x_1)$	**Point-slope form**
$y - 4 = 6(x - (-2))$	**Substitute.**
$y - 4 = 6(x + 2)$	**Simplify.**
$y - 4 = 6x + 12$	**Distributive Property**
$y = 6x + 16$	**Add 4 to each side.**

272 Chapter 4 Linear Functions and Relations

MIXED PROBLEM SOLVING
For mixed problem-solving practice, see page 848.

4-5 Scatter Plots and Lines of Fit (pp. 245–252)

8.A.4b, 10.A.4c

47. Determine whether the graph shows a *positive*, *negative*, or *no* correlation. If there is a positive or negative correlation, describe its meaning. **positive**

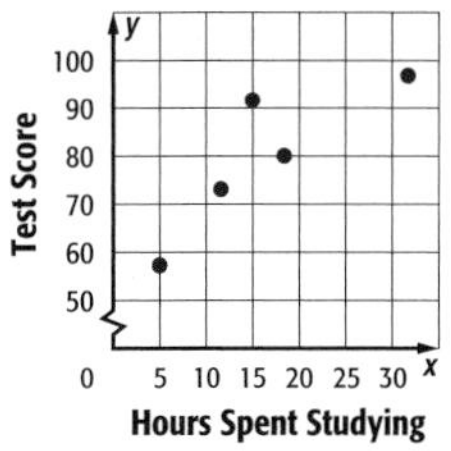

48. ATTENDANCE A scatter plot of data compares the number of years since a business has opened and its annual number of sales. It contains the ordered pairs (2, 650) and (5, 1280). Write an equation in slope-intercept form for the line of fit for this situation.
$y = 210x + 230$

EXAMPLE 6

The scatter plot displays the number of text messages and the number of phone calls made daily. Write an equation for the line of fit.

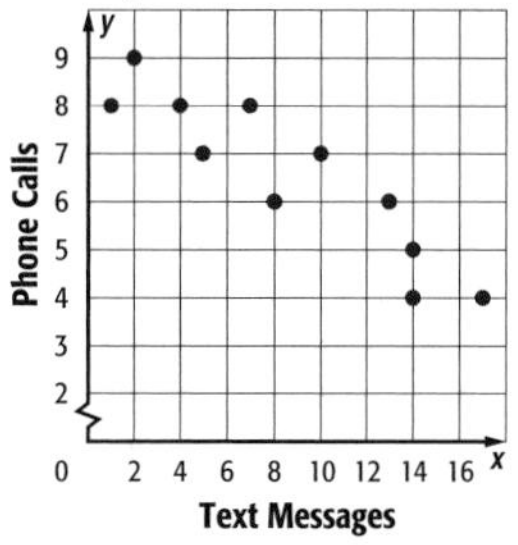

First, find the slope using (2, 9) and (17, 4).

$m = \frac{4-9}{17-2} = \frac{-5}{15}$ or $-\frac{1}{3}$ **Substitute and simplify.**

Then find the y-intercept.

$9 = -\frac{1}{3}(2) + b$ **Substitute.**

$9\frac{2}{3} = b$ **Add $\frac{2}{3}$ to each side.**

Write the equation. $y = -\frac{1}{3}x + 9\frac{2}{3}$

4-6 Regression and Median-Fit Lines (pp. 253–260)

10.A.4c

49. SALE The table shows the number of sales made at an outerwear store during a sale. Write an equation of the regression line. Then estimate the daily sales on day 10 of the sale.
$y = 5.36x + 11$; 65

Days Since Sale Began	1	2	3	4	5	6	7
Daily Sales ($)	15	21	32	30	40	38	51

50. MOVIES The table shows ticket sales during the first week. Write an equation of the regression line. Then estimate the daily ticket sales on the 15th day after the movie opens.

Days Since Movie Opened	1	2	3	4	5	6	7
Daily Ticket Sales ($)	85	92	89	78	65	68	55

$y = -5.79x + 99.14$; $12.29

EXAMPLE 7

ATTENDANCE The table shows the annual attendance at an amusement park. Write an equation of the regression line for the data.

Year (since 2000)	0	1	2	3	4	5	6
Attendance (thousands)	75	80	72	68	65	60	53

Step 1 Enter the data by pressing STAT and selecting the **Edit** option.

Step 2 Perform the regression by pressing STAT and selecting the **CALC** option. Scroll down to **LinReg (ax + b)** and press ENTER.

Step 3 Write the equation of the regression line by rounding the a- and b-values on the screen.
$y = -4.04x + 79.68$

Chapter 4 Study Guide and Review 273

Problem Solving Review

For additional practice in problem solving for Chapter 4, see the Mixed Problem Solving Appendix, p. 848, in the Student Handbook section.

Anticipation Guide

Have students complete the Chapter 4 Anticipation Guide and discuss how their responses have changed now that they have completed Chapter 4.

Additional Answers

51. D = all real numbers;
R = all integers

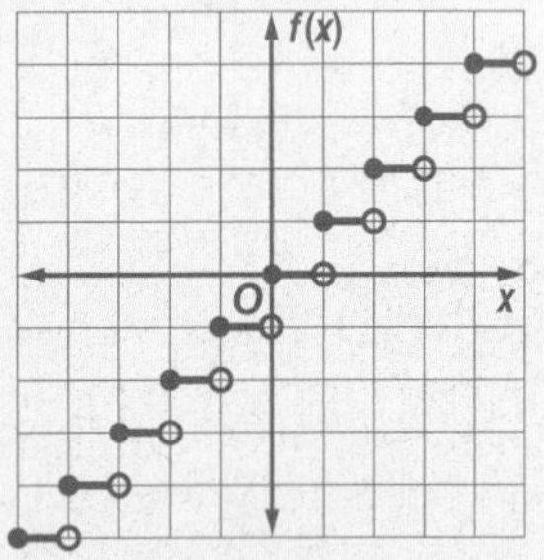

52. D = all real numbers;
R = all integers

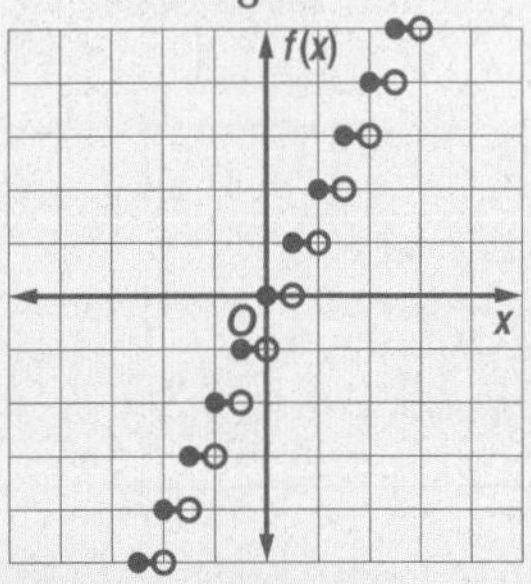

53. D = all real numbers;
R = $f(x) \geq 0$

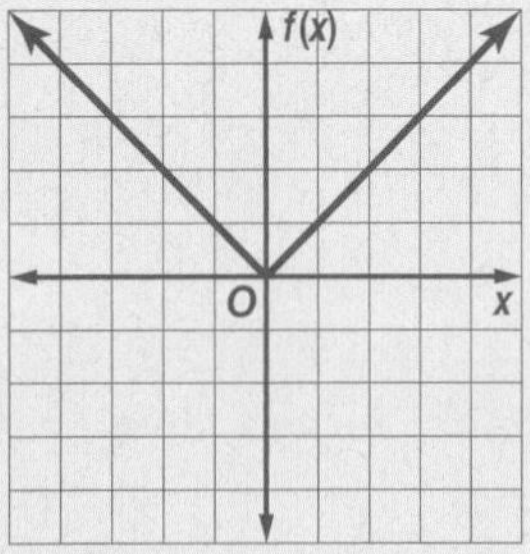

4-7 Special Functions (pp. 261–268)

8.B.4b, 8.C.4b

Graph each function. State the domain and range. 51–56. See margin.

51. $f(x) = [\![x]\!]$

52. $f(x) = [\![2x]\!]$

53. $f(x) = |x|$

54. $f(x) = |2x - 2|$

55. $f(x) = \begin{cases} x - 2 \text{ if } x < 1 \\ 3x \text{ if } x \geq 1 \end{cases}$

56. $f(x) = \begin{cases} 2x - 3 \text{ if } x \leq 2 \\ x + 1 \text{ if } x > 2 \end{cases}$

57. Determine the domain and range of the function graphed below.

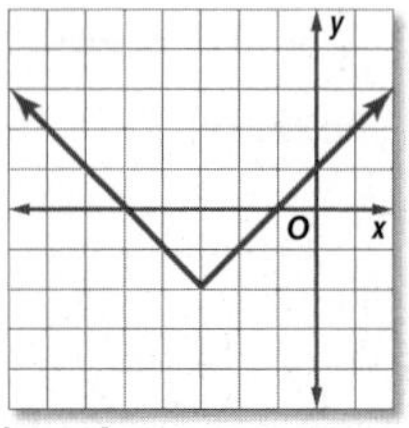

D = all real numbers
R = $y \geq -2$

EXAMPLE 8

Graph $f(x) = |x + 3|$. State the domain and range.

Since $f(x)$ cannot be negative, the minimum point of the graph is where $f(x) = 0$.

$f(x) = \lvert x + 3 \rvert$	**Original function**
$0 = x + 3$	**Replace f(x) with 0.**
$-3 = x$	**Subtract 3 from each side.**

Next, make a table of values. Include values for $x > -3$ and $x < -3$.

x	−5	−4	−3	−2	−1
f(x)	2	1	0	1	2

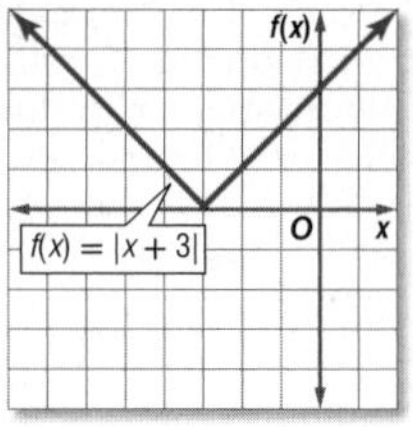

The domain is all real numbers, and the range is $f(x) \geq 0$.

54. D = all real numbers;
R = $f(x) \geq 0$

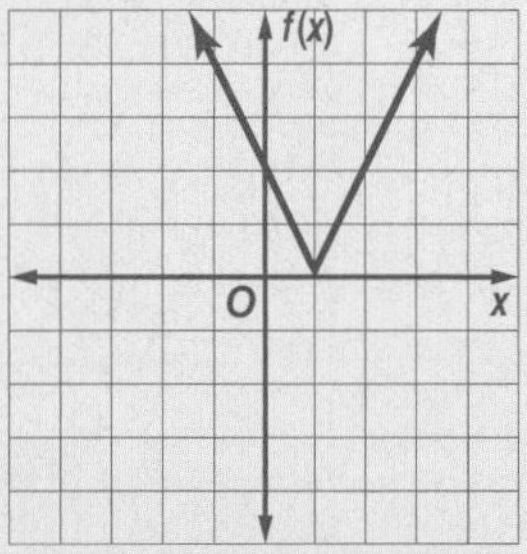

55. D = all real numbers;
R = $f(x) < -1$ or $f(x) \geq 3$

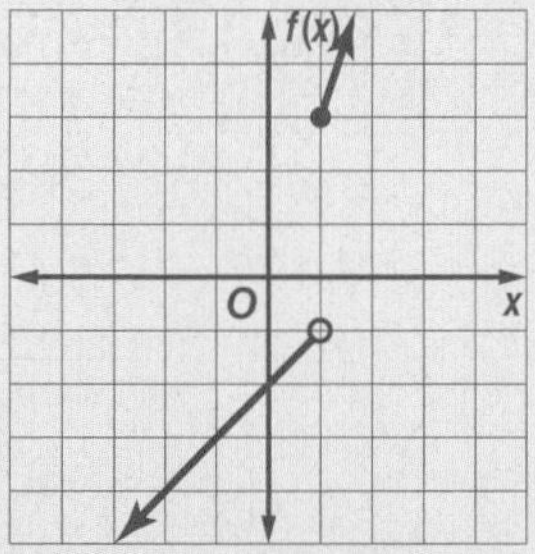

56. D = all real numbers;
R = $f(x) \leq -1$ or $f(x) > 3$

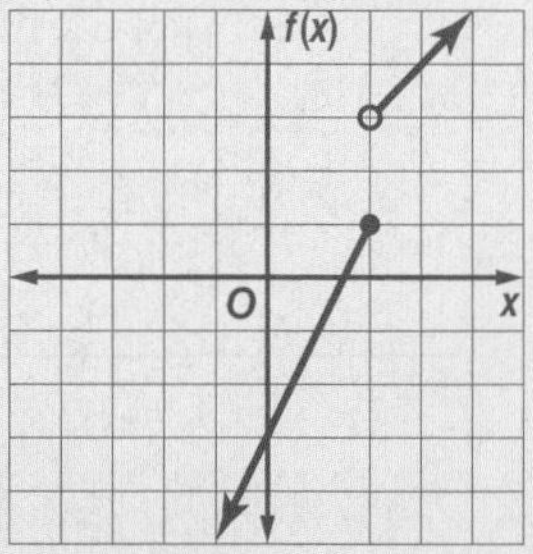

IL Math Online glencoe.com
Chapter Test

1. Graph $y = 2x - 3$. **See margin.**

2. **MULTIPLE CHOICE** A popular pizza parlor charges \$12 for a large cheese pizza plus \$1.50 for each additional topping. Write an equation in slope-intercept form for the total cost C of a pizza with t toppings. **C**

A $C = 12t + 1.50$

B $C = 13.50t$

C $C = 12 + 1.50t$

D $C = 1.50t - 12$

Write an equation of a line in slope-intercept form that passes through the given point and has the given slope.

3. $(-4, 2)$; slope -3 **$y = -3x - 10$**

4. $(3, -5)$; slope $\frac{2}{3}$ **$y = \frac{2}{3}x - 7$**

Write an equation of the line in slope-intercept form that passes through the given points.

5. $(1, 4), (3, 10)$ **$y = 3x + 1$**

6. $(2, 5), (-2, 8)$ **$y = -\frac{3}{4}x + \frac{13}{2}$**

7. $(0, 4), (-3, 0)$ **$y = \frac{4}{3}x + 4$**

8. $(7, -1), (9, -4)$ **$y = -\frac{3}{2}x + \frac{19}{2}$**

9. **PAINTING** The data in the table show the size of a room in square feet and the time it takes to paint the room in minutes.

Room Size	100	150	200	400	500
Painting Time	160	220	270	500	680

a. Use the points (100, 160) and (500, 680) to write an equation in slope-intercept form. **$y = 1.3x + 30$**

b. Predict the amount of time required to paint a room measuring 750 square feet. **1005 min**

10. **SALARY** The table shows the relationship between years of experience and teacher salary.

Years Experience	1	5	10	15	20
Salary (thousands of dollars)	28	31	42	49	64

a. Write an equation for the best-fit line. **$y = 1.89x + 23.57$**

b. Find the correlation coefficient and explain what it tells us about the relationship between experience and salary. **0.98**

Write an equation in slope-intercept form for the line that passes through the given point and is parallel to the graph of each equation.

11. $(2, -3), y = 4x - 9$ **$y = 4x - 11$**

12. $(-5, 1), y = -3x + 2$ **$y = -3x - 14$**

Write an equation in slope-intercept form for the line that passes through the given point and is perpendicular to the graph of the equation.

13. $(1, 4), y = -2x + 5$ **13. $y = \frac{1}{2}x + \frac{7}{2}$**

14. $(-3, 6), y = \frac{1}{4}x + 2$ **$y = -4x - 6$**

15. **MULTIPLE CHOICE** The graph shows the relationship between outside temperature and daily ice cream cone sales. What type of correlation is shown? **F**

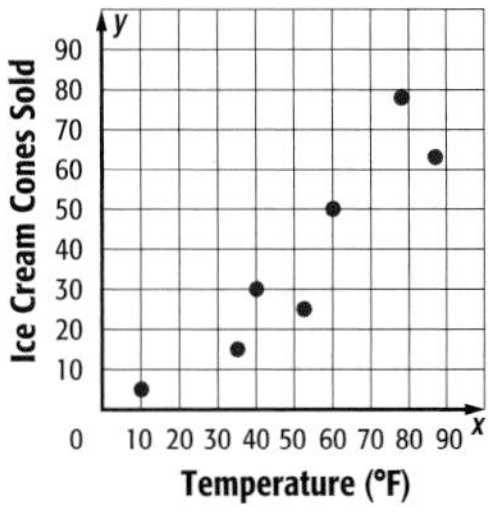

F positive correlation

G negative correlation

H no correlation

J not enough information

Graph each function. **16–19. See Ch. 4 Answer Appendix.**

16. $f(x) = |x - 1|$

17. $f(x) = -|2x|$

18. $f(x) = [\![x]\!]$

19. $f(x) = \begin{cases} 2x - 1 \text{ if } x < 2 \\ x - 3 \text{ if } x \geq 2 \end{cases}$

20. The table shows the number of children from Russia adopted by U.S. citizens.

Years Since 2000	0	1	2	3	4
Number of Children	4269	4279	4939	5209	6936

a. Write the slope-intercept form of the equation for the line of fit. **$y = 626.4x + 3873.6$**

b. Predict the number of children from Russia who will be adopted in 2025. **19,533**

CHAPTER 4 Practice Test

ExamView Assessment Suite — Customize and create multiple versions of your chapter tests and their answer keys. All of the questions from the leveled chapter tests in the *Chapter 4 Resource Masters* are also available on ExamView® Assessment Suite.

Additional Answer

1.

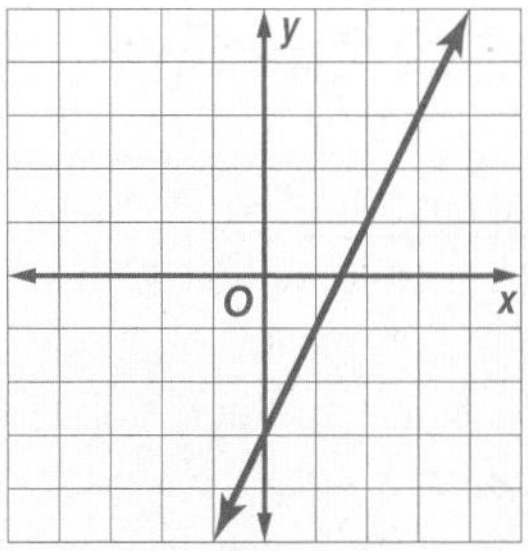

Intervention Planner

Tier 1 On Level	Tier 2 Strategic Intervention approaching grade level	Tier 3 Intensive Intervention 2 or more grades below level
If students miss about 25% of the exercises or less,	**If** students miss about 50% of the exercises,	**If** students miss about 75% of the exercises,
Then choose a resource:	**Then** choose a resource:	**Then** use *Math Triumphs, Alg. 1*, Ch. 4
SE Lessons 4-1, 4-2, 4-3, 4-4, 4-5, 4-6, and 4-7 **CRM** Skills Practice, pp. 7, 12, 19, 26, 32, 39, and 45 **TE** Chapter Project, p. 210 IL Math Online Self-Check Quiz	**CRM** Study Guide and Intervention, Chapter 4, pp. 5, 11, 17, 24, 30, 37, and 43 *Quick Review Math Handbook* IL Math Online Extra Examples, Personal Tutor, Homework Help	IL Math Online Extra Examples, Personal Tutor, Homework Help, Review Vocabulary

1 FOCUS

Objective Use strategies for solving short answer standardized test problems.

2 TEACH

Scaffolding Questions

Ask:

- How is a short answer question different from a multiple choice question? Sample answer: In a multiple choice question, you choose from several answers, but in a short answer question, your answer is the only answer.
- Why do you think math tests include short answer questions? Sample answer: To assess whether you understand a concept and know how to solve a problem.
- How can you show in a short answer response that you know how to solve a problem? Sample answer: Show the steps you used to solve the problem and/or explain how you solved it.

CHAPTER 4 Preparing for Standardized Tests

Short Answer Questions

Short answer questions require you to provide a solution to the problem, along with a method, explanation, and/or justification used to arrive at the solution.

Strategies for Solving Short Answer Questions

Step 1

Short answer questions are typically graded using a **rubric**, or a scoring guide. The following is an example of a short answer question scoring rubric.

Scoring Rubric	
Criteria	**Score**
Full Credit: The answer is correct and a full explanation is provided that shows each step.	2
Partial Credit: • The answer is correct, but the explanation is incomplete. • The answer is incorrect, but the explanation is correct.	1
No Credit: Either an answer is not provided or the answer does not make sense.	0

Step 2

In solving short answer questions, remember to...

- explain your reasoning or state your approach to solving the problem.
- show all of your work or steps.
- check your answer if time permits.

EXAMPLE

Read the problem. Identify what you need to know. Then use the information in the problem to solve. Show your work.

The table shows production costs for building different numbers of skateboards. Determine the missing value, x, that will result in a linear model.

Skateboards Built	Production Costs
14	$325
28	$500
x	$375
22	$425

Read the problem carefully. You are given several data points and asked to find the missing value that results in a linear model.

Example of a 2-point response:

Set up a coordinate grid and plot the three given points: (14, 325), (28, 500), (22, 425).

Then draw a straight line through them and find the x-value that produces a y-value of 375.

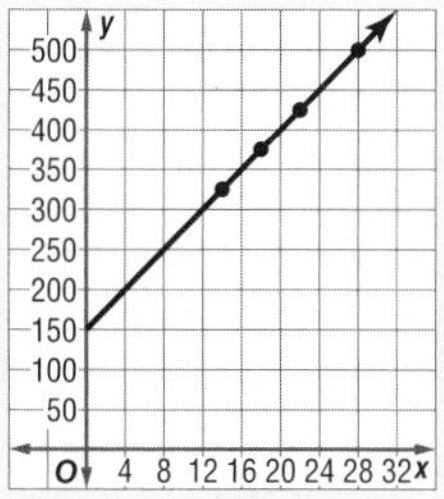

So, building 18 skateboards would result in production costs of \$375. These data form a linear model.

The steps, calculations, and reasoning are clearly stated. The student also arrives at the correct answer. So, this response is worth the full 2 points.

Exercises

Read each problem. Identify what you need to know. Then use the information in the problem to solve. Show your work.

1. Given points $M(-1, 7)$, $N(3, -5)$, $O(6, 1)$, and $P(-3, -2)$, determine two segments that are perpendicular to each other. **$\overline{MN} \perp \overline{OP}$**

2. Write the equation of a line that is parallel to $4x + 2y = 8$ and has a y-intercept of 5. **$y = -2x + 5$**

3. Three vertices of a quadrilateral are shown on the coordinate grid. Determine a fourth vertex that would result in a trapezoid. **Sample answer: (2, 6)**

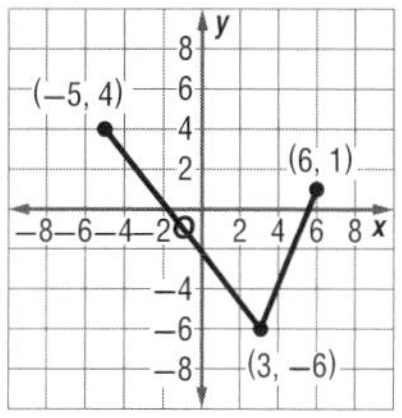

Additional Example

The table shows the earnings Nate makes in his job as a scuba diving instructor for a travel company. Write and use a linear equation to find the value of x in the table.

Hours	Earnings (\$)
9	710
25	1750
x	1490
17	1230

Sample 2-point response: Use two points in the table to write an equation of the line in slope-intercept form. Find the slope using the slope formula, and then use the slope to find the y-intercept. Write the equation of the line and use it to find the value of x.

$$m = \frac{y_2 - y_1}{x_2 - x_1}$$

$$m = \frac{1750 - 710}{25 - 9} = \frac{1040}{16} \text{ or } 65$$

$$y = mx + b$$

$$710 = 65(9) + b$$

$$710 = 585 + b$$

$$710 - 585 = b$$

$$125 = b$$

The equation of the line is $y = 65x + 125$.

$$y = 65x + 125$$

$$1490 = 65x + 125$$

$$1490 - 125 = 65x$$

$$1365 = 65x$$

$$21 = x$$

So Nate works 21 hours to earn \$1490.

3 ASSESS

Use Exercises 1–3 to assess students' understanding.

Diagnose Student Errors

Survey students' responses for each item. Class trends may indicate common errors and misconceptions.

1. A misunderstood how to represent each additional pound
B misunderstood concept of piecewise function
C misrepresented flat rate as price per pound
D correct
E misunderstood how to represent price over 1 pound

2. F guess
G correct
H guess
J calculation error, such as calculated a total of 7 pounds instead of 6
K used 11 pounds 5 ounces

3. A correct
B guess
C calculation error, such as used 1400 instead of 1600 as the pattern for yearly decrease
D guess
E guess

4. F does not understand relationship between slope and intercepts
G does not understand relationship between slope and intercepts
H does not understand relationship between slope and intercepts
J does not understand relationship between slope and intercepts
K correct

5. A partially correct for $x = 14$, but $x = -8$ not 8
B guess
C correct
D guess
E guess

6. F checked equation for 15° only
G checked equation for 10° only
H correct
J checked equation for 10° only
K checked equation for 10° only

PSAE Practice

Cumulative, Chapters 1 through 4

Multiple Choice

Read each question. Then fill in the correct answer on the answer document provided by your teacher or on a sheet of paper.

1. Which of the following piecewise-defined functions represents the cost C of shipping a package that weighs p pounds? D

A $C(p) = \begin{cases} 8.50 & \text{if } p \leq 1 \\ 8.50 + 7.25p & \text{if } p > 1 \end{cases}$

B $C(p) = \begin{cases} 7.25 & \text{if } p \leq 1 \\ 7.25 + 8.50p & \text{if } p > 1 \end{cases}$

C $C(p) = \begin{cases} 8.50 & \text{if } p \leq 1 \\ 8.50p + 7.25(p - 1) & \text{if } p > 1 \end{cases}$

D $C(p) = \begin{cases} 8.50 & \text{if } p \leq 1 \\ 8.50 + 7.25(p - 1) & \text{if } p > 1 \end{cases}$

E $C(p) = \begin{cases} 8.50 & \text{if } p < 1 \\ 7.25 + 8.50p & \text{if } p \geq 1 \end{cases}$

2. Refer to the information given in Exercise 1. How much would it cost a customer to ship a package that weighs 5 pounds 11 ounces if partial pounds are rounded up to the nearest whole pound? G

F $42.35
G $44.75
H $48.20
J $52.00
K $88.25

3. Jaime bought a car in 2005 for $28,500. By 2008, the car was worth $23,700. Based on a linear model, what will the value of the car be in 2012? A

A $17,300
B $17,550
C $18,100
D $18,475
E $22,100

4. If the graph of a line has a negative slope and a negative y-intercept, what happens to the x-intercept if the slope and the y-intercept are multiplied by 0.5? K

F The x-intercept becomes four times as great.

G The x-intercept becomes twice as great.

H The x-intercept becomes one-fourth as great.

J The x-intercept becomes one-half as great.

K The x-intercept remains the same.

5. Which absolute value equation has the graph below as its solution? C

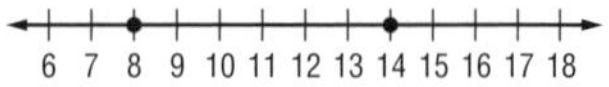

A $|x - 3| = 11$

B $|x - 4| = 12$

C $|x - 11| = 3$

D $|x - 12| = 4$

E $|x - 8| = 14$

6. The table below shows the relationship between certain temperatures in degrees Fahrenheit and degrees Celsius. Which of the following linear equations correctly models this relationship? H

F $F = \frac{8}{5}C + 35$

G $F = \frac{4}{5}C + 42$

H $F = \frac{9}{5}C + 32$

J $F = \frac{12}{5}C + 26$

K $F = \frac{1}{5}C + 48$

Celsius (C)	Fahrenheit (F)
10°	50°
15°	59°
20°	68°
25°	77°
30°	86°

Test-Taking Tip

Question 3 Find the average annual depreciation between 2005 and 2008. Then extend the pattern to find the car's value in 2012.

278 Chapter 4 Linear Functions and Relations

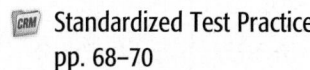

Short Response/Gridded Response

Record your answers on the answer sheet provided by your teacher or on a sheet of paper.

7. What is the equation of the line graphed below?

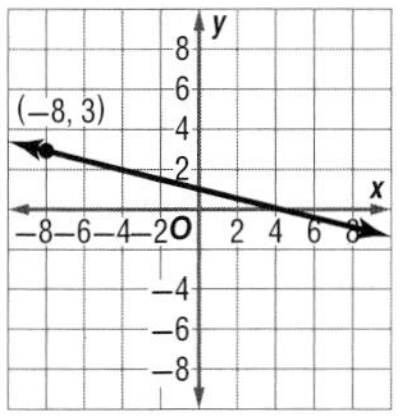

Express your answer in point-slope form using the point (−8, 3). $y - 3 = -\frac{1}{4}(x + 8)$

8. **GRIDDED RESPONSE** The linear equation below is a best fit model for the peak depth of the Mad River when x inches of rain fall. What would you expect the peak depth of the river to be after a storm that produces $1\frac{3}{4}$ inches of rain? Round your answer to the nearest tenth of a foot if necessary. **1.6**

$$y = 2.5x + 14.8$$

9. Jacob formed an advertising company in 1992. Initially, the company only had 14 employees. In 2008, the company had grown to a total of 63 employees. Find the percent of change in the number of employees working at Jacob's company. Round to the nearest tenth of a percent if necessary. **350%**

10. The table shows the total amount of rain during a storm.

Hour	1	2	3	4
Inches	0.45	0.9	1.35	1.8

a. Write an equation to fit the data in the table. $a_n = 0.45n$

b. Describe the relationship between the hour and the amount of rain received. **See margin.**

11. An electrician charges a $25 consultation fee plus $35 per hour for labor.

a. Copy and complete the following table showing the charges for jobs that take 1, 2, 3, 4, or 5 hours.

Hours, h	Total Cost, C
1	$60
2	$95
3	$130
4	$165
5	$200

b. Write an equation in slope-intercept form for the total cost of a job that takes h hours. $C = 35h + 25$

c. If the electrician bills in quarter hours, how much would it cost for a job that takes 3 hours 15 minutes to complete? **$138.75**

Extended Response

Record your answer on a sheet of paper. Show your work.

12. Explain how you can determine whether two lines are parallel or perpendicular.

12. Sample answer: Compare the slopes of the lines. If two lines have the same slope, they are parallel. If their slopes are opposite reciprocals, they are perpendicular.

Need Extra Help?

If you missed Question...	1	2	3	4	5	6	7	8	9	10	11	12
Go to Lesson or Page...	4-7	4-7	4-5	3-1	2-5	4-2	4-3	4-5	2-7	3-6	4-2	4-4
IL Assessment Objectives	8.11.14	8.11.06	8.11.14	8.11.10	8.11.19	8.11.07	8.11.07	8.11.06	6.11.18	8.11.08	8.11.07	8.11.08

Formative Assessment

You can use these two pages to benchmark student progress.

CRM Standardized Test Practice, pp. 68–70

Answer Sheet Practice

Have students simulate taking a standardized test by recording their answers on a practice recording sheet.

CRM Student Recording Sheet, p. 49

Chapter Resource Master
CRM p. 49

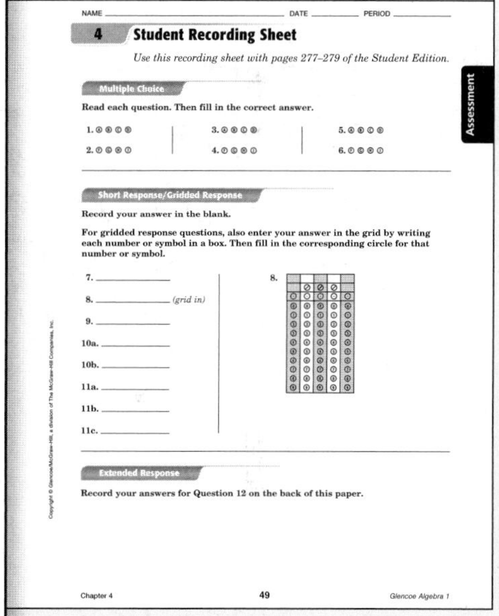

ExamView Assessment Suite Create practice worksheets or tests that align to your state's standards, as well as TIMSS and NAEP tests.

Homework Option

Get Ready for Chapter 5 Assign students the exercises on p. 281 as homework to assess whether they possess the prerequisite skills needed for the next chapter.

Page 214–215, Lesson 4-1 (Check Your Progress)

1A.

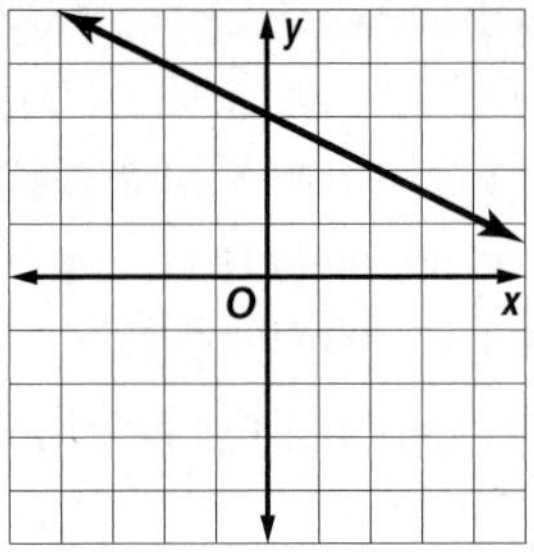

1B.

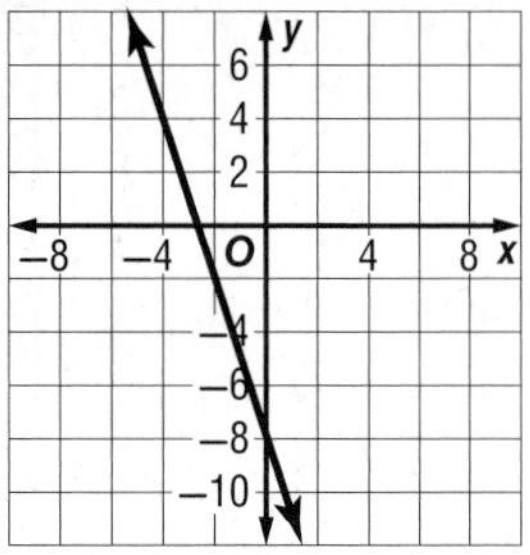

2A.

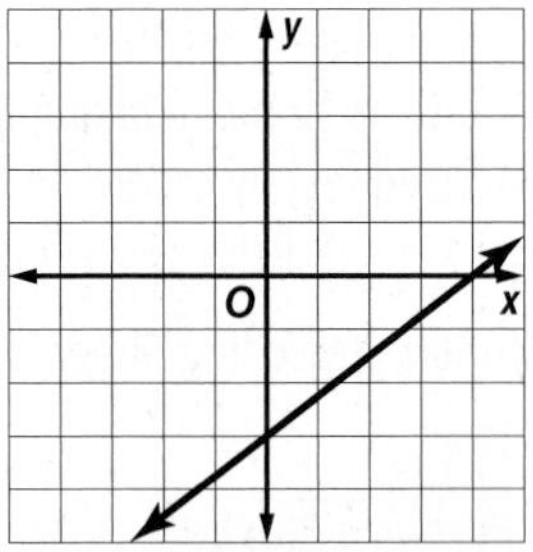

2B.

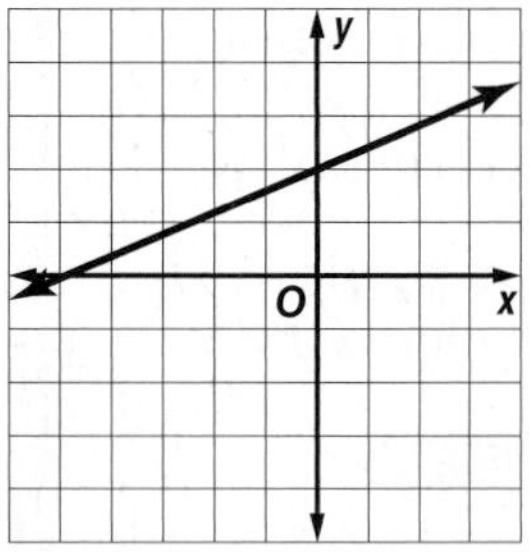

3A.

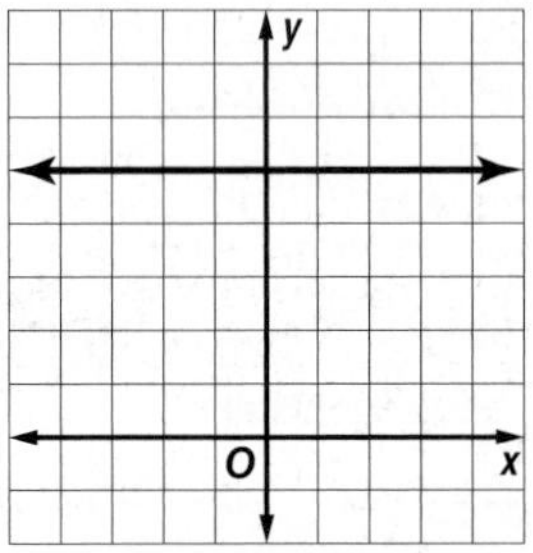

3B.

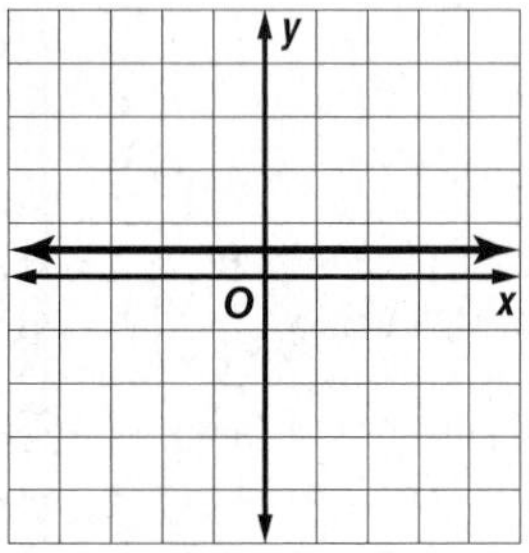

Pages 217–220, Lesson 4-1

1. $y = 2x + 4$

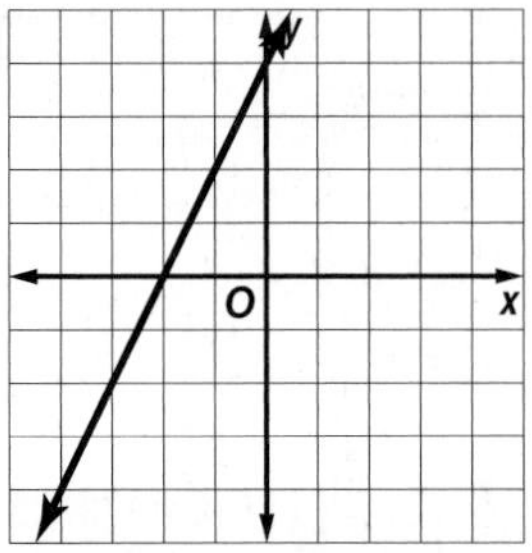

2. $y = -5x + 3$

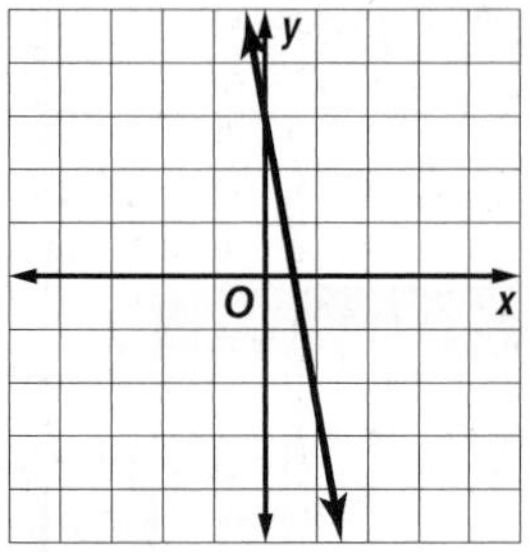

3. $y = \frac{3}{4}x - 1$

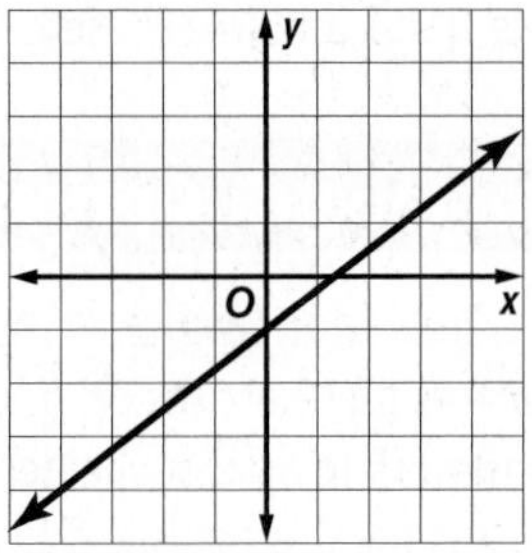

4. $y = -\frac{5}{7}x - \frac{2}{3}$

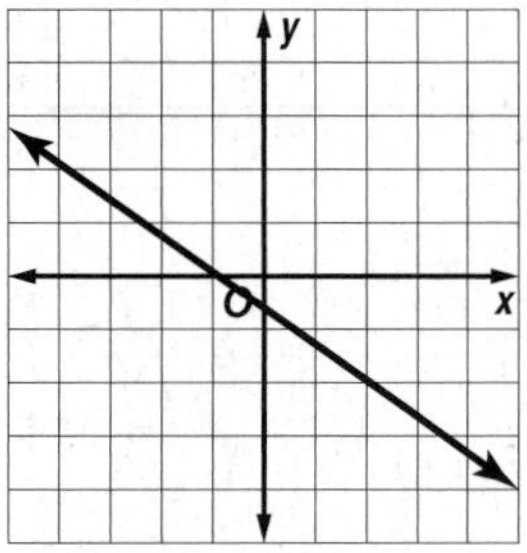

5.

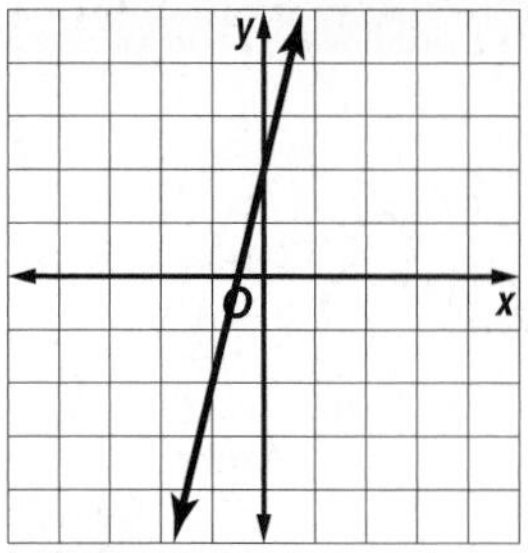

6.

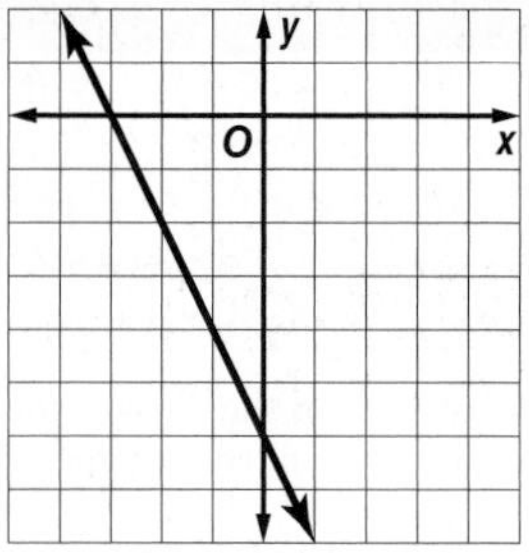

7.

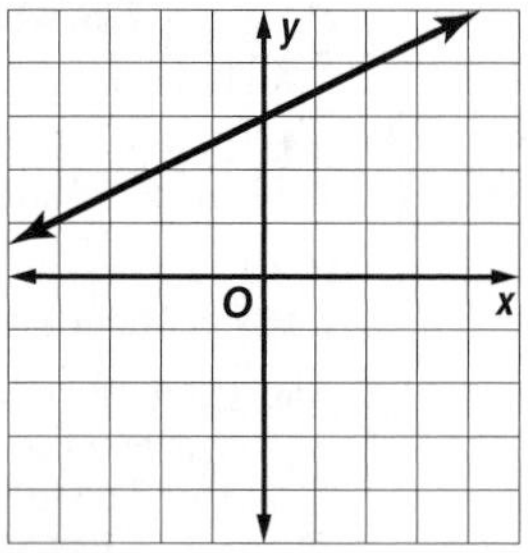

8.

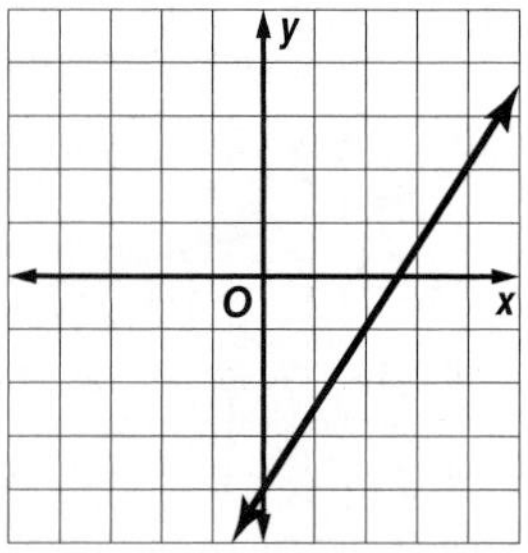

9.

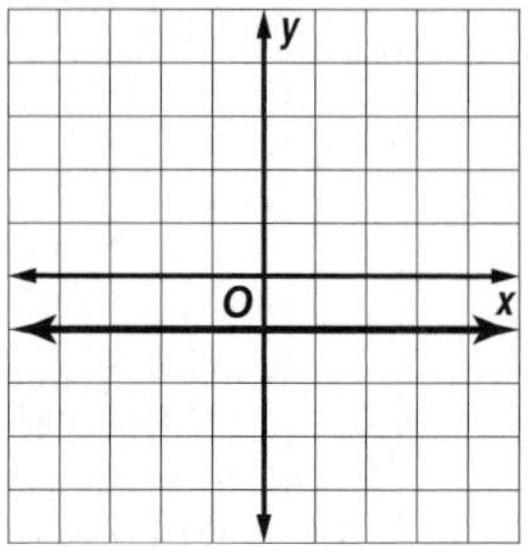

10.

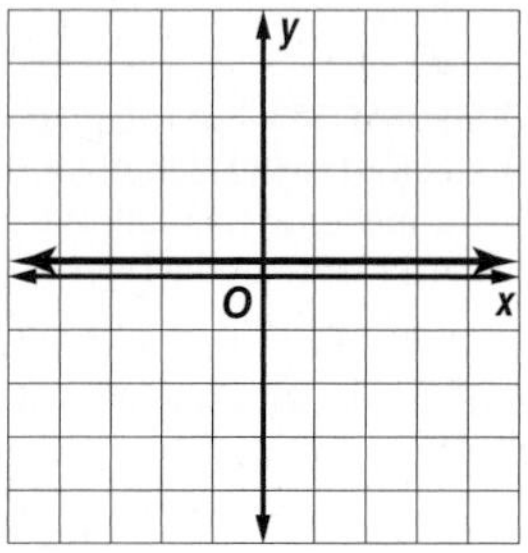

17. $y = 5x + 8$

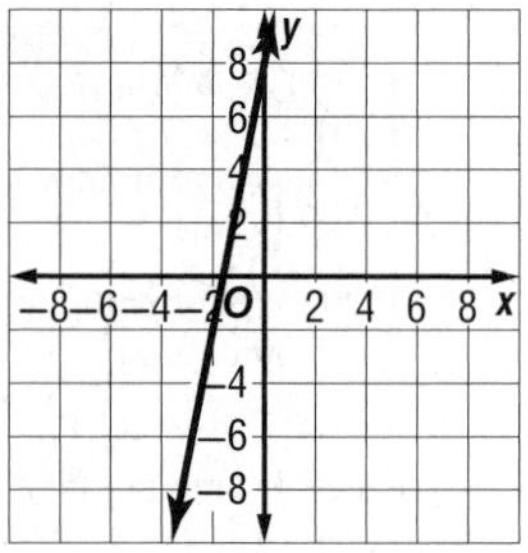

18. $y = 3x + 10$

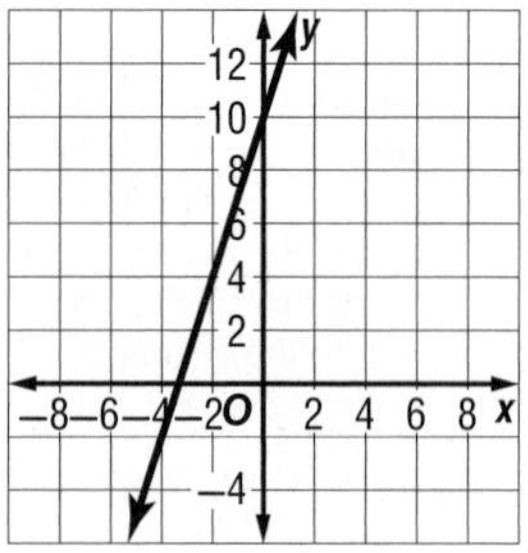

19. $y = -4x + 6$

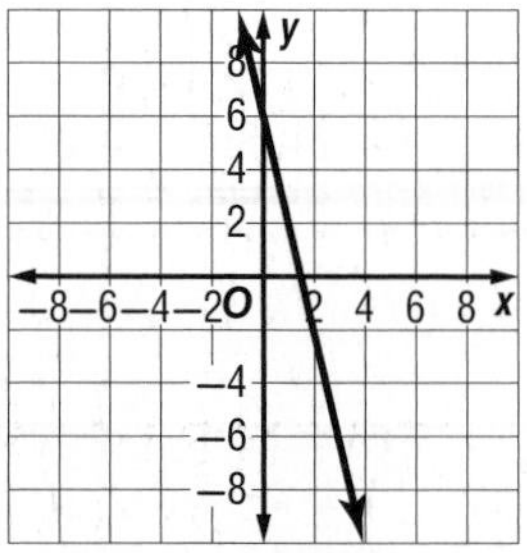

20. $y = -2x + 8$

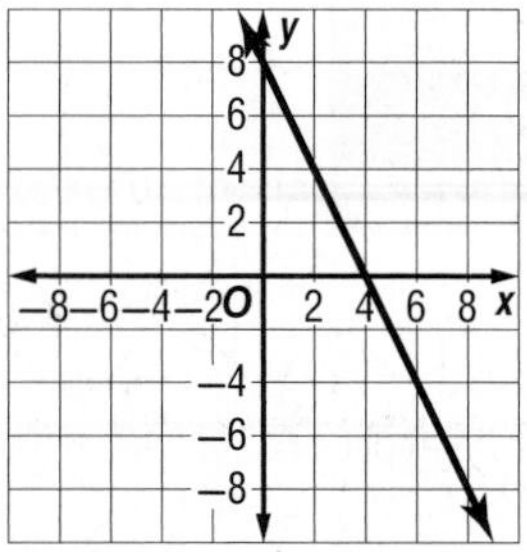

21. $y = 3x - 4$

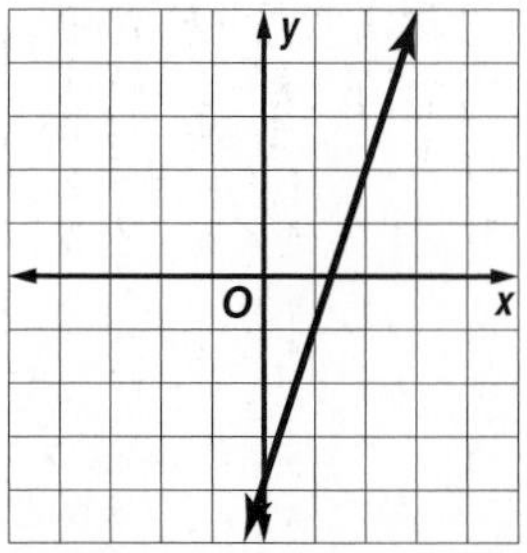

22. $y = 4x - 6$

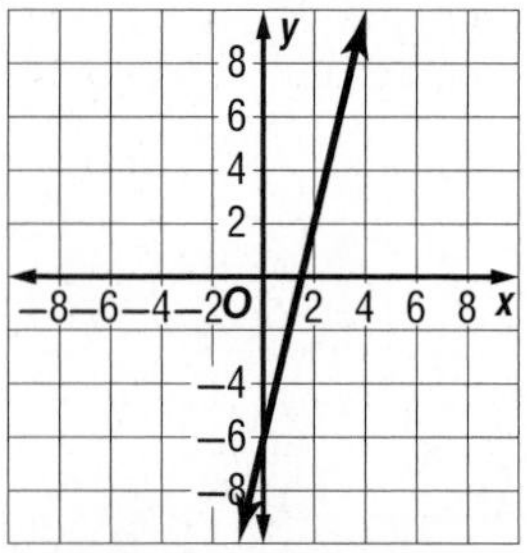

23. 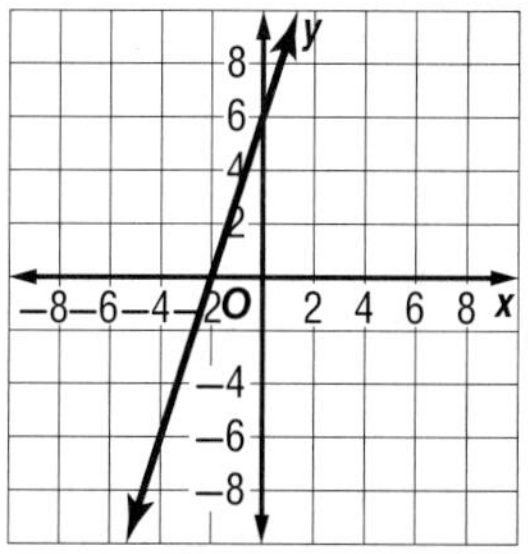

24. 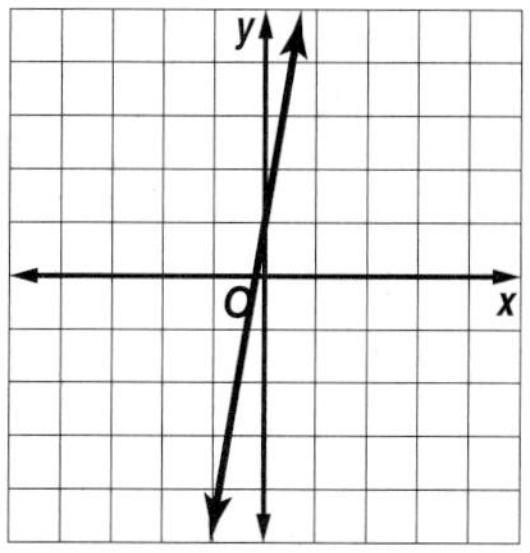

25. 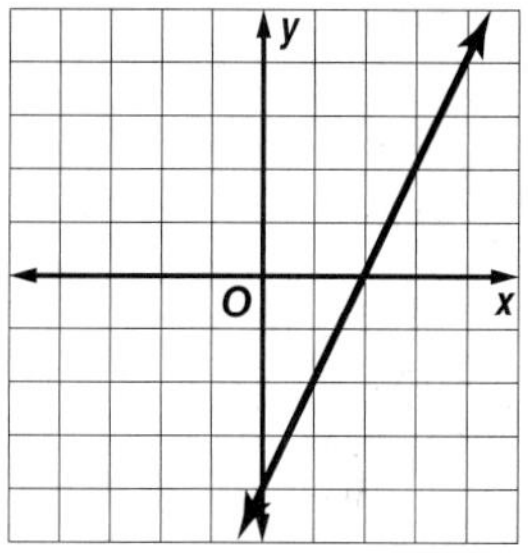

26. 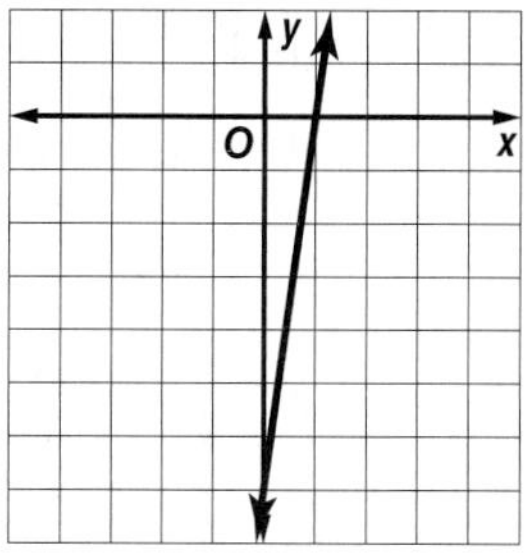

27. 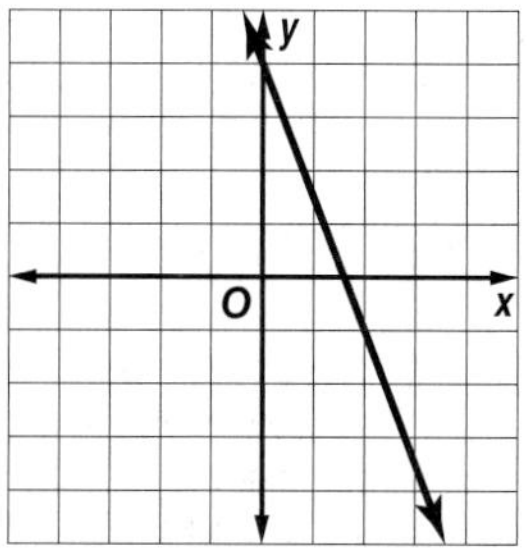

28. 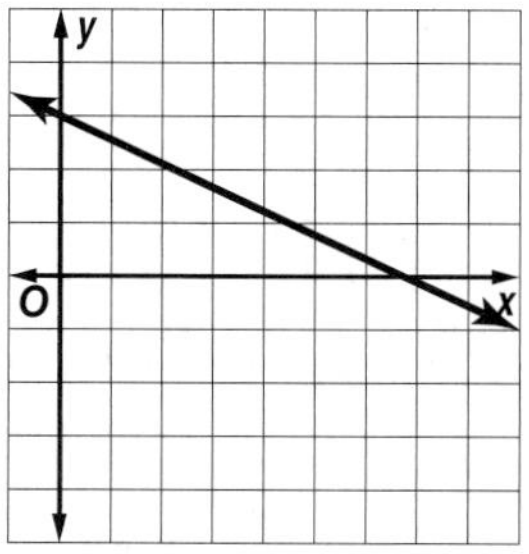

29. 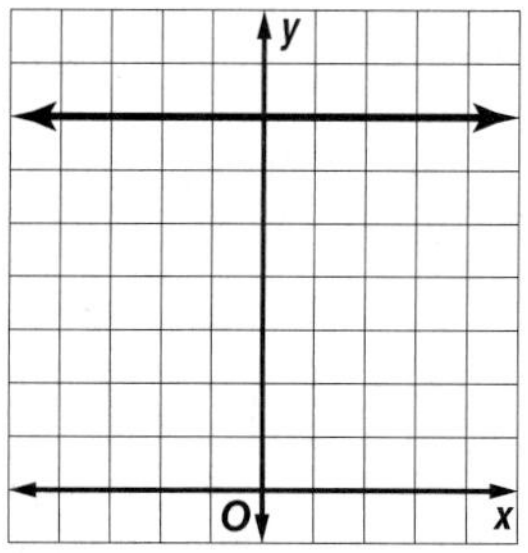

30. 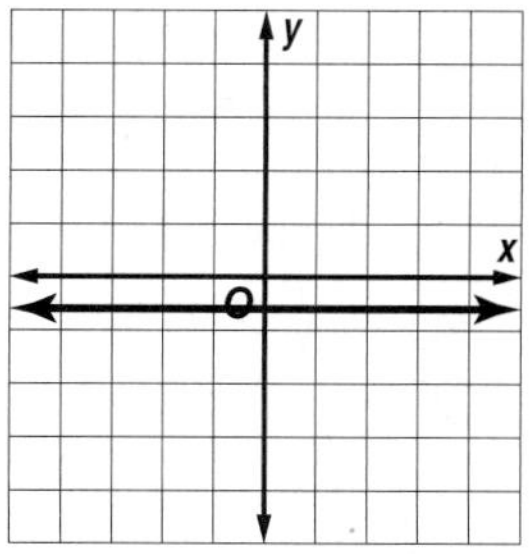

31. 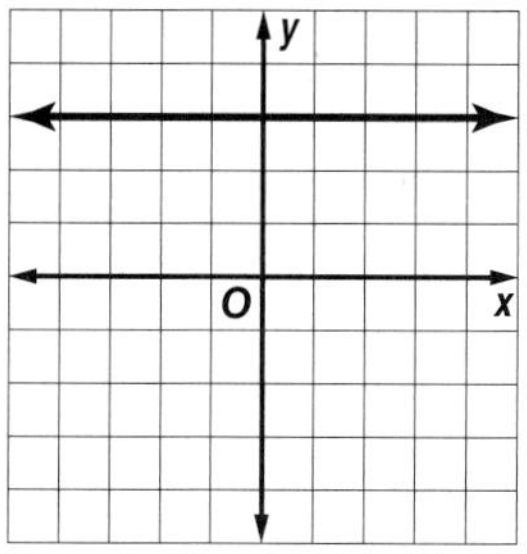

32. 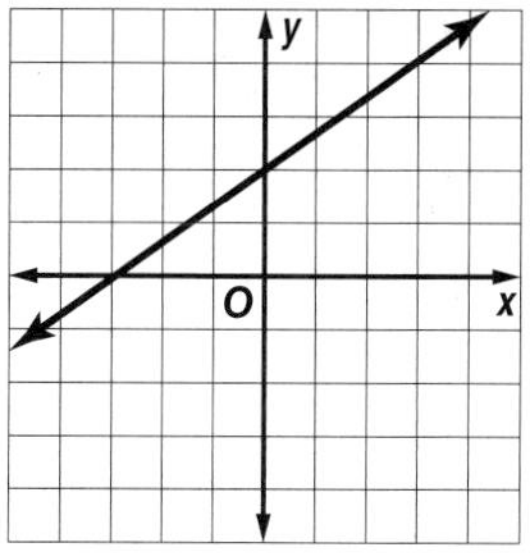

44. 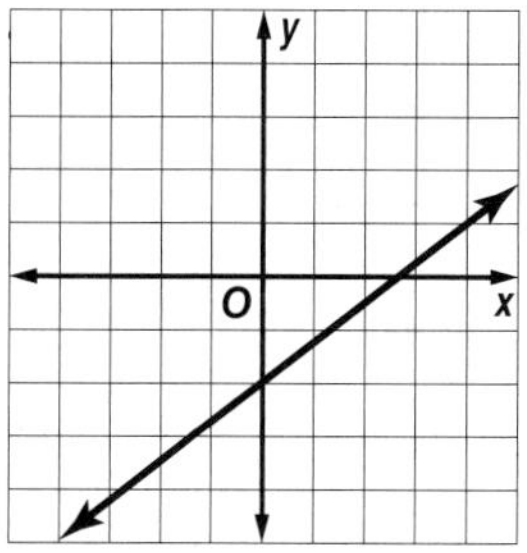

45. 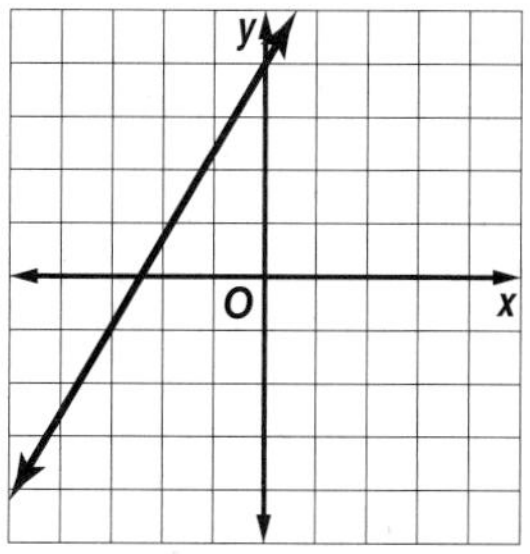

46. 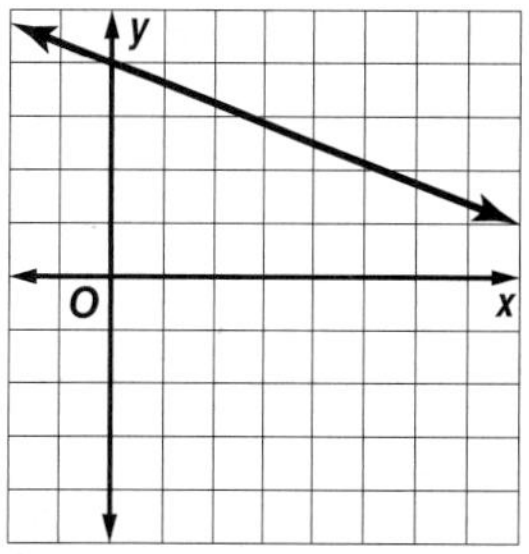

47. 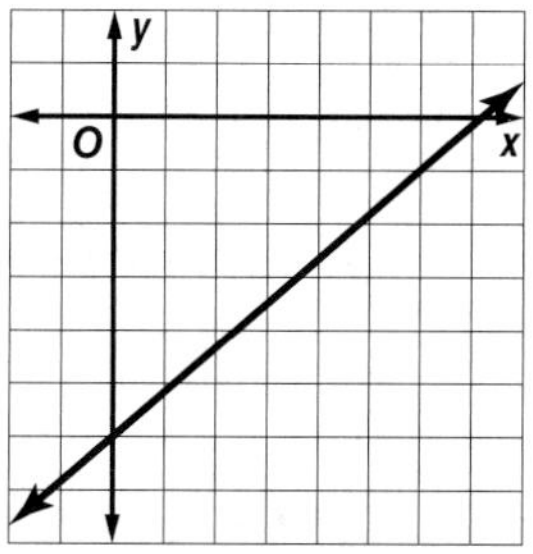

48. 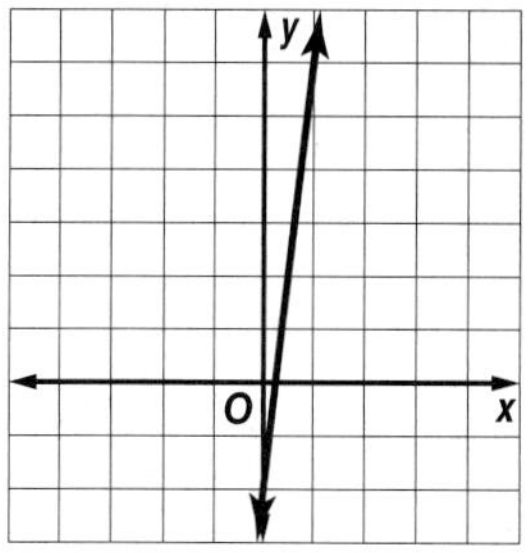

49. 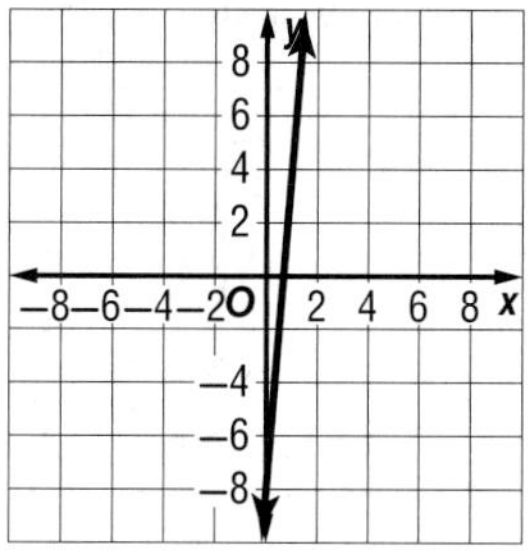

62. Sample answer: $y = x + 15$; The initial cost of joining a movie club is $15. Then each movie costs $1 for a 1-night rental.

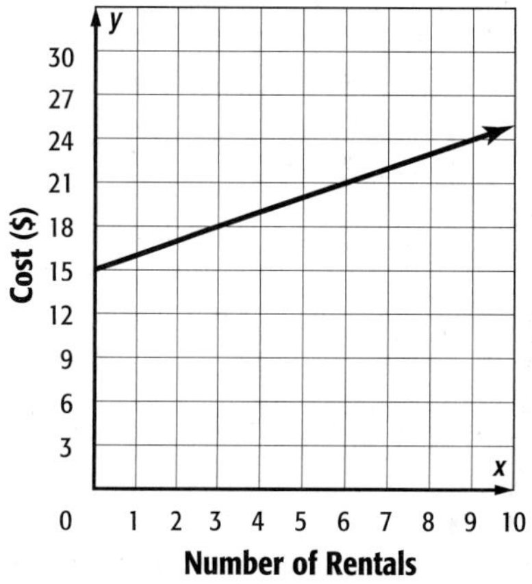

Page 221, Lesson 4-1

71. $a_n = 4n - 1$; nonproportional, does not contain (0, 0)
72. $a_n = -2n + 10$; nonproportional, does not contain (0, 0)
73. $a_n = 3n - 3$; nonproportional, does not contain (0, 0)
74. $a_n = n$; proportional, contains (0, 0)

Page 223, Extend 4-1

1. They have the same slope, but different y-intercepts.

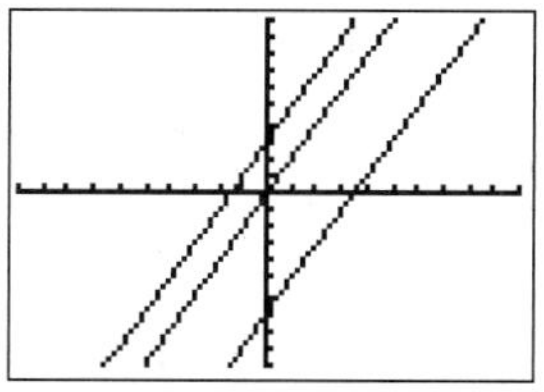

[−10, 10] scl: 1 by [−10, 10] scl: 1

2. They have the same *y*-intercept, but different slopes.

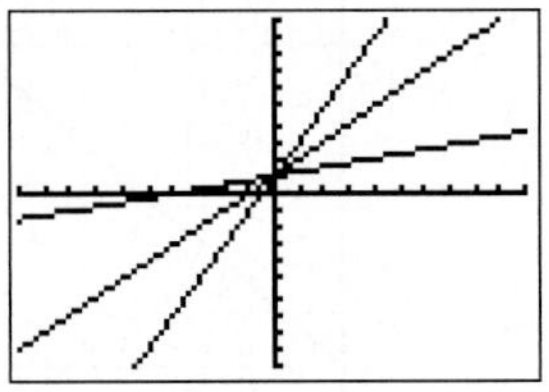

[−10, 10] scl: 1 by [−10, 10] scl: 1

3. They have the same *y*-intercept, but different slopes.

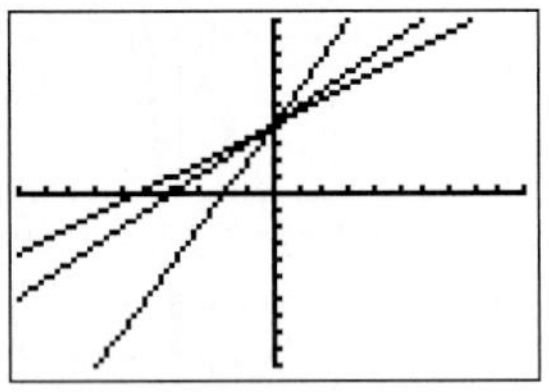

[−10, 10] scl: 1 by [−10, 10] scl: 1

4. They have the same slope, but different *y*-intercepts.

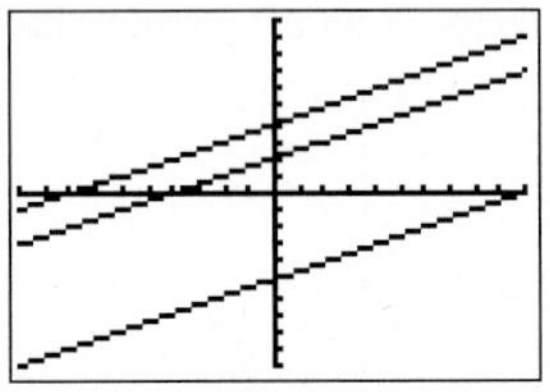

[−10, 10] scl: 1 by [−10, 10] scl: 1

5. They have the same *y*-intercept, but different slopes.

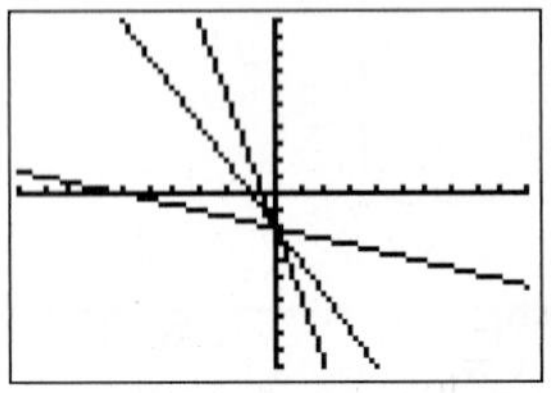

[−10, 10] scl: 1 by [−10, 10] scl: 1

6. They have the same slopes, but different intercepts.

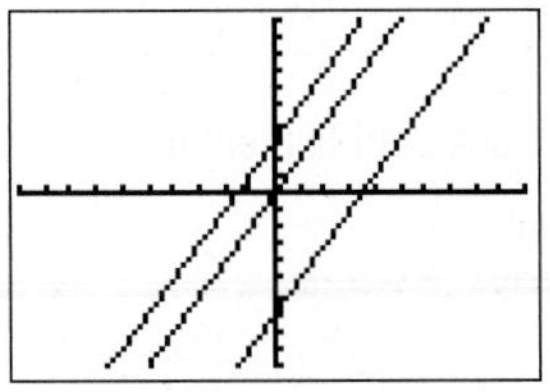

[−10, 10] scl: 1 by [−10, 10] scl: 1

Pages 229–230, Lesson 4-2

45b.

Number of Tickets	3	4	6	7
Cost ($)	171	223	327	379

45c. $431

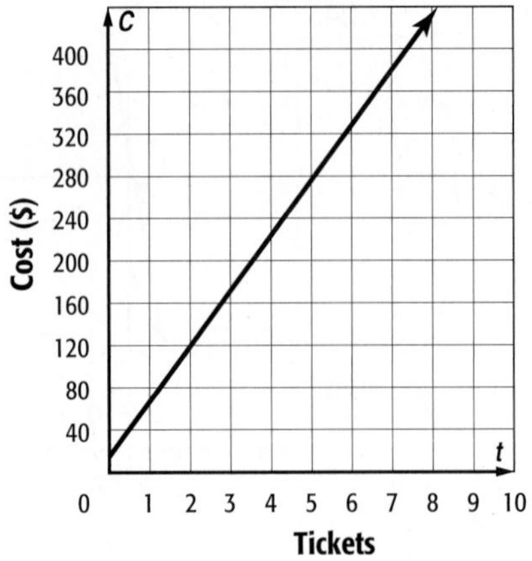

46c.

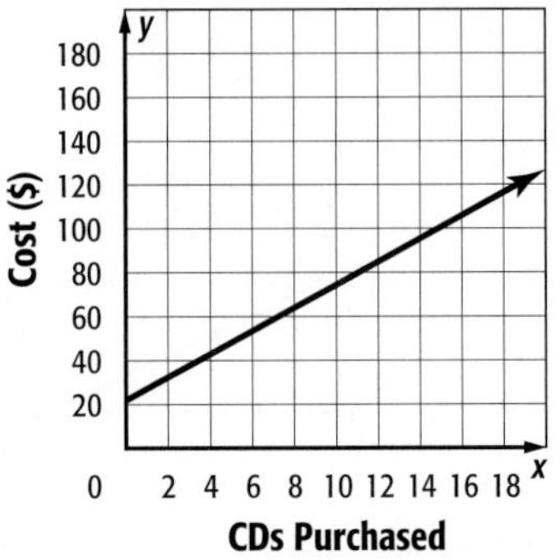

50. Sample answer: Let *y* represent the number of quarts of water in a pitcher, and let *x* represent the time in seconds that water is pouring from the pitcher. As time increases by 1 second, the amount of water in the pitcher decreases by $\frac{1}{2}$ qt. An equation is $y = -\frac{1}{2}x + 4$. The slope is the rate at which the water is leaving the pitcher, $\frac{1}{2}$ quart per second. The *y*-intercept represents the amount of water in the pitcher when it is full, 4 qt.

51. Sample answer: If the problem is about something that could suddenly change, such as weather or prices, the graph could suddenly spike up. You need a constant rate of change to produce a linear graph.

57.

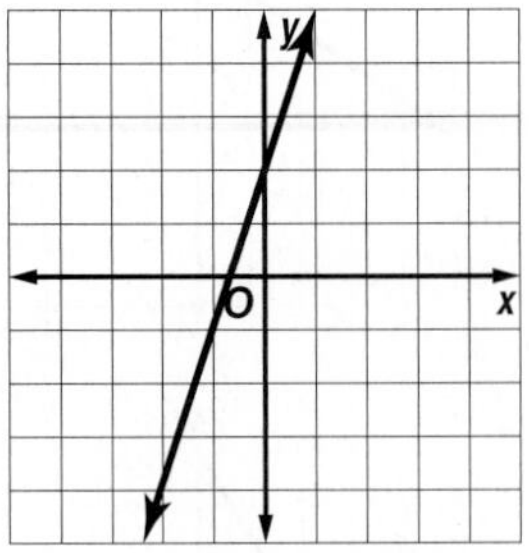

58.

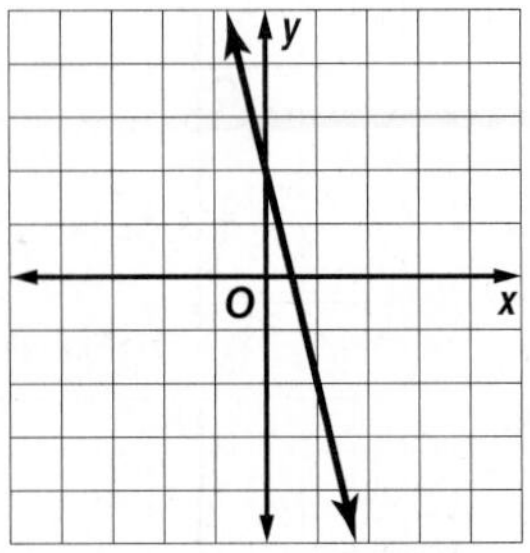

59.

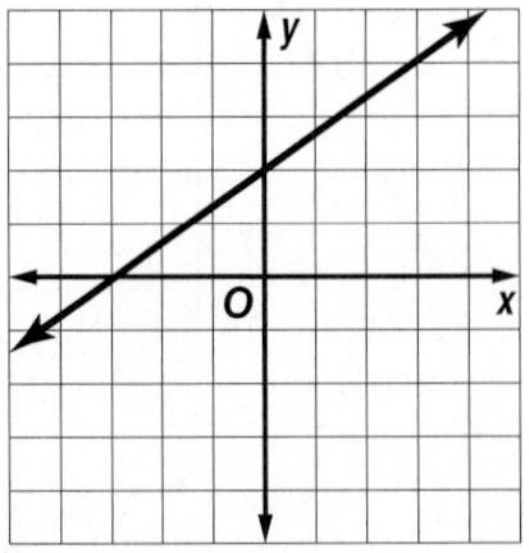

60.

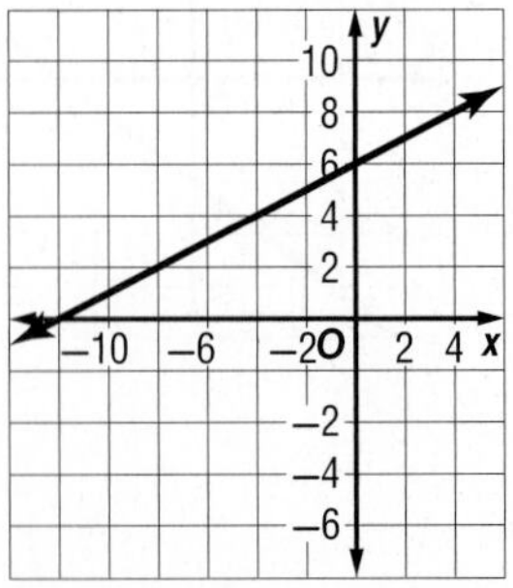

61.

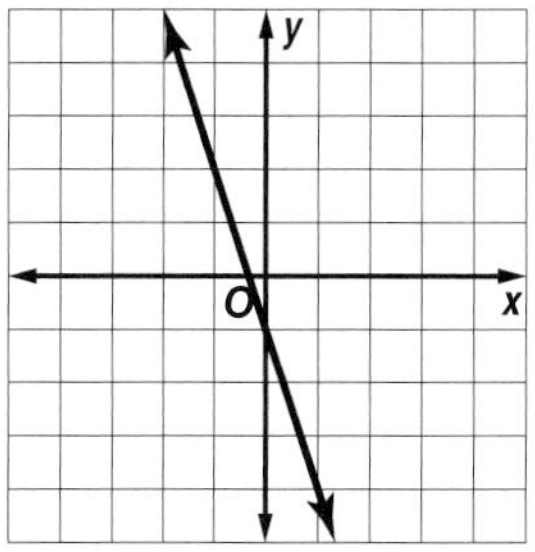

62.

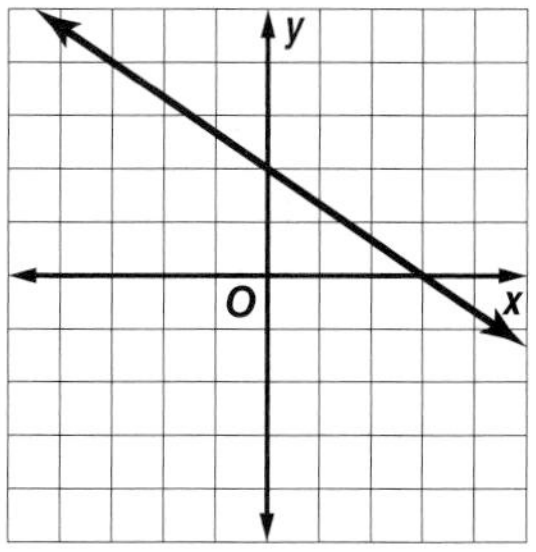

Page 231, Lesson 4-3 (Check Your Progress)

1.

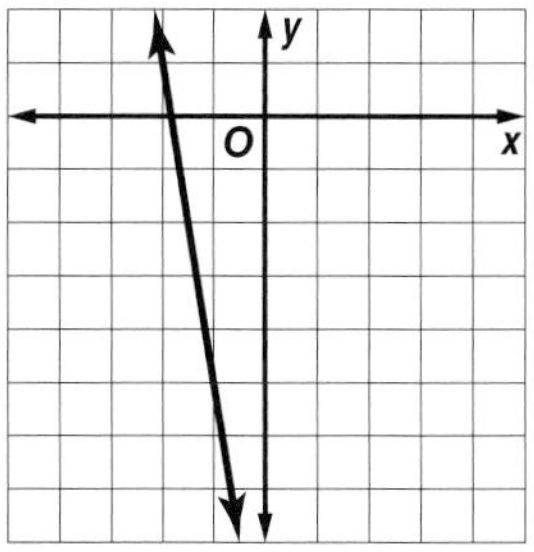

Pages 233–234, Lesson 4-3

1. $y - 5 = -6(x + 2)$

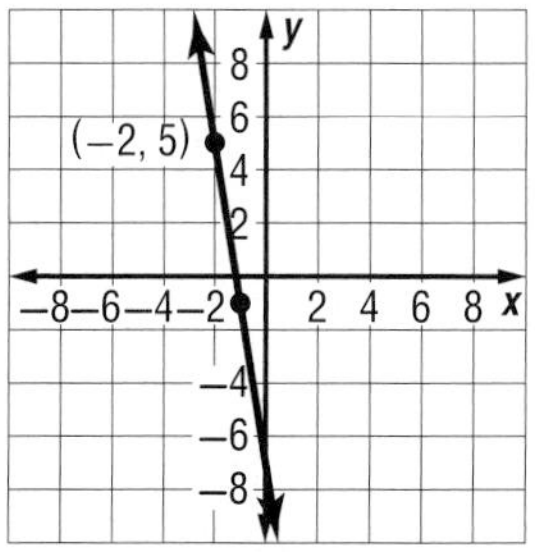

2. $y + 8 = \frac{5}{6}(x + 2)$

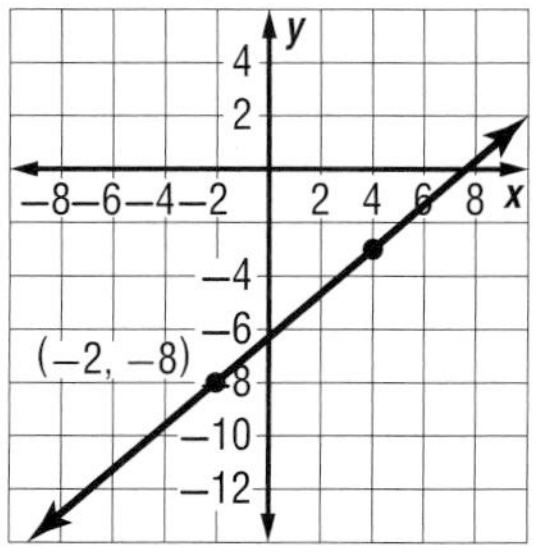

3. $y - 3 = -\frac{1}{2}(x - 4)$

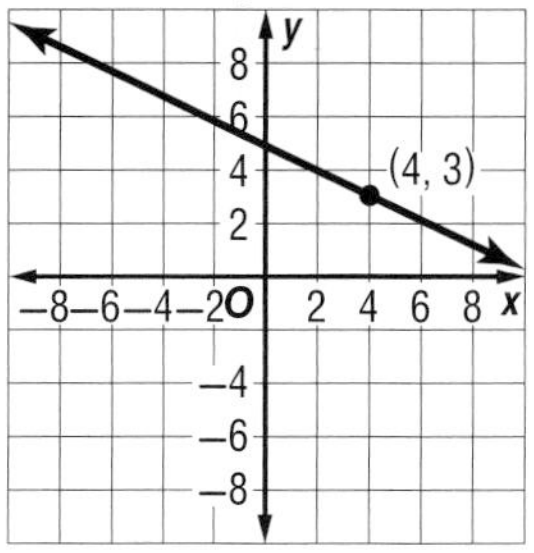

11.

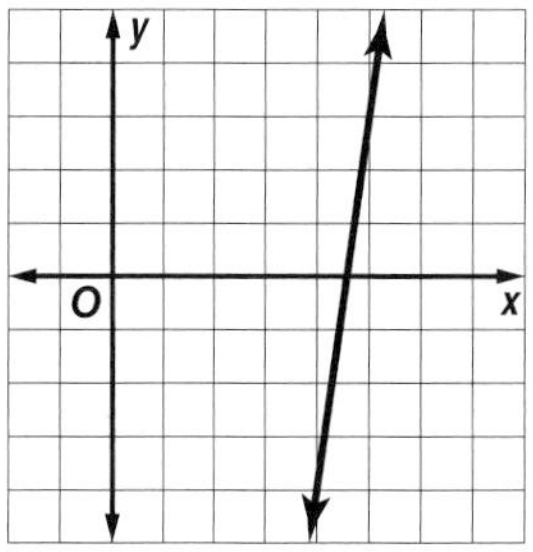

12.

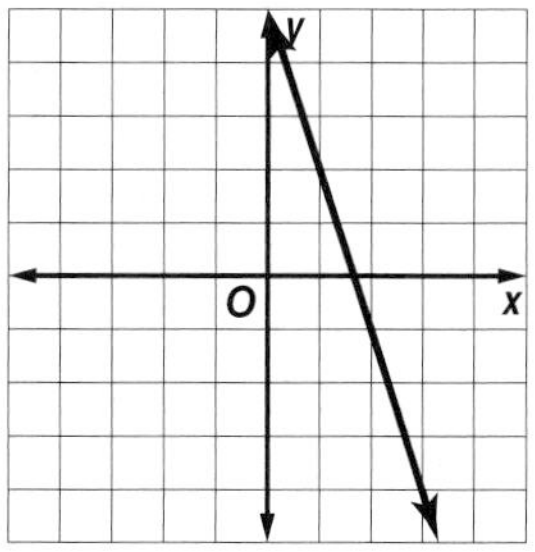

13.

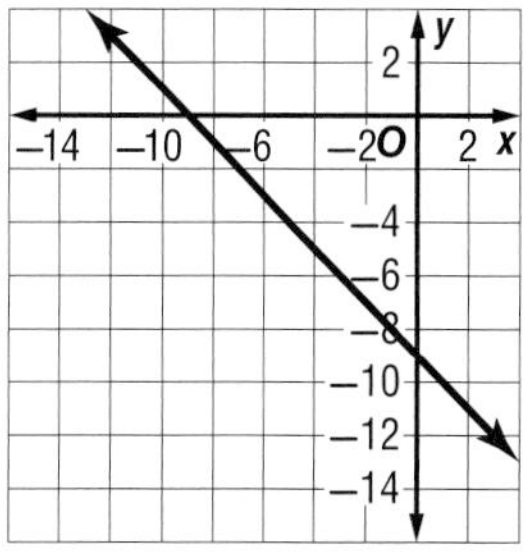

14.

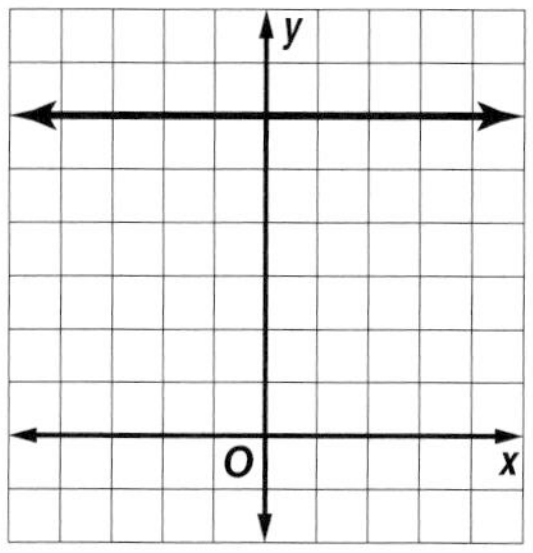

15.

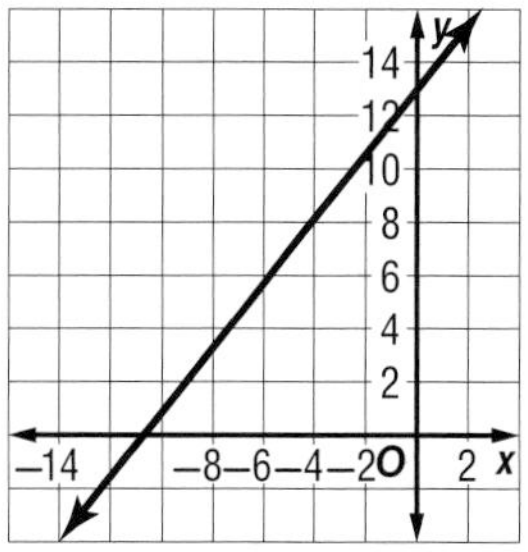

16.

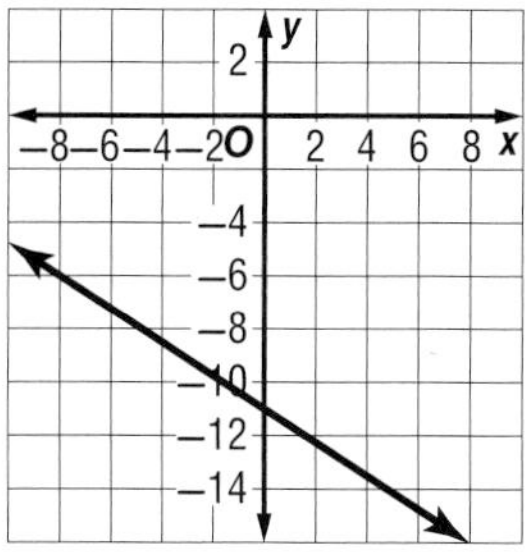

Pages 242–243, Lesson 4-4

43a.

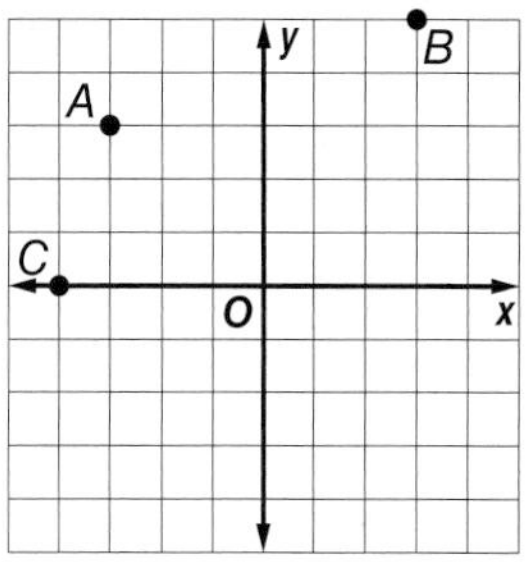

43b. Sample answer: (2, 2); $\overline{AB}$ and $\overline{CD}$ both have slope $\frac{1}{3}$, $\overline{AC}$ and $\overline{BD}$ both have slope 3.

43c. Two; sample answer: Move *C* to (−2, 0) and move *D* to (4, 2). Moving C changes the slope of $\overline{AC}$ to −3. This is the opposite reciprocal of the slope of $\overline{AB}$, $\frac{1}{3}$. Moving *D* also changes the slope of $\overline{BD}$ so $\overline{BD}$ is perpendicular to $\overline{AB}$ and $\overline{CD}$ and it is parallel to $\overline{AC}$.

48. Sample answer: If two lines have the same slope, then the lines are parallel. If the product of their slopes equals −1, then the lines are perpendicular. The graph of $y = \frac{3}{2}x$ is parallel to the graph of $y = \frac{2}{3}x - 1$ because they have the same slope, $\frac{3}{2}$. The graph of $y = -\frac{2}{3}x$ is perpendicular to the graph of $y = \frac{3}{2}x - 1$ because the slopes are opposite reciprocals of each other.

70.

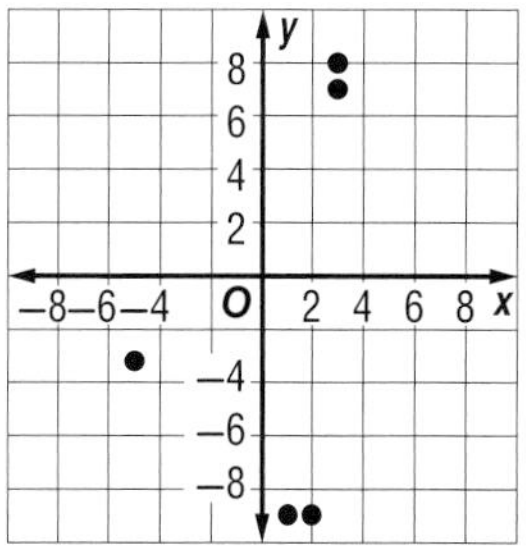

D = {3, 2, 1, −5};
R = {8, 7, −9, −3}

71.

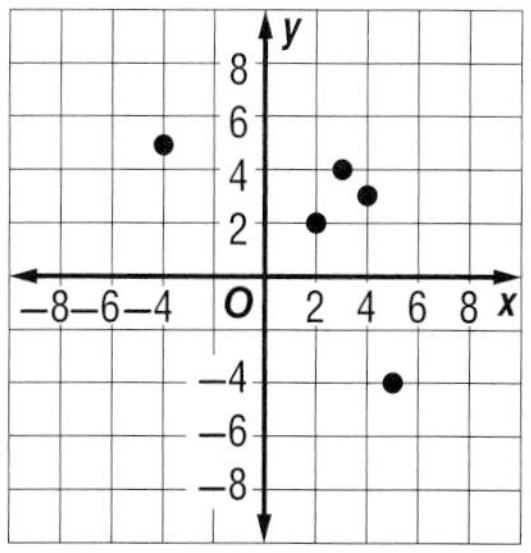

D = {3, 4, 2, 5, −4};
R = {4, 3, 2, −4, 5}

72.

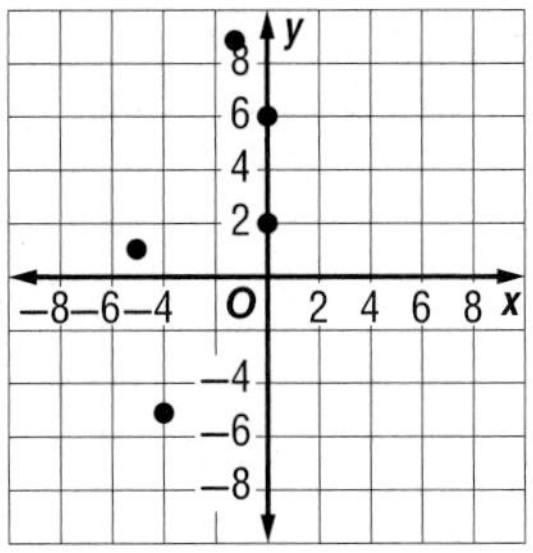

D = {0, −5, −1, −4}
R = {2, 1, 6, 9, −5}

73.

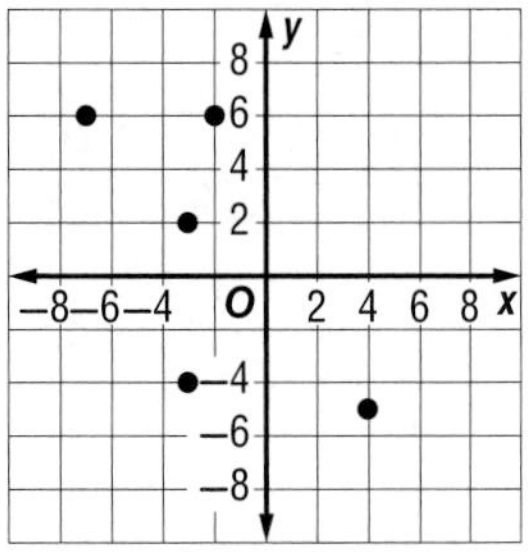

D = {−7, 4, −2, −3};
R = {6, 4, 5, 2}

Page 244, Mid-Chapter Quiz

3.

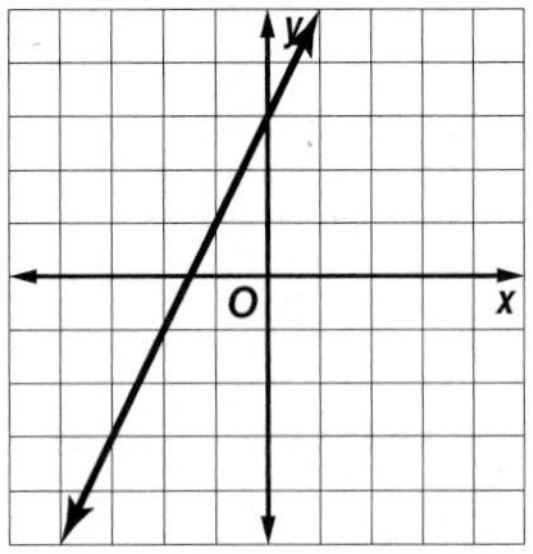

4.

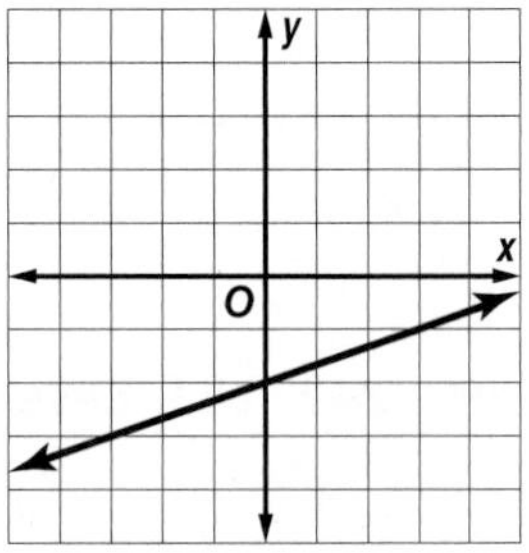

Page 247, Lesson 4-5 (Check Your Progress)

2. The independent variable is the year, and the dependent variable is the amount of sales; negative correlation.

CD Sales

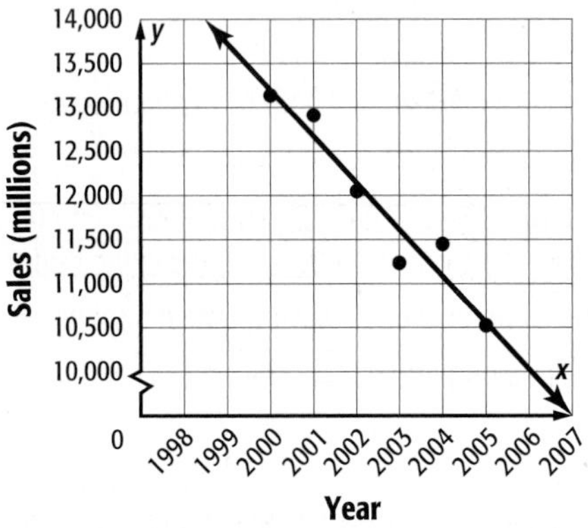

$y = -593x + 1{,}091{,}215$

Pages 249–251, Lesson 4-5

10a–b. **Height vs. Weight in 12 Men**

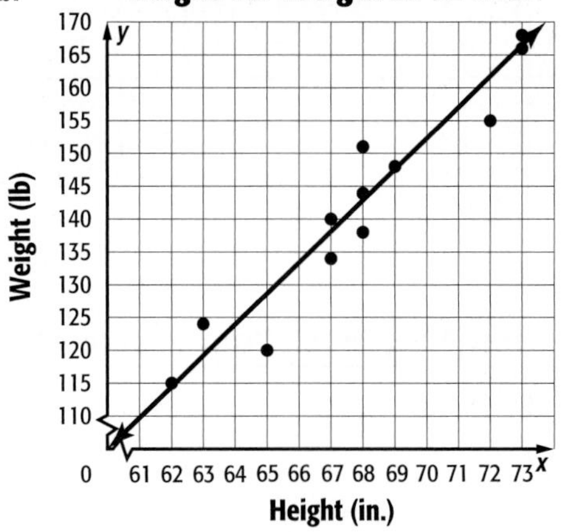

11a. **"Old Faithful"**

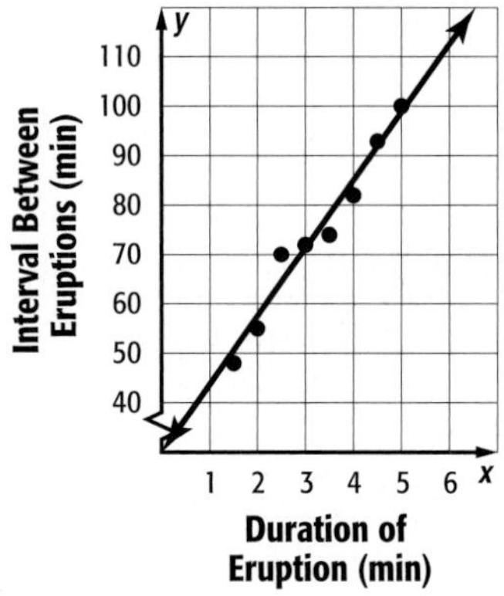

42.

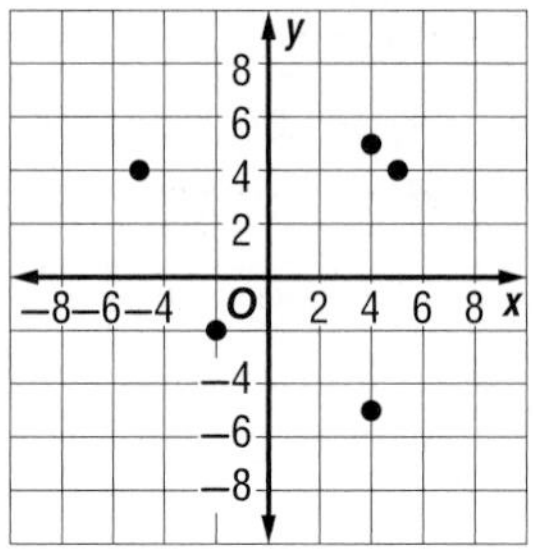

D = {4, 5, −2, −5};
R = {5, −2, −5, 4}

43.

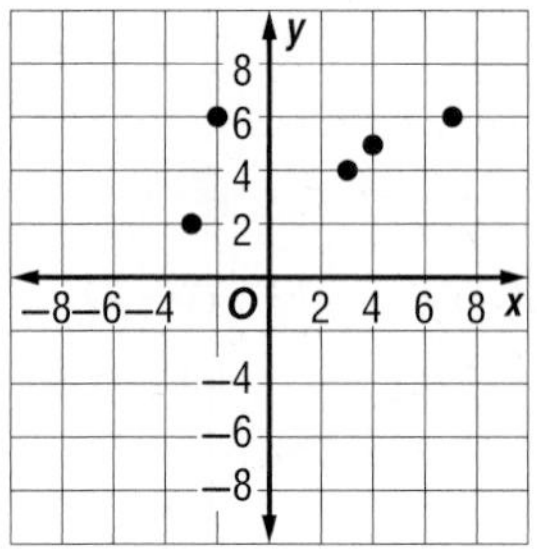

D = {7, 3, 4, −2, −3};
R = {6, 4, 5, 2}

Page 252, Extend 4-5

1. Correlation; a controlled experiment must be performed to show causation. This was just a survey. Other factors that might be involved could include an inherited trait from parents for nearsightedness or a disease.
2. Causation; this was a controlled experiment. Other factors that might be involved could include dangerous chemicals encountered in the environment or an inherited trait for developing cancer.
3. Correlation; a survey cannot show causation. Other factors that might be involved could be economic. Students riding the bus may come from families that do not have extra money to spare for alternate transportation or cell phones.

4. Causation; this was a controlled experiment. Other factors that might be involved could include loud noise encountered in the environment or workplace or an inherited trait for developing a hearing loss.

5. Correlation; it is not known if this was a controlled experiment or a survey. Other factors that might be involved include the fact the more people swim in the ocean and eat ice cream during hot months.

Page 259, Lesson 4-6

18a.

Year	Number of Launches
1993	7
1994	7
1995	7
1996	7
1997	8
1998	5
1999	3
2000	5
2001	6
2002	5
2003	1
2004	0
2005	1
2006	3

19.

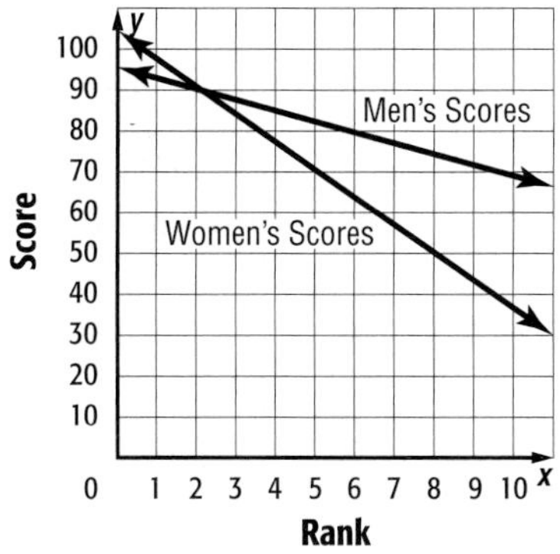

Sample answer: Men: $y = -2.92x + 95.92$; Women: $y = -7x + 106$; Women's scores have a steeper slope.

20. Apply a linear regression model to the data. Use the number of each test as the independent variable and the score on each test as the dependent variable. If there is no correlation, the r value will not be close to 1 or -1. If this is the case, the line of fit could not be used to predict the scores of the other students.

22. First, you would enter the data into the calculator with the year in L1 and the number of appearances in the L2 column. Then, you would use the linear regression function to find a linear regression equation of $y = 6.79x - 13{,}339$. Finally, enter the year 2012 into your equation for x to find that Spiderman should make approximately 322 visits in 2012.

Page 262, Lesson 4-7 (Check Your Progress)

2.

Parking

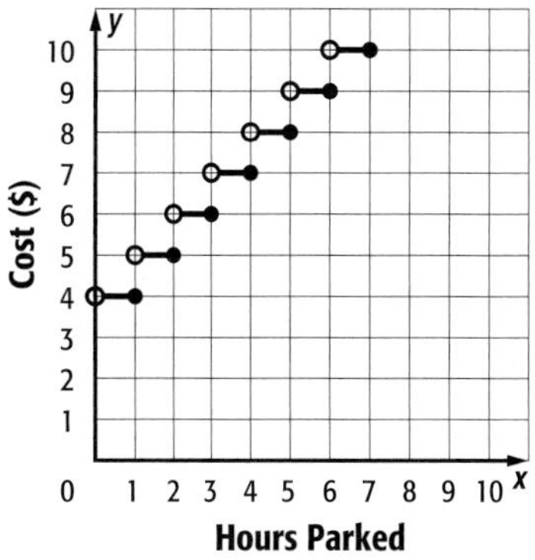

Pages 264–268, Lesson 4-7

5.

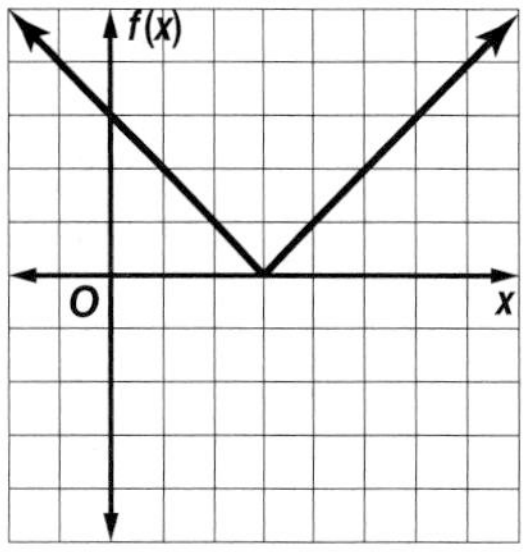

D = all real numbers,
R = $f(x) \geq 0$

6.

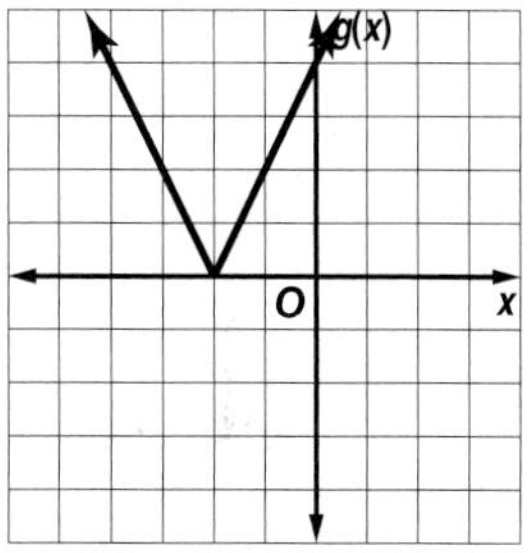

D = all real numbers,
R = $g(x) \geq 0$

7.

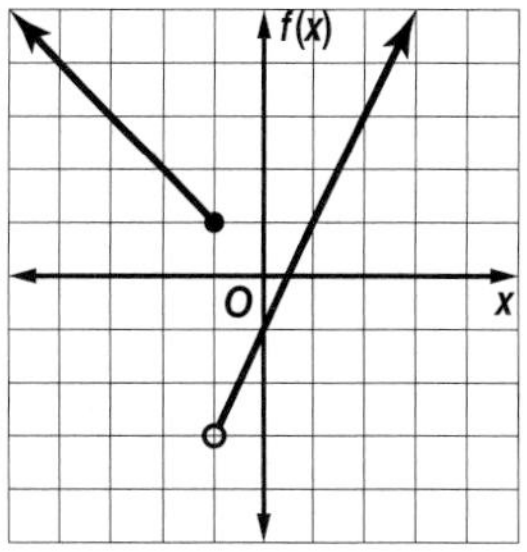

D = all real numbers,
R = $f(x) > -3$

8.

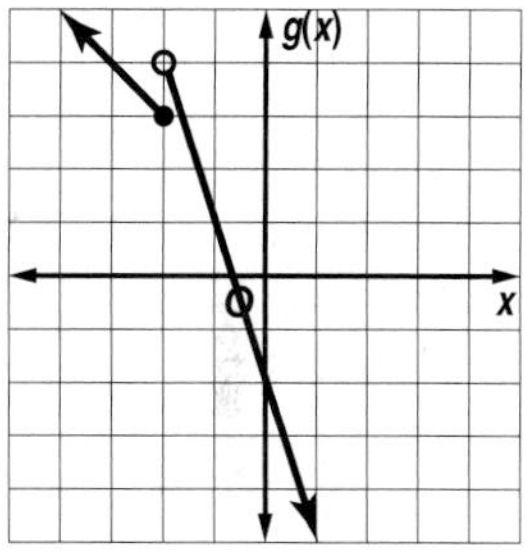

D = all real numbers,
R = all real numbers

9.

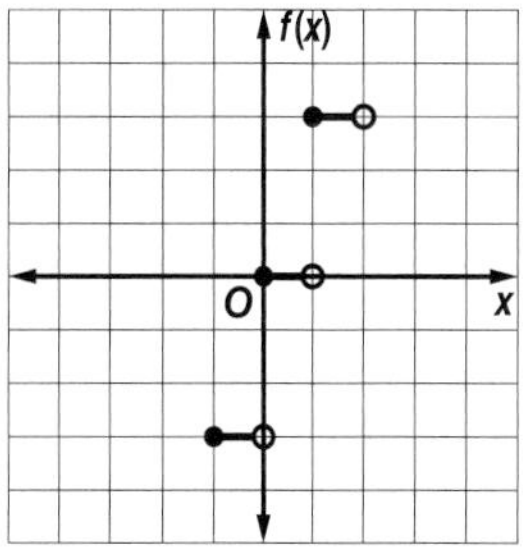

D = all real numbers,
R = all integer multiples of 3

10.

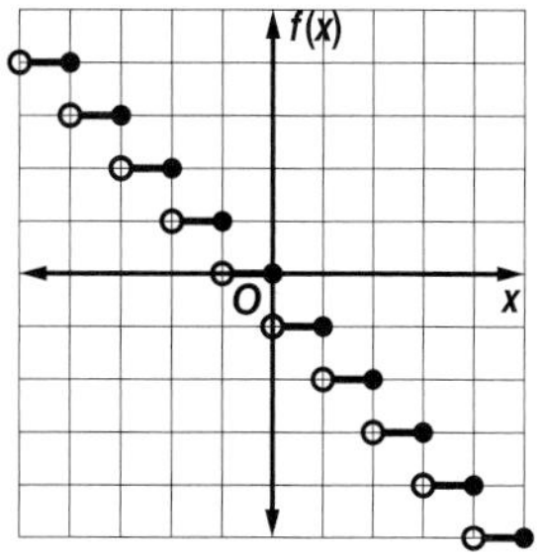

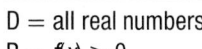

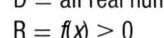

D = all real numbers,
R = all integers

11.

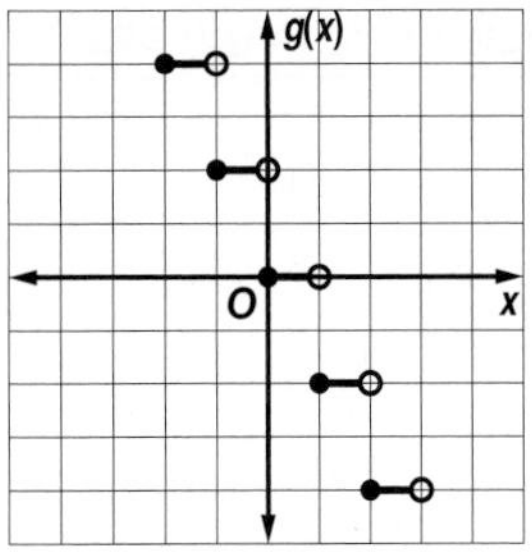

D = all real numbers,
R = all even integers

12.

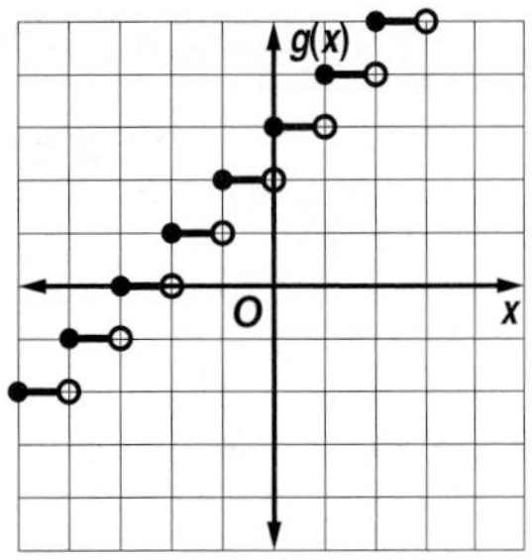

D = all real numbers,
R = all integers

13.

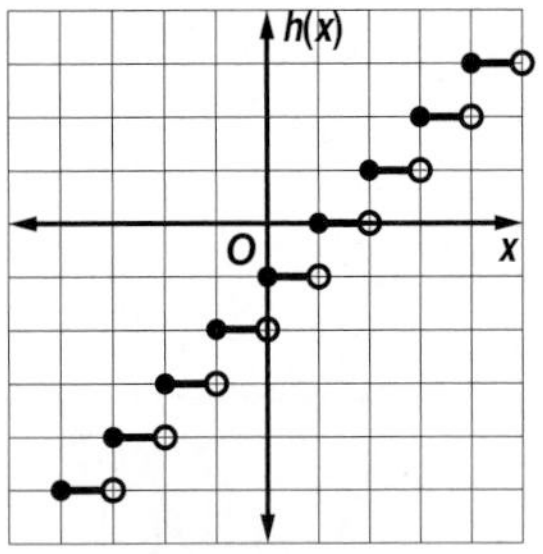

D = all real numbers,
R = all integers

14.

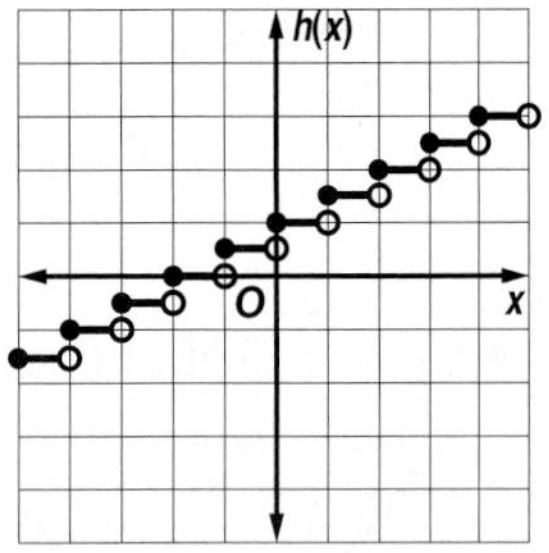

D = all real numbers,
R = all integer multiples of 0.5

17.

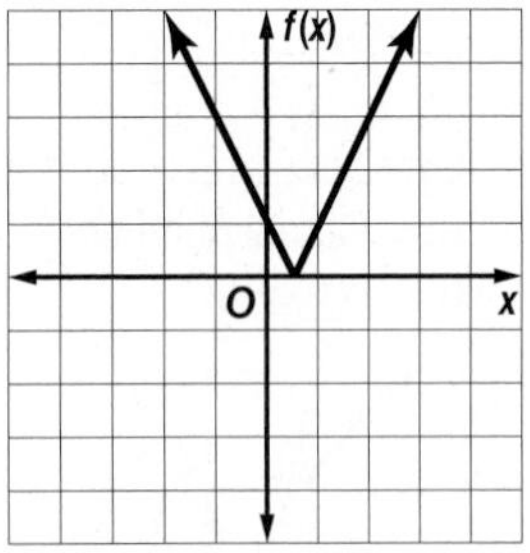

D = all real numbers,
R = $f(x) \geq 0$

18.

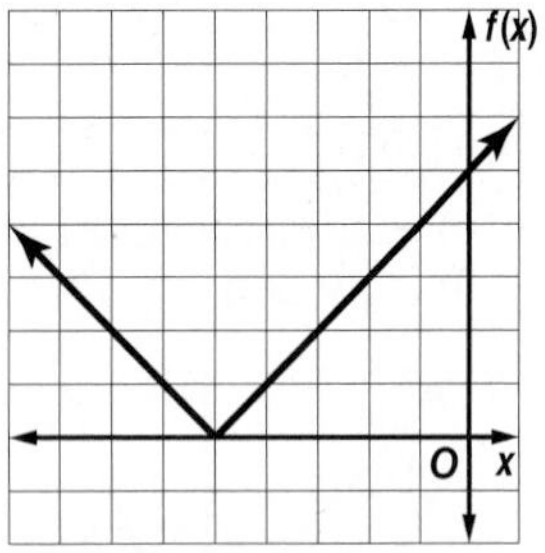

D = all real numbers,
R = $f(x) \geq 0$

19.

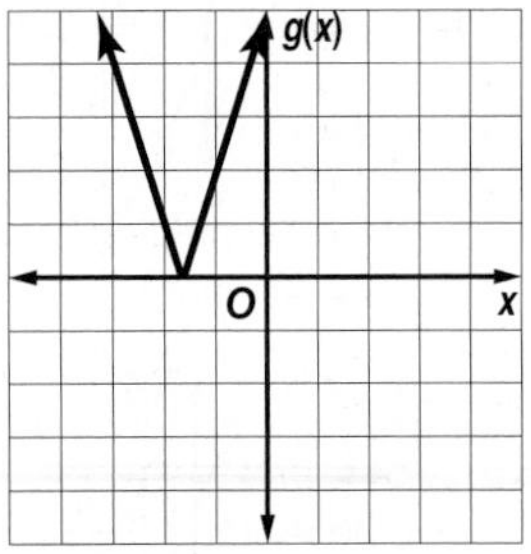

D = all real numbers,
R = $g(x) \geq 0$

20.

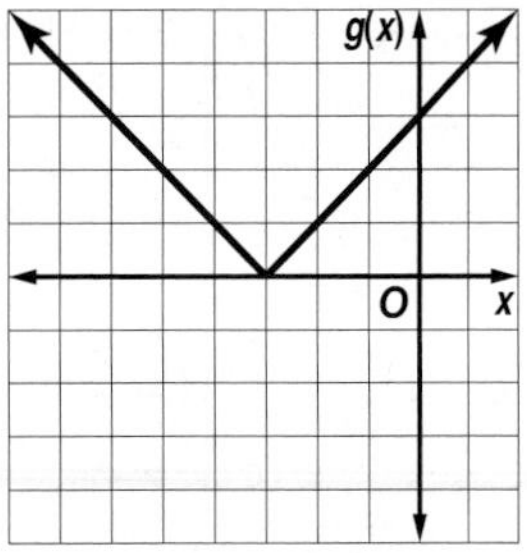

D = all real numbers,
R = $g(x) \geq 0$

21.

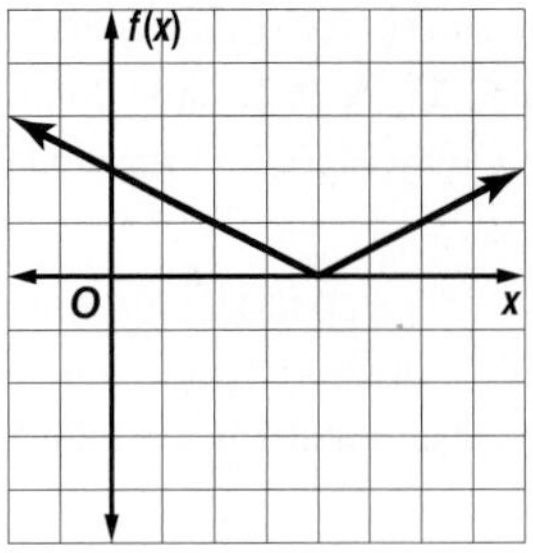

D = all real numbers,
R = $f(x) \geq 0$

22.

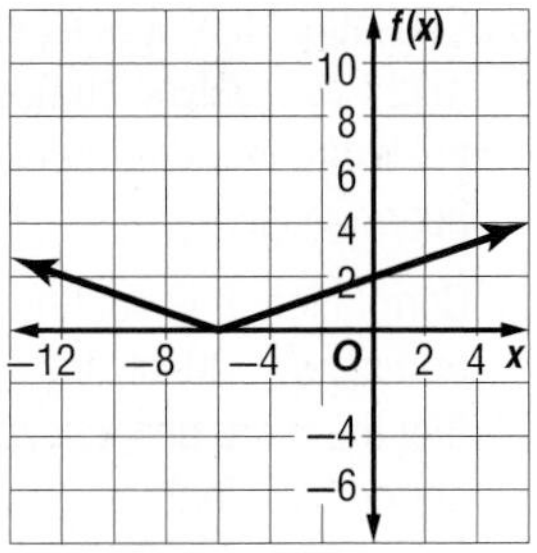

D = all real numbers,
R = $f(x) \geq 0$

23.

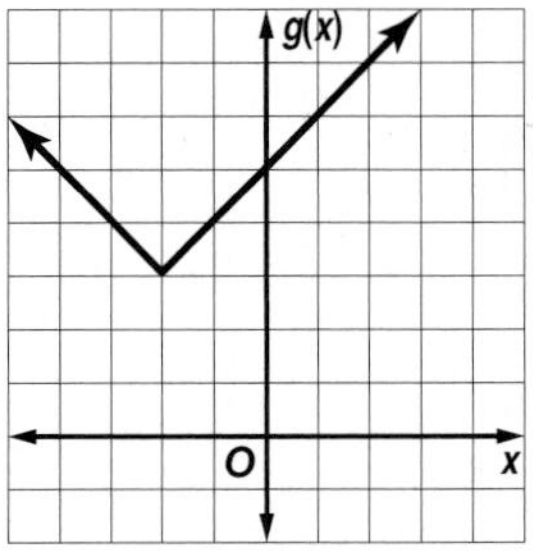

D = all real numbers,
R = $g(x) \geq 3$

24.

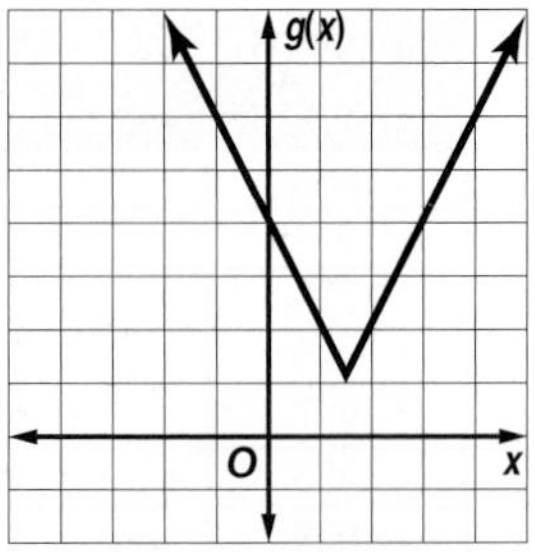

D = all real numbers,
R = $g(x) \geq 1$

25.

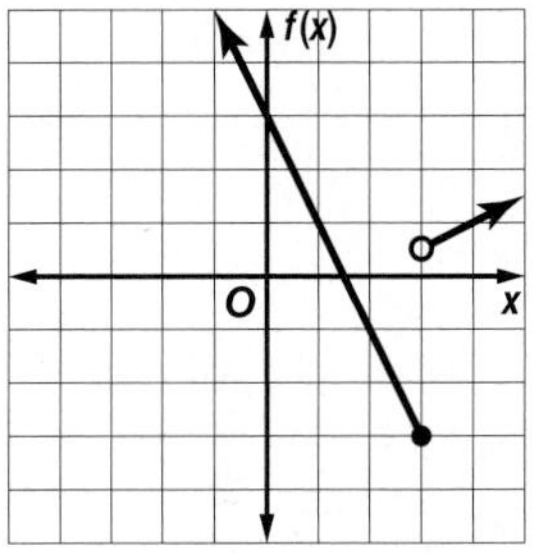

D = all real numbers,
R = $f(x) \geq -3$

26.

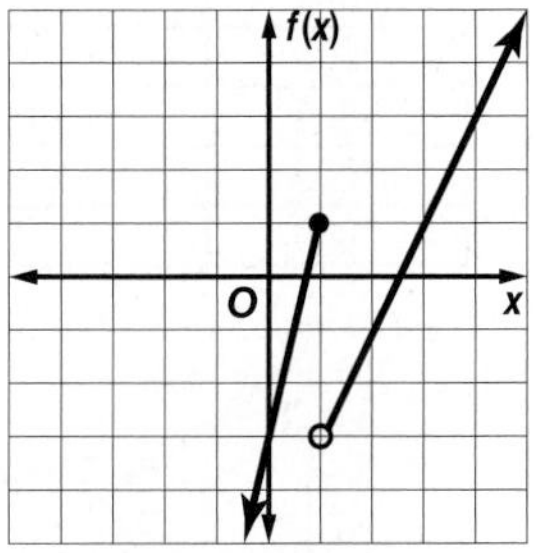

D = all real numbers,
R = all real numbers

27.

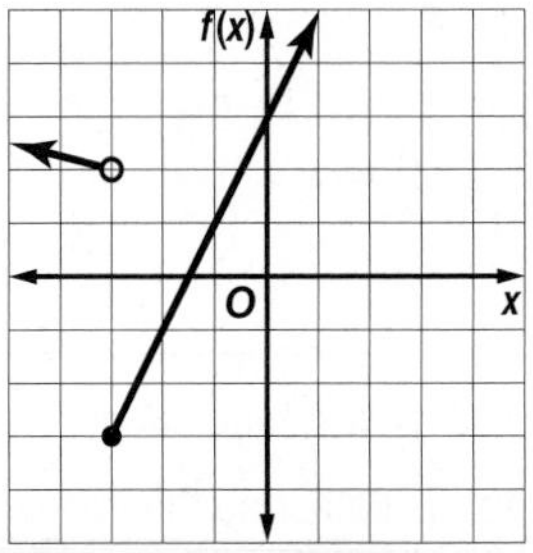

D = all real numbers,
R = all real numbers

28.

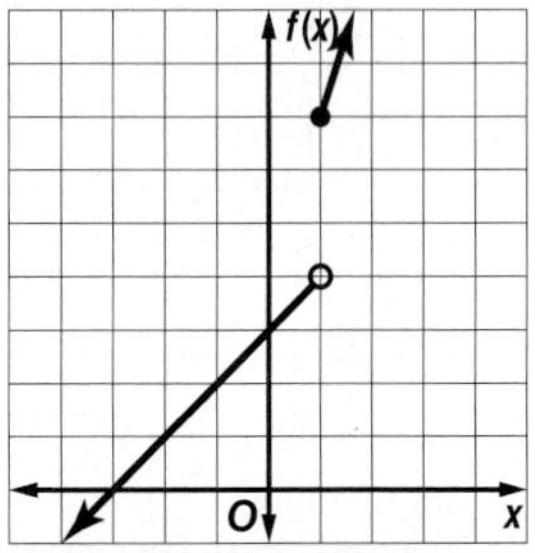

D = all real numbers,
R = $f(x) < 4$ or $f(x) \geq 7$

29.

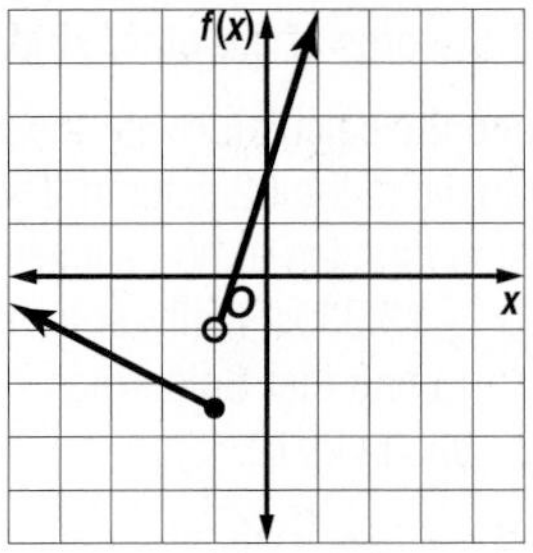

D = all real numbers,
R = $f(x) \geq -2.5$

30.

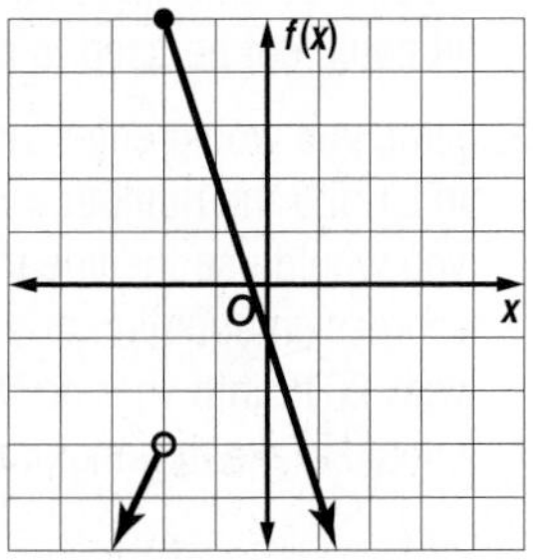

D = all real numbers,
R = $f(x) \leq 5$

43a.

Number of Orders	Total Price
$1 \le x \le 10$	$10 + (10 + 4 + 2)x = 10 + 16x$
$11 \le x < 20$	$(10 + 16x)(0.95) = 9.5 + 15.20x$
$x \ge 20$	$(10 + 16x)(0.90) = 9 + 14.40x$

43c.

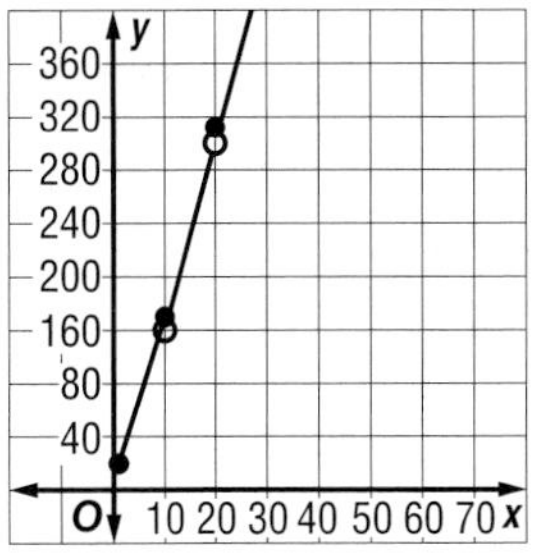

44a.

x	−5	−4	−3	−2	−1	0	1	2	3	4	5
$f(x)$	7	5	3	1	1	3	5	7	9	11	13

44b.

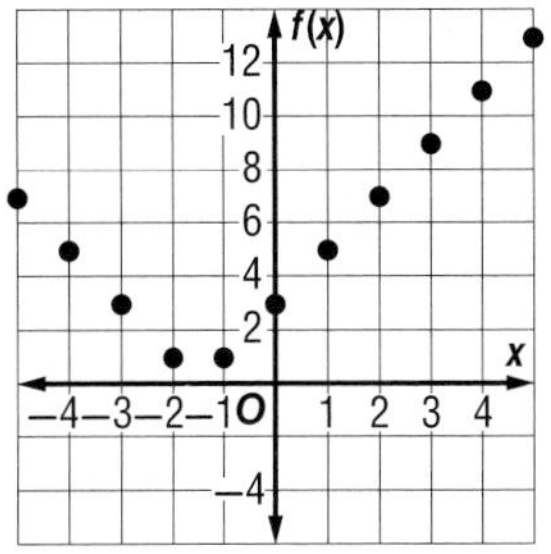

44c.

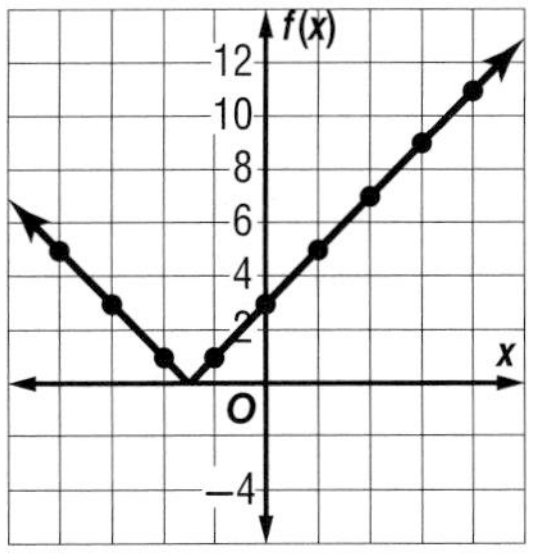

45a.

x	−5	−4	−3	−2	−1	0	1	2	3	4	5
$f(x)$	13	11	9	7	5	3	5	7	9	11	13

45b.

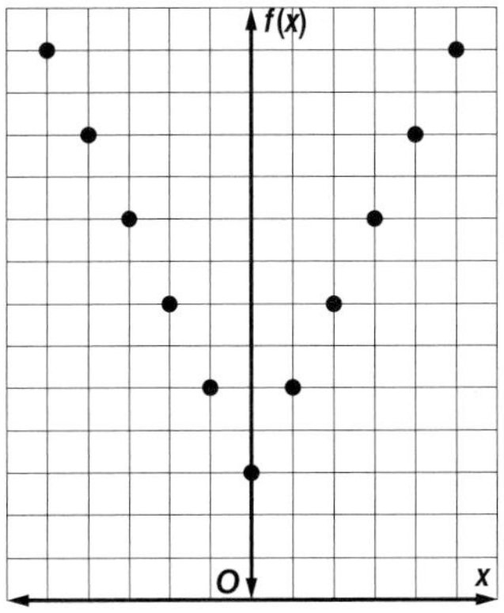

45c.

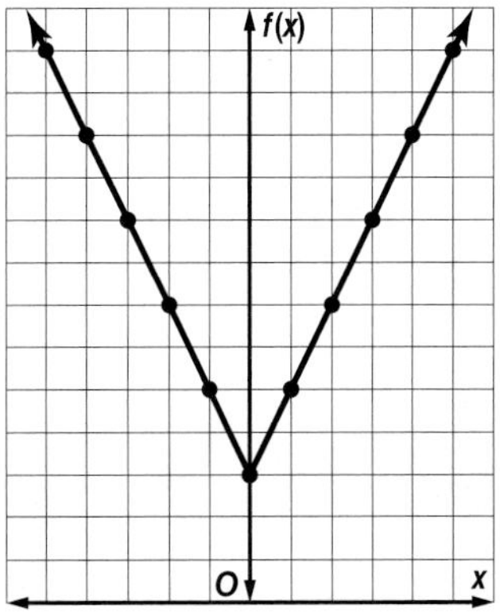

45d. The graph is shifted 1.5 units to the right and 3 units up.

48.

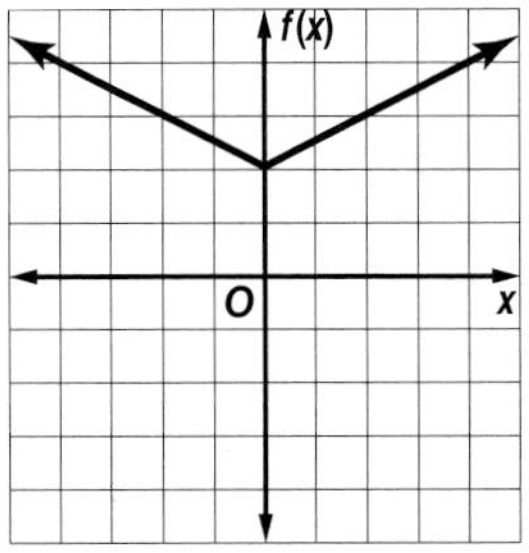

49.

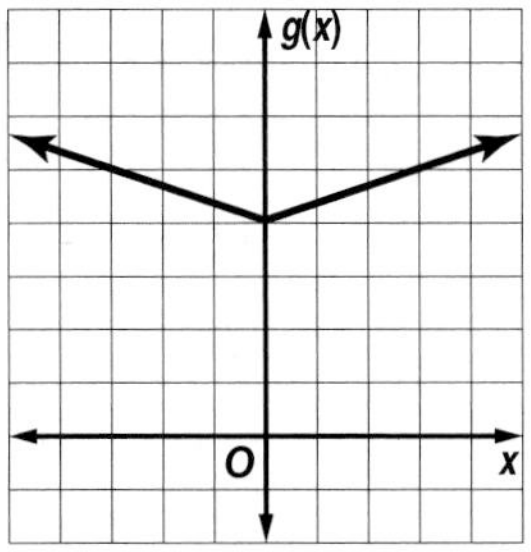

50.

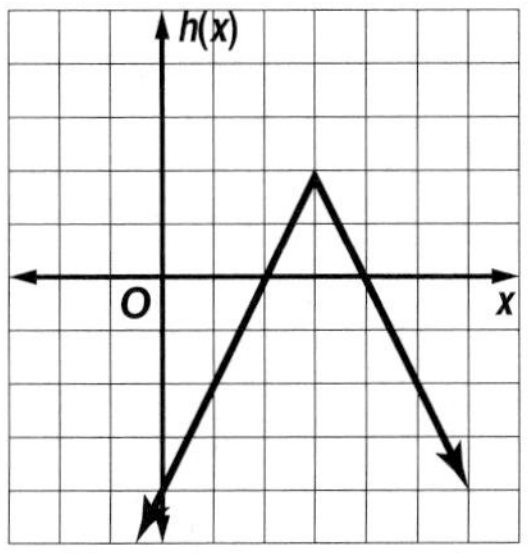

51.

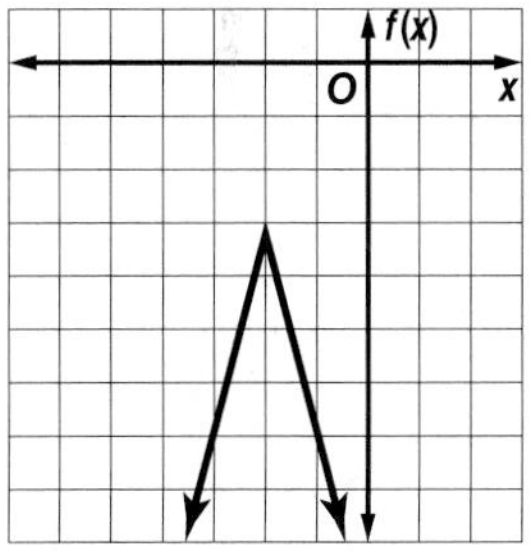

52.

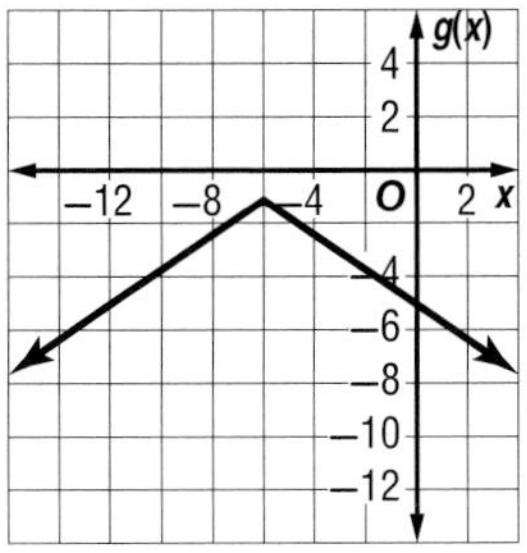

53.

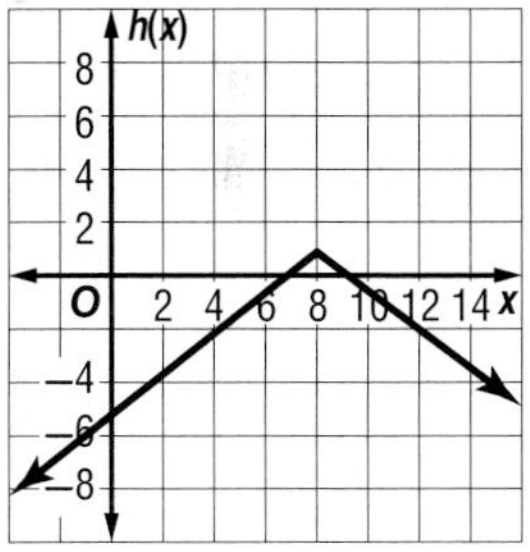

54b.

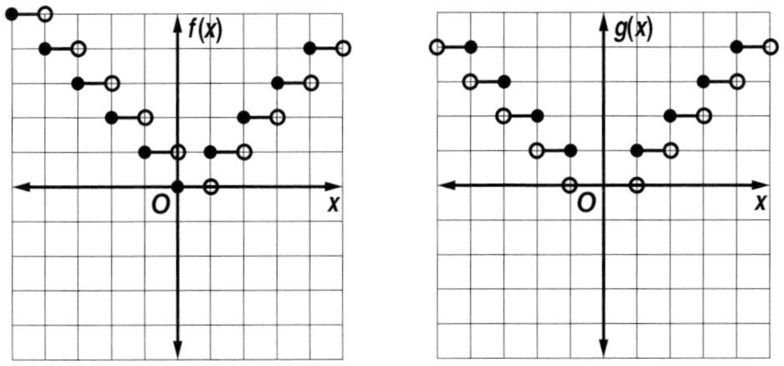

60b.

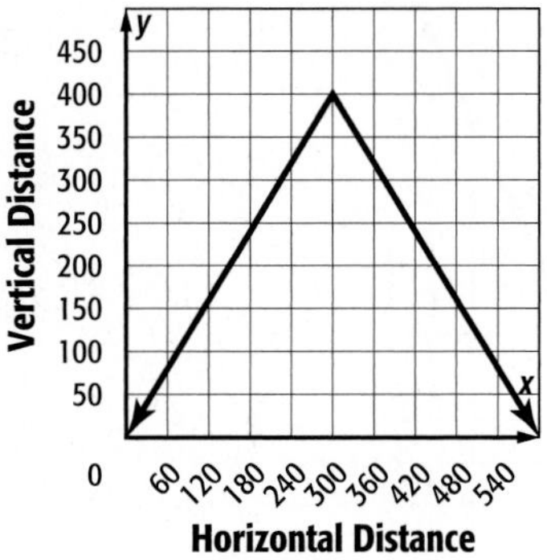

Ch. 4 Practice Test p. 275

16.

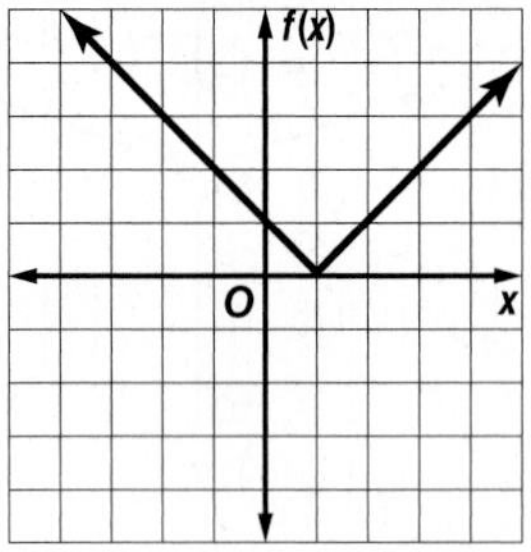

17.

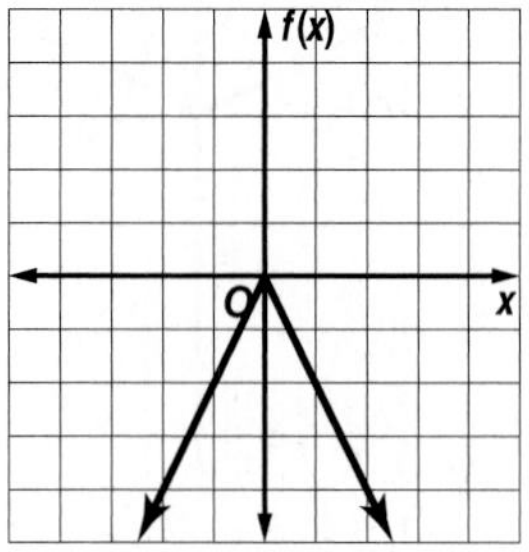

18.

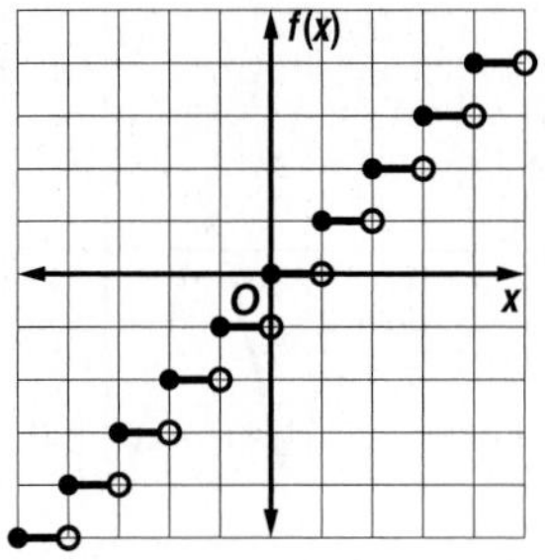

19.

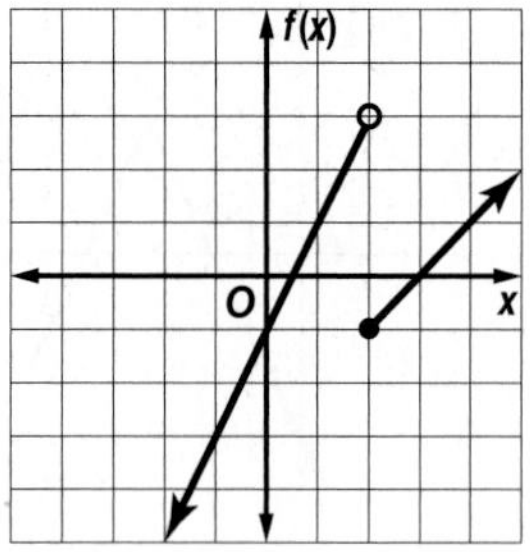

Chapter 4 Answer Appendix

NOTES

Chapter 5 Chapter Planner

Diagnostic Assessment
Quick Check, p. 281

	Lesson 5-1 Pacing: 1 day	Explore 5-2 Pacing: 0.5 day	Lesson 5-2 Pacing: 1.5 days	Lesson 5-3 Pacing: 1 day
Title	**Solving Inequalities by Addition and Subtraction**	**Algebra Lab: Solving Inequalities**	**Solving Inequalities by Multiplication and Division**	**Solving Multi-Step Inequalities**
Objectives	• Solve linear inequalities by using addition. • Solve linear inequalities by using subtraction.	• Use algebra tiles to model solving inequalities.	• Solve linear inequalities by using multiplication. • Solve linear inequalities by using division.	• Solve linear inequalities involving more than one operation. • Solve linear inequalities involving the Distributive Property.
Key Vocabulary	set-builder notation			
ILS	8.B.4a, 8.D.4	8.B.4a	8.B.4a, 8.D.4	8.B.4a, 8.D.4
Multiple Representations	p. 287		p. 294	p. 300
Lesson Resources	**Chapter 5 Resource Masters** • Study Guide and Intervention, pp. 5–6 AL OL ELL • Skills Practice, p. 7 AL OL ELL • Practice, p. 8 AL OL BL ELL • Word Problem Practice, p. 9 AL OL BL ELL • Enrichment, p. 10 OL BL **Transparencies** • 5-Minute Check Transparency 5-1 AL OL BL ELL **Additional Print Resources** • *Study Notebook* AL OL BL ELL • *Teaching Algebra with Manipulatives,* pp. 89–91 AL OL ELL	**Materials** • algebra tiles • equation mats • self-adhesive blank notes **Additional Print Resources** • *Teaching Algebra with Manipulatives,* pp. 10, 11, 16, 92 AL OL ELL	**Chapter 5 Resource Masters** • Study Guide and Intervention, pp. 11–12 AL OL ELL • Skills Practice, p. 13 AL OL ELL • Practice, p. 14 AL OL BL ELL • Word Problem Practice, p. 15 AL OL BL ELL • Enrichment, p. 16 OL BL • Quiz 1, p. 45 AL OL BL ELL **Transparencies** • 5-Minute Check Transparency 5-2 AL OL BL ELL **Additional Print Resources** • *Study Notebook* AL OL BL ELL • *Teaching Algebra with Manipulatives,* p. 93 AL OL ELL	**Chapter 5 Resource Masters** • Study Guide and Intervention, pp. 17–18 AL OL ELL • Skills Practice, p. 19 AL OL ELL • Practice, p. 20 AL OL BL ELL • Word Problem Practice, p. 21 AL OL BL ELL • Enrichment, p. 22 OL BL • Quiz 2, p. 45 AL OL BL ELL **Transparencies** • 5-Minute Check Transparency 5-3 AL OL BL ELL **Additional Print Resources** • *Study Notebook* AL OL BL ELL
Technology for Every Lesson	**IL Math Online** glencoe.com • Extra Examples • Self-Check Quizzes • Personal Tutor • Homework Help		**CD/DVD Resources** IWB INTERACTIVE WHITEBOARD READY IWB StudentWorks Plus IWB Interactive Classroom IWB Diagnostic and Assessment Planner	• TeacherWorks Plus • eSolutions Manual Plus • ExamView Assessment Suite
Math in Motion		Animation		BrainPOP, Intractive Lab
Differentiated Instruction	pp. 285, 288		pp. 291, 295	pp. 298, 301

Formative Assessment
Mid-Chapter Quiz, p. 302

KEY: AL Approaching Level OL On Level BL Beyond Level ELL English Learners

Suggested Pacing

Time Periods	Instruction	Review & Assessment	Total
45-minute	9	2	11
90-minute	5	1	6

Explore 5-4 Pacing: 0.5 day	Lesson 5-4 Pacing: 1.5 days	Lesson 5-5 Pacing: 1 day	Lesson 5-6 Pacing: 1.5 days	Extend 5-6 Pacing: 0.5 day
Algebra Lab: Reading Compound Statements	**Solving Compound Inequalities**	**Inequalities Involving Absolute Value**	**Graphing Inequalities in Two Variables**	**Graphing Technology Lab: Graphing Inequalities**
• Identify compound statements connected by the word *and* or *or* as true or false.	• Solve compound inequalities containing the word *and* and graph their solution set. • Solve compound inequalities containing the word *or* and graph their solution set.	• Solve and graph absolute value inequalities (<). • Solve and graph absolute value inequalities (>).	• Graph linear inequalities on the coordinate plane. • Solve inequalities by graphing.	• Use a graphing calculator to investigate the graphs of inequalities.
	compound inequality, intersection, union		boundary, half-plane closed (open) half-plane	
	8.B.4a, 8.D.4	8.B.4a	6.B.4, 8.D.4	8.B.4a, 8.D.4
	p. 308	p. 312	p. 319	
Additional Print Resources • *Teaching Algebra with Manipulatives,* p. 94 AL OL ELL	**Chapter 5 Resource Masters** • Study Guide and Intervention, pp. 23–24 AL OL ELL • Skills Practice, p. 25 AL OL ELL • Practice, p. 26 AL OL BL ELL • Word Problem Practice, p. 27 AL OL BL ELL • Enrichment, p. 28 OL BL **Transparencies** • 5-Minute Check Transparency 5-4 AL OL BL ELL **Additional Print Resources** • *Study Notebook* AL OL BL ELL • *Teaching Algebra with Manipulatives,* pp. 95–97 AL OL ELL	**Chapter 5 Resource Masters** • Study Guide and Intervention, pp. 29–30 AL OL ELL • Skills Practice, p. 31 AL OL ELL • Practice, p. 32 AL OL BL ELL • Word Problem Practice, p. 33 AL OL BL ELL • Enrichment, p. 34 OL BL • Graphing Calculator, p. 35 OL • Quiz 3, p. 46 AL OL BL ELL **Transparencies** • 5-Minute Check Transparency 5-5 AL OL BL ELL **Additional Print Resources** • *Study Notebook* AL OL BL ELL	**Chapter 5 Resource Masters** • Study Guide and Intervention, pp. 36–37 AL OL ELL • Skills Practice and Practice, pp. 38, 39 AL OL BL ELL • Word Problem Practice, p. 40 AL OL BL • Enrichment, p. 41 OL BL • Spreadsheet, p. 42 OL • Quiz 4, p. 46 AL OL BL ELL **Transparencies** • 5-Minute Check Transparency 5-6 AL OL BL ELL **Additional Print Resources** • *Study Notebook* AL OL BL ELL • *Teaching Algebra with Manipulatives,* pp. 98–99 AL OL ELL	**Materials** • TI-83/84 Plus or other graphing calculator

IL Math Online glencoe.com
- Extra Examples
- Self-Check Quizzes
- Personal Tutor
- Homework Help

CD/DVD Resources IWB INTERACTIVE WHITEBOARD READY
- IWB StudentWorks Plus
- IWB Interactive Classroom
- IWB Diagnostic and Assessment Planner
- TeacherWorks Plus
- eSolutions Manual Plus
- ExamView Assessment Suite

Explore 5-4	Lesson 5-4	Lesson 5-5	Lesson 5-6	Extend 5-6
Animation	Animation	Animation		
	pp. 308, 309	pp. 311, 314	pp. 317, 320	

Summative Assessment
- Study Guide and Review, pp. 322–324
- Practice Test, p. 325

Assessment and Intervention

SE = Student Edition, **TE** = Teacher Edition, **CRM** = Chapter Resource Masters

	Diagnosis	Prescription
Diagnostic Assessment	**Beginning Chapter 5**	
	Get Ready for Chapter 5 **SE**, p. 281	Response to Intervention **TE**, p. 281
	Beginning Every Lesson	
	Then, Now, Why? **SE** 5-Minute Check Transparencies	Chapter 0 **SE**, pp. **P**1–**P**45 Concepts and Skills Bank **SE**, pp. 857–867 *Quick Review Math Handbook*
Formative Assessment	**During/After Every Lesson**	
	Check Your Progress **SE**, every example Check Your Understanding **SE** H.O.T. Problems **SE** Spiral Review **SE** Additional Examples **TE** Watch Out! **TE** Step 4, Assess **TE** Chapter 5 Quizzes **CRM**, pp. 45–46 Self-Check Quizzes **glencoe.com**	**Tier 1 Intervention** Concepts and Skills Bank **SE**, pp. 857–867 Skills Practice **CRM**, Ch. 1–5 **glencoe.com** **Tier 2 Intervention** Differentiated Instruction **TE** Differentiated Homework Options **TE** Study Guide and Intervention Masters **CRM**, Ch. 1–5 *Quick Review Math Handbook* **Tier 3 Intervention** *Math Triumphs, Alg. 1*
	Mid-Chapter	
	Mid-Chapter Quiz **SE**, p. 302 Mid-Chapter Test **CRM**, p. 47 ExamView Assessment Suite	**Tier 1 Intervention** Concepts and Skills Bank **SE**, pp. 857–867 Skills Practice **CRM**, Ch. 1–5 **glencoe.com** **Tier 2 Intervention** Study Guide and Intervention Masters **CRM**, Ch. 1–5 *Quick Review Math Handbook* **Tier 3 Intervention** *Math Triumphs, Alg. 1*
	Before Chapter Test	
	Chapter Study Guide and Review **SE**, pp. 322–324 Practice Test **SE**, p. 325 Standardized Test Practice **SE**, pp. 326–329 Chapter Test **glencoe.com** Standardized Test Practice **glencoe.com** Vocabulary Review **glencoe.com** ExamView Assessment Suite	**Tier 1 Intervention** Concepts and Skills Bank **SE**, pp. 857–867 Skills Practice **CRM**, Ch. 1–5 **glencoe.com** **Tier 2 Intervention** Study Guide and Intervention Masters **CRM**, Ch. 1–5 *Quick Review Math Handbook* **Tier 3 Intervention** *Math Triumphs, Alg. 1*
Summative Assessment	**After Chapter 5**	
	Multiple-Choice Tests, Forms 1, 2A, 2B **CRM**, pp. 49–54 Free-Response Tests, Forms 2C, 2D, 3 **CRM**, pp. 54–56 Vocabulary Test **CRM**, p. 48 Extended Response Test **CRM**, p. 61 Standardized Test Practice **CRM**, pp. 62–64 ExamView Assessment Suite	Study Guide and Intervention Masters **CRM**, Ch. 1–5 *Quick Review Math Handbook* **glencoe.com**

Option 1 Reaching All Learners AL OL BL ELL

VISUAL/SPATIAL On a transparency sheet draw a large number line with two dashed horizontal guide-lines above it. Alternatively, the number line and guide-lines could be drawn on a sheet of paper that is then laminated. Give students a compound inequality written as two sentences. Have students use a dry-erase marker to plot the solution for each inequality on one of the dashed guide-lines. If the inequality involves "and," have students wipe away any parts that are not on both dashed lines. This leaves a clear picture of what part of the number line should be used for the solution.

LOGICAL Begin by writing $x - 12 = 8$ on the board. Review the Addition and Subtraction Properties of Equality as you solve for x. Then erase all the equals signs and replace them with $>$.

Discuss the similarities. Repeat using each of the inequality signs.

Option 2 Approaching Level AL

On self-sticking notes, write $+$, $-$, $>$, and $<$. Have students write an inequality involving a negative coefficient of x on their paper, such as [−] 4x [>] [+] 8, using the self-sticking notes for the symbols. Explain that since the coefficient of x is negative, all the signs in the inequality must change to their opposites, [+] 4x [<] [−] 8. Explain that by doing this they can solve for x without concern for the inequality sign.

Option 3 English Learners ELL

If students are having difficulty choosing the correct symbol for the problem's wording, have them use the chart on p. 285 to write each common inequality phrases on an index card and the appropriate inequality symbol on the back of the card. As students solve verbal problems, such as Example 4 on p. 285, they can pick the card that has the same wording as the problem. The back of the card will reveal the appropriate inequality symbol to use.

Option 4 Beyond Level BL

Have students work in pairs to develop two sets of inequalities. When graphed, the overlap of the solution sets of one pair form a triangle and the solution set of the other forms a square. This activity can be extended to include trapezoids and parallelograms. For example, when

$$\begin{cases} 2x - y \geq -1 \\ x + y \leq 4 \\ x + 4y \geq 4 \end{cases}$$

are graphed, a triangle is formed.

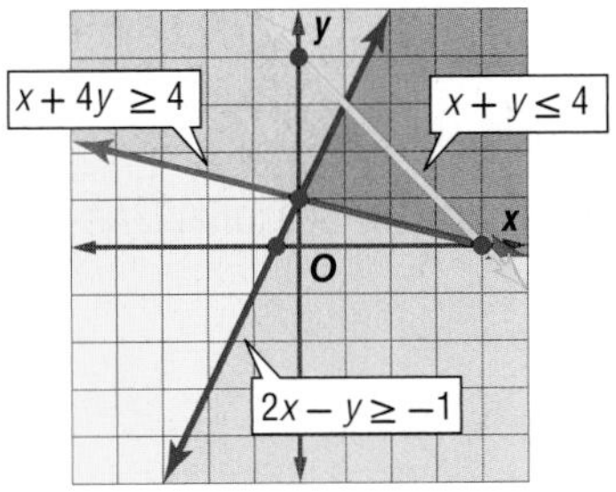

Students are often fascinated by the concept of infinity. Challenge students to think about the infinite nature of certain concepts using questions similar to the following:

- Is a half-plane really half of the plane or can it be more or less? Explain your reasoning.
- Does the solution set $\{x \mid x > 2\}$ contain an infinite set of numbers? Why or why not?
- Does the solution set $\{x \mid 2 < x < 2.5\}$ contain an infinite set of numbers? Why or why not?

CHAPTER 5

Focus on Mathematical Content

Vertical Alignment

Before Chapter 5

Related Topics before Grade 8
- use Venn diagrams for displaying relationships

Previous Topics from Algebra 1
- use the Distributive Property to simplify algebraic equations
- transform and solve linear equations
- graph equations of lines

Chapter 5

Related Topics from Algebra 1
- formulate linear inequalities to solve problems
- investigate methods for solving linear inequalities using the Properties of Inequality
- solve linear inequalities
- interpret and determine the reasonableness of solutions to linear inequalities

After Chapter 5

Preparation for Algebra 2
- use the necessary algebraic skills required to solve equations and inequalities in problem situations
- use algebraic methods, graphs, or tables to solve systems of inequalities
- solve quadratic inequalities using graphs, tables, and algebraic methods

Lesson-by-Lesson Preview

5-1 Solving Inequalities by Addition and Subtraction

Some equations are solved using the Addition and Subtraction Properties of Equality to isolate the variable, having a coefficient of 1, on one side of the equals sign (Lesson 2-2). Some inequalities are solved in much the same way.

The Addition and Subtraction Properties of Inequality state that any number added to or subtracted from each side of a true inequality, results in a true inequality.

The solution to inequalities can be expressed in more than one way.

- The solutions can be written in set-builder notation. For example: $\{x \mid x < 7\}$.
  This is read as *the set of all numbers x such that x is less than 7*. The inequality $<$ means that 7 is a boundary number and is *not* included in the solution.
- The solutions can be graphed on a number line. For example:

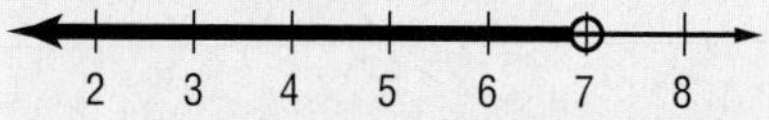

The open circle at 7 means that 7 is *not* included in the solution. The blackened arrowed line, pointing to the left, shows that the solutions are all numbers less than 7. If the arrow points to the right of a boundary number, it indicates the solutions are greater than the boundary.

If the inequality is $\geq$ or $\leq$, the boundary number is included in the solution, and a solid circle is placed at the boundary number on the number line.

5-2 Solving Inequalities by Multiplication and Division

Some equations are solved using the Multiplication and Division Properties of Equality to solve for a variable having a coefficient other than 1 (Lesson 2-2). Some inequalities are solved in much the same way, but there is one main difference.

When multiplying or dividing each side of an inequality by the same negative number, the direction of the inequality symbol must be reversed.

5-3 Solving Multi-Step Inequalities

Multi-step inequalities can be solved with the same process used for solving multi-step equations (Lesson 2-3). These equations can be solved using the Properties of Inequality and the strategy of undoing each operation by working backward. After each side is simplified using the Distributive Property and/or by combining like terms, work in the opposite order of the order of operations. The Addition and Subtraction Properties of Inequality are applied first, followed by the Multiplication or Division Property of Inequalities.

- If the inequality simplifies to a statement that is never true, such as $4 > 8$, the solution is the empty set, $\varnothing$, which has no members.
- If the solution results in a statement that is always true, such as $5 > 3$, then the solution is the set of all real numbers, $\{x \mid x \text{ is a real number}\}$.

5-4 Solving Compound Inequalities

If two inequalities are joined by the words *and* or *or*, the result is a compound inequality.

- If a compound inequality contains the word *and*, the solution must be a solution to both inequalities. The graph of the solution is the intersection of the graphs of the two inequalities.
- If the compound inequality contains the word *or*, the solution must be a solution to either *one* or *both* inequalities. The graph of the solution is the *union* of the graphs of the two inequalities.

The properties used to solve compound inequalities are the same as those used to solve any inequality.

5-5 Inequalities Involving Absolute Value

Absolute value inequalities can also be solved algebraically by writing them as compound inequalities.

When compound absolute inequalities are being solved, there are two cases to consider.

Case 1	The expression inside the absolute value symbol is positive or 0.
Case 2	The expression inside the absolute value symbol is negative.

If $n > 0$, then:

For $|x| < n$, the solution set is $\{x \mid -n < x < n\}$.

For $|x| \leq n$, the solution set is $\{x \mid -n \leq x \leq n\}$.

For $|x| > n$, the solution set is $\{x \mid x > n \text{ or } x < -n\}$.

For $|x| \geq n$, the solution set is $\{x \mid x \geq n \text{ or } x \leq -n\}$.

5-6 Graphing Inequalities in Two Variables

The solution set of a linear inequality, like that of a linear equation, is the set of all ordered pairs that makes the statement true. Like the solution set of an equation in two variables (Lesson 3-1), the solution set of an inequality in two variables is graphed on a coordinate plane. However, the solution set of a linear inequality is not linear. The graph of a linear inequality has the following characteristics.

- It has a linear boundary.

First graph the inequality as if it were an equation. This determines the boundary line. Use a solid line if the inequality is $\leq$ or $\geq$. Use a dashed line if the inequality is $<$ or $>$.

- It covers a region called a half-plane.

Select a point in either half-plane determined by the boundary line and test it in the inequality. If the resulting statement is true, shade the half-plane that contains that point. If the statement is false, shade the other half-plane.

Professional Development

Targeted professional development has been articulated throughout *Algebra 1*. More quality, customized professional development is available from McGraw-Hill Professional Development. Visit glencoe.com for details on each product.

- **Online Lessons** emphasize the strategies and techniques used to teach Algebra 1. Includes streaming video, interactive pages, and online tools.
- **Video Workshops** allow mentors, coaches, or leadership personnel to facilitate on-site workshops on educational strategies in mathematics and mathematical concepts.
- **MHPD Online** (www.mhpdonline.com) offers online professional development with video clips of instructional strategies, links, student activities, and news and issues in education.
- **Teaching Today** (teachingtoday.glencoe.com) gives secondary teachers practical strategies and materials that inspire excellence and innovation in teaching.

CHAPTER 5 Notes

Chapter Project

A "Yes" for the Animals

Students use what they have learned about writing, solving, and graphing inequalities and compound inequalities to work with animal facts.

- Divide students into groups. Have each group decide on a favorite pet. Ask each group member to research and bring to class feeding guidelines for their pet.
- Ask students why the guidelines vary. Name some of the criteria that must be taken into account when deciding how much to feed a pet.
- Have students write an inequality in words and in symbols that can be used to describe the amount of food, a, a pet should have per day. For example, a Beagle needs from $2\frac{1}{4}$ to $3\frac{3}{4}$ cups of food per day. This can be written as $2\frac{1}{4} \le a \le 3\frac{3}{4}$. Have students graph their inequalities.
- Have students conduct a survey of at least 50 people. Ask, "Has your family ever gotten a pet from an animal shelter?" Combine the data and calculate the following: total number surveyed, number of *yes* answers, and the fraction and percent of *yes* answers.
- Tell students that a shelter needs at least $600 for a vet to treat all their animals. A donor will give $20 for each *yes* answer and add $2 for each *no* answer on the survey. Ask students to write and graph an inequality for this situation. Will the results of the students' survey generate enough money to pay the vet?

CHAPTER 5 Linear Inequalities

Then

In Chapter 2, you solved equations.

Now

In Chapter 5, you will:

- Solve one-step and multi-step inequalities.
- Solve compound inequalities and inequalities involving absolute value.
- Graph inequalities in two variables.

IL Learning Standards

8.B.4a Represent algebraic concepts with physical materials, words, diagrams, tables, graphs, equations and inequalities and use appropriate technology.
8.D.4 Formulate and solve linear inequalities using graphs, tables, calculators and computers.

Why?

PETS In the United States, about 75 million dogs are kept as pets. Approximately 16% of these were adopted from animal shelters. About 14% of dog owners own more than 3 dogs.

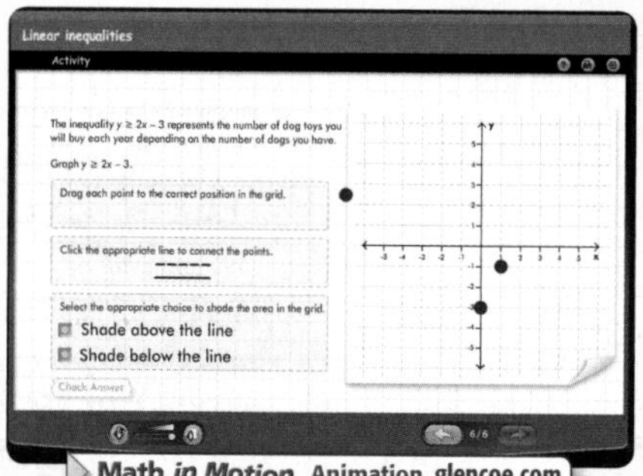

Math *in Motion,* Animation glencoe.com

Key Vocabulary Introduce the key vocabulary in the chapter using the routine below.

Define: A half-plane is a region on a coordinate plane where graphs of ordered pairs are filled.

Example:

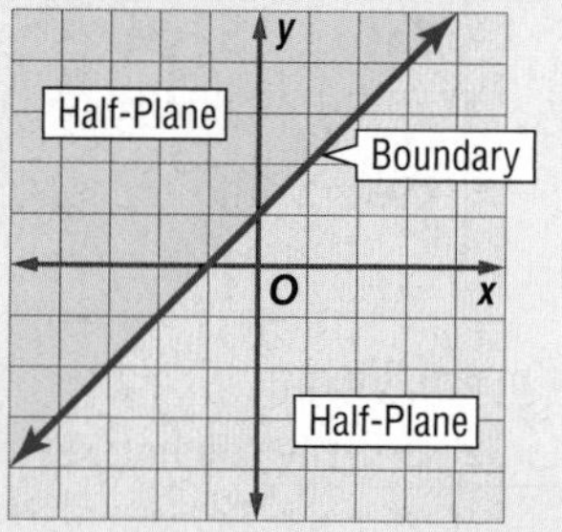

Ask: How many half-planes are in this graph? two

Get Ready for Chapter 5

Diagnose Readiness You have two options for checking Prerequisite Skills.

Text Option Take the Quick Check below. Refer to the Quick Review for help.

*Quick*Check

(Used in Lessons 5-1 through 5-6)
Evaluate each expression for the given values. (Lesson 1-2)

1. $3x + y$ if $x = -4$ and $y = 2$ **−10**
2. $-2m + 3k$ if $m = -8$ and $k = 3$ **25**
3. **CARS** The expression $\frac{m \text{ mi}}{g \text{ gal}}$ represents the gas mileage of a car. Find the gas mileage of a car that goes 295 miles on 12 gallons of gasoline. Round to the nearest tenth. **24.6**

(Used in Lessons 5-1 through 5-6)
Solve each equation. (Lesson 2-2)

4. $x - 4 = 9$ **13**
5. $x + 8 = -3$ **−11**
6. $4x = -16$ **−4**
7. $\frac{x}{3} = 7$ **21**
8. $2x + 1 = 9$ **4**
9. $4x - 5 = 15$ **5**
10. $9x + 2 = 3x - 10$ **−2**
11. $3(x - 2) = -2(x + 13)$ **−4**
12. **FINANCIAL LITERACY** Claudia opened a savings account with \$325. She saves \$100 per month. Write an equation to determine how much money d, she has after m months. (Lesson 2-1) $d = 100m + 325$

(Used in Lesson 5-5)
Solve each equation. (Lesson 2-5)

13. $|x + 11| = 18$ **{−29, 7}**
14. $|3x - 2| = 16$ **14.** $\left\{-\frac{14}{3}, 6\right\}$
15. **SURVEYS** In a survey, 32% of the people chose pizza as their favorite food. The results were reported to within 2% accuracy. What is the maximum and minimum percent of people who chose pizza? (Lesson 2-5) **34%, 30%**

*Quick*Review

EXAMPLE 1

Evaluate $-3x^2 + 4x - 6$ if $x = -2$.

$-3x^2 + 4x - 6$	**Original expression**
$= -3(-2)^2 + 4(-2) - 6$	**Replace x with −2.**
$= -3(4) + 4(-2) - 6$	**Evaluate the power.**
$= -12 + (-8) - 6$	**Multiply.**
$= -26$	**Add and subtract.**

EXAMPLE 2

Solve $-2(x - 4) = 7x - 19$.

$-2(x - 4) = 7x - 19$	**Original equation**
$-2x + 8 = 7x - 19$	**Distributive Property**
$-2x + 8 + 2x = 7x - 19 + 2x$	**Add 2x.**
$8 = 9x - 19$	**Simplify.**
$8 + 19 = 9x - 19 + 19$	**Add 19.**
$27 = 9x$	**Simplify.**
$3 = x$	**Divide by 3.**

EXAMPLE 3

Solve $|x - 4| = 9$.

If $|x - 4| = 9$, then $x - 4 = 9$ or $x - 4 = -9$.

$x - 4 = 9$	or	$x - 4 = -9$
$x - 4 + 4 = 9 + 4$		$x - 4 + 4 = -9 + 4$
$x = 13$		$x = -5$

So, the solution set is $\{-5, 13\}$.

Online Option IL Math Online Take a self-check Chapter Readiness Quiz at glencoe.com.

Response to Intervention (RtI)

Use the *Quick Check* results and the Intervention Planner chart to help you determine your Response to Intervention. The If-Then statements in the chart below help you decide the appropriate tier of RtI and suggest intervention resources for each tier.

Intervention Planner

Tier 1 — On Level

If students miss about 25% of the exercises or less,

Then choose a resource:

- **SE** Lessons 1-2, 2-2, and 2-5
- **CRM** Skills Practice, Chapter 1, p. 13, Chapter 2, pp. 13, 32
- **TE** Chapter Project, p. 280
- **IL Math Online** Self-Check Quiz

Tier 2 — Strategic Intervention approaching grade level

If students miss about 50% of the exercises,

Then choose a resource:

- **CRM** Study Guide and Intervention, Chapter 1, pp. 11–12, Chapter 2, pp. 11–12, 30–31
- **IL Math Online** Extra Examples, Personal Tutor, Homework Help

Tier 3 — Intensive Intervention 2 or more grades below level

If students miss about 75% of the exercises,

Then use *Math Triumphs, Alg. 1*

- **IL Math Online** Extra Examples, Personal Tutor, Homework Help, Review Vocabulary

CHAPTER 5 Notes

FOLDABLES® Study Organizer

Dinah Zike's Foldables®

Focus Students write about the different ways inequalities can be solved as these methods are presented in the lessons of this chapter.

Teach Have students make label their Foldables as illustrated. Students should fill in the appropriate sections with their notes, diagrams, and examples as they cover each lesson in this chapter.

When to Use It Encourage students to add to their Foldables as they work through the chapter and to use them to review for the chapter test.

Differentiated Instruction

CRM Student-Built Glossary, pp. 1–2 Students should complete the chart by providing a definition of each term and an example as they progress through Chapter 5. This study tool can also be used to review for the chapter test.

Get Started on Chapter 5

You will learn several new concepts, skills, and vocabulary terms as you study Chapter 5. To get ready, identify important terms and organize your resources. You may wish to refer to **Chapter 0** to review prerequisite skills.

FOLDABLES® Study Organizer

Linear Inequalities Make this Foldable to help you organize your Chapter 5 notes about linear inequalities. Begin with a sheet of 11″ by 17″ paper.

1. **Fold** each side so the edges meet in the center.

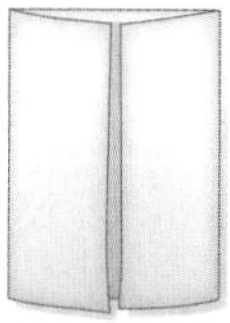

2. **Fold** in half.

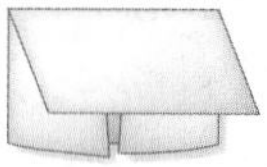

3. **Unfold** and cut from each end until you reach the vertical line.

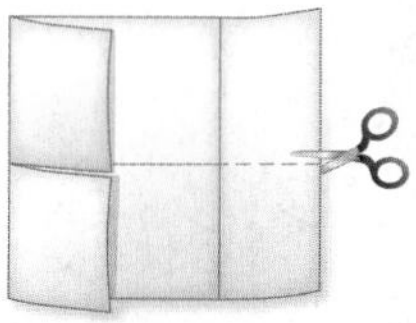

4. **Label** the front of each flap.

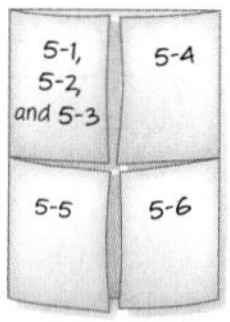

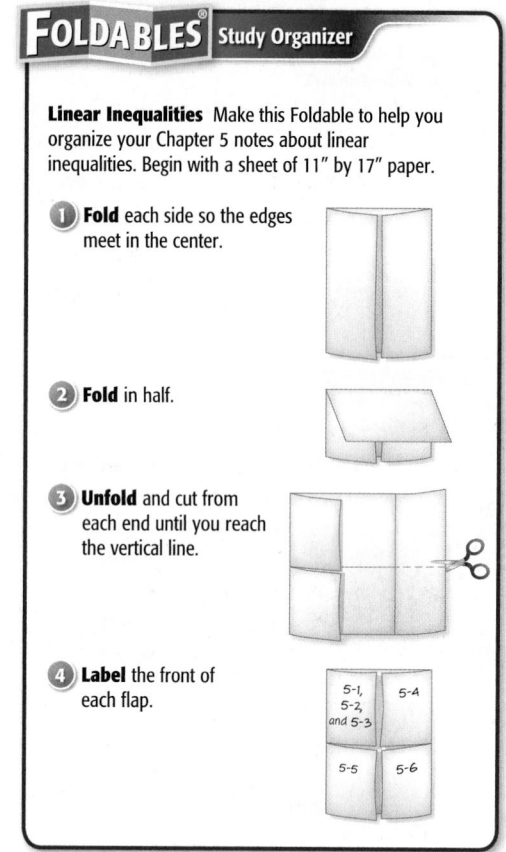

New Vocabulary

English		Español
set-builder notation	• p. 284 •	notación de construcción de conjuntos
compound inequality	• p. 304 •	desigualdad compuesta
intersection	• p. 304 •	intersección
union	• p. 305 •	unión
boundary	• p. 315 •	frontera
half-plane	• p. 315 •	semiplano
closed half-plane	• p. 315 •	semiplano cerrada
open half-plane	• p. 315 •	semiplano abierto

Review Vocabulary

equivalent equations • p. 83 • ecuaciones equivalentes equations that have the same solution

linear equation • p. 153 • ecuación lineal an equation in the form $Ax + By = C$, with a graph consisting of points on a straight line

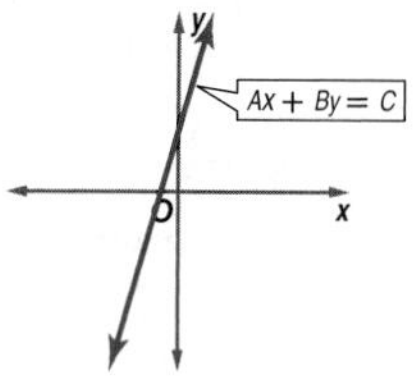

solution set • p. 31 • conjunto solución the set of elements from the replacement set that makes an open sentence true

Multilingual eGlossary glencoe.com

IL Math Online glencoe.com

- Study the chapter online
- Explore **Math in Motion**
- Get extra help from your own **Personal Tutor**
- Use **Extra Examples** for additional help
- Take a **Self-Check Quiz**
- **Review Vocabulary** in fun ways

5-1 Solving Inequalities by Addition and Subtraction

Then

You solved equations by using addition and subtraction. (Lesson 2-2)

Now

- Solve linear inequalities by using addition.
- Solve linear inequalities by using subtraction.

IL Learning Standards

8.B.4a Represent algebraic concepts with physical materials, words, diagrams, tables, graphs, equations and inequalities and use appropriate technology.
8.D.4 Formulate and solve linear and quadratic equations and **linear inequalities algebraically** and investigate nonlinear inequalities using graphs, tables, calculators and computers.

New Vocabulary

set-builder notation

IL Math Online

glencoe.com

- Extra Examples
- Personal Tutor
- Self-Check Quiz
- Homework Help

Why?

The data in the table show that the recommended daily allowance of Calories for girls 11–14 years old is less than that of girls between 15–18 years old.

Calories	
Girls 11–14 Years	Girls 15–18
1845	2110

Source: *Vital Health Zone*

$$1845 < 2110$$

If a 13-year-old girl and a 16-year-old girl each eat 150 more Calories in a day than is suggested, the 16-year-old will still eat more Calories.

$$1845 + 150 \ \underline{?}\ 2110 + 150$$
$$1995 < 2260$$

Solve Inequalities by Addition This example illustrates the Addition Property of Inequalities.

Key Concept Addition Property of Inequalities — For Your FOLDABLE

Words If the same number is added to each side of a true inequality, the resulting inequality is also true.

Symbols For all numbers a, b, and c, the following are true.
1. If $a > b$, then $a + c > b + c$.
2. If $a < b$, then $a + c < b + c$.

This property is also true for $\geq$ and $\leq$.

EXAMPLE 1 Solve by Adding

Solve $x - 12 \geq 8$. Check your solution.

$x - 12 \geq 8$	Original inequality
$x - 12 + 12 \geq 8 + 12$	Add 12 to each side.
$x \geq 20$	Simplify.

The solution is the set {all numbers greater than or equal to 20}.

CHECK To check, substitute three different values into the original inequality: 20, a number less than 20, and a number greater than 20.

Check Your Progress

Solve each inequality. Check your solution.

1A. $22 > m - 8$ {all numbers less than 30}

1B. $d - 14 \geq -19$ {all numbers greater than or equal to −5}

Personal Tutor glencoe.com

5-1 Lesson Notes

1 FOCUS

Vertical Alignment

Before Lesson 5-1
Solve equations by using addition and subtraction.

Lesson 5-1
Solve linear inequalities by using addition and subtraction.

After Lesson 5-1
Solve systems of inequalities.

2 TEACH

Scaffolding Questions

Have students read the *Why?* section of the lesson.

Ask:

- If both girls eat 200 fewer Calories than the recommended daily allowance, will the 13-year old eat fewer Calories than the 16-year old? Explain. Yes; $1845 - 200 = 1645$ and $2110 - 200 = 1910$, and $1645 < 1910$.
- If the two girls eat the same number of Calories over or under the daily allowance, is it ever possible that they will eat an equal number of Calories? Explain. No; the inequality between the two daily allowances is not changed by adding or subtracting the same amount on each side.

Lesson 5-1 Resources

Resource	Approaching-Level	On-Level	Beyond-Level	English Learners
Teacher Edition	• Differentiated Instruction, p. 285	• Differentiated Instruction, p. 288	• Differentiated Instruction, p. 288	• Differentiated Instruction, p. 285
Chapter Resource Masters	• Study Guide and Intervention, pp. 5–6 • Skills Practice, p. 7 • Practice, p. 8 • Word Problem Practice, p. 9	• Study Guide and Intervention, pp. 5–6 • Skills Practice, p. 7 • Practice, p. 8 • Word Problem Practice, p. 9 • Enrichment, p. 10	• Practice, p. 8 • Word Problem Practice, p. 9 • Enrichment, p. 10	• Study Guide and Intervention, pp. 5–6 • Skills Practice, p. 7 • Practice, p. 8 • Word Problem Practice, p. 9
Transparencies	• 5-Minute Check Transparency 5-1	• 5-Minute Check Transparency 5-1	• 5-Minute Check Transparency 5-1	• 5-Minute Check Transparency 5-1
Other	• Study Notebook • Teaching Algebra with Manipulatives	• Study Notebook • Teaching Algebra with Manipulatives	• Study Notebook	• Study Notebook • Teaching Algebra with Manipulatives

Solve Inequalities by Addition

Example 1 shows how to solve a linear inequality using the Addition Property of Inequalities.

Formative Assessment

Use the Check Your Progress exercises after each example to determine students' understanding of concepts.

Additional Example

1 Solve $c - 12 > 65$. Check your solution. $c > 77$ or {all numbers greater than 77}

Additional Examples also in:
Interactive Classroom PowerPoint® Presentations

IWB INTERACTIVE WHITEBOARD READY

Solve Inequalities by Subtraction

Example 2 shows how to solve a linear inequality using the Subtraction Property of Inequalities. **Example 3** shows how to solve and graph a linear inequality with variables on each side. **Example 4** shows how to write and solve a linear inequality for a real-world problem.

Additional Example

2 STANDARDIZED TEST PRACTICE
Solve the inequality $x + 23 < 14$.

A $\{x \mid x < -9\}$ **C** $\{x \mid x > -9\}$
B $\{x \mid x < 37\}$ **D** $\{x \mid x > 39\}$

A

ReadingMath

set-builder notation $\{x \mid x \geq 20\}$ is read *the set of all numbers x such that x is greater than or equal to 20.*

A more concise way of writing a solution set is to use **set-builder notation**. In set-builder notation, the solution set in Example 1 is $\{x \mid x \geq 20\}$.

This solution set can be graphed on a number line. Be sure to check if the endpoint of the graph of an inequality should be a circle or a dot. If the endpoint is not included in the graph, use a circle, otherwise use a dot.

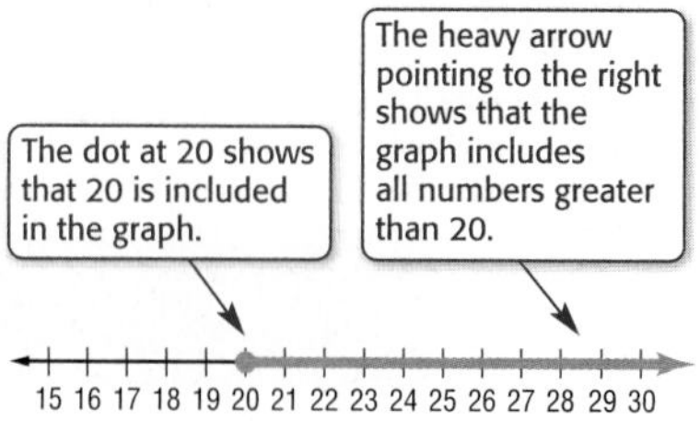

Solve Inequalities by Subtraction Subtraction can also be used to solve inequalities.

Key Concept — Subtraction Property of Inequalities (For Your FOLDABLE)

Words If the same number is subtracted from each side of a true inequality, the resulting inequality is also true.

Symbols For all numbers a, b, and c, the following are true.

1. If $a > b$, then $a - c > b - c$.
2. If $a < b$, then $a - c < b - c$.

This property is also true for $\geq$ and $\leq$.

Test-TakingTip

Isolating the Variable When solving inequalities, the goal is to isolate the variable on one side of the inequality. This is the same as with solving equations.

PSAE EXAMPLE 2 8.11.16

Solve $m + 19 > 56$.

A $\{m \mid m < 41\}$ **B** $\{m \mid m < 37\}$ **C** $\{m \mid m > 37\}$ **D** $\{m \mid m > 41\}$

Read the Test Item

You need to find the solution set for the inequality.

Solve the Test Item

Step 1 Solve the inequality.

$m + 19 > 56$	**Original inequality**
$m + 19 - 19 > 56 - 19$	**Subtract 19 from each side.**
$m > 37$	**Simplify.**

Step 2 Write in set-builder notation: $\{m \mid m > 37\}$. The answer is C.

Check Your Progress

2. Solve $p + 8 \leq 18$. G

F $\{p \mid p \geq 10\}$ **G** $\{p \mid p \leq 10\}$ **H** $\{p \mid p \leq 26\}$ **J** $\{p \mid p \geq 126\}$

Personal Tutor glencoe.com

Tips for New Teachers

Sense-Making Advise students that an equation such as $5 = x$ can be written as $x = 5$ because of the Symmetric Property of Equality, but an inequality such as $3 > y$ cannot be written as $y > 3$. Remind students that the inequality sign always points to the lesser value, so in $3 > y$, the expression should be written as $y < 3$ if y is on the left side of the inequality.

StudyTip

Writing Inequalities Simplifying the inequality so that the variable is on the left side, as in $a \geq 6$, prepares you to write the solution set in set-builder notation.

Terms that are constants are not the only terms that can be subtracted. Terms with variables can also be subtracted from each side to solve inequalities.

EXAMPLE 3 Variables on Each Side

Solve $3a + 6 \leq 4a$. Then graph the solution set on a number line.

$3a + 6 \leq 4a$	**Original inequality**
$3a - 3a + 6 \leq 4a - 3a$	**Subtract $3a$ from each side.**
$6 \leq a$	**Simplify.**

Since $6 \leq a$ is the same as $a \geq 6$, the solution set is $\{a \mid a \geq 6\}$.

Check Your Progress

Solve each inequality. Then graph the solution set on a number line.

3A. $9n - 1 < 10n$ **3B.** $5h \leq 12 + 4h$ **3A–3B. See margin.**

Personal Tutor glencoe.com

Verbal problems containing phrases like *greater than* or *less than* can be solved by using inequalities. The chart shows some other phrases that indicate inequalities.

Concept Summary Phrases for Inequalities

For Your FOLDABLE

<	>	≤	≥
less than fewer than	greater than more than	at most, no more than, less than or equal to	at least, no less than, greater than or equal to

Real-World EXAMPLE 4 Use an Inequality to Solve a Problem

PETS Felipe needs for the temperature of his leopard gecko's basking spot to be at least 82°F. Currently the basking spot is 62.5°F. How much warmer does the basking spot need to be?

Words	The current temperature needs to be at least 82°F.		
Variable	Let $t =$ the number of degrees that the temperature needs to rise.		
Inequality	$62.5 + t$	$\geq$	82

$62.5 + t \geq 82$	**Original inequality**
$62.5 + t - 62.5 \geq 82 - 62.5$	**Subtract 62.5 from each side.**
$t \geq 19.5$	**Simplify.**

Felipe needs to raise the temperature of the basking spot 19.5°F or more.

Check Your Progress

4. SHOPPING Sanjay has $65 to spend at the mall. He bought a T-shirt for $18 and a belt for $14. If Sanjay wants a pair of jeans, how much can he spend? no more than $33

Personal Tutor glencoe.com

Real-World Link

Leopard geckos are commonly yellow and white with black spots. They are nocturnal and easy to tame. They do not have toe pads like other geckos, so they do not climb.

Source: Exotic Pets

Additional Examples

3 Solve $12n - 4 \leq 13n$. Graph the solution set. $\{n \mid n \geq -4\}$

4 **ENTERTAINMENT** Panya wants to buy season passes to two theme parks. If one season pass costs $54.99 and Panya has $100 to spend on both passes, the second season pass must cost no more than what amount? The second season pass must cost no more than $45.01.

TEACH with TECH

INTERACTIVE WHITEBOARD Display a number line on the board. Give the class several exercises, and select students to come to the board to graph their solutions on the number line.

Focus on Mathematical Content

Producing Equivalent Inequalities You can substitute for either side of an inequality an expression equivalent to that side. For example, the inequality $2(3 + x) > 5$ is equivalent to the inequality $6 + 2x > 5$. You can also add (or subtract) the same real number to (or from) each side of an inequality.

Tips for New Teachers

Set Builder Notation Reading set builder notation is new to students. Give them opportunities to practice reading sets aloud.

Differentiated Instruction AL ELL

If students have trouble understanding some of the phrases used to indicate inequalities, such as *at most* or *no less than*,

Then have them work in pairs or groups to write word problems using the phrases. Have students write inequalities to represent the problem situations.

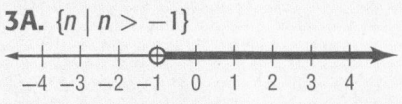

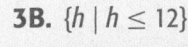

Additional Answers (Check Your Progress)

3A. $\{n \mid n > -1\}$

3B. $\{h \mid h \leq 12\}$

3 PRACTICE

Formative Assessment

Use Exercises 1–11 to check for understanding.

Use the chart at the bottom of this page to customize assignments for your students.

Additional Answers

1. $\{x \mid x > 10\}$

2. $\{y \mid y \leq -2\}$

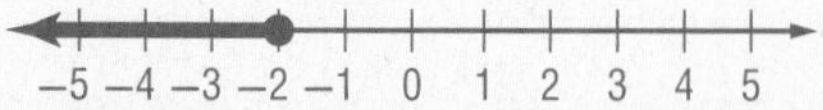

3. $\{g \mid g < -4\}$

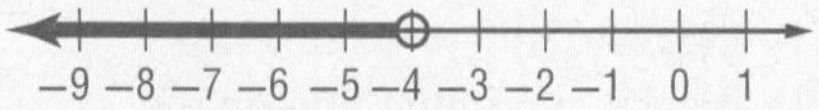

4. $\{p \mid p \geq 7\}$

5. $\{n \mid n < 11\}$

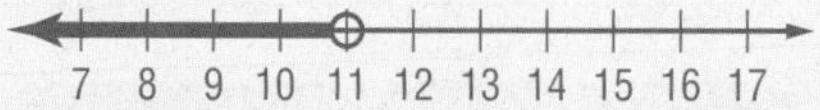

6. $\{k \mid k > -29\}$

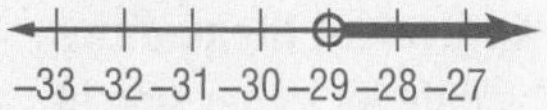

7. $\{r \mid r > 6\}$

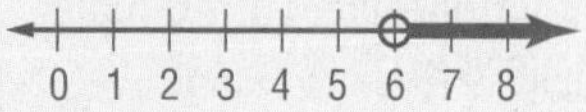

8. $\{n \mid n \geq -3\}$

35. Sample answer: Let n = the number of online teens that do not use the Internet at school in millions; $n > 21 - 16$; $\{n \mid n > 5\}$; at least 5 million teens use the Internet but not at school.

36. Sample answer: Let n = the original number of songs; $n + 20 > 61$; $\{n \mid n > 41\}$; there were originally more than 41 songs on the MP3 player.

Check Your Understanding

1–8. See margin.

Examples 1 and 2 pp. 283–284

Solve each inequality. Then graph the solution set on a number line.

1. $x - 3 > 7$

2. $5 \geq 7 + y$

3. $g + 6 < 2$

4. $11 \leq p + 4$

5. $10 > n - 1$

6. $k + 24 > -5$

7. $8r + 6 < 9r$

8. $8n \geq 7n - 3$

Example 3 p. 285

Define a variable, write an inequality, and solve each problem. Check your solution.

9. A number increased by 4 is at least 10. **Sample answer: Let n = the number, $n + 4 \geq 10$; $\{n \mid n \geq 6\}$.**

10. Three more than a number is less than twice the number. **10. Sample answer: Let n = the number, $3 + n < 2n$; $\{n \mid n > 3\}$.**

Example 4 p. 285

11. AMUSEMENT A thrill ride swings passengers back and forth, a little higher each time up to 137 feet. Suppose the height of the swing after 30 seconds is 45 feet. How much higher will the ride swing? **no more than 92 ft**

Practice and Problem Solving

● = **Step-by-Step Solutions** begin on page R12. **Extra Practice** begins on page 815.

12–29. See Ch. 5 Answer Appendix.

Examples 1 and 2 pp. 283–284

Solve each inequality. Then graph the solution set on a number line.

12. $m - 4 < 3$

13. $p - 6 \geq 3$

14. $r - 8 \leq 7$

15. $t - 3 > -8$

16. $b + 2 \geq 4$

17. $13 > 18 + r$

18. $5 + c \leq 1$

19. $-23 \geq q - 30$

20. $11 + m \geq 15$

21. $h - 26 < 4$

22. $8 \leq r - 14$

23. $-7 > 20 + c$

24. $2a \leq -4 + a$

25. $z + 4 \geq 2z$

26. $w - 5 \leq 2w$

27. $3y + 6 \leq 2y$

28. $6x + 5 \geq 7x$

29. $-9 + 2a < 3a$

Example 3 p. 285

Define a variable, write an inequality, and solve each problem. Check your solution.

30. The sum of a number and −4 is at least 8. **30–33. Sample answers given.** **Let n = the number, $n + (-4) \geq 8$; $\{n \mid n \geq 12\}$.**

31. A number decreased by 8 is less than 21. **Let n = the number, $n - 8 < 21$; $\{n \mid n < 29\}$.**

32. Twice a number is more than the sum of that number and 9. **Let n = the number, $2n > n + 9$; $\{n \mid n > 9\}$.**

33. The sum of twice a number and 5 is at most 3 less than the number. **Let n = the number, $2n + 5 \leq n - 3$; $\{n \mid n \leq -8\}$.**

Example 4 p. 285

Define a variable, write an inequality, and solve each problem. Then interpret your solution.

34. FINANCIAL LITERACY Keisha is babysitting at \$8 per hour to earn money for a car. So far she has saved \$1300. The car that Keisha wants to buy costs at least \$5440. How much money does Keisha still need to earn to buy the car?

34. Sample answer: Let b = the amount of money that Keisha still needs; $b + 1300 \geq 5440$; $\{b \mid b \geq 4140\}$; Keisha needs to earn at least \$4140.

35. TECHNOLOGY A recent survey found that more than 21 million people between the ages of 12 and 17 use the Internet. Of those, about 16 million said they use the Internet at school. How many teens that are online do not use the Internet at school? **See margin.**

B

36. MUSIC A DJ added 20 more songs to his MP3 player, making the total more than 61. How many songs were originally on the player? **See margin.**

Differentiated Homework Options

Level	Assignment	Two-Day Option	
AL Basic	12–35, 52, 54–81	13–35 odd, 57–60	12–34 even, 52, 54–56, 61–81
OL Core	13–35 odd, 36–40, 41–51 odd, 52, 54–81	12–35, 57–60	36–52, 54–56, 61–81
BL Advanced	36–73, (optional: 74–81)		

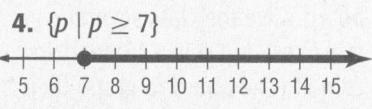

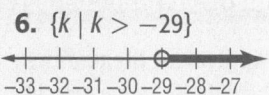

Real-World Link

In a recent year, 55% of American teenagers said they volunteered within the last year, nearly double the percentage of adults.

Source: Corporation for National and Community Service

37. **TEMPERATURE** The water temperature in a swimming pool increased 4°F this morning. The temperature is now less than 81°F. What was the water temperature this morning? **See Ch. 5 Answer Appendix.**

38. **BASKETBALL** A player's goal was to score at least 150 points this season. So far, she has scored 123 points. If there is one game left, how many points must she score to reach her goal? **See Ch. 5 Answer Appendix.**

39. **SPAS** Samantha received a $75 gift card for a local day spa for her birthday. She plans to get a haircut and a manicure. How much money will be left on her gift card after her visit?

Service	Cost ($)
haircut	at least 32
manicure	at least 26

40. **VOLUNTEER** Kono knows that he can only volunteer up to 25 hours per week. If he has volunteered for the times recorded at the right, how much more time can Kono volunteer this week? **19 h 15 min**

Center	Time (h)
Shelter	3 h 15 min
Kitchen	2 h 20 min

41–44. See Ch. 5 Answer Appendix.

Solve each inequality. Check your solution, and then graph it on a number line.

41. $c + (-1.4) \geq 2.3$
42. $9.1g + 4.5 < 10.1g$
43. $k + \frac{3}{4} > \frac{1}{3}$
44. $\frac{3}{2}p - \frac{2}{3} \leq \frac{4}{9} + \frac{1}{2}p$

C

45. **MULTIPLE REPRESENTATIONS** In this problem, you will explore multiplication and division in inequalities.

a. **GEOMETRIC** Suppose a balance has 12 pounds on the left side and 18 pounds on the right side. Draw a picture to represent this situation.

a–d. See Ch. 5 Answer Append

b. **NUMERICAL** Write an inequality to represent the situation.

c. **TABULAR** Create a table showing the result of doubling, tripling, or quadrupling the weight on each side of the balance. Create a second table showing the result of reducing the weight on each side of the balance by a factor of $\frac{1}{2}$, $\frac{1}{3}$, or $\frac{1}{4}$. Include a column in each table for the inequality representing each situation.

d. **VERBAL** Describe the effect multiplying or dividing each side of an inequality by the same positive value has on the inequality.

If $m + 7 \geq 24$, then complete each inequality.

46. $m \geq \underline{?}$ **17**
47. $m + \underline{?} \geq 27$ **10**
48. $m - 5 \geq \underline{?}$ **12**
49. $m - \underline{?} \geq 14$ **3**
50. $m - 19 \geq \underline{?}$ **−2**
51. $m + \underline{?} \geq 43$ **26**

H.O.T. Problems

Use Higher-Order Thinking Skills

52. **REASONING** Compare and contrast the graphs of $a < 4$ and $a \leq 4$.

53. **CHALLENGE** Suppose $b > d + \frac{1}{3}$, $c + 1 < a - 4$, and $d + \frac{5}{8} > a + 2$. Order a, b, c, and d from least to greatest. **$c < a < d < b$**

54. **OPEN ENDED** Write three linear inequalities that are equivalent to $y < -3$. **See Ch. 5 Answer Appendix.**

55. **WRITING IN MATH** Summarize the process of solving and graphing linear inequalities. **See Ch. 5 Answer Appendix.**

56. **WRITING IN MATH** Explain why $x - 2 > 5$ has the same solution set as $x > 7$. **See Ch. 5 Answer Appendix.**

39. Sample answer: Let m = the amount of money left on the gift card; $32 + 26 + m \leq 75$; $\{m \mid m \leq 17\}$; there will be no more than $17 left on her gift card.

40. Sample answer: Let t = time remaining in hours; $3\frac{1}{4} + 2\frac{1}{3} + t \leq 25$; $\{t \mid t \leq 19\frac{5}{12}\}$; the time remaining is at most 19 h 25 min.

52. In both graphs, the line is darkened to the left of 4. In the graph of $a < 4$, there is a circle at 4 to indicate that 4 is not included in the graph. In the graph of $a \leq 4$, there is a dot at 4 to indicate that 4 is included in the graph.

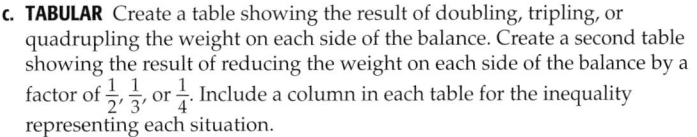

Multiple Representations In Exercise 45, students use a geometric sketch, a linear inequality, a table of values, and verbal analysis to show how inequalities are affected by multiplying or dividing each side by the same value.

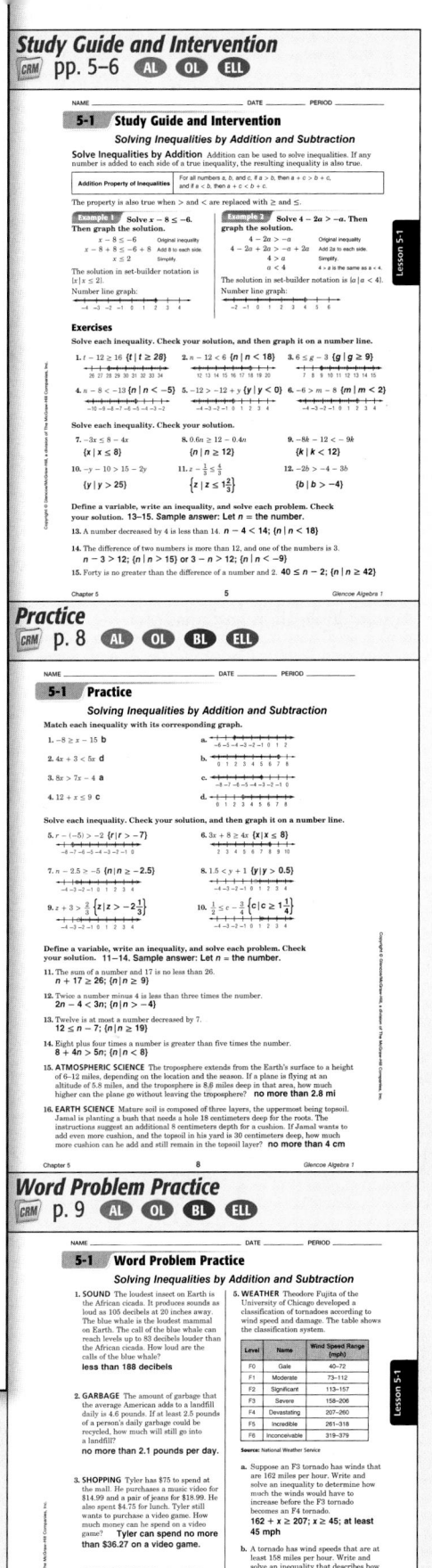

Study Guide and Intervention

CRM pp. 5–6 AL OL ELL

NAME ______ DATE ______ PERIOD ______

5-1 Study Guide and Intervention

Solving Inequalities by Addition and Subtraction

Solve Inequalities by Addition Addition can be used to solve inequalities. If any number is added to each side of a true inequality, the resulting inequality is also true.

Addition Property of Inequalities	For all numbers a, b, and c, if $a > b$, then $a + c > b + c$, and if $a < b$, then $a + c < b + c$.

The property is also true when > and < are replaced with ≥ and ≤.

Example 1 Solve $x - 8 \leq -6$. Then graph the solution.

$x - 8 \leq -6$ Original inequality
$x - 8 + 8 \leq -6 + 8$ Add 8 to each side.
$x \leq 2$ Simplify.

The solution in set-builder notation is $\{x \mid x \leq 2\}$.

Number line graph:

Example 2 Solve $4 - 2a > -a$. Then graph the solution.

$4 - 2a > -a$ Original inequality
$4 - 2a + 2a > -a + 2a$ Add $2a$ to each side.
$4 > a$ Simplify.
$a < 4$ $4 > a$ is the same as $a < 4$.

The solution in set-builder notation is $\{a \mid a < 4\}$.

Number line graph:

Lesson 5-1

Exercises

Solve each inequality. Check your solution, and then graph it on a number line.

1. $t - 12 \geq 16$ $\{t \mid t \geq 28\}$
2. $n - 12 < 6$ $\{n \mid n < 18\}$
3. $6 \leq g - 3$ $\{g \mid g \geq 9\}$
4. $n - 8 < -13$ $\{n \mid n < -5\}$
5. $-12 > -12 + y$ $\{y \mid y < 0\}$
6. $-6 > m - 8$ $\{m \mid m < 2\}$

Solve each inequality. Check your solution.

7. $-3x \leq 8 - 4x$ $\{x \mid x \leq 8\}$
8. $0.6n \geq 12 - 0.4n$ $\{n \mid n \geq 12\}$
9. $-8k - 12 < -9k$ $\{k \mid k < 12\}$
10. $-y - 10 > 15 - 2y$ $\{y \mid y > 25\}$
11. $z - \frac{1}{3} \leq \frac{4}{3}$ $\{z \mid z \leq 1\frac{2}{3}\}$
12. $-2b > -4 - 3b$ $\{b \mid b > -4\}$

Define a variable, write an inequality, and solve each problem. Check your solution. 13–15. Sample answer: Let n = the number.

13. A number decreased by 4 is less than 14. $n - 4 < 14$; $\{n \mid n < 18\}$
14. The difference of two numbers is more than 12, and one of the numbers is 3. $n - 3 > 12$; $\{n \mid n > 15\}$ or $3 - n > 12$; $\{n \mid n < -9\}$
15. Forty is no greater than the difference of a number and 2. $40 \leq n - 2$; $\{n \mid n \geq 42\}$

Chapter 5 5 Glencoe Algebra 1

Practice

CRM p. 8 AL OL BL ELL

NAME ______ DATE ______ PERIOD ______

5-1 Practice

Solving Inequalities by Addition and Subtraction

Match each inequality with its corresponding graph.

1. $-8 \geq x - 15$ **b**
2. $4x + 3 < 5x$ **d**
3. $8x > 7x - 4$ **a**
4. $12 + x \leq 9$ **c**

Solve each inequality. Check your solution, and then graph it on a number line.

5. $r - (-5) > -2$ $\{r \mid r > -7\}$
6. $3x + 8 \geq 4x$ $\{x \mid x \leq 8\}$
7. $n - 2.5 \geq -5$ $\{n \mid n \geq -2.5\}$
8. $1.5 < y + 1$ $\{y \mid y > 0.5\}$
9. $z + 3 > \frac{2}{3}$ $\{z \mid z > -2\frac{1}{3}\}$
10. $\frac{1}{2} \leq c - \frac{3}{4}$ $\{c \mid c \geq 1\frac{1}{4}\}$

Define a variable, write an inequality, and solve each problem. Check your solution. 11–14. Sample answer: Let n = the number.

11. The sum of a number and 17 is no less than 26. $n + 17 \geq 26$; $\{n \mid n \geq 9\}$
12. Twice a number minus 4 is less than three times the number. $2n - 4 < 3n$; $\{n \mid n > -4\}$
13. Twelve is at most a number decreased by 7. $12 \leq n - 7$; $\{n \mid n \geq 19\}$
14. Eight plus four times a number is greater than five times the number. $8 + 4n > 5n$; $\{n \mid n < 8\}$
15. **ATMOSPHERIC SCIENCE** The troposphere extends from the Earth's surface to a height of 6–12 miles, depending on the location and the season. If a plane is flying at an altitude of 5.8 miles, and the troposphere is 8.6 miles deep in that area, how much higher can the plane go without leaving the troposphere? **no more than 2.8 mi**
16. **EARTH SCIENCE** Mature soil is composed of three layers, the uppermost being topsoil. Jamal is planting a bush that needs a hole 18 centimeters deep for the roots. The instructions suggest an additional 8 centimeters depth for a cushion. If Jamal wants to add even more cushion, and the topsoil in his yard is 30 centimeters deep, how much more cushion can he add and still remain in the topsoil layer? **no more than 4 cm**

Chapter 5 8 Glencoe Algebra 1

Word Problem Practice

CRM p. 9 AL OL BL ELL

NAME ______ DATE ______ PERIOD ______

5-1 Word Problem Practice

Solving Inequalities by Addition and Subtraction

1. **SOUND** The loudest insect on Earth is the African cicada. It produces sounds as loud as 105 decibels at 20 inches away. The blue whale is the loudest mammal on Earth. The call of the blue whale can reach levels up to 83 decibels louder than the African cicada. How loud are the calls of the blue whale? **less than 188 decibels**

2. **GARBAGE** The amount of garbage that the average American adds to a landfill daily is 4.6 pounds. If at least 2.5 pounds of a person's daily garbage could be recycled, how much will still go into a landfill? **no more than 2.1 pounds per day.**

3. **SHOPPING** Tyler has $75 to spend at the mall. He purchases a music video for $14.99 and a pair of jeans for $18.99. He also spent $4.75 for lunch. Tyler still wants to purchase a video game. How much money can he spend on a video game? **Tyler can spend no more than $36.27 on a video game.**

4. **SUPREME COURT** The first Chief Justice of the U.S. Supreme Court, John Jay, served 2079 days as Chief Justice. He served 10,463 days fewer than John Marshall, who served as Supreme Court Chief Justice for the longest period of time. How many days must the current Supreme Court Chief Justice John Roberts serve to surpass John Marshall's record of service? **$x > 12{,}542$; more than 12,542 days**

5. **WEATHER** Theodore Fujita of the University of Chicago developed a classification of tornadoes according to wind speed and damage. The table shows the classification system.

Level	Name	Wind Speed Range (mph)
F0	Gale	40–72
F1	Moderate	73–112
F2	Significant	113–157
F3	Severe	158–206
F4	Devastating	207–260
F5	Incredible	261–318
F6	Inconceivable	319–379

Source: National Weather Service

a. Suppose an F3 tornado has winds that are 162 miles per hour. Write and solve an inequality to determine how much the winds would have to increase before the F3 tornado becomes an F4 tornado. **$162 + x \geq 207$; $x \geq 45$; at least 45 mph**

b. A tornado has wind speeds that are at least 158 miles per hour. Write and solve an inequality that describes how much greater these wind speeds are than the slowest tornado. **$40 + y \geq 158$; $y \geq 118$; at least 118 mph**

Lesson 5-1

Chapter 5 9 Glencoe Algebra 1

Enrichment

CRM p. 10 OL BL

NAME ______ DATE ______ PERIOD ______

5-1 Enrichment

Triangle Inequalities

Recall that a line segment can be named by the letters of its endpoints. Line segment AB (written as $\overline{AB}$) has points A and B for endpoints. The *length* of AB is written without the bar as AB.

$AB > BC$ $m\angle A < m\angle B$

The statement on the left above shows that $\overline{AB}$ is shorter than $\overline{BC}$. The statement on the right above shows that the measure of angle A is less than that of angle B.

These three inequalities are true for any triangle ABC, no matter how long the sides.

a. $AB + BC > AC$
b. If $AB > AC$, then $m\angle C > m\angle B$.
c. If $m\angle C > m\angle B$, then $AB > AC$.

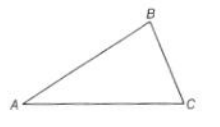

Use the three triangle inequalities for these problems.

1. List the sides of triangle DEF in order of increasing length.

Tips for New Teachers

Check Solutions Students should always check their solutions but often omit this step in their hurry to finish their assignments. Remind students that checking their solutions is especially important with inequalities because the direction of the inequality sign often is changed when writing solutions in set-builder notation

4 ASSESS

Crystal Ball Have students write how they think today's lesson will connect to the next lesson on solving inequalities by multiplication and division.

Additional Answers

61.

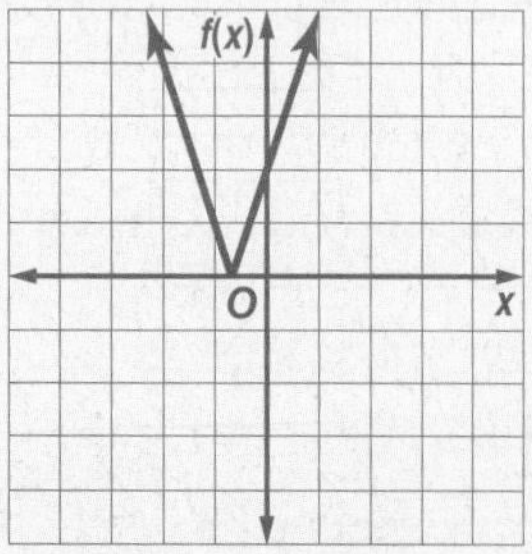

62.

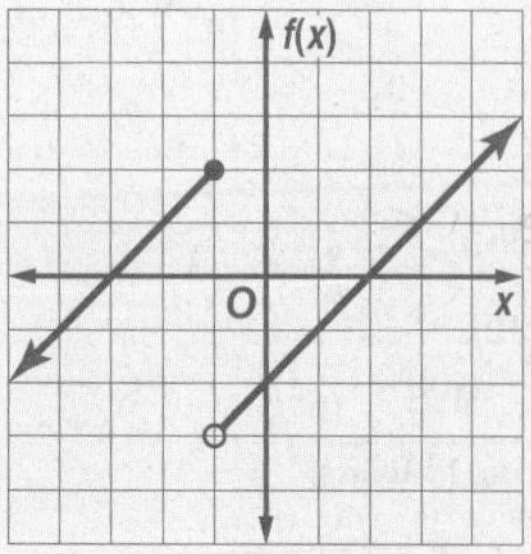

63.

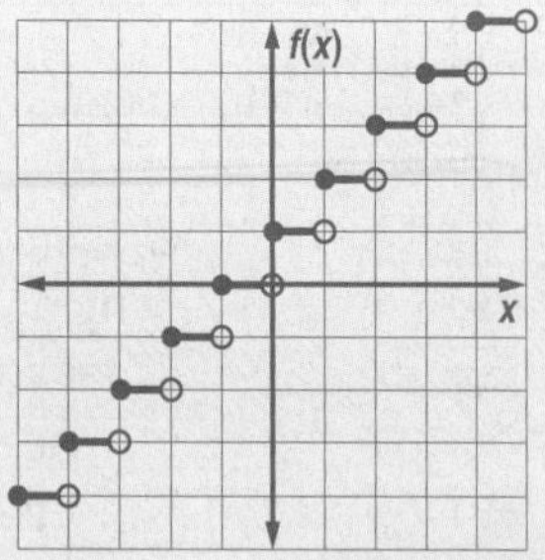

64.

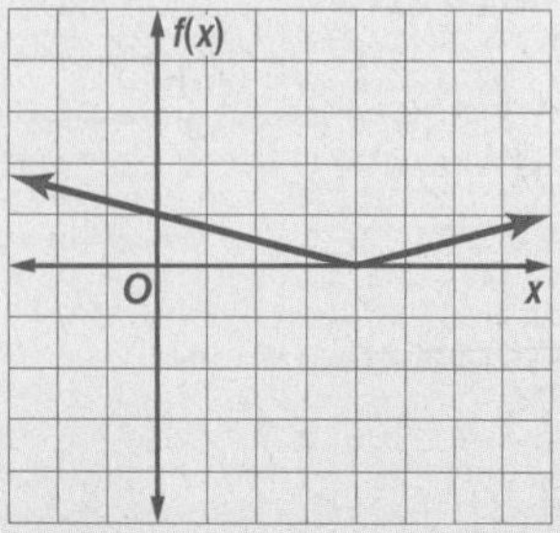

PSAE PRACTICE 8.11.07, 8.11.16, 8.11.02, 10.11.05

57. Which equation represents the relationship shown? **C**

x	y
1	1
2	9
3	17
4	25
5	33
6	41

A $y = 7x - 8$
B $y = 7x + 8$
C $y = 8x - 7$
D $y = 8x + 7$

58. What is the solution set of the inequality $7 + x < 5$? **H**

F $\{x \mid x < 2\}$
G $\{x \mid x > 2\}$
H $\{x \mid x < -2\}$
J $\{x \mid x > -2\}$

59. Francisco has \$3 more than $\frac{1}{4}$ the number of dollars that Kayla has. Which expression represents how much money Francisco has? **B**

A $3\left(\frac{1}{4}k\right)$
B $\frac{1}{4}k + 3$
C $3 - \frac{1}{4}k$
D $\frac{1}{4} + 3k$

60. GRIDDED RESPONSE The mean score for 10 students on the chemistry final exam was 178. However, the teacher had made a mistake and recorded one student's score as ten points less than the actual score. What should the mean score be? **179**

Spiral Review

Graph each function. (Lesson 4-7) **61–64. See margin.**

61. $f(x) = |3x + 2|$

62. $f(x) = \begin{cases} x - 2 \text{ if } x > -1 \\ x + 3 \text{ if } x \leq -1 \end{cases}$

63. $f(x) = [\![x + 1]\!]$

64. $f(x) = \left|\frac{1}{4}x - 1\right|$

Write the slope-intercept form of an equation for the line that passes through the given point and is perpendicular to the graph of each equation. (Lesson 4-4)

65. $(-2, 0), y = x - 6$ **$y = -x - 2$**

66. $(-3, 1), y = -3x + 7$ **$y = \frac{1}{3}x + 2$**

67. $(1, -3), y = \frac{1}{2}x + 4$ **$y = -2x - 1$**

68. $(-2, 7), 2x - 5y = 3$ **$y = -\frac{5}{2}x + 2$**

69. TRAVEL On an island cruise in Hawaii, each passenger is given a lei. A crew member hands out 3 red, 3 blue, and 3 green leis in that order. If this pattern is repeated, what color lei will the 50th person receive? (Lesson 3-6) **blue**

Find the *n*th term of each arithmetic sequence described. (Lesson 3-5)

70. $a_1 = 52, d = 12, n = 102$ **1264**

71. $-9, -7, -5, -3, \ldots$ for $n = 18$ **25**

72. $0.5, 1, 1.5, 2, \ldots$ for $n = 50$ **25**

73. JOBS Refer to the time card shown. Write a direct variation equation relating your pay to the hours worked and find your pay if you work 30 hours. (Lesson 3-4) **$y = 7x$; \$210**

Weekly Time Card

Day	Hours
FRIDAY	2.0
SATURDAY	3.5
SUNDAY	2.0
TOTAL HOURS	7.5
PAY	\$52.50

Skills Review

Solve each equation. (Lesson 2-2)

74. $8y = 56$ **7**

75. $4p = -120$ **−30**

76. $-3a = -21$ **7**

77. $2c = \frac{1}{5}$ **$\frac{1}{10}$**

78. $\frac{r}{2} = 21$ **42**

79. $-\frac{3}{4}g = -12$ **16**

80. $\frac{2}{5}w = -4$ **−10**

81. $-6x = \frac{2}{3}$ **$-\frac{1}{9}$**

Differentiated Instruction OL BL

Extension Write these three linear inequalities on the board:

$$y > 3 \qquad y + 1 > 4 \qquad 5 < y + 2$$

Have students solve each linear inequality and compare the solutions. Ask students to formulate three more linear inequalities that are equivalent to $y > 3$.

Solving Inequalities

IL Math Online glencoe.com
Math *in Motion*, Animation

IL Learning Standards **8.B.4a** Represent algebraic concepts with physical materials, words, diagrams, tables, graphs, equations and inequalities and use appropriate technology.

You can use algebra tiles to solve inequalities.

ACTIVITY Solve Inequalities

Solve $-2x \le 4$.

Step 1 Use a self-adhesive note to cover the equals sign on the equation mat. Then write a ≤ symbol on the note. Model the inequality.

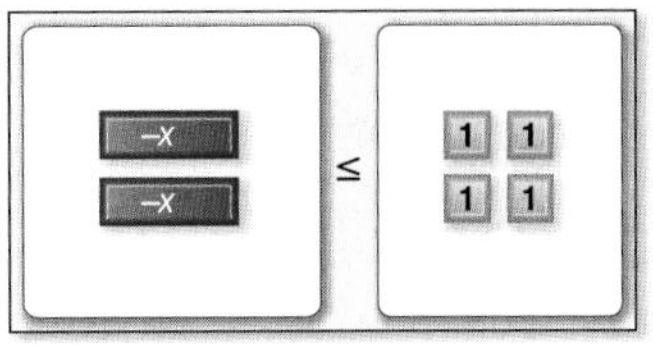

$-2x \le 4$

Step 2 Since you do not want to solve for a negative x-tile, eliminate the negative x-tiles by adding 2 positive x-tiles to each side. Remove the zero pairs.

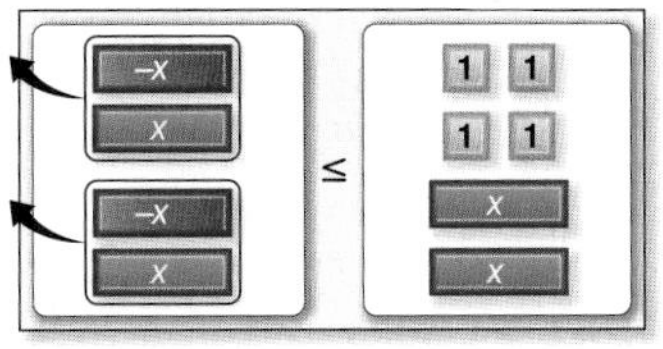

$-2x + 2x \le 4 + 2x$

Step 3 Add 4 negative 1-tiles to each side to isolate the x-tiles. Remove the zero pairs.

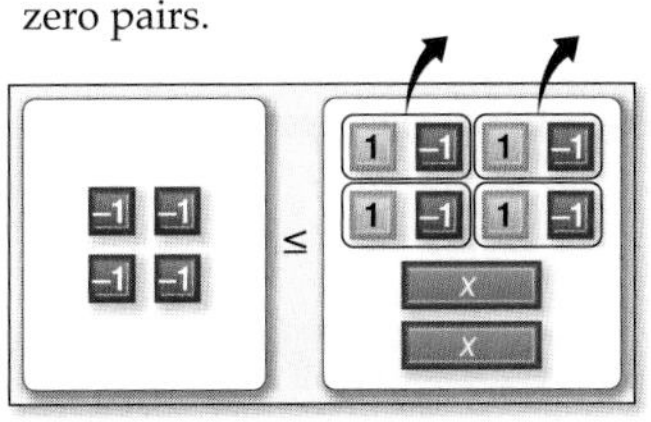

$-4 \le 2x$

Step 4 Separate the tiles into 2 groups.

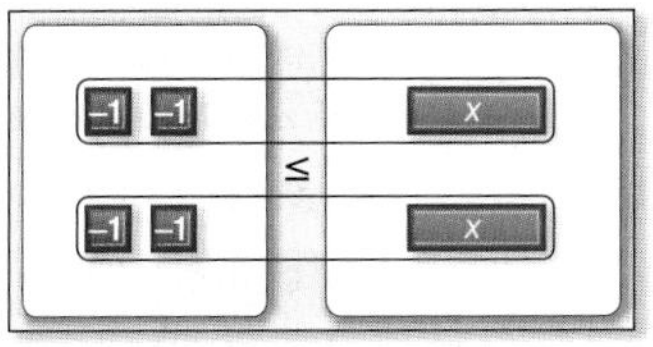

$-2 \le x$ or $x \ge -2$

Model and Analyze

Use algebra tiles to solve each inequality.

1. $-3x < 9$ $\{x \mid x > -3\}$ **2.** $-4x > -4$ $\{x \mid x < 1\}$ **3.** $-5x \ge 15$ $\{x \mid x \le -3\}$ **4.** $-6x \le -12$ $\{x \mid x \ge 2\}$

5. In Exercises 1–4, is the coefficient of x in each inequality positive or negative? **negative**

6. Compare the inequality symbols and locations of the variable in Exercises 1–4 with those in their solutions. What do you find? **See Ch. 5 Answer Appendix.**

7. Model the solution for $3x \le 12$. How is this different from solving $-3x \le 12$? **See Ch. 5 Answer Appendix.**

8. Write a rule for solving inequalities involving multiplication and division. (*Hint:* Remember that dividing by a number is the same as multiplying by its reciprocal.) **See Ch. 5 Answer Appendix.**

1 FOCUS

Objective Use algebra tiles to model solving inequalities.

Materials for Each Group

- algebra tiles and equation mats
- self-adhesive blank notes

Easy to Make Manipulatives

Teaching Algebra with Manipulatives
Templates for:

- algebra tiles, pp. 10–11
- equation mat, p. 16

Teaching Tip Have students use a self-adhesive note to cover the equals sign on the equation mat. Write a ≤ symbol on the note. This will allow students to model inequalities with the equation mat and algebra tiles.

2 TEACH

Working in Cooperative Groups Put students in groups of two or three and demonstrate the Activity. Have groups complete Exercises 1 and 2.

- Make sure the inequality sign on the self-adhesive note is pointed in the correct direction to match the inequality.
- Once students have isolated the x-tiles, remind them to separate the 1-tiles into equal groups to correspond to the number of x-tiles.
- If the x-tiles end up on the right side of the inequality, students may rotate the mat 180 degrees to read the inequality with the variable on the left side.

Practice Have students complete Exercises 3–8.

3 ASSESS

Formative Assessment

Use Exercises 5 and 6 to assess whether students understand that when they multiply or divide both sides of an inequality by a negative number, the direction of the inequality sign changes.

From Concrete to Abstract

Exercise 8 asks students to generalize what happens to the inequality when multiplying or dividing by positive or negative numbers.

5-2 Lesson Notes

1 FOCUS

Vertical Alignment

Before Lesson 5-2
Solve equations by using multiplication and division.

Lesson 5-2
Solve linear inequalities by using multiplication.
Solve linear inequalities by using division.

After Lesson 5-2
Solve systems of inequalities.

2 TEACH

Scaffolding Questions

Have students read the *Why?* section of the lesson.

Ask:

- In the inequality $0.89d \leq 20$, what does the variable d represent? the number of music downloads
- Why is the inequality symbol "$\leq$" used to represent the situation? Terrell has \$20 to spend, so the cost of music downloads times the number of downloads has to be less than or equal to \$20.
- What operation can you perform to get the variable on one side of the inequality? divide each side by 0.89

5-2 Solving Inequalities by Multiplication and Division

Then
You solved equations by using multiplication and division. (Lesson 2-3)

Now
- Solve linear inequalities by using multiplication.
- Solve linear inequalities by using division.

IL Learning Standards
8.B.4a Represent algebraic concepts with physical materials, words, diagrams, tables, graphs, equations and inequalities and use appropriate technology.
8.D.4 Formulate and solve linear and quadratic equations and **linear inequalities algebraically** and investigate nonlinear inequalities using graphs, tables, calculators and computers.

IL Math Online
glencoe.com
- Extra Examples
- Personal Tutor
- Self-Check Quiz
- Homework Help

Why?

Terrell received a gift card for \$20 of music downloads. If each download costs \$0.89, the number of downloads he can purchase can be represented by the inequality $0.89d \leq 20$.

Solve Inequalities by Multiplication If you multiply each side of an inequality by a positive number, then the inequality remains true.

$4 > 2$	**Original inequality**
$4(3) \overset{?}{\_} 2(3)$	**Multiply each side by 3.**
$12 > 6$	**Simplify.**

Notice that the direction of the inequality remains the same.

If you multiply each side of an inequality by a negative number, the inequality symbol changes direction.

$7 < 9$	**Original inequality**
$7(-2) \overset{?}{\_} 9(-2)$	**Multiply each side by −2.**
$-14 > -18$	**Simplify.**

These examples demonstrate the **Multiplication Property of Inequalities**.

Key Concept — Multiplication Property of Inequalities (For Your FOLDABLE)

Words	Symbols	Examples
If both sides of a true inequality are multiplied by a positive number, the resulting inequality is also true.	For any real numbers a and b and any positive real number c, if $a > b$, then $ac > bc$. And, if $a < b$, then $ac < bc$.	$6 > 3.5$ $6(2) > 3.5(2)$ $12 > 7$ and $2.1 < 5$ $2.1(0.5) < 5(0.5)$ $1.05 < 2.5$
If both sides of a true inequality are multiplied by a negative number, the direction of the inequality sign is reversed to make the resulting inequality also true.	For any real numbers a and b and any negative real number c, if $a > b$, then $ac < bc$. And, if $a < b$, then $ac > bc$.	$7 > 4.5$ $7(-3) < 4.5(-3)$ $-21 < -13.5$ and $3.1 < 5.2$ $3.1(-4) > 5.2(-4)$ $-12.4 > -20.8$

This property also holds for inequalities involving $\leq$ and $\geq$.

Lesson 5-2 Resources

Resource	Approaching-Level	On-Level	Beyond-Level	English Learners
Teacher Edition		• Differentiated Instruction, p. 291	• Differentiated Instruction, pp. 291, 295	
Chapter Resource Masters	• Study Guide and Intervention, pp. 11–12 • Skills Practice, p. 13 • Practice, p. 14 • Word Problem Practice, p. 15	• Study Guide and Intervention, pp. 11–12 • Skills Practice, p. 13 • Practice, p. 14 • Word Problem Practice, p. 15 • Enrichment, p. 16	• Practice, p. 14 • Word Problem Practice, p. 15 • Enrichment, p. 16	• Study Guide and Intervention, pp. 11–12 • Skills Practice, p. 13 • Practice, p. 14 • Word Problem Practice
Transparencies	• 5-Minute Check Transparency 5-2	• 5-Minute Check Transparency 5-2	• 5-Minute Check Transparency 5-2	• 5-Minute Check Transparency 5-2
Other	• Study Notebook • Teaching Algebra with Manipulatives	• Study Notebook • Teaching Algebra with Manipulatives	• Study Notebook	• Study Notebook • Teaching Algebra with Manipulatives

StudyTip

Checking Solutions In Example 1, you could also check the solution by substituting a number greater than 672 and verifying that the resulting inequality is false.

Real-World EXAMPLE 1 Write and Solve an Inequality

SURVEYS Of the students surveyed at Madison High School, fewer than eighty-four said they have never purchased an item online. This is about one eighth of those surveyed. How many students were surveyed?

Understand You know the number of students who have never purchased an item online and the portion this is of the number of students surveyed.

Plan Let n = the number of students surveyed. Write an open sentence that represents this situation.

Words	One eighth	times	the number of students surveyed	is less than	84.
Inequality	$\frac{1}{8}$	$\cdot$	n	$<$	84.

Solve Solve for n.

$\frac{1}{8}n < 84$ **Original inequality**

$(8)\frac{1}{8}n < (8)84$ **Multiply each side by 8.**

$n < 672$ **Simplify.**

Check To check this answer, substitute a number less than 672 into the original inequality. If $n = 80$, then $\frac{1}{8}(80)$ or $10 < 84$, so the solution checks.

The solution set is $\{n \mid n < 672\}$, so fewer than 672 students were surveyed at Madison High School.

Check Your Progress

1. **BIOLOGY** Mount Kinabalue in Malaysia has the greatest concentration of wild orchids on Earth. It contains more than 750 species, or about one fourth of all orchid species in Malaysia. How many orchid species are there in Malaysia? more than 3000 orchid species are in Malaysia

Personal Tutor glencoe.com

Real-World Link

More than 30,000 different orchid species flower in the wild on every continent except Antarctica.

Source: Aloha Orchid Nursery

You can also use multiplicative inverses with the Multiplication Property of Inequalities to solve an inequality.

EXAMPLE 2 Solve by Multiplying

Solve $-\frac{3}{7}r < 21$. Check your solution.

$-\frac{3}{7}r < 21$ **Original inequality**

$\left(-\frac{7}{3}\right)\left(-\frac{3}{7}r\right) > 21\left(-\frac{7}{3}\right)$ **Multiply each side by $-\frac{7}{3}$. Reverse the inequality symbol.**

$r > -49$ **Simplify. Check by substituting values.**

The solution set is $\{r \mid r > -49\}$.

Check Your Progress

Solve each inequality. Check your solution.

2A. $-\frac{n}{6} \leq 8$ $n \geq -48$

2B. $-\frac{4}{3}p > -10$ $p < 7\frac{1}{2}$

2C. $\frac{1}{5}m \geq -3$ $m \geq -15$

2D. $\frac{3}{8}t < 5$ $t < 13\frac{1}{3}$

Personal Tutor glencoe.com

Solve Inequalities by Multiplication

Example 1 shows how to solve an inequality by multiplying each side by a positive number. **Example 2** shows how to solve an inequality by multiplying each side by a negative number.

Formative Assessment

Use the Check Your Progress exercises after each example to determine students' understanding of concepts.

Additional Examples

1 **HIKING** Mateo walks at a rate of $\frac{3}{4}$ mile per hour. He knows that it is at least 9 miles to Onyx Lake. How long will it take Mateo to get there? Write and solve an inequality to find the time. $\frac{3}{4}t \geq 9$; $\{t \mid t \geq 12\}$; It will take Mateo at least 12 hours.

2 Solve $-\frac{3}{5}d \geq 6$. $\{d \mid d \leq -10\}$

Additional Examples also in Interactive Classroom PowerPoint® Presentations

IWB INTERACTIVE WHITEBOARD READY

Focus on Mathematical Content

Inequality Symbols The Multiplication Property of Inequalities also holds for inequalities involving $\leq$ and $\geq$.

TEACH with TECH

INTERACTIVE WHITEBOARD Have a student write an open sentence for a real-world situation. Highlight each value or key word. Have another student write the inequality and highlight the corresponding parts from the open sentence.

Differentiated Instruction OL BL

If students understand how to solve inequalities by multiplication,

Then challenge students to explain how they might already know how to solve inequalities by division. Students should suggest that since they know how to solve inequalities by multiplying, and since division is the same as multiplying by the reciprocal, then they already know how to solve inequalities by division.

Lesson 5-2 Solving Inequalities by Multiplication and Division 291

Solve Inequalities by Division

Example 3 shows how to solve an inequality by dividing each side by a positive number and by a negative number.

Additional Example

3 Solve each inequality.

a. $12k \geq 60.$ $k \geq 5$

b. $-8q < 136$ $q > -17$

Watch Out!

Preventing Errors Point out to students that an inequality is easier to solve using division when the inequality involves whole numbers and easier to solve using multiplication by reciprocals when the inequality involves fractions.

Preventing Errors Point out that the rules for the Division Property of Inequalities state that each side of an inequality can be divided by a positive or negative number. In neither case is zero included because division by zero is an undefined operation.

Tips for New Teachers

Checking Solutions Discuss numbers that could be used as a check after an inequality is solved. For example, could $t = 0$ be used to check the solution to Example 3a?

Watch Out!

Negatives A negative sign in an inequality does not necessarily mean that the direction of the inequality should change. For example, when solving $\frac{x}{6} > -3$, do not change the direction of the inequality.

Solve Inequalities by Division If you divide each side of an inequality by a positive number, then the inequality remains true.

$-10 < -5$	**Original inequality**
$\frac{-10}{5} \overset{?}{\_} \frac{-5}{5}$	**Divide each side by −5.**
$-2 < -1$	**Simplify.**

Notice that the direction of the inequality remains the same. If you divide each side of an inequality by a negative number, the inequality symbol changes direction.

$15 < 18$	**Original inequality**
$\frac{15}{-3} \overset{?}{\_} \frac{18}{-3}$	**Divide each side by −3.**
$-5 > -6$	**Simplify.**

These examples demonstrate the **Division Property of Inequalities.**

Key Concept — For Your FOLDABLE

Division Property of Inequalities

Words	Symbols	Examples
If both sides of a true inequality are divided by a positive number, the resulting inequality is also true.	For any real numbers a and b and any positive real number c, if $a > b$, then $\frac{a}{c} > \frac{b}{c}$. And, if $a < b$, then $\frac{a}{c} < \frac{b}{c}$.	$4.5 > 2.1$, $\frac{4.5}{3} > \frac{2.1}{3}$, $1.5 > 0.7$ and $1.5 < 5$, $\frac{1.5}{0.5} < \frac{5}{0.5}$, $3 < 10$
If both sides of a true inequality are divided by a negative number, the direction of the inequality sign is reversed to make the resulting inequality also true.	For any real numbers a and b and any negative real number c, if $a > b$, then $\frac{a}{c} < \frac{b}{c}$. And, if $a < b$, then $\frac{a}{c} > \frac{b}{c}$.	$6 > 2.4$, $\frac{6}{-6} < \frac{2.4}{-6}$, $-1 < -0.4$ and $-1.8 < 3.6$, $\frac{-1.8}{-9} < \frac{3.6}{-9}$, $0.2 > -0.4$

This property also holds for inequalities involving ≤ and ≥.

EXAMPLE 3 Divide to Solve an Inequality

Solve each inequality. Check your solution.

a. $60t > 8$

$60t > 8$	**Original inequality**
$\frac{60t}{60} > \frac{8}{60}$	**Divide each side by 60.**
$t > \frac{2}{15}$	**Simplify.**

b. $-7d \leq 147$

$-7d \leq 147$	**Original inequality**
$\frac{-7d}{-7} \geq \frac{147}{-7}$	**Divide each side by −7.**
$d \geq -21$	**Simplify.**

Check Your Progress

3A. $8p < 58$ **3B.** $-42 > 6r$ **3C.** $-12h > 15$ **3D.** $-\frac{1}{2}n < 6$

▷ Personal Tutor glencoe.com

3A. $p < 7\frac{1}{4}$
3B. $-7 > r$
3C. $h < -\frac{5}{4}$
3D. $n > -12$

292 Chapter 5 Linear Inequalities

Check Your Understanding

Example 1 p. 291

1. **FUNDRAISING** The Jefferson Band Boosters raised more than \$5500 from sales of their \$15 band DVD. Define a variable, and write an inequality to represent the number of DVDs they sold. Solve the inequality and interpret your solution. Let d = the number of DVDs sold; $15d > 5500$; $d > 366.67$; the band sold at least 367 DVDs.

Examples 2 and 3 pp. 291–292

Solve each inequality. Check your solution.

2. $30 > \frac{1}{2}n$ $n < 60$
3. $-\frac{3}{4}r \leq -6$ $r \geq 8$
4. $-\frac{c}{6} \geq 7$ $c \leq -42$
5. $\frac{h}{2} < -5$ $h < -10$
6. $9t > 108$ $t > 12$
7. $-84 < 7v$ $v > -12$
8. $-28 \leq -6x$ $x \leq 4\frac{2}{3}$
9. $40 \geq -5z$ $z \geq -8$

Practice and Problem Solving

● = **Step-by-Step Solutions** begin on page R12. **Extra Practice** begins on page 815.

Example 1 p. 291

Define a variable, write an inequality, and solve each problem. Then interpret your solution.

10. **CELL PHONE PLAN** Mario purchases a prepaid phone plan for \$50 at \$0.13 per minute. How many minutes can Mario talk on this plan?

10. Let m = the number of minutes that Mario can talk; $0.13m \leq 50$; $m \leq 384.6$; Mario can talk up to 384 minutes.

11. **FINANCIAL LITERACY** Rodrigo needs at least \$560 to pay for his spring break expenses, and he is saving \$25 from each of his weekly paychecks. How long will it be before he can pay for his trip? See margin.

Examples 2 and 3 pp. 291–292

Solve each inequality. Check your solution.

12. $\frac{1}{4}m \leq -17$ $m \leq -68$
13. $\frac{1}{2}a < 20$ $a < 40$
14. $-11 > -\frac{c}{11}$ $c > 121$
15. $-2 \geq -\frac{d}{34}$ $d \geq 68$
16. $-10 \leq \frac{x}{-2}$ $x \leq 20$
17. $-72 < \frac{f}{-6}$ $f < 432$
18. $\frac{2}{3}h > 14$ $h > 21$
19. $-\frac{3}{4}j \geq 12$ $j \leq -16$
20. $-\frac{1}{6}n \leq -18$ $n \geq 108$
21. $6p \leq 96$ $p \leq 16$
22. $4r < 64$ $r < 16$
23. $32 > -2y$ $y > -16$
24. $-26 < 26t$ $t > -1$
25. $-6v > -72$ $v < 12$
26. $-33 \geq -3z$ $z \geq 11$
27. $4b \leq -3$ $b \leq -\frac{3}{4}$
28. $-2d < 5$ $d > -2\frac{1}{2}$
29. $-7f > 5$ $f < -\frac{5}{7}$

Math History Link

Thomas Harriot (1560–1621)

Harriot was a prolific astronomer. He was the first to map the moon's surface and to see sunspots. Harriot is best known for his work in algebra.

30. **CHEERLEADING** To remain on the cheerleading squad, Lakita must attend at least $\frac{3}{5}$ of the study table sessions offered. She attends 15 sessions. If Lakita met the requirements, what is the least amount of study table sessions? 25

31. **BRACELETS** How many bracelets can Caitlin buy for herself and her friends if she wants to spend no more than \$22? no more than 4

32. **CHARITY** The National Honor Society at Pleasantville High School wants to raise at least \$500 for a local charity. Each student earns \$0.50 for every quarter of a mile walked in a walk-a-thon. How many miles will the students need to walk? at least 250 mi

33. **MUSEUM** The American history classes are planning a trip to a local museum. Admission is \$8 per person. Determine how many people can go for \$260. no more than 32 people

34. **GASOLINE** If gasoline costs \$3.15 per gallon, how many gallons of gasoline, to the nearest tenth, can Jan buy for \$24? no more than 7.6 gal

3 PRACTICE

Formative Assessment

Use Exercises 1–9 to check for understanding.

Use the chart at the bottom of this page to customize assignments for your students.

Additional Answer

11. Let p = the number of pay periods for which Rodrigo will need to save; $25p \geq 560$; $p \geq 22.4$; Rodrigo will need to save for 23 weeks.

Differentiated Homework Options

Level	Assignment	Two-Day Option	
AL Basic	10–29, 42, 45–62	11–29 odd, 48–51	10–28 even, 42, 45–47, 52–68
OL Core	11–29 odd, 30–35, 37, 39–42, 45–68	10–29, 48–51	30–42, 45–47, 52–68
BL Advanced	30–62, (optional: 63–68)		

Study Guide and Intervention
CRM pp. 11–12 AL OL ELL

NAME ______ DATE ______ PERIOD ______

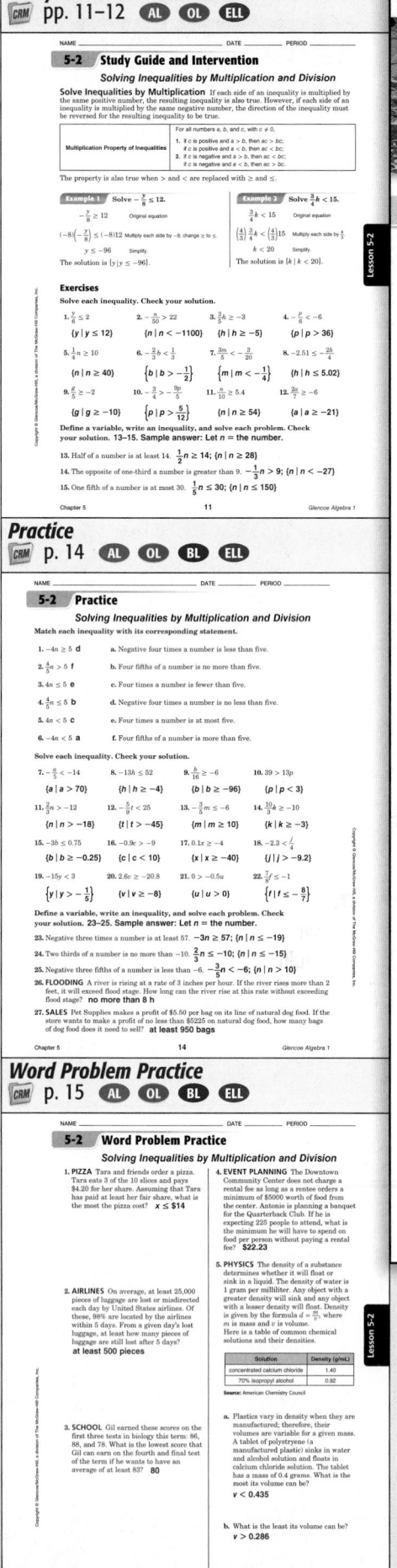

5-2 Study Guide and Intervention

Solving Inequalities by Multiplication and Division

Solve Inequalities by Multiplication If each side of an inequality is multiplied by the same positive number, the resulting inequality is also true. However, if each side of an inequality is multiplied by the same negative number, the direction of the inequality must be reversed for the resulting inequality to be true.

Multiplication Property of Inequalities	For all numbers a, b, and c, with $c \neq 0$, 1. if c is positive and $a > b$, then $ac > bc$; if c is positive and $a < b$, then $ac < bc$; 2. if c is negative and $a > b$, then $ac < bc$; if c is negative and $a < b$, then $ac > bc$.

The property is also true when > and < are replaced with ≥ and ≤.

Example 1 Solve $-\frac{y}{8} \leq 12$.

$-\frac{y}{8} \geq 12$ Original equation

$(-8)\left(-\frac{y}{8}\right) \leq (-8)12$ Multiply each side by −8; change ≥ to ≤.

$y \leq -96$ Simplify.

The solution is $\{y \mid y \leq -96\}$.

Example 2 Solve $\frac{3}{4}k < 15$.

$\frac{3}{4}k < 15$ Original equation

$\left(\frac{4}{3}\right)\frac{3}{4}k < \left(\frac{4}{3}\right)15$ Multiply each side by $\frac{4}{3}$.

$k < 20$ Simplify.

The solution is $\{k \mid k < 20\}$.

Exercises

Solve each inequality. Check your solution.

1. $\frac{y}{6} \leq 2$ $\{y \mid y \leq 12\}$
2. $-\frac{n}{50} > 22$ $\{n \mid n < -1100\}$
3. $\frac{3}{5}h \geq -3$ $\{h \mid h \geq -5\}$
4. $-\frac{p}{6} < -6$ $\{p \mid p > 36\}$
5. $\frac{1}{4}n \geq 10$ $\{n \mid n \geq 40\}$
6. $-\frac{2}{3}b < \frac{1}{3}$ $\left\{b \mid b > -\frac{1}{2}\right\}$
7. $\frac{3m}{5} < -\frac{3}{20}$ $\left\{m \mid m < -\frac{1}{4}\right\}$
8. $-2.51 \leq -\frac{2h}{4}$ $\{h \mid h \leq 5.02\}$
9. $\frac{g}{5} \geq -2$ $\{g \mid g \geq -10\}$
10. $-\frac{3}{4} > -\frac{9p}{5}$ $\left\{p \mid p > \frac{5}{12}\right\}$
11. $\frac{n}{10} \geq 5.4$ $\{n \mid n \geq 54\}$
12. $\frac{2a}{7} \geq -6$ $\{a \mid a \geq -21\}$

Define a variable, write an inequality, and solve each problem. Check your solution. 13–15. Sample answer: Let n = the number.

13. Half of a number is at least 14. $\frac{1}{2}n \geq 14$; $\{n \mid n \geq 28\}$
14. The opposite of one-third a number is greater than 9. $-\frac{1}{3}n > 9$; $\{n \mid n < -27\}$
15. One fifth of a number is at most 30. $\frac{1}{5}n \leq 30$; $\{n \mid n \leq 150\}$

Lesson 5-2

Practice
CRM p. 14 AL OL BL ELL

NAME ______ DATE ______ PERIOD ______

5-2 Practice

Solving Inequalities by Multiplication and Division

Match each inequality with its corresponding statement.

1. $-4n \geq 5$ **d** — a. Negative four times a number is less than five.
2. $\frac{4}{5}n > 5$ **f** — b. Four fifths of a number is no more than five.
3. $4n \leq 5$ **e** — c. Four times a number is fewer than five.
4. $\frac{4}{5}n \leq 5$ **b** — d. Negative four times a number is no less than five.
5. $4n < 5$ **c** — e. Four times a number is at most five.
6. $-4n < 5$ **a** — f. Four fifths of a number is more than five.

Solve each inequality. Check your solution.

7. $-\frac{a}{5} < -14$ $\{a \mid a > 70\}$
8. $-13h \leq 52$ $\{h \mid h \geq -4\}$
9. $\frac{b}{16} \geq -6$ $\{b \mid b \geq -96\}$
10. $39 > 13p$ $\{p \mid p < 3\}$
11. $\frac{2}{3}n > -12$ $\{n \mid n > -18\}$
12. $-\frac{5}{9}t < 25$ $\{t \mid t > -45\}$
13. $-\frac{3}{5}m \leq -6$ $\{m \mid m \geq 10\}$
14. $\frac{10}{3}k \geq -10$ $\{k \mid k \geq -3\}$
15. $-3b \leq 0.75$ $\{b \mid b \geq -0.25\}$
16. $-0.9c > -9$ $\{c \mid c < 10\}$
17. $0.1x \geq -4$ $\{x \mid x \geq -40\}$
18. $-2.3 < \frac{j}{4}$ $\{j \mid j > -9.2\}$
19. $-15y < 3$ $\left\{y \mid y > -\frac{1}{5}\right\}$
20. $2.6v \geq -20.8$ $\{v \mid v \geq -8\}$
21. $0 > -0.5u$ $\{u \mid u > 0\}$
22. $\frac{7}{8}f \leq -1$ $\left\{f \mid f \leq -\frac{8}{7}\right\}$

Define a variable, write an inequality, and solve each problem. Check your solution. 23–25. Sample answer: Let n = the number.

23. Negative three times a number is at least 57. $-3n \geq 57$; $\{n \mid n \leq -19\}$
24. Two thirds of a number is no more than −10. $\frac{2}{3}n \leq -10$; $\{n \mid n \leq -15\}$
25. Negative three fifths of a number is less than −6. $-\frac{3}{5}n < -6$; $\{n \mid n > 10\}$
26. **FLOODING** A river is rising at a rate of 3 inches per hour. If the river rises more than 2 feet, it will exceed flood stage. How long can the river rise at this rate without exceeding flood stage? **no more than 8 h**
27. **SALES** Pet Supplies makes a profit of $5.50 per bag on its line of natural dog food. If the store wants to make a profit of no less than $5225 on natural dog food, how many bags of dog food does it need to sell? **at least 950 bags**

Word Problem Practice
CRM p. 15 AL OL BL ELL

NAME ______ DATE ______ PERIOD ______

5-2 Word Problem Practice

Solving Inequalities by Multiplication and Division

1. **PIZZA** Tara and friends order a pizza. Tara eats 3 of the 10 slices and pays $4.20 for her share. Assuming that Tara has paid at least her fair share, what is the most the pizza cost? **$x \leq \$14$**

2. **AIRLINES** On average, at least 25,000 pieces of luggage are lost or misdirected each day by United States airlines. Of these, 98% are located by the airlines within 5 days. From a given day's lost luggage, at least how many pieces of luggage are still lost after 5 days? **at least 500 pieces**

3. **SCHOOL** Gil earned these scores on the first three tests in biology this term: 86, 88, and 78. What is the lowest score that Gil can earn on the fourth and final test of the term if he wants to have an average of at least 83? **80**

4. **EVENT PLANNING** The Downtown Community Center does not charge a rental fee as long as a rentee orders a minimum of $5000 worth of food from the center. Antonio is planning a banquet for the Quarterback Club. If he is expecting 225 people to attend, what is the minimum he will have to spend on food per person without paying a rental fee? **$22.23**

5. **PHYSICS** The density of a substance determines whether it will float or sink in a liquid. The density of water is 1 gram per milliliter. Any object with a greater density will sink and any object with a lesser density will float. Density is given by the formula $d = \frac{m}{v}$, where m is mass and v is volume. Here is a table of common chemical solutions and their densities.

Solution	Density (g/mL)
concentrated calcium chloride	1.40
70% isopropyl alcohol	0.92

Source: American Chemistry Council

a. Plastics vary in density when they are manufactured; therefore, their volumes are variable for a given mass. A tablet of polystyrene (a manufactured plastic) sinks in water and alcohol solution and floats in calcium chloride solution. The tablet has a mass of 0.4 grams. What is the most its volume can be? **$v < 0.435$**

b. What is the least its volume can be? **$v > 0.286$**

Lesson 5-2

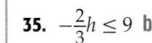

Real-World Link

At the FedNor Pavillion Royal Winter Fair in Toronto, Canada, the Northwest Fudge Factory made the world's largest slab of fudge. The fudge weighed 3010 pounds.

Source: *Guinness World Records*

Match each inequality to the graph of its solution.

35. $-\frac{2}{3}h \leq 9$ **b** **36.** $25j \geq 8$ **a** **37.** $3.6p < -4.5$ **d** **38.** $2.3 < -5t$ **c**

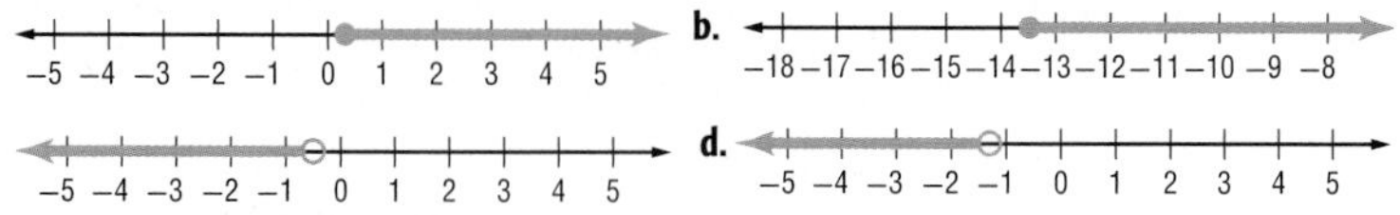

39. CANDY Fewer than 42 employees at a factory stated that they preferred fudge over fruit candy. This is about two thirds of the employees. How many employees are there? **fewer than 63 employees**

40. TRAVEL A certain travel agency employs more than 275 people at all of its branches. Approximately three fifths of all the people are employed at the west branch. How many people work at the west branch? **more than 165 employees**

C **41. MULTIPLE REPRESENTATIONS** The equation for the volume of a pyramid is $\frac{1}{3}$ the area of the base times the height.

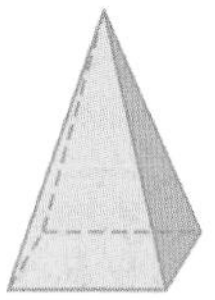

a. **GEOMETRIC** Draw a pyramid with a square base b cm long and a height of h cm.

b. **NUMERICAL** Suppose the pyramid has a volume of 72 cm³. Write an equation to find the height. $h = \frac{216}{b^2}$

c. **TABULAR** Create a table showing the value of h when b = 1, 3, 6, 9, and 12. **See margin.**

d. **NUMERICAL** Write an inequality for the possible lengths of b such that $b < h$. Write an inequality for the possible lengths of h such that $b > h$. $b < h$ **when** $0 < b < 6$; $b > h$ **when** $h < 6$.

41a.

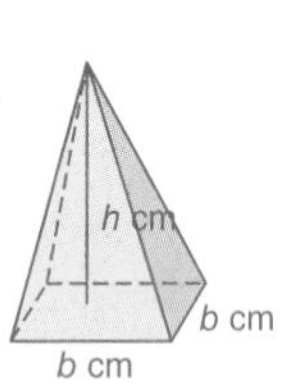

42. Taro; the inequality does not need to be reversed when dividing by a positive number.

43. $\frac{-96c}{-96} > \frac{12d}{-96}$

$c > -\frac{d}{8}$;

$-96c \cdot -\frac{1}{96} >$

$12d \cdot -\frac{1}{96}$;

$c > -\frac{d}{8}$

45. Sometimes; the statement is true when $a > 0$ and $b < 0$.

46. Sample answer: The temperature never exceeds $-\frac{5}{8}$°C.

H.O.T. Problems
Use Higher-Order Thinking Skills

42. FIND THE ERROR Taro and Jamie are solving $6d \geq -84$. Is either of them correct? Explain your reasoning.

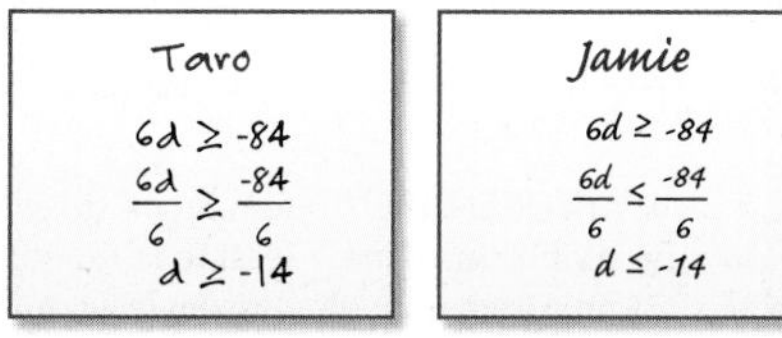

43. CHALLENGE Solve $-96c < 12d$ for c using two methods. Show your work.

44. CHALLENGE Determine whether $x^2 > 1$ and $x > 1$ are equivalent. Explain. **No; the solution set of $x^2 > 1$ includes values of $x < -1$.**

45. REASONING Explain whether the statement *If* $a > b$, *then* $\frac{1}{a} > \frac{1}{b}$ is *sometimes*, *always*, or *never* true.

46. OPEN ENDED Create a real-world situation to represent the inequality $-\frac{5}{8} \geq x$.

47. WRITING IN MATH Explain the circumstances under which the inequality symbol changes directions. Use examples to support your explanation. **See margin.**

Enrichment
CRM p. 16 OL BL

NAME ______ DATE ______ PERIOD ______

5-2 Enrichment

Quadratic Inequalities

Like linear inequalities, inequalities with higher degrees can also be solved. Quadratic Inequalities have a degree of 2. The following example shows how to solve quadratic inequalities.

Example Solve $(x + 3)(x - 2) > 0$.

Step 1 Determine what values of x will make the left side 0. In other words, what values of x will make either $x + 3 = 0$ or $x - 2 = 0$?

$x = -3$ or 2

Step 2 Plot these points on a number line. Above the number line, place a + if $x + 3$ is positive for that region or a − if $x + 3$ is negative for that region. Next, above the signs you have just entered; do the same for $x - 2$.

Step 3 Below the chart, enter the product of the two signs. Your sign chart should look like the following:

$x - 2$ − − +
$x + 3$ − + +

Multiple Representations In Exercise 41, students use a geometric sketch, an equation, a table of values, and numerical analysis to relate the dimensions of a square pyramid to its volume.

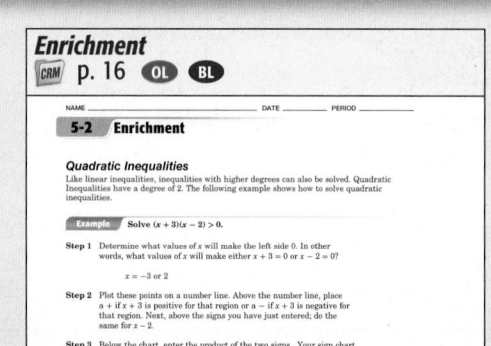

PSAE PRACTICE 8.11.02, 9.11.12, 8.11.05, 8.11.16

48. Juan's long-distance phone company charges 9¢ for each minute. Which inequality can be used to find how long he can talk to a friend if he does not want to spend more than $2.50 on the call? **D**

A $0.09 \geq 2.50m$
B $0.09 \leq 2.50m$
C $0.09m \geq 2.50$
D $0.09m \leq 2.50$

49. SHORT RESPONSE Find the value of x. **10 in.**

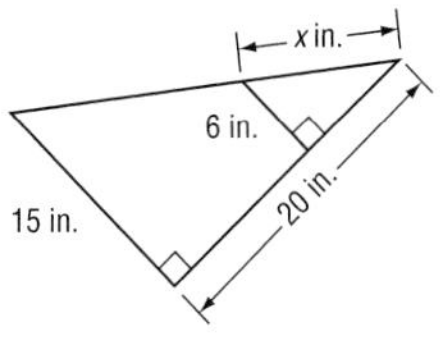

50. What is the greatest rate of decrease of this function? **F**

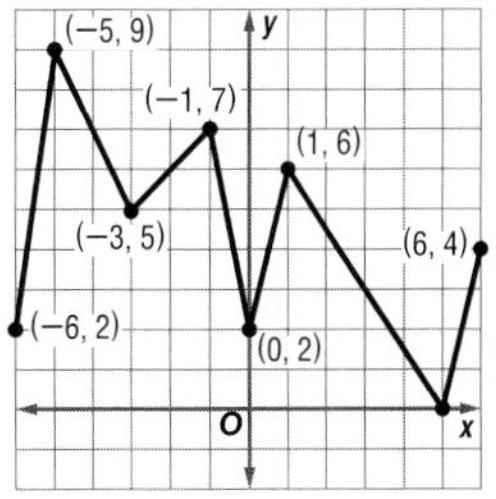

F −5 H −2
G −3 J 1

51. What is the value of x if $4x - 3 = -2x$? **C**

A −2 C $\frac{1}{2}$
B $-\frac{1}{2}$ D 2

Spiral Review

Solve each inequality. Check your solution, and then graph it on a number line. (Lesson 5-1) **52–54. See margin.**

52. $-8 + 4a < 6a$ **53.** $2y + 11 \geq -24y$ **54.** $7 - 2b > 12b$

Determine the domain and range for each function. (Lesson 4-7) **55–57. See margin.**

55. $f(x) = |2x - 5|$ **56.** $h(x) = |x - 1|$ **57.** $g(x) = \begin{cases} -3x + 4 \text{ if } x > 2 \\ x - 1 \text{ if } x \leq 2 \end{cases}$

58. HOME DECOR Pam is having blinds installed at her home. The cost c of installation for any number of blinds b can be described by $c = 25 + 6.5b$. Graph the equation and determine how much it would cost if Pam has 8 blinds installed. (Lesson 3-1) **See Ch. 5 Answer Appendix.**

59. RESCUE A boater radioed for a helicopter to pick up a sick crew member. At that time, the boat and the helicopter were at the positions shown. How long will it take for the helicopter to reach the boat? (Lesson 2-8) **2 hours**

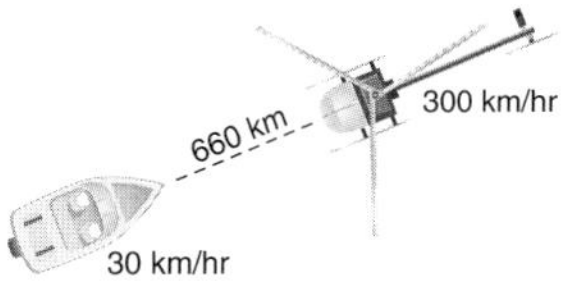

Solve each open sentence. (Lesson 2-5)

60. $|x + 3| = 10$ **{−13, 7}** **61.** $|2x - 8| = 6$ **{1, 7}** **62.** $|3x + 1| = -2$ **∅**

Skills Review

Solve each equation. (Lessons 2-3 and 2-4)

63. $4y + 11 = 19$ **2** **64.** $2x - 7 = 9 + 4x$ **−8** **65.** $\frac{1}{4} + 2x = 4x - 8$ **$\frac{33}{8}$**

66. $\frac{1}{3}(6w - 3) = 3w + 12$ **−13** **67.** $\frac{7r + 5}{2} = 13$ **3** **68.** $\frac{1}{2}a = \frac{a - 3}{4}$ **−3**

Differentiated Instruction OL BL

Extension Ask students to solve $2n + 4 \neq 12$. Have the students discuss the solution and write and solve a different inequality using the ≠ symbol. $\{n \mid n \neq 4\}$

Watch Out!

Find the Error In Exercise 42, students should see that the only difference between Taro's and Jamie's solutions is the inequality symbol. Since the solution involves division by a positive number, the inequality symbol of the solution is not reversed from the original equality.

4 ASSESS

Ticket Out the Door Have students write a short statement about what they think is the most important thing to remember about solving inequalities by multiplication and division.

Formative Assessment

Check for student understanding of the concepts in Lessons 5-1 and 5-2.

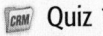

CRM Quiz 1, p. 45

Additional Answers

41c.

b	1	3	6	9	12
h	216	24	6	$\frac{8}{3}$	$\frac{3}{2}$

47. Sample answer: The inequality symbol changes directions when multiplying or dividing by a negative number so that the inequality remains true. For example, dividing $-2x > 4$ by −2 results in $x < -2$.

52. $\{a \mid a > -4\}$

53. $\left\{y \mid y \geq -\frac{11}{26}\right\}$

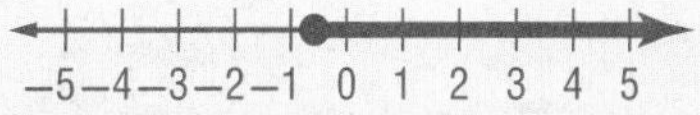

54. $\left\{b \mid b < \frac{1}{2}\right\}$

55. D = {all real numbers}; R = $\{y \mid y \geq 0\}$

56. D = {all real numbers}; R = $\{y \mid y \geq 0\}$

57. D = {all real numbers}; R = $\{y \mid y \leq 1\}$

5-3 Lesson Notes

1 FOCUS

Vertical Alignment

Before Lesson 5-3
Solve multi-step equations.

Lesson 5-3
Solve linear inequalities involving more than one operation.
Solve linear inequalities involving the Distributive Property.

After Lesson 5-3
Solve systems of inequality.

2 TEACH

Scaffolding Questions

Have students read the *Why?* section of the lesson.

Ask:

- What information is needed to solve the inequality for the number of sales? the base salary, the commission paid on each sale, and the income needed to pay the monthly bills
- Why is the inequality symbol "≥" used to represent the situation? The amount the salesperson earns from the base salary and commissions must be equal to at least the income needed to pay the bills.
- Which operations undo the operations represented in the inequality? subtraction and division

5-3 Solving Multi-Step Inequalities

Then

You solved multi-step equations. (Lesson 2-3)

Now

- Solve linear inequalities involving more than one operation.
- Solve linear inequalities involving the Distributive Property.

IL Learning Standards

8.B.4a Represent algebraic concepts with physical materials, words, diagrams, tables, graphs, equations and inequalities and use appropriate technology.
8.D.4 Formulate and solve linear and quadratic equations and **linear inequalities algebraically** and investigate nonlinear inequalities using graphs, tables, calculators and computers.

IL Math Online

glencoe.com

- Extra Examples
- Personal Tutor
- Self-Check Quiz
- Homework Help
- Math in Motion

Why?

A salesperson may make a base monthly salary and earn a commission on each of her sales. To find the number of sales she needs to make to pay her monthly bills, you can use a multi-step inequality.

Solve Multi-Step Inequalities Multi–step inequalities can be solved by undoing the operations in the same way you would solve a multi-step equation.

Real-World EXAMPLE 1 Solve a Multi-Step Inequality

SALES Write and solve an inequality to find the sales Mrs. Jones needs if she earns a salary of $2000 plus a 10% commission on her sales. Her goal is to make at least $4000 per month. What sales does she need to meet her goal?

base salary + (commission × sales) ≥ income needed

$2000 + 0.10x \geq 4000$ **Substitution**

$0.10x \geq 2000$ **Subtract 2000 from each side.**

$x \geq 20{,}000$ **Divide each side by 0.10.**

She must make at least $20,000 in sales to meet her monthly goal.

Check Your Progress

1. FINANCIAL LITERACY The Print Shop advertises a special to print 400 flyers for less than the competition. The price includes a $3.50 set-up fee. If the competition charges $35.50, what does the Print Shop charge for each flyer? less than 8¢

Personal Tutor glencoe.com

When multiplying or dividing by a negative number, the direction of the inequality symbol changes. This holds true for multi-step inequalities.

EXAMPLE 2 Inequality Involving a Negative Coefficient

Solve $-11y - 13 > 42$.

$-11y - 13 > 42$ **Original inequality**

$-11y > 55$ **Add 13 to each side and simplify.**

$\frac{-11y}{-11} < \frac{55}{-11}$ **Divide each side by −11, and reverse the inequality.**

$y < -5$ **Simplify.**

Check Your Progress Solve each inequality.

2A. $23 \geq 10 - 2w$ $\{w \mid w \geq -6.5\}$ **2B.** $43 > -4y + 11$ $\{y \mid y > -8\}$

Personal Tutor glencoe.com

Lesson 5-3 Resources

Resource	Approaching-Level	On-Level	Beyond-Level	English Learners
Teacher Edition	• Differentiated Instruction, p. 298	• Differentiated Instruction, pp. 298, 301	• Differentiated Instruction, pp. 298, 301	• Differentiated Instruction, p. 298
Chapter Resource Masters	• Study Guide and Intervention, pp. 17–18 • Skills Practice, p. 19 • Practice, p. 20 • Word Problem Practice, p. 21	• Study Guide and Intervention, pp. 17–18 • Skills Practice, p. 19 • Practice, p. 20 • Word Problem Practice, p. 21 • Enrichment, p. 22	• Practice, p. 20 • Word Problem Practice, p. 21 • Enrichment, p. 22	• Study Guide and Intervention, pp. 17–18 • Skills Practice, p. 19 • Practice, p. 20 • Word Problem Practice, p. 21
Transparencies	• 5-Minute Check Transparency 5-3	• 5-Minute Check Transparency 5-3	• 5-Minute Check Transparency 5-3	• 5-Minute Check Transparency 5-3
Other	• Study Notebook	• Study Notebook	• Study Notebook	• Study Notebook

You can translate sentences into multi-step inequalities and then solve them using the Properties of Inequalities.

Math *in Motion*, Interactive Lab glencoe.com

EXAMPLE 3 Write and Solve an Inequality

Define a variable, write an inequality, and solve the problem.

Five minus 6 times a number is more than four times the number plus 45.

Five	minus	six times a number	is more	four times a number	plus	forty-five.
5	$-$	$6n$	$>$	$4n$	$+$	45

$5 - 10n > 45$ **Subtract $4n$ from each side and simplify.**

$-10n > 40$ **Subtract 5 from each side and simplify.**

$\frac{-10n}{-10} < \frac{40}{-10}$ **Divide each side by -10, and reverse the inequality.**

$n < -4$ **Simplify.**

The solution set is $\{n \mid n < -4\}$.

3. Sample answer: Let $n =$ the number; $\frac{1}{2}n + 2 > 27$; $\{n \mid n > 50\}$.

Check Your Progress

3. *Two more than half of a number is greater than twenty-seven.*

Personal Tutor glencoe.com

Review Vocabulary

order of operations
1. Evaluate expressions inside grouping symbols.
2. Evaluate all powers.
3. Multiply and/or divide from left to right.
4. Add and/or subtract from left to right.
(Lesson 1-2)

Solve Inequalities Involving the Distributive Property When solving inequalities that contain grouping symbols, use the Distributive Property to remove the grouping symbols first. Then use the order of operations to simplify the resulting inequality.

EXAMPLE 4 Distributive Property

Solve $4(3t - 5) + 7 \geq 8t + 3$.

$4(3t - 5) + 7 \geq 8t + 3$ **Original inequality**

$12t - 20 + 7 \geq 8t + 3$ **Distributive Property**

$12t - 13 \geq 8t + 3$ **Combine like terms.**

$4t - 13 \geq 3$ **Subtract $8t$ from each side and simplify.**

$4t \geq 16$ **Add 13 to each side.**

$\frac{4t}{4} \geq \frac{16}{4}$ **Divide each side by 4.**

$t \geq 4$ **Simplify.**

The solution set is $\{t \mid t \geq 4\}$.

Check Your Progress

Solve each inequality. Check your solution.

4A. $6(5z - 3) \leq 36z$ $\{z \mid z \geq -3\}$

4B. $2(h + 6) > -3(8 - h)$ $\{h \mid h < 36\}$

Personal Tutor glencoe.com

Watch Out!

Distributive Property If a negative number is multiplied by a sum or difference, remember to distribute the negative sign along with the number to each term inside the parentheses.

If solving an inequality results in a statement that is always true, the solution set is the set of all real numbers. This solution set is written as $\{x \mid x \text{ is a real number.}\}$. If solving an inequality results in a statement that is never true, the solution set is the empty set, which is written as the symbol $\varnothing$. The empty set has no members.

Solve Multi-Step Inequalities

Example 1 shows how to solve a multi-step inequality. **Example 2** shows how to solve a multi-step inequality involving a negative coefficient. **Example 3** shows how to write and solve an inequality.

Formative Assessment

Use the Check Your Progress exercises after each example to determine students' understanding of concepts.

Additional Examples

1 **FAXES** Adriana has a budget of \$115 for faxes. The fax service she uses charges \$25 to activate an account and \$0.08 per page to send faxes. How many pages can Adriana fax and stay within her budget? Use the inequality $25 + 0.08p \leq 115$. She can send at most 1125 faxes.

2 Solve $13 - 11d \geq 79$. Check your solution. $\{d \mid d \leq -6\}$

3 Define a variable, write an inequality, and solve the problem. Then check your solution. *Four times a number plus twelve is less than the number minus three.* Let $n =$ the number; $4n + 12 < n - 3$; $\{n \mid n < -5\}$.

Additional Examples also in Interactive Classroom PowerPoint® Presentations

IWB INTERACTIVE WHITEBOARD READY

Solving Inequalities Involving the Distributive Property

Example 4 shows how to use the Distributive Property to solve a multi-step inequality. **Example 5** shows how to solve an inequality that results in the empty set or the set of all real numbers.

Focus on Mathematical Content

Distributive Property When evaluating an expression that contains grouping symbols, you can distribute the term outside the grouping symbols to each term inside the symbols. This allows you to remove grouping symbols. For example, in the expression $3(4c + 2)$, use the Distributive Property to remove the grouping symbols: $12c + 6$.

Additional Examples

4 Solve $6c + 3(2 - c) \geq -2c + 1$. Check your solution. $\{c \mid c \geq -1\}$

5 Solve each inequality. Check your solution.

a. $-7(k + 4) + 11k \geq 8k - 2(2k + 1)$. $\varnothing$

b. $2(4r + 3) \leq 22 + 8(r - 2)$ $\{r \mid r \text{ is a real number.}\}$

Watch Out!

Student Misconceptions Students may incorrectly assume that the solution of all inequalities in which the variable has been eliminated is the empty set. Remind students that they must simplify the inequality to determine whether it is a true statement. If the inequality is true, the solution set is the set of all real numbers. Only when the inequality is untrue is the solution the empty set.

TEACH with TECH

WIKI On your secure class wiki have students create a page explaining how they worked through solving a multi-step inequality. Be sure they explain how they decided whether or not to reverse the inequality sign. When all agree, save and have students use this as a reference.

StudyTip

Empty Set Set-builder notation is not required when the solution set is the empty set. Instead, the solution is written as the symbol $\varnothing$.

EXAMPLE 5 Empty Set and All Reals

Solve each inequality. Check your solution.

a. $9t - 5(t - 5) \leq 4(t - 3)$

$9t - 5(t - 5) \leq 4(t - 3)$	Original inequality
$9t - 5t + 25 \leq 4t - 12$	Distributive Property
$4t + 25 \leq 4t - 12$	Combine like terms.
$4t + 25 - 4t \leq 4t - 12 - 4t$	Subtract $4t$ from each side.
$25 \leq -12$	Simplify.

Since the inequality results in a false statement, the solution set is the empty set, $\varnothing$.

b. $3(4m + 6) \leq 42 + 6(2m - 4)$

$3(4m + 6) \leq 42 + 6(2m - 4)$	Original inequality
$12m + 18 \leq 42 + 12m - 24$	Distributive Property
$12m + 18 \leq 12m + 18$	Combine like terms.
$12m + 18 - 12m \leq 12m + 18 - 12m$	Subtract $12m$ from each side.
$18 \leq 18$	Simplify.

All values of m make the inequality true. All real numbers are solutions.

Check Your Progress

Solve each inequality. Check your solution.

5A. $18 - 3(8c + 4) \geq -6(4c - 1)$ **5B.** $46 \leq 8m - 4(2m + 5)$ $\varnothing$

5A. $\{c \mid c \text{ is a real number.}\}$

Personal Tutor glencoe.com

Check Your Understanding

Example 1 p. 296

1. **CANOEING** If four people plan to use the canoe with 60 pounds of supplies, write and solve an inequality to find the allowable average weight per person. $4n + 60 \leq 800$; $n \leq 185$; at most 185 lb per person

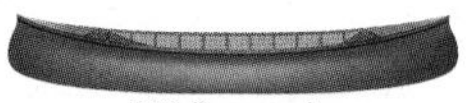

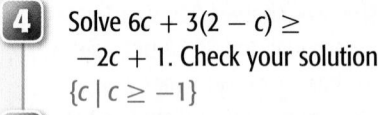

800-lb capacity

2. **SHOPPING** Rita is ordering a movie for \$11.95 and a few CDs. She has \$50 to spend. Shipping and sales tax will be \$10. If each CD costs \$9.99, write and solve an inequality to find the greatest number of CDs that she can buy. $9.99x + 11.95 + 10 \leq 50$; $x \leq 2.8$; Rita can buy 2 CDs.

Example 2 p. 296

Solve each inequality. Check your solution.

3. $6h - 10 \geq 32$ $\{h \mid h \geq 7\}$
4. $-3 \leq \frac{2}{3}r + 9$ $\{r \mid r \geq -18\}$
5. $-3x + 7 > 43$ $\{x \mid x < -12\}$
6. $4m - 17 < 6m + 25$ $\{m \mid m > -21\}$

Example 3 p. 297

Define a variable, write an inequality, and solve each problem. Then check your solution. 7. Sample answer: Let n = the number; $4n - 6 > 8 + 2n$; $\{n \mid n > 7\}$.

7. Four times a number minus 6 is greater than eight plus two times the number.
8. Negative three times a number plus 4 is less than five times the number plus 8. Sample answer: Let n = the number; $-3n + 4 < 5n + 8$; $\left\{n \mid n > -\frac{1}{2}\right\}$.

Examples 4 and 5 pp. 297–298

Solve each inequality. Check your solution.

9. $-6 \leq 3(5v - 2)$
10. $-5(g + 4) > 3(g - 4)$
11. $3 - 8x \geq 9 + 2(1 - 4x)$

9. $\{v \mid v \geq 0\}$
10. $\{g \mid g < -1\}$
11. $\varnothing$

Differentiated Instruction

AL OL BL ELL

If you have students who are interested in science,

Then point out that there are many natural settings, such as those in Exercises 36 and 41, that can be connected to linear inequalities. Have students write observations about possible connections in their notebooks and then share their observations with the class.

Practice and Problem Solving

● = **Step-by-Step Solutions** begin on page R12. **Extra Practice** begins on page 815.

Examples 1 and 2 p. 296

Solve each inequality. Check your solution.

12. $5b - 1 \geq -11$ $\{b \mid b \geq -2\}$
13. $21 > 15 + 2a$ $\{a \mid a < 3\}$
14. $-9 \geq \frac{2}{5}m + 7$ $\{m \mid m \leq -40\}$
15. $\frac{w}{8} - 13 > -6$ $\{w \mid w > 56\}$
16. $-a + 6 \leq 5$ $\{a \mid a \geq 1\}$
17. $37 < 7 - 10w$ $\{w \mid w < -3\}$
18. $8 - \frac{z}{3} \geq 11$ $\{z \mid z \leq -9\}$
19. $-\frac{5}{4}p + 6 < 12$ $\{p \mid p > -\frac{24}{5}\}$
20. $3b - 6 \geq 15 + 24b$ $\{b \mid b \leq -1\}$
21. $15h + 30 < 10h - 45$ $\{h \mid h < -15\}$

22. Sample answer: Let n = the number; $\frac{3}{4}n - 9 \geq 42$; $\{n \mid n \geq 68\}$

Example 3 p. 297

Define a variable, write an inequality, and solve each problem. Check your solution.

22. Three fourths of a number decreased by nine is at least forty-two.
23. Two thirds of a number added to six is at least twenty-two.
24. Seven tenths of a number plus 14 is less than forty-nine.
25. Eight times a number minus twenty-seven is no more than the negative of that number plus eighteen. Sample answer: Let n = the number; $8n - 27 \leq -n + 18$; $\{n \mid n \leq 5\}$.
26. Ten is no more than 4 times the sum of twice a number and three.
27. Three times the sum of a number and seven is greater than five times the number less thirteen. Sample answer: Let n = the number; $3(n + 7) > 5n - 13$; $\{n \mid n < 17\}$
28. The sum of nine times a number and fifteen is less than or equal to the sum of twenty-four and ten times the number. Sample answer: Let n = the number; $9n + 15 \leq 24 + 10n$; $\{n \mid n \geq -9\}$

23. Sample answer: Let n = the number; $\frac{2}{3}n + 6 \geq 22$; $\{n \mid n \geq 24\}$

24. Sample answer: Let n = the number; $\frac{7}{10}n + 14 < 49$; $\{n \mid n < 50\}$

26. Sample answer: Let n = the number; $10 \leq 4(2n + 3)$; $\left\{n \mid n \geq -\frac{1}{4}\right\}$

Examples 4 and 5 pp. 297–298

Solve each inequality. Check your solution.

29. $-3(7n + 3) < 6n$ $\left\{n \mid n > -\frac{1}{3}\right\}$
30. $21 \geq 3(a - 7) + 9$ $\{a \mid a \leq 11\}$
31. $2y + 4 > 2(3 + y)$ $\varnothing$
32. $3(2 - b) < 10 - 3(b - 6)$ $\{b \mid b$ is a real number.$\}$
33. $7 + t \leq 2(t + 3) + 2$ $\{t \mid t \geq -1\}$
34. $8a + 2(1 - 5a) \leq 20$ $\{a \mid a \geq -9\}$

Real-World Career

Veterinarian
Veterinarians take care of sick and injured animals. Vets can work anywhere from a zoo to a research facility to owning their own practice. Vets need to earn a bachelor's degree, attend vet college for 4 years, and take a test to get licensed.

B **Define a variable, write an inequality, and solve each problem. Then interpret your solution.**

35. **CARS** A car salesperson is paid a base salary of \$35,000 a year plus 8% of sales. What are the sales needed to have an annual income greater than \$65,000? See margin.
36. **ANIMALS** Keith's dog weighs 90 pounds. A healthy weight for his dog would be less than 75 pounds. If Keith's dog can lose an average of 1.25 pounds per week on a certain diet, how long until the dog reaches a healthy weight? See margin.
37. Solve $6(m - 3) > 5(2m + 4)$. Show each step and justify your work. See Ch. 5 Answer Appendix.
38. Solve $8(a - 2) \leq 10(a + 2)$. Show each step and justify your work. See Ch. 5 Answer Appendix.
39. **MUSICAL** A high school drama club is performing a musical to benefit a local charity. Tickets are \$5 each. They also received donations of \$565. They want to raise at least \$1500.
    a. Write an inequality that describes this situation. Then solve the inequality.
    b. Graph the solution.

39a. $5t + 565 \geq 1500$; $t \geq 187$

40. **ICE CREAM** Benito has \$6 to spend. A sundae costs \$3.25 plus \$0.65 per topping. Write and solve an inequality to find how many toppings he can order. Sample answer: $3.25 + 0.65t \leq 6$; 4 or fewer toppings

3 PRACTICE

Formative Assessment

Use Exercises 1–11 to check for understanding.

Use the chart at the bottom of this page to customize assignments for your students.

Additional Answers

35. Sample answer: Let s = the amount of sales made; $35{,}000 + 0.08s > 65{,}000$; $\{s \mid s > 375{,}000\}$; the sales must be more than \$375,000.

36. Sample answer: Let w = the number of weeks; $1.25w > 90 - 75$; $\{w \mid w > 12\}$; it will take more than 12 weeks for the dog to reach a healthy weight.

Differentiated Homework Options

Level	Assignment	Two-Day Option	
AL Basic	12–34, 55, 57–83	13–33 odd, 60–63	12–34 even, 55, 57–59, 64–83
OL Core	13–33 odd, 35–43, 45–53 odd, 54–55, 57–83	12–34, 60–63	35–55, 57–59, 64–83
BL Advanced	35–77, (optional: 78–83)		

Study Guide and Intervention
CRM pp. 17–18 AL OL ELL

NAME ______ DATE ______ PERIOD ______

5-3 Study Guide and Intervention
Solving Multi-Step Inequalities

Solve Multi-Step Inequalities To solve linear inequalities involving more than one operation, undo the operations in reverse of the order of operations, just as you would solve an equation with more than one operation.

Example 1 Solve $6x - 4 \le 2x + 12$.

$6x - 4 \le 2x + 12$ Original inequality
$6x - 4 - 2x \le 2x + 12 - 2x$ Subtract 2x from each side.
$4x - 4 \le 12$ Simplify.
$4x - 4 + 4 \le 12 + 4$ Add 4 to each side.
$4x \le 16$ Simplify.
$\frac{4x}{4} \le \frac{16}{4}$ Divide each side by 4.
$x \le 4$ Simplify.
The solution is $\{x \mid x \le 4\}$.

Example 2 Solve $3a - 15 > 4 + 5a$.

$3a - 15 > 4 + 5a$ Original inequality
$3a - 15 - 5a > 4 + 5a - 5a$ Subtract 5a from each side.
$-2a - 15 > 4$ Simplify.
$-2a - 15 + 15 > 4 + 15$ Add 15 to each side.
$-2a > 19$ Simplify.
$\frac{-2a}{-2} < \frac{19}{-2}$ Divide each side by −2 and change > to <.
$a < -9\frac{1}{2}$ Simplify.
The solution is $\left\{a \mid a < -9\frac{1}{2}\right\}$.

Exercises

Solve each inequality. Check your solution.

1. $11y + 13 \ge -1$ $\left\{y \mid y \ge -1\frac{3}{11}\right\}$
2. $8n - 10 < 6 - 2n$ $\left\{n \mid n < 1\frac{3}{5}\right\}$
3. $\frac{q}{7} + 1 > -5$ $\{q \mid q > -42\}$
4. $6n + 12 < 8 + 8n$ $\{n \mid n > 2\}$
5. $-12 - d > -12 + 4d$ $\{d \mid d < 0\}$
6. $5r - 6 > 8r - 18$ $\{r \mid r < 4\}$
7. $\frac{-3x + 6}{2} \le 12$ $\{x \mid x \ge -6\}$
8. $7.3y - 14.4 > 4.9y$ $\{y \mid y > 6\}$
9. $-8m - 3 < 18 - m$ $\{m \mid m > -3\}$
10. $-4y - 10 > 19 - 2y$ $\left\{y \mid y < -14\frac{1}{2}\right\}$
11. $9n - 24n + 45 > 0$ $\{n \mid n < 3\}$
12. $\frac{4x - 2}{5} \ge -4$ $\left\{x \mid x \ge -4\frac{1}{2}\right\}$

Define a variable, write an inequality, and solve each problem. Check your solution. 13–15. Sample answer: Let n = the number.

13. Negative three times a number plus four is no more than the number minus eight. $-3n + 4 \le n - 8$; $\{n \mid n \ge 3\}$
14. One fourth of a number decreased by three is at least two. $\frac{1}{4}n - 3 \ge 2$; $\{n \mid n \ge 20\}$
15. The sum of twelve and a number is no greater than the sum of twice the number and −8. $12 + n \le 2n + (-8)$; $\{n \mid n \ge 20\}$

Chapter 5 17 Glencoe Algebra 1

Lesson 5-3

Practice
CRM p. 20 AL OL BL ELL

NAME ______ DATE ______ PERIOD ______

5-3 Practice
Solving Multi-Step Inequalities

Justify each indicated step.

1. $x > \frac{5x - 12}{8}$
$8x > (8)\frac{5x - 12}{8}$ a. ?
$8x > 5x - 12$
$8x - 5x > 5x - 12 - 5x$ b. ?
$3x > -12$
$\frac{3x}{3} > \frac{-12}{3}$ c. ?
$x > -4$

a. Multiply each side by 8.
b. Subtract 5x from each side.
c. Divide each side by 3.

2. $2(2h + 2) < 2(3h + 5) - 12$
$4h + 4 < 6h + 10 - 12$ a. ?
$4h + 4 < 6h - 2$
$4h + 4 - 6h < 6h - 2 - 6h$ b. ?
$-2h + 4 < -2$
$-2h + 4 - 4 < -2 - 4$ c. ?
$-2h < -6$
$\frac{-2h}{-2} > \frac{-6}{-2}$ d. ?
$h > 3$

a. Distributive Property
b. Subtract 6h from each side.
c. Subtract 4 from each side.
d. Divide each side by −2 and change < to >.

Solve each inequality. Check your solution.

3. $-5 - \frac{t}{6} \ge -9$ $\{t \mid t \le 24\}$
4. $4u - 6 \ge 6u - 20$ $\{u \mid u \le 7\}$
5. $13 > \frac{2}{3}a - 1$ $\{a \mid a < 21\}$
6. $\frac{w + 3}{2} < -8$ $\{w \mid w < -19\}$
7. $\frac{3f - 10}{5} > 7$ $\{f \mid f > 15\}$
8. $h \le \frac{6h + 3}{5}$ $\{h \mid h \ge -3\}$
9. $3(z + 1) + 11 < -2(z + 13)$ $\{z \mid z < -8\}$
10. $3r + 2(4r + 2) \le 2(6r + 1)$ $\{r \mid r \ge 2\}$
11. $5n - 3(n - 6) \ge 0$ $\{n \mid n \ge -9\}$

Define a variable, write an inequality, and solve each problem. Check your solution. 12–13. Sample answer: Let n = the number.

12. A number is less than one fourth the sum of three times the number and four. $n < \frac{3n + 4}{4}$; $\{n \mid n < 4\}$
13. Two times the sum of a number and four is no more than three times the sum of the number and seven decreased by four. $2(n + 4) \le 3(n + 7) - 4$; $\{n \mid n \ge -9\}$
14. **GEOMETRY** The area of a triangular garden can be no more than 120 square feet. The base of the triangle is 16 feet. What is the height of the triangle? no more than 15 ft
15. **MUSIC PRACTICE** Nabuko practices the violin at least 12 hours per week. She practices for three fourths of an hour each session. If Nabuko has already practiced 3 hours in one week, how many sessions remain to meet or exceed her weekly practice goal? at least 12 sessions

Chapter 5 20 Glencoe Algebra 1

Word Problem Practice
CRM p. 21 AL OL BL ELL

NAME ______ DATE ______ PERIOD ______

5-3 Word Problem Practice
Solving Multi-Step Inequalities

1. **BEACHCOMBING** Jay has lost his mother's favorite necklace, so he will rent a metal detector to try to find it. A rental company charges a one-time rental fee of $15 plus $2 per hour to rent a metal detector. Jay has only $35 to spend. What is the maximum amount of time he can rent the metal detector? no more than 10 hours

2. **AGES** Bobby, Billy, and Barry Smith are each one year apart in age. The sum of their ages is greater than the age of their father, who is 60. What is the youngest age that the oldest brother can be? no younger than 22

3. **TAXI FARE** Jamal works in a city and sometimes takes a taxi to work. The taxicabs charge $1.50 for the first $\frac{1}{5}$ mile and $0.25 for each additional $\frac{1}{5}$ mile. Jamal has only $3.75 in his pocket. What is the maximum distance he can travel by cab if he does not intend to tip the cab driver? no more than 2 mi

4. **PLAYGROUND** The perimeter of a rectangular playground must be no greater than 120 meters, because that is the total length of the materials available for the border. The width of the playground cannot exceed 22 meters. What are the possible lengths of the playground? less than or equal to 38 meters

5. **MEDICINE** Clark's Rule is a formula used to determine pediatric dosages of over-the-counter medicines.

$\frac{\text{Weight of child (lb)}}{150} \times \text{adult dose} = \text{child dose}$

a. If an adult dose of acetaminophen is 1000 milligrams and a child weighs no more than 90 pounds, what is the recommended child's dose? $x \le 600$; no more than 600 mg

b. This label appears on a child's cold medicine. What is the adult minimum dosage in milliliters? $a \ge 15.79$ mL

Weight (lb)	Age (yr)	Dose
under 48	under 6	call a doctor
48-95	6-11	2 tsp or 10 mL

c. What is the maximum adult dosage in milliliters? $a \le 31.25$ mL

Chapter 5 21 Glencoe Algebra 1

Lesson 5-3

Real-World Link

Unlike most animals, camels move both legs on one side of their body at the same time as they walk.

Source: National Zoo

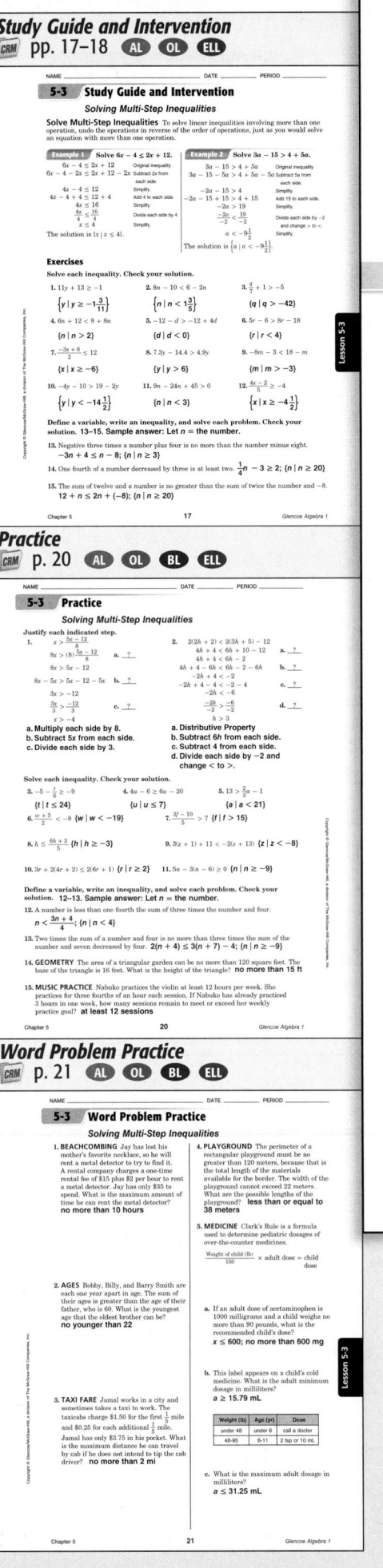

41. **SCIENCE** The normal body temperature of a camel is 97.7°F in the morning. If it has had no water by noon, its body temperature can be greater than 104°F.

a. Write an inequality that represents a camel's body temperature at noon if the camel had no water. $t > 104$

b. If C represents degrees Celsius, then $F = \frac{9}{5}C + 32$. Write and solve an inequality to find the camel's body temperature at noon in degrees Celsius.

42. **NUMBER THEORY** Find all sets of three consecutive positive even integers with a sum no greater than 36. 2, 4, 6; 4, 6, 8; 6, 8, 10; 8, 10, 12; 10, 12, 14

43. **NUMBER THEORY** Find all sets of four consecutive positive odd integers whose sum is less than 42. 1, 3, 5, 7; 3, 5, 7, 9; 5, 7, 9, 11; 7, 9, 11, 13

Solve each inequality. Check your solution.

44. $2(x - 4) \le 2 + 3(x - 6)$ $\{x \mid x \ge 8\}$
45. $\frac{2x - 4}{6} \ge -5x + 2$ $\left\{x \mid x \ge \frac{1}{2}\right\}$
46. $5.6z + 1.5 < 2.5z - 4.7$ $\{z \mid z < -2\}$
47. $0.7(2m - 5) \ge 21.7$ $\{m \mid m \ge 18\}$

GRAPHING CALCULATOR Use a graphing calculator to solve each inequality.

48. $3x + 7 > 4x + 9$
49. $13x - 11 \le 7x + 37$
50. $2(x - 3) < 3(2x + 2)$
51. $\frac{1}{2}x - 9 < 2x$
52. $2x - \frac{2}{3} \ge x - 22$
53. $\frac{1}{3}(4x + 3) \ge \frac{2}{3}x + 2$

C

54. **MULTIPLE REPRESENTATIONS** In this problem, you will solve compound inequalities. A number x is greater than 4, and the same number is less than 9.

a. **NUMERICAL** Write two separate inequalities for the statement. $x > 4$; $x < 9$

b. **GRAPHICAL** Graph the solution set for the first inequality in red. Graph the solution set for the second inequality in blue. Highlight the portion of the graph in which the red and blue overlap. See margin.

c. **TABULAR** Make a table using ten points from your number line, including points from each section. Use one column for each inequality and a third column titled "Both are True." Complete the table by writing true or false. See margin.

d. **VERBAL** Describe the relationship between the colored regions of the graph and the chart.

e. **LOGICAL** Make a prediction of what the graph of $4 < x < 9$ looks like. The graph would be the highlighted section of the number line.

41b. $\frac{9}{5}C + 32 > 104$; $C > 40$
48. $\{x \mid x < -2\}$
49. $\{x \mid x \le 8\}$
50. $\{x \mid x > -3\}$
51. $\{x \mid x > -6\}$
52. $\left\{x \mid x \ge -\frac{64}{3}\right\}$
53. $\{x \mid x \ge 1.5\}$
54d. The points that make $x > 4$ a true statement are in the blue section. The points that make $x < 9$ a true statement are in the red section. The points that make both true are in the highlighted section.
55. Add $3p$ and 2 to each side. The inequality becomes $9 \ge 3p$. Then divide each side by 3 to get $3 \ge p$.
56. ∅; if the first inequality is always true, the opposite inequality will always be false.

H.O.T. Problems
Use Higher-Order Thinking Skills

55. **REASONING** Explain how you could solve $-3p + 7 \ge -2$ without multiplying or dividing each side by a negative number.

56. **CHALLENGE** If $ax + b < ax + c$ has infinitely many solutions, what will be the solution of $ax + b > ax + c$? Explain how you know.

57. **OPEN ENDED** Write two different multi-step inequalities that have the same graph. See margin.

58. **WHICH ONE DOESN'T BELONG?** Name the inequality that does not belong. Explain. See margin.

$4y + 9 > -3$	$3y - 4 > 5$	$-2y + 1 < -5$	$-5y + 2 < -13$

59. **WRITING IN MATH** Explain when the solution set of an inequality will be the empty set or the set of all real numbers. Show an example of each. See margin.

Enrichment
CRM p. 22 OL BL

NAME ______ DATE ______ PERIOD ______

5-3 Enrichment

Carlos Montezuma

During his lifetime, Carlos Montezuma (1865?–1923) was one of the most influential Native Americans in the United States. He was recognized as a prominent physician and was also a passionate advocate of the rights of Native American peoples. The exercises that follow will help you learn some interesting facts about Dr. Montezuma's life.

Solve each inequality. The word or phrase next to the equivalent inequality will complete the statement correctly.

1. $-2k > 10$
Montezuma was born in the state of ? .
(a.) $k < -5$ Arizona
b. $k > -5$ Montana
c. $k > 12$ Utah

2. $5 \ge r - 9$
He was a Native American of the Yavapais, who are a ? people.
a. $r \le -4$ Navajo
b. $r \ge -4$ Mohawk
(c.) $r \le 14$ Mohave-Apache

3. $-y \le -9$
Montezuma received a medical degree ? in 1889

4. $-3 + q > 12$
As a physician, Montezuma's field of specialization was ?

Multiple Representations In Exercise 54, students use a number line, a table of values, and logical analysis to describe the solution of two linear inequalities.

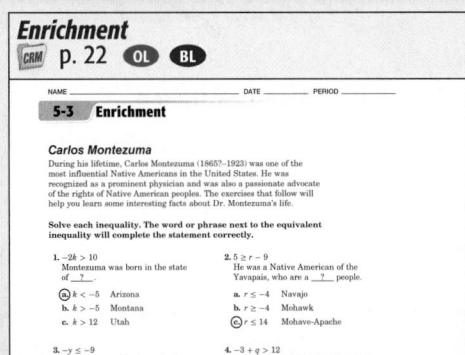

PSAE PRACTICE 8.11.16, 9.11.01, 6.11.17, 9.11.05

60. What is the solution set of the inequality $4t + 2 < 8t - (6t - 10)$? **C**

A $\{t \mid t < -6.5\}$ C $\{t \mid t < 4\}$
B $\{t \mid t > -6.5\}$ D $\{t \mid t > 4\}$

61. GEOMETRY The section of Liberty Ave. between 5th St. and King Ave. is temporarily closed. Traffic is being detoured right on 5th St., left on King Ave. and then back on Liberty Ave. How long is the closed section of Liberty Ave.? **G**

F 100 ft
G 120 ft
H 144 ft
J 180 ft

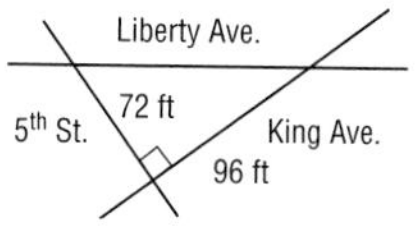

62. SHORT RESPONSE Rhiannon is paid \$52 for working 4 hours. At this rate, how many hours will it take her to earn \$845? **65 hours**

63. GEOMETRY Classify the triangle. **D**

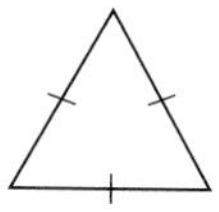

A right
B parallel
C obtuse
D equilateral

Spiral Review

Solve each inequality. Check your solution. (Lesson 5-2)

64. $\frac{y}{2} \le -5$ $\{y \mid y \le -10\}$ **65.** $12b > -48$ $\{b \mid b > -4\}$ **66.** $-\frac{2}{3}t \le -30$ $\{t \mid t \ge 45\}$

Solve each inequality. Check your solution, and graph it on a number line. (Lesson 5-1) **67–69. See Ch. 5 Answer Appendix.**

67. $6 - h > -8$ **68.** $p - 9 < 2$ **69.** $3 \ge 4 - m$

Solve each equation by graphing. Verify your answer algebraically. (Lesson 3-2) **70–72. See Ch. 5 Answer Appendix.**

70. $2x - 7 = 4x + 9$ **71.** $5 + 3x = 7x - 11$ **72.** $2(x - 3) = 5x + 12$

73. THEME PARKS In 2006, attendance at the top 20 theme parks in North America was 119.8 million. That represents an increase of about 1.5% from 2005. What was the approximate attendance in 2005? (Lesson 2-7) **118.0 million**

If $f(x) = 4x - 3$ and $g(x) = 2x^2 + 5$, find each value. (Lesson 1-7)

74. $f(-2)$ **−11** **75.** $g(2) - 5$ **8** **76.** $f(c + 3)$ **$4c + 9$**

77. COSMETOLOGY On average, a barber received a tip of \$4 for each of 12 haircuts. Write and evaluate an expression to determine the total amount that she earned. (Lesson 1-4) **12(29.95 + 4) or 12(29.95) + 12(4); \$407.40**

Skills Review

Graph each set of numbers on a number line. **78–83. See Ch. 5 Answer Appendix.**

78. $\{-4, -2, 2, 4\}$ **79.** $\{-3, 0, 1, 5\}$

80. {integers less than 3} **81.** {integers greater than or equal to −2}

82. {integers between −3 and 4} **83.** {integers less than −1}

Differentiated Instruction OL BL

Extension Ask students to explain how you can use the graph of $y = -2x + 6$ to solve the inequality $-2x + 6 < 0$. Sample explanation: The x-intercept ($x = 3$) is the value of x where $-2x + 6 = 0$. All values of x that are more than the x-intercept are solutions of $-2x + 6 < 0$. So, $x > 3$.

4 ASSESS

Yesterday's News Have students write an explanation of how the different methods they learned for solving multi-step linear inequalities relate to the methods learned in previous lessons, such as solving multi-step linear equations and using the Distributive Property.

Formative Assessment

Check for student understanding of Lesson 5-3.

CRM Quiz 2, p. 45

Additional Answers

54b.

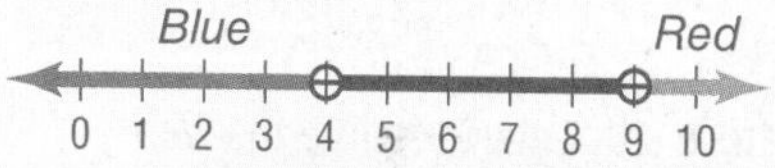

54c.

Point	$x > 4$	$x < 9$	Both are True
1	false	true	false
2	false	true	false
3	false	true	false
4	false	true	false
5	true	true	true
6	true	true	true
7	true	true	true
8	true	true	true
9	true	false	false
10	true	false	false

57. Sample answer: $2x + 4 > 2$ and $3x + 1 > -2$ both have the graph of $x > -1$.

58. $4y + 9 > -3$; it is the only inequality that does not have a solution set of $\{y \mid y > 3\}$.

59. Sample answer: The solution set for an inequality that results in a false statement is the empty set, as in $12 < -15$. The solution set for an inequality in which any value of x results in a true statement is all real numbers, as in $12 \le 12$.

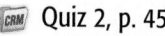

CHAPTER 5 Mid-Chapter Quiz

✓ Formative Assessment

Use the Mid-Chapter Quiz to assess students' progress in the first half of the chapter.

For problems answered incorrectly, have students review the lessons indicated in parentheses.

ExamView® Assessment Suite Customize and create multiple versions of your Mid-Chapter Test and their answer keys.

FOLDABLES® Follow-Up

Before students complete the Mid-Chapter Quiz, encourage them to review the information for Lessons 5-1 through 5-3 in their Foldables.

Additional Answers

1. $x > 12$

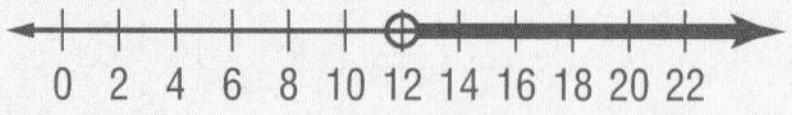

2. $m \geq 4$

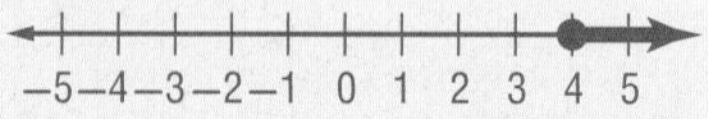

3. $p < -3$

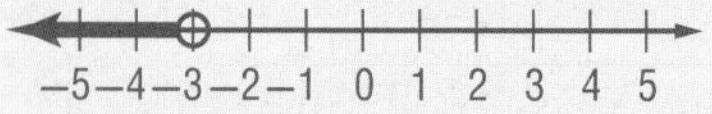

4. $t \geq 21$

CHAPTER 5 Mid-Chapter Quiz

Lessons 5-1 through 5-3

IL Learning Standards 8.B.4a, 8.D.4

Solve each inequality. Then graph it on a number line. (Lesson 5-1) **1–4. See margin.**

1. $x - 8 > 4$

2. $m + 2 \geq 6$

3. $p - 4 < -7$

4. $12 \leq t - 9$

5. CONCERTS Lupe's allowance for the month is \$60. She wants to go to a concert for which a ticket costs \$45. (Lesson 5-1)

a. Write and solve an inequality that shows how much money she can spend that month after buying a concert ticket. $m + 45 \leq 60$; $m \leq 15$

b. She spends \$9.99 on music downloads and \$2 on lunch in the cafeteria. Write and solve an inequality that shows how much she can spend after these purchases and the concert ticket. $m + 45 + 9.99 + 2 \leq 60$; $m \leq 3.01$

Define a variable, write an inequality, and solve each problem. Check your solution. (Lesson 5-2) **6–8. See Ch. 5 Answer Appendix.**

6. The sum of a number and −2 is no more than 6.

7. A number decreased by 4 is more than −1.

8. Twice a number increased by 3 is less than the number decreased by 4.

9. MULTIPLE CHOICE Jane is saving money to buy a new cell phone that costs no more than \$90. So far, she has saved \$52. How much more money does Jane need to save? (Lesson 5-2) **C**

A \$38

B more than \$38

C no more than \$38

D at least \$38

Solve each inequality. Check your solution. (Lesson 5-2)

10. $\frac{1}{3}y \geq 5$ $y \geq 15$

11. $4 < \frac{c}{5}$ $c > 20$

12. $-8x > 24$ $x < -3$

13. $2m \leq -10$ $m \leq -5$

14. $\frac{x}{2} < \frac{5}{8}$ $x < \frac{5}{4}$

15. $-9a \geq -45$ $a \leq 5$

16. $\frac{w}{6} > -3$ $w > -18$

17. $\frac{k}{7} < -2$ $k < -14$

18. ANIMALS The world's heaviest flying bird is the great bustard. A male bustard can be up to 4 feet long and weigh up to 40 pounds. (Lesson 5-2) $0 < \ell \leq 4$; $0 < w \leq 40$

a. Write inequalities to describe the ranges of lengths and weights of male bustards.

b. Male bustards are usually about four times as heavy as females. Write and solve an inequality that describes the range of weights of female bustards. $0 < 4w \leq 40$; $0 < w \leq 10$

19. GARDENING Bill is building a fence around a square garden to keep deer out. He has 60 feet of fencing. Find the maximum length of a side of the garden. (Lesson 5-3) $x \leq 15$; at most 15 ft on each side

Solve each inequality. Check your solution. (Lesson 5-3)

20. $4a - 2 > 14$ $a > 4$

21. $2x + 11 \leq 5x - 10$ $x \geq 7$

22. $-p + 4 < -9$ $p > 13$

23. $\frac{d}{4} + 1 \geq -3$ $d \geq -16$

24. $-2(4b + 1) < -3b + 8$ $b > -2$

Define a variable, write an inequality, and solve each problem. Check your solution. (Lesson 5-3)

25. Three times a number increased by 8 is no more than the number decreased by 4.

26. Two thirds of a number plus 5 is greater than 17. **25–26. See Ch. 5 Answer Appendix.**

27. MULTIPLE CHOICE Shoe rental costs \$2, and each game bowled costs \$3. How many games can Kyle bowl without spending more than \$15? (Lesson 5-3) **H**

F 2

G 3

H 4

J 5

Intervention Planner

Tier 1 On Level	Tier 2 Strategic Intervention approaching grade level	Tier 3 Intensive Intervention 2 or more grades below level
If students miss about 25% of the exercises or less,	**If** students miss about 50% of the exercises,	**If** students miss about 75% of the exercises,
Then choose a resource:	**Then** choose a resource:	**Then** use *Math Triumphs, Alg. 1*
SE Lessons 5-1, 5-2, and 5-3 **CRM** Skills Practice, pp. 7, 13, and 19 **TE** Chapter Project, p. 280 **IL Math Online** Self-Check Quiz	**CRM** Study Guide and Intervention, Chapter 5, pp. 5, 11, and 17 *Quick Review Math Handbook* **IL Math Online** Extra Examples, Personal Tutor, Homework Help	**IL Math Online** Extra Examples, Personal Tutor, Homework Help, Review Vocabulary

EXPLORE 5-4 Algebra Lab
Reading Compound Statements

A compound statement is made up of two simple statements connected by the word *and* or *or*. Before you can determine whether a compound statement is true or false, you must understand what the words *and* and *or* mean.

A spider has eight legs, *and* a dog has five legs.

For a compound statement connected by the word *and* to be true, both simple statements must be true.

A spider has eight legs. ⟶ true

A dog has five legs. ⟶ false

Since one of the statements is false, the compound statement is false.

A compound statement connected by the word *or* may be *exclusive* or *inclusive*. For example, the statement "With your lunch, you may have milk *or* juice," is exclusive. In everyday language, *or* means one or the other, but not both. However, in mathematics, *or* is inclusive. It means one or the other or both.

A spider has eight legs, *or* a dog has five legs.

For a compound statement connected by the word *or* to be true, at least one of the simple statements must be true. Since it is true that a spider has eight legs, the compound statement is true.

Exercises

1–10. See Ch. 5 Answer Appendix.

Is each compound statement *true* or *false*? Explain.

1. Most top 20 movies in 2004 were rated PG-13, *or* most top 20 movies in 2002 were rated G.
2. In 2005 more top 20 movies were rated PG than were rated G, *and* more were rated PG than rated PG-13.
3. For the years shown most top 20 movies are rated PG-13, *and* no top 20 movies in 2002 were rated R.
4. No top 20 movies in 2005 were rated G, *or* most top 20 movies in 2005 were *not* rated PG.
5. $11 < 5$ or $9 < 7$
6. $-2 > 0$ and $3 < 7$
7. $5 > 0$ and $-3 < 0$
8. $-2 > -3$ or $0 = 0$
9. $8 \neq 8$ or $-2 > -5$
10. $5 > 10$ and $4 > -2$

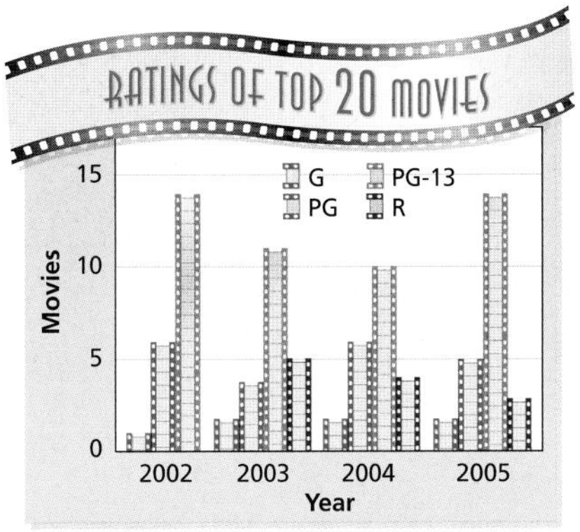

Source: National Association of Theater Owners

EXPLORE 5-4 Lesson Notes

1 FOCUS

Objective Identify compound statements connected by the word *and* or *or* as true or false.

Teaching Tip

Before the activity, ask students to recall the definition of a compound sentence from their language arts studies. Students should know that a compound sentence is a sentence made up of two independent clauses joined by a coordinating conjunction, punctuation mark, or both. Explain that the compound statements in this activity are made up of two independent clauses joined by *and* or *or*.

2 TEACH

Working in Cooperative Groups

Have students work in groups of three or four, mixing abilities, to complete Exercises 1–2 and 5–6.

Ask:

- What is a true compound statement that is connected by the word *and* that you can make about the legs of a spider and a dog? A spider has eight legs, *and* a dog has 4 legs.
- What is another true compound statement connected by the word *or* that you can make about the legs of a spider and a dog? A spider has eight legs, *or* a dog has 4 legs.
- Under what conditions is a compound statement that uses the word *or* false? It is false only if both statements are false.

Practice Have students complete Exercises 3–4 and 7–10.

3 ASSESS

Formative Assessment

Use Exercises 3 and 4 to assess whether students understand the conditions under which a compound statement using *and* or *or* is true or false.

From Concrete to Abstract

In Exercises 5–10, students apply their understanding of compound statements to compound inequalities.

5-4 Lesson Notes

1 FOCUS

Vertical Alignment

Before Lesson 5-4
Solve absolute value equations with two cases.

Lesson 5-4
Solve compound inequalities containing the word *and* and graph their solution sets.
Solve compound inequalities containing the word *or* and graph their solution sets.

After Lesson 5-4
Solve and graph systems of inequalities.

2 TEACH

Scaffolding Questions

Have students read the *Why?* section of the lesson.

Ask:

- What inequality symbol represents the term *at least* when we say that a rider must be at least 52 inches? $\geq$
- What is the minimum height a rider could be? 52 in.
- What is the maximum height a rider could be? 72 in.
- Could a rider who is 60 inches tall ride? Explain. Yes, because that rider would be more than 52 in. but less than 72 in.

5-4 Solving Compound Inequalities

Then
You solved absolute value equations with two cases. (Lesson 2-5)

Now
- Solve compound inequalities containing the word *and*, and graph their solution set.
- Solve compound inequalities containing the word *or*, and graph their solution set.

IL Learning Standards
8.B.4a Represent algebraic concepts with physical materials, words, diagrams, tables, graphs, equations and inequalities and use appropriate technology.
8.D.4 Formulate and solve linear and quadratic equations and **linear inequalities algebraically** and investigate nonlinear inequalities using graphs, tables, calculators and computers. *Also addresses 7.A.4a.*

New Vocabulary
compound inequality
intersection
union

IL Math Online
glencoe.com
- Extra Examples
- Personal Tutor
- Self-Check Quiz
- Homework Help
- Math in Motion

Why?

To ride the Mind Eraser roller coaster at Six Flags in Baltimore, Maryland, you must be at least 52 inches tall, and your height cannot exceed 72 inches. If h represents the height of a rider, we can write two inequalities to represent this.

at least 52 inches	cannot exceed 72 inches
$h \geq 52$	$h \leq 72$

The inequalities $h \geq 52$ and $h \leq 72$ can be combined and written without using *and* as $52 \leq h \leq 72$.

Inequalities Containing *and* When considered together, two inequalities such as $h \geq 52$ and $h \leq 72$ form a **compound inequality**. A compound inequality containing *and* is only true if both inequalities are true. Its graph is where the graphs of the two inequalities overlap. This is called the **intersection** of the two graphs.

The intersection can be found by graphing each inequality and then determining where the graphs intersect.

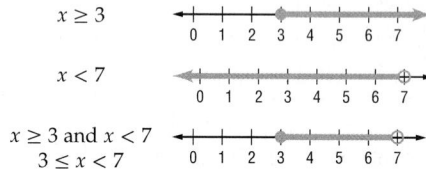

$x \geq 3$

$x < 7$

$x \geq 3$ and $x < 7$
$3 \leq x < 7$

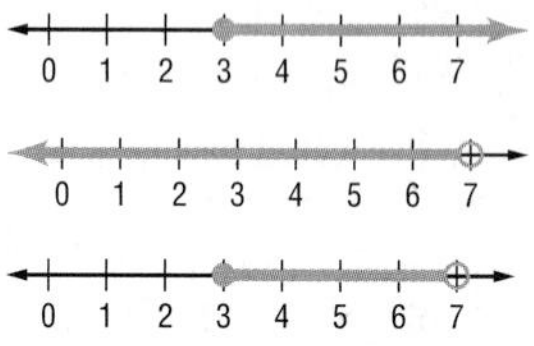

The statement $3 \leq x < 7$ can be read as *x is greater than or equal to 3 and less than 7* or *x is between 3 and 7 including 3*.

EXAMPLE 1 Solve and Graph an Intersection

Solve $-2 \leq x - 3 < 4$. Then graph the solution set.

First, express $-2 \leq x - 3 < 4$ using *and*. Then solve each inequality.

$-2 \leq x - 3$	and	$x - 3 < 4$	**Write the inequalities.**
$-2 + 3 \leq x - 3 + 3$		$x - 3 + 3 < 4 + 3$	**Add 3 to each side.**
$1 \leq x$		$x < 7$	**Simplify.**

The solution set is $\{x \mid 1 \leq x < 7\}$. Now graph the solution set.

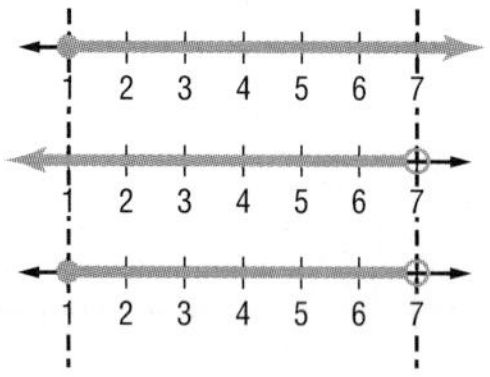

Graph $1 \leq x$ or $x \geq 1$.

Graph $x < 7$.

Find the intersection of the graphs.

Lesson 5-4 Resources

Resource	Approaching-Level	On-Level	Beyond-Level	English Learners
Teacher Edition	• Differentiated Instruction, p. 308	• Differentiated Instruction, p. 309	• Differentiated Instruction, p. 309	• Differentiated Instruction, p. 308
Chapter Resource Masters	• Study Guide and Intervention, pp. 23–24 • Skills Practice, p. 25 • Practice, p. 26 • Word Problem Practice, p. 27	• Study Guide and Intervention, pp. 23–24 • Skills Practice, p. 25 • Practice, p. 26 • Word Problem Practice, p. 27 • Enrichment, p. 28	• Practice, p. 26 • Word Problem Practice, p. 27 • Enrichment, p. 28	• Study Guide and Intervention, pp. 23–24 • Skills Practice, p. 26 • Practice, p. 26 • Word Problem Practice, p. 27
Transparencies	• 5-Minute Check Transparency 5-4	• 5-Minute Check Transparency 5-4	• 5-Minute Check Transparency 5-4	• 5-Minute Check Transparency 5-4
Other	• Study Notebook • Teaching Algebra with Manipulatives	• Study Notebook • Teaching Algebra with Manipulatives	• Study Notebook	• Study Notebook • Teaching Algebra with Manipulatives

Check Your Progress

Solve each compound inequality. Then graph the solution set.

1A. $y - 3 \geq -11$ and $y - 3 \leq -8$ **1B.** $6 \leq r + 7 < 10$

Personal Tutor glencoe.com

1A. $\{y \mid -8 \leq y \leq -5\}$

1B. $\{r \mid -1 \leq r < 3\}$

Inequalities Containing *or* Another type of compound inequality contains the word *or*. A compound inequality containing *or* is true if at least one of the inequalities is true. Its graph is the **union** of the graphs of two inequalities.

$x > 2$

$x \leq -1$

$x > 2$ or $x \leq -1$

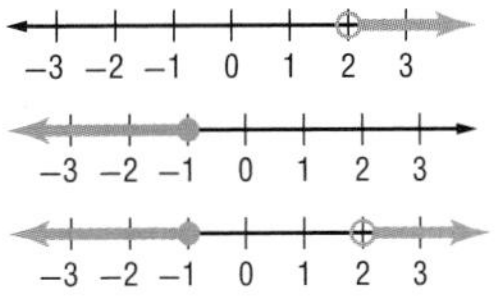

When solving problems involving inequalities, *within* is meant to be inclusive, so use $\geq$ or $\leq$. *Between* is meant to be exclusive, so use $<$ or $>$.

Real-World EXAMPLE 2 Write and Graph a Compound Inequality

SOUND The human ear can only detect sounds between the frequencies 20 Hertz and 20,000 Hertz. Write and graph a compound inequality that describes the frequency of sounds humans cannot hear.

The problem states that humans can hear the frequencies between 20 Hz and 20,000 Hz. We are asked to find the frequencies humans cannot hear.

Words	The frequency	is at most	20 Hertz	or	The frequency	is at least	20,000 Hertz.
Variable	Let *f* be the frequency.						
Inequality	f	$<$	20	or	f	$>$	20,000

Now, graph the solution set.

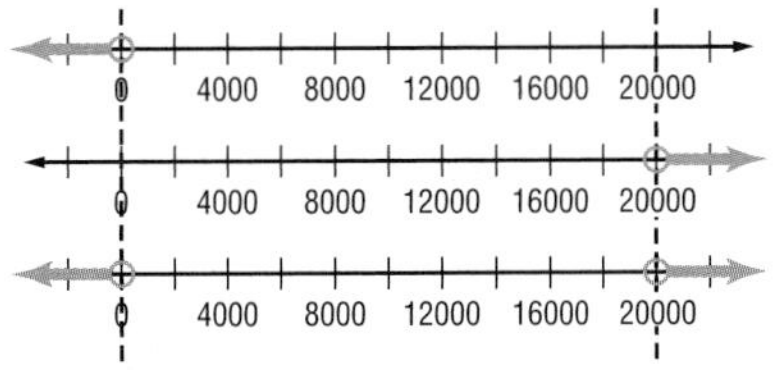
Graph $f < 20$.
Graph $f > 20,000$.
Find the union.

Notice that the graphs do not intersect. Humans cannot hear sounds at a frequency less than 20 Hertz or greater than 20,000 Hertz. The compound inequality is $\{f \mid f < 20 \text{ or } f > 20{,}000\}$.

2. $11.2 \leq h \leq 11.4$

Check Your Progress

2. MANUFACTURING A company is manufacturing an action figure that must be at least 11.2 centimeters and at most 11.4 centimeters tall. Write and graph a compound inequality that describes how tall the action figure can be.

Personal Tutor glencoe.com

ReadingMath

At Most The phrase *at most* in Example 2 indicates $\leq$. It could also have been phrased as *no more than* or *less than or equal to.*

Math *in Motion,* Animation glencoe.com

Inequalities Containing *and*

Example 1 shows how to solve a compound inequality containing *and* and how to graph the solution set.

Formative Assessment

Use the Check Your Progress exercises after each example to determine students' understanding of concepts.

Watch Out!

Student Misconceptions Students may assume that the solution set for $\{x \mid 1 \leq x < 7\}$ includes 7. However, because less than 7 does not include 7, the solution set does not include 7.

Additional Examples

1 Solve $7 < z + 2 \leq 11$. Then graph the solution set. $\{z \mid 5 < z \leq 9\}$

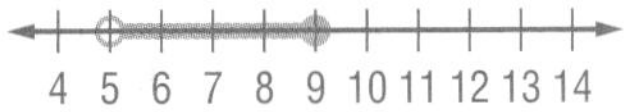

2 TRAVEL A ski resort has several types of hotel rooms and cabins. The hotel rooms cost at most \$89 per night, and the cabins cost at least \$109 per night. Write and graph a compound inequality that describes the amount a guest would pay per night at the resort. $\{n \mid n \leq 89$ or $n \geq 109\}$, where n is the amount a guest pays per night

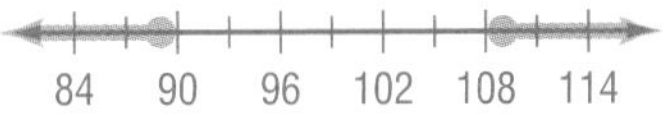

Additional Examples also in Interactive Classroom PowerPoint® Presentations

Tips for New Teachers

Intersection and Union Symbols Point out that the symbol for intersection is $\cap$. The solution set for Example 1 can be written as $\{x \mid x \geq 1\} \cap \{x \mid x < 7\}$. The symbol for union is $\cup$. The solution set for Example 3 can be written as $\{m \mid m \geq -3\} \cup \{m \mid m > 5\}$.

Focus on Mathematical Content

Conjunctions When the word *and* is used to join two inequalities to form a compound inequality, the resulting sentence is called a *conjunction*. To solve a conjunction, find the values of the variable for which *both* sentences are true.

Inequalities Containing *or*

Example 2 shows how to write and graph a compound inequality containing *or* for a real-world situation. **Example 3** shows how to solve and graph a compound inequality that involves *or*.

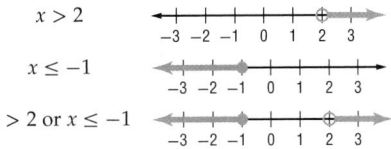

Additional Example

3 Solve $4k - 7 \leq 25$ or $12 - 9k \geq 30$. Then graph the solution set. $\{k \mid k \leq 8\}$

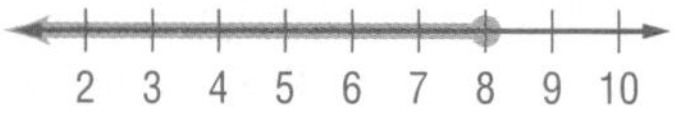

TEACH with TECH

DOCUMENT CAMERA Choose a student to work through an example using the document camera. Be sure the student uses a graph to find the solution to the inequality.

Tips for New Teachers

Reasoning Students may confuse the meaning of the words *intersection* and *union*. Have them compare the definitions of these two words in real-world situations. For intersection, students may suggest two roads overlapping at an intersection. For union, they might suggest the 50 states coming together to form a union.

3 PRACTICE

Formative Assessment

Use Exercises 1–5 to check for understanding.

Use the chart at the bottom of this page to customize assignments for your students.

Additional Answers

16. Sample answer: Let r = rate of speed, then $40 \leq r \leq 70$.

17. Sample answer: Let x = the smaller of two consecutive odd numbers, then $8 \leq 2x + 2 \leq 24$; $3 \leq x \leq 11$; 3, 5; 5, 7; 7, 9; 9, 11; 11, 13

EXAMPLE 3 Solve and Graph a Union

Solve $-2m + 7 \leq 13$ or $5m + 12 > 37$. Then graph the solution set.

$-2m + 7 \leq 13$	or	$5m + 12 > 37$
$-2m + 7 - 7 \leq 13 - 7$	**Subtract.**	$5m + 12 - 12 > 37 - 12$
$-2m \leq 6$	**Simplify.**	$5m > 25$
$\frac{-2m}{-2} \geq \frac{6}{-2}$	**Divide.**	$\frac{5m}{5} > \frac{25}{5}$
$m \geq -3$	**Simplify.**	$m > 5$

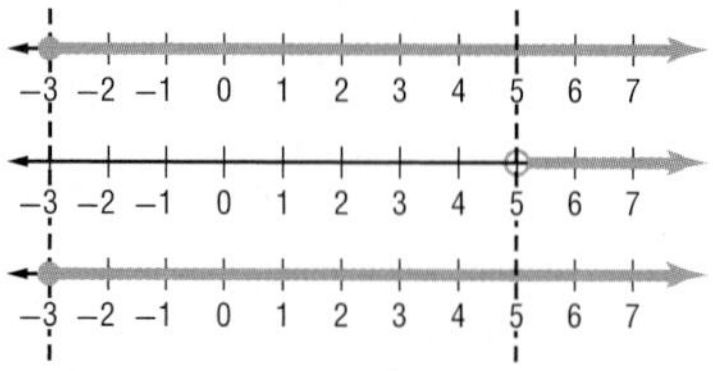

Graph $m \geq -3$.

Graph $m > 5$.

Find the union.

> **StudyTip**
>
> **Intersections and Unions** The graphs of compound inequalities containing *and* will be an intersection. The graphs of compound inequalities containing *or* will be a union.

Notice that the graph of $m \geq -3$ contains every point in the graph of $m > 5$. So, the union is the graph of $m \geq -3$. The solution set is $\{m \mid m \geq -3\}$.

3A. $\{a \mid a < 3$ or $a \geq 4\}$

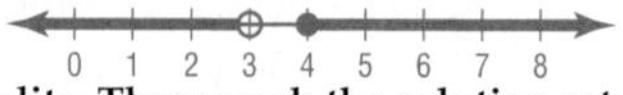

Check Your Progress

Solve each compound inequality. Then graph the solution set.

3A. $a + 1 < 4$ or $a - 1 \geq 3$

3B. $x \leq 9$ or $2 + 4x < 10$

Personal Tutor glencoe.com

3B. $\{x \mid x \leq 9\}$

Check Your Understanding

1–4. See Ch. 5 Answer Appendix.

Examples 1 and 3 pp. 304, 306

Solve each compound inequality. Then graph the solution set.

1. $4 \leq p - 8$ and $p - 14 \leq 2$

2. $r + 6 < -8$ or $r - 3 > -10$

3. $4a + 7 \geq 31$ or $a > 5$

4. $2 \leq g + 4 < 7$

Example 2 p. 305

5. BIKES The recommended air pressure for the tires of a mountain bike is at least 35 pounds per square inch (psi), but no more than 80 pounds per square inch. If a bike's tires have 24 pounds per square inch, what is the recommended range of air that should be put into the tires? **11 psi ≤ x ≤ 56 psi**

Practice and Problem Solving

● = **Step-by-Step Solutions** begin on page R12. **Extra Practice** begins on page 815.

6–15. See Ch. 5 Answer Appendix.

Examples 1 and 3 pp. 304, 306

Solve each compound inequality. Then graph the solution set.

6. $f - 6 < 5$ and $f - 4 \geq 2$

7. $n + 2 \leq -5$ and $n + 6 \geq -6$

8. $y - 1 \geq 7$ or $y + 3 < -1$

9. $t + 14 \geq 15$ or $t - 9 < -10$

10. $-5 < 3p + 7 \leq 22$

11. $-3 \leq 7c + 4 < 18$

12. $5h + -4 \geq 6$ and $7h + 11 < 32$

13. $22 \geq 4m - 2$ or $5 - 3m \leq -13$

14. $-4a + 13 \geq 29$ and $10 < 6a - 14$

15. $-y + 5 \geq 9$ or $3y + 4 < -5$

Differentiated Homework Options

Level	Assignment		Two-Day Option	
AL Basic	6–17, 39–41, 43–72	7–17 odd, 44–47	6–16 even, 39–41, 43, 48–72
OL Core	7–27 odd, 28–41, 43–72	6–17, 44–47	18–41, 43, 48–72
BL Advanced	18–63, (optional: 64–72)		

Example 2 p. 305

16–17. See margin.

16. SPEED The posted speed limit on an interstate highway is shown. Write an inequality that represents the sign. Graph the inequality.

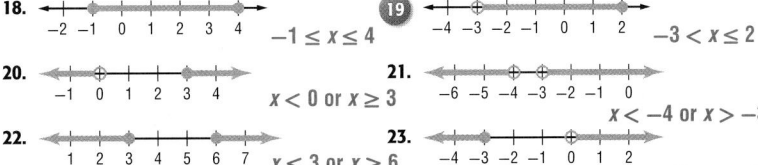

17. NUMBER THEORY Find all sets of two consecutive positive odd integers with a sum that is at least 8 and less than 24.

B

Write a compound inequality for each graph.

18. 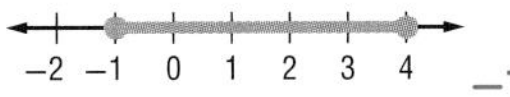

$-1 \le x \le 4$

19. 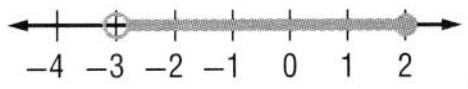

$-3 < x \le 2$

20. 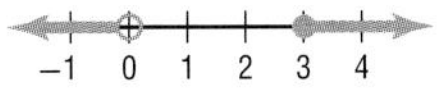

$x < 0$ or $x \ge 3$

21. 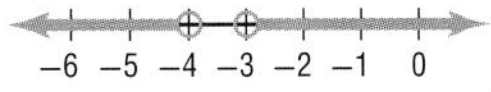

$x < -4$ or $x > -3$

22. 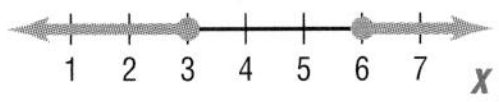

$x \le 3$ or $x \ge 6$

23. 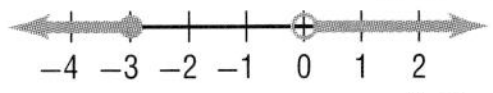

$x \le -3$ or $x > 0$

Solve each compound inequality. Then graph the solution set. 24–27. See Ch. 5 Answer Appendix.

24. $3b + 2 < 5b - 6 \le 2b + 9$

25. $-2a + 3 \ge 6a - 1 > 3a - 10$

26. $10m - 7 < 17m$ or $-6m > 36$

27. $5n - 1 < -16$ or $-3n - 1 < 8$

28. COUPON Juanita has a coupon for 10% off any digital camera at a local electronics store. She is looking at digital cameras that range in price from \$100 to \$250.

a. How much are the cameras after the coupon is used? from \$90 to \$225 inclusive

b. If the tax amount is 6.5%, how much should Juanita expect to spend? from \$95.85 to \$239.63 inclusive

Define a variable, write an inequality, and solve each problem. Then check your solution. 29–32. Sample answers given. Let n = the number.

29. Eight less than a number is no more than 14 and no less than 5.

30. The sum of 3 times a number and 4 is between −8 and 10.

31. The product of −5 and a number is greater than 35 or less than 10.

32. One half a number is greater than 0 and less than or equal to 1.

29. $5 \le n - 8 \le 14$; $\{n \mid 13 \le n \le 22\}$

30. $-8 < 3n + 4 < 10$; $\{n \mid -4 < n < 2\}$

31. $-5n > 35$ or $-5n < 10$; $\{n \mid n < -7$ or $n > -2\}$

32. $0 < \frac{1}{2}n \le 1$; $\{n \mid 0 < n \le 2\}$

33. SNAKES Most snakes live where the temperature ranges from 75°F to 90°F, inclusive. Write an inequality to represent temperatures where snakes will *not* thrive. $t < 75$ or $t > 90$

34. FUNDRAISING Yumas is selling gift cards to raise money for a class trip. He can earn prizes depending on how many cards he sells. So far, he has sold 34 cards. How many more does he need to sell to earn a prize in category 4? from 12 to 26, inclusive

Cards	Prize
1–15	1
16–30	2
31–45	3
46–60	4
+61	5

Real-World Link

The organization Field Trip Earth monitors the locations of Atlantic sea turtles. This data allows the scientists to track migration patterns as part of a wildlife conservation project.

Source: Field Trip Earth

35. TURTLES Atlantic sea turtle eggs that incubate below 23°C or above 33°C rarely hatch. Write an inequality for the temperatures at which the eggs should be incubated. $23 \le t \le 33$

36. GEOMETRY The *Triangle Inequality Theorem* states that the sum of the measures of any two sides of a triangle is greater than the measure of the third side. a. $x + 9 > 4$, $x > -5$; $x + 4 > 9$, $x > 5$; $4 + 9 > x$, $x < 13$

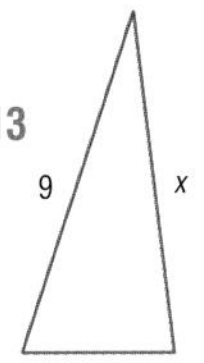

a. Write and solve three inequalities to express the relationships among the measures of the sides of the triangle shown at the right.

b. What are four possible lengths for the third side of the triangle? Sample answer: 6, 9, 10, 11

c. Write a compound inequality for the possible values of x. $5 < x < 13$

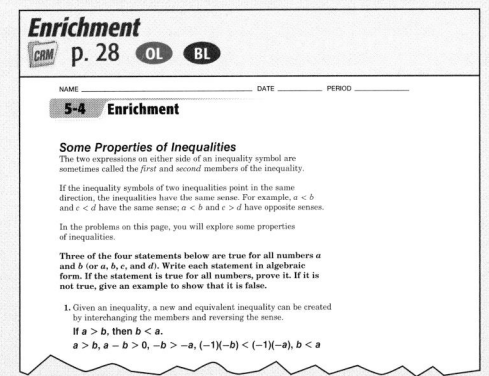

Study Guide and Intervention
CRM pp. 23–24 AL OL ELL

NAME ______ DATE ______ PERIOD ______

5-4 Study Guide and Intervention

Solving Compound Inequalities

Inequalities Containing *and* A compound inequality containing *and* is true only if both inequalities are true. The graph of a compound inequality containing *and* is the **intersection** of the graphs of the two inequalities. Every solution of the compound inequality must be a solution of both inequalities.

Example 1 Graph the solution set of $x < 2$ and $x \ge -1$.

−3 −2 −1 0 1 2 3 Graph $x < 2$.

−3 −2 −1 0 1 2 3 Graph $x \ge -1$.

−3 −2 −1 0 1 2 3 Find the intersection.

The solution set is $\{x \mid -1 \le x < 2\}$.

Example 2 Solve $-1 < x + 2 < 3$. Then graph the solution set.

$-1 < x + 2$ and $x + 2 < 3$

$-1 - 2 < x + 2 - 2$ $x + 2 - 2 < 3 - 2$

$-3 < x$ $x < 1$

−4 −3 −2 −1 0 1 2 Graph $x > -3$.

−4 −3 −2 −1 0 1 2 Graph $x < 1$.

−4 −3 −2 −1 0 1 2 Find the intersection.

The solution set is $\{x \mid -3 < x < 1\}$.

Exercises

Graph the solution set of each compound inequality.

1. $b > -1$ and $b \le 3$ (−4 −3 −2 −1 0 1 2 3 4)
2. $2 \ge q \ge -5$ (−6 −5 −4 −3 −2 −1 0 1 2)
3. $x > -3$ and $x \le 4$ (−4 −3 −2 −1 0 1 2 3 4)
4. $-2 \le p < 4$ (−3 −2 −1 0 1 2 3 4 5)
5. $-3 < d$ and $d < 2$ (−4 −3 −2 −1 0 1 2 3 4)
6. $-1 \le p \le 3$ (−4 −3 −2 −1 0 1 2 3 4)

Solve each compound inequality. Then graph the solution set.

7. $4 < w + 3 \le 5$ $\{w \mid 1 < w \le 2\}$ (−4 −3 −2 −1 0 1 2 3 4)
8. $-3 \le p - 5 < 2$ $\{p \mid 2 \le p < 7\}$ (0 1 2 3 4 5 6 7 8)
9. $-4 < x + 2 \le -2$ $\{x \mid -6 < x \le -4\}$ (−7 −6 −5 −4 −3 −2 −1 0 1)
10. $y - 1 < 2$ and $y + 2 \ge 1$ $\{y \mid -1 \le y < 3\}$ (−4 −3 −2 −1 0 1 2 3 4)
11. $n - 2 > -3$ and $n + 4 < 6$ $\{n \mid -1 < n < 2\}$ (−4 −3 −2 −1 0 1 2 3 4)
12. $d - 3 < 6d + 12 < 2d + 32$ $\{d \mid -3 < d < 5\}$ (−3 −2 −1 0 1 2 3 4 5)

Lesson 5-4

Chapter 5   23   Glencoe Algebra 1

Practice
CRM p. 26 AL OL BL ELL

NAME ______ DATE ______ PERIOD ______

5-4 Practice

Solving Compound Inequalities

Graph the solution set of each compound inequality.

1. $-4 \le n \le 1$ (−6 −5 −4 −3 −2 −1 0 1 2)
2. $x > 0$ or $x < 3$ (−4 −3 −2 −1 0 1 2 3 4)
3. $g < -3$ or $g \ge 4$ (−4 −3 −2 −1 0 1 2 3 4)
4. $-4 \le p \le 4$ (−4 −3 −2 −1 0 1 2 3 4)

Write a compound inequality for each graph.

5. (−4 −3 −2 −1 0 1 2 3 4) $x \le -3$ or $x \ge 3$
6. (−2 −1 0 1 2 3 4 5 6) $x < 2$ or $x \ge 3$
7. (−2 −1 0 1 2 3 4 5 6) $0 \le x < 5$
8. (−6 −5 −4 −3 −2 −1 0 1 2) $-5 < x < 0$

Solve each compound inequality. Then graph the solution set.

9. $k - 3 < -7$ or $k + 5 \ge 8$ $\{k \mid k < -4$ or $k \ge 3\}$ (−4 −3 −2 −1 0 1 2 3 4)
10. $-n < 2$ or $2n - 3 > 5$ $\{n \mid n > -2\}$ (−4 −3 −2 −1 0 1 2 3 4)
11. $5 < 3h + 2 \le 11$ $\{h \mid 1 < h \le 3\}$ (−4 −3 −2 −1 0 1 2 3 4)
12. $2c - 4 > -6$ and $3c + 1 < 13$ $\{c \mid -1 < c < 4\}$ (−2 −1 0 1 2 3 4 5 6)

Define a variable, write an inequality, and solve each problem. Check your solution. 13–14. Sample answer: Let n = the number.

13. Two times a number plus one is greater than five and less than seven.
$5 < 2n + 1 < 7$; $\{n \mid 2 < n < 3\}$

14. A number minus one is at most nine, or two times the number is at least twenty-four.
$n - 1 \le 9$ or $2n \ge 24$; $\{n \mid n \le 10$ or $n \ge 12\}$

15. **METEOROLOGY** Strong winds called the prevailing westerlies blow from west to east in a belt from 40° to 60° latitude in both the Northern and Southern Hemispheres.

a. Write an inequality to represent the latitude of the prevailing westerlies.
$\{w \mid 40 \le w \le 60\}$

b. Write an inequality to represent the latitudes where the prevailing westerlies are *not* located. $\{w \mid w < 40$ or $w > 60\}$

16. **NUTRITION** A cookie contains 9 grams of fat. If you eat no fewer than 4 and no more than 7 cookies, how many grams of fat will you consume?
between 36 g and 63 g inclusive

Chapter 5   26   Glencoe Algebra 1

Word Problem Practice
CRM p. 27 AL OL BL ELL

NAME ______ DATE ______ PERIOD ______

5-4 Word Problem Practice

Solving Compound Inequalities

1. **WEATHER** Ken saw this graph in the newspaper weather forecast. It shows the predicted temperature range for the following day. Write an inequality to represent the number line graph.

50°F 52° 54° 56° 58° 60° 62° 64° 66° 68° 70°

$54 \le x \le 68$

2. **POOLS** The pH of a person's eyes is 7.2. Therefore, the ideal pH for the water in a swimming pool is between 7.0 and 7.6. Write an inequality to represent pH levels that could cause physical discomfort to a person's eyes.
$x \le 7.0$ or $x \ge 7.6$

3. **STORE SIGNS** In Randy's town, street-side signs themselves must be exactly 8 feet high. When mounted on poles, the signs must be shorter than 20 feet or taller than 35 feet so that they do not interfere with the power and phone lines. Write a compound inequality to represent the possible height of the poles.

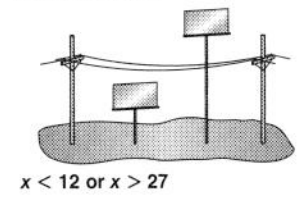

$x < 12$ or $x > 27$

4. **HEALTH** The human heart circulates from 770,000 to 1,600,000 gallons of blood through a person's body every year. How many gallons of blood does the heart circulate through the body in one day? between 2110 and 4384 gal

5. **HEALTH** Body mass index (BMI) is a measure of weight status. The BMI of a person over 20 years old is calculated using the following formula.
$\text{BMI} = 703 \times \frac{\text{weight in pounds}}{(\text{height in inches})^2}$
The table below shows the meaning of different BMI measures.

BMI	Weight Status
less than 18.5	underweight
18.5 – 24.9	normal
25 – 29.9	overweight
more than 30	obese

Source: Centers for Disease Control

a. Write a compound inequality to represent the normal BMI range.
$18.5 \le x < 25$

b. Write a compound inequality to represent an adult weight that is within the healthy BMI range for a person 6 feet tall.
$136.4 \le w \le 183.6$

Lesson 5-4

Chapter 5   27   Glencoe Algebra 1

Enrichment
CRM p. 28 OL BL

NAME ______ DATE ______ PERIOD ______

5-4 Enrichment

Some Properties of Inequalities

The two expressions on either side of an inequality symbol are sometimes called the *first* and *second* members of the inequality.

If the inequality symbols of two inequalities point in the same direction, the inequalities have the same sense. For example, $a < b$ and $c < d$ have the same sense; $a < b$ and $c > d$ have opposite senses.

In the problems on this page, you will explore some properties of inequalities.

Three of the four statements below are true for all numbers a and b (or a, b, c, and d). Write each statement in algebraic form. If the statement is true for all numbers, prove it. If it is not true, give an example to show that it is false.

1. Given an inequality, a new and equivalent inequality can be created by interchanging the members and reversing the sense.
If $a > b$, then $b < a$.
$a > b$, $a - b > 0$, $-b > -a$, $(-1)(-b) < (-1)(-a)$, $b < a$

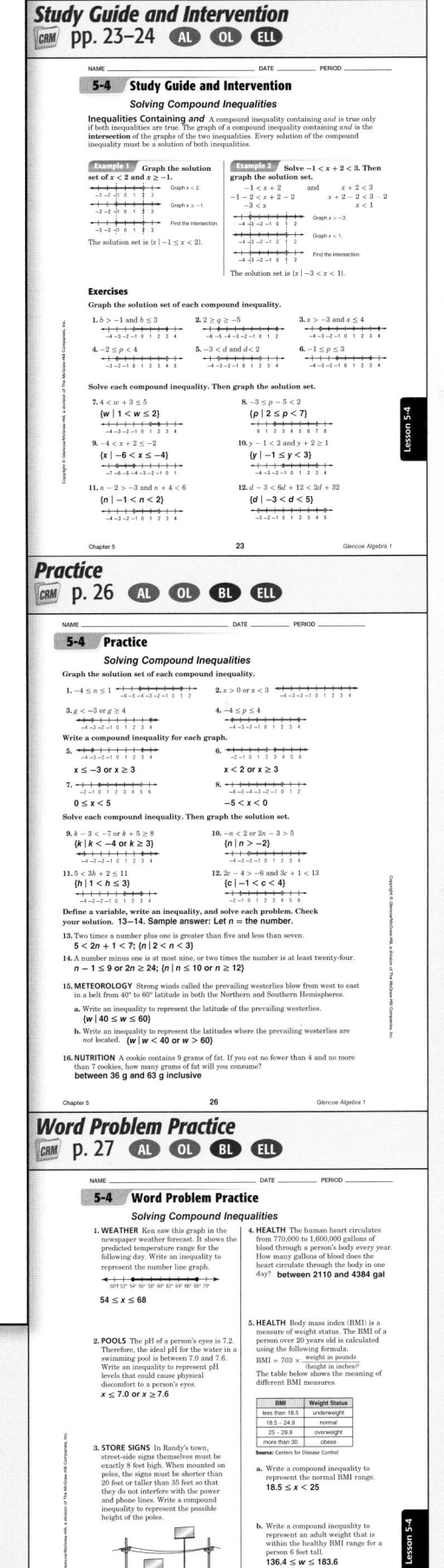

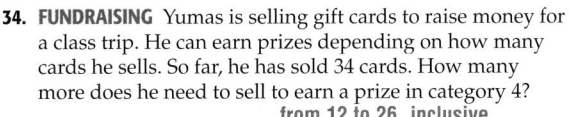

Multiple Representations In Exercise 38, students use a table of measures and logical analysis to compare the error in length measures.

Watch Out!

Find the Error For Exercise 39, point out that Chloe and Jonas show different results for the first step in the solution, so students should examine what needs to be done first to solve the inequality. An examination reveals that both Chloe and Jonas added 5 to only one side of the inequality. Remind students that you must perform the same operation on both sides of the inequality for the inequality to remain true.

Real-World Link

Between 2001 and 2004, a total of nine hurricanes struck the mainland United States. Of these, three were classified as Category 3, 4, or 5.

Source: National Weather Service

37. **HURRICANES** The Saffir-Simpson Hurricane Scale rates hurricanes on a scale from 1 to 5 based on their wind speed.

Category	Wind Speed (mph)	Example (year)
1	74–95	Gaston (2004)
2	96–110	Frances (2004)
3	111–130	Ivan (2004)
4	131–155	Charley (2004)
5	> 155	Andrew (1992)

a. Write a compound inequality for the wind speeds of a category 3 and a category 4 hurricane. $111 \le x \le 130$; $131 \le x \le 155$

b. What is the intersection of the two graphs of the inequalities you found in part **a**? $\varnothing$

38. **MULTIPLE REPRESENTATIONS** In this problem, you will investigate measurements. The **absolute error** of a measurement is equal to one half the unit of measure. The **relative error** of a measure is the ratio of the absolute error to the expected measure.

a. TABULAR Copy and complete the table.

Measure	Absolute Error	Relative Error
14.3 cm	$\frac{1}{2}(0.1) = 0.05$ cm	$\frac{\text{absolute error}}{\text{expected measure}} = \frac{0.05 \text{ cm}}{14.3 \text{ cm}}$ ≈ 0.0035 or 0.4%
1.85 cm	0.005 cm	≈ 0.0027 or 0.3%
61.2 cm	0.05 cm	≈ 0.00082 or 0.08%
237 cm	0.5 cm	≈ 0.0021 or 0.2%

b. ANALYTICAL You measured a length of 12.8 centimeters. Compute the absolute error and then write the range of possible measures. 0.05 cm; 12.75 cm – 12.085 cm

c. LOGICAL To what precision would you have to measure a length in centimeters to have an absolute error of less than 0.05 centimeter? to the nearest hundredths place

d. ANALYTICAL To find the relative error of an area or volume calculation, add the relative errors of each linear measure. If the measures of the sides of a rectangular box are 6.5 centimeters, 7.2 centimeters, and 10.25 centimeters, what is the relative error of the volume of the box? 0.105 cm

H.O.T. Problems Use Higher-Order Thinking Skills

39. **ERROR ANALYSIS** Chloe and Jonas are solving $3 < 2x - 5 < 7$. Is either of them correct? Explain your reasoning.

Chloe	Jonas
$3 < 2x - 5 < 7$	$3 < 2x - 5 < 7$
$3 < 2x < 12$	$8 < 2x < 7$
$\frac{3}{2} < x < 6$	$4 < x < \frac{7}{2}$

Neither; Chloe did not add 5 to 3, and Jonas did not add 5 to 7.

40. **REASONING** Write a compound inequality for which the graph is the empty set and one for which the graph is the set of all real numbers.

41. **OPEN ENDED** Create an example of a compound inequality containing *or* that has infinitely many solutions. Sample answer: $x \le 2$ or $x \ge 4$

42. **CHALLENGE** Determine whether the following statement is *always, sometimes,* or *never* true. Explain. *The graph of a compound inequality that involves an* or *statement is bounded on the left and right by two values of x.*

43. **WRITING IN MATH** Give an example of a compound inequality you might encounter at an amusement park. Does the example represent an intersection or a union?

40. Empty set: sample answer: $x \le -4$ and $x \ge 1$; All real numbers: sample answer: $x \le 5$ or $x \ge 1$

42. Sometimes; the graph of $x > 2$ or $x < 5$ includes the entire number line.

43. Sample answer: The speed at which a roller coaster runs while staying on the track could represent a compound inequality that is an intersection.

Differentiated Instruction

AL BL ELL

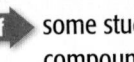

If some students are overwhelmed trying to discern whether word problems represent compound inequalities that contain *and* or *or* and whether the inequalities are inclusive or exclusive,

Then pair these students with more advanced students to discuss and solve Exercises 33–37. Encourage both students to take an active role in solving the problems.

PSAE PRACTICE 8.11.16, 7.11.03, 8.11.04, 8.11.17

44. What is the solution set of the inequality $-7 < x + 2 < 4$? **C**

A $\{x \mid -5 < x < 6\}$ C $\{x \mid -9 < x < 2\}$
B $\{x \mid -5 < x < 2\}$ D $\{x \mid -9 < x < 6\}$

45. GEOMETRY What is the surface area of the rectangular solid? **H**

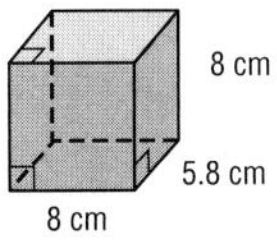

F 249.6 cm^2
G 278.4 cm^2
H 313.6 cm^2
J 371.2 cm^2

46. GRIDDED RESPONSE What is the next term in the sequence? **38/17**

$$\frac{13}{2}, \frac{18}{5}, \frac{23}{8}, \frac{28}{11}, \frac{33}{14}, \ldots$$

47. After paying a $15 membership fee, members of a video club can rent movies for $2. Nonmembers can rent movies for $4. What is the least number of movies which must be rented for it to be less expensive for members? **B**

A 9 C 7
B 8 D 6

Spiral Review

48. BABYSITTING Marilyn earns $150 per month delivering newspapers plus $7 an hour babysitting. If she wants to earn at least $300 this month, how many hours will she have to babysit? (Lesson 5-3) **at least 22 hours**

49. MAGAZINES Carlos has earned more than $260 selling magazine subscriptions. Each subscription was sold for $12. How many did Carlos sell? (Lesson 5-2) **at least 22 subscriptions**

50. PUNCH Raquel is mixing lemon-lime soda and a fruit juice blend that is 45% juice. If she uses 3 quarts of soda, how many quarts of fruit juice must be added to produce punch that is 30% juice? (Lesson 2-9) **6 qt**

Solve each proportion. If necessary, round to the nearest hundredth. (Lesson 2-6)

51. $\frac{14}{x} = \frac{20}{8}$ **5.6** **52.** $\frac{0.47}{6} = \frac{1.41}{m}$ **18** **53.** $\frac{16}{7} = \frac{9}{b}$ **3.94**

54. $\frac{2+y}{5} = \frac{10}{3}$ **14.67** **55.** $\frac{8}{9} = \frac{2r-3}{4}$ **3.28** **56.** $\frac{6-2y}{8} = \frac{2}{18}$ **2.56**

Determine whether a valid conclusion follows from the statement below for each given condition. If a valid conclusion does not follow, write *no valid conclusion* and explain why. (Lesson 1-8)

If a DVD box set costs less than $70, then Ian will buy one.

57. A DVD box set costs $59. **Ian will buy a DVD box set.**
58. A DVD box set costs $89.
59. Ian will not buy a DVD box set. **The DVD box set cost $70 or more.**
60. Ian bought 2 DVD box sets.

58. No valid conclusion; the hypothesis does not say that Ian won't buy a DVD box set if it costs more than $70.
60. No valid conclusion; the conditional does not mention Ian buying 2 DVD box sets.

Evaluate each expression. Name the property used in each step. (Lesson 1-2) **61–63. See margin.**

61. $5 + (4 - 2^2)$ **62.** $\frac{3}{8}[8 \div (7 - 4)]$ **63.** $2(4 \cdot 9 - 3) + 5 \cdot \frac{1}{5}$

Skills Review

Solve each equation. (Lesson 2-3)

64. $4p - 2 = -6$ **−1** **65.** $18 = 5p + 3$ **3** **66.** $9 = 1 + \frac{m}{7}$ **56**

67. $1.5a - 8 = 11$ $\mathbf{12\frac{2}{3}}$ **68.** $20 = -4c - 8$ **−7** **69.** $\frac{b+4}{-2} = -17$ **30**

70. $\frac{n-3}{8} = 20$ **163** **71.** $6y - 16 = 44$ **10** **72.** $130 = 11k + 9$ **11**

4 ASSESS

Name the Math Have each student tell a partner the difference between a compound inequality that contains *or* and a compound inequality that contains *and*.

Additional Answers

61. $5 + (4 - 2^2)$
$= 5 + (4 - 4)$ Substitution
$= 5 + 0$ Substitution
$= 5$ Additive Identity

62. $\frac{3}{8}[8 \div (7 - 4)]$
$= \frac{3}{8}[8 \div 3]$ Substitution
$= \frac{3}{8} \cdot \frac{8}{3}$ Substitution
$= 1$ Multiplicative Inverse

63. $2(4 \cdot 9 - 3) + 5 \cdot \frac{1}{5}$
$= 2(36 - 3) + 5 \cdot \frac{1}{5}$ Substitution
$= 2(33) + 5 \cdot \frac{1}{5}$ Substitution
$= 66 + 5 \cdot \frac{1}{5}$ Substitution
$= 66 + 1$ Multiplicative Inverse
$= 67$ Substitution

Differentiated Instruction OL BL

Extension Have students find a value of k so that the solution set of $k - 5 \leq x - 6 \leq 3$ is $\{x \mid 6 \leq x \leq 9\}$. 5

5-5 Lesson Notes

1 FOCUS

Vertical Alignment

Before Lesson 5-5
Solve equations involving absolute value.

Lesson 5-5
Solve and graph absolute value inequalities (<). Solve and graph absolute value inequalities (>).

After Lesson 5-5
Graph inequalities in two variables.

2 TEACH

Scaffolding Questions

Have students read the *Why?* section of the lesson.

Ask:

- How would you represent the length of a baby carrot x sliced by the machine with an absolute value inequality? $|x - 3| \leq \frac{1}{8}$
- What graph would represent the length of baby carrots sliced by the machine?

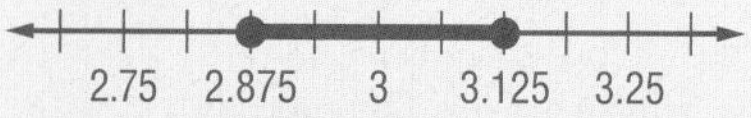

- If the accuracy of the machine were within $\frac{1}{4}$ of an inch, would the margin of error be less or greater? greater

5-5 Inequalities Involving Absolute Value

Then
You solved equations involving absolute value. (Lesson 2-5)

Now
- Solve and graph absolute value inequalities (<).
- Solve and graph absolute value inequalities (>).

IL Learning Standards
8.B.4a Represent algebraic concepts with physical materials, words, diagrams, tables, graphs, equations and inequalities and use appropriate technology.

IL Math Online
glencoe.com
- Extra Examples
- Personal Tutor
- Self-Check Quiz
- Homework Help
- Math in Motion

Why?

Some companies use absolute value inequalities to control the quality of their product. To make baby carrots, long carrots are sliced into 3-inch sections and peeled. If the machine is accurate to within $\frac{1}{8}$ of an inch, the length ranges from $2\frac{7}{8}$ inches to $3\frac{1}{8}$ inches.

Absolute Value Inequalities (<) The inequality $|x| < 3$ means that the distance between x and 0 is less than 3.

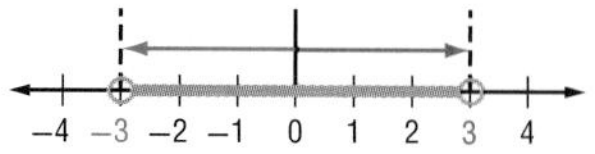

So, $x > -3$ and $x < 3$. The solution set is $\{x \mid -3 < x < 3\}$.

When solving absolute value inequalities, there are two cases to consider.

Case 1 The expression inside the absolute value symbols is nonnegative.

Case 2 The expression inside the absolute value symbols is negative.

The solution is the union of the solutions of these two cases.

EXAMPLE 1 Solve Absolute Value Inequalities (<)

Solve each inequality. Then graph the solution set.

a. $|m + 2| < 11$

Rewrite $|m + 2| < 11$ for Case 1 *and* Case 2.

Case 1 $m + 2$ is nonnegative. **and** **Case 2** $m + 2$ is negative.

$$m + 2 < 11 \qquad\qquad -(m + 2) < 11$$
$$m + 2 - 2 < 11 - 2 \qquad\qquad m + 2 > -11$$
$$m < 9 \qquad\qquad m + 2 - 2 > -11 - 2$$
$$m > -13$$

So, $m < 9$ and $m > -13$. The solution set is $\{m \mid -13 < m < 9\}$.

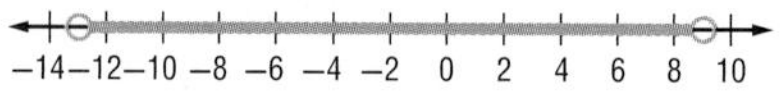

b. $|y - 1| < -2$

$|y - 1|$ cannot be negative. So it is not possible for $|y - 1|$ to be less than −2. Therefore, there is no solution, and the solution set is the empty set, Ø.

Check Your Progress 1A. $\{n \mid 6 \leq n \leq 10\}$

1A. $|n - 8| \leq 2$ **1B.** $|2c - 5| < -3$ Ø

Personal Tutor glencoe.com

Lesson 5-5 Resources

Resource	Approaching-Level	On-Level	Beyond-Level	English Learners
Teacher Edition	• Differentiated Instruction, p. 311	• Differentiated Instruction, p. 311, 314	• Differentiated Instruction, p. 314	
Chapter Resource Masters	• Study Guide and Intervention, pp. 29–30 • Skills Practice, p. 31 • Practice, p. 32 • Word Problem Practice, p. 33	• Study Guide and Intervention, pp. 29–30 • Skills Practice, p. 31 • Practice, p. 32 • Word Problem Practice, p. 33 • Enrichment, p. 34 • Graphing Calculator, p. 35	• Practice, p. 32 • Word Problem Practice, p. 33 • Enrichment, p. 34	• Study Guide and Intervention, pp. 29–30 • Skills Practice, p. 31 • Practice, p. 32 • Word Problem Practice, p. 33
Transparencies	• 5-Minute Check Transparency 5-5	• 5-Minute Check Transparency 5-5	• 5-Minute Check Transparency 5-5	• 5-Minute Check Transparency 5-5
Other	• Study Notebook	• Study Notebook	• Study Notebook	• Study Notebook

Real-World EXAMPLE 2 Apply Absolute Value Inequalities

INTERNET **A recent survey showed that 65% of young adults watched online video clips. The margin of error was within 3 percentage points. Find the range of young adults who use video sharing sites.**

The difference between the actual number of viewers and the number from the survey is less than or equal to 3. Let x be the actual number of viewers. Then $|x - 65| \leq 3$.

Solve each case of the inequality.

Case 1 $x - 65$ is nonnegative. **and** **Case 2** $x - 65$ is negative.

$x - 65 \leq 3$	$-(x - 65) \leq 3$
$x - 65 + 65 \leq 3 + 65$	$x - 65 \geq -3$
$x \leq 68$	$x \geq 62$

The range of young adults who use video sharing sites is $\{x \mid 62 \leq x \leq 68\}$.

Real-World Link

One in five Americans use the Internet to view videos. Young adults tend to watch funny videos, while other age groups tend to watch the news.

Source: Pew Internet and American Life Project

Check Your Progress

2. **CHEMISTRY** The melting point of ice is 0°C. During a chemistry experiment, Jill observed ice melting within 2°C of this measurement. Write the range of temperatures that Jill observed. $\{t \mid 0 \leq t \leq 2\}$

Personal Tutor glencoe.com

Absolute Value Inequalities (>) The inequality $|x| > 3$ means that the distance between x and 0 is greater than 3.

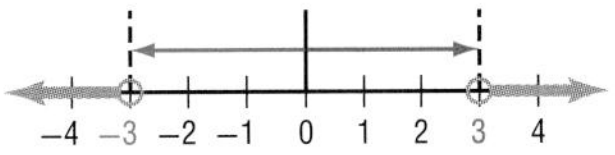

So, $x < -3$ or $x > 3$. The solution set is $\{x \mid x < -3 \text{ or } x > 3\}$.

As in the previous example, we must consider both cases.

Case 1 The expression inside the absolute value symbols is nonnegative.

Case 2 The expression inside the absolute value symbols is negative.

StudyTip

Absolute Value For $|a| \geq b$, where a is any linear expression in one variable and b is a negative number, the solution set will always be the set of all real numbers. Since $|a|$ is always greater than or equal to zero, $|a|$ is always greater than or equal to b.

EXAMPLE 3 Solve Absolute Value Inequalities (>)

Solve $|3n + 6| \geq 12$. Then graph the solution set.

Rewrite $|3n + 6| \geq 12$ for Case 1 *or* Case 2.

Case 1 $3n + 6$ is nonnegative. **or** **Case 2** $3n + 6$ is negative.

$3n + 6 \geq 12$	$-(3n + 6) \geq 12$
$3n + 6 - 6 \geq 12 - 6$	$3n + 6 \leq -12$
$3n \geq 6$	$3n \leq -18$
$n \geq 2$	$n \leq -6$

So, $n \geq 2$ or $n \leq -6$. The solution set is $\{n \mid n \geq 2 \text{ or } n \leq -6\}$.

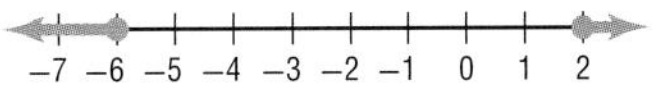

Check Your Progress

Solve each inequality. Then graph the solution set. **3A–3B. See margin.**

3A. $|2k + 1| > 7$

3B. $|r - 6| \geq -5$

Personal Tutor glencoe.com

Differentiated Instruction

AL OL

If students do not understand why $|m + 2| < 11$ is rewritten as $m + 2 < 11$ and $m + 2 > -11$,

Then have them rewrite the second inequality as $-(m + 2) < 11$ and multiply each side by -1 to yield $m + 2 > -11$. This method makes the switch of the direction of the inequality more obvious, as students must make the switch when they multiply each side by -1.

Absolute Value Inequalities

Example 1 shows how to solve an absolute value inequality of the form $|x| < n$. **Example 2** shows how to solve an absolute value inequality involving a real-world situation. **Example 3** shows how to solve an absolute value inequality of the form $|x| > n$.

Formative Assessment

Use the Check Your Progress exercises after each Example to determine students' understanding of concepts.

Additional Example

1 Solve each inequality. Then graph the solution set.

a. $|n - 3| \leq 12$
$\{n \mid -9 \leq n \leq 15\}$

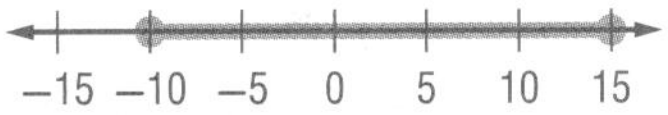

b. $|x + 6| < -8$ $\varnothing$

Additional Examples also in Interactive Classroom PowerPoint® Presentations

IWB INTERACTIVE WHITEBOARD READY

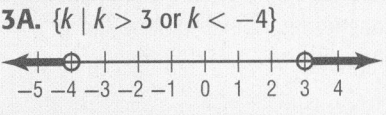

Focus on Mathematical Content

Conjunction or Disjunction When $b > 0$, inequalities of the form $|x| < b$ are equivalent to the conjunction $x < b$ and $x > -b$. Inequalities of the form $|x| > b$ are equivalent to the disjunction $x > b$ or $x < -b$.

Additional Answers (Check Your Progress)

3A. $\{k \mid k > 3 \text{ or } k < -4\}$

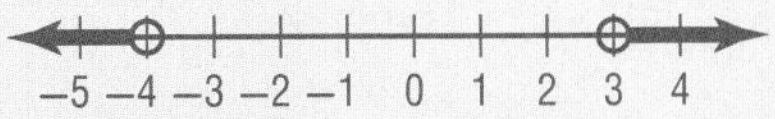

3B. $\{r \mid r \text{ is a real number.}\}$

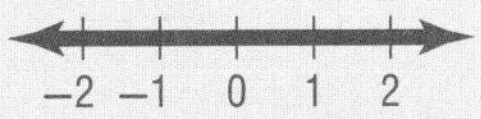

Additional Examples

2 Solve each inequality. Then graph the solution set.

a. $|3y - 3| > 9$

$\{y \mid y < -2 \text{ or } y > 4\}$

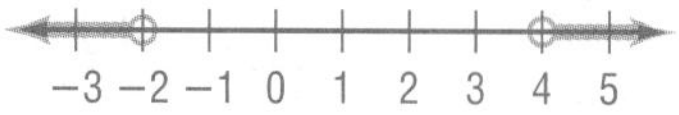

b. $|2x + 7| \geq -11$

$\{x \mid x \text{ is a real number.}\}$

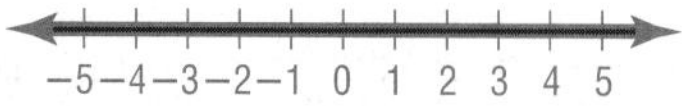

3 **RAINFALL** The average annual rainfall in California for the last 100 years is 23 inches. However, the annual rainfall can differ by 10 inches from the 100 year average. What is the range of annual rainfall for California?

$\{x \mid 13 \leq x \leq 33\}$

TEACH with TECH

DIGITAL CAMERA Have students use a camera to take step-by-step photos of their work. Then choose several students to display their photos as a slide show, and explain their work in each step.

3 PRACTICE

Formative Assessment

Use Exercises 1–7 to check for understanding.

Use the chart at the bottom of this page to customize assignments for your students.

Multiple Representations In Exercise 42, students use a table of values and a graph in the coordinate plane to describe absolute-value inequalities.

Check Your Understanding

Examples 1 and 3 pp. 310–311

Solve each inequality. Then graph the solution set. 1–6. See Ch. 5 Answer Appendix.

1. $|a - 5| < 3$ **2.** $|u + 3| < 7$ **3.** $|t + 4| \leq -2$

4. $|c + 2| > -2$ **5.** $|n + 5| \geq 3$ **6.** $|p - 2| \geq 8$

Example 2 p. 311

7. FINANCIAL LITERACY Jerome bought stock in his favorite fast-food restaurant chain at \$70.85. However, it has fluctuated up to \$0.75 in a day. Find the range of prices for which the stock could trade in a day. $\{m \mid 70.10 \leq m \leq 71.60\}$

Practice and Problem Solving

● = **Step-by-Step Solutions** begin on page R12. **Extra Practice** begins on page 815.

Examples 1 and 3 pp. 310–311

Solve each inequality. Then graph the solution set. 8–19. See Ch. 5 Answer Appendix.

8. $|x + 8| < 16$ **9.** $|r + 1| \leq 2$ **10.** $|2c - 1| \leq 7$

11. $|3h - 3| < 12$ **12.** $|m + 4| < -2$ **13.** $|w + 5| < -8$

14. $|r + 2| > 6$ **15.** $|k - 4| > 3$ **16.** $|2h - 3| \geq 9$

17. $|4p + 2| \geq 10$ **18.** $|5v + 3| > -9$ **19.** $|-2c - 3| > -4$

Example 2 p. 311

20. SCUBA DIVING The pressure of a scuba tank should be within 500 pounds per square inch (psi) of 2500 psi. Write the range of optimum pressures. $\{p \mid 2000 \leq p \leq 3000\}$

B **Solve each inequality. Then graph the solution set.** 21–29. See Ch. 5 Answer Appendix.

21. $|4n + 3| \geq 18$ **22.** $|5t - 2| \leq 6$ **23.** $\left|\frac{3h + 1}{2}\right| < 8$

24. $\left|\frac{2p - 8}{4}\right| \geq 9$ **25.** $\left|\frac{7c + 3}{2}\right| \leq -5$ **26.** $\left|\frac{2g + 3}{2}\right| > -7$

27. $|-6r - 4| < 8$ **28.** $|-3p - 7| > 5$ **29.** $|-h + 1.5| < 3$

30. MUSIC DOWNLOADS Kareem is allowed to download \$10 worth of music each month. This month he has spent within \$3 of his allowance.

a. What is the range of money he has spent on music downloads this month? $\{m \mid 7 \leq m \leq 13\}$

b. Graph the range of the money that he spent. See Ch. 5 Answer Appendix.

31. CHEMISTRY Water can be present in our atmosphere as a solid, liquid, or gas. Water freezes at 32°F and vaporizes at 212°F.

a. Write the range of temperatures in which water is not a liquid. $\{t \mid t < 32 \text{ or } t > 212\}$

b. Graph this range.

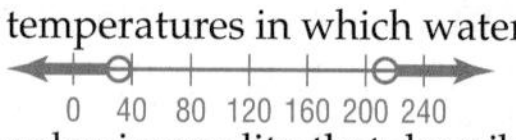

c. Write the absolute value inequality that describes this situation. $|t - 122| > 90$

Write an open sentence involving absolute value for each graph.

32.

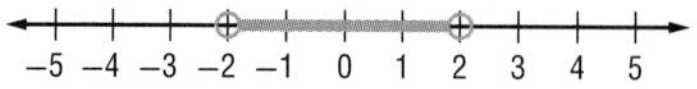

$|x| < 2$

33.

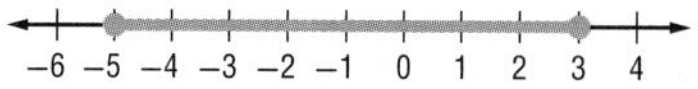

$|x + 1| \leq 4$

34.

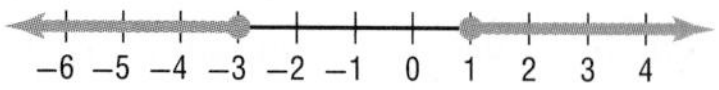

$|x + 1| \geq 2$

35.

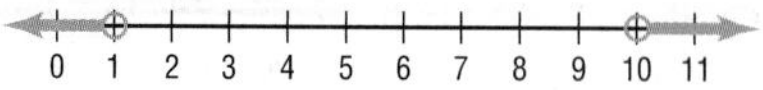

$|x - 5.5| > 4.5$

Differentiated Homework Options

Level	Assignment	Two-Day Option	
AL Basic	8–20, 43–44, 46–68	9–19 odd, 48–51	8–20 even, 43–44, 46–47, 52–68
OL Core	9–29 odd, 30, 31–35 odd, 36–44, 46–68	8–20, 48–51	21–47, 52–68
BL Advanced	21–60, (optional: 61–68)		

Real-World Link

In the 1930s, there were about 20,000 miniature golf courses in the United States. Today there are about 4000 courses.

Source: Professional Miniature Golf Association

36. ANIMALS A sheep's normal body temperature is 39°C. However, a healthy sheep may have body temperatures 1°C above or below this temperature. What is the range of body temperatures for a sheep? $\{t \mid 38 \le t \le 40\}$

37. MINIATURE GOLF Ginger's score was within 5 strokes of her average score of 52. Determine the range of scores for Ginger's game. $\{g \mid 47 \le g \le 57\}$

Express each statement using an inequality involving absolute value. Do *not* solve.

38. The pH of a swimming pool must be within 0.3 of a pH of 7.5. $|p - 7.5| \le 0.3$

39. The temperature inside a refrigerator should be within 1.5 degrees of 38°F. $|t - 38| \le 1.5$

40. Ramona's bowling score was within 6 points of her average score of 98. $|b - 98| \le 6$

41. The cruise control of a car should keep the speed within 3 miles per hour of 55. $|c - 55| \le 3$

42. MULTIPLE REPRESENTATIONS In this problem, you will investigate the graphs of absolute value inequalities on a coordinate plane.

a. TABULAR Copy and complete the table. Substitute the x and $f(x)$ values for each point into each inequality. Mark whether the resulting statement is *true* or *false*.

Point	$f(x) \ge \|x - 1\|$	true/false	$f(x) \le \|x - 1\|$	true/false
(−4, 2)	$2 \ge 5$	false	$2 \le 5$	true
(−2, 2)	$2 \ge 3$	false	$2 \le 3$	true
(0, 2)	$2 \ge 1$	true	$2 \le 1$	false
(2, 2)	$2 \ge 1$	true	$2 \le 1$	false
(4, 2)	$2 \ge 3$	false	$2 \le 3$	true

b. GRAPHICAL Graph $f(x) = |x - 1|$. See Ch. 5 Answer Appendix.

c. GRAPHICAL Plot each point that made $f(x) \ge |x - 1|$ a true statement on the graph in red. Plot each point that made $f(x) \le |x - 1|$ on the graph in blue.

c–e. See Ch. 5 Answer Appendix.

d. LOGICAL Make a conjecture about what the graphs of $f(x) \ge |x - 1|$ and $f(x) \le |x - 1|$ look like. Complete the table with other points to verify your conjecture.

e. GRAPHICAL Use what you discovered to graph $f(x) \ge |x - 3|$.

H.O.T. Problems

Use Higher-Order Thinking Skills

43. FIND THE ERROR Lucita sketched a graph of her solution to $|2a - 3| > 1$. Is she correct? Explain your reasoning.

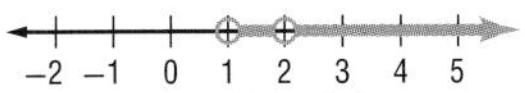

Sample answer: Lucita forgot to change the direction of the inequality sign for the negative case of the absolute value.

44. REASONING The graph of an absolute value inequality is *sometimes, always,* or *never* the union of two graphs. Explain.

45. CHALLENGE Demonstrate why the solution of $|t| > 0$ is not all real numbers. Explain your reasoning. Sample answer: If $t = 0$, then the absolute value is equal to 0, not greater than 0.

46. OPEN ENDED Write an absolute value inequality to represent a real-world situation. Interpret the solution.

47. WRITING IN MATH Explain how to determine whether an absolute value inequality uses a compound inequality with *and* or a compound inequality with *or*. Then summarize how to solve absolute value inequalities.

44. Sometimes; the graph could be the intersection of two graphs, the empty set, or all real numbers.

46. Sample answer: $|t - 98.6| < 1.4$; The range of normal body temperature of a healthy human is $\{t \mid 97.2 < t < 100\}$.

47. Sample answer: When an absolute value is on the left and the inequality symbol is $<$ or $\le$, the compound sentence uses *and*, and if the inequality symbol is $>$ or $\ge$, the compound sentence uses *or*. To solve, if $|x| < n$, then set up and solve the inequalities $x < n$ and $x > -n$, and if $|x| > n$, then set up and solve the inequalities $x > n$ or $x < -n$.

Watch Out!

Find the Error In Exercise 43, suggest that students solve the inequality to determine the error Lucita made. Ask them to explain what they must do to solve the inequality for Case 2 and how that might relate to the error in the graph.

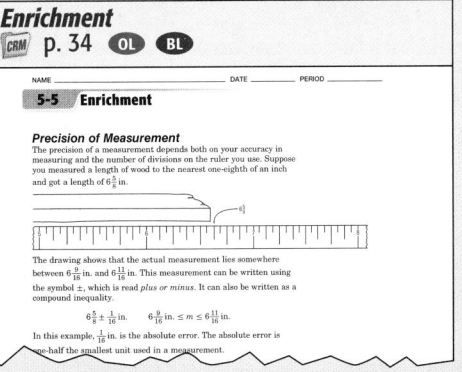

Study Guide and Intervention

CRM pp. 29–30 AL OL ELL

NAME ______ DATE ______ PERIOD ______

5-5 Study Guide and Intervention

Inequalities Involving Absolute Value

Inequalities Involving Absolute Value (<) When solving inequalities that involve absolute value, there are two cases to consider for inequalities involving < (or ≤).

If $|x| < n$, then $x > -n$ and $x < n$.

Remember that inequalities with *and* are related to intersections.

Example Solve $|3a + 4| < 10$. Then graph the solution set.

Write $|3a + 4| < 10$ as $3a + 4 < 10$ and $3a + 4 > -10$.

$3a + 4 < 10$ and $3a + 4 > -10$

$3a + 4 - 4 < 10 - 4$ $\quad$ $3a + 4 - 4 > -10 - 4$

$3a < 6$ $\quad$ $3a > -14$

$\frac{3a}{3} < \frac{6}{3}$ $\quad$ $\frac{3a}{3} > \frac{-14}{3}$

$a < 2$ $\quad$ $a > -4\frac{2}{3}$

Now graph the solution set.

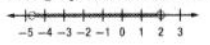

The solution set is $\left\{a \mid -4\frac{2}{3} < a < 2\right\}$.

Exercises

Solve each inequality. Then graph the solution set.

1. $|y| < 3$ $\{y \mid -3 < y < 3\}$
2. $|x - 4| < 4$ $\{x \mid 0 < x < 8\}$
3. $|y + 3| \le 2$ $\{y \mid -5 \le y \le -1\}$
4. $|b + 2| \le 3$ $\{b \mid -5 \le b \le 1\}$
5. $|w - 2| \le 5$ $\{w \mid -3 \le w \le 7\}$
6. $|t + 2| \le 4$ $\{t \mid -6 \le t \le 2\}$
7. $|2x| \le 8$ $\{x \mid -4 \le x \le 4\}$
8. $|5y - 2| \le 7$ $\left\{y \mid -1 \le y \le 1\frac{4}{5}\right\}$
9. $|p - 0.2| < 0.5$ $\{p \mid -0.3 < p < 0.7\}$

Lesson 5-5

Chapter 5 29 Glencoe Algebra 1

Practice

CRM p. 32 AL OL BL ELL

NAME ______ DATE ______ PERIOD ______

5-5 Practice

Inequalities Involving Absolute Value

Match each open sentence with the graph of its solution set.

1. $|x - 3| \ge 1$ **a**
2. $|2x + 1| < 5$ **c**
3. $|5 - x| \ge 3$ **b**

Express each statement using an inequality involving absolute value.

4. The height of the plant must be within 2 inches of the standard 13-inch show size. $|h - 13| \le 2$
5. The majority of grades in Sean's English class are within 4 points of 85. $|g - 85| \le 4$

Solve each inequality. Then graph the solution set.

6. $|2z - 9| \le 1$ $\{z \mid 4 \le z \le 5\}$
7. $|3 - 2r| > 7$ $\{r \mid r < -2 \text{ or } r > 5\}$
8. $|3t + 6| < 9$ $\{t \mid -5 < t < 1\}$
9. $|2g - 5| \ge 9$ $\{g \mid g \le -2 \text{ or } g \ge 7\}$

Write an open sentence involving absolute value for each graph.

10. $|x - 6| < 5$
11. $|x + 4| > 2$
12. $|x + 3| \ge 4$
13. $|x - 2| \le 4$

14. **RESTAURANTS** The menu at Jeanne's favorite restaurant states that the roasted chicken with vegetables entree typically contains 480 Calories. Based on the size of the chicken, the actual number of Calories in the entree can vary by as many as 40 Calories from this amount.
    a. Write an absolute value inequality to represent the situation. $|x - 480| \le 40$
    b. What is the range of the number of Calories in the chicken entree? $440 \le x \le 520$

Chapter 5 32 Glencoe Algebra 1

Word Problem Practice

CRM p. 33 AL OL BL ELL

NAME ______ DATE ______ PERIOD ______

5-5 Word Problem Practice

Solving Open Sentences Involving Absolute Value

1. **SPEEDOMETERS** The government requires speedometers on cars sold in the United States to be accurate within ±2.5% of the actual speed of the car. If your speedometer reads 60 miles per hour while you are driving on a highway, what is the range of possible actual speeds your car could be traveling at? $\{x \mid 58.5 \le x \le 61.5\}$

2. **BAKING** Pete is making muffins for a bake sale. Before he starts baking, he goes online to research different muffin recipes. The recipes that he finds all specify baking temperatures between 350°F and 400°F. Write an absolute value expression to represent the possible temperatures t called for in the muffin recipes Pete is researching. $|t - 375| \le 25$

3. **ARCHERY** In an Olympic archery event, the center of the target is set exactly 130 centimeters off the ground. To get the highest score of ten points, an archer must shoot an arrow no further than 3.05 centimeters from the exact center of the target.
    a. Write an absolute value expression to represent the possible distances d from the ground an archer can hit the target and still score ten points. $|d - 130| \le 3.05$
    b. Graph the solution set of the expression you wrote in part a.

4. **CATS** During a recent visit to the veterinarian's office, the Mrs. Van Allen was informed that a healthy weight for her cat is approximately 10 pounds, plus or minus one pound. Write an absolute value equation that represents unhealthy weights w for her cat. $|w - 10| \ge 1$

5. **STATISTICS** The most familiar statistical measure is the arithmetic mean, or average. A second important statistical measure is the standard deviation, which is a measure of how far the individual scores deviate from the mean. For example, in 2007 the mean score on the mathematics section of the SAT test was 515 and the standard deviation was 114. This means that people within one deviation of the mean have SAT math scores that are 114 points higher or 114 points lower than the mean.
    a. Write an absolute value inequality to find the range of 2007 SAT mathematics test scores within one standard deviation of the mean. $|x - 515| \le 114$
    b. What is the range of SAT mathematics test scores ±2 standard deviation from the mean? 287 to 743

Lesson 5-5

Chapter 5 33 Glencoe Algebra 1

Enrichment

CRM p. 34 OL BL

NAME ______ DATE ______ PERIOD ______

5-5 Enrichment

Precision of Measurement

The precision of a measurement depends both on your accuracy in measuring and the number of divisions on the ruler you use. Suppose you measured a length of wood to the nearest one-eighth of an inch and got a length of $6\frac{5}{8}$ in.

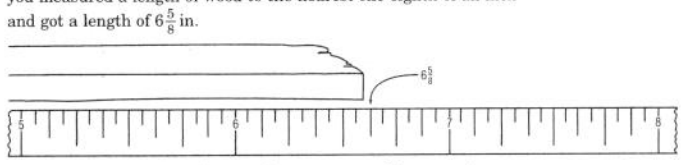

The drawing shows that the actual measurement lies somewhere between $6\frac{9}{16}$ in. and $6\frac{11}{16}$ in. This measurement can be written using the symbol ±, which is read *plus or minus*. It can also be written as a compound inequality.

$6\frac{5}{8} \pm \frac{1}{16}$ in. $\qquad 6\frac{9}{16}$ in. $\le m \le 6\frac{11}{16}$ in.

In this example, $\frac{1}{16}$ in. is the absolute error. The absolute error is one-half the smallest unit used in a measurement.

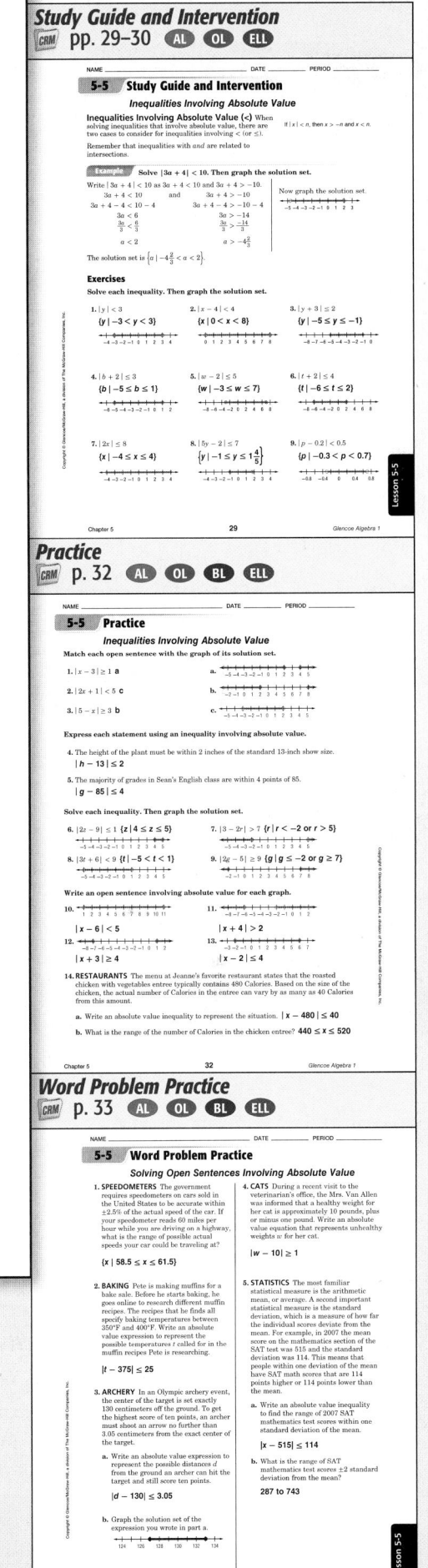

4 ASSESS

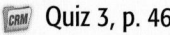

Crystal Ball Have students write how they think what they learned in today's lesson will connect to the next lesson *Graphing Inequalities in Two Variables.*

Formative Assessment

Check for student understanding of concepts in Lessons 5-4 and 5-5.

CRM Quiz 3, p. 46

Additional Answers

52. $\{b \mid -5 < b < 8\}$

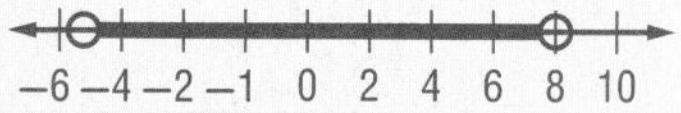

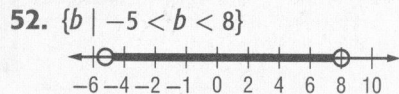

53. $\{t \mid 5 \le t \le 6\}$

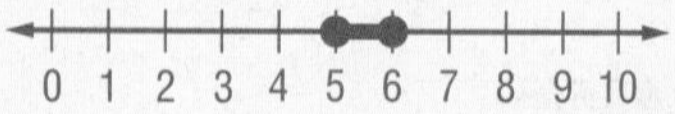

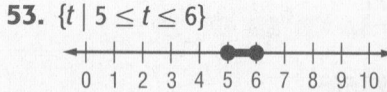

54. $\{c \mid c \ge 4 \text{ or } c \le -4\}$

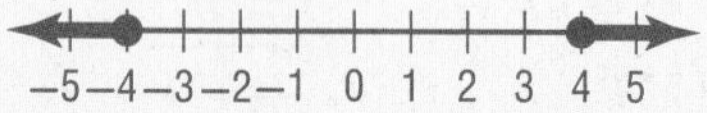

PSAE PRACTICE 8.11.01, 8.11.08, 10.11.07, 8.11.19

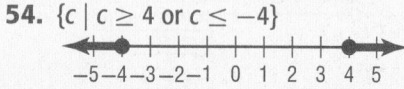

48. The formula for acceleration in a circle is $a = \frac{v^2}{r}$. Which of the following shows the equation solved for v? **B**

A $v = ar$

B $v = \sqrt{ar}$

C $v^2 = ar$

D $v = \frac{\sqrt{a}}{r}$

49. An engraver charges a \$3 set-up fee and \$0.25 per word. Which table shows the total price p for w words? **J**

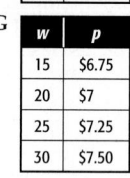

F

w	p
15	\$3
20	\$4.25
25	\$5.50
30	\$7.75

G

w	p
15	\$6.75
20	\$7
25	\$7.25
30	\$7.50

H

w	p
15	\$3.75
20	\$5
25	\$6.25
30	\$8.50

J

w	p
15	\$6.75
20	\$8
25	\$9.25
30	\$10.50

50. SHORT RESPONSE The table shows the items in stock at the school store the first day of class. What is the probability that an item chosen at random was a notebook? $\frac{1}{8}$

Item	Number Purchased
pencil	57
pen	38
eraser	6
folder	25
notebook	18

51. Solve for n. **B**

$$|2n - 3| = 5$$

A $\{-4, -1\}$

B $\{-1, 4\}$

C $\{1, 1\}$

D $\{4, 4\}$

Spiral Review

Solve each compound inequality. Then graph the solution set. (Lesson 5-4) **52–54. See margin.**

52. $b + 3 < 11$ and $b + 2 > -3$ **53.** $6 \le 2t - 4 \le 8$ **54.** $2c - 3 \ge 5$ or $3c + 7 \le -5$

55. FINANCIAL LITERACY In a recent year, the sum of the number of \$2 bills and \$50 bills in circulation was 1,857,573,945. The number of \$50 bills was 494,264,809 more than the number of \$2 bills. How many of each type of bill was in circulation? (Lesson 5-3)

55. 681,654,568 \$2 bills and 1,175,919,377 \$50 bills

56. GEOMETRY One angle of a triangle measures 10° more than the second. The measure of the third angle is twice the sum of the measure of the first two angles. Find the measure of each angle. (Lesson 2-4) **25°, 35°, 120°**

Solve each equation. Then check your solution. (Lesson 2-2)

57. $c - 7 = 11$ **18** **58.** $2w = 24$ **12** **59.** $9 + p = -11$ **−20** **60.** $\frac{t}{5} = 20$ **100**

Skills Review

Graph each equation. (Lesson 3-1) **61–68. See Ch. 5 Answer Appendix.**

61. $y = 4x - 1$ **62.** $y - x = 3$ **63.** $2x - y = -4$ **64.** $3y + 2x = 6$

65. $4y = 4x - 16$ **66.** $2y - 2x = 8$ **67.** $-9 = -3x - y$ **68.** $-10 = 5y - 2x$

Differentiated Instruction OL BL

Extension Draw a number line on the board or overhead. Have a student use your number line to create the graph of an absolute value inequality. Ask the rest of the class to write the inequality that the graph models.

5-6 Graphing Inequalities in Two Variables

Then

You graphed linear equations. (Lesson 3-1)

Now

- Graph linear inequalities on the coordinate plane.
- Solve inequalities by graphing.

IL Learning Standards

6.B.4 Select and use appropriate arithmetic operations in practical situations including calculating wages after taxes, developing a budget and balancing a checkbook. **8.D.4 Formulate and solve** linear and quadratic equations and **linear inequalities** algebraically and investigate nonlinear inequalities using graphs, tables, calculators and computers.

New Vocabulary

boundary
half-plane
closed half-plane
open half-plane

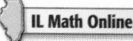

IL Math Online

glencoe.com

- Extra Examples
- Personal Tutor
- Self-Check Quiz
- Homework Help

Why?

Hannah has budgeted \$35 every three months for car maintenance. From this she must buy oil costing \$3 and filters that cost \$7 each. How much oil and how many filters can Hannah buy and stay within her budget?

Graph Linear Inequalities The graph of a linear inequality is the set of points that represent all of the possible solutions of that inequality. An equation defines a **boundary**, which divides the coordinate plane into two **half-planes**.

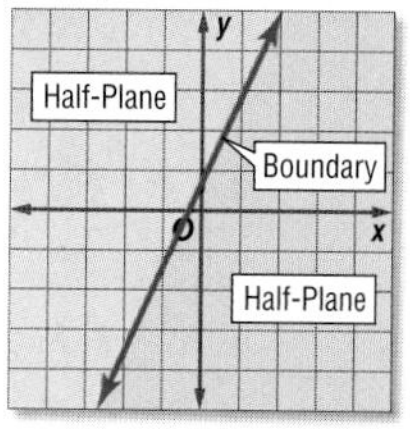

The boundary may or may not be included in the graph of an inequality. When it is included, the solution is a **closed half-plane**. When not included, the solution is an **open half-plane**.

Key Concept — Graphing Linear Inequalities (For Your FOLDABLE)

Step 1 Graph the boundary. Use a solid line when the inequality contains $\leq$ or $\geq$. Use a dashed line when the inequality contains $<$ or $>$.

Step 2 Use a test point to determine which half-plane should be shaded.

Step 3 Shade the half-plane that contains the solution.

EXAMPLE 1 Graph an Inequality ($<$ or $>$)

Graph $3x - y < 2$.

Step 1 First, solve for y in terms of x.

$$3x - y < 2$$
$$-y < -3x + 2$$
$$y > 3x - 2$$

Then, graph $y = 3x - 2$. Because the inequality involves $>$, graph the boundary with a dashed line.

Step 2 Select a test point in either half-plane. A simple choice is (0, 0).

$3x - y < 2$	**Original inequality**
$3(0) - 0 < 2$	**$x = 0$ and $y = 0$**
$0 < 2$	**true**

Step 3 So, the half-plane containing the origin is the solution. Shade this half-plane.

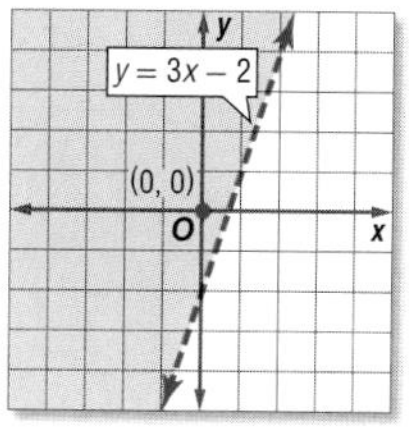

Check Your Progress Graph each inequality. 1A–1B. See Ch. 5 Answer Appendix.

1A. $y > \frac{1}{2}x + 3$ **1B.** $x - 1 > y$

Personal Tutor glencoe.com

5-6 Lesson Notes

1 FOCUS

Vertical Alignment

Before Lesson 5-6
Graph linear equations.

Lesson 5-6
Graph linear inequalities on the coordinate plane.
Solve inequalities by graphing.

After Lesson 5-6
Graph systems of linear inequalities.

2 TEACH

Scaffolding Questions

Have students read the *Why?* section of the lesson.

Ask:

- How many variables do you need if you want to write an inequality for Hannah's budget? Explain. Two; you need a variable to represent the number of units of oil and a variable to represent the number of filters.
- Which inequality symbol would you use to write the inequality? Explain. the symbol for less than or equal to, $\leq$, because Hannah can spend up to \$35
- What inequality can you write to represent the situation? $3x + 7y \leq 35$, where x is the number of units of oil, and y is the number of filters.

Lesson 5-6 Resources

Resource	Approaching-Level	On-Level	Beyond-Level	English Learners
Teacher Edition	• Differentiated Instruction, p. 317	• Differentiated Instruction, p. 320	• Differentiated Instruction, p. 320	
Chapter Resource Masters	• Study Guide and Intervention, pp. 36–37 • Skills Practice, p. 38 • Practice, p. 39 • Word Problem Practice, p. 40	• Study Guide and Intervention, pp. 36–37 • Skills Practice, p. 38 • Practice, p. 39 • Word Problem Practice, p. 40 • Enrichment, p. 41 • Spreadsheet Activity, p. 42	• Practice, p. 39 • Word Problem Practice, p. 40 • Enrichment, p. 41	• Study Guide and Intervention, pp. 36–37 • Skills Practice, p. 38 • Practice, p. 39 • Word Problem Practice, p. 40
Transparencies	• 5-Minute Check Transparency 5-6	• 5-Minute Check Transparency 5-6	• 5-Minute Check Transparency 5-6	• 5-Minute Check Transparency 5-6
Other	• Study Notebook	• Study Notebook	• Study Notebook	• Study Notebook

Graph Linear Inequalities

Example 1 shows how to graph an inequality that contains $<$ or $>$. **Example 2** shows how to graph an inequality that contains $\leq$ or $\geq$.

Formative Assessment

Use the Check Your Progress exercises after each example to determine students' understanding of concepts.

Watch Out!

Preventing Errors Students may need a quick refresher on slope-intercept form before they graph inequalities. Remind students that slope-intercept form is $y = mx + b$.

Additional Examples

1 Graph $2y - 4x > 6$.

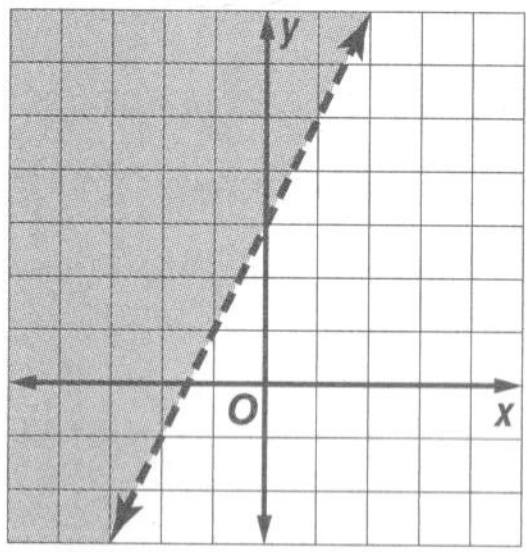

2 Graph $x + 4y \geq 2$.

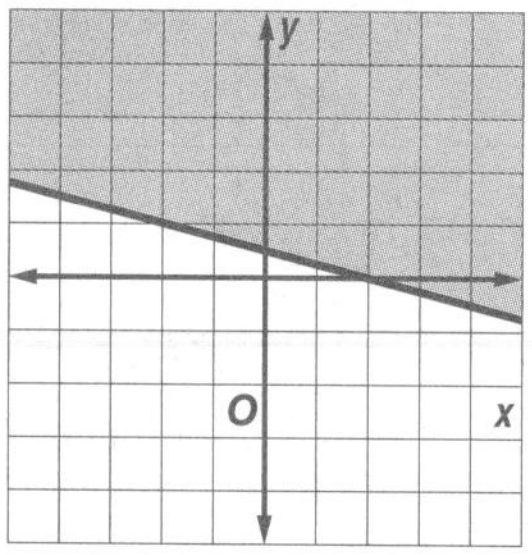

Additional Examples also in Interactive Classroom PowerPoint® Presentations

IWB INTERACTIVE WHITEBOARD READY

StudyTip

Selecting a Test Point When selecting a test point, a standard choice is the origin because it offers easy calculations. However, if it lies on the border, you must choose another point that is not on the border.

EXAMPLE 2 Graph an Inequality ($\leq$ or $\geq$)

Graph $x + 5y \leq 10$.

Step 1 Solve for y in terms of x.

$x + 5y \leq 10$	**Original inequality**
$5y \leq -x + 10$	**Subtract x from each side and simplify.**
$y \leq -\frac{1}{5}x + 2$	**Divide each side by 5.**

Graph $y = -\frac{1}{5}x + 2$. Because the inequality symbol is $\leq$, graph the boundary with a solid line.

Step 2 Select a test point. Let's use (3, 3). Substitute the values into the original inequality.

$x + 5y \leq 10$	**Original inequality**
$3 + 5(3) \leq 10$	**$x = 3$ and $y = 3$**
$18 \nleq 10$	**Simplify.**

Step 3 Since this statement is false, shade the other half-plane.

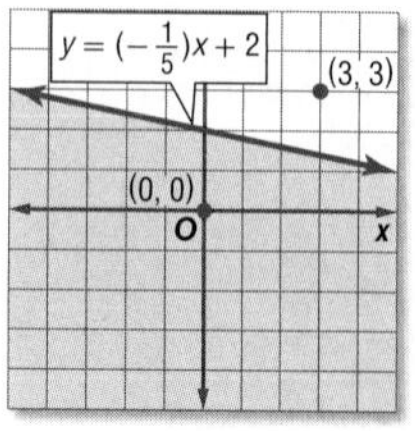

Check Your Progress Graph each inequality. **2A–2B. See Ch. 5 Answer Appendix.**

2A. $x - y \leq 3$

2B. $2x + 3y \geq 18$

Personal Tutor glencoe.com

Solve Linear Inequalities We can use a coordinate plane to solve inequalities with one variable.

EXAMPLE 3 Solve Inequalities From Graphs

Use a graph to solve $3x + 5 < 14$.

Step 1 First graph the boundary, which is the related equation. Replace the inequality sign with an equals sign, and solve for x.

$3x + 5 < 14$	**Original inequality**
$3x + 5 = 14$	**Change $<$ to $=$.**
$3x = 9$	**Subtract 5 from each side and simplify.**
$x = 3$	**Divide each side by 3.**

Graph $x = 3$ with a dashed line.

Step 2 Choose (0, 0) as a test point. These values in the original inequality give us $5 < 14$.

Step 3 Since this statement is true, shade the half-plane that contains the point (0, 0).

Notice that the x-intercept of the graph is at 3. Since the half-plane to the left of the x-intercept is shaded, the solution is $x < 3$.

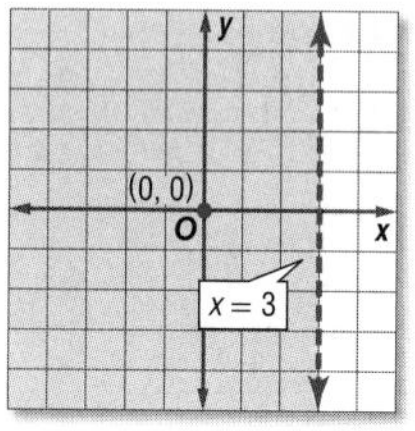

Check Your Progress Use a graph to solve each inequality.

3A. $4x - 3 \geq 17$ **$x \geq 5$**

3B. $-2x + 6 > 12$ **$x < -3$**

3A–3B. See Ch. 5 Answer Appendix for graphs.

Personal Tutor glencoe.com

Focus on Mathematical Content

Graphing Inequalities To graph an inequality, begin by solving the inequality for y in terms of x. Then graph the related equation $y = mx + b$. Use a dashed line when the boundary is not part of the solution set and use a solid line when the boundary is included. If the origin is not on the boundary line, use it as a test point to determine which half-plane is the graph of the solution set of the inequality.

When using inequalities to solve real-world problems, the domain and the range are often restricted to nonnegative or whole numbers.

Real-World EXAMPLE 4 Write and Solve an Inequality

CLASS PICNIC A yearbook company promises to give the junior class a picnic if they spend at least \$28,000 on yearbooks and class rings. Each yearbook costs \$35, and each class ring costs \$140. How many yearbooks and class rings must the junior class buy to get their picnic?

Understand You know the cost of each item and the minimum amount the class needs to spend.

Plan Let x = the number of yearbooks and y = the number of class rings the class must buy. Write an inequality.

\$35	times	the number of yearbooks	plus	\$140	times	the number of rings	is at least	\$28,000.
35	$\cdot$	x	$+$	140	$\cdot$	y	$\geq$	28,000

Solve Solve for y in terms of x.

$35x + 140y - 35x \geq 28{,}000 - 35x$ **Subtract 35x from each side.**

$140y \geq -35x + 28{,}000$ **Divide each side by 140.**

$\frac{140y}{140} \geq \frac{-35x}{140} + \frac{28000}{140}$ **Simplify.**

$y \geq -0.25x + 200$ **Simplify.**

Because the yearbook company cannot sell a negative number of items, the domain and range must be nonnegative numbers. Graph the boundary with a solid line. If we test (0, 0), the result is $0 \geq 28{,}000$, which is false. Shade the closed half-plane that does not include the origin. One solution is (500, 100), or 500 yearbooks and 100 class rings.

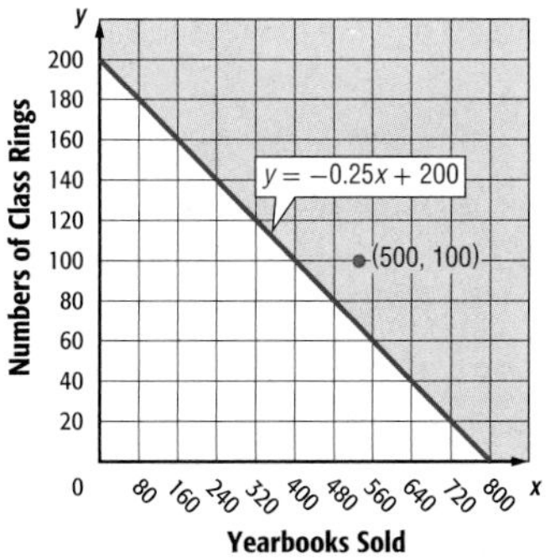

Check If we test (500, 100), the result is $100 \geq 75$, which is true. Because the company cannot sell a fraction of an item, only points with whole-number coordinates can be solutions.

Check Your Progress

4. **MARATHONS** Neil wants to run a marathon at a pace of at least 6 miles per hour. Write and graph an inequality for the miles y he will run in x hours.

Personal Tutor glencoe.com

Real-World Link

As a supplement to traditional yearbooks, many schools are producing digital versions. They include features that allow you to click on a picture and see a short video clip.

Source: *eSchool News*

Problem-SolvingTip

Use a Graph You can use a graph to visualize data, analyze trends, and make predictions.

4. $y \geq 6x$

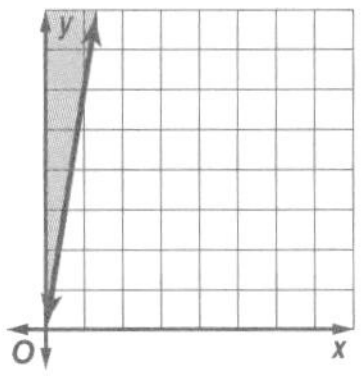

Solve Linear Inequalities

Example 3 shows how to use a graph to solve an inequality. **Example 4** shows how to write, solve, and graph an inequality involving a real-world situation.

Additional Examples

3 Use a graph to solve $2x + 3 \leq 7$. $x \leq 2$

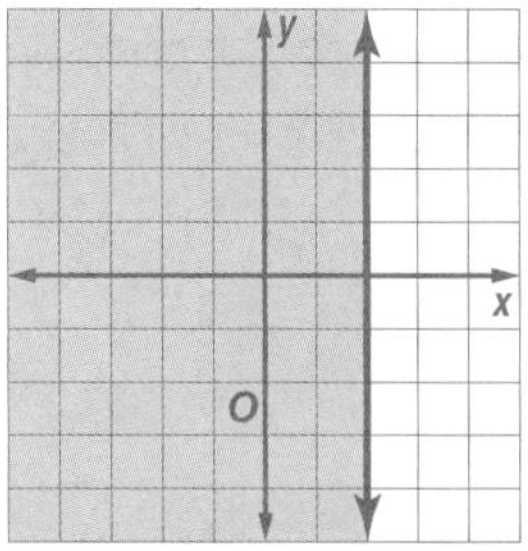

4 **JOURNALISM** Ranjan writes and edits short articles for a local newspaper. It takes him about an hour to write an article and about a half-hour to edit an article. If Ranjan works up to 8 hours a day, how many articles can he write and edit in one day?

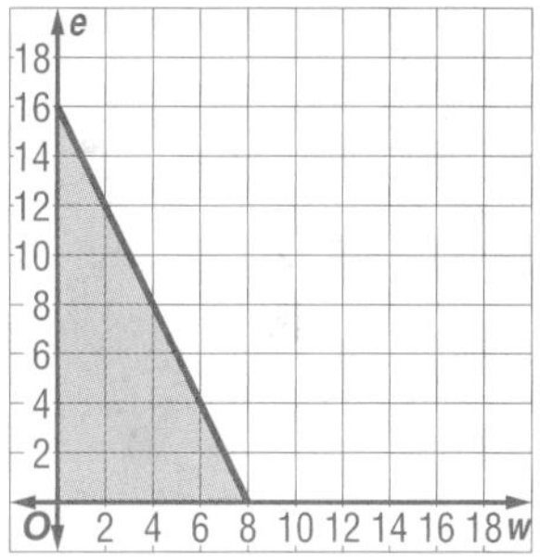

$e \leq -2w + 16$
One solution is (2, 3) or write 2 articles and edit 3. Consider other possibilities.

Differentiated Instruction AL

If some students have trouble working with the numbers in Example 4,

Then as an alternative problem, have them write and solve an inequality for the budget situation in the *Why?* section at the beginning of the lesson. The inequality they should write, solve, and then graph is $3x + 7y \leq 35$.

TEACH with TECH

PORTABLE MEDIA PLAYER Create a video showing your students how to graph inequalities in two variables. Post the video on your class Web page for students to download onto their portable media players for use as an additional reference outside of class.

3 PRACTICE

Formative Assessment

Use Exercises 1–11 to check for understanding.

Use the chart at the bottom of this page to customize assignments for your students.

Multiple Representations In Exercise 45, students use graphing and shading in the coordinate plane along with algebraic analysis to solve a system of inequalities.

Additional Answers

11b. Sample answer: 1 skim board and 4 surfboards

37a. $x + 1.25y \geq 2000$

37b.

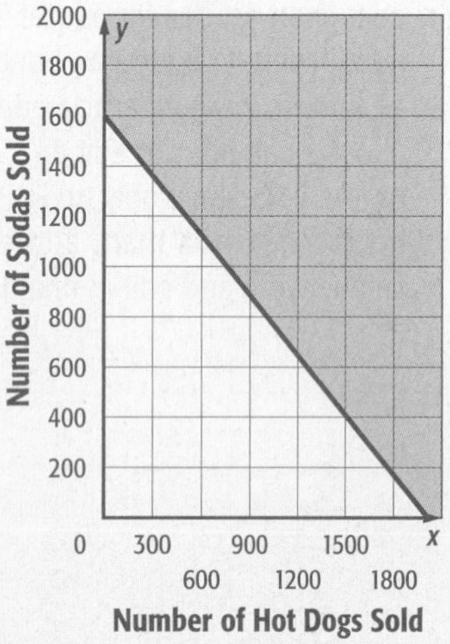

37c. Sample answer: (400, 1600), (200,1500), (300, 1400), (400, 1300), (1000, 1000)

37d. Sample points should be in the shaded region of the graph in part b.

Check Your Understanding

Examples 1 and 2 pp. 315–316

Graph each inequality. **1–6. See Ch. 5 Answer Appendix.**

1. $y > x + 3$ **2.** $y \geq -8$ **3.** $x + y > 1$

4. $y \leq x - 6$ **5.** $y < 2x - 4$ **6.** $x - y \leq 4$

Example 3 p. 316

Use a graph to solve each inequality. **7–10. See Ch. 5 Answer Appendix for graphs.**

7. $7x + 1 < 15$ $x < 2$ **8.** $-3x - 2 \geq 11$ $x \leq -4\frac{1}{3}$

9. $3y - 5 \leq 34$ $y \leq 13$ **10.** $4y - 21 > 1$ $y > 5\frac{1}{2}$

Example 4 p. 317

11. FINANCIAL LITERACY The surf shop has a weekly overhead of $2300.

a. Write an inequality to describe this situation. $115x + 685y \geq 2300$

b. How many skimboards and longboards must the shop sell each week to make a profit? **See margin.**

Practice and Problem Solving

= **Step-by-Step Solutions** begin on page R12. **Extra Practice** begins on page 815.

Examples 1 and 2 pp. 315–316

Graph each inequality. **12–23. See Ch. 5 Answer Appendix.**

12. $y < x - 3$ **13.** $y > x + 12$ **14.** $y \geq 3x - 1$

15. $y \leq -4x + 12$ **16.** $6x + 3y > 12$ **17.** $2x + 2y < 18$

18. $5x + y > 10$ **19.** $2x + y < -3$ **20.** $-2x + y \geq -4$

21. $8x + y \leq 6$ **22.** $10x + 2y \leq 14$ **23.** $-24x + 8y \geq -48$

Example 3 p. 316

Use a graph to solve each inequality. **24–29. See Ch. 5 Answer Appendix for graphs.**

24. $10x - 8 < 22$ $x < 3$ **25.** $20x - 5 > 35$ $x > 2$ **26.** $4y - 77 \geq 23$ $y \geq 25$

27. $5y + 8 \leq 33$ $y \leq 5$ **28.** $35x + 25 < 6$ $x < -\frac{19}{35}$ **29.** $14x - 12 > -31$

29. $x > -\frac{19}{14}$

Example 4 p. 317

30. DECORATING Sybrina is decorating her bedroom. She has $300 to spend on paint and bed linens. A gallon of paint costs $14, while a set of bed linens costs $60.

a. Write an inequality for this situation. $14x + 60y \leq 300$

b. How many gallons of paint and bed linen sets can Sybrina buy and stay within her budget? **Sample answer: 5 gallons of paint and 3 bed linen sets**

Use a graph to solve each inequality. **31–36. See Ch. 5 Answer Appendix for graphs.**

B

31. $3x + 2 < 0$ $x < -\frac{2}{3}$ **32.** $4x - 1 > 3$ $x > 1$ **33.** $-6x - 8 \geq -4$ $x \leq -\frac{2}{3}$

34. $-5x + 1 < 3$ $x > -\frac{2}{5}$ **35.** $-7x + 13 < 10$ $x > \frac{3}{7}$ **36.** $-4x - 4 \leq -6$ $x \geq \frac{1}{2}$

37. SOCCER The girls' soccer team wants to raise $2000 to buy new goals. How many of each item must they sell to buy the goals? **a–d. See margin.**

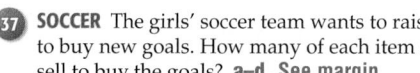

a. Write an inequality that represents this situation.

b. Graph this inequality.

c. Make a table of values that shows at least five possible solutions.

d. Plot the solutions from part **c**.

Differentiated Homework Options

Level	Assignment	Two-Day Option	
AL Basic	12–30, 46, 48–65	13–29 odd, 51–54	12–30 even, 46, 48–50, 55–65
OL Core	13–43 odd, 44–46, 48–65	12–30, 51–54	31–46, 48–50, 55–65
BL Advanced	31–64, (optional: 65)		

38–43. See Ch. 5 Answer Appendix.

Graph each inequality. Determine which of the ordered pairs are part of the solution set for each inequality.

38. $y \geq 6$; {(0, 4), (−2, 7), (4, 8), (−4, −8), (1, 6)}

39. $x < -4$; {(2, 1), (−3, 0), (0, −3), (−5, −5), (−4, 2)}

40. $2x - 3y \leq 1$; {(2, 3), (3, 1), (0, 0), (0, −1), (5, 3)}

41. $5x + 7y \geq 10$; {(−2, −2), (1, −1), (1, 1), (2, 5), (6, 0)}

42. $-3x + 5y < 10$; {(3, −1), (1, 1), (0, 8), (−2, 0), (0, 2)}

43. $2x - 2y \geq 4$; {(0, 0), (0, 7), (7, 5), (5, 3), (2, −5)}

44c.

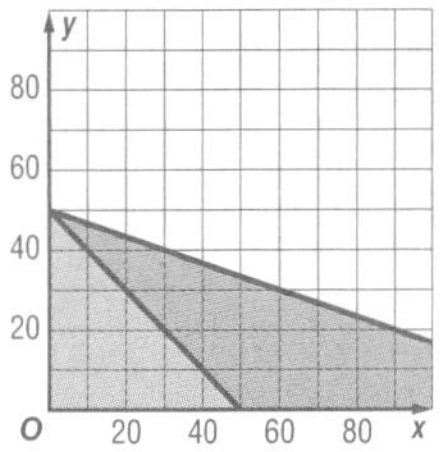

Real-World Link

The energy saved when recycling one glass bottle is enough to light a traditional light bulb for four hours.

Source: PlanetPals

44. RECYCLING A curbside recycling service will remove up to 50 pounds of plastic bottles and paper products each week. They charge \$0.25 per pound of plastic and \$0.75 per pound for paper products.

a. Write an inequality that describes the pounds of each kind of product that can be included in the curbside service. $x + y \leq 50$

b. Write an inequality that describes the charge. $0.25x + 0.75y \leq 37.50$

c. Graph each inequality.

d. Compare the two graphs.

44d. Sample answer: Both boundaries cross the y-axis at (0, 50). Both domains and ranges contain only nonnegative numbers.

45. MULTIPLE REPRESENTATIONS Use inequalities A and B to investigate graphing compound inequalities on a coordinate plane.

A. $7(y + 6) \leq 21x + 14$ **B.** $-3y \leq 3x - 12$

a. **NUMERICAL** Solve each inequality for y.

b. **GRAPHICAL** Graph both inequalities on one graph. Shade the half-plane that makes A true in red. Shade the half-plane that makes B true in blue.

c. **VERBAL** What does the overlapping region represent?

45a. $y \leq 3x - 4$
$y \geq -x + 4$

45b. See Ch. 5 Answer Appendix.

45c. The overlapping region represents the solutions that make both A and B true.

H.O.T. Problems

Use Higher-Order Thinking Skills

46. FIND THE ERROR Reiko and Kristin are solving $4y \leq \frac{8}{3}x$ by graphing. Is either of them correct? Explain your reasoning.

47–50. See Ch. 5 Answer Appendix.

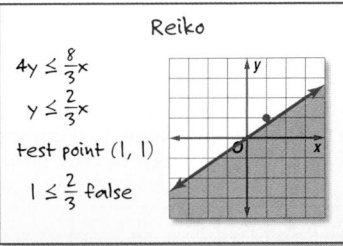

Reiko

$4y \leq \frac{8}{3}x$

$y \leq \frac{2}{3}x$

test point (1, 1)

$1 \leq \frac{2}{3}$ false

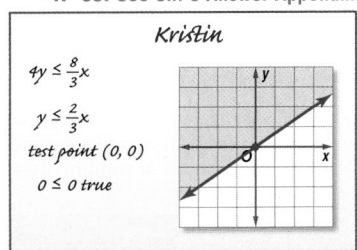

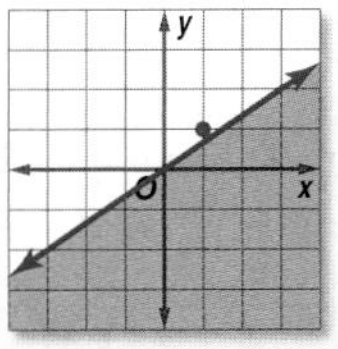

Kristin

$4y \leq \frac{8}{3}x$

$y \leq \frac{2}{3}x$

test point (0, 0)

$0 \leq 0$ true

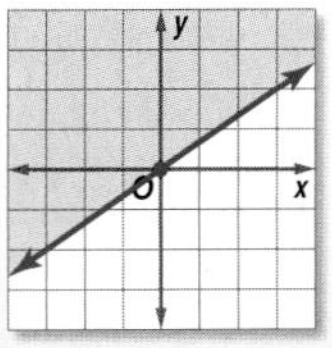

46. Reiko; Kristin used a test point located on the line and shaded the incorrect half-plane.

47. CHALLENGE Graph $y > |x + 5|$.

48. REASONING Explain why a point on the boundary should not be used as a test point.

49. OPEN ENDED Write a two-variable inequality with a restricted domain and range to represent a real-world situation. Give the domain and range, and explain why they are restricted.

50. WRITING IN MATH Summarize the steps to graph an inequality in two variables.

Watch Out!

Find the Error In Exercise 46, since Reiko and Kristin graphed the same solutions, have students examine the two graphs to find any differences. They should see that Reiko and Kristin shaded different half-planes. They should also notice that the test points they used are different. Ask students why one set of test points is better than the other.

Study Guide and Intervention

CRM pp. 36–37 AL OL ELL

NAME ______ DATE ______ PERIOD ______

5-6 Study Guide and Intervention

Graphing Inequalities in Two Variables

Graph Linear Inequalities The solution set of an inequality that involves two variables is graphed by graphing a related linear equation that forms a boundary of a **half-plane**. The graph of the ordered pairs that make up the solution set of the inequality fill a region of the coordinate plane on one side of the half-plane.

Example Graph $y \leq -3x - 2$.

Graph $y = -3x - 2$.

Since $y \leq -3x - 2$ is the same as $y < -3x - 2$ and $y = -3x - 2$, the boundary is included in the solution set and the graph should be drawn as a solid line.

Select a point in each half plane and test it. Choose (0, 0) and (−2, −2).

$y \leq -3x - 2$	$y \leq -3x - 2$
$0 \leq -3(0) - 2$	$-2 \leq -3(-2) - 2$
$0 \leq -2$ is false.	$-2 \leq 6 - 2$
	$-2 \leq 4$ is true.

The half-plane that contains (−2, −2) contains the solution. Shade that half-plane.

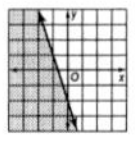

Exercises

Graph each inequality.

1. $y < 4$ 2. $x \geq 1$ 3. $3x \leq y$

4. $-x > y$ 5. $x - y \geq 1$ 6. $2x - 3y \leq 6$

7. $y < -\frac{1}{2}x - 3$ 8. $4x - 3y < 6$ 9. $3x + 6y \geq 12$

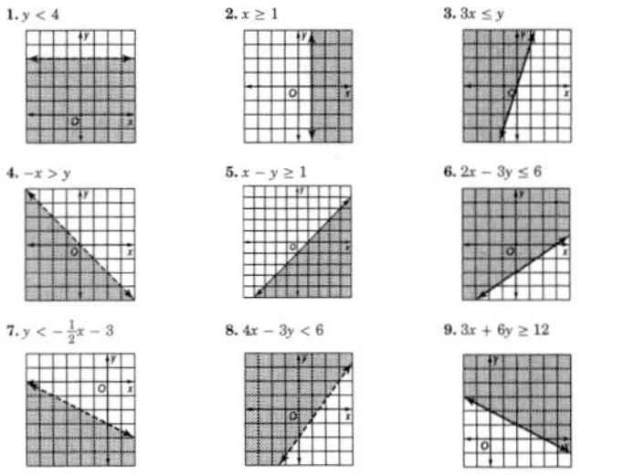

Chapter 5 36 Glencoe Algebra 1

Practice

CRM p. 39 AL OL BL ELL

NAME ______ DATE ______ PERIOD ______

5-6 Practice

Graphing Inequalities in Two Variables

Determine which ordered pairs are part of the solution set for each inequality.

1. $3x + y \geq 6$, {(4, 3), (−2, 4), (−5, −3), (3, −3)} **{(4, 3), (3, −3)}**

2. $y \geq x + 3$, {(6, 3), (−3, 2), (3, −2), (4, 3)} **{(−3, 2)}**

3. $3x - 2y < 5$, {(4, −4), (3, 5), (5, 2), (−3, 4)} **{(3, 5), (−3, 4)}**

Graph each inequality.

4. $2y - x < -4$ 5. $2x - 2y \geq 8$ 6. $3y > 2x - 3$

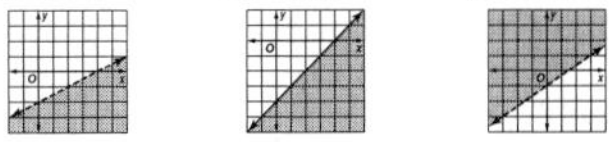

Use a graph to solve each inequality.

7. $-5 \leq x - 9$ 8. $6 > \frac{2}{3}x + 5$ 9. $\frac{1}{2} > -2x + \frac{7}{2}$

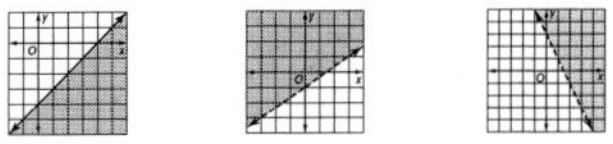

$x \geq 4$ $x < 1\frac{1}{2}$ $x > 1\frac{1}{2}$

10. **MOVING** A moving van has an interior height of 7 feet (84 inches). You have boxes in 12 inch and 15 inch heights, and want to stack them as high as possible to fit. Write an inequality that represents this situation. **$12x + 15y \leq 84$**

11. **BUDGETING** Satchi found a used bookstore that sells pre-owned videos and CDs. Videos cost \$9 each, and CDs cost \$7 each. Satchi can spend no more than \$35.

a. Write an inequality that represents this situation. **$9x + 7y \leq 35$**

b. Does Satchi have enough money to buy 2 videos and 3 CDs?
No, the purchases will be \$39, which is greater than \$35.

Chapter 5 39 Glencoe Algebra 1

Lesson 5-6

Word Problem Practice

CRM p. 40 AL OL BL ELL

NAME ______ DATE ______ PERIOD ______

5-6 Word Problem Practice

Graphing Inequalities in Two Variables

1. **FAMILY** Tyrone said that the ages of his siblings are all part of the solution set of $y > 2x$, where x is the age of a sibling and y is Tyrone's age. Which of the following ages is possible for Tyrone and a sibling?
Tyrone is 23; Maxine is 14. **no**
Tyrone is 18; Camille is 8. **yes**
Tyrone is 12; Francis is 4. **yes**
Tyrone is 11; Martin is 6. **no**
Tyrone is 19; Paul is 9. **yes**

2. **FARMING** The average value of U.S. farm cropland has steadily increased in recent years. In 2000, the average value was \$1490 per acre. Since then, the value has increased at least an average of \$77 per acre per year. Write an inequality to show land values above the average for farmland. **$y > 77x + 1490$**

3. **SHIPPING** An international shipping company has established size limits for packages with all their services. The total of the length of the longest side and the girth (distance completely around the package at its widest point perpendicular to the length) must be less than or equal to 419 centimeters. Write and graph an inequality that represents this situation.

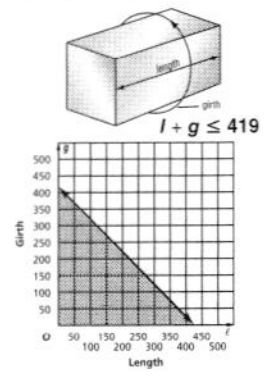

4. **FUNDRAISING** Troop 200 sold cider and donuts to raise money for charity. They sold small boxes of donut holes for \$1.25 and cider for \$2.50 a gallon. In order to cover their expenses, they needed to raise at least \$100. Write and graph an inequality that represents this situation.
$1.25d + 2.5c \geq 100$

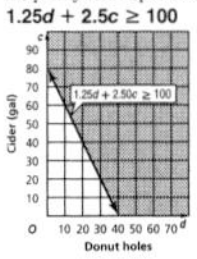

5. **INCOME** In 2006 the median yearly family income was about \$48,200 per year. Suppose the average annual rate of change since then is \$1240 per year.

a. Write and graph an inequality for the annual family incomes y that are less than the median for x years after 2006.
$y < 1240x + 48,200$

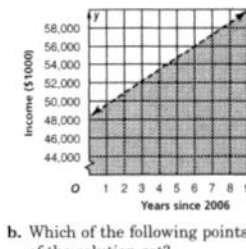

b. Which of the following points is part of the solution set?
(2, 51,000) **no** (8, 69,200) **no**
(5, 50,000) **yes** (10, 61,000) **no**

Chapter 5 40 Glencoe Algebra 1

Enrichment

CRM p. 41 OL BL

NAME ______ DATE ______ PERIOD ______

5-6 Enrichment

Lesson 5-6

Linear Programming

Linear programming can be used to maximize or minimize costs. It involves graphing a set of linear inequalities and using the region of intersection. You will use linear programming to solve the following problem.

Example **Layne's Gift Shoppe sells at most 500 items per week. To meet her customers' demands, she sells at least 100 stuffed animals and 75 greeting cards. If the profit for each stuffed animal is \$2.50 and the profit for each greeting card is \$1.00, the equation $P(a, g) = 2.50a + 1.00g$ can be used to represent the profit. How many of each should she sell to maximize her profit?**

Write the inequalities:
$a + g \leq 500$
$a \geq 100$
$g \geq 75$

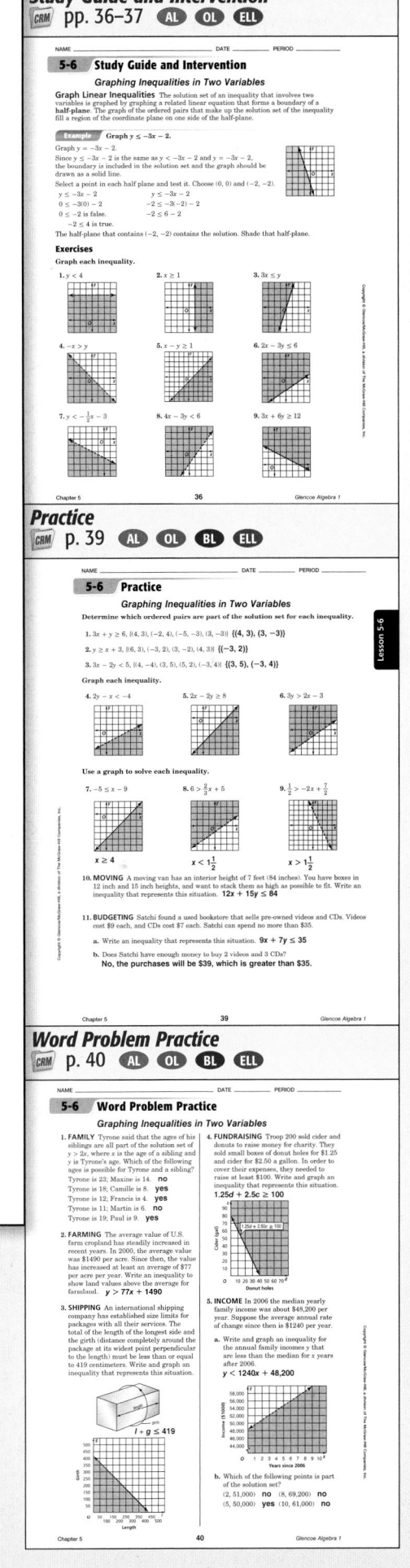

Graph the inequalities:

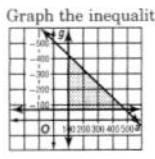

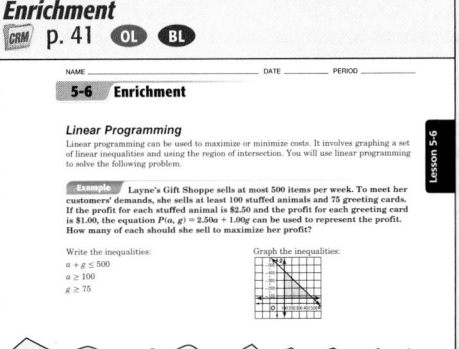

4 ASSESS

Ticket Out the Door Ask students to write, on a slip on paper, whether the boundary of the graph of $y < 2x + 1$ has a dashed or solid line and what this means.

Additional Answers

52b. 390; the y-intercept represents the number of trees with leaves in the arboretum on day 0.

52c. The arboretum will close after 30 days; I found the solution of $0 = 390 - 13d$.

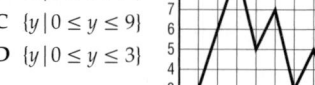

PSAE PRACTICE 8.11.11, 8.11.03, 8.11.02, 8.11.16

51. What is the domain of this function? **B**

A $\{x \mid 0 \leq x \leq 3\}$
B $\{x \mid 0 \leq x \leq 9\}$
C $\{y \mid 0 \leq y \leq 9\}$
D $\{y \mid 0 \leq y \leq 3\}$

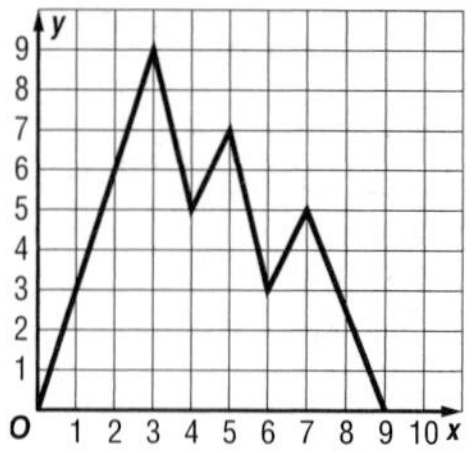

52. EXTENDED RESPONSE An arboretum will close for the winter when all of the trees have lost their leaves. The table shows the number of trees each day that still have leaves.

Day	5	10	15	20
Trees with Leaves	325	260	195	130

a. Write an equation that represents the number of trees with leaves y after d days. $y = 390 - 13d$

b. Find the y-intercept. What does it mean in the context of this problem? **b–c. See margin.**

c. After how many days will the arboretum close? Explain how you got your answer.

53. Which inequality best represents the statement below? **F**

A jar contains 832 gumballs. Ebony's guess was within 46 pieces.

F $|g - 832| \leq 46$
G $|g + 832| \leq 46$
H $|g - 832| \geq 46$
J $|g + 832| \geq 46$

54. GEOMETRY If the rectangular prism has a volume of 10,080 cm^3, what is the value of x? **D**

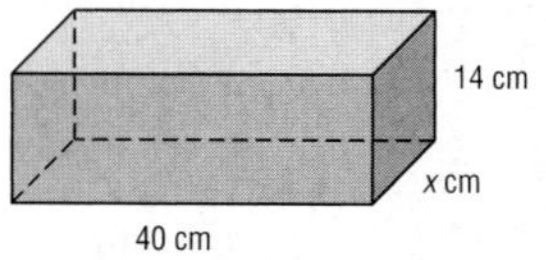

A 12
B 14
C 16
D 18

Spiral Review

62. $y = -\frac{7}{5}x - \frac{34}{5}$ 63. $y = -\frac{3}{2}x - 17$

Solve each open sentence. (Lesson 5-5)

55. $|y - 2| > 4$ $\{y \mid y > 6 \text{ or } y < -2\}$ **56.** $|t - 6| \leq 5$ $\{t \mid 1 \leq t \leq 11\}$ **57.** $|3 + d| < -4$ $\varnothing$

Solve each compound inequality. (Lesson 5-4)

58. $4c - 4 < 8c - 16 < 6c - 6$ $\{c \mid 3 < c < 5\}$ **59.** $5 < \frac{1}{2}p + 3 < 8$ $\{p \mid 4 < p < 10\}$ **60.** $0.5n \geq -7$ or $2.5n + 2 \leq 9$ $\{n \mid n \text{ is a real number.}\}$

Write an equation of the line that passes through each pair of points. (Lesson 4-2)

61. (1, −3) and (2, 5) $y = 8x - 11$ **62.** (−2, −4) and (−7, 3) **63.** (−6, −8) and (−8, −5)

64. FITNESS The table shows the maximum heart rate to maintain during aerobic activities. Write an equation in function notation for the relation. Determine what would be the maximum heart rate to maintain in aerobic training for an 80-year-old. (Lesson 3-5) $f(a) = -0.9a + 193$; 121 beats/min

Age (yr)	20	30	40	50	60	70
Pulse rate (beats/min)	175	166	157	148	139	130

Skills Review

65. WORK The formula $s = \frac{w - 10r}{m}$ is used to find keyboarding speeds. In the formula, s represents the speed in words per minute, w the number of words typed, r the number of errors, and m the number of minutes typed. Solve for r. (Lesson 2-8) $r = \frac{w - sm}{10}$

Differentiated Instruction OL BL

Extension Challenge students to write an inequality for the graph whose boundary passes through the points at (4, −2) and (−3, −2) and whose solution set contains the boundary and all the points above the boundary. $y \geq -2$

EXTEND 5-6

Graphing Technology Lab
Graphing Inequalities

IL Math Online glencoe.com
- Other Calculator Keystrokes
- Graphing Technology Personal Tutor

IL Learning Standards

8.B.4a Represent algebraic concepts with physical materials, words, diagrams, tables, graphs, equations and inequalities and use appropriate technology.
8.D.4 **Formulate and solve** linear and quadratic equations and **linear inequalities** algebraically and investigate nonlinear inequalities using graphs, tables, calculators and computers.

You can use a graphing calculator to investigate the graphs of inequalities.

ACTIVITY 1 Less Than

Graph $y \le 2x + 5$.

Clear all functions from the Y= list.

KEYSTROKES: [Y=] [CLEAR]

Graph $y \le 2x + 5$ in the standard window.

KEYSTROKES: 2 [X,T,θ,n] [+] 5 [◀] [◀] [◀] [◀] [◀] [◀] [ENTER] [ENTER] [ENTER] [Zoom] 6

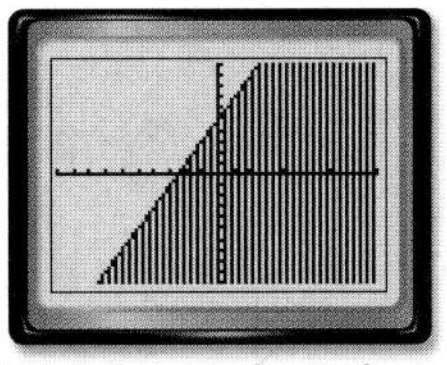

[−10, 10] scl: 1 by [−10, 10] scl: 1

All ordered pairs for which y is *less than or equal to* $2x + 5$ lie *below or on* the line and are solutions.

ACTIVITY 2 Greater Than

Graph $y - 2x \ge 5$.

Clear the graph that is currently displayed.

KEYSTROKES: [Y=] [CLEAR]

Rewrite $y - 2x \ge 5$ as $y \ge 2x + 5$ and graph it.

KEYSTROKES: 2 [X,T,θ,n] [+] 5 [◀] [◀] [◀] [◀] [◀] [◀] [ENTER] [ENTER] [Zoom] 6

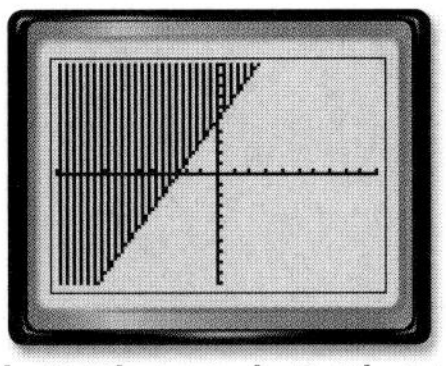

[−10, 10] scl: 1 by [−10, 10] scl: 1

All ordered pairs for which y is *greater than or equal to* $2x + 5$ lie *above or on* the line and are solutions.

Exercises

1. Both graphs contain the line $y = 2x + 5$. The first graph is shaded below $y = 2x + 5$, while the second graph is shaded above $y = 2x + 5$.

1. Compare and contrast the two graphs shown above.
2. Graph $y \ge -3x + 1$ in the standard viewing window. Using your graph, name four solutions of the inequality. Sample answer: {(0, 1), (−1, 7), (2, 6), (4.2, −1.5)}
3. Suppose student water park tickets cost $16, and adult water park tickets cost $20. You would like to buy at least 10 tickets but spend no more than $200.
   a. Let x = number of student tickets and y = number of adult tickets. Write two inequalities, one representing the total number of tickets and the other representing the total cost of the tickets. $x + y \ge 10$; $16x + 20y \le 200$
   b. Graph the inequalities. Use the viewing window [0, 20] scl: 1 by [0, 20] scl: 1. See margin.
   c. Name four possible combinations of student and adult tickets. Sample answer: {(0, 10), (6, 5), (8, 3), (11, 1)}

EXTEND 5-6

Lesson Notes

1 FOCUS

Objective Use a graphing calculator to investigate the graphs of inequalities.

Materials for Each Group

- TI–83/84 Plus or other graphing calculator

Teaching Tip You may also need students to reset the viewing windows. Have them enter ZOOM 6 to graph in the standard viewing window.

2 TEACH

Working in Cooperative Groups

Put students in groups of two or three, mixing abilities. Have groups complete the Activities and Exercise 1.

- To graph inequalities, enter the function in the Y= table editor at Y_1=. Then highlight the symbol in front of the Y_1 entry and press [ENTER] until either shading above or below the symbol appears.

Practice Have students complete Exercises 2 and 3.

3 ASSESS

Formative Assessment

Use Exercise 2 to assess whether students understand that the coordinates of all the points on the line or in the shaded region are solutions of the inequality.

Additional Answer

3b.

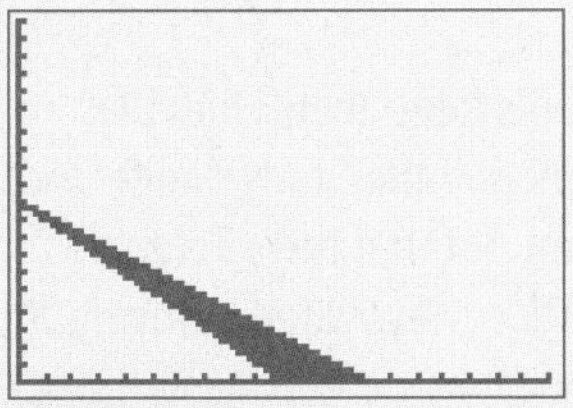

From Concrete to Abstract

Ask: Why do the ordered pairs that lie on the line belong to the solution set of the inequality for Exercise 2? Sample answer: The equals sign is included with the inequality.

Formative Assessment

Key Vocabulary The page reference after each word denotes where that term was first introduced. If students have difficulty answering questions 1–10, remind them that they can use these page references to refresh their memories about the vocabulary terms.

Summative Assessment

CRM Vocabulary Test, p. 48

IL Math Online glencoe.com

Vocabulary PuzzleMaker improves students' mathematics vocabulary using four puzzle formats–crossword, scramble, word search using a word list, and word search using clues. Students can work online or from a printed worksheet.

CHAPTER 5 Study Guide and Review

IL Math Online glencoe.com
- STUDY TO GO
- Vocabulary Review

Chapter Summary

Key Concepts

Solving One-Step Inequalities (Lessons 5-1 and 5-2)

For all numbers a, b, and c, the following are true.

- If $a > b$ and c is positive, $ac > bc$.
- If $a > b$ and c is negative, $ac < bc$.

Multi-Step and Compound Inequalities (Lessons 5-3 and 5-4)

- Multi-step inequalities can be solved by undoing the operations in the same way you would solve a multi-step equation.
- A compound inequality containing *and* is only true if both inequalities are true.
- A compound inequality containing *or* is true if at least one of the inequalities is true.

Absolute Value Inequalities (Lesson 5-5)

- The absolute value of any number x is its distance from zero on a number line and is written as $|x|$. If $x \geq 0$, then $|x| = x$. If $x < 0$, then $|x| = -x$.
- If $|x| < n$ and $n > 0$, then $-n < x < n$.
- If $|x| > n$ and $n > 0$, then $x > n$ or $x < -n$.

Inequalities in Two Variables (Lesson 5-6)

To graph an inequality:

Step 1 Graph the boundary. Use a solid line when the inequality contains $\leq$ or $\geq$. Use a dashed line when the inequality contains $<$ or $>$.

Step 2 Use a test point to determine which half-plane should be shaded.

Step 3 Shade the half-plane.

FOLDABLES® Study Organizer

Be sure the Key Concepts are noted in your Foldable.

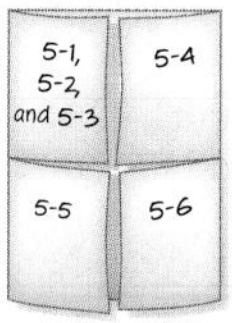

Key Vocabulary

boundary (p. 315)
closed half-plane (p. 315)
compound inequality (p. 304)
half plane (p. 315)
intersection (p. 304)
open half-plane (p. 315)
set-builder notation (p. 284)
union (p. 305)

Vocabulary Check

State whether each sentence is *true* or *false*. If *false*, replace the underlined term to make a true sentence.

1. Set-builder notation is a <u>less</u> concise way of writing a solution set. **false; more**
2. There are <u>two</u> types of compound inequalities. **true**
3. The graph of a compound inequality containing *and* shows the <u>union</u> of the individual graphs. **false; intersection**
4. A compound inequality containing *or* is true if one or both of the inequalities is true. Its graph is the <u>union</u> of the graphs of the two inequalities. **true**
5. The graph of an inequality of the form $y < ax + b$ is a region on the coordinate plane called a <u>half-plane</u>. **true**
6. A <u>point</u> defines the boundary of an open half-plane. **false; line**
7. The <u>boundary</u> is the graph of the equation of the line that defines the edge of each half-plane. **true**
8. The solution set to the inequality $y \geq x$ includes the <u>boundary</u>. **true**
9. When solving an inequality, <u>multiplying</u> each side by a negative number reverses the inequality symbol. **true**
10. The graph of a compound inequality that contains <u>*and*</u> is the intersection of the graphs of the two inequalities. **true**

FOLDABLES® Study Organizer

Dinah Zike's Foldables®

Have students look through the chapter to make sure they have included examples in their Foldables.

Suggest that students keep their Foldables handy while completing the Study Guide and Review pages. Point out that their Foldables can serve as a quick review when studying for the chapter test.

322 Chapter 5 Linear Inequalities

Lesson-by-Lesson Review

5-1 Solving Inequalities by Addition and Subtraction (pp. 283–288)

8.B.4a, 8.D.4

Solve each inequality. Then graph it on a number line. **11–16. See margin.**

11. $w - 4 > 9$
12. $x + 8 \leq 3$
13. $6 + h < 1$
14. $-5 < a + 2$
15. $13 - p \geq 15$
16. $y + 1 \leq 8$
17. **FIELD TRIP** A bus can hold 44 people. If there are 35 students in Samantha's class, how many more people can ride on the bus? **no more than 9**

EXAMPLE 1

Solve $x - 9 < -4$. Then graph it on a number line.

$x - 9 < -4$	**Original inequality**
$x - 9 + 9 < -4 + 9$	**Add 9 to each side.**
$x < 5$	**Simplify.**

The solution set is $\{x \mid x < 5\}$.

5-2 Solving Inequalities by Multiplication and Division (pp. 290–295)

8.B.4a, 8.D.4

Solve each inequality. Check your solution.

18. $\frac{1}{3}x > 6$ **$x > 18$**
19. $\frac{1}{5}g \geq -4$ **$g \geq -20$**
20. $4p < 32$ **$p < 8$**
21. $-55 \leq -5w$ **$w \leq 11$**
22. $-2m > 100$ **$m < -50$**
23. $\frac{2}{3}t < -48$ **$t < -72$**
24. **MOVIE RENTAL** Jack has no more than \$24 to spend on DVDs for a party. Each DVD rents for \$4. Find the maximum number of DVDs Jack can rent for his party. **6**

EXAMPLE 2

Solve $-14h < 56$. Check your solution.

$-14h < 56$	**Original inequality**
$\frac{-14h}{-14} > \frac{56}{-14}$	**Divide each side by −14.**
$h > -4$	**Simplify.**

CHECK To check, substitute three different values into the original inequality: -4, a number less than -4, and a number greater than -4.

5-3 Solving Multi-Step Inequalities (pp. 296–301)

8.B.4a, 8.D.4

Solve each inequality. Check your solution.

25. $3h - 7 < 14$ **$h < 7$**
26. $4 + 5b > 34$ **$b > 6$**
27. $18 \leq -2x + 8$ **$x \leq -5$**
28. $\frac{t}{3} - 6 > -4$ **$t > 6$**
29. Four times a number decreased by 6 is less than -2. Define a variable, write an inequality, and solve for the number. **See margin.**
30. **TICKET SALES** The drama club collected \$160 from ticket sales for the spring play. They need to collect at least \$400 to pay for new lighting for the stage. If tickets sell for \$3 each, how many more tickets need to be sold? **at least 80 more**

EXAMPLE 3

Solve $-6y - 13 > 29$. Check your solution.

$-6y - 13 > 29$	**Original inequality**
$-6y - 13 + 13 > 29 + 13$	**Add 13 to each side.**
$-6y > 42$	**Simplify.**
$\frac{-6y}{-6} < \frac{42}{-6}$	**Divide each side by −6 and change > to <.**
$y < -7$	**Simplify.**

The solution set is $\{y \mid y < -7\}$.

CHECK	$-6y - 13 > 29$	**Original inequality**
	$-6(-10) - 13 \stackrel{?}{>} 29$	**Substitute −10 for y.**
	$47 > 29$ ✓	**Simplify.**

Lesson-by-Lesson Review

Intervention If the given examples are not sufficient to review the topics covered by the questions, remind students that the page references tell them where to review that topic in their textbook.

Two-Day Option Have students complete the Lesson-by-Lesson Review on pp. 323–324. Then you can use ExamView® Assessment Suite to customize another review worksheet that practices all the objectives of this chapter or only the objectives on which your students need more help.

Differentiated Instruction

Super DVD: Mindjogger Videoquizzes
Use this DVD as an alternative format of review for the test.

Additional Answers

11. $\{w \mid w > 13\}$

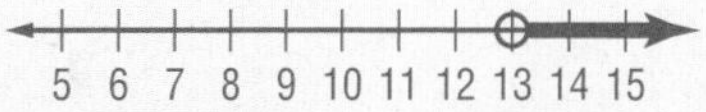

12. $\{x \mid x \leq -5\}$

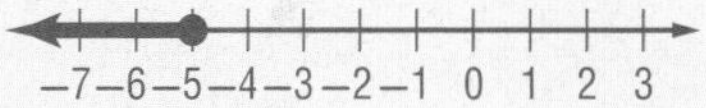

13. $\{h \mid h < -5\}$

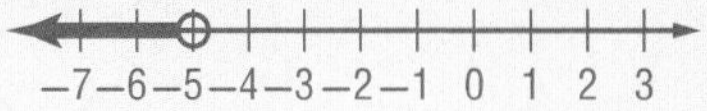

14. $\{a \mid a > -7\}$

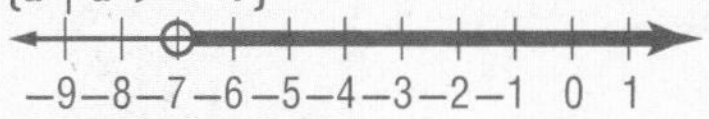

15. $\{p \mid p \leq -2\}$

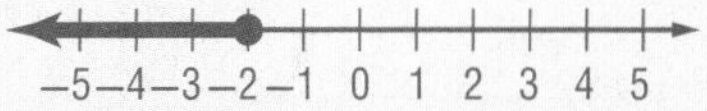

16. $\{y \mid y \leq 7\}$

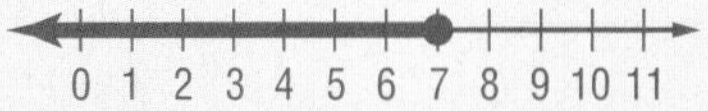

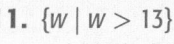

29. Sample answer: Let x = the number, $4x - 6 < -2$; $x < 1$; $\{x \mid x < 1\}$

Problem Solving Review

For additional practice in problem solving for Chapter 5, see the Mixed Problem Solving Appendix, p. 849, in the Student Handbook section.

Anticipation Guide

Have students complete the Chapter 5 Anticipation Guide and discuss how their responses have changed now that they have completed Chapter 5.

5-4 Solving Compound Inequalities (pp. 304–309)

8.B.4a, 8.D.4

Solve each compound inequality. Then graph the solution set. 31–33. See margin.

31. $m - 3 < 6$ and $m + 2 > 4$
32. $-4 < 2t - 6 < 8$
33. $3x + 2 \leq 11$ or $5x - 8 > 22$
34. **KITES** A kite can be flown in wind speeds no less than 7 miles per hour and no more than 16 miles per hour. Write an inequality for the wind speeds at which the kite can fly. $7 \leq x \leq 16$

EXAMPLE 4

Solve $-3w + 4 > -8$ and $2w - 11 > -19$. Then graph the solution set.

$-3w + 4 > -8$ and $2w - 11 > -19$

$w < 4$ $\quad$ $w > -4$

To graph the solution set, graph $w < 4$ and graph $w > -4$. Then find the intersection.

5-5 Inequalities Involving Absolute Value (pp. 310–314)

8.B.4a

Solve each inequality. Then graph the solution set. 35–44. See margin.

35. $\lvert x - 4\rvert < 9$	36. $\lvert p + 2\rvert > 7$
37. $\lvert 2c + 3\rvert \leq 11$	38. $\lvert f - 9\rvert \geq 2$
39. $\lvert 3d - 1\rvert \leq 8$	40. $\left\lvert \frac{4b - 2}{3}\right\rvert < 12$
41. $\left\lvert \frac{2t + 6}{2}\right\rvert > 10$	42. $\lvert -4y - 3\rvert < 13$
43. $\lvert m + 19\rvert \leq 1$	44. $\lvert -k - 7\rvert \geq 4$

EXAMPLE 5

Solve $|x - 6| < 9$. Then graph the solution set.

Case 1 $x - 6$ is nonnegative.

$x - 6 < 9$

$x < 15$

Case 2 $x - 6$ is negative.

$-(x - 6) < 9$

$x > -3$

The solution set is $\{x \mid -3 < x < 15\}$.

5-6 Graphing Inequalities in Two Variables (pp. 315–320)

6.B.4, 8.D.4

Graph each inequality. 45–50. See Ch. 5 Answer Appendix.

45. $y > x - 3$	46. $y < 2x + 1$
47. $3x - y \leq 4$	48. $y \geq -2x + 6$
49. $5x - 2y < 10$	50. $3x + 4y > 12$

Graph each inequality. Determine which of the ordered pairs are part of the solution set for each inequality. 52. (0, 4) (1, 2), (3, –2)

51. $y \leq 4$; {(3, 6), (1, 2), (–4, 8), (3, –2), (1, 7)}
52. $-2x + 3y \geq 12$; {(–2, 2), (–1, 1), (0, 4), (2, 2)}
53. **BAKERY** Ben has $24 to spend on cookies and cupcakes. Write and graph an inequality that represents what Ben can buy. $2x + 3y \leq 24$

51–53. See Ch. 5 Answer Appendix for graphs.

$2

$3

EXAMPLE 6

Graph $2x - y > 3$.

Solve for y in terms of x.

$2x - y > 3$	**Original inequality**
$-y > -2x + 3$	**Subtract 2x from each side.**
$y < 2x - 3$	**Multiply each side by –1.**

Graph the boundary using a dashed line. Choose (0, 0) as a test point.

$2(0) - 0 \overset{?}{>} 3$

$0 \not> 3$

Since 0 is not greater than 3, shade the plane that does not contain (0, 0).

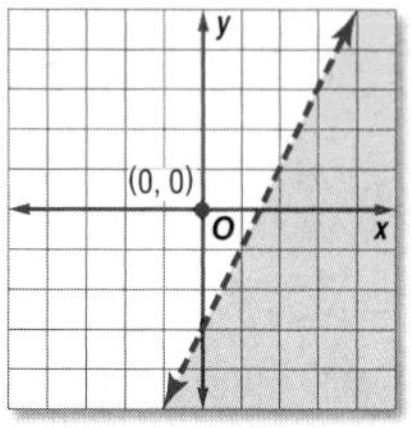

Additional Answers

31. $\{m \mid 2 < m < 9\}$

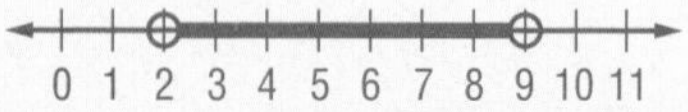

32. $\{t \mid 1 < t < 7\}$

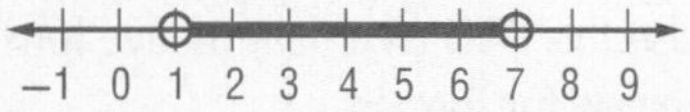

33. $\{x \mid x \leq 3 \text{ or } x > 6\}$

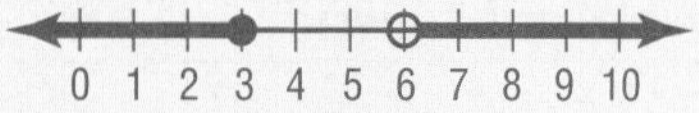

35. $\{x \mid -5 < x < 13\}$

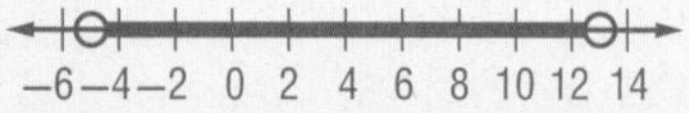

36. $\{p \mid p < -9 \text{ or } p > 5\}$

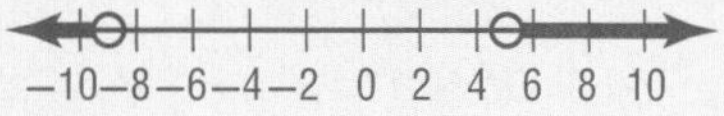

37. $\{c \mid -7 \leq c \leq 4\}$

38. $\{f \mid f \leq 7 \text{ or } f \geq 11\}$

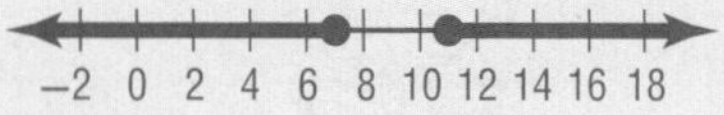

39. $\{d \mid -\frac{7}{3} \leq d \leq 3\}$

40. $\{b \mid -\frac{17}{2} < b < \frac{19}{2}\}$

41. $\{t \mid t < -13 \text{ or } t > 7\}$

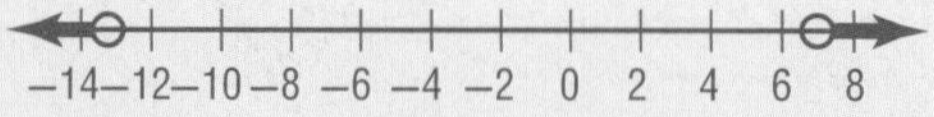

42. $\{y \mid -4 < y < \frac{5}{2}\}$

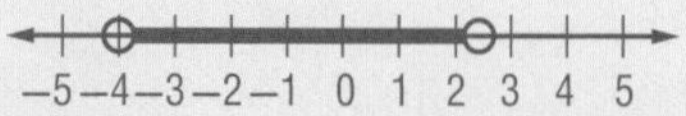

43. $\{m \mid -20 \leq m \leq -18\}$

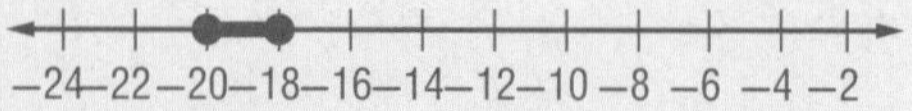

44. $\{k \mid k \geq -3 \text{ or } k \leq -11\}$

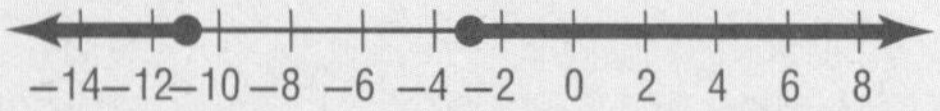

IL Math Online glencoe.com
Chapter Test

Solve each inequality. Then graph it on a number line.

1. $x - 9 < -4$ $x < 5$
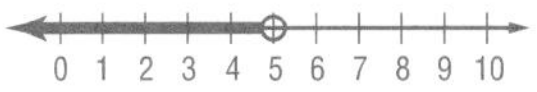

2. $6p \geq 5p - 3$ $p \geq -3$

3. **MULTIPLE CHOICE** Drew currently has 31 comic books in his collection. His friend Connor has 58 comic books. How many more comic books does Drew need to add to his collection in order to have a larger collection than Connor? **C**

   A no more than 21

   B 27

   C at least 28

   D more than 30

Solve each inequality. Check your solution.

4. $\frac{1}{5}h > 3$ $h > 15$
5. $7w \leq -42$ $w \leq -6$
6. $-\frac{2}{3}t \geq 24$ $t \leq -36$
7. $-9m < -36$ $m > 4$
8. $3c - 7 < 11$ $c < 6$
9. $\frac{g}{4} + 3 \leq -9$ $g \leq -48$
10. $-2(x - 4) > 5x - 13$ $x < 3$

11. **ZOO** The 8th grade science class is going to the zoo. The class can spend up to $300 on admission.

Zoo Admission	
Visitor	**Cost**
Student	$8
Adult	$10

   a. Write an inequality for this situation. $8s + 10a \leq 300$

   b. If there are 32 students in the class and 1 adult will attend for every 8 students, how much will admission be? **$296**

Solve each compound inequality. Then graph the solution set. 12–13. See margin.

12. $y - 8 < -3$ or $y + 5 > 19$
13. $-11 \leq 2h - 5 \leq 13$
14. $3z - 2 > -5$ and $7z + 4 < -17$ $\emptyset$

Define a variable, write an inequality, and solve the problem. Check your solution.

15. The difference of a number and 4 is no more than 8. See margin.

16. Nine times a number decreased by four is at least twenty-three. See margin.

17. **MULTIPLE CHOICE** Write a compound inequality for the graph shown below. **G**

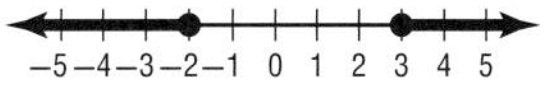

   F $-2 \leq x < 3$

   G $x \leq -2$ or $x \geq 3$

   H $x < -2$ or $x \geq 3$

   J $-2 < x \leq 3$

18–21. See Ch. 5 Answer Appendix.

Solve each inequality. Then graph the solution set.

18. $|p - 5| < 3$
19. $|2f + 7| \geq 21$
20. $|-4m + 3| \leq 15$
21. $\left|\frac{x - 3}{4}\right| > 5$

22. **RETAIL** A sporting goods store is offering a $15 coupon on any pair of shoes.

   a. The most and least expensive pairs of shoes are $149.95 and $24.95. What is the range of costs for customers with coupons? $9.95 \leq p \leq 134.95$

   b. When buying a pair of $109.95 shoes, you can use a coupon or a 15% discount. Which option is best? **15% discount**

23–24. See Ch. 5 Answer Appendix.

Graph each inequality.

23. $y < 4x - 1$
24. $2x + 3y \geq 12$

25. Graph $y > -2x + 5$. Then determine which of the ordered pairs in {(−2, 0), (−1, 5), (2, 3), (7, 3)} are in the solution set. See Ch. 5 Answer Appendix.

26. **PRESCHOOL** Mrs. Jones is buying new books and puzzles for her preschool classroom. Each book costs $6, and each puzzle costs $4. Write and graph an inequality to determine how many books and puzzles she can buy for $96. $6x + 4y \leq 96$; see Ch. 5 Answer Appendix for graph.

ExamView Assessment Suite — Customize and create multiple versions of your chapter tests and their answer keys. All of the questions from the leveled chapter tests in the *Chapter 5 Resource Masters* are also available on ExamView® Assessment Suite.

Additional Answers

12. $\{y \mid y < 5 \text{ or } y > 14\}$
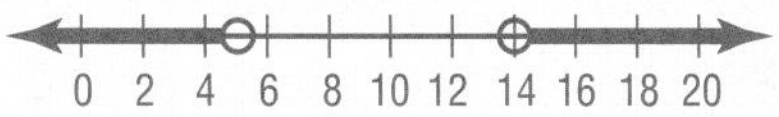

13. $\{h \mid -3 \leq h \leq 9\}$
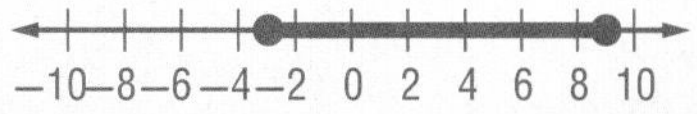

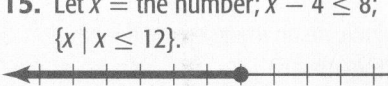

15. Let x = the number; $x - 4 \leq 8$; $\{x \mid x \leq 12\}$.
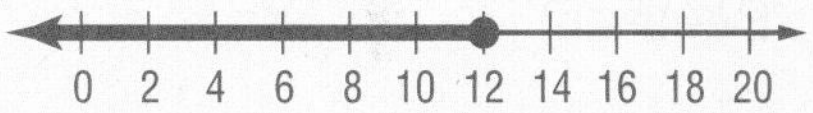

16. Let x = the number; $9x - 4 \geq 23$; $\{x \mid x \geq 3\}$.
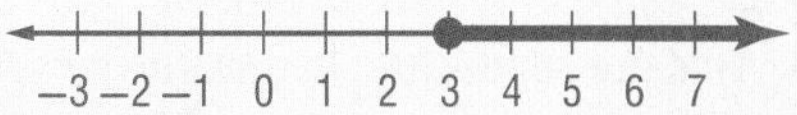

Intervention Planner

Tier 1 On Level	Tier 2 Strategic Intervention approaching grade level	Tier 3 Intensive Intervention 2 or more grades below level
If students miss about 25% of the exercises or less,	**If** students miss about 50% of the exercises,	**If** students miss about 75% of the exercises,
Then choose a resource: **SE** Lessons 5-1, 5-2, 5-3, 5-4, 5-5, and 5-6 **CRM** Skills Practice, pp. 7, 13, 19, 25, 31, and 38 **TE** Chapter Project, p. 280 IL Math Online Self-Check Quiz	**Then** choose a resource: **CRM** Study Guide and Intervention, Chapter 5, p. 5, 11, 17, 23, 29, and 36 *Quick Review Math Handbook* IL Math Online Extra Examples, Personal Tutor, Homework Help	**Then** use *Math Triumph, Alg. 1* IL Math Online Extra Examples, Personal Tutor, Homework Help, Review Vocabulary

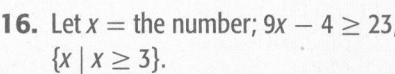

1 FOCUS

Objective Use the strategy of writing and solving an inequality to solve standardized test problems.

2 TEACH

Scaffolding Questions

Ask:

- What are some situations in which you could use an inequality to represent the situation? Answers will vary.
- What are the symbols used to indicate an inequality and what do they mean? The symbols are $<$, which means less than, $>$, which means greater than, $\leq$, which means less than or equal to, and $\geq$, which means greater than or equal to.
- What are some clues in a word problem that suggest that writing and solving an inequality will solve the problem? Answers will vary.

CHAPTER 5 Preparing for Standardized Tests

Write and Solve an Inequality

Many multiple-choice items will require writing and solving inequalities. Follow the steps below to help you successfully solve these types of problems.

Strategies for Writing and Solving Inequalities

Step 1

Read the problem statement carefully.

Ask yourself:

- What am I being asked to solve?
- What information is given in the problem?
- What are the unknowns for which I need to solve?

Step 2

Translate the problem statement into an inequality.

- Assign variables to the unknown(s).
- Write the word sentence as a mathematical number sentence looking for words such as *greater than, less than, no more than, up to,* or *at least to* indicate the type of inequality as well as where to place the inequality sign.

Step 3

Solve the inequality.

- Solve for the unknowns in the inequality.
- Remember that multiplying or dividing each side by a negative number reverses the direction of the inequality.
- Check your answer to make sure it makes sense.

EXAMPLE

Read the problem. Identify what you need to know. Then use the information in the problem to solve. Show your work.

Pedro has earned scores of 89, 74, 79, 85, and 88 on his tests this semester. He needs a test average of at least 85 in order to earn an A for the semester. There will be one more test given this semester.

A Write an inequality to model the situation.

B What score must he have on his final test to earn an A for the semester?

326 Chapter 5 Linear Inequalities

Read the problem carefully. You are given Pedro's first 5 test scores and told that he needs an average of *at least* 85 after his next test to earn an A for the semester.

a. Write the inequality.

Words	Pedro needs a test average of *at least* 85.
Variable	Let *t* represent Pedro's score on the final test.
Equation	$\frac{89 + 74 + 79 + 85 + 88 + t}{6} \geq 85$

b. Solve the inequality for *t*.

$$\frac{89 + 74 + 79 + 85 + 88 + t}{6} \geq 85$$

$$89 + 74 + 79 + 85 + 88 + t \geq 85(6)$$

$$415 + t \geq 510$$

$$t \geq 95$$

So, Pedro's final test score must be greater than or equal to 95 in order for him to earn an A for the semester.

Exercises

Read each problem. Identify what you need to know. Then use the information in the problem to solve.

1. Craig has $20 to order a pizza. The pizza costs $12.50 plus $0.95 per topping. If there is also a $3 deliver fee, how many toppings can Craig order? **up to 4 toppings**
2. To join an archery club, Nina had to pay an initiation fee of $75, plus $40 per year in membership dues.
   a. Write an equation to model the total cost, y, of belonging to the club for x years. $y = 40x + 75$
   b. How many years will it take her to spend more than $400 to belong to the club? **9 years**
3. The area of the triangle below is no more than 84 square millimeters. What is the height of the triangle? **no more than 12 mm**

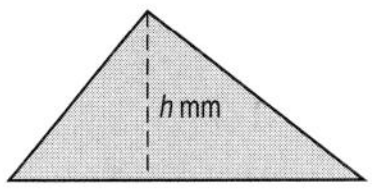

4. Rosa earns $200 a month delivering newspapers, plus an average of $11 per hour babysitting. If her goal is to earn at least $295 this month, how many hours will she have to babysit? **at least 9 hours**
5. To earn money for a new bike, Ethan is selling some of his baseball cards. He has saved $245. If the bike costs $1400, and he can sell 154 cards, for how much money will he need to sell each card to reach his goal? **at least $7.50 per card**
6. In a certain lacrosse league, there can be no more than 22 players on each team, and no more than 10 teams per age group. There are 6 age groups.
   a. Write an inequality to represent this situation. $p \leq 22 \cdot 10 \cdot 6$
   b. What is the greatest number of players that can play lacrosse in this league? **1320 players**
7. Sarah has $120 to shop for herself and to buy some gifts for 6 of her friends. She has purchased a shirt for herself for $32. What is the maximum that she can spend on each friend? **$14.66**

Additional Example

SHORT RESPONSE A company plans to buy, at most, 115 spots of radio airtime to advertise a new line of sporting goods. The company will use 40 spots to advertise the new line and 5 weeks of spots to advertise sales of the new line. The company plans to run an equal number of spots each week.

a. Write an inequality to model the situation.

b. What is the greatest number of spots the company will run each week?

Sample 2-point response:

a. Let a equal the number of advertising spots per week. Let the symbol $\leq$ represent the inequality *at most*. The inequality $5a + 40 \leq 115$ models the situation.

b. Solve the inequality for a to find the greatest number of spots the company will run per week.

$$5a + 40 \leq 115$$

$$5a \leq 115 - 40$$

$$5a \leq 75$$

$$a \leq 15$$

So, the company will run at most 15 spots per week.

3 ASSESS

Use Exercises 1–7 to assess students' understanding.

Chapter 5 Preparing for Standardized Tests 327

Diagnose Student Errors

Survey students' responses for each item. Class trends may indicate common errors and misconceptions.

1. A rounded answer up instead of down
   B used the inequality symbol for *at least* instead of *at most*
   C used the inequality symbol for *less* than instead of *at most* or *less than or equal to*
   D correct
   E guess
2. F chose hours that represent less than \$600
   G chose hours that represent less than \$600
   H correct
   J chose hours that represent at least \$600, but not the minimum hours
   K too many overtime hours
3. A confused slope and *y*-intercept and chose positive instead of negative slope
   B chose negative instead of positive *y*-intercept
   C correct
   D confused slope and *y*-intercept
   E chose positive slope
4. F chose highest score only
   G chose lowest score only
   H misunderstood difference between *greater than* and *greater than or equal to* and *less than* and *less than or equal to*
   J correct
   K chose highest score only
5. A misinterpreted *over* to mean *less than* instead of *greater than*
   B correct
   C calculation error
   D calculation error and misinterpreted *over* to mean *less than* instead of *greater than*
   E calculation error
6. F chose result for *less than* instead of *more than*
   G chose result for *less than* instead of *more than*
   H chose result for \$250
   J exactly \$250, not *more than* \$250
   K correct
7. A misunderstood concept of undefined slope
   B misunderstood concept of undefined slope
   C misunderstood concept of undefined slope
   D correct
   E misunderstood concept of unidefined slope
8. F chose Commutative Property instead of Associative Property
   G chose Distributive Property instead of Associative Property
   H correct
   J chose Additive Inverse Property instead of Associative Property
   K chose Identity Property

Multiple Choice

Read each question. Then fill in the correct answer on the answer document provided by your teacher or on a sheet of paper.

1. Miguel received a \$100 gift certificate. He wants to buy a CD player that costs \$38 and CDs that cost \$12 each. Which of the following inequalities represents how many CDs Miguel can buy? D

   A $n \leq 6$ D $n \leq 5$
   B $n \geq 5$ E $n \leq 2$
   C $n < 5$

2. Craig is paid time-and-a-half for any additional hours over 40 that he works.

Time	Pay Rate
Up to 40 hours	\$12.80/hr
Additional hours worked over 40	\$19.20/hr

   If Craig's goal is to earn at least \$600 next week, what is the minimum number of hours he needs to work? H

   F 43 hours   J 46 hours
   G 44 hours   K 48 hours
   H 45 hours

3. Which equation has a slope of $-\frac{2}{3}$ and a *y*-intercept of 6? C

   A $y = 6x + \frac{2}{3}$ D $y = 6x - \frac{2}{3}$
   B $y = -\frac{2}{3}x - 6$ E $y = \frac{2}{3}x + 6$
   C $y = -\frac{2}{3}$

4. The highest score that is on record on a video game is 10,219 points. The lowest score on record is 257 points. Which of the following inequalities best shows the range of scores recorded on the game? J

   F $x \leq 10{,}219$ J $257 \leq x \leq 10{,}219$
   G $x \geq 257$ K $x \leq 9{,}962$
   H $257 < x < 10{,}219$

5. Kyle scored 14 points in his last game, so his total is over 100 points. Which number line represents the number of points Kyle had scored prior to the last game? B

   A
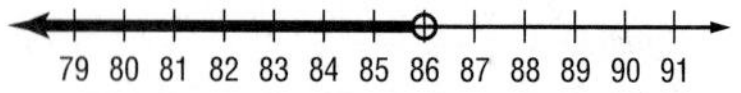

   B
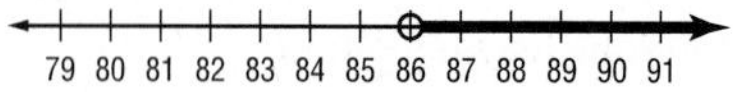

   C
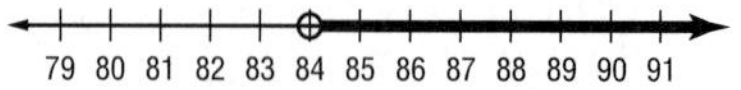

   D
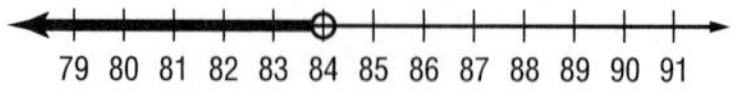

   E
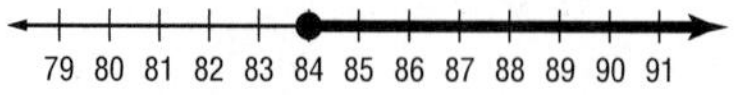

6. The girls' volleyball team is selling T-shirts and pennants to raise money for new uniforms.

Item	Price
T-shirt	\$10
Pennant	\$4

   Which of the following combinations of items sold would raise more than \$250? K

   F 16 T-shirts and 20 pennants
   G 20 T-shirts and 12 pennants
   H 17 T-shirts and 20 pennants
   J 15 T-shirts and 25 pennants
   K 18 T-shirts and 18 pennants

7. What type of line does not have a defined slope? D

   A horizontal   D vertical
   B parallel   E diagonal
   C perpendicular

8. Which expression below illustrates the Associative Property? H

   F $abc = bac$ J $5 + (-5) = 0$
   G $2(x - 3) = 2x - 6$ K $5 \cdot 1 = 5$
   H $(p + 3) - t = p + (3 - t)$

Test-Taking Tip

Question 2 You can check your answer by finding Craig's earnings for the hours worked.

328 Chapter 5 Linear Inequalities

Short Response/Gridded Response

Record your answers on the answer sheet provided by your teacher or on a sheet of paper.

9. Solve $-4 < 3x + 8 \leq 23$. **$-4 < x \leq 5$**

10. GRIDDED RESPONSE Tien is saving money for a new television. She needs to save at least $720 to pay for her expenses. Each week Tien saves $50 toward her new television. How many weeks will it take so she can pay for the television? **15 weeks**

11. Write an inequality that best represents the graph. **$y \leq -\frac{2}{3}x + 1$**

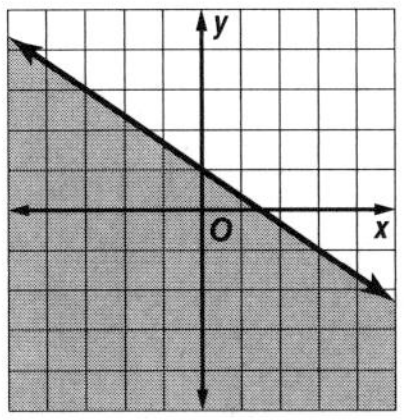

12. Solve $|x - 4| < 2$. **$2 < x < 6$**

13. GRIDDED RESPONSE Daniel wants to ship a set of golf clubs and several boxes of golf balls in a box that can hold up to 20 pounds. If the set of clubs weighs 9 pounds and each box of golf balls weighs 12 ounces, how many boxes of golf balls can Daniel ship? **14 boxes**

14. Graph the solution set for the inequality $3x - 6 \leq 4x - 4 \leq 3x + 1$.

15. Write an equation that represents the data in the table. **$y = 3.5x + 2$**

x	y
3	12.5
4	16
5	19.5
6	23
7	26.5

16. A sporting goods company near the beach rents bicycles for $10 plus $5 per hour. Write an equation in slope-intercept form that shows the total cost, y, of renting a bicycle for x hours. How much would it cost Emily to rent a bicycle for 6 hours? **$y = 5x + 10$; $40**

Extended Response

Record your answers on a sheet of paper. Show your work.

17. Theresa is saving money for a vacation. She needs to save at least $640 to pay for her expenses. Each week, she puts $35 towards her vacation savings.

a. Let w represent the number of weeks Theresa saves money. Write an inequality to model the situation. **$35w \geq 640$**

b. Solve the inequality from part a. What is the minimum number of weeks Theresa must save money in order to reach her goal? **19 weeks**

c. If Theresa were to save $45 each week instead, by how many weeks would the minimum savings time be decreased? **by 4 weeks**

Need Extra Help?																	
If you missed Question...	1	2	3	4	5	6	7	8	9	10	11	12	13	14	15	16	17
Go to Lesson or Page...	5-3	5-2	4-1	5-4	5-1	5-6	3-3	1-3	5-4	5-2	5-6	5-5	5-3	5-4	2-1	4-2	5-2
IL Assessment Objectives	8.11.16	8.11.16	8.11.09	8.11.16	8.11.16	6.11.13	8.11.08	6.11.05	8.11.16	8.11.16	8.11.16	8.11.19	8.11.16	8.11.16	8.11.07	8.11.02	8.11.02

Formative Assessment

You can use these two pages to benchmark student progress.

CRM Standardized Test Practice, pp. 62–64

Answer Sheet Practice

Have students simulate taking a standardized test by recording their answers on a practice recording sheet.

CRM Student Recording Sheet, p. 43

Chapter Resource Master
CRM p. 43

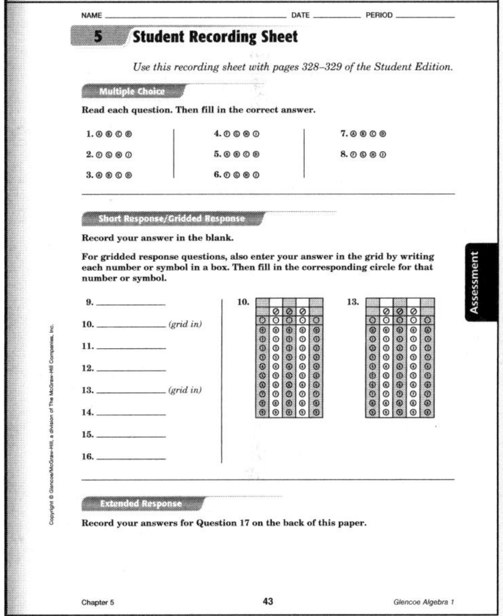
NAME DATE PERIOD

5 Student Recording Sheet

Use this recording sheet with pages 328–329 of the Student Edition.

Multiple Choice

Read each question. Then fill in the correct answer.

1. 2. 3. 4. 5. 6. 7. 8.

Short Response/Gridded Response

Record your answer in the blank.

For gridded response questions, also enter your answer in the grid by writing each number or symbol in a box. Then fill in the corresponding circle for that number or symbol.

9. 10. (grid in) 11. 12. 13. (grid in) 14. 15. 16.

Extended Response

Record your answers for Question 17 on the back of this paper.

Chapter 5 43 Glencoe Algebra 1

Assessment

ExamView Assessment Suite Create practice worksheets or tests that align to your state's standards, as well as TIMSS and NAEP tests.

Homework Option

Get Ready for Chapter 6 Assign students the exercises on p. 331 as homework to assess whether they possess the prerequisite skills needed for the next chapter.

Pages 286–287, Lesson 5-1

12. $\{m \mid m < 7\}$

13. $\{p \mid p \geq 9\}$

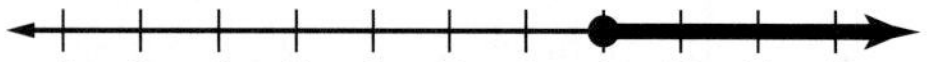

14. $\{r \mid r \leq 15\}$

15. $\{t \mid t > -5\}$

16. $\{b \mid b \geq 2\}$

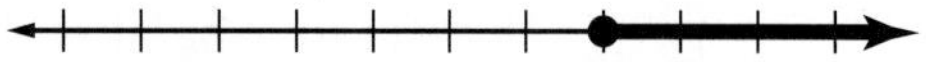

17. $\{r \mid r < -5\}$

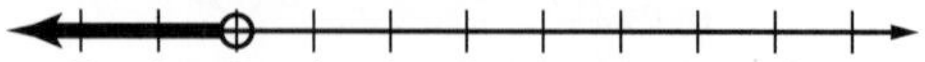

18. $\{c \mid c \leq -4\}$

19. $\{q \mid q \leq 7\}$

20. $\{m \mid m \geq 4\}$

21. $\{h \mid h < 30\}$

22. $\{r \mid r \geq 22\}$

23. $\{c \mid c < -27\}$

24. $\{a \mid a \leq -4\}$

25. $\{z \mid z \leq 4\}$

26. $\{w \mid w \geq -5\}$

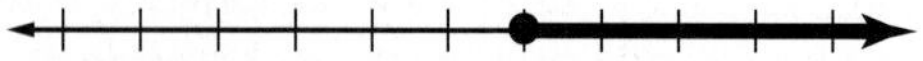

27. $\{y \mid y \leq -6\}$

28. $\{x \mid x \leq 5\}$

29. $\{a \mid a > -9\}$

37. Sample answer: Let $t =$ the original water temperature; $t + 4 < 81$; $\{t \mid t < 77\}$; the water temperature was originally less than 77°.

38. Sample answer: Let $p =$ points needed to score; $p + 123 \geq 150$; $\{p \mid p \geq 27\}$; she must score at least 27 points.

41. $\{c \mid c \geq 3.7\}$

42. $\{g \mid g > 4.5\}$

43. $\left\{k \,\middle|\, k > -\frac{5}{12}\right\}$

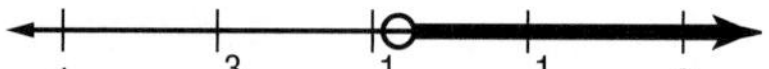

44. $\left\{p \,\middle|\, p \leq 1\frac{1}{9}\right\}$

45a.

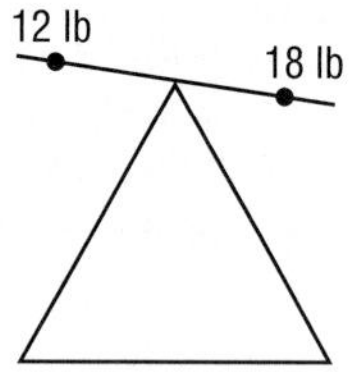

45b. 12 lb < 18 lb

45c.

	12	<	18
2	24	<	36
3	36	<	54
4	48	<	72
$\frac{1}{2}$	6	<	9
$\frac{1}{3}$	4	<	6
$\frac{1}{4}$	3	<	$4\frac{1}{2}$

45d. If a true inequality is multiplied by a positive number, the resulting inequality is also true. If a true inequality is divided by a positive number, the resulting inequality is also true.

54. Sample answers: $y + 1 < -2$, $y - 1 < -4$, $y + 3 < 0$

55. Solving linear inequalities is similar to solving linear equations. You must isolate the variable on one side of the inequality. To graph, if the problem is a less than or a greater than inequality, an open circle is used. Otherwise a dot is used. If the variable is on the left hand side of the inequality, and the inequality sign is less than (or less than or equal to), the graph extends to the left; otherwise it extends to the right.

56. The inequalities are equivalent. By adding 2 to each side of the first inequality, you get the second inequality.

Page 289, Explore 5-2

6. Sample answer: When the solution is written so that the variable remains on the same side as in the original inequality, the inequality symbol is reversed in the solution.
7. Sample answer: $x \leq 4$; The inequality symbol remains the same in the solution for $3x \leq 12$, but is reversed in the solution for $-3x \leq 12$.
8. Sample answer: When solving inequalities involving multiplication, the inequality symbol remains unchanged when multiplying by a positive number, but is reversed when multiplying by a negative number. When solving inequalities involving division, the inequality symbol remains unchanged when dividing by a positive number, but is reversed when dividing by a negative number or multiplying by a negative reciprocal.

Page 295, Lesson 5-2

58.

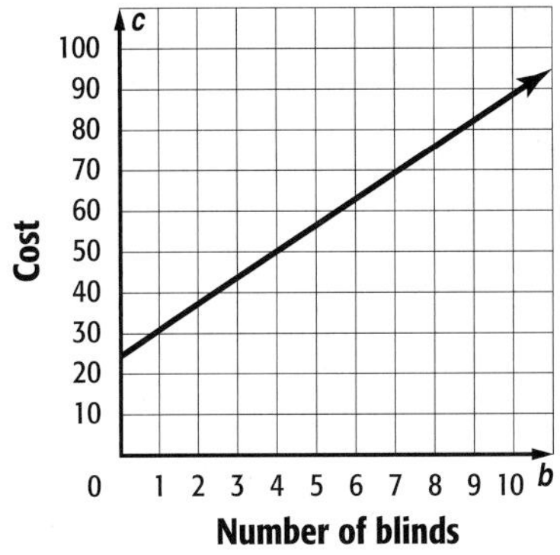

$77

Pages 299–301, Lesson 5-3

37.

$6(m-3) > 5(2m+4)$	Original inequality
$6m - 18 > 10m + 20$	Distributive Property
$6m - 18 - 6m > 10m + 20 - 6m$	Subtract $6m$ from each side.
$-18 > 4m + 20$	Simplify.
$-18 - 20 > 4m + 20 - 20$	Subtract 20 from each side.
$-38 > 4m$	Simplify.
$-\frac{38}{4} > \frac{4m}{4}$	Divide each side by 4.
$-9.5 > m$	Simplify.
$\{m \mid m < -9.5\}$	

38.

$8(a-2) \leq 10(a+2)$	Original inequality
$8a - 16 \leq 10a + 20$	Distributive Property
$8a - 16 - 8a \leq 10a + 20 - 8a$	Subtract $8a$ from each side.
$-16 \leq 2a + 20$	Simplify.
$-16 - 20 \leq 2a + 20 - 20$	Subtract 20 from each side.
$-36 \leq 2a$	Simplify.
$\frac{-36}{2} \leq \frac{2a}{2}$	Divide each side by 2.
$-18 \leq a$	Simplify.
$\{a \mid a \geq -18\}$	

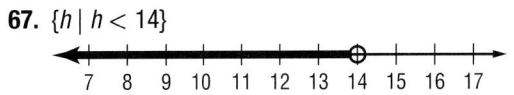

67. $\{h \mid h < 14\}$

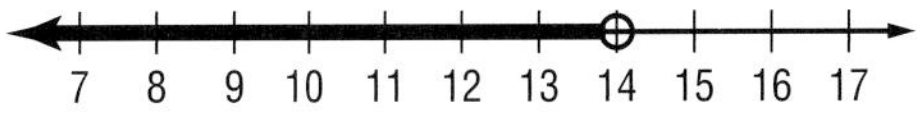

68. $\{p \mid p < 11\}$

69. $\{m \mid m \geq 1\}$

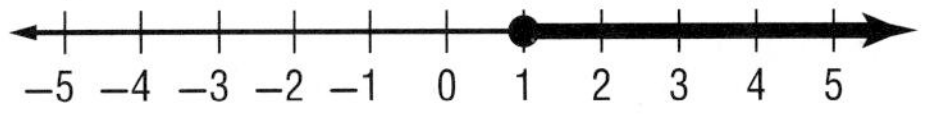

70. -8

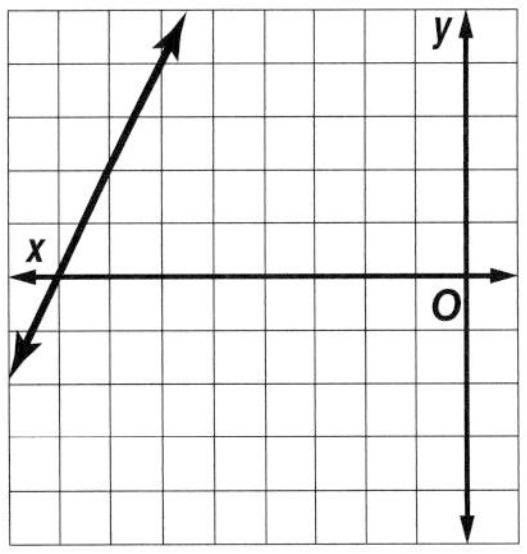

71. 4

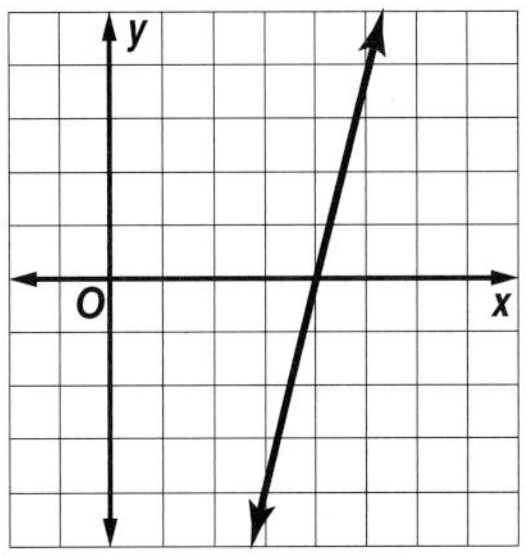

72. -6

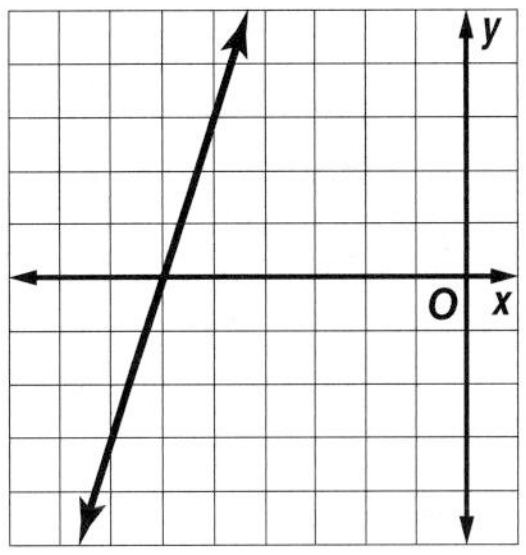

78.

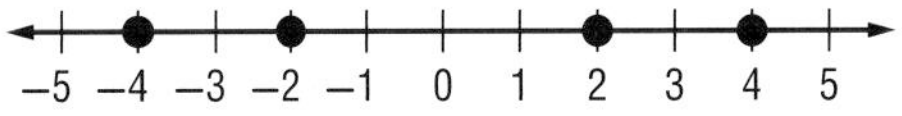

79.

80.

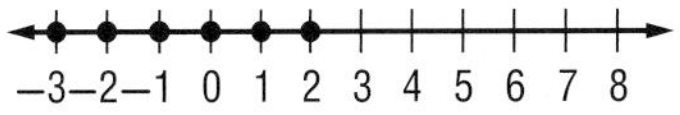

81.

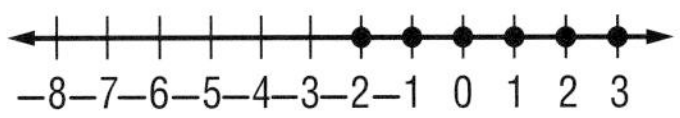

82.

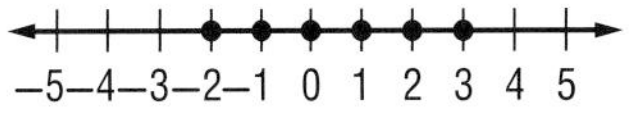

83.

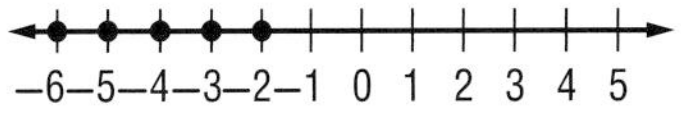

Page 302, Mid-Chapter Quiz

6. Sample answer: Let x = the number; $x + (-2) \leq 6$; $x \leq 8$
7. Sample answer: Let x = the number; $x - 4 > -1$; $x > 3$
8. Sample answer: Let x = the number; $2x + 3 < x - 4$; $x < -7$
25. Sample answer: Let x = the number; $3x + 8 \leq x - 4$; $x \leq -6$
26. Sample answer: Let x = the number; $\frac{2}{3}x + 5 > 17$; $x > 18$

Page 303, Explore 5-4

1. True; since most top 20 movies in 2004 were rated PG-13, one of the statements is true. Thus the compound statement is true.

2. False; since more movies were not rated PG than rated PG-13, one of the statements is false. Thus the compound statement is false.

3. True; both parts of the compound statement are true. Thus the compound statement is true.

4. True; most top 20 movies in 2005 were not rated PG, one of the statements is true. Thus the compound statement is true.

5. False; both statements are false. Thus the compound statement is false.

6. False; since (−2) is not greater than 0, one of the statements is false. Thus the compound statement is false.

7. True; both parts of the compound statement are true. Thus the compound statement is true.

8. True; both parts of the compound statement are true. Thus the compound statement is true.

9. True; since −2 is greater than −5, one of the statements is true. Thus the compound statement is true.

10. False; since 5 is not greater than 10, one of the statements is false. Thus the compound statement is false.

Pages 306–307, Lesson 5-4

1. $\{p \mid 12 \leq p \leq 16\}$

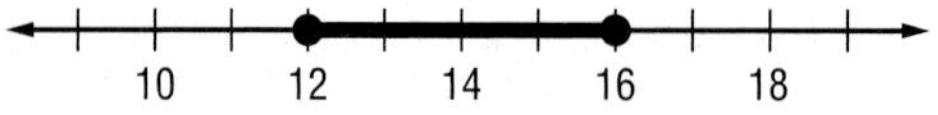

2. $\{r \mid r < -14 \text{ or } r > -7\}$

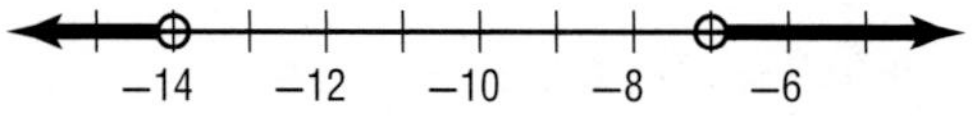

3. $\{a \mid a > 5\}$

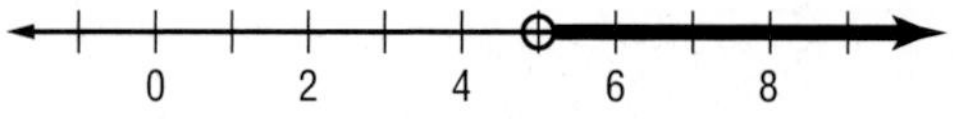

4. $\{g \mid -2 \leq g < 3\}$

6. $\{f \mid 6 \leq f < 11\}$

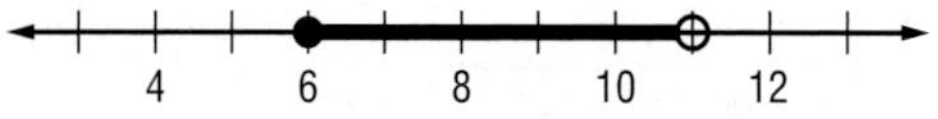

7. $\{n \mid -12 \leq n \leq -7\}$

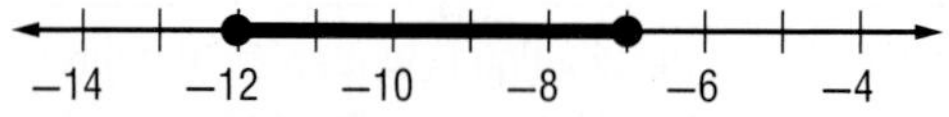

8. $\{y \mid y \geq 8 \text{ or } y < -4\}$

9. $\{t \mid t \geq 1 \text{ or } t < -1\}$

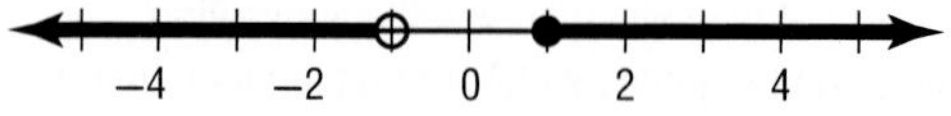

10. $\{p \mid -4 < p \leq 5\}$

11. $\{c \mid -1 \leq c < 2\}$

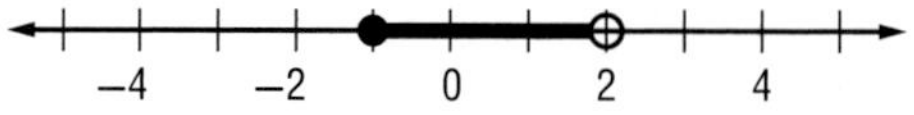

12. $\{h \mid 2 \leq h < 3\}$

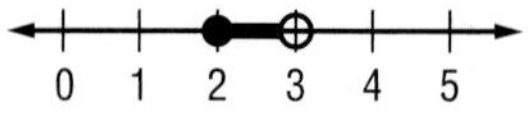

13. $\{m \mid m$ is a real number.$\}$

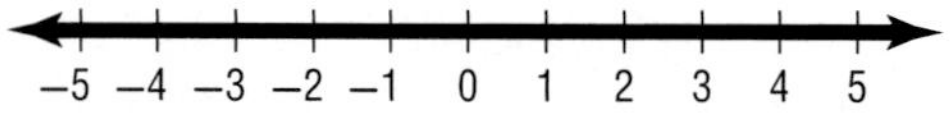

14. $\varnothing$

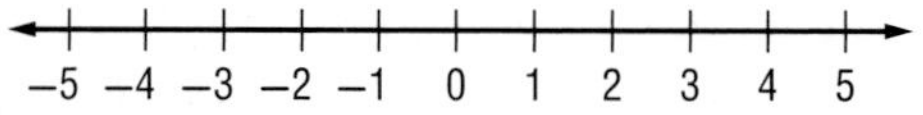

15. $\{y \mid y < -3\}$

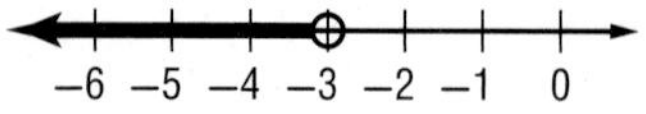

24. $\{b \mid 4 < b \leq 5\}$

25. $\left\{a \mid -3 < a \leq \frac{1}{2}\right\}$

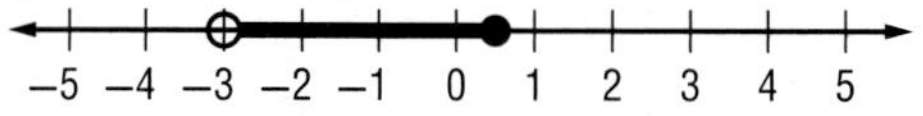

26. $\{m \mid m < -6 \text{ or } m > -1\}$

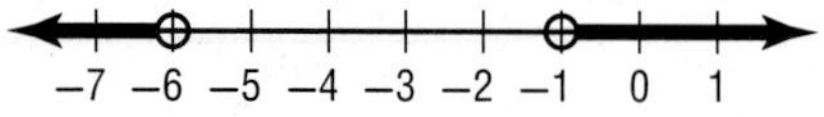

27. $\{n \mid n < -3 \text{ or } n > -3\}$

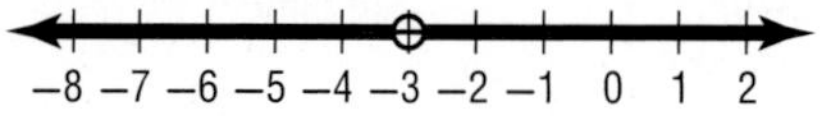

Pages 312–314, Lesson 5-5

1. $\{a \mid 2 < a < 8\}$

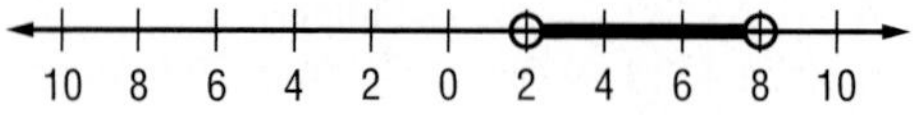

2. $\{u \mid -10 < u < 4\}$

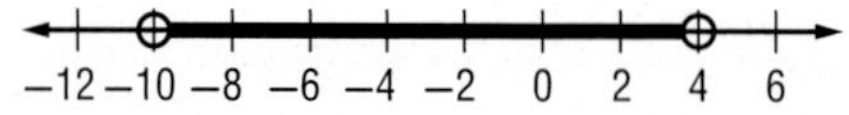

3. ∅

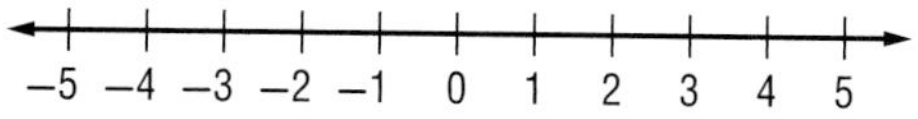

4. {c | c is a real number.}

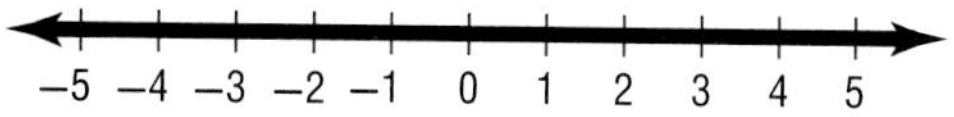

5. {n | $n \leq -8$ or $n \geq -2$}

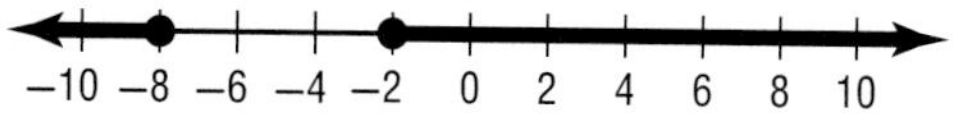

6. {p | $p \leq -6$ or $p \geq 10$}

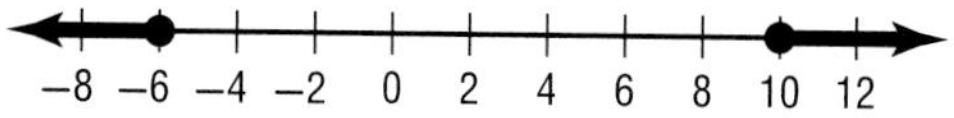

8. {x | $-24 < x < 8$}

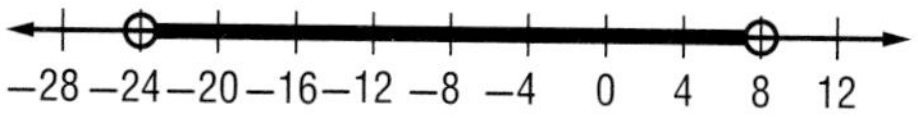

9. {r | $-3 \leq r \leq 1$}

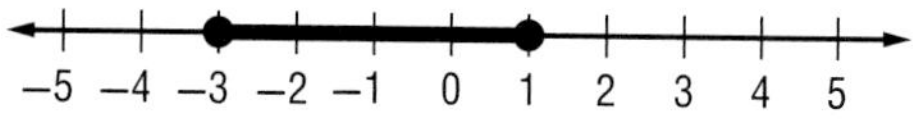

10. {c | $-3 \leq c \leq 4$}

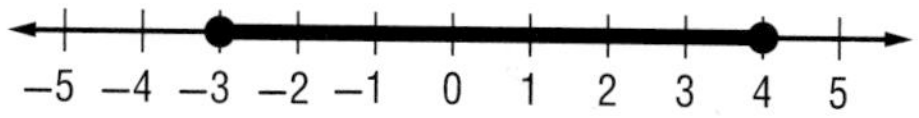

11. {h | $-3 < h < 5$}

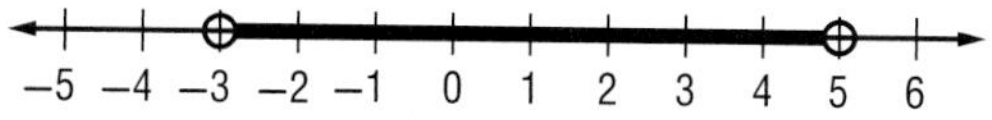

12. ∅

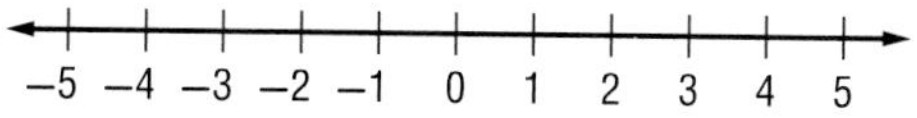

13. ∅

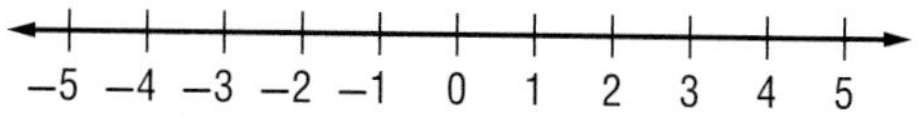

14. {r | $r < -8$ or $r > 4$}

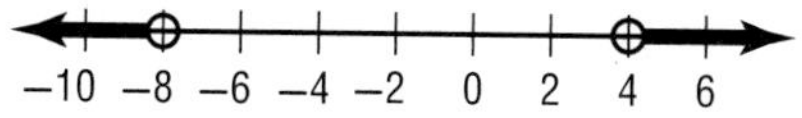

15. {k | $k < 1$ or $k > 7$}

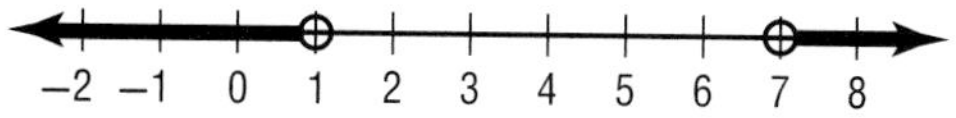

16. {h | $h \leq -3$ or $h \geq 6$}

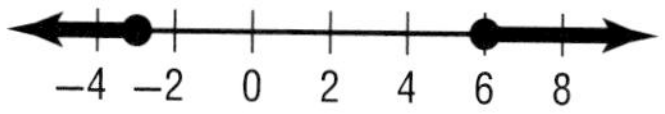

17. {p | $p \leq -3$ or $p \geq 2$}

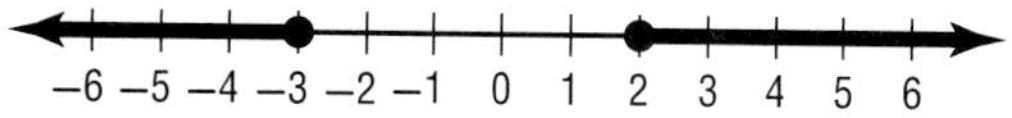

18. {v | v is a real number.}

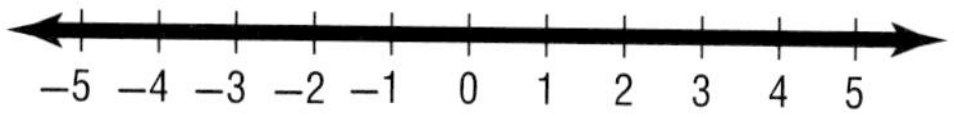

19. {c | c is a real number.}

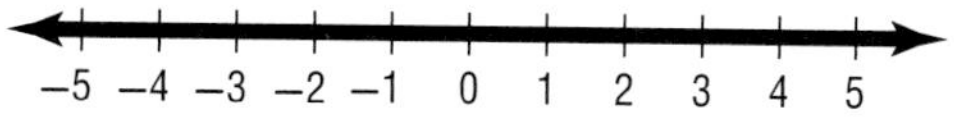

21. $\left\{n \,\middle|\, n \leq -5\frac{1}{4} \text{ or } n \geq 3\frac{3}{4}\right\}$

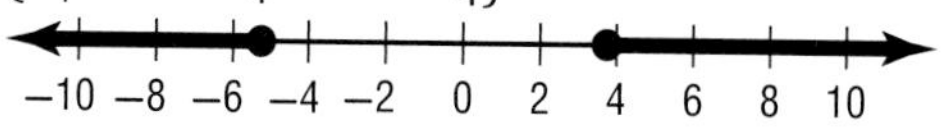

22. $\left\{t \,\middle|\, -\frac{4}{5} \leq t \leq 1\frac{3}{5}\right\}$

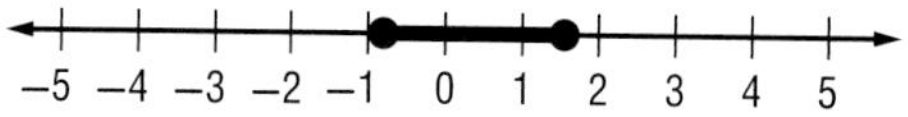

23. $\left\{h \,\middle|\, -5\frac{2}{3} < h < 5\right\}$

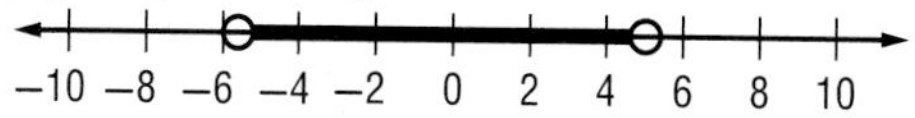

24. {p | $p \leq -14$ or $p \geq 22$}

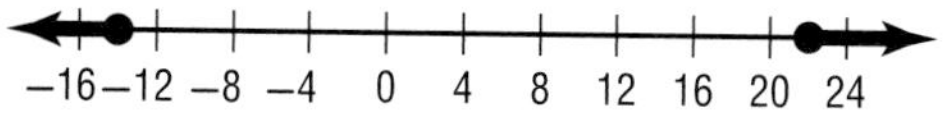

25. ∅

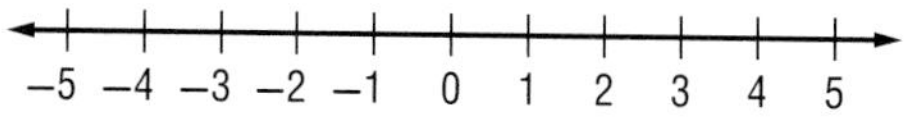

26. {g | g is a real number.}

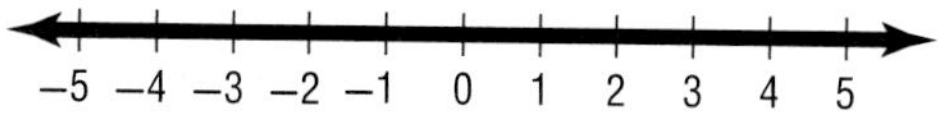

27. $\left\{r \,\middle|\, -2 < r < \frac{2}{3}\right\}$

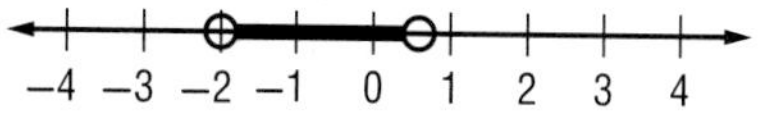

28. $\left\{p \,\middle|\, p < -4 \text{ or } p > -\frac{2}{3}\right\}$

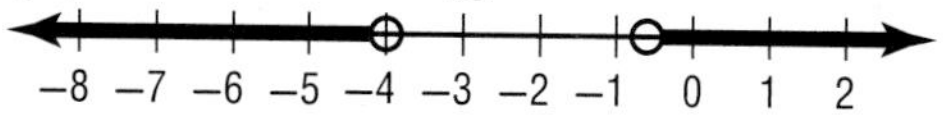

29. {h | $-1.5 < h < 4.5$}

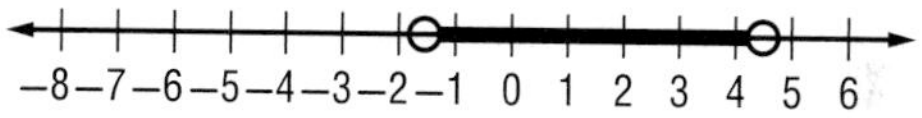

30b.

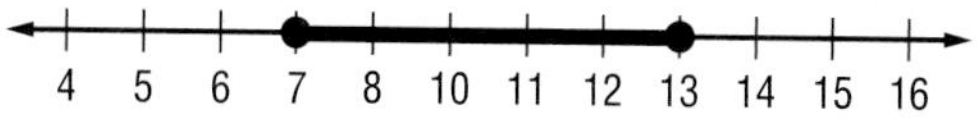

42b.

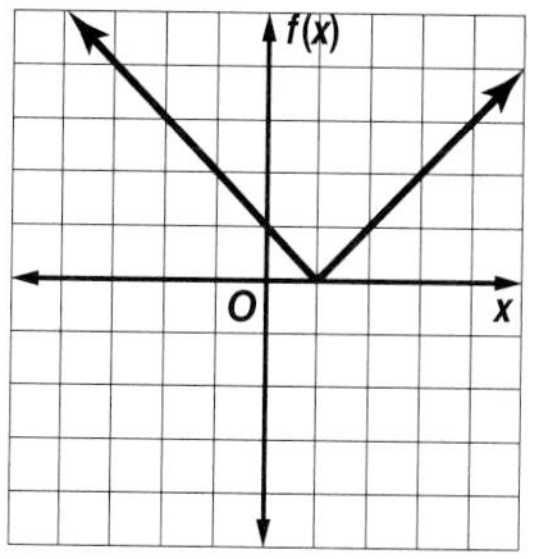

42c.

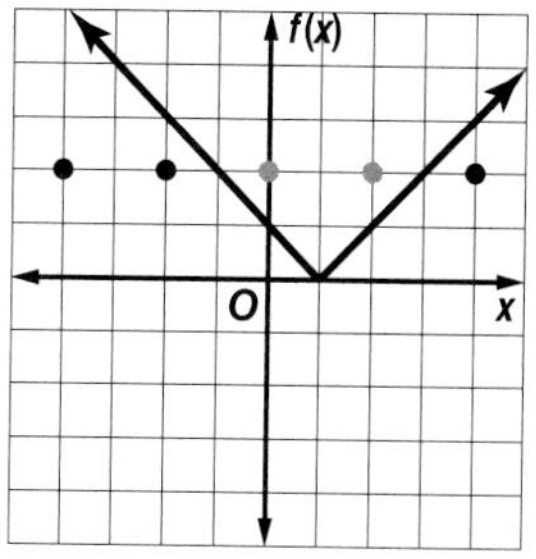

42d. $f(x) > |x - 1|$

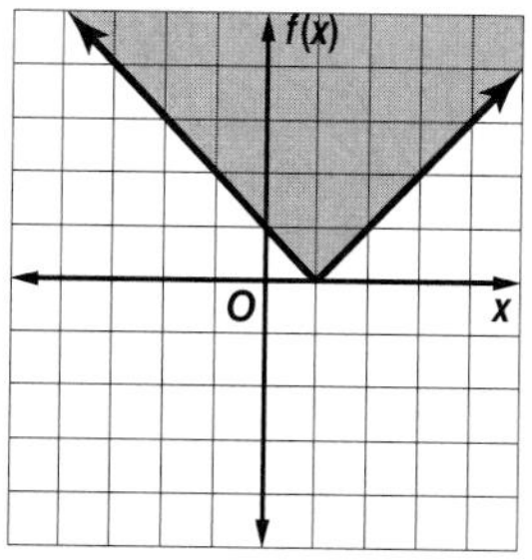

42e. Sample answer:

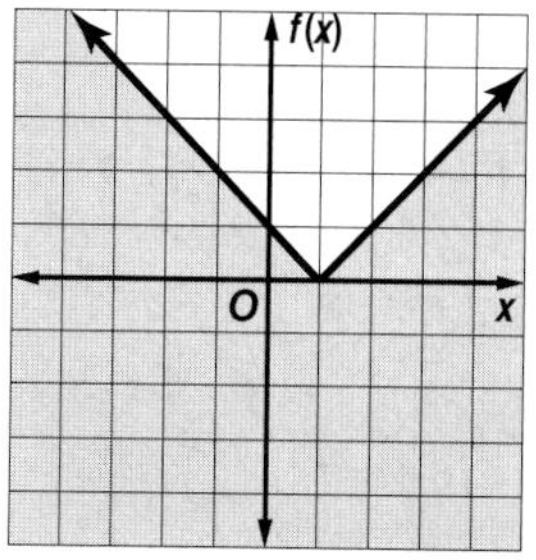

61.

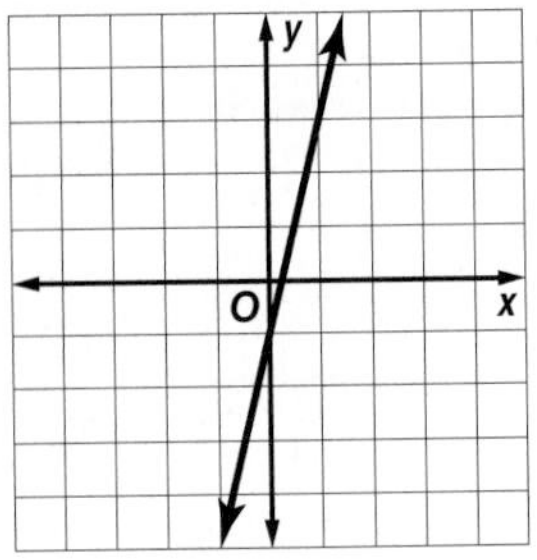

62.

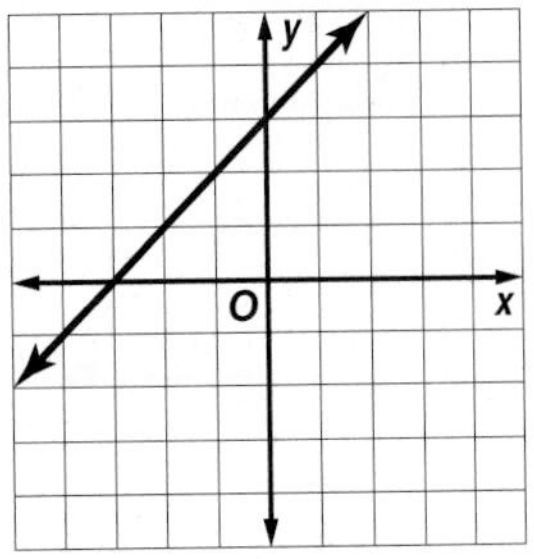

63.

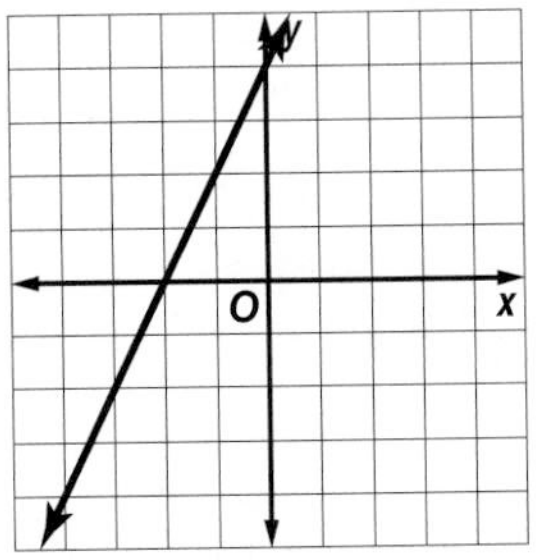

64.

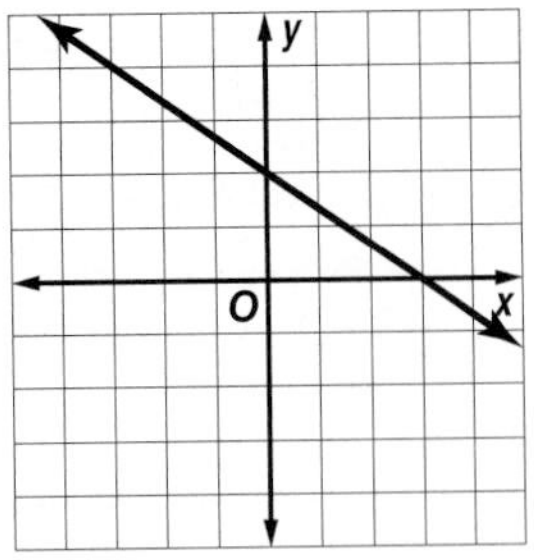

65.

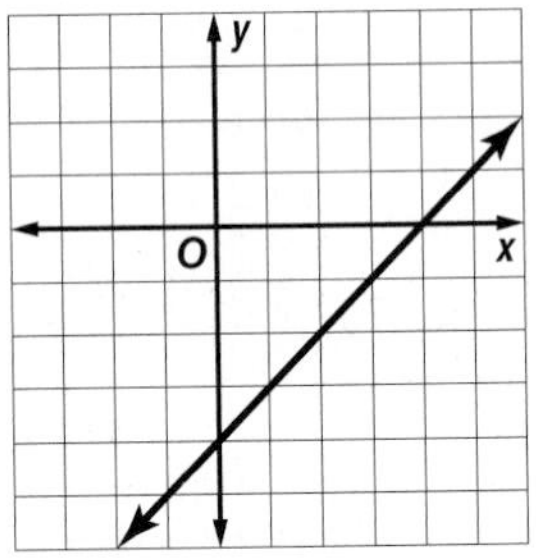

66.

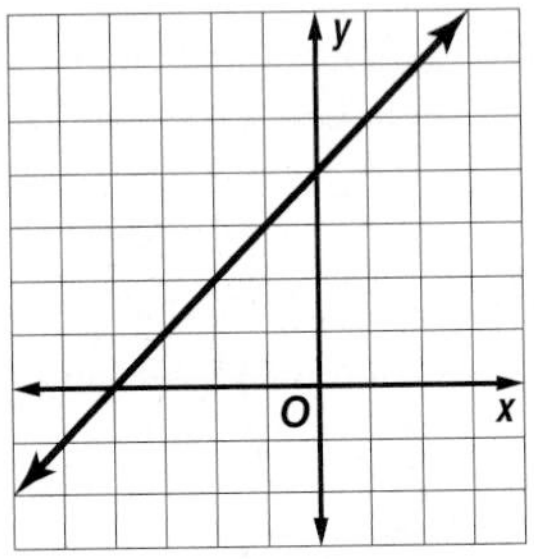

67.

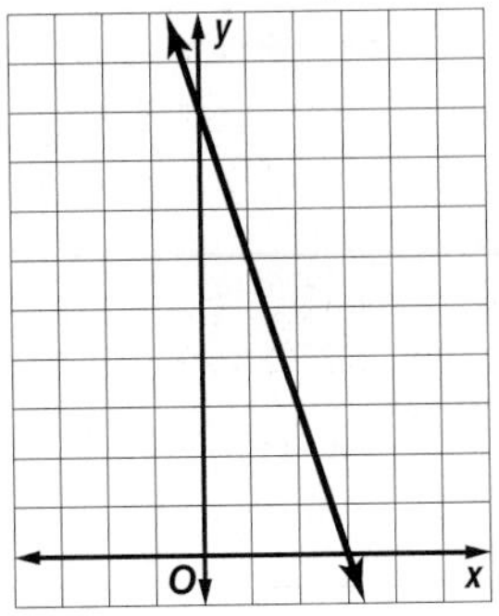

68.

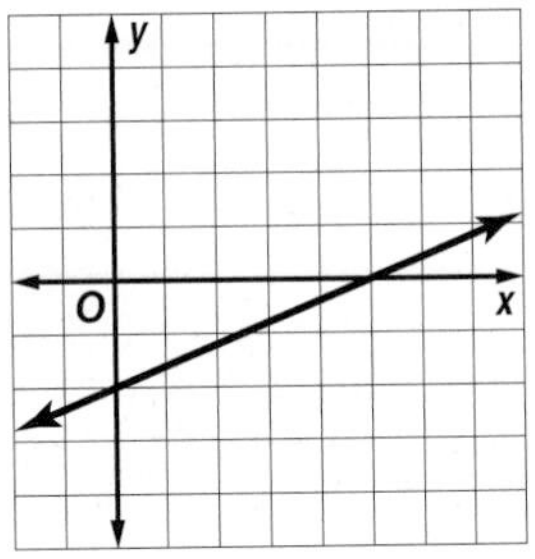

Pages 315–316, Lesson 5-6 (Check Your Progress)

1A.

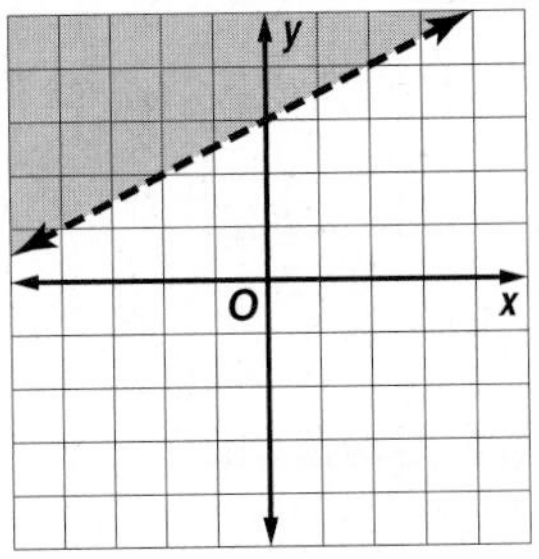

1B.

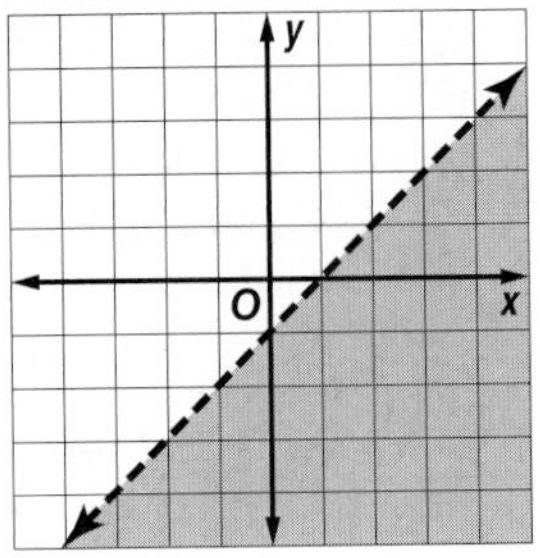

2A.

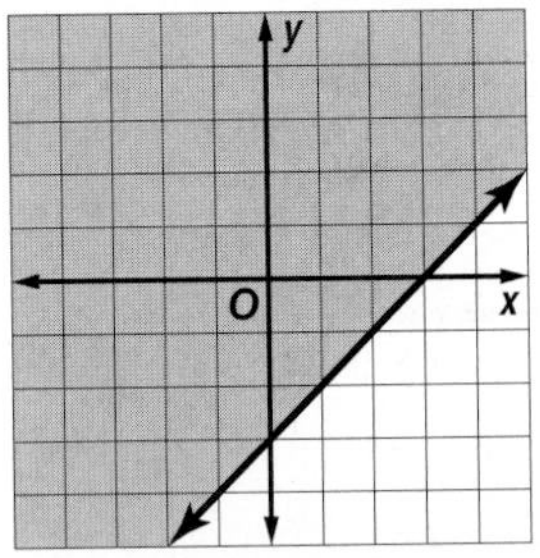

2B.

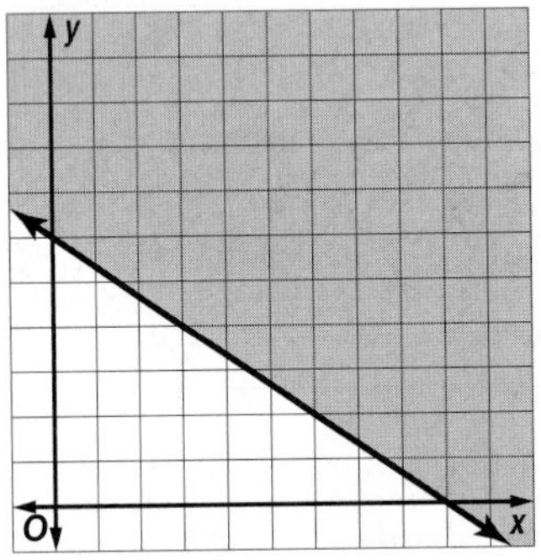

3A.

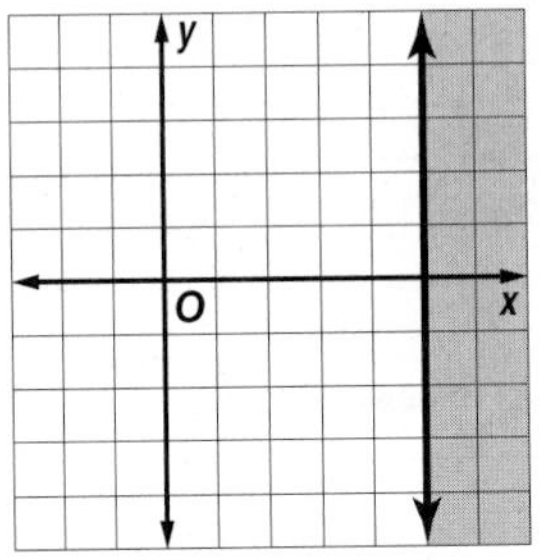

3B.

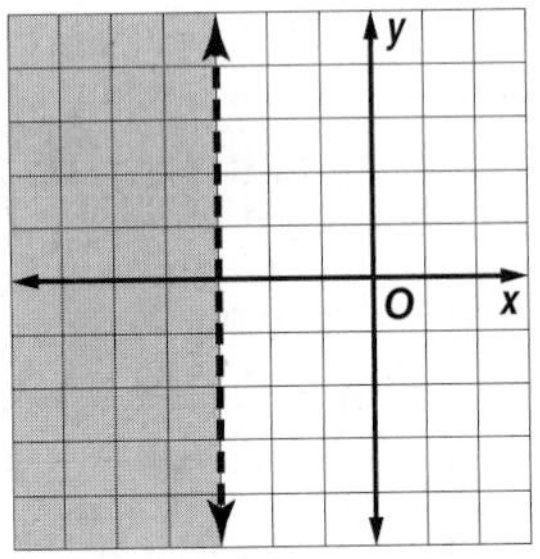

Pages 318–319, Lesson 5-6

1.

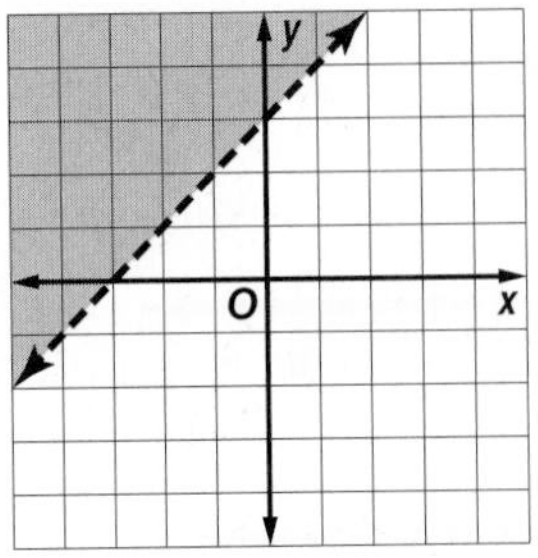

2.

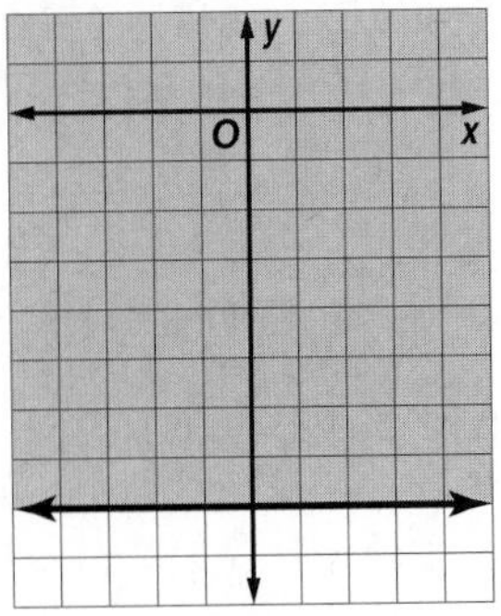

3.
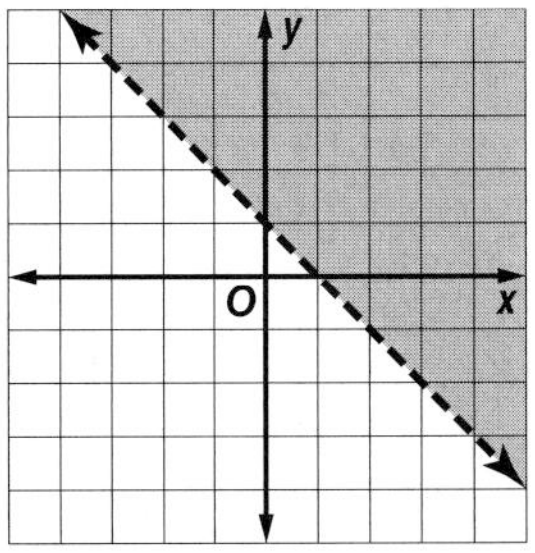

4.
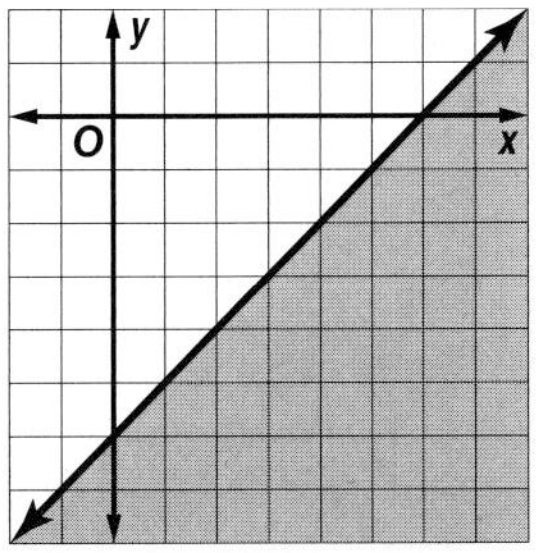

5.
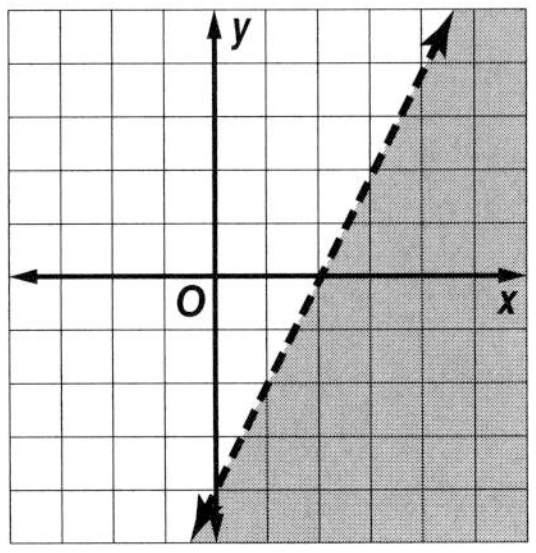

6.
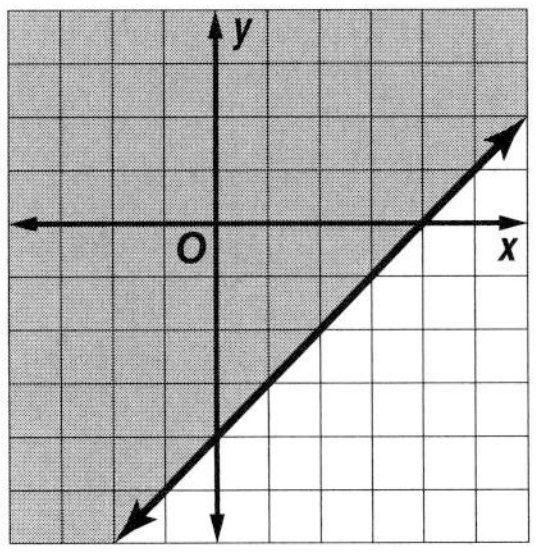

7.
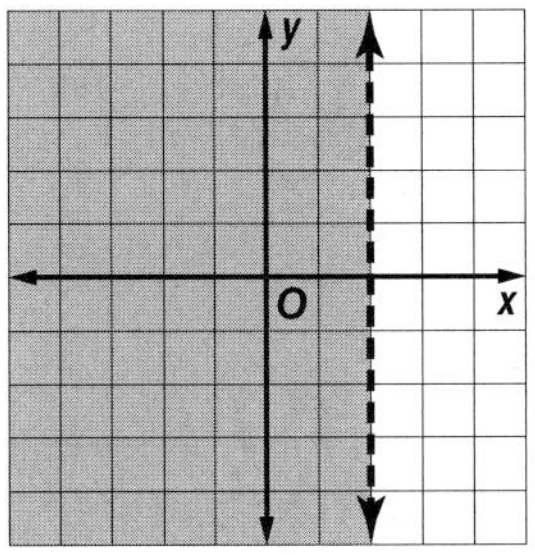

8.
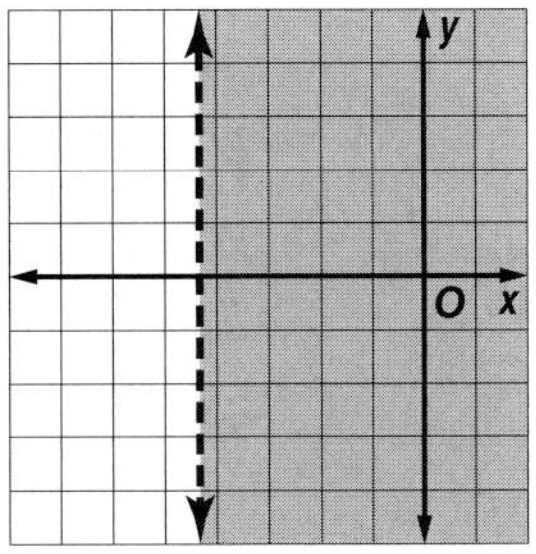

9.
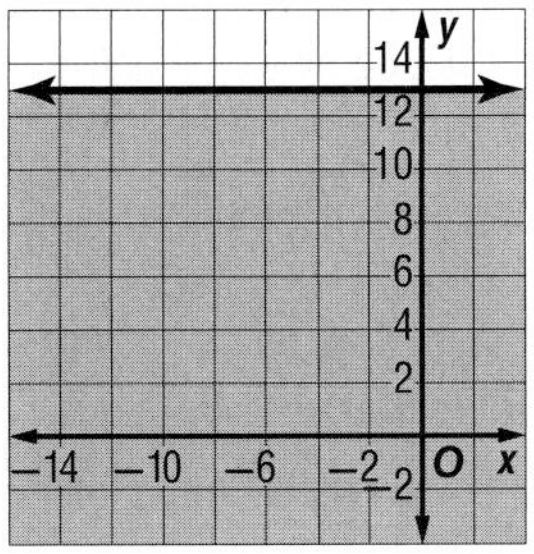

10.
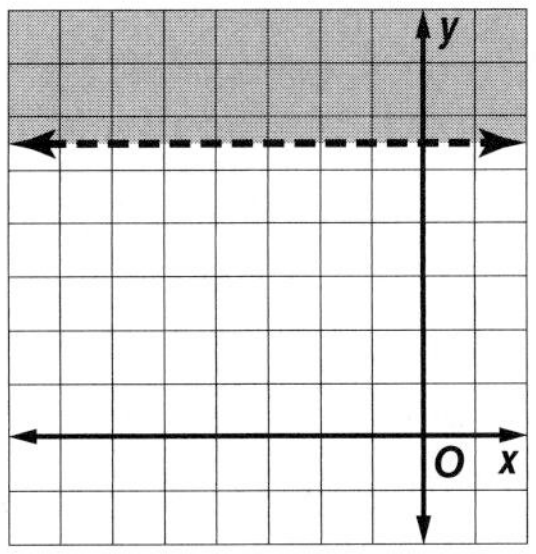

12.
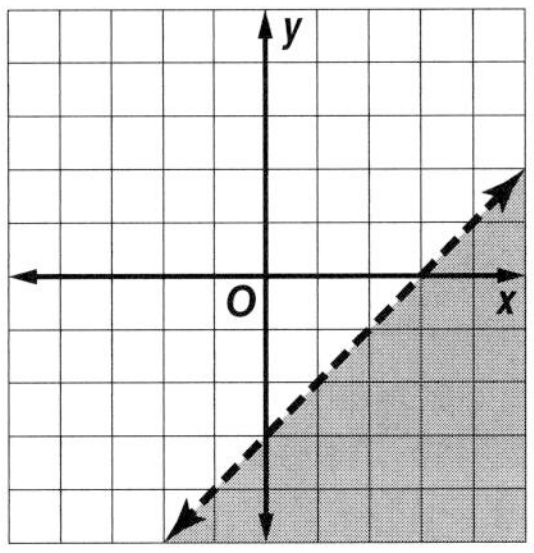

13.
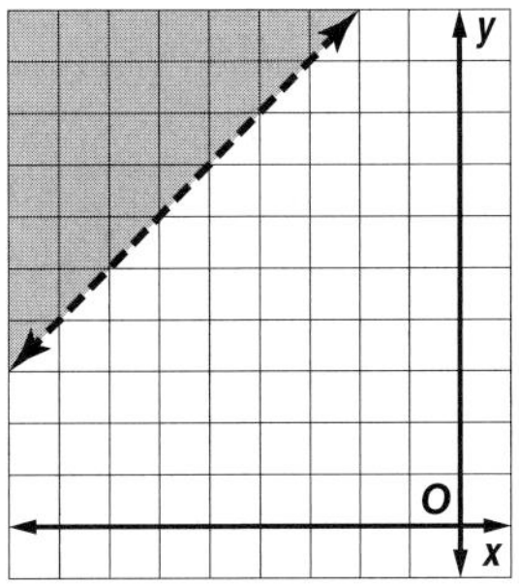

14.
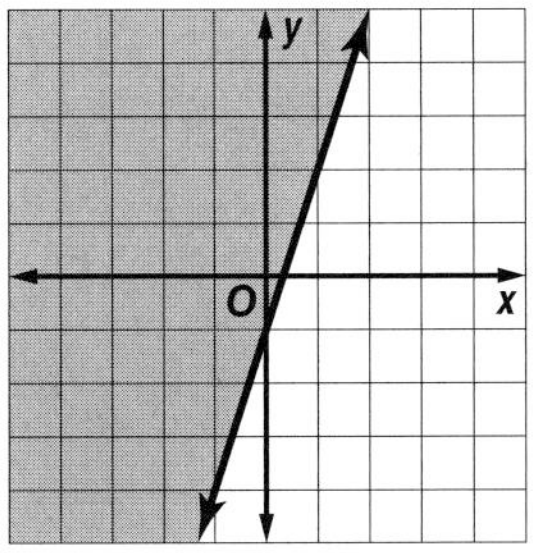

15.
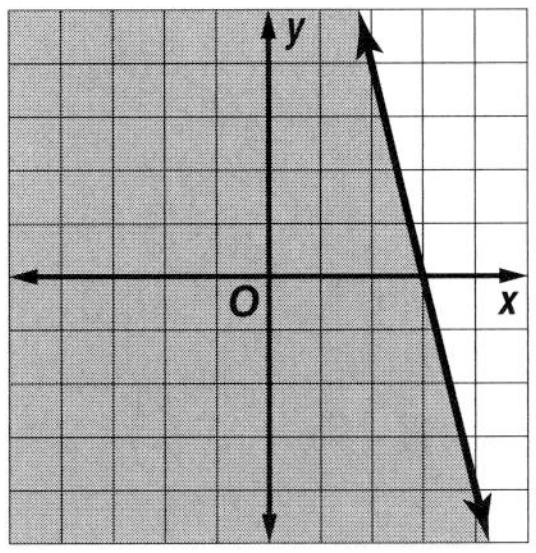

16.
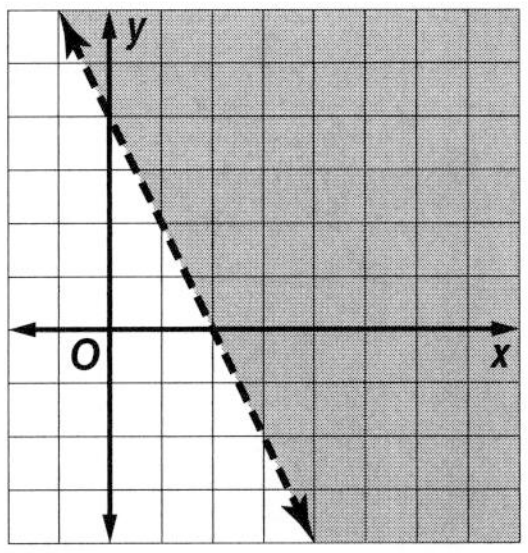

17.
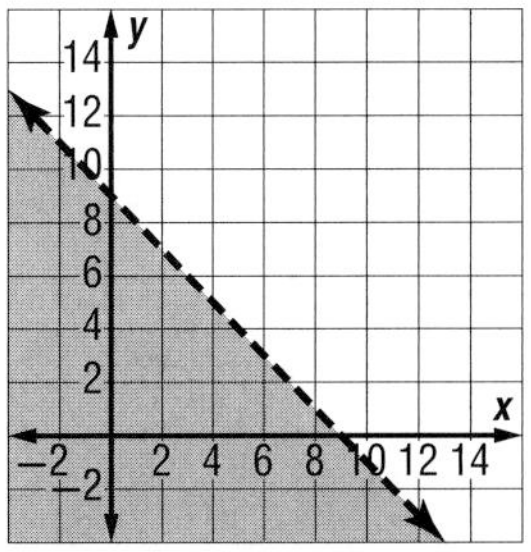

18.
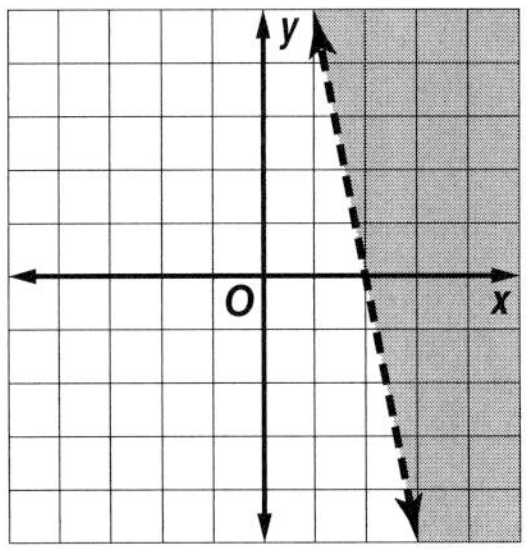

19.
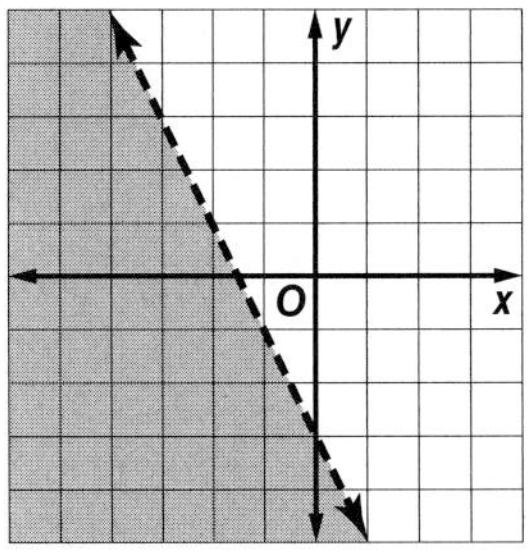

20.
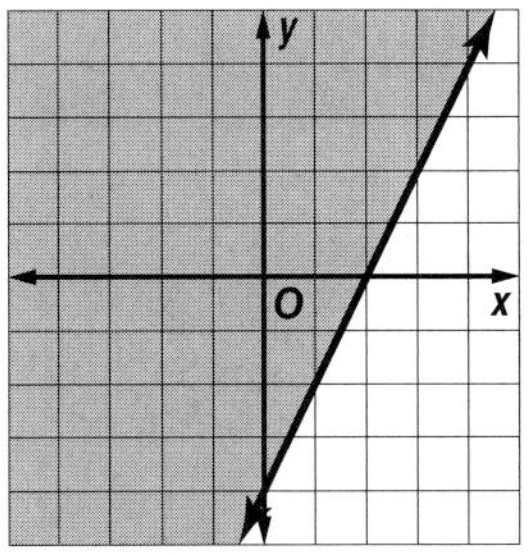

21.
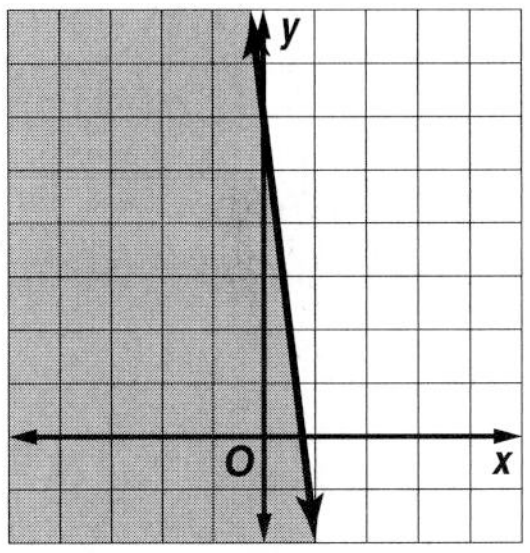

22.
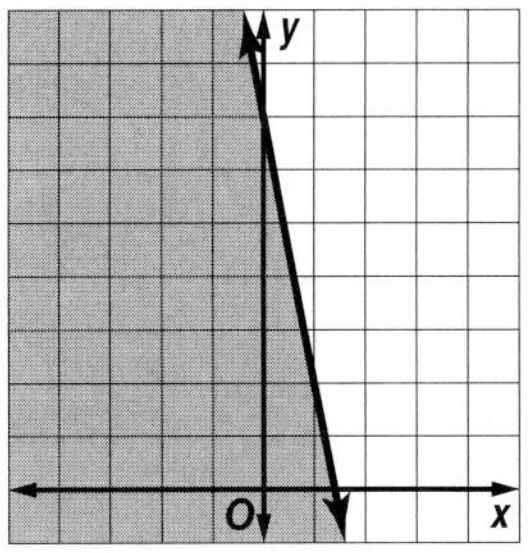

23.
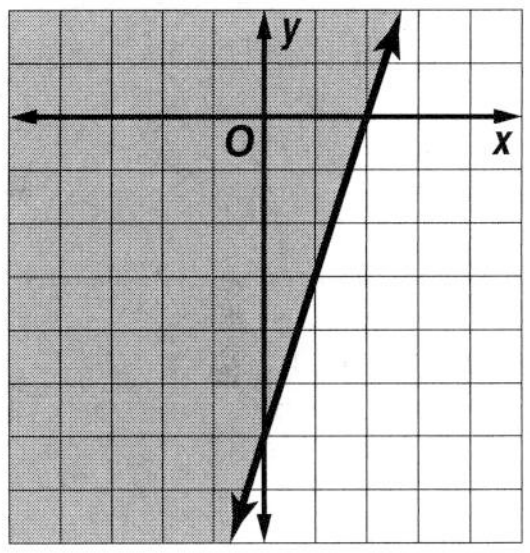

24.
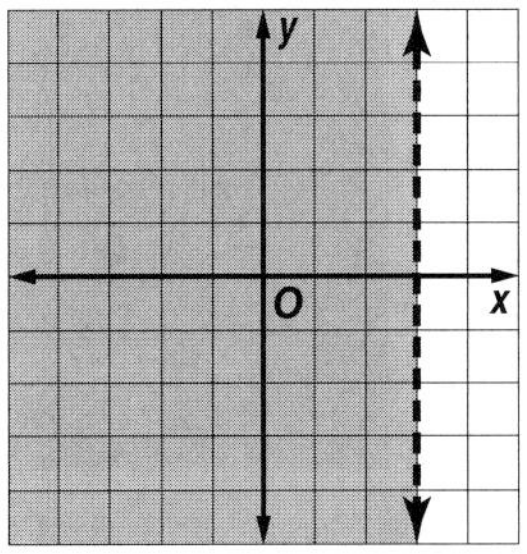

25.
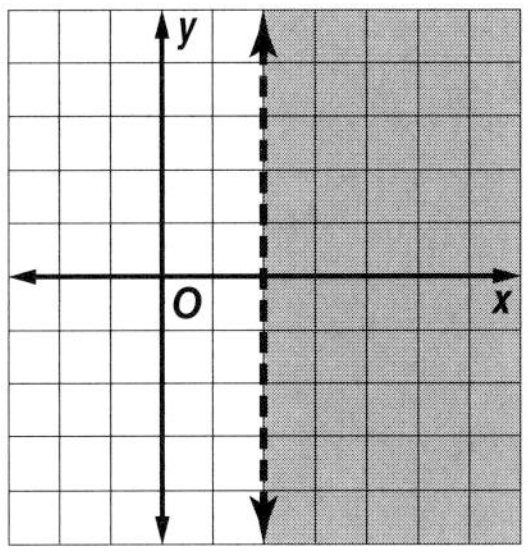

26.
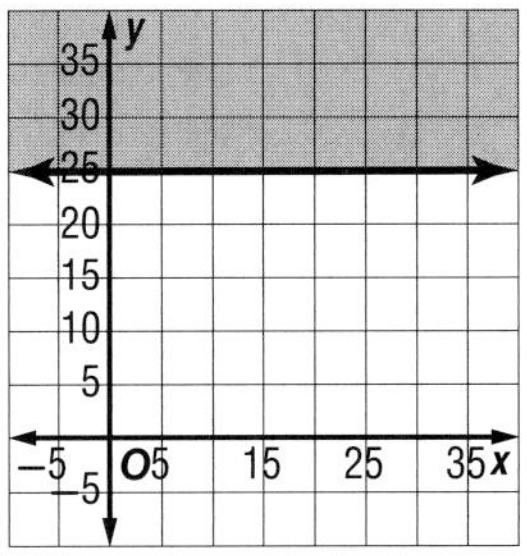

27.
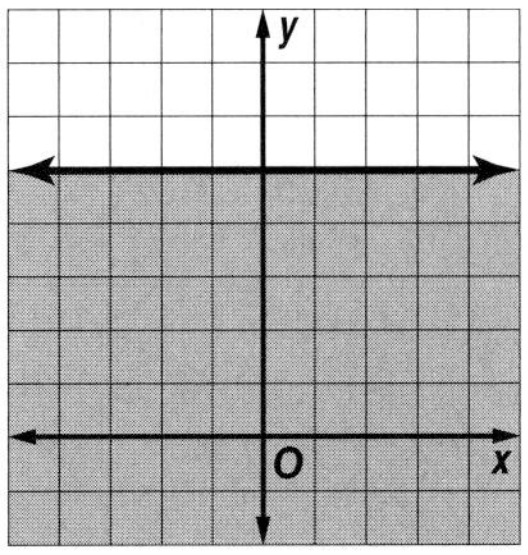

28.
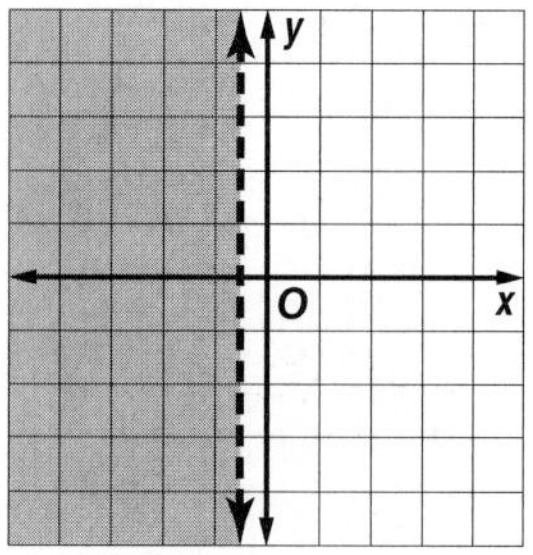

29.
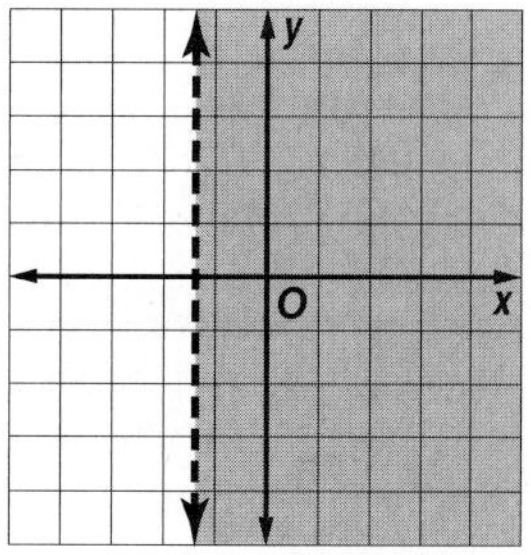

31.
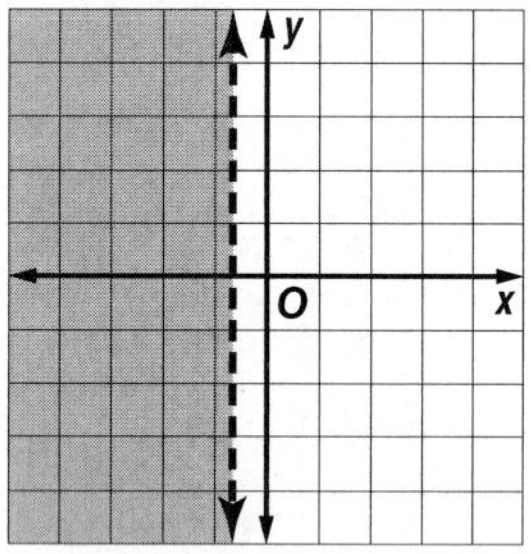

32.
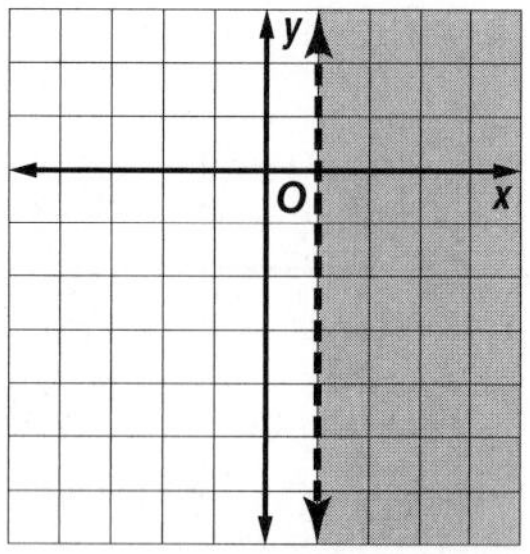

33.
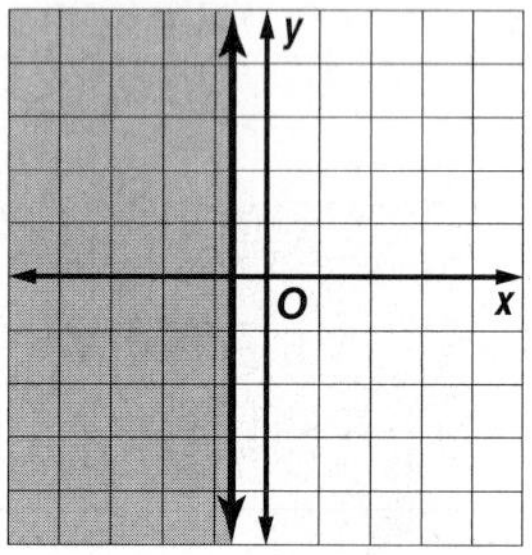

34.
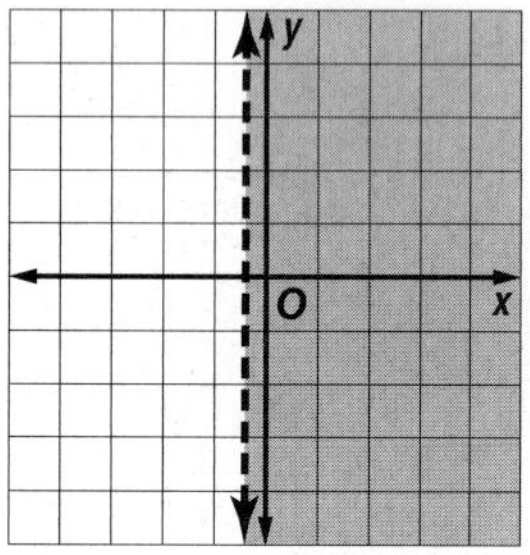

35.
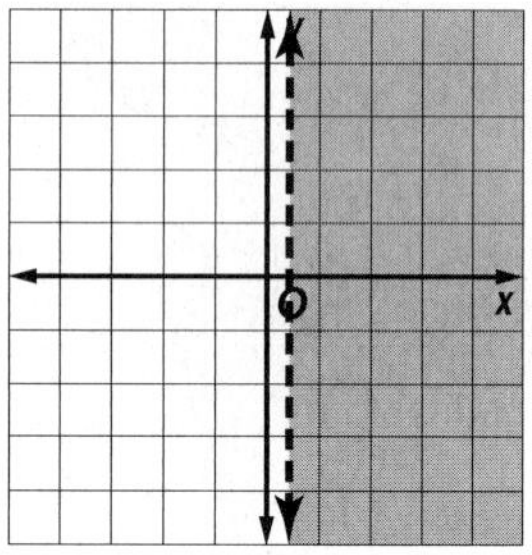

36.
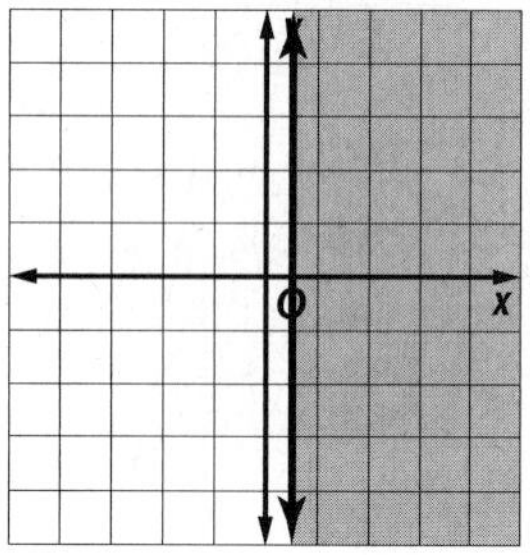

38. (−2, 7), (4, 8), (1, 6)
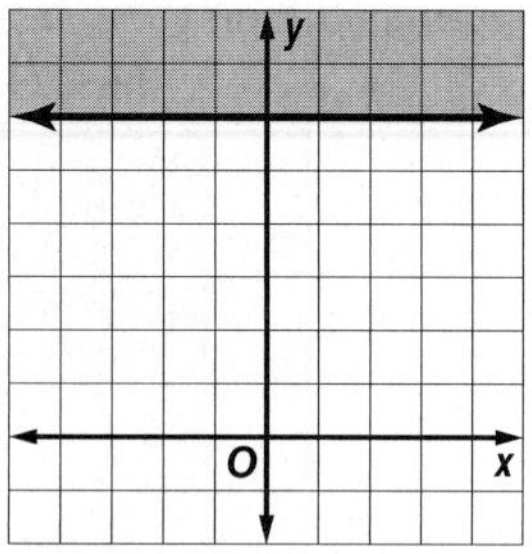

39. (−5, −5)
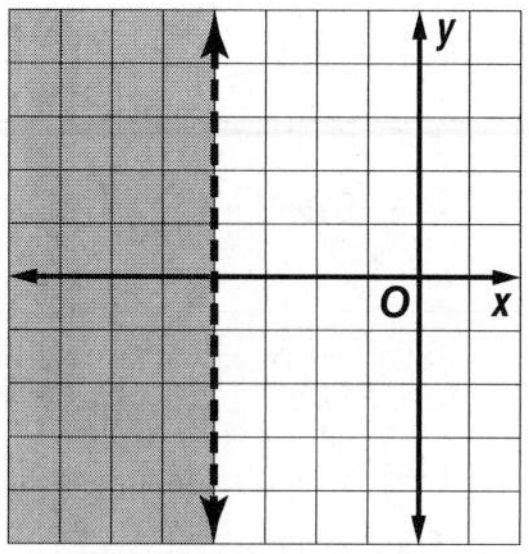

40. (2, 3), (0, 0), (5, 3)
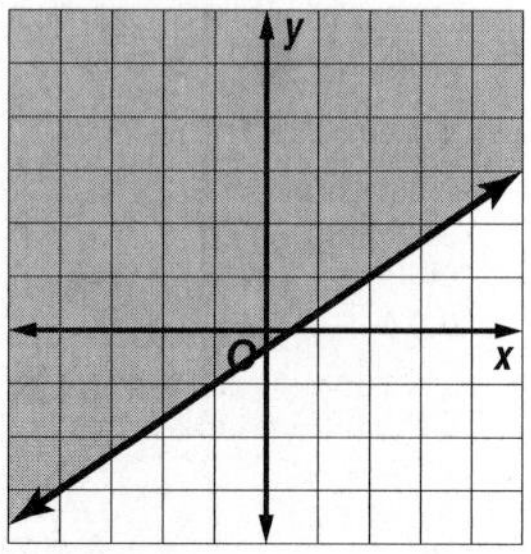

41. (1, 1), (2, 5), (6, 0)
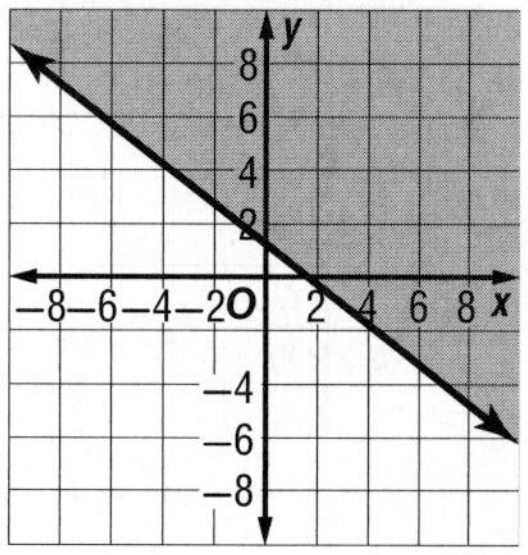

42. (3, −1), (1, 1), (−2, 0)
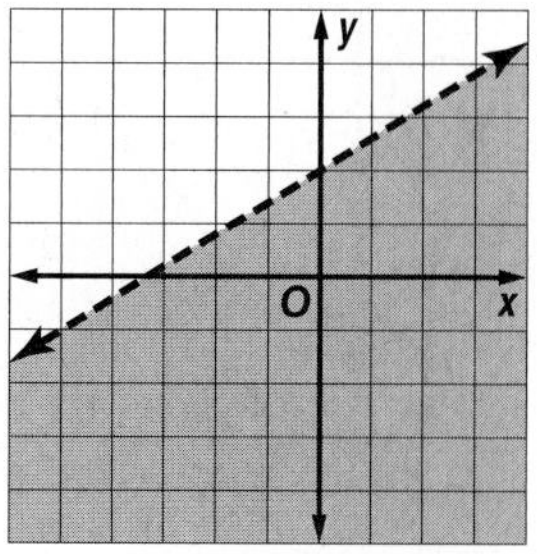

43. (7, 5), (5, 3), (2, −5)
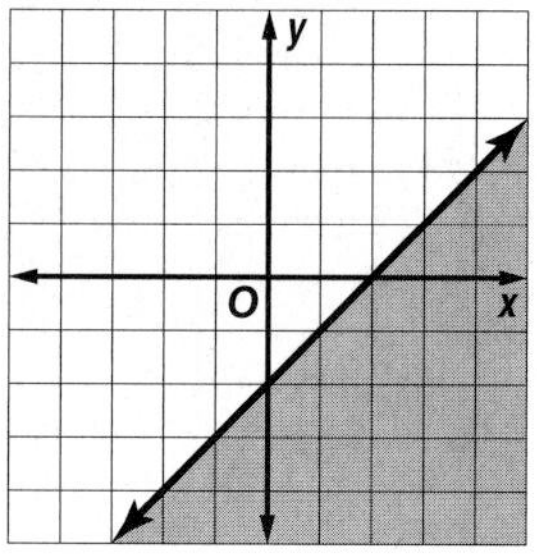

45b.
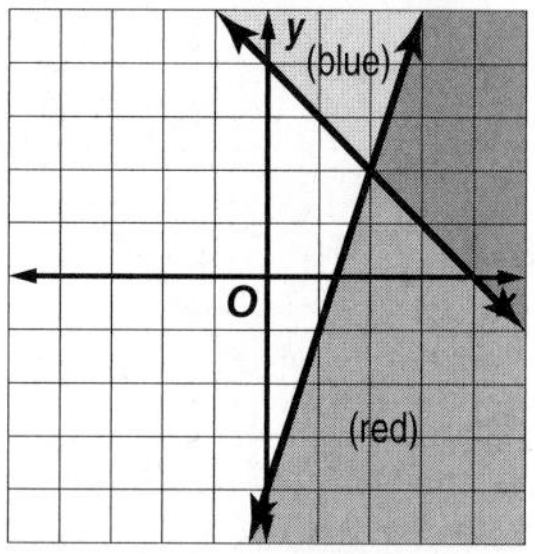

47.
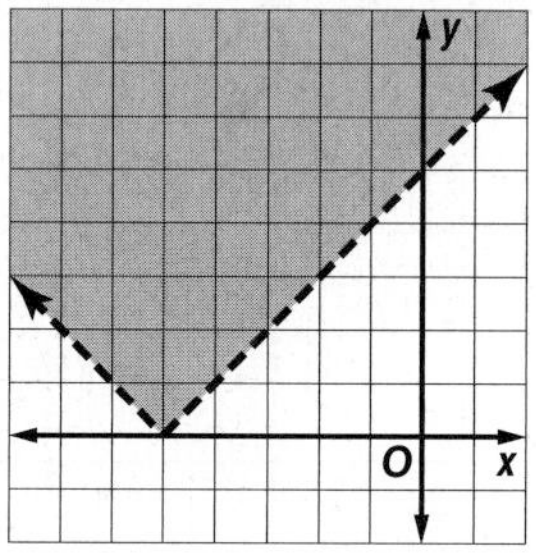

48. A test point on the boundary does not show which half-plane contains points that make the inequality true.

49. Sample answer: The inequality $y > 7x$ represents an employee earning $7 per hour plus the possibility of earning tips. Both the domain and range are nonnegative real numbers because hours worked and pay cannot be negative.

50. Sample answer: First solve the inequality for y. Then change the inequality sign to an equal sign and graph the boundary. If $<$ or $>$ is used, the boundary is not included in the graph and the line is dashed. Otherwise, the boundary is included and the line is solid. Then choose a test point not on the boundary. Substitute the coordinates of the test point into the original inequality. If the result makes the inequality true, then shade the half-plane that includes the test point. If the result makes the inequality false, shade the half-plane that does not include the test point. Lastly, check your solution by choosing a test point that is in the half-plane that is not shaded. This second test point should make the inequality false if the solution is correct.

Page 324, Study Guide and Review

45.
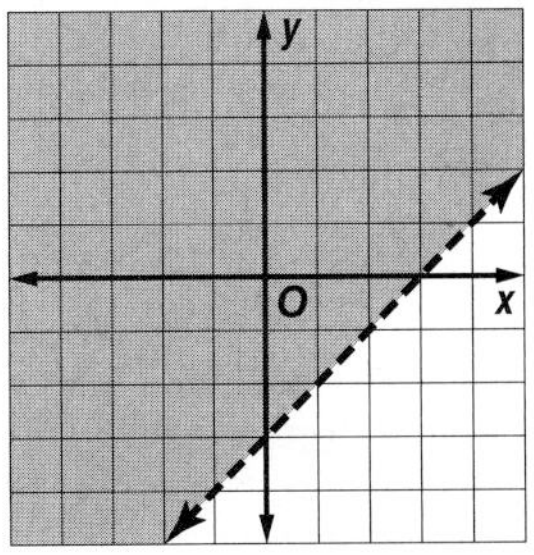

46.
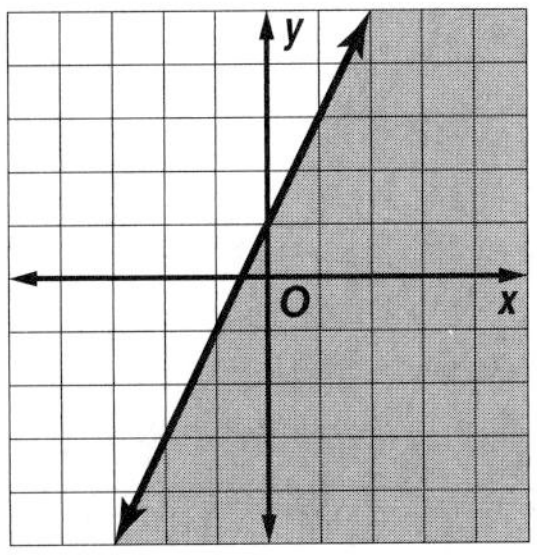

47.
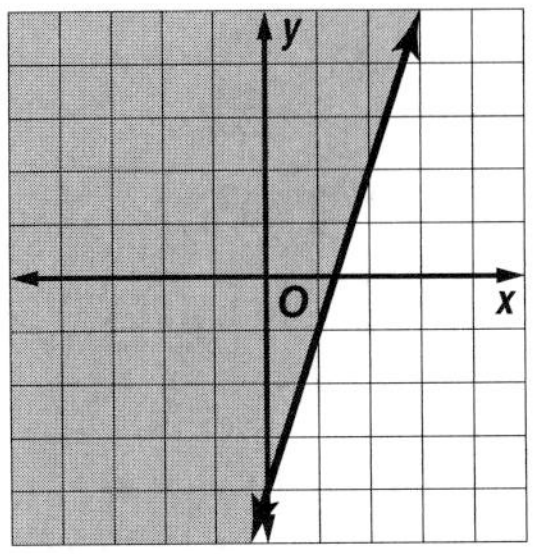

48.
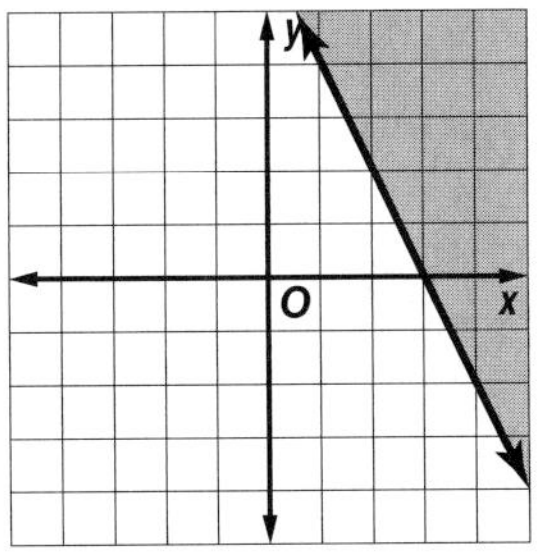

49.
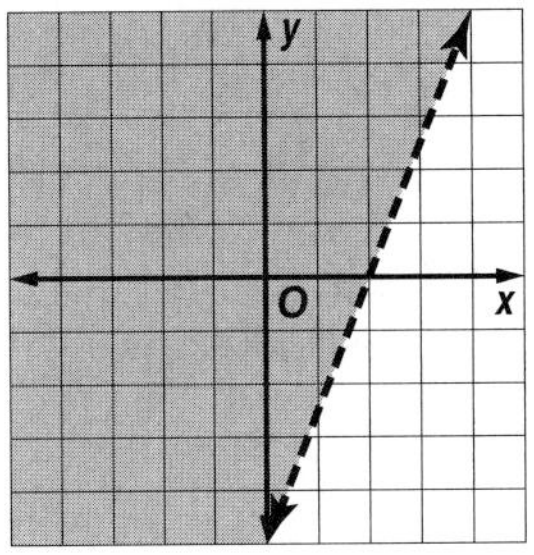

50.
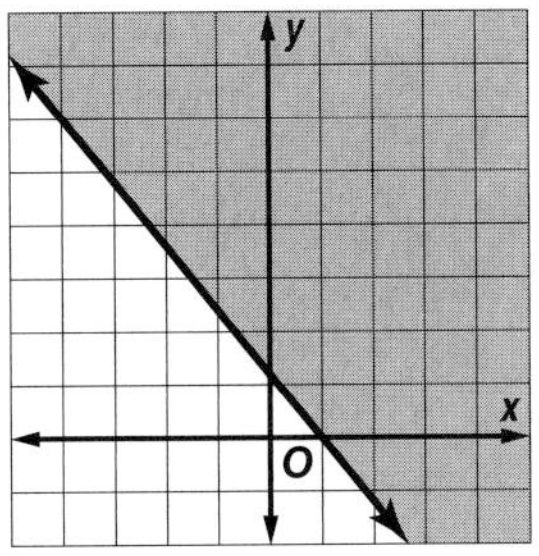

51.
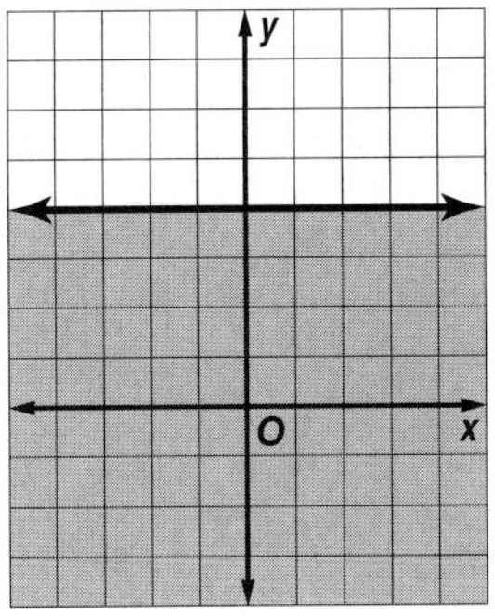

52.
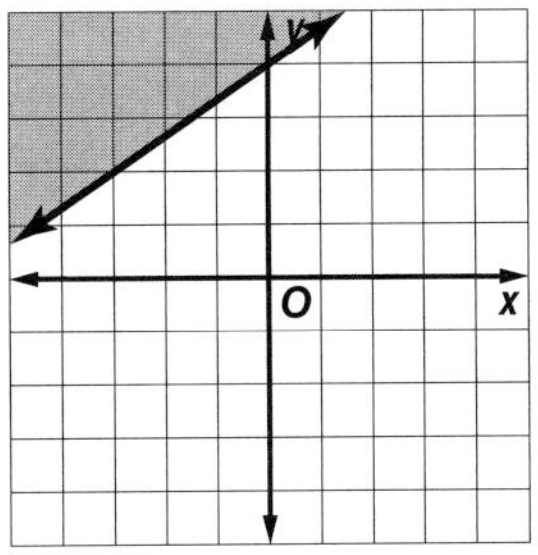

53.
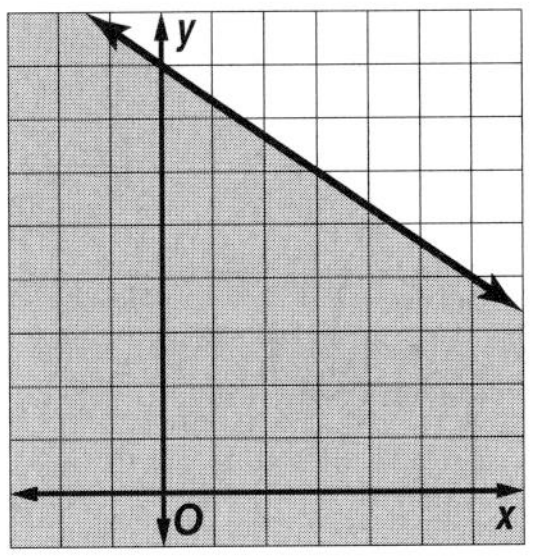

Page 325, Practice Test

18. $2 < p < 8$
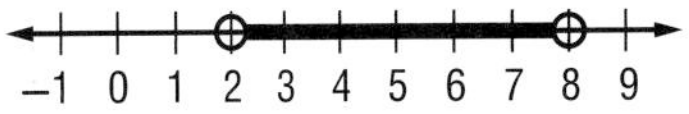

19. $f \leq -14$ or $f \geq 7$
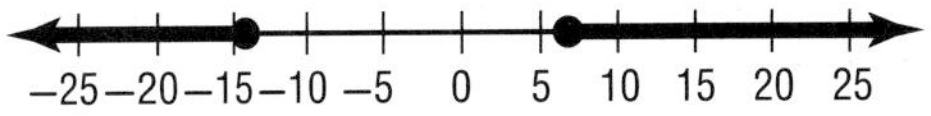

20. $-3 \leq m \leq \frac{9}{2}$

21. $x < -17$ or $x > 23$
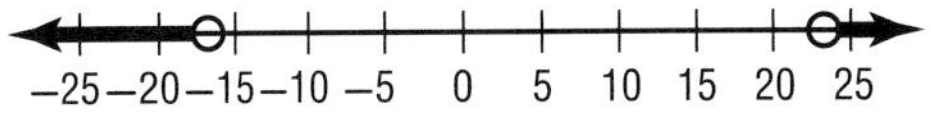

23.
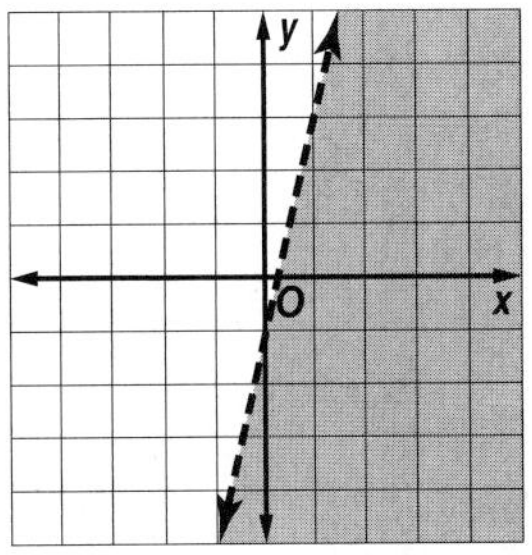

24.
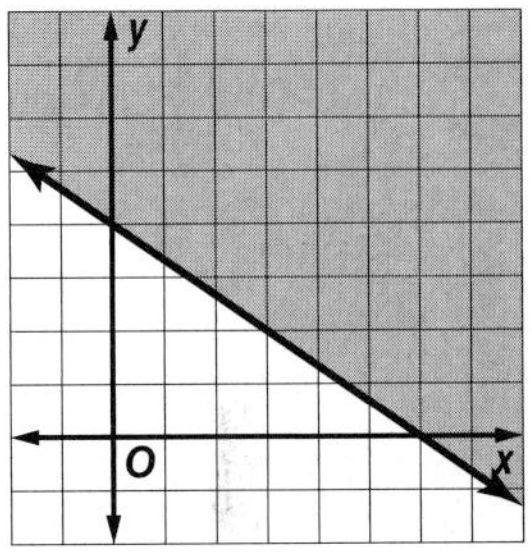

25. (2, 3), (7, 3)
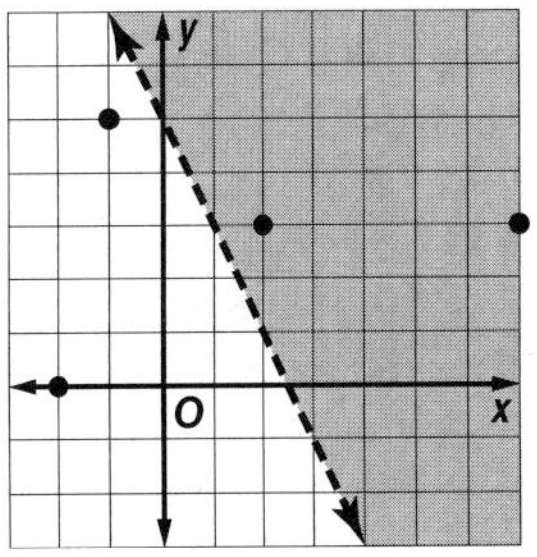

26.
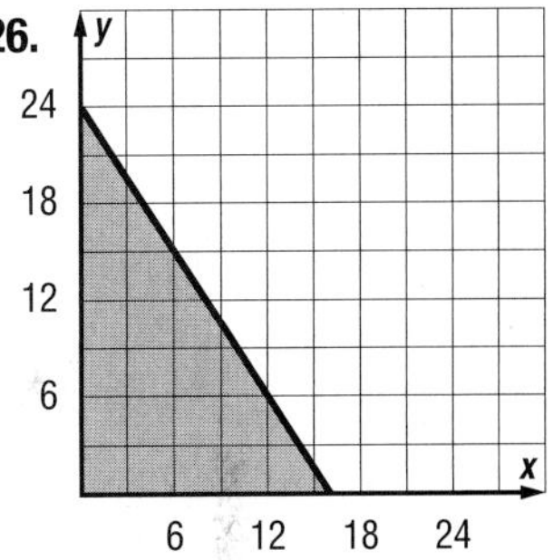

Chapter 5 Answer Appendix

Chapter Planner

Diagnostic Assessment
Quick Check, p. 331

	Lesson 6-1 Pacing: 1.5 days	Extend 6-1 Pacing: 0.5 day	Lesson 6-2 Pacing: 1 day
Title	**Graphing Systems of Equations**	**Graphing Technology Lab: Systems of Equations**	**Substitution**
Objectives	• Determine the number of solutions a system of linear equations has, if any. • Solve systems of linear equations by graphing.	• Use a graphing calculator to solve a system of equations.	• Solve systems of equations by using substitution. • Solve real-world problems involving systems of equations by using substitution.
Key Vocabulary	system of equations consistent independent dependent inconsistent		substitution
ILS	8.B.4a	8.B.4a	8.B.4a
Multiple Representations	p. 338		
Lesson Resources	**Chapter 6 Resource Masters** • Study Guide and Intervention, pp. 5–6 AL OL ELL • Skills Practice, p. 7 AL OL ELL • Practice, p. 8 AL OL BL ELL • Word Problem Practice, p. 9 AL OL BL ELL • Enrichment, p. 10 OL BL • Graphing Calculator Activity, p. 11 OL **Transparencies** • 5-Minute Check Transparency 6-1 AL OL BL ELL **Additional Print Resources** • *Study Notebook* AL OL BL ELL • *Teaching with Manipulatives,* p. 101 AL OL ELL	**Materials** • TI-83/84 Plus or other graphing calculator	**Chapter 6 Resource Masters** • Study Guide and Intervention, pp. 12–13 AL OL ELL • Skills Practice, p. 14 AL OL ELL • Practice, p. 15 AL OL BL ELL • Word Problem Practice, p. 16 AL OL BL ELL • Enrichment, p. 17 OL BL • Quiz 1, p. 59 AL OL BL ELL **Transparencies** • 5-Minute Check Transparency 6-2 AL OL BL ELL **Additional Print Resources** • *Study Notebook* AL OL BL ELL
Technology for Every Lesson	IL Math Online glencoe.com • Extra Examples • Self-Check Quizzes • Personal Tutor • Homework Help	**CD/DVD Resources** IWB INTERACTIVE WHITEBOARD READY IWB StudentWorks Plus IWB Interactive Classroom IWB Diagnostic and Assessment Planner	• TeacherWorks Plus • eSolutions Manual Plus • ExamView Assessment Suite
Math in Motion	Animation, Interactive Lab	Animation	
Differentiated Instruction	pp. 334, 338		pp. 343, 347

KEY: AL Approaching Level OL On Level BL Beyond Level ELL English Learners

Suggested Pacing			
Time Periods	Instruction	Review & Assessment	Total
45-minute	14	2	16
90-minute	7	1	8

Lesson 6-3 Pacing: 2 days	**Lesson 6-4** Pacing: 1 day	**Lesson 6-5** Pacing: 1.5 days	**Extend 6-5** Pacing: 0.5 day
Elimination Using Addition and Subtraction	**Elimination Using Multiplication**	**Applying Systems of Linear Equations**	**Spreadsheet Lab: Credit Cards and Cash**
• Solve systems of equations by using elimination with addition. • Solve systems of equations by using elimination with subtraction.	• Solve systems of equations by using elimination with multiplication. • Solve real-world problems involving systems of equations.	• Determine the best method for solving systems of equations. • Apply systems of equations.	• Use a spreadsheet to compare using cash and using a credit card to pay for a purchase.
elimination			
8.B.4a	8.B.4a	8.B.4a	6.B.4
p. 353			
Chapter 6 Resource Masters • Study Guide and Intervention, pp. 18–19 AL OL ELL • Skills Practice, p. 20 AL OL ELL • Practice, p. 21 AL OL BL ELL • Word Problem Practice, p. 22 AL OL BL ELL • Enrichment, p. 23 OL BL **Transparencies** • 5-Minute Check Transparency 6-3 AL OL BL ELL **Additional Print Resources** • *Study Notebook* AL OL BL ELL • Teaching Algebra with Manipulatives, p. 102 AL OL ELL	**Chapter 6 Resource Masters** • Study Guide and Intervention, pp. 24–25 AL OL ELL • Skills Practice, p. 26 AL OL ELL • Practice, p. 27 AL OL BL ELL • Word Problem Practice, p. 28 AL OL BL ELL • Enrichment, p. 29 OL BL • Quiz 2, p. 59 AL OL BL ELL **Transparencies** • 5-Minute Check Transparency 6-4 AL OL BL ELL **Additional Print Resources** • *Study Notebook* AL OL BL ELL	**Chapter 6 Resource Masters** • Study Guide and Intervention, pp. 30–31 AL OL ELL • Skills Practice, p. 32 AL OL ELL • Practice, p. 33 AL OL BL ELL • Word Problem Practice, p. 34 AL OL BL ELL • Enrichment, p. 35 OL BL **Transparencies** • 5-Minute Check Transparency 6-5 AL OL BL ELL **Additional Print Resources** • *Study Notebook* AL OL BL ELL	**Materials** • computer • spreadsheet software

IL Math Online glencoe.com
- Extra Examples
- Self-Check Quizzes
- Personal Tutor
- Homework Help

CD/DVD Resources IWB INTERACTIVE WHITEBOARD READY
- IWB StudentWorks Plus
- IWB Interactive Classroom
- IWB Diagnostic and Assessment Planner
- TeacherWorks Plus
- eSolutions Manual Plus
- ExamView Assessment Suite

			Animation
pp. 350, 354	pp. 357, 360	pp. 364, 367	

Formative Assessment
Mid-Chapter Quiz, p. 361

Chapter Planner

	Lesson 6-6 Pacing: 2 days	Lesson 6-7 Pacing: 2 days	Lesson 6-8 Pacing: 1 day	Extend 6-8 Pacing: 1 day
Title	**Organizing Data Using Matrices**	**Using Matrices to Solve Systems of Equations**	**Systems of Inequalities**	**Graphing Technology Lab: Systems of Inequalities**
Objectives	• Organize data in matrices. • Perform matrix operations.	• Write systems of equations as augmented matrices. • Solve systems of equations by using elementary row operations.	• Graph systems of linear inequalities. • Solve systems of linear inequalities by graphing.	• Use a graphing calculator to explore systems of inequalities.
Key Vocabulary	matrix dimension scalar multiplication element scalar	augmented matrix row reduction identity matrix	system of inequalities	
ILS	8.C.4b	8.C.4b	8.B.4a	8.B.4a
Multiple Representations		p. 380		
Lesson Resources	**Chapter 6 Resource Masters** • Study Guide and Intervention, pp. 36–37 AL OL ELL • Skills Practice, p. 38 AL OL ELL • Practice, p. 39 AL OL BL ELL • Word Problem Practice, p. 40 AL OL BL ELL • Enrichment, p. 41 OL BL • Quiz 3, p. 60 AL OL BL ELL **Transparencies** • 5-Minute Check Transparency 6-6 AL OL BL ELL **Additional Print Resources** • *Study Notebook* AL OL BL ELL	**Chapter 6 Resource Masters** • Study Guide and Intervention, pp. 42–43 AL OL ELL • Skills Practice, p. 44 AL OL ELL • Practice, p. 45 AL OL BL ELL • Word Problem Practice, p. 46 AL OL BL ELL • Enrichment, p. 47 OL BL • Quiz 3, p. 60 AL OL BL ELL **Transparencies** • 5-Minute Check Transparency 6-7 AL OL BL ELL **Additional Print Resources** • *Study Notebook* AL OL BL ELL	**Chapter 6 Resource Masters** • Study Guide and Intervention, pp. 48–49 AL OL ELL • Skills Practice, p. 50 AL OL ELL • Practice, p. 51 AL OL BL ELL • Word Problem Practice, p. 52 AL OL BL ELL • Enrichment, p. 53 OL BL • Graphing Calculator Activity, p. 54 OL • Quiz 4, p. 60 AL OL BL ELL **Transparencies** • 5-Minute Check Transparency 6-8 AL OL BL ELL **Additional Print Resources** • *Study Notebook* AL OL BL ELL • *Teaching Algebra with Manipulatives,* pp. 103–104 AL OL ELL	**Materials** • TI-Nspire calculator
Technology for Every Lesson	IL Math Online glencoe.com • Extra Examples • Self-Check Quizzes • Personal Tutor • Homework Help	**CD/DVD Resources** IWB INTERACTIVE WHITEBOARD READY IWB StudentWorks Plus IWB Interactive Classroom IWB Diagnostic and Assessment Planner	• TeacherWorks Plus • eSolutions Manual Plus • ExamView Assessment Suite	
Math in Motion	Animation		Animation	Animation
Differentiated Instruction	pp. 370, 375	pp. 377, 381	pp. 383, 386	

KEY: AL Approaching Level OL On Level BL Beyond Level ELL English Learners

Summative Assessment
• Study Guide and Review, pp. 388–392
• Practice Test, p. 393

Professional Development

Targeted professional development has been articulated throughout *Algebra 1.* More quality, customized professional development is available from McGraw-Hill Professional Development. Visit glencoe.com for details on each product.

- **Online Lessons** emphasize the strategies and techniques used to teach Algebra 1. Includes streaming video, interactive pages, and online tools.
- **Video Workshops** allow mentors, coaches, or leadership personnel to facilitate on-site workshops on educational strategies in mathematics and mathematical concepts.
- **MHPD Online** (www.mhpdonline.com) offers online professional development with video clips of instructional strategies, links, student activities, and news and issues in education.
- **Teaching Today** (teachingtoday.glencoe.com) gives secondary teachers practical strategies and materials that inspire excellence and innovation in teaching.

What the Research Says...

According to Smith (1997), current technology allows readily accessible representations of systems of equations in algebraic, numeric, and geometric forms. Integrating these different representations into the curriculum helps students to think more critically about systems, to foster new perspectives, and to feel more confident in their results.

- In Extend 6-1, students use graphing calculators to visualize systems, based on concepts discussed in Lesson 6-1.
- Throughout Chapter 6, algebraic methods for solving systems are related to graphical representations.

[Source: Smith, K.B. (1997). "Exploration and Visualization: Making Critical Connections About Linear Systems of Equations," *School Science and Mathematics*, 97(1), pp. 13–19.]

Notes

CHAPTER 6 Assessment and Intervention

SE = Student Edition, **TE** = Teacher Edition, **CRM** = Chapter Resource Masters

	Diagnosis	Prescription
Diagnostic Assessment	**Beginning Chapter 6**	
	Get Ready for Chapter 6 **SE**, p. 331	Response to Intervention **TE**, p. 331
	Beginning Every Lesson	
	Then, Now, Why? **SE** 5-Minute Check Transparencies	Chapter 0 **SE**, pp. P1 through P45 Concepts and Skills Bank **SE**, pp. 857–867 *Quick Review Math Handbook*
Formative Assessment	**During/After Every Lesson**	
	Check Your Progress **SE**, every example Check Your Understanding **SE** H.O.T. Problems **SE** Spiral Review **SE** Additional Examples **TE** Watch Out! **TE** Step 4, Assess **TE** Chapter 6 Quizzes **CRM**, pp. 59–60 Self-Check Quizzes glencoe.com	**Tier 1 Intervention** Concepts and Skills Bank **SE**, pp. 857–867 Skills Practice **CRM**, Ch. 1–6 glencoe.com **Tier 2 Intervention** Differentiated Instruction **TE** Differentiated Homework Options **TE** Study Guide and Intervention Masters **CRM**, Ch. 1–6 *Quick Review Math Handbook* **Tier 3 Intervention** *Math Triumphs, Alg. 1*
	Mid-Chapter	
	Mid-Chapter Quiz **SE**, p. 361 Mid-Chapter Test **CRM**, p. 61 ExamView Assessment Suite	**Tier 1 Intervention** Concepts and Skills Bank **SE**, pp. 857–867 Skills Practice **CRM**, Ch. 1–6 glencoe.com **Tier 2 Intervention** Study Guide and Intervention Masters **CRM**, Ch. 1–6 *Quick Review Math Handbook* **Tier 3 Intervention** *Math Triumphs, Alg. 1*
	Before Chapter Test	
	Chapter Study Guide and Review **SE**, pp. 388–392 Practice Test **SE**, p. 393 Standardized Test Practice **SE**, pp. 394–397 Chapter Test glencoe.com Standardized Test Practice glencoe.com Vocabulary Review glencoe.com ExamView Assessment Suite	**Tier 1 Intervention** Concepts and Skills Bank **SE**, pp. 857–867 Skills Practice **CRM**, Ch. 1–6 glencoe.com **Tier 2 Intervention** Study Guide and Intervention Masters **CRM**, Ch. 1–6 *Quick Review Math Handbook* **Tier 3 Intervention** *Math Triumphs, Alg. 1*
Summative Assessment	**After Chapter 6**	
	Multiple-Choice Tests, Forms 1, 2A, 2B **CRM**, pp. 63–68 Free-Response Tests, Forms 2C, 2D, 3 **CRM**, pp. 69–74 Vocabulary Test **CRM**, p. 62 Extended Response Test **CRM**, p. 75 Standardized Test Practice **CRM**, pp. 76–78 ExamView Assessment Suite	Study Guide and Intervention Masters **CRM**, Ch. 1–6 *Quick Review Math Handbook* glencoe.com

CHAPTER 6

Differentiated Instruction

Option 1 Reaching All Learners AL OL BL ELL

INTERPERSONAL Place students in pairs or small groups and assign systems of equations for them to solve. Tell students to use the Concept Summary on p. 362 or discuss which method is best to use to solve the system of equations they have been assigned. Make sure all group members participate in the discussion.

VISUAL Write several linear equations on the board. Graph each of these equations on a separate transparency coordinate grid. Then take a pair of equations and write them as a system of equations. Overlap the transparencies of their graphs to find their point of intersection. Repeat for a different pair of equations.
Then, change all the equations to inequalities. Shade their corresponding graphs to reflect the inequality. Then take a pair of inequalities and write them as a system of inequalities. Overlap the transparencies of their graphs to find their points of intersection.

Option 2 Approaching Level AL

Provide students with a copy of the graph of a system of linear equations and write the equations of the system on the board. Ask students to identify which line belongs to which equation. Then ask students to check that the solution works for both equations. Similarly, provide students with a graph of a system of linear inequalities. Ask students to identify which line and shading belongs to which inequality. Then ask students to check that several solutions within the overlapped shading work for both inequalities.

Option 3 English Learners ELL

Help students understand the vocabulary in the first lesson of this chapter by creating a set of flashcards. On one side of the card draw a graph of intersecting lines, one line, or a pair of parallel lines. On the flip side, write *consistent and independent*, *consistent and dependent*, or *inconsistent*.

Option 4 Beyond Level BL

Ask students to write a sentence about a two-digit number on one side of an index card. On the back of the card, students write and solve a system of equations to find the number. Have students trade cards and solve each other's number puzzle.

The sum of the digits of a two-digit number is 7. If the digits are reversed, the new number is 9 more than the original number."

$t + u = 7$
$10u + t = 9 + 10t + u$
$u = 4, t = 3$
The original number is 34.

CHAPTER 6 Focus on Mathematical Content

Vertical Alignment

Before Chapter 6

Related Topics before Grade 8

- use a coordinate system to graph ordered pairs
- use Venn diagrams for displaying relationships

Previous Topics from Algebra 1

- graph equations of lines
- use properties of equality to solve equations
- analyze situations involving linear functions and formulate linear equations to solve problems

Chapter 6

Related Topics from Algebra 1

- analyze situations and formulate systems of linear equations in two unknowns to solve problems
- solve systems of linear equations and linear inequalities using graphs and algebraic methods
- interpret and determine the reasonableness of solutions to systems of linear equations and linear inequalities

After Chapter 6

Preparation for Algebra 2

- analyze situations and formulate systems of equations in two or more unknowns, or inequalities in two unknowns to solve problems
- use algebraic methods, graphs, tables, or matrices to solve systems of equations or inequalities
- interpret and determine the reasonableness of solutions to systems of equations or inequalities for given contexts

Lesson-by-Lesson Preview

6-1 Graphing Systems of Equations

A system of equations can be solved by graphing the equations on the same coordinate plane. A solution of a system of two linear equations is an ordered pair that satisfies both equations in the system. A system of two linear equations can have the following:

- *exactly one solution*–The graphs of the equations intersect at one point. This system is said to be consistent and independent.
- *no solution*–The graphs of the equation are parallel. There are no ordered pairs that satisfy both equations. This system is said to be inconsistent.
- *infinite number of solutions*–The graphs of the equations are the same line. An infinite number of points will satisfy both equations. This system is said to be consistent and dependent.

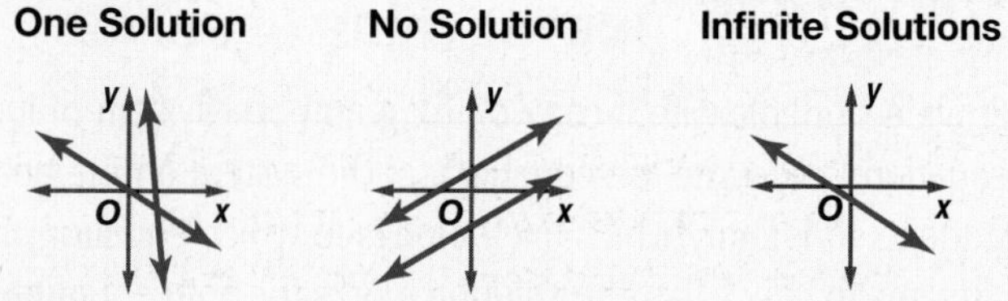

6-2 Substitution

Determining the exact solution to a system of equations from a graph can be difficult at times. When an exact solution is needed, algebraic methods can be used. Substitution is one method. To use substitution,

- Solve one equation for one variable in terms of the other variable.
- Next, substitute this expression into the other equation, thus eliminating one of the variables.
- Solve the resulting equation for the other variable.
- Substitute this value into either original equation to find the value of the eliminated variable.

If the system has *one solution*, the two values are written as an ordered pair.

The system has an *infinite number of solutions* if solving the system results in a true statement (such as $3 = 3$). There is *no solution* if solving the system results in a false statement (such as $-2 = 4$).

6-3 Elimination Using Addition and Subtraction

Elimination using addition or subtraction is another algebraic method used in solving a system of equations. When using this method, the two equations are combined to eliminate one of the variables. One equation can be added or subtracted from the other using the Addition/Subtraction Properties of Equality.

To use this method of elimination,

- Add the two equations if the coefficients of one of the variables are additive inverses, or opposites.
- Subtract the two equations if the coefficients of one of the variables are the same.

After eliminating one of the variables, solve for the remaining variable. Then substitute this value back into either original equation to find the value of the eliminated variable. The solution to the system is the two values written as an ordered pair.

6-4 Elimination Using Multiplication

When the coefficients of one of the variables are neither the same nor additive inverses, multiplication is used. This method requires that either one or both equations be changed using the Multiplication Property of Equality.

To use multiplication,

- multiply each term of one equation by the same number, or multiply both equations by different numbers in order to get one of the variables to have coefficients that are additive inverses of each other or the same number
- then solve the system by following the steps for solving a system by elimination using addition or subtraction.

6-5 Applying Systems of Linear Equations

Five methods of solving systems of equations have been studied. Each method works best for certain systems.

- Graphing can be used when an estimate will do.
- Substitution is used when one of the variables in either equation has a coefficient of 1 or -1.
- Elimination using addition is used if the coefficients of one of the variables are additive inverses.
- Elimination using subtraction is used if the coefficients of one of the variables are the same.
- Elimination using multiplication is used when none of the coefficients are 1 or -1 and neither of the variables can be eliminated by addition or subtraction.
- For real-world problems, check solutions in the context of the situation.

6-6 Organizing Data Using Matrices

Matrices provide a way to organize data. A matrix is a rectangular arrangement of numbers in rows and columns enclosed in brackets. A matrix with m rows and n columns is an $m \times n$ matrix.

- Matrices with the same dimensions can be added or subtracted by adding or subtracting the corresponding elements of the matrices.
- Matrices can be multiplied by a scalar (a constant). To perform scalar multiplication, multiply each element of the matrix by the scalar.

6-7 Using Matrices to Solve Systems of Equations

A matrix called an augmented matrix can provide an efficient way to solve a system of equations.

Linear System	Augmented Matrix
$\begin{cases} 2x - 3y = 6 \\ -4x + y = 9 \end{cases}$	$\begin{bmatrix} 2 & -3 & 6 \\ -4 & 1 & 9 \end{bmatrix}$

Row operations are performed to change the form of the matrix. These operations are the same as the ones used when working with the equations. The goal is to get the coefficient portion of the matrix (columns 1 and 2) to have the form $\begin{bmatrix} 1 & 0 \\ 0 & 1 \end{bmatrix}$, the identity matrix. Then, the solution to the system can be found in the third column of the matrix.

6-8 Systems of Inequalities

A solution of a system of inequalities is the set of all points that satisfy both inequalities. To solve the system, graph each inequality. The points that are solutions lie in the region where the graphs overlap, or intersect. There are two possibilities.

- *no solution*–The boundary lines are parallel, and the shaded regions have no points in common.
- *infinitely many solutions*–The overlapping shaded region extends on indefinitely.

CHAPTER 6 Notes

Chapter Project

Matrices of Music

Students use what they have learned about writing and solving systems of equations and using matrices to work with different categories of music.

- Ask each student to determine the total number of music CDs they own.
- Assign each student a partner. Let x stand for one student's total and y for their partner's. Have partners write a system of equations, with coefficients for x and y, to describe the total number of CDs they have together. For example, if one student has 8 CDs and the other has 10 CDs, one system they could write is $2x + 3y = 46$ and $3x + 4y = 64$.
- Have pairs trade systems and determine the number of CDs owned by each person in the other pair using elimination by adding and subtracting, by multiplying, and by using an augmented matrix. Then ask pairs to graph the system. Are all the results the same?
- Ask each student to determine the number of R & B, Rock, and Country CDs he or she owns.
- Ask each pair to make a table and then a 2×3 matrix to organize the number of R & B, Rock, and Country CDs owned by each. Have each pair add, then subtract, their matrix to the matrix made by another pair.

CHAPTER 6 Systems of Linear Equations and Inequalities

Then

In Chapter 2, you solved linear equations in one variable.

Now

In Chapter 6, you will:

- Solve systems of linear equations by graphing, substitution, and elimination.
- Solve systems of linear inequalities by graphing.

IL Learning Standards

8.B.4a Represent algebraic concepts with physical materials, words, diagrams, tables, graphs, equations and inequalities and use appropriate technology.
8.C.4b Apply algebraic properties and procedures with matrices using data found in business, industry and consumer situations.

Why?

MUSIC $1500 worth of tickets were sold for a marching band competition. Adult tickets were $12 each, and student tickets were $8 each. If you knew how many total tickets were sold, you could use a system of equations to determine how many adult tickets and how many student tickets were sold.

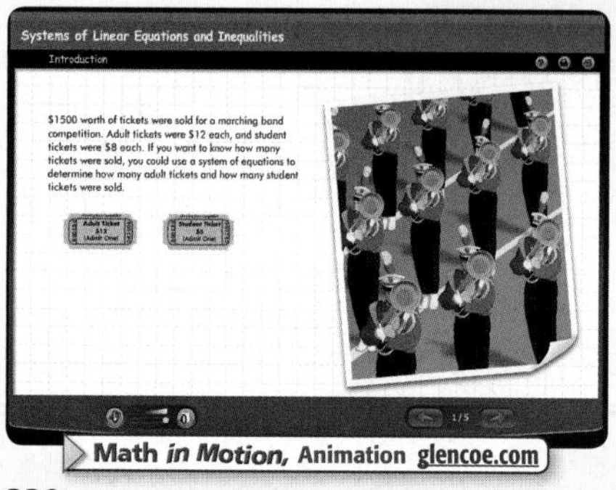

Math *in Motion*, Animation glencoe.com

330 Chapter 6

Key Vocabulary Introduce the key vocabulary in the chapter using the routine below.

Define: A system of equations is a set of equations with the same variables.

Example: $y = 34.2 - 14.9x$ and $y = 3.3 + 4.7x$

Ask: What variables do both equations have in common? x and y

Get Ready for Chapter 6

Diagnose Readiness You have two options for checking Prerequisite Skills.

Text Option

Take the Quick Check below. Refer to the Quick Review for help.

*Quick*Check

(Used in Lessons 6-1 and 6-5.)

Name the ordered pair for each point on the coordinate plane. (Lesson 1-6)

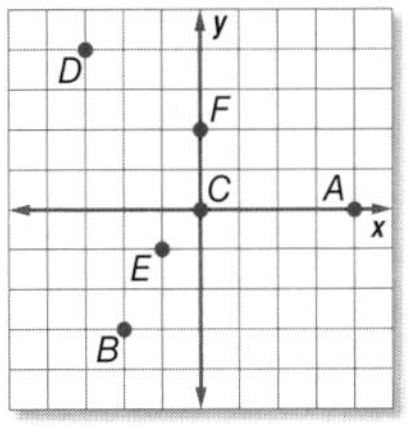

1. A (4, 0)
2. D (−3, 4)
3. B (−2, −3)
4. C (0, 0)
5. E (−1, −1)
6. F (0, 2)

(Used in Lessons 6-1 through 6-5.)

Solve each equation or formula for the variable specified. (Lesson 2-8)

7. $2x + 4y = 12$, for x $x = 6 - 2y$
8. $x = 3y - 9$, for y $y = \frac{x + 9}{3}$
9. $m - 2n = 6$, for m $m = 2n + 6$
10. $y = mx + b$, for x $x = \frac{y - b}{m}$
11. $P = 2\ell + 2w$, for ℓ $\ell = \frac{P - 2w}{2}$
12. $5x - 10y = 40$, for y $y = \frac{x - 8}{2}$
13. **GEOMETRY** The formula for the area of a triangle is $A = \frac{1}{2}bh$, where A represents the area, b is the base, and h is the height of the triangle. Solve the equation for b. $b = \frac{2A}{h}$

*Quick*Review

EXAMPLE 1

Name the ordered pair for Q on the coordinate plane.

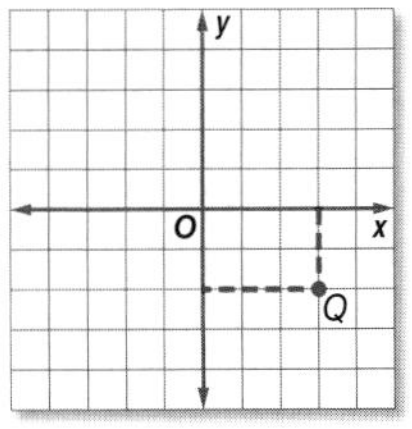

Follow a vertical line from the point to the x-axis. This gives the x-coordinate, 3.

Follow a horizontal line from the point to the y-axis. This gives the y-coordinate, −2.

The ordered pair is (3, −2).

EXAMPLE 2

Solve $12x + 3y = 36$ for y.

$12x + 3y = 36$	**Original equation**
$12x + 3y - 12x = 36 - 12x$	**Subtract 12x from each side.**
$3y = 36 - 12x$	**Simplify.**
$\frac{3y}{3} = \frac{36 - 12x}{3}$	**Divide each side by 3.**
$y = 12 - 4x$	**Simplify.**

Online Option

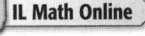

IL Math Online Take a self-check Chapter Readiness Quiz at glencoe.com.

Get Ready for Chapter 6

Response to Intervention (RtI)

Use the *Quick Check* results and the Intervention Planner chart to help you determine your Response to Intervention. The If-Then statements in the chart below help you decide the appropriate tier of RtI and suggest intervention resources for each tier.

Intervention Planner

Tier 1 — On Level

If students miss about 25% of the exercises or less,

Then choose a resource:

- **SE** Lessons 1–6 and 2–8
- **CRM** Skills Practice, Chapter 1, p. 39, Chapter 2, p. 51
- **TE** Chapter Project, p. 330
- IL Math Online Self-Check Quiz

Tier 2 — Strategic Intervention approaching grade level

If students miss about 50% of the exercises,

Then choose a resource:

- **CRM** Study Guide and Intervention, Chapter 1, pp. 37–38, Chapter 2, pp. 49–50
- *Quick Review Math Handbook*
- IL Math Online Extra Examples, Personal Tutor, Homework Help

Tier 3 — Intensive Intervention 2 or more grades below level

If students miss about 75% of the exercises,

Then use *Math Triumphs, Alg. 1*

- IL Math Online Extra Examples, Personal Tutor, Homework Help, Review Vocabulary

CHAPTER 6 Notes

FOLDABLES® Study Organizer

Dinah Zike's Foldables®

Focus Students write notes about solving systems of linear equations and inequalities as they are presented in the lessons of this chapter.

Teach Have students make and label their Foldables as illustrated. Have students write a word or concept from the lesson on the back of each lesson's tab. Under the word or concept, ask students to include a definition and an example.

When to Use It Encourage students to add to their Foldables as they work through the chapter and to use them to review for the chapter test.

Differentiated Instruction

CRM Student-Built Glossary, pp. 1–2 Students should complete the chart by providing the definition of each term and an example as they progress through Chapter 6. This study tool can also be used to review for the chapter test.

Get Started on Chapter 6

You will learn several new concepts, skills, and vocabulary terms as you study Chapter 6. To get ready, identify important terms and organize your resources. You may wish to refer to **Chapter 0** to review prerequisite skills.

FOLDABLES® Study Organizer

Linear Functions Make this Foldable to help you organize your Chapter 6 notes about solving systems of equations and inequalities. Begin with a sheet of notebook paper.

1. **Fold** lengthwise to the holes.

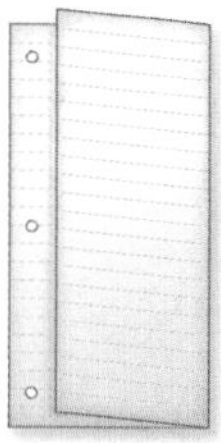

2. **Cut** 8 tabs.

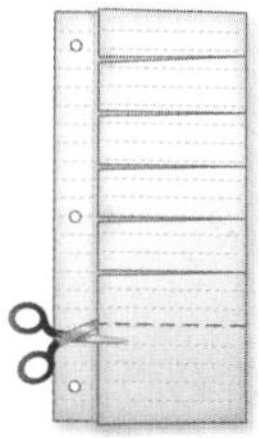

3. **Label** the tabs using the lesson numbers and lesson titles.

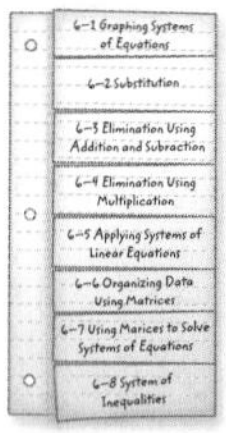

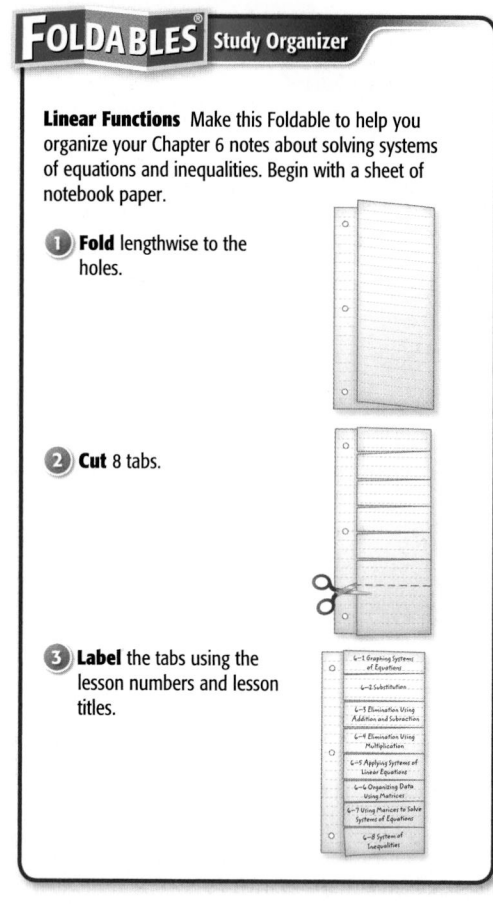

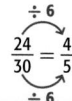

IL Math Online glencoe.com

- Study the chapter online
- Explore **Math in Motion**
- Get extra help from your own **Personal Tutor**
- Use **Extra Examples** for additional help
- Take a **Self-Check Quiz**
- **Review Vocabulary** in fun ways

New Vocabulary

English		Español
system of equations	• p. 333 •	sistema de ecuaciones
consistent	• p. 333 •	consistente
independent	• p. 333 •	independiente
dependent	• p. 333 •	dependiente
inconsistent	• p. 333 •	inconsistente
substitution	• p. 342 •	sustitución
elimination	• p. 348 •	eliminación
matrix	• p. 369 •	matriz
element	• p. 369 •	elemento
dimension	• p. 369 •	dimensión
scalar	• p. 371 •	escalar
scalar multiplication	• p. 371 •	multiplicación por escalares
augmented matrix	• p. 376 •	matriz ampliada
row reduction	• p. 377 •	reducción de fila
identity matrix	• p. 377 •	matriz
system of inequalities	• p. 382 •	sistema de desigualdades

Review Vocabulary

domain • p. 39 • dominio the set of the first numbers of the ordered pairs in a relation

intersection • p. 304 • intersección the graph of a compound inequality containing *and*; the solution is the set of elements common to both graphs

proportion • p. 111 • proporción an equation stating that two ratios are equal

Proportion

$$\frac{24}{30} = \frac{4}{5}$$

(÷ 6 numerator, ÷ 6 denominator)

Multilingual eGlossary glencoe.com

332 Chapter 6 Systems of Linear Equations and Inequalities

6-1 Graphing Systems of Equations

Then

You graphed linear equations. (Lesson 3-1)

Now

- Determine the number of solutions a system of linear equations has.
- Solve systems of linear equations by graphing.

IL Learning Standards

8.B.4a Represent algebraic concepts with physical materials, words, diagrams, tables, graphs, equations and inequalities and use appropriate technology.

New Vocabulary

system of equations
consistent
independent
dependent
inconsistent

IL Math Online

glencoe.com

- Extra Examples
- Personal Tutor
- Self-Check Quiz
- Homework Help
- Math in Motion

Why?

The cost to begin production on a band's CD is \$1500. Each CD costs \$4 to produce and will sell for \$10. The band wants to know how many CDs they will have to sell to earn a profit.

Graphing a system can show when a company makes a profit. The cost of producing the CD can be modeled by the equation $y = 4x + 1500$, where y represents the cost of production and x is the number of CDs produced.

The income from the CDs sold can be modeled by the equation $y = 10x$, where y represents the total income of selling the CDs, and x is the number of CDs sold.

Band's CD Sales

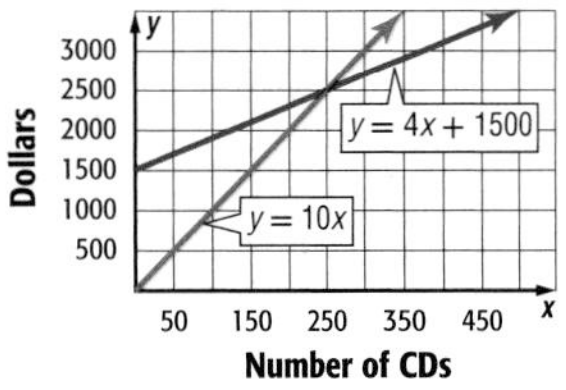

If we graph these equations, we can see at which point the band begins making a profit. The point where the two graphs intersect is where the band breaks even. This happens when the band sells 250 CDs. If the band sells more than 250 CDs, they will make a profit.

Possible Number of Solutions The two equations, $y = 4x + 1500$ and $y = 10x$, form a **system of equations**. The ordered pair that is a solution of both equations is the solution of the system. A system of two linear equations can have one solution, an infinite number of solutions, or no solution.

- If a system has at least one solution, it is said to be **consistent**. The graphs intersect at one point or are the same line.
- If a consistent system has exactly one solution, it is said to be **independent**. If it has an infinite number of solutions, it is **dependent**. This means that there are unlimited solutions that satisfy both equations.
- If a system has no solution, it is said to be **inconsistent**. The graphs are parallel.

Concept Summary — **Possible Solutions** (For Your FOLDABLE)

Number of Solutions	exactly one	infinite	no solution
Terminology	consistent and independent	consistent and dependent	inconsistent
Graph	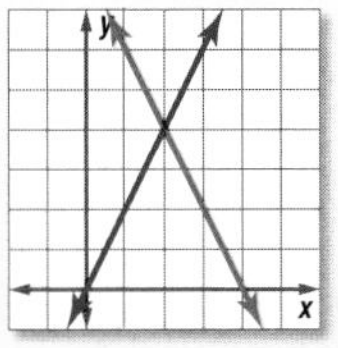	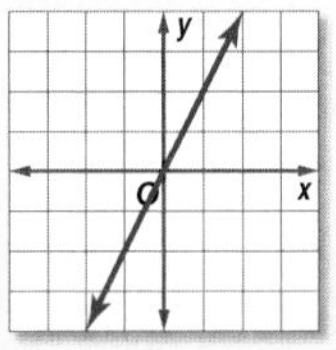	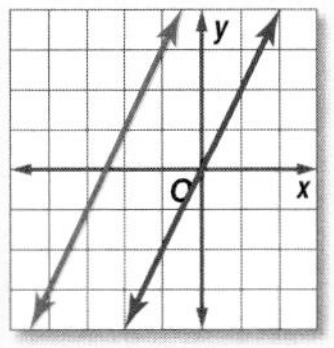

6-1 Lesson Notes

1 FOCUS

Vertical Alignment

Before Lesson 6-1
Graph linear functions.

Lesson 6-1
Determine the number of solutions a system of linear equations has, if any.
Solve systems of linear equations by graphing.

After Lesson 6-1
Solve systems of linear equations using algebraic methods.

2 TEACH

Scaffolding Questions

Have students read the *Why?* section of the lesson.

- What does it mean to *break even* in this situation? The income from CD sales and the cost of producing the CDs are equal.
- What is the break-even dollar amount? \$2500
- How many solutions does the system have? Explain. One; there can be only one break-even point, and that is where the graphs intersect.

Lesson 6-1 Resources

Resource	Approaching-Level	On-Level	Beyond-Level	English Learners
Teacher Edition	• Differentiated Instruction, p. 338	• Differentiated Instruction, pp. 334, 338	• Differentiated Instruction, p. 334	• Differentiated Instruction, p. 338
Chapter Resource Masters	• Study Guide and Intervention, pp. 5–6 • Skills Practice, p. 7 • Practice, p. 8 • Word Problem Practice, p. 9 • Graphing Calculator Activity, p. 11	• Study Guide and Intervention, pp. 5–6 • Skills Practice, p. 7 • Practice, p. 8 • Word Problem Practice, p. 9 • Enrichment, p. 10 • Graphing Calculator Activity, p. 11	• Practice, p. 8 • Word Problem Practice, p. 9 • Enrichment, p. 10 • Graphing Calculator Activity, p. 11	• Study Guide and Intervention, pp. 5–6 • Skills Practice, p. 7 • Practice, p. 8 • Graphing Calculator Activity, p. 11
Transparencies	• 5-Minute Check Transparency 6-1	• 5-Minute Check Transparency 6-1	• 5-Minute Check Transparency 6-1	• 5-Minute Check Transparency 6-1
Other	• Study Notebook • Teaching Algebra with Manipulatives	• Study Notebook • Teaching Algebra with Manipulatives	• Study Notebook	• Study Notebook • Teaching Algebra with Manipulatives

Possible Number of Solutions

Example 1 shows how to find the number of solutions of a system of equations, and if it is consistent, inconsistent, dependent, or independent.

Formative Assessment

Use the Check Your Progress exercises after each Example to determine students' understanding of concepts.

Additional Example

1 Use the graph to determine whether each system is *consistent* or *inconsistent* and if it is *independent* or *dependent*.

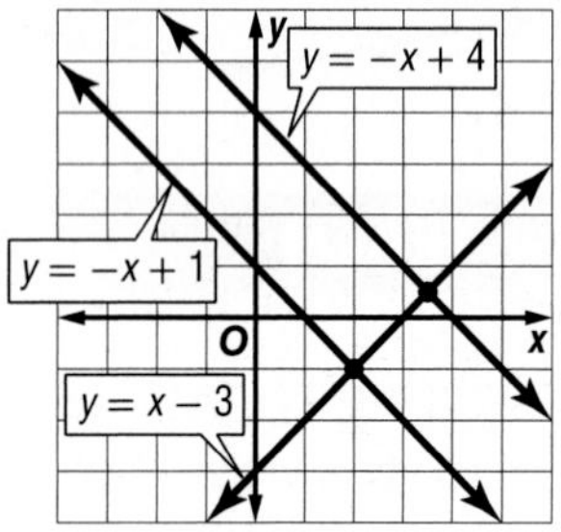

a. $y = -x + 1$
$y = -x + 4$
inconsistent

b. $y = x - 3$
$y = -x + 1$
consistent and independent

Additional Examples also in Interactive Classroom PowerPoint® Presentations

IWB INTERACTIVE WHITEBOARD READY

TEACH with TECH

INTERACTIVE WHITEBOARD Create a table with columns: *no solutions*, *1 solution*, and *infinitely many solutions*. Write several systems of equations on the board. Have students drag each system to the correct column.

StudyTip

Number of Solutions When both equations are of the form $y = mx + b$, the values of m and b can determine the number of solutions.

Compare m and b	Number of Solutions
different m values	one
same m value, but different b values	none
same m value, and same b value	infinite

Math *in Motion*, Animation glencoe.com

EXAMPLE 1 Number of Solutions

Use the graph at the right to determine whether each system is *consistent* or *inconsistent* and if it is *independent* or *dependent*.

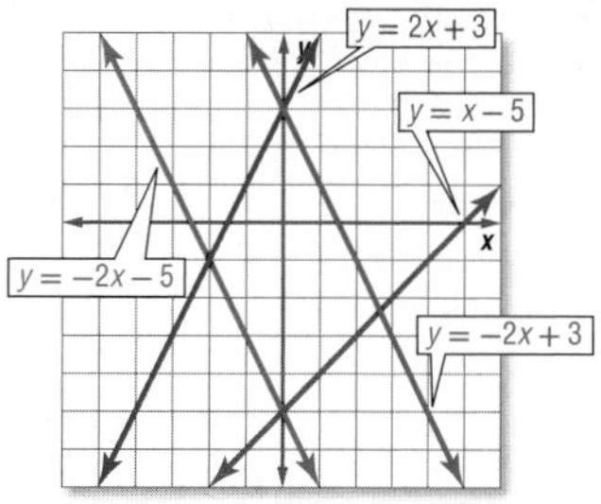

a. $y = -2x + 3$
$y = x - 5$

Since the graphs of these two lines intersect at one point, there is exactly one solution. Therefore, the system is consistent and independent.

b. $y = -2x - 5$
$y = -2x + 3$

Since the graphs of these two lines are parallel, there is no solution of the system. Therefore, the system is inconsistent.

Check Your Progress

1A. $y = 2x + 3$, $y = -2x - 5$ consistent and independent

1B. $y = x - 5$, $y = -2x - 5$ consistent and independent

Personal Tutor glencoe.com

Solve by Graphing One method of solving a system of equations is to graph the equations carefully on the same coordinate grid and find their point of intersection. This point is the solution of the system.

EXAMPLE 2 Solve by Graphing

Graph each system and determine the number of solutions that it has. If it has one solution, name it.

a. $y = -3x + 10$
$y = x - 2$

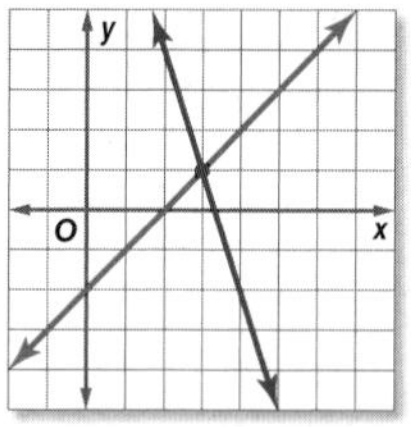

The graphs appear to intersect at the point (3, 1). You can check this by substituting 3 for x and 1 for y.

CHECK

$y = -3x + 10$	**Original equation**
$1 \stackrel{?}{=} -3(3) + 10$	**Substitution**
$1 \stackrel{?}{=} -9 + 10$	**Multiply.**
$1 = 1$ ✓	
$y = x - 2$	**Original equation**
$1 \stackrel{?}{=} 3 - 2$	**Substitution**
$1 = 1$ ✓	**Multiply.**

The solution is (3, 1).

b. $2x - y = -1$
$4x - 2y = 6$

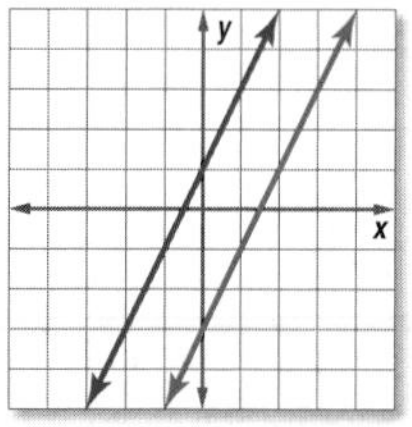

The lines have the same slope but different y-intercepts, so the lines are parallel. Since they do not intersect, there is no solution of this system. The system is inconsistent.

Review Vocabulary

parallel lines never intersect and have the same slope (Lesson 4-4)

Differentiated Instruction

OL BL

Extension Write a system of three equations in two variables on the board. Have the students determine if the system has *one* solution, *no* solution, or *infinitely many* solutions. If it has one solution, name it. For example,

$x + y = 2$
$x - y = 0$
$y = -2$

has *no* solution because the three lines do not intersect at one point.

Check Your Progress

Graph each system and determine the number of solutions that it has. If it has one solution, name it. 2A–2B. See Ch. 6 Answer Appendix for graphs.

2A. $x - y = 2$
$3y + 2x = 9$ 1 solution; (3, 1)

2B. $y = -2x - 3$
$6x + 3y = -9$ infinitely many

Personal Tutor glencoe.com

We can use what we know about systems of equations to solve many real-world problems that involve two or more different functions.

Real-World Link

In 2004, 2.9 million girls participated in high school sports. This was an all-time high for female participation.

Source: National Federation of State High School Associations

Real-World EXAMPLE 3 Write and Solve a System of Equations

SPORTS The number of girls participating in high school soccer and track and field has steadily increased over the past few years. Use the information in the table to predict the approximate year when the number of girls participating in these two sports will be the same.

High School Sport	Number of Girls Participating in 2004 (thousands)	Average rate of increase (thousands per year)
soccer	309	8
track and field	418	3

Source: National Federation of State High School Associations

Words	Number of girls participating	equals	rate of increase	times	number of years after 2004	plus	number participating in 2004.		
Variables	Let y = number of girls competing. Let x = number of years after 2004.								
Equations	Soccer: y	=	8	•	x	+	309		
	Track and field: y	=	3	•	x	+	418		

Graph $y = 8x + 309$ and $y = 3x + 418$. The graphs appear to intersect at approximately (22, 485).

CHECK Use substitution to check this answer.

$y = 8x + 309$ $\qquad$ $y = 3x + 418$

$485 \stackrel{?}{=} 8(22) + 309$ $\qquad$ $485 \stackrel{?}{=} 3(22) + 418$

$485 = 485$ ✓ $\qquad$ $485 \approx 484$ ✓

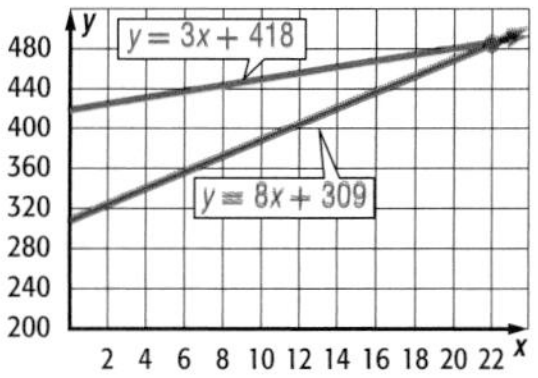

The solution means that approximately 22 years after 2004, or in 2026, the number of girls participating in high school soccer and track and field will be the same, about 485,000.

Math in Motion, Interactive Lab glencoe.com

Check Your Progress

3. VIDEO GAMES Joe and Josh each want to buy a video game. Joe has \$14 and saves \$10 a week. Josh has \$26 and saves \$7 a week. In how many weeks will they have the same amount? 4 weeks

Personal Tutor glencoe.com

Focus on Mathematical Content

Graphing Systems of Equations If the graphs of a system intersect in one point, the system is consistent and independent and has one solution. If the graphs coincide or lie on the same line, the system is consistent and dependent, and the system has an infinite number of solutions. If the graphs are parallel, the system is inconsistent, there are no points of intersection, and there is no solution.

Solve By Graphing

Example 2 shows how to solve a system of equations by graphing. **Example 3** shows how to use a system of equations to solve a real-world problem.

Additional Examples

2 Graph each system and determine the number of solutions that it has. If it has one solution, name it.

a. $y = 2x + 3$
$8x - 4y = -12$ infinitely many solutions

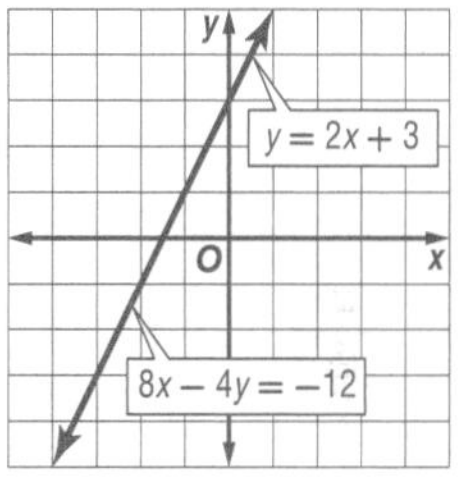

b. $x - 2y = 4$
$x - 2y = -2$ no solution

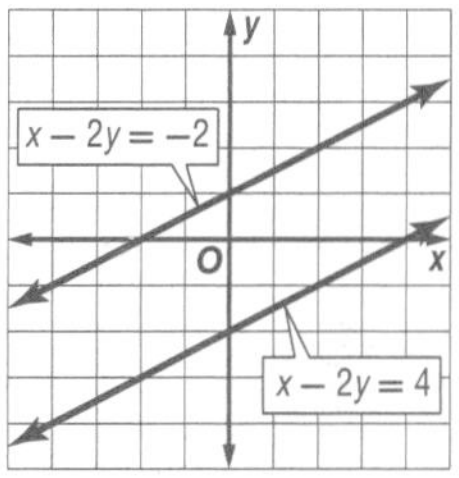

3 BICYCLING Naresh rode 20 miles last week and plans to ride 35 miles per week. Diego rode 50 miles last week and plans to ride 25 miles per week. Predict the week in which Naresh and Diego will have ridden the same number of miles. week 3

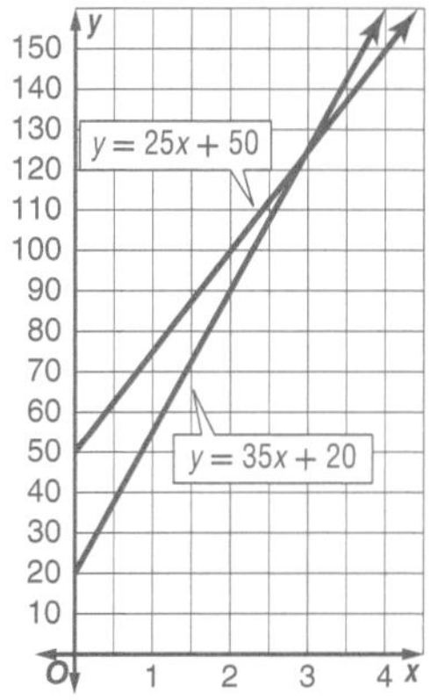

3 PRACTICE

Formative Assessment

Use Exercises 1–9 to check for understanding.

Use the chart at the bottom of this page to customize assignments for your students.

Additional Answers

7. 1 solution, $(-4, 0)$

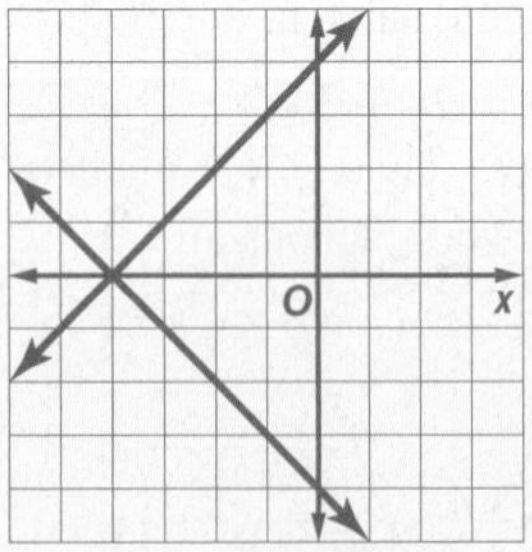

8. 1 solution, $(-1, 2)$

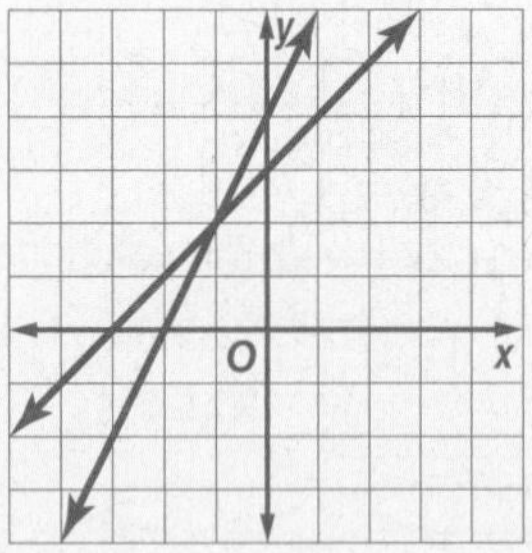

9b.

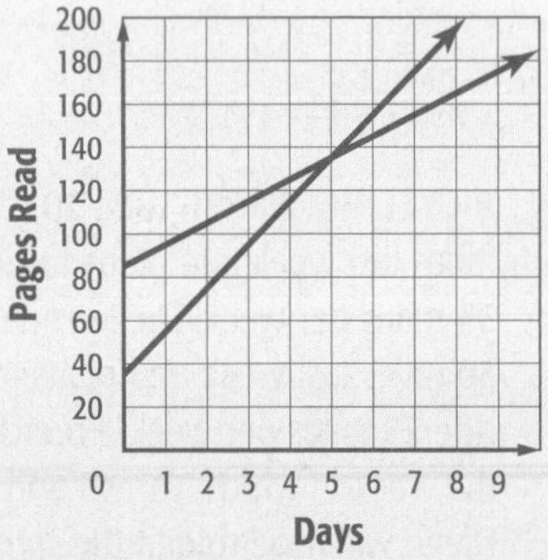

16–24. See Ch. 6 Answer Appendix for graphs.

16. 1 solution, $(0, -3)$

17. 1 solution; $\left(-\frac{5}{6}, -\frac{4}{3}\right)$, -1

18. no solution

19. infinitely many

20. infinitely many

21. 1 solution; $(5, -1)$

22. 1 solution; $(3, 2)$

23. no solution

24. infinitely many

Check Your Understanding

Example 1 p. 334

Use the graph at the right to determine whether each system is *consistent* or *inconsistent* and if it is *independent* or *dependent*.

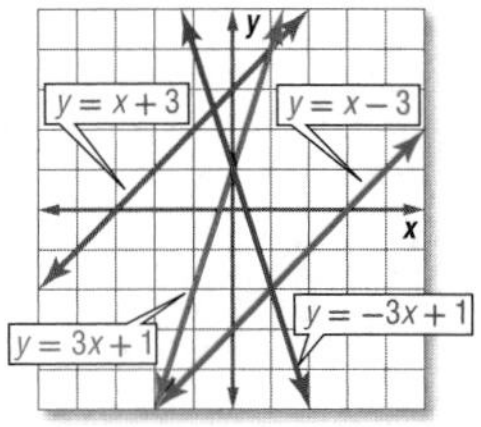

1. $y = -3x + 1$; $y = 3x + 1$ — 1. consistent and independent

2. $y = 3x + 1$; $y = x - 3$ — 2. consistent and independent

3. $y = x - 3$; $y = x + 3$ — 3. inconsistent

4. $y = x + 3$; $x - y = -3$ — 4. consistent and dependent

5. $x - y = -3$; $y = -3x + 1$ — 5. consistent and independent

6. $y = -3x + 1$; $y = x - 3$ — 6. consistent and independent

Example 2 p. 334

Graph each system and determine the number of solutions that it has. If it has one solution, name it. 7–8. See margin.

7. $y = x + 4$; $y = -x - 4$

8. $y = x + 3$; $y = 2x + 4$

Example 3 p. 335

9. **READING** Alberto and Ashanti are reading a graphic novel.

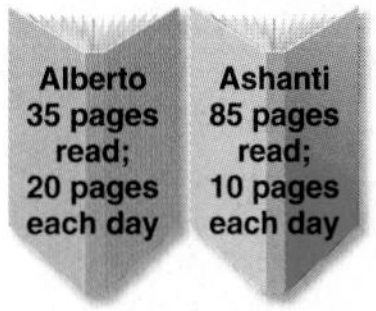

a. Write an equation to represent the pages each boy has read. 9a. Alberto: $y = 20x + 35$; Ashanti: $y = 10x + 85$

b. Graph each equation. See margin.

c. How long will it be before Alberto has read more pages than Ashanti? Check and interpret your solution. (5, 135); Alberto will have read more after 5 days.

Practice and Problem Solving

● = **Step-by-Step Solutions** begin on page R12.
Extra Practice begins on page 815.

Example 1 p. 334

Use the graph at the right to determine whether each system is *consistent* or *inconsistent* and if it is *independent* or *dependent*.

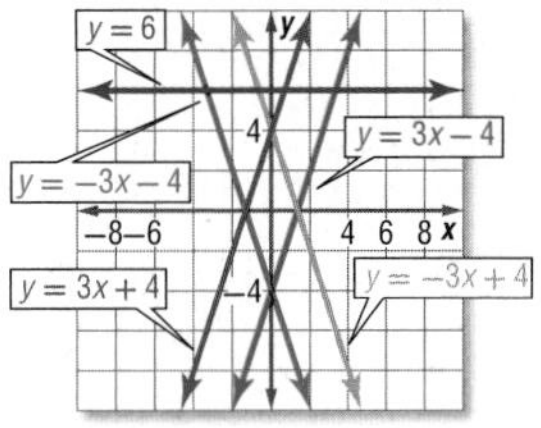

10. $y = 6$; $y = 3x + 4$ — 10. consistent and independent

11. $y = 3x + 4$; $y = -3x + 4$ — 11. consistent and independent

12. $y = -3x + 4$; $y = -3x - 4$ — 12. inconsistent

● 13. $y = -3x - 4$; $y = 3x - 4$ — 13. consistent and independent

14. $3x - y = -4$; $y = -3x + 4$ — 14. consistent and independent

15. $3x - y = 4$; $3x + y = 4$ — 15. consistent and independent

Example 2 p. 334

Graph each system and determine the number of solutions that it has. If it has one solution, name it. 16–24. See margin.

16. $y = -3$; $y = x - 3$

17. $y = 4x + 2$; $y = -2x - 3$

18. $y = x - 6$; $y = x + 2$

19. $x + y = 4$; $3x + 3y = 12$

20. $x - y = -2$; $-x + y = 2$

21. $x + 2y = 3$; $x = 5$

22. $2x + 3y = 12$; $2x - y = 4$

23. $2x + y = -4$; $y + 2x = 3$

24. $2x + 2y = 6$; $5y + 5x = 15$

Differentiated Homework Options

Level	Assignment	Two-Day Option	
AL Basic	10–26, 47, 49–76	11–25 odd, 53–56	10–26 even, 47, 49–52, 57–76
OL Core	11–25 odd, 26, 27–41 odd, 42–47, 49–76	10–26, 53–56	27–47, 49–52, 57–76
BL Advanced	27–68, (optional: 69–76)		

Example 3 p. 335

25. **SCHOOL DANCE** Akira and Jen are competing to see who can sell the most tickets for the Winter Dance. On Monday, Akira sold 22 and then sold 30 per day after that. Jen sold 53 one Monday and then sold 20 per day after that.
   a. Write equations for the number of tickets each person has sold. **Akira: $y = 30x + 22$; Jen: $y = 20x + 53$**
   b. Graph each equation. **See margin.**
   c. Solve the system of equations. Check and interpret your solution. **(3.1, 115); After about 3 days Akira will have sold more tickets.**

26. **TRAVEL** If x is the number of years since 2000 and y is the percent of people using travel services, the following equations represent the percent of people using travel agents and the percent of the people using the Internet to plan travel.

   Travel agents: $y = -2x + 30$ Internet: $y = 6x + 41$

   a. Graph the system of equations. **See Ch. 6 Answer Appendix.**
   b. Estimate the year travel agents and the Internet were used equally. **1999**

42d. The domain of each of these equations is the set of real numbers greater than or equal to 0. The range of each of these equations is the set of real numbers greater than or equal to 0.

Graph each system and determine the number of solutions that it has. If it has one solution, name it. **27–41. See Ch. 6 Answer Appendix for graphs.**

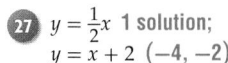

B

27. $y = \frac{1}{2}x$, $y = x + 2$ **1 solution; (−4, −2)**
28. $y = 6x + 6$, $y = 3x + 6$ **1 solution; (0, 6)**
29. $y = 2x - 17$, $y = x - 10$ **1 solution; (7, −3)**
30. $8x - 4y = 16$, $-5x - 5y = 5$ **1 solution; (1, −2)**
31. $3x + 5y = 30$, $3x + y = 18$ **1 solution; (5, 3)**
32. $-3x + 4y = 24$, $4x - y = 7$ **1 solution (4, 9)**
33. $2x - 8y = 6$, $x - 4y = 3$ **infinitely many**
34. $4x - 6y = 12$, $-2x + 3y = -6$ **infinitely many**
35. $2x + 3y = 10$, $4x + 6y = 12$ **no solution**
36. $3x + 2y = 10$, $2x + 3y = 10$ **1 solution; (2, 2)**
37. $3y - x = -2$, $y - \frac{1}{3}x = 2$ **no solution**
38. $\frac{8}{5}y = \frac{2}{5}x + 1$, $\frac{2}{5}y = \frac{1}{10}x + \frac{1}{4}$ **infinitely many**
39. $\frac{1}{3}x + \frac{1}{3}y = 1$, $x + y = 1$ **no solution**
40. $\frac{3}{4}x + \frac{1}{2}y = \frac{1}{4}$, $\frac{2}{3}x + \frac{1}{6}y = \frac{1}{2}$ **1 solution; (1, −1)**
41. $\frac{5}{6}x + \frac{2}{3}y = \frac{1}{2}$, $\frac{2}{5}x + \frac{1}{5}y = \frac{3}{5}$ **1 solution; (3, −3)**

Real-World Link

Many photographers feel that the most useful aspect of digital cameras is the ability to see photos instantly. The second most important aspect is the ability to manipulate and correct digital photos.

Source: Photography

42. **PHOTOGRAPHY** Suppose x represents the number of cameras sold and y represents the number of years since 2000. Then the number of digital cameras sold each year since 2000, in millions, can be modeled by the equation $y = 12.5x + 10.9$. The number of film cameras sold each year since 2000, in millions, can be modeled by the equation $y = -9.1x + 78.8$.
   a. Graph each equation. **See Ch. 6 Answer Appendix.**
   b. In which year did digital camera sales surpass film camera sales? **2003**
   c. In what year will film cameras stop selling altogether? **2008**
   d. What are the domain and range of each of the functions in this situation?

C

Graph each system and determine the number of solutions that it has. If it has one solution, name it. **43–44. See Ch. 6 Answer Appendix for graphs.**

43. $2y = 1.2x - 10$, $4y = 2.4x$ **no solution**
44. $x = 6 - \frac{3}{8}y$, $4 = \frac{2}{3}x + \frac{1}{4}y$ **infinitely many**

Study Guide and Intervention

CRM pp. 5–6 AL OL ELL

NAME ______ DATE ______ PERIOD ______

6-1 Study Guide and Intervention

Graphing Systems of Equations

Possible Number of Solutions Two or more linear equations involving the same variables form a **system of equations**. A solution of the system of equations is an ordered pair of numbers that satisfies both equations. The table below summarizes information about systems of linear equations.

Graph of a System	intersecting lines	same line	parallel lines
Number of Solutions	exactly one solution	infinitely many solutions	no solution
Terminology	consistent and independent	consistent and dependent	inconsistent

Example Use the graph at the right to determine whether each system is *consistent* or *inconsistent* and if it is *independent* or *dependent*.

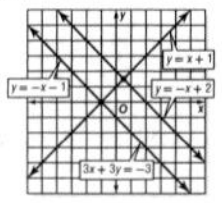

a. $y = -x + 2$, $y = x + 1$
Since the graphs of $y = -x + 2$ and $y = x + 1$ intersect, there is one solution. Therefore, the system is consistent and independent.

b. $y = -x + 2$, $3x + 3y = -3$
Since the graphs of $y = -x + 2$ and $3x + 3y = -3$ are parallel, there are no solutions. Therefore, the system is inconsistent.

c. $3x + 3y = -3$, $y = -x - 1$
Since the graphs of $3x + 3y = -3$ and $y = -x - 1$ coincide, there are infinitely many solutions. Therefore, the system is consistent and dependent.

Exercises

Use the graph at the right to determine whether each system is *consistent* or *inconsistent* and if it is *independent* or *dependent*.

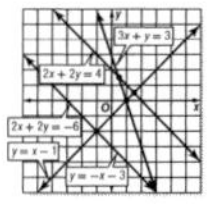

1. $y = -x - 3$, $y = x - 1$ **consistent; independent**
2. $2x + 2y = -6$, $y = -x - 3$ **consistent; dependent**
3. $y = -x - 3$, $2x + 2y = 4$ **inconsistent**
4. $2x + 2y = -6$, $3x + y = 3$ **consistent; independent**

Practice

CRM p. 8 AL OL BL ELL

NAME ______ DATE ______ PERIOD ______

6-1 Practice

Graphing Systems of Equations

Use the graph at the right to determine whether each system is *consistent* or *inconsistent* and if it is *independent* or *dependent*.

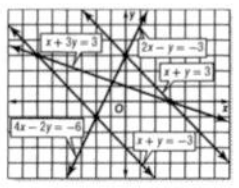

1. $x + y = 3$, $x + y = -3$ **inconsistent**
2. $2x - y = -3$, $4x - 2y = -6$ **consistent and dependent**
3. $x + 3y = 3$, $x + y = -3$ **consistent and independent**
4. $x + 3y = 3$, $2x - y = -3$ **consistent and independent**

Graph each system and determine the number of solutions that it has. If it has one solution, name it.

5. $3x - y = -2$, $3x - y = 0$ **no solution**

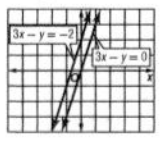

6. $y = 2x - 3$, $4x = 2y + 6$ **infinitely many**

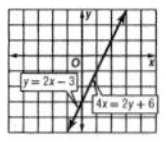

7. $x + 2y = 3$, $3x - y = -5$ **one; (−1, 2)**

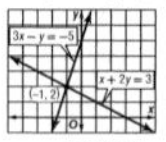

8. **BUSINESS** Nick plans to start a home-based business producing and selling gourmet dog treats. He figures it will cost \$20 in operating costs per week plus \$0.50 to produce each treat. He plans to sell each treat for \$1.50.
   a. Graph the system of equations $y = 0.5x + 20$ and $y = 1.5x$ to represent the situation.
   b. How many treats does Nick need to sell per week to break even? **20**

9. **SALES** A used book store also started selling used CDs and videos. In the first week, the store sold 40 used CDs and videos, at \$4.00 per CD and \$6.00 per video. The sales for both CDs and videos totaled \$180.00
   a. Write a system of equations to represent the situation. **c + v = 40, 4c + 6v = 180**
   b. Graph the system of equations.
   c. How many CDs and videos did the store sell in the first week? **30 CDs and 10 videos**

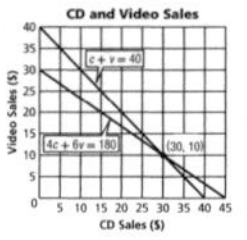

Word Problem Practice

CRM p. 9 AL OL BL ELL

NAME ______ DATE ______ PERIOD ______

6-1 Word Problem Practice

Graphing Systems of Equations

1. **BUSINESS** The widget factory will sell a total of y widgets after x days according to the equation $y = 200x + 300$. The gadget factory will sell y gadgets after x days according to the equation $y = 200x + 100$. Look at the graph of the system of equations and determine whether it has *no* solution, *one* solution, or *infinitely many* solutions. **no solution**

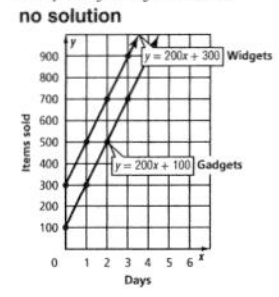

2. **ARCHITECTURE** An office building has two elevators. One elevator starts out on the 4th floor, 35 feet above the ground, and is descending at a rate of 2.2 feet per second. The other elevator starts out at ground level and is rising at a rate of 1.7 feet per second. Write a system of equations to represent the situation. **Sample answer: $y = 35 - 2.2x$; $y = 1.7x$**

3. **FITNESS** Olivia and her brother William had a bicycle race. Olivia rode at a speed of 20 feet per second while William rode at a speed of 15 feet per second. To be fair, Olivia decided to give William a 150-foot head start. The race ended in a tie. How far away was the finish line from where Olivia started? **600 ft**

4. **AVIATION** Two planes are in flight near a local airport. One plane is at an altitude of 1000 meters and is ascending at a rate of 400 meters per minute. The second plane is at an altitude of 5900 meters and is descending at a rate of 300 meters per minute.
   a. Write a system of equations that represents the progress of each plane **$y = 400x + 1000$; $y = 5900 - 300x$**
   b. Make a graph that represents the progress of each plane.

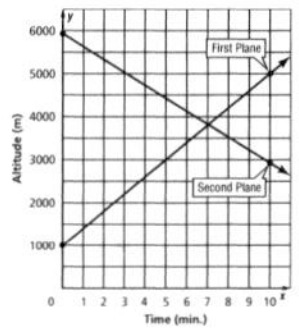

Additional Answer

25b.

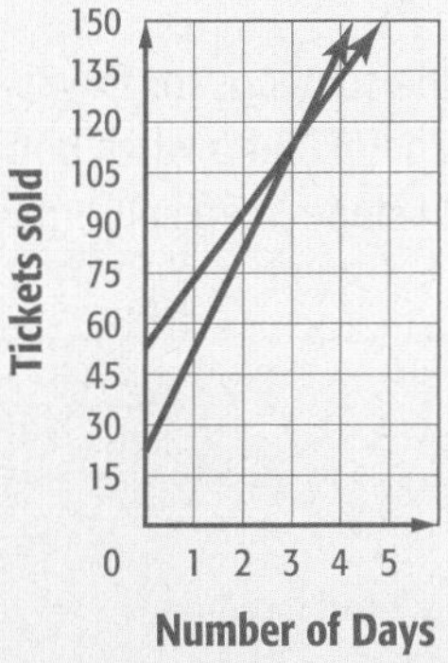

Enrichment

CRM p. 10 OL BL

NAME ______ DATE ______ PERIOD ______

6-1 Enrichment

Graphing a Trip

The distance formula, $d = rt$, is used to solve many types of problems. If you graph an equation such as $d = 50t$, the graph is a model for a car going at 50 mi/h. The time the car travels is t; the distance in miles the car covers is d. The slope of the line is the speed.

Suppose you drive to a nearby town and return. You average 50 mi/h on the trip out but only 25 mi/h on the trip home. The round trip takes 5 hours. How far away is the town?

The graph at the right represents your trip. Notice that the return trip is shown with a negative slope because you are driving in the opposite direction.

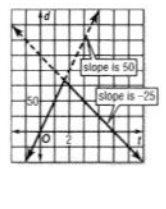

Solve each problem.

1. Estimate the answer to the problem in the above example. About how far away is the town? **about 80 miles**

Graph each trip and solve the problem.

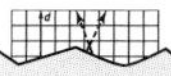

2. An airpl... has enough fuel for 3 h... of

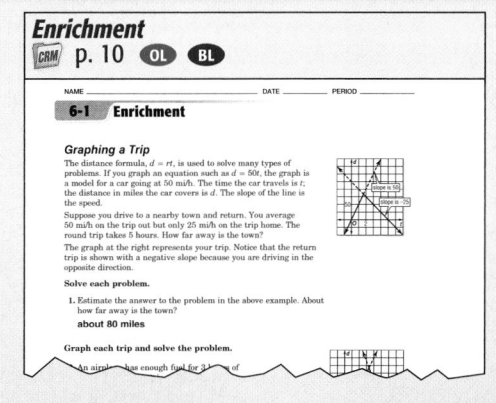

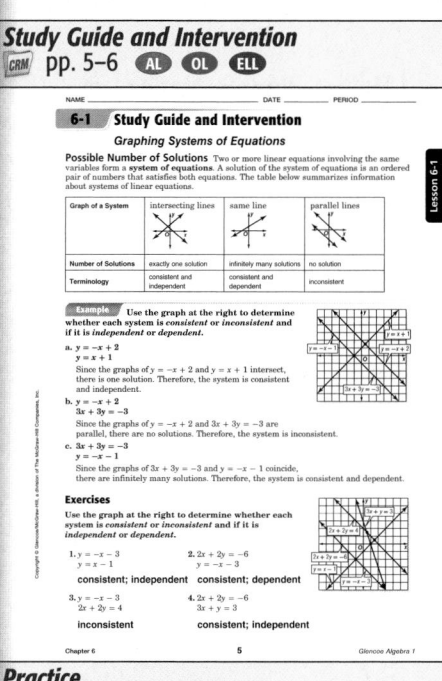

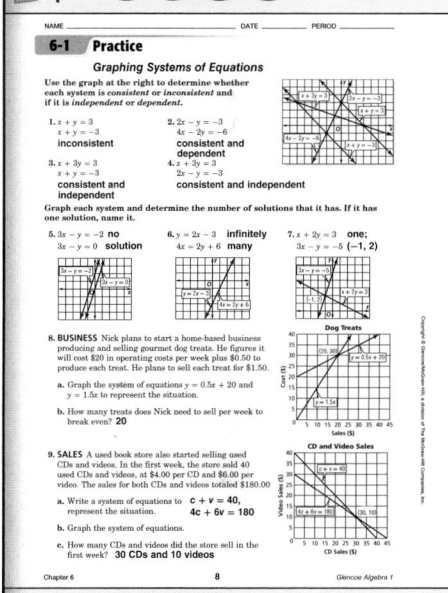

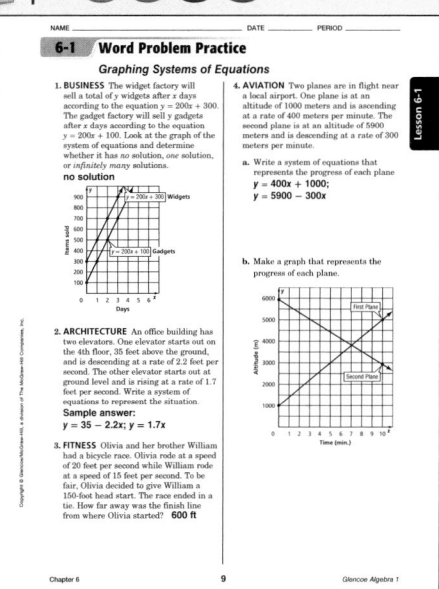

Multiple Representations In Exercise 46, students use algebra and a graph in the coordinate plane to solve a system of equations and interpret the results.

Watch Out!

Find the Error For Exercise 47, suggest that students try several prices at both discounts, such as \$50, \$100, and \$150, and then decide whether Francisca or Alan is correct.

Additional Answers

45b.

Years Since 2005	Lookatme Visitors (mln)	Buyourstuff Visitors (mln)
0	2.5	59
1	15.6	57
2	28.7	55
3	41.8	53
4	54.9	51

45c.

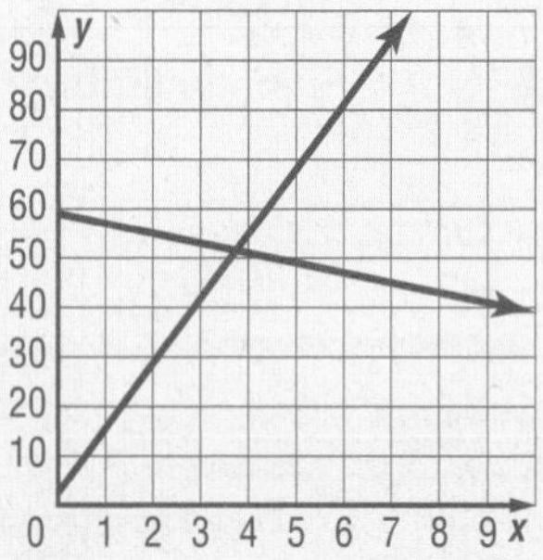

46b. (6, 6)

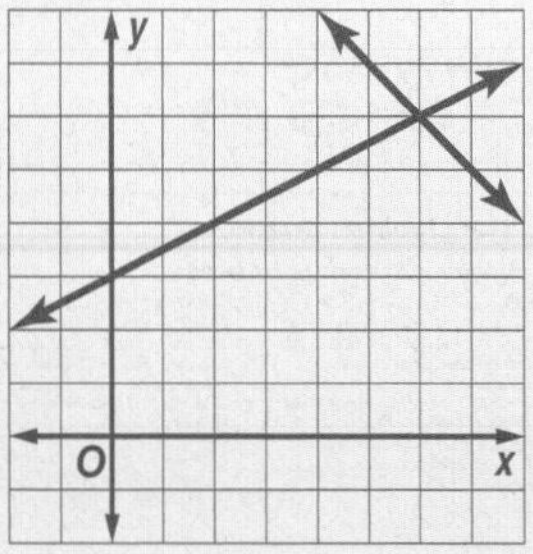

48.

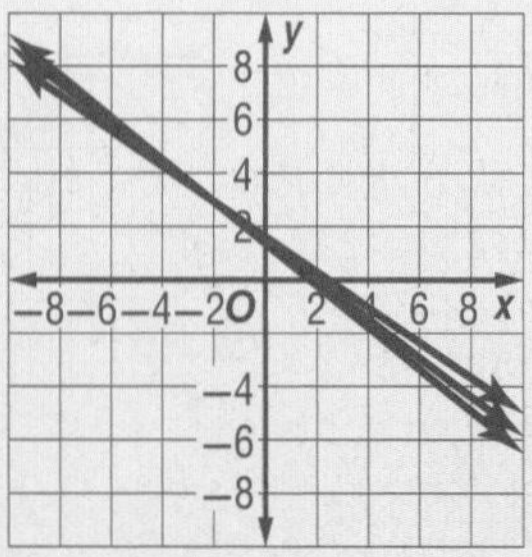

Real-World Link

Social networking sites have grown in popularity in recent years. Approximately 2 out of every 3 people online visit a social networking site.

Source: Read/Write Web

45. **WEB SITES** Personal publishing site *Lookatme* had 2.5 million visitors in 2005. Each year after that, the number of visitors rose by 13.1 million. Online auction site *Buyourstuff* had 59 million visitors in 2005, but each year after that the number of visitors fell by 2 million.

a. Write an equation for each of the companies. **Lookatme: $y = 13.1x + 2.5$; Buyourstuff: $y = -2x + 59$**

b. Make a table of values for 5 years for each of the companies. **See margin.**

c. Graph each equation. **See margin.**

d. When will *Lookatme* and *Buyourstuff's* sites have the same number of visitors? **sometime during 2008**

e. Name the domain and range of these functions in this situation. **$D = \{x \mid x \geq 0\}$; $R = \{y \mid y \geq 0\}$**

46. **MULTIPLE REPRESENTATIONS** In this problem, you will explore different methods for finding the intersection of the graphs of two linear equations.

a. **ALGEBRAIC** Use algebra to solve the equation $\frac{1}{2}x + 3 = -x + 12$. **6**

b. **GRAPHICAL** Use a graph to solve $y = \frac{1}{2}x + 3$ and $y = -x + 12$. **See margin.**

c. **ANALYTICAL** How is the equation in part **a** related to the system in part **b**?

d. **VERBAL** Explain how to use the graph in part b to solve the equation in part a.

46c. Both sides of the equation in part a are set equal to y in the system of linear equations in part b.

46d. You can find the solution from the x-coordinate of the intersection of the two lines in the system of equation.

47. Francisca; if the item is less than \$100, then \$10 off is better. If the item is more than \$100, then the 10% is better.

49. Always; if the equations are linear and have more than one common solution, they must be consistent and dependent, which means that they have an infinite number of solutions in common.

50. Sample answer: $4x + 2y = 14$, $12x + 6y = 18$; This system is inconsistent while the others are consistent and independent.

H.O.T. Problems Use Higher-Order Thinking Skills

47. **FIND THE ERROR** Store A is offering a 10% discount on the purchase of all electronics in their store. Store B is offering \$10 off all the electronics in their store. Francisca and Alan are deciding which offer will save them more money. Is either of them correct? Explain your reasoning.

Francisca	Alan
You can't determine which store has the better offer unless you know the price of the items you want to buy.	*Store A has the better offer because 10% of the sale price is a greater discount than \$10.*

48. **CHALLENGE** Use graphing to find the solution of the system of equations $2x + 3y = 5$, $3x + 4y = 6$, and $4x + 5y = 7$. **(−2, 3); See margin for graph.**

49. **REASONING** Determine whether a system of two linear equations with (0, 0) and (2, 2) as solutions *sometimes*, *always*, or *never* has other solutions. Explain.

50. **WHICH ONE DOESN'T BELONG?** Which one of the following systems of equations doesn't belong with the other three? Explain your reasoning.

$4x - y = 5$	$-x + 4y = 8$	$4x + 2y = 14$	$3x - 2y = 1$
$-2x + y = -1$	$3x - 6y = 6$	$12x + 6y = 18$	$2x + 3y = 18$

51. **OPEN ENDED** Write three equations such that they form three systems of equations with $y = 5x - 3$. The three systems should be inconsistent, consistent and independent, and consistent and dependent, respectively. **Sample answers: $y = 5x + 3$; $y = -5x - 3$; $2y = 10x - 6$**

52. **WRITING IN MATH** Describe the advantages and disadvantages to solving systems of equations by graphing. **See margin.**

Differentiated Instruction AL OL ELL

Interpersonal Learners Have students work in pairs or groups to check the solutions for Exercises 16–21 and 27–41. Suggest that they use the Study Tip (p. 344) on comparing m and b when both equations are in the form of $y = mx + b$. Have students write equations in slope-intercept form, if necessary.

PSAE PRACTICE 7.11.03, 8.11.19, 8.11.17

53. SHORT RESPONSE Certain bacteria can reproduce every 20 minutes, doubling the population. If there are 450,000 bacteria in a population at 9:00 A.M., how many bacteria will be in the population at 2:00 P.M.? **14,745,600,000 bacteria**

54. GEOMETRY An 84-centimeter piece of wire is cut into equal segments and then attached at the ends to form the edges of a cube. What is the volume of the cube? **B**

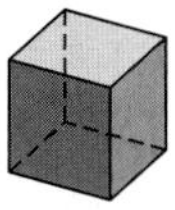

A 294 cm^3 C 1158 cm^3
B 343 cm^3 D 2744 cm^3

55. What is the solution of the inequality $-9 < 2x + 3 < 15$? **H**

F $-x \geq 0$ H $-6 < x < 6$
G $x \leq 0$ J $-5 < x < 5$

56. What is the solution of the system of equations? **D**

$$x + 2y = -1$$
$$2x + 4y = -2$$

A $(-1, -1)$ C no solution
B $(2, 1)$ D infinitely many solutions

Spiral Review

Graph each inequality. (Lesson 5-6) **57–62. See margin.**

57. $3x + 6y > 0$
58. $4x - 2y < 0$
59. $3y - x \leq 9$
60. $4y - 3x \geq 12$
61. $y < -4x - 8$
62. $3x - 1 > y$

63. LIBRARY To get a grant from the city's historical society, the number of history books must be within 25 of 1500. What is the range of the number of historical books that must be in the library? (Lesson 5-5) **1475 to 1525 books**

64. SCHOOL Camilla's scores on three math tests are shown in the table. The fourth and final test of the grading period is tomorrow. She needs an average of at least 92 to receive an A for the grading period. (Lesson 5-3)

Test	Score
1	91
2	95
3	88

a. If m represents her score on the fourth math test, write an inequality to represent this situation. $\frac{91 + 95 + 88 + m}{4} \geq 92$

b. If Camilla wants an A in math, what must she score on the test? **94 or higher**

c. Is your solution reasonable? Explain. **Yes; the score is attainable and Camilla has scored higher than that before.**

Write the slope-intercept form of an equation for the line that passes through the given point and is perpendicular to the graph of the equation. (Lesson 4-4)

65. $(-3, 1), y = \frac{1}{3}x + 2$ $y = -3x - 8$
66. $(6, -2), y = \frac{3}{5}x - 4$ $y = -\frac{5}{3}x + 8$
67. $(2, -2), 2x + y = 5$ $y = \frac{1}{2}x - 3$
68. $(-3, -3), -3x + y = 6$ $y = -\frac{1}{3}x - 4$

Skills Review

Find the solution of each equation using the given replacement set. (Lesson 1-5)

69. $f - 14 = 8$; {12, 15, 19, 22} **22**
70. $15(n + 6) = 165$; {3, 4, 5, 6, 7} **5**
71. $23 = \frac{d}{4}$; {91, 92, 93, 94, 95} **92**
72. $36 = \frac{t - 9}{2}$; {78, 79, 80, 81} **81**

Evaluate each expression if $a = 2$, $b = -3$, and $c = 11$. (Lesson 1-2)

73. $a + 6b$ **−16**
74. $7 - ab$ **13**
75. $(2c + 3a) \div 4$ **7**
76. $b^2 + (a^3 - 8)5$ **9**

4 ASSESS

Ticket Out the Door Give students a small piece of grid paper. Have them draw a graph that represents a system of equations that is consistent and dependent.

Additional Answers

52. Graphing clearly shows whether a system of equations has one solution, no solution, or infinitely many solutions. However, finding the exact values of x and y from a graph can be difficult.

57.

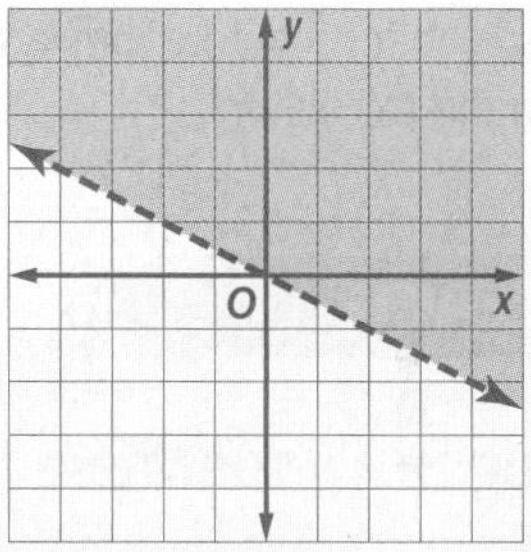

58.

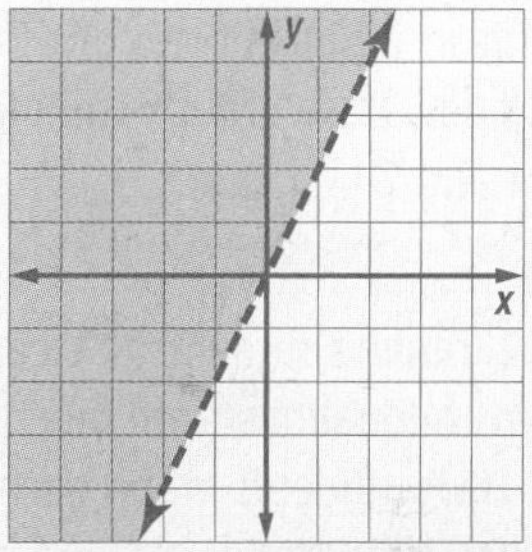

59.

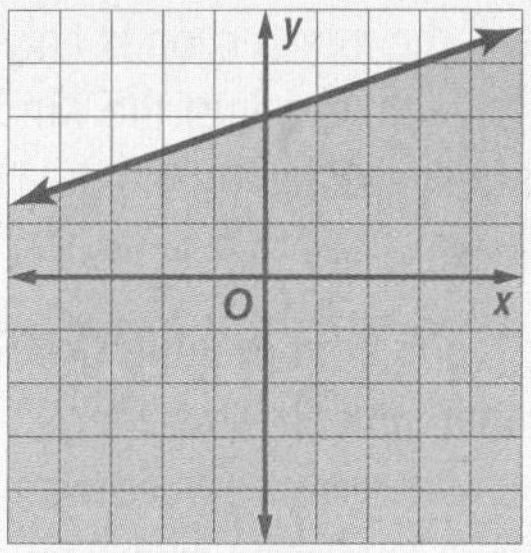

60.

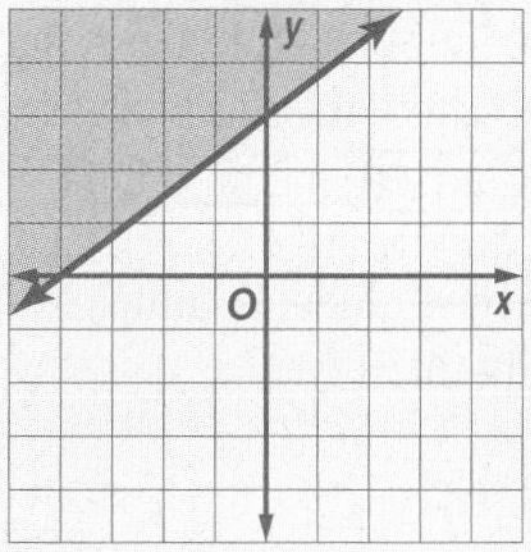

61.

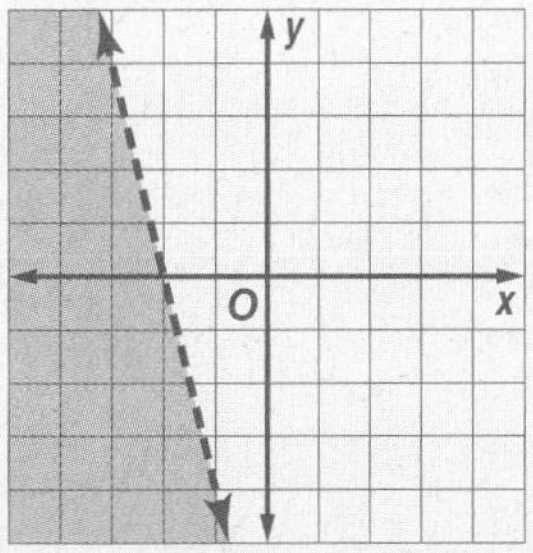

62.

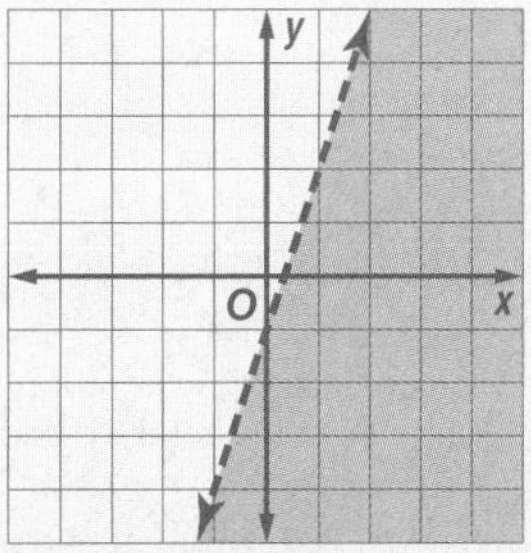

Lesson 6-1 Graphing Systems of Equations 339

1 FOCUS

Objective Use a graphing calculator to solve a system of equations.

Materials

- TI–83/84 Plus or other graphing calculator

Teaching Tip

Remind students that the equations must be solved for *y* before they are entered in the calculator.

2 TEACH

Working in Cooperative Groups

Put students in groups of two or three, mixing abilities. Have groups complete Activities 1 and 2.

Activity 1

- In Step 2, remind students to clear all previous equations from the Y= list. Have students graph each system using the standard viewing window. If the intersection is not visible, have them adjust the window to an area suggested by the directions of the lines.
- In Step 3, point out that the **GUESS** feature that appears after the second ENTER gives students an opportunity to use the arrow keys to estimate the solution to the system and then check their estimates by pressing ENTER the third time.

Practice Have students complete Exercises 1–10.

Systems of Equations

IL Math Online glencoe.com
- Other Calculator Keystrokes
- Graphing Technology Personal Tutor

IL Learning Standards **8.B.4a** Represent algebraic concepts with physical materials, words, diagrams, tables, graphs, equations and inequalities and use appropriate technology.

You can use a graphing calculator to graph and solve a system of equations.

ACTIVITY 1 Solve a System of Equations

Solve the system of equations. State the decimal solution to the nearest hundredth.

$$5.23x + y = 7.48$$
$$6.42x - y = 2.11$$

Step 1 Solve each equation for y to enter them into the calculator.

$5.23x + y = 7.48$	**First equation**
$5.23x + y - 5.23x = 7.48 - 5.23x$	**Subtract 5.23*x* from each side.**
$y = 7.48 - 5.23x$	**Simplify.**
$6.42x - y = 2.11$	**Second equation**
$6.42x - y - 6.42x = 2.11 - 6.42x$	**Subtract 6.42*x* from each side.**
$-y = 2.11 - 6.42x$	**Simplify.**
$(-1)(-y) = (-1)(2.11 - 6.42x)$	**Multiply each side by −1.**
$y = -2.11 + 6.42x$	**Simplify.**

Step 2 Enter these equations in the Y= list and graph.

KEYSTROKES: *Review on pages 167–168.*

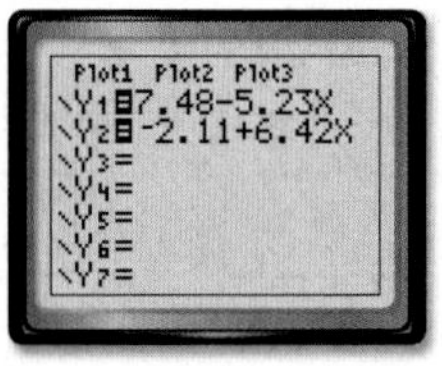

Step 3 Use the CALC menu to find the point of intersection.

KEYSTROKES: 2nd [CALC] 5 ENTER ENTER ENTER

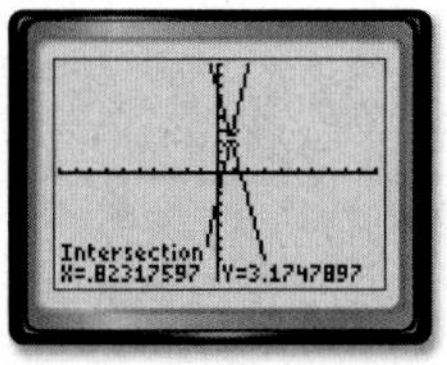

[−10, 10] scl: 1 by [−10, 10] scl: 1

The solution is approximately (0.82, 3.17).

One method you can use to solve an equation with one variable is by graphing and solving a system of equations based on the equation. To do this, write a system using both sides of the equation. Then use a graphing calculator to solve the system.

ACTIVITY 2 Use a System to Solve a Linear Equation

Use a system of equations to solve $5x + 6 = -4$.

Step 1 Write a system of equations.
Set each side of the equation equal to y.

$y = 5x + 6$ **First equation**

$y = -4$ **Second equation**

Step 2 Enter these equations in the Y= list and graph.

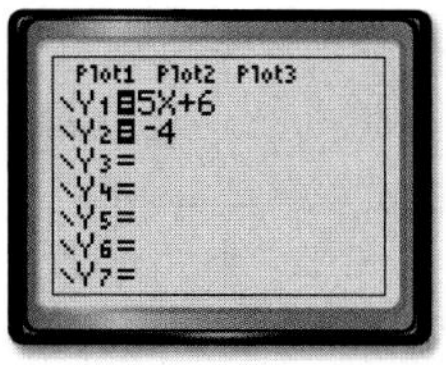

Step 3 Use the CALC menu to find the point of intersection.

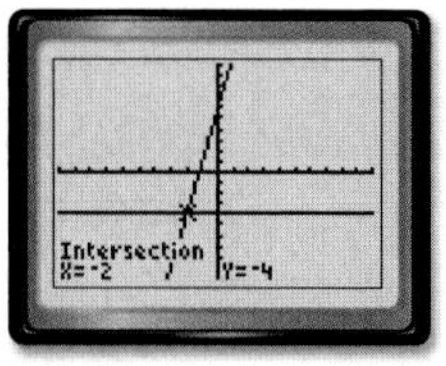

[−10, 10] scl: 1 by [−10, 10] scl: 1

The solution is −2.

Exercises

Use a graphing calculator to solve each system of equations. Write decimal solutions to the nearest hundredth.

1. $y = 2x - 3$
$y = -0.4x + 5$ **(3.33, 3.67)**

2. $y = 6x + 1$
$y = -3.2x - 4$ **(−0.54, −2.26)**

3. $x + y = 9.35$
$5x - y = 8.75$ **(3.02, 6.33)**

4. $2.32x - y = 6.12$
$4.5x + y = -6.05$ **(0.01, −6.10)**

5. $5.2x - y = 4.1$
$1.5x + y = 6.7$ **(1.61, 4.28)**

6. $1.8 = 5.4x - y$
$y = -3.8 - 6.2x$ **(−0.17, −2.73)**

7. $7x - 2y = 16$
$11x + 6y = 32.3$ **(2.51, 0.78)**

8. $3x + 2y = 16$
$5x + y = 9$ **(0.29, 7.57)**

9. $0.62x + 0.35y = 1.60$
$-1.38x + y = 8.24$ **(−1.16, 6.63)**

10. $75x - 100y = 400$
$33x - 10y = 70$ **(1.18, −3.12)**

Use a graphing calculator to solve each equation. Write decimal solutions to the nearest hundredth.

11. $4x - 2 = -6$ **−1**

12. $3 = 1 + \frac{x}{2}$ **4**

13. $\frac{x + 4}{-2} = -1$ **−2**

14. $\frac{x}{7} - 3 = -2$ **7**

15. $-9 = 7 + 3x$ **−5.33**

16. $-2 + 10x = 8x - 1$ **0.5**

17. WRITING IN MATH Explain why you can solve an equation like $r = ax + b$ by solving the system of equations $y = r$ and $y = ax + b$.

17. At the intersection of the graphs of $y = r$ and $y = ax + b$, the y-values are equal. Therefore, at that point $r = ax + b$.

Activity 2

- For Activity 2, students will need to clear the Y= list to begin the activity. Remind students to press (−) to enter −4 rather than the key for the subtraction symbol.
- In Step 3, students should use the same keystrokes used in Activity 1, Step 3.

Ask:

- What does the solution in Step 3 mean? For the equation $y = 5x + 6$, $x = -2$ when $y = -4$.
- How can you check your solution? Substitute −2 for x in the original equation to check whether the equation is true.

Practice Have students complete Exercises 11–17.

3 Assess

Formative Assessment

- Use Exercise 7 to assess whether students can use a graphing calculator to solve a system of equations.
- Use Exercise 15 to assess whether students can graph a system to solve an equation with one variable.

From Concrete to Abstract

Exercise 17 asks students to give an algebraic justification for using a system of equations to solve a linear equation with one variable.

Extending the Concept

Ask:

- When would a system of two linear equations not have a point of intersection? Sample answer: Two linear equations will not have a point of intersection if their graphs are parallel.

Extend 6-1 Graphing Technology Lab: Systems of Equations 341

6-2 Lesson Notes

1 FOCUS

Vertical Alignment

Before Lesson 6-2
Solve systems of equations by graphing.

Lesson 6-2
Solve systems of equations by using substitution.
Solve real-world problems involving systems of equations by using substitution.

After Lesson 6-2
Solve systems of equations by using elimination.

2 TEACH

Scaffolding Questions

Have students read the *Why?* section of the lesson.

Ask:

- What are the rates of decrease for Movies A and B? $16 million per week; $10 million per week
- If $x =$ the number of weeks from the opening week, and $y =$ total earnings, what equation represents the earnings in week x for Movie A? $y = -16x + 31$ for Movie B? $y = -10x + 21$

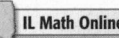

(continued on the next page)

6-2 Substitution

Then
You solved systems of equations by graphing. (Lesson 6-1)

Now
- Solve systems of equations by using substitution.
- Solve real-world problems involving systems of equations by using substitution.

IL Learning Standards
8.B.4a Represent algebraic concepts with physical materials, words, diagrams, tables, graphs, equations and inequalities and use appropriate technology.

New Vocabulary
substitution

IL Math Online
glencoe.com
- Extra Examples
- Personal Tutor
- Self-Check Quiz
- Homework Help

Why?

Two movies were released at the same time. Movie A earned \$31 million in its opening week, but fell to \$15 million the following week. Movie B opened earning \$21 million and fell to \$11 million the following week. If the earnings for each movie continue to decrease at the same rate, when will they earn the same amount?

Solve by Substitution You can use a system of equations to find when the movie earnings are the same. One method of finding an exact solution of a system of equations is called **substitution**.

Key Concept Solving by Substitution — For Your FOLDABLE

Step 1 When necessary, solve at least one equation for one variable.

Step 2 Substitute the resulting expression from Step 1 into the other equation to replace the variable. Then solve the equation.

Step 3 Substitute the value from Step 2 into either equation, and solve for the other variable. Write the solution as an ordered pair.

EXAMPLE 1 Solve a System by Substitution

Use substitution to solve the system of equations.

$y = 2x + 1$ ← **Step 1** One equation is already solved for y.
$3x + y = -9$

Step 2 Substitute $2x + 1$ for y in the second equation.

$3x + y = -9$	**Second equation**
$3x + 2x + 1 = -9$	**Substitute $2x + 1$ for y.**
$5x + 1 = -9$	**Combine like terms.**
$5x = -10$	**Subtract 1 from each side.**
$x = -2$	**Divide each side by 5.**

Step 3 Substitute -2 for x in either equation to find y.

$y = 2x + 1$	**First equation**
$= 2(-2) + 1$	**Substitute -2 for x.**
$= -3$	**Simplify.**

The solution is $(-2, -3)$.

CHECK You can check your solution by graphing.

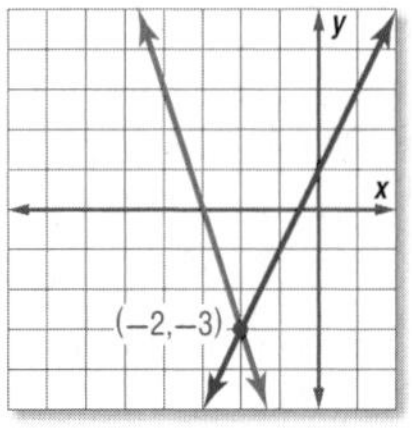

Check Your Progress

1A. $y = 4x - 6$
$5x + 3y = -1$ **(1, −2)**

1B. $2x + 5y = -1$
$y = 3x + 10$ **(−3, 1)**

Personal Tutor glencoe.com

Lesson 6-2 Resources

Resource	Approaching-Level	On-Level	Beyond-Level	English Learners
Teacher Edition	• Differentiated Instruction, p. 343	• Differentiated Instruction, pp. 343, 347	• Differentiated Instruction, p. 347	
Chapter Resource Masters	• Study Guide and Intervention, pp. 12–13 • Skills Practice, p. 14 • Practice, p. 15 • Word Problem Practice, p. 16	• Study Guide and Intervention, pp. 12–13 • Skills Practice, p. 14 • Practice, p. 15 • Word Problem Practice, p. 16 • Enrichment, p. 17	• Practice, p. 15 • Word Problem Practice, p. 16 • Enrichment, p. 17	• Study Guide and Intervention, pp. 12–13 • Skills Practice, p. 14 • Practice, p. 15
Transparencies	• 5-Minute Check Transparency 6-2	• 5-Minute Check Transparency 6-2	• 5-Minute Check Transparency 6-2	• 5-Minute Check Transparency 6-2
Other	• Study Notebook	• Study Notebook	• Study Notebook	• Study Notebook

If a variable is not isolated in one of the equations in a system, solve an equation for a variable first. Then you can use substitution to solve the system.

StudyTip

Slope-Intercept Form If both equations are in the form $y = mx + b$, they can simply be set equal to each other and then solved for x. The solution for x can then be used to find the value of y.

EXAMPLE 2 Solve and then Substitute

Use substitution to solve the system of equations.

$x + 2y = 6$
$3x - 4y = 28$

Step 1 Solve the first equation for x since the coefficient is 1.

$x + 2y = 6$	**First equation**
$x + 2y - 2y = 6 - 2y$	**Subtract $2y$ from each side.**
$x = 6 - 2y$	**Simplify.**

Step 2 Substitute $6 - 2y$ for x in the second equation to find the value of y.

$3x - 4y = 28$	**Second equation**
$3(6 - 2y) - 4y = 28$	**Substitute $6 - 2y$ for x.**
$18 - 6y - 4y = 28$	**Distributive Property**
$18 - 10y = 28$	**Combine like terms.**
$18 - 10y - 18 = 28 - 18$	**Subtract 18 from each side.**
$-10y = 10$	**Simplify.**
$y = -1$	**Divide each side by -10.**

Step 3 Find the value of x.

$x + 2y = 6$	**First equation**
$x + 2(-1) = 6$	**Substitute -1 for y.**
$x - 2 = 6$	**Simplify.**
$x = 8$	**Add 2 to each side.**

The solution is $(8, -1)$.

Check Your Progress

2A. $4x + 5y = 11$
$y - 3x = -13$ **(4, −1)**

2B. $x - 3y = -9$
$5x - 2y = 7$ **(3, 4)**

Personal Tutor glencoe.com

Generally, if you solve a system of equations and the result is a false statement such as $3 = -2$, there is no solution. If the result is an identity, such as $3 = 3$, then there are an infinite number of solutions.

StudyTip

Dependent Systems There are infinitely many solutions of the system in Example 3 because the equations in slope-intercept form are equivalent, and they have the same graph.

EXAMPLE 3 No Solution or Infinitely Many Solutions

Use substitution to solve the system of equations.

$y = 2x - 4$
$-6x + 3y = -12$

Substitute $2x - 4$ for y in the second equation.

$-6x + 3y = -12$	**Second equation**
$-6x + 3(2x - 4) = -12$	**Substitute $2x - 4$ for y.**
$-6x + 6x - 12 = -12$	**Distributive Property**
$-12 = -12$	**Combine like terms.**

This statement is an identity. Thus, there are an infinite number of solutions.

- Why might solving the system of equations using substitution be better than graphing the equations to determine when the movies have the same earnings? Sample answer: Using substitution might give a more exact answer since the graphs might intersect between weeks.

Solve by Substitution

Example 1 shows how to solve a system of equations using substitution. **Example 2** shows how to solve one of the equations for one variable and then substitute to solve the system of equations. **Example 3** shows how to solve a system of equations that has an infinite number of solutions.

Formative Assessment

Use the Check Your Progress exercises after each example to determine students' understanding of concepts.

Additional Examples

1 Use substitution to solve the system of equations.

$y = -4x + 12$
$2x + y = 2$ (5, −8)

2 Use substitution to solve the system of equations.

$x - 2y = -3$
$3x + 5y = 24$ (3, 3)

Additional Examples also in Interactive Classroom PowerPoint® Presentations

IWB INTERACTIVE WHITEBOARD READY

Differentiated Instruction

AL OL

If students have difficulty solving a system using substitution,

Then suggest that they use the Study Tip to write both equations in slope-intercept form, set the expressions in x equal to each other, solve for x, and then use the value for x to find y. Have students compare the methods and decide which method they prefer.

Watch Out!

Preventing Errors Point out that if neither of the equations gives one variable in terms of the other, you must solve for one variable first. The easiest choice in Example 2 is to solve the first equation for x by subtracting $2y$ from both sides.

Additional Example

3 Use substitution to solve the system of equations.

$2x + 2y = 8$

$x + y = -2$ no solution

Solve Real-World Problems

Example 4 shows how to write and solve a system of equations for a real-world problem that can be solved by substitutions.

Additional Example

4 **NATURE CENTER** A nature center charges $35.25 for a yearly membership and $6.25 for a single admission. Last week it sold a combined total of 50 yearly memberships and single admissions for $660.50. How many memberships and how many single admissions were sold? 12 memberships and 38 single admissions

Focus on Mathematical Content

Infinitely Many or No Solutions If solving a system of equations results in a true sentence (such as $3 = 3$), then the system has infinitely many solutions. This happens when the two equations represent the same line. When solving a system of equations results in a false sentence (such as $3 = 2$), the system has no solution. The equations represent two parallel lines. If both equations are solved for y, the equations will have the same slope but different y-intercepts.

Check Your Progress

Use substitution to solve each system of equations.

3A. $2x - y = 8$
$y = 2x - 3$ no solution

3B. $4x - 3y = 1$
$6y - 8x = -2$ infinite number

Personal Tutor glencoe.com

Solve Real-World Problems You can use substitution to find the solution of a real-world problem involving a system of equations.

Real-World Career

Sound Engineering Technician
Sound engineering technicians record, synchronize, mix, and reproduce music, voices, and sound effects in recording studios, sporting arenas, and theater, movie, or video productions. They need to have at least a 2-year associate's degree in electronics.

Real-World EXAMPLE 4 Write and Solve a System of Equations

MUSIC A store sold a total of 125 car stereo systems and speakers in one week. The stereo systems sold for $104.95, and the speakers sold for $18.95. The sales from these two items totaled $6926.75. How many of each item were sold?

Let c = the number of car stereo systems sold, and let t = the number of speakers sold.

Number of Units Sold	c	t	125
Sales ($)	$104.95c$	$18.95t$	6926.75

So, the two equations are $c + t = 125$ and $104.95c + 18.95t = 6926.75$.

Step 1 Solve the first equation for c.

$c + t = 125$ **First equation**

$c + t - t = 125 - t$ **Subtract t from each side.**

$c = 125 - t$ **Simplify.**

Step 2 Substitute $125 - t$ for c in the second equation.

$104.95c + 18.95t = 6926.75$ **Second equation**

$104.95(125 - t) + 18.95t = 6926.75$ **Substitute $125 - t$ for c.**

$13{,}118.75 - 104.95t + 18.95t = 6926.75$ **Distributive Property**

$13{,}118.75 - 86t = 6926.75$ **Combine like terms.**

$-86t = -6192$ **Subtract 13118.75 from each side.**

$t = 72$ **Divide each side by −86.**

Step 3 Substitute 72 for t in either equation to find the value of c.

$c + t = 125$ **First equation**

$c + 72 = 125$ **Substitute 72 for t.**

$c = 53$ **Subtract 72 from each side.**

The store sold 53 car stereo systems and 72 speakers.

Check Your Progress

4. BASEBALL As of 2007, the New York Yankees and the Cincinnati Reds together had won a total of 31 World Series. The Yankees had won 5.2 times as many as the Reds. How many World Series had each team won? Cincinnati, 5; New York, 26

Personal Tutor glencoe.com

TEACH with TECH

AUDIO RECORDING Have students work in groups to record a song to a common tune about how to solve a system of equations by substitution. Have students use each song to solve a problem to determine if it really explains how to solve systems by substitution.

344 **Chapter 6** Systems of Linear Equations and Inequalities

Check Your Understanding

Examples 1–3 pp. 342–343

Use substitution to solve each system of equations.

1. $y = x + 5$
   $3x + y = 25$ **(5, 10)**
2. $x = y - 2$
   $4x + y = 2$ **(0, 2)**
3. $3x + y = 6$
   $4x + 2y = 8$ **(2, 0)**
4. $2x + 3y = 4$
   $4x + 6y = 9$ **no solution**
5. $x - y = 1$
   $3x = 3y + 3$ **infinitely many**
6. $2x - y = 6$
   $-3y = -6x + 18$ **infinitely many**

Example 4 p. 344

7. **GEOMETRY** The sum of the measures of angles X and Y is 180°. The measure of angle X is 24° greater than the measure of angle Y.
   a. Define the variables, and write equations for this situation. **$x = m\angle X$, $y = m\angle Y$; $x + y = 180$, $x = 24 + y$**
   b. Find the measure of each angle. **$x = 102°$, $y = 78°$**

Practice and Problem Solving

● = **Step-by-Step Solutions** begin on page R12. **Extra Practice** begins on page 815.

Examples 1–3 pp. 342–343

Use substitution to solve each system of equations.

8. $y = 5x + 1$
   $4x + y = 10$ **(1, 6)**
9. $y = 4x + 5$
   $2x + y = 17$ **(2, 13)**
10. $y = 3x - 34$
    $y = 2x - 5$ **(29, 53)**
11. $y = 3x - 2$
    $y = 2x - 5$ **(−3, −11)**
12. $2x + y = 3$
    $4x + 4y = 8$ **(1, 1)**
13. $3x + 4y = -3$
    $x + 2y = -1$ **(−1, 0)**
14. $y = -3x + 4$
    $-6x - 2y = -8$ **infinitely many**
15. $-1 = 2x - y$
    $8x - 4y = -4$ **infinitely many**
16. $x = y - 1$
    $-x + y = -1$ **no solution**
17. $y = -4x + 11$
    $3x + y = 9$ **(2, 3)**
18. $y = -3x + 1$
    $2x + y = 1$ **(0, 1)**
19. $3x + y = -5$
    $6x + 2y = 10$ **no solution**
20. $5x - y = 5$
    $-x + 3y = 13$ **(2, 5)**
21. $2x + y = 4$
    $-2x + y = -4$ **(2, 0)**
22. $-5x + 4y = 20$
    $10x - 8y = -40$ **infinitely many**

23a. Let x = number of years since 2000, and let y = the number of nurses; supply, $y = -8000x + 1{,}890{,}000$; demand, $y = 82{,}000x + 2{,}000{,}000$

Example 4 p. 344

23. **ECONOMICS** In 2000, the demand for nurses was 2,000,000, while the supply was only 1,890,000. The projected demand for nurses in 2010 is 2,820,000, while the supply is only projected to be 1,810,000.
    a. Define the variables, and write equations to represent these situations.
    b. Use substitution to determine during which year the supply of nurses was equal to the demand. **during 1998**

Real-World Link

As the population's age increases, the need for nursing and home care is also increasing. Employment among RNs is expected to grow faster than the average for all occupations.

24. **TOURISM** The table shows the approximate number of tourists in two areas of the world during a recent year and the average rates of change in tourism.

Destination	Number of Tourists	Average Rates of Change in Tourists (millions per year)
South America and the Caribbean	40.3 million	increase of 0.8
Middle East	17.0 million	increase of 1.8

    a. Define the variables, and write an equation for each region's tourism rate. **See margin.**
    b. If the trends continue, in how many years would you expect the number of tourists in the regions to be equal? **in 23.3 yr, or about 23 yr 4 mo**

3 PRACTICE

Formative Assessment

Use Exercises 1–7 to check for understanding.

Use the chart at the bottom of this page to customize assignments for your students.

Additional Answer

24a. Let x = number of years since base year, and y = number of tourists in millions; South America and Caribbean, $y = 0.8x + 40.3$; Middle East, $y = 1.8x + 17.0$.

Differentiated Homework Options

Level	Assignment	Two-Day Option	
AL Basic	8–23, 27, 29–50	9–23 odd, 32–35	18–22 even, 27, 29–31, 36–50
OL Core	9–23 odd, 25–27, 29–50	8–23, 32–35	24–27, 29–31, 36–50
BL Advanced	24–46, (optional: 47–50)		

Study Guide and Intervention
CRM pp. 12–13 AL OL ELL

NAME ______________ DATE ________ PERIOD ________

6-2 Study Guide and Intervention

Substitution

Solve by Substitution One method of solving systems of equations is **substitution**.

Example 1 **Use substitution to solve the system of equations.**
$y = 2x$
$4x - y = -4$

Substitute $2x$ for y in the second equation.

$4x - y = -4$	Second equation
$4x - 2x = -4$	$y = 2x$
$2x = -4$	Combine like terms.
$x = -2$	Divide each side by 2 and simplify.

Use $y = 2x$ to find the value of y.

$y = 2x$	First equation
$y = 2(-2)$	$x = -2$
$y = -4$	Simplify.

The solution is $(-2, -4)$.

Example 2 **Solve for one variable, then substitute.**
$x + 3y = 7$
$2x - 4y = -6$

Solve the first equation for x since the coefficient of x is 1.

$x + 3y = 7$	First equation
$x + 3y - 3y = 7 - 3y$	Subtract 3y from each side.
$x = 7 - 3y$	Simplify.

Find the value of y by substituting $7 - 3y$ for x in the second equation.

$2x - 4y = -6$	Second equation
$2(7 - 3y) - 4y = -6$	$x = 7 - 3y$
$14 - 6y - 4y = -6$	Distributive Property
$14 - 10y = -6$	Combine like terms.
$14 - 10y - 14 = -6 - 14$	Subtract 14 from each side.
$-10y = -20$	Simplify.
$y = 2$	Divide each side by −10 and simplify.

Use $y = 2$ to find the value of x.
$x = 7 - 3y$
$x = 7 - 3(2)$
$x = 1$
The solution is $(1, 2)$.

Exercises

Use substitution to solve each system of equations.

1. $y = 4x$, $3x - y = 1$ **(−1, −4)**
2. $x = 2y$, $y = x - 2$ **(4, 2)**
3. $x = 2y - 3$, $x = 2y + 4$ **no solution**
4. $x - 2y = -1$, $3y = x + 4$ **(5, 3)**
5. $x - 4y = 1$, $2x - 8y = 2$ **infinitely many**
6. $x + 2y = 0$, $3x + 4y = 4$ **(4, −2)**
7. $2b = 6a - 14$, $3a - b = 7$ **infinitely many**
8. $x + y = 16$, $2y = -2x + 2$ **no solution**
9. $y = -x + 3$, $2y + 2x = 4$ **no solution**
10. $x = 2y$, $0.25x + 0.5y = 10$ **(20, 10)**
11. $x - 2y = -5$, $x + 2y = -1$ **(−3, 1)**
12. $-0.2x + y = 0.5$, $0.4x + y = 1.1$ **(1, 0.7)**

Chapter 6 12 Glencoe Algebra 1

Practice
CRM p. 15 AL OL BL ELL

NAME ______________ DATE ________ PERIOD ________

6-2 Practice

Substitution

Use substitution to solve each system of equations.

1. $y = 6x$, $2x + 3y = -20$ **(−1, −6)**
2. $x = 3y$, $3x - 5y = 12$ **(9, 3)**
3. $x = 2y + 7$, $x = y + 4$ **(1, −3)**
4. $y = 2x - 2$, $y = x + 2$ **(4, 6)**
5. $y = 2x + 6$, $2x - y = 2$ **no solution**
6. $3x + y = 12$, $y = -x - 2$ **(7, −9)**
7. $x + 2y = 13$, $-2x - 3y = -18$ **(−3, 8)**
8. $x - 2y = 3$, $4x - 8y = 12$ **infinitely many**
9. $x - 5y = 36$, $2x + y = -16$ **(−4, −8)**
10. $2x - 3y = -24$, $x + 6y = 18$ **(−6, 4)**
11. $x + 14y = 84$, $2x - 7y = -7$ **(14, 5)**
12. $0.3x - 0.2y = 0.5$, $x - 2y = -5$ **(5, 5)**
13. $0.5x + 4y = -1$, $x + 2.5y = 3.5$ **(6, −1)**
14. $3x - 2y = 11$, $x - \frac{1}{2}y = 4$ **(5, 2)**
15. $\frac{1}{2}x + 2y = 12$, $x - 2y = 6$ **(12, 3)**
16. $\frac{1}{3}x - y = 3$, $2x + y = 25$ **(12, 1)**
17. $4x - 5y = -7$, $y = 5x$ $\left(\frac{1}{3}, 1\frac{2}{3}\right)$
18. $x + 3y = -4$, $2x + 6y = 5$ **no solution**

19. **EMPLOYMENT** Kenisha sells athletic shoes part-time at a department store. She can earn either \$500 per month plus a 4% commission on her total sales, or \$400 per month plus a 5% commission on total sales.
   a. Write a system of equations to represent the situation. **$y = 0.04x + 500$ and $y = 0.05x + 400$**
   b. What is the total price of the athletic shoes Kenisha needs to sell to earn the same income from each pay scale? **\$10,000**
   c. Which is the better offer? **the first offer if she expects to sell less than \$10,000 in shoes, and the second offer if she expects to sell more than \$10,000 in shoes**

20. **MOVIE TICKETS** Tickets to a movie cost \$7.25 for adults and \$5.50 for students. A group of friends purchased 8 tickets for \$52.75.
   a. Write a system of equations to represent the situation. **$x + y = 8$ and $7.25x + 5.5y = 52.75$**
   b. How many adult tickets and student tickets were purchased? **5 adult and 3 student**

Lesson 6-2

Chapter 6 15 Glencoe Algebra 1

Word Problem Practice
CRM p. 16 AL OL BL ELL

NAME ______________ DATE ________ PERIOD ________

6-2 Word Problem Practice

Substitution

1. **BUSINESS** Mr. Randolph finds that the supply and demand for gasoline at his station are generally given by the following equations.
$$x - y = -2$$
$$x + y = 10$$
Use substitution to find the equilibrium point where the supply and demand lines intersect. **(4, 6)**

2. **GEOMETRY** The measures of complementary angles have a sum of 90 degrees. Angle A and angle B are complementary, and their measures have a difference of 20°. What are the measures of the angles? **35° and 55°**

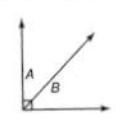

3. **MONEY** Harvey has some \$1 bills and some \$5 bills. In all, he has 6 bills worth \$22. Let x be the number of \$1 bills and let y be the number of \$5 bills. Write a system of equations to represent the information and use substitution to determine how many bills of each denomination Harvey has. **$x + y = 6$, $x + 5y = 22$; he has four \$5 bills and two \$1 bills.**

4. **POPULATION** Sanjay is researching population trends in South America. He found that experts expect the population of Ecuador to increase by 1,000,000 and the population of Chile to increase by 600,000 from 2004 to 2009. The table displays the information he found.

Country	2004 Population	Predicted 5-Year Change
Ecuador	13,000,000	+1,000,000
Chile	16,000,000	+600,000

Source: *World Almanac 2005*

If the population growth for each country continues at the same rate, in what year are the populations of Ecuador and Chile predicted to be equal? **2041**

5. **CHEMISTRY** Shelby and Calvin are doing a chemistry experiment. They need 5 ounces of a solution that is 65% acid and 35% distilled water. There is no undiluted acid in the chemistry lab, but they do have two flasks of diluted acid: Flask A contains 70% acid and 30% distilled water. Flask B contains 20% acid and 80% distilled water.
   a. Write a system of equations that Shelby and Calvin could use to determine how many ounces they need to pour from each flask to make their solution. **Sample answer: $a + b = 5$; $0.7a + 0.2b = 0.65(5)$**
   b. Solve your system of equations. How many ounces from each flask do Shelby and Calvin need? **4.5 oz from Flask A and 0.5 oz from Flask B.**

Chapter 6 16 Glencoe Algebra 1

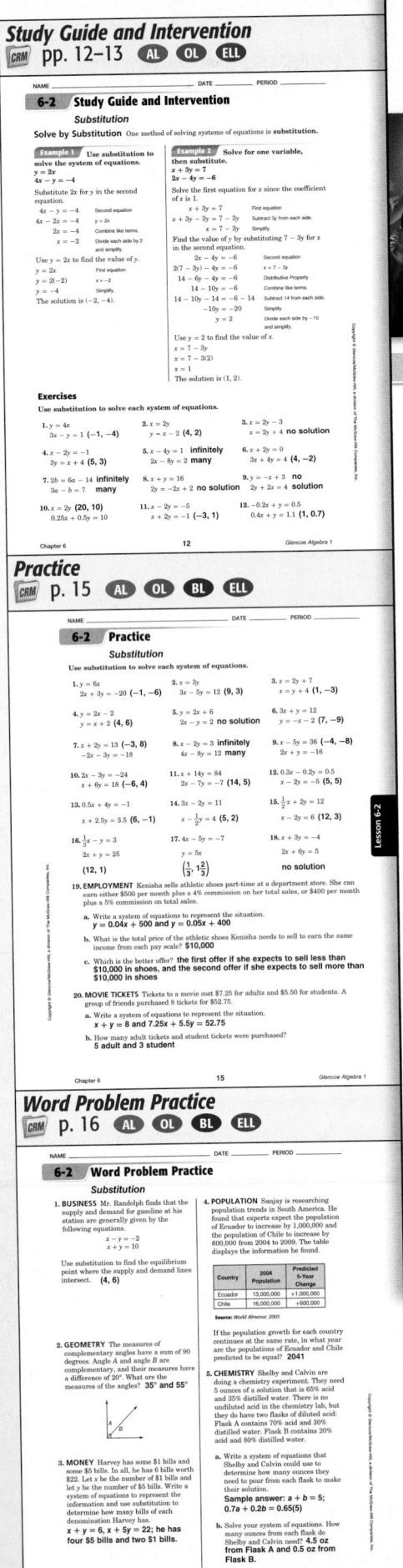

25. **SPORTS** The table shows the winning times for the Triathlon World Championship.

Year	Men's	Women's
2000	1:51:39	1:54:43
2005	1:49:31	1:58:03

   a. The times are in hours, minutes, and seconds. Rewrite the times rounded to the nearest minute. **men: 112, 110; women: 115, 118**
   b. Let the year 2000 be 0. Assume that the rate of change remains the same for years after 2000. Write an equation to represent each of the men's and women's winning times y in any year x. **$y = -0.4x + 112$; $y = 0.6x + 115$**
   c. If the trend continues, when would you expect the men's and women's winning times to be the same? Explain your reasoning. **Never; the graphs never intersect.**

Real-World Link

Recent marketing surveys reveal that two thirds of concert attendees are female, and one third are male.

Source: Concert Promotions Company

26. **CONCERT TICKETS** Booker is buying tickets online for a concert. He finds tickets for himself and his friends for \$65 each plus a one-time fee of \$10. Paula is looking for tickets to the same concert. She finds them at another Web site for \$69 and a one-time fee of \$13.60. **a–d. See Ch. 6 Answer Appendix.**
   a. Define the variables, and write equations to represent this situation.
   b. Create a table of values for 1 to 5 tickets for each person's purchase.
   c. Graph each of these equations.
   d. Analyze the graph. How many solutions are there? Explain why.

H.O.T. Problems Use Higher-Order Thinking Skills

27. **FIND THE ERROR** In the system $a + b = 7$ and $1.29a + 0.49b = 6.63$, a represents pounds of apples and b represents pounds of bananas. Guillermo and Cara are finding and interpreting the solution. Is either of them correct? Explain.

Guillermo

$1.29a + 0.49b = 6.63$
$1.29a + 0.49(a + 7) = 6.63$
$1.29 + 0.49a + 3.43 = 6.63$
$0.49a = 3.2$
$a = 1.9$

$a + b = 7$, so $b = 5$. The solution (2, 5) means that 2 pounds of apples and 5 pounds of bananas were bought.

Cara

$1.29a + 0.49b = 6.63$
$1.29(7 - b) + 0.49b = 6.63$
$9.03 - 1.29b + 0.49b = 6.63$
$-0.8b = -2.4$
$b = 3$

The solution $b = 3$ means that 3 pounds of apples and 3 pounds of bananas were bought.

28. **CHALLENGE** A local charity has 60 volunteers. The ratio of boys to girls is 7:5. Find the number of boy and the number of girl volunteers.

29. **REASONING** Compare and contrast the solution of a system found by graphing and the solution of the same system found by substitution.

30. **OPEN ENDED** Create a system of equations that has one solution. Illustrate how the system could represent a real-world situation and describe the significance of the solution in the context of the situation. **See Ch. 6 Answer Appendix.**

31. **WRITING IN MATH** Explain how to determine what to substitute when using the substitution method of solving systems of equations.

27. Neither; Guillermo substituted incorrectly for b. Cara solved correctly for b, but misinterpreted the pounds of apples bought.
28. 25 girls and 35 boys
29. Sample answer: The solutions found by each of these methods should be the same. However, it may be necessary to estimate using a graph. So, when a precise solution is needed, you should use substitution.
31. An equation containing a variable with a coefficient of 1 can easily be solved for the variable. That expression can then be substituted into the second equation for the variable.

Enrichment
CRM p. 17 OL BL

NAME ______________ DATE ________ PERIOD ________

6-2 Enrichment

Intersection of Two Parabolas

Substitution can be used to find the intersection of two parabolas. Replace the y-value in one of the equations with the y-value in terms of x from the other equation.

Example **Find the intersection of the two parabolas.**
$y = x^2 + 5x + 6$
$y = x^2 + 4x + 3$

Graph the equations.

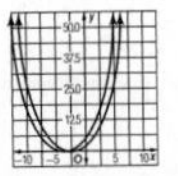

From the graph, notice that the two graphs intersect in one point.

Use substitution to solve for the point of intersection.

Lesson 6-2

Additional Answer

36.

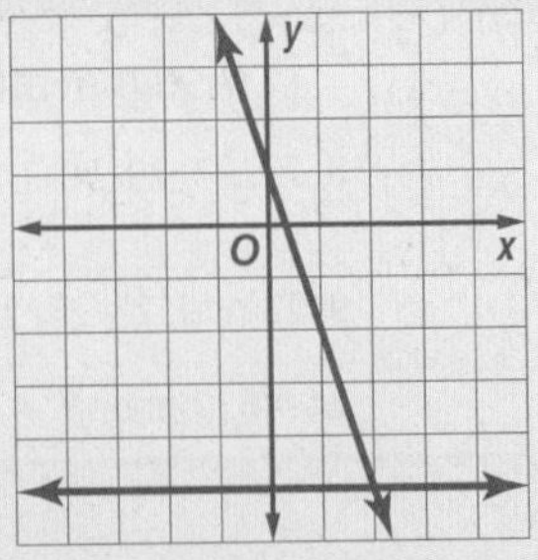

one solution; (2, −5)

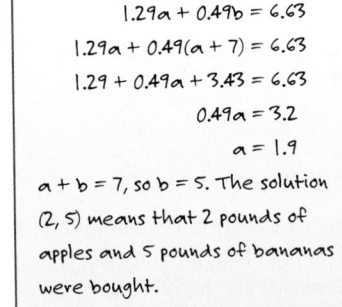

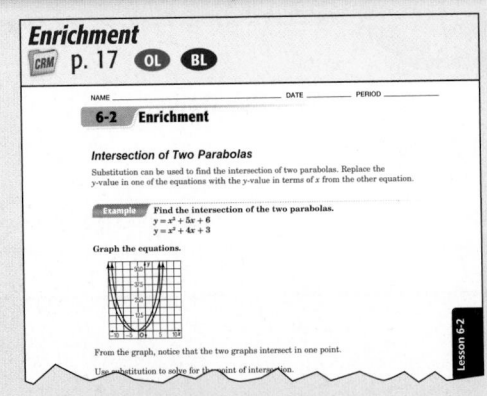

PSAE PRACTICE 8.11.17, 9.11.12, 8.11.13, 8.11.19

32. The debate team plans to make and sell trail mix. They can spend $34.

Item	Cost Per Pound
sunflower seeds	$4.00
raisins	$1.50

The pounds of raisins in the mix are to be 3 times the pounds of sunflower seeds. Which system can be used to find r, the pounds of raisins, and p, pounds of sunflower seeds, they should buy? **A**

A $3p = r$
$4p + 1.5r = 34$

C $3r = p$
$4p + 1.5r = 34$

B $3p = r$
$4r + 1.5p = 34$

D $3r = p$
$4r + 1.5p = 34$

33. GRIDDED RESPONSE The perimeters of two similar polygons are 250 centimeters and 300 centimeters, respectively. What is the scale factor between the two polygons? **5/6**

34. Based on the graph, which statement is true? **G**

Sports Drinks Supply

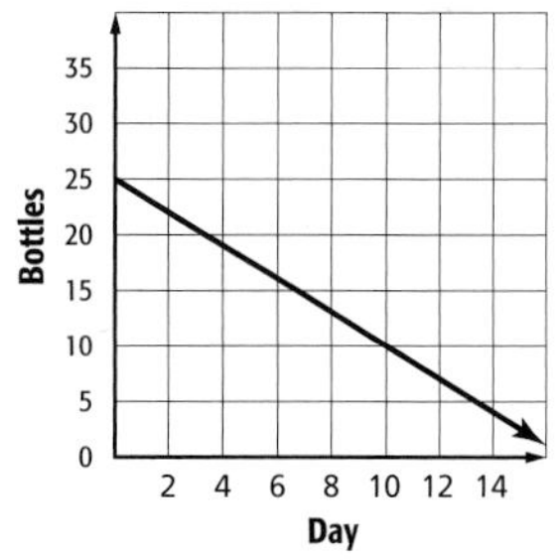

F Mary started with 30 bottles.
G On day 10, Mary will have 10 bottles left.
H Mary will be out of sports drinks on day 14.
J Mary drank 5 bottles the first two days.

35. If p is an integer, which of the following is the solution set for $2|p| = 16$? **C**

A $\{0, 8\}$
C $\{-8, 8\}$
B $\{-8, 0\}$
D $\{-8, 0, 8\}$

40b. $0 \le p < 6$, $0 \le d \le 35$, and p and d are integers; The coach cannot purchase a fractional part of a pizza or pitcher of drinks.

Spiral Review

40a. Let p represent the number of pizzas, and let d represent the number of pitchers of soft drinks; $12p + 2d \le 70$.

Graph each system of equations. Then determine whether the system has *no* solution, *one* solution, or *infinitely many* solutions. If the system has one solution, name it. (Lesson 6-1) **36–39. See margin.**

36. $y = -5$
$3x + y = 1$

37. $x = 1$
$2x - y = 7$

38. $y = x + 5$
$y = x - 2$

39. $x + y = 1$
$3y + 3x = 3$

40. ENTERTAINMENT Coach Ross wants to take the soccer team out for pizza after their game. Her budget is at most $70. (Lesson 5-6)

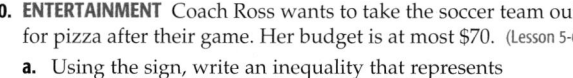

a. Using the sign, write an inequality that represents this situation.

b. Are there any restrictions on the domain or range? Explain.

Solve each inequality. Check your solution. (Lesson 5-3)

41. $6v + 1 \ge -11$ **$v \ge -2$**

42. $24 > 18 + 2n$ **$n < 3$**

43. $-11 \ge \frac{2}{5}q + 5$ **$q \le -40$**

44. $\frac{a}{8} - 10 > -3$ **$a > 56$**

45. $-3t + 9 \le 0$ **$t \ge 3$**

46. $54 > -10 - 8n$ **$n > -8$**

Skills Review

Rewrite each product using the Distributive Property. Then simplify. (Lesson 1-4)

47. $10b + 5(3 + 9b)$ **$55b + 15$**

48. $5(3t^2 + 4) - 8t$ **$15t^2 - 8t + 20$**

49. $7h^2 + 4(3h + h^2)$ **$11h^2 + 12h$**

50. $-2(7a + 5b) + 5(2a - 7b)$ **$-4a - 45b$**

Differentiated Instruction OL BL

Extension Have students write a system of equations that produces one solution using $y = \frac{1}{3}x - 2$ as one of the equations. Ask them to solve the system. Sample answer: Using the equation $2x - y = 7$, the solution is $(3, -1)$.

Watch Out!

Find the Error In Exercise 27, remind students that both Guillermo and Cara could be wrong, and that errors can be made in interpreting a solution as well as finding it.

4 ASSESS

Name the Math Write a system of equations on the board. Have students pair up and tell each other how they would solve the system.

Formative Assessment

Check for student understanding of concepts in Lessons 6-1 and 6-2.

CRM Quiz 1, p. 59

Additional Answers

37.

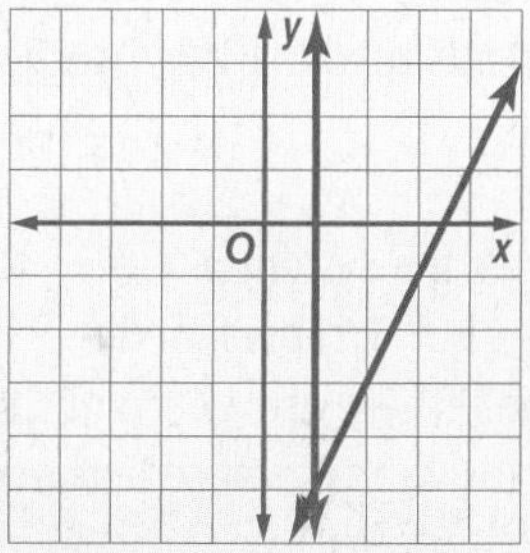

one solution; $(1, -5)$

38.

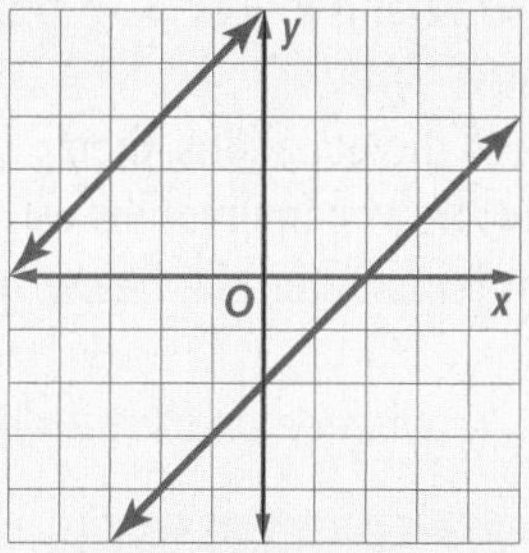

no solution

39.

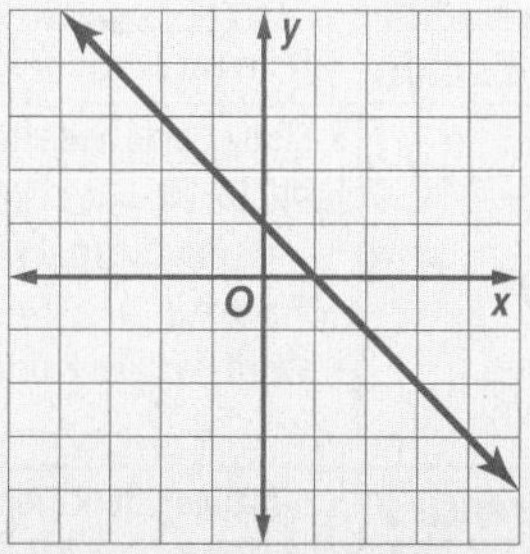

infinitely many solutions

6-3 Lesson Notes

1 FOCUS

Vertical Alignment

Before Lesson 6-3
Use properties of equality to solve equations.

Lesson 6-3
Solve systems of equations by using elimination with addition.
Solve systems of equations by using elimination with subtraction.

After Lesson 6-3
Solve systems of equations by using elimination with multiplication.

2 TEACH

Scaffolding Questions

Have students read the *Why?* section of the lesson.

Ask:

- Why does the system $a + b = 12$ and $a - b = 2$ represent the situation? There are 12 months in a year and the difference between a and b is 2.
- Why is b eliminated when you add $a + b = 12$ and $a - b = 2$? b is eliminated because $b + (-b) = 0$
- If you add the equations, then $2a = 14$. How many months will the high temperature be below 70° F? 7 months

(continued on the next page)

6-3 Elimination Using Addition and Subtraction

Then
You solved systems of equations by using substitution. (Lesson 6-2)

Now
- Solve systems of equations by using elimination with addition.
- Solve systems of equations by using elimination with subtraction.

IL Learning Standards
8.B.4a Represent algebraic concepts with physical materials, words, diagrams, tables, graphs, equations and inequalities and use appropriate technology.

New Vocabulary
elimination

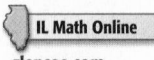

IL Math Online
glencoe.com
- Extra Examples
- Personal Tutor
- Self-Check Quiz
- Homework Help

Why?

In Chicago, Illinois, there are two more months a when the mean high temperature is below 70°F than there are months b when it is above 70°F. The system of equations, $a + b = 12$ and $a - b = 2$, represents this situation.

Elimination Using Addition If you add these equations, the variable b will be eliminated. Using addition or subtraction to solve a system is called **elimination**.

> **Key Concept** Solving by Elimination — *For Your FOLDABLE*
>
> **Step 1** Write the system so like terms with the same or opposite coefficients are aligned.
>
> **Step 2** Add or subtract the equations, eliminating one variable. Then solve the equation.
>
> **Step 3** Substitute the value from Step 2 into one of the equations and solve for the other variable. Write the solution as an ordered pair.

EXAMPLE 1 Elimination Using Addition

Use elimination to solve the system of equations.

$4x + 6y = 32$
$3x - 6y = 3$ ← **Step 1** $6y$ and $-6y$ have opposite coefficients.

Step 2 Add the equations.

$$\begin{aligned} 4x + 6y &= 32 \\ (+)\ 3x - 6y &= 3 \\ \hline 7x \quad &= 35 \end{aligned}$$ The variable y is eliminated.

$\frac{7x}{7} = \frac{35}{7}$ Divide each side by 7.

$x = 5$ Simplify.

Step 3 Substitute 5 for x in either equation to find the value of y.

$4x + 6y = 32$	First equation
$4(5) + 6y = 32$	Replace x with 5.
$20 + 6y = 32$	Multiply.
$20 + 6y - 20 = 32 - 20$	Subtract 20 from each side.
$6y = 12$	Simplify.
$\frac{6y}{6} = \frac{12}{6}$	Divide each side by 6.
$y = 2$	Simplify.

The solution is (5, 2).

Lesson 6-3 Resources

Resource	Approaching-Level	On-Level	Beyond-Level	English Learners
Teacher Edition	• Differentiated Instruction, p. 350	• Differentiated Instruction, pp. 350, 354	• Differentiated Instruction, p. 354	• Differentiated Instruction, p. 350
Chapter Resource Masters	• Study Guide and Intervention, pp. 18–19 • Skills Practice, p. 20 • Practice, p. 21 • Word Problem Practice, p. 22	• Study Guide and Intervention, pp. 18–19 • Skills Practice, p. 20 • Practice, p. 21 • Word Problem Practice, p. 22 • Enrichment, p. 23	• Practice, p. 21 • Word Problem Practice, p. 22 • Enrichment, p. 23	• Study Guide and Intervention, pp. 18–19 • Skills Practice, p. 20 • Practice, p. 21
Transparencies	• 5-Minute Check Transparency 6-3	• 5-Minute Check Transparency 6-3	• 5-Minute Check Transparency 6-3	• 5-Minute Check Transparency 6-3
Other	• Study Notebook • Teaching Algebra with Manipulatives	• Study Notebook • Teaching Algebra with Manipulatives	• Study Notebook	• Study Notebook • Teaching Algebra with Manipulatives

Check Your Progress

1A. $-4x + 3y = -3$
$4x - 5y = 5$ (0, −1)

1B. $4y + 3x = 22$
$3x - 4y = 14$ (6, 1)

Personal Tutor glencoe.com

ReadingMath

Elimination When adding or subtracting two equations causes the coefficients of a variable to result in 0, the variable is said to be *eliminated.*

We can use elimination to find specific numbers that are described as being related to each other.

EXAMPLE 2 Write and Solve a System of Equations

Negative three times one number plus five times another number is −11. Three times the first number plus seven times the other number is −1. Find the numbers.

Negative three times one number	plus	five times another number	is	−11.
$-3x$	$+$	$5y$	$=$	-11
Three times the first number	plus	seven times the other number	is	−1.
$3x$	$+$	$7y$	$=$	-1

Steps 1 and 2 Write the equations vertically and add.

$$\begin{array}{r} -3x + 5y = -11 \\ (+)\ 3x + 7y = -1 \\ \hline 12y = -12 \end{array}$$ The variable x is eliminated.

$\frac{12y}{12} = \frac{-12}{12}$ Divide each side by 12.

$y = -1$ Simplify.

Step 3 Substitute −1 for y in either equation to find the value of x.

$3x + 7y = -1$ Second equation

$3x + 7(-1) = -1$ Replace y with −1.

$3x + (-7) = -1$ Simplify.

$3x + (-7) + 7 = -1 + 7$ Add 7 to each side.

$3x = 6$ Simplify.

$\frac{3x}{3} = \frac{6}{3}$ Divide each side by 3.

$x = 2$ Simplify.

The numbers are 2 and −1.

CHECK $-3x + 5y = -11$ First equation

$-3(2) + 5(-1) \stackrel{?}{=} -11$ Substitute 2 for x and −1 for y.

$-11 = -11$ ✓ Simplify.

$3x + 7y = -1$ Second equation

$3(2) + 7(-1) \stackrel{?}{=} -1$ Substitute 2 for x and −1 for y.

$-1 = -1$ ✓ Simplify.

StudyTip

Coefficients When the coefficients of a variable are the same, subtracting the equations will eliminate the variable. When the coefficients are opposites, adding the equations will eliminate the variable.

Check Your Progress

2. The sum of two numbers is −10. Negative three times the first number minus the second number equals 2. Find the numbers. 4, −14

Personal Tutor glencoe.com

- If you know the value of a, how can you find the value of b? Substitute the value of a for a in one of the equations and solve for b.
- When might you use elimination with addition to solve a system of equations? when the coefficients of one variable are opposites

Elimination Using Addition

Example 1 shows how to solve a system of equations by using elimination with addition. **Example 2** shows how to write a system of equations and then use elimination with addition to solve it.

Formative Assessment

Use the Check Your Progress exercises after each example to determine students' understanding of concepts.

Additional Examples

1 Use elimination to solve the system of equations.

$-3x + 4y = 12$

$3x - 6y = 18$ (−24, −15)

2 Four times one number minus three times another number is 12. Two times the first number added to three times the second number is 6. Find the numbers. The numbers are 3 and 0.

Additional Examples also in Interactive Classroom PowerPoint® Presentations

IWB INTERACTIVE WHITEBOARD READY

Focus on Mathematical Content

Elimination Using Addition Solving a system of equations by using elimination with addition requires adding the two equations together to eliminate one of the variables. The resulting equation is then solved for the remaining variable. Once the value of one variable is known, it can be substituted into one of the original equations to determine the value of the other variable. In order to use this method, the coefficients of either x or y need to be additive inverses.

TEACH with TECH

VIDEO RECORDING Have students work in groups, and record themselves teaching each other how to solve an equation using elimination. Then share all of the videos with the class.

Elimination Using Subtraction

Example 3 shows how to solve a system of equations using elimination with subtraction. **Example 4** shows how to write and solve a system of equations by elimination for a real-world problem.

Additional Examples

3 Use elimination to solve the system of equations.

$4x + 2y = 28$

$4x - 3y = 18$ (6, 2)

4 **RENTALS** A hardware store earned $956.50 from renting ladders and power tools last week. The store charged 36 days for ladders and 85 days for power tools. This week the store charged 36 days for ladders, 70 days for power tools, and earned $829. How much does the store charge per day for ladders and for power tools? $6.50 per day for ladders and $8.50 per day for power tools

Focus on Mathematical Content

Elimination Using Subtraction Solving a system of equations by subtraction requires subtracting one equation from the other to eliminate one of the variables. The coefficients of either x or y must be the same in order to use this method.

Watch Out!

Preventing Errors When using elimination with subtraction to solve systems of equations, many students forget to distribute the negative sign over every term of the equation that is subtracted. Since subtraction is the same as adding the inverse, you might suggest that students change the signs of the terms and then add to eliminate the variable.

Elimination Using Subtraction Sometimes we can eliminate a variable by subtracting one equation from another.

PSAE EXAMPLE 3 8.11.15

Solve the system of equations. $2t + 5r = 6$
$9r + 2t = 22$

A $(-7, 15)$ B $\left(7, \frac{8}{9}\right)$ C $(4, -7)$ D $\left(4, -\frac{2}{5}\right)$

Read the Test Item

Since both equations contain $2t$, use elimination by subtraction.

Solve the Test Item

Step 1 Subtract the equations.

$5r + 2t = 6$	**Write the system so like terms are aligned.**
$(-)\ 9r + 2t = 22$	
$-4r = -16$	**The variable *t* is eliminated.**
$r = 4$	**Simplify.**

Step 2 Substitute 4 for r in either equation to find the value of t.

$5r + 2t = 6$	**First equation**
$5(4) + 2t = 6$	**$r = 4$**
$20 + 2t = 6$	**Simplify.**
$20 + 2t - 20 = 6 - 20$	**Subtract 20 from each side.**
$2t = -14$	**Simplify.**
$t = -7$	**Simplify.**

The solution is $(4, -7)$. The correct answer is C .

Check Your Progress

3. Solve the system of equations. H $8b + 3c = 11$
$8b + 7c = 7$

F $(1.5, -1)$ G $(1.75, -1)$ H $(1.75, 1)$ J $(1.5, 1)$

Personal Tutor glencoe.com

Real-World Link

The five most dangerous jobs for teenagers are: delivery and other driving jobs, working alone in cash-based businesses, traveling youth crews, cooking, and construction.

Source: National Consumers League

Real-World EXAMPLE 4 Write and Solve a System of Equations

JOBS Cheryl and Jackie work at an ice cream shop. Cheryl earns $8.50 per hour and Jackie earns $7.50 per hour. During a typical week, Cheryl and Jackie earn $299.50 together. One week, Jackie doubles her work hours, and the girls earn $412. How many hours does each girl work during a typical week?

Understand You know how much Cheryl and Jackie each earn per hour and how much they earned together.

Plan Let c = Cheryl's hours and j = Jackie's hours.

Cheryl's pay	plus	Jackie's pay	equals	$299.50.
$8.50c$	$+$	$7.50j$	$=$	299.50
Cheryl's pay	**plus**	**Jackie's pay**	**equals**	**$412.**
$8.50c$	$+$	$7.50(2)j$	$=$	412

Differentiated Instruction AL OL ELL

Kinesthetic Learners Students may benefit from using concrete models to solve systems of equations with elimination. Have students write the terms of the equations on pieces of paper or use algebra tiles or other models to represent the equations. When they eliminate a variable, have them remove the model for that variable. The act of removing the terms should help them remember eliminating the variable.

Solve Subtract the equations to eliminate one of the variables. Then solve for the other variable.

$$\begin{aligned} 8.50c + 7.50j &= 299.50 && \text{Write the equations vertically.} \\ (-)\ 8.50c + 7.50(2)j &= 412 \end{aligned}$$

$$\begin{aligned} 8.50c + 7.50j &= 299.50 \\ (-)\ 8.50c + 15j &= 412 && \text{Simplify.} \\ -7.50j &= -112.50 && \text{Subtract. The variable } c \text{ is eliminated.} \\ \frac{-7.50j}{-7.50} &= \frac{-112.50}{-7.50} && \text{Divide each side by } -7.50. \\ j &= 15 && \text{Simplify.} \end{aligned}$$

Now substitute 15 for j in either equation to find the value of c.

$$\begin{aligned} 8.50c + 7.50j &= 299.50 && \text{First equation} \\ 8.50c + 7.50(15) &= 299.50 && \text{Substitute 15 for } j. \\ 8.50c + 112.50 &= 299.50 && \text{Simplify.} \\ 8.50c &= 187 && \text{Subtract 112.50 from each side.} \\ c &= 22 && \text{Divide each side by 8.50.} \end{aligned}$$

Check Substitute both values into the other equation to see if the equation holds true. If $c = 22$ and $j = 15$, then $8.50(22) + 15(15)$ or 412.

Cheryl works 22 hours, while Jackie works 15 hours during a typical week.

StudyTip

Another Method Instead of subtracting the equations, you could also multiply one equation by −1 and then add the equations.

Check Your Progress

4. **PARTIES** Tamera and Adelina are throwing a birthday party for their friend. Tamera invited 5 fewer friends than Adelina. Together they invited 47 guests. How many guests did each girl invite? **Tamera, 21; Adelina, 26**

Personal Tutor glencoe.com

Check Your Understanding

6. recycling and reuse, 1,150,000; waste management, 125,000

Examples 1 and 3 pp. 348 and 350

Use elimination to solve each system of equations.

1. $5m - p = 7$
   $7m - p = 11$ **(2, 3)**
2. $8x + 5y = 38$
   $-8x + 2y = 4$ **(1, 6)**
3. $7f + 3g = -6$
   $7f - 2g = -31$ **(−3, 5)**
4. $6a - 3b = 27$
   $2a - 3b = 11$ **(4, −1)**

Example 2 p. 349

5. The sum of two numbers is 24. Five times the first number minus the second number is 12. What are the two numbers? **6, 18**

Example 4 pp. 350–351

6. **RECYCLING** The recycling and reuse industry employs approximately 1,025,000 more workers than the waste management industry. Together they provide 1,275,000 jobs. How many jobs does each industry provide?

3 PRACTICE

Formative Assessment

Use Exercises 1–6 to check for understanding.

Use the chart at the bottom of this page to customize assignments for your students.

Differentiated Homework Options

Level	Assignment	Two-Day Option	
AL Basic	7–23, 34–37, 39–59	7–23 odd, 40–43	8–22 even, 34–37, 39, 44–59
OL Core	7–29 odd, 30–37, 39–59	7–23, 40–43	24–37, 39, 44–59
BL Advanced	24–55, (optional: 56–59)		

Study Guide and Intervention
CRM pp. 18–19 AL OL ELL

NAME ________ DATE ________ PERIOD ________

6-3 Study Guide and Intervention
Elimination Using Addition and Subtraction

Elimination Using Addition In systems of equations in which the coefficients of the x or y terms are additive inverses, solve the system by adding the equations. Because one of the variables is eliminated, this method is called **elimination**.

Example 1 **Use elimination to solve the system of equations.**
$x - 3y = 7$
$3x + 3y = 9$

Write the equations in column form and add to eliminate y.

$$\begin{array}{r} x - 3y = 7 \\ (+)\ 3x + 3y = 9 \\ \hline 4x \quad = 16 \end{array}$$

Solve for x.

$$\frac{4x}{4} = \frac{16}{4}$$
$$x = 4$$

Substitute 4 for x in either equation and solve for y.

$$4 - 3y = 7$$
$$4 - 3y - 4 = 7 - 4$$
$$-3y = 3$$
$$\frac{-3y}{-3} = \frac{3}{-3}$$
$$y = -1$$

The solution is $(4, -1)$.

Example 2 **The sum of two numbers is 70 and their difference is 24. Find the numbers.**

Let x represent one number and y represent the other number.

$$\begin{array}{r} x + y = 70 \\ (+)\ x - y = 24 \\ \hline 2x \quad = 94 \end{array}$$
$$\frac{2x}{2} = \frac{94}{2}$$
$$x = 47$$

Substitute 47 for x in either equation.

$$47 + y = 70$$
$$47 + y - 47 = 70 - 47$$
$$y = 23$$

The numbers are 47 and 23.

Exercises

Use elimination to solve each system of equations.

1. $x + y = -4$; $x - y = 2$ **(−1, −3)**
2. $2x - 3y = 14$; $x + 3y = -11$ **(1, −4)**
3. $3x - y = -9$; $-3x - 2y = 0$ **(−2, 3)**
4. $-3x - 4y = -1$; $3x - y = -4$ **(−1, 1)**
5. $3x + y = 4$; $2x - y = 6$ **(2, −2)**
6. $-2x + 2y = 9$; $2x - y = -6$ $\left(-\frac{3}{2}, 3\right)$
7. $2x + 2y = -2$; $3x - 2y = 12$ **(2, −3)**
8. $4x - 2y = -1$; $-4x + 4y = -2$ $\left(-1, -\frac{3}{2}\right)$
9. $x - y = 2$; $x + y = -3$ $\left(-\frac{1}{2}, -\frac{5}{2}\right)$
10. $2x - 3y = 12$; $4x + 3y = 24$ **(6, 0)**
11. $-0.2x + y = 0.5$; $0.2x + 2y = 1.6$ **(1, 0.7)**
12. $0.1x + 0.3y = 0.9$; $0.1x - 0.3y = 0.2$ $\left(\frac{11}{2}, \frac{7}{6}\right)$

13. Rema is older than Ken. The difference of their ages is 12 and the sum of their ages is 50. Find the age of each. **Rema is 31 and Ken is 19.**

14. The sum of the digits of a two-digit number is 12. The difference of the digits is 2. Find the number if the units digit is larger than the tens digit. **57**

Chapter 6 18 *Glencoe Algebra 1*

Practice
CRM p. 21 AL OL BL ELL

NAME ________ DATE ________ PERIOD ________

6-3 Practice
Elimination Using Addition and Subtraction

Use elimination to solve each system of equations.

1. $x - y = 1$; $x + y = -9$ **(−4, −5)**
2. $p + q = -2$; $p - q = 8$ **(3, −5)**
3. $4x + y = 23$; $3x - y = 12$ **(5, 3)**
4. $2x + 5y = -3$; $2x + 2y = 6$ **(6, −3)**
5. $3x + 2y = -1$; $4x + 2y = -6$ **(−5, 7)**
6. $5x + 3y = 22$; $5x - 2y = 2$ **(2, 4)**
7. $5x + 2y = 7$; $-2x + 2y = -14$ **(3, −4)**
8. $3x - 9y = -12$; $3x - 15y = -6$ **(−7, −1)**
9. $-4c - 2d = -2$; $2c - 2d = -14$ **(−2, 5)**
10. $2x - 6y = 6$; $2x + 3y = 24$ **(9, 2)**
11. $7x + 2y = 2$; $7x - 2y = -30$ **(−2, 8)**
12. $4.25x - 1.28y = -9.2$; $x + 1.28y = 17.6$ **(1.6, 12.5)**
13. $2x + 4y = 10$; $x - 4y = -2.5$ **(2.5, 1.25)**
14. $2.5x + y = 10.7$; $2.5x + 2y = 12.9$ **(3.4, 2.2)**
15. $6m - 8n = 3$; $2m - 8n = -3$ $\left(1\frac{1}{2}, \frac{3}{4}\right)$
16. $4a + b = 2$; $4a + 3b = 10$ $\left(-\frac{1}{2}, 4\right)$
17. $-\frac{1}{3}x - \frac{4}{3}y = -2$; $\frac{1}{3}x - \frac{2}{3}y = 4$ **(10, −1)**
18. $\frac{3}{4}x - \frac{1}{2}y = 8$; $\frac{3}{2}x + \frac{1}{2}y = 19$ **(12, 2)**

19. The sum of two numbers is 41 and their difference is 5. What are the numbers? **18, 23**

20. Four times one number added to another number is 36. Three times the first number minus the other number is 20. Find the numbers. **8, 4**

21. One number added to three times another number is 24. Five times the first number added to three times the other number is 36. Find the numbers. **3, 7**

22. **LANGUAGES** English is spoken as the first or primary language in 78 more countries than Farsi is spoken as the first language. Together, English and Farsi are spoken as a first language in 130 countries. In how many countries is English spoken as the first language? In how many countries is Farsi spoken as the first language? **English: 104 countries, Farsi: 26 countries**

23. **DISCOUNTS** At a sale on winter clothing, Cody bought two pairs of gloves and four hats for \$43.00. Tori bought two pairs of gloves and two hats for \$30.00. What were the prices for the gloves and hats? **gloves: \$8.50, hats: \$6.50.**

Chapter 6 21 *Glencoe Algebra 1*

Lesson 6-3

Word Problem Practice
CRM p. 22 AL OL BL ELL

NAME ________ DATE ________ PERIOD ________

6-3 Word Problem Practice
Elimination Using Addition and Subtraction

1. **NUMBER FUN** Ms. Simms, the sixth grade math teacher, gave her students this challenge problem.

   Twice a number added to another number is 15. The sum of the two numbers is 11.

   Lorenzo, an algebra student who was Ms. Simms aide, realized he could solve the problem by writing the following system of equations.

   $$2x + y = 15$$
   $$x + y = 11$$

   Use the elimination method to solve the system and find the two numbers. **(4, 7)**

2. **GOVERNMENT** The Texas State Legislature is comprised of state senators and state representatives. The sum of the number of senators and representatives is 181. There are 119 more representatives than senators. How many senators and how many representatives make up the Texas State Legislature? **31 state senators and 150 state representatives**

3. **RESEARCH** Melissa wondered how much it cost to send a letter by mail in 1990, so she asked her father. Rather than answer directly, Melissa's father gave her the following information. It would have cost \$3.70 to send 13 postcards and 7 letters, and it would have cost \$2.65 to send 6 postcards and 7 letters. Use a system of equations and elimination to find how much it cost to send a letter in 1990. **\$0.25**

4. **SPORTS** As of 2007 the New York Yankees had won more Major League Baseball World Series than any other team. In fact The Yankees had won 1 fewer than 3 times the number of World Series won by the Oakland A's. The sum of the two teams' World Series championships is 35. How many times has each team won the World Series? **The A's have won 9 times and the Yankees have won 26 times.**

5. **BASKETBALL** In 2005, the average ticket prices for Dallas Mavericks games and Boston Celtics games are shown in the table below. The change in price is from the 2004 season to the 2005 season.

Team	Average Ticket Price	Change in Price
Dallas	\$53.60	\$0.53
Boston	\$55.93	−\$1.08

Source: Team Marketing Report

   a. Assume that tickets continue to change at the same rate each year after 2005. Let x be the number of years after 2005, and y be the price of an average ticket. Write a system of equations to represent the information in the table.
   $y = 0.53x + 53.60$
   $y = -1.08x + 55.93$

   b. In how many years will the average ticket price for Dallas approximately equal that of Boston?
   $x = 1.45$; 1 or 2 yr

Chapter 6 22 *Glencoe Algebra 1*

Practice and Problem Solving

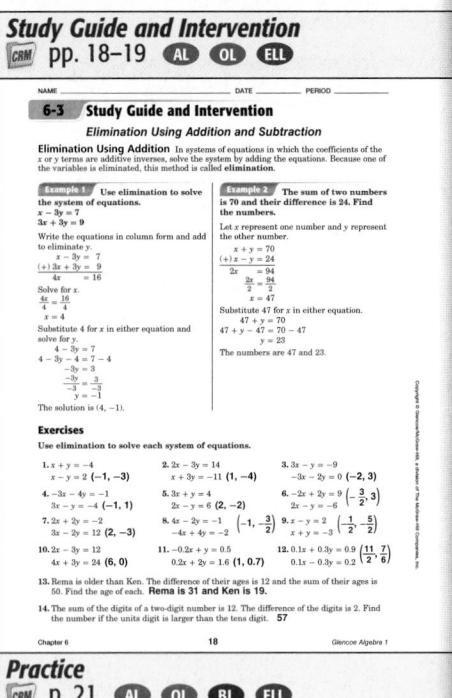

= Step-by-Step Solutions begin on page R12.
Extra Practice begins on page 815.

Examples 1 and 3 pp. 348 and 350

Use elimination to solve each system of equations.

7. $-v + w = 7$; $v + w = 1$ **(−3, 4)**
8. $y + z = 4$; $y - z = 8$ **(6, −2)**
9. $-4x + 5y = 17$; $4x + 6y = -6$ **(−3, 1)**
10. $5m - 2p = 24$; $3m + 2p = 24$ **(6, 3)**
11. $a + 4b = -4$; $a + 10b = -16$ **(4, −2)**
12. $6r - 6t = 6$; $3r - 6t = 15$ **(−3, −4)**
13. $6c - 9d = 111$; $5c - 9d = 103$ **(8, −7)**
14. $11f + 14g = 13$; $11f + 10g = 25$ **(5, −3)**
15. $9x + 6y = 78$; $3x - 6y = -30$ **(4, 7)**
16. $3j + 4k = 23.5$; $8j - 4k = 4$ **(2.5, 4)**
17. $-3x - 8y = -24$; $3x - 5y = 4.5$ **(4, 1.5)**
18. $6x - 2y = 1$; $10x - 2y = 5$ **(1, 2.5)**

Example 2 p. 349

19. The sum of two numbers is 22, and their difference is 12. What are the numbers? **5, 17**

20. Find the two numbers with a sum of 41 and a difference of 9. **25, 16**

21. Three times a number minus another number is −3. The sum of the numbers is 11. Find the numbers. **2, 9**

22. A number minus twice another number is 4. Three times the first number plus two times the second number is 12. What are the numbers? **4, 0**

Example 4 pp. 350–351

23. **TOURS** The Blackwells and Joneses are going to Hershey's Really Big 3D Show in Pennsylvania. Find the adult price and the children's price of the show.

Adult, \$5.95; children, \$3.95

Family	Number of Adults	Number of Children	Total Cost
Blackwell	2	5	\$31.65
Jones	2	3	\$23.75

B **Use elimination to solve each system of equations.**

24. $4(x + 2y) = 8$; $4x + 4y = 12$ **(4, −1)**
25. $3x - 5y = 11$; $5(x + y) = 5$ **(2, −1)**
26. $4x + 3y = 6$; $3x + 3y = 7$ $\left(-1, 3\frac{1}{3}\right)$
27. $6x - 7y = -26$; $6x + 5y = 10$ $\left(-\frac{5}{6}, 3\right)$
28. $\frac{1}{2}x + \frac{2}{3}y = 2\frac{3}{4}$; $\frac{1}{4}x - \frac{2}{3}y = 6\frac{1}{4}$ $\left(12, -4\frac{7}{8}\right)$
29. $\frac{3}{5}x + \frac{1}{2}y = 8\frac{1}{3}$; $-\frac{3}{5}x + \frac{3}{4}y = 8\frac{1}{3}$ $\left(2\frac{7}{9}, 13\frac{1}{3}\right)$

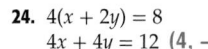

Real-World Link

Cross-country mountain bike racing became an Olympic event in 1996. Dutch cyclist Bart Brentjens earned the first gold medal in the event with a time of 2:17:36.

Source: Cycling News

30. **ARCHITECTURE** The total height of an office building b and the granite statue that stands on top of it g is 326.6 feet. The difference in heights between the building and the statue is 295.4 feet.
    a. How tall is the statue? **15.6 ft**
    b. How tall is the building? **311 ft**

31. **BIKE RACING** Professional Mountain Bike Racing currently has 66 teams. The number of non-U.S. teams is 30 more than the number of U.S. teams.
    a. Let x represent the number of non-U.S. teams and y represent the number of U.S. teams. Write a system of equations that represents the number of U.S. teams and non-U.S. teams. **$x + y = 66$; $x = 30 + y$**
    b. Use elimination to find the solution of the system of equations. **(48, 18)**
    c. Interpret the solution in the context of the situation. **See margin.**
    d. Graph the system of equations to check your solution. **See margin.**

Enrichment
CRM p. 23 OL BL

NAME ________ DATE ________ PERIOD ________

6-3 Enrichment
Solving Systems of Equations in Three Variables

Systems of equations can involve more than 2 equations and 2 variables. It is possible to solve a system of 3 equations and 3 variables using elimination.

Example **Solve the following system.**
$x + y + z = 6$
$3x - y + z = 8$
$x - z = 2$

Step 1: Use elimination to get rid of the y in the first two equations.

$$\begin{array}{r} x + y + z = 6 \\ 3x - y + z = 8 \\ \hline 4x + 2z = 14 \end{array}$$

Step 2: Use the equation you found in step 1 and the third equation to eliminate the z.

$$4x + 2z = 14$$
$$x - z = 2$$

Multiply the second equation by 2 so that the z's will eliminate.

$$\begin{array}{r} 4x + 2z = 14 \\ 2x - 2z = 4 \\ \hline 6x = 18 \end{array}$$

So, $x = 3$.

Additional Answer

31c. There are 48 teams that are not from the U.S., and 18 teams that are from the U.S.

Math History Link

Leonardo Pisano (1170–1250)

Leonardo Pisano is better known by his nickname *Fibonacci*. His book introduced the Hindu-Arabic place-valued decimal system. Systems of linear equations are studied in this work.

32. ONLINE CATALOGS Let x represent the number of years since 2004 and y represent the number of catalogs.

Catalogs	Number in 2004	Growth Rate (number per year)
online	7440	1293
print	3805	−1364

Source: MediaPost Publications

a. Write a system of equations to represent this situation.

b. Use elimination to find the solution to the system of equations. about (−1.4, 5671.1)

c. Analyze the solution in terms of the situation. Determine the reasonableness of the solution. About 1.4 years before 2004, or in 2002, the number of online catalogs and the number of print catalogs were both 5671.

33. C **MULTIPLE REPRESENTATIONS** Collect 9 pennies and 9 paper clips. For this game, you may use a maximum of 9 objects to create a certain required number of points. Each paper clip is worth 1 point and each penny is worth 3 points. Let p represent a penny and c represent a paper clip.

9 points = 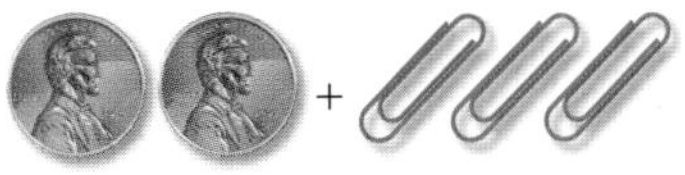 $= 2p + 3c$

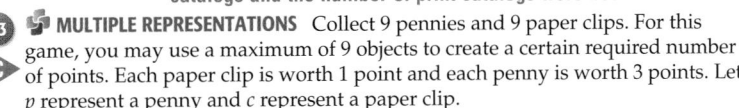

a. CONCRETE You must have exactly 15 points using at least one of each piece. Compare your pattern to other students. Sample answer: 4 pennies, and 3 paper clips

b. ANALYTICAL Write and solve a system of equations to find the number of paper clips and pennies used. $p + c = 9$, $3p + c = 15$, $p = 3$, $c = 6$

c. TABULAR Make a table showing the number of paper clips used and the total number of points when the number of pennies is 0, 1, 2, 3, 4, or 5. See margin.

d. VERBAL Does the result in the table match the results in part **b**? Explain. See margin.

H.O.T. Problems

Use **H**igher-**O**rder **T**hinking Skills

34. REASONING Describe the solution of a system of equations if after you added two equations the result was $0 = 0$. If the result is a true statement such as $0 = 0$, then there would be an infinite number of solutions.

35. REASONING What is the solution of a system of equations if the sum of the equations is $0 = 2$? See margin.

36. OPEN ENDED Create a system of equations that can be solved by using addition to eliminate one variable. Formulate a general rule for creating such systems.

37. REASONING The solution of a system of equations is $(-3, 2)$. One equation in the system is $x + 4y = 5$. Find a second equation for the system. Explain how you derived this equation.

38. CHALLENGE If a number is multiplied by 7, the result is 182. The sum of that number's two digits is 8. Define the variables and write the system of equations that you would use to find the number. Then solve the system and find the number. See margin.

39. WRITING IN MATH Describe when it would be most beneficial to use elimination to solve a system of equations. See margin.

36. Sample answer: $2a + b = 5$, $a - b = 4$; a system that can be solved by using addition to eliminate one variable must have one variable with coefficients that are additive inverses.

37. Sample answer: $-x + y = 5$; I used the solution to create another equation with the coefficient of the x-term being the opposite of its corresponding coefficient.

Multiple Representations In Exercise 33, students use a concrete model and a table of values to illustrate the solution of a system of equations.

Additional Answers

31d.

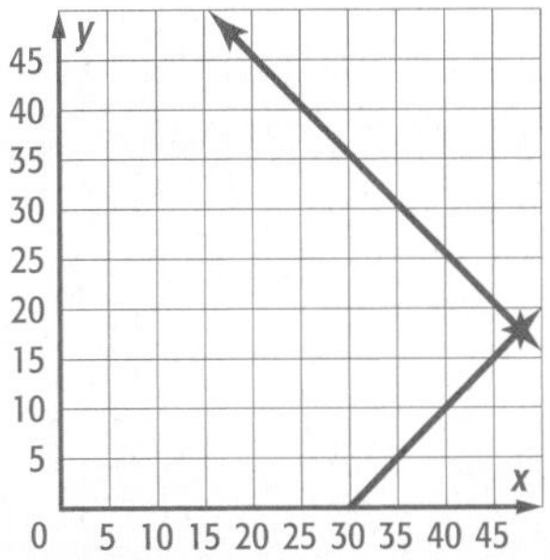

33c. Sample answer:

Pennies (p)	0	1	2	3	4	5
Paper clips ($9 - p$)	9	8	7	6	5	4
Points ($3p + c$)	9	11	13	15	17	19

33d. Yes; since the pennies are 3 points each, 3 of them makes 9 points. Add the 6 points from 6 paper clips and you get 15 points.

35. The result of the statement is false, so there is no solution.

38. Let a = the tens digit of the number, and let b = the ones digit of the number; $7 \cdot (10a + b) = 182$; $a + b = 8$; 26 is the number.

39. Sample answer: It would be most beneficial when one variable has either the same coefficient or opposite coefficients in the equations.

4 ASSESS

Ticket Out the Door Have students write a system of equations that can be solved by using elimination with subtraction.

PSAE PRACTICE 6.11.17, 7.11.03, 8.11.04, 8.11.17

40. SHORT RESPONSE Martina is on a train traveling at a speed of 188 mph between two cities 1128 miles apart. If the train has been traveling for an hour, how many more hours is her train ride? **5 hours**

41. GEOMETRY Ms. Miller wants to tile her rectangular kitchen floor. She knows the dimensions of the floor. Which formula should she use to find the area? **A**

A $A = \ell w$
B $V = Bh$
C $P = 2\ell + 2w$
D $c^2 = a^2 + b^2$

42. If the pattern continues, what is the 8th number in the sequence? **F**

$$2, 3, \frac{9}{2}, \frac{27}{4}, \frac{81}{8}, \ldots$$

F $\frac{2187}{64}$
G $\frac{2245}{64}$
H $\frac{2281}{64}$
J $\frac{2445}{64}$

43. What is the solution of this system of equations? **B**

$$x + 4y = 1$$
$$2x - 3y = -9$$

A $(2, -8)$
B $(-3, 1)$
C no solution
D infinitely many solutions

Spiral Review

Use substitution to solve each system of equations. If the system does not have exactly one solution, state whether it has no solution or infinitely many solutions. (Lesson 6-2)

44. $y = 6x$
$2x + 3y = 40$ **(2, 12)**

45. $x = 3y$
$2x + 3y = 45$ **(15, 5)**

46. $x = 5y + 6$
$x = 3y - 2$ **(−14, −4)**

47. $y = 3x + 2$
$y = 4x - 1$ **(3, 11)**

48. $3c = 4d + 2$
$c = d - 1$ **(−6, −5)**

49. $z = v + 4$
$2z - v = 6$ **(−2, 2)**

50. FINANCIAL LITERACY Gregorio and Javier each want to buy a bicycle. Gregorio has already saved \$35 and plans to save \$10 per week. Javier has \$26 and plans to save \$13 per week. (Lesson 6-1)

a. In how many weeks will Gregorio and Javier have saved the same amount of money? **3 wk**

b. How much will each person have saved at that time? **\$65**

51. GEOMETRY A *parallelogram* is a quadrilateral in which opposite sides are parallel. Determine whether *ABCD* is parallelogram. Explain your reasoning. (Lesson 4-4) **Yes; each pair of opposite sides have the same or an undefined slope, so they are parallel.**

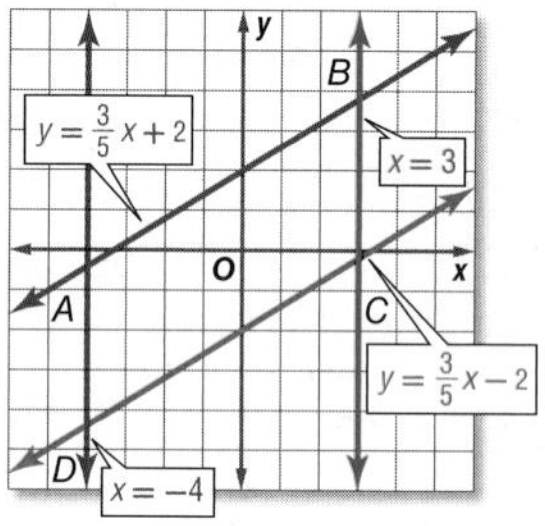

Solve each equation. Check your solution. (Lesson 2-2)

52. $6u = -48$ **−8**

53. $75 = -15p$ **−5**

54. $\frac{2}{3}a = 8$ **12**

55. $-\frac{3}{4}d = 15$ **−20**

Skills Review

Simplify each expression. If not possible, write *simplified*. (Lesson 1-4)

56. $6q - 3 + 7q + 1$ **$13q - 2$**

57. $7w^2 - 9w + 4w^2$ **$11w^2 - 9w$**

58. $10(2 + r) + 3r$ **$13r + 20$**

59. $5y - 7(y + 5)$ **$-2y - 35$**

Differentiated Instruction OL BL

Extension Write two equations on the board with the constants missing. Have students find the missing constants that ensure the given solution. For example, write the system $3x + 2y = ?$, $5x - 2y = ?$ and tell students that the solution is (1.5, 0.25). $3x + 2y = 5$, $5x - 2y = 7$

354 Chapter 6 Systems of Linear Equations and Inequalities

Elimination Using Multiplication

Why?

The table shows the number of cars at Scott's Auto Repair Shop for each type of service.

Item	Repairs	Maintenance
body	3	4
engine	2	2

The manager has allotted 1110 minutes for body work and 570 minutes for engine work. The system $3r + 4m = 1110$ and $2r + 2m = 570$ can be used to find the average time for each service.

Then

You used elimination with addition and subtraction to solve systems of equations. (Lesson 6-3)

Now

- Solve systems of equations by using elimination with multiplication.
- Solve real-world problems involving systems of equations.

IL Learning Standards

8.B.4a Represent algebraic concepts with physical materials, words, diagrams, tables, graphs, equations and inequalities and use appropriate technology.

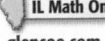

IL Math Online

glencoe.com

- Extra Examples
- Personal Tutor
- Self-Check Quiz
- Homework Help

Elimination Using Multiplication In the system above, neither variable can be eliminated by adding or subtracting. You can use multiplication to solve.

Key Concept Solving by Elimination — For Your FOLDABLE

Step 1 Multiply at least one equation by a constant to get two equations that contain opposite terms.

Step 2 Add or subtract the equations, eliminating one variable. Then solve the equation.

Step 3 Substitute the value from Step 2 into one of the equations and solve for the other variable. Write the solution as an ordered pair.

EXAMPLE 1 Multiply One Equation to Eliminate a Variable

Use elimination to solve the system of equations.

$5x + 6y = -8$

$2x + 3y = -5$

Steps 1 and 2 $5x + 6y = -8$ → $5x + 6y = -8$

$2x + 3y = -5$ **Multiply each term by −2.** → $(+)\ -4x - 6y = 10$ **Add.**

$x = 2$ ***y* is eliminated.**

Step 3

$2x + 3y = -5$ **Second equation**

$2(2) + 3y = -5$ **Substitution, $x = 2$**

$4 + 3y = -5$ **Simplify.**

$3y = -9$ **Subtract 4 from each side and simplify.**

$y = -3$ **Divide each side by 3 and simplify.**

The solution is (2, −3).

Check Your Progress

1A. $6x - 2y = 10$, $3x - 7y = -19$ **(3, 4)**

1B. $9r + q = 13$, $3r + 2q = -4$ **(2, −5)**

Personal Tutor glencoe.com

6-4 Lesson Notes

1 FOCUS

Vertical Alignment

Before Lesson 6-4
Use properties of equality to solve equations.

Lesson 6-4
Solve systems of equations by using elimination with multiplication.
Solve real-world problems involving systems of equations.

After Lesson 6-4
Use matrices to solve systems of equations.

2 TEACH

Scaffolding Questions

Have students read the *Why?* section of the lesson.

Ask:

- What does the first equation in the system of equations represent? the amount of time to perform body repair for 3 cars and body maintenance for 4 cars
- What does the second equation in the system represent? the amount of time to perform engine repair for 2 cars and engine maintenance for 2 cars

(continued on the next page)

Lesson 6-4 Resources

Resource	Approaching-Level	On-Level	Beyond-Level	English Learners
Teacher Edition	• Differentiated Instruction, p. 357	• Differentiated Instruction, p. 360	• Differentiated Instruction, p. 360	• Differentiated Instruction, p. 357
Chapter Resource Masters	• Study Guide and Intervention, pp. 24–25 • Skills Practice, p. 26 • Practice, p. 27 • Word Problem Practice, p. 28	• Study Guide and Intervention, pp. 24–25 • Skills Practice, p. 26 • Practice, p. 27 • Word Problem Practice, p. 28 • Enrichment, p. 29	• Practice, p. 27 • Word Problem Practice, p. 28 • Enrichment, p. 29	• Study Guide and Intervention, pp. 24–25 • Skills Practice, p. 26 • Practice, p. 27
Transparencies	• 5-Minute Check Transparency 6-4	• 5-Minute Check Transparency 6-4	• 5-Minute Check Transparency 6-4	• 5-Minute Check Transparency 6-4
Other	• Study Notebook	• Study Notebook	• Study Notebook	• Study Notebook

- What will the solution to the system represent? the average number of minutes allotted per body repair and the average number of minutes allotted per engine maintenance
- If you multiply the second equation by -2, what variable could you eliminate by adding the equations? the variable m

Elimination Using Multiplication

Example 1 shows how to multiply one equation of a system by a number to eliminate a variable. **Example 2** shows how to multiply both equations of a system to eliminate a variable.

Formative Assessment

Use the Check Your Progress exercises after each example to determine students' understanding of concepts.

Additional Examples

1 Use elimination to solve the system of equations.

$2x + y = 23$

$3x + 2y = 37$ (9, 5)

2 Use elimination to solve the system of equations.

$4x + 3y = 8$

$3x - 5y = -23$ $(-1, 4)$

Additional Examples also in Interactive Classroom PowerPoint® Presentations

IWB INTERACTIVE WHITEBOARD READY

TEACH with TECH

BLOG On your secure classroom blog have students write a blog entry explaining how they decide when to use each of the different methods for solving a system of equations.

StudyTip

Choosing a Variable to Eliminate Unless the problem is asking for the value of a specific variable, you may use multiplication to eliminate either variable.

Sometimes you have to multiply each equation by a different number in order to solve the system.

EXAMPLE 2 Multiply Both Equations to Eliminate a Variable

Use elimination to solve the system of equations.

$4x + 2y = 8$

$3x + 3y = 9$

Method 1 Eliminate x.

$4x + 2y = 8$ **Multiply by 3.** → $12x + 6y = 24$

$3x + 3y = 9$ **Multiply by −4.** → $(+)\ -12x - 12y = -36$ **Add equations.**

$-6y = -12$ ***x* is eliminated.**

$\frac{-6y}{-6} = \frac{-12}{-6}$ **Divide each side by −6.**

$y = 2$ **Simplify.**

Now substitute 2 for y in either equation to find the value of x.

$3x + 3y = 9$	**Second equation**
$3x + 3(2) = 9$	**Substitute 2 for *y*.**
$3x + 6 = 9$	**Simplify.**
$3x = 3$	**Subtract 6 from each side and simplify.**
$\frac{3x}{3} = \frac{3}{3}$	**Divide each side by 3.**
$x = 1$	**The solution is (1, 2).**

Method 2 Eliminate y.

$4x + 2y = 8$ **Multiply by 3.** → $12x + 6y = 24$

$3x + 3y = 9$ **Multiply by −2.** → $(+)\ -6x - 6y = -18$ **Add equations.**

$6x = 6$ ***y* is eliminated.**

$\frac{6x}{6} = \frac{6}{6}$ **Divide each side by 6.**

$x = 1$ **Simplify.**

Now substitute 1 for x in either equation to find the value of y.

$3x + 3y = 9$	**Second equation**
$3(1) + 3y = 9$	**Substitute 1 for *x*.**
$3 + 3y = 9$	**Simplify.**
$3y = 6$	**Subtract 3 from each side and simplify.**
$\frac{3y}{3} = \frac{6}{3}$	**Divide each side by 3.**
$y = 2$	**Simplify.**

The solution is (1, 2), which matches the result obtained with Method 1.

CHECK Substitute 1 for x and 2 for y in the first equation.

$4x + 2y = 8$	**Original equation**
$4(1) + 2(2) \stackrel{?}{=} 8$	**Substitute (1, 2) for (*x*, *y*).**
$4 + 4 \stackrel{?}{=} 8$	**Multiply.**
$8 = 8$ ✓	**Add.**

Check Your Progress

2A. $5x - 3y = 6$
$2x + 5y = -10$ **(0, −2)**

2B. $6a + 2b = 2$
$4a + 3b = 8$ **(−1, 4)**

Personal Tutor glencoe.com

Focus on Mathematical Content

Elimination Using Multiplication This method of solving a system must be used when neither x nor y can be eliminated by adding or subtracting the two equations. The Multiplication Property of Equality is used in order to add or subtract the equations to eliminate one of the variables. Multiply one or both of the equations by numbers so that a variable will be eliminated when the equations of the new system are added or subtracted.

356 Chapter 6 Systems of Linear Equations and Inequalities

Solve Real-World Problems Sometimes it is necessary to use multiplication before elimination in real-world problem solving too.

Real-World EXAMPLE 3 Solve a System of Equations

FLIGHT A personal aircraft traveling with the wind flies 520 miles in 4 hours. On the return trip, the airplane takes 5 hours to travel the same distance. Find the speed of the airplane if the air is still.

You are asked to find the speed of the airplane in still air.

Let a = the rate of the airplane if the air is still.
Let w = the rate of the wind.

	r	t	d	$r \cdot t = d$
With the Wind	$a + w$	4	520	$(a + w)4 = 520$
Against the Wind	$a - w$	5	520	$(a - w)5 = 520$

So, our two equations are $4a + 4w = 520$ and $5a - 5w = 520$.

$4a + 4w = 520$ **Multiply by 5.** → $20a + 20w = 2600$

$5a - 5w = 520$ **Multiply by 4.** → $(+)\ 20a - 20w = 2080$

$40a = 4680$ **w is eliminated.**

$\frac{40a}{40} = \frac{4680}{40}$ **Divide each side by 40.**

$a = 117$ **Simplify.**

The rate of the airplane in still air is 117 miles per hour.

Check Your Progress

$3\frac{1}{3}$ mi/h

3. CANOEING A canoeist travels 4 miles downstream in 1 hour. The return trip takes the canoeist 1.5 hours. Find the rate of the boat in still water.

Personal Tutor glencoe.com

Check Your Understanding

Examples 1 and 2 pp. 355–356

Use elimination to solve each system of equations.

1. $2x - y = 4$
$7x + 3y = 27$ (3, 2)

2. $2x + 7y = 1$
$x + 5y = 2$ (−3, 1)

3. $4x + 2y = -14$
$5x + 3y = -17$ (−4, 1)

4. $9a - 2b = -8$
$-7a + 3b = 12$ (0, 4)

Example 3 p. 357

5. KAYAKING A kayaking group with a guide travels 16 miles downstream, stops for a meal, and then travels 16 miles upstream. The speed of the current remains constant throughout the trip. Find the speed of the kayak in still water. 6 mph

6. 8 Hobbies and Recreation, 2 Soliloquies

6. PODCASTS Steve subscribed to 10 podcasts for a total of 340 minutes. He used his two favorite tags, Hobbies and Recreation and Soliloquies. Each of the Hobbies and Recreation episodes lasted about 32 minutes. Each Soliloquies episode lasted 42 minutes. To how many of each tag did Steve subscribe?

Solve Real-World Problems

Example 3 shows how to write and solve a system of equations by elimination for a real-world situation.

Additional Example

3 **TRANSPORTATION** A fishing boat travels 10 miles downstream in 30 minutes. The return trip takes the boat 40 minutes. Find the rate in miles per hour of the boat in still water. 17.5 mi/h

Watch Out!

Common Errors When using elimination with multiplication, many students forget to multiply each term on both sides of the equation by the number. Suggest that they include an extra step in the solutions that shows the multiplication:

$3x + 2y = 7 \Rightarrow 2(3x + 2y) = 2(7)$

$2x - 7y = -12 \Rightarrow$

$-3(2x - 7y) = -3(-12)$

3 PRACTICE

Formative Assessment

Use Exercises 1–6 to check for understanding.

Use the chart at the bottom of the next page to customize assignments for your students.

Differentiated Instruction

AL ELL

If students have trouble solving Exercises 1–4,

Then suggest that they form groups of two or three to discuss the best strategy for solving each problem and then work through the solution together. Encourage all students to participate and remind students to check their solutions.

Lesson 6-4 Elimination Using Multiplication 357

Watch Out!

Find the Error For Exercise 30, tell students to look at the original system of equations before they evaluate Jason's and Daniela's work. Did they both find a way to eliminate one variable completely?

Additional Answers

26b.

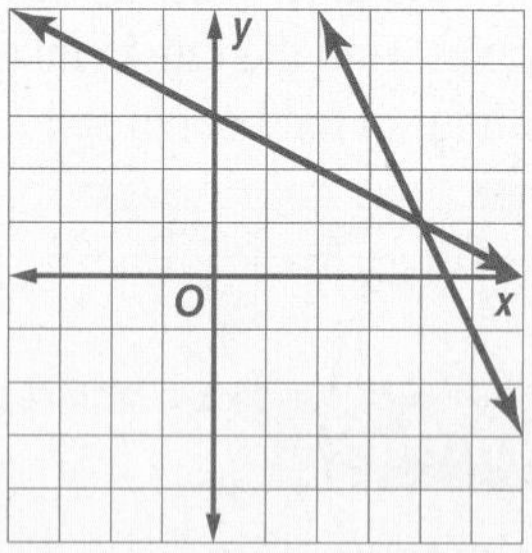

26c.

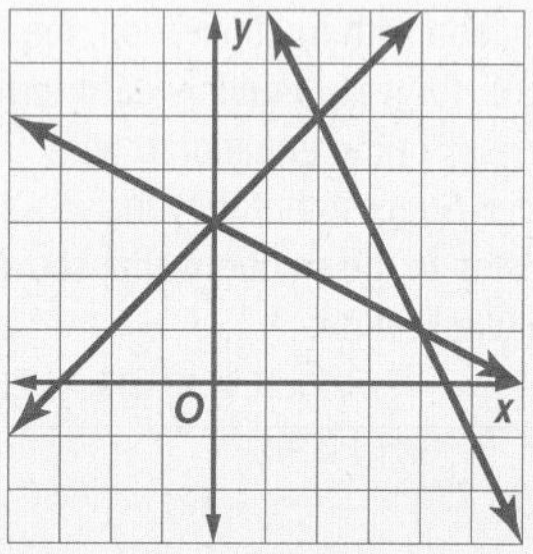

32. $a = -2, b = 22$; Substitute 3 for x and a for y in the first equation and then solve for a to get $a = -2$. Then substitute 3 for x and -2 for y in the second equation and simplify to get $b = 22$.

33. Sample answer: A variable that has a nonzero coefficient in each equation may be eliminated using multiplication. Calculations may be easier if a variable requiring only one equation to be multiplied or a variable with a smaller coefficient is eliminated.

Practice and Problem Solving

= **Step-by-Step Solutions** begin on page R12.
Extra Practice begins on page 815.

Examples 1 and 2
pp. 355–356

Use elimination to solve each system of equations.

7. $x + y = 2$
$-3x + 4y = 15$ **(−1, 3)**

8. $x - y = -8$
$7x + 5y = 16$ **(−2, 6)**

9. $x + 5y = 17$
$-4x + 3y = 24$ **(−3, 4)**

10. $6x + y = -39$
$3x + 2y = -15$ **(−7, 3)**

11. $2x + 5y = 11$
$4x + 3y = 1$ **(−2, 3)**

12. $3x - 3y = -6$
$-5x + 6y = 12$ **(0, 2)**

13. $3x + 4y = 29$
$6x + 5y = 43$ **(3, 5)**

14. $8x + 3y = 4$
$-7x + 5y = -34$ **(2, −4)**

15. $8x + 3y = -7$
$7x + 2y = -3$ **(1, −5)**

16. $4x + 7y = -80$
$3x + 5y = -58$ **(−6, −8)**

17. $12x - 3y = -3$
$6x + y = 1$ **(0, 1)**

18. $-4x + 2y = 0$
$10x + 3y = 8$ **$\left(\frac{1}{2}, 1\right)$**

19. 2, −5
20. 14 field goals; 7 extra points

Example 3
p. 357

19. **NUMBER THEORY** Seven times a number plus three times another number equals negative one. The sum of the two numbers is negative three. What are the numbers?

25c. (5, 5); To be cost-effective, the robots must save the time of 5 nurses and 5 support staff.

20. **FOOTBALL** A field goal is 3 points and the extra point after a touchdown is 1 point. In a recent post-season, Adam Vinatieri of the Indianapolis Colts made a total of 21 field goals and extra point kicks for 49 points. Find the number of field goals and extra points that he made.

B Use elimination to solve each system of equations.

21. $2.2x + 3y = 15.25$
$4.6x + 2.1y = 18.325$ **(2.5, 3.25)**

22. $-0.4x + 0.25y = -2.175$
$2x + y = 7.5$ **(4.5, −1.5)**

23. $\frac{1}{4}x + 4y = 2\frac{3}{4}$
$3x + \frac{1}{2}y = 9\frac{1}{4}$ **$\left(3, \frac{1}{2}\right)$**

24. $\frac{2}{5}x + 6y = 24\frac{1}{5}$
$3x + \frac{1}{2}y = 3\frac{1}{2}$ **$\left(\frac{1}{2}, 4\right)$**

Real-World Link

TOBOR, *robot* spelled backward, is a robot that delivers medications directly from the pharmacy to a patient's room. TOBOR can talk, detect when someone is blocking its path, and interface with an elevator.

Source: *U.S. Medicine Magazine*

25. **ROBOTS** TOBOR saves 120 minutes of a nurse's time n and 180 minutes of support staff time s each day. Another robot that aids stroke patients' limbs is estimated to save 90 minutes of nursing time and 120 minutes of support staff time each day.

a. To be cost effective, TOBOR must save a total of 1500 minutes per day. Write an equation that represents this relationship. **$120n + 180s = 1500$**

b. To make the stroke assistant cost effective, it must save a total of 1050 minutes per day. Write an equation that represents this relationship. **$90n + 120s = 1050$**

c. Solve the system of equations, and interpret the solution in the context of the situation.

26. **GEOMETRY** The graphs of $x + 2y = 6$ and $2x + y = 9$ contain two of the sides of a triangle. A vertex of the triangle is at the intersection of the graphs.

a. What are the coordinates of the vertex? **(4, 1)**

b. Draw the graph of the two lines. Identify the vertex of the triangle. **See margin.**

c. The line that forms the third side of the triangle is the line $x - y = -3$. Draw this line on the previous graph. **See margin.**

d. Name the other two vertices of the triangle. **(0, 3); (2, 5)**

Differentiated Homework Options

Level	Assignment	Two-Day Option	
AL Basic	7–20, 29–31, 33–54	7–19 odd, 34–37	8–20 even, 29–31, 33, 38–54
OL Core	7–25 odd, 26–31, 33–54	7–20, 34–37	21–31, 33, 38–54
BL Advanced	21–48, (optional: 49–54)		

Real-World Link

In addition to batting cages and miniature golf, many entertainment centers offer go-karts, bumper boats, and a video arcade.

Source: Camelot Park

27. ENTERTAINMENT At an entertainment center, two groups of people bought batting tokens and miniature golf games, as shown in the table.

Group	Number of Batting Tokens	Number of Miniature Golf Games	Total Cost
A	16	3	$30
B	22	5	$43

a. Define the variables, and write a system of linear equations from this situation.

b. Solve the system of equations, and explain what the solution represents.

28. TESTS Mrs. Henderson discovered that she had accidentally reversed the digits of a test score and did not give a student 36 points. Mrs. Henderson told the student that the sum of the digits was 14 and agreed to give the student his correct score plus extra credit if he could determine his actual score. What was his correct score? **95**

H.O.T. Problems Use Higher-Order Thinking Skills

29. REASONING Explain how you could recognize a system of linear equations with infinitely many solutions. **One of the equations will be a multiple of the other.**

30. FIND THE ERROR Jason and Daniela are solving a system of equations. Is either of them correct? Explain your reasoning.

Jason

$2r + 7t = 11$
$r - 9t = -7$

$2r + 7t = 11$
$(-)\ 2r - 18t = -14$
$25t = 25$
$t = 1$

$2r + 7t = 11$
$2r + 7(1) = 11$
$2r + 7 = 11$
$2r = 4$
$\frac{2r}{2} = \frac{4}{2}$
$r = 2$

The solution is (2, 1).

Daniela

$2r + 7t = 11$
$(-)\ r - 9t = -7$
$r = 18$

$2r + 7t = 11$
$2(18) + 7t = 11$
$36 + 7t = 11$
$7t = -25$
$\frac{7t}{7} = -\frac{25}{7}$
$t = -3.6$

The solution is (18, -3.6).

31. OPEN ENDED Write a system of equations that can be solved by multiplying one equation by −3 and then adding the two equations together.

32. CHALLENGE The solution of the system $4x + 5y = 2$ and $6x - 2y = b$ is $(3, a)$. Find the values of a and b. Discuss the steps that you used. **See margin.**

33. WRITING IN MATH Explain how to decide which variable to eliminate when using multiplication. **See margin.**

27a. Let x = the cost of a batting token and let y = the cost of a miniature golf game; $16x + 3y = 30$ and $22x + 5y = 43$.

27b. (1.5, 2); A batting token costs $1.50 and a game of miniature golf costs $2.00.

30. Jason; in order to eliminate the r-terms, you can multiply the second equation by 2 and then subtract, or multiply the equation by −2 and then add. Daniela did not subtract the equations correctly.

31. Sample answer: $2x + 3y = 6$, $4x + 9y = 5$

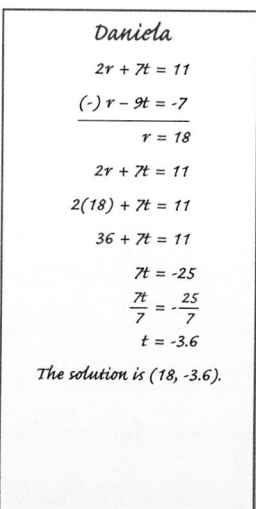

Study Guide and Intervention
CRM pp. 24–25 AL OL ELL

NAME ______ DATE ______ PERIOD ______

6-4 Study Guide and Intervention

Elimination Using Multiplication

Elimination Using Multiplication Some systems of equations cannot be solved simply by adding or subtracting the equations. In such cases, one or both equations must first be multiplied by a number before the system can be solved by elimination.

Example 1 Use elimination to solve the system of equations.
$x + 10y = 3$
$4x + 5y = 5$

If you multiply the second equation by −2, you can eliminate the y terms.

$x + 10y = 3$
$(+)\ -8x - 10y = -10$
$-7x = -7$
$\frac{7x}{-7} = \frac{-7}{-7}$
$x = 1$

Substitute 1 for x in either equation.

$1 + 10y = 3$
$1 + 10y - 1 = 3 - 1$
$10y = 2$
$\frac{10y}{10} = \frac{2}{10}$
$y = \frac{1}{5}$

The solution is $\left(1, \frac{1}{5}\right)$.

Example 2 Use elimination to solve the system of equations.
$3x - 2y = -7$
$2x - 5y = 10$

If you multiply the first equation by 2 and the second equation by −3, you can eliminate the x terms.

$6x - 4y = -14$
$(+)\ -6x + 15y = -30$
$11y = -44$
$\frac{11y}{11} = -\frac{44}{11}$
$y = -4$

Substitute −4 for y in either equation.

$3x - 2(-4) = -7$
$3x + 8 = -7$
$3x + 8 - 8 = -7 - 8$
$3x = -15$
$\frac{3x}{3} = -\frac{15}{3}$
$x = -5$

The solution is (−5, −4).

Exercises

Use elimination to solve each system of equations.

1. $2x + 3y = 6$, $x + 2y = 5$ **(−3, 4)**
2. $2m + 3n = 4$, $-m + 2n = 5$ **(−1, 2)**
3. $3a - b = 2$, $a + 2b = 3$ **(1, 1)**
4. $4x + 5y = 6$, $6x - 7y = -20$ **(−1, 2)**
5. $4x - 3y = 22$, $2x - y = 10$ **(4, −2)**
6. $3x - 4y = -4$, $x + 3y = -10$ **(−4, −2)**
7. $4x - y = 9$, $5x + 2y = 8$ **(2, −1)**
8. $4a - 3b = -8$, $2a + 2b = 3$ **$\left(-\frac{1}{2}, 2\right)$**
9. $2x + 2y = 5$, $4x - 4y = 10$ **$\left(\frac{5}{2}, 0\right)$**
10. $6x - 4y = -8$, $4x + 2y = -3$ **$\left(-1, \frac{1}{2}\right)$**
11. $4x + 2y = -5$, $-2x - 4y = 1$ **$\left(-\frac{3}{2}, \frac{1}{2}\right)$**
12. $2x + y = 3.5$, $-x + 2y = 2.5$ **(0.9, 1.7)**

13. **GARDENING** The length of Sally's garden is 4 meters greater than 3 times the width. The perimeter of her garden is 72 meters. What are the dimensions of Sally's garden? **28 m by 8 m**

Chapter 6 24 Glencoe Algebra 1

Practice
CRM p. 27 AL OL BL ELL

NAME ______ DATE ______ PERIOD ______

6-4 Practice

Elimination Using Multiplication

Use elimination to solve each system of equations.

1. $2x - y = -1$, $3x - 2y = 1$ **(−3, −5)**
2. $5x - 2y = -10$, $3x + 6y = 66$ **(2, 10)**
3. $7x + 4y = -4$, $5x + 8y = 28$ **(−4, 6)**
4. $2x - 4y = -22$, $3x + 3y = 30$ **(3, 7)**
5. $3x + 2y = -9$, $5x - 3y = 4$ **(−1, −3)**
6. $4x - 2y = 32$, $-3x - 5y = -11$ **(7, −2)**
7. $3x + 4y = 27$, $5x - 3y = 16$ **(5, 3)**
8. $0.5x + 0.5y = -2$, $x - 0.25y = 6$ **(4, −8)**
9. $2x - \frac{3}{4}y = -7$, $x + \frac{1}{2}y = 0$ **(−2, 4)**
10. $6x - 3y = 21$, $2x + 2y = 22$ **(6, 5)**
11. $3x + 2y = 11$, $2x + 6y = -2$ **(5, −2)**
12. $-3x + 2y = -15$, $2x - 4y = 26$ **(1, −6)**

13. Eight times a number plus five times another number is −13. The sum of the two numbers is 1. What are the numbers? **−6, 7**

14. Two times a number plus three times another number equals 4. Three times the first number plus four times the other number is 7. Find the numbers. **5, −2**

15. **FINANCE** Gunther invested $10,000 in two mutual funds. One of the funds rose 6% in one year, and the other rose 9% in one year. If Gunther's investment rose a total of $684 in one year, how much did he invest in each mutual fund? **$7200 in the 6% fund and $2800 in the 9% fund**

16. **CANOEING** Laura and Brent paddled a canoe 6 miles upstream in four hours. The return trip took three hours. Find the rate at which Laura and Brent paddled the canoe in still water. **1.75 mi/h**

17. **NUMBER THEORY** The sum of the digits of a two-digit number is 11. If the digits are reversed, the new number is 45 more than the original number. Find the number. **38**

Chapter 6 27 Glencoe Algebra 1

Word Problem Practice
CRM p. 28 AL OL BL ELL

NAME ______ DATE ______ PERIOD ______

6-4 Word Problem Practice

Elimination Using Multiplication

1. **SOCCER** Suppose a youth soccer field has a perimeter of 320 yards and its length measures 40 yards more than its width. Ms. Hughey asks her players to determine the length and width of their field. She gives them the following system of equations to represent the situation. Use elimination to solve the system to find the length and width of the field.

$2L + 2W = 320$
$L - W = 40$

width = 60 yd; length = 100 yd

2. **SPORTS** The Fan Cost Index (FCI) tracks the average costs for attending sporting events, including tickets, drinks, food, parking, programs, and souvenirs. According to the FCI, a family of four would spend a total of $592.30 to attend two Major League Baseball (MLB) games and one National Basketball Association (NBA) game. The family would spend $691.31 to attend one MLB and two NBA games. Write and solve a system of equations to find the family's costs for each kind of game according to the FCI. **NBA: $263.44; MLB: $164.43**

3. **ART** Mr. Santos, the curator of the children's museum, recently made two purchases of clay and wood for a visiting artist to sculpt. Use the table to find the cost of each product per kilogram.

Clay (kg)	Wood (kg)	Total Cost
5	4	$35.50
3.5	6	$50.45

Clay was $0.70 per kilogram and wood was $8.00 per kilogram.

4. **TRAVEL** Antonio flies from Houston to Philadelphia, a distance of about 1340 miles. His plane travels with the wind and takes 2 hours and 20 minutes. At the same time, Paul is on a plane from Philadelphia to Houston. Since his plane is heading against the wind, Paul's flight takes 2 hours and 50 minutes. What was the speed of the wind in miles per hour? **about 50.67 mph**

5. **BUSINESS** Suppose you start a business assembling and selling motorized scooters. It costs you $1500 for tools and equipment to get started, and the materials cost $200 for each scooter. Your scooters sell for $300 each.

a. Write and solve a system of equations representing the total costs and revenue of your business. **$y = 200x + 1500$ (cost); $y = 300x$ (revenue); solution: (15, 4500)**

b. Describe what the solution means in terms of the situation. **The solution represents the point at which cost equals revenue. This is the break-even point for the business owner.**

c. Give an example of a reasonable number of scooters you could assemble and sell in order to make a profit, and find the profit you would make for that number of scooters. **Sample answer: 20 scooters: It costs $5500 to assemble these scooters, which sell for $6000, leaving a $500 profit.**

Chapter 6 28 Glencoe Algebra 1

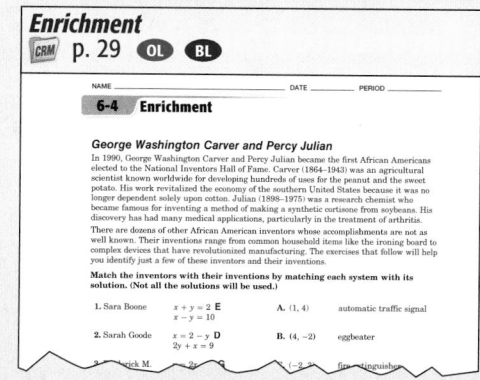

Enrichment
CRM p. 29 OL BL

NAME ______ DATE ______ PERIOD ______

6-4 Enrichment

George Washington Carver and Percy Julian

In 1990, George Washington Carver and Percy Julian became the first African Americans elected to the National Inventors Hall of Fame. Carver (1864–1943) was an agricultural scientist known worldwide for developing hundreds of uses for the peanut and the sweet potato. His work revitalized the economy of the southern United States because it was no longer dependent solely upon cotton. Julian (1898–1975) was a research chemist who became famous for inventing a method of making a synthetic cortisone from soybeans. His discovery has had many medical applications, particularly in the treatment of arthritis.

There are dozens of other African American inventors whose accomplishments are not as well known. Their inventions range from common household items like the ironing board to complex devices that have revolutionized manufacturing. The exercises that follow will help you identify just a few of these inventors and their inventions.

Match the inventors with their inventions by matching each system with its solution. (Not all the solutions will be used.)

1. Sara Boone	$x + y = 2$, $x - y = 10$ **E**	A. (1, 4)	automatic traffic signal
2. Sarah Goode	$x = 2 - y$, $2y + x = 9$ **D**	B. (4, −2)	eggbeater

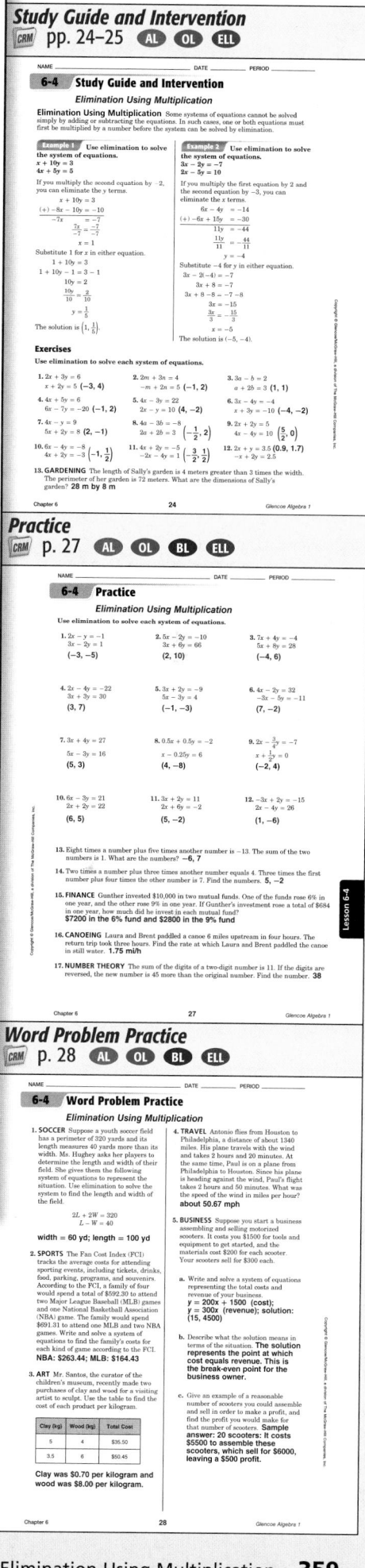

4 ASSESS

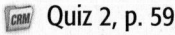

Crystal Ball Have students write how they think what they learned today about using multiplication before elimination to solve a system of equations will help them in the next lesson on applying systems of linear equations.

Formative Assessment

Check for student understanding of the concepts in Lessons 6-3 and 6-4.

CRM Quiz 2, p. 59

Additional Answers

45. $m \leq 13$ and $m \geq -3$

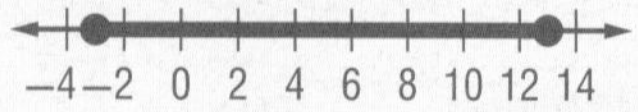

46. $q < -6$ and $q > -16$

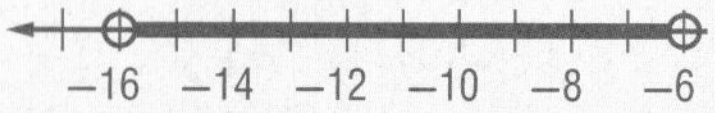

47. $w > 1$ or $w < -10$

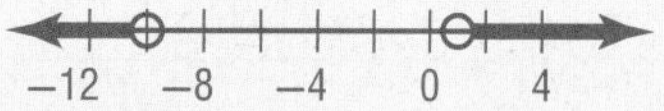

48. $r \geq 4$ or $r \leq -5$

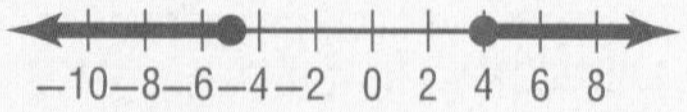

PSAE PRACTICE 8.11.17, 8.11.14, 6.11.17, 10.11.07

34. What is the solution of this system of equations? **C**

$2x - 3y = -9$

$-x + 3y = 6$

A $(3, 3)$ C $(-3, 1)$

B $(-3, 3)$ D $(1, -3)$

35. A buffet has one price for adults and another for children. The Taylor family has two adults and three children, and their bill was \$40.50. The Wong family has three adults and one child. Their bill was \$38. Which system of equations could be used to determine the price for an adult and for a child? **G**

F $x + y = 40.50$; $x + y = 38$ H $2x + 3y = 40.50$; $x + 3y = 38$

G $2x + 3y = 40.50$; $3x + y = 38$ J $2x + 2y = 40.50$; $3x + y = 38$

36. SHORT RESPONSE A customer at the paint store has ordered 3 gallons of ivy green paint. Melissa mixes the paint in a ratio of 3 parts blue to one part yellow. How many quarts of blue paint does she use? **9 qt**

37. PROBABILITY The table shows the results of a number cube being rolled. What is the experimental probability of rolling a 3? **D**

Outcome	Frequency
1	4
2	8
3	2
4	0
5	5
6	1

A $\frac{2}{3}$ B $\frac{1}{3}$ C 0.2 D 0.1

Spiral Review

Use elimination to solve each system of equations. (Lesson 6-3)

38. $f + g = -3$; $f - g = 1$ **(−1, −2)**

39. $6g + h = -7$; $6g + 3h = -9$ **(−1, −1)**

40. $5j + 3k = -9$; $3j + 3k = -3$ **(−3, 2)**

41. $2x - 4z = 6$; $x - 4z = -3$ **(9, 3)**

42. $-5c - 3v = 9$; $5c + 2v = -6$ **(0, −3)**

43. $4b - 6n = -36$; $3b - 6n = -36$ **(0, 6)**

44. JOBS Brandy and Adriana work at an after-school child care center. Together they cared for 32 children this week. Brandy cared for 0.6 times as many children as Adriana. How many children did each girl care for? (Lesson 6-2) **Brandy: 12; Adriana: 20**

Solve each inequality. Then graph the solution set. (Lesson 5-5) **45–48. See margin.**

45. $|m - 5| \leq 8$ **46.** $|q + 11| < 5$ **47.** $|2w + 9| > 11$ **48.** $|2r + 1| \geq 9$

Skills Review

Translate each sentence into a formula. (Lesson 2-1)

49. The area A of a triangle equals one half times the base b times the height h. $A = \frac{1}{2}bh$

50. The circumference C of a circle equals the product of 2, π, and the radius r. $C = 2\pi r$

51. The volume V of a rectangular box is the length ℓ times the width w multiplied by the height h. $V = \ell wh$

52. The volume of a cylinder V is the same as the product of π and the radius r to the second power multiplied by the height h. $V = \pi r^2 h$

53. The area of a circle A equals the product of π and the radius r squared. $A = \pi r^2$

54. Acceleration A equals the increase in speed s divided by time t in seconds. $A = \frac{s}{t}$

Differentiated Instruction OL BL

Extension Have students solve this system or a similar system using elimination.

$\frac{1}{2}x - \frac{2}{3}y = \frac{7}{3}$

$\frac{3}{2}x + 2y = -25$

$(-6, -8)$

360 Chapter 6 Systems of Linear Equations and Inequalities

IL Learning Standards
8.B.4a

Use the graph to determine whether each system is *consistent* or *inconsistent* and if it is *independent* or *dependent*.

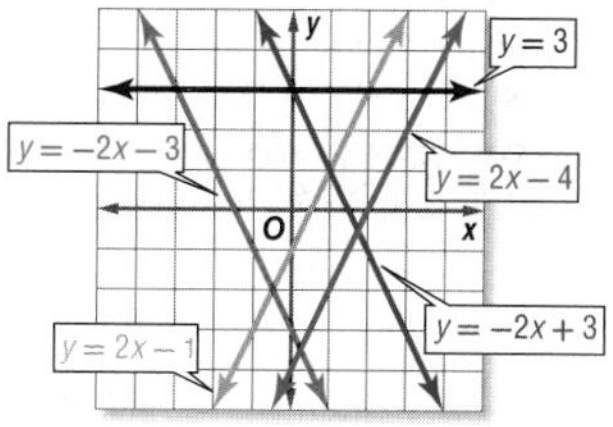

1. $y = 2x - 1$
   $y = -2x + 3$
   consistent, independent
2. $y = -2x + 3$
   $y = -2x - 3$
   inconsistent

Graph each system and determine the number of solutions that it has. If it has one solution, name it.

3. $y = 2x - 3$ (7, 11)
   $y = x + 4$
4. $x + y = 6$ (5, 1)
   $x - y = 4$
5. $x + y = 8$ infinitely many solutions
   $3x + 3y = 24$
6. $x - 4y = -6$ (−10, −1)
   $y = -1$
7. $3x + 2y = 12$ no solutions
   $3x + 2y = 6$
8. $2x + y = -4$ (−6, 8)
   $5x + 3y = -6$

3–8. See Ch. 6 Answer Appendix for graphs.

Use substitution to solve each system of equations.

9. $y = x + 4$ (4, 8)
   $2x + y = 16$
10. $y = -2x - 3$ (−12, 21)
    $x + y = 9$
11. $x + y = 6$ (7, −1)
    $x - y = 8$
12. $y = -4x$ (3, −12)
    $6x - y = 30$

13. **FOOD** The cost of two meals at a restaurant is shown in the table below.

Meal	Total Cost
3 tacos, 2 burritos	\$7.40
4 tacos, 1 burrito	\$6.45

a. Define variables to represent the cost of a taco and the cost of a burrito. a–c. See margin.

b. Write a system of equations to find the cost of a single taco and a single burrito.

c. Solve the systems of equations, and explain what the solution means.

d. How much would a customer pay for 2 tacos and 2 burritos? \$6.30

14. **AMUSEMENT PARKS** The cost of two groups going to an amusement park is shown in the table. a–c. See Ch. 6 Answer Appendix.

Group	Total Cost
4 adults, 2 children	\$184
4 adults, 3 children	\$200

a. Define variables to represent the cost of an adult ticket and the cost of a child ticket.

b. Write a system of equations to find the cost of an adult ticket and a child ticket.

c. Solve the system of equations, and explain what the solution means.

d. How much will a group of 3 adults and 5 children be charged for admission? \$194

15. **MULTIPLE CHOICE** Angelina needs to buy 12 pieces of candy to take to a meeting. She has \$16. Each chocolate bar costs \$2, and each lollipop costs \$1. Determine how many of each she can buy. B

A 6 chocolate bars, 6 lollipops

B 4 chocolate bars, 8 lollipops

C 7 chocolate bars, 5 lollipops

D 3 chocolate bars, 9 lollipops

Use elimination to solve each system of equations.

16. $x + y = 9$ (3, 6)
    $x - y = -3$
17. $x + 3y = 11$ (5, 2)
    $x + 7y = 19$
18. $9x - 24y = -6$ (2, 1)
    $3x + 4y = 10$
19. $-5x + 2y = -11$ (3, 2)
    $5x - 7y = 1$

20. **MULTIPLE CHOICE** The Blue Mountain High School Drama Club is selling tickets to their spring musical. Adult tickets are \$4 and student tickets are \$1. A total of 285 tickets are sold for \$765. How many of each type of ticket are sold? J

F 145 adult, 140 student

G 120 adult, 165 student

H 180 adult, 105 student

J 160 adult, 125 student

CHAPTER 6 Mid-Chapter Quiz

Formative Assessment

Use the Mid-Chapter Quiz to assess students' progress in the first half of the chapter.

For problems answered incorrectly, have students review the lessons indicated in parentheses.

ExamView Assessment Suite Customize and create multiple versions of your Mid-Chapter Quiz and their answer keys.

FOLDABLES® Follow-Up

Before students complete the Mid-Chapter Quiz, encourage them to review the information for Lessons 6-1 through 6-4 in their Foldables.

Additional Answers

13a. Let t = the cost of a taco and b = the cost of a burrito.

13b. $3t + 2b = 7.4$
$4t + b = 6.45$

13c. (1.10, 2.05); The cost of a single taco is \$1.10, and the cost of a single burrito is \$2.05.

Intervention Planner

Tier 1 On Level	Tier 2 Strategic Intervention approaching grade level	Tier 3 Intensive Intervention 2 or more grades below level
If students miss about 25% of the exercises or less,	**If** students miss about 50% of the exercises,	**If** students miss about 75% of the exercises,
Then choose a resource:	**Then** choose a resource:	**Then** use *Math Triumphs, Alg. 1*
SE Lessons 6-1, 6-2, 6-3, and 6-4 **CRM** Skills Practice, pp. 7, 14, 20, and 26 **TE** Chapter Project, p. 330	**CRM** Study Guide and Intervention, Chapter 6, pp. 5, 12, 18, 24 *Quick Review Math Handbook*	
IL Math Online Self-Check Quiz	IL Math Online Extra Examples, Personal Tutor, Homework Help	IL Math Online Extra Examples, Personal Tutor, Homework Help, Review Vocabulary

6-5 Lesson Notes

1 FOCUS

Vertical Alignment

Before Lesson 6-5
Solve systems of equations by using substitution and elimination.

Lesson 6-5
Determine the best method for solving systems of equations.
Apply systems of equations.

After Lesson 6-5
Use matrices to solve systems of equations.

2 TEACH

Scaffolding Questions

Have students read the *Why?* section of the lesson.

Ask:

- What do the variables *x* and *y* represent in the problem? The length of the official track is represented by *x* and the length of the short track by *y* in meters.
- What method could you use to solve the system? substitution or elimination

6-5 Applying Systems of Linear Equations

Then
You solved systems of equations by using substitution and elimination.
(Lessons 6-2, 6-3, and 6-4)

Now
- Determine the best method for solving systems of equations.
- Apply systems of equations.

IL Learning Standards
8.B.4a Represent algebraic concepts with physical materials, words, diagrams, tables, graphs, equations and inequalities and use appropriate technology.

IL Math Online
glencoe.com
- Extra Examples
- Personal Tutor
- Self-Check Quiz
- Homework Help

Why?

In speed skating, competitors race two at a time on a double track. Indoor speed skating rinks have two track sizes for race events: an official track and a short track.

Speed Skating Tracks	
official track	x
short track	y

The total length of the two tracks is 511 meters. The official track is 44 meters less than four times the short track. The total length is represented by $x + y = 511$. The length of the official track is represented by $x = 4y - 44$.

You can solve the system of equations to find the length of each track.

Determine the Best Method You have learned five methods for solving systems of linear equations. The table summarizes the methods and the types of systems for which each method works best.

Concept Summary — Solving Systems of Equations — For Your FOLDABLE

Method	The Best Time to Use
Graphing	To estimate solutions, since graphing usually does not give an exact solution.
Substitution	If one of the variables in either equation has a coefficient of 1 or −1.
Elimination Using Addition	If one of the variables has opposite coefficients in the two equations.
Elimination Using Subtraction	If one of the variables has the same coefficient in the two equations.
Elimination Using Multiplication	If none of the coefficients are 1 or −1 and neither of the variables can be eliminated by simply adding or subtracting the equations.

Substitution and elimination are algebraic methods for solving systems of equations. An algebraic method is best for an exact solution. Graphing, with or without technology, is a good way to estimate a solution.

Lesson 6-5 Resources

Resource	Approaching-Level	On-Level	Beyond-Level	English Learners
Teacher Edition	• Differentiated Instruction, p. 364	• Differentiated Instruction, pp. 364, 367	• Differentiated Instruction, p. 367	• Differentiated Instruction, p. 364
Chapter Resource Masters	• Study Guide and Intervention, pp. 30–31 • Skills Practice, p. 32 • Practice, p. 33 • Word Problem Practice, p. 34	• Study Guide and Intervention, pp. 30–31 • Skills Practice, p. 32 • Practice, p. 33 • Word Problem Practice, p. 34 • Enrichment, p. 35	• Practice, p. 33 • Word Problem Practice, p. 34 • Enrichment, p. 35	• Study Guide and Intervention, pp. 30–31 • Skills Practice, p. 32 • Practice, p. 33
Transparencies	• 5-Minute Check Transparency 6-5	• 5-Minute Check Transparency 6-5	• 5-Minute Check Transparency 6-5	• 5-Minute Check Transparency 6-5
Other	• Study Notebook	• Study Notebook	• Study Notebook	• Study Notebook

EXAMPLE 1 Choose the Best Method

Determine the best method to solve the system of equations. Then solve the system.

$4x - 4y = 8$
$-8x + y = 19$

Understand To determine the best method to solve the system of equations, look closely at the coefficients of each term.

Plan Neither the coefficients of x nor y are the same or additive inverses, so you cannot add or subtract to eliminate a variable. Since the coefficient of y in the second equation is 1, you can use substitution.

Solve First, solve the second equation for y.

$-8x + y = 19$	**Second equation**
$-8x + y + 8x = 19 + 8x$	**Add 8x to each side.**
$y = 19 + 8x$	**Simplify.**

Next, substitute $19 + 8x$ for y in the first equation.

$4x - 4y = 8$	**First equation**
$4x - 4(19 + 8x) = 8$	**Substitution**
$4x - 76 - 32x = 8$	**Distributive Property**
$-28x - 76 = 8$	**Simplify.**
$-28x - 76 + 76 = 8 + 76$	**Add 76 to each side.**
$-28x = 84$	**Simplify.**
$\frac{-28x}{-28} = \frac{84}{-28}$	**Divide each side by −28.**
$x = -3$	**Simplify.**

Last, substitute -3 for x in the second equation.

$-8x + y = 19$	**Second equation**
$-8(-3) + y = 19$	**$x = -3$**
$y = -5$	**Simplify.**

The solution of the system of equations is $(-3, -5)$.

Check Use a graphing calculator to check your solution. If your algebraic solution is correct, then the graphs will intersect at $(-3, -5)$.

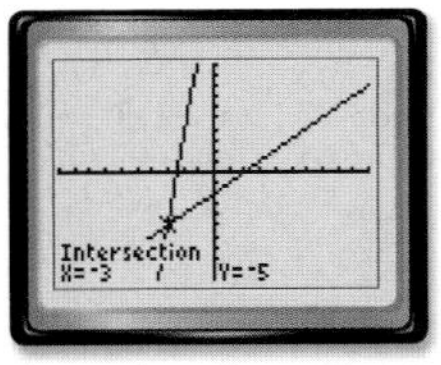

[−10, 10] scl: 1 [−10, 10] scl: 1

Check Your Progress

1A. $5x + 7y = 2$ elimination (−); (−1, 1)
$-2x + 7y = 9$

1B. $3x - 4y = -10$ elimination (×); (−2, 1)
$5x + 8y = -2$

1C. $x - y = 9$ elimination (+); (2, −7)
$7x + y = 7$

1D. $5x - y = 17$ substitution; (3, −2)
$3x + 2y = 5$

Personal Tutor glencoe.com

StudyTip

Alternate Method The system of equations in Example 1 can also be solved by using elimination with multiplication. You can multiply the first equation by 2 and then add to eliminate the x-term.

Determine the Best Method

Example 1 shows how to determine the best method to use in solving a system of equations.

Formative Assessment

Use the Check Your Progress exercises after each example to determine students' understanding of concepts.

Additional Example

1 Determine the best method to solve the system of equations. Then solve the system.

$2x + 3y = 23$
$4x + 2y = 34$

The best method is elimination using multiplication. The solution is (7, 3).

Additional Examples also in Interactive Classroom PowerPoint® Presentations

IWB INTERACTIVE WHITEBOARD READY

Tips for New Teachers

Reasoning Encourage students to take time to plan a problem-solving strategy before starting calculations. Advise students that taking this time may provide them with insight into the best strategy.

TEACH with TECH

DIGITAL CAMERA Have students find the capacity of the memory card in their camera, and the file size of photos of different resolutions. Use this information to create an in class example. For example, if the camera has 64MB of memory and photos can be either 2MB or 3MB, have students find the number of each type of photo that can be taken to have a total of 30 photos and fill the memory card.

Focus on Mathematical Content

Best Method for Solving a System of Equations Systems of equations can be solved by graphing, substitution, or elimination. Graphing can be used to approximate a solution and to provide a visual model of the problem. To find an exact solution, substitution or elimination should be used. Use substitution if one of the variables has a 1 or −1 for its coefficient. Use elimination with addition if the coefficients of one of the variables are opposites. Use elimination with subtraction if the coefficients of one of the variables are the same. Use elimination with multiplication in all other situations.

Lesson 6-5 Applying Systems of Linear Equations 363

Apply Systems of Linear Equations

Example 2 shows how to solve a real-world problem by writing and solving a system of equations.

Additional Example

2 **CAR RENTAL** Ace Car Rental rents a car for \$45 and \$0.25 per mile. Star Car Rental rents a car for \$35 and \$0.30 per mile. How many miles would a driver need to drive before the cost of renting a car at Ace Car Rental and renting a car at Star Car Rental were the same?

Let x = number of miles and y = cost of renting car.
$y = 45 + 0.25x$
$y = 35 + 0.30x$
The solution is (200, 95). This means that when the car has been driven 200 miles, the cost of renting a car will be the same (\$95) at both rental companies.

Real-World Link

Four species of penguins are on the endangered species list. The colonies of penguins that live closest to human inhabitants are the most at risk for extinction.

Source: PBS

Apply Systems of Linear Equations When applying systems of linear equations to problems, it is important to analyze each solution in the context of the situation.

Real-World EXAMPLE 2 Apply Systems of Linear Equations

PENGUINS Of the 17 species of penguins in the world, the largest species is the emperor penguin. One of the smallest is the Galapagos penguin. The total height of the two penguins is 169 centimeters. The emperor penguin is 22 centimeters more than twice the height of the Galapagos penguin. Find the height of each penguin.

The total height of the two species can be represented by $p + g = 169$, where p represents the height of the emperor penguin and g the height of the Galapagos penguin. Next write an equation to represent the height of the emperor penguin.

Words	The emperor penguin	is	22 centimeters	more than	twice the height of the Galapagos penguin.
Variables	Let p = the height of the emperor penguin and g = the height of the Galapagos penguin.				
Equation	p	$=$	22	$+$	$2g$

First rewrite the second equation.

$p = 22 + 2g$ **Second equation**
$p - 2g = 22$ **Subtract 2g from each side.**

You can use elimination by subtraction to solve this system of equations.

$p + g = 169$ **First equation**
$(-)\ p - 2g = 22$ **Subtract the second equation.**
$3g = 147$ **Eliminate p.**
$\frac{3g}{3} = \frac{147}{3}$ **Divide each side by 3.**
$g = 49$ **Simplify.**

Next substitute 49 for g in one of the equations.

$p = 22 + 2g$ **Second equation**
$= 22 + 2(49)$ **g = 49**
$= 120$ **Simplify.**

The height of the emperor penguin is 120 centimeters, and the height of the Galapagos penguin is 49 centimeters.

Does the solution make sense in the context of the problem?
Check by verifying the given information. The penguins' heights added together would be 120 + 49 or 169 centimeters and 22 + 2(49) is 120 centimeters.

Check Your Progress

2. VOLUNTEERING Jared has volunteered 50 hours and plans to volunteer 3 hours in each coming week. Clementine is a new volunteer who plans to volunteer 5 hours each week. Write and solve a system of equations to find how long it will be before they will have volunteered the same number of hours.
$y = 50 + 3x$, $y = 5x$; 25 wk

Personal Tutor glencoe.com

Differentiated Instruction
AL OL ELL

If students have trouble writing the necessary equations for a system in a real-world situation,

Then give them these steps to help them explore, plan, solve, and check.

- Determine the question.
- Describe the variables used for the unknowns.
- Translate the conditions in the problem into two equations.
- Solve the system by the best method.
- Analyze the solution in the context of the situation.

Check Your Understanding

Example 1 p. 363

1. elim (×); (2, −5)
2. subst.; (−3, 5)

Determine the best method to solve each system of equations. Then solve the system.

1. $2x + 3y = -11$, $-8x - 5y = 9$

2. $3x + 4y = 11$, $2x + y = -1$

3. $3x - 4y = -5$, $-3x + 2y = 3$

4. $3x + 7y = 4$, $5x - 7y = -12$

Example 2 p. 364

3. elim (+); $\left(-\frac{1}{3}, 1\right)$
4. elim (+); (−1, 1)

5. SHOPPING At a sale, Salazar bought 4 T-shirts and 3 pairs of jeans for $181. At the same store, Jenna bought 1 T-shirt and 2 pairs of jeans for $94. The T-shirts were all the same price, and the jeans were all the same price.

a. Write a system of equations that can be used to represent this situation. See margin.

b. Determine the best method to solve the system of equations. substitution

c. Solve the system. Each T-shirt cost $16 and each pair of jeans cost $39.

Practice and Problem Solving

● = **Step-by-Step Solutions** begin on page R12.
Extra Practice begins on page 815.

Example 1 p. 363

Determine the best method to solve each system of equations. Then solve the system. 6–11. See margin.

12. Sample answer: $3s + 5p = 233$ and $s = p + 11$; (25, 36); Denzell sold 25 pizzas and 36 subs.

6. $-3x + y = -3$, $4x + 2y = 14$

7. $2x + 6y = -8$, $x - 3y = 8$

8. $3x - 4y = -5$, $-3x - 6y = -5$

9. $5x + 8y = 1$, $-2x + 8y = -6$

10. $y + 4x = 3$, $y = -4x - 1$

11. $-5x + 4y = 7$, $-5x - 3y = -14$

Example 2 p. 364

13. $m + t = 40$ and $m = 3t - 4$; 29 movies, 11 television shows

12. FINANCIAL LITERACY For a Future Teachers of America fundraiser, Denzell sold food as shown in the table. He sold 11 more subs than pizzas and earned a total of $233. Write and solve a system of equations to represent this situation. Then describe what the solution means.

Item	Selling Price
pizza	$5.00
sub	$3.00

13. DVDs Manuela has a total of 40 DVDs of movies and television shows. The number of movies is 4 less than 3 times the number of television shows. Write and solve a system of equations to find the numbers of movies and television shows that she has on DVD.

14. CAVES The Caverns of Sonora have two different tours: the Crystal Palace tour and the Horseshoe Lake tour. The total length of both tours is 3.25 miles. The Crystal Palace tour is a half-mile less than twice the distance of the Horseshoe Lake tour. Determine the length of each tour. See margin.

15. YEARBOOKS The *break-even point* is the point at which income equals expenses. Ridgemont High School is paying $13,200 for the writing and research of their yearbook plus a printing fee of $25 per book. If they sell the books for $40 each, how many will they have to sell to break even? Explain. See margin.

Real-World Link

Anyone can create their own yearbook using the Internet and layout software. The yearbook is all in color, and you can order exactly as many as you need and order more anytime you want.

Source: dotPhoto Inc

16. PAINTBALL Clara and her friends are planning a trip to a paintball park. Find the cost of lunch and the cost of each paintball. What would be the cost for 400 paintballs and lunch? The cost of lunch is $8.33 and the cost of each paintball is $0.03. The cost of 400 paintballs and lunch would be $20.33.

PAINTBALL IN THE PARK
- $25 for 500 paintballs
- $15 for 200 paintballs

Lunch is included

3 PRACTICE

Formative Assessment

Use Exercises 1–5 to check for understanding.

Use the chart at the bottom of this page to customize assignments for your students.

Watch Out!

Preventing Errors Students frequently do not understand what their answers mean in the context of the problem. Stress that they should go back and read the problem again to make sure they have answered the question. It is also helpful to have them give their answers to a word problem in sentence form.

Additional Answers

5a. $4t + 3j = 181$; $t + 2j = 94$

6. subst.; (2, 3)

7. subst.; (2, −2)

8. elim (+); $\left(-\frac{1}{3}, 1\right)$

9. elim (−); $\left(1, -\frac{1}{2}\right)$

10. subst.; no solution

11. elim (−); (1, 3)

14. Horseshoe Lake = 1.25 mi, Crystal Palace = 2 mi

15. 880 books; If they sell this number, then their income and expenses both equal $35,200

Differentiated Homework Options

Level	Assignment	Two-Day Option	
AL Basic	6–15, 21–22, 24–44	7–15 odd, 27–30	6–14 even, 21–22, 24–26, 31–44
OL Core	7–15 odd, 16–22, 24–44	6–15, 27–30	16–22, 24–26, 31–44
BL Advanced	16–38, (optional: 39–44)		

Study Guide and Intervention

CRM pp. 30–31 AL OL ELL

NAME ________ DATE ________ PERIOD ________

6-5 Study Guide and Intervention

Applying Systems of Linear Equations

Determine The Best Method You have learned five methods for solving systems of linear equations: graphing, substitution, elimination using addition, elimination using subtraction, and elimination using multiplication. For an exact solution, an algebraic method is best.

Example At a baseball game, Henry bought 3 hotdogs and a bag of chips for $14. Scott bought 2 hotdogs and a bag of chips for $10. Each of the boys paid the same price for their hotdogs, and the same price for their chips. The following system of equations can be used to represent the situation. Determine the best method to solve the system of equations. Then solve the system.

$3x + y = 14$
$2x + y = 10$

- Since neither the coefficients of x nor the coefficients of y are additive inverses, you cannot use elimination using addition.
- Since the coefficient of y in both equations is 1, you can use elimination using subtraction. You could also use the substitution method or elimination using multiplication

The following solution uses elimination by subtraction to solve this system.

$3x + y = 14$ Write the equations in column form and subtract.
$(-)\ 2x + (-)\ y = (-)10$
$x = 4$ The variable y is eliminated.
$3(4) + y = 14$ Substitute the value for x back into the first equation.
$y = 2$ Solve for y.

This means that hot dogs cost $4 each and a bag of chips costs $2.

Exercises

Determine the best method to solve each system of equations. Then solve the system.

1. $5x + 3y = 16$, $3x - 5y = -4$ **elimination (×); (2, 2)**
2. $3x - 5y = 7$, $2x + 5y = 13$ **elimination (+); (4, 1)**
3. $y + 3x = 24$, $5x - y = 8$ **elimination (+); (4, 12)**
4. $-11x - 10y = 17$, $5x - 7y = 50$ **elimination (×); (3, −5)**

Chapter 6 30 Glencoe Algebra 1

Practice

CRM p. 33 AL OL BL ELL

NAME ________ DATE ________ PERIOD ________

6-5 Practice

Applying Systems of Linear Equations

Determine the best method to solve each system of equations. Then solve the system.

1. $1.5x - 1.9y = -29$, $x - 0.9y = 4.5$ **substitution; (63, 65)**
2. $1.2x - 0.8y = -6$, $4.8x + 2.4y = 60$ **elimination (×); (5, 15)**
3. $18x - 16y = -312$, $78x - 16y = 408$ **elimination (−); (12, 33)**
4. $14x + 7y = 217$, $14x + 3y = 189$ **elimination (−); (12, 7)**
5. $x = 3.6y + 0.7$, $2x + 0.2y = 38.4$ **substitution; (18.7, 5)**
6. $5.3x - 4y = 43.5$, $x + 7y = 78$ **substitution; (15, 9)**

7. BOOKS A library contains 2000 books. There are 3 times as many non-fiction books as fiction books. Write and solve a system of equations to determine the number of non-fiction and fiction books. **$x + y = 2000$ and $x = 3y$; 1500 non-fiction, 500 fiction**

8. SCHOOL CLUBS The chess club has 16 members and gains a new member every month. The film club has 4 members and gains 4 new members every month. Write and solve a system of equations to find when the number of members in both clubs will be equal. **$y = 16 + x$ and $y = 4 + 4x$; 4 months**

9. Tia and Ken each sold snack bars and magazine subscriptions for a school fund-raiser, as shown in the table. Tia earned $132 and Ken earned $190.

Item	Number Sold: Tia	Number Sold: Ken
snack bars	16	20
magazine subscriptions	4	6

a. Define variable and formulate a system of linear equation from this situation. **Let x = the cost per snack bar and let y = the cost per magazine subscriptions; $16x + 4y = 132$ and $20x + 6y = 190$.**

b. What was the price per snack bar? Determine the reasonableness of your solution. **$2**

Chapter 6 33 Glencoe Algebra 1

Lesson 6-5

Word Problem Practice

CRM p. 34 AL OL BL ELL

NAME ________ DATE ________ PERIOD ________

6-5 Word Problem Practice

Applying Systems of Linear Equations

1. MONEY Veronica has been saving dimes and quarters. She has 94 coins in all, and the total value is $19.30. How many dimes and how many quarters does she have? **28 dimes; 66 quarters**

2. CHEMISTRY How many liters of 15% acid and 33% acid should be mixed to make 40 liters of 21% acid solution?

Concentration of Solution	Amount of Solution (L)	Amount of Acid
15%	x	
33%	y	
21%	40	

$26\frac{2}{3}$ L of 15%; $13\frac{1}{3}$ L of 33%

3. BUILDINGS The Sears Tower in Chicago is the tallest building in North America. The total height of the tower t and the antenna that stands on top of it a is 1729 feet. The difference in heights between the building and the antenna is 279 feet. How tall is the Sears Tower? **1450 ft**

4. PRODUCE Roger and Trevor went shopping for produce on the same day. They each bought some apples and some potatoes. The amount they bought and the total price they paid are listed in the table below.

	Apples (lb)	Potatoes (lb)	Total Cost ($)
Roger	8	7	18.85
Trevor	2	10	12.88

What was the price of apples and potatoes per pound? **Apples: $1.49 per lb; Potatoes: $0.99 per lb**

5. SHOPPING Two stores are having a sale on T-shirts that normally sell for $20. Store S is advertising an s percent discount, and Store T is advertising a t dollar discount. Rose spends $63 for three T-shirts from Store S and one from Store T. Manny spends $140 on five T-shirts from Store S and four from Store T. Find the discount at each store. **Store S: 20%; Store T: $5**

6. TRANSPORTATION A Speedy River barge bound for New Orleans leaves Baton Rouge, Louisiana, at 9:00 A.M. and travels at a speed of 10 miles per hour. A Rail Transport freight train also bound for New Orleans leaves Baton Rouge at 1:30 P.M. the same day. The train travels at 25 miles per hour, and the river barge travels at 10 miles per hour. Both the barge and the train will travel 100 miles to reach New Orleans.

a. How far will the train travel before catching up to the barge? **75 mi**

b. Which shipment will reach New Orleans first? At what time? **The train will arrive first. It will arrive in New Orleans at 5:30 P.M. of the same day.**

c. If both shipments take an hour to unload before heading back to Baton Rouge, what is the earliest time that either one of the companies can begin to load grain to ship in Baton Rouge? **at 10:30 P.M. the same day**

Chapter 6 34 Glencoe Algebra 1

Real-World Link

There are many things for teenagers at a library besides books. Public libraries may have DVDs of new movies, current music, free Internet access, magazines, free online homework help, and SAT workshops.

Source: MSN Encarta

17a. Let x = the cost per pound of aluminum cans, and let y = the cost per pound of newspaper; $9x + 26y = 3.77$ and $9x + 114y = 4.65$.

22. Sample answer: You should always check that the answer makes sense in the context of the original problem. If it does not, you may have made an incorrect calculation. If (−1, 7) was the solution, then it is probably incorrect, since time in this case cannot be a negative number. The solution should be recalculated.

25. The third system; this system is the only one that is not a system of linear equations.

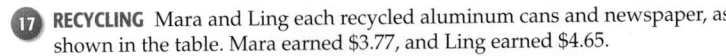

17. RECYCLING Mara and Ling each recycled aluminum cans and newspaper, as shown in the table. Mara earned $3.77, and Ling earned $4.65.

Materials	Pounds Recycled: Mara	Pounds Recycled: Ling
aluminum cans	9	9
newspaper	26	114

a. Define variables and write a system of linear equations from this situation.

b. What was the price per pound of aluminum? Determine the reasonableness of your solution. **$0.39; This solution is reasonable.**

18. BOOKS The library is having a book sale. Hardcover books sell for $4 each, and paperback books are $2 each. If Connie spends $26 for 8 books, how many hardcover books did she buy? **5**

19. MUSIC An online music club offers individual songs for one price or entire albums for another. Kendrick pays $14.90 to download 5 individual songs and 1 album. Geoffrey pays $21.75 to download 3 individual songs and 2 albums.

a. How much does the music club charge to download a song? **$1.15**

b. How much does the music club charge to download an entire album? **$9.15**

20. DRIVING Malik drove his car for 45 miles at an average speed of r miles per hour. On the return trip, traffic has increased, and Malik's average speed is $\frac{3}{4}r$. The round trip took a total of 1 hour and 45 minutes. Find the average speed for each portion of the trip. **first portion: 60 mph; second portion: 45 mph**

H.O.T. Problems

Use Higher-Order Thinking Skills

21. OPEN ENDED Formulate a system of equations that represents a situation in your school. Describe the method that you would use to solve the system. Then solve the system and explain what the solution means. **See margin.**

22. REASONING In a system of equations, x represents the time spent riding a bike, and y represents the distance traveled. You determine the solution to be $(-1, 7)$. Use this problem to discuss the importance of analyzing solutions in the context of real-world problems.

23. CHALLENGE Solve the following system of equations by using three different methods. Show your work. **See margin.**

$$4x + y = 13$$
$$6x - y = 7$$

24. WRITE A QUESTION A classmate says that elimination is the best way to solve a system of equations. Write a question to challenge his conjecture. **See margin.**

25. WHICH ONE DOESN'T BELONG? Which system is different? Explain.

$x - y = 3$, $x + \frac{1}{2}y = 1$	$-x + y = 0$, $5x = 2y$	$y = x - 4$, $y = \frac{2}{x}$	$y = x + 1$, $y = 3x$

26. WRITING IN MATH Explain when graphing would be the best method of solving a system of equations. When would solving a system of equations algebraically be the best method? **See margin.**

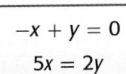

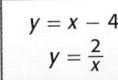

Enrichment

CRM p. 35 OL BL

NAME ________ DATE ________ PERIOD ________

6-5 Enrichment

Cramer's Rule

Cramer's Rule is a method for solving a system of equations. To use Cramer's Rule, set up a matrix to represent the equations. A matrix is a way of organizing data.

Example Solve the following system of equations using Cramer's Rule.
$2x + 3y = 13$
$x + y = 5$

Step 1: Set up a matrix representing the coefficients of x and y.

$A = \begin{vmatrix} 2 & 3 \\ 1 & 1 \end{vmatrix}$

Step 2: Find the determinant of matrix A.

If a matrix $A = \begin{vmatrix} a & b \\ c & d \end{vmatrix}$, then the determinant, $\det(A) = ad - bc$.

$\det(A) = 2(1) - 1(3) = -1$

Step 3: Replace the first column in A with 13 and 5 and find the determinant of the new matrix.

Additional Answer

21. Sample answer: $x + y = 12$ and $3x + 2y = 29$, where x represents the cost of a student ticket for the basketball game and y represents the cost of an adult ticket; substitution could be used to solve the system; (5, 7) means the cost of a student ticket is $5 and the cost of an adult ticket is $7.

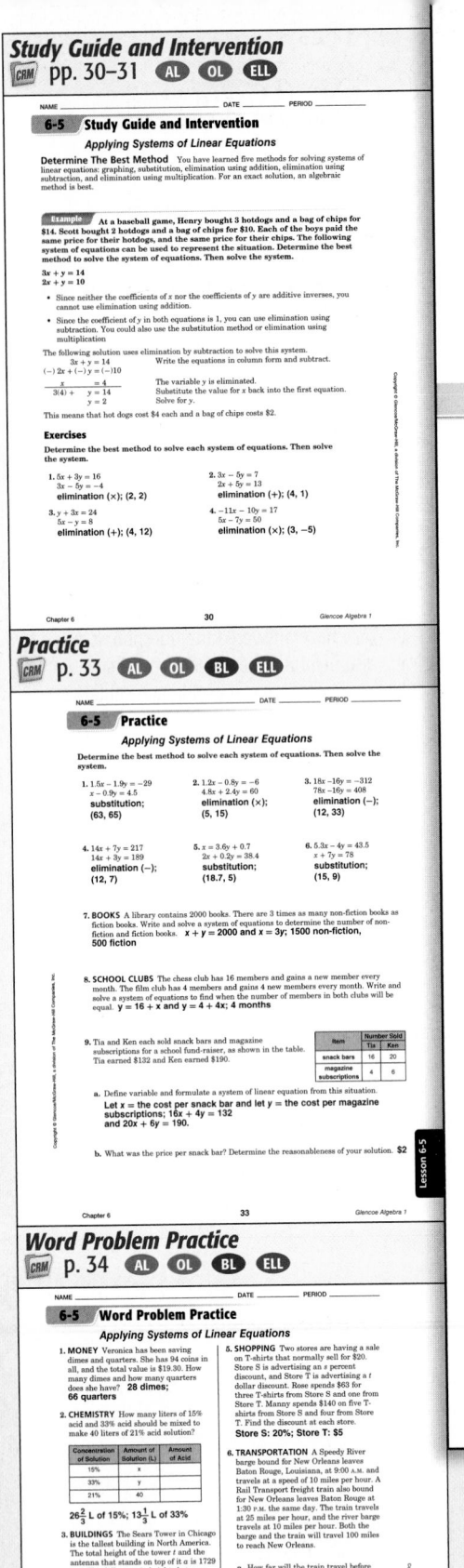

PSAE PRACTICE 8.11.17, 10.11.01, 9.11.12, 8.11.15

27. If $5x + 3y = 12$ and $4x - 5y = 17$, what is y? **A**

A -1 B 3 C $(-1, 3)$ D $(3, -1)$

28. STATISTICS The scatter plot shows the number of hay bales used on the Bostwick farm during the last year. **J**

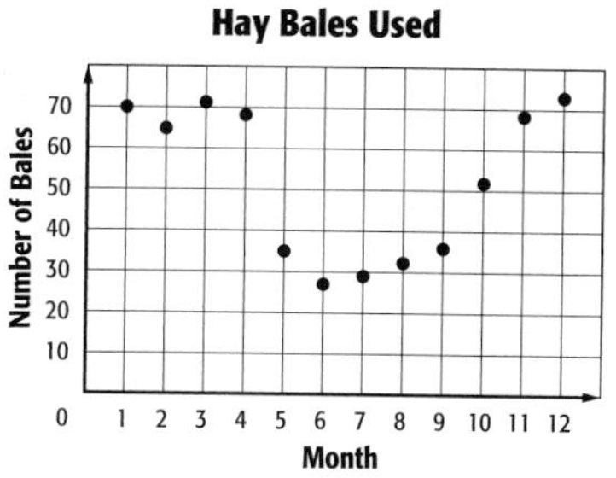

Which is an invalid conclusion?

F The Bostwicks used less hay in the summer than they did in the winter.

G The Bostwicks used about 629 bales of hay during the year.

H On average, the Bostwicks used about 52 bales each month.

J The Bostwicks used the most hay in February.

29. SHORT RESPONSE At noon, Cesar cast a shadow 0.15 foot long. Next to him a streetlight cast a shadow 0.25 foot long. If Cesar is 6 feet tall, how tall is the streetlight? **10 ft**

30. The graph shows the solution to which of the following systems of equations? **A**

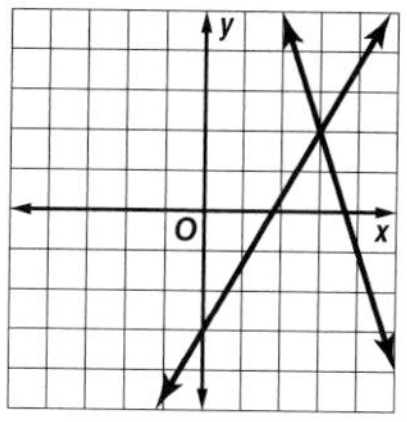

A $y = -3x + 11$
$3y = 5x - 9$

B $y = 5x - 15$
$2y = x + 7$

C $y = -3x + 11$
$2y = 4x - 5$

D $y = 5x - 15$
$3y = 2x + 18$

Spiral Review

Use elimination to solve each system of equations. (Lesson 6-4)

31. $x + y = 3$
$3x - 4y = -12$ **(0, 3)**

32. $-4x + 2y = 0$
$2x - 3y = 16$ **(−4, −8)**

33. $4x + 2y = 10$
$5x - 3y = 7$ **(2, 1)**

34. TRAVELING A youth group is traveling in two vans to visit an aquarium. The number of people in each van and the cost of admission for that van are shown. What are the adult and student prices? (Lesson 6-3) **$16; $9**

Van	Number of Adults	Number of Students	Total Cost
A	2	5	$77
B	2	7	$95

Graph each inequality. (Lesson 5-6) **35–38. See Ch. 6 Answer Appendix.**

35. $y < 4$ **36.** $x \geq 3$ **37.** $7x + 12y > 0$ **38.** $y - 3x \leq 4$

Skills Review

Find each sum or difference. (Lesson 0-4)

39. $(-3.81) + (-8.5)$ **−12.31**

40. $12.625 + (-5.23)$ **7.395**

41. $21.65 + (-15.05)$ **6.6**

42. $(-4.27) + 1.77$ **−2.5**

43. $(-78.94) - 14.25$ **−93.19**

44. $(-97.623) - (-25.14)$ **−72.483**

Differentiated Instruction OL BL

Extension Have students make up their own real-world problem that can be solved using a system of linear equations. This will help all students understand the concept of solving systems of linear equations.

4 ASSESS

Yesterday's News Have students write how yesterday's concept of using elimination with multiplication to solve systems of equations helped them with today's concept of determining the best method for solving systems of equations.

Additional Answers

23. Graphing: (2, 5);

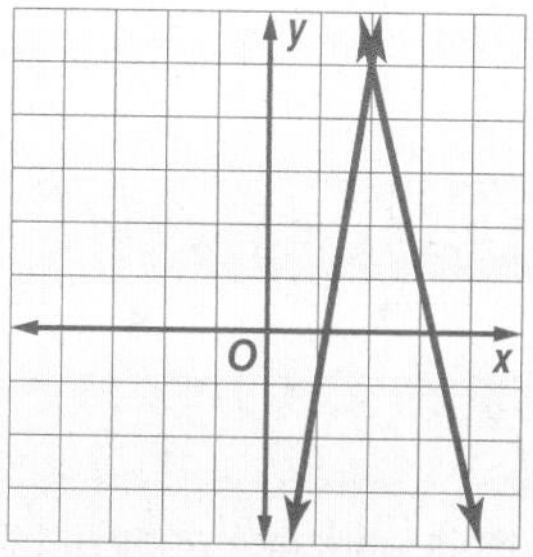

elimination by addition:

$$\begin{aligned} 4x + y &= 13 \\ 6x - y &= 7 \\ \hline 10x &= 20 \\ x &= 2 \\ 4(2) + y &= 13 \\ y &= 5 \end{aligned}$$

substitution:

$$\begin{aligned} y &= -4x + 13 \\ 6x - (-4x + 13) &= 7 \\ 6x + 4x - 13 &= 7 \\ 10x &= 20 \\ x &= 2 \\ 4(2) + y &= 13 \\ y &= 5 \end{aligned}$$

24. Sample answer: Would another method work better if one of the equations is in the form $y = mx + b$?

26. Sample answer: Graphing is the best method of showing how many solutions a system of equations has and finding an estimated answer. Solving a system algebraically provides an exact solution.

EXTEND 6-5

Lesson Notes

1 FOCUS

Objective Use a spreadsheet to compare using cash and using a credit card to pay for a purchase.

Materials for Each Student

- computer
- spreadsheet software

2 TEACH

Working in Cooperative Groups

Have students work in groups of three or four, mixing abilities, to complete the Activity and Exercises 1–4.

- For columns A and B, students can grab the right corner to drag a series of numbers or copy the cells. In column A, right click after dragging for 2 or 3 cells and choose the *fill series* button to list numbers 0–30. In column B, 200 will be copied as the cell is dragged.
- To have the spreadsheet calculate the interest, enter in D the formula $= C2 * \frac{0.15}{12}$
- To calculate the principal paid, enter in E2 the formula $= 200 - D2$.
- To have the spreadsheet calculate the remaining balance, enter in C3 the formula $= C2 - E2$). The formula subtracts from the previous remaining balance the difference between the principal paid and the interest paid. Caution students that they must use parentheses to ensure the correct order of operations.

Practice Have students complete Exercise 5.

EXTEND 6-5

Spreadsheet Lab: Credit Cards and Cash

IL Math Online glencoe.com
• Graphing Technology Personal Tutor

IL Learning Standards **6.B.4** Select and use appropriate arithmetic operations in practical situations including calculating wages after taxes, developing a budget and balancing a checkbook.

You can use a spreadsheet to compare the advantages and disadvantages of using cash versus using a credit card for a purchase.

ACTIVITY

Jun wants to purchase a car for $4000. He can save $350 per month toward the purchase of the car. Or he can use a credit card that charges 15% interest and pay $200 a month on the card. How much money will Jun save on his purchase if he waits and pays cash?

Part 1 To find out how long it will take Jun to pay cash for the car, divide $4000 by $350. This is about 11.4 months. So Jun would need to save for 12 months to pay cash for the car.

Part 2 If Jun uses his credit card to pay for the car, he would have the car right away, but he would have to pay interest. You can use a spreadsheet to find the costs by month.

Column A: List months from 0–30.

Column B: List each of the $200 payments.

Column C: Place the remaining balance. Begin with 4000 in C2.

Column D: Find the amount of interest paid each month by using the formula =C2•0.15/12.

Column E: Find the principal paid by subtracting the interest from 200 using the formula =200−D2.

Spreadsheet.xls

	A	B	C	D	E
1	Month	Payment	Remaining Balance	Interest Paid	Principal Paid
2	0	200	4000	50	150
3	1	200	3850.00	48.13	151.875
4	2	200	3698.13	46.23	153.77
5	3	200	3544.35	44.30	155.70
6	4	200	3388.66	42.36	157.64
21	19	200	805.48	10.07	189.93
22	20	200	615.55	7.69	192.31
23	21	200	423.25		
24	22	200			

Sheet 1 Sheet 2 Sheet 3

Analyze the Results

5. Jun would save $631.79 in interest. The car would be paid for in 12 months instead of 24.

1. How long will it take Jun to pay for his car using his credit card? 24 mo or 2 yr
2. What is the amount of Jun's last payment? $31.39
3. How can you find how much Jun pays in interest as he pays back his credit card? Add the numbers in the Interest Paid column.
4. How much total interest did Jun pay? $631.79
5. What are the benefits of using cash to pay for the car instead of using a credit card?

3 ASSESS

Formative Assessment

Use Exercise 5 to assess whether students understand how to use a spreadsheet to make comparisons.

From Concrete to Abstract

Ask: Suppose Jun pays $350 per month on his credit card. How would that affect the benefits of using cash to pay for the car? Sample answer: Even though interest would be less and it would take less time to pay off the car, Jun would still pay more for the car because of interest, and it would take longer than a year to pay for the car.

368 Chapter 6 Systems of Linear Equations and Inequalities

6-6 Organizing Data Using Matrices

Why?

The table shows high school participation in various sports.

Sport	Girls		Boys	
	Schools	Participation	Schools	Participation
basketball	17,175	456,543	17,482	545,497
cross country	12,345	170,450	12,727	201,719
lacrosse	1270	48,086	1334	59,993
tennis	9646	169,292	9426	148,530

Source: The National Federation of State High School Associations

These data can be organized into two matrices with the figures for girls and boys.

Organize Data Using Matrices A **matrix** is a rectangular arrangement of numbers in rows and columns enclosed in brackets. Each number in a matrix is called an **element**. A matrix is usually named using an uppercase letter. A matrix can be described by its **dimensions** or the number of rows and columns in the matrix. A matrix with m rows and n columns is an $m \times n$ matrix (read "m by n").

$$A = \begin{bmatrix} 7 & -9 & 5 & 3 \\ -1 & 3 & -3 & 6 \\ 0 & -4 & 8 & 2 \end{bmatrix}$$

3 rows

4 columns

The element -1 is in Row 2, Column 1.

The element 2 is in Row 3, Column 4.

Matrix A above is a 3×4 matrix because it has 3 rows and 4 columns.

EXAMPLE 1 Dimensions of a Matrix

State the dimensions of each matrix. Then identify the position of the circled element in each matrix.

a. $A = \begin{bmatrix} 1 & \textcircled{7} \\ -4 & 0 \\ 2 & -5 \end{bmatrix}$

$\begin{bmatrix} 1 & \textcircled{7} \\ -4 & 0 \\ 2 & -5 \end{bmatrix}$ 3 rows, 2 columns

Matrix A has 3 rows and 2 columns. Therefore, it is a 3×2 matrix. The circled element is in the first row and the second column.

b. $B = \begin{bmatrix} -5 & 10 & \textcircled{2} & -3 \end{bmatrix}$

$\begin{bmatrix} -5 & 10 & \textcircled{2} & -3 \end{bmatrix}$ 1 row, 4 columns

Matrix B has 1 row and 4 columns. Therefore, it is a 1×4 matrix. The circled element is in the first row and the third column.

Check Your Progress

1A. $C = \begin{bmatrix} -1 & 7 & 12 \\ 4 & \textcircled{-5} & -2 \end{bmatrix}$ 2×3; 2nd row and 2nd column

1B. $D = \begin{bmatrix} -3 & 6 \\ 4 & \textcircled{-8} \end{bmatrix}$ 2×2; 2nd row and 2nd column

Personal Tutor glencoe.com

Then

You represented data using statistical graphs. (Lesson 0-13)

Now

- Organize data in matrices.
- Perform matrix operations.

IL Learning Standards

8.C.4b Apply algebraic properties and procedures with matrices, vectors, functions and sequences **using data found in business, industry and consumer situations.**

New Vocabulary

matrix
element
dimension
scalar
scalar multiplication

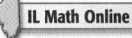

IL Math Online

glencoe.com

- Extra Examples
- Personal Tutor
- Self-Check Quiz
- Homework Help

6-6 Lesson Notes

1 FOCUS

Vertical Alignment

Before Lesson 6-6
Represent data using statistical graphs.

Lesson 6-6
Organize data in matrices.
Perform matrix operations.

After Lesson 6-6
Use matrices to solve systems of equations.

2 TEACH

Scaffolding Questions

Have students read the *Why?* section of the lesson and the paragraph on organizing data using matrices.

Ask:

- If you organize the data in the table into two matrices, one for girls and one for boys, how many rows will each matrix have? 4 How many columns? 2 What will be the dimensions of each matrix? 4×2
- In the matrix for boys, in which row and column would you place the number of boys who participated in lacrosse? row 3, column 2
- Why might it be helpful to organize the data into matrices? Sample answer: It makes it easier to analyze and compare data.

Lesson 6-6 Resources

Resource	Approaching-Level	On-Level	Beyond-Level	English Learners
Teacher Edition	• Differentiated Instruction, p. 370	• Differentiated Instruction, pp. 370, 375	• Differentiated Instruction, p. 375	• Differentiated Instruction, p. 370
Chapter Resource Masters	• Study Guide and Intervention, pp. 36–37 • Skills Practice, p. 38 • Practice, p. 39 • Word Problem Practice, p. 40	• Study Guide and Intervention, pp. 36–37 • Skills Practice, p. 38 • Practice, p. 39 • Word Problem Practice, p. 40 • Enrichment, p. 41	• Practice, p. 39 • Word Problem Practice, p. 40 • Enrichment, p. 41	• Study Guide and Intervention, pp. 36–37 • Skills Practice, p. 38 • Practice, p. 39
Transparencies	• 5-Minute Check Transparency 6-6	• 5-Minute Check Transparency 6-6	• 5-Minute Check Transparency 6-6	• 5-Minute Check Transparency 6-6
Other	• Study Notebook	• Study Notebook	• Study Notebook	• Study Notebook

Organize Data Using Matrices

Example 1 shows how to determine the dimensions of a matrix and identify the position of an element. **Example 2** shows how to organize real-world data into a matrix to solve a problem.

Formative Assessment

Use the Check Your Progress exercises after each example to determine students' understanding of concepts.

Additional Example

1 State the dimensions of each matrix. Then identify the position of the circled element in each matrix.

a. $\begin{bmatrix} -8 & \textcircled{4} \\ 3 & 9 \end{bmatrix}$

2 × 2; row 1, column 2

b. $\begin{bmatrix} -1 & 12 & 3 & 4 & -2 \\ 8 & 1 & 15 & -5 & 6 \\ 2 & 8 & 4 & \textcircled{-3} & -5 \end{bmatrix}$

3 × 5; row 3, column 4

Additional Examples also in Interactive Classroom PowerPoint® Presentations

IWB INTERACTIVE WHITEBOARD READY

Additional Answer (Check Your Progress)

2. $\begin{matrix} & \text{Matinee} & \text{Evening} \\ \text{Adult} & 5.25 & 8.75 \\ \text{Child} & 4.50 & 5.75 \end{matrix}$; 2 × 2

TEACH with TECH

WEB SEARCH Search the Web to find the home attendance for 3 sports teams on 3 days. Show students how to use a 3 × 3 matrix to organize the data. Then estimate an average ticket price and show how you can use scalar multiplication to find the total ticket sales for each team for each day.

Real-World Link

In June 2007, the Projecte Home Balear set a world record by having the most participants swim one pool length each in a 24-hour relay. A total of 3,168 people participated in the relay at the Municipal Sports Complex in Palma de Mallorca, Spain.

Source: Guinness World Records

Real-World EXAMPLE 2 Organize Data into a Matrix

SWIMMING At a meet, 10 points were awarded for each first-place finish, 8 points for each second-place finish, and 5 points for each third-place finish. Use a matrix to organize each team's points. Which school had the most first-place finishes?

School	Freestyle	Backstroke	Breaststroke	Butterfly
North	10	8	8	10
South	5	5	10	8
Jefferson	8	10	5	5

Organize the points awarded into labeled columns and rows.

$$\begin{array}{r} \\ \text{North} \\ \text{South} \\ \text{Jefferson} \end{array} \begin{array}{c} \text{Freestyle} \quad \text{Backstroke} \quad \text{Breaststroke} \quad \text{Butterfly} \\ \begin{bmatrix} 10 & 8 & 8 & 10 \\ 5 & 5 & 10 & 8 \\ 8 & 10 & 5 & 5 \end{bmatrix} \end{array}$$

North High School earned 10 points in both the freestyle event and the butterfly event, so they had the most first-place finishes.

Check Your Progress

2. MOVIES For a matinee, a movie theater charges \$5.25 for an adult and \$4.50 for a child. Evening admission is \$8.75 for an adult and \$5.75 for a child. Organize the prices into a matrix. What are the dimensions of the matrix? **See margin.**

Personal Tutor glencoe.com

Matrix Operations If two matrices have the same dimensions, they can be added together. You add matrices by adding the corresponding elements of the matrices.

StudyTip

Corresponding Elements *Corresponding* means that the elements are in the exact same position in each matrix.

EXAMPLE 3 Add Matrices

Find each sum for $A = \begin{bmatrix} 12 & 2 \\ -9 & 15 \end{bmatrix}$, $B = \begin{bmatrix} -4 & 4 \\ -3 & -10 \end{bmatrix}$, and $C = \begin{bmatrix} -2 \\ 8 \end{bmatrix}$.

a. $A + B$

$A + B = \begin{bmatrix} 12 & 2 \\ -9 & 15 \end{bmatrix} + \begin{bmatrix} -4 & 4 \\ -3 & -10 \end{bmatrix}$ **Substitution**

$= \begin{bmatrix} 12 + (-4) & 2 + 4 \\ -9 + (-3) & 15 + (-10) \end{bmatrix}$ or $\begin{bmatrix} 8 & 6 \\ -12 & 5 \end{bmatrix}$ **Simplify.**

b. $B + C$

$B + C = \begin{bmatrix} -4 & 4 \\ -3 & -10 \end{bmatrix} + \begin{bmatrix} -2 \\ 8 \end{bmatrix}$ **Substitution**

Matrix B is a 2 × 2 matrix, and matrix C is a 2 × 1 matrix. Since the matrices do not have the same dimensions, it is not possible to add these matrices.

Check Your Progress

3A. $\begin{bmatrix} 7 & -2 & 11 \\ -14 & 8 & 1 \end{bmatrix} + \begin{bmatrix} -3 & 4 & 5 \\ -4 & 6 & -1 \end{bmatrix}$

3B. $\begin{bmatrix} 12 & 8 \\ -3 & -7 \\ -6 & 9 \end{bmatrix} + \begin{bmatrix} -2 & 4 \\ 1 & -1 \\ -9 & 5 \end{bmatrix}$

Personal Tutor glencoe.com

3A. $\begin{bmatrix} 4 & 2 & 16 \\ -18 & 14 & 0 \end{bmatrix}$

3B. $\begin{bmatrix} 10 & 12 \\ -2 & -8 \\ -15 & 14 \end{bmatrix}$

Differentiated Instruction

AL OL ELL

If students have trouble understanding matrices,

Then write a matrix on the board and have students identify the positions of various elements. Ask one volunteer to point out the row of the element and another to point out the column. Emphasize that numbers in rows are arranged horizontally and numbers in columns are arranged vertically. Have students repeat the position of the element to reinforce the idea that row, then column is used to describe the matrix. Suggest students develop a mnemonic device to remember the order in which to state the dimensions.

If two matrices have the same dimensions, then they can also be subtracted. You subtract matrices by subtracting the corresponding elements of the matrices.

EXAMPLE 4 Subtract Matrices

Find each difference for $A = \begin{bmatrix} 4 & -2 & 8 \\ -17 & 10 & 6 \end{bmatrix}$, $B = \begin{bmatrix} 6 & -14 & 2 \end{bmatrix}$, and $C = \begin{bmatrix} 1 & -3 & 5 \\ -10 & 8 & 7 \end{bmatrix}$. If the difference does not exist, write *impossible*.

a. $B - A$

$B - A = \begin{bmatrix} 6 & -14 & 2 \end{bmatrix} - \begin{bmatrix} 4 & -2 & 8 \\ -7 & 10 & 6 \end{bmatrix}$ **Substitution**

Matrix B is a 1×3 matrix, while matrix A is a 2×3 matrix. Since the dimensions are not the same, it is not possible to subtract these matrices.

b. $A - C$

$A - C = \begin{bmatrix} 4 & -2 & 8 \\ -17 & 10 & 6 \end{bmatrix} - \begin{bmatrix} 1 & -3 & 5 \\ -10 & 8 & 7 \end{bmatrix}$ **Substitution**

$= \begin{bmatrix} 4 - 1 & -2 - (-3) & 8 - 5 \\ -17 - (-10) & 10 - 8 & 6 - 7 \end{bmatrix}$ or $\begin{bmatrix} 3 & 1 & 3 \\ -7 & 2 & -1 \end{bmatrix}$ **Simplify.**

Check Your Progress

4A. $\begin{bmatrix} 2 & -5 \\ 8 & 12 \end{bmatrix} - \begin{bmatrix} 6 & -3 \\ -9 & 1 \end{bmatrix}$ $\begin{bmatrix} -4 & -2 \\ 17 & 11 \end{bmatrix}$

4B. $\begin{bmatrix} 16 & -6 & 1 \\ -2 & 5 & -1 \end{bmatrix} - \begin{bmatrix} 21 & 3 & -6 \\ -12 & -2 & 1 \end{bmatrix}$

Personal Tutor glencoe.com

Watch Out!

Dimensions When working with matrices, remember that the dimensions are always given as rows by columns.

4B. $\begin{bmatrix} -5 & -9 & 7 \\ 10 & 7 & -2 \end{bmatrix}$

You can multiply any matrix by a constant called a **scalar**. This operation is called **scalar multiplication** and is done by multiplying each element of the matrix by the scalar.

EXAMPLE 5 Multiply a Matrix by a Scalar

If $A = \begin{bmatrix} 2 & -4 & -7 & 9 \\ 1 & -10 & 8 & 6 \end{bmatrix}$, find $4A$.

$4A = 4\begin{bmatrix} 2 & -4 & -7 & 9 \\ 1 & -10 & 8 & 6 \end{bmatrix}$ **Substitution**

$= \begin{bmatrix} 4(2) & 4(-4) & 4(-7) & 4(9) \\ 4(1) & 4(-10) & 4(8) & 4(6) \end{bmatrix}$ **Definition of scalar multiplication**

$= \begin{bmatrix} 8 & -16 & -28 & 36 \\ 4 & -40 & 32 & 24 \end{bmatrix}$ **Simplify.**

Check Your Progress

5A. If $A = \begin{bmatrix} -9 & 3 \\ 5 & -11 \\ -2 & 7 \end{bmatrix}$, find $-3A$.

5B. If $B = \begin{bmatrix} -12 & 8 \\ -3 & 0 \end{bmatrix}$, find $2B$. $\begin{bmatrix} -24 & 16 \\ -6 & 0 \end{bmatrix}$

Personal Tutor glencoe.com

StudyTip

Matrix Operations The order of operations for matrices is similar to that of real numbers. You would perform scalar multiplication before matrix addition and subtraction.

5A. $\begin{bmatrix} 27 & -9 \\ -15 & 33 \\ 6 & -21 \end{bmatrix}$

Additional Example

2 **HORSEBACK RIDING** At a particular horseback riding competition, blue ribbons go to the highest score in an event. Use a matrix to organize the scores for each participant for each event. Which participant won the most blue ribbons? Mandy

Participant	Jumping	Cutting	Reining
Lukden	7	8	6
Hamida	10	10	8
Mandy	12	9	11
Rozene	11	7	10

	Jumping	Cutting	Reining
Lukden	7	8	6
Hamida	10	10	8
Mandy	12	9	11
Rozene	11	7	10

Matrix Operations

Example 3 shows how to add matrices. **Example 4** shows how to subtract matrices. **Example 5** shows how to multiply a matrix by a scalar.

Additional Example

3 Find each sum for $A = \begin{bmatrix} -8 & 15 & 9 \\ 4 & -3 & 7 \end{bmatrix}$, $B = \begin{bmatrix} -12 & 10 & -13 \\ -8 & 11 & -6 \end{bmatrix}$, and $C = \begin{bmatrix} -4 & 8 & 12 \end{bmatrix}$.

a. $A + B$ $\begin{bmatrix} -20 & 25 & -4 \\ -4 & 8 & 1 \end{bmatrix}$

b. $A + C$ not possible to add

Focus on Mathematical Content

Matrix Operations Two or more matrices that have the same dimensions can be added or subtracted by adding or subtracting corresponding elements in the matrices. A matrix can be multiplied by a scalar or real number by multiplying each element in the matrix by the scalar. If two or more matrices combine several operations, multiply first and then add or subtract.

Additional Examples

4 Find each difference for $A = \begin{bmatrix} 8 & 10 \\ -3 & -8 \end{bmatrix}$, $B = \begin{bmatrix} -1 & 12 \\ 4 & -2 \end{bmatrix}$, and $C = \begin{bmatrix} -7 \\ 6 \end{bmatrix}$. If the difference does not exist, write *impossible*.

a. $B - C$ impossible

b. $A - B$ $\begin{bmatrix} 9 & -2 \\ -7 & -6 \end{bmatrix}$

5 If $A = \begin{bmatrix} 9 & -3 & 4 & 8 & -7 \\ -5 & -12 & 2 & 6 & -10 \end{bmatrix}$, find $3A$.

$\begin{bmatrix} 27 & -9 & 12 & 24 & -21 \\ -15 & -36 & 6 & 18 & -30 \end{bmatrix}$

3 PRACTICE

Formative Assessment

Use Exercises 1–9 to check for understanding.

Use the chart at the bottom of this page to customize assignments for your students.

Additional Answers

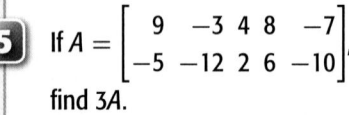

5a.

	Weekday	Weekend
Single	69	89
Double	79	109
Suite	99	139

20. $\begin{bmatrix} -18 & 24 & -27 & -3 & 9 \\ 0 & -21 & 6 & 12 & -15 \end{bmatrix}$

Check Your Understanding

Example 1 (p. 369)

State the dimensions of each matrix. Then identify the position of the circled element in each matrix.

1. $\begin{bmatrix} 8 & -2 & 1 & -3 \\ \textcircled{0} & 5 & 7 & -11 \end{bmatrix}$

2. $\begin{bmatrix} 6 \\ -7 \\ 2 \\ \textcircled{1} \end{bmatrix}$

3. $\begin{bmatrix} 9 & -12 & \textcircled{6} & 2 \end{bmatrix}$

4. $\begin{bmatrix} 6 & -8 & 12 & 9 & -1 \\ 2 & 9 & 7 & \textcircled{11} & -5 \\ 5 & 0 & 1 & 3 & 4 \end{bmatrix}$

1. 2 × 4; second row and first column
2. 4 × 1; fourth row and first column
3. 1 × 4; first row and third column
4. 3 × 5; second row and fourth column

Example 2 (p. 370)

5. **HOTELS** The costs for an overnight stay at a hotel are listed in the table at the right.

Room	Weekday	Weekend
single	\$69	\$89
double	\$79	\$109
suite	\$99	\$139

a. Write a matrix to organize the costs of an overnight stay at the hotel. See margin.

b. What are the dimensions of the matrix? 3 × 2

c. Which room and night is the most expensive? least expensive? suite on a weekend; single on a weekday

Examples 3–5 (pp. 370–371)

Perform the indicated matrix operations. If the matrix does not exist, write *impossible*.

6. $\begin{bmatrix} 5 & -2 \\ 7 & -6 \end{bmatrix} + \begin{bmatrix} -5 & -8 \\ 3 & 1 \end{bmatrix}$ $\begin{bmatrix} 0 & -10 \\ 10 & -5 \end{bmatrix}$

7. $\begin{bmatrix} 8 & 11 & 5 \\ -3 & 7 & 8 \\ -1 & -2 & 0 \end{bmatrix} - \begin{bmatrix} -4 & 10 & -9 \\ 6 & -12 & -1 \\ 7 & 5 & 3 \end{bmatrix}$

7. $\begin{bmatrix} 12 & 1 & 14 \\ -9 & 19 & 9 \\ -8 & -7 & -3 \end{bmatrix}$

8. $-2\begin{bmatrix} 7 & -2 & 0 & 1 \\ -8 & 11 & -9 & 3 \\ -4 & -7 & 5 & 6 \end{bmatrix}$

8. $\begin{bmatrix} -14 & 4 & 0 & -2 \\ 16 & -22 & 18 & -6 \\ 8 & 14 & -10 & -12 \end{bmatrix}$

9. $\begin{bmatrix} 15 \\ -8 \\ 4 \end{bmatrix} - \begin{bmatrix} -3 & -2 & 7 \end{bmatrix}$ impossible

Practice and Problem Solving

● = **Step-by-Step Solutions** begin on page R12. **Extra Practice** begins on page 815.

Example 1 (p. 369)

State the dimensions of each matrix. Then identify the position of the circled element in each matrix.

10. $\begin{bmatrix} 6 & 8 & -2 & 3 \\ -7 & -12 & 58 & 1 \\ 86 & \textcircled{12} & 7 & -9 \\ 0 & -6 & 21 & 79 \end{bmatrix}$

11. $\begin{bmatrix} 2 & 9 \\ \textcircled{-3} & -5 \\ 7 & -8 \\ 1 & -1 \\ -2 & 3 \end{bmatrix}$

12. $\begin{bmatrix} 8 & -10 & 4 & 6 & -2 \\ \textcircled{3} & 7 & 9 & 5 & -1 \end{bmatrix}$

13. $\begin{bmatrix} 8 & 2 & -1 & 4 & 3 & -7 \\ 9 & 10 & -17 & 0 & 1 & -8 \\ -1 & 5 & -2 & \textcircled{7} & -3 & 0 \\ -9 & 7 & 5 & 3 & -6 & 6 \end{bmatrix}$

14. $\begin{bmatrix} 1 & -20 & -16 \\ -5 & 0 & 7 \\ 9 & -13 & 12 \\ 8 & \textcircled{-9} & 2 \\ -3 & 5 & 10 \\ 6 & -14 & 25 \end{bmatrix}$

15. $\begin{bmatrix} 3 & 2 & 7 & 0 \\ 4 & 9 & 10 & \textcircled{4} \\ -1 & 7 & 6 & 5 \\ 0 & -3 & 12 & -5 \\ 8 & -5 & -10 & -8 \\ -2 & 4 & 11 & -2 \end{bmatrix}$

16. $\begin{bmatrix} 8 & 6 & -4 & 2 & 1 & 3 \\ -8 & -4 & 0 & \textcircled{9} & -5 & 6 \\ 2 & 3 & -1 & 7 & -9 & 0 \end{bmatrix}$

10. 4 × 4; third row and second column
11. 5 × 2; second row and first column
12. 2 × 5; second row and first column
13. 4 × 6; third row and fourth column
14. 6 × 3; fourth row and second column
15. 6 × 4; second row and fourth column
16. 3 × 6; second row and fourth column

Differentiated Homework Options

Level	Assignment	Two-Day Option	
AL Basic	10–23, 33, 35–57	11–23 odd, 39–42	10–22 even, 33, 35–38, 43–57
OL Core	11–23 odd, 24–26, 27–33 odd, 35–57	10–23, 39–42	24–33, 35–38, 43–57
BL Advanced	24–51, (optional: 52–57)		

Example 2 p. 370

17. GEOGRAPHY The land area in square miles and the number of people per square mile in 2000 are shown.

State	Land Area	People per Square Mile
Ohio	40,948	277.3
Florida	53,926	296.4
New York	47,213	401.9
North Carolina	48,710	165.2

17a.

$$\begin{array}{l} \\ \text{Ohio} \\ \text{Florida} \\ \text{New York} \\ \text{North Carolina} \end{array} \begin{array}{c} \text{Land Area}\quad\text{People} \\ \begin{bmatrix} 40{,}948 & 277.3 \\ 53{,}926 & 296.4 \\ 47{,}213 & 401.9 \\ 48{,}710 & 165.2 \end{bmatrix} \end{array}$$

a. Write a matrix to organize the given data.

b. What are the dimensions of the matrix? **4 × 2**

c. Which state has the most people per square mile? the fewest people per square mile?

17c. New York; North Carolina

Examples 3–5 pp. 370–371

Perform the indicated matrix operations. If the matrix does not exist, write *impossible*.

18. $\begin{bmatrix} 8 & -5 & 1 \\ 3 & -7 & -4 \end{bmatrix} - \begin{bmatrix} 6 & -2 & -7 & 9 \\ 10 & -3 & 1 & -4 \end{bmatrix}$

18. impossible

19. $\begin{bmatrix} -9 & 5 & 1 \\ 14 & -6 & 7 \end{bmatrix} + \begin{bmatrix} 3 & -4 & -1 \\ -7 & -2 & 8 \end{bmatrix}$

19. $\begin{bmatrix} -6 & 1 & 0 \\ 7 & -8 & 15 \end{bmatrix}$

20. $-3\begin{bmatrix} 6 & -8 & 9 & 1 & -3 \\ 0 & 7 & -2 & -4 & 5 \end{bmatrix}$

20. See margin.

21. $5\begin{bmatrix} 2 & -1 & 0 \\ 1 & -3 & 5 \\ 7 & 10 & -11 \\ 8 & -9 & -4 \end{bmatrix}$ $\begin{bmatrix} 10 & -5 & 0 \\ 5 & -15 & 25 \\ 35 & 50 & -55 \\ 40 & -45 & -20 \end{bmatrix}$

22. $\begin{bmatrix} 17 & 10 \\ -5 & 1 \\ 7 & 6 \\ -8 & -2 \\ 3 & 8 \end{bmatrix} - \begin{bmatrix} 20 & 6 \\ -4 & -5 \\ -9 & 0 \\ -1 & 9 \\ 6 & -12 \end{bmatrix}$

22. $\begin{bmatrix} -3 & 4 \\ -1 & 6 \\ 16 & 6 \\ -7 & -11 \\ -3 & 20 \end{bmatrix}$

23. $\begin{bmatrix} 6 & 8 & -4 & -2 \end{bmatrix} - \begin{bmatrix} 9 & -4 & 7 & 8 \end{bmatrix}$ $\begin{bmatrix} -3 & 12 & -11 & -10 \end{bmatrix}$

24. VOTING The results of a recent poll are organized in the matrix shown at the right. B

$$\begin{array}{l} \\ \text{Propositon 1} \\ \text{Propositon 2} \\ \text{Propositon 3} \end{array} \begin{array}{c} \text{For}\quad\text{Against} \\ \begin{bmatrix} 562 & 1025 \\ 789 & 921 \\ 1255 & 301 \end{bmatrix} \end{array}$$

a. How many people voted for Proposition 1? **562**

b. How many more people voted against Proposition 2 than for Proposition 2? **132**

c. How many votes were cast against the propositions? **2247**

25. SALES The manager of The Donut Delight Shop keeps records of the types of donuts sold each day. Two days of sales are shown.

Day	Store	Sales of Each Type of Donut ($)			
		Chocolate	Glazed	Powdered	Lemon Filled
Saturday	Main St.	95	205	70	51
	Elm St.	105	245	79	49
Sunday	Main St.	167	295	99	79
	Elm St.	159	289	107	88

a. Describe what 245 represents.

b. Write a matrix that represents the sales for each day. **See margin.**

c. How much did each store make in sales over the two days for each type of donut? **See margin.**

d. Which donut made the company the most money? **glazed**

25a. On Saturday at the store on Elm St., $245 in glazed donuts were sold.

Real-World Link

Some Dutch settlers brought donuts to Colonial America. Since ovens were not always available, people began frying the dough. Then sugar and spices were added.

Source: Oracle Education Foundation

Additional Answers

25b. $\begin{bmatrix} 95 & 205 & 70 & 51 \\ 105 & 245 & 79 & 49 \end{bmatrix}$; $\begin{bmatrix} 167 & 295 & 99 & 79 \\ 159 & 289 & 107 & 88 \end{bmatrix}$

25c. $\begin{bmatrix} 262 & 500 & 169 & 130 \\ 264 & 534 & 186 & 137 \end{bmatrix}$

Main Street: Chocolate 262, Glazed 500, Powdered 169, Lemon filled 130

Elm Street: Chocolate 264, Glazed 534, Powdered 186, Lemon filled 137

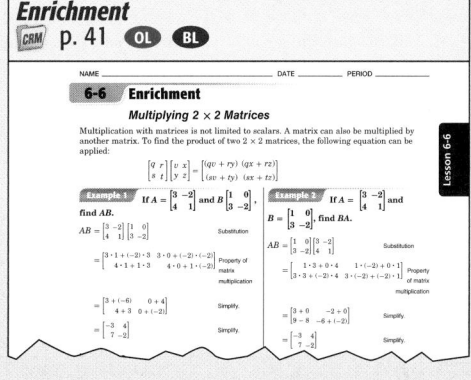

Study Guide and Intervention

CRM pp. 36–37 AL OL ELL

NAME ____ DATE ____ PERIOD ____

6-6 Study Guide and Intervention

Organizing Data Using Matrices

Organize Data Using Matrices A **matrix** is a rectangular arrangement of numbers in rows and columns enclosed in brackets. Matrices can be described by its dimensions or the number of rows and columns in the matrix. A matrix with m rows and n columns is an $m \times n$ matrix.

Example **State the dimensions of the matrix. Then identify the position of the circled element in the matrix.**

$A = \begin{bmatrix} -1 & 0 & \textcircled{4} \\ 2 & 2 & -7 \end{bmatrix}$

Matrix A has 2 rows and 3 columns. Therefore, it is a 2 × 3 matrix. The circled element is in the first row and third column.

Exercises

State the dimensions of each matrix. Then identify the position of the circled element in each matrix.

1. $\begin{bmatrix} 9 & 1 & -2 & 8 \\ 0 & \textcircled{-3} & 1 & 4 \end{bmatrix}$ **2 × 4; second row, second column**

2. $\begin{bmatrix} 2 & 10 & -3 \\ -1 & 1 & 5 \\ -4 & \textcircled{0} & 8 \end{bmatrix}$ **3 × 3; third row, second column**

3. $\begin{bmatrix} 2 & \textcircled{-1} & 5 & 14 & 0 \end{bmatrix}$ **1 × 5; first row, second column**

4. The selling prices for various luxury condominiums are listed in the table to the right.

Condo Development	1 Bedroom	2 Bedrooms	3 Bedrooms
Foxpointe Estates	$349,000	$449,000	$499,000
Condos at Salmon Brook	$329,900	$389,900	$439,900
Kean Mills	$499,000	$649,000	$799,000

a. Write a matrix to organize the selling prices of the condos.

$$\begin{array}{l} \\ \text{Foxpoine Estates} \\ \text{Condos at Salmon Brook} \\ \text{Kean Mills} \end{array} \begin{array}{c} \text{1 Bedroom}\quad\text{2 Bedrooms}\quad\text{3 Bedrooms} \\ \begin{bmatrix} 349{,}000 & 449{,}000 & 499{,}000 \\ 329{,}900 & 389{,}900 & 439{,}900 \\ 499{,}000 & 649{,}000 & 799{,}000 \end{bmatrix} \end{array}$$

b. What are the dimensions of the matrix? **3 × 3**

c. Which condo is the most expensive? least expensive? **most expensive: 3 bedrooms at Kean Mills; least expensive: 1 bedroom at Condos at Salmon Brook**

Chapter 6 36 *Glencoe Algebra 1*

Practice

CRM p. 39 AL OL BL ELL

NAME ____ DATE ____ PERIOD ____

6-6 Practice

Organizing Data Using Matrices

Exercises

State the dimensions of each matrix. Then identify the position of the circled element in each matrix.

1. $\begin{bmatrix} 0 & 1 & -4 & 9 \\ 2 & \textcircled{7} & 0 & -3 \end{bmatrix}$ **2 × 4; second row, second column**

2. $\begin{bmatrix} 14 & -2 & 5 \\ 9 & 1 & 0 \\ -6 & \textcircled{20} & 3 \end{bmatrix}$ **3 × 3; third row, second column**

3. $\begin{bmatrix} 9 & 1 & 0 & 0 \\ -3 & 2 & -4 & 1 \\ \textcircled{-6} & 4 & 1 & 4 \end{bmatrix}$ **3 × 4; third row, first column**

4. $\begin{bmatrix} 3 & \textcircled{-2} & 6 & 1 & 1 \end{bmatrix}$ **1 × 5; first row, second column**

Perform the indicated matrix operations. If the matrix does not exist, write *impossible*.

5. $\begin{bmatrix} 0 & 3 \\ -1 & 8 \end{bmatrix} + \begin{bmatrix} 7 & 1 \\ 2 & 1 \end{bmatrix}$ $\begin{bmatrix} 7 & 4 \\ 1 & 9 \end{bmatrix}$

6. $\begin{bmatrix} 3 & 2 \\ 1 & -4 \end{bmatrix} - \begin{bmatrix} 6 & -3 \\ -1 & 2 \end{bmatrix}$ $\begin{bmatrix} -3 & 5 \\ 2 & -6 \end{bmatrix}$

7. $\begin{bmatrix} 6 & -2 & 1 \\ 3 & 4 & 0 \end{bmatrix} - \begin{bmatrix} 1 & 5 & -3 \\ 2 & -1 & 4 \end{bmatrix}$ $\begin{bmatrix} 5 & -7 & 4 \\ 1 & 5 & -4 \end{bmatrix}$

8. $\begin{bmatrix} 7 & -1 & 3 \\ 0 & 2 & -4 \\ 3 & 1 & 5 \end{bmatrix} \begin{bmatrix} 3 & -2 & 6 & 1 & 1 \end{bmatrix}$ **impossible**

9. $-2\begin{bmatrix} 4 & -1 & 3 & 0 \end{bmatrix}$ $\begin{bmatrix} -8 & 2 & -6 & 0 \end{bmatrix}$

10. $6\begin{bmatrix} 2 & -1 & 5 \\ -3 & 2 & -1 \end{bmatrix}$ $\begin{bmatrix} 12 & -6 & 30 \\ -18 & 12 & -6 \end{bmatrix}$

11. $5\begin{bmatrix} 0 & 2 & -1 & 7 \\ 4 & 1 & 0 & 2 \\ -3 & 1 & 9 & -4 \\ 0 & -2 & 6 & 1 \end{bmatrix}$ $\begin{bmatrix} 0 & 10 & -5 & 35 \\ 20 & 5 & 0 & 10 \\ -15 & 5 & 45 & -20 \\ 0 & -10 & 30 & 5 \end{bmatrix}$

12. $-2\begin{bmatrix} 2 & 11 & -5 & 4 \\ -1 & 0 & 6 & 3 \\ 9 & -2 & 1 & 0 \end{bmatrix}$ $\begin{bmatrix} -4 & -22 & 10 & -8 \\ 2 & 0 & -12 & -6 \\ -18 & 4 & -2 & 0 \end{bmatrix}$

13. **FOOD SALES** The daily sales at various fast food restaurants in various cities are shown in the table below.

City	McPizza	Burger Hut	QuikSubs
Dulles	$25,000	$17,400	$21,000
Fitchburg	$ 3,600	$ 4,400	$ 5,900
Newton	$ 19,200	$20,100	$17,400

a. Write a matrix to organize the sales data.

$$\begin{array}{l} \\ \text{Dulles} \\ \text{Fitchburg} \\ \text{Newton} \end{array} \begin{array}{c} \text{McPizza}\quad\text{Burger Hut}\quad\text{QuikSubs} \\ \begin{bmatrix} 25{,}000 & 17{,}400 & 21{,}000 \\ 3{,}600 & 4{,}400 & 5{,}900 \\ 19{,}200 & 20{,}100 & 17{,}400 \end{bmatrix} \end{array}$$

b. What are the dimensions of the matrix? **3 × 3**

c. In which city does Burger Hut sell more food than its competitors? **Newton**

Chapter 6 39 *Glencoe Algebra 1*

Lesson 6-6

Word Problem Practice

CRM p. 40 AL OL BL ELL

NAME ____ DATE ____ PERIOD ____

6-6 Word Problem Practice

Organizing Data Using Matrices

1. **AP EXAMS** The College Board regularly administers Advanced Placement (AP) exams to students in high schools nationwide. The highest score possible on an AP exam is a 5; Below is a table showing the percentage of students taking selected AP exams in 2007 and the percentage of students who achieved various scores.

AP Grade	Calculus AB	Calculus BC	Chemistry	Chinese
5 points	21.0%	43.5%	15.3%	81.0%
4 points	18.7%	17.9%	18.0%	11.8%

Source: The College Board

Write a matrix to organize the test scores, and state its dimensions. In which test did most students score a 5?

$$\begin{array}{l} \\ \text{5 points} \\ \text{4 points} \end{array} \begin{array}{c} \text{Calc AB}\quad\text{Calc BC}\quad\text{Chemistry}\quad\text{Chinese} \\ \begin{bmatrix} 21.0 & 43.5 & 15.3 & 81.0 \\ 18.7 & 17.9 & 18.0 & 11.8 \end{bmatrix} \end{array}$$ **2 × 4; "Chinese"**

2. **STOCK PRICES** The chart below shows the performance of one share of PQR Corp. and ABC Corp. over the last week.

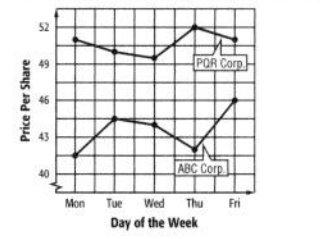

Organize the data in the chart into a matrix and perform the matrix operation to find the value of 50 shares of PQR Corp. and ABC Corp. on each day.

$$\begin{array}{c} \text{Mon}\quad\text{Tue}\quad\text{Wed}\quad\text{Thu}\quad\text{Fri} \\ \begin{bmatrix} 2{,}550 & 2{,}500 & 2{,}475 & 2{,}600 & 2{,}550 \\ 2{,}100 & 2{,}225 & 2{,}200 & 2{,}100 & 2{,}300 \end{bmatrix} \end{array}$$

3. **BASEBALL** In Tuesday's baseball game, Reggie scored 1 run and had 4 hits and 1 stolen base. Jeremy scored 2 runs, had 5 hits, and stole no bases. In Wednesday's baseball game, Reggie didn't score any runs, but did have 3 hits and 1 stolen base. Jeremy had 1 run, 4 hits, and 1 stolen base.

a. Create a matrix showing Reggie and Jeremy's performance in Tuesday's baseball game. $\begin{bmatrix} 1 & 4 & 1 \\ 2 & 5 & 0 \end{bmatrix}$

b. Create a matrix showing Reggie and Jeremy's performance in Wednesday's baseball game. $\begin{bmatrix} 0 & 3 & 1 \\ 1 & 4 & 1 \end{bmatrix}$

c. Add the two matrices together to show Reggie and Jeremy's total performance over both games. $\begin{bmatrix} 1 & 7 & 2 \\ 3 & 9 & 1 \end{bmatrix}$

d. Subtract the matrix representing Tuesday's game from the matrix representing Wednesday's game to show Reggie and Jeremy's change in performance. $\begin{bmatrix} -1 & -1 & 0 \\ -1 & -1 & 1 \end{bmatrix}$

Chapter 6 40 *Glencoe Algebra 1*

Enrichment

CRM p. 41 OL BL

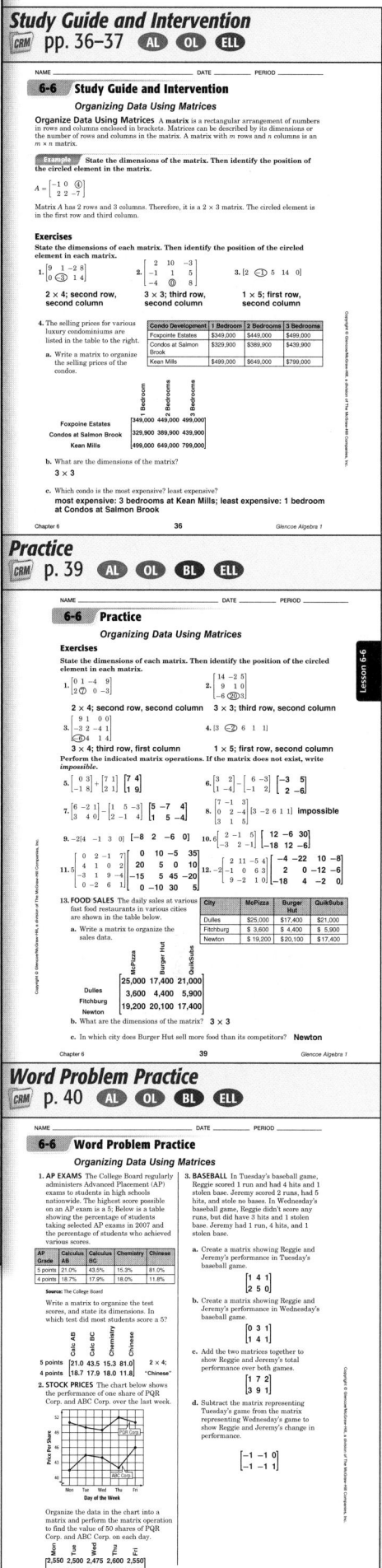

NAME ____ DATE ____ PERIOD ____

6-6 Enrichment

Multiplying 2 × 2 Matrices

Multiplication with matrices is not limited to scalars. A matrix can also be multiplied by another matrix. To find the product of two 2 × 2 matrices, the following equation can be applied:

$$\begin{bmatrix} q & r \\ s & t \end{bmatrix}\begin{bmatrix} v & x \\ y & z \end{bmatrix} = \begin{bmatrix} (qv + ry) & (qx + rz) \\ (sv + ty) & (sx + tz) \end{bmatrix}$$

Example 1 **If $A = \begin{bmatrix} 3 & -2 \\ 4 & 1 \end{bmatrix}$ and $B \begin{bmatrix} 1 & 0 \\ 3 & -2 \end{bmatrix}$, find AB.**

$AB = \begin{bmatrix} 3 & -2 \\ 4 & 1 \end{bmatrix}\begin{bmatrix} 1 & 0 \\ 3 & -2 \end{bmatrix}$ Substitution

$= \begin{bmatrix} 3 \cdot 1 + (-2) \cdot 3 & 3 \cdot 0 + (-2) \cdot (-2) \\ 4 \cdot 1 + 1 \cdot 3 & 4 \cdot 0 + 1 \cdot (-2) \end{bmatrix}$ Property of matrix multiplication

$= \begin{bmatrix} 3 + (-6) & 0 + 4 \\ 4 + 3 & 0 + (-2) \end{bmatrix}$ Simplify.

$= \begin{bmatrix} -3 & 4 \\ 7 & -2 \end{bmatrix}$ Simplify.

Example 2 **If $A = \begin{bmatrix} 3 & -2 \\ 4 & 1 \end{bmatrix}$ and $B = \begin{bmatrix} 1 & 0 \\ 3 & -2 \end{bmatrix}$, find BA.**

$AB = \begin{bmatrix} 1 & 0 \\ 3 & -2 \end{bmatrix}\begin{bmatrix} 3 & -2 \\ 4 & 1 \end{bmatrix}$ Substitution

$= \begin{bmatrix} 1 \cdot 3 + 0 \cdot 4 & 1 \cdot (-2) + 0 \cdot 1 \\ 3 \cdot 3 + (-2) \cdot 4 & 3 \cdot (-2) + (-2) \cdot 1 \end{bmatrix}$ Property of matrix multiplication

$= \begin{bmatrix} 3 + 0 & -2 + 0 \\ 9 - 8 & -6 + (-2) \end{bmatrix}$ Simplify.

$= \begin{bmatrix} -3 & 4 \\ 7 & -2 \end{bmatrix}$ Simplify.

Lesson 6-6

Tips for New Teachers

Assessment For Exercise 26c, check that students understand that negative numbers in the matrix mean that the verbal score is less than the mathematical score, and positive numbers mean that the verbal score is greater than the mathematical score. You may want to ask students to make a generalization about the scores based on the matrix for part c.

Additional Answers

26a. $\begin{bmatrix} 509 & 502 \\ 507 & 504 \\ 507 & 502 \\ 512 & 504 \\ 513 & 505 \end{bmatrix}$; $\begin{bmatrix} 531 & 496 \\ 533 & 498 \\ 534 & 500 \\ 537 & 501 \\ 538 & 504 \end{bmatrix}$

26c. $\begin{bmatrix} -22 & 6 \\ -26 & 6 \\ -27 & 2 \\ -25 & 3 \\ -25 & 1 \end{bmatrix}$

34. Sample answer: $-1\begin{bmatrix} 1 & 1 \\ 1 & 1 \\ 1 & 1 \end{bmatrix}$, $\begin{bmatrix} 5 & 0 \\ 10 & 7 \\ -4 & 10 \end{bmatrix}$, and $\begin{bmatrix} 1 & 0 \\ 0 & 1 \\ 0 & -1 \end{bmatrix}$

36. No; the matrices have different dimensions. The matrix $\begin{bmatrix} 1 & 2 & 3 \\ 4 & 5 & 6 \end{bmatrix}$ is a 2×3 matrix and the matrix $\begin{bmatrix} 1 & 2 \\ 3 & 4 \\ 5 & 6 \end{bmatrix}$ is a 3×2 matrix. These matrices cannot be added.

37. Sample answer: The number of miles hiked on a 3-day hiking trip. On the first day, 5 miles were hiked. On the second day, 8 miles were hiked. On the third day, 10 miles were hiked.

	Miles
Day 1	5
Day 2	8
Day 3	10

26. SCORES The average SAT scores for males and females are shown.

Real-World Link

The SAT test consists of three parts: math, critical reading, and writing. Each part is worth 800 points, and 2400 is the best possible score. The average SAT score is about 1518.

Source: *The Washington Post*

Year	Verbal Score		Mathematical Score	
	Male	Female	Male	Female
1998	509	502	531	496
2000	507	504	533	498
2002	507	502	534	500
2004	512	504	537	501
2005	513	505	538	504

See margin.

a. Organize the verbal scores and mathematical scores into two matrices.

b. Find the total score that males and females earned on the SATs each year.

c. Express the difference between the verbal and mathematical scores in a matrix. See margin.

26b. $\begin{bmatrix} 1040 & 998 \\ 1040 & 1002 \\ 1041 & 1002 \\ 1049 & 1005 \\ 1051 & 1009 \end{bmatrix}$

C **Perform the indicated matrix operations. If an operation cannot be performed, write *impossible*.**

27. $2\begin{bmatrix} -5 & 8 & 2 \end{bmatrix} + \begin{bmatrix} -6 & 9 & 5 \end{bmatrix}$ $\begin{bmatrix} -16 & 25 & 9 \end{bmatrix}$

28. $\begin{bmatrix} 9 & -5 \\ -3 & 4 \end{bmatrix} + (-9)\begin{bmatrix} 2 & -1 \\ 0 & -7 \end{bmatrix}$ $\begin{bmatrix} -9 & 4 \\ -3 & 67 \end{bmatrix}$

29. $-3\begin{bmatrix} 7 \\ -4 \\ -2 \\ 1 \end{bmatrix} - 2\begin{bmatrix} 7 \\ -5 \\ -3 \end{bmatrix}$ impossible

30. $-1\begin{bmatrix} 5 & -8 & 14 \\ 12 & -7 & -3 \\ 1 & 0 & 8 \end{bmatrix} + \begin{bmatrix} 7 & 8 & 2 \\ -7 & -2 & 6 \\ -6 & 3 & -1 \end{bmatrix}$

31. $\begin{bmatrix} -5 & 2 \\ 12 & -11 \\ 9 & 0 \\ -1 & 7 \\ 6 & 5 \\ -4 & 2 \end{bmatrix} + 4\begin{bmatrix} 10 & 4 \\ -1 & -3 \\ 5 & -8 \\ -9 & 0 \\ 1 & 4 \\ -3 & 2 \end{bmatrix}$

32. $2\begin{bmatrix} 4 & 0 \\ -1 & 7 \\ -3 & 2 \end{bmatrix} - 3\begin{bmatrix} 1 & -4 \\ -8 & 9 \\ 10 & 7 \end{bmatrix} + \begin{bmatrix} 6 & 3 \\ 8 & -4 \\ -1 & -2 \end{bmatrix}$

30. $\begin{bmatrix} 2 & 16 & -12 \\ -19 & 5 & 9 \\ -7 & 3 & -9 \end{bmatrix}$

31. $\begin{bmatrix} 35 & 18 \\ 8 & -23 \\ 29 & -32 \\ -37 & 7 \\ 10 & 21 \\ -16 & 10 \end{bmatrix}$

32. $\begin{bmatrix} 11 & 15 \\ 30 & -17 \\ -37 & -19 \end{bmatrix}$

33. Sample answer: $\begin{bmatrix} 6 & 1 & 9 \\ 1 & 3 & 2 \end{bmatrix}$ and $\begin{bmatrix} 1 & 3 & 2 \\ 4 & 2 & 2 \end{bmatrix}$

35. Sample answer: $\begin{bmatrix} 4 & 5 \\ 5 & 1 \end{bmatrix}$

H.O.T. Problems

Use Higher-Order Thinking Skills

33. OPEN ENDED Write two matrices with a difference of $\begin{bmatrix} 5 & -2 & 7 \\ -3 & 1 & 0 \end{bmatrix}$.

34. CHALLENGE Write three matrices with a sum of $\begin{bmatrix} 5 & -1 \\ 9 & 7 \\ -5 & 8 \end{bmatrix}$ if at least one of the addends is shown as the product of a scalar and a matrix. See margin.

35. REASONING For matrix $A = \begin{bmatrix} 1 & 2 \\ 3 & 4 \end{bmatrix}$, the *transpose* of A is $A^T = \begin{bmatrix} 1 & 3 \\ 2 & 4 \end{bmatrix}$. Write a matrix B that is equal to its transpose B^T.

36. REASONING Is it possible to add a 3×2 matrix and a 2×3 matrix? Explain. Include an example or counterexample to support your answer. See margin.

37. OPEN ENDED Describe a real-world situation that can be modeled by using a matrix. Then write a matrix to model the situation. See margin.

38. WRITING IN MATH Summarize how to perform matrix operations on matrices. See margin.

38. Matrix addition and subtraction can only be performed on matrices that have exactly the same dimensions. Each of the corresponding elements of the matrices are either added or subtracted. In scalar multiplication, each element of the matrix is multiplied by the same scalar (a real number).

PSAE PRACTICE 6.11.12, 8.11.02, 8.11.17, 8.11.16

39. If $A = \begin{bmatrix} 5 & -8 & 1 \\ 7 & -3 & 4 \end{bmatrix}$ and $B = \begin{bmatrix} 9 & -5 & 2 \\ -1 & -7 & 6 \end{bmatrix}$, find $A + B$. **C**

A $\begin{bmatrix} 14 & -13 & 3 \\ 7 & -3 & 4 \end{bmatrix}$ **C** $\begin{bmatrix} 14 & -13 & 3 \\ 6 & -10 & 10 \end{bmatrix}$

B $\begin{bmatrix} 5 & -8 & 1 \\ 6 & -10 & 10 \end{bmatrix}$ **D** $\begin{bmatrix} -4 & -3 & -1 \\ 8 & 4 & -2 \end{bmatrix}$

40. SHORT RESPONSE The difference between the length and width of a rectangle is 9 inches. Find the dimensions of the rectangle if its perimeter is 52 inches. **17.5 in. × 8.5 in.**

41. At a movie theater, the costs for various amounts of popcorn and hot dogs are shown. **G**

Hot Dogs	Boxes of Popcorn	Total Cost
1	1	$8.50
2	4	$21.60

Which pair of equations can be used to find p, the cost of a box of popcorn, and h, the cost of a hot dog?

F $p + h = 8.5$, $p + 2h = 10.8$ **H** $p + h = 8.5$, $2p + 4h = 21.6$

G $p + h = 8.5$, $2h + 4p = 21.6$ **J** $p + h = 8.5$, $2p + 2h = 21.6$

42. What is the solution set for $9 + x \geq 3$? **A**

A $\{x \mid x \geq -6\}$ **C** $\{x \mid x \leq -6\}$

B $\{x \mid x \geq 6\}$ **D** $\{x \mid x \leq 6\}$

Spiral Review

43. CHEMISTRY Orion Labs needs to make 500 gallons of 34% acid solution. The only solutions available are a 25% acid solution and a 50% acid solution. Write and solve a system of equations to find the number of gallons of each solution that should be mixed to make the 34% solution. (Lesson 6-5) **$x + y = 500$, $0.25x + 0.5y = 170$; 320 gal of 25%; 180 gal of 50%**

Use elimination to solve each system of equations. (Lesson 6-4)

44. $x + y = 7$, $2x + y = 11$ **(4, 3)**

45. $a - b = 9$, $7a + b = 7$ **(2, −7)**

46. $q + 4r = -8$, $3q + 2r = 6$ **(4, −3)**

47. SALES Marissa wants to make at least $75 selling caramel apples at the school carnival. She plans to sell each apple for $1.50. Write and solve an inequality to find the number of apples a she needs to make and sell to reach her goal if it costs her $0.30 per apple. (Lesson 5-3) **$1.5a - 0.3a \geq 75$; $a \geq 62.5$; at least 63 apples**

Find the next three terms of each arithmetic sequence. (Lesson 3-5)

48. 4, 7, 10, 13, . . . **16, 19, 22**

49. 18, 24, 30, 36, . . . **42, 48, 54**

50. −66, −70, −74, −78, . . . **−82, −86, −90**

51. CRAFTS Mandy makes baby blankets and stuffed rabbits to sell at craft fairs. She sells blankets for $28 and rabbits for $18. Write and evaluate an expression to find her total amount of sales if she sells 25 blankets and 25 rabbits. (Lesson 1-4) **25(28 + 18) = $1150**

Skills Review

Solve each equation. (Lesson 2-3)

52. $5 = 4t - 7$ **3**

53. $-3x + 10 = 19$ **−3**

54. $\frac{c}{-4} - 2 = -36$ **136**

55. $6 + \frac{y}{3} = -45$ **−153**

56. $9 = \frac{d + 5}{8}$ **67**

57. $\frac{r + 1}{3} = 8$ **23**

4 ASSESS

Crystal Ball Have students write a short sentence on how they think today's lesson will prepare them for tomorrow's lesson on using matrices to solve systems of equations.

Formative Assessment

Check for student understanding of concepts in Lessons 6-5 and 6-6.

CRM Quiz 3, p. 60

Differentiated Instruction OL BL

Extension Have students use matrix operations and the meaning of equivalent matrices to solve the following equation for x and y.

$$2\begin{bmatrix} x & 2 \\ -4 & 5 \end{bmatrix} + \begin{bmatrix} -3 & 7 \\ 2 & y \end{bmatrix} = \begin{bmatrix} 9 & 11 \\ -6 & 3 \end{bmatrix}$$ $x = 6$; $y = -7$

6-7 Lesson Notes

1 FOCUS

Vertical Alignment

Before Lesson 6-7
Solve systems of equations by graphing, using substitution, and using elimination.

Lesson 6-7
Write systems of equations as augmented matrices.
Solve systems of equations by using elementary row operations.

After Lesson 6-7
Use matrices to transform figures on a coordinate plane.

2 TEACH

Scaffolding Questions

Have students read the *Why?* section of the lesson and the paragraph on augmented matrices.

Ask:

- What system of equations represents the situation? $x + y = 30$; $22x + 24y = 700$
- What are the coefficients in the system? 1, 1; 22, 24 What are the constant terms? 30, 700
- Which numbers are entered to the right of the dashed line in an augmented matrix? 30, 700

(continued on the next page)

6-7 Using Matrices to Solve Systems of Equations

Then
You solved systems of equations by graphing, using substitution, and using elimination. (Lesson 6-1 through 6-4)

Now
- Write systems of equations as augmented matrices.
- Solve systems of equations by using elementary row operations.

IL Learning Standards
8.C.4b Apply algebraic properties and procedures with matrices, vectors, functions and sequences **using data found in business, industry and consumer situations.**

New Vocabulary
augmented matrix
row reduction
identity matrix

IL Math Online
glencoe.com
- Extra Examples
- Personal Tutor
- Self-Check Quiz
- Homework Help

Why?

The 30 members of the Washington High School's Ski Club went on a one-day ski trip. Members can rent skis for \$22 per day or snowboards for \$24 per day. The club paid a total of \$700 for rental equipment.

The resort can use this information to find how many members rented each type of equipment.

Augmented Matrices You can use a matrix called an **augmented matrix** to solve a system of equations. An augmented matrix consists of the coefficients and the constant terms of a system of equations. The coefficients and constant terms are usually separated by a dashed line.

Linear System	Augmented Matrix
$x - 3y = 8$ $-9x + 2y = -4$	$\left[\begin{array}{rr:r} 1 & -3 & 8 \\ -9 & 2 & -4 \end{array}\right]$

Make sure that the coefficients of the x-terms are listed in one column, the coefficients of the y-terms are in another column, and the constant terms are in a third column.

EXAMPLE 1 Write an Augmented Matrix

Write an augmented matrix for each system of equations.

a. $-2x + 7y = 11$
$6x - 4y = 2$

Place the coefficients of the equations and the constant terms into a matrix.

$$\begin{aligned} -2x + 7y &= 11 \\ 6x - 4y &= 2 \end{aligned} \quad \rightarrow \quad \left[\begin{array}{rr:r} -2 & 7 & 11 \\ 6 & -4 & 2 \end{array}\right]$$

b. $x - 2y = 5$
$y = -4$

$$\begin{aligned} x - 2y &= 5 \\ y &= -4 \end{aligned} \quad \rightarrow \quad \left[\begin{array}{rr:r} 1 & -2 & 5 \\ 0 & 1 & -4 \end{array}\right]$$

Check Your Progress

1A. $6x - 8y = -10$, $-5x = -20$ $\left[\begin{array}{rr:r} 6 & -8 & -10 \\ -5 & 0 & -20 \end{array}\right]$

1B. $3x - 2y = 6$, $2x + 3y = 12$ $\left[\begin{array}{rr:r} 3 & -2 & 6 \\ 2 & 3 & 12 \end{array}\right]$

Personal Tutor glencoe.com

Solve Systems of Equations You can solve a system of equations by using an augmented matrix. By performing row operations, you can change the form of the matrix.

Lesson 6-7 Resources

Resource	Approaching-Level	On-Level	Beyond-Level	English Learners
Teacher Edition		• Differentiated Instruction, pp. 377, 381	• Differentiated Instruction, pp. 377, 381	
Chapter Resource Masters	• Study Guide and Intervention, pp. 42–43 • Skills Practice, p. 44 • Practice, p. 45 • Word Problem Practice, p. 46	• Study Guide and Intervention, pp. 42–43 • Skills Practice, p. 44 • Practice, p. 45 • Word Problem Practice, p. 46 • Enrichment, p. 47	• Practice, p. 45 • Word Problem Practice, p. 46 • Enrichment, p. 47	• Study Guide and Intervention, pp. 42–43 • Skills Practice, p. 44 • Practice, p. 45
Transparencies	• 5-Minute Check Transparency 6-7	• 5-Minute Check Transparency 6-7	• 5-Minute Check Transparency 6-7	• 5-Minute Check Transparency 6-7
Other	• Study Notebook	• Study Notebook	• Study Notebook	• Study Notebook

Key Concept — Elementary Row Operations

For Your FOLDABLE

The following operations can be performed on an augmented matrix.

- Interchange any two rows.
- Multiply all elements in a row by a nonzero constant.
- Replace one row with the sum of that row and a multiple of another row.

Row reduction is the process of performing elementary row operations on an augmented matrix to solve a system. The goal is to get the coefficients portion of the matrix to have the form $\begin{bmatrix} 1 & 0 \\ 0 & 1 \end{bmatrix}$, also known as the **identity matrix**.

The first row will give you the solution for x, because the coefficient of y is 0 and the coefficient of x is 1. The second row will give you the solution for y, because the coefficient of x is 0 and the coefficient of y is 1.

EXAMPLE 2 Use Row Operations to Solve a System

Use an augmented matrix to solve the system of equations.

$-5x + 3y = 6$

$x - y = 4$

Step 1 Write the augmented matrix: $\left[\begin{array}{cc|c} -5 & 3 & 6 \\ 1 & -1 & 4 \end{array}\right]$.

Step 2 Notice that the first element in the second row is 1. Interchange the rows so 1 can be in the upper left-hand corner.

$$\left[\begin{array}{cc|c} -5 & 3 & 6 \\ 1 & -1 & 4 \end{array}\right] \xrightarrow{\text{Interchange } R_1 \text{ and } R_2.} \left[\begin{array}{cc|c} 1 & -1 & 4 \\ -5 & 3 & 6 \end{array}\right]$$

Step 3 To make the first element in the second row a 0, multiply the first row by 5 and add the result to row 2.

$$\left[\begin{array}{cc|c} 1 & -1 & 4 \\ -5 & 3 & 6 \end{array}\right] \xrightarrow{5R_1 + R_2} \left[\begin{array}{cc|c} 1 & -1 & 4 \\ 0 & -2 & 26 \end{array}\right]$$

The result is placed in row 2.

Step 4 To make the second element in the second row a 1, multiply the second row by $-\frac{1}{2}$.

$$\left[\begin{array}{cc|c} 1 & -1 & 4 \\ 0 & -2 & 26 \end{array}\right] \xrightarrow{-\frac{1}{2}R_2} \left[\begin{array}{cc|c} 1 & -1 & 4 \\ 0 & 1 & -13 \end{array}\right]$$

The result is placed in row 2.

Step 5 To make the second element in the first row a 0, add the rows together.

$$\left[\begin{array}{cc|c} 1 & -1 & 4 \\ 0 & 1 & -13 \end{array}\right] \xrightarrow{R_1 + R_2} \left[\begin{array}{cc|c} 1 & 0 & -9 \\ 0 & 1 & -13 \end{array}\right]$$

The result is placed in row 1.

The solution is $(-9, -13)$.

StudyTip

Alternate Method Row operations can be performed in different orders to arrive at the same result. In Example 2, you could have started by multiplying the first row, R_1, by $-\frac{1}{5}$ instead of interchanging the rows.

Check Your Progress

2A. $x + 2y = 6$ $(4, 1)$
$2x + y = 9$

2B. $2x - 3y = 3$ $(9, 5)$
$x + y = 14$

Personal Tutor glencoe.com

- What is an advantage in using an augmented matrix to solve a system of equations? Sample answer: It is easier to manipulate numbers only rather than numbers and variables.

Augmented Matrices

Example 1 shows how to write an augmented matrix for a system of linear equations.

Formative Assessment

Use the Check Your Progress exercises after each Example to determine students' understanding of concepts.

Additional Example

1 Write an augmented matrix for each system of equations.

a. $4x + 2y = 22$

$-2x + y = -5$

$\left[\begin{array}{cc|c} 4 & 2 & 22 \\ -2 & 1 & -5 \end{array}\right]$

b. $2x + y = 10$

$-3x = -18$

$\left[\begin{array}{cc|c} 2 & 1 & 10 \\ -3 & 0 & -18 \end{array}\right]$

Additional Examples also in Interactive Classroom PowerPoint® Presentations

IWB INTERACTIVE WHITEBOARD READY

Solve Systems of Equations

Example 2 shows how to use row operations to solve a system.

Additional Example

2 Use an augmented matrix to solve the system of equations.

$-3x + 2y = 2$

$x + y = 6$ $(2, 4)$

Differentiated Instruction OL BL

Logical Learners Have students use a different order of row operations to solve the system of equations in Example 2. Suggest that they use the Study Tip or start by solving for the second element in row 1 or row 2. Have them compare their steps with the steps in Example 2 and then share their results with the class.

Example 3 shows how to write an augmented matrix for a real-world problem and solve the system.

Additional Example

3 **THEATER** Mr. Gomez and Mr. Bates took their families to a play. The total number of people in each family and the total cost of tickets are shown in the table.

Family	Number of Adults	Number of Children	Total Cost
Gomez	2	2	\$80
Bates	2	3	\$92

a. Write a system of linear equations to model the situation. Then write the augmented matrix. $2a + 2c = 80$, $2a + 3c = 92$; $\left[\begin{array}{cc|c} 2 & 2 & 80 \\ 2 & 3 & 92 \end{array}\right]$

b. Find the cost of a ticket for an adult and a child. adult ticket = \$28; child ticket = \$12

Focus on Mathematical Content

Row Operations Row operations include interchanging two rows any number of times, multiplying all of the elements in a row by a nonzero constant, adding the rows, or performing a combination of multiplying and adding rows in a single row operation. The purpose of row operations is to get the identity matrix. The order in which row operations are applied can vary, just as the order of using operations can vary in solving systems by elimination.

Real-World Link

Yellowstone National Park is America's first national park. It is located in Wyoming, Montana, and Idaho. The park was established in 1872. The most popular geyser in the world, Old Faithful, is located there.

Source: National Park Service

Matrices are useful for solving real-world problems. First, model the situation with a system of equations and then write the augmented matrix.

Real-World EXAMPLE 3

PARKS A youth group traveling in two vans visited Yellowstone National Park. The number of people in each van and the park fees are shown in the table.

Van	Number of Adults	Number of Students	Total Cost
A	2	6	\$102
B	2	7	\$114

a. Write a system of linear equations to model the situation. Then write the augmented matrix.

Let a represent the adult fee, and let s represent the student fee.

$$\begin{array}{l} 2a + 6s = 102 \\ 2a + 7s = 114 \end{array} \longrightarrow \left[\begin{array}{cc|c} 2 & 6 & 102 \\ 2 & 7 & 114 \end{array}\right]$$

b. Find the entrance fee for an adult and a student.

Step 1 To make the first element in the first row a 1, multiply the first row by $\frac{1}{2}$.

$$\left[\begin{array}{cc|c} 2 & 6 & 102 \\ 2 & 7 & 114 \end{array}\right] \xrightarrow{\frac{1}{2}R_1} \left[\begin{array}{cc|c} 1 & 3 & 51 \\ 2 & 7 & 114 \end{array}\right]$$

Step 2 To make the first element in the second row a 0, multiply the first row by −2 and add the result to row 2.

$$\left[\begin{array}{cc|c} 1 & 3 & 51 \\ 2 & 7 & 114 \end{array}\right] \xrightarrow{-2R_1 + R_2} \left[\begin{array}{cc|c} 1 & 3 & 51 \\ 0 & 1 & 12 \end{array}\right]$$

Step 3 To make the second element in the first row a 0, multiply the second row by −3 and add the result to row 1.

$$\left[\begin{array}{cc|c} 1 & 3 & 51 \\ 0 & 1 & 12 \end{array}\right] \xrightarrow{-3R_2 + R_1} \left[\begin{array}{cc|c} 1 & 0 & 15 \\ 0 & 1 & 12 \end{array}\right]$$

The solution is (15, 12). The adult fee is \$15, and the student fee is \$12.

Check Your Progress

3. CARNIVAL At a carnival, 44 tickets are required for 4 meals and 8 rides, and 58 tickets are required for 6 meals and 10 rides. How many tickets are required for each item? **3 tickets for a meal and 4 tickets for a ride**

Personal Tutor glencoe.com

Check Your Understanding

Example 1 p. 376

Write an augmented matrix for each system of equations. **1–6. See margin.**

1. $-x + 3y = -10$; $5x - 2y = 7$

2. $x - 4y = 5$; $-2x + 8y = 1$

3. $x + 2y = -1$; $2x - 2y = -9$

4. $-4x + 6y = 2$; $-x - 8y = 0$

5. $3x + 4y = -5$; $2x - y = 6$

6. $-x + 3y = 8$; $6x - 3y = -3$

TEACH with TECH

VIDEO RECORDING Record yourself working through the examples in class. Post the videos to a video sharing Web site so that students can watch them outside of class as an additional reference.

Additional Answers

1. $\left[\begin{array}{cc|c} -1 & 3 & -10 \\ 5 & -2 & 7 \end{array}\right]$

2. $\left[\begin{array}{cc|c} 1 & -4 & 5 \\ -2 & 8 & 1 \end{array}\right]$

3. $\left[\begin{array}{cc|c} 1 & 2 & -1 \\ 2 & -2 & -9 \end{array}\right]$

4. $\left[\begin{array}{cc|c} -4 & 6 & 2 \\ -1 & -8 & 0 \end{array}\right]$

5. $\left[\begin{array}{cc|c} 3 & 4 & -5 \\ 2 & -1 & 6 \end{array}\right]$

6. $\left[\begin{array}{cc|c} -1 & 3 & 8 \\ 6 & -3 & -3 \end{array}\right]$

Example 2 p. 377

Use an augmented matrix to solve each system of equations.

7. $x + y = -3$ **(−1, −2)**
$x - y = 1$

8. $x - y = -2$
$2x + 2y = 12$ **(2, 4)**

9. $3x - 4y = -27$ **(−1, 6)**
$x + 2y = 11$

10. $x + 4y = -6$
$2x - 5y = 1$ **(−2, −1)**

Example 3 p. 378

11a. $3n + 4b = 22.25$
$3n + 10b = 29.75$

11b. $\left[\begin{array}{cc|c} 3 & 4 & 22.25 \\ 3 & 10 & 29.75 \end{array}\right]$

11. **SHOPPING** Darnell and Sandra went shopping for graphic novels. The store charges one price for all new books and another for all old books.

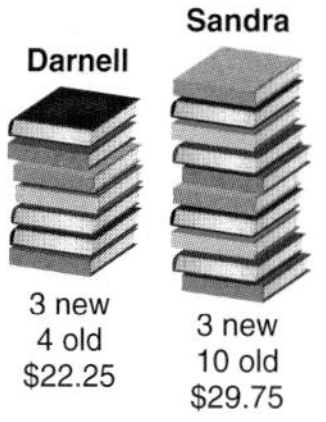

a. Write a system of linear equations to model the situation. Let n represent new books, and let b represent old books.

b. Write the augmented matrix.

c. What is the price for each type of book? **new: $5.75; used: $1.25**

Practice and Problem Solving

= **Step-by-Step Solutions** begin on page R12.
Extra Practice begins on page 815.

Example 1 p. 376

Write an augmented matrix for each system of equations. **12–17. See margin.**

12. $x + 2y = -3$
$3x - y = 2$

13. $-4x - 3y = -8$
$x + y = -12$

14. $2x + y = 1$
$x + 4y = -5$

15. $-6x + y = -15$
$x - 2y = 13$

16. $3x + y = -6$
$x - 5y = -7$

17. $x - y = 7$
$9x - 5y = 23$

Example 2 p. 377

Use an augmented matrix to solve each system of equations.

18. $x - 3y = -2$ **(7, 3)**
$4x + y = 31$

19. $x + 2y = 3$
$-3x + 3y = 27$ **(−5, 4)**

20. $2x - 3y = -20$ **(−1, 6)**
$x + 2y = 11$

21. $x - y = 2$
$3x - 2y = 2$ **(−2, −4)**

22. $x - 2y = -15$ **(9, 12)**
$2x + 5y = 78$

23. $4x + 3y = -9$
$x + 4y = -25$ **(3, −7)**

24. $-2x - 2y = 8$ **(2, −6)**
$5x + 2y = -2$

25. $3x - 6y = 36$
$2x + 4y = -40$ **(−4, −8)**

26. $2x + 3y = 11$ **(−2, 5)**
$3x - y = -11$

27. $4x - 3y = 24$
$2x + 5y = -14$ **(3, −4)**

28. $3x + 2y = 6$ $\left(-1, \frac{9}{2}\right)$
$x + 2y = 8$

29. $4x - 3y = 5$
$2x + 9y = 6$ $\left(\frac{3}{2}, \frac{1}{3}\right)$

Example 3 p. 378

30a. $8u + 6p = 378$
$6u + 9p = 333$

30b. $\left[\begin{array}{cc|c} 8 & 6 & 378 \\ 6 & 9 & 333 \end{array}\right]$

30. **CHEERLEADING** If the Franklin High School cheerleaders replace 8 uniforms and 6 poms, the cost is $378. If they replace 6 uniforms and 9 poms, the cost is $333.

a. Write a system of linear equations to model the situation. Let u represent uniforms, and let p represent poms.

b. Write the augmented matrix.

c. What is the cost of each uniform and each pom? **uniform: $39; pom: $11**

B **Write a system of equations for each augmented matrix.** **31–36. See margin.**

31. $\left[\begin{array}{cc|c} 1 & 0 & 16 \\ 0 & 1 & -2 \end{array}\right]$

32. $\left[\begin{array}{cc|c} 1 & 7 & 3 \\ -5 & 10 & 4 \end{array}\right]$

33. $\left[\begin{array}{cc|c} 3 & 2 & 7 \\ -1 & -4 & 5 \end{array}\right]$

34. $\left[\begin{array}{cc|c} 1 & 0 & -10 \\ 0 & 4 & 8 \end{array}\right]$

35. $\left[\begin{array}{cc|c} -1 & 9 & 12 \\ 2 & 3 & -7 \end{array}\right]$

36. $\left[\begin{array}{cc|c} 6 & -6 & 5 \\ -8 & 11 & 0 \end{array}\right]$

Differentiated Homework Options

Level	Assignment	Two-Day Option	
AL Basic	12–30, 47–48, 50–73	13–29 odd, 52–55	12–30 even, 47–48, 50–51, 56–73
OL Core	13–35 odd, 37–39, 41–45 odd, 46–48, 50–73	12–30, 52–55	31–48, 50–51, 56–73
BL Advanced	31–67, (optional: 68–73)		

3 PRACTICE

Formative Assessment

Use Exercises 1–11 to check for understanding.

Use the chart at the bottom of this page to customize assignments for your students.

Tips for New Teachers

Sense-Making Remind students to check that they entered the coefficients for x in one column, the coefficients for y in one column, and the constant terms in one column when writing an augmented matrix. Point out that if either x or y is missing from the equation, students should enter its coefficient as zero.

Additional Answers

12. $\left[\begin{array}{cc|c} 1 & 2 & -3 \\ 3 & -1 & 2 \end{array}\right]$

13. $\left[\begin{array}{cc|c} -4 & -3 & -8 \\ 1 & 1 & -12 \end{array}\right]$

14. $\left[\begin{array}{cc|c} 2 & 1 & 1 \\ 1 & 4 & -5 \end{array}\right]$

15. $\left[\begin{array}{cc|c} -6 & 1 & -15 \\ 1 & -2 & 13 \end{array}\right]$

16. $\left[\begin{array}{cc|c} 3 & 1 & -6 \\ 1 & -5 & -7 \end{array}\right]$

17. $\left[\begin{array}{cc|c} 1 & -1 & 7 \\ 9 & -5 & 23 \end{array}\right]$

31. $x = 16$
$y = -2$

32. $x + 7y = 3$
$-5x + 10y = 4$

33. $3x + 2y = 7$
$-x - 4y = 5$

34. $x = -10$
$4y = 8$

35. $-x + 9y = 12$
$2x + 3y = -7$

36. $6x - 6y = 5$
$-8x + 11y = 0$

Study Guide and Intervention
CRM pp. 42–43 AL OL ELL

NAME ________________ DATE ________ PERIOD ________

6-7 Study Guide and Intervention
Using Matrices to Solve Systems of Equations

Augmented Matrices An augmented matrix consists of the coefficients and constant terms of a system of equations, separated by a dashed line.

Example 1 Write an augmented matrix for each system of equations.

$2x + 3y = 8$
$-x + 4y = 7$

Place the coefficients of the equations and the constant terms into a matrix.

$\begin{matrix} 2x + 3y = 8 \\ -x + 4y = 7 \end{matrix} \rightarrow \left[\begin{array}{cc|c} 2 & 3 & 8 \\ -1 & 4 & 7 \end{array}\right]$

Example 2 Write an augmented matrix for each system of equations.

$x + 3y = 6$
$2y = 6$

Place the coefficients of the equations and the constant terms into a matrix.

$\begin{matrix} x + 3y = 6 \\ 2y = 6 \end{matrix} \rightarrow \left[\begin{array}{cc|c} 1 & 3 & 6 \\ 0 & 2 & 6 \end{array}\right]$

Exercises

1. $2x - 2y = 10$, $-4x + y = -35$ $\left[\begin{array}{cc|c} 2 & -2 & 10 \\ -4 & 1 & -35 \end{array}\right]$
2. $x - y = 3$, $x - 2y = -1$ $\left[\begin{array}{cc|c} 1 & -1 & 3 \\ 1 & -2 & -1 \end{array}\right]$
3. $-x = -4$, $3x - 2y = 2$ $\left[\begin{array}{cc|c} -1 & 0 & -4 \\ 3 & -2 & 2 \end{array}\right]$
4. $-x + y = 9$, $4x - y = -6$ $\left[\begin{array}{cc|c} -1 & 1 & 9 \\ 4 & -1 & -6 \end{array}\right]$
5. $-2x + 5y = 11$, $3x - y = 0$ $\left[\begin{array}{cc|c} -2 & 5 & 11 \\ 3 & -1 & 0 \end{array}\right]$
6. $2y = 8$, $-3x = 12$ $\left[\begin{array}{cc|c} 0 & 2 & 8 \\ -3 & 0 & 12 \end{array}\right]$
7. $x - y = 3$, $2x = 12$ $\left[\begin{array}{cc|c} 1 & -1 & 3 \\ 2 & 0 & 12 \end{array}\right]$
8. $2x - y = 1$, $3x + y = 4$ $\left[\begin{array}{cc|c} 2 & -1 & 1 \\ 3 & 1 & 4 \end{array}\right]$
9. $2x - y = 4$, $10x - y = 24$ $\left[\begin{array}{cc|c} 2 & -1 & 4 \\ 10 & -1 & 24 \end{array}\right]$
10. $-2x = -4$, $x + 3y = 8$ $\left[\begin{array}{cc|c} -2 & 0 & -4 \\ 1 & 3 & 8 \end{array}\right]$
11. $5x - 2y = 7$, $x + 4y = 19$ $\left[\begin{array}{cc|c} 5 & -2 & 7 \\ 1 & 4 & 19 \end{array}\right]$
12. $x - y = 5$, $2x + 3y = 15$ $\left[\begin{array}{cc|c} 1 & -1 & 5 \\ 2 & 3 & 15 \end{array}\right]$
13. $x + 4y = 10$, $x - y = 0$ $\left[\begin{array}{cc|c} 1 & 4 & 10 \\ 1 & -1 & 0 \end{array}\right]$
14. $3x - y = 1$, $x + 2y = 19$ $\left[\begin{array}{cc|c} 3 & -1 & 1 \\ 1 & 2 & 19 \end{array}\right]$
15. $4y = -2$, $x + 2y = 3$ $\left[\begin{array}{cc|c} 0 & 4 & -2 \\ 1 & 2 & 3 \end{array}\right]$

Chapter 6 42 Glencoe Algebra 1

Practice
CRM p. 45 AL OL BL ELL

NAME ________________ DATE ________ PERIOD ________

6-7 Practice
Using Matrices to Solve Systems of Equations

Exercises

Write an augmented matrix for each system of equations.

1. $4x - 2y = 10$, $x + 8y = -22$ $\left[\begin{array}{cc|c} 4 & -2 & 10 \\ 1 & 8 & -22 \end{array}\right]$
2. $-12y = 6$, $3x + 2y = 11$ $\left[\begin{array}{cc|c} 0 & -12 & 6 \\ 3 & 2 & 11 \end{array}\right]$
3. $x + y = 10$, $2y - 3y = 0$ $\left[\begin{array}{cc|c} 1 & 1 & 10 \\ 2 & -3 & 0 \end{array}\right]$
4. $-x + 2y = 8$, $3x - y = 5$ $\left[\begin{array}{cc|c} -1 & 2 & 8 \\ 3 & -1 & 5 \end{array}\right]$
5. $4x - y = 11$, $2x - 3y = 3$ $\left[\begin{array}{cc|c} 4 & -1 & 11 \\ 2 & -3 & 3 \end{array}\right]$
6. $2x = 9$, $x - 5y = -5.5$ $\left[\begin{array}{cc|c} 2 & 0 & 9 \\ 1 & -5 & -5.5 \end{array}\right]$

Write a system of equations for each augmented matrix.

7. $\left[\begin{array}{cc|c} 2 & 0 & 8 \\ 3 & 4 & -2 \end{array}\right]$ $2x = 8$, $3x + 4y = -2$
8. $\left[\begin{array}{cc|c} 1 & 1 & 9 \\ -2 & 3 & -3 \end{array}\right]$ $x + y = 9$, $-2x + 3y = -3$
9. $\left[\begin{array}{cc|c} 2 & 3 & -6 \\ 1 & -4 & -14 \end{array}\right]$ $2x + 3y = -6$, $x - 4y = -14$

Use an augmented matrix to solve each system of equations.

10. $4x - y = 4$, $3y = 12$ (2, 4)
11. $2x + 5y = 1$, $-x - y = -2$ (3, –1)
12. $2x + 3y = 0$, $-x + 2y = 14$ (–6, 4)
13. $2x - y = 3$, $7x + y = 24$ (3, 3)
14. $2x - y = 4$, $9x - 3y = 12$ (0, –4)
15. $4x - y = 7$, $-2x + 3y = -16$ (0.5, –5)
16. **COMMUTER RAIL** The cost of a commuter rail ticket varies with the distance traveled. This month, Marcelo bought 5 round-trip tickets to visit his grandmother and 3 round-trip tickets to his friend's house for \$31.50. Last month, Marcelo bought 2 round-trip tickets to visit his grandmother and 6 round-trip tickets to visit his friend's house for \$27.00.
    a. Write a system of linear equations to represent the situations. $5x + 3y = 31.50$, $2x + 6y = 27.00$
    b. Write the augmented matrix. $\left[\begin{array}{cc|c} 5 & 3 & 31.50 \\ 2 & 6 & 27.00 \end{array}\right]$
    c. What is the cost of each type of ticket?
    round-trip ticket to his grandmother's: \$4.50; round-trip ticket to his friend's: \$3.00

Chapter 6 45 Glencoe Algebra 1

Word Problem Practice
CRM p. 46 AL OL BL ELL

NAME ________________ DATE ________ PERIOD ________

6-7 Word Problem Practice
Using Matrices to Solve Systems of Equations

1. **RENOVATIONS** A contractor is renovating a pair of bathrooms. The contractor buys 20 marble tiles and a can of paint to renovate the first bathroom, spending \$290. The contractor buys 35 marble tiles and 2 cans of paint for the second bathroom, spending \$470. Write an augmented matrix to model the situation.
   $\left[\begin{array}{cc|c} 20 & 1 & 290 \\ 35 & 2 & 470 \end{array}\right]$
2. **CATERING** The Mitchell Family is spending \$122 on 4 trays of ziti and 3 trays of grilled chicken for their family reunion. The Arroyo Family is spending \$208 on 7 trays of ziti and 5 trays of chicken from the same caterer. Use an augmented matrix to find out how much the caterer charges for a tray of ziti and a tray of grilled chicken.
   ziti: \$14; chicken: \$22
3. **DIAMONDS** As of 2007, the most expensive stone ever sold at auction is The Star of the Season, a pear-shaped diamond, which was sold in May 1995. The second most expensive diamond is the Chloe Diamond, which was sold in November 2007. The two diamonds together sold for \$32.7 million. The Chloe Diamond sold for \$33.3 million less than 3 times the selling price of the Star of the Season. Write an augmented matrix to model the situation. Then find the selling price of each diamond.
   $\left[\begin{array}{cc|c} 1 & -3 & -33.3 \\ 1 & 1 & 32.7 \end{array}\right]$; Star of the Season = \$16.5 million; Chloe Diamond = \$16.2 million.
4. **FOOTBALL** During the 2006–2007 season, the New York Jets scored a total of 59 times by getting touchdowns or kicking field goals, for a combined total of 282 points. If each touchdown is worth 6 points and each field goal is worth 3 points, write an augmented matrix to model the situation. Then find the number of touchdowns scored by the Jets.
   $\left[\begin{array}{cc|c} 1 & 1 & 59 \\ 3 & 6 & 282 \end{array}\right]$; 35
5. **POOLS** The design plans for a swimming pool call for a cement walkway of width x feet to surround the entire pool. The pool will be y feet long and $16x$ feet wide. The perimeter of the pool is 560 feet, and the outer perimeter of the walkway is 600 feet.

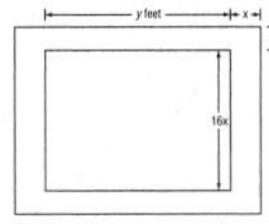

   a. Write a system of linear equations to model the situation.
   $32x + 2y = 560$
   $40x + 2y = 600$
   b. Write the augmented matrix.
   $\left[\begin{array}{cc|c} 32 & 2 & 560 \\ 40 & 2 & 600 \end{array}\right]$
   c. What are the dimensions of the pool?
   200 feet by 80 feet

Chapter 6 46 Glencoe Algebra 1

Real-World Link

According to a survey of girls between the ages of 8 and 15, watching videos is a popular slumber party activity.

Source: Blockbuster

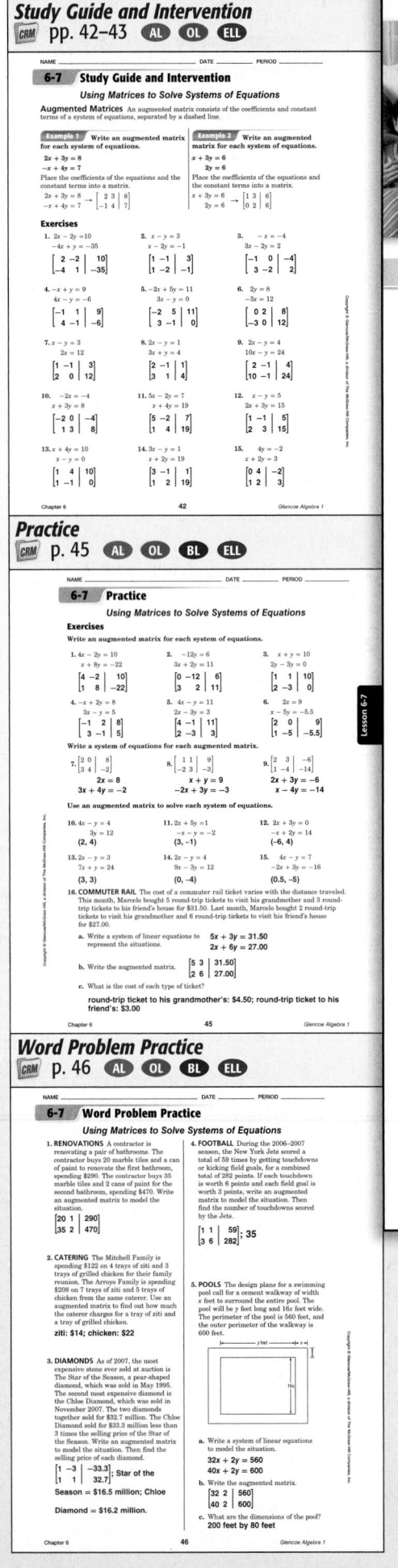

37. **SCHOOL STORE** Nari is checking items being shipped to the school store. The shipment contains notebooks that cost \$22 per box and mugs that cost \$40 per box. She counts 16 boxes, and the invoice states that the order totals \$460. How many boxes of each item were received? **10 boxes of notebooks, 6 boxes of mugs**

38. **PARTIES** Mel is having a few friends over, and she is buying subs and cans of sodas for them. Mel bought 28 items. If Mel spent \$56.70, how many subs did she buy? How many sodas did she buy? **10 subs and 18 cans of soda**

39. **RENTALS** Makya and his three sisters rented 2 items each at the video store. Members can rent movies for \$4 and video games for \$4.50. If Makya and his sisters spent \$33.50, how many movies did they rent? How many games did they rent? **5 movies and 3 games**

Use an augmented matrix to solve each system of equations.

40. $2x + y = -1$
    $-2x + y = -4$
41. $x + 2y = 3$
    $2x + 4y = 6$
42. $3x - y = 1$
    $-12x + 4y = 3$
43. $3x - 9y = 12$
    $-2x + 6y = 9$
44. $4x - 3y = 1$
    $-8x + 6y = -2$
45. $6x - 2y = -4$
    $-3x + y = 2$

40. $\left(\frac{3}{4}, -\frac{5}{2}\right)$
41. infinitely many
42. no solution
43. no solution
44. infinitely many
45. infinitely many

46. **MULTIPLE REPRESENTATIONS** In this problem, you will investigate the different representations of the following problem and their impact on the solution.

    Paloma exercises every morning for 40 minutes. She does a combination of aerobics, which burns about 11 Calories per minute, and stretching, which burns about 4 Calories per minute. Her goal is to burn 335 Calories during her routine. How long should she do each activity to burn 335 Calories?

    a. **VERBAL** List the representations that would be appropriate to solve the problem. **system of equations, graph, matrix, table of values**
    b. **ALGEBRAIC** Select a representation and solve the problem.
    c. **ALGEBRAIC** Select a different representation and solve the problem.
    d. **VERBAL** Write about the relationship between the representations of the problem. How did each affect your solution? **See margin.**

b–c. See students' representations; 25 minutes of aerobics, 15 minutes of stretching

H.O.T. Problems
Use Higher-Order Thinking Skills

47. **REASONING** Explain why the system represented by $\left[\begin{array}{cc|c} 6 & 2 & 3 \\ 6 & 2 & -5 \end{array}\right]$ has no solution.

47. Sample answer: The graphs of these two lines are parallel, so the system has no solution.

48. **WRITING IN MATH** Describe the advantages and disadvantages of using an augmented matrix to solve a system of equations. **See margin.**

49. **CHALLENGE** For $a \neq 0$, what is the solution of the system represented by $\left[\begin{array}{cc|c} a & 2 & 4 \\ a & -3 & -6 \end{array}\right]$? **(0, 2)**

50. **OPEN ENDED** Write a word problem for the system represented by $\left[\begin{array}{cc|c} 3 & 1 & 13 \\ 2 & 1 & 9.5 \end{array}\right]$. Solve the system, and explain its meaning in this situation. **See margin.**

51. **WRITING IN MATH** Summarize how to write and use an augmented matrix to solve a system of linear equations. **See margin.**

Problem-Solving Tip

Look for a Pattern Looking for a pattern can help to identify a function and write an equation.

Enrichment
CRM p. 47 OL BL

NAME ________________ DATE ________ PERIOD ________

6-7 Enrichment
Using Matrices to Solve Larger Systems of Equations

Augmented matrices can also be used to solve systems of equations with three variables. In this type of problem, the goal is to get the coefficients portion of the matrix to have the form $\begin{bmatrix} 1 & 0 & 0 \\ 0 & 1 & 0 \\ 0 & 0 & 1 \end{bmatrix}$, or a three-row identity matrix.

Example Use an augmented matrix to solve the system of equations.

$x + y + z = 4$
$x - y - z = 2$
$2x - y + 4z = 0$

First, create the augmented matrix: $\left[\begin{array}{ccc|c} 1 & 1 & -1 & 4 \\ 1 & -1 & -1 & 2 \\ 2 & -1 & 4 & 0 \end{array}\right]$.

You must now use row reduction to create the three-row identity matrix. First, perform row reduction to get the first column to match the identity matrix.

$\left[\begin{array}{ccc|c} 1 & 1 & 1 & 4 \\ 1 & -1 & -1 & 2 \\ 2 & -1 & 4 & 0 \end{array}\right] \xrightarrow{-R_1 + R_2} \left[\begin{array}{ccc|c} 1 & 1 & 1 & 4 \\ 0 & -2 & -2 & -2 \\ 2 & -1 & 4 & 0 \end{array}\right] \xrightarrow{-2R_1 + R_3} \left[\begin{array}{ccc|c} 1 & 1 & 1 & 4 \\ 0 & -2 & -2 & -2 \\ 0 & -3 & 2 & -8 \end{array}\right]$

Next, perform row reduction to get the second column in the form of the identity matrix.

Multiple Representations In Exercise 46, students use an augmented matrix and a graph in the coordinate plane to illustrate solving a system of equations.

PSAE PRACTICE 8.11.17, 10.11.04, 6.11.18

52. SHORT RESPONSE Tonisha paid \$25.75 for 3 games of miniature golf and 2 rides on go-karts. Trevor paid \$35.75 for 4 games of miniature golf and 3 rides on go-karts. How much did each activity cost?

52. miniature golf, \$5.75; go-karts, \$4.25

53. What is the solution of this system of equations? **A**

$$\begin{cases} 0.5x - 2y = 17 \\ 2x + y = 104 \end{cases}$$

A (50, 4)
B (4, 50)
C no solution
D infinitely many solutions

54. PROBABILITY Lexis scored 88, 95, 77, and 93 on her first four tests. What grade must she get on her fifth test to earn an average of 90 for all five tests? **J**

F 85
G 90
H 96
J 97

55. Pablo's Pizza Place estimates that 42% of their annual sales go toward paying employees. If the pizza place makes \$4156.50 on Friday, approximately how much went for paying employees? **B**

A \$98.96
B \$1745.73
C \$174.57
D \$17457.30

Spiral Review

Perform the indicated matrix operations. If an operation cannot be performed, write *impossible*. (Lesson 6-6)

56. $\begin{bmatrix} 5 & -2 & 4 \\ -3 & 7 & 9 \\ 12 & -1 & 8 \end{bmatrix} + \begin{bmatrix} -6 & 7 & -12 \\ 15 & -8 & 1 \\ 9 & 3 & -5 \end{bmatrix}$ $\begin{bmatrix} -1 & 5 & -8 \\ 12 & -1 & 10 \\ 21 & 2 & 3 \end{bmatrix}$

57. $\begin{bmatrix} 8 & -13 \\ 4 & 2 \\ -4 & -6 \end{bmatrix} - \begin{bmatrix} -3 & 5 \\ 10 & -16 \\ 8 & -2 \end{bmatrix}$ $\begin{bmatrix} 11 & -18 \\ -6 & 18 \\ -12 & -4 \end{bmatrix}$

58. $-3\begin{bmatrix} -7 & -1 & 3 & 0 \\ -1 & 5 & 7 & 9 \end{bmatrix}$ $\begin{bmatrix} 21 & 3 & -9 & 0 \\ 3 & -15 & -21 & -27 \end{bmatrix}$

59. $\begin{bmatrix} 5 \\ -8 \\ 3 \end{bmatrix} + \begin{bmatrix} 9 & -4 & 2 \end{bmatrix}$ **impossible**

60. SPORTS In the 2006 Winter Olympic Games, the total number of gold and silver medals won by the U.S. was 18. The total points scored for gold and silver medals was 45. Write and solve a system of equations to find how many gold and silver medals were won by the U.S. (Lesson 6-5) $3g + 2v = 45$; $g + v = 18$; **9 gold, 9 silver**

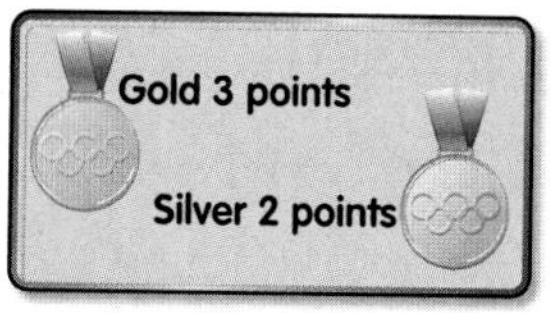

61. DRIVING Tires should be kept within 2 pounds per square inch (psi) of the manufacturer's recommended tire pressure. If the recommendation for a tire is 30 psi, what is the range of acceptable pressures? (Lesson 5-5) $\{p \mid 28 \le p \le 32\}$

Write an equation in slope-intercept form for the line that passes through the given point and is parallel to the graph of each equation. (Lesson 4-4)

62. $(-3, 2); y = x - 6$ $y = x + 5$

63. $(2, -1); y = 2x + 2$ $y = 2x - 5$

64. $(-5, -4); y = \frac{1}{2}x + 1$ $y = \frac{1}{2}x - \frac{3}{2}$

65. $(3, 3); y = \frac{2}{3}x - 1$ $y = \frac{2}{3}x + 1$

66. $(-4, -3); y = -\frac{1}{3}x + 3$ $y = -\frac{1}{3}x - \frac{13}{3}$

67. $(-1, 2); y = -\frac{1}{2}x - 4$ $y = -\frac{1}{2}x + \frac{3}{2}$

Skills Review

Simplify each expression. (Lesson 1-4)

68. $2(7p + 4)$ $14p + 8$

69. $-3(3 - 8x)$ $-9 + 24x$

70. $-3y + 5(4y)$ $17y$

71. $-2(4m - 6 + 8m)$ $-24m + 12$

72. $5g - 8g + 2(-4g)$ $-11g$

73. $12(4c + 3b)$ $48c + 36b$

Differentiated Instruction OL BL

Extension Have students write an augmented matrix for a system of equations that is consistent and dependent, and then explain why it is consistent and dependent.

Sample answer: $\left[\begin{array}{cc|c} 3 & 2 & -12 \\ 6 & 4 & -24 \end{array}\right]$; the graphs of the equations of the system coincide, so the system is consistent, and there are an infinite number of solutions, so the system is dependent.

4 ASSESS

Yesterday's News Have students write a sentence on how yesterday's lesson on adding and subtracting matrices helped with today's lesson on using augmented matrices to solve systems of equations.

Additional Answers

46d. See students' explanations. Each representation should yield the same solution, but students may feel more comfortable with one solution method. Solving by graphing may sometimes only be accurate enough for estimation of the solution.

48. Sample answer: An advantage is that only the coefficients and constant terms are used rather than the variables. Sometimes it is easier to solve a system by substitution or elimination and it can be confusing knowing where to place the results once a row operation is performed.

50. Sample answer: Lindsey and Zach were changing the oil in each of their cars. Lindsey bought 3 quarts of oil and an oil filter that totaled \$13. Zach bought 2 quarts of the same oil and the same oil filter that totaled \$9.50. How much did each quart of oil cost? How much did the oil filter cost? Solution: (3.5, 2.5) oil: \$3.50/qt, oil filter: \$2.50 ea.

51. Sample answer: An augmented matrix consists of the coefficients and constant terms of a system. Row operations are used until the coefficient portion of the matrix is the identity matrix. The *x*-coordinate is the top number in the constant portion of the matrix, and the *y*-coordinate is the bottom number in the constant portion of the matrix.

6-8 Lesson Notes

1 FOCUS

Vertical Alignment

Before Lesson 6-8
Graph and solve linear inequalities.

Lesson 6-8
Graph systems of inequalities. Solve systems of linear inequalities by graphing.

After Lesson 6-8
Analyze situations and formulate systems of inequalities in two unknowns to solve problems.

2 TEACH

Scaffolding Questions

Have students read the *Why?* section of the lesson.

Ask:

- According to the graph, what are three possible heart rates in the preferred range for Jacui? Sample answers: 110, 146, and 168
- What are three heart rates that fall outside the range? Sample answers: 100, 180, 195
- What happens to the range of preferred heart rates as Jacui becomes older? The lower and upper limits for the range decrease, and the overall range decreases.

6-8 Systems of Inequalities

Then
You graphed and solved linear inequalities. (Lesson 5-6)

Now
- Graph systems of linear inequalities.
- Solve systems of linear inequalities by graphing.

IL Learning Standards
8.B.4a Represent algebraic concepts with physical materials, words, diagrams, tables, graphs, equations and inequalities and use appropriate technology.

New Vocabulary
system of inequalities

IL Math Online
glencoe.com
- Extra Examples
- Personal Tutor
- Self-Check Quiz
- Homework Help
- Math in Motion

Why?

Jacui is beginning an exercise program that involves an intense cardiovascular workout. Her trainer recommends that for a person her age, her heart rate should stay within the following range as she exercises.

- It should be higher than 102 beats per minute.
- It should not exceed 174 beats per minute.

The graph shows the maximum and minimum target heart rate for people ages 0 to 30 as they exercise. If the preferred range is in light green, how old do you think Jacui is?

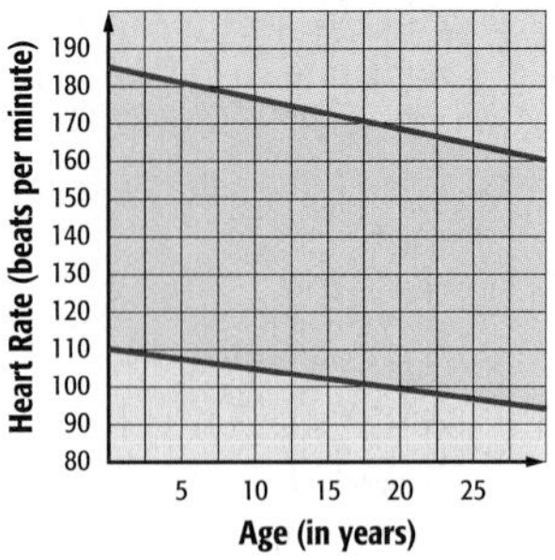

Systems of Inequalities The graph above is a graph of two inequalities. A set of two or more inequalities with the same variables is called a **system of inequalities**.

The solution of a system of inequalities with two variables is the set of ordered pairs that satisfy all of the inequalities in the system. The solution set is represented by the overlap, or intersection, of the graphs of the inequalities.

EXAMPLE 1 Solve by Graphing

Solve the system of inequalities by graphing.

$y > -2x + 1$
$y \leq x + 3$

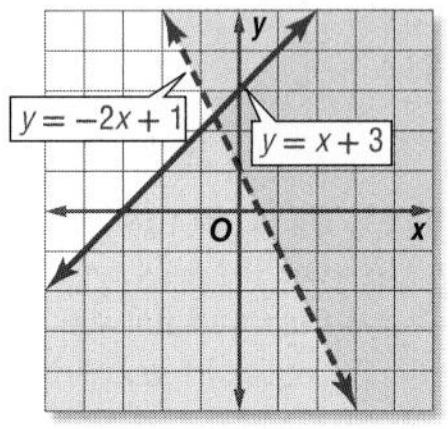

The graph of $y = -2x + 1$ is dashed and is not included in the graph of the solution. The graph of $y = x + 3$ is solid and is included in the graph of the solution.

The solution of the system is the set of ordered pairs in the intersection of the graphs of $y > -2x + 1$ and $y \leq x + 3$. This region is shaded in green.

When graphing more than one region, it is helpful to use two different colored pencils or two different patterns for each region. This will make it easier to see where the regions intersect and find possible solutions.

Check Your Progress 1A–1D. See Ch. 6 Answer Appendix.

1A. $y \leq 3$
$x + y \geq 1$

1B. $2x + y \geq 2$
$2x + y < 4$

1C. $y \geq -4$
$3x + y \leq 2$

1D. $x + y > 2$
$-4x + 2y < 8$

Personal Tutor glencoe.com

Sometimes the regions never intersect. When this happens, there is no solution because there are no points in common.

Lesson 6-8 Resources

Resource	Approaching-Level	On-Level	Beyond-Level	English Learners
Teacher Edition	• Differentiated Instruction, p. 383	• Differentiated Instruction, pp. 383, 386	• Differentiated Instruction, p. 386	
Chapter Resource Masters	• Study Guide and Intervention, pp. 48–49 • Skills Practice, p. 50 • Practice, p. 51 • Word Problem Practice, p. 52 • Graphing Calculator Activity, p. 54 • Spreadsheet Activity, p. 55	• Study Guide and Intervention, pp. 48–49 • Skills Practice and Practice, pp. 50–51 • Word Problem Practice, p. 52 • Enrichment, p. 53 • Graphing Calculator Activity, p. 54 • Spreadsheet Activity, p. 55	• Practice, p. 51 • Word Problem Practice, p. 52 • Enrichment, p. 53 • Graphing Calculator Activity, p. 54 • Spreadsheet Activity, p. 55	• Study Guide and Intervention, pp. 48–49 • Skills Practice, p. 50 • Practice, p. 51 • Graphing Calculator Activity, p. 54 • Spreadsheet Activity, p. 55
Transparencies	• 5-Minute Check Transparency 6-8	• 5-Minute Check Transparency 6-8	• 5-Minute Check Transparency 6-8	• 5-Minute Check Transparency 6-8
Other	• Study Notebook • Teaching Algebra with Manipulatives	• Study Notebook • Teaching Algebra with Manipulatives	• Study Notebook	• Study Notebook • Teaching Algebra with Manipulatives

StudyTip

Parallel Boundaries A system of equations that are parallel lines does not have a solution. However, a system of inequalities with parallel boundaries can have a solution. For example:

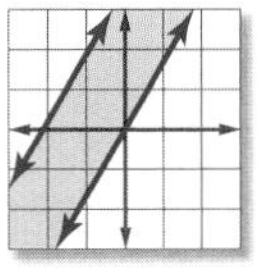

EXAMPLE 2 No Solution

Solve the system of inequalities by graphing.

$3x - y \geq 2$
$3x - y < -5$

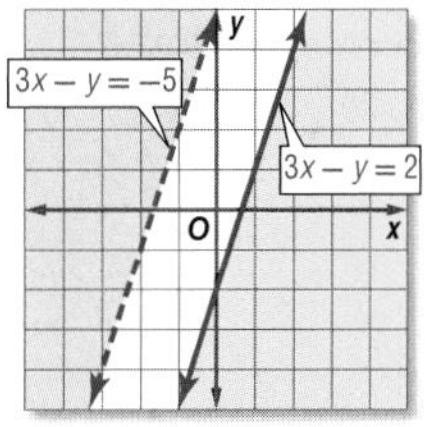

The graphs of $3x - y = 2$ and $3x - y = -5$ are parallel lines. The two regions do not intersect at any point, so the system has no solution.

2A–2B. See Ch. 6 Answer Appendix.

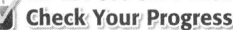

Check Your Progress

2A. $y > 3$
$y < 1$

2B. $x + 6y \leq 2$
$y \geq -\frac{1}{6}x + 7$

Personal Tutor glencoe.com

When using a system of inequalities in a real-world problem, sometimes only whole-number solutions will make sense.

Math *in Motion*, Animation glencoe.com

Real-World EXAMPLE 3 Whole-Number Solutions

ELECTIONS **Monifa is running for student council. The election rules say that for the election to be valid, at least 80% of the 900 students must vote. Monifa knows that she needs more than 330 votes to win.**

a. Define the variables, and write a system of inequalities to represent this situation. Then graph the system.

Let r = the number of votes required by the election rules; 80% of 900 students is 720 students. So $r \geq 720$.

Let v = the number of votes that Monifa needs to win. So $v > 330$.

The system of inequalities is $r \geq 720$ and $v > 330$.

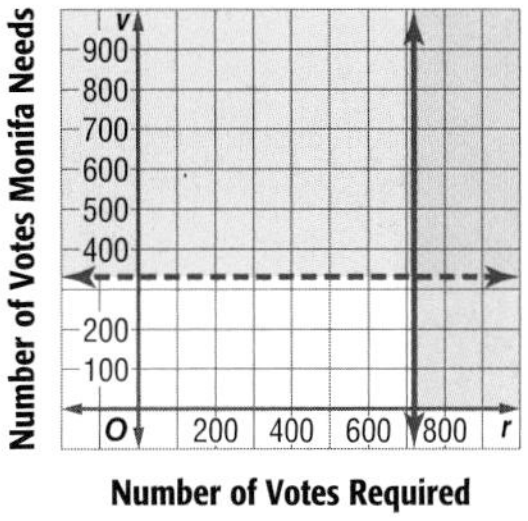

b. Name one possible solution.

Only whole-number solutions make sense in this problem. One possible solution is (800, 400); 800 students voted and Monifa received 400 votes.

Real-World Link

Student government might be a good activity for you if you like to bring about change, plan events, and work with others.

Check Your Progress

3. FUNDRAISING The Theater Club is selling shirts. They have only enough supplies to print 120 shirts. They will sell sweatshirts for \$22 and T-shirts for \$15, with a goal of at least \$2000 in sales.

A. Define the variables, and write a system of inequalities to represent this situation. **3A–3B. See Ch. 6 Answer Appendix.**

B. Then graph the system.

C. Name one possible solution. **95 sweatshirts and 10 T-shirts**

D. Is (45, 30) a solution? Explain. **No, the point does not fall in the overlapping region.**

Personal Tutor glencoe.com

Systems of Inequalities

Example 1 shows how to solve a system of inequalities by graphing. **Example 2** shows how to determine that a system of inequalities has no solution. **Example 3** shows how to use a system of inequalities to solve a real-world problem.

Formative Assessment

Use the Check Your Progress exercises after each Example to determine students' understanding of concepts.

Additional Examples

1 Solve the system of inequalities by graphing.

$y < 2x + 2$
$y \geq -x - 3$

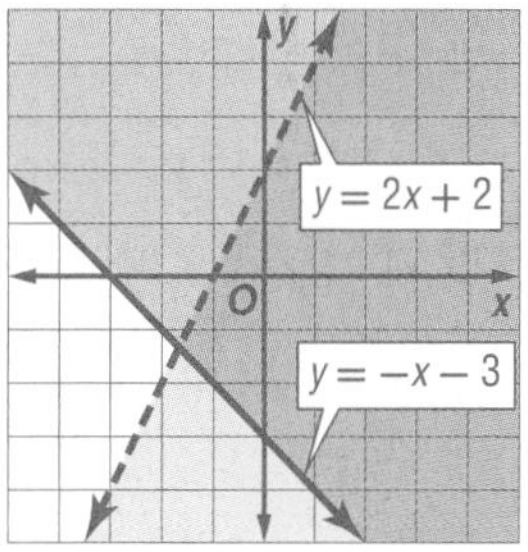

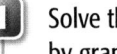

2 Solve the system of inequalities by graphing.

$y \geq -3x + 1$
$y \leq -3x - 2$ ∅

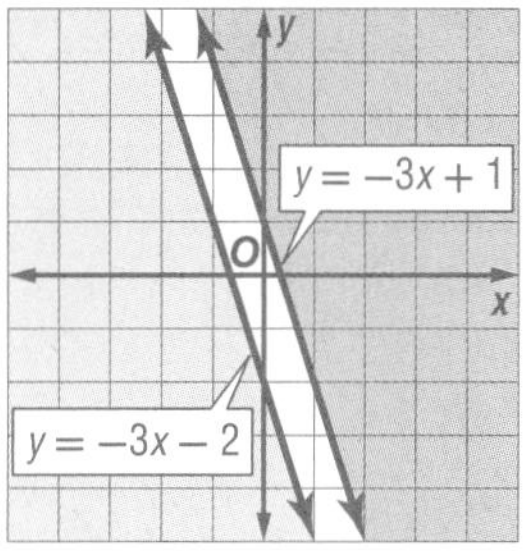

Additional Examples also in Interactive Classroom PowerPoint® Presentations

IWB INTERACTIVE WHITEBOARD READY

Differentiated Instruction AL OL

If students have difficulty graphing systems of inequalities,

Then suggest that they graph each inequality on a separate coordinate graph and then put the two graphs together on the same coordinate graph by copying them over or tracing them.

Additional Example

3 **SERVICE** A college service organization requires that its members maintain at least a 3.0 grade point average and volunteer at least 10 hours a week.

a. Define the variables and write a system of inequalities to represent this situation. Then graph the system.
Let g = grade point average; let v = the number of volunteer hours; $g \geq 3.0$, $v \geq 10$.

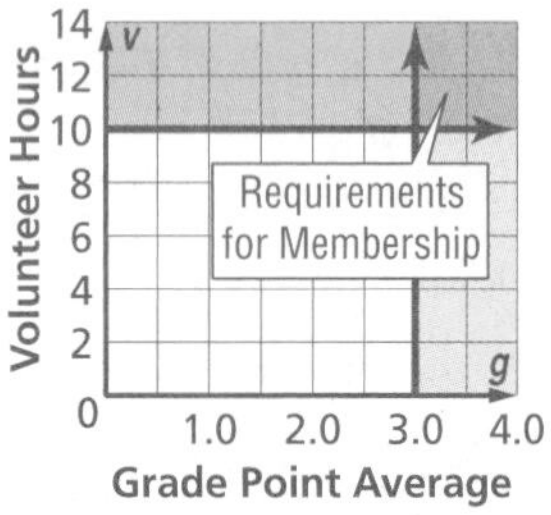

b. Name one possible solution.
(3.5, 12); a grade point average of 3.5 and 12 hours of volunteering

3 PRACTICE

Formative Assessment

Use Exercises 1–9 to check for understanding.

Use the chart at the bottom of this page to customize assignments for your students.

Additional Answer

42. 9 units^2

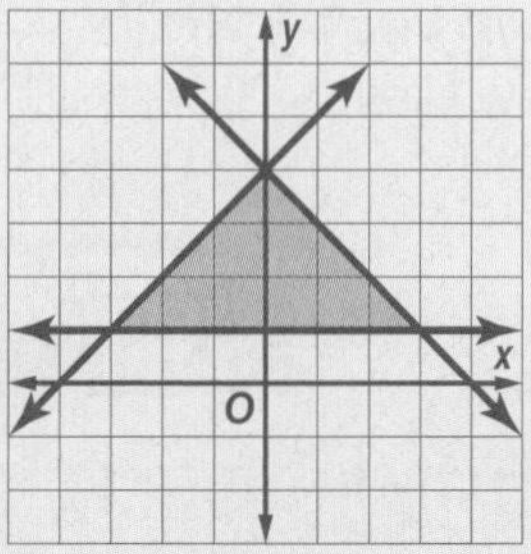

Check Your Understanding

Examples 1 and 2 pp. 382–383

Solve each system of inequalities by graphing. **1–8. See Ch. 6 Answer Appendix.**

1. $x \geq 4$
$y \leq x - 3$

2. $y > -2$
$y \leq x + 9$

3. $y < 3x + 8$
$y \geq 4x$

4. $3x - y \geq -1$
$2x + y \geq 5$

5. $y \leq 2x - 7$
$y \geq 2x + 7$

6. $y > -2x + 5$
$y \geq -2x + 10$

7. $2x + y \leq 5$
$2x + y \leq 7$

8. $5x - y < -2$
$5x - y > 6$

Example 3 p. 383

9. **AUTO RACING** At a racecar driving school there are safety requirements.

a. Define the variables, and write a system of inequalities to represent the height and weight requirements in this situation. Then graph the system. **See Ch. 6 Answer Appendix.**

b. Name one possible solution. **Sample answer: 72 in. and 220 lb**

c. Is (50, 180) a solution? Explain. **Yes, the point falls in the overlapping region.**

Practice and Problem Solving

● = **Step-by-Step Solutions** begin on page R12.
Extra Practice begins on page 815.

Examples 1 and 2 pp. 382–383

Solve each system of inequalities by graphing. **10–24. See Ch. 6 Answer Appendix.**

10. $y < 6$
$y > x + 3$

11. $y \geq 0$
$y \leq x - 5$

12. $y \leq x + 10$
$y > 6x + 2$

13. $y < 5x - 2$
$y > -6x + 2$

14. $2x - y \leq 6$
$x - y \geq -1$

15. $3x - y > -5$
$5x - y < 9$

16. $y \geq x + 10$
$y \leq x - 3$

17. $y < 5x - 5$
$y > 5x + 9$

18. $y \geq 3x - 5$
$3x - y > -4$

19. $4x + y > -1$
$y < -4x + 1$

20. $3x - y \geq -2$
$y < 3x + 4$

21. $y > 2x - 3$
$2x - y \geq 1$

22. $5x - y < -6$
$3x - y \geq 4$

23. $x - y \leq 8$
$y < 3x$

24. $4x + y < -2$
$y > -4x$

Example 3 p. 383

25. **ICE RINKS** Ice resurfacers are used for rinks of at least 1000 square feet and up to 17,000 square feet. The price ranges from as little as \$10,000 to as much as \$150,000.

a. Define the variables, and write a system of inequalities to represent this situation. Then graph the system. **See Ch. 6 Answer Appendix.**

b. Name one possible solution.

c. Is (15,000, 30,000) a solution? Explain. **Yes; the point satisfies each inequality.**

25b. Sample answer: an ice resurfacer for a rink of 5000 ft^2 and a price of \$20,000

26. **PIZZERIA** Josefina works between 10 and 30 hours per week at a pizzeria. She earns \$6.50 an hour, but can earn tips when she delivers pizzas.

a. Write a system of inequalities to represent the dollars d she could earn for working h hours in a week. $d \geq 6.50h$, $10 \leq h \leq 30$

b. Graph this system. **See Ch. 6 Answer Appendix.**

c. If Josefina received \$17.50 in tips and earned a total of \$180 for the week, how many hours did she work? **25 hours**

Differentiated Homework Options

Level	Assignment	Two-Day Option	
AL Basic	10–26, 39–41, 43–66	11–25 odd, 44–47	10–26 even, 39–41, 43, 48–66
OL Core	11–25 odd, 26, 27–35 odd, 36, 37, 39–41, 43–66	10–26, 44–47	27–35, 36, 37, 39–41, 43, 48–66
BL Advanced	27–63, (optional: 64–66)		

384 Chapter 6 Systems of Linear Equations and Inequalities

B Solve each system of inequalities by graphing. **27–35. See Ch. 6 Answer Appendix.**

27. $x + y \geq 1$
$x + y \leq 2$

28. $3x - y < -2$
$3x - y < 1$

29. $2x - y \leq -11$
$3x - y \geq 12$

30. $y < 4x + 13$
$4x - y \geq 1$

31. $4x - y < -3$
$y \geq 4x - 6$

32. $y \leq 2x + 7$
$y < 2x - 3$

33. $y > -12x + 1$
$y \leq 9x + 2$

34. $2y \geq x$
$x - 3y > -6$

35. $x - 5y > -15$
$5y \geq x - 5$

Real-World Link

Junior Achievement is a worldwide organization of volunteers that teaches students about entrepreneurship, work readiness, and finance through hands-on programs.

Source: *Junior Achievement*

36. CLASS PROJECT An economics class formed a company to sell school supplies. They would like to sell at least 20 notebooks and 50 pens per week, with a goal of earning at least $60 per week. **a–b. See Ch. 6 Answer Appendix.**

School Supplies
Notebooks........$2.50
Pens $1.25

a. Define the variables, and write a system of inequalities to represent this situation.

b. Graph the system.

c. Name one possible solution. **Sample answer: 25 notebooks and 100 pens**

37 C FINANCIAL LITERACY Opal makes $15 per hour working for a photographer. She also coaches a competitive soccer team for $10 per hour. Opal needs to earn at least $90 per week, but she does not want to work more than 20 hours per week.

a. Define the variables, and write a system of inequalities to represent this situation.

b. Graph this system. **See Ch. 6 Answer Appendix.**

c. Give two possible solutions to describe how Opal can meet her goals.

d. Is (2, 2) a solution? Explain.

37a. Let x = the hours worked for the photographer, let y = the hours coaching, $x + y \leq 20$, $15x + 10y \geq 90$.

37c. Sample answer: 6 hours at the photographer, 10 hours of coaching; 8 hours at the photographer, 10 hours of coaching

37d. No; the point does not fall in the shaded region. She would not earn enough money.

H.O.T. Problems
Use **H**igher-**O**rder **T**hinking Skills

38. CHALLENGE Create a system of inequalities equivalent to $|x| \leq 4$. $x \leq 4$, $x \geq -4$

39. REASONING State whether the following statement is *sometimes*, *always*, or *never* true. Explain your answer with an example or counterexample. **See Ch. 6 Answer Appendix.**

Systems of inequalities with parallel boundaries have no solutions.

40. REASONING Describe the graph of the solution of this system without graphing.
$6x - 3y \leq -5$
$6x - 3y \geq -5$ **It is the line $6x - 3y = -5$.**

41. OPEN ENDED One inequality in a system is $3x - y > 4$. Write a second inequality so that the system will have no solution. **Sample answer: $3x - y < -4$**

42. CHALLENGE Graph the system of inequalities. Estimate the area of the solution. **See margin.**
$y \geq 1$
$y \leq x + 4$
$y \leq -x + 4$

43. WRITING IN MATH Refer to the beginning of the lesson. Explain what each colored region of the graph represents. Explain how shading in various colors can help to clearly show the solution set of a system of inequalities. **See Ch. 6 Answer Appendix.**

Study Guide and Intervention
CRM pp. 48–49 AL OL ELL

NAME ______ DATE ______ PERIOD ______

6-8 Study Guide and Intervention *(continued)*

Systems of Inequalities

Real-World Problems In real-world problems, sometimes only whole numbers make sense for the solution, and often only positive values of x and y make sense.

Example **BUSINESS AAA Gem Company produces necklaces and bracelets. In a 40-hour week, the company has 400 gems to use. A necklace requires 40 gems and a bracelet requires 10 gems. It takes 2 hours to produce a necklace and a bracelet requires one hour. How many of each type can be produced in a week?**

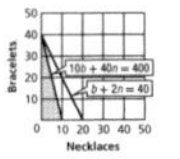

Let n = the number of necklaces that will be produced and b = the number of bracelets that will be produced. Neither n or b can be a negative number, so the following system of inequalities represents the conditions of the problems.

$n \geq 0$
$b \geq 0$
$b + 2n \leq 40$
$10b + 40n \leq 400$

The solution is the set ordered pairs in the intersection of the graphs. This region is shaded at the right. Only whole-number solutions, such as (5, 20) make sense in this problem.

Exercises

For each exercise, graph the solution set. List three possible solutions to the problem.

1. HEALTH Mr. Flowers is on a restricted diet that allows him to have between 1600 and 2000 Calories per day. His daily fat intake is restricted to between 45 and 55 grams. What daily Calorie and fat intakes are acceptable?

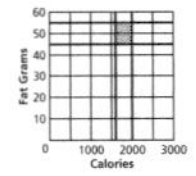

Sample answers: 1600 Calories, 45 fat grams; 1800 Calories, 50 fat grams; 2000 Calories, 55 fat grams

2. RECREATION Maria had $150 in gift certificates to use at a record store. She bought fewer than 20 recordings. Each tape cost $5.95 and each CD cost $8.95. How many of each type of recording might she have bought?

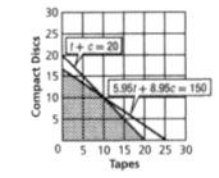

Sample answers: 10 tapes, 9 CDs; 0 tapes, 16 CDs; 14 tapes, 5 CDs

Lesson 6-8

Chapter 6 49 *Glencoe Algebra 1*

Practice
CRM p. 51 AL OL BL ELL

NAME ______ DATE ______ PERIOD ______

6-8 Practice

Systems of Inequalities

Solve each system of inequalities by graphing.

1. $y > x - 2$, $y \leq x$
2. $y \geq x + 2$, $y > 2x + 3$
3. $x + y \geq 1$, $x + 2y > 1$

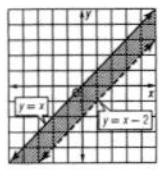
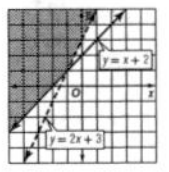

4. $y < 2x - 1$, $y > 2 - x$
5. $y > x - 4$, $2x + y \leq 2$
6. $2x - y \geq 2$, $x - 2y \geq 2$

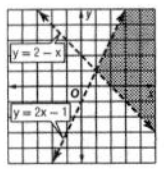
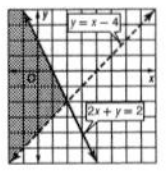
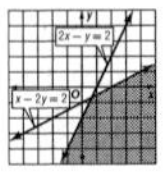

7. FITNESS Diego started an exercise program in which each week he works out at the gym between 4.5 and 6 hours and walks between 9 and 12 miles.

a. Make a graph to show the number of hours Diego works out at the gym and the number of miles he walks per week.

b. List three possible combinations of working out and walking that meet Diego's goals. **Sample answers: gym 5 h, walk 9 mi; gym 6 h, walk 10 mi, gym 5.5 h, walk 11 mi**

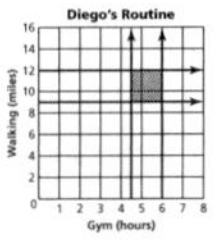

8. SOUVENIRS Emily wants to buy turquoise stones on her trip to New Mexico to give to at least 4 of her friends. The gift shop sells stones for either $4 or $6 per stone. Emily has no more than $30 to spend.

a. Make a graph showing the numbers of each price of stone Emily can purchase.

b. List three possible solutions. **Sample answer: one $4 stone and four $6 stones; three $4 stones and three $6 stones; five $4 stones and one $6 stone**

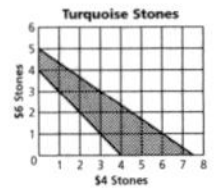

Lesson 6-8

Chapter 6 51 *Glencoe Algebra 1*

Word Problem Practice
CRM p. 52 AL OL BL ELL

NAME ______ DATE ______ PERIOD ______

6-8 Word Problem Practice

Systems of Inequalities

1. PETS Renée's Pet Store never has more than a combined total of 20 cats and dogs and never more than 8 cats. This is represented by the inequalities $x \leq 8$ and $x + y \leq 20$. Solve the system of inequalities by graphing.

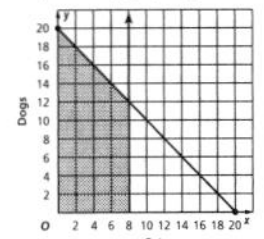

2. WAGES The minimum wage for one group of workers in Texas is $7.25 per hour effective Sept. 1, 2008. The graph below shows the possible weekly wages for a person who makes at least minimum wages and works at most 40 hours. Write the system of inequalities for the graph.

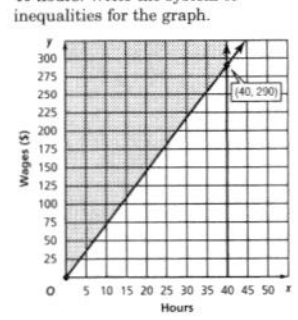

$x \leq 40$, $y \geq 7.25x$

3. FUND RAISING The Camp Courage Club plans to sell tins of popcorn and peanuts as a fundraiser. The Club members have $900 to spend on products to sell and want to order up to 200 tins in all. They also want to order at least as many tins of popcorn as tins of peanuts. Each tin of popcorn costs $3 and each tin of peanuts costs $4. Write a system of equations to represent the conditions of this problem. **$x + y \leq 200$; $x \geq y$; $3x + 4y \leq 900$ Students may also include $x \geq 0$ and $y \geq 0$.**

4. BUSINESS For maximum efficiency, a factory must have at least 100 workers, but no more than 200 workers on a shift. The factory also must manufacture at least 30 units per worker.

a. Let x be the number of workers and let y be the number of units. Write four inequalities expressing the conditions in the problem given above. **$x \leq 200$; $x \geq 100$; $y \geq 3000$; $y \geq 30x$**

b. Graph the systems of inequalities.

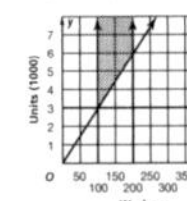

c. List at least three possible solutions. **Sample answer: (110, 3410), (150, 5100), (180, 6300)**

Chapter 6 52 *Glencoe Algebra 1*

TEACH with TECH

WIKI On your secure class wiki have students work in pairs to create a wiki page describing how to graph a system of inequalities. Describe how to decide whether to use a solid or dashed line and which side of the line to shade. Also, explain how to interpret the graph to determine the solutions of the system.

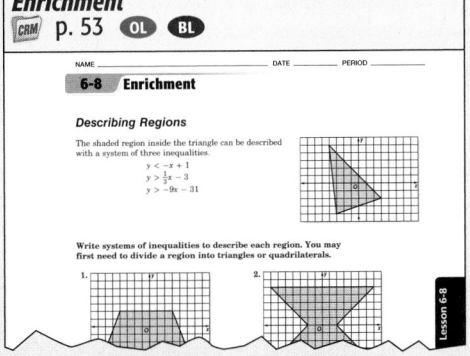

Enrichment
CRM p. 53 OL BL

NAME ______ DATE ______ PERIOD ______

6-8 Enrichment

Describing Regions

The shaded region inside the triangle can be described with a system of three inequalities.

$y < -x + 1$
$y > \frac{1}{3}x - 3$
$y > -9x - 31$

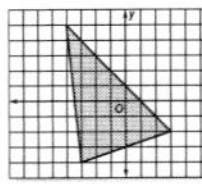

Write systems of inequalities to describe each region. You may first need to divide a region into triangles or quadrilaterals.

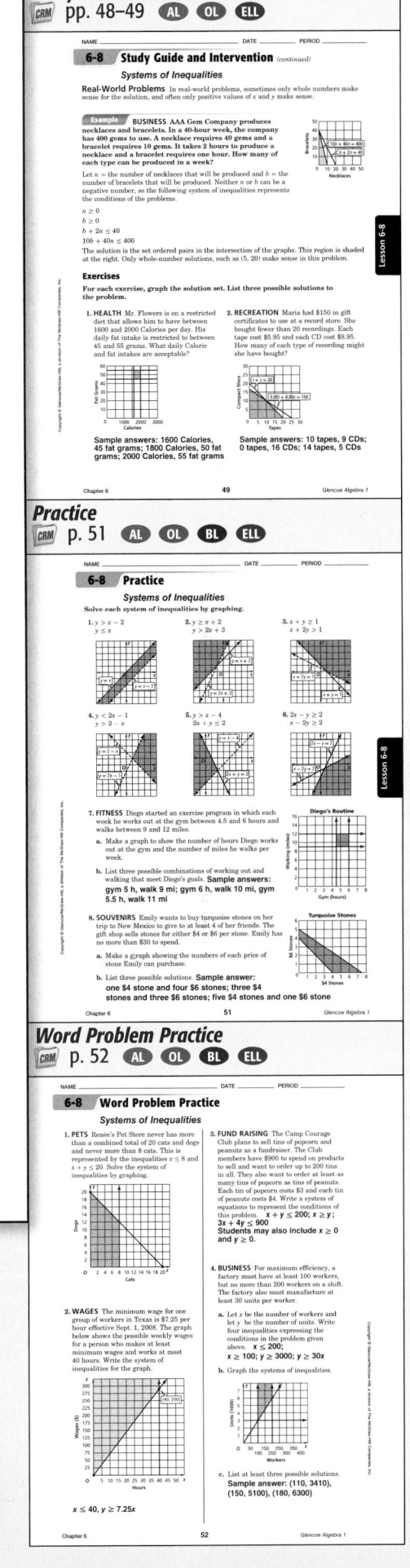

1. 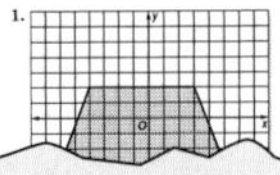

2. 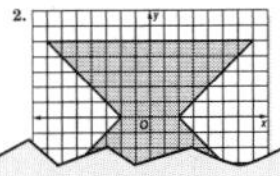

Lesson 6-8

4 ASSESS

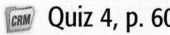

Name the Math Have each student write the method for determining whether to shade above or below the line when graphing an inequality and how to determine the common solutions when graphing a system of inequalities.

Formative Assessment

Check for student understanding of concepts in Lessons 6-7 and 6-8.

CRM Quiz 4, p. 60

Additional Answers

44a. $c \geq 20$ and $g \geq 3.75$
$c \geq 40$ and $g \geq 3.0$

44b. **Scholarship**

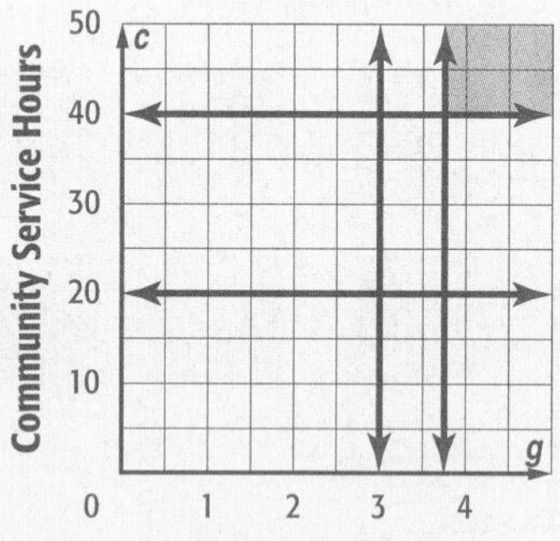

44c. Sample answer: 40 community service hours and a 3.75 grade points average

54. $\begin{bmatrix} 7 & 14 & 7 \\ -3 & 4 & -6 \\ 3 & -1 & 13 \end{bmatrix}$

55. $\begin{bmatrix} 1 & -4 & 5 \\ 3 & -6 & 0 \\ 1 & -5 & 1 \end{bmatrix}$ **56.** $\begin{bmatrix} 12 & 15 & 18 \\ 0 & -3 & -9 \\ 6 & -9 & 21 \end{bmatrix}$

57. $\begin{bmatrix} 7 & 14 & 7 \\ -3 & 4 & -6 \\ 3 & -1 & 13 \end{bmatrix}$

58. $\begin{bmatrix} -1 & 4 & -5 \\ -3 & 6 & 0 \\ -1 & 5 & -1 \end{bmatrix}$

59. $\begin{bmatrix} -6 & -18 & -2 \\ 6 & -10 & 6 \\ -2 & -4 & -12 \end{bmatrix}$

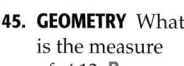

PSAE PRACTICE 8.11.17, 9.11.05, 7.11.03, 6.11.17

44. EXTENDED RESPONSE To apply for a scholarship, you must have a minimum of 20 hours of community service and a grade-point average of at least 3.75. Another scholarship requires at least 40 hours of community service and a minimum grade-point average of 3.0. **a–c. See margin.**

a. Write a system of inequalities to represent the grade point average g and community service hours c you must have to apply.

b. Graph the system of inequalities.

c. If you are eligible for both scholarships, give one possible solution.

45. GEOMETRY What is the measure of $\angle 1$? **D**

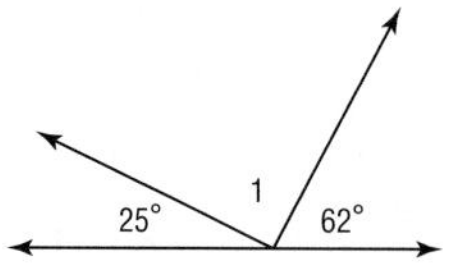

A 83°
B 87°
C 90°
D 93°

46. GEOMETRY What is the volume of the triangular prism? **H**

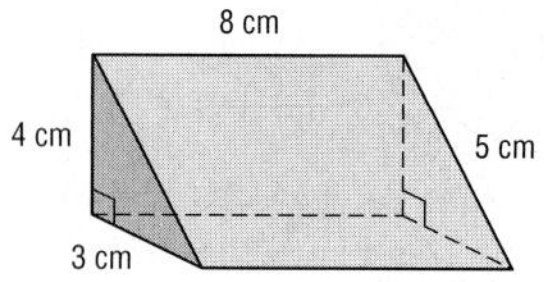

F 120 cm^3
G 96 cm^3
H 48 cm^3
J 30 cm^3

47. Ten pounds of fresh tomatoes make about 15 cups of cooked tomatoes. How many cups of cooked tomatoes does one pound of fresh tomatoes make? **A**

A $1\frac{1}{2}$ cups
B 3 cups
C 4 cups
D 5 cups

Spiral Review

Solve each system by using matrices. (Lesson 6-7)

48. $3x + 2y = 12$ **(2, 3)**
$-2x - 2y = -10$

49. $-2x + 5y = -9$ **(−3, −3)**
$2x - 4y = 6$

50. $2x + y = 2$ **(3, −4)**
$5x + 2y = 7$

51. $-3x - 6y = -42$ **(−2, 8)**
$x + 4y = 30$

52. $-5x + 6y = 41$ **(−1, 6)**
$3x - 4y = -27$

53. $-3x - 4y = -46$ **(6, 7)**
$7x - 6y = 0$

If $A = \begin{bmatrix} 4 & 5 & 6 \\ 0 & -1 & -3 \\ 2 & -3 & 7 \end{bmatrix}$ and $B = \begin{bmatrix} 3 & 9 & 1 \\ -3 & 5 & -3 \\ 1 & 2 & 6 \end{bmatrix}$, **find each sum, difference, or product.** (Lesson 6-6) **54–59. See margin.**

54. $A + B$
55. $A - B$
56. $3A$
57. $B + A$
58. $B - A$
59. $-2B$

60. ENTERTAINMENT A group of 11 adults and children bought tickets for the baseball game. If the total cost was $156, how many of each type of ticket did they buy? (Lesson 6-4) **8 adult, 3 children**

Graph each inequality. (Lesson 5-6) **61–63. See Ch. 6 Answer Appendix.**

61. $4x - 2 \geq 2y$
62. $9x - 3y < 0$
63. $2y \leq -4x - 6$

Skills Review

Evaluate each expression. (Lesson 1-1)

64. 3^3 **27**
65. 2^4 **16**
66. $(-4)^3$ **−64**

Differentiated Instruction OL BL

Extension Have students graph $2 \leq x \leq 5$ and $1 \leq y \leq 4$ on the same coordinate plane. Have them describe what polygon is formed by their intersection. a square with vertices at (2, 4), (5, 4), (2, 1) and (5, 1)

Systems of Inequalities

IL Math Online glencoe.com
• Graphing Technology Personal Tutor

IL Learning Standards **8.B.4a** Represent algebraic concepts with physical materials, words, diagrams, tables, graphs, equations and inequalities and use appropriate technology.

You can use a TI-Nspire™ or TI-Nspire™ CAS technology to explore systems of inequalities. To prepare your calculator, select New Document from the Home screen. Then select Add Graphs & Geometry.

ACTIVITY Graph Systems of Inequalities

Mr. Jackson owns a car washing and detailing business. It takes 20 minutes to wash a car and 60 minutes to detail a car. He works at most 8 hours per day and does at most 4 details per day. Write a system of linear inequalities to represent this situation.

First, write a linear inequality that represents the time it takes for car washing and car detailing. Let x represent the number of car washes, and let y represent the number of car details. Then $20x + 60y \leq 480$.

To graph this using a graphing calculator, solve for y.

$20x + 60y \leq 480$	**Original inequality**
$60y \leq -20x + 480$	**Subtract 20x from each side and simplify.**
$y \leq -\frac{1}{3}x + 8$	**Divide each side by 60 and simplify.**

Mr. Jackson does at most 4 details per day. This means that $y \leq 4$.

Step 1 Graph $y \leq 4$. Press (menu) Window; Window Settings (enter) −4, 30, −2, 10 (enter). Press clear to delete = and then type (<) (=) 4 (enter).

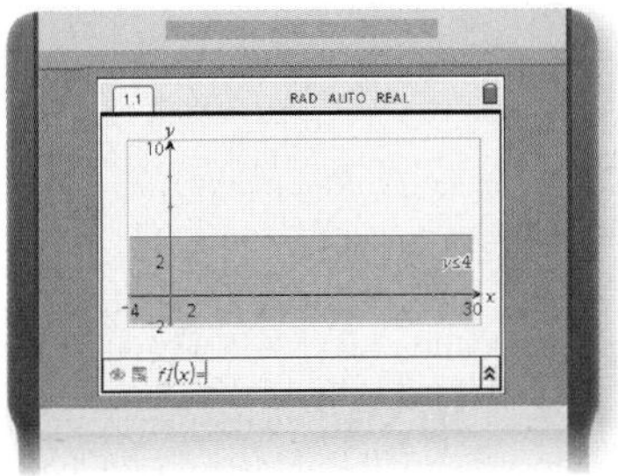

Step 2 Graph $y \leq -\frac{1}{3}x + 8$. Press clear once, delete =, and then type (<)(=)(−) (1 ÷ 3) x + 8 (enter).

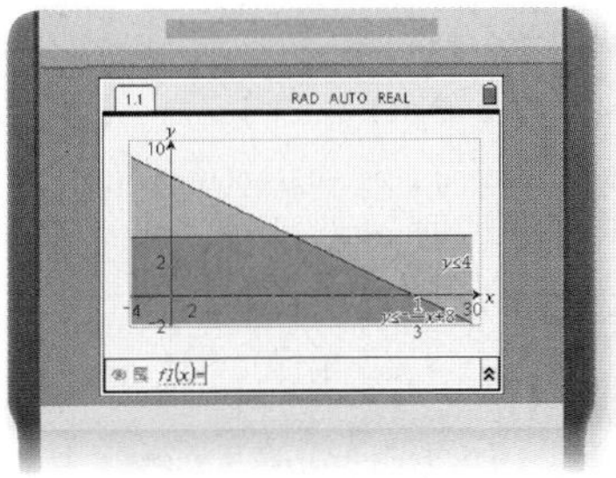

The darkest shaded half-plane of the graph represents the solutions.

Analyze the Results

1. If Mr. Jackson charges $75 for each car he details and $25 for each car wash, what is the maximum amount of money he could earn in one day? **$600**
2. What is the greatest number of car washes that Mr. Jackson could do in a day? Explain your reasoning. **24; It is the x-intercept of $y = -\frac{1}{3}x + 8$.**

1 FOCUS

Objective Use a graphing calculator to explore systems of inequalities.

Materials for Each Student

- TI-Nspire graphing calculator

Teaching Tip

To start a new document, students can press CTRL N and then select 2: Add Graphs & Geometry.

2 TEACH

Working in Cooperative Groups

Have students work in groups of two or three, mixing abilities, to complete Steps 1 and 2 of the Activity.

- In Step 1, when changing the window settings, students should press TAB or the down navigating arrow to move through the settings.
- In Steps 1 and 2, students can type CTRL < for the symbol ≤. To remove or return the entry line press CTRL G.
- If more or less contrast is needed to view the overlap of the graphs, press CTRL + for greater contrast and CTRL – for less contrast.

Practice Have students complete Exercises 1 and 2.

3 ASSESS

Formative Assessment

Use Exercise 1 to assess whether students can use a system of inequalities to solve a problem.

From Concrete to Abstract

Exercise 2 asks students to interpret the graph of a system of inequalities to determine a maximum value.

Formative Assessment

Key Vocabulary The page reference after each word denotes where that term was first introduced. If students have difficulty answering questions 1–10, remind them that they can use these page references to refresh their memories about the vocabulary terms.

Summative Assessment

CRM Vocabulary Test, p. 62

IL Math Online glencoe.com

Vocabulary PuzzleMaker improves students' mathematics vocabulary using four puzzle formats–crossword, scramble, word search using a word list, and word search using clues. Students can work online or from a printed worksheet.

Additional Answers

11.

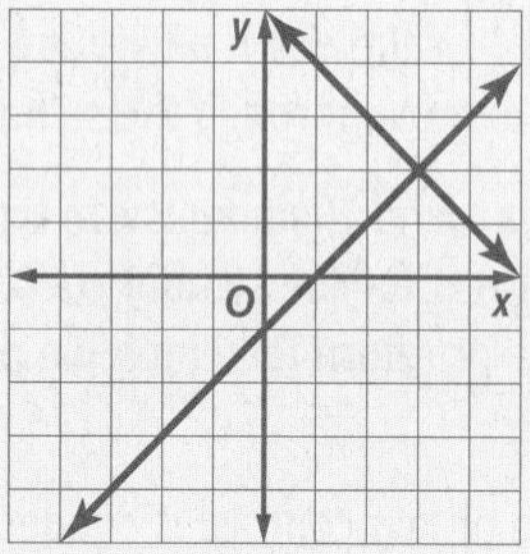

12.

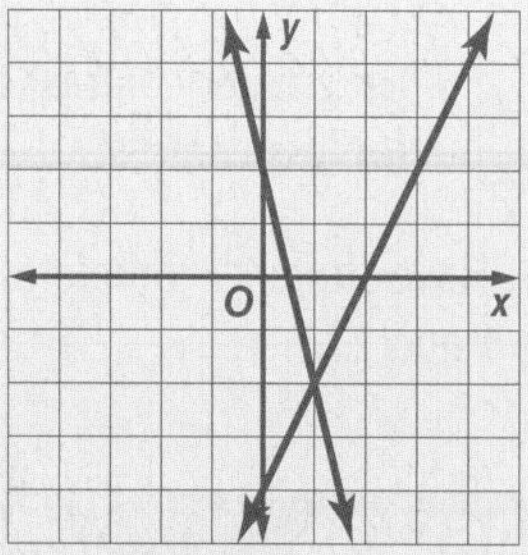

CHAPTER 6 Study Guide and Review

IL Math Online glencoe.com
- STUDY TO GO
- Vocabulary Review

Chapter Summary

Key Concepts

Systems of Equations (Lessons 6-1 through 6-4)

- A system with a graph of two intersecting lines has one solution and is *consistent and independent.*
- Graphing a system of equations can only provide approximate solutions. For exact solutions, you must use algebraic methods.
- In the substitution method, one equation is solved for a variable and the expression substituted to find the value of another variable.
- In the elimination method, one variable is eliminated by adding or subtracting the equations. Sometimes multiplying one equation by a constant makes it easier to use the elimination method.

Matrices (Lessons 6-6 and 6-7)

- Matrices can be added or subtracted only if they have the same dimensions. Add or subtract corresponding elements.
- To multiply a matrix by a scalar k, multiply each element in the matrix by k.
- An augmented matrix can be used to solve a system of equations.

Systems of Inequalities (Lesson 6-8)

- A system of inequalities is a set of two or more inequalities with the same variables.
- The solution of a system of inequalities is the intersection of the graphs.

FOLDABLES® Study Organizer

Be sure the Key Concepts are noted in your Foldable.

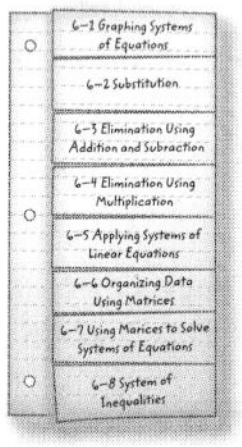

Key Vocabulary

augmented matrix (p. 376)	**independent** (p. 333)
consistent (p. 333)	**matrix** (p. 369)
dependent (p. 333)	**scalar** (p. 371)
dimension (p. 369)	**scalar multiplication** (p. 371)
element (p. 369)	**substitution** (p. 342)
elimination (p. 348)	**system of equations** (p. 333)
inconsistent (p. 333)	**system of inequalities** (p. 382)

Vocabulary Check

State whether each sentence is *true* or *false*. If *false*, replace the underlined term to make a true sentence.

1. If a system has at least one solution, it is said to be <u>consistent</u>. **true**
2. If a consistent system has exactly <u>two</u> solution(s), it is said to be independent. **false; one**
3. If a consistent system has an infinite number of solutions, it is said to be <u>inconsistent</u>. **false; dependent**
4. If a system has no solution, it is said to be <u>inconsistent</u>. **true**
5. <u>Substitution</u> involves substituting an expression from one equation for a variable in the other. **true**
6. In some cases, <u>dividing</u> two equations in a system together will eliminate one of the variables. This process is called elimination. **false; adding or subtracting**
7. Each number in a matrix is called a(n) <u>dimension</u>. **false; element**
8. A constant by which you multiply a matrix is called a <u>scalar</u>. **true**
9. An <u>augmented matrix</u> consists of the coefficients and the constant terms of a system of equations. **true**
10. A set of two or more inequalities with the same variables is called a <u>system of equations</u>. **false; system of inequalities**

FOLDABLES® Study Organizer

Dinah Zike's Foldables®

Have students look through the chapter to make sure they have included examples in their Foldables.

Suggest that students keep their Foldables handy while completing the Study Guide and Review pages. Point out that their Foldables can serve as a quick review tool when studying for the chapter test.

388 Chapter 6 Systems of Linear Equations and Inequalities

Lesson-by-Lesson Review

6-1 Graphing Systems of Equations (pp. 333–339)

8.B.4a

Graph each system and determine the number of solutions that it has. If it has one solution, name it. 11–16. See margin for graphs.

11. $x - y = 1$
$x + y = 5$ one; (3, 2)

12. $y = 2x - 4$
$4x + y = 2$ one; (1, −2)

13. $2x - 3y = -6$
$y = -3x + 2$ one; (0, 2)

14. $-3x + y = -3$
$y = x - 3$ one; (0, −3)

15. $x + 2y = 6$
$3x + 6y = 8$ no solution

16. $3x + y = 5$
$6x = 10 - 2y$ infinitely many solutions

17. **MAGIC NUMBERS** Sean is trying to find two numbers with a sum of 14 and a difference of 4. Define two variables, write a system of equations, and solve by graphing. See margin.

EXAMPLE 1

Graph the system and determine the number of solutions it has. If it has one solution, name it.

$y = 2x + 2$
$y = -3x - 3$

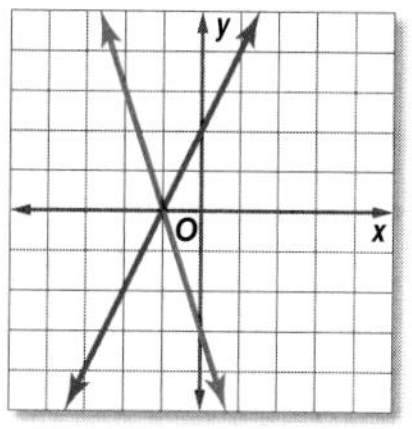

The lines appear to intersect at the point (−1, 0). You can check this by substituting −1 for x and 0 for y.

CHECK	$y = 2x + 2$	Original equation
	$0 \stackrel{?}{=} 2(-1) + 2$	Substitution
	$0 \stackrel{?}{=} -2 + 2$	Multiply.
	$0 = 0$ ✓	
	$y = -3x - 3$	Original equation
	$0 \stackrel{?}{=} -3(-1) - 3$	Substitution
	$0 \stackrel{?}{=} 3 - 3$	Multiply.
	$0 = 0$ ✓	

The solution is (−1, 0).

6-2 Substitution (pp. 342–347)

8.B.4a

Use substitution to solve each system of equations.

18. $x + y = 3$
$x = 2y$ (2, 1)

19. $x + 3y = -28$
$y = -5x$ (2, −10)

20. $3x + 2y = 16$
$x = 3y - 2$ (4, 2)

21. $x - y = 8$
$y = -3x$ (2, −6)

22. $y = 5x - 3$
$x + 2y = 27$ (3, 12)

23. $x + 3y = 9$
$x + y = 1$ (−3, 4)

24. **GEOMETRY** The perimeter of a rectangle is 48 inches. The length is 6 inches greater than the width. Define the variables, and write equations to represent this situation. Solve the system by using substitution.
Sample answer: Let w be the width and let ℓ be the length; $2w + 2\ell = 48$, $\ell = w + 6$; 9 is the width and 15 is the length.

EXAMPLE 2

Use substitution to solve the system.

$3x - y = 18$
$y = x - 4$

$3x - y = 18$	First equation
$3x - (x - 4) = 18$	Substitute $x - 4$ for y.
$2x + 4 = 18$	Simplify.
$2x = 14$	Subtract 4 from each side.
$x = 7$	Divide each side by 2.

Use the value of x and either equation to find the value for y.

$y = x - 4$	Second equation
$= 7 - 4$ or 3	Substitute and simplify.

The solution is (7, 3).

Lesson-by-Lesson Review

Intervention If the given examples are not sufficient to review the topics covered by the questions, remind students that the page references tell them where to review that topic in their textbook.

Two-Day Option Have students complete the Lesson-by-Lesson Review on pp. 389–392. Then you can use ExamView® Assessment Suite to customize another review worksheet that practices all the objectives of this chapter or only the objectives on which your students need more help.

Differentiated Instruction

Super DVD: Mindjogger Videoquizzes
Use this DVD as an alternative format of review for the test.

Additional Answers

13.
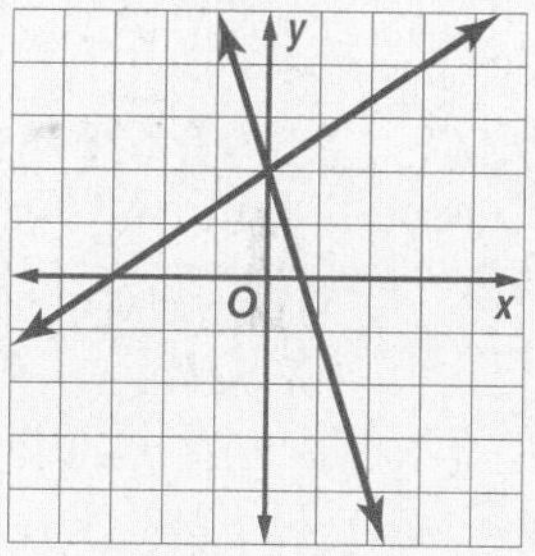

14.
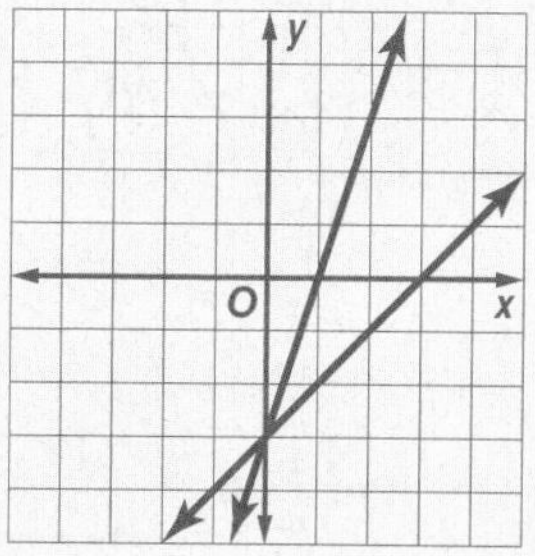

15.
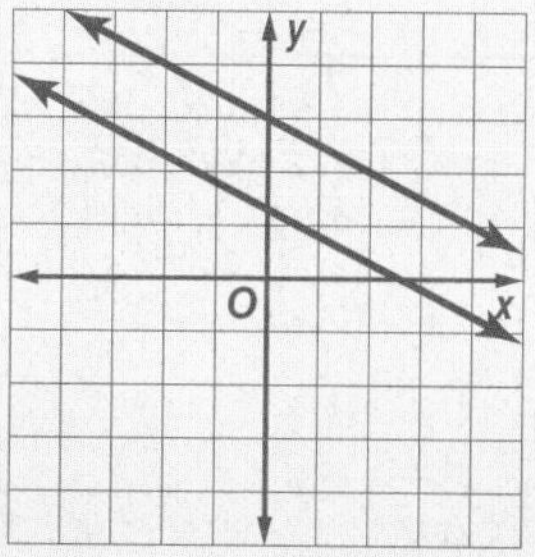

16.
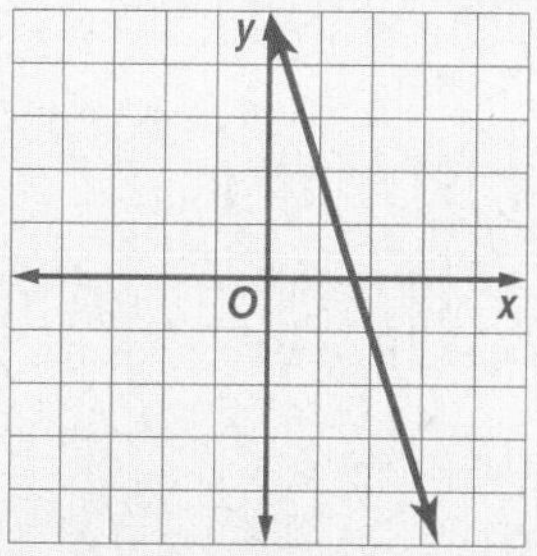

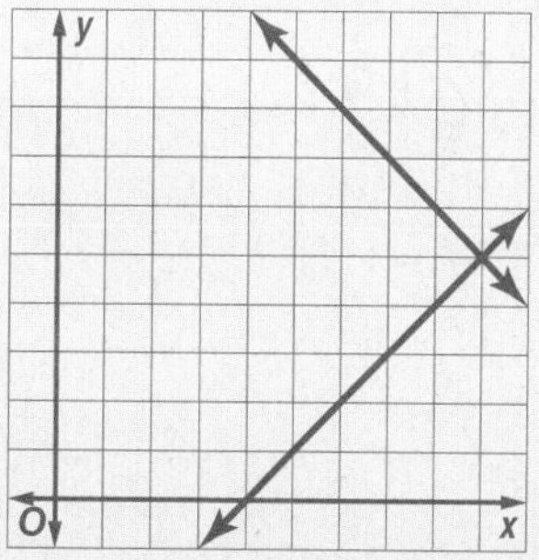

17. Sample answer: Let x be one number and y the other number; $x + y = 14$; $x - y = 4$; 9 and 5

Additional Answers

33. Sample answer: Let f be the number of the first type of card, and let c be the number of the second type of card; $f + c = 24$, $f + 3c = 50$; 11 \$1 cards and 13 \$3 cards.

42. Sample answer: Let c represent the number of cakes, and let p represent the number of pies; $8c + 10p = 356$, $p + c = 40$; 22 cakes, 18 pies

CHAPTER 6 Study Guide and Review

6-3 Elimination Using Addition and Subtraction (pp. 348–354)

8.B.4a

Use elimination to solve each system of equations.

25. $x + y = 13$, $x - y = 5$ **(9, 4)**

26. $-3x + 4y = 21$, $3x + 3y = 14$ $\left(-\frac{1}{3}, 5\right)$

27. $x + 4y = -4$, $x + 10y = -16$ **(4, −2)**

28. $2x + y = -5$, $x - y = 2$ **(−1, −3)**

29. $6x + y = 9$, $-6x + 3y = 15$ $\left(\frac{1}{2}, 6\right)$

30. $x - 4y = 2$, $3x + 4y = 38$ **(10, 2)**

31. $2x + 2y = 4$, $2x - 8y = -46$ **(−3, 5)**

32. $3x + 2y = 8$, $x + 2y = 2$ $\left(3, -\frac{1}{2}\right)$

33. BASEBALL CARDS Cristiano bought 24 baseball cards for \$50. One type cost \$1 per card, and the other cost \$3 per card. Define the variables, and write equations to find the number of each type of card he bought. Solve by using elimination. **See margin.**

EXAMPLE 3

Use elimination to solve the system of equations.

$$3x - 5y = 11$$
$$x + 5y = -3$$

$$\begin{aligned} 3x - 5y &= 11 \\ (+)\quad x + 5y &= -3 \\ \hline 4x \quad &= 8 \\ x &= 2 \end{aligned}$$

The variable y is eliminated. Divide each side by 4.

Now, substitute 2 for x in either equation to find the value of y.

$3x - 5y = 11$	First equation
$3(2) - 5y = 11$	Substitute.
$6 - 5y = 11$	Multiply.
$-5y = 5$	Subtract 6 from each side.
$y = -1$	Divide each side by −5.

The solution is (2, −1).

6-4 Elimination Using Multiplication (pp. 355–360)

8.B.4a

Use elimination to solve each system of equations.

34. $x + y = 4$, $-2x + 3y = 7$ **(1, 3)**

35. $x - y = -2$, $2x + 4y = 38$ **(5, 7)**

36. $3x + 4y = 1$, $5x + 2y = 11$ **(3, −2)**

37. $-9x + 3y = -3$, $3x - 2y = -4$ **(2, 5)**

38. $8x - 3y = -35$, $3x + 4y = 33$ **(−1, 9)**

39. $2x + 9y = 3$, $5x + 4y = 26$ **(6, −1)**

40. $-7x + 3y = 12$, $2x - 8y = -32$ **(0, 4)**

41. $8x - 5y = 18$, $6x + 6y = -6$ **(1, −2)**

42. BAKE SALE On the first day, a total of 40 items were sold for \$356. Define the variables, and write a system of equations to find the number of cakes and pies sold. Solve by using elimination. **See margin.**

EXAMPLE 4

Use elimination to solve the system of equations.

$$3x + 6y = 6$$
$$2x + 3y = 5$$

Notice that if you multiply the second equation by −2, the coefficients of the y-terms are additive inverses.

$3x + 6y = 6$

$2x + 3y = 5$ **Multiply by −2.** →

$$\begin{aligned} 3x + 6y &= 6 \\ (+)\ -4x - 6y &= -10 \\ \hline -x \quad &= -4 \\ x &= 4 \end{aligned}$$

Now, substitute 4 for x in either equation to find the value of y.

$2x + 3y = 5$	Second equation
$2(4) + 3y = 5$	Substitution
$8 + 3y = 5$	Multiply.
$3y = -3$	Subtract 8 from both sides.
$y = -1$	Divide each side by 3.

The solution is (4, −1).

MIXED PROBLEM SOLVING
For mixed problem-solving practice, see page 850.

6-5 Applying Systems of Linear Equations (pp. 362–367)

8.B.4a

Determine the best method to solve each system of equations. Then solve the system.

43. $y = x - 8$; $y = -3x$ **(2, −6)**

44. $y = -x$; $y = 2x$ **(0, 0)**

45. $x + 3y = 12$; $x = -6y$ **(24, −4)**

46. $x + y = 10$; $x - y = 18$ **(14, −4)**

47. $3x + 2y = -4$; $5x + 2y = -8$ **(−2, 1)**

48. $6x + 5y = 9$; $-2x + 4y = 14$ **(−1, 3)**

49. $3x + 4y = 26$; $2x + 3y = 19$ **(2, 5)**

50. $11x - 6y = 3$; $5x - 8y = -25$ **(3, 5)**

51. COINS Tionna has saved dimes and quarters in her piggy bank. Define the variables, and write a system of equations to determine the number of dimes and quarters. Then solve the system using the best method for the situation.

EXAMPLE 5

Determine the best method to solve the system of equations. Then solve the system.

$3x + 5y = 4$
$4x + y = -6$

Solve the second equation for y.

$4x + y = -6$	Second equation
$y = -6 - 4x$	Subtract $4x$ from each side.

Substitute $-6 - 4x$ for y in the first equation.

$3x + 5(-6 - 4x) = 4$	Substitute.
$3x - 30 - 20x = 4$	Distributive Property
$-17x - 30 = 4$	Simplify.
$-17x = 34$	Add 30 to each side.
$x = -2$	Divide by −17.

Last, substitute −2 for x in either equation to find y.

$4x + y = -6$	Second equation
$4(-2) + y = -6$	Substitute.
$-8 + y = -6$	Multiply.
$y = 2$	Add 8 to each side.

The solution is (−2, 2).

51. Sample answer: Let d represent the dimes and q represent the quarters; $d + q = 25$; $0.10d + 0.25q = 4$; 15 dimes, 10 quarters.

6-6 Organizing Data Using Matrices (pp. 369–375)

8.C.4b

Perform the indicated matrix operation.

52. $\begin{bmatrix} 5 & -6 \\ -9 & 4 \end{bmatrix} + \begin{bmatrix} 2 & -3 \\ -4 & 2 \end{bmatrix}$ $\begin{bmatrix} 7 & -9 \\ -13 & 6 \end{bmatrix}$

53. $\begin{bmatrix} 5 & -8 & 4 \\ -6 & 2 & -9 \end{bmatrix} - \begin{bmatrix} 6 & -4 & -3 \\ 8 & 2 & 1 \end{bmatrix}$ **See margin.**

54. $3\begin{bmatrix} 5 & -3 & -1 & 4 \\ 7 & -6 & 8 & 1 \end{bmatrix}$ $\begin{bmatrix} 15 & -9 & -3 & 12 \\ 21 & -18 & 24 & 3 \end{bmatrix}$

55. POLLS The results of a poll are shown. How many votes were cast against both tax levies? **176**

	For	Against
Tax Levy 1	68	105
Tax Levy 2	69	71

EXAMPLE 6

Find $\begin{bmatrix} 3 & 9 & -6 \\ 7 & 2 & 1 \end{bmatrix} + \begin{bmatrix} -2 & -1 & 6 \\ -6 & 4 & -5 \end{bmatrix}$.

To add the 2 × 3 matrices, add the corresponding elements.

$$\begin{bmatrix} 3 & 9 & -6 \\ 7 & 2 & 1 \end{bmatrix} + \begin{bmatrix} -2 & -1 & 6 \\ -6 & 4 & -5 \end{bmatrix}$$

$$= \begin{bmatrix} 3 + (-2) & 9 + (-1) & -6 + 6 \\ 7 + (-6) & 2 + 4 & 1 + (-5) \end{bmatrix}$$

$$= \begin{bmatrix} 1 & 8 & 0 \\ 1 & 6 & -4 \end{bmatrix}$$

Additional Answer

53. $\begin{bmatrix} -1 & -4 & 7 \\ -14 & 0 & -10 \end{bmatrix}$

Chapter 6 Study Guide and Review 391

Problem Solving Review

For additional practice in problem solving for Chapter 6, see the Mixed Problem Solving Appendix, p. 850, in the Student Handbook section.

Anticipation Guide

Have students complete the Chapter 6 Anticipation Guide and discuss how their responses have changed now that they have completed Chapter 6.

Additional Answers

67.

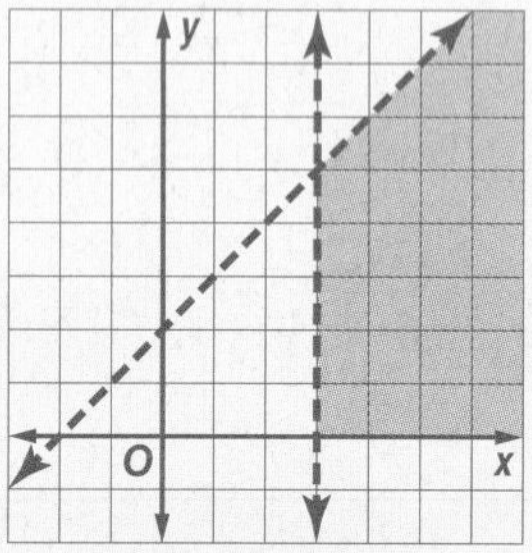

68.

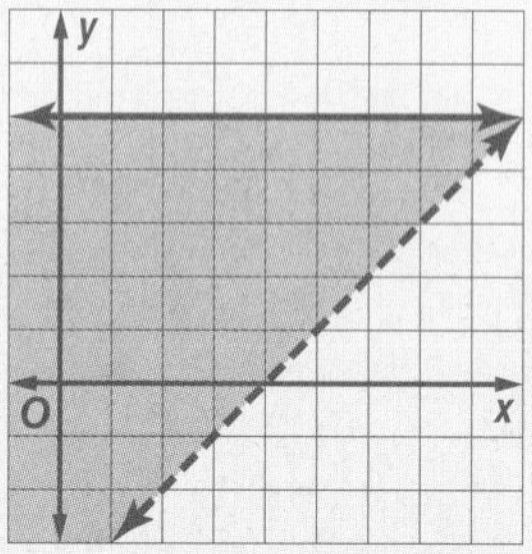

69.

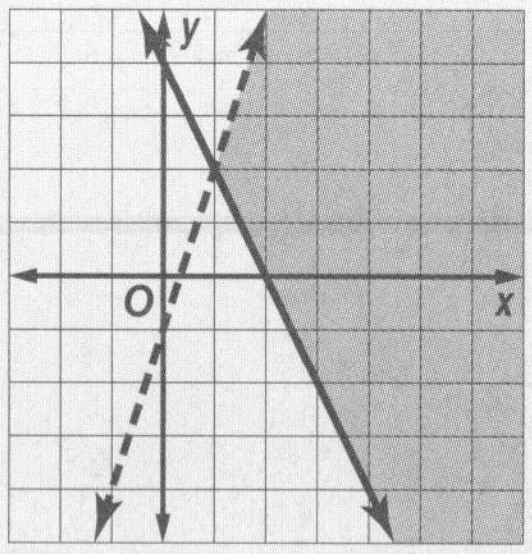

CHAPTER 6 Study Guide and Review

6-7 Using Matrices to Solve Systems of Equations (pp. 376–381)

8.C.4b

Use an augmented matrix to solve each system of equations.

56. $x - 2y = -5$
$2x + 3y = 4$ **(−1, 2)**

57. $x - y = 5$
$3x + 3y = 3$ **(3, −2)**

58. $2x + 3y = 8$
$x - 5y = -22$ **(−2, 4)**

59. $2x + 4y = -16$
$x - 2y = 0$ **(−4, −2)**

60. $2x - 4y = 10$
$x + 2y = 5$ **(5, 0)**

61. $x - 4y = 11$
$3x + 5y = -1$ **(3, −2)**

62. $x - 2y = -26$
$2x - 3y = -42$ **(−6, 10)**

63. $x - 3y = 24$
$5x - 2y = 29$ **(3, −7)**

64. $x - 2y = -16$
$3x + 4y = 72$ **(8, 12)**

65. $x + 3y = 12$
$2x - 4y = 14$ **(9, 1)**

66. ART Mateo spent a total of \$36 on 10 art supply items. How many bottles of paint and paint brushes did Mateo buy?
6 bottles of paint and 4 paint brushes

EXAMPLE 7

Use an augmented matrix to solve the system of equations.

$x + 3y = 11$
$3x + 4y = 18$

Step 1 Write the augmented matrix.

$$\left[\begin{array}{cc|c} 1 & 3 & 11 \\ 3 & 4 & 18 \end{array}\right]$$

Step 2 Multiply the first row by −3 and add the result to row 2.

$$\left[\begin{array}{cc|c} 1 & 3 & 11 \\ 3 & 4 & 18 \end{array}\right] \xrightarrow{-3R_1 + R_2} \left[\begin{array}{cc|c} 1 & 3 & 11 \\ 0 & -5 & -15 \end{array}\right]$$

Step 3 Multiply the second row by $-\frac{1}{5}$.

$$\left[\begin{array}{cc|c} 1 & 3 & 11 \\ 0 & -5 & -15 \end{array}\right] \xrightarrow{-\frac{1}{5}R_2} \left[\begin{array}{cc|c} 1 & 3 & 11 \\ 0 & 1 & 3 \end{array}\right]$$

Step 4 Multiply the second row by −3 and add the result to row 1.

$$\left[\begin{array}{cc|c} 1 & 3 & 11 \\ 0 & 1 & 3 \end{array}\right] \xrightarrow{-3R_2 + R_1} \left[\begin{array}{cc|c} 1 & 0 & 2 \\ 0 & 1 & 3 \end{array}\right]$$

The solution is (2, 3).

6-8 Systems of Inequalities (pp. 382–387)

8.B.4a

Solve each system of inequalities by graphing.

67. $x > 3$
$y < x + 2$

68. $y \le 5$
$y > x - 4$

69. $y < 3x - 1$
$y \ge -2x + 4$

70. $y \le -x - 3$
$y \ge 3x - 2$

67–70. See margin.

71. JOBS Kishi makes \$7 an hour working at the grocery store and \$10 an hour delivering newspapers. She cannot work more than 20 hours per week. Graph two inequalities that Kishi can use to determine how many hours she needs to work at each job if she wants to earn at least \$90 per week. **See margin.**

EXAMPLE 8

Solve the system of inequalities by graphing.

$y < 3x + 1$
$y \ge -2x + 3$

The solution set of the system is the set of ordered pairs in the intersection of the two graphs. This portion is shaded in the graph below.

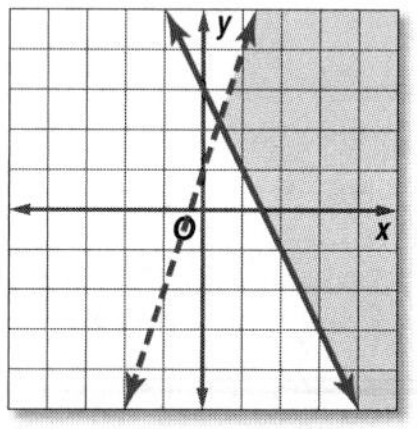

70.

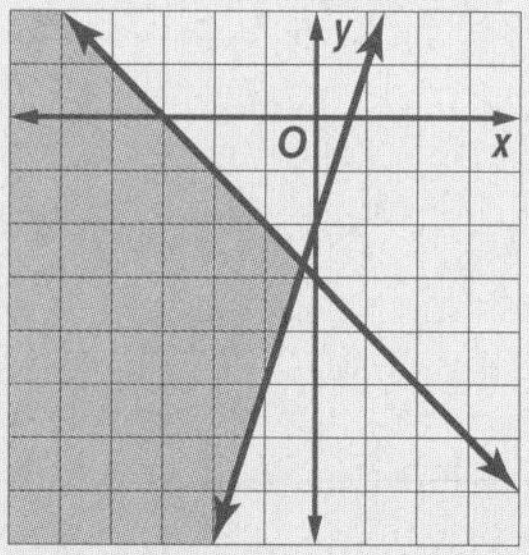

71. **Jobs**

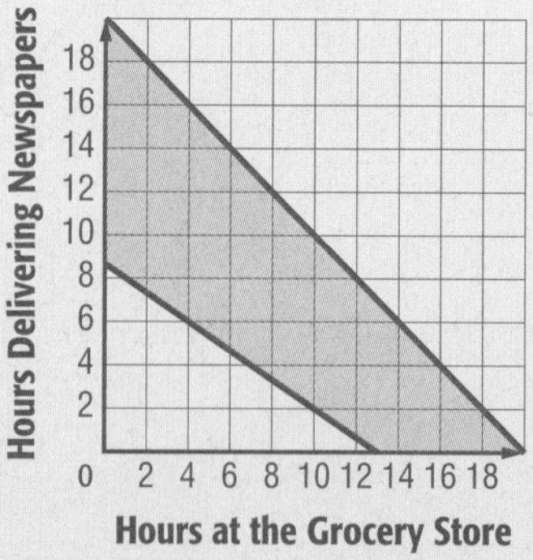

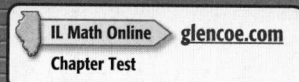

IL Math Online glencoe.com
Chapter Test

Graph each system and determine the number of solutions that it has. If it has one solution, name it.

1. $y = 2x$
   $y = 6 - x$ one; (2, 4)

2. $y = x - 3$
   $y = -2x + 9$ one; (4, 1)

3. $x - y = 4$
   $x + y = 10$ one; (7, 3)

4. $2x + 3y = 4$
   $2x + 3y = -1$ no solution

1–4. See Ch. 6 Answer Appendix for graphs.

Use substitution to solve each system of equations.

5. $y = x + 8$
   $2x + y = -10$ (−6, 2)

6. $x = -4y - 3$
   $3x - 2y = 5$ (1, −1)

7. **GARDENING** Corey has 42 feet of fencing around his garden. The garden is rectangular in shape, and its length is equal to twice the width minus 3 feet. Define the variables, and write a system of equations to find the length and width of the garden. Solve the system by using substitution. See margin.

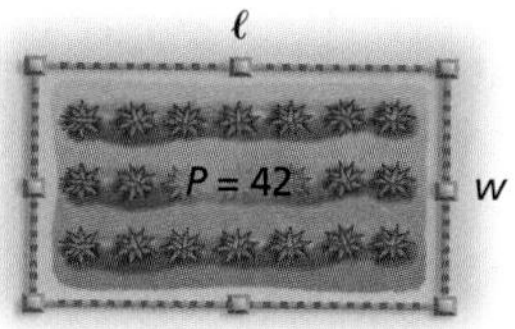

8. **MULTIPLE CHOICE** Use elimination to solve the system. B

$$6x - 4y = 6$$
$$-6x + 3y = 0$$

A (5, 6)

B (−3, −6)

C (1, 0)

D (4, −8)

9. **SHOPPING** Shelly has $175 to shop for jeans and sweaters. Each pair of jeans costs $25, each sweater costs $20, and she buys 8 items. Determine the number of pairs of jeans and sweaters Shelly bought. 3 jeans, 5 sweaters

Use elimination to solve each system of equations.

10. $x + y = 13$
    $x - y = 5$ (9, 4)

11. $3x + 7y = 2$
    $3x - 4y = 13$ (3, −1)

12. $x + y = 8$
    $x - 3y = -4$ (5, 3)

13. $2x + 6y = 18$
    $3x + 2y = 13$ (3, 2)

14. **MAGAZINES** Julie subscribes to a sports magazine and a fashion magazine. She received 24 issues this year. The number of fashion issues is 6 less than twice the number of sports issues. Define the variables, and write a system of equations to find the number of issues of each magazine. See margin.

Perform the indicated matrix operations. If an operation cannot be performed, write *impossible*.

15. $\begin{bmatrix} 3 & -5 & 2 \end{bmatrix} + \begin{bmatrix} 12 & -7 & -6 \end{bmatrix}$ $\begin{bmatrix} 15 & -12 & -4 \end{bmatrix}$

16. $\begin{bmatrix} 1 & 8 & -4 \\ -2 & 6 & 7 \\ 0 & 9 & -6 \end{bmatrix} - \begin{bmatrix} -4 & 2 & 0 \\ -5 & 3 & 8 \\ -9 & -7 & 1 \end{bmatrix}$ $\begin{bmatrix} 5 & 6 & -4 \\ 3 & 3 & -1 \\ 9 & 16 & -7 \end{bmatrix}$

17. $-2\begin{bmatrix} -2 & 7 \\ 6 & -4 \\ 8 & 5 \end{bmatrix}$ $\begin{bmatrix} 4 & -14 \\ -12 & 8 \\ -16 & -10 \end{bmatrix}$

Use an augmented matrix to solve each system of equations.

18. $y = 3x$
    $x + 2y = 21$ (3, 9)

19. $x + y = 12$
    $y = x - 4$ (8, 4)

20. $x + y = 15$
    $x - y = 9$ (12, 3)

21. $3x + 5y = 7$
    $2x - 3y = 11$ (4, −1)

22–25. See Ch. 6 Answer Appendix.

Solve each system of inequalities by graphing.

22. $x > 2$
    $y < 4$

23. $x + y \leq 5$
    $y \geq x + 2$

24. $3x - y > 9$
    $y > -2x$

25. $y \geq 2x + 3$
    $-4x - 3y > 12$

ExamView Assessment Suite Customize and create multiple versions of your chapter test and their answer keys. All of the questions from the leveled chapter tests in the *Chapter 6 Resource Masters* are also available on ExamView® Assessment Suite.

Additional Answers

7. Sample answer: Let w be the width and let ℓ be the length; $2w + 2\ell = 42$, $\ell = 2w - 3$; $w = 8$ ft, $\ell = 13$ ft

14. Let $f =$ the number of fashion magazines and $s =$ the number of sports magazines. Then $f + s = 24$, and $f = 2s - 6$. So $s = 10$ and $f = 14$.

Intervention Planner

Tier 1 On Level	Tier 2 Strategic Intervention approaching grade level	Tier 3 Intensive Intervention 2 or more grades below level
If students miss about 25% of the exercises or less,	**If** students miss about 50% of the exercises,	**If** students miss about 75% of the exercises,
Then choose a resource: SE Lessons 6-1–6-8 CRM Skills Practice, pp. 7, 14, 20, 26, 32, 38, 44 and 50 TE Chapter Project, p. 330 IL Math Online Self-Check Quiz	**Then** choose a resource: CRM Study Guide and Intervention, Chapter 6, pp. 5, 12, 18, 24, 30, 36, 42 and 48 *Quick Review Math Handbook* IL Math Online Extra Examples, Personal Tutor, Homework Help	**Then** use *Math Triumphs, Alg. 1* IL Math Online Extra Examples, Personal Tutor, Homework Help, Review Vocabulary

1 FOCUS

Objective Use the strategy of guess and check to solve standardized test problems.

2 TEACH

Scaffolding Questions

Ask:

- Have you ever used a guess to choose an answer on a test? If yes, why did you guess the answer? Answers will vary.
- Did you check the guess? If yes, how did you check it? Answers will vary.
- Why do you think it makes sense to check a guess? Sample answer: A guess could be wrong, so checking it could show that it is wrong and that you need to make another guess.

CHAPTER 6 Preparing for Standardized Tests

Guess and Check

It is very important to pace yourself and keep track of how much time you have when taking a standardized test. If time is running short, or if you are unsure how to solve a problem, the guess and check strategy may help you determine the correct answer quickly.

Strategies for Guessing and Checking

Step 1

Carefully look over each possible answer choice, and evaluate for reasonableness. Eliminate unreasonable answers.

Ask yourself:

- Are there any answer choices that are clearly incorrect?
- Are there any answer choices that are not in the proper format?
- Are there any answer choices that do not have the proper units for the correct answer?

Step 2

For the remaining answer choices, use the guess and check method.

- **Equations:** If you are solving an equation, substitute the answer choice for the variable and see if this results in a true number sentence.
- **Inequalities:** Likewise, you can substitute the answer choice for the variable and see if it satisfies the inequality.
- **System of Equations:** Find the answer choice that satisfies both equations of the system.

Step 3

Choose an answer choice and see if it satisfies the constraints of the problem statement. Identify the correct answer.

- If the answer choice you are testing does not satisfy the problem, move on to the next reasonable guess and check it.
- When you find the correct answer choice, stop. You do not have to check the other answer choices.

394 Chapter 6 Systems of Linear Equations and Inequalities

EXAMPLE

Read the problem. Identify what you need to know. Then use the information in the problem to solve.

Solve $\begin{cases} 4x - 8y = 20 \\ -3x + 5y = -14 \end{cases}$.

A (5, 0) C (3, –1)

B (4, –2) D (–6, –5)

The solution of a system of equations is an ordered pair, (x, y). Since all four answer choices are of this form, they are all possible correct answers and must be checked. Begin with the first answer choice and substitute it in each equation. Continue until you find the ordered pair that satisfies both equations of the system.

	First Equation	Second Equation
Guess: (5, 0)	$4x - 8y = 20$ $4(5) - 8(0) = 20$ ✓	$-3x + 5y = -14$ $-3(5) + 5(0) \neq -14$ ✗

	First Equation	Second Equation
Guess: (4, –2)	$4x - 8y = 20$ $4(4) - 8(-2) \neq 20$ ✗	$-3x + 5y = -14$ $-3(4) + 5(-2) \neq -14$ ✗

	First Equation	Second Equation
Guess: (3, –1)	$4x - 8y = 20$ $4(3) - 8(-1) = 20$ ✓	$-3x + 5y = -14$ $-3(3) + 5(-1) = -14$ ✓

The ordered pair (3, –1) satisfies both equations of the system. So, the correct answer is C.

Exercises

Read each problem. Eliminate any unreasonable answers. Then use the information in the problem to solve.

1. Gina bought 5 hot dogs and 3 soft drinks at the ball game for \$11.50. Renaldo bought 4 hot dogs and 2 soft drinks for \$8.50. How much does a single hot dog and a single drink cost? B

   A hot dogs: \$1.25 soft drinks: \$1.50

   B hot dogs: \$1.25 soft drinks: \$1.75

   C hot dogs: \$1.50 soft drinks: \$1.25

   D hot dogs: \$1.50 soft drinks: \$1.75

2. The bookstore hopes to sell at least 30 binders and calculators each week. The store also hopes to have sales revenue of at least \$200 in binders and calculators. How many binders and calculators could be sold to meet both of these sales goals? H

Store Prices	
Item	**Price**
binders	\$3.65
calculators	\$14.80

   F 25 binders, 5 calculators

   G 12 binders, 15 calculators

   H 22 binders, 9 calculators

   J 28 binders, 6 calculators

Additional Example

Solve $2x + 5y = -18$
$-4x + 3y = 10$ C

A (6, –6)

B (1, –4)

C (–4, –2)

D (–9, 0)

3 ASSESS

Use Exercises 1 and 2 to assess students' understanding.

PSAE Practice

Cumulative, Chapters 1 through 6

Multiple Choice

Read each question. Then fill in the correct answer on the answer document provided by your teacher or on a sheet of paper.

1. Which of the following terms ***best*** describes the system of equations shown in the graph? D

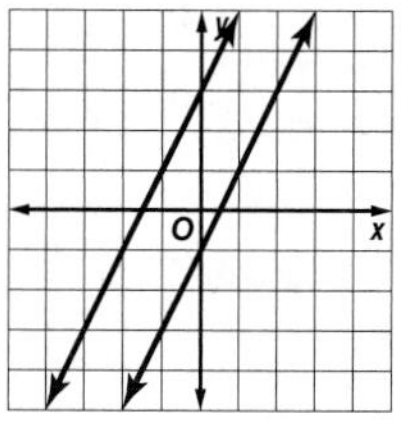

A consistent
B consistent and dependent
C consistent and independent
D inconsistent
E independent

2. Use substitution to solve the system of equations below. K

$$\begin{cases} y = 4x - 7 \\ 3x - 2y = -1 \end{cases}$$

F (3, 1)
G (4, −1)
H (5, −2)
J (−6, 2)
K (3, 5)

3. Solve the system of equations below. B

$$\begin{cases} 3x - 8y = -50 \\ 3x - 5y = -38 \end{cases}$$

A (4, −6)
B (−6, 4)
C $\left(-\frac{44}{3}, \frac{88}{13}\right)$
D $\left(-\frac{2}{7}, \frac{4}{9}\right)$
E (0, 3)

4. Bob payed $881 for 4 table saws and 9 drills. If the cost of the saws exceeded the cost of the drills by $71, what is the price of a drill? F

F $45
G $59
H $90
J $108
K $119

5. In which quadrant(s) of the coordinate plane is the region defined by this system located? C

$$y > -\frac{1}{2}x - 1$$
$$y > -x + 3$$

A I and IV only
B III only
C I, II, and IV only
D II and III only
E I and III only

6. Which of the following terms ***best*** describes the system of equations shown in the graph? G

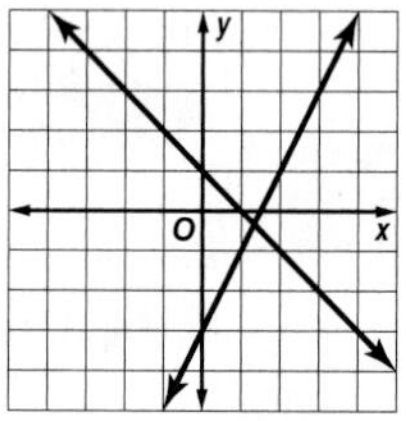

F consistent
G consistent and independent
H consistent and dependent
J inconsistent
K independent

7. Solve the system of equations below. D

$$3x + 2y = -2$$
$$2x - 2y = -18$$

A (−16, −25)
B (−14, 5)
C (3, −6)
D (−4, 5)
E (1, 4)

8. What is the solution of the following system of equations? J

$$\begin{cases} y = 6x - 1 \\ y = 6x + 4 \end{cases}$$

F (2, 11)
G (−3, −14)
H (7, 5)
J no solution
K (0, 5)

Test-TakingTip

Question 8 You can subtract the second equation from the first equation to eliminate the x-variable. Then solve for y.

Diagnose Student Errors

Survey students' responses for each item. Class trends may indicate common errors and misconceptions.

1. A misunderstood concept of possible solutions for a system of equations
B misunderstood concept of possible solutions for a system of equations
C misunderstood concept of possible solutions for a system of equations
D correct
E misunderstood concept of independent systems

2. F guess
G added x-terms and constants incorrectly
H added y-terms incorrectly
J added constant terms incorrectly
K correct

3. A transposed the results
B correct
C guess
D guess
E guess

4. F correct
G guess or calculation error
H guess or calculation error
J guess or calculation error
K guess or calculation error

5. A error in identifying quadrants
B misunderstood how to solve system of inequalities
C correct
D shaded below boundary line
E error in identifying quadrants

6. F did not choose the *best* answer
G correct
H confused one solution and infinite number of solutions
J misunderstood concept of possible solutions for a system of equations
K need to include *consistent*

7. A guess
B guess
C guess
D correct
E guess

8. F solved for the first equation only
G solved for the second equation only
H guess
J correct
K guess

Short Response/Gridded Response

Record your answers on the answer sheet provided by your teacher or on a sheet of paper.

9. GRIDDED RESPONSE Angie and her sister have \$15 to spend on pizza. A medium pizza costs \$11.50 plus \$0.75 per topping. What is the maximum number of toppings Angie and her sister can get on their pizza? **4**

10. Write an inequality for the graph below. $y \geq \frac{3}{4}x - 1$

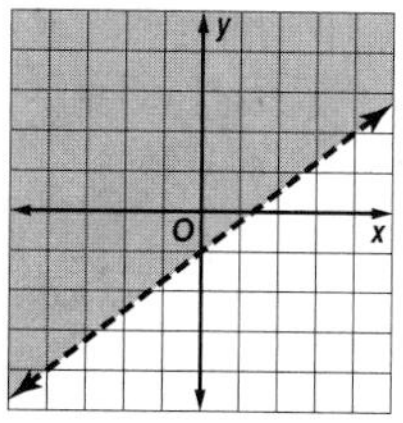

11. GRIDDED RESPONSE Christy is taking a road trip. After she drives 12 more miles, she will have driven at least half of the 108-mile trip. What is the least number of miles she has driven so far? **42**

12 Write an equation in slope-intercept form with a slope of $-\frac{2}{3}$ and a y-intercept of 6. $y = -\frac{2}{3}x + 6$

13. A rental company charges \$9.50 per hour for a scooter plus a \$15 fee. Write an equation in slope-intercept form for the total rental cost C of renting a scooter for h hours. $C = 9.5h + 15$

14. GRIDDED RESPONSE A computer supplies store is having a storewide sale this weekend. An inkjet printer that normally sells for \$179.00 is on sale for \$143.20. What is the percent discount of the sale price? **20**

15. In 1980, the population of Kentucky was about 3.66 million people. By 2000, this number had grown to about 4.04 million people. What was the annual rate of change in population from 1980 to 2000? **about 19,000 people per year**

16. Joseph's cell phone service charges him \$0.15 per each text message sent. Write an equation that represents the cost C of his cell phone service for text messages t sent each month. $C = 0.15t$

17. A store is offering a \$15 mail-in-rebate on all printers. If Mark is looking at printers that range from \$45 to \$89, how much can he expect to pay? **\$30 to \$74**

Extended Response

Record your answers on a sheet of paper. Show your work.

18. The table shows how many canned goods were collected during the first day of a charity food drive.

Food Drive Day 1 Results	
Class	**Number Collected**
10th graders	78
11th graders	80
12th graders	92

a. Estimate how many canned goods will be collected during the 5-day food drive. Explain your answer. **a–b. See margin.**

b. Is this estimate a reasonable expectation? Explain.

Need Extra Help?																		
If you missed Question...	1	2	3	4	5	6	7	8	9	10	11	12	13	14	15	16	17	18
Go to Lesson or Page...	6-1	6-2	6-3	6-3	6-8	6-1	6-3	6-3	5-3	5-6	5-3	4-2	4-2	3-3	2-7	2-1	1-4	1-3
IL Assessment Objectives	8.11.15	8.11.17	8.11.17	8.11.17	8.11.15	8.11.15	8.11.17	8.11.17	8.11.16	8.11.16	8.11.16	8.11.07	8.11.02	6.11.18	6.11.17	8.11.02	6.11.13	6.11.09

Formative Assessment

You can use these two pages to benchmark student progress.

CRM Standardized Test Practice, pp. 76–78

Answer Sheet Practice

Have students simulate taking a standardized test by recording their answers on a practice recording sheet.

CRM Student Recording Sheet, p. 57

Chapter Resource Master

CRM p. 57

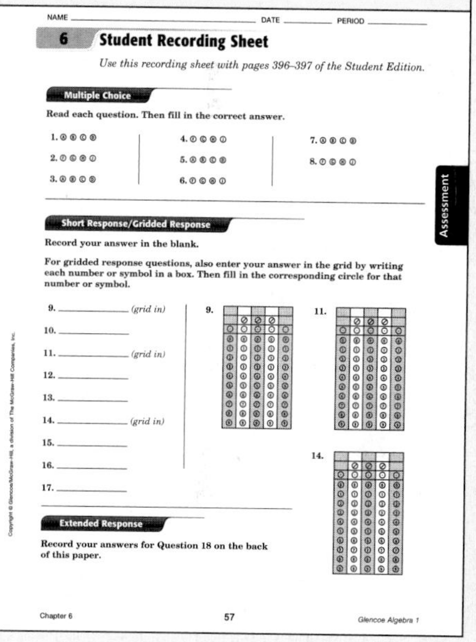
NAME DATE PERIOD

6 Student Recording Sheet

Use this recording sheet with pages 396–397 of the Student Edition.

Multiple Choice

Read each question. Then fill in the correct answer.

Short Response/Gridded Response

Record your answer in the blank.

For gridded response questions, also enter your answer in the grid by writing each number or symbol in a box. Then fill in the corresponding circle for that number or symbol.

Extended Response

Record your answers for Question 18 on the back of this paper.

Chapter 6 57 Glencoe Algebra 1

ExamView Assessment Suite Create practice worksheets or tests that align to your state's standards, as well as TIMSS and NAEP tests.

Additional Answers

18a. 250 canned goods were collected on Day 1. So after 5 days 1,250 will be collected.

18b. Sample answer: No, because the number of canned goods will likely fluctuate from day-today.

Homework Option

Get Ready for Chapter 7 Assign students the exercises on p. 399 as homework to assess whether they possess the prerequisite skills needed for the next chapter.

Page 335, Lesson 6-1 (Check Your Progress)

2A.

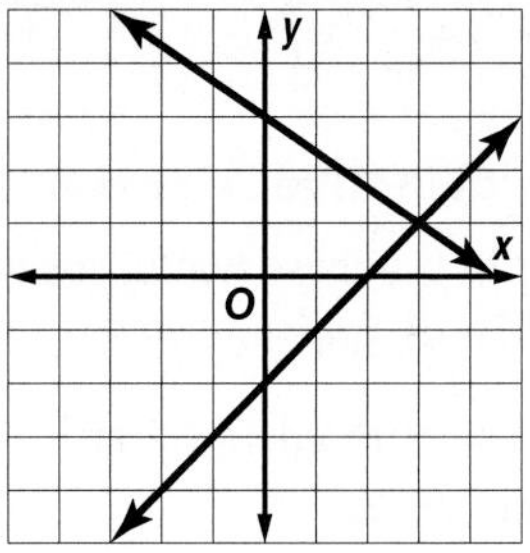

2B.

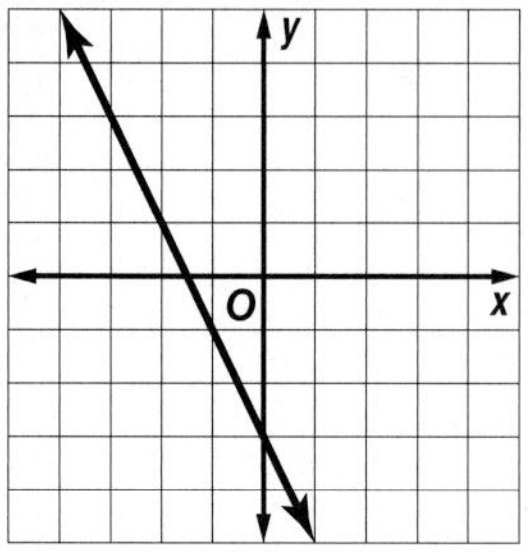

Pages 336–338, Lesson 6-1

16.

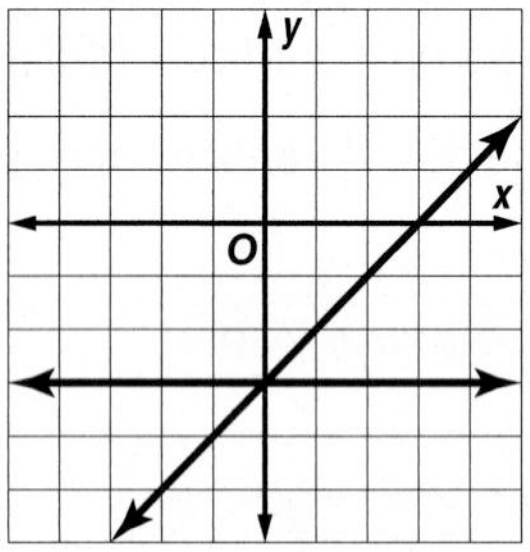

17.

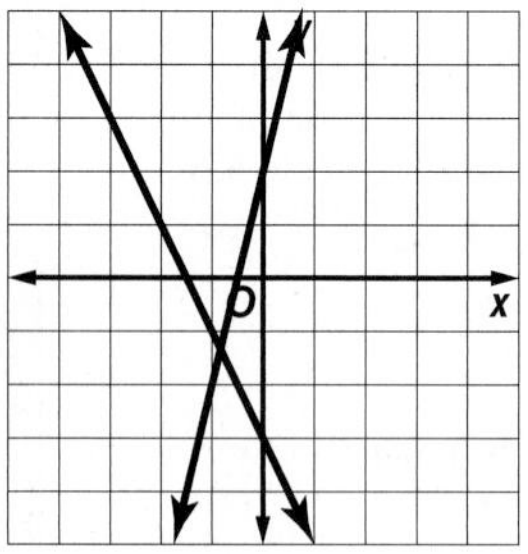

18.

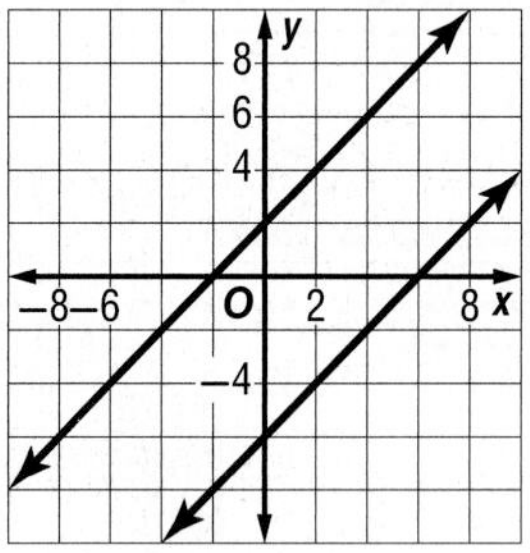

19.

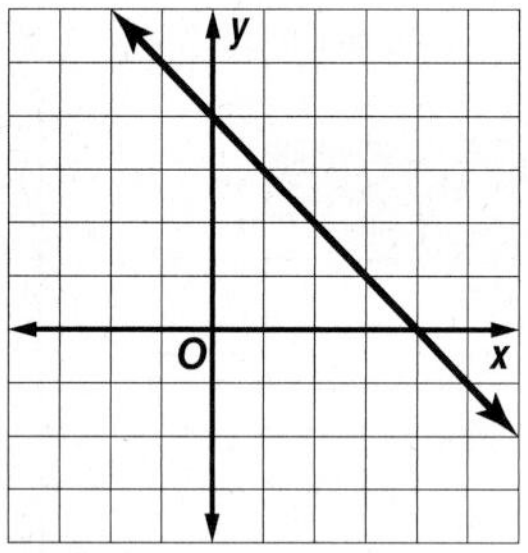

20.

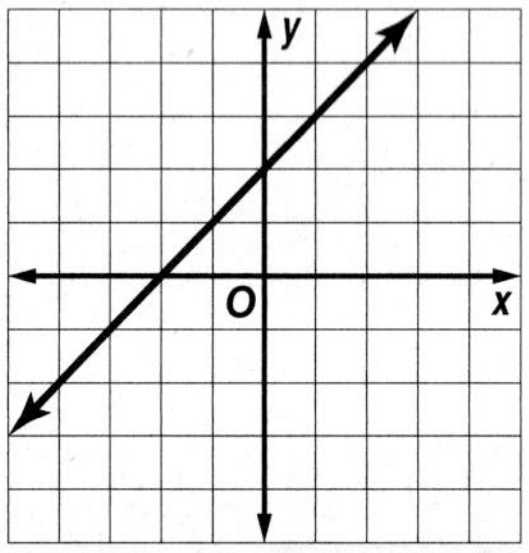

21.

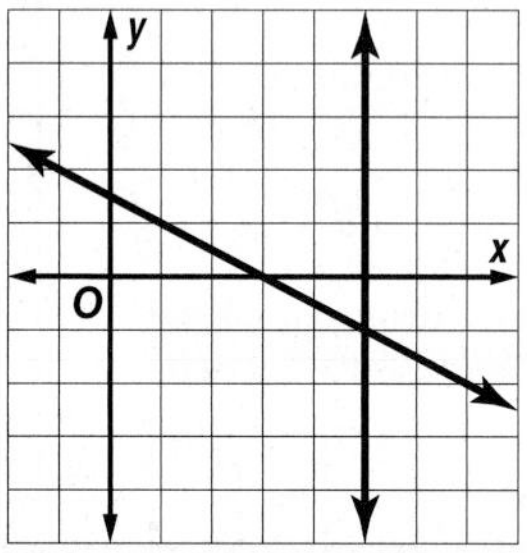

22.

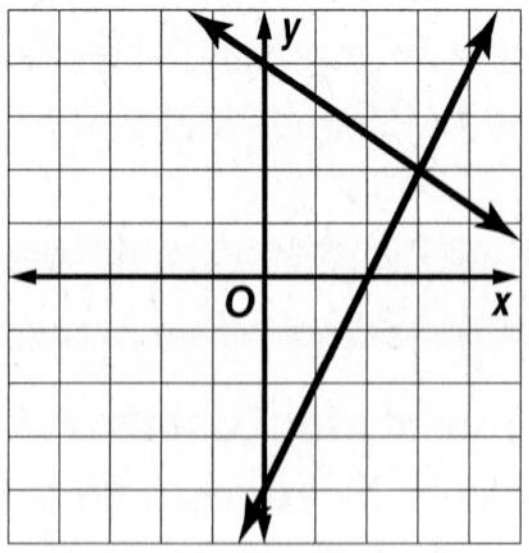

23.

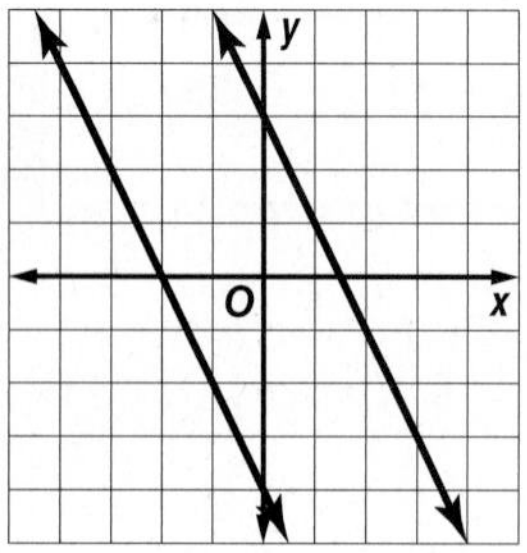

24.

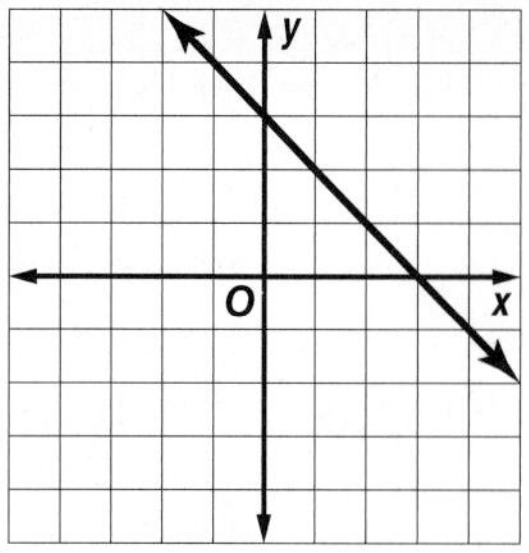

26a.

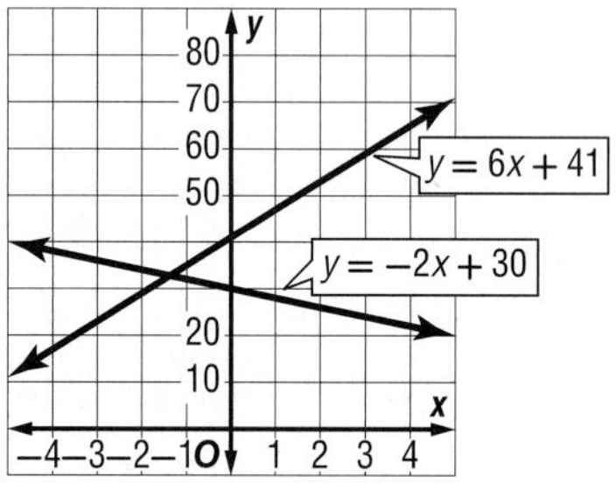

27.

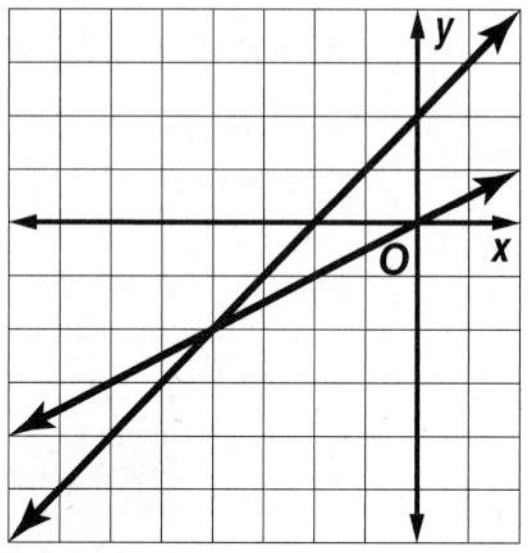

28.

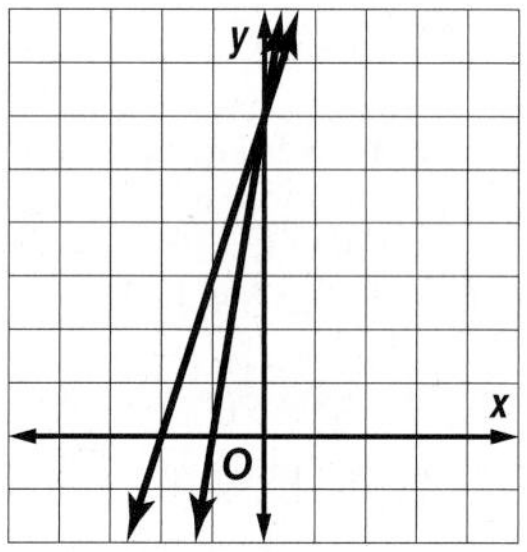

29.

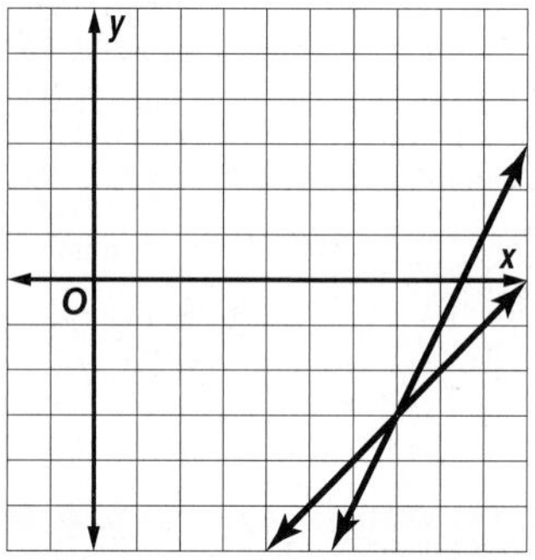

30.

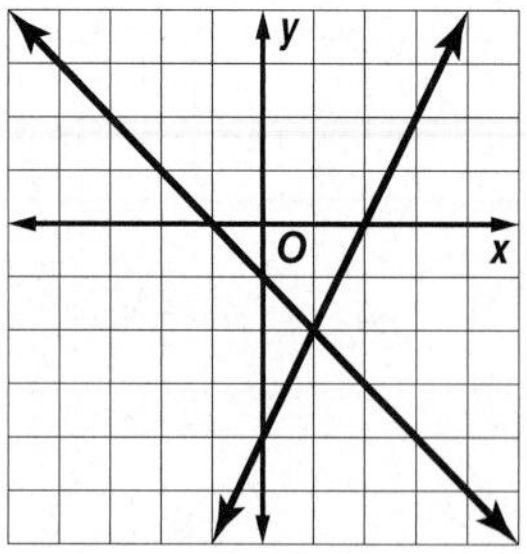

31.

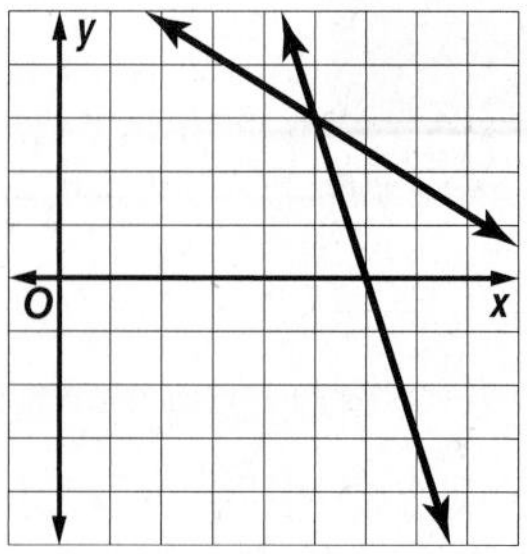

32.
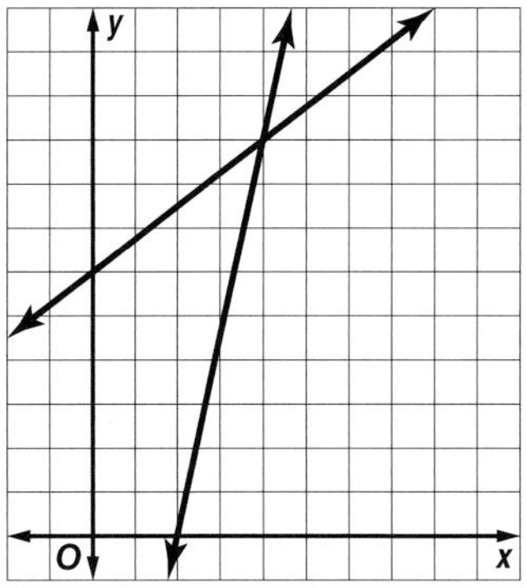

33.
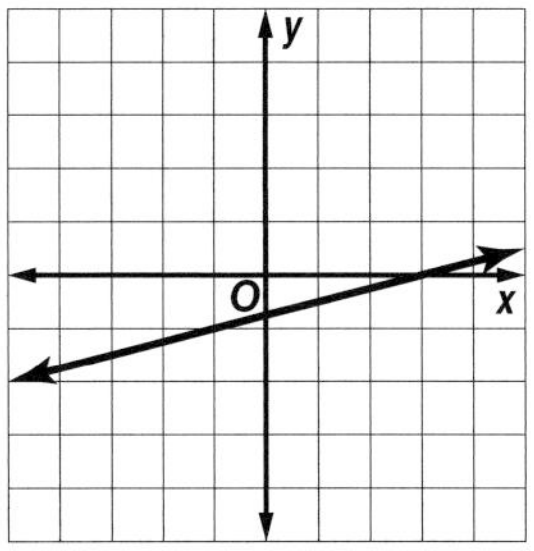

34.
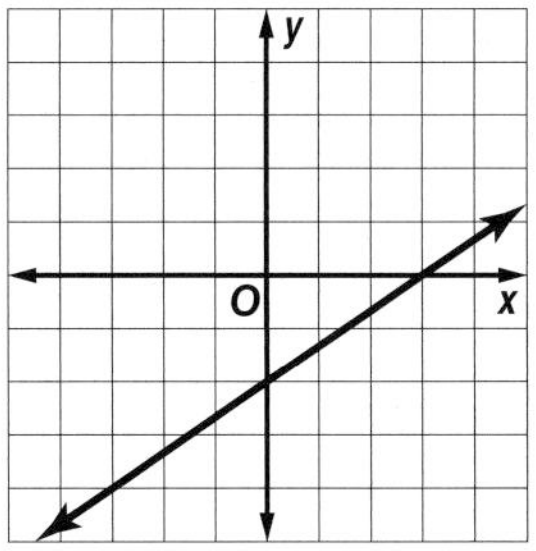

35.
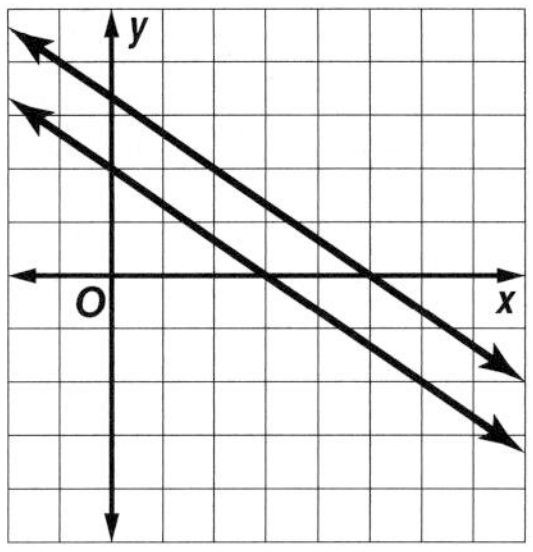

36.
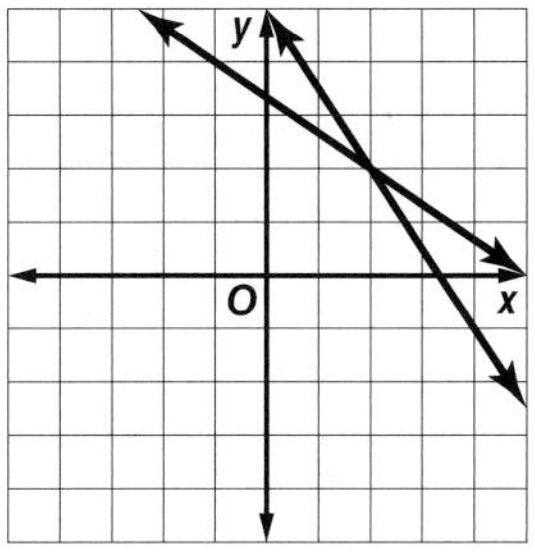

37.
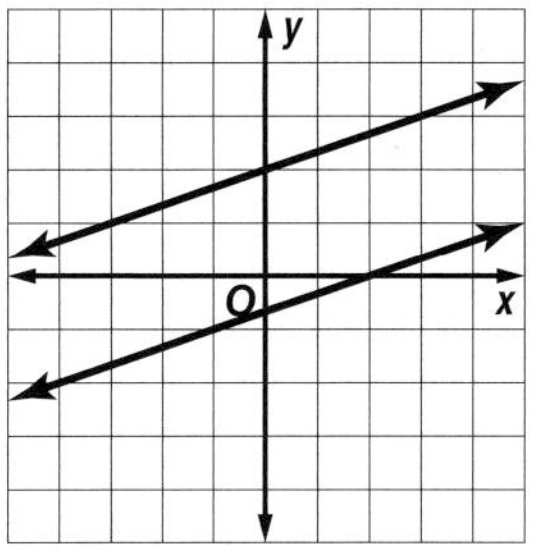

38.
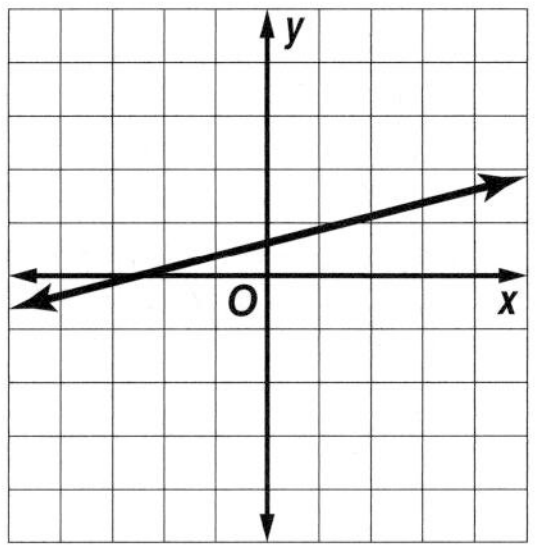

39.
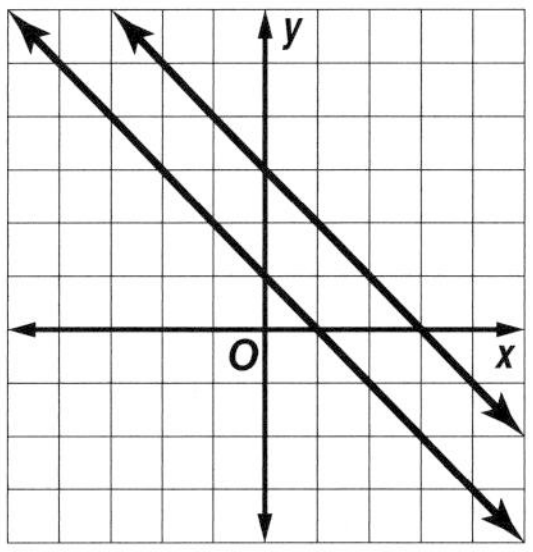

40.
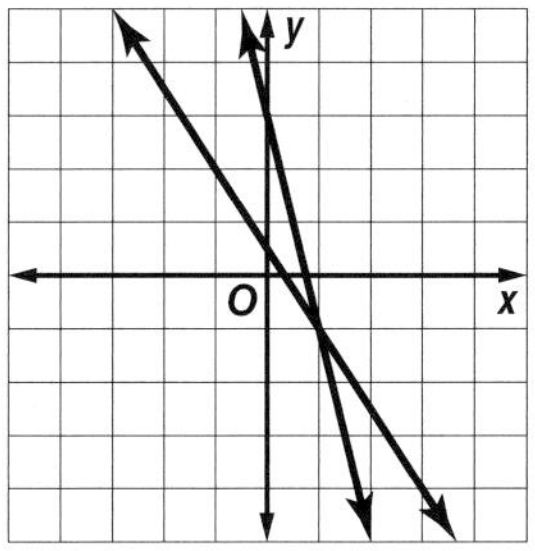

41.
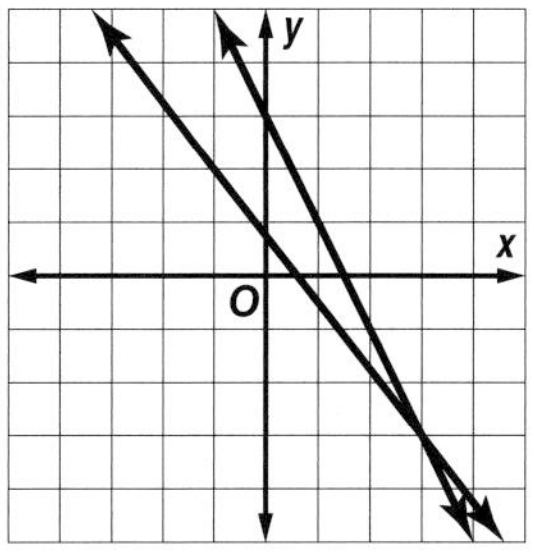

42a.
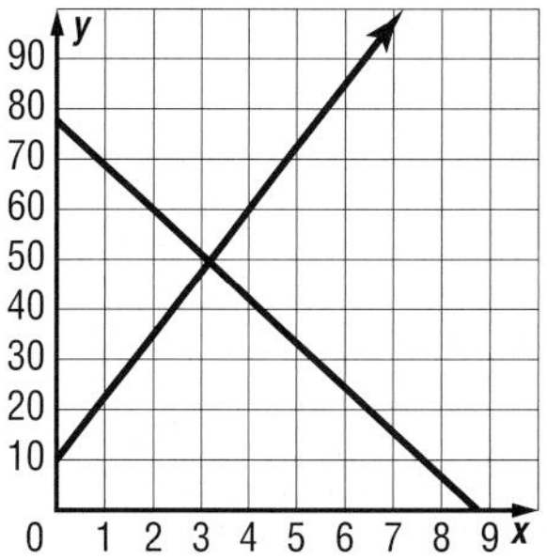

43.
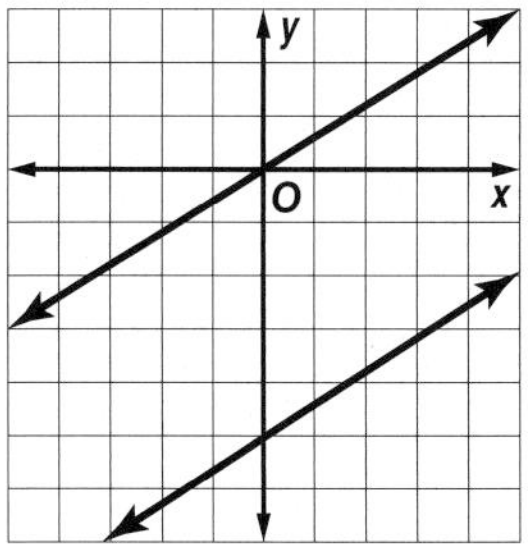

44.
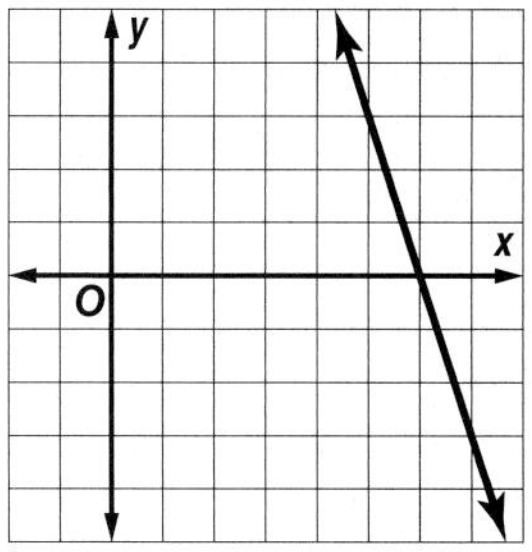

Pages 346–347, Lesson 6-2

26a. Let x = number of tickets purchased and let y = the cost; $y = 65x + 10$, $y = 69x + 13.60$.

26b.

Booker's Concert Tickets	
Number of Tickets	Cost($)
1	75
2	140
3	205
4	270
5	335

Paula's Concert Tickets	
Number of Tickets	Cost($)
1	82.60
2	151.60
3	220.60
4	289.60
5	358.60

26c.

Tickets

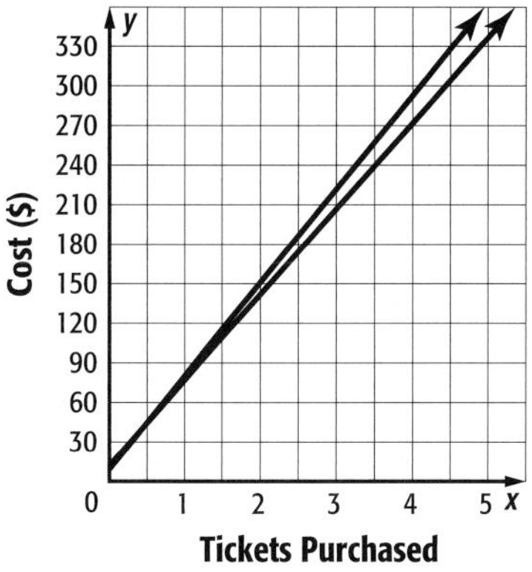

26d. No solution; sample answer: The graphs do not intersect in the first quadrant.

30. Sample answer: $a + b = 25$, $24a + 16b = 464$; Let a = the number of tops Allison bought, and let b = the number of tops Beth bought; together, Allison and Beth bought 25 tops. Allison spent $24 per top, and Beth spent $16 per top. Together they spent $464. How many tops did each girl buy? Allison bought 8 tops, and Beth bought 17 tops.

Page 361, Mid-Chapter Quiz

3.

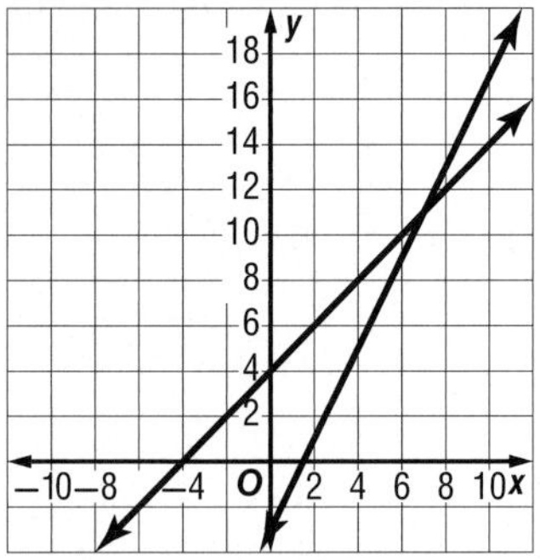

4.

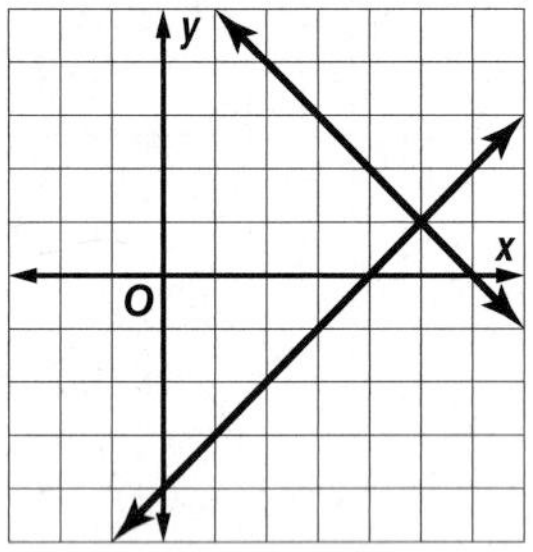

5.

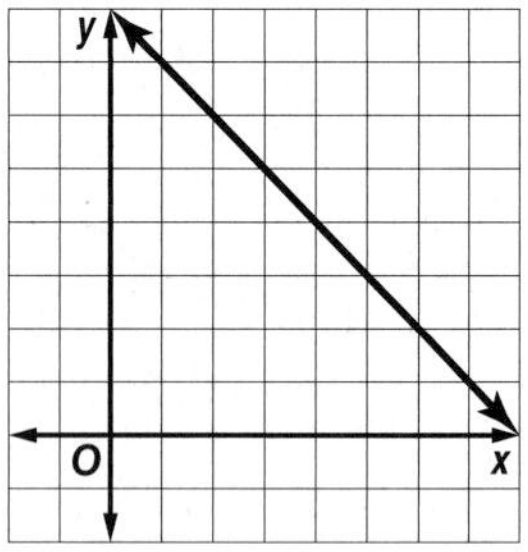

6.

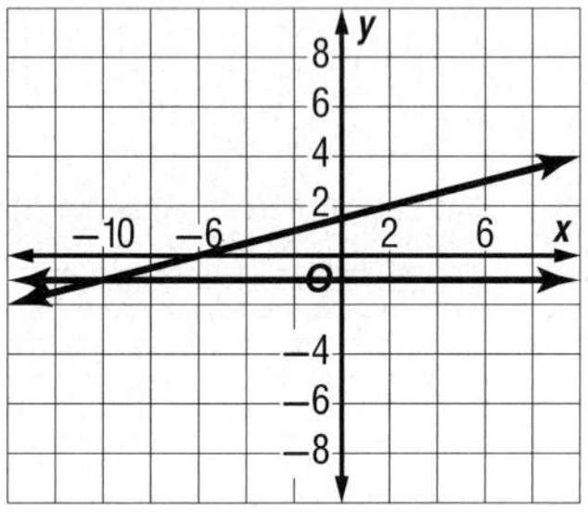

7.

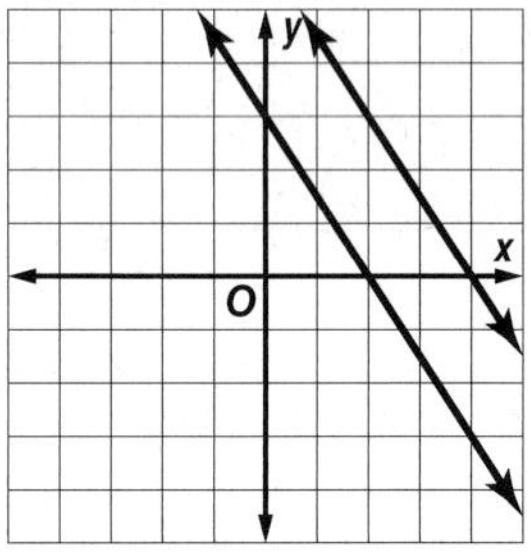

8.

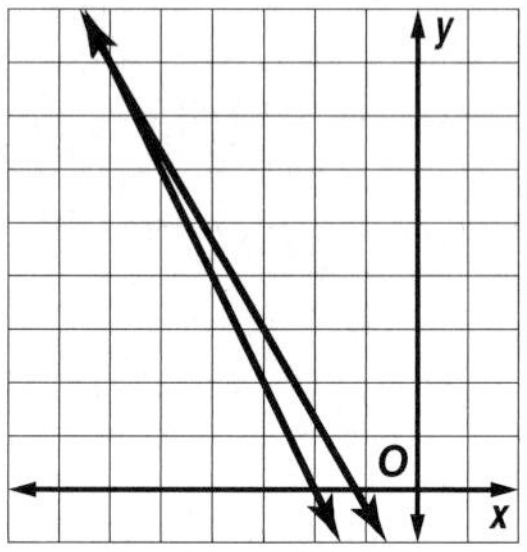

14a. Let a = cost of an adult ticket and c = the cost of a child ticket.

14b. $4a + 2c = 184$
$4a + 3c = 200$

14c. (38, 16); The cost of an adult's ticket is \$38, and the cost of a child's ticket is \$16.

Page 367, Lesson 6-5

35.

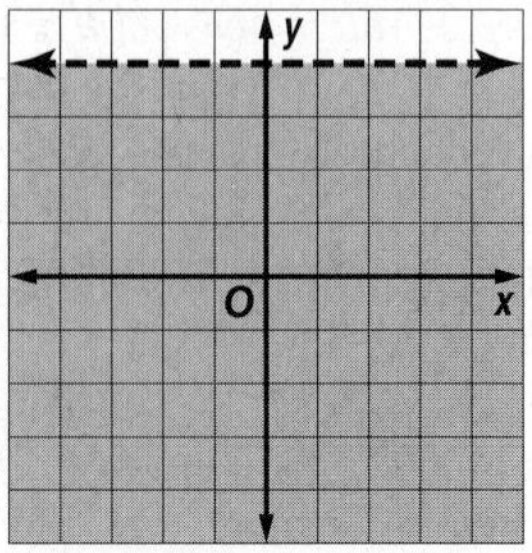

36.

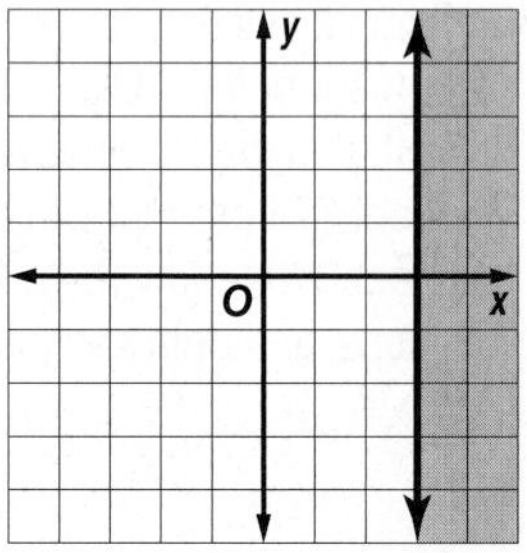

37.

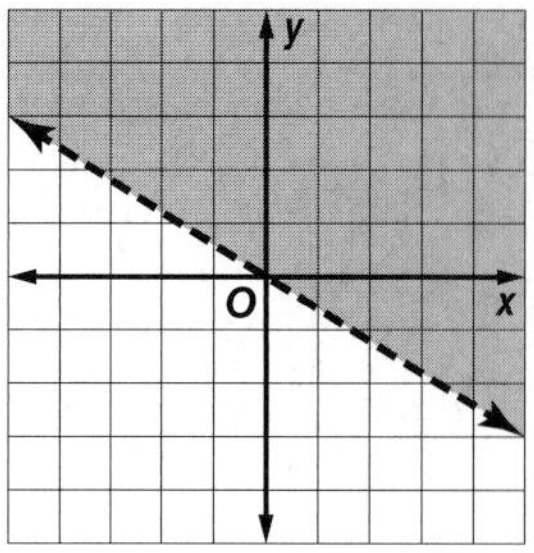

38.

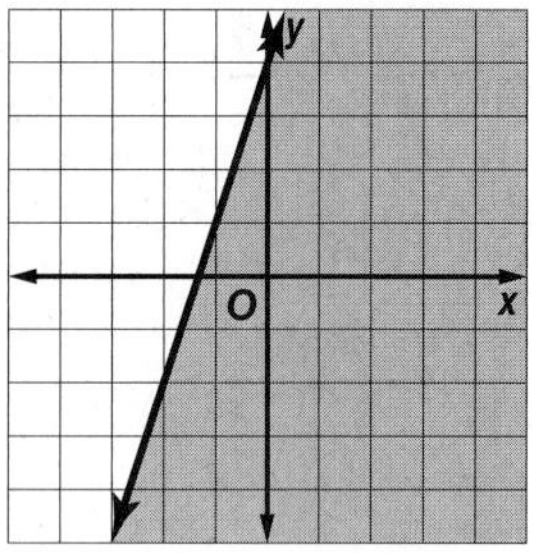

Pages 382–383, Lesson 6-8 (Check Your Progress)

1A.

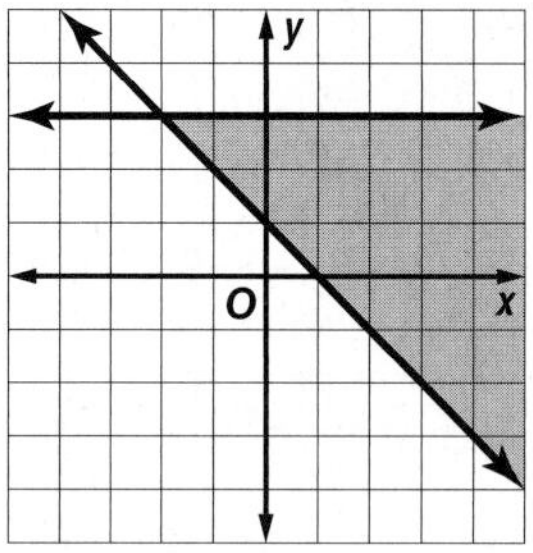

1B.

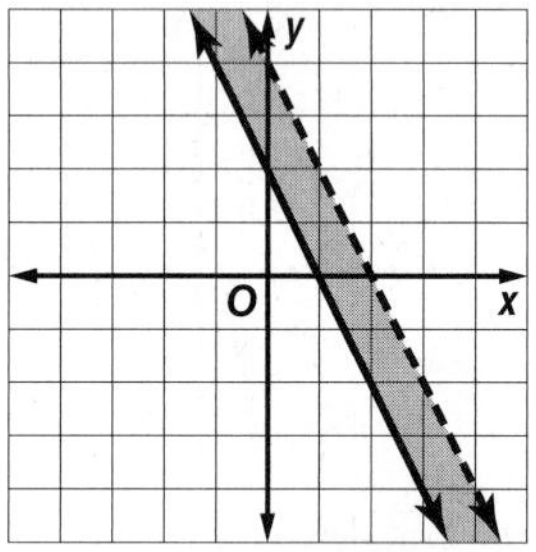

1C.

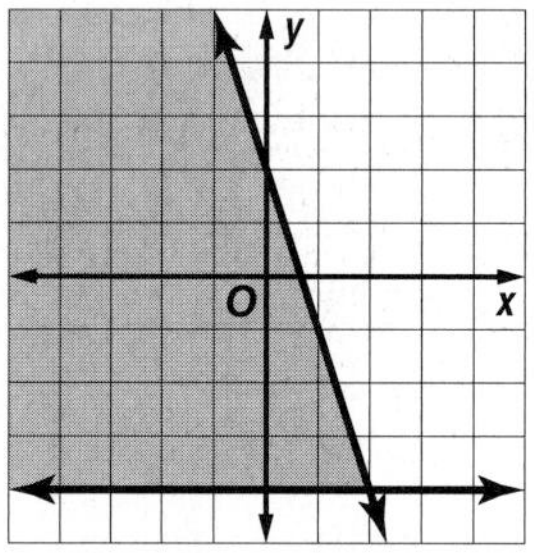

1D.

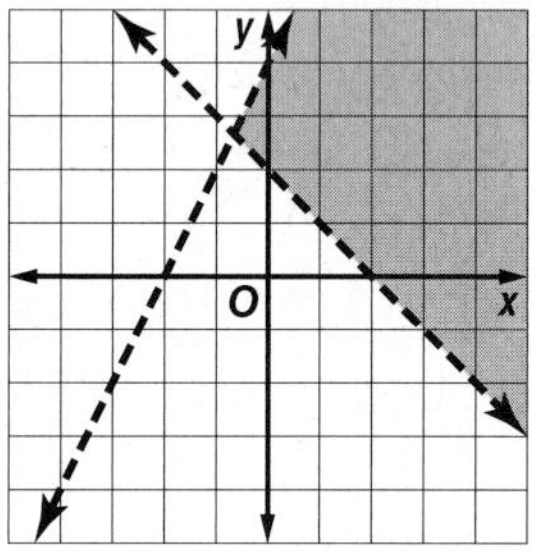

2A. no solution

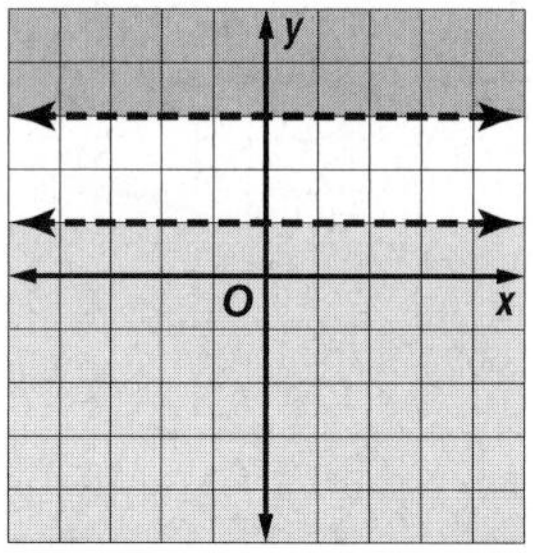

2B. no solution

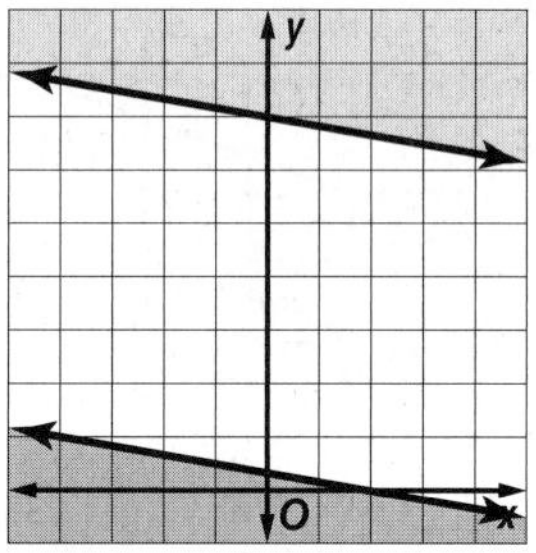

3A. Let w = the number of sweatshirts and t = the number of T-shirts; $w + t \leq 120$ and $22w + 15t \geq 2000$.

3B.

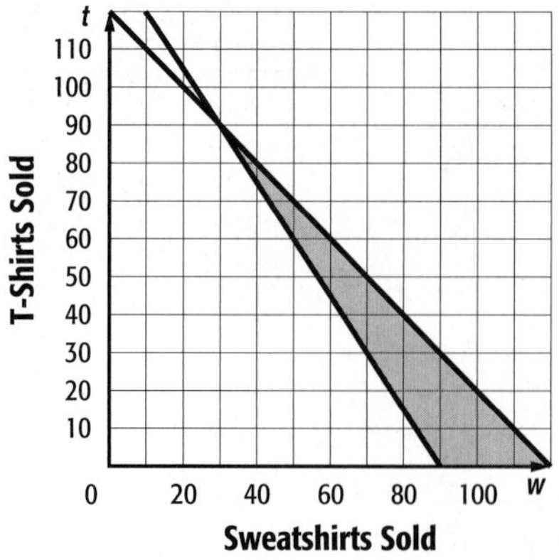

Pages 384–386, Lesson 6-8

1.

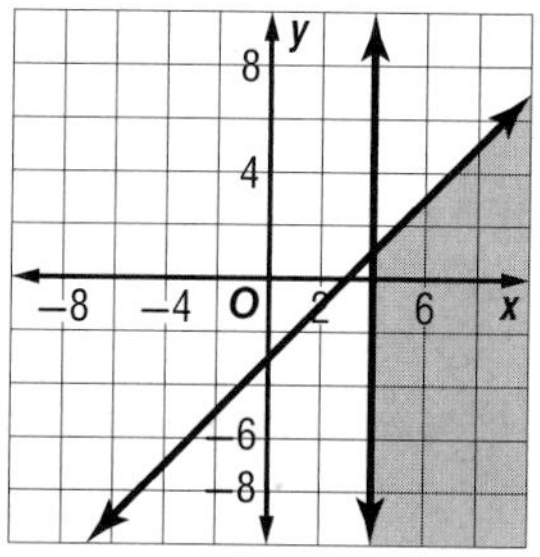

2.

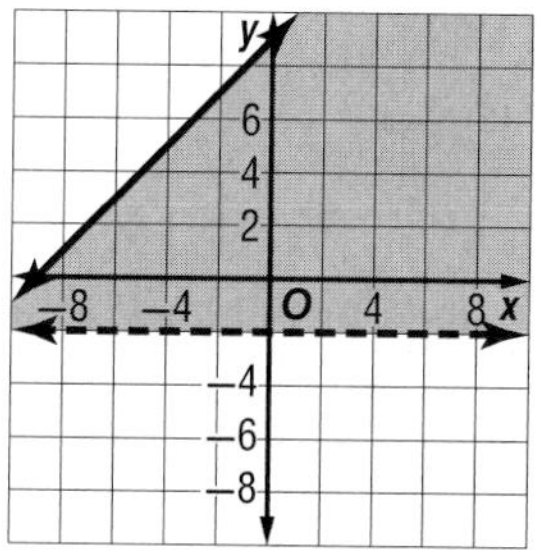

3.

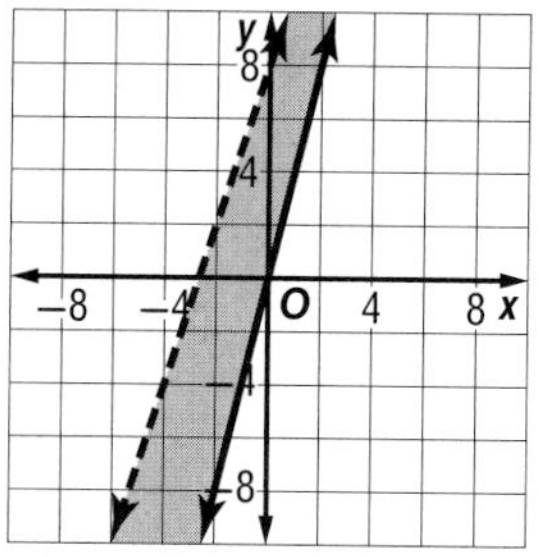

4.

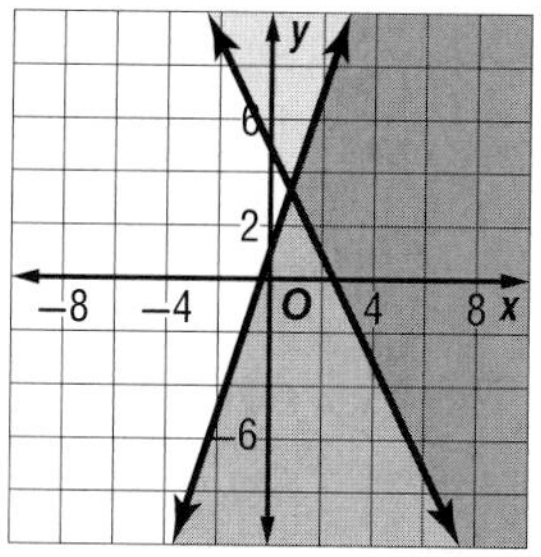

5. no solution

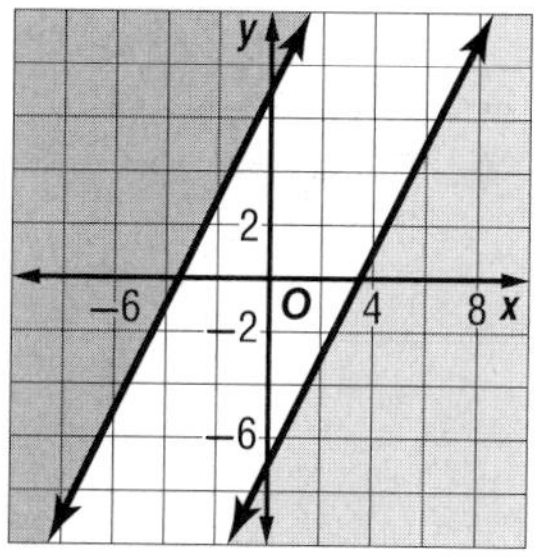

6.

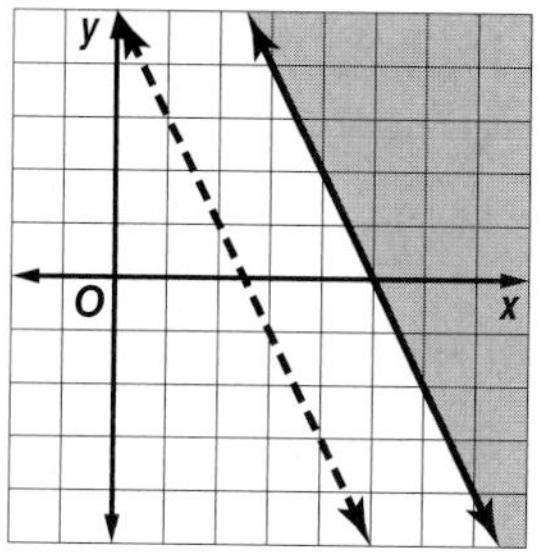

7.

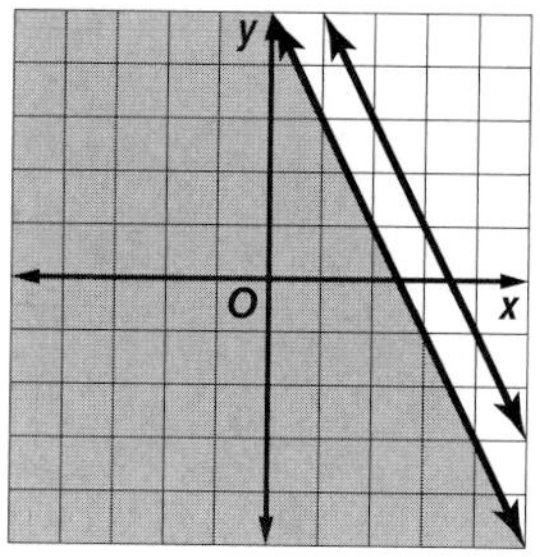

8. no solution

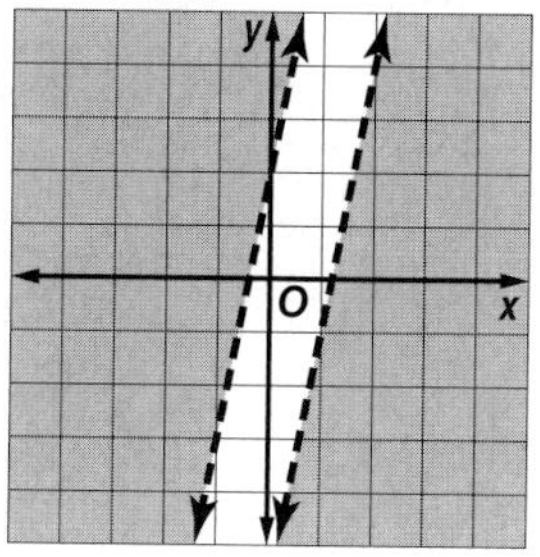

9a. Let h = the height of the driver in inches and w = the weight of the driver in pounds; $h < 79$ and $w < 295$.

Driving Requirements

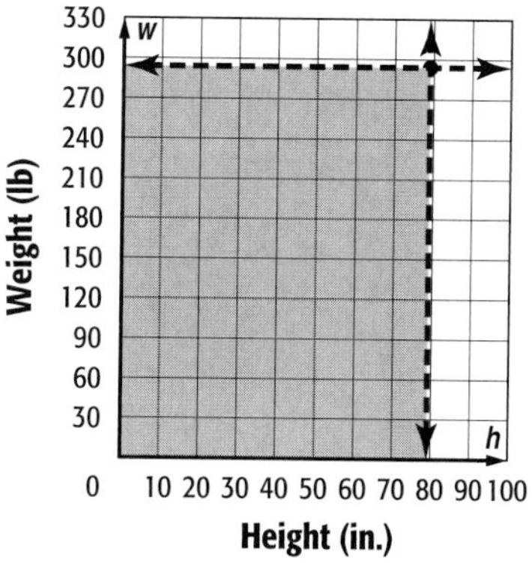

10.

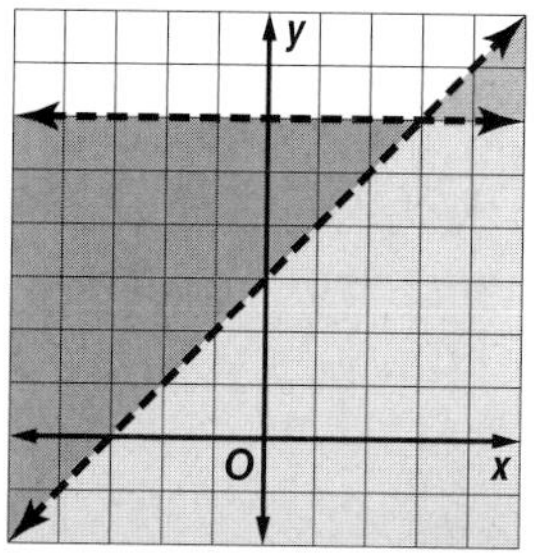

11.

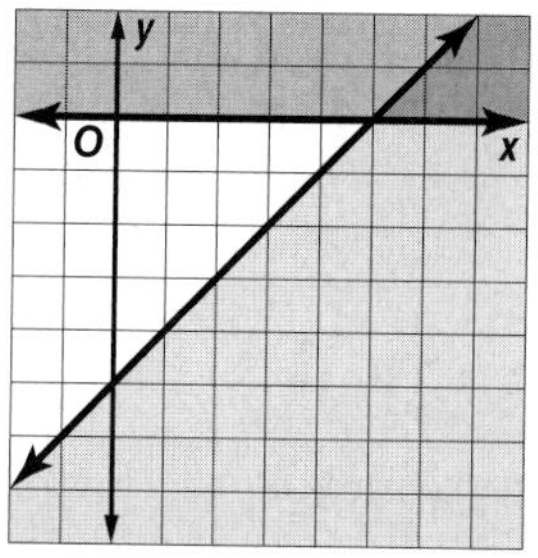

12.

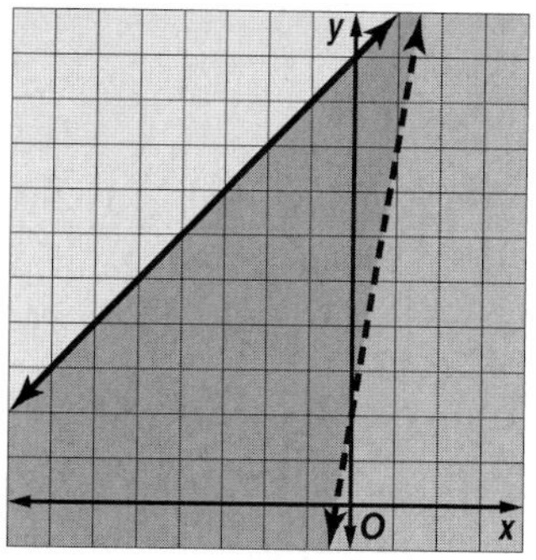

13.

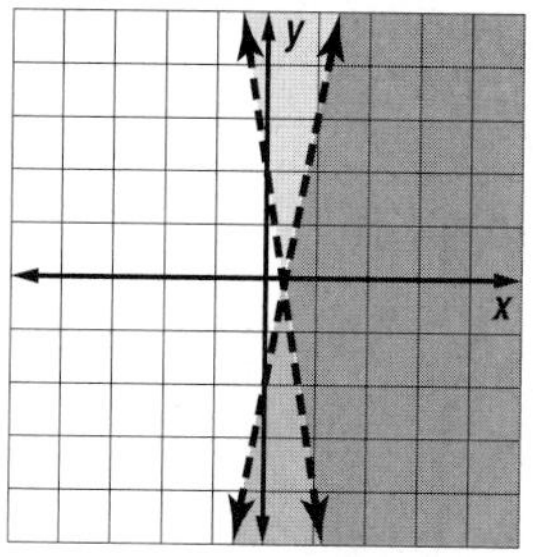

14.

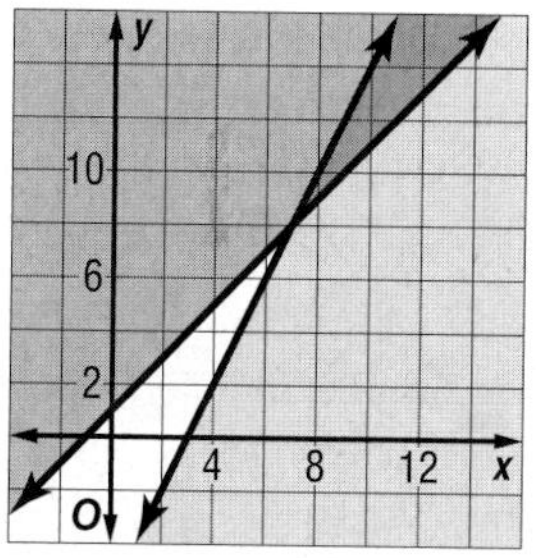

15.

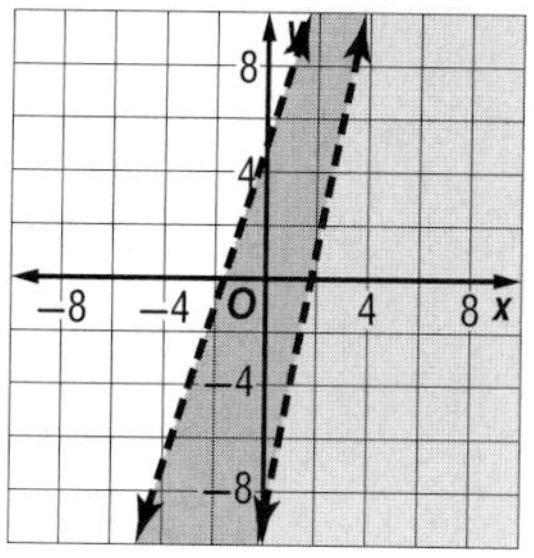

16. no solution

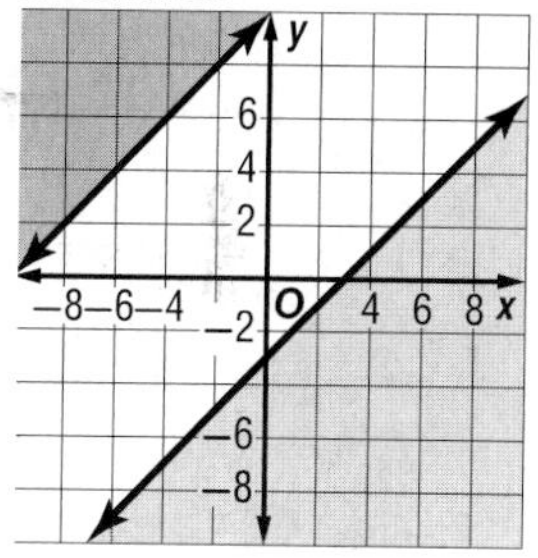

17. no solution

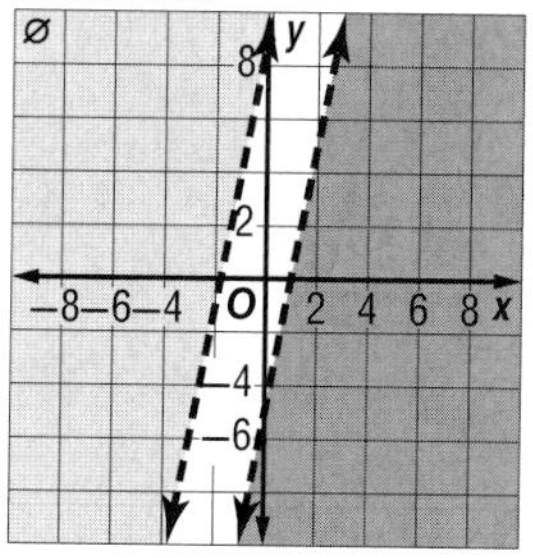

18.

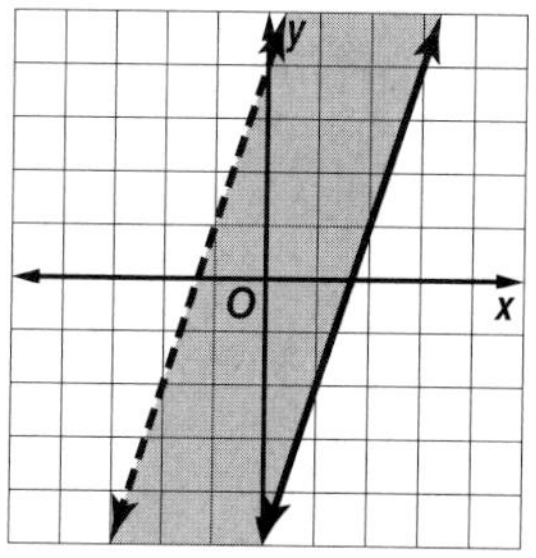

19.

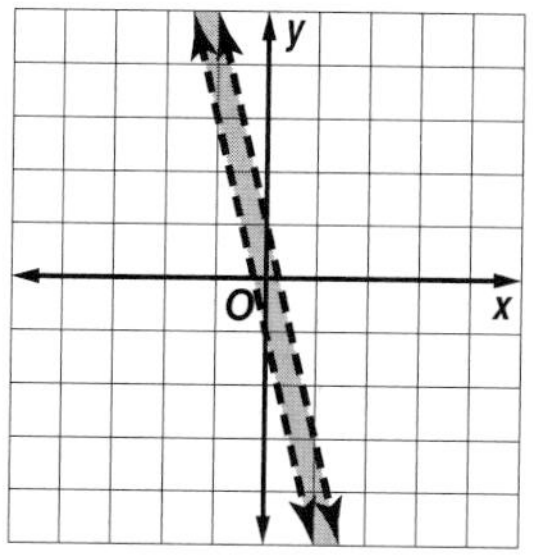

20.

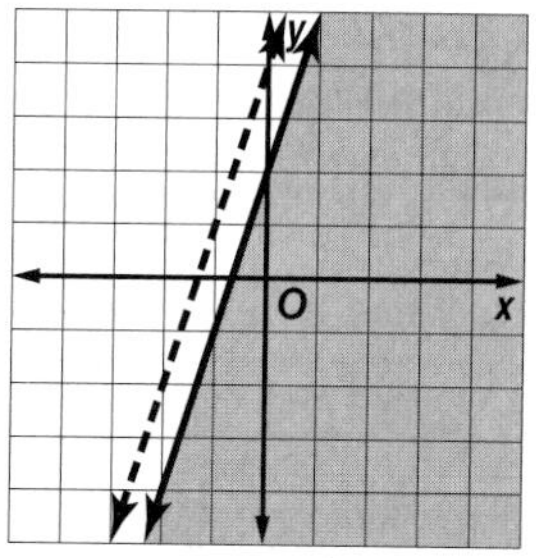

21.

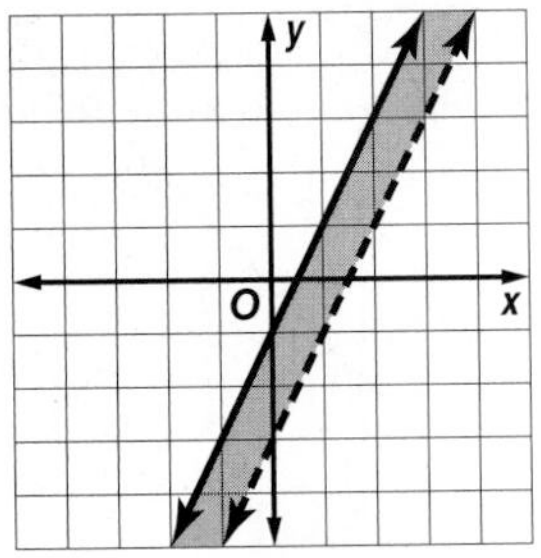

22.

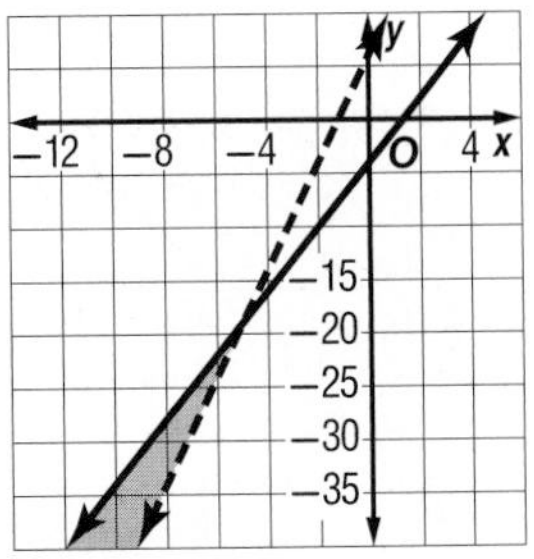

23.

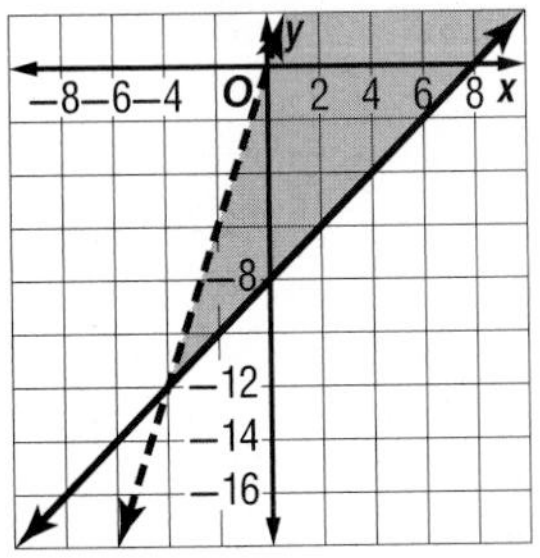

24. no solution

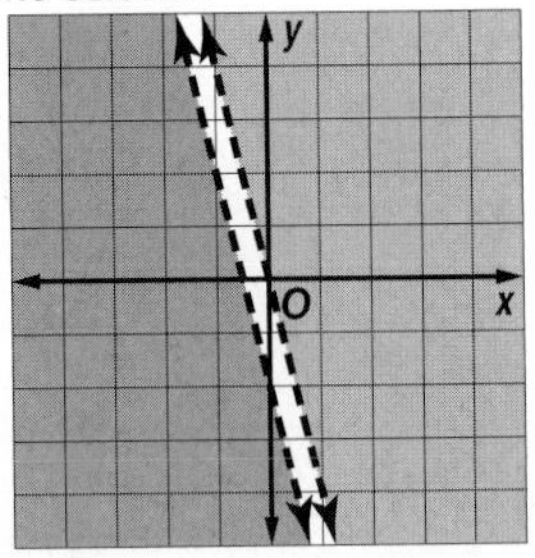

25a. Let f = square footage and p = price; $1000 \leq f \leq 17{,}000$ and $10{,}000 \leq p \leq 150{,}000$.

Ice Rink Resurfacers

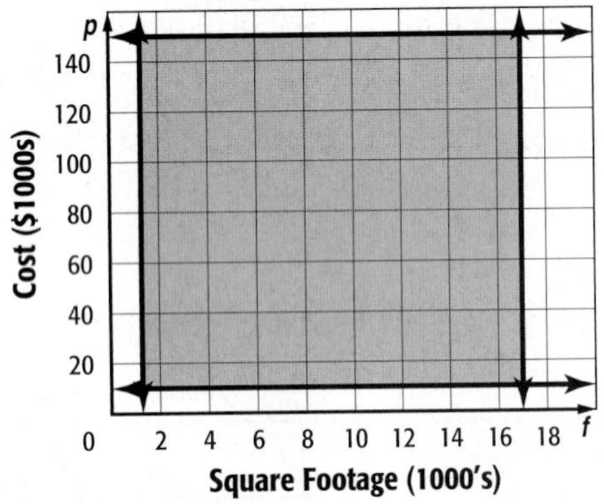

26b.

Earnings

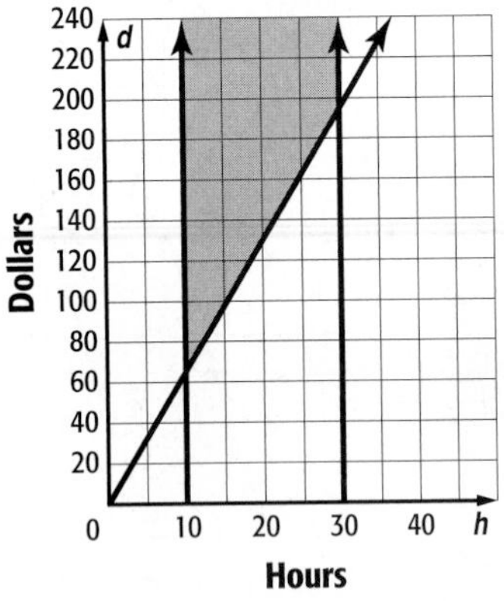

27.

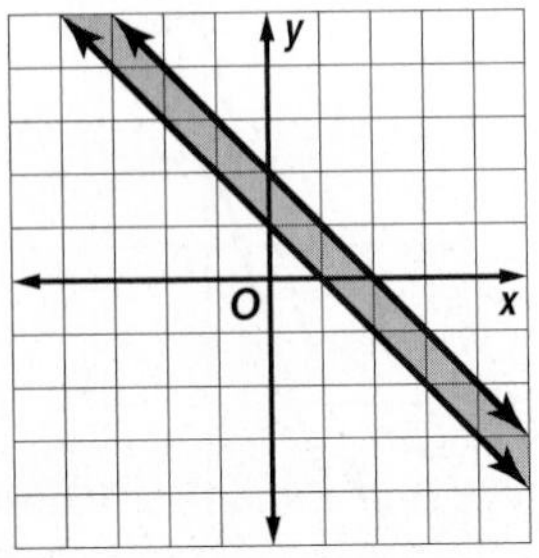

28.

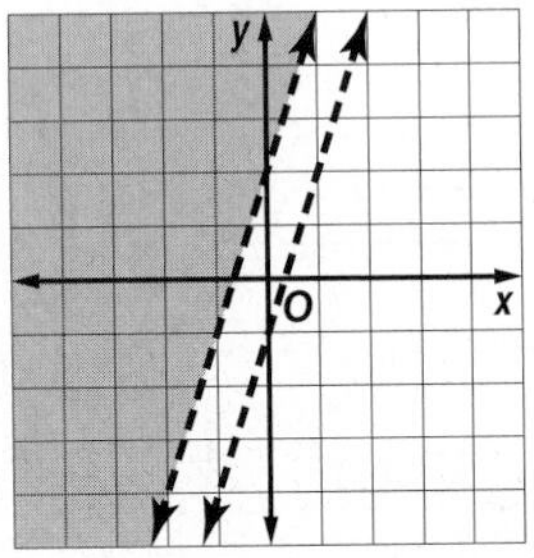

29.

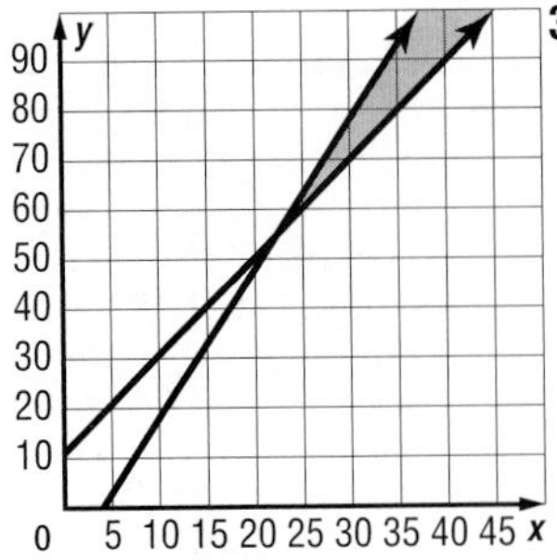

30.

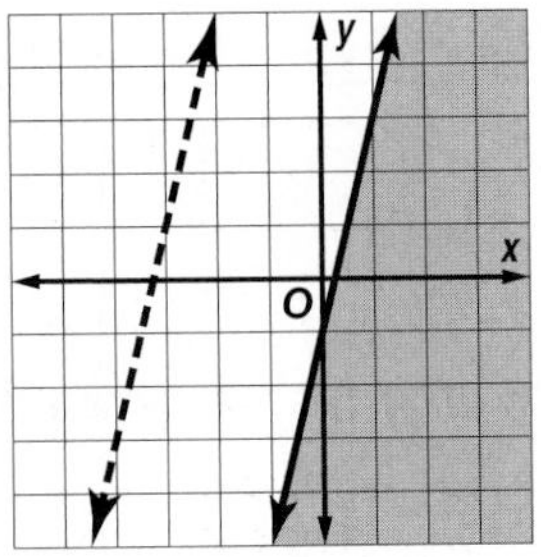

31.

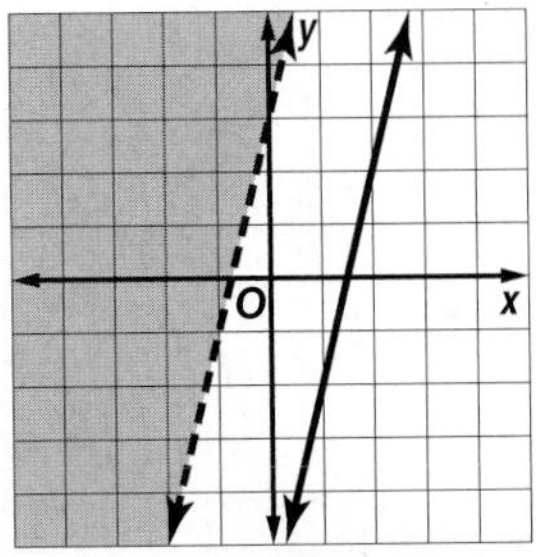

32.

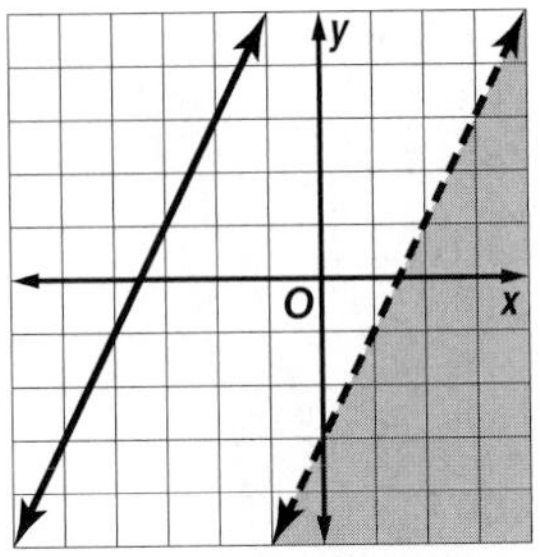

33.

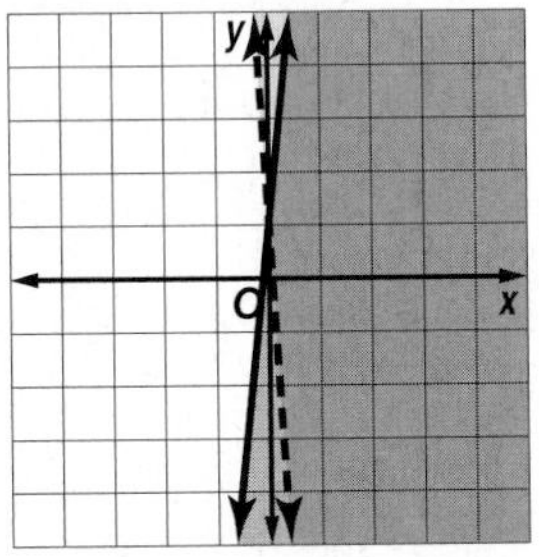

34.

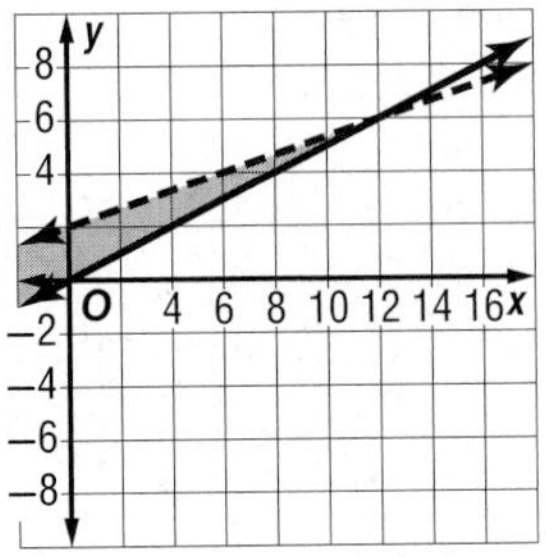

35.

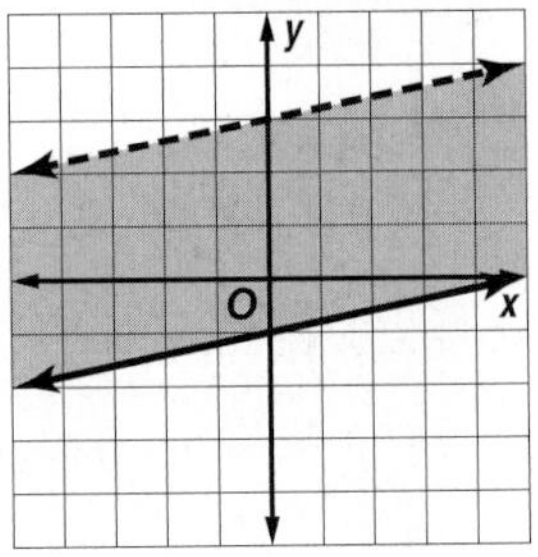

36a. Let n = the number of notebooks and p = the number of pens; $n \geq 20$, $p \geq 50$, $\$2.50n + \$1.25p \geq 60$.

36b.

Class Project

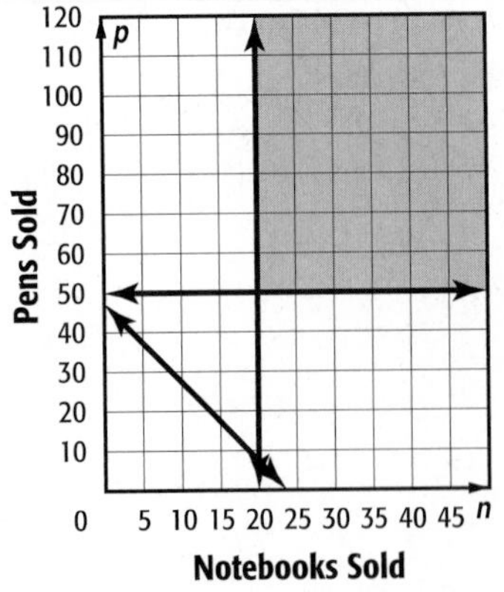

37b.

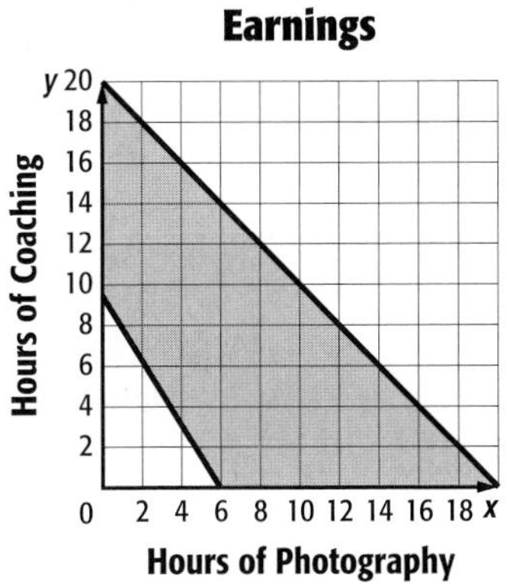

39. Sometimes; sample answer: $y > 3$, $y < -3$ will have no solution, but $y > -3$, $y < 3$ will have solutions.

43. Sample answer: The yellow region represents the beats per minute below the target heart rate. The blue region represents the beats per minute above the target heart rate. The green region represents the beats per minute within the target heart rate. Shading in different colors clearly shows the overlapping solution set of the system of inequalities.

61.

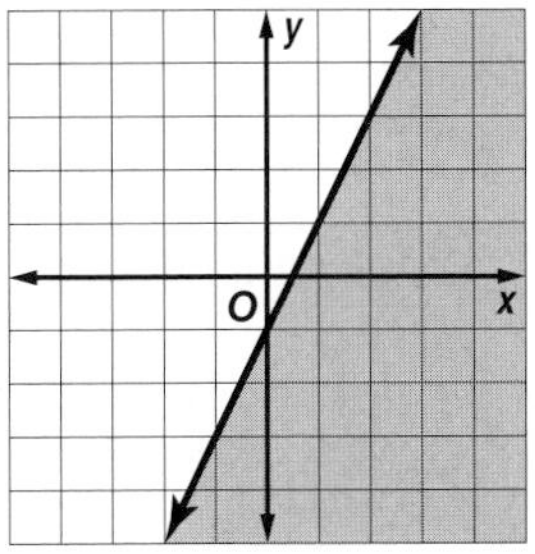

62.

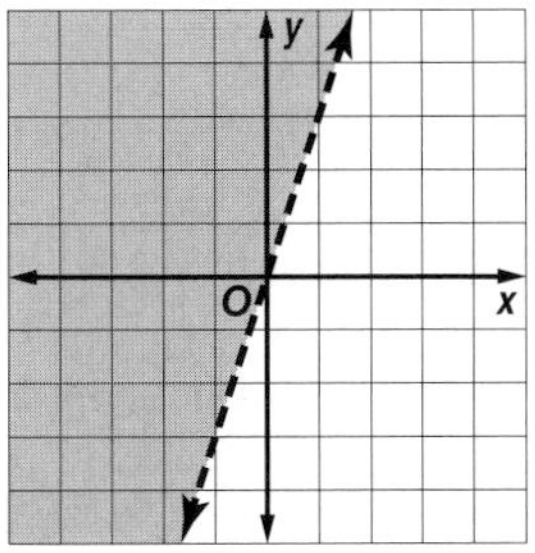

63.

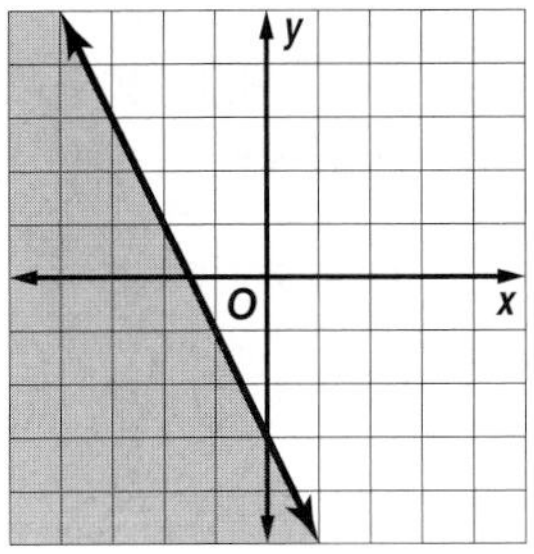

Page 393, Practice Test

1.

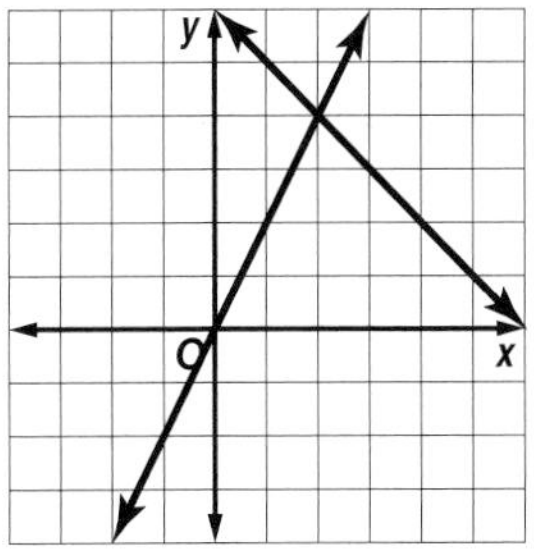

2.

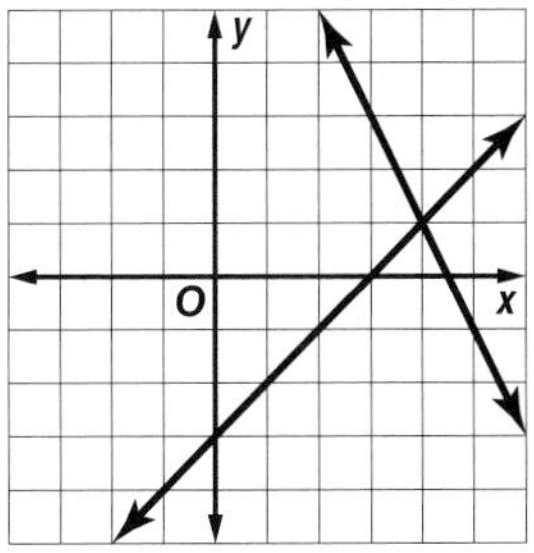

3.

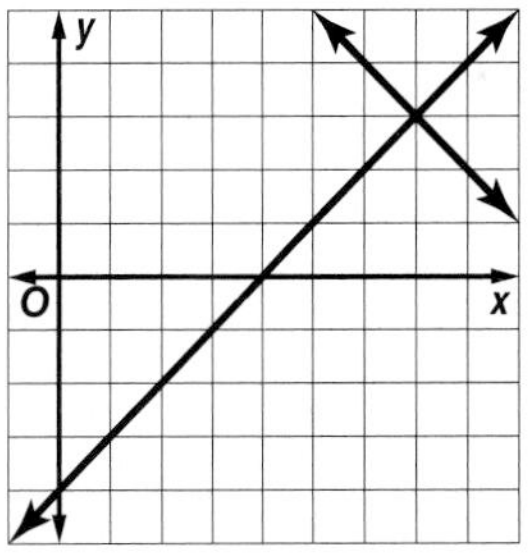

4.

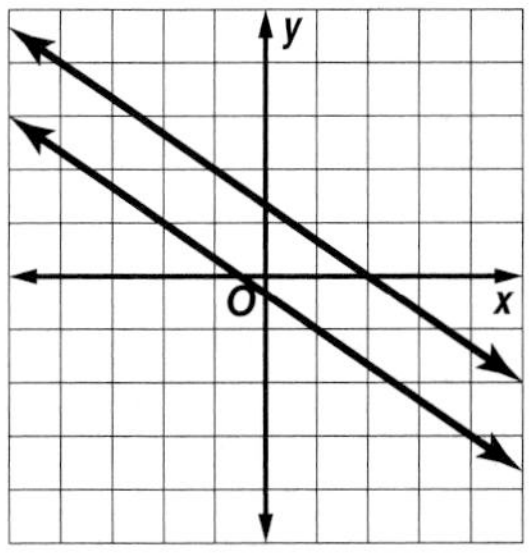

22.

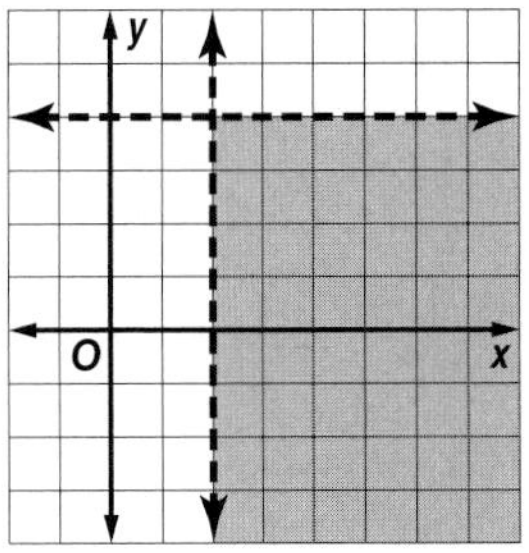

23.

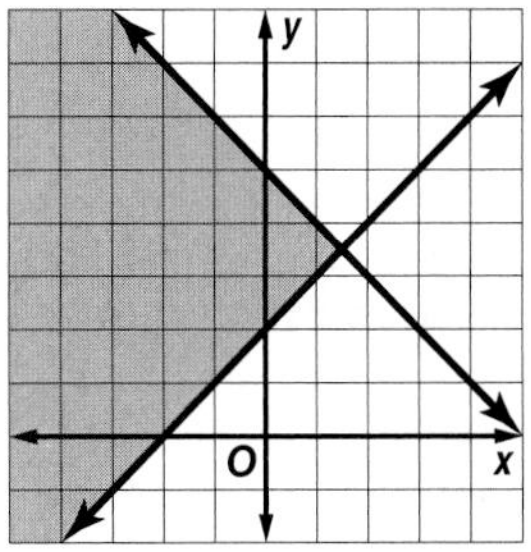

24.

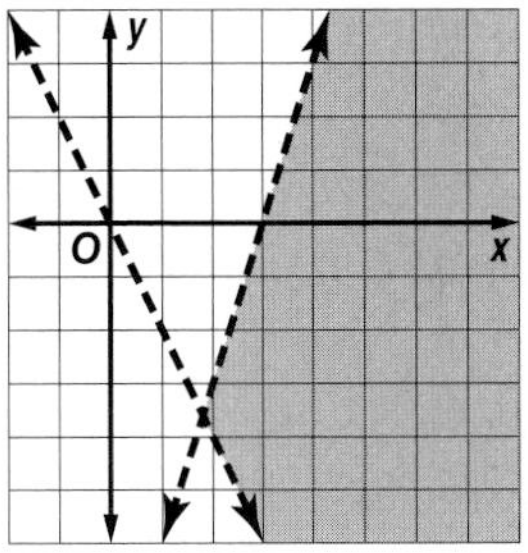

25.

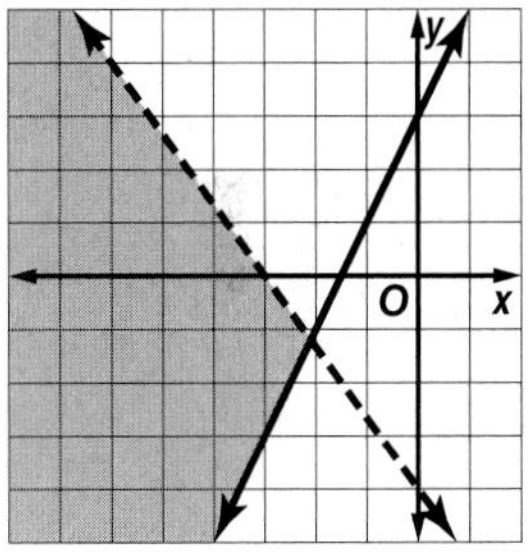

Chapter Planner

Diagnostic Assessment
Quick Check, p. 399

	Lesson 7-1 Pacing: 1 day	Lesson 7-2 Pacing: 1 day	Lesson 7-3 Pacing: 1 day
Title	**Multiplying Monomials**	**Dividing Monomials**	**Scientific Notation**
Objectives	• Multiply monomials. • Simplify expressions involving monomials.	• Find the quotient of two monomials. • Simplify expressions containing negative and zero exponents.	• Express numbers in scientific notation. • Find products and quotients of numbers expressed in scientific notation.
Key Vocabulary	monomial constant	zero exponents negative exponent order of magnitude	scientific notation
ILS	7.A.4b, 8.A.4b	8.A.4b	7.A.4b
Multiple Representations	p. 406	p. 414	
Lesson Resources	**Chapter 7 Resource Masters** • Study Guide and Intervention, pp. 5–6 AL OL ELL • Skills Practice, p. 7 AL OL ELL • Practice, p. 8 AL OL BL ELL • Word Problem Practice, p. 9 AL OL BL ELL • Enrichment, p. 10 OL BL • Quiz 1, p. 57 AL OL BL ELL **Transparencies** • 5-Minute Check Transparency 7-1 AL OL BL ELL **Additional Print Resources** • *Study Notebook* AL OL BL ELL • *Teaching Algebra with Manipulatives*, p. 110 AL OL ELL	**Chapter 7 Resource Masters** • Study Guide and Intervention, pp. 11–12 AL OL ELL • Skills Practice, p. 13 AL OL ELL • Practice, p. 14 AL OL BL ELL • Word Problem Practice, p. 15 AL OL BL ELL • Enrichment, p. 16 OL BL • Quiz 1, p. 57 AL OL BL ELL **Transparencies** • 5-Minute Check Transparency 7-2 AL OL BL ELL **Additional Print Resources** • *Study Notebook* AL OL BL ELL	**Chapter 7 Resource Masters** • Study Guide and Intervention, pp. 17–18 AL OL ELL • Skills Practice, p. 19 AL OL ELL • Practice, p. 20 AL OL BL ELL • Word Problem Practice, p. 21 AL OL BL ELL • Enrichment, p. 22 OL BL **Transparencies** • 5-Minute Check Transparency 7-3 AL OL BL ELL **Additional Print Resources** • *Study Notebook* AL OL BL ELL
Technology for Every Lesson	**IL Math Online** glencoe.com • Extra Examples • Self-Check Quizzes • Personal Tutor • Homework Help	**CD/DVD Resources** IWB INTERACTIVE WHITEBOARD READY IWB StudentWorks Plus IWB Interactive Classroom IWB Diagnostic and Assessment Planner	• TeacherWorks Plus • eSolutions Manual Plus • ExamView Assessment Suite
Math in Motion		BrainPOP	
Differentiated Instruction	pp. 403, 407	pp. 410, 415	pp. 417, 420

KEY: AL Approaching Level OL On Level BL Beyond Level ELL English Learners

Suggested Pacing			
Time Periods	Instruction	Review & Assessment	Total
45-minute	10	2	12
90-minute	6	1	7

Explore 7-4 Pacing: 0.5 day	Lesson 7-4 Pacing: 1 day	Explore 7-5 Pacing: 0.5 day	Lesson 7-5 Pacing: 1 day
Algebra Lab: Polynomials	**Polynomials**	**Algebra Lab: Adding and Subtracting Polynomials**	**Adding and Subtracting Polynomials**
• Use algebra tiles to model polynomials.	• Find the degree of a polynomial. • Write polynomials in standard form.	• Use algebra tiles to add and subtract polynomials.	• Add polynomials. • Subtract polynomials.
	polynomial binomial trinomial degree of a monomial degree of a polynomial standard form of a polynomial leading coefficient		
8.B.4a	7.A.4b, 8.C.4b	8.B.4a	8.C.4b
	p. 428		
Materials • algebra tiles **Additional Print Resources** • *Teaching Algebra with Manipulatives,* pp. 10, 11, 111 AL OL ELL	**Chapter 7 Resource Masters** • Study Guide and Intervention, pp. 23–24 AL OL ELL • Skills Practice, p. 25 AL OL ELL • Practice, p. 26 AL OL BL ELL • Word Problem Practice, p. 27 AL OL BL ELL • Enrichment, p. 28 OL BL • Graphing Calculator Activity, p. 29 OL • Quiz 2, p. 57 AL OL BL ELL **Transparencies** • 5-Minute Check Transparency 7-4 AL OL BL ELL **Additional Print Resources** • *Study Notebook* AL OL BL ELL	**Materials** • algebra tiles **Additional Print Resources** • *Teaching Algebra with Manipulatives,* pp. 10, 11, 112 AL OL ELL	**Chapter 7 Resource Masters** • Study Guide and Intervention, pp. 30–31 AL OL ELL • Skills Practice, p. 32 AL OL ELL • Practice, p. 33 AL OL BL ELL • Word Problem Practice, p. 34 AL OL BL ELL • Enrichment, p. 35 OL BL **Transparencies** • 5-Minute Check Transparency 7-5 AL OL BL ELL **Additional Print Resources** • *Study Notebook* AL OL BL ELL • *Teaching Algebra with Manipulatives,* pp. 113–115 AL OL ELL
	IL Math Online glencoe.com • Extra Examples • Self-Check Quizzes • Personal Tutor • Homework Help	**CD/DVD Resources** IWB INTERACTIVE WHITEBOARD READY IWB StudentWorks Plus IWB Interactive Classroom IWB Diagnostic and Assessment Planner	• TeacherWorks Plus • eSolutions Manual Plus • ExamView Assessment Suite
Animation		Animation	
	pp. 426, 429		pp. 435, 438

Formative Assessment
Mid-Chapter Quiz, p. 430

CHAPTER 7

Chapter Planner

	Lesson 7-6 Pacing: 1 day	Explore 7-7 Pacing: 0.5 day	Lesson 7-7 Pacing: 1.5 days	Lesson 7-8 Pacing: 1 day
Title	**Multiplying a Polynomial by a Monomial**	**Algebra Lab: Multiplying Polynomials**	**Multiplying Polynomials**	**Special Products**
Objectives	• Multiply a polynomial by a monomial. • Solve equations involving the products of monomials and polynomials.	• Use algebra tiles to multiply polynomials.	• Multiply polynomials by using the Distributive Property. • Multiply binomials by using the FOIL method.	• Find squares of sums and differences. • Find the product of a sum and a difference.
Key Vocabulary			• FOIL method • quadratic expression	
ILS	8.A.4b	8.B.4a	8.A.4b	8.A.4b
Multiple Representations	p. 442		p. 451	p. 456
Lesson Resources	**Chapter 7 Resource Masters** • Study Guide and Intervention, pp. 36–37 AL OL ELL • Skills Practice, p. 38 AL OL ELL • Practice, p. 39 AL OL BL ELL • Word Problem Practice, p. 40 AL OL BL ELL • Enrichment, p. 41 OL BL • Quiz 3, p. 58 AL OL BL ELL **Transparencies** • 5-Minute Check Transparency 7-6 AL OL BL ELL **Additional Print Resources** • *Study Notebook* AL OL BL ELL • *Teaching Algebra with Manipulatives*, pp. 116–117 AL OL ELL	**Materials** • algebra tiles • product mat **Additional Print Resources** • *Teaching Algebra with Manipulatives*, pp. 10, 11, 17, 119 AL OL ELL	**Chapter 7 Resource Masters** • Study Guide and Intervention, pp. 42–43 AL OL ELL • Skills Practice, p. 44 AL OL ELL • Practice, p. 45 AL OL BL ELL • Word Problem Practice, p. 46 AL OL BL • Enrichment, p. 47 OL BL • Spreadsheet Activity, p. 48 OL **Transparencies** • 5-Minute Check Transparency 7-7 AL OL BL ELL **Additional Print Resources** • *Study Notebook* AL OL BL ELL • *Teaching Algebra with Manipulatives*, pp. 120–123 AL OL ELL	**Chapter 7 Resource Masters** • Study Guide and Intervention, pp. 49–50 AL OL ELL • Skills Practice, p. 51 AL OL ELL • Practice, p. 52 AL OL BL ELL • Word Problem Practice, p. 53 AL OL BL ELL • Enrichment, p. 54 OL BL • Quiz 4, p. 58 AL OL BL ELL **Transparencies** • 5-Minute Check Transparency 7-3 AL OL BL ELL **Additional Print Resources** • *Study Notebook* AL OL BL ELL • *Teaching Algebra with Manipulatives*, pp. 124–126 AL OL ELL
Technology for Every Lesson	**IL Math Online glencoe.com** • Extra Examples • Personal Tutor • Self-Check Quizzes • Homework Help	**CD/DVD Resources** IWB INTERACTIVE WHITEBOARD READY IWB StudentWorks Plus IWB Interactive Classroom IWB Diagnostic and Assessment Planner		• TeacherWorks Plus • eSolutions Manual Plus • ExamView Assessment Suite
Math in Motion		Animation	Animation	
Differentiated Instruction	pp. 441, 444		pp. 448, 452	pp. 455, 458

Summative Assessment
- Study Guide and Review, pp. 459–462
- Practice Test, p. 463

KEY: AL Approaching Level OL On Level BL Beyond Level ELL English Learners

Quick Review Math Handbook*

is Glencoe's mathematical handbook for students and parents.

Hot Words includes a glossary of terms.

Hot Topics consists of two parts:

- explanations of key mathematical concepts
- exercises to check students' understanding.

Lesson	Hot Topics Section	Lesson	Hot Topics Section
7-1	2.1, 6.2	7-5	6.2
7-2	3.4, 6.2	7-6	3.4, 6.2
7-3	3.3	7-7	3.4, 6.2
7-4	6.2	7-8	3.4, 6.2

Also available in Spanish

What the Research Says...

Wenglinsky (2000) found that students whose teachers conduct hands-on learning activities outperform their peers by more than 70% of a grade level in mathematics on the National Assessment of Educational Progress (a study of over 7000 students).

- Explores 7-4, 7-5, and 7-7 all involve activities-based investigations of polynomial properties.
- Algebra tiles are used in Explores 7-4, 7-5, and 7-7 to provide students with concrete models for their understanding polynomials.

[Source: Wenglinsky, H. (2000). *How Teaching Matters: Bringing the Classroom Back into Discussion of Teacher Quality,* Princeton, New Jersey: Educational Testing Service, p. 7]

McGraw Hill Professional Development

Targeted professional development has been articulated throughout *Algebra 1.* More quality, customized professional development is available from McGraw-Hill Professional Development. Visit glencoe.com for details on each product.

- **Online Lessons** emphasize the strategies and techniques used to teach Algebra 1. Includes streaming video, interactive pages, and online tools.
- **Video Workshops** allow mentors, coaches, or leadership personnel to facilitate on-site workshops on educational strategies in mathematics and mathematical concepts.
- **MHPD Online** (www.mhpdonline.com) offers online professional development with video clips of instructional strategies, links, student activities, and news and issues in education.
- **Teaching Today** (teachingtoday.glencoe.com) gives secondary teachers practical strategies and materials that inspire excellence and innovation in teaching.

CHAPTER 7

Assessment and Intervention

SE = Student Edition, **TE** = Teacher Edition, **CRM** = Chapter Resource Masters

	Diagnosis	Prescription
Diagnostic Assessment	**Beginning Chapter 7**	
	Get Ready for Chapter 7 **SE**, p. 399	Response to Intervention **TE**, p. 399
	Beginning Every Lesson	
	Then, Now, Why? **SE** 5-Minute Check Transparencies	Chapter 0 **SE**, P1–P45 Concepts and Skills Bank **SE**, pp. 845–867 *Quick Review Math Handbook*
Formative Assessment	**During/After Every Lesson**	
	Check Your Progress **SE**, every example Check Your Understanding **SE** H.O.T. Problems **SE** Spiral Review **SE** Additional Examples **TE** Watch Out! **TE** Step 4, Assess **TE** Chapter 7 Quizzes **CRM**, pp. 57–58 Self-Check Quizzes **glencoe.com**	Tier 1 Intervention Concepts and Skills Bank **SE**, pp. 845–867 Skills Practice **CRM**, Ch. 1–7 **glencoe.com** Tier 2 Intervention Differentiated Instruction **TE** Study Guide and Intervention Masters **CRM**, Ch. 1–7 *Quick Review Math Handbook* Tier 3 Intervention *Math Triumphs, Alg. 1*
	Mid-Chapter	
	Mid-Chapter Quiz **SE**, p. 430 Mid-Chapter Test **CRM**, p. 59 ExamView Assessment Suite	Tier 1 Intervention Concepts and Skills Bank **SE**, pp. 845–867 Skills Practice **CRM**, Ch. 1–7 **glencoe.com** Tier 2 Intervention Study Guide and Intervention Masters **CRM**, Ch. 1–7 *Quick Review Math Handbook* Tier 3 Intervention *Math Triumphs, Alg.1*
	Before Chapter Test	
	Chapter Study Guide and Review **SE**, pp. 459–462 Practice Test **SE**, p. 463 Standardized Test Practice **SE**, pp. 464–467 Chapter Test **glencoe.com** Standardized Test Practice **glencoe.com** Vocabulary Review **glencoe.com** ExamView Assessment Suite	Tier 1 Intervention Concepts and Skills Bank **SE**, pp. 845–867 Skills Practice **CRM**, Ch. 1–7 **glencoe.com** Tier 2 Intervention Study Guide and Intervention Masters **CRM**, Ch. 1–7 *Quick Review Math Handbook* Tier 3 Intervention *Math Triumphs, Alg. 1*
Summative Assessment	**After Chapter 7**	
	Multiple-Choice Tests, Forms 1, 2A, 2B **CRM**, pp. 61–66 Free-Response Tests, Forms 2C, 2D, 3 **CRM**, pp. 67–72 Vocabulary Test **CRM**, p. 60 Extended Response Test **CRM**, p. 73 Standardized Test Practice **CRM**, pp. 74–76 ExamView Assessment Suite	Study Guide and Intervention Masters **CRM**, Ch. 1–7 *Quick Review Math Handbook* **glencoe.com**

Differentiated Instruction

Option 1 Reaching All Learners AL OL BL ELL

AUDITORY/MUSICAL Music can be a powerful memory tool. Suggest that groups of students make up a song or poem to explain how to use the FOIL method to multiply binomials. Have the groups perform their songs or read their poems for the class.

VISUAL To help students remember the patterns in the operations in the special products, have students highlight the operations using two different colors. Students can make their own study cards and/or posters to hang in the classroom.

$$(a + b)^2 = (a + b)(a + b) = a^2 + 2ab + b^2$$
$$(a - b)^2 = (a - b)(a - b) = a^2 - 2ab + b^2$$
$$(a + b)(a - b) = a^2 - b^2$$

Option 2 Approaching Level AL

Make a set of "problem" cards showing a monomial times a polynomial, such as $-3x(5x^2 - 2x + 3)$. Make a set of "simplification" cards showing the simplification of the problems on the "problem" cards. Make enough cards so that students from half the class gets one card from the "problem" set and the other students get cards from the "simplification" set. Ask each student holding a card from the "problem" set to find the classmate holding the "simplification" card that corresponds to his or her problem.

Option 3 English Learners ELL

Tell students that learning mathematics involves learning the language of mathematics.

On the board write several very large and very small numbers, such as 12,000,000,000,000,000 and 0.00000000067. Ask students to read these numbers using any language of their choice. Tell students that these numbers are written in standard notation, a type of math language.

Then ask students to use what they have learned to express these numbers in a shorter way using a different mathematical language. 1.2×10^{16}; 6.7×10^{-10}

Option 4 Beyond Level BL

Challenge students to a competition. Have pairs go to the board. Have one student multiply two 2-digit numbers using the FOIL method while the other student multiplies the same numbers using the multiplication algorithm. Repeat with other numbers. Which method appears to be faster? Then, extend the competition to include a mixed number times a mixed number.

Focus on Mathematical Content

Vertical Alignment

Before Chapter 7

Related Topics before Grade 8

- make conjectures from patterns or sets of examples
- compare and order rational numbers including integers
- select appropriate operations to solve problems involving rational numbers

Previous Topics from Algebra 1

- use symbols to represent unknowns and variables

Chapter 7

- use the Commutative, Associative, and Distributive Properties to simplify algebraic expressions
- simplify polynomial expressions and apply the laws of exponents in problem-solving situations

After Chapter 7

Preparation for Algebra 2

- use the necessary algebraic skills required to simplify algebraic expressions and inequalities in problem-solving situations
- use tools including factoring and properties of exponents to simplify expressions and to transform and solve equations

Lesson-by-Lesson Preview

7-1 Multiplying Monomials

A *monomial* is a number, a variable, or a product of a number and one or more variables. An expression involving negative integer exponents is not a monomial. Monomials that are real numbers are called *constants.* When multiplying monomials, use the Commutative and Associative Properties to group constants together and to group powers with the same base together.

- To multiply two powers that have the same base, add their exponents.
- To find the power of a power, multiply the exponents.
- To find the power of a product, find the power of each factor and multiply.

A monomial expression is simplified when

- each base appears exactly once,
- there are no powers of powers, and
- all fractions are in simplest form.

7-2 Dividing Monomials

Monomials may also be divided.

- To divide two powers that have the same base, subtract the exponents.
- To find the power of a quotient, find the power of the numerator and the power of the denominator.
- Any nonzero number raised to the zero power is equal to 1.

Expressions can also have negative exponents.

- A nonzero number raised to a negative integer power is the reciprocal of the same number with the opposite, or positive power.
- A fraction that has a negative exponent can be rewritten as its reciprocal with a positive power.

The order of magnitude of a quantity is the number rounded to the nearest power of 10.

7-3 Scientific Notation

A number is in *scientific notation* when it is written in the form $a \times 10^n$, where $1 \leq a < 10$ and n is an integer. To translate from standard form to scientific notation,

- move the decimal point until it is to the right of the first non-zero digit, then
- write the appropriate power of 10 to the right of the number.

The direction the decimal point is moved indicates the sign of the power.

To translate from scientific notation to standard form

- move the decimal point the number of places indicated by the exponent. A positive exponent is used to represent a number that is greater than or equal to 10 in standard form. A negative exponent represents a number that is less than 1 in standard form.

To multiply or divide numbers in scientific notation,

- multiply or divide the decimals;
- apply either the Product of Powers or the Quotient of Powers to simplify the powers of 10;
- rewrite the decimal in scientific notation and simplify the powers of 10. The result is in scientific notation, but it can also be presented in standard form if preferred.

7-4 Polynomials

A *polynomial* is a monomial or a sum or difference of monomials. The sum of two monomials is called a *binomial,* and the sum of three monomials is called a *trinomial.* Polynomials with more than three monomials have no special names.

- The degree of a polynomial is the greatest degree of any monomial in the polynomial.
- The degree of a monomial is the sum of the exponents of all its variables.

The terms of a polynomial are usually arranged so that the powers of one variable are in increasing or decreasing order. This aids in reading and understanding the polynomial.

7-5 Adding and Subtracting Polynomials

Polynomials can be added or subtracted.

- To add polynomials, add the coefficients of like terms using the rules for adding real numbers.
- To subtract polynomials, first replace each term of the polynomial being subtracted with its additive inverse. Then combine the like terms.

To aid in adding and subtracting polynomials, like terms can be grouped using a horizontal or vertical format.

7-6 Multiplying a Polynomial by a Monomial

The Distributive Property can be used to find the product of a polynomial and a monomial.

- Each term of the polynomial is multiplied by the monomial using the rules for monomial multiplication.
- Apply the rules for multiplying real numbers if the monomial is negative.
- Simplify the product by combining like terms.

Equations often contain polynomials that must be added, subtracted, or multiplied before they can be solved. To solve such equations, first simplify each side. Then apply the rules for solving multi-step equations and equations with variables on each side.

7-7 Multiplying Polynomials

When multiplying two binomials, use the Distributive Property in either a vertical or horizontal format.

- Multiply the terms of the first binomial by one term of the second binomial.
- Then, multiply the terms of the first binomial by the other term of the second binomial. Combine like terms.

A shortcut, called the FOIL method, can be used to multiply two binomials. To use this method, find the sum of the products of the First terms (F), the Outer terms (O), the Inner terms (I), and the Last terms (L).

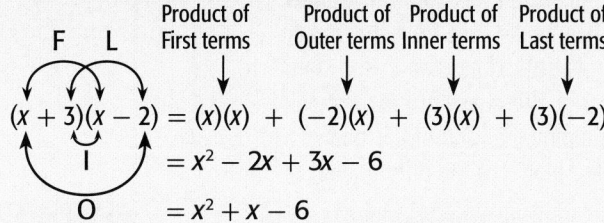

F L — Product of First terms, Product of Outer terms, Product of Inner terms, Product of Last terms; I; O

$$(x+3)(x-2) = (x)(x) + (-2)(x) + (3)(x) + (3)(-2)$$
$$= x^2 - 2x + 3x - 6$$
$$= x^2 + x - 6$$

The Distributive Property can be used to multiply any two polynomials. Products are not in simplest form until all like terms have been combined.

7-8 Special Products

Some binomials have products that follow a specific pattern. Some patterns are the

- *square of a sum or a difference:* $(a+b)^2 = a^2 + 2ab + b^2$ or $(a-b)^2 = a^2 - 2ab + b^2$
- *product of a sum and a difference* of the same two terms: $(a+b)(a-b) = a^2 - b^2$

Being able to identify and use these patterns can make it easier to simplify these special products.

CHAPTER 7 Notes

Chapter Project

Space for Data

Students use what they have learned about bases and exponents, properties of powers, scientific notation, and multiplying and adding polynomials to work with data about planets.

- Ask each student to bring to class numerical data about his or her favorite planet and also a picture or drawing of it.
- Ask students to identify each base and exponent in their data. Then, have them choose two powers that have the same base and then find the product of the powers. Next, have students find the quotient of the two powers. For example,

$$10^3 \cdot 10^5 = 10^8$$
$$\frac{10^3}{10^5} = 10^{3-5}$$
$$= 10^{-2}$$

- Divide students into groups. Have each group choose two different planets from their group. Then, have them write the numerical data for a similar measure for both planets, such as distance from the Sun, in both scientific notation and standard form. Then have groups write and simplify the ratio of this quantity for one planet to the other planet
- Have students measure their planet's picture and design a wooden frame to surround the picture that is x inches wide. Ask students to write an expression for the total area of the photo and the frame. How many inches of frame wood are needed?

CHAPTER 7 Polynomials

Then

In Chapter 1, you performed operations on expressions with exponents.

Now

In Chapter 7, you will:

- Simplify expressions involving monomials.
- Use scientific notation.
- Find degrees of polynomials, write polynomials in standard form, and add, subtract, and multiply polynomials.

IL Learning Standards

7.A.4b Apply formulas in a wide variety of theoretical and practical real-world measurement applications.
8.A.4b Represent mathematical patterns and describe their properties using variables and mathematical symbols.

Why?

SPACE The Very Large Array is an arrangement of 27 radio antennas in a Y pattern. The data the antennas collect is used by astronomers around the world to study the planets and stars. Astrophysicists use and apply properties of exponents to model the distance and orbit of celestial bodies.

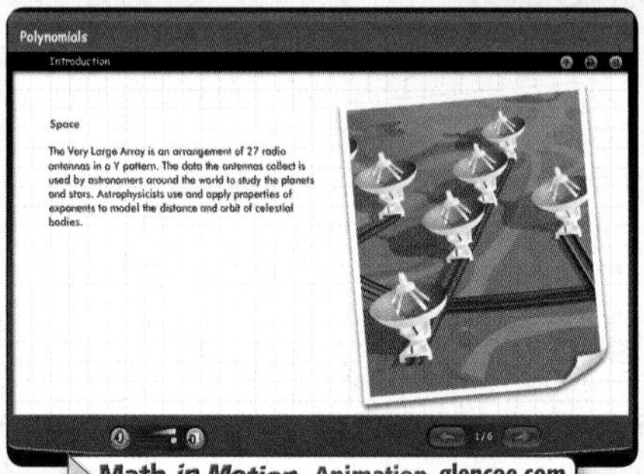

Math *in Motion*, Animation glencoe.com

Key Vocabulary Introduce the key vocabulary in the chapter using the routine below.

Define: A monomial is a number, a variable, or a product of a number and one or more variables.

Example: $\frac{1}{20}n^2$

Ask: Can you name another monomial? Possible answers: $32ab$, 175, x, y

Get Ready for Chapter 7

Diagnose Readiness You have two options for checking Prerequisite Skills.

Text Option

Take the Quick Check below. Refer to the Quick Review for help.

QuickCheck

(Used in Lessons 7-1, 7-2, and 7-4)

Write each expression using exponents. (Lesson 1-1)

1. $4 \cdot 4 \cdot 4 \cdot 4 \cdot 4$ 4^5
2. $y \cdot y \cdot y$ y^3
3. $6 \cdot 6$ 6^2
4. $2 \cdot 2 \cdot 2 \cdot 2 \cdot 2 \cdot 2 \cdot 2 \cdot 2 \cdot 2$ 2^9
5. $b \cdot b \cdot b \cdot b \cdot b \cdot b$ b^6
6. $m \cdot m \cdot m \cdot p \cdot p \cdot p \cdot p \cdot p \cdot p$ m^3p^6
7. $\frac{1}{3} \cdot \frac{1}{3} \cdot \frac{1}{3} \cdot \frac{1}{3} \cdot \frac{1}{3} \cdot \frac{1}{3} \cdot \frac{1}{3} \cdot \frac{1}{3}$ $\left(\frac{1}{3}\right)^8$ or $\frac{1}{3^8}$
8. $\frac{x}{y} \cdot \frac{x}{y} \cdot \frac{x}{y} \cdot \frac{x}{y} \cdot \frac{w}{z} \cdot \frac{w}{z}$ $\frac{x^4w^3}{y^4z^2}$

(Used in Lessons 7-1 through 7-3)

Evaluate each expression. (Lesson 1-2)

9. 2^3 8
10. $(-5)^2$ 25
11. 3^3 27
12. $(-4)^3$ -64
13. $\left(\frac{2}{3}\right)^2$ $\frac{4}{9}$
14. $\left(\frac{1}{2}\right)^4$ $\frac{1}{16}$
15. **SCHOOL** The probability of guessing correctly on 5 true-false questions is $\left(\frac{1}{2}\right)^5$. Express this probability as a fraction without exponents. $\frac{1}{32}$

(Used in Lessons 7-1, 7-2, 7-5, 7-6, 7-7, 7-8)

Find the area or volume of each figure. (Lessons 0-8 and 0-9)

16.

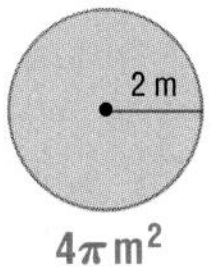

4π m^2

17.

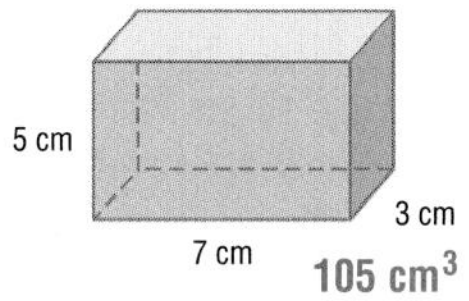

105 cm^3

18. **PHOTOGRAPHY** A photo is 4 inches by 6 inches. What is the area of the photo? 24 in^2

QuickReview

EXAMPLE 1

Write $5 \cdot 5 \cdot 5 \cdot 5 + x \cdot x \cdot x$ using exponents.

4 factors of 5 is 5^4.

3 factors of x is x^3.

So, $5 \cdot 5 \cdot 5 \cdot 5 + x \cdot x \cdot x = 5^4 + x^3$.

EXAMPLE 2

Evaluate $\left(\frac{5}{7}\right)^2$.

$\left(\frac{5}{7}\right)^2 = \frac{5^2}{7^2}$ **Power of a Quotient**

$= \frac{25}{49}$ **Simplify.**

EXAMPLE 3

Find the volume of the figure.

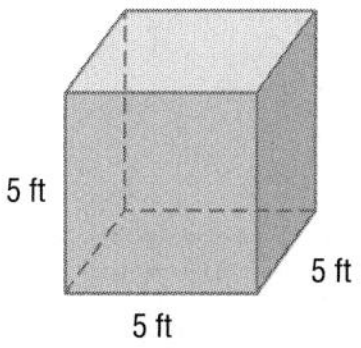

$V = \ell wh$ **Volume of a rectangular prism**

$= 5 \cdot 5 \cdot 5$ or 125 **$\ell = 5$, $w = 5$, and $h = 5$**

The volume is 125 cubic feet.

Online Option

IL Math Online Take a self-check Chapter Readiness Quiz at glencoe.com.

Response to Intervention (RtI)

Use the *Quick Check* results and the Intervention Planner chart to help you determine your Response to Intervention. The If-Then statements in the chart below help you decide the appropriate tier of RtI and suggest intervention resources for each tier.

Intervention Planner

Tier 1 — On Level

If students miss about 25% of the exercises or less,

Then choose a resource:

SE Lessons 1-1, 1-2, 0-8, and 0-9

CRM Skills Practice, Chapter 1, pp. 7 and 13

IL Math Online Self-Check Quiz

Tier 2 — Strategic Intervention approaching grade level

If students miss about 50% of the exercises,

Then choose a resource:

CRM Study Guide and Intervention, Chapter 1, pp. 5 and 11

Quick Review Math Handbook

IL Math Online Extra Examples, Personal Tutor, Homework Help

Tier 3 — Intensive Intervention 2 or more grades below level

If students miss about 75% of the exercises,

Then use *Math Triumphs, Alg. 1*

IL Math Online Extra Examples, Personal Tutor, Homework Help, Review Vocabulary

CHAPTER 7 Notes

FOLDABLES® Study Organizer

Dinah Zike's Foldables®

Focus Students create a tabbed book on which they organize information about polynomials.

Teach Have students make and label their Foldables as illustrated. Before beginning each lesson, ask students to think of one question that comes to mind as they skim through the lesson. Have them write the questions on the tabbed page of the corresponding lesson. As they read and work through the lesson, ask them to record the answers to their questions under the tabs.

When to Use It Encourage students to add to their Foldables as they work through the chapter and to use them to review for the chapter test.

Differentiated Instruction

CRM Student-Built Glossary, pp. 1–2 Students should complete the chart by providing a definition of each term and an example as they progress through Chapter 7. This study tool can also be used to review for the chapter test.

Get Started on Chapter 7

You will learn several new concepts, skills, and vocabulary terms as you study Chapter 7. To get ready, identify important terms and organize your resources. You may wish to refer to **Chapter 0** to review prerequisite skills.

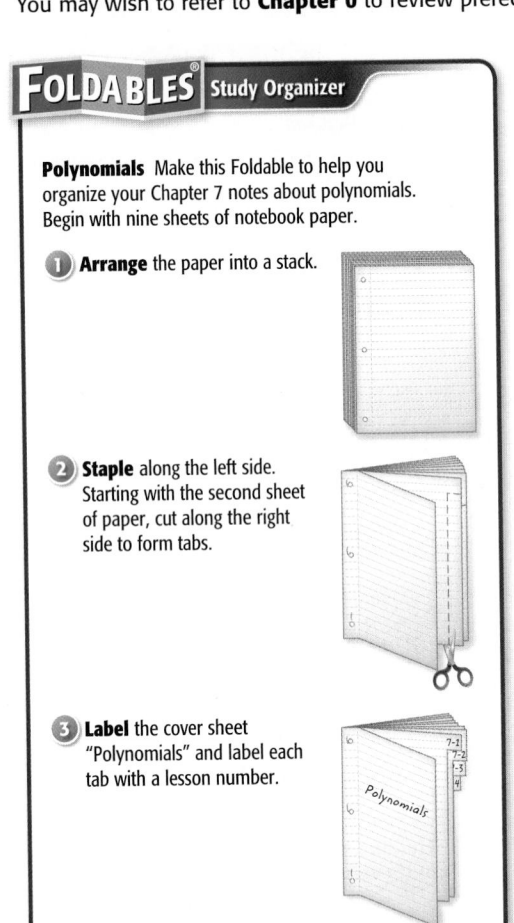

FOLDABLES® Study Organizer

Polynomials Make this Foldable to help you organize your Chapter 7 notes about polynomials. Begin with nine sheets of notebook paper.

1. **Arrange** the paper into a stack.

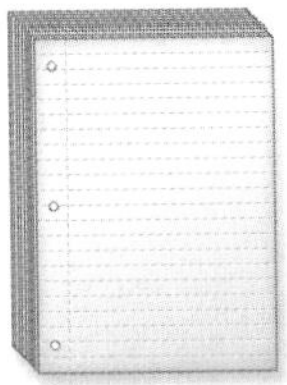

2. **Staple** along the left side. Starting with the second sheet of paper, cut along the right side to form tabs.

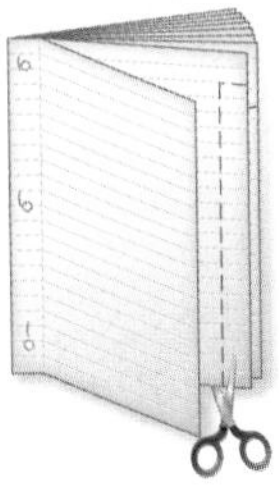

3. **Label** the cover sheet "Polynomials" and label each tab with a lesson number.

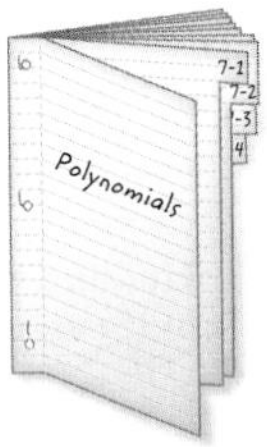

IL Math Online glencoe.com

- Study the chapter online
- Explore **Math in Motion**
- Get extra help from your own **Personal Tutor**
- Use **Extra Examples** for additional help
- Take a **Self-Check Quiz**
- **Review Vocabulary** in fun ways

New Vocabulary

English		Español
constant	p. 401	constante
monomial	p. 401	monomio
negative exponent	p. 410	exponente negativo
zero exponent	p. 410	cero exponente
order of magnitude	p. 411	ordenar de magnitud
scientific notation	p. 416	notación científica
binomial	p. 424	binomio
degree of a monomial	p. 424	grado de un monomio
degree of a polynomial	p. 424	grado de un polinomio
polynomial	p. 424	polinomio
trinomial	p. 424	trinomio
leading coefficient	p. 425	coeficiente líder
standard form of a polynomial	p. 425	forma estándar de polinomio
FOIL method	p. 448	método foil
quadratic expression	p. 448	expresion cuadrática

Review Vocabulary

base • p. 5 • base In an expression of the form x^n, the base is x.

Distributive Property • p. 23 • Propiedad distributiva For any numbers a, b, and c, $a(b + c) = ab + ac$ and $a(b - c) = ab - ac$.

exponent • p. 5 • exponente In an expression of the form x^n, the exponent is n. It indicates the number of times x is used as a factor.

exponent

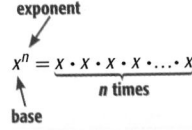

$$x^n = \underbrace{x \cdot x \cdot x \cdot x \cdot \ldots \cdot x}_{n \text{ times}}$$

base

Multilingual eGlossary glencoe.com

Additional Answers (p. 401, Check Your Progress)

1A. No; the expression has addition and more than one term.

1B. Yes; this is a product of a number and variables.

1C. Yes; this is a product of variables, with a constant in the denominator.

1D. No; this expression has a variable in the denominator.

7-1 Multiplying Monomials

Then

You performed operations on expressions with exponents. (Lesson 1-1)

Now

- Multiply monomials.
- Simplify expressions involving monomials.

IL Learning Standards

7.A.4b Apply formulas in a wide variety of theoretical and practical real-world measurement applications involving perimeter, area, volume, angle, time, temperature, mass, speed, distance, density and monetary values.
8.A.4b Represent mathematical patterns and describe their properties using variables and mathematical symbols.

New Vocabulary

monomial
constant

IL Math Online

glencoe.com

- Extra Examples
- Personal Tutor
- Self-Check Quiz
- Homework Help

Why?

Many formulas contain *monomials*. For example, the formula for the horsepower of a car is $H = w\left(\frac{v}{234}\right)^3$. H represents the horsepower produced by the engine, w equals the weight of the car with passengers, and v is the velocity of the car at the end of a quarter of a mile. As the velocity increases, the horsepower increases.

Monomials A **monomial** is a number, a variable, or the product of a number and one or more variables with nonnegative integer exponents. It has only one term. In the formula to calculate the horsepower of a car, the term $w\left(\frac{v}{234}\right)^3$ is a monomial. An expression that involves division by a variable, like $\frac{ab}{c}$, is not a monomial.

A **constant** is a monomial that is a real number. The monomial $3x$ is an example of a *linear expression* since the exponent of x is 1. The monomial $2x^2$ is a *nonlinear expression* since the exponent is a positive number other than 1.

EXAMPLE 1 Identify Monomials

Determine whether each expression is a monomial. Write *yes* or *no*. Explain your reasoning.

a. 10 — Yes; this is a constant, so it is a monomial.

b. $f + 24$ — No; this expression has addition, so it has more than one term.

c. h^2 — Yes; this expression is a product of variables.

d. j — Yes; single variables are monomials.

Check Your Progress

1A. $-x + 5$ **1A–1D. See margin.**
1B. $23abcd^2$
1C. $\frac{xyz^2}{2}$
1D. $\frac{mp}{n}$

Personal Tutor glencoe.com

Recall that an expression of the form x^n is called a *power* and represents the result of multiplying x by itself n times. x is the *base*, and n is the *exponent*. The word *power* is also used sometimes to refer to the exponent.

exponent → $3^4 = \underbrace{3 \cdot 3 \cdot 3 \cdot 3}_{\text{4 factors}} = 81$ ← base

7-1 Lesson Notes

1 FOCUS

Vertical Alignment

Before Lesson 7-1
Perform operations on expressions with exponents.

Lesson 7-1
Multiply monomials.
Simplify expressions involving monomials.

After Lesson 7-1
Find quotients of two monomials and simplify expressions containing negative exponents.

2 TEACH

Scaffolding Questions

Have students read the *Why?* section of the lesson.

Ask:

- What two values do you need to know to be able to use the formula to find the horsepower of a car? weight of the car, *w*, with passengers; velocity of the car, *v*, at the end of a quarter of a mile
- Which values in the formula are raised to the third power? *v*, 234
- When would the horsepower of a car be equal to or greater than the weight of a car with passengers? when $v \geq 234$

Lesson 7-1 Resources

Resource	Approaching-Level	On-Level	Beyond-Level	English Learners
Teacher Edition		• Differentiated Instruction, pp. 403, 407	• Differentiated Instruction, pp. 403, 407	
Chapter Resource Masters	• Study Guide and Intervention, pp. 5–6 • Skills Practice, p. 7 • Practice, p. 8 • Word Problem Practice, p. 9	• Study Guide and Intervention, pp. 5–6 • Skills Practice, p. 7 • Practice, p. 8 • Word Problem Practice, p. 9 • Enrichment, p. 10	• Practice, p. 8 • Word Problem Practice, p. 9 • Enrichment, p. 10	• Study Guide and Intervention, pp. 5–6 • Skills Practice, p. 7 • Practice, p. 8
Transparencies	• 5-Minute Check Transparency 7-1	• 5-Minute Check Transparency 7-1	• 5-Minute Check Transparency 7-1	• 5-Minute Check Transparency 7-1
Other	• Study Notebook • Teaching Algebra with Manipulatives	• Study Notebook • Teaching Algebra with Manipulatives	• Study Notebook	• Study Notebook • Teaching Algebra with Manipulatives

Monomials

Example 1 shows how to determine whether an expression is a monomial. **Example 2** shows how to find the product of powers. **Example 3** shows how to find the power of a power. **Example 4** shows how to find the power of a product.

Formative Assessment

Use the Check Your Progress exercises after each Example to determine students' understanding of concepts.

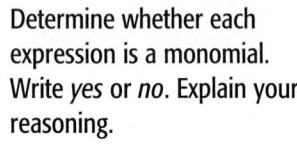

Additional Examples

1 Determine whether each expression is a monomial. Write *yes* or *no*. Explain your reasoning.

a. $17 - c$ No; this expression involves subtraction, so it involves more than one term.

b. $8f^2g$ Yes; this expression is the product of a number and two variables.

c. $\frac{3}{4}$ Yes; The expression is a constant.

d. $\frac{5}{t}$ No; this expression has a variable in the denominator.

2 Simplify each expression.

a. $(r^4)(-12r^7)$ $-12r^{11}$

b. $(6cd^5)(5c^5d^2)$ $30c^6d^7$

Additional Examples also in Interactive Classroom PowerPoint® Presentations

IWB INTERACTIVE WHITEBOARD READY

By applying the definition of a power, you can find the product of powers. Look for a pattern in the exponents.

$$2^2 \cdot 2^4 = \underbrace{\overbrace{2 \cdot 2}^{2\text{ factors}} \cdot \overbrace{2 \cdot 2 \cdot 2 \cdot 2}^{4\text{ factors}}}_{2+4=6\text{ factors}} \qquad 4^3 \cdot 4^2 = \underbrace{\overbrace{4 \cdot 4 \cdot 4}^{3\text{ factors}} \cdot \overbrace{4 \cdot 4}^{2\text{ factors}}}_{3+2=5\text{ factors}}$$

These examples demonstrate the property for the product of powers.

Key Concept — Product of Powers (For Your FOLDABLE)

Words To multiply two powers that have the same base, add their exponents.

Symbols For any real number a and any integers m and p, $a^m \cdot a^p = a^{m+p}$.

Examples $b^3 \cdot b^5 = b^{3+5}$ or b^8 $\quad g^4 \cdot g^6 = g^{4+6}$ or g^{10}

EXAMPLE 2 Product of Powers

Simplify each expression.

a. $(6n^3)(2n^7)$

$(6n^3)(2n^7) = (6 \cdot 2)(n^3 \cdot n^7)$ — Group the coefficients and the variables.

$= (6 \cdot 2)(n^{3+7})$ — Product of Powers

$= 12n^{10}$ — Simplify.

b. $(3pt^3)(p^3t^4)$

$(3pt^3)(p^3t^4) = (3 \cdot 1)(p \cdot p^3)(t^3 \cdot t^4)$ — Group the coefficients and the variables.

$= (3 \cdot 1)(p^{1+3})(t^{3+4})$ — Product of Powers

$= 3p^4t^7$ — Simplify.

StudyTip

Coefficients and Powers of 1 A variable with no exponent or coefficient shown can be assumed to have an exponent and coefficient of 1. For example, $x = 1x^1$.

Check Your Progress

2A. $(3y^4)(7y^5)$ $21y^9$

2B. $(-4rx^2t^3)(-6r^5x^2t)$ $24r^6x^4t^4$

Personal Tutor glencoe.com

We can use the Product of Powers Property to find the power of a power. In the following examples, look for a pattern in the exponents.

$$(3^2)^4 = \overbrace{(3^2)(3^2)(3^2)(3^2)}^{4\text{ factors}} = 3^{2+2+2+2} = 3^8 \qquad (r^4)^3 = \overbrace{(r^4)(r^4)(r^4)}^{3\text{ factors}} = r^{4+4+4} = r^{12}$$

These examples demonstrate the property for the power of a power.

Key Concept — Power of a Power (For Your FOLDABLE)

Words To find the power of a power, multiply the exponents.

Symbols For any real number a and any integers m and p, $(a^m)^p = a^{m \cdot p}$.

Examples $(b^3)^5 = b^{3 \cdot 5}$ or b^{15} $\quad (g^6)^7 = g^{6 \cdot 7}$ or g^{42}

Focus on Mathematical Content

Variables with No Exponents A variable without an exponent can be rewritten with an exponent of 1. For example, x can be written as x^1, and ab can be written as a^1b^1. In order for students to find the products of powers correctly, suggest that they rewrite variables without an exponent with an exponent of 1.

TEACH with TECH

VIDEO RECORDING Have students record themselves multiplying monomials and explaining their work. Share the videos with the class.

StudyTip

Power Rules If you are unsure about when to multiply the exponents and when to add the exponents, write the expression in expanded form.

EXAMPLE 3 Power of a Power

Simplify $[(2^3)^2]^4$.

$[(2^3)^2]^4 = (2^{3 \cdot 2})^4$	**Power of a Power**
$= (2^6)^4$	**Simplify.**
$= 2^{6 \cdot 4}$	**Power of a Power**
$= 2^{24}$ or 16,777,216	**Simplify.**

Check Your Progress

Simplify each expression.

3A. $[(2^2)^2]^4$ **2^{16} or 65,536**

3B. $[(3^2)^3]^2$ **3^{12} or 531,441**

Personal Tutor glencoe.com

We can use the Product of Powers Property and the Power of a Power Property to find the power of a product. In the following examples, look for a pattern in the exponents.

$$(tw)^3 = \overbrace{(tw)(tw)(tw)}^{\text{3 factors}} = (t \cdot t \cdot t)(w \cdot w \cdot w) = t^3w^3$$

$$(2yz^2)^3 = \overbrace{(2yz^2)(2yz^2)(2yz^2)}^{\text{3 factors}} = (2 \cdot 2 \cdot 2)(y \cdot y \cdot y)(z^2 \cdot z^2 \cdot z^2) = 2^3y^3z^6 \text{ or } 8y^3z^6$$

These examples demonstrate the property for the power of a product.

Key Concept Power of a Product

For Your FOLDABLE

Words To find the power of a product, find the power of each factor and multiply.

Symbols For any real numbers a and b and any integer m, $(ab)^m = a^mb^m$.

Example $(-2xy^3)^5 = (-2)^5x^5y^{15}$ or $-32x^5y^{15}$

EXAMPLE 4 Power of a Product

GEOMETRY **Express the area of the circle as a monomial.**

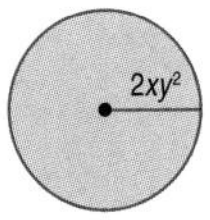

Area $= \pi r^2$	**Formula for the area of a circle**
$= \pi(2xy^2)^2$	**Replace r with $2xy^2$.**
$= \pi(2^2x^2y^4)$	**Power of a Product**
$= 4x^2y^4\pi$	**Simplify.**

The area of the circle is $4x^2y^4\pi$ square units.

Check Your Progress

4A. Express the area of a square with sides of length $3xy^2$ as a monomial. **$9x^2y^4$**

4B. Express the area of a triangle with a height of $4a$ and a base of $5ab^2$ as a monomial. **$10a^2b^2$**

Personal Tutor glencoe.com

Additional Examples

3 Simplify $[(2^3)^3]^2$. 2^{18} or 262,144

4 **GEOMETRY** Express the volume of a cube with side length $5xyz$ as a monomial. $(5xyz)^3 = 125x^3y^3z^3$

Watch Out!

Student Misconceptions Students may simplify an expression such as $\frac{4}{6}(x^2y^5)^3[2(xy)^7]$ into $\frac{8}{6}x^{13}y^{22}$, not realizing that the simplification is incomplete because the fraction is not in the simplest form.

Differentiated Instruction

OL BL

Logical Learners Give students an expression such as $240x^{12}y^8$ and challenge them to write ten different monomial expressions that, when simplified, equal the given expression.

Simplify Expressions

Example 5 shows how to simplify expressions involving monomials by using the power and product rules.

Tips for New Teachers

Reasoning Remind students that there is often more than one strategy that can be used to simplify an expression. For example, in Example 5, the first step could be to simplify $(-2y)^2$ first and then raise the product to the third power.

Additional Example

5 Simplify $[(8g^3h^4)^2]^2(2gh^5)^4$. $65{,}536g^{16}h^{36}$

3 PRACTICE

Formative Assessment

Use Exercises 1–20 to check for understanding.

Use the chart at the bottom of the next page to customize assignments for your students.

Additional Answers

1. Yes; constants are monomials.
2. No; there is subtraction and more than one term.
3. No; there is a variable in the denominator.
4. Yes; this is a product of a number and variables.
5. Yes; this is a product of a number and variables.
6. No; there is addition and more than one term.

StudyTip

Simplify When simplifying expressions with multiple grouping symbols, begin at the innermost expression and work outward.

Simplify Expressions We can combine and use these properties to simplify expressions involving monomials.

Key Concept — Simplify Expressions

For Your FOLDABLE

To simplify a monomial expression, write an equivalent expression in which:

- each variable base appears exactly once,
- there are no powers of powers, and
- all fractions are in simplest form.

EXAMPLE 5 Simplify Expressions

Simplify $(3xy^4)^2[(-2y)^2]^3$.

$(3xy^4)^2[(-2y)^2]^3 = (3xy^4)^2(-2y)^6$	**Power of a Power**
$= (3)^2x^2(y^4)^2(-2)^6y^6$	**Power of a Product**
$= 9x^2y^8(64)y^6$	**Power of a Power**
$= 9(64)x^2 \cdot y^8 \cdot y^6$	**Commutative**
$= 576x^2y^{14}$	**Product of Powers**

Check Your Progress

5. Simplify $\left(\frac{1}{2}a^2b\ ^2\right)^3[(-4b)^2]^2$. $32a^6b^{10}$

Personal Tutor glencoe.com

Check Your Understanding

Example 1 p. 401

Determine whether each expression is a monomial. Write *yes* or *no*. Explain your reasoning. 1–6. See margin.

1. 15 **2.** $2 - 3a$ **3.** $\frac{5c}{d}$

4. $-15g^2$ **5.** $\frac{r}{2}$ **6.** $7b + 9$

Examples 2 and 3 pp. 402–403

Simplify each expression.

7. $k(k^3)$ k^4 **8.** $m^4(m^2)$ m^6 **9.** $2q^2(9q^4)$ $18q^6$

10. $(5u^4v)(7u^4v^3)$ $35u^8v^4$ **11.** $[(3^2)^2]^2$ 3^8 or 6561 **12.** $(xy^4)^6$ x^6y^{24}

13. $(4a^4b^9c)^2$ $16a^8b^{18}c^2$ **14.** $(-2f^2g^3h^2)^3$ $-8f^6g^9h^6$ **15.** $(-3p^5t^6)^4$ $81p^{20}t^{24}$

Example 4 p. 403

16. GEOMETRY The formula for the surface area of a cube is $SA = 6s^2$, where SA is the surface area and s is the length of any side.

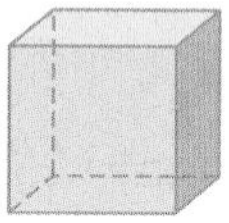

a^3b

a. Express the surface area of the cube as a monomial. $6a^6b^2$

b. What is the surface area of the cube if $a = 3$ and $b = 4$? 69,984 units²

Example 5 p. 404

Simplify each expression.

17. $(5x^2y)^2(2xy^3z)^3(4xyz)$ $800x^8y^{12}z^4$ **18.** $(-3d^2f\ ^3g)^2[(-3d^2f)^3]^2$ $6561d^{16}f^{12}g^2$

19. $(-2g^3h)(-3gj^4)^2(-ghj)^2$ $-18g^7h^3j^{10}$ **20.** $(-7ab^4c)^3[(2a^2c)^2]^3$ $-21{,}952a^{15}b^{12}c^9$

Practice and Problem Solving

= Step-by-Step Solutions begin on page R12.
Extra Practice begins on page 815.

Example 1 p. 401

Determine whether each expression is a monomial. Write *yes* or *no*. Explain your reasoning. **21–26. See margin.**

21. 122
22. $3a^4$
23. $2c + 2$
24. $\frac{-2g}{4h}$
25. $\frac{5k}{10}$
26. $6m + 3n$

Examples 2 and 3 pp. 402–403

Simplify each expression.

27. $(q^2)(2q^4)$ **$2q^6$**
28. $(-2u^2)(6u^6)$ **$-12u^8$**
29. $(9w^2x^8)(w^6x^4)$ **$9w^8x^{12}$**
30. $(y^6z^9)(6y^4z^2)$ **$6y^{10}z^{11}$**
31. $(b^8c^6d^5)(7b^6c^2d)$ **$7b^{14}c^8d^6$**
32. $(14fg^2h^2)(-3f^4g^2h^2)$ **$-42f^5g^4h^4$**
33. $(j^5k^7)^4$ **$j^{20}k^{28}$**
34. $(n^3p)^4$ **$n^{12}p^4$**
35. $[(2^2)^2]^2$ **2^8 or 256**
36. $[(3^2)^2]^4$ **3^{16} or 43,046,721**
37. $[(4r^2t)^3]^2$ **$4096r^{12}t^6$**
38. $[(-2xy^2)^3]^2$ **$64x^6y^{12}$**

Example 4 p. 403

GEOMETRY Express the area of each triangle as a monomial.

39. **$20c^5d^5$**

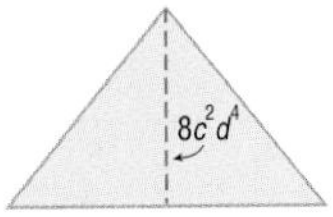

40. **$3g^3h^6$**

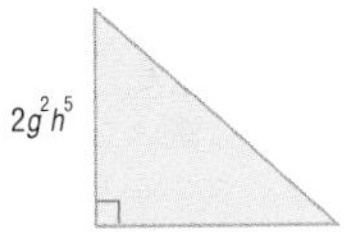

Example 5 p. 404

Simplify each expression.

41. $(2a^3)^4(a^3)^3$ **$16a^{21}$**
42. $(c^3)^2(-3c^5)^2$ **$9c^{16}$**
43. $(2gh^4)^3[(-2g^4h)^3]^2$ **$512g^{27}h^{18}$**
44. $(5k^2m)^3[(4km^4)^2]^2$ **$32{,}000k^{10}m^{19}$**
45. $(p^5r^2)^4(-7p^3r^4)^2(6pr^3)$ **$294p^{27}r^{19}$**
46. $(5x^2y)^2(2xy^3z)^3(4xyz)$ **$800x^8y^{12}z^4$**
47. $(5a^2b^3c^4)(6a^3b^4c^2)$ **$30a^5b^7c^6$**
48. $(10xy^5z^3)(3x^4y^6z^3)$ **$30x^5y^{11}z^6$**
49. $(0.5x^3)^2$ **$0.25x^6$**
50. $(0.4h^5)^3$ **$0.064h^{15}$**
51. $\left(-\frac{3}{4}c\right)^3$ **$-\frac{27}{64}c^3$**
52. $\left(\frac{4}{5}a^2\right)^2$ **$\frac{16}{25}a^4$**
53. $(8y^3)(-3x^2y^2)\left(\frac{3}{8}xy^4\right)$ **$-9x^3y^9$**
54. $\left(\frac{4}{7}m\right)^2(49m)(17p)\left(\frac{1}{34}p^5\right)$ **$8m^3p^6$**

B

55. $(-3r^3w^4)^3(2rw)^2(-3r^2)^3(4rw^2)^3(2r^2w^3)^4$ **$2{,}985{,}984r^{28}w^{32}$**
56. $(3ab^2c)^2(-2a^2b^4)^2(a^4c^2)^3(a^2b^4c^5)^2(2a^3b^2c^4)^3$ **$288a^{31}b^{26}c^{30}$**

57. **FINANCIAL LITERACY** Cleavon has money in an account that earns 3% simple interest. The formula for computing simple interest is $I = Prt$, where I is the interest earned, P represents the principal that he put into the account, r is the interest rate (in decimal form), and t represents time in years.

   a. Cleavon makes a deposit of \$2*c* and leaves it for 2 years. Write a monomial that represents the interest earned. **$0.12c$**

   b. If *c* represents a birthday gift of \$250, how much will Cleavon have in this account after 2 years? **\$280**

Real-World Link

84% of teens have some money saved. The average teen has saved \$1044.

Source: Charles Schwab Teens & Money Survey

GEOMETRY Express the volume of each solid as a monomial.

58. **$12x^4\pi$**

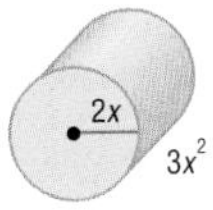

59. **$15x^7$**

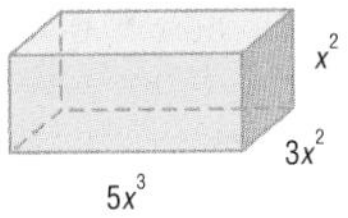

60. **$16x^9$**

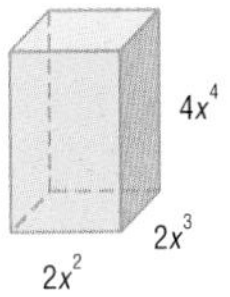

Exercise Alert

Formulas For Exercises 39, 40, and 58–60, students will need to know the formulas for area of a triangle and for volume of solids.

Additional Answers

21. Yes; constants are monomials.
22. Yes; this is a product of a number and variables.
23. No; there is addition and more than one term.
24. No; there is a variable in the denominator.
25. Yes; this can be written as the product of a number and a variable.
26. No; there is addition and more than one term.

Differentiated Homework Options

Level	Assignment	Two-Day Option	
AL Basic	21–57, 65–86	21–57 odd, 68–71	22–56 even, 65–67, 72–86
OL Core	21–57 odd, 59, 61–63, 65–86	21–57, 68–71	58–63, 65–67, 72–86
BL Advanced	58–80, (optional: 81–86)		

Study Guide and Intervention
CRM pp. 5–6 AL OL ELL

NAME ______________ DATE ________ PERIOD ________

7-1 Study Guide and Intervention
Multiplying Monomials

Monomials A **monomial** is a number, a variable, or the product of a number and one or more variables with nonnegative integer exponents. An expression of the form x^n is called a **power** and represents the product you obtain when x is used as a factor n times. To multiply two powers that have the same base, add the exponents.

Product of Powers	For any number a and all integers m and n, $a^m \cdot a^n = a^{m+n}$.

Example 1 Simplify $(3x^6)(5x^2)$.

$(3x^6)(5x^2) = (3)(5)(x^6 \cdot x^2)$ Group the coefficients and the variables
$= (3 \cdot 5)(x^{6+2})$ Product of Powers
$= 15x^8$ Simplify.
The product is $15x^8$.

Example 2 Simplify $(-4a^3b)(3a^2b^5)$.

$(-4a^3b)(3a^2b^5) = (-4)(3)(a^3 \cdot a^2)(b \cdot b^5)$
$= -12(a^{3+2})(b^{1+5})$
$= -12a^5b^6$
The product is $-12a^5b^6$.

Exercises

Simplify each expression.

1. $y(y^5)$ y^6
2. $n^2 \cdot n^7$ n^9
3. $(-7x^2)(x^4)$ $-7x^6$
4. $x(x^2)(x^4)$ x^7
5. $m \cdot m^5$ m^6
6. $(-x^3)(-x^4)$ x^7
7. $(2a^2)(8a)$ $16a^3$
8. $(rs)(rn^3)(n^2)$ r^2n^6
9. $(x^2y)(4xy^3)$ $4x^3y^4$
10. $\frac{1}{3}(2a^3b)(6b^3)$ $4a^3b^4$
11. $(-4x^3)(-5x^7)$ $20x^{10}$
12. $(-3j^2k^4)(2jk^6)$ $-6j^3k^{10}$
13. $(5a^2bc^3)\left(\frac{1}{5}abc^4\right)$ $a^3b^2c^7$
14. $(-5xy)(4x^2)(y^4)$ $-20x^3y^5$
15. $(10x^3yz^2)(-2xy^5z)$ $-20x^4y^6z^3$

Lesson 7-1

Chapter 7 5 Glencoe Algebra 1

Practice
CRM p. 8 AL OL BL ELL

NAME ______________ DATE ________ PERIOD ________

7-1 Practice
Multiplying Monomials

Determine whether each expression is a monomial. Write *yes* or *no*. Explain your reasoning.

1. $\frac{21a^2}{7b}$ No; this involves the quotient, not the product, of variables.
2. $\frac{b^3c^2}{2}$ Yes; this is the product of a number, $\frac{1}{2}$, and two variables.

Simplify each expression.

3. $(-5x^2y)(3x^4)$ $-15x^6y$
4. $(2ab^2f^2)(4a^3b^2f^2)$ $8a^4b^4f^4$
5. $(3ad^4)(-2a^2)$ $-6a^3d^4$
6. $(4g^3h)(-2g^5)$ $-8g^8h$
7. $(-15xy^4)\left(-\frac{1}{3}xy^3\right)$ $5x^2y^7$
8. $(-xy)^3(xz)$ $-x^4y^3z$
9. $(-18m^2n)^2\left(-\frac{1}{6}mn^2\right)$ $-54m^5n^4$
10. $(0.2a^2b^3)^2$ $0.04a^4b^6$
11. $\left(\frac{2}{3}p\right)^2$ $\frac{4}{9}p^2$
12. $\left(\frac{1}{4}ad^3\right)^2$ $\frac{1}{16}a^2d^6$
13. $(0.4k^3)^3$ $0.064k^9$
14. $[(4^2)^2]^2$ 4^8 or 65,536

GEOMETRY Express the area of each figure as a monomial.

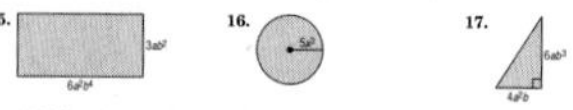

15. $18a^3b^6$ 16. $(25x^6)\pi$ 17. $12a^3b^4$

GEOMETRY Express the volume of each solid as a monomial.

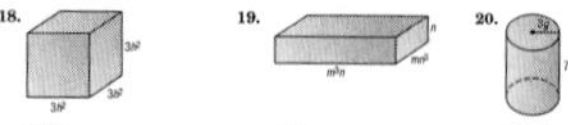

18. $27h^6$ 19. m^4n^5 20. $(63g^4)\pi$

21. **COUNTING** A panel of four light switches can be set in 2^4 ways. A panel of five light switches can set in twice this many ways. In how many ways can five light switches be set? 2^5 or 32

22. **HOBBIES** Tawa wants to increase her rock collection by a power of three this year and then increase it again by a power of two next year. If she has 2 rocks now, how many rocks will she have after the second year? 2^6 or 64

Chapter 7 8 Glencoe Algebra 1

Word Problem Practice
CRM p. 9 AL OL BL ELL

NAME ______________ DATE ________ PERIOD ________

7-1 Word Problem Practice
Multiplying Monomials

1. **GRAVITY** An egg that has been falling for x seconds has dropped at an average speed of $16x$ feet per second. If the egg is dropped from the top of a building, its total distance traveled is the product of the average rate times the time. Write a simplified expression to show the distance the egg has traveled after x seconds. $16x^2$

2. **CIVIL ENGINEERING** A developer is planning a sidewalk for a new development. The sidewalk can be installed in rectangular sections that have a fixed width of 3 feet and a length that can vary. Assuming that each section is the same length, express the area of a 4-section sidewalk as a monomial. $12x$

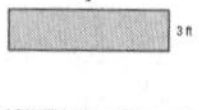

3. **PROBABILITY** If you flip a coin 3 times in a row, there are 2^3 outcomes that can occur.

Outcomes	
HHH	TTT
HTT	THH
HTH	TTH
HHT	THT

If you then flip the coin two more times, there are $2^3 \times 2^2$ outcomes that can occur. How many outcomes can occur if you flip the quarter as mentioned above plus four more times? Write your answer in the form 2^x. 2^9

4. **SPORTS** The volume of a sphere is given by the formula $V = \frac{4}{3}\pi r^3$, where r is the radius of the sphere. Find the volume of air in three different basketballs. Use $\pi = 3.14$. Round your answers to the nearest whole number.

Ball	Radius (in.)	Volume (in³)
Child's	4	268
Women's	4.5	382
HTH	4.8	463

Source: WikiAnswers

5. **ELECTRICITY** An electrician uses the formula $W = I^2R$, where W is the power in watts, I is the current in amperes, and R is the resistance in ohms.

a. Find the power in a household circuit that has 20 amperes of current and 5 ohms of resistance. 2000 watts

b. If the current is reduced by one half, what happens to the power?
The power is one-fourth the previous amount.

Lesson 7-1

Chapter 7 9 Glencoe Algebra 1

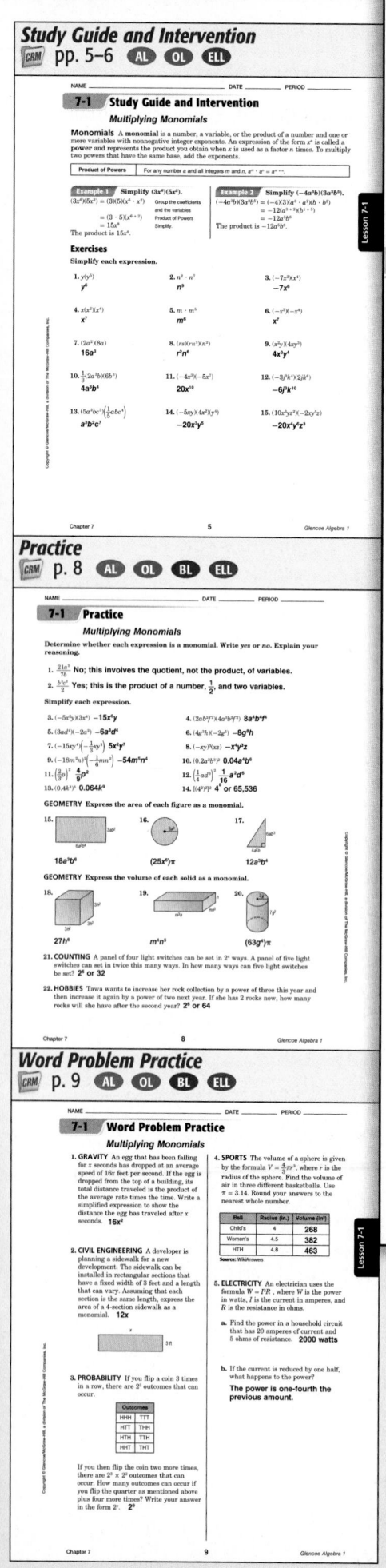

Math History Link

Albert Einstein (1879–1955)

Albert Einstein is perhaps the most well-known scientist of the 20th century. His formula $E = mc^2$, where E represents the energy, m is the mass of the material, and c is the speed of light, shows that if mass is accelerated enough, it could be converted into usable energy.

61. **PACKAGING** For a commercial art class, Aiko must design a new container for individually wrapped pieces of candy. The shape that she chose is a cylinder. The formula for the volume of a cylinder is $V = \pi r^2 h$.

a. The radius that Aiko would like to use is $2p^3$, and the height is $4p^3$. Write a monomial that represents the volume of her container. $16\pi p^9$

b. Make a table of values for five possible radius widths and heights if the volume is to remain the same.

c. What is the volume of Aiko's container if the height is doubled? $32\pi p^9$

62. **ENERGY** Matter can be converted completely into energy by using the formula at the left. Energy is measured in joules, mass in kilograms, and the speed of light is about 300 million meters per second.

a. Complete the calculations to convert 3 kilograms of gasoline completely into energy. 270,000,000,000,000,000 joules

b. What happens to the energy if the amount of gasoline is doubled? The energy is also doubled.

63. **MULTIPLE REPRESENTATIONS** In this problem, you will explore exponents.

a. **TABULAR** Copy and use a calculator to complete the table.

Power	3^4	3^3	3^2	3^1	3^0	3^{-1}	3^{-2}	3^{-3}	3^{-4}
Value	81	27	9	3	1	$\frac{1}{3}$	$\frac{1}{9}$	$\frac{1}{27}$	$\frac{1}{81}$

b. **ANALYTICAL** What do you think the values of 5^0 and 5^{-1} are? Verify your conjecture using a calculator. 1 and $\frac{1}{5}$

c. **ANALYTICAL** Complete: For any nonzero number a and any integer n, $a^{-n} =$ ______. $\frac{1}{a^n}$

d. **VERBAL** Describe the value of a nonzero number raised to the zero power. **63d.** Any nonzero number raised to the zero power is 1.

61b. Sample answer:

Radius	Height
$4p$	p^7
$4p^2$	p^5
$2p^3$	$4p^3$
$2p^4$	$4p$
$2p$	$4p^7$

66. Sample answer: $x^4 \cdot x^2$; $x^5 \cdot x$; $(x^3)^2$

H.O.T. Problems
Use **H**igher-**O**rder **T**hinking Skills

64. **CHALLENGE** For any nonzero real numbers a and b and any integers m and t, simplify the expression $\left(-\frac{a^m}{b^t}\right)^{2t}$ and describe each step.

65. **REASONING** Copy the table below.

Equation	Related Expression	Power of x	Linear or Nonlinear
$y = x$	x	1	linear
$y = x^2$	x^2	2	nonlinear
$y = x^3$	x^3	3	nonlinear

a. For each equation, write the related expression and record the power of x.

b. Graph each equation using a graphing calculator. See Ch. 7 Answer Appendix.

c. Classify each graph as *linear* or *nonlinear*. See chart above.

d. Explain how to determine whether an equation, or its related expression, is linear or nonlinear without graphing. See Ch. 7 Answer Appendix.

66. **OPEN ENDED** Write three different expressions that can be simplified to x^6.

67. **WRITING IN MATH** Write two formulas that have monomial expressions in them. Explain how each is used in a real-world situation.

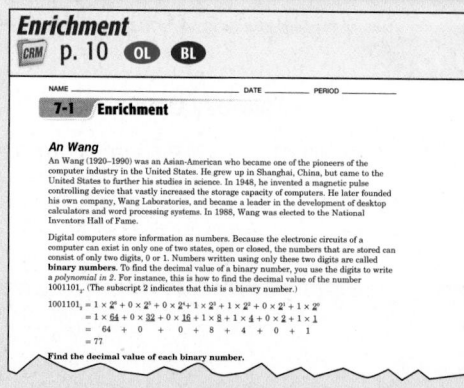

64. Sample answer: First use the power of a power rule to simplify the expression to $\frac{a^{2tm}}{b^{2t^2}}$.

67. Sample answer: The area of a circle or $A = \pi r^2$, where the radius r can be used to find the area of any circle. The area of a rectangle or $A = w \cdot \ell$, where w is the width and ℓ is the length, can be used to find the area of any rectangle.

Enrichment
CRM p. 10 OL BL

NAME ______________ DATE ________ PERIOD ________

7-1 Enrichment

An Wang

An Wang (1920–1990) was an Asian-American who became one of the pioneers of the computer industry in the United States. He grew up in Shanghai, China, but came to the United States to further his studies in science. In 1948, he invented a magnetic pulse controlling device that vastly increased the storage capacity of computers. He later founded his own company, Wang Laboratories, and became a leader in the development of desktop calculators and word processing systems. In 1988, Wang was elected to the National Inventors Hall of Fame.

Digital computers store information as numbers. Because the electronic circuits of a computer can exist in only one of two states, open or closed, the numbers that are stored can consist of only two digits, 0 or 1. Numbers written using only these two digits are called **binary numbers**. To find the decimal value of a binary number, you use the digits to write a *polynomial in 2*. For instance, this is how to find the decimal value of the number 1001101_2. (The subscript 2 indicates that this is a binary number.)

$1001101_2 = 1 \times 2^6 + 0 \times 2^5 + 0 \times 2^4 + 1 \times 2^3 + 1 \times 2^2 + 0 \times 2^1 + 1 \times 2^0$
$= 1 \times 64 + 0 \times 32 + 0 \times 16 + 1 \times 8 + 1 \times 4 + 0 \times 2 + 1 \times 1$
$= 64 + 0 + 0 + 8 + 4 + 0 + 1$
$= 77$

Find the decimal value of each binary number.

Multiple Representations In Exercise 63, students use a calculator, a table of values, and verbal analysis to relate the values of expressions involving positive and negative exponents.

PSAE PRACTICE 9.11.02, 8.11.14, 8.11.10

68. Which of the following is not a monomial? C

A $-6xy$

B $\frac{1}{2}a^2$

C $-\frac{1}{2b^3}$

D $5gh^4$

69. GEOMETRY The accompanying diagram shows the transformation of $\triangle XYZ$ to $\triangle X'Y'Z'$. F

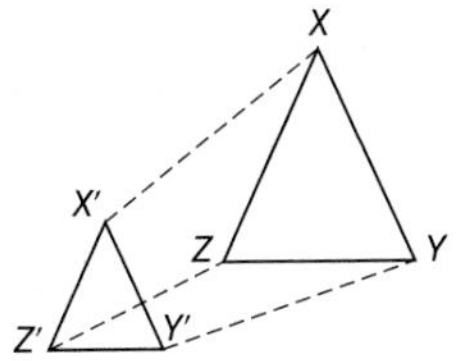

This transformation is an example of a

F dilation

G line reflection

H rotation

J translation

70. CARS In 1994, the average price of a new domestic car was $16,930. In 2002, the average price was $19,126. Based on a linear model, what is the predicted average price for 2010? B

A $22,969

B $21,322

C $20,773

D $18,577

71. SHORT RESPONSE If a line has a positive slope and a negative y-intercept, what happens to the x-intercept if the slope and the y-intercept are both doubled? The x-intercept does not change.

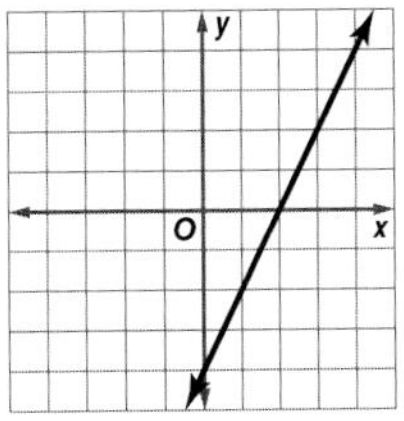

Spiral Review

Solve each system of inequalities by graphing. (Lesson 6-8) 72–75. See margin.

72. $y < 4x$
$2x + 3y \geq -21$

73. $y \geq 2$
$2y + 2x \leq 4$

74. $y > -2x - 1$
$2y \leq 3x + 2$

75. $3x + 2y < 10$
$2x + 12y < -6$

Perform the indicated matrix operations. If an operation cannot be performed, write *impossible*. (Lesson 6-7)

76. $\begin{bmatrix} 2 & 5 & 3 \\ -5 & -1 & 10 \\ 4 & -4 & 0 \end{bmatrix} + \begin{bmatrix} -8 & 2 & -6 \\ 3 & 6 & -1 \\ -6 & -10 & 6 \end{bmatrix}$

76. $\begin{bmatrix} -6 & 7 & -3 \\ -2 & 5 & 9 \\ -2 & -14 & 6 \end{bmatrix}$

77. $\begin{bmatrix} 11 & 0 & 7 \\ 8 & 11 & -10 \end{bmatrix} - \begin{bmatrix} -3 & 0 & 4 \end{bmatrix}$ impossible

78. $\begin{bmatrix} -5 & 2 & -11 \\ 2 & -2 & 1 \end{bmatrix} + \begin{bmatrix} 2 & 5 \\ 3 & -9 \end{bmatrix}$ impossible

79. $\begin{bmatrix} 2 & -5 & -7 \\ -1 & 11 & 1 \\ 6 & -3 & 4 \end{bmatrix} + \begin{bmatrix} -4 & 0 & -9 \\ 12 & -12 & 8 \\ 12 & 0 & 8 \end{bmatrix}$ $\begin{bmatrix} -2 & -5 & -16 \\ 11 & -1 & 9 \\ 18 & -3 & 12 \end{bmatrix}$

80. BABYSITTING Alexis charges $10 plus $4 per hour to babysit. Alexis needs at least $40 more to buy a television for which she is saving. Write an inequality for this situation. Will she be able to get her television if she babysits for 5 hours? (Lesson 5-6) $10 + 4h \geq 40$; no

Skills Review

Find each quotient. (Lesson 0-3)

81. $-64 \div (-8)$ 8

82. $-78 \div 1.3$ -60

83. $42.3 \div (-6)$ -7.05

84. $-23.94 \div 10.5$ -2.28

85. $-32.5 \div (-2.5)$ 13

86. $-98.44 \div 4.6$ -21.4

Exercise Alert

Grid Paper For Exercises 72–75, students will need grid paper.

4 ASSESS

Ticket Out the Door Make several copies each of five monomial expressions that need to be simplified. Give one expression to each student. As students leave the room, ask them to tell you the simplified versions of the expressions they possess.

Additional Answers

72.

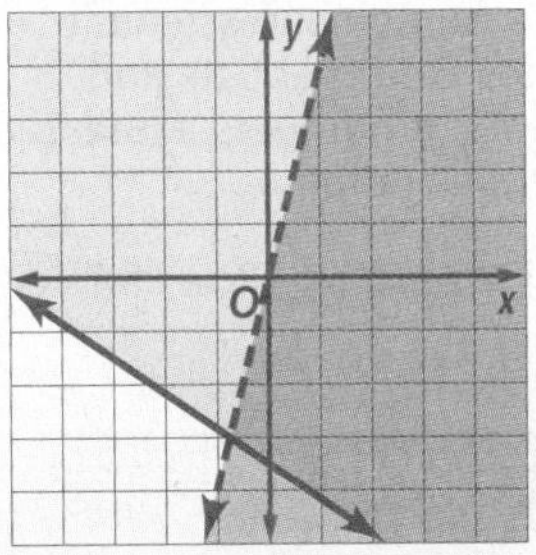

73.

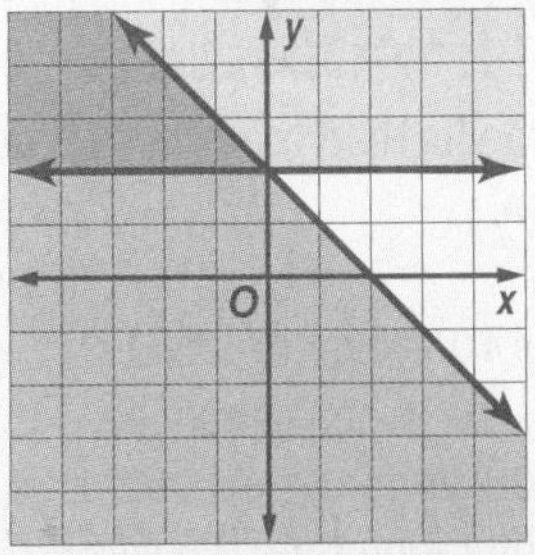

74.

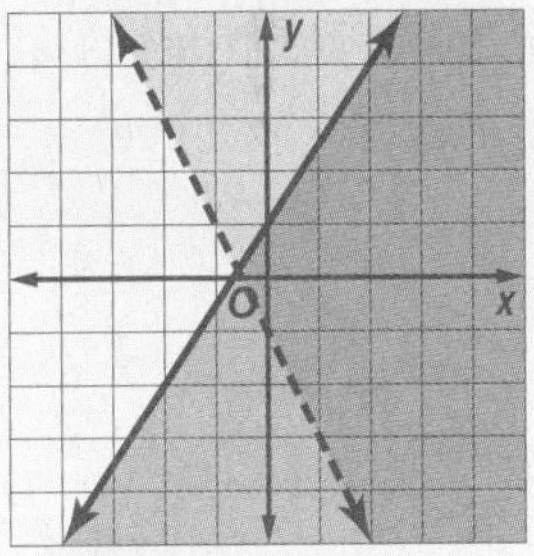

75.

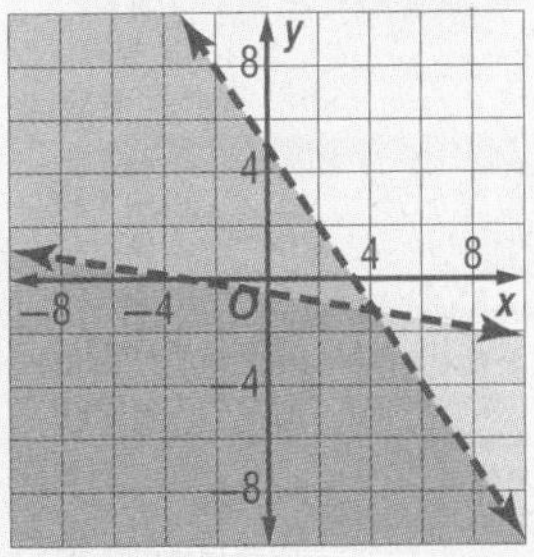

Differentiated Instruction

OL BL

Extension Tell students that a sports car on a drag-racing strip can reach 100 miles per hour in a quarter mile. If s represents the speed in miles per hour, then the approximate number of feet that the driver must apply the brakes before stopping is $\frac{1}{20}s^2$. Calculate how far the car would travel on the drag strip, from start to stop, if the driver started braking when the car reached 100 miles per hour. A mile is 5280 feet. 1820 ft; the initial quarter mile (1320 ft) plus braking distance (500 ft)

7-2 Lesson Notes

1 FOCUS

Vertical Alignment

Before Lesson 7-2
Multiply monomials.

Lesson 7-2
Find the quotient of two monomials.
Simplify expressions containing negative and zero exponents.

After Lesson 7-2
Express numbers in scientific notation. Find products and quotients of numbers expressed in scientific notation.

2 TEACH

Scaffolding Questions

Have students read the *Why?* section of the lesson.

Ask:

- What is 10^2 when simplified? 100
- What is 10^1 when simplified? 10
- How could you use exponents to write the ratio of the height of a skyscraper that is 900 meters tall to the height of the tallest tree? $\frac{10^3}{10^2}$ or 10^1

7-2 Dividing Monomials

Then

You multiplied monomials. (Lesson 7-1)

Now

- Find the quotient of two monomials.
- Simplify expressions containing negative and zero exponents.

IL Learning Standards

8.A.4b Represent mathematical patterns and describe their properties using variables and mathematical symbols.

New Vocabulary

order of magnitude

IL Math Online

glencoe.com

- Extra Examples
- Personal Tutor
- Self-Check Quiz
- Homework Help
- Math in Motion

Why?

The tallest redwood tree is 112 feet or about 10^2 meters tall. The average height of a woman in the United States is 1.62 meters. The closest power of ten to 1.62 is 10^0, so a woman is about 10^0 meters tall. The ratio of the tree's height to the woman's height is $\frac{10^2}{10^0}$ or 10^2. This means the tallest redwood tree is approximately 100 times as tall as the average woman.

Quotients of Monomials We can use the principles for reducing fractions to find quotients of monomials like $\frac{10^2}{10^0}$. In the following examples, look for a pattern in the exponents.

$$\frac{2^7}{2^4} = \frac{\overbrace{\cancel{2}\cdot\cancel{2}\cdot\cancel{2}\cdot\cancel{2}\cdot 2\cdot 2\cdot 2}^{7\text{ factors}}}{\underbrace{\cancel{2}\cdot\cancel{2}\cdot\cancel{2}\cdot\cancel{2}}_{4\text{ factors}}} = 2\cdot 2\cdot 2 \text{ or } 2^3 \qquad \frac{t^4}{t^3} = \frac{\overbrace{\cancel{t}\cdot\cancel{t}\cdot\cancel{t}\cdot t}^{4\text{ factors}}}{\underbrace{\cancel{t}\cdot\cancel{t}\cdot\cancel{t}}_{3\text{ factors}}} = t$$

These examples demonstrate the Quotient of Powers Rule.

Key Concept — Quotient of Powers (For Your FOLDABLE)

Words To divide two powers with the same base, subtract the exponents.

Symbols For any nonzero number a, and any integers m and p, $\frac{a^m}{a^p} = a^{m-p}$.

Examples $\frac{c^{11}}{c^8} = c^{11-8}$ or c^3 $\qquad \frac{r^5}{r^2} = r^{5-2} = r^3$

Math *in Motion*, BrainPOP® glencoe.com

EXAMPLE 1 Quotient of Powers

Simplify $\frac{g^3h^5}{gh^2}$. Assume that no denominator equals zero.

$\frac{g^3h^5}{gh^2} = \left(\frac{g^3}{g}\right)\left(\frac{h^5}{h^2}\right)$ **Group powers with the same base.**

$= (g^{3-1})(h^{5-2})$ **Quotient of Powers**

$= g^2h^3$ **Simplify.**

Check Your Progress

Simplify each expression. Assume that no denominator equals zero.

1A. $\frac{x^3y^4}{x^2y}$ xy^3

1B. $\frac{k^7m^{10}p}{k^5m^3p}$ k^2m^7

Personal Tutor glencoe.com

Lesson 7-2 Resources

Resource	Approaching-Level	On-Level	Beyond-Level	English Learners
Teacher Edition	• Differentiated Instruction, p. 410	• Differentiated Instruction, pp. 410, 415	• Differentiated Instruction, p. 415	• Differentiated Instruction, p. 410
Chapter Resource Masters	• Study Guide and Intervention, pp. 11–12 • Skills Practice, p. 13 • Practice, p. 14 • Word Problem Practice, p. 15	• Study Guide and Intervention, pp. 11–12 • Skills Practice, p. 13 • Practice, p. 14 • Word Problem Practice, p. 15 • Enrichment, p. 16	• Practice, p. 14 • Word Problem Practice, p. 15 • Enrichment, p. 16	• Study Guide and Intervention, pp. 11–12 • Skills Practice, p. 13 • Practice, p. 14
Transparencies	• 5-Minute Check Transparency 7-2	• 5-Minute Check Transparency 7-2	• 5-Minute Check Transparency 7-2	• 5-Minute Check Transparency 7-2
Other	• Study Notebook	• Study Notebook	• Study Notebook	• Study Notebook

We can use the Product of Powers Rule to find the powers of quotients for monomials. In the following example, look for a pattern in the exponents.

$$\left(\frac{3}{4}\right)^3 = \overbrace{\left(\frac{3}{4}\right)\left(\frac{3}{4}\right)\left(\frac{3}{4}\right)}^{3\text{ factors}} = \frac{\overbrace{3\cdot 3\cdot 3}^{3\text{ factors}}}{\underbrace{4\cdot 4\cdot 4}_{3\text{ factors}}} = \frac{3^3}{4^3}$$

$$\left(\frac{c}{d}\right)^2 = \overbrace{\left(\frac{c}{d}\right)\left(\frac{c}{d}\right)}^{2\text{ factors}} = \frac{\overbrace{c\cdot c}^{2\text{ factors}}}{\underbrace{d\cdot d}_{2\text{ factors}}} = \frac{c^2}{d^2}$$

StudyTip

Power Rules with Variables The power rules apply to variables as well as numbers. For example, $\left(\frac{3a}{4b}\right)^3 = \frac{(3a)^3}{(4b)^3}$ or $\frac{27a^3}{64b^3}$.

Key Concept Power of a Quotient — For Your FOLDABLE

Words To find the power of a quotient, find the power of the numerator and the power of the denominator.

Symbols For any real numbers a and $b \neq 0$, and any integer m, $\left(\frac{a}{b}\right)^m = \frac{a^m}{b^m}$.

Examples $\left(\frac{3}{5}\right)^4 = \frac{3^4}{5^4}$ $\left(\frac{r}{t}\right)^5 = \frac{r^5}{t^5}$

EXAMPLE 2 Power of a Quotient

Simplify $\left(\frac{3p^3}{7}\right)^2$.

$\left(\frac{3p^3}{7}\right)^2 = \frac{(3p^3)^2}{7^2}$ Power of a Quotient

$= \frac{3^2(p^3)^2}{7^2}$ Power of a Product

$= \frac{9p^6}{49}$ Power of a Power

Check Your Progress

Simplify each expression.

2A. $\left(\frac{3x^4}{4}\right)^3$ $\frac{27x^{12}}{64}$ **2B.** $\left(\frac{5x^5y}{6}\right)^2$ $\frac{25x^{10}y^2}{36}$ **2C.** $\left(\frac{2y^2}{3z^3}\right)^2$ $\frac{4y^4}{9z^6}$ **2D.** $\left(\frac{4x^3}{5y^4}\right)^3$ $\frac{64x^9}{125y^{12}}$

Personal Tutor glencoe.com

A calculator can be used to explore expressions with 0 as the exponent. There are two methods to explain why a calculator gives a value of 1 for 3^0.

Method 1

$\frac{3^5}{3^5} = 3^{5-5}$ Quotient of Powers

$= 3^0$ Simplify.

Method 2

$\frac{3^5}{3^5} = \frac{\cancel{3}\cdot\cancel{3}\cdot\cancel{3}\cdot\cancel{3}\cdot\cancel{3}}{\cancel{3}\cdot\cancel{3}\cdot\cancel{3}\cdot\cancel{3}\cdot\cancel{3}}$ Definition of powers

$= 1$ Simplify.

Since $\frac{3^5}{3^5}$ can only have one value, we can conclude that $3^0 = 1$.

TEACH with TECH

BLOG On your secure classroom blog have students create a blog entry explaining how to find the quotient of powers and the power of a quotient.

Quotients of Monomials

Example 1 shows how to find the quotient of powers. **Example 2** shows how to find the power of a quotient. **Example 3** shows how to simplify expressions involving zero exponents.

Formative Assessment

Use the Check Your Progress exercises after each example to determine students' understanding of concepts.

Additional Examples

1 Simplify $\frac{x^7y^{12}}{x^6y^3}$. Assume that no denominator equals zero. xy^9

2 Simplify $\left(\frac{4c^3d^2}{5}\right)^3$. $\frac{64c^9d^6}{125}$

Additional Examples also in Interactive Classroom PowerPoint® Presentations

IWB INTERACTIVE WHITEBOARD READY

Watch Out!

Preventing Errors Remind students to also find the powers of the constant terms of the monomials.

Focus on Mathematical Content

Powers of Negative Numbers Students may assume that the expression -6^3 means $(-6)(-6)(-6)$. Explain that -6^3 means $-(6^3)$. To express -6 to the third power, they must use parentheses, $(-6)^3$.

Tips for New Teachers

Properties Point out to students that the definition of the Quotient of Powers restricts a to being nonzero. Ask why must a be nonzero? If $a = 0$, we would be dividing by 0, which is undefined.

Watch Out!

Preventing Errors Ask students why the negative sign in Example 3 does not affect the outcome. Students should explain that any nonzero number raised to the zero power is 1, and a negative number is a nonzero number.

Additional Example

3 Simplify each expression. Assume that no denominator equals zero.

a. $\left(\frac{12m^8n^7}{8m^5n^{10}}\right)^0$ 1

b. $\frac{m^0n^3}{n^2}$ n

Tips for New Teachers

Zero to the Zero Power Ask students to write an expression involving division that will be equivalent to 0^0, for example, $\frac{0^6}{0^6}$. Show students that $\frac{0^6}{0^6} = \frac{0}{0}$ and remind them that division by zero is undefined.

Negative Exponents

Example 4 shows how to simplify expressions involving negative exponents. **Example 5** shows how to apply the properties of exponents in real-world situations.

Key Concept — Zero Exponent Property

For Your FOLDABLE

Words Any nonzero number raised to the zero power is equal to 1.

Symbols For any nonzero number a, $a^0 = 1$.

Examples $15^0 = 1$ $\left(\frac{b}{c}\right)^0 = 1$ $\left(\frac{2}{7}\right)^0 = 1$

EXAMPLE 3 Zero Exponent

Simplify each expression. Assume that no denominator equals zero.

a. $\left(-\frac{4n^2q^5r^2}{9n^3q^2r}\right)^0$

$\left(-\frac{4n^2q^5r^2}{9n^3q^2r}\right)^0 = 1$ $a^0 = 1$

b. $\frac{x^5y^0}{x^3}$

$\frac{x^5y^0}{x^3} = \frac{x^5(1)}{x^3}$ $a^0 = 1$

$= x^2$ Quotient of Powers

StudyTip

Zero Exponent Be careful of parentheses. The expression $(5x)^0$ is 1 but $5x^0 = 5$.

Check Your Progress

3A. $\frac{b^4c^2d^0}{b^2c}$ b^2c

3B. $\left(\frac{2f^4g^7h^3}{15f^3g^9h^6}\right)^0$ 1

Personal Tutor glencoe.com

Negative Exponents To investigate the meaning of a negative exponent, we can simplify expressions like $\frac{c^2}{c^5}$ using two methods.

Method 1

$\frac{c^2}{c^5} = c^{2-5}$ Quotient of Powers

$= c^{-3}$ Simplify.

Method 2

$\frac{c^2}{c^5} = \frac{\cancel{c}\cdot\cancel{c}}{\cancel{c}\cdot\cancel{c}\cdot c\cdot c\cdot c}$ Definition of powers

$= \frac{1}{c^3}$ Simplify.

Since $\frac{c^2}{c^5}$ can only have one value, we can conclude that $c^{-3} = \frac{1}{c^3}$.

Key Concept — Negative Exponent Property

For Your FOLDABLE

Words For any nonzero number a and any integer n, a^{-n} is the reciprocal of a^n. Also, the reciprocal of a^{-n} is a^n.

Symbols For any nonzero number a and any integer n, $a^{-n} = \frac{1}{a^n}$ and $\frac{1}{a^{-n}} = a^n$.

Examples $2^{-4} = \frac{1}{2^4} = \frac{1}{16}$ $\frac{1}{j^{-4}} = j^4$

Differentiated Instruction

AL OL ELL

If students have difficulty relating the Key Concepts in this lesson to expressions,

Then have students make flash cards to illustrate each Key Concept. Write an expression that is an example of a Key Concept on the board. Tell students to show their card that correlates to the example. Then ask a student to describe the process of simplifying the expression.

StudyTip

Negative Signs Be aware of where a negative sign is placed. $5^{-1} = \frac{1}{5}$, while $-5^1 \neq \frac{1}{5}$.

An expression is considered simplified when it contains only positive exponents, each base appears exactly once, there are no powers of powers, and all fractions are in simplest form.

EXAMPLE 4 Negative Exponents

Simplify each expression. Assume that no denominator equals zero.

a. $\frac{n^{-5}p^4}{r^{-2}}$

$\frac{n^{-5}p^4}{r^{-2}} = \left(\frac{n^{-5}}{1}\right)\left(\frac{p^4}{1}\right)\left(\frac{1}{r^{-2}}\right)$ Write as a product of fractions.

$= \left(\frac{1}{n^5}\right)\left(\frac{p^4}{1}\right)\left(\frac{r^2}{1}\right)$ $a^{-n} = \frac{1}{a^n}$ and $\frac{1}{a^{-n}} = a^n$

$= \frac{p^4r^2}{n^5}$ Multiply.

b. $\frac{5r^{-3}t^4}{-20r^2t^7u^{-5}}$

$\frac{5r^{-3}t^4}{-20r^2t^7u^{-5}} = \left(\frac{5}{-20}\right)\left(\frac{r^{-3}}{r^2}\right)\left(\frac{t^4}{t^7}\right)\left(\frac{1}{u^{-5}}\right)$ Group powers with the same base.

$= \left(-\frac{1}{4}\right)(r^{-3-2})(t^{4-7})(u^5)$ Quotient of Powers and Negative Exponents Property

$= -\frac{1}{4}r^{-5}t^{-3}u^5$ Simplify.

$= -\frac{1}{4}\left(\frac{1}{r^5}\right)\left(\frac{1}{t^3}\right)(u^5)$ Negative Exponent Property

$= -\frac{u^5}{4r^5t^3}$ Multiply.

c. $\frac{2a^2b^3c^{-5}}{10a^{-3}b^{-1}c^{-4}}$

$\frac{2a^2b^3c^{-5}}{10a^{-3}b^{-1}c^{-4}} = \left(\frac{2}{10}\right)\left(\frac{a^2}{a^{-3}}\right)\left(\frac{b^3}{b^{-1}}\right)\left(\frac{c^{-5}}{c^{-4}}\right)$ Group powers with the same base.

$= \left(\frac{1}{5}\right)(a^{2-(-3)})(b^{3-(-1)})(c^{-5-(-4)})$ Quotient of Powers and Negative Exponents Property

$= \frac{1}{5}a^5b^4c^{-1}$ Simplify.

$= \frac{1}{5}(a^5)(b^4)\left(\frac{1}{c}\right)$ Negative Exponent Property

$= \frac{a^5b^4}{5c}$ Multiply.

Check Your Progress

Simplify each expression. Assume that no denominator equals zero.

4A. $\frac{v^{-3}wx^2}{wy^{-6}}$ $\frac{x^2y^6}{v^3}$ **4B.** $\frac{32a^{-8}b^3c^{-4}}{4a^3b^5c^{-2}}$ $\frac{8}{a^{11}b^2c^2}$ **4C.** $\frac{5j^{-3}k^2m^{-6}}{25k^{-4}m^{-2}}$ $\frac{k^6}{5j^3m^4}$

Personal Tutor glencoe.com

Real-World Link

An adult human weighs about 70 kilograms and an adult dairy cow weighs about 700 kilograms. Their weights differ by 1 order of magnitude.

Order of magnitude is used to compare measures and to estimate and perform rough calculations. The **order of magnitude** of a quantity is the number rounded to the nearest power of 10. For example, the power of 10 closest to 95,000,000,000 is 10^{11}, or 100,000,000,000. So the order of magnitude of 95,000,000,000 is 10^{11}.

Watch Out!

Preventing Errors Have students look at the first step of the solution of Example 4. Point out that rewriting an expression as a product of fractions makes applying the Negative Exponent Property easier. Fractions that have negative exponents can be rewritten as their reciprocals.

Additional Example

4 Simplify each expression. Assume that no denominator equals zero.

a. $\frac{x^{-4}y^9}{z^{-6}}$ $\frac{y^9z^6}{x^4}$

b. $\frac{75p^3m^{-5}}{15p^5m^{-4}r^{-8}}$ $\frac{5r^8}{p^2m}$

Tips for New Teachers

Monomials Point out to students that a variable with a negative exponent such as x^{-2} is not a monomial. A monomial does not involve division by variables and $x^{-2} = \frac{1}{x^2}$.

Lesson 7-2 Dividing Monomials 411

Additional Example

5 **SAVINGS** Darin has \$123,456 in his savings account. Tabo has \$156 in his savings account. Determine the order of magnitude of Darin's account and Tabo's account. How many orders of magnitude as great is Darin's account as Tabo's account? Darin: 10^5, Tabo: 10^2; Darin's account is 3 orders of magnitude as great as Tabo's account.

3 PRACTICE

Formative Assessment

Use Exercise 1–18 to check for understanding.

Use the chart at the bottom of the next page to customize assignments for your students.

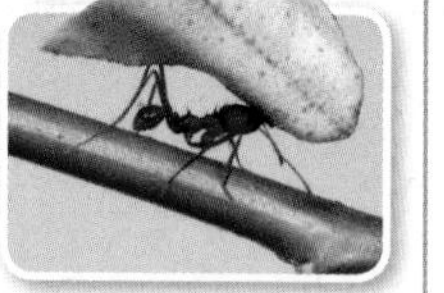

Real-World Link

There are over 14,000 species of ants living all over the world. Some ants can carry objects that are 50 times their own weight.

Source: Maine Animal Coalition

Real-World EXAMPLE 5 Apply Properties of Exponents

HEIGHT Suppose the average height of a man is about 1.7 meters, and the average height of an ant is 0.0008 meter. How many orders of magnitude as tall as an ant is a man?

Understand We must find the order of magnitude of the heights of the man and ant. Then find the ratio of the orders of magnitude of the man's height to that of the ant's height.

Plan Round each height to the nearest power of ten. Then find the ratio of the height of the man to the height of the ant.

Solve The average height of a man is close to 1 meter. So, the order of magnitude is 10^0 meter. The average height of an ant is about 0.001 meter. So, the order of magnitude is 10^{-3} meters.

The ratio of the height of a man to the height of an ant is about $\frac{10^0}{10^{-3}}$.

$\frac{10^0}{10^{-3}} = 10^{0-(-3)}$ **Quotient of Powers**

$= 10^3$ **$0-(-3) = 0+3$ or 3**

$= 1000$ **Simplify.**

So, a man is approximately 1000 times as tall as an ant, or a man is 3 orders of magnitude as tall as an ant.

Check The ratio of the man's height to the ant's height is $\frac{1.7}{0.0008} = 2125$. The order of magnitude of 2125 is 10^3. ✓

Check Your Progress

5. ASTRONOMY The order of magnitude of the mass of Earth is about 10^{27}. The order of magnitude of the Milky Way galaxy is about 10^{44}. How many orders of magnitude as big is the Milky Way galaxy as Earth? 17

Personal Tutor glencoe.com

Check Your Understanding

Examples 1–4 pp. 408–411

Simplify each expression. Assume that no denominator equals zero.

1. $\frac{t^5u^4}{t^2u}$ t^3u^3
2. $\frac{a^6b^4c^{10}}{a^3b^2c}$ $a^3b^2c^9$
3. $\frac{m^6r^5p^3}{m^5r^2p^3}$ mr^3
4. $\frac{b^4c^6f^8}{b^4c^3f^5}$ c^3f^3
5. $\frac{g^8h^2m}{hg^7}$ ghm
6. $\frac{r^4t^7v^2}{t^7v^2}$ r^4
7. $\frac{x^3y^2z^6}{z^5x^2y}$ xyz
8. $\frac{n^4q^4w^6}{q^2n^3w}$ nq^2w^5
9. $\left(\frac{2a^3b^5}{3}\right)^2$ $\frac{4a^6b^{10}}{9}$
10. $\frac{r^3v^{-2}}{t^{-7}}$ $\frac{r^3t^7}{v^2}$
11. $\left(\frac{2c^3d^5}{5g^2}\right)^5$ $\frac{32c^{15}d^{25}}{3125g^{10}}$
12. $\left(-\frac{3xy^4z^2}{x^3yz^4}\right)^0$ 1
13. $\left(\frac{3f^4gh^4}{32f^3g^4h}\right)^0$ 1
14. $\frac{4r^2v^0t^5}{2rt^3}$ $2rt^2$
15. $\frac{f^{-3}g^2}{h^{-4}}$ $\frac{g^2h^4}{f^3}$
16. $\frac{-8x^2y^8z^{-5}}{12x^4y^{-7}z^7}$ $\frac{-2y^{15}}{3x^2z^{12}}$
17. $\frac{2a^2b^{-7}c^{10}}{6a^{-3}b^2c^{-3}}$ $\frac{a^5c^{13}}{3b^9}$

Example 5 p. 412

18. **FINANCIAL LITERACY** The gross domestic product (GDP) for the United States in 2006 was \$13.06 trillion, and the GDP per person was \$43,800. Use order of magnitude to approximate the population of the United States in 2006. 10^8 or 100,000,000

Practice and Problem Solving

● = Step-by-Step Solutions begin on page R12.
Extra Practice begins on page 815.

Examples 1–4 pp. 408–411

Simplify each expression. Assume that no denominator equals zero.

19. $\frac{m^4p^2}{m^2p}$ m^2p
20. $\frac{p^{12}t^3r}{p^2tr}$ $p^{10}t^2$
21. $\frac{3m^{-3}r^4p^2}{12t^4}$ $\frac{r^4p^2}{4m^3t^4}$
22. $\frac{c^4d^4f^3}{c^2d^4f^3}$ c^2
23. $\left(\frac{3xy^4}{5z^2}\right)^2$ $\frac{9x^2y^8}{25z^4}$
24. $\left(\frac{3t^6u^2v^5}{9tuv^{21}}\right)^0$ 1
25. $\left(\frac{p^2t^7}{10}\right)^3$ $\frac{p^6t^{21}}{1000}$
26. $\frac{x^{-4}y^9}{z^{-2}}$ $\frac{y^9z^2}{x^4}$
27. $\frac{a^7b^8c^8}{a^5bc^7}$ a^2b^7c
28. $\left(\frac{3np^3}{7q^2}\right)^2$ $\frac{9n^2p^6}{49q^4}$
29. $\left(\frac{2r^3t^6}{5u^9}\right)^4$ $\frac{16r^{12}t^{24}}{625u^{36}}$
30. $\left(\frac{3m^5r^3}{4p^8}\right)^4$ $\frac{81m^{20}r^{12}}{256p^{32}}$
31. $\left(-\frac{5f^9g^4h^2}{fg^2h^3}\right)^0$ 1
32. $\frac{p^{12}t^7r^2}{p^2t^7r}$ $p^{10}r$
33. $\frac{p^4t^{-3}}{r^{-2}}$ $\frac{p^4r^2}{t^3}$
34. $-\frac{5c^2d^5}{8cd^5f^0}$ $-\frac{5c}{8}$
35. $\frac{-2f^3g^2h^0}{8f^2g^2}$ $\frac{-f}{4}$
36. $\frac{12m^{-4}p^2}{-15m^3p^{-9}}$ $\frac{4p^{11}}{-5m^7}$
37. $\frac{k^4m^3p^2}{k^2m^2}$ k^2mp^2
38. $\frac{14f^{-3}g^2h^{-7}}{21k^3}$ $\frac{2g^2}{3f^3h^7k^3}$
39. $\frac{39t^4uv^{-2}}{13t^{-3}u^7}$ $\frac{3t^7}{u^6v^2}$
40. $\left(\frac{a^{-2}b^4c^5}{a^{-4}b^{-4}c^3}\right)^2$ $a^4b^{16}c^4$
41. $\frac{r^3t^{-1}x^{-5}}{tx^5}$ $\frac{r^3}{t^2x^{10}}$
42. $\frac{g^0h^7j^{-2}}{g^{-5}h^0j^{-2}}$ g^5h^7

Example 5 p. 412

43. **INTERNET** In a recent year, there were approximately 3.95 million Internet hosts. Suppose there were 208 million Internet users. Determine the order of magnitude for the Internet hosts and Internet users. Using the orders of magnitude, how many Internet users were there compared to Internet hosts?

43. 10^6; 10^8; about 10^2 or 100 times as many users as hosts

B

44. **PROBABILITY** The probability of rolling a die and getting an even number is $\frac{1}{2}$. If you roll the die twice, the probability of getting an even number both times is $\left(\frac{1}{2}\right)\left(\frac{1}{2}\right)$ or $\left(\frac{1}{2}\right)^2$. Write an expression to represent the probability of rolling a die d times and getting an even number every time. Write the expression as a power of 2. $\left(\frac{1}{2}\right)^d$; 2^{-d}

Simplify each expression. Assume that no denominator equals zero.

45. $\frac{-4w^{12}}{12w^3}$ $-\frac{w^9}{3}$
46. $\frac{13r^7}{39r^4}$ $\frac{r^3}{3}$
47. $\frac{(4k^3m^2)^3}{(5k^2m^{-3})^{-2}}$ $1600k^{13}$
48. $\frac{3wy^{-2}}{(w^{-1}y)^3}$ $\frac{3w^4}{y^5}$
49. $\frac{20qr^{-2}t^{-5}}{4q^0r^4t^{-2}}$ $\frac{5q}{r^6t^3}$
50. $\frac{-12c^3d^0f^{-2}}{6c^5d^{-3}f^4}$ $\frac{-2d^3}{c^2f^6}$
51. $\frac{(2g^3h^{-2})^2}{(g^2h^0)^{-3}}$ $\frac{4g^{12}}{h^4}$
52. $\frac{(5pr^{-2})^{-2}}{(3p^{-1}r)^3}$ $\frac{pr}{675}$
53. $\left(\frac{-3x^{-6}y^{-1}z^{-2}}{6x^{-2}yz^{-5}}\right)^{-2}$ $\frac{4x^8y^4}{z^6}$
54. $\left(\frac{2a^{-2}b^4c^2}{-4a^{-2}b^{-5}c^{-7}}\right)^{-1}$ $\frac{-2}{b^9c^9}$
55. $\frac{(16x^2y^{-1})^0}{(4x^0y^{-4}z)^{-2}}$ $\frac{16z^2}{y^8}$
56. $\left(\frac{4^0c^2d^3f}{2c^{-4}d^{-5}}\right)^{-3}$ $\frac{8}{c^{18}d^{24}f^3}$

57. **COMPUTERS** In 1993, the processing speed of a desktop computer was about 10^8 instructions per second. By 2004, it had increased to 10^{10} instructions per second. The newer computer is how many times as fast as the older one? 100

Differentiated Homework Options

Level	Assignment	Two-Day Option	
AL Basic	19–43, 61–62, 64–89	19–43 odd, 66–69	20–42 even, 61–62, 64–65, 70–89
OL Core	19–43 odd, 44, 45–55 odd, 57–62, 64–89	19–43, 66–69	44–62, 64–65, 70–89
BL Advanced	44–81, (optional: 82–89)		

Real-World Career

Astronomer
An astronomer studies the universe and analyzes space travel and satellite communications. To be a technician or research assistant, a bachelor's degree is required.

58. ASTRONOMY The brightness of a star is measured in magnitudes. The lower the magnitude, the brighter the star. A magnitude 9 star is 2.51 times as bright as a magnitude 10 star. A magnitude 8 star is 2.51 • 2.51 or 2.51^2 times as bright as a magnitude 10 star.

a. How many times as bright is a magnitude 3 star as a magnitude 10 star? **2.51^7 or 627.647857**

b. Write an expression to compare a magnitude m star to a magnitude 10 star. **2.51^{10-m}**

c. Magnitudes can be measured in negative numbers. Does your expression hold true? Give an example or counterexample.

59. PROBABILITY The probability of rolling a die and getting a 3 is $\frac{1}{6}$. If you roll the die twice, the probability of getting a 3 both times is $\frac{1}{6} \cdot \frac{1}{6}$ or $\left(\frac{1}{6}\right)^2$.

a. Write an expression to represent the probability of rolling a die d times and getting a 3 each time. **$\left(\frac{1}{6}\right)^d$**

b. Write the expression as a power of 6. **6^{-d}**

C **60. MULTIPLE REPRESENTATIONS** To find the area of a circle, use $A = \pi r^2$. The formula for the area of a square is $A = s^2$.

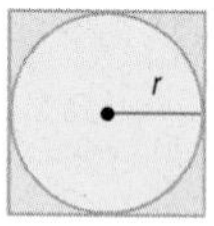

a. **ALGEBRAIC** Find the ratio of the area of the circle to the area of the square. **$\frac{\pi}{4}$**

b. **ALGEBRAIC** If the radius of the circle and the length of each side of the square are doubled, find the ratio of the area of the circle to the square. **$\frac{\pi}{4}$**

c. **TABULAR** Copy and complete the table.

Radius	Area of Circle	Area of Square	Ratio
r	πr^2	$4r^2$	$\frac{\pi}{4}$
$2r$	$\pi 4r^2$	$16r^2$	$\frac{\pi}{4}$
$3r$	$\pi 9r^2$	$36r^2$	$\frac{\pi}{4}$
$4r$	$\pi 16r^2$	$64r^2$	$\frac{\pi}{4}$
$5r$	$\pi 25r^2$	$100r^2$	$\frac{\pi}{4}$
$6r$	$\pi 36r^2$	$144r^2$	$\frac{\pi}{4}$

d. **ANALYTICAL** What conclusion can be drawn from this? **The ratio of the area of the circle to the area of the square will always be $\frac{\pi}{4}$.**

H.O.T. Problems
Use Higher-Order Thinking Skills

61. REASONING Is $x^y \cdot x^z = x^{yz}$ *sometimes, always,* or *never* true? Explain.

62. OPEN ENDED Name two monomials with a quotient of $24a^2b^3$.

63. CHALLENGE Use the Quotient of Powers Property to explain why $x^{-n} = \frac{1}{x^n}$.

64. REASONING Write a convincing argument to show why $3^0 = 1$ using the following pattern: $3^5 = 243$, $3^4 = 81$, $3^3 = 27$, $3^2 = 9$. **See margin.**

65. WRITING IN MATH Explain how to use the Quotient of Powers property and the Power of a Quotient property. **See margin.**

58c. Sample answer: No; if we measured a magnitude 12 star according to the formula, the magnitude would be $2.51^{10-12} = 2.51^{-2} = \frac{1}{2.51^2} = 0.1587$. There is no way to get a negative value for the expression.

61. Sometimes; sample answer: The equation is true when $x = 0$, $y = 2$, and $z = 3$, but it is false when $x = 1$, $y = 2$, and $z = 3$.

62. Sample answer: $24a^4b^6$ and a^2b^3

63. $\frac{1}{x^n} = \frac{x^0}{x^n} = x^{0-n} = x^{-n}$

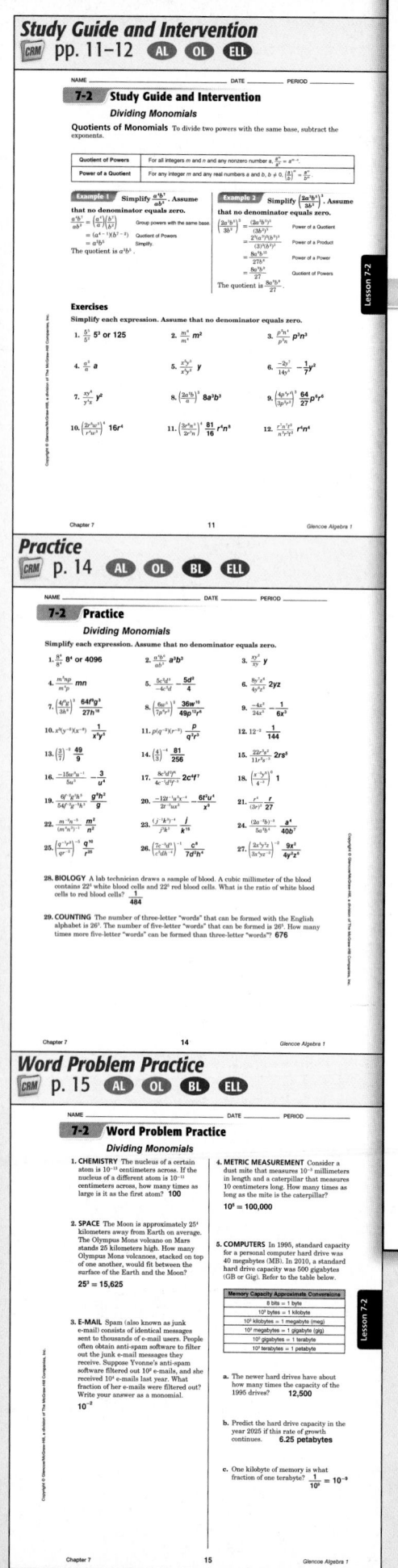

Study Guide and Intervention
CRM pp. 11–12 AL OL ELL

NAME ______ DATE ______ PERIOD ______

7-2 Study Guide and Intervention

Dividing Monomials

Quotients of Monomials To divide two powers with the same base, subtract the exponents.

Quotient of Powers	For all integers m and n and any nonzero number a, $\frac{a^m}{a^n} = a^{m-n}$.
Power of a Quotient	For any integer m and any real numbers a and b, $b \neq 0$, $\left(\frac{a}{b}\right)^m = \frac{a^m}{b^m}$.

Example 1 Simplify $\frac{a^4b^7}{ab^2}$. Assume that no denominator equals zero.

$\frac{a^4b^7}{ab^2} = \left(\frac{a^4}{a}\right)\left(\frac{b^7}{b^2}\right)$ Group powers with the same base.
$= (a^{4-1})(b^{7-2})$ Quotient of Powers
$= a^3b^5$ Simplify.
The quotient is a^3b^5.

Example 2 Simplify $\left(\frac{2a^3b^5}{3b^2}\right)^3$. Assume that no denominator equals zero.

$\left(\frac{2a^3b^5}{3b^2}\right)^3 = \frac{(2a^3b^5)^3}{(3b^2)^3}$ Power of a Quotient
$= \frac{2^3(a^3)^3(b^5)^3}{(3)^3(b^2)^3}$ Power of a Product
$= \frac{8a^9b^{15}}{27b^6}$ Power of a Power
$= \frac{8a^9b^9}{27}$ Quotient of Powers
The quotient is $\frac{8a^9b^9}{27}$.

Exercises

Simplify each expression. Assume that no denominator equals zero.

1. $\frac{5^5}{5^2}$ **5^3 or 125**
2. $\frac{m^6}{m^4}$ **m^2**
3. $\frac{p^5n^4}{p^2n}$ **p^3n^3**
4. $\frac{a^2}{a}$ **a**
5. $\frac{x^5y^3}{x^5y^2}$ **y**
6. $\frac{-2y^7}{14y^5}$ **$-\frac{1}{7}y^2$**
7. $\frac{xy^6}{y^4x}$ **y^2**
8. $\left(\frac{2a^2b}{a}\right)^3$ **$8a^3b^3$**
9. $\left(\frac{4p^4r^4}{3p^2r^2}\right)^3$ **$\frac{64}{27}p^6r^6$**
10. $\left(\frac{2r^5w^3}{r^4w^3}\right)^4$ **$16r^4$**
11. $\left(\frac{3r^6n^3}{2r^5n}\right)^4$ **$\frac{81}{16}r^4n^8$**
12. $\frac{r^7n^7t^2}{n^3r^3t^2}$ **r^4n^4**

Lesson 7-2

Chapter 7 11 Glencoe Algebra 1

Practice
CRM p. 14 AL OL BL ELL

NAME ______ DATE ______ PERIOD ______

7-2 Practice

Dividing Monomials

Simplify each expression. Assume that no denominator equals zero.

1. $\frac{8^8}{8^4}$ **8^4 or 4096**
2. $\frac{a^4b^6}{ab^3}$ **a^3b^3**
3. $\frac{xy^2}{xy}$ **y**
4. $\frac{m^5np}{m^4p}$ **mn**
5. $\frac{5c^2d^3}{-4c^2d}$ **$-\frac{5d^2}{4}$**
6. $\frac{8y^7z^6}{4y^6z^5}$ **$2yz$**
7. $\left(\frac{4f^3g}{3h^6}\right)^3$ **$\frac{64f^9g^3}{27h^{18}}$**
8. $\left(\frac{6w^5}{7p^6r^3}\right)^2$ **$\frac{36w^{10}}{49p^{12}r^6}$**
9. $\frac{-4x^2}{24x^5}$ **$-\frac{1}{6x^3}$**
10. $x^3(y^{-5})(x^{-8})$ **$\frac{1}{x^5y^5}$**
11. $p(q^{-2})(r^{-3})$ **$\frac{p}{q^2r^3}$**
12. 12^{-2} **$\frac{1}{144}$**
13. $\left(\frac{3}{7}\right)^{-2}$ **$\frac{49}{9}$**
14. $\left(\frac{4}{3}\right)^{-4}$ **$\frac{81}{256}$**
15. $\frac{22r^3s^2}{11r^2s^{-3}}$ **$2rs^5$**
16. $\frac{-15w^0u^{-1}}{5u^3}$ **$-\frac{3}{u^4}$**
17. $\frac{8c^3d^2f^4}{4c^{-1}d^2f^{-3}}$ **$2c^4f^7$**
18. $\left(\frac{x^{-3}y^5}{4^{-3}}\right)^0$ **1**
19. $\frac{6f^{-2}g^3h^5}{54f^{-2}g^{-5}h^3}$ **$\frac{g^8h^2}{g}$**
20. $\frac{-12t^{-1}u^5x^{-4}}{2t^{-3}ux^5}$ **$-\frac{6t^2u^4}{x^9}$**
21. $\frac{r^4}{(3r)^3}$ **$\frac{r}{27}$**
22. $\frac{m^{-2}n^{-5}}{(m^4n^3)^{-1}}$ **$\frac{m^2}{n^2}$**
23. $\frac{(j^{-1}k^3)^{-4}}{j^3k^3}$ **$\frac{j}{k^{15}}$**
24. $\frac{(2a^{-2}b)^{-3}}{5a^2b^4}$ **$\frac{a^4}{40b^7}$**
25. $\left(\frac{q^{-1}r^3}{qr^{-2}}\right)^{-5}$ **$\frac{q^{10}}{r^{25}}$**
26. $\left(\frac{7c^{-3}d^3}{c^5dh^{-4}}\right)^{-1}$ **$\frac{c^8}{7d^2h^4}$**
27. $\left(\frac{2x^3y^2z}{3x^4yz^{-2}}\right)^{-2}$ **$\frac{9x^2}{4y^2z^6}$**

28. **BIOLOGY** A lab technician draws a sample of blood. A cubic millimeter of the blood contains 22^3 white blood cells and 22^5 red blood cells. What is the ratio of white blood cells to red blood cells? **$\frac{1}{484}$**

29. **COUNTING** The number of three-letter "words" that can be formed with the English alphabet is 26^3. The number of five-letter "words" that can be formed is 26^5. How many times more five-letter "words" can be formed than three-letter "words"? **676**

Chapter 7 14 Glencoe Algebra 1

Word Problem Practice
CRM p. 15 AL OL BL ELL

NAME ______ DATE ______ PERIOD ______

7-2 Word Problem Practice

Dividing Monomials

1. **CHEMISTRY** The nucleus of a certain atom is 10^{-13} centimeters across. If the nucleus of a different atom is 10^{-11} centimeters across, how many times as large is it as the first atom? **100**

2. **SPACE** The Moon is approximately 25^4 kilometers away from Earth on average. The Olympus Mons volcano on Mars stands 25 kilometers high. How many Olympus Mons volcanoes, stacked on top of one another, would fit between the surface of the Earth and the Moon? **$25^3 = 15{,}625$**

3. **E-MAIL** Spam (also known as junk e-mail) consists of identical messages sent to thousands of e-mail users. People often obtain anti-spam software to filter out the junk e-mail messages they receive. Suppose Yvonne's anti-spam software filtered out 10^2 e-mails, and she received 10^4 e-mails last year. What fraction of her e-mails were filtered out? Write your answer as a monomial. **10^{-2}**

4. **METRIC MEASUREMENT** Consider a dust mite that measures 10^{-3} millimeters in length and a caterpillar that measures 10 centimeters long. How many times as long as the mite is the caterpillar? **$10^5 = 100{,}000$**

5. **COMPUTERS** In 1995, standard capacity for a personal computer hard drive was 40 megabytes (MB). In 2010, a standard hard drive capacity was 500 gigabytes (GB or Gig). Refer to the table below.

Memory Capacity Approximate Conversions
8 bits = 1 byte
10^3 bytes = 1 kilobyte
10^3 kilobytes = 1 megabyte (meg)
10^3 megabytes = 1 gigabyte (gig)
10^3 gigabytes = 1 terabyte
10^3 terabytes = 1 petabyte

a. The newer hard drives have about how many times the capacity of the 1995 drives? **12,500**

b. Predict the hard drive capacity in the year 2025 if this rate of growth continues. **6.25 petabytes**

c. One kilobyte of memory is what fraction of one terabyte? **$\frac{1}{10^9} = 10^{-9}$**

Lesson 7-2

Chapter 7 15 Glencoe Algebra 1

Enrichment
CRM p. 16 OL BL

NAME ______ DATE ______ PERIOD ______

7-2 Enrichment

Patterns with Powers

Use your calculator, if necessary, to complete each pattern.

a.		b.		c.	
2^{10} =	1024	5^{10} =	9,765,625	4^{10} =	1,048,576
2^9 =	512	5^9 =	1,953,125	4^9 =	262,144
2^8 =	256	5^8 =	390,625	4^8 =	65,536
2^7 =	128	5^7 =	78,125	4^7 =	16,384
2^6 =	64	5^6 =	15,625	4^6 =	4096
2^5 =	32	5^5 =	3125	4^5 =	1024
2^4 =	16	5^4 =	625	4^4 =	256
2^3 =	8	5^3 =	125	4^3 =	64
2^2 =	4	5^2 =	25	4^2 =	16
2^1 =	2	5^1 =	5	4^1 =	4

Study the patterns for a, b, and c above. Then answer the questions.

1. Describe the pattern of the exponents from the top of each column to the bottom. **The exponents decrease by one from each row to the one below.**

Multiple Representations In Exercise 60, students use a geometric sketch, algebraic formulas, and a table of values to analyze the relation between a square and an inscribed circle.

414 Chapter 7 Polynomials

PSAE PRACTICE 7.11.03, 6.11.17, 10.11.08, 6.11.04

66. GEOMETRY What is the perimeter of the figure in meters? B

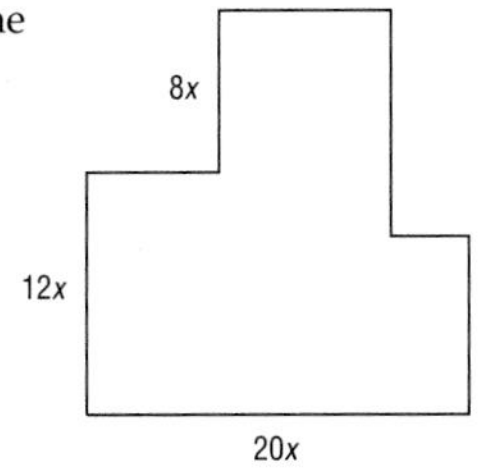

A $40x$

B $80x$

C $160x$

D $400x$

67. In researching her science project, Leigh learned that light travels at a constant rate and that it takes 500 seconds for light to travel the 93 million miles from the Sun to Earth. Mars is 142 million miles from the Sun. About how many seconds will it take for light to travel from the Sun to Mars? J

F 235 seconds

G 327 seconds

H 642 seconds

J 763 seconds

68. EXTENDED RESPONSE Jessie and Jonas are playing a game using the spinners below. Each spinner is equally likely to stop on any of the four numbers. In the game, a player spins both spinners and calculates the product of the two numbers on which the spinners have stopped.

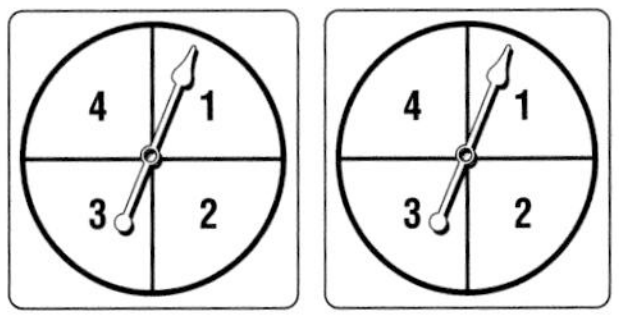

a. What product has the greatest probability of occurring? 4

b. What is the probability of that product occurring? $\frac{3}{16}$

69. Simplify $(4^{-2} \cdot 5^0 \cdot 64)^3$. B

A $\frac{1}{64}$ C 320

B 64 D 1024

Spiral Review

70. GEOLOGY The seismic waves of a magnitude 6 earthquake are 10^2 times as great as a magnitude 4 earthquake. The seismic waves of a magnitude 4 earthquake are 10 times as great as a magnitude 3 earthquake. How many times as great are the seismic waves of a magnitude 6 earthquake as those of a magnitude 3 earthquake? (Lesson 7-1) 10^3

Solve each system of inequalities by graphing. (Lesson 6-8) **71–74. See Ch. 7 Answer Appendix.**

71. $y \geq 1$, $x < -1$

72. $y \geq -3$, $y - x < 1$

73. $y < 3x + 2$, $y \geq -2x + 4$

74. $y - 2x < 2$, $y - 2x > 4$

Solve each inequality. Check your solution. (Lesson 5-3)

75. $5(2h - 6) > 4h$ $h > 5$

76. $22 \geq 4(b - 8) + 10$ $b \leq 11$

77. $5(u - 8) \leq 3(u + 10)$ $u \leq 35$

78. $8 + t \leq 3(t + 4) + 2$ $t \geq -3$

79. $9n + 3(1 - 6n) \leq 21$ $n \geq -2$

80. $-6(b + 5) > 3(b - 5)$ $b < -\frac{5}{3}$

81. GRADES In a high school science class, a test is worth three times as much as a quiz. What is the student's average grade? (Lesson 2-9) 87

Science Grades

Tests	Quizzes
85	82
92	75
	95

Skills Review

Evaluate each expression. (Lesson 1-1)

82. 9^2 81

83. 11^2 121

84. 10^6 1,000,000

85. 10^4 10,000

86. 3^5 243

87. 5^3 125

88. 12^3 1728

89. 4^6 4096

Exercise Alert

Grid Paper For Exercises 71–74, students will need grid paper.

4 ASSESS

Yesterday's News Ask students to write two ways in which the concepts of multiplying monomials helped them to understand dividing monomials.

Formative Assessment

Check for student understanding of Lessons 7-1 and 7-2.

CRM Quiz 1, p. 57

Additional Answers

64. Since each number is obtained by dividing the previous number by 3, $3^1 = 3$ and $3^0 = 1$.

65. The Quotient of Powers Property is used when dividing two powers with the same base. The exponents are subtracted. The Power of a Quotient Property is used to find the power of a quotient. You find the power of the numerator and the power of the denominator.

Differentiated Instruction OL BL

Extension Tell students that if you roll a color cube, the probability of getting red is $\frac{1}{2}$. If you throw the cube n times, the probability of getting red each time is $\left(\frac{1}{2}\right)^n$. Ask them to determine how many times the cube is rolled if the probability of getting red each time is $\frac{1}{512}$. $\frac{1}{512} = \left(\frac{1}{2}\right)^9$, $n = 9$, so 9 times

7-3 Lesson Notes

1 FOCUS

Vertical Alignment

Before Lesson 7-3
Find products and quotients of monomials.

Lesson 7-3
Express numbers in scientific notation.
Find products and quotients of numbers expressed in scientific notation.

After Lesson 7-3
Perform dimensional analysis with numbers in scientific notation.

2 TEACH

Scaffolding Questions

Have students read the *Why?* section of the lesson.

Ask:

- What would $20 million look like when written out? $20,000,000
- What would you have to multiply $2 by to get $20 million? 10,000,000
- How can you write 10,000,000 as a power of 10? 10^7
- What would you have to multiply 1.4 by to get 0.0000000014? 0.000000001
- How can you write 0.000000001 as a power of 10? 10^{-9}
- What is 2×10^7? $20,000,000 What is 1.4×10^{-9}? 0.0000000014

7-3 Scientific Notation

Then
You found products and quotients of monomials. (Lessons 7-1 and 7-2)

Now
- Express numbers in scientific notation.
- Find products and quotients of numbers expressed in scientific notation.

IL Learning Standards
7.A.4b Apply formulas in a wide variety of theoretical and practical real-world measurement applications involving perimeter, area, volume, angle, time, temperature, mass, speed, distance, density and monetary values.

New Vocabulary
scientific notation

IL Math Online
glencoe.com
- Extra Examples
- Personal Tutor
- Self-Check Quiz
- Homework Help

Why?

Space tourism is a multibillion dollar industry. For a price of $20 million, a civilian can travel on a rocket or shuttle and visit the International Space Station (ISS) for a week.

Scientific Notation Very large and very small numbers such as $20 million can be cumbersome to use in calculations. For this reason, numbers are often expressed in scientific notation. A number written in **scientific notation** is of the form $a \times 10^n$, where $1 \leq a < 10$ and n is an integer.

Key Concept Standard Form to Scientific Notation — For Your FOLDABLE

Step 1 Move the decimal point until it is to the right of the first nonzero digit. The result is a real number a.

Step 2 Note the number of places n and the direction that you moved the decimal point.

Step 3 If the decimal point is moved left, write the number as $a \times 10^n$. If the decimal point is moved right, write the number as $a \times 10^{-n}$.

Step 4 Remove the unnecessary zeros.

EXAMPLE 1 Standard Form to Scientific Notation

Express each number in scientific notation.

a. 201,000,000

Step 1 201,000,000 ⟶ 2.01000000 $a = 2.01000000$

Step 2 The decimal point moved 8 places to the left, so $n = 8$.

Step 3 $201,000,000 = 2.01000000 \times 10^8$

Step 4 2.01×10^8

b. 0.000051

Step 1 0.000051 ⟶ 00005.1 $a = 00005.1$

Step 2 The decimal point moved 5 places to the right, so $n = 5$.

Step 3 $0.000051 = 00005.1 \times 10^{-5}$

Step 4 5.1×10^{-5}

Check Your Progress

1A. 68,700,000,000 6.87×10^{10}

1B. 0.0000725 7.25×10^{-5}

Personal Tutor glencoe.com

Lesson 7-3 Resources

Resource	Approaching-Level	On-Level	Beyond-Level	English Learners
Teacher Edition	• Differentiated Instruction, p. 417	• Differentiated Instruction, p. 420	• Differentiated Instruction, p. 420	
Chapter Resource Masters	• Study Guide and Intervention, pp. 17–18 • Skills Practice, p. 19 • Practice, p. 20 • Word Problem Practice, p. 21	• Study Guide and Intervention, pp. 17–18 • Skills Practice, p. 19 • Practice, p. 20 • Word Problem Practice, p. 21 • Enrichment, p. 22	• Practice, p. 20 • Word Problem Practice, p. 21 • Enrichment, p. 22	• Study Guide and Intervention, pp. 17–18 • Skills Practice, p. 19 • Practice, p. 20
Transparencies	• 5-Minute Check Transparency 7-3	• 5-Minute Check Transparency 7-3	• 5-Minute Check Transparency 7-3	• 5-Minute Check Transparency 7-3
Other	• Study Notebook	• Study Notebook	• Study Notebook	• Study Notebook

Watch Out!

Negative Signs Be careful about the placement of negative signs. A negative sign in the exponent means that the number is between 0 and 1. A negative sign before the number means that it is less than 0.

You can also rewrite numbers in scientific notation in standard form.

Key Concept Scientific Notation to Standard Form — For Your FOLDABLE

Step 1 In $a \times 10^n$, note whether $n > 0$ or $n < 0$.

Step 2 If $n > 0$, move the decimal point n places right.
If $n < 0$, move the decimal point $-n$ places left.

Step 3 Insert zeros, decimal point, and commas as needed for place value.

EXAMPLE 2 Scientific Notation to Standard Form

Express each number in standard form.

a. 6.32×10^9

Step 1 The exponent is 9, so $n = 9$.

Step 2 Since $n > 0$, move the decimal point 9 places to the right.
$6.32 \times 10^9 \longrightarrow 6320000000$

Step 3 $6.32 \times 10^9 = 6{,}320{,}000{,}000$ **Rewrite; insert commas.**

b. 4×10^{-7}

Step 1 The exponent is -7, so $n = -7$.

Step 2 Since $n < 0$, move the decimal point 7 places to the left.
$4 \times 10^{-7} \longrightarrow 0000004$

Step 3 $4 \times 10^{-7} = 0.0000004$ **Rewrite; insert a 0 before the decimal point.**

Check Your Progress

2A. 3.201×10^6 **3,201,000**

2B. 9.03×10^{-5} **0.0000903**

Personal Tutor glencoe.com

Product and Quotients in Scientific Notation You can use scientific notation to simplify multiplying and dividing very large and very small numbers.

Problem-SolvingTip

Estimate Reasonable Answers Estimating an answer before computing the solution can help you determine if your answer is reasonable.

EXAMPLE 3 Multiply with Scientific Notation

Evaluate $(3.5 \times 10^{-3})(7 \times 10^5)$. Express the result in both scientific notation and standard form.

$(3.5 \times 10^{-3})(7 \times 10^5)$	Original expression
$= (3.5 \times 7)(10^{-3} \times 10^5)$	Commutative and Associative Properties
$= 24.5 \times 10^2$	Product of Powers
$= (2.45 \times 10^1) \times 10^2$	$24.5 = 2.45 \times 10$
$= 2.45 \times 10^3$	Product of Powers
$= 2450$	Standard form

Check Your Progress

Evaluate each product. Express the results in both scientific notation and standard form. **3A–3B. See margin.**

3A. $(6.5 \times 10^{12})(8.7 \times 10^{-15})$

3B. $(1.95 \times 10^{-8})(7.8 \times 10^{-2})$

Personal Tutor glencoe.com

Scientific Notation

Example 1 shows how to express a very large and a very small number in scientific notation. **Example 2** shows how to express a number written in scientific notation in standard form.

Formative Assessment

Use the Check Your Progress exercises after each Example to determine students' understanding of concepts.

Additional Examples

1 Express each number in scientific notation.

a. 4,062,000,000,000 4.062×10^{12}

b. 0.000000823 8.23×10^{-7}

2 Express each number in standard form.

a. 6.49×10^5 649,000

b. 1.8×10^{-3} 0.0018

Additional Examples also in Interactive Classroom PowerPoint® Presentations

IWB INTERACTIVE WHITEBOARD READY

Products and Quotients in Scientific Notation

Example 3 shows how to multiply with scientific notation. **Example 4** shows how to divide with scientific notation. **Example 5** shows how to solve a real-world problem using scientific notation.

Additional Example

3 Evaluate $(5 \times 10^{-6})(2.3 \times 10^{12})$. Express the result in both scientific notation and standard form. 1.15×10^7; 11,500,000

Differentiated Instruction AL

If students have trouble keeping track of a moving decimal point,

Then have students write each digit in the number 201,000,000, for example, on an index card. Using an object such as a paper clip or penny as the decimal point, students can actually move the decimal point and count the number of places it moved. Repeat using other numbers from the examples, such as 0.000051.

Additional Answers (Check Your Progress)

3A. 5.655×10^{-2}; 0.05655

3B. 1.521×10^{-9}; 0.000000001521

Additional Examples

4 Evaluate $\frac{4.5 \times 10^8}{1.5 \times 10^{10}}$. Express the result in both scientific notation and standard form. 3×10^{-2}; 0.03

5 **WATERCRAFT** Last year Afyu's state registered over 400 thousand watercraft. Boat sales in her state generated more than \$15.4 million in state sales taxes that same year.

a. Express the number of watercraft registered and the state sales tax generated from boat sales last year in Afyu's state in standard notation. Watercraft registered: 400,000; state sales tax generated: \$15,400,000

b. Write each number in scientific notation. 4×10^5; 1.54×10^7

c. How many watercraft have been registered in Afyu's state if 12 times the number registered last year have been registered in all? Write your answer in scientific notation and standard form. 4,800,000; 4.8×10^6

Tips for New Teachers

E Notation On some calculators, the powers of 10 are written using E notation. For example, 3×10^{-6}, would be displayed as **3 E −6.** The E means *times 10 to the given power.*

TEACH with TECH

INTERACTIVE WHITEBOARD Write a number not in scientific notation on the board. Grab the decimal point and drag it to the left or right as you count the number of places you have moved it.

StudyTip

Quotient of Powers Recall that the Quotient of Powers Property is only valid for powers that have the same base. Since 10^8 and 10^3 have the same base, the property applies.

EXAMPLE 4 Divide with Scientific Notation

Evaluate $\frac{3.066 \times 10^8}{7.3 \times 10^3}$. Express the result in both scientific notation and standard form.

$$\begin{aligned} \frac{3.066 \times 10^8}{7.3 \times 10^3} &= \left(\frac{3.066}{7.3}\right)\left(\frac{10^8}{10^3}\right) && \text{Product rule for fractions} \\ &= 0.42 \times 10^5 && \text{Quotient of Powers} \\ &= 4.2 \times 10^{-1} \times 10^5 && 0.42 = 4.2 \times 10^{-1} \\ &= 4.2 \times 10^4 && \text{Product of Powers} \\ &= 42{,}000 && \text{Standard form} \end{aligned}$$

Check Your Progress

Evaluate each quotient. Express the results in both scientific notation and standard form.

4A. $\frac{2.3958 \times 10^3}{1.98 \times 10^8}$ 1.21×10^{-5}; 0.0000121 **4B.** $\frac{1.305 \times 10^3}{1.45 \times 10^{-4}}$ 9×10^6; 9,000,000

Personal Tutor glencoe.com

Real-World Link

The platinum award was created in 1976. In 2004, the criteria for the award was extended to digital sales. The top-selling artist of all time is the Beatles with 170 million units sold.

Source: Recording Industry Association of America

Real-World EXAMPLE 5 Use Scientific Notation

MUSIC In the United States, a CD reaches gold status once 500 thousand copies are sold. A CD reaches platinum status once 1 million or more copies are sold.

a. Express the number of copies of CDs that need to be sold to reach each status in standard notation.

gold status: 500 thousand = 500,000; platinum status: 1 million = 1,000,000

b. Write each number in scientific notation.

gold status: $500{,}000 = 5 \times 10^5$; platinum status: $1{,}000{,}000 = 1 \times 10^6$

c. How many copies of a CD have sold if it has gone platinum 13 times? Write your answer in scientific notation and standard form.

A CD reaches platinum status once it sells 1 million records. Since the CD has gone platinum 13 times, we need to multiply by 13.

$$\begin{aligned} &(13)(1 \times 10^6) && \text{Original expression} \\ &= (13 \times 1)(10^6) && \text{Associative Property} \\ &= 13 \times 10^6 && 13 \times 1 = 13 \\ &= (1.3 \times 10^1) \times 10^6 && 13 = 1.3 \times 10 \\ &= 1.3 \times 10^7 && \text{Product of Powers} \\ &= 13{,}000{,}000 && \text{Standard form} \end{aligned}$$

Check Your Progress

5. SATELLITE RADIO Suppose a satellite radio company earned \$125.4 million in one year.

A. Write this number in standard form. 125,400,000

B. Write this number in scientific notation. 1.254×10^8

C. If the following year the company earned 2.5 times the amount earned the previous year, determine the amount earned. Write your answer in scientific notation and standard form. 3.135×10^8; 313,500,000

Personal Tutor glencoe.com

Focus on Mathematical Content

Multiplying and Dividing with Scientific Notation If students think of numbers in scientific notation as monomials, then the procedures for multiplying and dividing are the same. For example, think of $(3 \times 10^{-2})(1.2 \times 10^5)$ as $(3x^{-2})(1.2x^5)$. In this case, you first multiply the constants and then the powers with the same bases. Similarly, with scientific notation, you multiply the constants, then the powers of 10.

Check Your Understanding

Example 1 p. 416

Express each number in scientific notation.

1. 185,000,000 **1.85×10^8**
2. 1,902,500,000 **1.9025×10^9**
3. 0.000564 **5.64×10^{-4}**
4. 0.00000804 **8.04×10^{-6}**

MONEY **Express each number in scientific notation.**

5. Teenagers spend $13 billion annually on clothing. **1.3×10^{10}**
6. Teenagers have an influence on their families' spending habit. They control about $1.5 billion of discretionary income. **1.5×10^9**

Example 2 p. 417

Express each number in standard form.

7. 1.98×10^7 **19,800,000**
8. 4.052×10^6 **4,052,000**
9. 3.405×10^{-8} **0.00000003405**
10. 6.8×10^{-5} **0.000068**

Example 3 p. 417

Evaluate each product. Express the results in both scientific notation and standard form. **11–14. See margin.**

11. $(1.2 \times 10^3)(1.45 \times 10^{12})$
12. $(7.08 \times 10^{14})(5 \times 10^{-9})$
13. $(5.18 \times 10^2)(9.1 \times 10^{-5})$
14. $(2.9 \times 10^{-2})(5.2 \times 10^{-9})$

Example 4 p. 418

Evaluate each quotient. Express the results in both scientific notation and standard form. **15–18. See margin.**

15. $\dfrac{1.035 \times 10^8}{2.3 \times 10^4}$
16. $\dfrac{2.542 \times 10^5}{4.1 \times 10^{-10}}$
17. $\dfrac{1.445 \times 10^{-7}}{1.7 \times 10^5}$
18. $\dfrac{2.05 \times 10^{-8}}{4 \times 10^{-2}}$

Example 5 p. 418

19. **AIR FILTERS** Salvador bought an air purifier to help him deal with his allergies. The filter in the purifier will stop particles as small as one hundredth of a micron. A micron is one millionth of a millimeter.
    a. Write one hundredth and one micron in standard form. **0.01, 0.000001**
    b. Write one hundredth and one micron in scientific notation. **1×10^{-2}, 1×10^{-6}**
    c. What is the smallest size particle in meters that the filter will stop? Write the result in both standard form and scientific notation. **0.00000000001; 1×10^{-11}**

Practice and Problem Solving

● = **Step-by-Step Solutions** begin on page R12. **Extra Practice** begins on page 815.

Example 1 p. 416

Express each number in scientific notation.

20. 1,220,000 **1.22×10^6**
21. 58,600,000 **5.86×10^7**
22. 1,405,000,000,000
23. 0.0000013 **1.3×10^{-6}**
24. 0.000056 **5.6×10^{-5}**
25. 0.000000000709

E-MAIL **Express each number in scientific notation.**

26. Approximately 100 million e-mails sent to the President are put into the National Archives. **1×10^8**
27. By 2010, the e-mail security market will generate $5.5 billion. **$5.5 \times 10^9$**

Example 2 p. 417

Express each number in standard form.

28. 1×10^{12}
29. 9.4×10^7
30. 8.1×10^{-3}
31. 5×10^{-4}
32. 8.73×10^{11}
33. 6.22×10^{-6}

22. 1.405×10^{12}
25. 7.09×10^{-10}
28. 1,000,000,000,000
29. 94,000,000
30. 0.0081
31. 0.0005
32. 873,000,000,000
33. 0.00000622

Tips for New Teachers

Sense-Making Students may have encountered the use of scientific notation in their science classes, where they rounded numbers to two decimal places when converting from standard to scientific notation. Make sure that students do not automatically round numbers to two decimal places when they convert to scientific notation in this lesson.

3 PRACTICE

Formative Assessment

Use Exercises 1–19 to check for understanding.

Use the chart at the bottom of this page to customize assignments for your students.

Additional Answers

11. 1.74×10^{15}; 1,740,000,000,000,000
12. 3.54×10^6; 3,540,000
13. 4.7138×10^{-2}; 0.047138
14. 1.508×10^{-10}; 0.0000000001508
15. 4.5×10^3; 4,500
16. 6.2×10^{14}; 620,000,000,000,000
17. 8.5×10^{-13}; 0.00000000000085
18. 5.125×10^{-7}; 0.0000005215

Differentiated Homework Options

Level	Assignment	Two-Day Option	
AL Basic	20–54, 70–71, 73–98	21–53 odd, 76–79	20–54 even, 70–71, 73–75, 80–98
OL Core	21–61 odd, 63–71, 73–98	20–54, 76–79	55–71, 73–75, 80–98
BL Advanced	55–92, (optional: 93–98)		

Lesson 7-3 Scientific Notation **419**

Exercise Alert

Change in Units For Exercises 63–66, students are given the speed of light in meters per second but are asked to find results in kilometers per second.

Watch Out!

Find the Error For Exercise 71, help students see that everything is the same in the two methods except the exponent in the power of 10 in the last line. Ask students if the decimal point was moved to the left or right, and how the direction affects the exponent of the power of 10.

Additional Answers

65.

Time	Kilometers Traveled
1 day	2.592×10^{10}
1 week	1.8144×10^{11}
1 month	7.776×10^{11}
1 year	9.4608×10^{12}

75. Sample answer: Divide the numbers to the left of the × symbols. Then divide the powers of 10. If necessary, rewrite the results in scientific notation. To convert that to standard form, check to see if the exponent is positive or negative. If positive, move the decimal point to the right, and if negative, to the left. The number of places to move the decimal point is the absolute value of the exponent. Fill in with zeros as needed.

Example 2 p. 417

INTERNET **Express each number in standard form.**

34. About 2.1×10^7 people, aged 12 to 17, use the Internet. **21,000,000**

35. Approximately 1.1×10^7 teens go online daily. **11,000,000**

Examples 3 and 4 pp. 417–418

Evaluate each product or quotient. Express the results in both scientific notation and standard form.

36. $(3.807 \times 10^3)(5 \times 10^2)$ **1.9035×10^6; 1,903,500**

37. $\frac{9.6 \times 10^3}{1.2 \times 10^{-4}}$ **8×10^7; 80,000,000**

38. $\frac{2.88 \times 10^3}{1.2 \times 10^{-5}}$ **2.4×10^8; 240,000,000**

39. $(6.5 \times 10^7)(7.2 \times 10^{-2})$ **4.68×10^6; 4,680,000**

40. $(9.5 \times 10^{-18})(9 \times 10^9)$ **8.55×10^{-8}; 0.0000000855**

41. $\frac{8.8 \times 10^3}{4 \times 10^{-4}}$ **2.2×10^7; 22,000,000**

42. $\frac{9.15 \times 10^{-3}}{6.1 \times 10}$ **1.5×10^{-4}; 0.00015**

43. $(2.01 \times 10^{-4})(8.9 \times 10^{-3})$ **1.7889×10^{-6}; 0.0000017889**

44. $(2.58 \times 10^2)(3.6 \times 10^6)$ **9.288×10^8; 928,800,000**

45. $\frac{5.6498 \times 10^{10}}{8.2 \times 10^4}$ **6.89×10^5; 689,000**

46. $\frac{1.363 \times 10^{16}}{2.9 \times 10^6}$ **4.7×10^9; 4,700,000,000**

47. $(9.04 \times 10^6)(5.2 \times 10^{-4})$ **4.7008×10^3; 4700.8**

48. $(1.6 \times 10^{-5})(2.3 \times 10^{-3})$ **3.68×10^{-8}; 0.0000000368**

49. $\frac{6.25 \times 10^{-4}}{1.25 \times 10^2}$ **5×10^{-6}; 0.000005**

50. $\frac{3.75 \times 10^{-9}}{1.5 \times 10^{-4}}$ **2.5×10^{-5}; 0.000025**

51. $(3.4 \times 10^4)(7.2 \times 10^{-15})$ **2.448×10^{-10}; 0.0000000002448**

52. $\frac{8.6 \times 10^4}{2 \times 10^{-6}}$ **4.3×10^{10}; 43,000,000,000**

53. $(6.3 \times 10^{-2})(3.5 \times 10^{-4})$ **2.205×10^{-5}; 0.00002205**

Example 5 p. 418

54. ASTRONOMY The distance between Earth and the Sun varies throughout the year. Earth is closest to the Sun in January when the distance is 91.4 million miles. In July, the distance is greatest at 94.4 million miles. **a. 91,400,000; 9.14×10^7**

a. Write 91.4 million in both standard form and in scientific notation.

b. Write 94.4 million in both standard form and in scientific notation.

c. What is the percent increase in distance from January to July? Round to the nearest tenth of a percent. **3.3%** **b. 94,400,000; 9.44×10^7**

Real-World Link

The distance from Earth to the Sun does not determine the seasons. The seasons are determined by the tilt of the Earth's axis and the elliptical orbit around the Sun.

Source: University of British Columbia Okanagan

63. 3×10^5
64. 1.08×10^9

B **Evaluate each product or quotient. Express the results in both scientific notation and standard form.**

55. $(4.65 \times 10^{-2})(5 \times 10^6)$ **2.325×10^5; 232,500**

56. $\frac{2.548 \times 10^5}{2.8 \times 10^{-2}}$ **9.1×10^6; 9,100,000**

57. $\frac{2.135 \times 10^5}{3.5 \times 10^{12}}$ **6.1×10^{-8}; 0.000000061**

58. $(4.8 \times 10^5)(3.16 \times 10^{-5})$ **1.5168×10; 15.168**

59. $(4.3 \times 10^{-3})(4.5 \times 10^4)$ **1.935×10^2; 193.5**

60. $\frac{5.184 \times 10^{-5}}{7.2 \times 10^3}$ **7.2×10^{-9}; 0.0000000072**

61. $(5 \times 10^3)(1.8 \times 10^{-7})$ **9×10^{-4}; 0.0009**

62. $\frac{1.032 \times 10^{-4}}{8.6 \times 10^{-5}}$ **1.2×10^0; 1.2**

LIGHT **The speed of light is approximately 3×10^8 meters per second.**

63. Write an expression to represent the speed of light in kilometers per second.

64. Write an expression to represent the speed of light in kilometers per hour.

65. Make a table to show how many kilometers light travels in a day, a week, a 30-day month, and a 365-day year. Express your results in scientific notation. **See margin.**

66. The distance from Earth to the Moon is approximately 3.844×10^5 kilometers. How long would it take light to travel from Earth to the Moon? **≈1.2813 seconds**

Differentiated Instruction

OL BL

Extension Write the expression $0.00042 \times 316{,}000{,}000$ on the board. Ask students to write this expression using scientific notation. Then have students evaluate the product.
$4.2 \times 10^{-4} \times 3.16 \times 10^8$; 132,720

420 Chapter 7 Polynomials

Real-World Link

The longest river on Earth is the Nile River in Africa. It is 4,160 miles long, beginning in Burundi to its mouth at the Mediterranean Sea. The Nile River basin covers an area of 1.293×10^6 square miles.

Source: *Encarta Encyclopedia*

67. **EARTH** The population of Earth is about 6.623×10^9. The land surface of Earth is 1.483×10^8 square kilometers. What is the population density for the land surface area of Earth? **about 44.7 persons/km^2**

68. **RIVERS** A drainage basin separated from adjacent basins by a ridge, hill, or mountain is known as a watershed. The watershed of the Amazon River is 2,300,000 square miles. The watershed of the Mississippi River is 1,200,000 square miles.

   a. Write each of these numbers in scientific notation. **2.3×10^6; 1.2×10^6**

   b. How many times as large is the Amazon River watershed as the Mississippi River watershed? **about 1.9 times as large**

69. **AGRICULTURE** In a recent year, farmers planted approximately 92.9 million acres of corn. They also planted 64.1 million acres of soybeans and 11.1 million acres of cotton. **a. corn: 9.29×10^7, 92,900,000; soybeans: 6.41×10^7, 64,100,000; cotton: 1.11×10^7, 11,100,000**

   a. Write each of these numbers in scientific notation and in standard form.

   b. How many times as much corn was planted as soybeans? Write your results in standard form and in scientific notation. Round your answer to four decimal places. **about 1.4493×10^0; 1.4493**

   c. How many times as much corn was planted as cotton? Write your results in standard form and in scientific notation. Round your answer to four decimal places. **about 8.3694×10^0; 8.3694**

H.O.T. Problems Use Higher-Order Thinking Skills

70. **REASONING** Which is greater, 100^{10} or 10^{100}? Explain your reasoning.

71. **FIND THE ERROR** Syreeta and Pete are solving a division problem with scientific notation. Is either of them correct? Explain your reasoning.

Syreeta

$$\frac{3.65 \times 10^{-12}}{5 \times 10^{5}} = 0.73 \times 10^{-17}$$
$$= 7.3 \times 10^{-16}$$

Pete

$$\frac{3.65 \times 10^{-12}}{5 \times 10^{5}} = 0.73 \times 10^{-17}$$
$$= 7.3 \times 10^{-18}$$

72. **CHALLENGE** Order these numbers from least to greatest without converting them to standard form. -4.65×10^5, -5.64×10^4, 4.56×10^{-4}, 5.46×10^{-3}, 6.54×10^3

   5.46×10^{-3}, 6.54×10^3, 4.56×10^{-4}, -5.64×10^4, -4.65×10^5

73. **REASONING** Determine whether the statement is *always*, *sometimes*, or *never* true. Give examples or a counterexample to verify your reasoning.

   When multiplying two numbers written in scientific notation, the resulting number can have no more than two digits to the left of the decimal point.

74. **OPEN ENDED** Write two numbers in scientific notation with a product of 1.3×10^{-3}. Then name two numbers in scientific notation with a quotient of 1.3×10^{-3}.

75. **WRITING IN MATH** Write the steps that you would use to divide two numbers written in scientific notation. Then describe how you would write the results in standard form. **See margin.**

70. $100^{10} = (10^2)^{10}$ or 10^{20} and $10^{100} > 10^{20}$, so $10^{100} > 100^{10}$

71. Pete; Syreeta moved the decimal point in the wrong direction.

73. Sample answer: Always; if the numbers are $a \times 10^m$ and $b \times 10^n$ in scientific notation, then $1 \le a < 10$ and $1 \le b < 10$. So $1 \le ab < 100$.

74. Sample answer: product: 2.5×10^5, 5.2×10^{-9}; quotient: 2.6×10^3, 2×10^6

Study Guide and Intervention

CRM pp. 17–18 AL OL ELL

NAME ______ DATE ______ PERIOD ______

7-3 Study Guide and Intervention

Scientific Notation

Scientific Notation Very large and very small numbers are often best represented using a method known as **scientific notation**. Numbers written in scientific notation take the form $a \times 10^n$, where $1 \le a < 10$ and n is an integer. Any number can be written in scientific notation.

Example 1 **Express 34,020,000,000 in scientific notation.**

Step 1 Move the decimal point until it is to the right of the first nonzero digit. The result is a real number a. Here, $a = 3.402$.

Step 2 Note the number of places n and the direction that you moved the decimal point. The decimal point moved 10 places to the left, so $n = 10$.

Step 3 Because the decimal moved to the left, write the number as $a \times 10^n$.
$34{,}020{,}000{,}000 = 3.4020000000 \times 10^{10}$

Step 4 Remove the extra zeros. 3.402×10^{10}

Example 2 **Express 4.11×10^{-6} in standard notation.**

Step 1 The exponent is –6, so $n = -6$.

Step 2 Because $n < 0$, move the decimal point 6 places to the left.
$4.11 \times 10^{-6} \Rightarrow .00000411$

Step 3 $4.11 \times 10^{-6} \Rightarrow 0.00000411$
Rewrite; insert a 0 before the decimal point.

Exercises

Express each number in scientific notation.

1. 5,100,000 **5.1×10^6**
2. 80,300,000,000 **8.03×10^{10}**
3. 14,250,000 **1.425×10^7**
4. 68,070,000,000,000 **6.807×10^{13}**
5. 14,000 **1.4×10^4**
6. 901,050,000,000 **9.0105×10^{11}**
7. 0.0049 **4.9×10^{-3}**
8. 0.000301 **3.01×10^{-4}**
9. 0.0000000519 **5.19×10^{-8}**
10. 0.000000185 **1.85×10^{-7}**
11. 0.002002 **2.002×10^{-3}**
12. 0.00000771 **7.71×10^{-6}**

Express each number in standard form.

13. 4.91×10^4 **49,100**
14. 3.2×10^{-5} **0.000032**
15. 6.03×10^8 **603,000,000**
16. 2.001×10^{-6} **0.000002001**
15. 1.00024×10^{10} **10,002,400,000**
18. 5×10^5 **500,000**
19. 9.09×10^{-5} **0.0000909**
20. 3.5×10^{-2} **0.035**
21. 1.7087×10^7 **17,087,000**

Lesson 7-3

Chapter 7 17 Glencoe Algebra 1

Practice

CRM p. 20 AL OL BL ELL

NAME ______ DATE ______ PERIOD ______

7-3 Practice

Scientific Notation

Express each number in scientific notation.

1. 1,900,000 **1.9×10^6**
2. 0.000704 **7.04×10^{-4}**
3. 50,040,000,000 **5.004×10^{10}**
4. 0.0000000661 **6.61×10^{-8}**

Express each number in standard form.

5. 5.3×10^7 **53,000,000**
6. 1.09×10^{-4} **0.000109**
7. 9.13×10^3 **9130**
8. 7.902×10^{-6} **0.000007902**

Evaluate each product. Express the results in both scientific notation and standard form.

9. $(4.8 \times 10^4)(6 \times 10^6)$ **2.88×10^{11}; 288,000,000,000**
10. $(7.5 \times 10^{-5})(3.2 \times 10^7)$ **2.4×10^3; 2400**
11. $(2.06 \times 10^4)(5.5 \times 10^{-9})$ **1.133×10^{-4}; 0.0001133**
12. $(8.1 \times 10^{-6})(1.96 \times 10^{11})$ **1.5876×10^6; 1,587,600**
13. $(5.29 \times 10^8)(9.7 \times 10^4)$ **5.1313×10^{13}; 51,313,000,000,000**
14. $(1.45 \times 10^{-6})(7.2 \times 10^{-5})$ **1.044×10^{-10}; 0.0000000001044**

Evaluate each quotient. Express the results in both scientific notation and standard form.

15. $\frac{(4.2 \times 10^5)}{(3 \times 10^{-3})}$ **1.4×10^8; 140,000,000**
16. $\frac{(1.76 \times 10^{-11})}{(2.2 \times 10^{-5})}$ **8×10^{-7}; 0.0000008**
17. $\frac{(7.05 \times 10^{12})}{(9.4 \times 10^7)}$ **7.5×10^4; 75,000**
18. $\frac{(2.04 \times 10^{-4})}{(3.4 \times 10^5)}$ **6×10^{-10}; 0.0000000006**

19. **GRAVITATION** Issac Newton's theory of universal gravitation states that the equation $F = G\frac{m_1 m_2}{r^2}$ can be used to calculate the amount of gravitational force in newtons between two point masses m_1 and m_2 separated by a distance r. G is a constant equal to 6.67×10^{-11} N m^2 kg^{-2}. The mass of the earth m_1 is equal to 5.97×10^{24} kg, the mass of the moon m_2 is equal to 7.36×10^{22} kg, and the distance r between the two is 384,000,000 m.

   a. Express the distance r in scientific notation. **3.84×10^8 m**

   b. Compute the amount of gravitational force between the earth and the moon. Express your answer in scientific notation. **1.99×10^{20} newtons**

Chapter 7 20 Glencoe Algebra 1

Word Problem Practice

CRM p. 21 AL OL BL ELL

NAME ______ DATE ______ PERIOD ______

7-3 Word Problem Practice

Scientific Notation

1. **PLANETS** Neptune's mean distance from the sun is 4,500,000,000 kilometers. Uranus' mean distance from the sun is 2,870,000,000 kilometers. Express these distances in scientific notation. **Neptune: 4.5×10^9 km; Uranus: 2.87×10^9 km**

2. **PATHOLOGY** The common cold is caused by the rhinovirus, which commonly measures 2×10^{-8} m in diameter. The E. coli bacterium, which causes food poisoning, commonly measures 3×10^{-6} m in length. Express these measurements in standard form. **Rhinovirus: 0.00000002 m; E. coli: 0.000003 m**

3. **COMMERCIALS** A 30-second commercial aired during the 2007 Super Bowl cost $2,600,000. A 30-second commercial aired during the 1967 Super Bowl cost $40,000. Express these values in scientific notation. How many times more expensive was it to air an advertisement during the 2007 Super Bowl than the 1967 Super Bowl? **2007 Super Bowl: $\$2.6 \times 10^6$; 1967 Super Bowl: $\$4 \times 10^4$; 6.5×10^1 or 65 times more expensive**

4. **AVOGADRO'S NUMBER** Avogadro's number is an important concept in chemistry. It states that the number 6.022×10^{23} is approximately equal to the number of molecules in 12 grams of carbon 12. Use Avogadro's number to determine the number of molecules in 5×10^{-7} grams of carbon 12. **2.509×10^{16} molecules**

5. **COAL RESERVES** The table below shows the number of kilograms of coal select countries had in proven reserve at the end of 2006.

Coal Reserves, 2006	
Country	Coal (kg)
United States	2.46×10^{14}
Russia	1.57×10^{14}
India	9.24×10^{13}
Romania	4.94×10^{11}

Source: British Petroleum

   a. Express each country's coal reserves in standard form. **United States: 246,000,000,000,000 kg; Russia: 157,000,000,000,000 kg; India: 92,400,000,000,000 kg; Romania: 494,000,000,000 kg**

   b. How many times more coal does the United States have than Romania? **4.98×10^2 or 498 times**

   c. One kilogram of coal has an energy density of 2.4×10^7 joules. What is the total energy density of the United States' coal reserve? Express your answer in scientific notation. **5.90×10^{21} joules**

Lesson 7-3

Chapter 7 21 Glencoe Algebra 1

Enrichment

CRM p. 22 OL BL

NAME ______ DATE ______ PERIOD ______

7-3 Enrichment

Engineering Notation

Engineering notation is a variation on scientific notation where numbers are expressed as powers of 1000 rather than as powers of 10. Engineering notation takes the familiar form of $a \times 10^n$, but n is restricted to multiples of three and $1 \le |a| < 1000$.

One advantage to engineering notation is that numbers can be neatly expressed using SI prefixes. These prefixes are typically used for scientific measurements.

1000^n	10^n	SI Prefix	Symbol
1000^5	10^{15}	peta	P
1000^4	10^{12}	tera	T
1000^3	10^9	giga	G
1000^2	10^6	mega	M
1000^1	10^3	kilo	k
1000^{-1}	10^{-3}	milli	m
1000^{-2}	10^{-6}	micro	μ
1000^{-3}	10^{-9}	nano	n
1000^{-4}	10^{-12}	pico	p
1000^{-5}	10^{-15}	femto	f

Example NUCLEAR POWER **The output of a nuclear power plant is measured to be 620,000,000 watts. Express this number in engineering notation and using SI prefixes.**

...express ... number in engineering ...tion, first conv... the number to scientific notation.

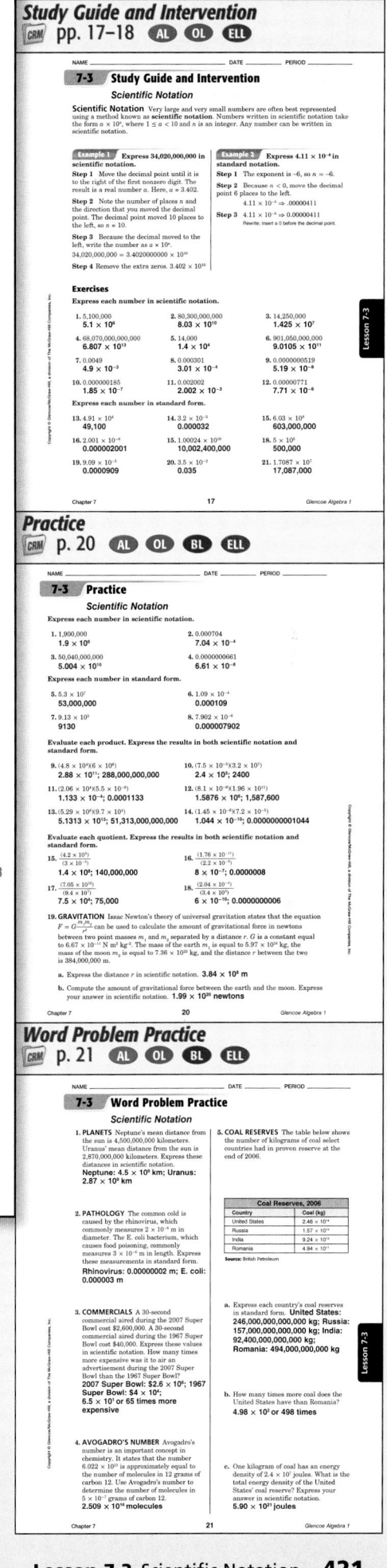

4 ASSESS

Name the Math Ask students to describe how they would evaluate $(3.5 \times 10^{-5})(4 \times 10^2)$.

PSAE PRACTICE 6.11.02, 8.11.13, 10.11.04, 8.11.07

76. Which number represents 0.05604×10^8 written in standard form? **C**

A 0.0000000005604
B 560,400
C 5,604,000
D 50,604,000

77. Toni left school and rode her bike home. The graph below shows the relationship between her distance from the school and time.

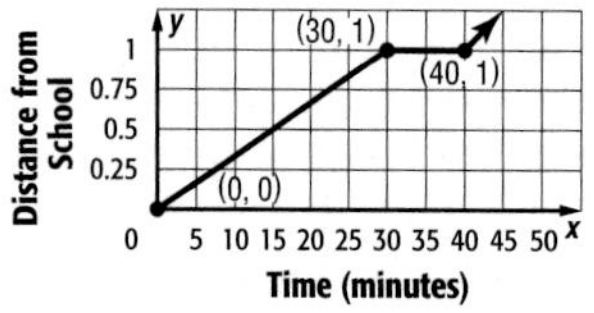

Which explanation could account for the section of the graph from $t = 30$ to $t = 40$? **H**

F Toni rode her bike down a hill.
G Toni ran all the way home.
H Toni stopped at a friend's house on her way home.
J Toni returned to school to get her mathematics book.

78. SHORT RESPONSE In his first four years of coaching football, Coach Delgato's team won 5 games the first year, 10 games the second year, 8 games the third year, and 7 games the fourth year. How many games does the team need to win during the fifth year to have an average of 8 wins per year? **10 games**

79. The table shows the relationship between Calories and grams of fat contained in an order of fried chicken from various restaurants.

Calories	305	410	320	500	510	440
Fat (g)	28	34	28	41	42	38

Assuming that the data can best be described by a linear model, about how many grams of fat would you expect to be in a 275-Calorie order of fried chicken? **B**

A 22
B 25
C 27
D 28

Spiral Review

Simplify. Assume that no denominator is equal to zero. (Lesson 7-2)

80. $\frac{8^9}{8^6}$ **8^3 or 512**

81. $\frac{6^5}{6^3}$ **6^2 or 36**

82. $\frac{r^8t^{12}}{r^2t^7}$ **r^6t^5**

83. $\left(\frac{3a^4b^4}{8c^2}\right)^4$ **$\frac{81a^{16}b^{16}}{4096c^8}$**

84. $\left(\frac{5d^3g^2}{3h^4}\right)^2$ **$\frac{25d^6g^4}{9h^8}$**

85. $\left(\frac{4n^2p^4}{8p^3}\right)^3$ **$\frac{n^6p^3}{8}$**

86. CHEMISTRY Lemon juice is 10^2 times as acidic as tomato juice. Tomato juice is 10^3 times as acidic as egg whites. How many times as acidic is lemon juice as egg whites? (Lesson 7-1) **10^5**

Write each equation in slope-intercept form. (Lesson 4-2)

87. $y - 2 = 3(x - 1)$ **$y = 3x - 1$**

88. $y - 5 = 6(x + 1)$ **$y = 6x + 11$**

89. $y + 2 = -2(x + 5)$ **$y = -2x - 12$**

90. $y + 3 = \frac{1}{2}(x + 4)$ **$y = \frac{1}{2}x - 1$**

91. $y - 1 = \frac{2}{3}(x + 9)$ **$y = \frac{2}{3}x + 7$**

92. $y + 3 = -\frac{1}{4}(x + 2)$ **$y = -\frac{1}{4}x - \frac{7}{2}$**

Skills Review

Simplify each expression. If not possible, write *simplified*. (Lesson 1-4)

93. $3u + 10u$ **$13u$**

94. $5a - 2 + 6a$ **$11a - 2$**

95. $6m^2 - 8m$ **simplified**

96. $4w^2 + w + 15w^2$ **$19w^2 + w$**

97. $13(5 + 4a)$ **$65 + 52a$**

98. $(4t - 6)16$ **$64t - 96$**

Additional Answers (p. 423, Explore 7-4)

1.
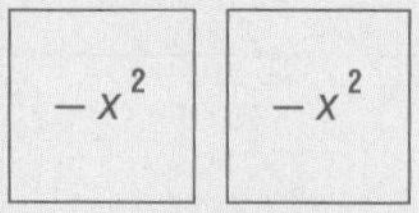

2.
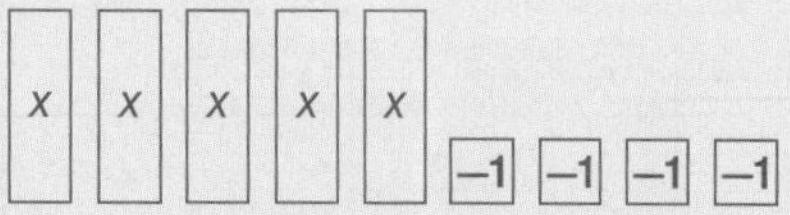

3.
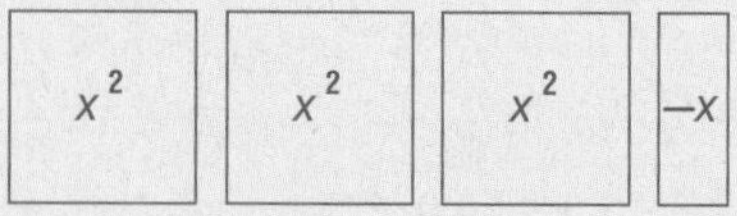

4.
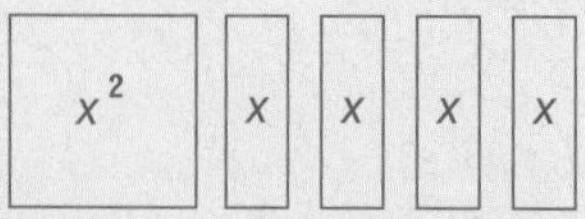

Polynomials

IL Math Online glencoe.com
Math *in Motion*, Animation

IL Learning Standards **8.B.4a** Represent algebraic concepts with physical materials, words, diagrams, tables, graphs, equations and inequalities and use appropriate technology.

Algebra tiles can be used to model polynomials. A polynomial is a monomial or the sum of monomials. The diagram at the right shows the models.

Polynomial Models	
Polynomials are modeled using three types of tiles.	
Each tile has an opposite.	

ACTIVITY Use algebra tiles to model each polynomial.

- $5x$

  To model this polynomial, you will need 5 green x-tiles.

- $3x^2 - 1$

  To model this polynomial, you will need 3 blue x^2-tiles and 1 red -1-tile.

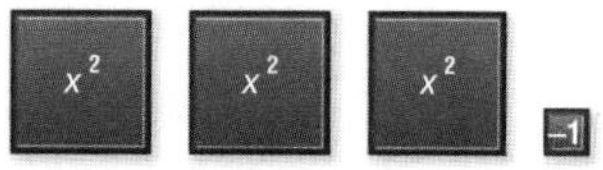

- $-2x^2 + x + 3$

  To model this polynomial, you will need 2 red $-x^2$-tiles, 1 green x-tile, and 3 yellow 1-tiles.

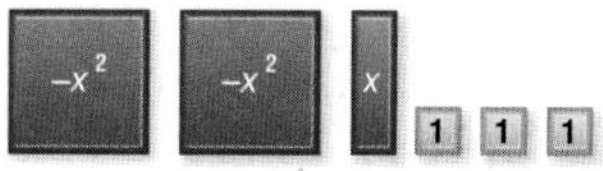

Model and Analyze

Use algebra tiles to model each polynomial. Then draw a diagram of your model. 1–4. See margin.

1. $-4x^2$ **2.** $3x - 5$

3. $2x^2 - 3x$ **4.** $x^2 + 2x + 1$

Write an algebraic expression for each model.

5. 

$2x^2 - 5x$

6. 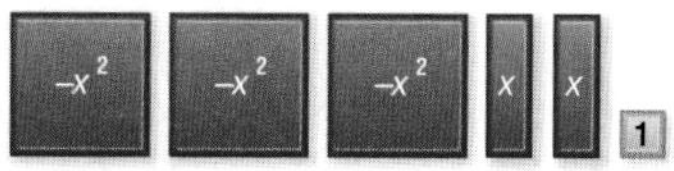

$-3x^2 + 2x + 1$

7. 

$-x^2 + 4x - 2$

8. 

$x^2 - x + 6$

9. MAKE A CONJECTURE Write a sentence or two explaining why algebra tiles are sometimes called *area tiles*. x^2, x, and 1 represent the areas of the tiles.

From Concrete to Abstract

Place a set of tiles in a bag. Have each group of students draw seven tiles from the bag and write an algebraic expression for the model.

Extending the Concept

Ask student to use their tiles to model $x^2 + 3x$ and $x^2 + 2x$. Ask them to make conjectures about the sum of the two polynomials and to use their algebra tiles to support their conjectures.

EXPLORE 7-4 Lesson Notes

1 FOCUS

Objective Use algebra tiles to model polynomials.

Materials for Each Student

- algebra tiles

Easy-to-Make Manipulatives

Teaching Algebra with Manipulatives
Template for algebra tiles, pp. 10–11

2 TEACH

Working in Cooperative Groups

Put students in groups of two or three, mixing abilities. Have groups complete the Activity and Exercises 1 and 2.

- Make sure students understand that the number of x-tiles and x^2-tiles represent the coefficients of x and x^2, respectively. The number of 1-tiles represents the constant in the expression.
- Tell students to be careful to use the tiles with the correct colors. It is easy to incorrectly substitute an x-tile for a $-x$-tile.

Practice Have students complete Exercises 3–9.

3 ASSESS

Formative Assessment

Use Exercises 3 and 4 to assess whether students can use algebra tiles to model a polynomial correctly.

Use Exercises 5–8 to assess whether students can write a polynomial from an algebra-tile model.

7-4 Lesson Notes

1 FOCUS

Vertical Alignment

Before Lesson 7-4
Identify monomials and their characteristics.

Lesson 7-4
Find the degree of a polynomial.
Write polynomials in standard form.

After Lesson 7-4
Add and subtract polynomials.

2 TEACH

Scaffolding Questions

Have students read the *Why?* section of the lesson.

Ask:

- What is the value of t for the year 2007? 2
- What would be the value of t for the year 2010? 5
- Using the equation, find the value of U for the year 2007. 216.7
- How many monomials make up the expression that equals U? 3
- What are they? $-2.7t^2$; $49.4t$; 128.7

7-4 Polynomials

Then

You identified monomials and their characteristics. (Lesson 7-1)

Now

- Find the degree of a polynomial.
- Write polynomials in standard form.

IL Learning Standards

7.A.4b Apply formulas in a wide variety of theoretical and practical real-world measurement applications involving perimeter, area, volume, angle, time, temperature, mass, speed, distance, density and monetary values.
8.C.4b Apply algebraic properties and procedures with matrices, vectors, functions and sequences using data found in business, industry and consumer situations.

New Vocabulary

polynomial
binomial
trinomial
degree of a monomial
degree of a polynomial
standard form of a polynomial
leading coefficient

IL Math Online

glencoe.com

- Extra Examples
- Personal Tutor
- Self-Check Quiz
- Homework Help
- Math in Motion

Why?

In 2011, sales of digital audio players are expected to reach record numbers. The sales data can be modeled by the equation $U = -2.7t^2 + 49.4t + 128.7$, where U is the number of units shipped in millions and t is the number of years since 2005.

The expression $-2.7t^2 + 49.4t + 128.7$ is an example of a polynomial. Polynomials can be used to model situations.

Degree of a Polynomial A **polynomial** is a monomial or the sum of monomials, each called a *term* of the polynomial. Some polynomials have special names. A **binomial** is the sum of *two* monomials, and a **trinomial** is the sum of *three* monomials.

EXAMPLE 1 Identify Polynomials

Determine whether each expression is a polynomial. If so, identify the polynomial as a *monomial, binomial,* or *trinomial*.

Expression	Is it a polynomial?	Monomial, binomial, or trinomial?
a. $4y - 5xz$	Yes; $4y - 5xz$ is the sum of the two monomials $4y$ and $-5xz$.	binomial
b. -6.5	Yes; -6.5 is a real number.	monomial
c. $7a^{-3} + 9b$	No; $7a^{-3} = \frac{7}{a^3}$, which is not a monomial.	none of these
d. $6x^3 + 4x + x + 3$	Yes; $6x^3 + 4x + x + 3 = 6x^3 + 5x + 3$, the sum of three monomials.	trinomial

Check Your Progress

1A. x yes; monomial
1B. $-3y^2 - 2y + 4y - 1$ yes; trinomial
1C. $5rx + 7tuv$ yes; binomial
1D. $10x^{-4} - 8x^a$

1D. No; $10x^{-4}$ is not a monomial and $8x^a$ has a variable exponent.

Personal Tutor glencoe.com

The **degree of a monomial** is the sum of the exponents of all its variables. A nonzero constant has degree 0. Zero has no degree.

The **degree of a polynomial** is the greatest degree of any term in the polynomial. To find the degree of a polynomial, you must find the degree of each term. Some polynomials have special names based on their degree.

Degree	Name
0	constant
1	linear
2	quadratic
3	cubic
4	quartic
5	quintic
6 or more	6th degree, 7th degree, and so on

Lesson 7-4 Resources

Resource	Approaching-Level	On-Level	Beyond-Level	English Learners
Teacher Edition	• Differentiated Instruction, p. 426	• Differentiated Instruction, pp. 426, 429	• Differentiated Instruction, p. 429	
Chapter Resource Masters	• Study Guide and Intervention, pp. 23–24 • Skills Practice, p. 25 • Practice, p. 26 • Word Problem Practice, p. 27	• Study Guide and Intervention, pp. 23–24 • Skills Practice, p. 25 • Practice, p. 26 • Word Problem Practice, p. 27 • Enrichment, p. 28 • Graphing Calculator Activity, p. 29	• Practice, p. 26 • Word Problem Practice, p. 27 • Enrichment, p. 28	• Study Guide and Intervention, pp. 23–24 • Skills Practice, p. 25 • Practice, p. 26
Transparencies	• 5-Minute Check Transparency 7-4	• 5-Minute Check Transparency 7-4	• 5-Minute Check Transparency 7-4	• 5-Minute Check Transparency 7-4
Other	• Study Notebook	• Study Notebook	• Study Notebook	• Study Notebook

ReadingMath

Prefixes The prefixes *mono*, *bi*, and *tri* mean one, two, and three, respectively. Hence, a monomial has one term, a binomial has two terms, and a trinomial has three terms.

Math *in Motion*, BrainPOP® glencoe.com

EXAMPLE 2 Degree of a Polynomial

Find the degree of each polynomial.

a. $3a^2b^3 + 6$

Step 1 Find the degree of each term.

$3a^2b^3$: degree = 2 + 3 or 5   6: degree 0

Step 2 The degree of the polynomial is the greatest degree, 5.

b. $2d^3 - 5c^5d - 7$

$2d^3$: degree = 3 $-5c^5d$: degree = 5 + 1 or 6

-7: degree 0   The degree of the polynomial is 6.

Check Your Progress

2A. $7xy^5z$ 7   **2B.** $2rt - 3rt^2 - 7r^2t^2 - 13$ 4

Personal Tutor glencoe.com

Polynomials in Standard Form The terms of a polynomial may be written in any order. Polynomials written in only one variable are usually written in standard form.

The **standard form of a polynomial** is written with the terms in order from greatest degree to least degree. When a polynomial is written in standard form, the coefficient of the first term is called the **leading coefficient**.

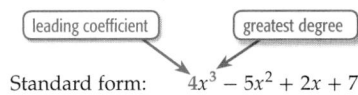

leading coefficient   greatest degree

Standard form: $4x^3 - 5x^2 + 2x + 7$

EXAMPLE 3 Standard Form of a Polynomial

Write each polynomial in standard form. Identify the leading coefficient.

a. $3x^2 + 4x^5 - 7x$

Step 1 Find the degree of each term.

Degree: 2   5   1

Polynomial: $3x^2 + 4x^5 - 7x$

Step 2 Write the terms in descending order: $4x^5 + 3x^2 - 7x$.

The leading coefficient is 4.

b. $5y - 9 - 2y^4 - 6y^3$

Step 1 Degree: 1   0   4   3

Polynomial: $5y - 9 - 2y^4 - 6y^3$

Step 2 $-2y^4 - 6y^3 + 5y - 9$ The leading coefficient is −2.

Math *in Motion*, Interactive Lab glencoe.com

Check Your Progress

3A. $8 - 2x^2 + 4x^4 - 3x$ **3B.** $y + 5y^3 - 2y^2 - 7y^6 + 10$

3A. $4x^4 - 2x^2 - 3x + 8$; 4
3B. $-7y^6 + 5y^3 - 2y^2 + y + 10$; −7

Personal Tutor glencoe.com

Focus on Mathematical Content

Degree of a Polynomial The degree of a polynomial should not be confused with the number of terms. For example, $x^3 + 1$ is a binomial, but the degree is 3, not 2, because the greatest degree of any of the terms is 3.

TEACH with TECH

INTERACTIVE WHITEBOARD Write numbers 1 thru 10 on the board. Then write several polynomials on the board. For each polynomial, ask students to identify the degree of the polynomial. Grab the correct number and drag it underneath that polynomial.

Degree of a Polynomial

Example 1 shows how to determine whether an expression is a polynomial. **Example 2** shows how to find the degree of a polynomial.

Formative Assessment

Use the Check Your Progress exercises after each example to determine students' understanding of concepts.

Additional Examples

1 Determine whether each expression is a polynomial. If so, identify the polynomial as a *monomial, binomial,* or *trinomial.*

a. $6x - 4$ yes; binomial

b. $x^2 + 2xy - 7$ yes; trinomial

c. $\frac{14d + 19e^3}{5d^4}$ no

d. $26b^2$ yes; monomial

2 Find the degree of each polynomial.

a. $12 + 5b + 6bc + 8bc^2$ 3

b. $9x^2 - 2x - 4$ 2

Additional Examples also in Interactive Classroom PowerPoint® Presentations

IWB INTERACTIVE WHITEBOARD READY

Polynomials in Standard Form

Example 3 shows how to write a polynomial in standard form and identify the leading coefficient. **Example 4** shows how to use polynomials to estimate values between two points and predict values.

Additional Example

3 Write each polynomial in standard form. Identify the leading coefficient.

a. $9x^2 + 3x^6 - 4x$
$3x^6 + 9x^2 - 4x$; 3

b. $12 + 5y + 6xy + 8xy^2$
$8xy^2 + 6xy + 5y + 12$; 8

Additional Example

4 **MEDICINE** From 2000 to 2006, the number N (in thousands) of patients seen by a medical facility can be modeled by the equation $N = t^2 + 2.1t + 0.8$, where t is the number of years since 2000. How many patients were seen in 2005? 36,300

3 PRACTICE

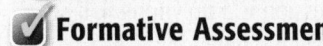

Formative Assessment

Use Exercises 1–19 to check for understanding.

Use the chart at the bottom of the next page to customize assignments for your students.

Watch Out!

Preventing Errors For Exercise 4, remind students that monomials are the products of a number and one or more variables, so expressions such as $\frac{1}{b^2}$ are not monomials.

We can use polynomials to estimate values between two points. We can also use them to predict values of events before they occur.

Real-World Link

The world's biggest skateboard was built in 1996. The skateboard is 10 feet long, 4 feet wide, 3 feet tall and is fully functional. It is on display in San Diego, California.

Source: Foundation Skateboard Company

Real-World EXAMPLE 4 Use a Polynomial

BUSINESS From 2000 through 2006, the number U of skateboards (in thousands) produced at a manufacturing plant can be modeled by the equation $U = 3t^2 - 2t + 10$, where t is the number of years since 2000. How many skateboards were produced in 2002?

Find the value of t, and substitute the value of t to find the number of skateboards produced.

Since t is the number of years since 2000, t equals 2002 − 2000 or 2.

$U = 3t^2 - 2t + 10$	**Original equation**
$= 3(2)^2 - 2(2) + 10$	**$t = 2$**
$= 3(4) - 4 + 10$	**Simplify.**
$= 12 - 4 + 10$	**Multiply.**
$= 18$	**Simplify.**

Since U is in thousands, the number of skateboards produced was 18 thousand or 18,000.

Check Your Progress 4B. 655,000 skateboards

4A. How many skateboards were produced in 2005? 75,000 skateboards

4B. If this trend continues, how many skateboards will be produced in 2015?

Personal Tutor glencoe.com

Check Your Understanding

Example 1 p. 424

4. No; a monomial cannot have a variable in the denominator.

Determine whether each expression is a polynomial. If so, identify the polynomial as a *monomial*, *binomial*, or *trinomial*.

1. $7ab + 6b^2 - 2a^3$ yes; trinomial
2. $2y - 5 + 3y^2$ yes; trinomial
3. $3x^2$ yes; monomial
4. $\frac{4m}{3p}$
5. $5m^2p^3 + 6$ yes; binomial
6. $5q^{-4} + 6q$

6. No; $5q^{-4} = \frac{5}{q^4}$, a monomial cannot have a variable in the denominator.

Example 2 p. 425

16. $-y^3 - 3y^2 + 3y + 2$; −1

18. $4a^3 - 5a^2 + 2a - 1$; 4

Find the degree of each polynomial.

7. -3 0
8. $6p^3 - p^4$ 4
9. $-7z$ 1
10. $\frac{3}{4}$ 0
11. $12 - 7q^2t + 8r$ 3
12. $2a^2b^5 + 5 - ab$ 7
13. $6df^3 + 3d^2f^2 + 2d + 1$ 4
14. $9hjk - 4h^2j^3 + 5j^2k^2 - h^3k^3$ 6

Example 3 p. 425

Write each polynomial in standard form. Identify the leading coefficient.

15. $2x^5 - 12 + 3x$ $2x^5 + 3x - 12$; 2
16. $-y^3 + 3y - 3y^2 + 2$
17. $4z - 2z^2 - 5z^4$ $-5z^4 - 2z^2 + 4z$, −5
18. $2a + 4a^3 - 5a^2 - 1$

Example 4 p. 426

19. **ENROLLMENT** Suppose the number N (in hundreds) of students projected to attend a high school from 1998 to 2007 can be modeled by the equation $N = t^2 + 1.5t + 0.5$, where t is the number of years since 1998.

 a. How many students were enrolled in the high school in 2003? 3300 students

 b. How many students were enrolled in the high school in 2005? 6000 students

Differentiated Instruction AL OL

If some students have a problem determining the degree of a polynomial,

Then have students work in pairs and give each pair a list of polynomials. For each monomial term, have one student tap out its degree. Have the partner record the total number of beats for each monomial. After tapping the degree of all the monomials in the polynomial, have the partner tell the degree of the polynomial.

Practice and Problem Solving

● = **Step-by-Step Solutions** begin on page R12.
Extra Practice begins on page 815.

Example 1 p. 424

20. No; a monomial cannot have a variable in the denominator.

Example 2 p. 425

23. No; the exponent is a variable.

Determine whether each expression is a polynomial. If so, identify the polynomial as a *monomial, binomial,* or *trinomial.*

20. $\frac{5y^3}{x^2} + 4x$ **21.** 21 yes; monomial **22.** $c^4 - 2c^2 + 1$ yes; trinomial

23. $d + 3d^{-c}$ **24.** $a - a^2$ yes; binomial **25.** $5n^3 + nq^3$ yes; binomial

Find the degree of each polynomial.

26. $13 - 4ab + 5a^3b$ 4 **27.** $3x - 8$ 1 **28.** -4 0

29. $17g^2h$ 3 **30.** $10 + 2cd^4 - 6d^2g$ 5 **31.** $2z^2y^2 - 7 + 5y^3w^4$ 7

Example 3 p. 425

Write each polynomial in standard form. Identify the leading coefficient.

32. $5x^2 - 2 + 3x$ $5x^2 + 3x - 2; 5$ **33.** $8y + 7y^3$ $7y^3 + 8y; 7$

34. $4 - 3c - 5c^2$ $-5c^2 - 3c + 4; -5$ **35.** $-4d^4 + 1 - d^2$ $-4d^4 - d^2 + 1; -4$

36. $11t + 2t^2 - 3 + t^5$ $t^5 + 2t^2 + 11t - 3; 1$ **37.** $2 + r - r^3$ $-r^3 + r + 2; -1$

38. $\frac{1}{2}x - 3x^4 + 7$ $-3x^4 + \frac{1}{2}x + 7; -3$ **39.** $-9b^2 + 10b - b^6$ $-b^6 - 9b^2 + 10b; -1$

Example 4 p. 426

40. FIREWORKS A firework shell is launched two feet from the ground at a speed of 150 feet per second. The height H of the firework shell is modeled by the equation $H = -16t^2 + 150t + 2$, where t is time in seconds.

a. How high will the firework be after 3 seconds? 308 ft

b. How high will the firework be after 5 seconds? 352 ft

41. quadratic trinomial
42. cubic monomial
43. quartic binomial
44. cubic binomial
45. quintic polynomial
46. cubic trinomial
48. $2(4x^2 + 2x - 1) + 2(2x^2 - x + 3)$; $(4x^2 + 2x - 1) \cdot (2x^2 - x + 3)$

B **Classify each polynomial according to its degree and number of terms.**

41. $4x - 3x^2 + 5$ **42.** $11z^3$ **43.** $9 + y^4$

44. $3x^3 - 7$ **45.** $-2z^5 - x^2 + 5x - 8$ **46.** $10t - 4t^2 + 6t^3$

47. ICE CREAM An ice cream shop is changing the size of their cone.

a. If the volume of a cone is the product of $\frac{1}{3}$, π, the square of the radius r, and the height h, write a polynomial that represents the volume. $\frac{1}{3}\pi r^2 h$

b. How much will the cone hold if the radius is 1.5 inches and the height is 4 inches? about 9.42 in^3

c. If the volume of the cone must be 63 cubic inches and the radius of the cone is 3 inches, how tall is the cone? about 6.7 in.

48. GEOMETRY Write two expressions for the perimeter and area of the rectangle.

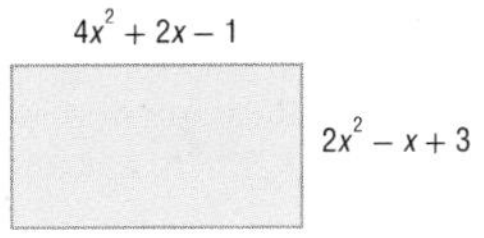

49. GEOMETRY Write a polynomial for the area of the shaded region shown. $6x^2$

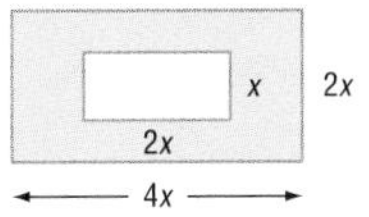

Differentiated Homework Options

Level	Assignment	Two-Day Option	
AL Basic	20–40, 52, 54–79	21–39 odd, 57–60	20–40 even, 52, 54–56, 61–79
OL Core	21–45 odd, 47–52, 54–79	20–40, 57–60	41–52, 54–56, 61–79
BL Advanced	41–73, (optional: 74–79)		

Study Guide and Intervention
CRM pp. 23–24 AL OL ELL

NAME ____________ DATE ________ PERIOD ________

7-4 Study Guide and Intervention

Polynomials

Degree of a Polynomial A **polynomial** is a monomial or a sum of monomials. A **binomial** is the sum of two monomials, and a **trinomial** is the sum of three monomials. Polynomials with more than three terms have no special name. The **degree** of a monomial is the sum of the exponents of all its variables. The **degree of the polynomial** is the same as the degree of the monomial term with the highest degree.

Example **Determine whether each expression is a polynomial. If so, identify the polynomial as a *monomial, binomial,* or *trinomial*. Then find the degree of the polynomial.**

Expression	Polynomial?	Monomial, Binomial, or Trinomial?	Degree of the Polynomial
$3x - 7xyz$	Yes. $3x - 7xyz = 3x + (-7xyz)$, which is the sum of two monomials	binomial	3
-25	Yes. -25 is a real number.	monomial	0
$7n^3 + 3n^{-4}$	No. $3n^{-4} = \frac{3}{n^4}$, which is not a monomial	none of these	—
$9x^3 + 4x + x + 4 + 2x$	Yes. The expression simplifies to $9x^3 + 7x + 4$, which is the sum of three monomials	trinomial	3

Exercises

Determine whether each expression is a polynomial. If so, identify the polynomial as a *monomial, binomial,* or *trinomial*.

1. 36 **yes; monomial**
2. $\frac{3}{q^2} + 5$ **no**
3. $7x - x + 5$ **yes; binomial**
4. $8g^2h - 7gh + 2$ **yes; trinomial**
5. $\frac{1}{4y^2} + 5y - 8$ **no**
6. $6x + x^2$ **yes; binomial**

Find the degree of each polynomial.

7. $4x^2y^3z$ **6**
8. $-2abc$ **3**
9. $15m$ **1**
10. $r + 5t$ **1**
11. 22 **0**
12. $18x^2 + 4yz - 10y$ **2**
13. $x^4 - 6x^2 - 2x^3 - 10$ **4**
14. $2x^3y^2 - 4xy^3$ **5**
15. $-2r^8x^4 + 7r^2x - 4r^7x^6$ **13**
16. $9x^2 + yz^8$ **9**
17. $8b + bc^5$ **6**
18. $4x^4y - 8zx^2 + 2x^5$ **5**
19. $4x^2 - 1$ **2**
20. $9abc + bc - n^5$ **5**
21. $h^3m + 6h^4m^2 - 7$ **6**

Lesson 7-4

Chapter 7 23 Glencoe Algebra 1

Practice
CRM p. 26 AL OL BL ELL

NAME ____________ DATE ________ PERIOD ________

7-4 Practice

Polynomials

Determine whether each expression is a polynomial. If so, identify the polynomial as a *monomial, binomial,* or *trinomial*.

1. $7a^2b + 3b^2 - a^2b$ **yes; binomial**
2. $\frac{1}{5}y^3 + y^2 - 9$ **yes; trinomial**
3. $6g^2h^3k$ **yes; monomial**

Find the degree of each polynomial.

4. $x + 3x^4 - 21x^2 + x^3$ **4**
5. $3g^2h^3 + g^3h$ **5**
6. $-2x^2y + 3xy^3 + x^2$ **4**
7. $5n^3m - 2m^3 + n^2m^4 + n^2$ **6**
8. $a^3b^2c + 2a^5c + b^3c^2$ **6**
9. $10r^3t^2 + 4rt^2 - 5r^3t^2$ **5**

Write each polynomial in standard form. Identify the leading coefficient.

10. $8x^2 - 15 + 5x^5$ **$5x^5 + 8x^2 - 15$; 5**
11. $10x - 7 + x^4 + 4x^3$ **$x^4 + 4x^3 + 10x - 7$; 1**
12. $13x^2 - 5 + 6x^3 - x$ **$6x^3 + 13x^2 - x - 5$; 6**
13. $4x + 2x^5 - 6x^3 + 2$ **$2x^5 - 6x^3 + 4x + 2$; 2**

GEOMETRY Write a polynomial to represent the area of each shaded region.

14. 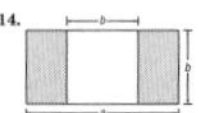

$ab - b^2$

15. 

$d^2 - \frac{1}{4}\pi d^2$

16. **MONEY** Write a polynomial to represent the value of t ten-dollar bills, f fifty-dollar bills, and h one-hundred-dollar bills. **$10t + 50f + 100h$**

17. **GRAVITY** The height above the ground of a ball thrown up with a velocity of 96 feet per second from a height of 6 feet is $6 + 96t - 16t^2$ feet, where t is the time in seconds. According to this model, how high is the ball after 7 seconds? Explain.
−106 ft; The height is negative because the model does not account for the ball hitting the ground when the height is 0 feet.

Chapter 7 26 Glencoe Algebra 1

Word Problem Practice
CRM p. 27 AL OL BL ELL

NAME ____________ DATE ________ PERIOD ________

7-4 Word Problem Practice

Polynomials

1. **PRIMES** Mei is trying to list as many prime numbers as she can for a challenge problem for her math class. She finds that the polynomial expression $n^2 - n + 41$ can be used to generate some, but not all, prime numbers. What is the degree of Mei's polynomial? **2**

2. **PHONE CALLS** A long-distance telephone company charges a \$19.95 standard monthly service fee plus \$0.05 per minute of long-distance use. Write a polynomial to express the monthly cost of the phone plan if x minutes of long-distance time are used per month. What is the degree of the polynomial?
\$0.05x + \$19.95; 1

3. **COSTUMES** Jack's mother is sewing the cape of his costume for a charity masked ball. The pattern for the cape (lying flat) is shown below. The radius of the neck hole is 6 inches. What is the area, in square feet, of the finished cape?
27.5 ft²

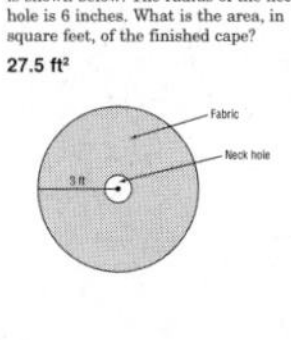

4. **ARCHITECTURE** Graphing the polynomial function $y = -x^2 + 3$ produces an accurate drawing of the shape of an archway inside a historical library, where x is the horizontal distance in meters from the base of the arch and y is the height of the arch. At $x = 0$, what is the height of the arch? **3 m**

5. **DRIVING** A truck and a car leave an intersection. The truck travels south, and the car travels east. When the truck had gone 24 miles, the distance between the car and truck was four miles more than three times the distance traveled by the car heading east.

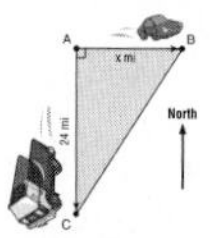

a. Suppose the truck stops at point C and the car stops at point B. Write a polynomial in standard form to express the sum of the distances traveled by the car and the truck.
$x + 24$

b. Write a simplified polynomial to express the perimeter of triangle ABC.
$4x + 28$ mi

Lesson 7-4

Chapter 7 27 Glencoe Algebra 1

Real-World Link

A space shuttle has three parts: the orbiter, an external tank, and two solid rocket boosters. Including fuel, the shuttle weighs a total of 4.4 million pounds at launch.

Source: How Stuff Works

50. PROJECT Rocky and Arturo are designing a rocket for a competition. The top must be cone-shaped and the body of the rocket must be cylindrical. The volume of a cone is the product of $\frac{1}{3}$, π, the height h, and the square of the radius r. The volume of a cylinder is the product of π, the height t, and the square of the radius r. **50a. $\frac{1}{3}\pi hr^2 + \pi tr^2$**

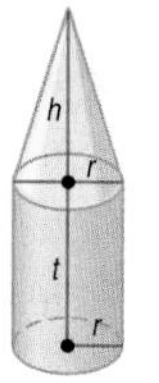

a. Write a polynomial that represents the volume of the rocket.

b. If the height of the body of the rocket is 8 inches, the height of the top is 6 inches, and the radius is 3 inches, find the volume of the rocket. **about 282.7 in³**

c. If the height of the body of the rocket is 9 inches, the height of the top is 5 inches, and the radius is 4 inches, find the volume of the rocket. **about 536.17 in³**

51. MULTIPLE REPRESENTATIONS In this problem, you will explore perimeter and area. **See Ch. 7 Answer Appendix.**

a. **GEOMETRIC** Draw three rectangles that each have a perimeter of 400 feet.

b. **TABULAR** Record the width and length of each rectangle in a table like the one shown below. Find the area of each rectangle.

Rectangle	Length	Width	Area
1	100 ft	**100 ft**	**10,000 ft²**
2	50 ft	**150 ft**	**7500 ft²**
3	75 ft	**125 ft**	**9375 ft²**
4	x ft	**$(200 - x)$ ft**	**$x(200 - x)$ ft²**

See Ch. 7 Answer Appendix.

c. **GRAPHICAL** On a coordinate system, graph the area of rectangle 4 in terms of the length, x. Use the graph to determine the largest area possible.

d. **ANALYTICAL** Determine the length and width that produce the largest area. **The length and width of the rectangle must be 100 feet each to have the largest area.**

H.O.T. Problems
Use **H**igher-**O**rder **T**hinking Skills

52. FIND THE ERROR Chuck and Claudio are writing $2x^2 - 3 + 5x$ in standard form. Is either of them correct? Explain your reasoning.

Chuck	Claudio
$2x^2$: degree 2	$2x^2$: degree 2
-3 : degree 0	-3 : degree 0
$5x$: degree 1	$5x$: degree 1
$2x^2 - 5x + 3$	$2x^2 + 5x - 3$

53. CHALLENGE Write a polynomial that represents any odd integer if x is an integer. Explain. **$2x + 1$, where x is an integer**

54. REASONING Is the following statement *sometimes, always,* or *never* true? Explain.

A binomial can have a degree of zero.

55. OPEN ENDED Write an example of a cubic trinomial. **Sample answer: $x^3 - x^2 + 1$**

56. WRITING IN MATH Explain how to write a polynomial in standard form and how to identify the leading coefficient. **See margin.**

52. Claudio; Chuck did not move the signs along with the 3 and 5x.

54. Never; a binomial must have at least one monomial term with degree greater than zero.

Enrichment
CRM p. 28 OL BL

NAME ____________ DATE ________ PERIOD ________

7-4 Enrichment

Polynomial Functions

Suppose a linear equation such as $-3x + y = 4$ is solved for y. Then an equivalent equation, $y = 3x + 4$, is found. Expressed in this way, y is a function of x, or $f(x) = 3x + 4$. Notice that the right side of the equation is a binomial of degree 1.

Higher-degree polynomials in x may also form functions. An example is $f(x) = x^3 + 1$, which is a polynomial function of degree 3. You can graph this function using a table of ordered pairs, as shown at the right.

x	y
$-1\frac{1}{2}$	$-2\frac{3}{8}$
-1	0
0	1
1	2
$1\frac{1}{2}$	$4\frac{3}{8}$

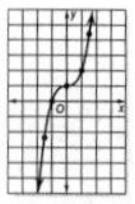

For each of the following polynomial functions, make a table of values for x and $y = f(x)$. Then draw the graph on the grid.

1. $f(x) = 1 - x^2$

x	y
−2	−3

2. $f(x) = x^2 - 5$

x	y
−2	−1

Additional Answer

56. First find the degree of every term. Then arrange the terms in descending order of degree. The leading coefficient is always the coefficient of the first term, that is, the term with the highest degree.

PSAE PRACTICE 6.11.12, 6.11.10, 10.11.01, 8.11.17

57. Matrices P and Q are given below.

$$P = \begin{bmatrix} 3 & 2 \\ 6 & 9 \\ 1 & 0 \end{bmatrix} \qquad Q = \begin{bmatrix} -3 & -2 \\ -6 & -9 \\ 4 & 0 \end{bmatrix}$$

What is $P - Q$? **D**

A $\begin{bmatrix} -6 & -9 \\ -8 & -15 \\ 3 & 0 \end{bmatrix}$ C $\begin{bmatrix} 0 & -5 \\ 4 & 3 \\ 5 & 0 \end{bmatrix}$

B $\begin{bmatrix} 0 & 5 \\ -4 & -3 \\ -5 & 0 \end{bmatrix}$ D $\begin{bmatrix} 6 & 4 \\ 12 & 18 \\ -3 & 0 \end{bmatrix}$

58. You have a coupon from The Really Quick Lube Shop for an \$8 off oil change this month. An oil change costs \$19.95, and a new oil filter costs \$4.95. You use the coupon for an oil change and filter. Before adding tax, how much should you pay? **G**

F \$11.95
G \$16.90
H \$24.90
J \$27.95

59. SHORT RESPONSE In a recent poll, 3000 people were asked to pick their favorite baseball team. The accompanying circle graph shows the results of that poll. How many people polled picked the Black Sox as their favorite team? **500**

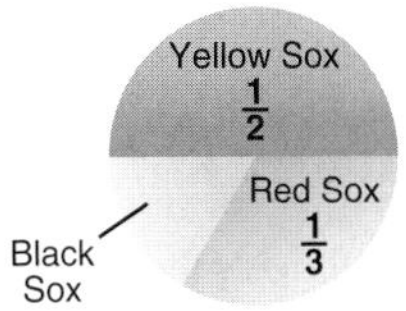

60. What value for y satisfies the system of equations below? **A**

$$2x + y = 19$$
$$4x - 6y = -2$$

A 5
B 7
C 8
D 10

Spiral Review

Express each number in standard notation. (Lesson 7-3)

61. 6×10^{-7} **0.0000006**
62. 7.2×10^{-10} **0.00000000072**
63. 8.1×10^{5} **810,000**
64. 7×10^{6} **7,000,000**
65. 0.132×10^{-6} **0.000000132**
66. 1.88×10^{0} **1.88**

Simplify. Assume that no denominator is equal to zero. (Lesson 7-2)

67. $a^0(a^4)(a^{-8})$ $\frac{1}{a^4}$
68. $\frac{(4m^{-3}c^6)^0}{mc}$ $\frac{1}{mc}$
69. $\frac{(3f^2g^6)^0}{(18f^6g^2)^0}$ 1
70. 12^{-1} $\frac{1}{12}$
71. $\frac{k^{-4}}{m^2p^{-8}}$ $\frac{p^8}{k^4m^2}$
72. $\frac{(nq^{-1})^3}{(n^4q^8)^{-1}}$ n^7q^5

73. FINANCIAL LITERACY The owners of a new restaurant have hired enough servers to handle 17 tables of customers. The fire marshal has approved the restaurant for a limit of 56 customers. How many two-seat tables and how many four-seat tables should the owners buy? (Lesson 6-4) **6 two-seat, 11 four-seat**

Skills Review

Simplify each expression. If not possible, write *simplified*. (Lesson 1-5)

74. $7b^2 + 14b - 10b$ $7b^2 + 4b$
75. $5t + 12t^2 - 8t$ $12t^2 - 3t$
76. $3y^4 + 2y^4 + 2y^5$ $5y^4 + 2y^5$
77. $7h^5 - 7j^5 + 8k^5$ simplified
78. $n + \frac{n}{3} + \frac{2}{3}n$ $2n$
79. $2u + \frac{u}{2} + u^2$ $\frac{5u}{2} + u^2$

Exercise Alert

Grid Paper For Exercise 51, students will need grid paper.

Multiple Representations In Exercise 51, students explore perimeter and area of rectangles graphically and analyze their results to determine the length and width that produces the largest area possible.

Watch Out!

Find the Error For Exercise 52, students should notice that both Chuck and Claudio have identified the same degree for each term. Chuck, however, did not remember to keep the sign of each term with its assigned term.

4 ASSESS

Crystal Ball Ask students to predict how the mathematical procedures they used to determine the degree of a polynomial will help them with tomorrow's lesson on adding and subtracting polynomials.

Formative Assessment

Check for student understanding of Lessons 7-3 and 7-4.

CRM Quiz 2, p. 57

Differentiated Instruction OL BL

Extension Tell students that the degree of a polynomial function determines the maximum number of times the graph of the function intersects the x-axis. Ask students to tell the maximum number of times the graphs of the following functions could intersect the x-axis: $f(x) = 5$, $f(x) = 3x + 1$, and $f(x) = x^2 + x - 5$. 0; 1; 2 Then ask students to describe the graph of each function. horizontal line, line, U-shaped (parabola)

Formative Assessment

Use the Mid-Chapter Quiz to assess students' progress in the first half of the chapter.

For problems answered incorrectly, have students review the lessons indicated in parentheses.

ExamView Assessment Suite: Customize and create multiple versions of your Mid-Chapter Quiz and their answer keys.

FOLDABLES Follow-Up

Before students complete the Mid-Chapter Quiz, encourage them to review the information for Lessons 7-1 through 7-4 in their Foldables.

Additional Answers

29b. 2

29c. 30.07 people/mi^2; Since 2020 is 90 years after 1930, substitute 90 for y in the equation.

29d. 38.3 people/mi^2; Since 2030 is 100 years after 1930, substitute 100 for y in the equation.

CHAPTER 7 Mid-Chapter Quiz

Lessons 7-1 through 7-4

IL Learning Standards 7.A.4b

Simplify each expression. (Lesson 7-1)

1. $(x^3)(4x^5)$ **$4x^8$**
2. $(m^2p^5)^3$ **m^6p^{15}**
3. $[(2xy^3)^2]^3$ **$64x^6y^{18}$**
4. $(6ab^3c^4)(-3a^2b^3c)$ **$-18a^3b^6c^5$**
5. **MULTIPLE CHOICE** Express the volume of the solid as a monomial. (Lesson 7-1) **B**

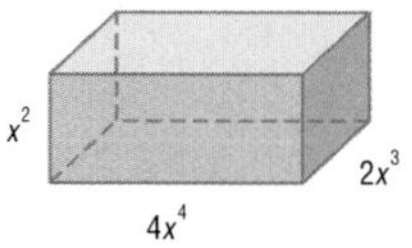

A $6x^9$ C $8x^{24}$

B $8x^9$ D $7x^{24}$

Simplify each expression. Assume that no denominator equals 0. (Lesson 7-2)

6. $\left(\frac{2a^4b^3}{c^6}\right)^3$ **$\frac{8a^{12}b^9}{c^{18}}$**
7. $\frac{2xy^0}{6x}$ **$\frac{1}{3}$**
8. $\frac{m^7n^4p}{m^3n^3p}$ **m^4n**
9. $\frac{p^4t^{-2}}{r^{-5}}$ **$\frac{p^4r^5}{t^2}$**

10. **ASTRONOMY** Physicists estimate that the number of stars in the universe has an order of magnitude of 10^{21}. The number of stars in the Milky Way galaxy is around 100 billion. Using orders of magnitude, how many times as many stars are there in the universe as the Milky Way? (Lesson 7-2) **10^{10}**

Express each number in scientific notation. (Lesson 7-3)

11. 0.00000054 **5.4×10^{-7}**
12. 0.0042 **4.2×10^{-3}**
13. 234,000 **2.34×10^5**
14. 418,000,000 **4.18×10^8**

Express each number in standard form. (Lesson 7-3)

15. 4.1×10^{-3} **0.0041**
16. 2.74×10^5 **274,000**
17. 3×10^9 **3,000,000,000**
18. 9.1×10^{-5} **0.000091**

Evaluate each product or quotient. Express the results in scientific notation. (Lesson 7-3)

19. $(2.13 \times 10^2)(3 \times 10^5)$ **6.39×10^7**
20. $(7.5 \times 10^6)(2.5 \times 10^{-2})$ **1.875×10^5**
21. $\frac{7.5 \times 10^8}{2.5 \times 10^4}$ **3×10^4**
22. $\frac{6.6 \times 10^5}{2 \times 10^{-3}}$ **3.3×10^8**

Determine whether each expression is a polynomial. If so, identify the polynomial as a *monomial*, *binomial*, or *trinomial*. (Lesson 7-4)

23. $3y^2 - 2$ **binomial**
24. $4t^5 + 3t^2 + t$ **trinomial**
25. $\frac{3x}{5y}$ **not a polynomial**
26. ax^{-3} **not a polynomial**
27. $3b^2$ **monomial**
28. $2x^{-3} - 4x + 1$ **not a polynomial**

29. **POPULATION** The table shows the population density for Nevada for various years. (Lesson 7-4) **b–d. See margin.**

Year	Years Since 1930	People/ Square Mile
1930	0	0.8
1960	30	2.6
1980	50	7.3
1990	60	10.9
2000	70	18.2

a. The population density d of Nevada from 1930 to 2000 can be modeled by $d = 0.005y^2 - 0.127y + 1$, where y represents the number of years since 1930. Identify the type of polynomial for $0.005y^2 - 0.127y + 1$. **quadratic trinomial**

b. What is the degree of the polynomial?

c. Predict the population density of Nevada for 2020. Explain your method.

d. Predict the population density of Nevada for 2030. Explain your method.

Intervention Planner

Tier 1 On Level	Tier 2 Strategic Intervention approaching grade level	Tier 3 Intensive Intervention 2 or more grades below level
If students miss about 25% of the exercises or less,	**If** students miss about 50% of the exercises,	**If** students miss about 75% of the exercises,
Then choose a resource:	**Then** choose a resource:	**Then** use *Math Triumphs, Alg. 1*
SE Lessons 7-1, 7-2, 7-3, and 7-4 **CRM** Skills Practice, pp. 7, 13, 19, and 25 **TE** Chapter Project, p. 398 **IL Math Online** Self-Check Quiz	**CRM** Study Guide and Intervention, Chapter 7, pp. 5, 11, 17, and 23 *Quick Review Math Handbook* **IL Math Online** Extra Examples, Personal Tutor, Homework Help	**IL Math Online** Extra Examples, Personal Tutor, Homework Help, Review Vocabulary

Algebra Lab
Adding and Subtracting Polynomials

IL Math Online glencoe.com
Math *in Motion*, Animation

IL Learning Standards **8.B.4a** Represent algebraic concepts with physical materials, words, diagrams, tables, graphs, equations and inequalities and use appropriate technology.

Monomials such as $3x$ and $-2x$ are called *like terms* because they have the same variable to the same power. When you use algebra tiles, you can recognize like terms because the individual tiles have the same size and shape.

Polynomial Models	
Like terms are represented by tiles that have the same shape and size.	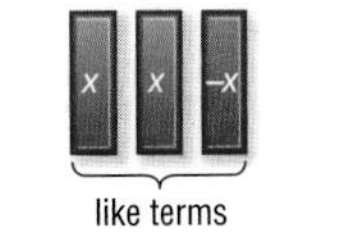
A *zero pair* may be formed by pairing one tile with its opposite. You can remove or add zero pairs without changing the polynomial.	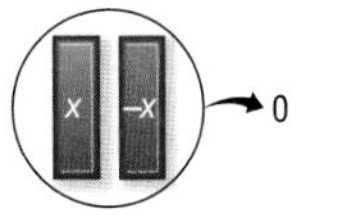

ACTIVITY 1 Add Polynomials

Use algebra tiles to find $(2x^2 - 3x + 5) + (x^2 + 6x - 4)$.

Step 1 Model each polynomial.

$2x^2 - 3x + 5 \rightarrow$

$x^2 + 6x - 4 \rightarrow$

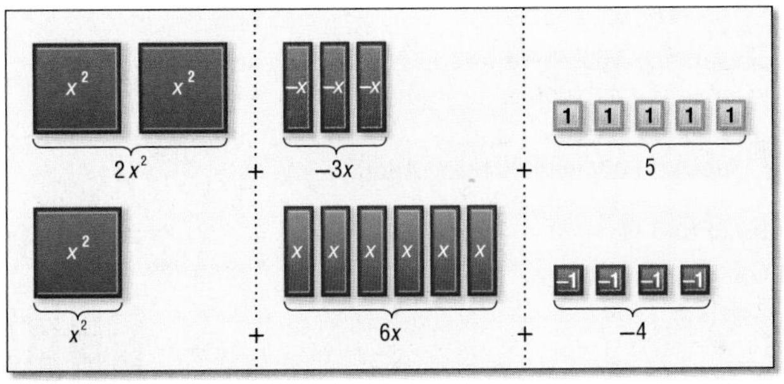

Step 2 Combine like terms and remove zero pairs.

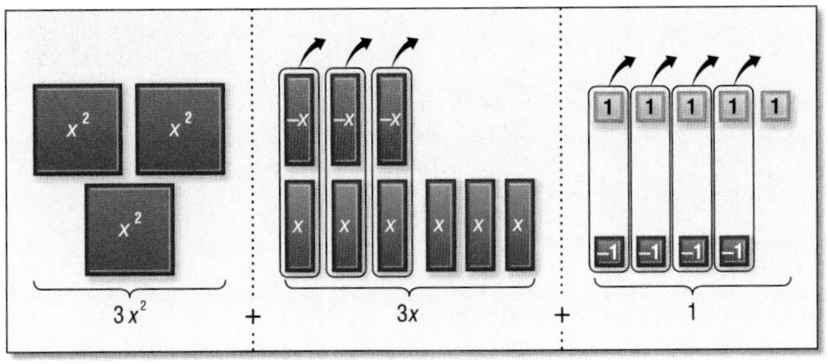

Step 3 Write the polynomial for the tiles that remain.

$(2x^2 - 3x + 5) + (x^2 + 6x - 4) = 3x^2 + 3x + 1$

1 FOCUS

Objective Use algebra tiles to add and subtract polynomials.

Materials for Each Student

- algebra tiles

Easy to Make Manipulatives

Teaching Algebra with Manipulatives
Template for algebra tiles, pp. 10–11

Tips for New Teachers

Zero Pairs Prior to the Activities, discuss the concept of a zero pair. Have students form zero pairs using 1-tiles, x-tiles, and x^2-tiles and their opposites.

2 TEACH

Working in Cooperative Groups

Put students in groups of two or three, mixing abilities. Have groups complete Activities 1–3 and Exercise 1.

- Talk about like terms in the context of the tiles. Tiles with the same shape and size represent like terms.
- For Activity 1, tell students that it is easier to model the polynomials if they arrange the tiles in the same order as the monomials within each polynomial. In this case, the monomials are arranged in descending order of degree. Therefore, students should arrange the tiles in descending order from left to right.
- After groups have completed Activity 1, write the addition of the two polynomials vertically so students can see that the coefficients of like terms are added.
- For Activity 2, explain that adding a zero pair to the polynomial does not change its value because the zero pair is equal to zero.

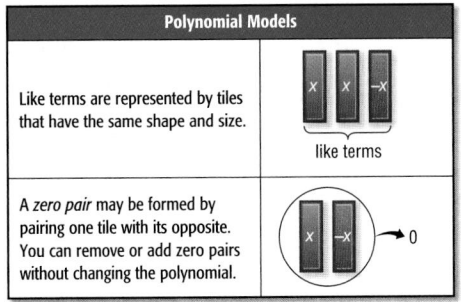

- After groups complete Activity 2, write the difference vertically so students can see that coefficients of like terms are subtracted.
- For Activity 3, students may find that it is easier to add the additive inverse when using algebra tiles. By doing so, they can avoid adding zero pairs.

Practice Have students complete Exercises 2–4.

Formative Assessment

Use Exercise 4 to assess whether students can use models to compare polynomials.

From Concrete to Abstract

Write a polynomial addition or subtraction problem on the board. Have students determine the sum or difference without using tiles. If they answer incorrectly, have them use their tiles to help them find their errors.

ACTIVITY 2 Subtract Polynomials

Use algebra tiles to find $(4x + 5) - (-3x + 1)$.

Step 1 Model the polynomial $4x + 5$.

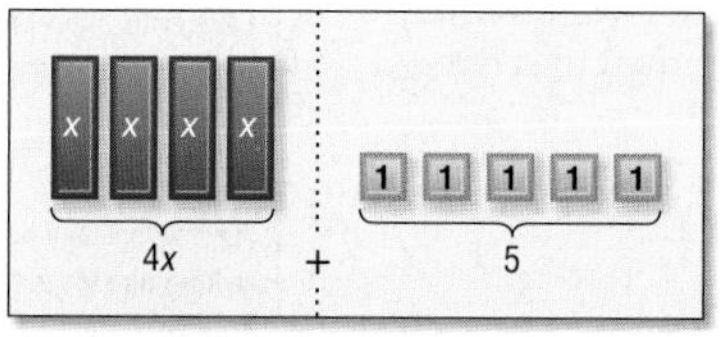

Step 2 To subtract $-3x + 1$, you must remove 3 red $-x$-tiles and 1 yellow 1-tile. You can remove the yellow 1-tile, but there are no red $-x$-tiles. Add 3 zero pairs of x-tiles. Then remove the 3 red $-x$-tiles.

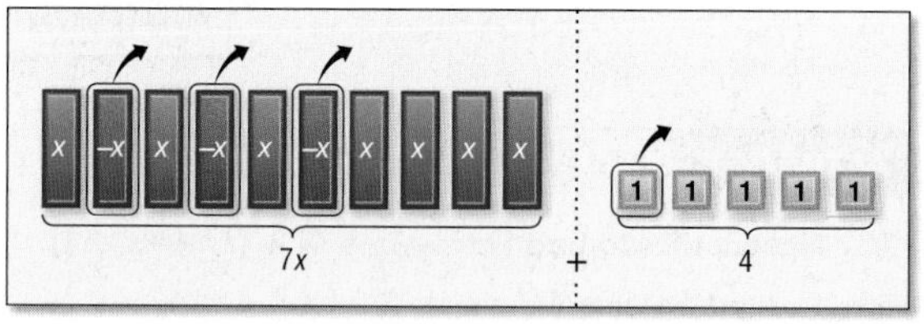

Step 3 Write the polynomial for the tiles that remain. $(4x + 5) - (-3x + 1) = 7x + 4$

Recall that you can subtract a number by adding its additive inverse or opposite. Similarly, you can subtract a polynomial by adding its opposite.

ACTIVITY 3 Subtract Polynomials Using Additive Inverse

Use algebra tiles to find $(4x + 5) - (-3x + 1)$.

Step 1 To find the difference of $4x + 5$ and $-3x + 1$, add $4x + 5$ and the opposite of $-3x + 1$.

$4x + 5$ →

The opposite of $-3x + 1$ is $3x - 1$. →

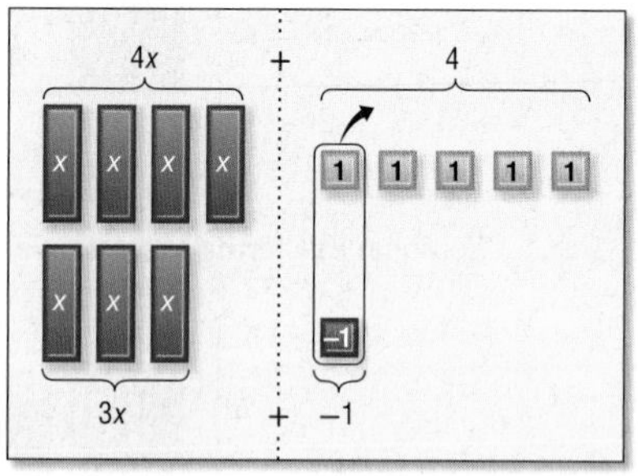

Step 2 Write the polynomial for the tiles that remain.
$(4x + 5) - (-3x + 1) = 7x + 4$. **Notice that this is the same answer as in Activity 2.**

Model and Analyze

Use algebra tiles to find each sum or difference. **1. $4x^2 + 3x + 4$** **2. $x^2 + 12x + 3$** **3. $-5x^2 + 4x$**

1. $(x^2 + 5x - 2) + (3x^2 - 2x + 6)$
2. $(2x^2 + 8x + 1) - (x^2 - 4x - 2)$
3. $(-4x^2 + x) - (x^2 + 5x)$
4. **WRITING IN MATH** Find $(4x^2 - x + 3) - (2x + 1)$ using each method from Activity 2 and Activity 3. Illustrate with drawings, and explain in writing how zero pairs are used in each case. **See Ch. 7 Answer Appendix.**

7-5 Adding and Subtracting Polynomials

Then

You wrote polynomials in standard form. (Lesson 7-4)

Now

- Add polynomials.
- Subtract polynomials.

IL Learning Standards

8.C.4b Apply algebraic properties and procedures with matrices, vectors, functions and sequences using data found in business, industry and consumer situations.

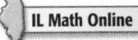

IL Math Online

glencoe.com

- Extra Examples
- Personal Tutor
- Self-Check Quiz
- Homework Help

Why?

From 2000 to 2003, sales (in millions of dollars) of rap/hip-hop music R and country music C in the United States can be modeled by the following equations, where t is the number of years since 2000.

$R = -132.3t^3 + 624.7t^2 - 773.6t + 1847.7$

$C = -3.4t^3 + 8.6t^2 - 95t + 1532.6$

The total music sales T of rap/hip-hop music and country music is $R + C$.

Add Polynomials Adding polynomials involves adding like terms. You can group like terms by using a horizontal or vertical format.

EXAMPLE 1 Add Polynomials

Find each sum.

a. $(2x^2 + 5x - 7) + (3 - 4x^2 + 6x)$

Horizontal Method

$(2x^2 + 5x - 7) + (3 - 4x^2 + 6x)$

$= [2x^2 + (-4x^2)] + [5x + 6x] + [-7 + 3]$ — Group like terms.

$= -2x^2 + 11x - 4$ — Combine like terms.

Vertical Method

$$\begin{array}{r} 2x^2 + 5x - 7 \\ (+)\ -4x^2 + 6x + 3 \\ \hline -2x^2 + 11x - 4 \end{array}$$

Align like terms in columns and combine.

b. $(3y + y^3 - 5) + (4y^2 - 4y + 2y^3 + 8)$

Horizontal Method

$(3y + y^3 - 5) + (4y^2 - 4y + 2y^3 + 8)$

$= [y^3 + 2y^3] + 4y^2 + [3y + (-4y)] + [(-5) + 8]$ — Group like terms.

$= 3y^3 + 4y^2 - y + 3$ — Combine like terms.

Vertical Method

$$\begin{array}{r} y^3 + 0y^2 + 3y - 5 \\ (+)\ 2y^3 + 4y^2 - 4y + 8 \\ \hline 3y^3 + 4y^2 - y + 3 \end{array}$$

Insert a placeholder to help align the terms.
Align and combine like terms.

Check Your Progress

1A. Find $(5x^2 - 3x + 4) + (6x - 3x^2 - 3)$. $2x^2 + 3x + 1$

1B. Find $(y^4 - 3y + 7) + (2y^3 + 2y - 2y^4 - 11)$. $-y^4 + 2y^3 - y - 4$

Personal Tutor glencoe.com

1 FOCUS

Vertical Alignment

Before Lesson 7-5
Write polynomials in standard form.

Lesson 7-5
Add polynomials.
Subtract polynomials.

After Lesson 7-5
Simplify the product of a polynomial by a monomial.

2 TEACH

Scaffolding Questions

Have students read the *Why?* section of the lesson.

Ask:

- Look at the polynomials that represent rap/hip-hop and country music sales. How many terms does each have? 4
- Compare the two polynomials. Are the terms like terms? yes
- How would you add the two polynomials? Combine the like terms.

Add Polynomials

Example 1 shows how to add polynomials by grouping like terms.

Lesson 7-5 Resources

Resource	Approaching-Level	On-Level	Beyond-Level	English Learners
Teacher Edition	• Differentiated Instruction, p. 435	• Differentiated Instruction, pp. 435, 438	• Differentiated Instruction, p. 438	• Differentiated Instruction, p. 435
Chapter Resource Masters	• Study Guide and Intervention, pp. 30–31 • Skills Practice, p. 32 • Practice, p. 33 • Word Problem Practice, p. 34	• Study Guide and Intervention, pp. 30–31 • Skills Practice, p. 32 • Practice, p. 33 • Word Problem Practice, p. 34 • Enrichment, p. 35	• Practice, p. 33 • Word Problem Practice, p. 34 • Enrichment, p. 35	• Study Guide and Intervention, pp. 30–31 • Skills Practice, p. 32 • Practice, p. 33
Transparencies	• 5-Minute Check Transparency 7-5	• 5-Minute Check Transparency 7-5	• 5-Minute Check Transparency 7-5	• 5-Minute Check Transparency 7-5
Other	• Study Notebook • Teaching Algebra with Manipulatives	• Study Notebook • Teaching Algebra with Manipulatives	• Study Notebook	• Study Notebook • Teaching Algebra with Manipulatives

Formative Assessment

Use the Check Your Progress exercises after each example to determine students' understanding of concepts.

Additional Example

1 Find each sum.

a. $(7y^2 + 2y - 3) + (2 - 4y + 5y^2)$ $12y^2 - 2y - 1$

b. $(4x^2 - 2x + 7) + (3x - 7x^2 - 9)$ $-3x^2 + x - 2$

Additional Examples also in Interactive Classroom PowerPoint® Presentations

IWB INTERACTIVE WHITEBOARD READY

Subtract Polynomials

Example 2 shows how to subtract a polynomial by adding its additive inverse. **Example 3** shows how to use addition or subtraction of polynomials to model a real-world situation.

Additional Example

2 Find each difference.

a. $(6y^2 + 8y^4 - 5y) - (9y^4 - 7y + 2y^2)$ $-y^4 + 4y^2 + 2y$

b. $(6n^2 + 11n^3 + 2n) - (4n - 3 + 5n^2)$ $11n^3 + n^2 - 2n + 3$

Watch Out!

Preventing Errors Some students may find it helpful to mark through like terms as they mentally combine them. This saves time spent on rewriting to group like terms.

StudyTip

Additive Inverse When finding the additive inverse of a polynomial, you are multiplying every term by −1.

Subtract Polynomials Recall that you can subtract a real number by adding its opposite or additive inverse. Similarly, you can subtract a polynomial by adding its additive inverse.

To find the additive inverse of a polynomial, write the opposite of each term in the polynomial.

$$-(3x^2 + 2x - 6) = \underbrace{-3x^2 - 2x + 6}_{\text{Additive Inverse}}$$

EXAMPLE 2 Subtract Polynomials

Find each difference.

a. $(3 - 2x + 2x^2) - (4x - 5 + 3x^2)$

Horizontal Method

Subtract $4x - 5 + 3x^2$ by adding its additive inverse.

$(3 - 2x + 2x^2) - (4x - 5 + 3x^2)$

$= (3 - 2x + 2x^2) + (-4x + 5 - 3x^2)$ — **The additive inverse of $4x - 5 + 3x^2$ is $-4x + 5 - 3x^2$.**

$= [2x^2 + (-3x^2)] + [(-2x) + (-4x)] + [3 + 5]$ — **Group like terms.**

$= -x^2 - 6x + 8$ — **Combine like terms.**

Vertical Method

Align like terms in columns and subtract by adding the additive inverse.

$$\begin{array}{r} 2x^2 - 2x + 3 \\ (-)\ 3x^2 + 4x - 5 \\ \hline \end{array} \quad \xrightarrow{\text{Add the opposite.}} \quad \begin{array}{r} 2x^2 - 2x + 3 \\ (+)\ -3x^2 - 4x + 5 \\ \hline -x^2 - 6x + 8 \end{array}$$

Thus, $(3 - 2x + 2x^2) - (4x - 5 + 3x^2) = -x^2 - 6x + 8$.

StudyTip

Vertical Method Notice that the polynomials are written in standard form with like terms aligned.

b. $(7p + 4p^3 - 8) - (3p^2 + 2 - 9p)$

Horizontal Method

Subtract $3p^2 + 2 - 9p$ by adding its additive inverse.

$(7p + 4p^3 - 8) - (3p^2 + 2 - 9p)$

$= (7p + 4p^3 - 8) + (-3p^2 - 2 + 9p)$ — **The additive inverse of $3p^2 + 2 - 9p$ is $-3p^2 - 2 + 9p$.**

$= [7p + 9p] + 4p^3 + (-3p^2) + [(-8) + (-2)]$ — **Group like terms.**

$= 4p^3 - 3p^2 + 16p - 10$ — **Combine like terms.**

Vertical Method

Align like terms in columns and subtract by adding the additive inverse.

$$\begin{array}{r} 4p^3 + 0p^2 + 7p - 8 \\ (-)\quad 3p^2 - 9p + 2 \\ \hline \end{array} \quad \xrightarrow{\text{Add the opposite.}} \quad \begin{array}{r} 4p^3 + 0p^2 + 7p - 8 \\ (+)\quad -3p^2 + 9p - 2 \\ \hline 4p^3 - 3p^2 + 16p - 10 \end{array}$$

Thus, $(7p + 4p^3 - 8) - (3p^2 + 2 - 9p) = 4p^3 - 3p^2 + 16p - 10$.

Check Your Progress

2A. Find $(4x^3 - 3x^2 + 6x - 4) - (-2x^3 + x^2 - 2)$. $6x^3 - 4x^2 + 6x - 2$

2B. Find $(8y - 10 + 5y^2) - (7 - y^3 + 12y)$. $y^3 + 5y^2 - 4y - 17$

Personal Tutor glencoe.com

Focus on Mathematical Content

Number of Terms When adding or subtracting polynomials, the number of terms in the sum or difference may or may not be the same number as in the polynomials being added or subtracted. Students may assume that having more or fewer terms in the sum or difference must be the sign of an error or an unsimplified answer. Use an example to explain why this is faulty thinking.

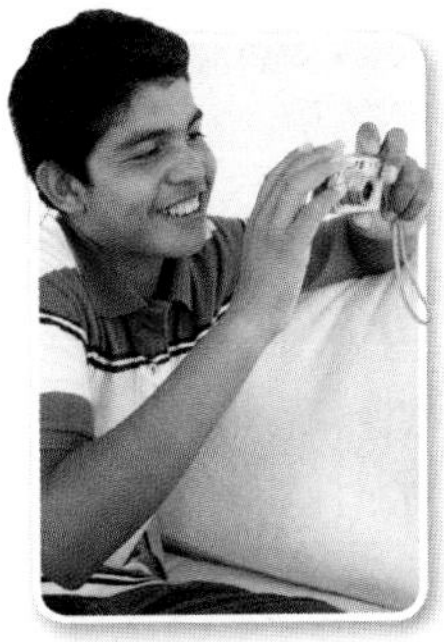

Real-World Link

Sales of digital cameras recently increased by 42% in one year. Sales are expected to increase by at least 15% each year as consumers upgrade their cameras.

Source: Big Planet Marketing Company

Real-World EXAMPLE 3 Add and Subtract Polynomials

CONSUMER ELECTRONICS **An electronics store is starting to track sales of cell phones and digital cameras. The equations below represent the number of cell phones P and the number of digital cameras C sold in m months.**

$$P = 7m + 137 \qquad C = 4m + 78$$

a. Write an equation for the monthly sales T of phones and cameras.

Add the polynomial for P with the polynomial for C.

total sales = cell phone sales + digital camera sales

$T = 7m + 137 + 4m + 78$ **Substitution**

$= 11m + 215$ **Combine like terms.**

An equation is $T = 11m + 215$.

b. Use the equation to predict the number of cell phones and digital cameras sold in 10 months.

$T = 11(10) + 215$ **Substitute 10 for *m*.**

$= 110 + 215$ **Simplify.**

$= 325$

Thus, a total of 325 cell phones and digital cameras will be sold in 10 months.

Check Your Progress

3. Use the information above to write an equation that represents the difference in the monthly sales of cell phones and the monthly sales of digital cameras. Use the equation to predict the difference in monthly sales in 24 months. $D = 3m - 59$; 13

Personal Tutor glencoe.com

Check Your Understanding

Examples 1 and 2 pp. 433–434

Find each sum or difference.

1. $(6x^3 - 4) + (-2x^3 + 9)$ $4x^3 + 5$
2. $(g^3 - 2g^2 + 5g + 6) - (g^2 + 2g)$ $g^3 - 3g^2 + 3g + 6$
3. $(4 + 2a^2 - 2a) - (3a^2 - 8a + 7)$ $-a^2 + 6a - 3$
4. $(8y - 4y^2) + (3y - 9y^2)$ $-13y^2 + 11y$
5. $(-4z^3 - 2z + 8) - (4z^3 + 3z^2 - 5)$ $-8z^3 - 3z^2 - 2z + 13$
6. $(-3d^2 - 8 + 2d) + (4d - 12 + d^2)$ $-2d^2 + 6d - 20$
7. $(2c^2 + 6c + 4) + (5c^2 - 7)$ $7c^2 + 6c - 3$
8. $(3n^3 - 5n + n^2) - (-8n^2 + 3n^3)$ $9n^2 - 5n$

Example 3 p. 435

9. **VACATION** The total number of students T who traveled for spring break consists of two groups: students who flew to their destinations F and students who drove to their destination D. The number (in thousands) of students who flew and the total number of students who flew or drove can be modeled by the following equations, where n is the number of years since 1995.

$$T = 14n + 21 \qquad F = 8n + 7$$

a. Write an equation that models the number of students who drove to their destination for this time period. $D = 6n + 14$

b. Predict the number of students who will drive to their destination in 2012. 116,000 students

c. How many students will drive or fly to their destination in 2015? 301,000 students

Additional Example

3 **VIDEO GAMES** The total amount of toy sales T (in billions of dollars) consists of two groups: sales of video games V and sales of traditional toys R. In recent years, the sales of traditional toys and total sales could be represented by the following equations, where n is the number of years since 2000.

$R = 0.46n^3 - 1.9n^2 + 3n + 19$

$T = 0.45n^3 - 1.85n^2 + 4.4n + 22.6$

a. Write an equation that represents the sales of video games V.
$V = -0.01n^3 + 0.05n^2 + 1.4n + 3.6$

b. Use the equation to predict the amount of video game sales in the year 2009.
12.96 billion dollars

3 PRACTICE

Formative Assessment

Use Exercises 1–9 to check for understanding.

Use the chart at the bottom of the next page to customize assignments for your students.

TEACH with TECH

INTERACTIVE WHITEBOARD Write an expression on the board to add or subtract two polynomials. Drag the like terms to group them together. Then combine like terms and simplify the expression.

Differentiated Instruction AL OL ELL

Interpersonal Learners Have students work in pairs to find the sums and differences in Exercises 1–8. Then compare answers and steps used to get their answers. When they differ, pairs should consult with another pair of students. Students should offer constructive reinforcement to each other.

Watch Out!

Find the Error For Exercise 36, have students check each step of Cheyenne and Sebastian's work. Remind students that both need to add the additive inverse of each term in the polynomial being subtracted.

Additional Answer

41. Sample answer: To add polynomials in a horizontal format, you combine like terms. For the vertical format, you write the polynomials in standard form, align like terms in columns, and combine like terms. To subtract polynomials in a horizontal format you find the additive inverse of the polynomial you are subtracting, and then combine like terms. For the vertical format you write the polynomials in standard form, align like terms in columns, and subtract by adding the additive inverse.

Practice and Problem Solving

(●) = **Step-by-Step Solutions** begin on page R12. **Extra Practice** begins on page 815.

Examples 1 and 2 pp. 433–434

14. $-2x - 5y + 1$
15. $-2b^2 + 2a + 9$
16. $-x^2y - 3x^2 + 4y$
17. $7x^2 - 2xy - 7y$
18. $-6p^2 + 2np + n$
19. $3x^2 - rxt - 8r^2x - 6rx^2$
20. $7ab^2 + 3a^2b - 2ab$
21. $-cd^2 + 6cd - 10$

Find each sum or difference. **10.** $4y^2 + 3y + 3$ **12.** $3c^3 - c^2 - 3c + 3$

10. $(y + 5) + (2y + 4y^2 - 2)$

11. $(2x + 3x^2) - (7 - 8x^2)$ $11x^2 + 2x - 7$

12. $(3c^3 - c + 11) - (c^2 + 2c + 8)$

13. $(z^2 + z) + (z^2 - 11)$ $2z^2 + z - 11$

14. $(2x - 2y + 1) - (3y + 4x)$

15. $(4a - 5b^2 + 3) + (6 - 2a + 3b^2)$

16. $(x^2y - 3x^2 + y) + (3y - 2x^2y)$

17. $(-8xy + 3x^2 - 5y) + (4x^2 - 2y + 6xy)$

18. $(5n - 2p^2 + 2np) - (4p^2 + 4n)$

19. $(4rxt - 8r^2x + x^2) - (6rx^2 + 5rxt - 2x^2)$

20. $(6ab^2 + 2ab) + (3a^2b - 4ab + ab^2)$

21. $(cd^2 + 2cd - 4) + (-6 + 4cd - 2cd^2)$

Example 3 p. 435

22. PETS From 1997 through 2007, the number of dogs D and the number of cats C (in hundreds) adopted from animal shelters in the United States are modeled by the following equations, where n is the number of years since 1997.

$$D = 2n + 3 \qquad C = n + 4$$

a. Write an equation that models the total number T of dogs and cats adopted in hundreds for this time period. $T = 3n + 7$

b. If this trend continues, how many dogs and cats will be adopted in 2011? **4900 dogs and cats**

B Find each sum or difference.

23. $(4x + 2y - 6z) + (5y - 2z + 7x) + (-9z - 2x - 3y)$ $9x + 4y - 17z$

24. $(5a^2 - 4) + (a^2 - 2a + 12) + (4a^2 - 6a + 8)$ $10a^2 - 8a + 16$

25. $(3c^2 - 7) + (4c + 7) - (c^2 + 5c - 8)$ $2c^2 - c + 8$

26. $(3n^3 + 3n - 10) - (4n^2 - 5n) + (4n^3 - 3n^2 - 9n + 4)$ $7n^3 - 7n^2 - n - 6$

27. GEOMETRY Write a polynomial that represents the perimeter of the figure at the right. $12x + 1\frac{1}{4}$

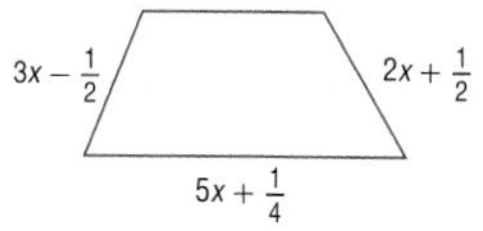

28. PAINTING Kin is painting two walls of her bedroom. The area of one wall can be modeled by $3x^2 + 14$, and the area of the other wall can be modeled by $2x - 3$. What is the total area of the two walls? $3x^2 + 2x + 11$

29. GEOMETRY The perimeter of the figure at the right is represented by the expression $3x^2 - 7x + 2$. Write a polynomial that represents the measure of the third side. $4x$

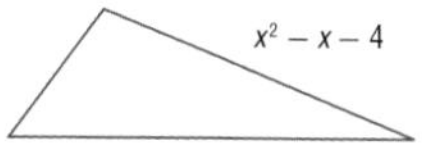

Real-World Link

The Pro Football Hall of Fame located in Canton, Ohio, is approximately 83,000 square feet and has had more than eight million visitors.

Source: Pro Football Hall of Fame

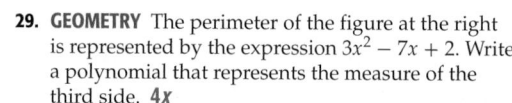

30. FOOTBALL The National Football League is divided into two conferences, the American A and the National N. From 1996 through 2004, the total attendance T (in thousands) for both conferences and for the American Conference games are modeled by the following equations, where y is the number of years since 1996.

$$T = 35y^3 + 27y^2 + 1899 \qquad A = 16y^3 + 13y^2 + 2y + 905$$

Determine how many people attended a National Conference football game in 2002. **5,590,000 people**

31. GEOMETRY The width of a rectangle is represented by $5x + 2y$, and the length is represented by $6y - 2x$. Write a polynomial that represents the perimeter. $6x + 16y$

Differentiated Homework Options

Level	Assignment	Two-Day Option	
AL Basic	10–22, 36–37, 39–69	11–21 odd, 42–45	10–22 even, 36–37, 39–41, 46–69
OL Core	11–25 odd, 27–37, 39–69	10–22, 42–45	23–37, 39–41, 46–69
BL Advanced	23–61, (optional: 62–69)		

32. **GARDENING** Candida is planting flowers on the perimeter of a rectangular patio.

a. If the perimeter of the patio is $210x$ and one side measures $32x$, find the length of the other side. **$73x$**

b. Write a polynomial that represents the area of the rectangular patio. **$2336x^2$**

33. **GEOMETRY** The sum of the measures of the angles in a triangle is 180°.

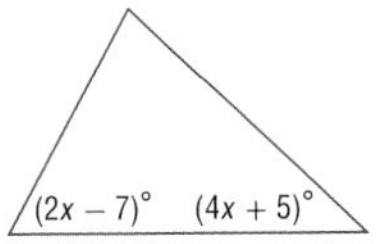

a. Write an expression to represent the measure of the third angle of the triangle. **$182 - 6x$**

b. If $x = 23$, find the measures of the three angles. **39, 97, 44**

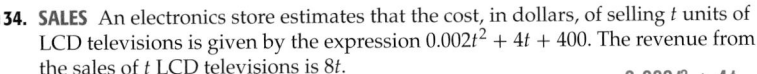

34. **SALES** An electronics store estimates that the cost, in dollars, of selling t units of LCD televisions is given by the expression $0.002t^2 + 4t + 400$. The revenue from the sales of t LCD televisions is $8t$.

a. Write a polynomial that represents the profit of selling t units. **$-0.002t^2 + 4t - 400$**

b. If 750 LCD televisions are sold, how much did the store earn? **\$1475**

c. If 575 LCD televisions are sold, how much did the store earn? **\$1238.75**

35. **CAR RENTAL** The cost to rent a car for a day is \$15 plus \$0.15 for each mile driven.

a. Write a polynomial that represents the cost of renting a car for m miles. **$15 + 0.15m$**

b. If a car is driven 145 miles, how much would it cost to rent? **\$36.75**

c. If a car is driven 105 miles each day for four days, how much would it cost to rent a car? **\$123**

d. If a car is driven 220 miles each day for seven days, how much would it cost to rent a car? **\$336**

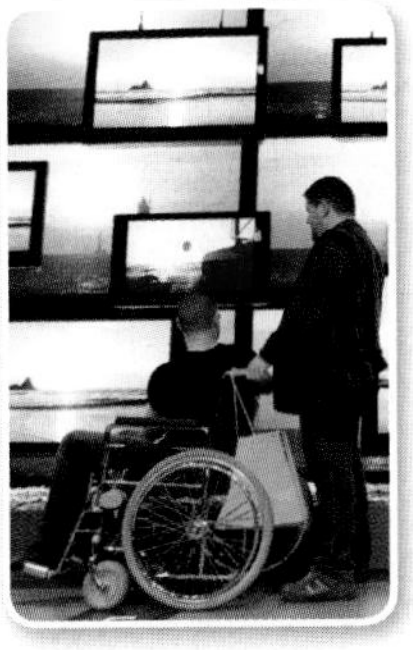

Real-World Link

On average, an LCD television lasts about 60,000 hours. This means the lifespan of an LCD television can be 20 years or more if the television is used less than 8 hours per day.

Source: LCD TV Buying Guide

H.O.T. Problems

Use Higher-Order Thinking Skills

36. **FIND THE ERROR** Cheyenne and Sebastian are finding $(2x^2 - x) - (3x + 3x^2 - 2)$. Is either of them correct? Explain your reasoning.

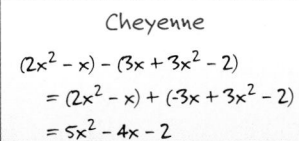

Cheyenne	Sebastian
$(2x^2 - x) - (3x + 3x^2 - 2)$	$(2x^2 - x) - (3x + 3x^2 - 2)$
$= (2x^2 - x) + (-3x + 3x^2 - 2)$	$= (2x^2 - x) + (-3x - 3x^2 - 2)$
$= 5x^2 - 4x - 2$	$= -x^2 - 4x - 2$

37. **OPEN ENDED** Write two trinomials with a difference of $2x^3 - 7x + 8$.

38. **CHALLENGE** Write a polynomial that represents the sum of an odd integer $2n + 1$ and the next two consecutive odd integers. **$6n + 9$**

39. **REASONING** Find a counterexample to the following statement.

The order in which polynomials are subtracted does not matter.

40. **OPEN ENDED** Write three trinomials with a sum of $4x^4 + 3x^2$.

41. **WRITING IN MATH** Describe how to add and subtract polynomials using both the vertical and horizontal formats. Which one do you think is easier? Why? **See margin.**

36. Neither; neither of them found the additive inverse correctly. All terms should be multiplied by −1.

37. Sample answer: $3x^3 - 8x + 9$, $x^3 - x + 1$

39. Sample answer: $(2x - 3) - (4x - 3) = -2x$ but $(4x - 3) - (2x - 3) = 2x$

40. Sample answer: $2x^4 + 5x^2 + 2x$, $x^4 - x^2 - x$, $x^4 - x^2 - x$

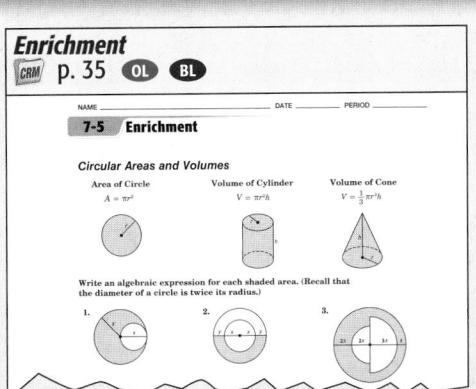

Study Guide and Intervention
CRM pp. 30–31 AL OL ELL

NAME ______ DATE ______ PERIOD ______

7-5 Study Guide and Intervention

Adding and Subtracting Polynomials

Add Polynomials To add polynomials, you can group like terms horizontally or write them in column form, aligning like terms vertically. **Like terms** are monomial terms that are either identical or differ only in their coefficients, such as $3p$ and $-5p$ or $2x^2y$ and $8x^2y$.

Example 1 Find $(2x^2 + x - 8) + (3x - 4x^2 + 2)$.

Horizontal Method

Group like terms.

$(2x^2 + x - 8) + (3x - 4x^2 + 2)$

$= [(2x^2 + (-4x^2)] + (x + 3x) + [(-8) + 2)]$

$= -2x^2 + 4x - 6.$

The sum is $-2x^2 + 4x - 6$.

Example 2 Find $(3x^2 + 5xy) + (xy + 2x^2)$.

Vertical Method

Align like terms in columns and add.

$3x^2 + 5xy$

$(+)\ 2x^2 + xy$ Put the terms in descending order.

$5x^2 + 6xy$

The sum is $5x^2 + 6xy$.

Exercises

Find each sum.

1. $(4a - 5) + (3a + 6)$ **$7a + 1$**
2. $(6x + 9) + (4x^2 - 7)$ **$4x^2 + 6x + 2$**
3. $(6xy + 2y + 6x) + (4xy - x)$ **$10xy + 5x + 2y$**
4. $(x^2 + y^2) + (-x^2 + y^2)$ **$2y^2$**
5. $(3p^2 - 2p + 3) + (p^2 - 7p + 7)$ **$4p^2 - 9p + 10$**
6. $(2x^2 + 5xy + 4y^2) + (-xy - 6x^2 + 2y^2)$ **$-4x^2 + 4xy + 6y^2$**
7. $(5p + 2q) + (2p^2 - 8q + 1)$ **$2p^2 + 5p - 6q + 1$**
8. $(4x^2 - x + 4) + (5x + 2x^2 + 2)$ **$6x^2 + 4x + 6$**
9. $(6x^2 + 3x) + (x^2 - 4x - 3)$ **$7x^2 - x - 3$**
10. $(x^2 + 2xy + y^2) + (x^2 - xy - 2y^2)$ **$2x^2 + xy - y^2$**
11. $(2a - 4b - c) + (-2a - b - 4c)$ **$-5b - 5c$**
12. $(6xy^2 + 4xy) + (2xy - 10xy^2 + y^2)$ **$-4xy^2 + 6xy + y^2$**
13. $(2p - 5r) + (3p + 6r) + (p - r)$ **$6p$**
14. $(2x^2 - 6) + (5x^2 + 2) + (-x^2 - 7)$ **$6x^2 - 11$**
15. $(3z^2 + 5z) + (z^2 + 2z) + (z - 4)$ **$4z^2 + 8z - 4$**
16. $(8x^2 + 4x + 3y^2 + y) + (6x^2 - x + 4y)$ **$14x^2 + 3x + 3y^2 + 5y$**

Chapter 7 30 Glencoe Algebra 1

Practice
CRM p. 33 AL OL BL ELL

NAME ______ DATE ______ PERIOD ______

7-5 Practice

Adding and Subtracting Polynomials

Find each sum or difference.

1. $(4y + 5) + (-7y - 1)$ **$-3y + 4$**
2. $(-x^2 + 3x) - (5x + 2x^2)$ **$-3x^2 - 2x$**
3. $(4k^2 + 8k + 2) - (2k + 3)$ **$4k^2 + 6k - 1$**
4. $(2m^2 + 6m) + (m^2 - 5m + 7)$ **$3m^2 + m + 7$**
5. $(5a^2 + 6a + 2) - (7a^2 - 7a + 5)$ **$-2a^2 + 13a - 3$**
6. $(-4p^2 - p + 9) + (p^2 + 3p - 1)$ **$-3p^2 + 2p + 8$**
7. $(x^3 - 3x + 1) - (x^3 + 7 - 12x)$ **$9x - 6$**
8. $(6x^2 - x + 1) - (-4 + 2x^2 + 8x)$ **$4x^2 - 9x + 5$**
9. $(4y^2 + 2y - 8) - (7y^2 + 4 - y)$ **$-3y^2 + 3y - 12$**
10. $(w^2 - 4w - 1) + (-5 + 5w^2 - 3w)$ **$6w^2 - 7w - 6$**
11. $(4u^2 - 2u - 3) + (3u^2 - u + 4)$ **$7u^2 - 3u + 1$**
12. $(5b^2 - 8 + 2b) - (b + 9b^2 + 5)$ **$-4b^2 + b - 13$**
13. $(4d^2 + 2d + 2) + (5d^2 - 2 - d)$ **$9d^2 + d$**
14. $(8x^2 + x - 6) - (-x^2 + 2x - 3)$ **$9x^2 - x - 3$**
15. $(3h^2 + 7h - 1) - (4h + 8h^2 + 1)$ **$-5h^2 + 3h - 2$**
16. $(4m^2 - 3m + 10) + (m^2 + m - 2)$ **$5m^2 - 2m + 8$**
17. $(x^2 + y^2 - 6) - (5x^2 - y^2 - 5)$ **$-4x^2 + 2y^2 - 1$**
18. $(7t^2 + 2 - t) + (t^2 - 7 - 2t)$ **$8t^2 - 3t - 5$**
19. $(k^3 - 2k^2 + 4k + 6) - (-4k + k^2 - 3)$ **$k^3 - 3k^2 + 8k + 9$**
20. $(9j^2 + j + jk) + (-3j^2 - jk - 4j)$ **$6j^2 - 3j$**
21. $(2x + 6y - 3z) + (4x + 6z - 8y) + (x - 3y + z)$ **$7x - 5y + 4z$**
22. $(6f^2 - 7f - 3) - (5f^2 - 1 + 2f) - (2f^2 - 3 + f)$ **$-f^2 - 10f + 1$**
23. **BUSINESS** The polynomial $s^3 - 70s^2 + 1500s - 10{,}800$ models the profit a company makes on selling an item at a price s. A second item sold at the same price brings in a profit of $s^3 - 30s^2 + 450s - 5000$. Write a polynomial that expresses the total profit from the sale of both items. **$2s^3 - 100s^2 + 1950s - 15{,}800$**
24. **GEOMETRY** The measures of two sides of a triangle are given. If P is the perimeter, and $P = 10x + 5y$, find the measure of the third side. **$2x + 2y$**

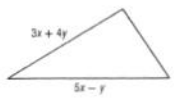

Chapter 7 33 Glencoe Algebra 1

Word Problem Practice
CRM p. 34 AL OL BL ELL

NAME ______ DATE ______ PERIOD ______

7-5 Word Problem Practice

Adding and Subtracting Polynomials

1. **BUILDING** Find the simplest expression for the perimeter of the triangular roof truss. **$5a^2 + 6a - 3$**

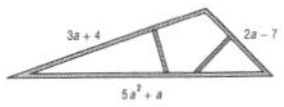

2. **GEOMETRY** Write a polynomial to show the area of the large square below. **$a^2 + 2ab + b^2$**

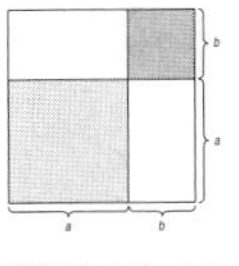

3. **FIREWORKS** Two bottle rockets are launched straight up into the air. The height, in feet, of each rocket at t seconds after launch is given by the polynomial equations below. Write an equation to show how much higher Rocket A traveled.
Rocket A: $H_1 = -16t^2 + 122t$
Rocket B: $H_1 = -16t^2 + 84t$
$D = 38t$

4. **ENVELOPES** An office supply company produces yellow document envelopes. The envelopes come in a variety of sizes, but the length is always 4 centimeters more than double the width. Write a polynomial expression to give the perimeter of any of the envelopes. **$6x + 8$**

5. **INDUSTRY** Two identical right cylindrical steel drums containing oil need to be covered with a fire-resistant sealant. In order to determine how much sealant to purchase, George must find the surface area of the two drums. The surface area (including the top and bottom bases) is given by the following formula.

$$S = 2\pi rh + 2\pi r^2$$

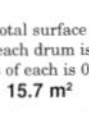

a. Write a polynomial to represent the total surface area of the two drums. **$4\pi rh + 4\pi r^2$**

b. Find the total surface area if the height of each drum is 2 meters and the radius of each is 0.5 meters. Let $\pi = 3.14$. **15.7 m²**

c. The fire resistant sealant must be applied while they are stacked vertically in groups of three. If h is the height of each drum and r is the radius, write a polynomial to represent the exposed surface area. **$6\pi rh + \pi r^2$**

Chapter 7 34 Glencoe Algebra 1

Enrichment
CRM p. 35 OL BL

NAME ______ DATE ______ PERIOD ______

7-5 Enrichment

Circular Areas and Volumes

Area of Circle	Volume of Cylinder	Volume of Cone
$A = \pi r^2$	$V = \pi r^2 h$	$V = \frac{1}{3}\pi r^2 h$

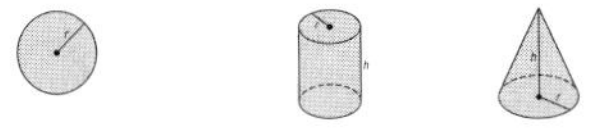

Write an algebraic expression for each shaded area. (Recall that the diameter of a circle is twice its radius.)

1. 2. 3.

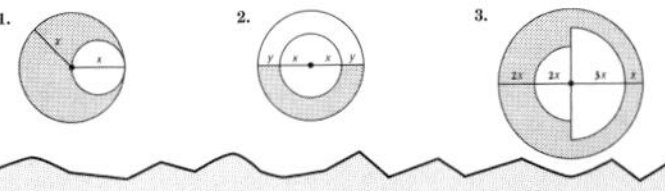

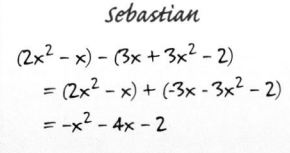

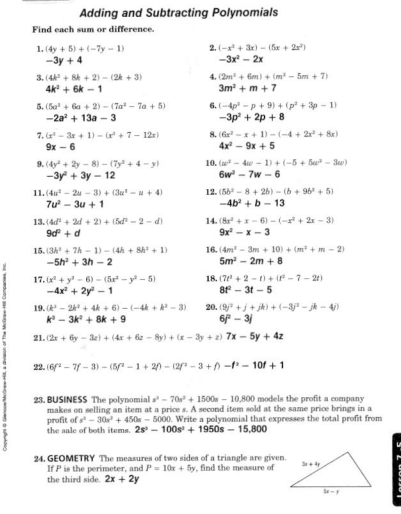

4 ASSESS

Ticket Out the Door Make several copies each of five polynomial expressions. Give one expression to each student. As the students leave the room, ask them to tell you the additive inverses of their expressions.

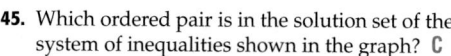

PSAE PRACTICE 6.11.13, 7.11.03, 6.11.10, 8.11.15

42. Three consecutive integers can be represented by x, $x + 1$, and $x + 2$. What is the sum of these three integers? **C**

A $x(x + 1)(x + 2)$ C $3x + 3$

B $x^3 + 3$ D $x + 3$

43. SHORT RESPONSE What is the perimeter of a square with sides that measure $2x + 3$ units? **$8x + 12$ units**

44. Jim cuts a board in the shape of a regular hexagon and pounds in a nail at each vertex, as shown. How many rubber bands will he need to stretch a rubber band across every possible pair of nails? **F**

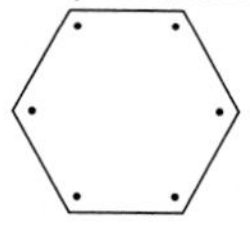

F 15 G 12 H 14 J 9

45. Which ordered pair is in the solution set of the system of inequalities shown in the graph? **C**

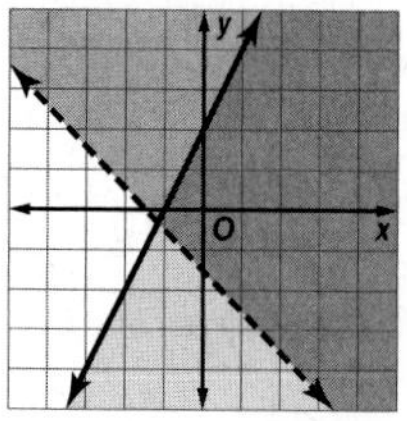

A $(-3, 0)$ C $(5, 0)$

B $(0, -3)$ D $(0, 5)$

Spiral Review

Find the degree of each polynomial. (Lesson 7-4)

46. $6b^4$ **4** **47.** $10t$ **1** **48.** $5g^2h$ **3**

49. $7np^4$ **5** **50.** 25 **0** **51.** $t^3 + 6u$ **3**

52. $2 + 3ab^3 - a^2b + 4a^6$ **6** **53.** $6 - v^4 + v^2z^3 + 6v^3$ **5**

54. POPULATION The 2005 population of North Carolina's Beaufort County was approximately 46,000. Express this number in scientific notation. (Lesson 7-3) **4.6×10^4**

55. JOBS Kimi received an offer for a new job. She wants to compare the offer with her current job. What is total amount of sales that Kimi must get each month to make the same income at either job? (Lesson 6-2) **$80,000**

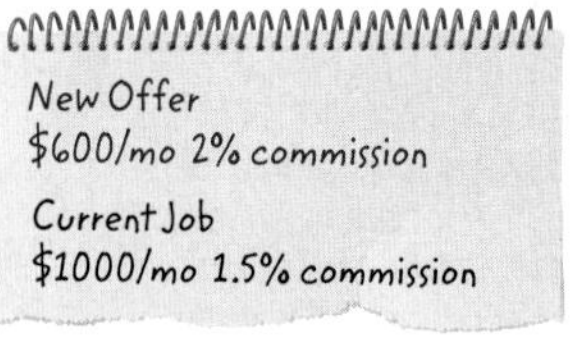

Determine whether each sequence is an arithmetic sequence. If it is, state the common difference. (Lesson 3-5)

56. 24, 16, 8, 0, … **yes; −8** **57.** $3\frac{1}{4}, 6\frac{1}{2}$, 13, 26, … **no** **58.** 7, 6, 5, 4, … **yes; −1**

59. 10, 12, 15, 18, … **no** **60.** −15, −11, −7, −3, … **yes; 4** **61.** −0.3, 0.2, 0.7, 1.2, … **yes; 0.5**

Skills Review

Simplify. (Lesson 7-1)

62. $t(t^5)(t^7)$ **t^{13}** **63.** $n^3(n^2)(-2n^3)$ **$-2n^8$**

64. $(5t^5v^2)(10t^3v^4)$ **$50t^8v^6$** **65.** $(-8u^4z^5)(5uz^4)$ **$-40u^5z^9$**

66. $[(3)^2]^3$ **729** **67.** $[(2)^3]^2$ **64**

68. $(2m^4k^3)^2(-3mk^2)^3$ **$-108m^{11}k^{12}$** **69.** $(6xy^2)^2(2x^2y^2z^2)^3$ **$288x^8y^{10}z^6$**

Differentiated Instruction OL BL

Extension Tell students the equations for the monthly unit sales of CDs C and DVDs D are $C = 7m + 87$ and $D = 9m + 152$, where m represents time in months since a store opened. Suppose the total monthly sales of CDs, DVDs, and videos is represented by $T = 15m + 248$. Write an equation that can be used to calculate monthly video sales V. How many videos did the store sell in the sixth month when $m = 5$? $V = (-1)m + 9$; 4

7-6

Multiplying a Polynomial by a Monomial

Then

You multiplied monomials. (Lesson 7-1)

Now

- Multiply a polynomial by a monomial.
- Solve equations involving the products of monomials and polynomials.

IL Learning Standards

8.A.4b Represent mathematical patterns and describe their properties using variables and mathematical symbols.

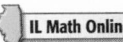

IL Math Online

glencoe.com

- Extra Examples
- Personal Tutor
- Self-Check Quiz
- Homework Help

Why?

Charmaine Brooks is opening a fitness club. She tells the contractor that the length of the fitness room should be three times the width plus 8 feet.

To cover the floor with mats for exercise classes, Ms. Brooks needs to know the area of the floor. So she multiplies the width times the length, $w(3w + 8)$.

Polynomial Multiplied by Monomial To find the product of a polynomial and a monomial, you can use the Distributive Property.

EXAMPLE 1 Multiply a Polynomial by a Monomial

Find $-3x^2(7x^2 - x + 4)$.

Horizontal Method

$-3x^2(7x^2 - x + 4)$	Original expression
$= -3x^2(7x^2) - (-3x^2)(x) + (-3x^2)(4)$	Distributive Property
$= -21x^4 - (-3x^3) + (-12x^2)$	Multiply.
$= -21x^4 + 3x^3 - 12x^2$	Simplify.

Vertical Method

$7x^2 - x + 4$	
$(\times) \quad -3x^2$	Distributive Property
$-21x^4 + 3x^3 - 12x^2$	Multiply.

Check Your Progress

Find each product.

1A. $5a^2(-4a^2 + 2a - 7)$ $-20a^4 + 10a^3 - 35a^2$

1B. $-6d^3(3d^4 - 2d^3 - d + 9)$ $-18a^7 + 12d^6 + 6d^4 - 54d^3$

Personal Tutor glencoe.com

We can use this same method more than once to simplify large expressions.

EXAMPLE 2 Simplify Expressions

Simplify $2p(-4p^2 + 5p) - 5(2p^2 + 20)$.

$2p(-4p^2 + 5p) - 5(2p^2 + 20)$	Original expression
$= (2p)(-4p^2) + (2p)(5p) + (-5)(2p^2) + (-5)(20)$	Distributive Property
$= -8p^3 + 10p^2 - 10p^2 - 100$	Multiply.
$= -8p^3 + (10p^2 - 10p^2) - 100$	Commutative and Associative Properties
$= -8p^3 - 100$	Combine like terms.

7-6 Lesson Notes

1 FOCUS

Vertical Alignment

Before Lesson 7-6
Multiply monomials.

Lesson 7-6
Multiply a polynomial by a monomial.
Solve equations involving the products of monomials and polynomials.

After Lesson 7-6
Multiply binomials and polynomials.

2 TEACH

Scaffolding Questions

Have students read the *Why?* section of the lesson.

Ask:

- What is the formula for finding the area of a rectangle? $A = \ell w$, where ℓ is the length and w is the width.
- What are ℓ and w for the expression shown? ℓ is $(3w + 8)$ and w is w.
- Which of the dimensions is a monomial? w
- Describe how you would find the area of the room if the width is 20 feet. $20(3 \cdot 20 + 8) = 20(60 + 8) = 1200 + 160 = 1360$ ft^2

Lesson 7-6 Resources

Resource	Approaching-Level	On-Level	Beyond-Level	English Learners
Teacher Edition	• Differentiated Instruction, p. 441	• Differentiated Instruction, pp. 441, 444	• Differentiated Instruction, p. 444	
Chapter Resource Masters	• Study Guide and Intervention, pp. 36–37 • Skills Practice, p. 38 • Practice, p. 39 • Word Problem Practice, p. 40	• Study Guide and Intervention, pp. 36–37 • Skills Practice, p. 38 • Practice, p. 39 • Word Problem Practice, p. 40 • Enrichment, p. 41	• Practice, p. 39 • Word Problem Practice, p. 40 • Enrichment, p. 41	• Study Guide and Intervention, pp. 36–37 • Skills Practice, p. 38 • Practice, p. 39
Transparencies	• 5-Minute Check Transparency 7-6	• 5-Minute Check Transparency 7-6	• 5-Minute Check Transparency 7-6	• 5-Minute Check Transparency 7-6
Other	• Study Notebook • Teaching Algebra with Manipulatives	• Study Notebook • Teaching Algebra with Manipulatives	• Study Notebook	• Study Notebook • Teaching Algebra with Manipulatives

Lesson 7-6 Multiplying a Polynomial by a Monomial 439

Polynomial Multiplied by Monomial

Example 1 shows how the Distributive Property can be used to multiply a polynomial by a monomial. **Example 2** shows how to use the Distributive Property more than once to simplify large expressions. **Example 3** shows how to write and evaluate a polynomial expression for a real-world problem.

Formative Assessment

Use the Check Your Progress exercises after each example to determine students' understanding of concepts.

Additional Examples

1 Find $6y(4y^2 - 9y - 7)$. $24y^3 - 54y^2 - 42y$

2 Simplify $3(2t^2 - 4t - 15) + 6t(5t + 2)$. $36t^2 - 45$

3 **GRIDDED RESPONSE** Admission to the Super Fun Amusement Park is \$10. Once in the park, super rides are an additional \$3 each, and regular rides are an additional \$2. Wyome goes to the park and rides 15 rides, of which s of those 15 are super rides. Find the cost if Wyome rode 9 super rides. \$49

Additional Examples also in Interactive Classroom PowerPoint® Presentations

IWB INTERACTIVE WHITEBOARD READY

TEACH with TECH

DOCUMENT CAMERA Display a square photograph. Label each side as p. Discuss how to find the area of the photo. Then add a portion of a frame to the top of the photo. Discuss the new length of the photo and frame, and how to find the new area of the view.

Check Your Progress

Simplify each expression.

2A. $3(5x^2 + 2x - 4) - x(7x^2 + 2x - 3)$ **2B.** $15t(10y^3t^5 + 5y^2t) - 2y(yt^2 + 4y^2)$

2A. $-7x^3 + 13x^2 + 9x - 12$
2B. $150y^3t^6 + 73y^2t^2 - 8y^3$

Personal Tutor glencoe.com

We can use the Distributive Property to multiply monomials by polynomials and solve real world problems.

Test-Taking Tip

Formulas Many standardized tests provide formula sheets with commonly used formulas. If you are unsure of the correct formula, check the sheet before beginning to solve the problem.

PSAE EXAMPLE 3 9.11.05

GRIDDED RESPONSE The theme for a school dance is "Solid Gold." For one decoration, Kana is covering a trapezoid-shaped piece of poster board with metallic gold paper to look like a bar of gold. If the height of the poster board is 18 inches, how much metallic paper will Kana need in square inches?

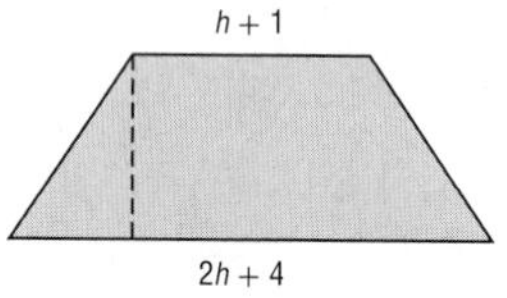

Read the Test Item

The question is asking you to find the area of the trapezoid with a height of h and bases of $h + 1$ and $2h + 4$.

Solve the Test Item

Write an equation to represent the area of the trapezoid.
Let $b_1 = h + 1$, let $b_2 = 2h + 4$ and let h = height of the trapezoid.

$A = \frac{1}{2}h(b_1 + b_2)$	**Area of a trapezoid**
$= \frac{1}{2}h[(h + 1) + (2h + 4)]$	**$b_1 = h + 1$ and $b_2 = 2h + 4$**
$= \frac{1}{2}h(3h + 5)$	**Add and simplify.**
$= \frac{3}{2}h^2 + \frac{5}{2}h$	**Distributive Property**
$= \frac{3}{2}(18)^2 + \frac{5}{2}(18)$	**$h = 18$**
$= 531$	**Simplify.**

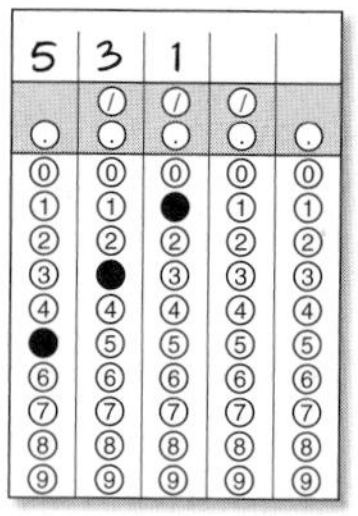

Kana will need 531 square inches of metallic paper.
Grid in your response of 531.

Real-World Link

In a recent year, the pet supply business hit an estimated \$7.05 billion in sales. This business ranges from gourmet food to rhinestone tiaras, pearl collars, and cashmere coats.

Source: *Entrepreneur Magazine*

Check Your Progress

3. Kachima is making triangular bandanas for the dogs and cats in her pet club. The base of the bandana is the length of the collar with 4 inches added to each end to tie it on. The height is $\frac{1}{2}$ of the collar length.

A. If Kachima's dog has a collar length of 12 inches, how much fabric does she need in square inches? **60**

B. If Kachima makes a bandana for her friend's cat with a 6-inch collar, how much fabric does Kachima need in square inches? **21**

Personal Tutor glencoe.com

Focus on Mathematical Content

Order of Operations When simplifying expressions involving products of monomials and polynomials, the order of operations must be followed. Multiplication precedes addition, unless parentheses indicate otherwise.

> **StudyTip**
>
> **Combining Like Terms** When simplifying a long expression, it may be helpful to put a circle around one set of like terms, a rectangle around another set, a triangle around another set, and so on.

Solve Equations with Polynomial Expressions We can use the Distributive Property to solve equations that involve the products of monomials and polynomials.

EXAMPLE 4 Equations with Polynomials on Both Sides

Solve $2a(5a - 2) + 3a(2a + 6) + 8 = a(4a + 1) + 2a(6a - 4) + 50$.

$2a(5a - 2) + 3a(2a + 6) + 8 = a(4a + 1) + 2a(6a - 4) + 50$	**Original equation**
$10a^2 - 4a + 6a^2 + 18a + 8 = 4a^2 + a + 12a^2 - 8a + 50$	**Distributive Property**
$16a^2 + 14a + 8 = 16a^2 - 7a + 50$	**Combine like terms.**
$14a + 8 = -7a + 50$	**Subtract $16a^2$ from each side.**
$21a + 8 = 50$	**Add $7a$ to each side.**
$21a = 42$	**Subtract 8 from each side.**
$a = 2$	**Divide each side by 21.**

CHECK

$2a(5a - 2) + 3a(2a + 6) + 8 = a(4a + 1) + 2a(6a - 4) + 50$	
$2(2)[5(2) - 2] + 3(2)[2(2) + 6] + 8 \stackrel{?}{=} 2[4(2) + 1] + 2(2)[6(2) - 4] + 50$	
$4(8) + 6(10) + 8 \stackrel{?}{=} 2(9) + 4(8) + 50$	**Simplify.**
$32 + 60 + 8 \stackrel{?}{=} 18 + 32 + 50$	**Multiply.**
$100 = 100$ ✓	**Add and subtract.**

Check Your Progress

Solve each equation.

4A. $2x(x + 4) + 7 = (x + 8) + 2x(x + 1) + 12$ $2\frac{3}{5}$

4B. $d(d + 3) - d(d - 4) = 9d - 16$ 8

Personal Tutor glencoe.com

1. $-15w^3 + 10w^2 - 20w$ **2.** $18g^5 + 24g^4 + 60g^3 - 6g^2$ **3.** $32k^2m^4 + 8k^3m^3 + 20k^2m^2$

Check Your Understanding

Example 1 p. 439

Find each product. **4.** $-6p^6r^7 + 18p^{10}r^6 + 15p^4r^3$

5. $14a^5b^3 + 2a^6b^2 - 4a^2b$
6. $5c^3d^{10} - 3c^5d^5 - 4c^2d^6$

1. $5w(-3w^2 + 2w - 4)$
2. $6g^2(3g^3 + 4g^2 + 10g - 1)$
3. $4km^2(8km^2 + 2k^2m + 5k)$
4. $-3p^4r^3(2p^2r^4 - 6p^6r^3 - 5)$
5 $2ab(7a^4b^2 + a^5b - 2a)$
6. $c^2d^3(5cd^7 - 3c^3d^2 - 4d^3)$

Example 2 p. 439

Simplify each expression. **10.** $-40w^4x + 55w^3x^2 + 54wx^5 - 24wx - 18x^3$

7. $4t^3 + 15t^2 - 8t + 4$

7. $t(4t^2 + 15t + 4) - 4(3t - 1)$
8. $x(3x^2 + 4) + 2(7x - 3)$ $3x^3 + 18x - 6$
9. $-2d(d^3c^2 - 4dc^2 + 2d^2c) + c^2(dc^2 - 3d^4)$ $-5d^4c^2 + 8d^2c^2 - 4d^3c + dc^4$
10. $-5w^2(8w^2x - 11wx^2) + 6x(9wx^4 - 4w - 3x^2)$

Example 3 p. 440

11. **GRIDDED RESPONSE** Marlene is buying a new plasma television. The height of the screen of the television is one half the width plus 5 inches. The width is 30 inches. Find the height of the screen in inches. 20

Example 4 p. 441

Solve each equation.

12. $-6(11 - 2c) = 7(-2 - 2c)$ 2
13. $t(2t + 3) + 20 = 2t(t - 3)$ $\frac{-20}{9}$
14. $-2(w + 1) + w = 7 - 4w$ 3
15. $3(y - 2) + 2y = 4y + 14$ 20
16. $a(a + 3) + a(a - 6) + 35 = a(a - 5) + a(a + 7)$ 7
17. $n(n - 4) + n(n + 8) = n(n - 13) + n(n + 1) + 16$ 1

Solve Equations with Polynomial Expressions

Example 4 shows how to solve equations that contain polynomials on both sides.

Additional Example

4 Solve $b(12 + b) - 7 = 2b + b(-4 + b)$. $\frac{1}{2}$

3 PRACTICE

Formative Assessment

Use Exercises 1–17 to check for understanding.

Use the chart at the bottom of the next page to customize assignments for your students.

Tips for New Teachers

Multiplying by a Negative Monomial If students are having difficulty multiplying by a monomial with a negative sign, you may want to have them apply the negative first (by multiplying all terms by -1) and then multiply by the rest of the monomial.

Differentiated Instruction AL OL

Visual/Spatial Learners Have students group algebra tiles to form a rectangle with a wide of $2x$ and a length of $x + 3$ using 2 blue x^2-tiles and 6 green x-tiles. Ask students to use their models to write an expression for the area of the rectangle. Then ask students to use the formula for area to calculate the area. $2x^2 + 6x$; $2x(x + 3) = 2x^2 + 6x$

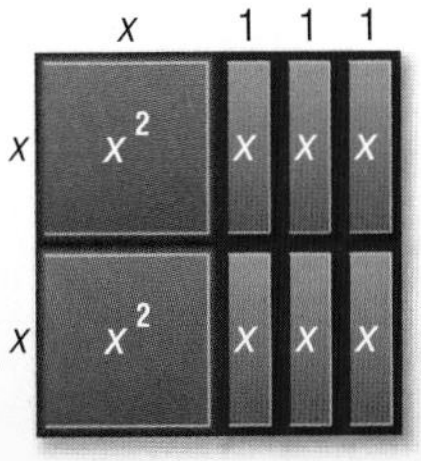

Tips for New Teachers

Multiplication Facts In Exercises 18 through 29, some students may prefer using the horizontal method for multiplying a polynomial by a monomial. Others may prefer the vertical method. Since these two methods are equivalent, either may be used.

Exercise Alert

Formula For Exercises 30 and 42, suggest students refer to Example 3 to help them with the formula for the area of a trapezoid.

Multiple Representations In Exercise 44, students use algebraic expressions and a table of values to show the degree of a product of a monomial and a polynomial.

Watch Out!

Find the Error For Exercise 45, point out to students that Pearl's method should draw a critical eye because her final polynomial has only two terms. When a monomial is multiplied by a polynomial with three different degree terms, the result will be a polynomial with three terms.

Additional Answers

18. $b^3 - 12b^2 + b$
19. $f^3 + 2f^2 + 25f$
20. $-6m^6 + 36m^5 - 6m^4 - 75m^3$
21. $10j^5 - 30j^4 + 4j^3 + 4j^2$
22. $4p^2r^3 + 10p^3r^3 - 30p^2r^2$
23. $8t^5u^3 - 40t^4u^5 + 8t^3u$

Practice and Problem Solving

= Step-by-Step Solutions begin on page R12.
Extra Practice begins on page 815.

Example 1 p. 439

Find each product. 18–23. See margin.

18. $b(b^2 - 12b + 1)$
19. $f(f^2 + 2f + 25)$
20. $-3m^3(2m^3 - 12m^2 + 2m + 25)$
21. $2j^2(5j^3 - 15j^2 + 2j + 2)$
22. $2pr^2(2pr + 5p^2r - 15p)$
23. $4t^3u(2t^2u^2 - 10tu^4 + 2)$

Example 2 p. 439

Simplify each expression. 24. $-13x^2 - 9x - 27$ 25. $-8a^3 + 20a^2 + 4a - 12$

24. $-3(5x^2 + 2x + 9) + x(2x - 3)$
25. $a(-8a^2 + 2a + 4) + 3(6a^2 - 4)$
26. $-4d(5d^2 - 12) + 7(d + 5)$
27. $-9g(-2g + g^2) + 3(g^2 + 4)$
28. $2j(7j^2k^2 + jk^2 + 5k) - 9k(-2j^2k^2 + 2k^2 + 3j)$ $14j^3k^2 + 2j^2k^2 - 17jk + 18j^2k^3 - 18k^3$
29. $4n(2n^3p^2 - 3np^2 + 5n) + 4p(6n^2p - 2np^2 + 3p)$

26. $-20d^3 + 55d + 35$
27. $-9g^3 + 21g^2 + 12$
29. $8n^4p^2 + 12n^2p^2 + 20n^2 - 8np^3 + 12p^2$

Example 3 p. 440

30. **DAMS** A new dam being built has the shape of a trapezoid. The base at the bottom of the dam is 2 times the height. The base at the top of the dam is $\frac{1}{5}$ times the height minus 30 feet.

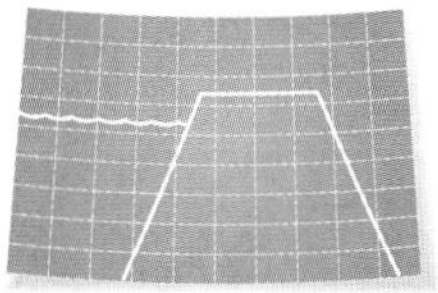

   a. Write an expression to find the area of the trapezoidal cross section of the dam. $\frac{11}{10}h^2 - 15h$
   b. If the height of the dam is 180 feet, find the area of this cross section. 32,940 ft²

Example 4 p. 441

Solve each equation.

31. $7(t^2 + 5t - 9) + t = t(7t - 2) + 13$ 2
32. $w(4w + 6) + 2w = 2(2w^2 + 7w - 3)$ 1
33. $5(4z + 6) - 2(z - 4) = 7z(z + 4) - z(7z - 2) - 48$ $\frac{43}{6}$
34. $9c(c - 11) + 10(5c - 3) = 3c(c + 5) + c(6c - 3) - 30$ 0
35. $2f(5f - 2) - 10(f^2 - 3f + 6) = -8f(f + 4) + 4(2f^2 - 7f)$ $\frac{30}{43}$
36. $2k(-3k + 4) + 6(k^2 + 10) = k(4k + 8) - 2k(2k + 5)$ -6

B **Simplify each expression.** 37. $20np^4 + 6n^3p^3 - 8np^2$ 38. $6r^5t + 3r^3t^4 + 9r^2t^3$

37. $\frac{2}{3}np^2(30p^2 + 9n^2p - 12)$
38. $\frac{3}{5}r^2t(10r^3 + 5rt^3 + 15t^2)$
39. $-5q^2w^3(4q + 7w) + 4qw^2(7q^2w + 2q) - 3qw(3q^2w^2 + 9)$
40. $-x^2z(2z^2 + 4xz^3) + xz^2(xz + 5x^3z) + x^2z^3(3x^2z + 4xz)$ $-x^2z^3 + 5x^4z^3 + 3x^4z^4$

39. $-q^3w^3 - 35q^2w^4 + 8q^2w^2 - 27qw$

41. **PARKING** A parking garage charges \$30 per month plus \$0.50 per daytime hour and \$0.25 per hour during nights and weekends. Suppose Trent parks in the garage for 47 hours in January and h of those are night and weekend hours.
   a. Find an expression for Trent's January bill. $53.50 - 0.25h$
   b. Find the cost if Trent had 12 hours of night and weekend hours. \$50.50

42. **PETS** Che is building a dog house for his new puppy. The upper face of the dog house is a trapezoid. If the height of the trapezoid is 12 inches, find the area of the face of this piece of the dog house. 318 in²

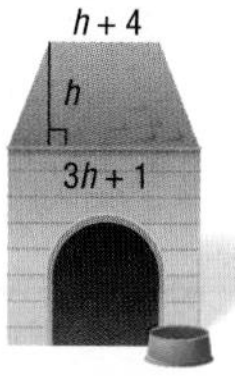

Differentiated Homework Options

Level	Assignment	Two-Day Option	
AL Basic	18–36, 45, 48–75	19–35 odd, 51–54	18–36 even, 45, 48–50, 55–75
OL Core	19–39 odd, 41–45, 48–75	18–36, 51–54	37–45, 48–50, 55–75
BL Advanced	37–69, (optional: 70–75)		

Real-World Link

Arthur Ashe is the only African-American male tennis player to win both Wimbledon and the U.S. Open and the first and only African-American player to be ranked the #1 tennis player in the world.

Source: CMG Worldwide

43. **TENNIS** The tennis club is building a new tennis court with a path around it.

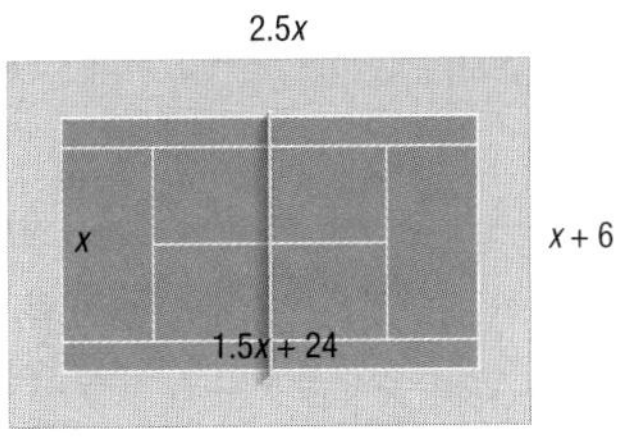

a. Write an expression for the area of the tennis court. **$1.5x^2 + 24x$**

b. Write an expression for the area of the path. **$x^2 - 9x$**

c. Every three feet around the court, there will be a stepping stone placed in the path. If $x = 36$, how many stones will there be? **88**

44. **MULTIPLE REPRESENTATIONS** In this problem, you will investigate the degree of the product of a monomial and a polynomial.

a. **TABULAR** Write three monomials of different degrees and three polynomials of different degrees. Determine the degree of each monomial and polynomial. Multiply the monomials by the polynomials. Determine the degree of each product. Record your results in a table like the one shown below.

Monomial	Degree	Polynomial	Degree	Product of Monomial and Polynomial	Degree
$2x$	1	$x^2 - 1$	2	$2x^3 - 2x$	3
$3x^2$	2	$x^5 + 1$	5	$3x^7 + 3x^2$	7
$4x^3$	3	$x^6 + 1$	6	$4x^9 + 4x^3$	9

b. **VERBAL** Make a conjecture about the degree of the product of a monomial and a polynomial. What is the degree of the product of a monomial of degree a and a polynomial of degree b? **The degree of the product is the sum of the degree of the monomial and the degree of the polynomial; $a + b$.**

H.O.T. Problems

Use Higher-Order Thinking Skills

45. **FIND THE ERROR** Pearl and Ted both worked on this problem. Is either of them correct? Explain your reasoning.

Pearl	Ted
$2x^2(3x^2 + 4x + 2)$	$2x^2(3x^2 + 4x + 2)$
$6x^4 + 8x^2 + 4x^2$	$6x^4 + 8x^3 + 4x^2$
$6x^4 + 12x^2$	

46. **CHALLENGE** Find p such that $3x^p(4x^{2p+3} + 2x^{3p-2}) = 12x^{12} + 6x^{10}$. **3**

47. **CHALLENGE** Simplify $4x^{-3}y^2(2x^5y^{-4} + 6x^{-7}y^6 - 4x^0y^{-2})$. **$8x^2y^{-2} + 24x^{-10}y^8 - 16x^{-3}$**

48. **REASONING** Is there a value for x that makes the statement $(x + 2)^2 = x^2 + 2^2$ true? If so, find a value for x. Explain your reasoning.

49. **OPEN ENDED** Write a monomial and a polynomial using n as the variable. Find their product. **Sample answer: $3n$, $4n + 1$; $12n^2 + 3n$**

50. **WRITING IN MATH** Describe the steps to multiply a polynomial by a monomial.

45. Ted; Pearl used the Distributive Property incorrectly.

48. Yes; 0; when 0 is substituted in for x in the equation, both sides are 2^2 or 4, which makes the equation true.

50. Sample answer: To multiply a polynomial by a monomial, use the Distributive Property. Multiply each term of the polynomial by the monomial. Then simplify by multiplying the coefficients together and using the Product of Powers Property for the variables.

Study Guide and Intervention

CRM pp. 36–37 AL OL ELL

NAME ______ DATE ______ PERIOD ______

7-6 Study Guide and Intervention

Multiplying a Polynomial by a Monomial

Polynomial Multiplied by Monomial The Distributive Property can be used to multiply a polynomial by a monomial. You can multiply horizontally or vertically. Sometimes multiplying results in like terms. The products can be simplified by combining like terms.

Example 1 Find $-3x^2(4x^2 + 6x - 8)$.

Horizontal Method

$-3x^2(4x^2 + 6x - 8)$
$= -3x^2(4x^2) + (-3x^2)(6x) - (-3x^2)(8)$
$= -12x^4 + (-18x^3) - (-24x^2)$
$= -12x^4 - 18x^3 + 24x^2$

Vertical Method

$$\begin{array}{lr} & 4x^2 + 6x - 8 \\ (\times) & -3x^2 \\ \hline & -12x^4 - 18x^3 + 24x^2 \end{array}$$

The product is $-12x^4 - 18x^3 + 24x^2$.

Example 2 Simplify $-2(4x^2 + 5x) - x(x^2 + 6x)$.

$-2(4x^2 + 5x) - x(x^2 + 6x)$
$= -2(4x^2) + (-2)(5x) + (-x)(x^2) + (-x)(6x)$
$= -8x^2 + (-10x) + (-x^3) + (-6x^2)$
$= (-x^3) + [-8x^2 + (-6x^2)] + (-10x)$
$= -x^3 - 14x^2 - 10x$

Exercises

Find each product.

1. $x(5x + x^2)$ **$5x^2 + x^3$**
2. $x(4x^2 + 3x + 2)$ **$4x^3 + 3x^2 + 2x$**
3. $-2xy(2y + 4x^2)$ **$-4xy^2 - 8x^3y$**
4. $-2g(g^2 - 2g + 2)$ **$-2g^3 + 4g^2 - 4g$**
5. $3x(x^4 + x^3 + x^2)$ **$3x^5 + 3x^4 + 3x^3$**
6. $-4x(2x^3 - 2x + 3)$ **$-8x^4 + 8x^2 - 12x$**
7. $-4ax(10 + 3x)$ **$-40ax - 12ax^2$**
8. $3y(-4x - 6x^3 - 2y)$ **$-12xy - 18x^3y - 6y^2$**
9. $2x^2y^2(3xy + 2y + 5x)$ **$6x^3y^3 + 4x^2y^3 + 10x^3y^2$**

Simplify each expression.

10. $x(3x - 4) - 5x$ **$3x^2 - 9x$**
11. $-x(2x^2 - 4x) - 6x^2$ **$-2x^3 - 2x^2$**
12. $6a(2a - b) + 2a(-4a + 5b)$ **$4a^2 + 4ab$**
13. $4r(2r^2 - 3r + 5) + 6r(4r^2 + 2r + 8)$ **$32r^3 + 68r$**
14. $4n(3n^2 + n - 4) - n(3 - n)$ **$12n^3 + 5n^2 - 19n$**
15. $2b(b^2 + 4b + 8) - 3b(3b^2 + 9b - 18)$ **$-7b^3 - 19b^2 + 70b$**
16. $-2z(4z^2 - 3z + 1) - z(3z^2 + 2z - 1)$ **$-11z^3 + 4z^2 - z$**
17. $2(4x^2 - 2x) - 3(-6x^2 + 4) + 2x(x - 1)$ **$28x^2 - 6x - 12$**

Practice

CRM p. 39 AL OL BL ELL

NAME ______ DATE ______ PERIOD ______

7-6 Practice

Multiplying a Polynomial by a Monomial

Lesson 7-6

Find each product.

1. $2h(-7h^2 - 4h)$ **$-14h^3 - 8h^2$**
2. $6pq(3p^2 + 4q)$ **$18p^3q + 24pq^2$**
3. $5jk(3jk + 2k)$ **$15j^2k^2 + 10jk^2$**
4. $-3rt(-2t^2 + 3r)$ **$6rt^3 - 9r^2t$**
5. $-\frac{1}{4}m(8m^2 + m - 7)$ **$-2m^3 - \frac{1}{4}m^2 + \frac{7}{4}m$**
6. $-\frac{2}{3}n^2(-9n^2 + 3n + 6)$ **$6n^4 - 2n^3 - 4n^2$**

Simplify each expression.

7. $-2\ell(3\ell - 4) + 7\ell$ **$-6\ell^2 + 15\ell$**
8. $5w(-7w + 3) + 2w(-2w^2 + 19w + 2)$ **$-4w^3 + 3w^2 + 19w$**
9. $6t(2t - 3) - 5(2t^2 + 9t - 3)$ **$2t^2 - 63t + 15$**
10. $-2(3m^3 + 5m + 6) + 3m(2m^2 + 3m + 1)$ **$9m^2 - 7m - 12$**
11. $-3g(7g - 2) + 3(g^2 + 2g + 1) - 3g(-5g + 3)$ **$-3g^2 + 3g + 3$**

Solve each equation.

12. $5(2t - 1) + 3 = 3(3t + 2)$ **8**
13. $3(3u + 2) + 5 = 2(2u - 2)$ **-3**
14. $4(8n + 3) - 5 = 2(6n + 8) + 1$ **$\frac{1}{2}$**
15. $8(3b + 1) = 4(b + 3) - 9$ **$-\frac{1}{4}$**
16. $t(t + 4) - 1 = t(t + 2) + 2$ **$\frac{3}{2}$**
17. $u(u - 5) + 8u = u(u + 2) - 4$ **-4**

18. **NUMBER THEORY** Let x be an integer. What is the product of twice the integer added to three times the next consecutive integer? **$5x + 3$**

19. **INVESTMENTS** Kent invested $5000 in a retirement plan. He allocated x dollars of the money to a bond account that earns 4% interest per year and the rest to a traditional account that earns 5% interest per year.

a. Write an expression that represents the amount of money invested in the traditional account. **$5000 - x$**

b. Write a polynomial model in simplest form for the total amount of money T Kent has invested after one year. (*Hint:* Each account has $A + IA$ dollars, where A is the original amount in the account and I is its interest rate.) **$T = 5250 - 0.01x$**

c. If Kent put $500 in the bond account, how much money does he have in his retirement plan after one year? **$5245**

Word Problem Practice

CRM p. 40 AL OL BL ELL

NAME ______ DATE ______ PERIOD ______

7-6 Word Problem Practice

Multiplying a Polynomial by a Monomial

1. **NUMBER THEORY** The sum of the first n whole numbers is given by the expression $\frac{1}{2}(n^2 + n)$. Expand the equation by multiplying, then find the sum of the first 12 whole numbers. **$\frac{n^2}{2} + \frac{n}{2}$; 78**

2. **COLLEGE** Troy's boss gave him $700 to start his college savings account. Troy's boss also gives him $40 each month to add to the account. Troy's mother gives him $50 each month, but has been doing so for 4 fewer months than Troy's boss. Write a simplified expression for the amount of money Troy has received from his boss and mother after m months. **$90m + $500**

3. **LANDMARKS** A circle of 50 flags surrounds the Washington Monument. Suppose a new sidewalk 12 feet wide is installed just around the outside of the circle of flags. The outside circumference of the sidewalk is 1.10 times the circumference of the circle of flags.

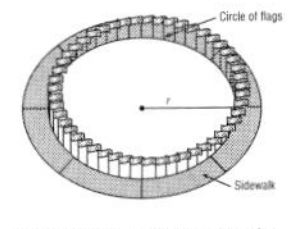

Write an equation that equates the outside circumference of the sidewalk to 1.10 times the circumference of the circle of flags. Solve the equation for the radius of the circle of flags. Recall that circumference of a circle is $2\pi r$. **$1.10(2\pi r) = 2\pi(r + 12)$; $r = 120$ ft**

4. **MARKET** Sophia went to the farmers' market to purchase some vegetables. She bought peppers and potatoes. The peppers were $0.39 each and the potatoes were $0.29 each. She spent $3.88 on vegetables, and bought 4 more potatoes than peppers. If x = the number of peppers, write and solve an equation to find out how many of each vegetable Sophia bought. **$3.88 = x(0.39) + (x + 4)(0.29); 4 peppers and 8 potatoes**

5. **GEOMETRY** Some monuments are constructed as rectangular pyramids. The volume of a pyramid can be found by multiplying the area of its base B by one third of its height. The area of the rectangular base of a monument in a local park is given by the polynomial equation $B = x^2 - 4x - 12$.

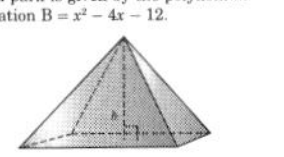

a. Write a polynomial equation to represent V, the volume of a rectangular pyramid if its height is 10 centimeters. **$V = \frac{10}{3}x^2 - \frac{40}{3}x - 40$**

b. Find the volume of the pyramid if $x = 12$. **280 cm^3**

Enrichment

CRM p. 41 OL BL

NAME ______ DATE ______ PERIOD ______

7-6 Enrichment

Lesson 7-6

Figurate Numbers

The numbers below are called **pentagonal numbers**. They are the numbers of dots or disks that can be arranged as pentagons.

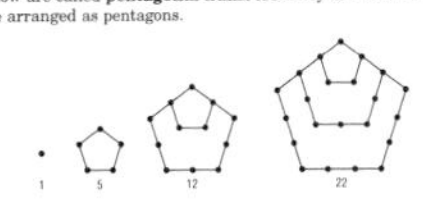

1. Find the product $\frac{1}{2}n(3n - 1)$. **$\frac{3n^2}{2} - \frac{n}{2}$**
2. Evaluate the product in Exercise 1 for values of n from 1 through 4. **1, 5, 12, 22**
3. What do you notice? **They are the first four pentagonal numbers.**
4. Find the next six pentagonal numbers. **35, 51, 70, 92, 117, 145**
5. Find the product $\frac{1}{2}n(n + 1)$. **$\frac{n^2}{2} + \frac{n}{2}$**

Lesson 7-6 Multiplying a Polynomial by a Monomial 443

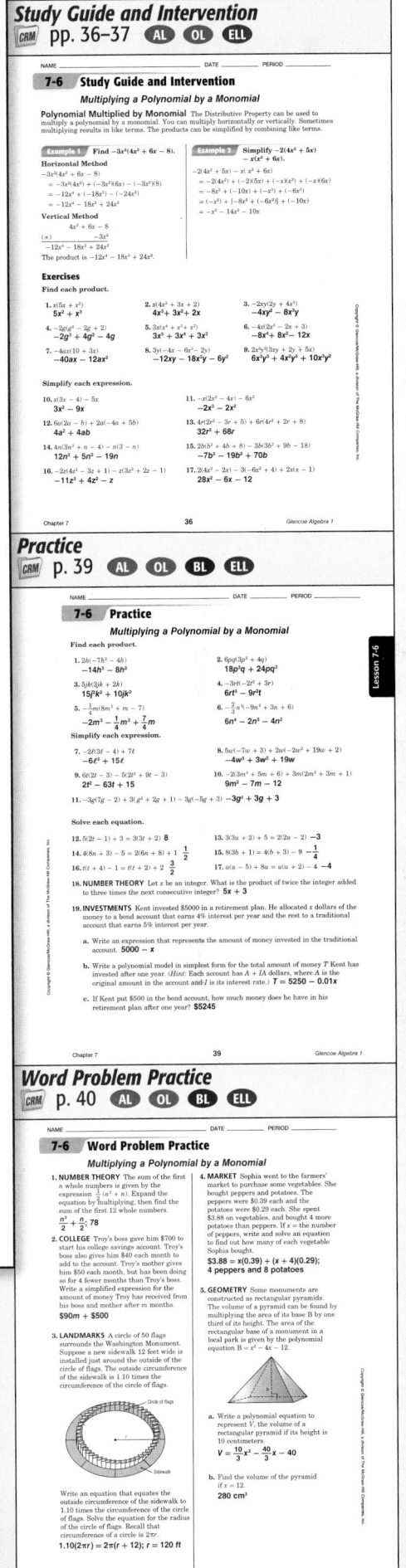

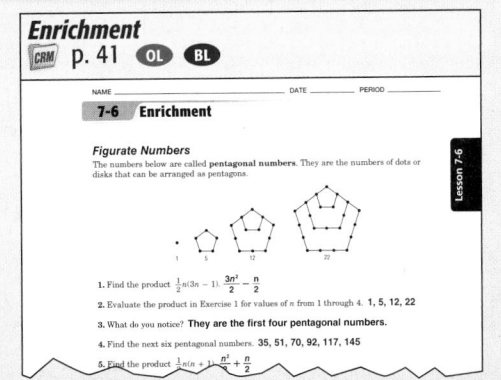

4 ASSESS

Crystal Ball Ask students to write a sentence predicting how learning to multiply a polynomial by a monomial will help them to learn to multiply polynomials by other polynomials in the next lesson.

Formative Assessment

Check for student understanding of Lessons 7-5 and 7-6.

CRM Quiz 3, p. 58

PSAE PRACTICE 8.11.02, 6.11.04, 9.11.05, 6.11.19

51. Every week a store sells j jeans and t T-shirts. The store makes \$8 for each T-shirt and \$12 for each pair of jeans. Which of the following expressions represents the total amount of money, in dollars, the store makes every week? **B**

A $8j + 12t$ C $20(j + t)$
B $12j + 8t$ D $96jt$

52. If $a = 5x + 7y$ and $b = 2y - 3x$, what is $a + b$? **H**

F $2x - 9y$ H $2x + 9y$
G $3y + 4x$ J $2x - 5y$

53. GEOMETRY A triangle has sides of length 5 inches and 8.5 inches. Which of the following cannot be the length of the third side? **A**

A 3.5 inches
B 4 inches
C 5.5 inches
D 12 inches

54. SHORT RESPONSE Write an equation in which x varies directly as the cube of y and inversely as the square of z. **Sample answer: $x = \frac{y^3}{z^2}$**

Spiral Review

Find each sum or difference. (Lesson 7-5) **56. $4z^2 + 2z - 7$ 57. $-9a^2 + 4a + 7$ 58. $a^3 - 7a^2 - 3$**

55. $(2x^2 - 7) + (8 - 5x^2)$ **$-3x^2 + 1$**
56. $(3z^2 + 2z - 1) + (z^2 - 6)$
57. $(2a - 4a^2 + 1) - (5a^2 - 2a - 6)$
58. $(a^3 - 3a^2 + 4) - (4a^2 + 7)$
59. $(2ab - 3a + 4b) + (5a + 4ab)$ **$6ab + 2a + 4b$**
60. $(8c^3 - 3c^2 + c - 2) - (3c^3 + 9)$ **$5c^3 - 3c^2 + c - 11$**

Find the degree of each polynomial. (Lesson 7-4)

61. $12y$ **1**
62. -10 **0**
63. $2x^2 - 5$ **2**
64. $9a - 8a^3 + 6$ **3**
65. $7b^2c^3$ **5**
66. $-3p^4r^5t^2$ **11**

67. TRAVEL In 1990, about 3.6 million people took cruises. Between 1990 and 2000, the number increased by about 300,000 each year. Write the point-slope form of an equation to find the total number of people y taking a cruise for any year x. Estimate the number of people who will take a cruise in 2010. (Lesson 4-3)
$y - 3{,}600{,}000 = 300{,}000(x - 1990)$; 9,600,000 people

Write an equation in function notation for each relation. (Lesson 3-6)

68.
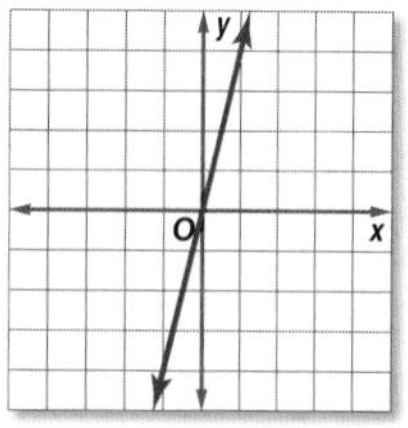

$f(x) = 4x$

69.
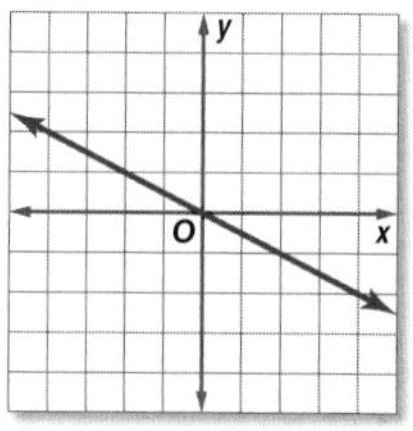

$f(x) = -0.5x$

Skills Review

Simplify. (Lesson 7-1)

70. $b(b^2)(b^3)$ **b^6**
71. $2y(3y^2)$ **$6y^3$**
72. $-y^4(-2y^3)$ **$2y^7$**
73. $-3z^3(-5z^4 + 2z)$ **$15z^7 - 6z^4$**
74. $2m(-4m^4) - 3(-5m^3)$ **$-8m^5 + 15m^3$**
75. $4p^2(-2p^3) + 2p^4(5p^6)$ **$-8p^5 + 10p^{10}$**

Differentiated Instruction OL BL

Extension Give students this problem: Nate multiplied a polynomial by a monomial and got $6x^8 - 3x^4 + 9x^2$. If the polynomial factor was $2x^6 - x^2 + 3$, what was the monomial factor? $3x^2$

Multiplying Polynomials

IL Math Online glencoe.com
Math *in Motion,* Animation

IL Learning Standards **8.B.4a** Represent algebraic concepts with physical materials, words, diagrams, tables, graphs, equations and inequalities and use appropriate technology.

You can use algebra tiles to find the product of two binomials.

ACTIVITY 1 Multiply Binomials

Use algebra tiles to find $(x + 3)(x + 4)$.

The rectangle will have a width of $x + 3$ and a length of $x + 4$. Use algebra tiles to mark off the dimensions on a product mat. Then complete the rectangle with algebra tiles.

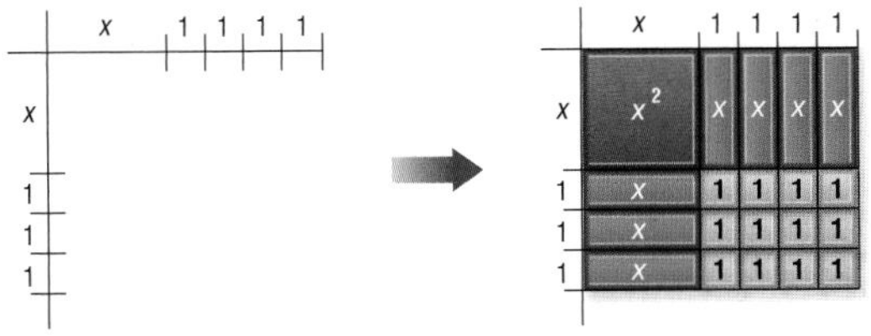

The rectangle consists of 1 blue x^2-tile, 7 green x-tiles, and 12 yellow 1-tiles. The area of the rectangle is $x^2 + 7x + 12$. So, $(x + 3)(x + 4) = x^2 + 7x + 12$.

ACTIVITY 2 Multiply Binomials

Use algebra tiles to find $(x - 2)(x - 5)$.

Step 1 The rectangle will have a width of $x - 2$ and a length of $x - 5$. Use algebra tiles to mark off the dimensions on a product mat. Then begin to make the rectangle with algebra tiles.

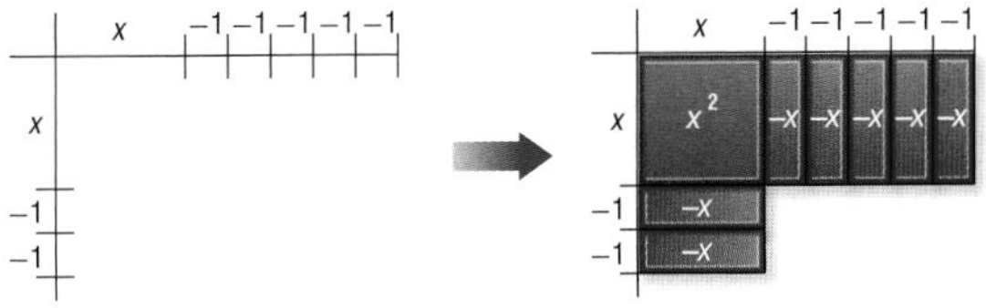

Step 2 Determine whether to use 10 yellow 1-tiles or 10 red −1-tiles to complete the rectangle. The area of each yellow tile is the product of −1 and −1. Fill in the space with 10 yellow 1-tiles to complete the rectangle.

The rectangle consists of 1 blue x^2-tile, 7 red $-x$-tiles, and 10 yellow 1-tiles. The area of the rectangle is $x^2 - 7x + 10$. So, $(x - 2)(x - 5) = x^2 - 7x + 10$.

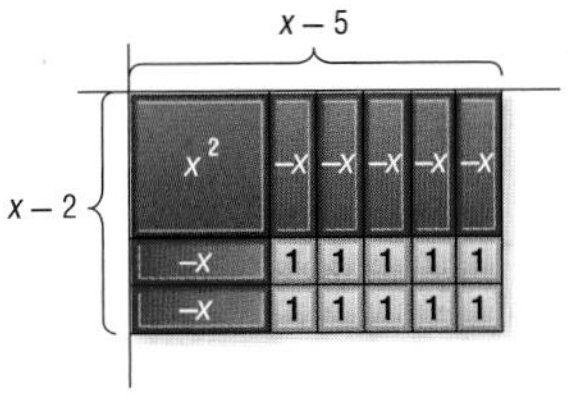

(continued on the next page)

1 FOCUS

Objective Use algebra tiles to multiply polynomials.

Materials for Each Student

- algebra tiles
- product mat

Easy to Make Manipulatives

Teaching Algebra with Manipulatives
Template for:

- algebra tiles, pp. 10–11
- product mat , p. 17

Tips for New Teachers

Some students may benefit from laying tiles along the top and side of the product mat to model each expression. Have them remove the two factors before determining their final product.

2 TEACH

Working in Cooperative Groups

Put students in groups of two or three, mixing abilities. Have groups complete Activities 1–3 and Exercise 1.

- For Activity 1, make sure groups mark the dimensions properly on the product mat. Since x-tiles are rectangular, remind students that the long side is the correct side to use to mark a value of x on the mat.
- When students are filling in the mats with the tiles, remind them to look carefully at the horizontal and vertical dimensions of each tile on the product mat. If both dimensions have a value of x, then use an x^2-tile. If one dimension is x and the other is 1, then use an x-tile. If both dimensions are 1, then use a 1-tile.

- For Activity 2, Step 2, have students pay close attention to whether the dimensions for each tile are positive or negative, as this affects which tile to use. If both dimensions are positive, then the tile is positive. If one is positive and the other is negative, the tile is negative. If both are negative, then the tile is positive.
- For Activity 3, as an alternative to removing zero pairs, have students write the expression based on the tiles without removing zero pairs. They can then simplify the expression by combining like terms.

Practice Have students complete Exercises 2–9.

3 ASSESS

Formative Assessment

Use Exercise 9 to assess whether students can model a product correctly.

From Concrete to Abstract

After students have completed Exercise 9, help them to see that when using the Distributive Property to multiply polynomials, each term from the first polynomial is multiplied by each term from the second polynomial.

ACTIVITY 3 Multiply Binomials

Use algebra tiles to find $(x - 4)(2x + 3)$.

Step 1 The rectangle will have a width of $x - 4$ and a length of $2x + 3$. Use algebra tiles to mark off the dimensions on a product mat. Then begin to make the rectangle with algebra tiles.

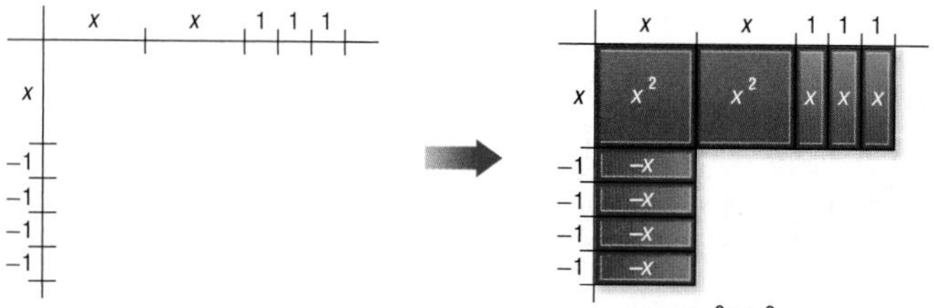

Step 2 Determine what color x-tiles and what color 1-tiles to use to complete the rectangle. The area of each red x-tile is the product of x and -1. The area of each red -1-tile is represented by the product of 1 and -1 or 1.

Complete the rectangle with 4 red x-tiles and 12 red -1-tiles.

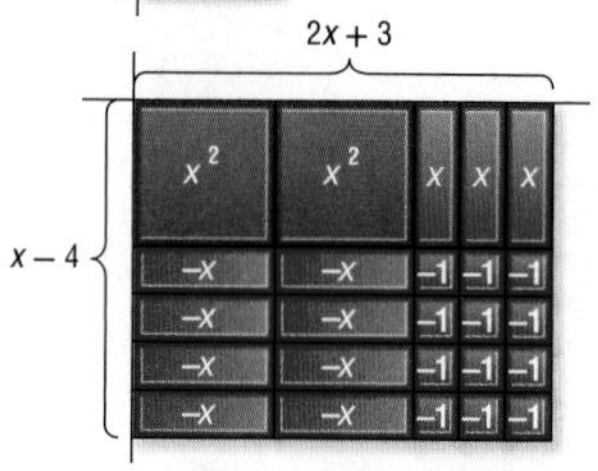

Step 3 Rearrange the tiles to simplify the polynomial you have formed. Notice that a 3 zero pair are formed by three positive and three negative x-tiles.

There are 2 blue x^2-tiles, 5 red $-x$-tiles, and 12 red -1-tiles left. In simplest form, $(x - 4)(2x + 3) = 2x^2 - 5x - 12$.

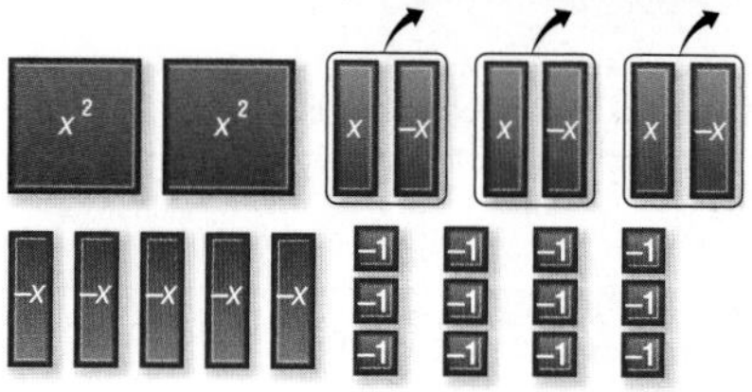

Model and Analyze

Use algebra tiles to find each product. **7–8. See Ch. 7 Answer Appendix for drawings.**

1. $(x + 1)(x + 4)$ $x^2 + 5x + 4$
2. $(x - 3)(x - 2)$ $x^2 - 5x + 6$
3. $(x + 5)(x - 1)$ $x^2 + 4x - 5$
4. $(x + 2)(2x + 3)$ $2x^2 + 7x + 6$
5. $(x - 1)(2x - 1)$ $2x^2 - 3x + 1$
6. $(x + 4)(2x - 5)$ $2x^2 + 3x - 20$

Is each statement *true* or *false*? Justify your answer with a drawing of algebra tiles.

7. $(x - 4)(x - 2) = x^2 - 6x + 8$ **true**
8. $(x + 3)(x + 5) = x^2 + 15$ **false**
9. **WRITING IN MATH** You can also use the Distributive Property to find the product of two binomials. The figure at the right shows the model for $(x + 4)(x + 5)$ separated into four parts. Write a sentence or two explaining how this model shows the use of the Distributive Property.
   By the Distributive Property, $(x + 4)(x + 5) = x(x + 5) + 4(x + 5)$. The top row represents $x(x + 5)$ or $x^2 + 5x$. The bottom row represents $4(x + 5)$ or $4x + 20$.

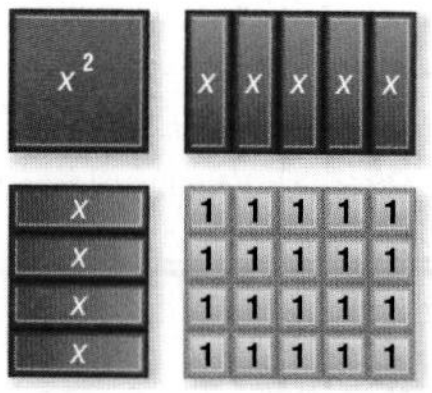

Extending the Concept

Ask students to model $(x - 3)(x + 2)$ using algebra tiles. Then ask students to write the expression based on the tiles without removing zero pairs. $x^2 + 2x - 3x - 6$

Finally, ask students to find the sum of the product of the two first terms, outer terms, inner terms, and last terms of $(x - 3)(x + 2)$ and then compare the results to the expression they wrote. The two expressions are the same.

7-7 Multiplying Polynomials

Why?

Bodyboards, which are used to ride waves, are made of foam and are more rectangular than surfboards. A bodyboard's dimensions are determined by the height and skill level of the user.

The length of Ann's bodyboard should be Ann's height h minus 32 inches or $h - 32$. The board's width should be half of Ann's height plus 11 inches or $\frac{1}{2}h + 11$. To approximate the area of the bodyboard, you need to find $(h - 32)\left(\frac{1}{2}h + 11\right)$.

Then
You multiplied polynomials by monomials. (Lesson 7-6)

Now
- Multiply polynomials by using the Distributive Property.
- Multiply binomials by using the FOIL method.

IL Learning Standards
8.A.4b Represent mathematical patterns and describe their properties using variables and mathematical symbols.

New Vocabulary
FOIL method
quadratic expression

IL Math Online
- Extra Examples
- Personal Tutor
- Self-Check Quiz
- Homework Help
- Math in Motion

Multiply Binomials To multiply two binomials such as $h - 32$ and $\frac{1}{2}h + 11$, the Distributive Property is used. Binomials can be multiplied horizontally or vertically.

EXAMPLE 1 The Distributive Property

Find each product.

a. $(2x + 3)(x + 5)$

Vertical Method

Multiply by 5.

$$\begin{array}{r} 2x + 3 \\ (\times)\ x + 5 \\ \hline 10x + 15 \end{array}$$

$5(2x + 3) = 10x + 15$

Multiply by x.

$$\begin{array}{r} 2x + 3 \\ (\times)\ x + 5 \\ \hline 10x + 15 \\ 2x^2 + 3x \\ \hline \end{array}$$

$x(2x + 3) = 2x^2 + 3x$

Combine like terms.

$$\begin{array}{r} 2x + 3 \\ (\times)\ x + 5 \\ \hline 10x + 15 \\ 2x^2 + 3x \\ \hline \end{array}$$

$2x^2 + 13x + 15$

Horizontal Method

$(2x + 3)(x + 5) = 2x(x + 5) + 3(x + 5)$	Rewrite as the sum of two products.
$= 2x^2 + 10x + 3x + 15$	Distributive Property
$= 2x^2 + 13x + 15$	Combine like terms.

b. $(x - 2)(3x + 4)$

Vertical Method

Multiply by 4.

$$\begin{array}{r} x - 2 \\ (\times)\ 3x + 4 \\ \hline 4x - 8 \end{array}$$

$4(x - 2) = 4x - 8$

Multiply by $3x$.

$$\begin{array}{r} x - 2 \\ (\times)\ 3x + 4 \\ \hline 4x - 8 \\ 3x^2 - 6x \\ \hline \end{array}$$

$3x(x - 2) = 3x^2 - 6x$

Combine like terms.

$$\begin{array}{r} x - 2 \\ (\times)\ 3x + 4 \\ \hline 4x - 8 \\ 3x^2 - 6x \\ \hline \end{array}$$

$3x^2 - 2x - 8$

Horizontal Method

$(x - 2)(3x + 4) = x(3x + 4) - 2(3x + 4)$	Rewrite as the difference of two products.
$= 3x^2 + 4x - 6x - 8$	Distributive Property
$= 3x^2 - 2x - 8$	Combine like terms.

7-7 Lesson Notes

1 FOCUS

Vertical Alignment

Before Lesson 7-7
Multiply polynomials by monomials.

Lesson 7-7
Multiply polynomials by using the Distributive Property.
Multiply binomials by using the FOIL method.

After Lesson 7-7
Find squares of binomials involving sums and differences.

2 TEACH

Scaffolding Questions

Have students read the *Why?* section of the lesson.

Ask:

- What expression would you get if you multiplied the first term in $(h - 32)$ times $\left(\frac{1}{2}h + 11\right)$? $\frac{1}{2}h^2 + 11h$
- What expression would you get if you multiplied the second term in $(h - 32)$ by $\left(\frac{1}{2}h + 11\right)$? $-16h - 352$
- What expression do you get when you add these two answers together? $\frac{1}{2}h^2 - 5h - 352$

Lesson 7-7 Resources

Resource	Approaching-Level	On-Level	Beyond-Level	English Learners
Teacher Edition	• Differentiated Instruction, p. 448	• Differentiated Instruction, pp. 448, 452	• Differentiated Instruction, p. 452	
Chapter Resource Masters	• Study Guide and Intervention, pp. 42–43 • Skills Practice, p. 44 • Practice, p. 45 • Word Problem Practice, p. 46	• Study Guide and Intervention, pp. 42–43 • Skills Practice, p. 44 • Practice, p. 45 • Word Problem Practice, p. 46 • Enrichment, p. 47 • Spreadsheet Activity, p. 48	• Practice, p. 45 • Word Problem Practice, p. 46 • Enrichment, p. 47	• Study Guide and Intervention, pp. 42–43 • Skills Practice, p. 44 • Practice, p. 45 • Word Problem Practice, p. 46
Transparencies	• 5-Minute Check Transparency 7-7	• 5-Minute Check Transparency 7-7	• 5-Minute Check Transparency 7-7	• 5-Minute Check Transparency 7-7
Other	• Study Notebook • Teaching Algebra with Manipulatives	• Study Notebook • Teaching Algebra with Manipulatives	• Study Notebook	• Study Notebook • Teaching Algebra with Manipulatives

Multiply Binomials

Example 1 shows how to multiply two binomials using the Distributive Property. **Example 2** shows how to multiply two binomials using a shortcut of the Distributive Property called the FOIL method. **Example 3** shows how to use the FOIL method to solve a real-world problem.

Formative Assessment

Use the Check Your Progress exercises after each example to determine students' understanding of concepts.

Additional Examples

1 Find each product.

a. $(y + 8)(y - 4)$
$y^2 + 4y - 32$

b. $(2x + 1)(x + 6)$
$2x^2 + 13x + 6$

2 Find each product.

a. $(z - 6)(z - 12)$
$z^2 - 18z + 72$

b. $(5x - 4)(2x + 8)$
$10x^2 + 32x - 32$

Additional Examples also in Interactive Classroom PowerPoint® Presentations

IWB INTERACTIVE WHITEBOARD READY

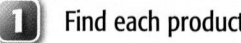

Focus on Mathematical Content

Multiplying Other Polynomials The FOIL method only works for multiplying two binomials. To multiply any other polynomials, the Distributive Property must be used.

Tips for New Teachers

FOIL Point out that FOIL is a memory tool. The order in which the terms are multiplied is not important, as long as all four products are found.

Check Your Progress

1A. $(3m + 4)(m + 5)$ $3m^2 + 19m + 20$ **1B.** $(5y - 2)(y + 8)$ $5y^2 + 38y - 16$

Personal Tutor glencoe.com

A shortcut version of the Distributive Property for multiplying binomials is called the **FOIL method**.

ReadingMath

Polynomials as Factors The expression $(x + 4)(x - 2)$ is read *the quantity x plus 4 times the quantity x minus 2.*

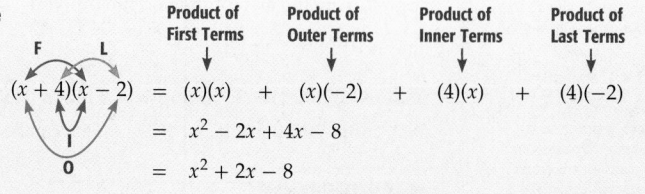

Key Concept — For Your FOLDABLE

FOIL Method

Words To multiply two binomials, find the sum of the products of **F** the *First* terms, **O** the *Outer* terms, **I** the *Inner* terms, **L** and the *Last* terms.

Example

	Product of First Terms		Product of Outer Terms		Product of Inner Terms		Product of Last Terms
$(x + 4)(x - 2) =$	$(x)(x)$	+	$(x)(-2)$	+	$(4)(x)$	+	$(4)(-2)$

$= x^2 - 2x + 4x - 8$

$= x^2 + 2x - 8$

(F, O, I, L arrows connect the terms.)

Math *in Motion,* Animation glencoe.com

EXAMPLE 2 FOIL Method

Find each product.

a. $(2y - 7)(3y + 5)$

$(2y - 7)(3y + 5) = (2y)(3y) + (2y)(5) + (-7)(3y) + (-7)(5)$ FOIL method
$= 6y^2 + 10y - 21y - 35$ Multiply.
$= 6y^2 - 11y - 35$ Combine like terms.

b. $(4a - 5)(2a - 9)$

$(4a - 5)(2a - 9)$
$= (4a)(2a) + (4a)(-9) + (-5)(2a) + (-5)(-9)$ FOIL method
$= 8a^2 - 36a - 10a + 45$ Multiply.
$= 8a^2 - 46a + 45$ Combine like terms.

Check Your Progress

2A. $(x + 3)(x - 4)$ $x^2 - x - 12$ **2B.** $(4b - 5)(3b + 2)$ $12b^2 - 7b - 10$

2C. $(2y - 5)(y - 6)$ $2y^2 - 17y + 30$ **2D.** $(5a + 2)(3a - 4)$ $15a^2 - 14a - 8$

Personal Tutor glencoe.com

Notice that when two linear expressions are multiplied, the result is a quadratic expression. A **quadratic expression** is an expression in one variable with a degree of 2. When three linear expressions are multiplied, the result has a degree of 3.

The FOIL method can be used to find an expression that represents the area of a rectangular object when the lengths of the sides are given as binomials.

Differentiated Instruction (AL OL)

If students are less familiar with the Distributive Property,

Then they may wish to use the vertical method for multiplying binomials because it is similar to multiplying two-digit numbers. Suggest that students use the method with which they are most comfortable.

Real-World Link

The cost of a swimming pool depends on many factors, including the size of the pool, whether the pool is an above-ground or an in-ground pool, and the material used.

Source: American Dream Homes

Real-World EXAMPLE 3 FOIL Method

SWIMMING POOL **A contractor is building a deck around a rectangular swimming pool. The deck is x feet from every side of the pool. Write an expression for the total area of the pool and deck.**

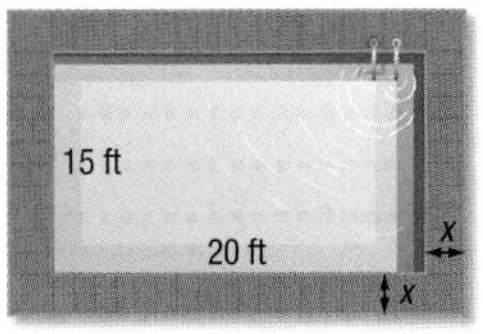

Understand We need to find an expression for the total area of the pool and deck.

Plan Use the formula for the area of a rectangle and determine the length and width of the pool with the deck.

Solve Since the deck is the same distance from every side of the pool, the length and width of the pool are $2x$ longer. So, the length can be represented by $2x + 20$ and the width can be represented by $2x + 15$.

Area = length · width	**Area of a rectangle**
$= (2x + 20)(2x + 15)$	**Substitution**
$= (2x)(2x) + (2x)(15) + (20)(2x) + (20)(15)$	**FOIL Method**
$= 4x^2 + 30x + 40x + 300$	**Multiply.**
$= 4x^2 + 70x + 300$	**Combine like terms.**

So, the total area of the deck and pool is $4x^2 + 70x + 300$.

Check Choose a value for x. Substitute this value into $(2x + 20)(2x + 15)$ and $4x^2 + 70x + 300$. The result should be the same for both expressions.

Check Your Progress

3. If the pool is 25 feet long and 20 feet wide, find the area of the pool and deck. **$4x^2 + 90x + 500$**

Personal Tutor glencoe.com

Multiply Polynomials The Distributive Property can also be used to multiply any two polynomials.

EXAMPLE 4 The Distributive Property

Find each product.

a. $(6x + 5)(2x^2 - 3x - 5)$

$(6x + 5)(2x^2 - 3x - 5)$	
$= 6x(2x^2 - 3x - 5) + 5(2x^2 - 3x - 5)$	**Distributive Property**
$= 12x^3 - 18x^2 - 30x + 10x^2 - 15x - 25$	**Multiply.**
$= 12x^3 - 8x^2 - 45x - 25$	**Combine like terms.**

b. $(2y^2 + 3y - 1)(3y^2 - 5y + 2)$

$(2y^2 + 3y - 1)(3y^2 - 5y + 2)$	
$= 2y^2(3y^2 - 5y + 2) + 3y(3y^2 - 5y + 2) - 1(3y^2 - 5y + 2)$	**Distributive Property**
$= 6y^4 - 10y^3 + 4y^2 + 9y^3 - 15y^2 + 6y - 3y^2 + 5y - 2$	**Multiply.**
$= 6y^4 - y^3 - 14y^2 + 11y - 2$	**Combine like terms.**

StudyTip

Multiplying Polynomials If a polynomial with c terms and a polynomial with d terms are multiplied together, there will be $c \cdot d$ terms before simplifying. In Example 4a, there are $2 \cdot 3$ or 6 terms before simplifying.

Check Your Progress

4A. $(3x - 5)(2x^2 + 7x - 8)$ **$6x^3 + 11x^2 - 59x + 40$**

4B. $(m^2 + 2m - 3)(4m^2 - 7m + 5)$ **$4m^4 + m^3 - 21m^2 + 31m - 15$**

Personal Tutor glencoe.com

Additional Example

3 **PATIO** A patio in the shape of the triangle shown below is being built in Lavali's backyard. The dimensions given are in feet. The area A of the triangle is one half the height h times the base b. Write an expression for the area of the patio.

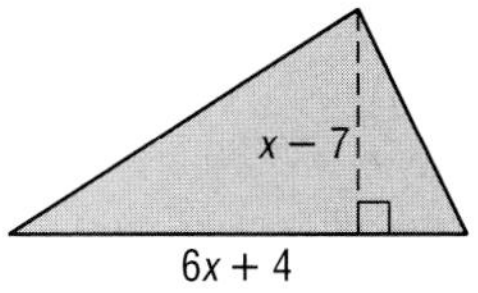

$(3x^2 - 19x - 14)$ ft^2

Multiply Polynomials

Example 4 shows how the Distributive Property can be used to multiply any two polynomials.

Additional Example

4 Find each product.

a. $(3a + 4)(a^2 - 12a + 1)$ $3a^3 - 32a^2 - 45a + 4$

b. $(2b^2 + 7b + 9)(b^2 + 3b - 1)$ $2b^4 + 13b^3 + 28b^2 + 20b - 9$

TEACH with TECH

INTERACTIVE WHITEBOARD Work through an example multiplying two binomials. Write the example on the board and use a different color for each of the four terms. Then create a table with four columns, one for each of the four parts of FOIL. In each column, write the expression for the two terms to be multiplied using the color coding from the original expression.

Lesson 7-7 Multiplying Polynomials 449

3 PRACTICE

Formative Assessment

Use Exercises 1–11 to check for understanding.

Use the chart at the bottom of this page to customize assignments for your students.

Watch Out!

Common Errors When students multiply polynomials horizontally, they often try to combine terms that are not like terms. For students who are having difficulty finding the product in Exercises 12–23, suggest that they try multiplying the polynomials in vertical form, aligning like terms.

Exercise Alert

Formula For Exercise 33, students will need to know the formula for the area of a circle, $A = \pi r^2$.

Additional Answers

25. $2y^3 - 17y^2 + 37y - 22$

26. $36a^3 + 71a^2 - 14a - 49$

27. $m^4 + 2m^3 - 34m^2 + 43m - 12$

28. $5x^4 + 19x^3 - 34x^2 + 11x - 1$

29. $6b^5 - 3b^4 - 35b^3 - 10b^2 + 43b + 63$

30. $18z^5 - 15z^4 - 18z^3 - 14z^2 + 24z + 8$

37. $a^2 - 4ab + 4b^2$

38. $9c^2 + 24cd + 16d^2$

39. $x^2 - 10xy + 25y^2$

40. $8r^3 - 36r^2t + 54rt^2 - 27t^3$

41. $125g^3 + 150g^2h + 60gh^2 + 8h^3$

42. $64y^3 - 48y^2z - 36yz^2 + 27z^3$

43a. $x > 4$; If $x = 4$ the width of the rectangular sandbox would be zero and if $x < 4$ the width of the rectangular sandbox would be negative.

Check Your Understanding

1. $x^2 + 7x + 10$ **2.** $y^2 + 2y - 8$ **3.** $b^2 - 4b - 21$ **4.** $4n^2 + 39n + 27$ **5.** $16h^2 - 26h + 3$ **6.** $10a^2 + 33a - 54$

Examples 1 and 2 pp. 447–448

Find each product.

1. $(x + 5)(x + 2)$ **2.** $(y - 2)(y + 4)$ **3.** $(b - 7)(b + 3)$

4. $(4n + 3)(n + 9)$ **5.** $(8h - 1)(2h - 3)$ **6.** $(2a + 9)(5a - 6)$

Example 3 p. 449

7. FRAME Hugo is designing a frame to surround the picture shown at the right. The frame is the same distance all the way around. Write an expression that represents the total area of the picture and frame. $4x^2 + 72x + 320$

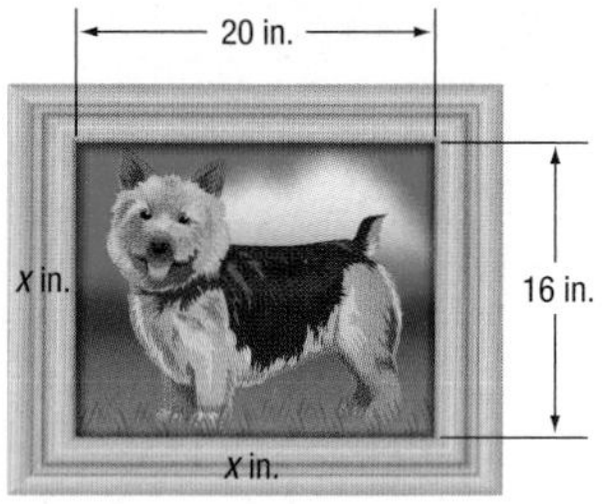

Example 4 p. 449

Find each product.

8. $(2a - 9)(3a^2 + 4a - 4)$

9. $(4y^2 - 3)(4y^2 + 7y + 2)$

10. $(x^2 - 4x + 5)(5x^2 + 3x - 4)$ $5x^4 - 17x^3 + 9x^2 + 31x - 20$

11. $(2n^2 + 3n - 6)(5n^2 - 2n - 8)$ $10n^4 + 11n^3 - 52n^2 - 12n + 48$

8. $6a^3 - 19a^2 - 44a + 36$

9. $16y^4 + 28y^3 - 4y^2 - 21y - 6$

Practice and Problem Solving

● = **Step-by-Step Solutions** begin on page R12. **Extra Practice** begins on page 815.

Examples 1 and 2 pp. 447–448

Find each product. **12.** $3c^2 + 4c - 15$ **13.** $2g^2 + 15g - 50$ **14.** $30a^2 + 43a + 15$

15. $24x^2 + 18x + 3$
16. $15y^2 - 17y + 4$
17. $24d^2 - 62d + 35$
18. $6m^2 + 19m + 15$

12. $(3c - 5)(c + 3)$ **13.** $(g + 10)(2g - 5)$ **14.** $(6a + 5)(5a + 3)$

15 $(4x + 1)(6x + 3)$ **16.** $(5y - 4)(3y - 1)$ **17.** $(6d - 5)(4d - 7)$

18. $(3m + 5)(2m + 3)$ **19.** $(7n - 6)(7n - 6)$ **20.** $(12t - 5)(12t + 5)$

21. $(5r + 7)(5r - 7)$ $25r^2 - 49$ **22.** $(8w + 4x)(5w - 6x)$ $40w^2 - 28wx - 24x^2$ **23.** $(11z - 5y)(3z + 2y)$ $33z^2 + 7yz - 10y^2$

Example 3 p. 449

19. $49n^2 - 84n + 36$
20. $144t^2 - 25$

24. GARDEN A walkway surrounds a rectangular garden. The width of the garden is 8 feet, and the length is 6 feet. The width x of the walkway around the garden is the same on every side. Write an expression that represents the total area of the garden and walkway. $4x^2 + 28x + 48$

Example 4 p. 449

Find each product. **25–30.** See margin.

25. $(2y - 11)(y^2 - 3y + 2)$ **26.** $(4a + 7)(9a^2 + 2a - 7)$

27. $(m^2 - 5m + 4)(m^2 + 7m - 3)$ **28.** $(x^2 + 5x - 1)(5x^2 - 6x + 1)$

29. $(3b^3 - 4b - 7)(2b^2 - b - 9)$ **30.** $(6z^2 - 5z - 2)(3z^3 - 2z - 4)$

B Simplify.

31. $(m + 2)[(m^2 + 3m - 6) + (m^2 - 2m + 4)]$ $2m^3 + 5m^2 - 4$

32. $[(t^2 + 3t - 8) - (t^2 - 2t + 6)](t - 4)$ $5t^2 - 34t + 56$

GEOMETRY Find an expression to represent the area of each shaded region.

33. $4\pi x^2 + 12\pi x + 9\pi - 3x^2 - 5x - 2$
34. $24x^2 - \frac{3}{2}$

33.

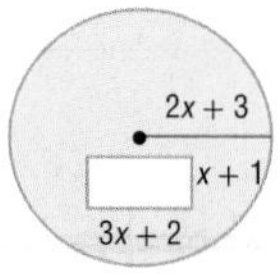

34.

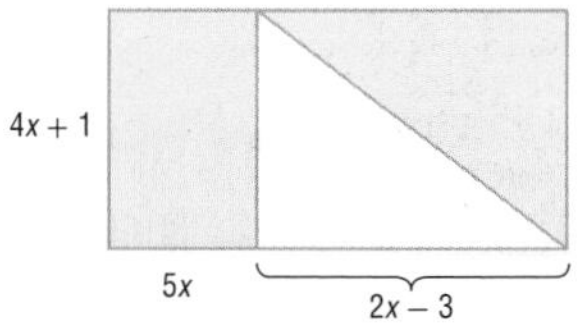

Differentiated Homework Options

Level	Assignment		Two-Day Option	
AL Basic	12–30, 45, 47–66	13–29 odd, 50–53		12–30 even, 45, 47–49, 54–66
OL Core	13–33 odd, 35–36, 37–41 odd, 43–45, 47–66	12–30, 50–53		31–45, 47–49, 54–66
BL Advanced	31–62, (optional: 63–66)			

450 Chapter 7 Polynomials

Real-World Link

On May 20, 2007, Misty May-Treanor won her 73rd professional beach volleyball title. May-Treanor has more wins than any other woman.

Source: Association of Volleyball Professionals

35. VOLLEYBALL The dimensions of a sand volleyball court are represented by a width of $6y - 5$ feet and a length of $3y + 4$ feet.

a. Write an expression that represents the area of the court. $18y^2 + 9y - 20$

b. The length of a sand volleyball court is 31 feet. Find the area of the court. 1519 ft^2

36. GEOMETRY Write an expression for the area of a triangle with a base of $2x + 3$ and a height of $3x - 1$. $3x^2 + \frac{7}{2}x - \frac{3}{2}$

Find each product. 37–42. See margin.

37. $(a - 2b)^2$ **38.** $(3c + 4d)^2$ **39.** $(x - 5y)^2$

40. $(2r - 3t)^3$ **41.** $(5g + 2h)^3$ **42.** $(4y + 3z)(4y - 3z)^2$

43. CONSTRUCTION A sandbox kit allows you to build a square sandbox or a rectangular sandbox as shown.

a. What are the possible values of x? Explain. See margin.

b. Which shape has the greater area? square

c. What is the difference in areas between the two? 4 ft^2

44. MULTIPLE REPRESENTATIONS In this problem, you will investigate the square of a sum.

a. **TABULAR** Copy and complete the table for each sum.

Expression	$(\text{Expression})^2$
$x + 5$	$x^2 + 10x + 25$
$3y + 1$	$9y^2 + 6y + 1$
$z + q$	$z^2 + 2zq + q^2$

b. **VERBAL** Make a conjecture about the terms of the square of a sum. See Chapter 7 Answer Appendix.

c. **SYMBOLIC** For a sum of the form $a + b$, write an expression for the square of the sum. $a^2 + 2ab + b^2$

H.O.T. Problems

Use Higher-Order Thinking Skills

45. REASONING Determine if the following statement is *sometimes*, *always*, or *never* true. Explain your reasoning.

The FOIL method can be used to multiply a binomial and a trinomial.

46. CHALLENGE Find $(x^m + x^p)(x^{m-1} - x^{1-p} + x^p)$. $x^{2m-1} - x^{m-p+1} + x^{m+p} + x^{m+p-1} - x + x^{2p}$

47. OPEN ENDED Write a binomial and a trinomial involving a single variable. Then find their product. Sample answer: $x - 1$, $x^2 - x - 1$; $(x - 1)(x^2 - x - 1) = x^3 - 2x^2 + 1$

48. REASONING Compare and contrast the procedure used to multiply a trinomial by a binomial using the vertical method with the procedure used to multiply a three-digit number by a two-digit number.

49. WRITING IN MATH Summarize the methods that can be used to multiply polynomials. See Ch. 7 Answer Appendix.

45. Always; you can group two adjacent terms of a trinomial, treat the trinomial as a sum of two quantities, and apply the FOIL method. For example, $(2x + 3)(x^2 + 5x + 7) = (2x + 3)[x^2 + (5x + 7)] = 2x(x^2) + 2x(5x + 7) + 3(x^2) + 3(5x + 7)$. Then use the Distributive Property and simplify.

48. The three monomials that make up the trinomial are similar to the three digits that make up the 3-digit number. The single monomial is similar to a 1-digit number. With each procedure you perform 3 multiplications. The difference is that polynomial multiplication involves variables and the resulting product is often the sum of two or more monomials, while numerical multiplication results in a single number.

Multiple Representations In Exercise 44, students use a table of values and analysis to express the results of squaring a sum of the form $(a + b)$.

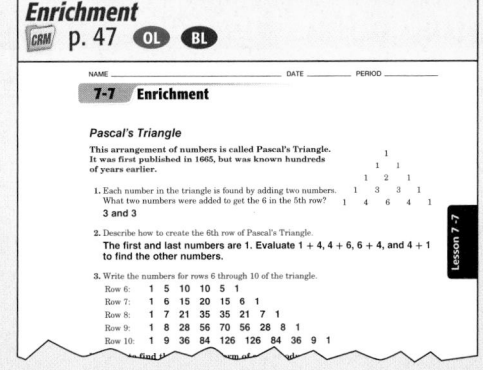

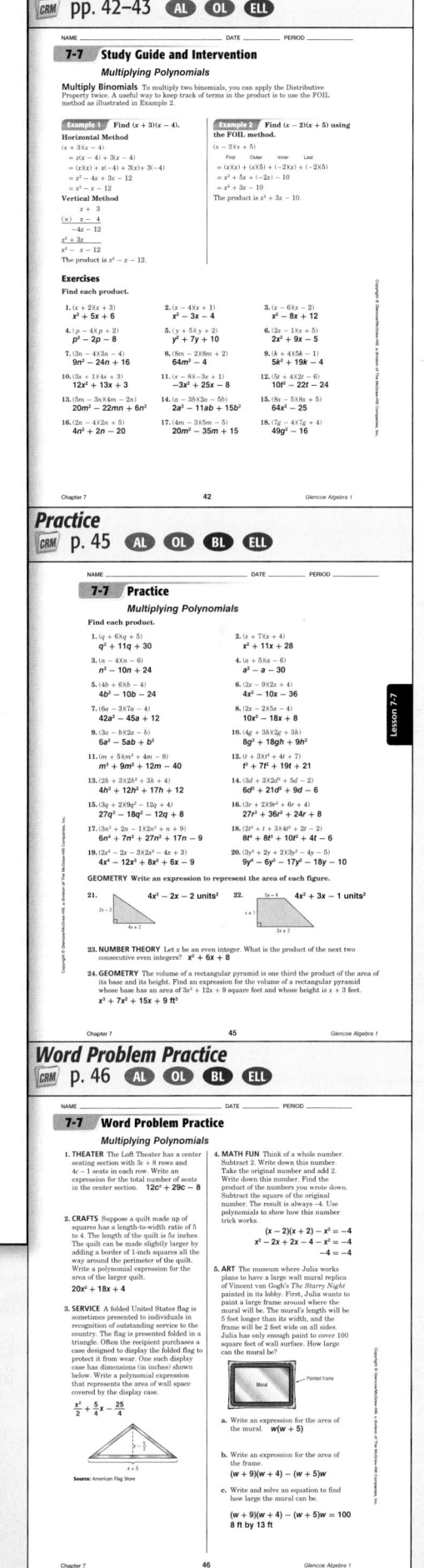

Study Guide and Intervention

CRM pp. 42–43 AL OL ELL

NAME ______ DATE ______ PERIOD ______

7-7 Study Guide and Intervention

Multiplying Polynomials

Multiply Binomials To multiply two binomials, you can apply the Distributive Property twice. A useful way to keep track of terms in the product is to use the FOIL method as illustrated in Example 2.

Example 1 Find $(x + 3)(x - 4)$.

Horizontal Method

$(x + 3)(x - 4)$
$= x(x - 4) + 3(x - 4)$
$= (x)(x) + x(-4) + 3(x) + 3(-4)$
$= x^2 - 4x + 3x - 12$
$= x^2 - x - 12$

Vertical Method

$$\begin{array}{r} x + 3 \\ (\times)\quad x - 4 \\ \hline -4x - 12 \\ x^2 + 3x \quad \\ \hline x^2 - x - 12 \end{array}$$

The product is $x^2 - x - 12$.

Example 2 Find $(x - 2)(x + 5)$ using the FOIL method.

$(x - 2)(x + 5)$
First Outer Inner Last
$= (x)(x) + (x)(5) + (-2)(x) + (-2)(5)$
$= x^2 + 5x + (-2x) - 10$
$= x^2 + 3x - 10$

The product is $x^2 + 3x - 10$.

Exercises

Find each product.

1. $(x + 2)(x + 3)$ $x^2 + 5x + 6$
2. $(x - 4)(x + 1)$ $x^2 - 3x - 4$
3. $(x - 6)(x - 2)$ $x^2 - 8x + 12$
4. $(p - 4)(p + 2)$ $p^2 - 2p - 8$
5. $(y + 5)(y + 2)$ $y^2 + 7y + 10$
6. $(2x - 1)(x + 5)$ $2x^2 + 9x - 5$
7. $(3n - 4)(3n - 4)$ $9n^2 - 24n + 16$
8. $(8m - 2)(8m + 2)$ $64m^2 - 4$
9. $(k + 4)(5k - 1)$ $5k^2 + 19k - 4$
10. $(3x + 1)(4x + 3)$ $12x^2 + 13x + 3$
11. $(x - 8)(-3x + 1)$ $-3x^2 + 25x - 8$
12. $(5t + 4)(2t - 6)$ $10t^2 - 22t - 24$
13. $(5m - 3n)(4m - 2n)$ $20m^2 - 22mn + 6n^2$
14. $(a - 3b)(2a - 5b)$ $2a^2 - 11ab + 15b^2$
15. $(8x - 5)(8x + 5)$ $64x^2 - 25$
16. $(2n - 4)(2n + 5)$ $4n^2 + 2n - 20$
17. $(4m - 3)(5m - 5)$ $20m^2 - 35m + 15$
18. $(7g - 4)(7g + 4)$ $49g^2 - 16$

Chapter 7 42 Glencoe Algebra 1

Practice

CRM p. 45 AL OL BL ELL

NAME ______ DATE ______ PERIOD ______

7-7 Practice

Multiplying Polynomials

Find each product.

1. $(q + 6)(q + 5)$ $q^2 + 11q + 30$
2. $(x + 7)(x + 4)$ $x^2 + 11x + 28$
3. $(n - 4)(n - 6)$ $n^2 - 10n + 24$
4. $(a + 5)(a - 6)$ $a^2 - a - 30$
5. $(4b + 6)(b - 4)$ $4b^2 - 10b - 24$
6. $(2x - 9)(2x + 4)$ $4x^2 - 10x - 36$
7. $(6a - 3)(7a - 4)$ $42a^2 - 45a + 12$
8. $(2x - 2)(5x - 4)$ $10x^2 - 18x + 8$
9. $(3a - b)(2a - b)$ $6a^2 - 5ab + b^2$
10. $(4g + 3h)(2g + 3h)$ $8g^2 + 18gh + 9h^2$
11. $(m + 5)(m^2 + 4m - 8)$ $m^3 + 9m^2 + 12m - 40$
12. $(t + 3)(t^2 + 4t + 7)$ $t^3 + 7t^2 + 19t + 21$
13. $(2h + 3)(2h^2 + 3h + 4)$ $4h^3 + 12h^2 + 17h + 12$
14. $(3d + 3)(2d^2 + 5d - 2)$ $6d^3 + 21d^2 + 9d - 6$
15. $(3q + 2)(9q^2 - 12q + 4)$ $27q^3 - 18q^2 - 12q + 8$
16. $(3r + 2)(9r^2 + 6r + 4)$ $27r^3 + 36r^2 + 24r + 8$
17. $(3n^2 + 2n - 1)(2n^2 + n + 9)$ $6n^4 + 7n^3 + 27n^2 + 17n - 9$
18. $(2t^2 + t + 3)(4t^2 + 2t - 2)$ $8t^4 + 8t^3 + 10t^2 + 4t - 6$
19. $(2x^2 - 2x - 3)(2x^2 - 4x + 3)$ $4x^4 - 12x^3 + 8x^2 + 6x - 9$
20. $(3y^2 + 2y + 2)(3y^2 - 4y - 5)$ $9y^4 - 6y^3 - 17y^2 - 18y - 10$

GEOMETRY Write an expression to represent the area of each figure.

21. 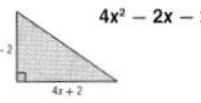

$4x^2 - 2x - 2$ units²

22. 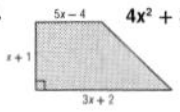

$4x^2 + 3x - 1$ units²

23. **NUMBER THEORY** Let x be an even integer. What is the product of the next two consecutive even integers? $x^2 + 6x + 8$

24. **GEOMETRY** The volume of a rectangular pyramid is one third the product of the area of its base and its height. Find an expression for the volume of a rectangular pyramid whose base has an area of $3x^2 + 12x + 9$ square feet and whose height is $x + 3$ feet. $x^3 + 7x^2 + 15x + 9\text{ ft}^3$

Chapter 7 45 Glencoe Algebra 1

Word Problem Practice

CRM p. 46 AL OL BL ELL

NAME ______ DATE ______ PERIOD ______

7-7 Word Problem Practice

Multiplying Polynomials

1. **THEATER** The Loft Theater has a center seating section with $3c + 8$ rows and $4c - 1$ seats in each row. Write an expression for the total number of seats in the center section. $12c^2 + 29c - 8$

2. **CRAFTS** Suppose a quilt made up of squares has a length-to-width ratio of 5 to 4. The length of the quilt is $5x$ inches. The quilt can be made slightly larger by adding a border of 1-inch squares all the way around the perimeter of the quilt. Write a polynomial expression for the area of the larger quilt. $20x^2 + 18x + 4$

3. **SERVICE** A folded United States flag is sometimes presented to individuals in recognition of outstanding service to the country. The flag is presented folded in a triangle. Often the recipient purchases a case designed to display the folded flag to protect it from wear. One such display case has dimensions (in inches) shown below. Write a polynomial expression that represents the area of wall space covered by the display case. $\frac{x^2}{2} + \frac{5}{4}x - \frac{25}{4}$

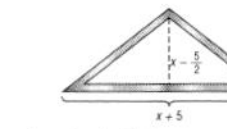

Source: American Flag Store

4. **MATH FUN** Think of a whole number. Subtract 2. Write down this number. Take the original number and add 2. Write down this number. Find the product of the numbers you wrote down. Subtract the square of the original number. The result is always –4. Use polynomials to show how this number trick works.

$(x - 2)(x + 2) - x^2 = -4$
$x^2 - 2x + 2x - 4 - x^2 = -4$
$-4 = -4$

5. **ART** The museum where Julia works plans to have a large wall mural replica of Vincent van Gogh's *The Starry Night* painted in its lobby. First, Julia wants to paint a large frame around where the mural will be. The mural's length will be 5 feet longer than its width, and the frame will be 2 feet wide on all sides. Julia has only enough paint to cover 100 square feet of wall surface. How large can the mural be?

a. Write an expression for the area of the mural. $w(w + 5)$

b. Write an expression for the area of the frame. $(w + 9)(w + 4) - (w + 5)w$

c. Write and solve an equation to find how large the mural can be. $(w + 9)(w + 4) - (w + 5)w = 100$; 8 ft by 13 ft

Chapter 7 46 Glencoe Algebra 1

Enrichment

CRM p. 47 OL BL

NAME ______ DATE ______ PERIOD ______

7-7 Enrichment

Pascal's Triangle

This arrangement of numbers is called Pascal's Triangle. It was first published in 1665, but was known hundreds of years earlier.

1
1 1
1 2 1
1 3 3 1
1 4 6 4 1

1. Each number in the triangle is found by adding two numbers. What two numbers were added to get the 6 in the 5th row? 3 and 3

2. Describe how to create the 6th row of Pascal's Triangle. The first and last numbers are 1. Evaluate 1 + 4, 4 + 6, 6 + 4, and 4 + 1 to find the other numbers.

3. Write the numbers for rows 6 through 10 of the triangle.

Row 6:	1 5 10 10 5 1
Row 7:	1 6 15 20 15 6 1
Row 8:	1 7 21 35 35 21 7 1
Row 9:	1 8 28 56 70 56 28 8 1
Row 10:	1 9 36 84 126 126 84 36 9 1

4 ASSESS

Name the Math Ask students to name the mathematical procedures they use when multiplying two binomials with the FOIL method.

PSAE PRACTICE 6.11.05, 9.11.05, 6.11.01, 8.11.09

50. What is the product of $2x - 5$ and $3x + 4$? **B**

A $5x - 1$
B $6x^2 - 7x - 20$
C $6x^2 - 20$
D $6x^2 + 7x - 20$

51. Which statement is correct about the symmetry of this design? **F**

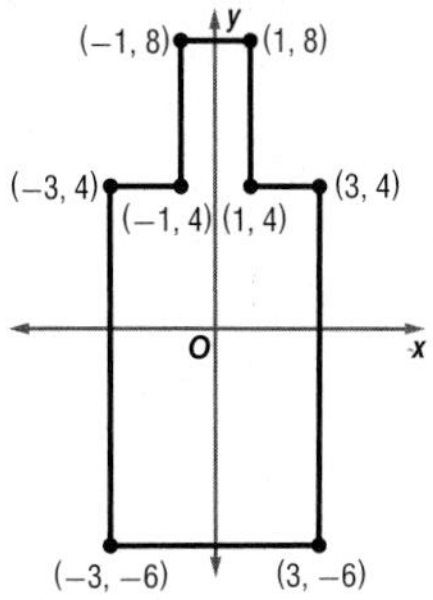

F The design is symmetrical only about the y-axis.
G The design is symmetrical only about the x-axis.
H The design is symmetrical about both the y- and the x-axes.
J The design has no symmetry.

52. Which point on the number line represents a number that, when cubed, will result in a number greater than itself? **D**

A P
B Q
C R
D T

53. SHORT RESPONSE For a science project, Jodi selected three bean plants of equal height. Then, for five days, she measured their heights in centimeters and plotted the values on the graph below.

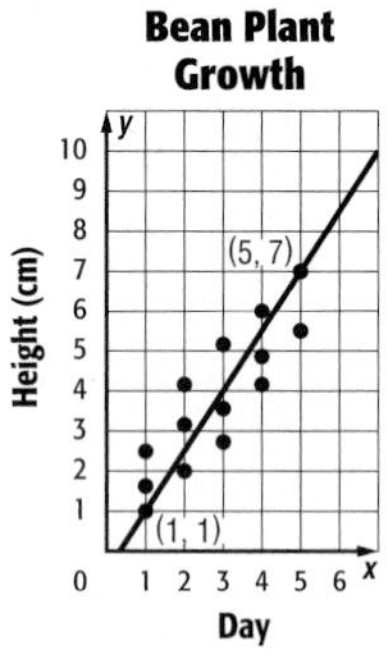

She drew a line of best fit on the graph. What is the slope of the line that she drew? $\frac{3}{2}$

Spiral Review

54. SAVINGS Carrie has \$6000 to invest. She puts x dollars of this money into a savings account that earns 2% interest per year. She uses the rest of the money to purchase a certificate of deposit that earns 4% interest. Write an equation for the amount of money that Carrie will have in one year. (Lesson 7-6) $T = 1.02x + 1.04(6000 - x)$

Find each sum or difference. (Lesson 7-5)

55. $(7a^2 - 5) + (-3a^2 + 10)$ $4a^2 + 5$

56. $(8n - 2n^2) + (4n - 6n^2)$ $12n - 8n^2$

57. $(4 + n^3 + 3n^2) + (2n^3 - 9n^2 + 6)$ $3n^3 - 6n^2 + 10$

58. $(-4u^2 - 9 + 2u) + (6u + 14 + 2u^2)$ $-2u^2 + 8u + 5$

59. $(b + 4) + (c + 3b - 2)$ $4b + c + 2$

60. $(3a^3 - 6a) - (3a^3 + 5a)$ $-11a$

61. $(-4m^3 - m + 10) - (3m^3 + 3m^2 - 7)$ $-7m^3 - 3m^2 - m + 17$

62. $(3a + 4ab + 3b) - (2b + 5a + 8ab)$ $-2a - 4ab + b$

Skills Review

Simplify. (Lesson 7-1)

63. $(-2t^4)^3 - 3(-2t^3)^4$ $-56t^{12}$

64. $(-3h^2)^3 - 2(-h^3)^2$ $-29h^6$

65. $2(-5y^3)^2 + (-3y^3)^3$ $50y^6 - 27y^9$

66. $3(-6n^4)^2 + (-2n^2)^2$ $108n^8 + 4n^4$

Differentiated Instruction OL BL

Extension Tell students that one way to multiply 25 and 18 mentally is to multiply (20 + 5) by (20 − 2). Have them show how the FOIL method can be used to find each product.

a. 35(19) $35(19) = (30 + 5)(10 + 9) = (30)(10) + (30)(9) + 5(10) + 5(9) = 300 + 270 + 50 + 45 = 665$

b. 67(102) $67(102) = (60 + 7)(100 + 2) = (60)(100) + (60)(2) + 7(100) + 7(2) = 6000 + 120 + 700 + 14 = 6834$

452 Chapter 7 Polynomials

Special Products

Why?

Then

You multiplied binomials by using the FOIL method. (Lesson 7-7)

Now

- Find squares of sums and differences.
- Find the product of a sum and a difference.

IL Learning Standards

8.A.4b Represent mathematical patterns and describe their properties using variables and mathematical symbols.

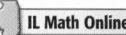

IL Math Online

glencoe.com

- Extra Examples
- Personal Tutor
- Self-Check Quiz
- Homework Help
- Math in Motion

Colby wants to attach a dartboard to a square piece of corkboard. If the radius of the dartboard is $r + 12$, how large does the square corkboard need to be?

Colby knows that the diameter of the dartboard is $2(r + 12)$ or $2r + 24$. Each side of the square also measures $2r + 24$. To find how much corkboard is needed, Colby must find the area of the square: $A = (2r + 24)^2$.

Squares of Sums and Differences Some pairs of binomials, such as squares like $(2r + 24)^2$, have products that follow a specific pattern. Using the pattern can make multiplying easier. The square of a sum, $(a + b)^2$ or $(a + b)(a + b)$, is one of those products.

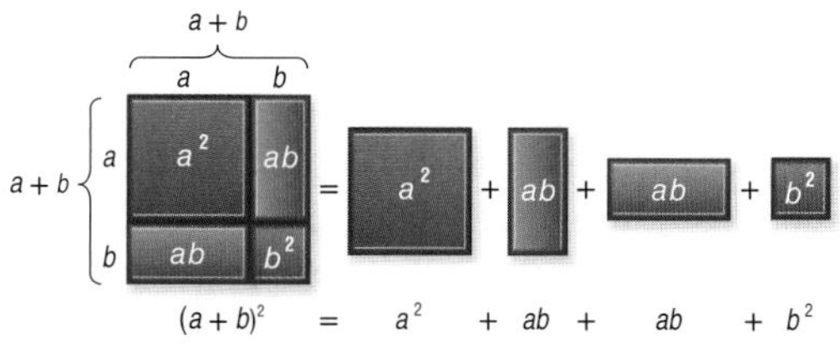

Key Concept — Square of a Sum

For Your FOLDABLE

Words The square of $a + b$ is the square of a plus twice the product of a and b plus the square of b.

Symbols $(a + b)^2 = (a + b)(a + b)$
$= a^2 + 2ab + b^2$

Example $(x + 4)^2 = (x + 4)(x + 4)$
$= x^2 + 8x + 16$

Math *in Motion*, Animation glencoe.com

EXAMPLE 1 Square of a Sum

Find $(3x + 5)^2$.

$(a + b)^2 = a^2 + 2ab + b^2$	Square of a sum
$(3x + 5)^2 = (3x)^2 + 2(3x)(5) + 5^2$	$a = 3x$, $b = 5$
$= 9x^2 + 30x + 25$	Simplify. Use FOIL to check your solution.

Check Your Progress

Find each product.

1A. $(8c + 3d)^2$ $64c^2 + 48cd + 9d^2$

1B. $(3x + 4y)^2$ $9x^2 + 24xy + 16y^2$

Personal Tutor glencoe.com

7-8 Lesson Notes

1 FOCUS

Vertical Alignment

Before Lesson 7-8
Multiply binomials by using the FOIL method.

Lesson 7-8
Find squares of sums and differences.
Find the product of a sum and a difference.

After Lesson 7-8
Factor a polynomial using the Distributive Property.

2 TEACH

Scaffolding Questions

Have students read the *Why?* section of the lesson.

Ask:

- What two factors equal $(2r + 24)^2$ when multiplied? $(2r + 24)(2r + 24)$
- Use the FOIL method to find $(2r + 24)^2$. $4r^2 + 96r + 576$
- If $2r = a$ and $24 = b$, does $(2r + 24)^2$ equal $a^2 + 2ab + b^2$? Explain. Yes; $(2r + 24)^3 = (2r)^2 + 2(2r)(24) + 24^2 = 4r^2 + 96r + 576$.

Lesson 7-8 Resources

Resource	Approaching-Level	On-Level	Beyond-Level	English Learners
Teacher Edition	• Differentiated Instruction, p. 455	• Differentiated Instruction, p. 458	• Differentiated Instruction, p. 458	• Differentiated Instruction, p. 455
Chapter Resource Masters	• Study Guide and Intervention, pp. 49–50 • Skills Practice, p. 51 • Practice, p. 52 • Word Problem Practice, p. 53	• Study Guide and Intervention, pp. 49–50 • Skills Practice, p. 51 • Practice, p. 52 • Word Problem Practice, p. 53 • Enrichment, p. 54	• Practice, p. 52 • Word Problem Practice, p. 53 • Enrichment, p. 54	• Study Guide and Intervention, pp. 49–50 • Skills Practice, p. 51 • Practice, p. 52 • World Problem Practice, p. 53
Transparencies	• 5-Minute Check Transparency 7-8	• 5-Minute Check Transparency 7-8	• 5-Minute Check Transparency 7-8	• 5-Minute Check Transparency 7-8
Other	• Study Notebook • Teaching Algebra with Manipulatives	• Study Notebook • Teaching Algebra with Manipulatives	• Study Notebook	• Study Notebook • Teaching Algebra with Manipulatives

Squares of Sums and Differences

Example 1 shows how to follow a specific pattern to find the square of a sum. **Example 2** shows how to find the square of a difference. **Example 3** shows how to use the square of a difference to write an expression that models a real-world situation.

Formative Assessment

Use the Check Your Progress exercises after each example to determine students' understanding of concepts.

Additional Examples

1 Find $(7z + 2)^2$. $49z^2 + 28z + 4$

2 Find $(3c - 4)^2$. $9c^2 - 24c + 16$

3 **GEOMETRY** Write an expression that represents the area of a square that has a side length of $3x + 12$ units. $(9x^2 + 72x + 144)$ units^2

Additional Examples also in Interactive Classroom PowerPoint® Presentations

IWB INTERACTIVE WHITEBOARD READY

Tips for New Teachers

Alternative Method Even though it is important to learn the special products, point out to students that they can always find these products using methods from previous lessons in the chapter.

There is also a pattern for the *square of a difference*. Write $a - b$ as $a + (-b)$ and square it using the square of a sum pattern.

$$(a - b)^2 = [a + (-b)]^2$$
$$= a^2 + 2(a)(-b) + (-b)^2 \quad \textbf{Square of a sum}$$
$$= a^2 - 2ab + b^2 \quad \textbf{Simplify.}$$

Key Concept — Square of a Difference

For Your FOLDABLE

Words The square of $a - b$ is the square of a minus twice the product of a and b plus the square of b.

Symbols $(a + b)^2 = (a + b)(a + b) = a^2 + 2ab + b^2$

Example $(x - 3)^2 = (x - 3)(x - 3) = x^2 - 6x + 9$

Watch Out!

Square of a Difference Remember that $(x - 7)^2$ does not equal $x^2 - 7^2$, or $x^2 - 49$.

$(x - 7)^2$
$= (x - 7)(x - 7)$
$= x^2 - 14x + 49$

EXAMPLE 2 Square of a Difference

Find $(2x - 5y)^2$.

$(a - b)^2 =$	$a^2 - 2ab + b^2$	**Square of a difference**
$(2x - 5y)^2 =$	$(2x)^2 - 2(2x)(5y) + (5y)^2$	**$a = 2x$ and $b = 5y$**
	$= 4x^2 - 20xy + 25y^2$	**Simplify.**

Check Your Progress

Find each product.

2A. $(6p - 1)^2$ $36p^2 - 12p + 1$

2B. $(a - 2b)^2$ $a^2 - 4ab + 4b^2$

Personal Tutor glencoe.com

The product of the square of a sum or the square of a difference is called a *perfect square trinomial*. We can use these to find patterns to solve real-world problems.

Real-World EXAMPLE 3 Square of a Difference

PHYSICAL SCIENCE Each edge of a cube of aluminum is 4 centimeters less than each edge of a cube of copper. Write an equation to model the surface area of the aluminum cube.

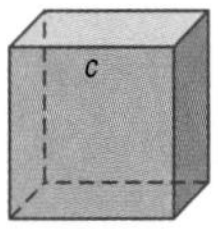

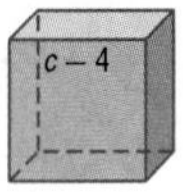

Let c = the length of each edge of the cube of copper.
So, each edge of the cube of aluminum is $c - 4$.

$SA = 6s^2$	**Formula for surface area of a cube**
$SA = 6(c - 4)^2$	**Replace s with $c - 4$.**
$SA = 6[c^2 - 2(4)(c) + 4^2]$	**Square of a difference**
$SA = 6(c^2 - 8c + 16)$	**Simplify.**

Check Your Progress

3. **GARDENING** Alano has a garden that is g feet long and g feet wide. He wants to add 3 feet to the length and the width.

A. Show how the new area of the garden can be modeled by the square of a binomial. $(g + 3)^2$

B. Find the square of this binomial. $g^2 + 6g + 9$

Personal Tutor glencoe.com

Focus on Mathematical Content

Squares of Sums and Differences Since the square of a sum and the square of a difference are the same except for the sign of the middle term, the risk of making a careless mistake when finding the sum or difference of a square is high. Tell students to pay close attention to the signs when finding squares of sums or differences.

TEACH with TECH

WIKI On your secure classroom wiki have students write a real world situation that uses their choice of the square of sums, the square of differences, or the product of a sum and difference. These situations can be used as a review for a chapter test.

454 Chapter 7 Polynomials

StudyTip

Patterns When using any of these patterns, *a* and *b* can be numbers, variables, or expressions with numbers and variables.

Product of a Sum and a Difference Now we will see what the result is when we multiply a sum and a difference, or $(a + b)(a - b)$. Recall that $a - b$ can be written as $a + (-b)$.

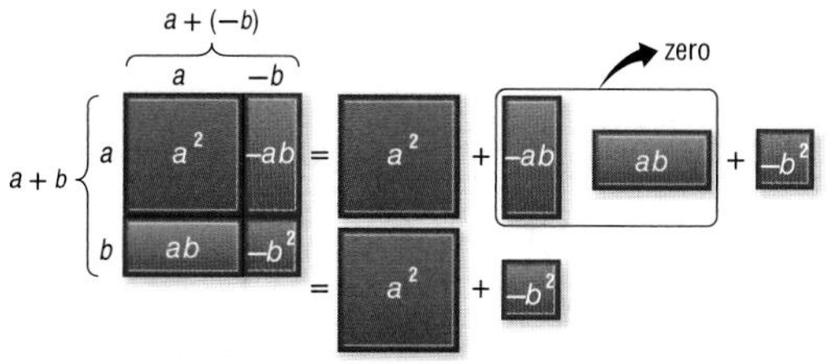

Notice that the middle terms are opposites and add to a zero pair. So $(a + b)(a - b) = a^2 - ab + ab - b^2 = a^2 - b^2$.

Key Concept — Product of a Sum and a Difference

For Your FOLDABLE

Words The product of $a + b$ and $a - b$ is the square of a minus the square of b.

Symbols $(a + b)(a - b) = (a - b)(a + b)$
$= a^2 - b^2$

Math *in Motion*, Animation glencoe.com

EXAMPLE 4 Product of a Sum and a Difference

Find $(2x^2 + 3)(2x^2 - 3)$.

$(a + b)(a - b) = a^2 - b^2$	Product of a sum and difference
$(2x^2 + 3)(2x^2 - 3) = (2x^2)^2 - (3)^2$	$a = 2x^2$ and $b = 3$
$= 4x^4 - 9$	Simplify.

Check Your Progress

Find each product.

4A. $(3n + 2)(3n - 2)$ $9n^2 - 4$ **4B.** $(4c - 7d)(4c + 7d)$ $16c^2 - 49d^2$

Personal Tutor glencoe.com

Check Your Understanding

Examples 1 and 2 pp. 453–454

Find each product. 4. $9m^2 - 24m + 16$ 5. $g^2 - 8gh + 16h^2$ 6. $9c^2 + 36cd + 36d^2$

1. $(x + 5)^2$ $x^2 + 10x + 25$ **2.** $(11 - a)^2$ $121 - 22a + a^2$ **3.** $(2x + 7y)^2$ $4x^2 + 28xy + 49y^2$

4. $(3m - 4)(3m - 4)$ **5.** $(g - 4h)(g - 4h)$ **6.** $(3c + 6d)^2$

Example 3 p. 454

7. GENETICS The color of a Labrador retriever's fur is genetic. Dark genes D are dominant over yellow genes y. A dog with genes DD or Dy will have dark fur. A dog with genes yy will have yellow fur. Pepper's genes for fur color are Dy, and Ramiro's are yy.

	D	y
D	DD	Dy
y	Dy	yy

a. Write an expression for the possible fur colors of Pepper's and Ramiro's puppies. $0.5Dy + 0.5y^2$

b. What is the probability that a puppy will have yellow fur? 50%

Product of a Sum and a Difference

Example 4 shows how to use the pattern for the product of the sum and difference of the same two terms.

Additional Example

4 Find $(9d + 4)(9d - 4)$. $81d^2 - 16$

Focus on Mathematical Content

Difference of Squares The product of a sum and difference of the same two terms, $(a + b)(a - b)$, is $a^2 - b^2$. This resulting product has a special name, the *difference of squares.*

3 PRACTICE

Formative Assessment

Use Exercises 1–7 to check for understanding.

Use the chart at the bottom of the next page to customize assignments for your students.

Differentiated Instruction AL ELL

If students have trouble remembering the pattern for special products studied in this lesson,

Then have them write the symbols for and examples of each Key Concept in this lesson on separate index cards. They can use their note cards for a quick reminder on how to proceed when they are finding products of squares of sums or differences or the product of a sum and a difference.

Exercise Alerts

Formula For Exercises 46 and 55, students will need to know the formula for the area of a circle, $A = \pi r^2$.

Construction Paper For Exercise 56, students will need a square piece of construction paper.

Isometric Dot Paper For Exercise 58, students may want to use isometric dot paper to draw their models for the cube of a sum.

Additional Answers

56a. The area of the larger square is a^2. The area of the smaller square is b^2.

57. Sample answer: $(2c + d) \bullet (2c - d)$; The product of these binomials is a difference of two squares and does not have a middle term. The other three do.

61. Sample answer: To find the square of a sum, apply the FOIL method or apply the pattern. The square of the sum of two quantities is the first quantity squared plus two times the product of the two quantities plus the second quantity squared. The square of the difference of two quantities is the first quantity squared minus two times the product of the two quantities plus the second quantity squared. The product of the sum and difference of two quantities is the square of the first quantity minus the square of the second quantity.

Example 4 p. 455

Find each product.

8. $(a - 3)(a + 3)$ $a^2 - 9$

9. $(x + 5)(x - 5)$ $x^2 - 25$

10. $(6y - 7)(6y + 7)$ $36y^2 - 49$

11. $(9t + 6)(9t - 6)$ $81t^2 - 36$

Practice and Problem Solving

● = **Step-by-Step Solutions** begin on page R12. **Extra Practice** begins on page 815.

Examples 1 and 2 pp. 453–454

Find each product.

12. $(a + 10)(a + 10)$ $a^2 + 20a + 100$

13. $(b - 6)(b - 6)$ $b^2 - 12b + 36$

14. $(h + 7)^2$ $h^2 + 14h + 49$

15. $(x + 6)^2$ $x^2 + 12x + 36$

16. $(8 - m)^2$ $64 - 16m + m^2$

17. $(9 - 2y)^2$ $81 - 36y + 4y^2$

18. $(2b + 3)^2$ $4b^2 + 12b + 9$

19. $(5t - 2)^2$ $25t^2 - 20t + 4$

20. $(8h - 4n)^2$ $64h^2 - 64hn + 16n^2$

Example 3 p. 454

21. GENETICS The ability to roll your tongue is inherited genetically from parents if either parent has the dominant trait T. Children of two parents without the trait will not be able to roll their tongues.

	T	t
T	TT	Tt
t	Tt	tt

a. Show how the combinations can be modeled by the square of a sum. $(T + t)^2 = T^2 + 2Tt + t^2$

b. Predict the percent of children that will have both dominant genes, one dominant gene, and both recessive genes. *TT*: 25%; *Tt*: 50%; *tt*: 25%

Example 4 p. 455

Find each product. **26.** $4q^2 - 25r^2$ **27.** $9a^4 - 49b^2$ **28.** $25y^2 + 70y + 49$

22. $(u + 3)(u - 3)$ $u^2 - 9$

23 ● $(b + 7)(b - 7)$ $b^2 - 49$

24. $(2 + x)(2 - x)$ $4 - x^2$

25. $(4 - x)(4 + x)$ $16 - x^2$

26. $(2q + 5r)(2q - 5r)$

27. $(3a^2 + 7b)(3a^2 - 7b)$

28. $(5y + 7)^2$

29. $(8 - 10a)^2$

30. $(10x - 2)(10x + 2)$

31. $(3t + 12)(3t - 12)$

32. $(a + 4b)^2$

33. $(3q - 5r)^2$

34. $(2c - 9d)^2$

35. $(g + 5h)^2$

36. $(6y - 13)(6y + 13)$

37. $(3a^4 - b)(3a^4 + b)$

38. $(5x^2 - y^2)^2$

39. $(8a^2 - 9b^3)(8a^2 + 9b^3)$

40. $\left(\frac{3}{4}k + 8\right)^2$

41. $\left(\frac{2}{5}y - 4\right)^2$

42. $(7z^2 + 5y^2)(7z^2 - 5y^2)$ $49z^4 - 25y^4$

Answers: **29.** $64 - 160a + 100a^2$ **30.** $100x^2 - 4$ **31.** $9t^2 - 144$ **32.** $a^2 + 8ab + 16b^2$ **33.** $9q^2 - 30qr + 25r^2$ **34.** $4c^2 - 36cd + 81d^2$ **35.** $g^2 + 10gh + 25h^2$ **36.** $36y^2 - 169$ **37.** $9a^8 - b^2$ **38.** $25x^4 - 10x^2y^2 + y^4$ **39.** $64a^4 - 81b^6$ **40.** $\frac{9}{16}k^2 + 12k + 64$ **41.** $\frac{4}{25}y^2 - \frac{16}{5}y + 16$

43. $(2m + 3)(2m - 3)(m + 4)$ $4m^3 + 16m^2 - 9m - 36$

44. $(r + 2)(r - 5)(r - 2)(r + 5)$ $r^4 - 29r^2 + 100$

45. GEOMETRY Write a polynomial that represents the area of the figure at the right. $2x^2 + 2x + 5$

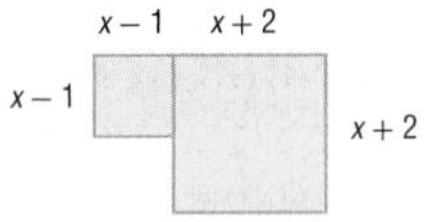

Real-World Link

In the 1870s, a baker named William Frisbie put his name on the bottom of tin pie pans. In the 1940s, students from Yale University began throwing the pie pans through the air. Eventually, the pie tins became known as Frisbees.

Source: Idea Finder

46. FLYING DISKS A flying disk shaped like a circle has a radius of $x + 3$ inches.

a. Write an expression representing the area of the flying disk. $\pi x^2 + 6\pi x + 9\pi$

b. If the diameter of the flying disk is 8 inches, what is its area? about 50.3 in²

GEOMETRY Find the area of each shaded region.

47. $6x + 3$

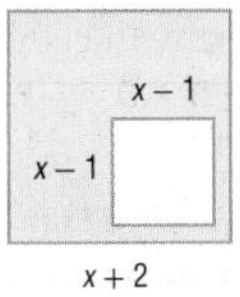

48. $x^2 + 11x - 6$

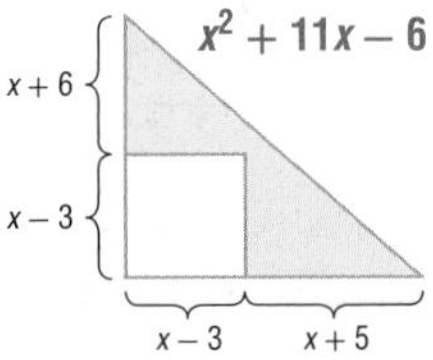

Differentiated Homework Options

Level	Assignment	Two-Day Option	
AL Basic	12–45, 57, 59–89	13–45 odd, 62–65	12–44 even, 57, 59–61, 66–89
OL Core	13–53 odd, 55–57, 59–89	12–45, 62–65	46–57, 59–61, 66–89
BL Advanced	46–85, (optional: 84–89)		

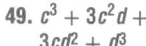

Real-World Link

Cael Sanderson of Iowa State University is the only wrestler in NCAA Division I history to be undefeated for four years. He compiled a 159-0 record from 1999–2002.

Source: Team Sanderson

Find each product.

49. $(c + d)(c + d)(c + d)$ **50.** $(2a - b)^3$ **51.** $(f + g)(f - g)(f + g)$

52. $(k - m)(k + m)(k - m)$ **53.** $(n - p)^2(n + p)$ **54.** $(q + r)^2(q - r)$

55. WRESTLING A high school wrestling mat must be a square with 38-foot sides and contain two circles as shown. Suppose the inner circle has a radius of r feet, and the radius of the outer circle is nine feet longer than the inner circle.

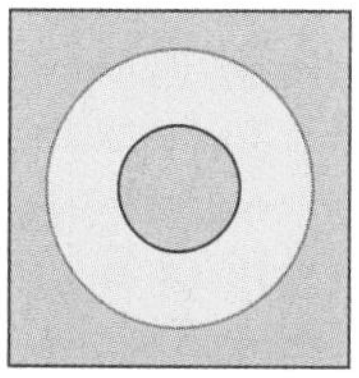

a. Write an expression for the area of the larger circle. **about $(3.14r^2 + 56.52r + 254.34)$ ft²**

b. Write an expression for the area of the portion of the square outside the larger circle. **about $(1189.66 - 3.14r^2 - 56.52r)$ ft²**

56. MULTIPLE REPRESENTATIONS In this problem, you will investigate a pattern. Begin with a square piece of construction paper. Label each edge of the paper a. In any of the corners, draw a smaller square and label the edges b.

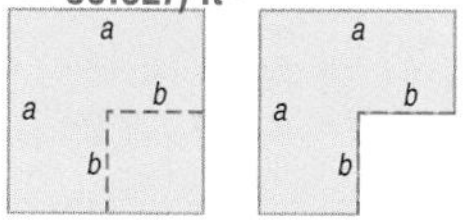

a. NUMERICAL Find the area of each of the squares. **See margin.**

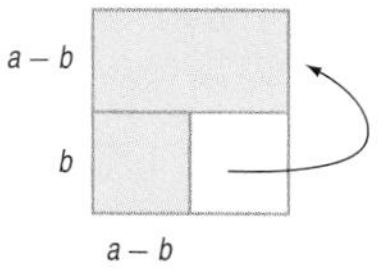

b. CONCRETE Cut the smaller square out of the corner. What is the area of the shape? **$a^2 - b^2$**

c. ANALYTICAL Remove the smaller rectangle on the bottom. Turn it and slide it next to the top rectangle. What is the length of the new arrangement? What is the width? What is the area? **$a + b$, $a - b$, $(a + b)(a - b)$**

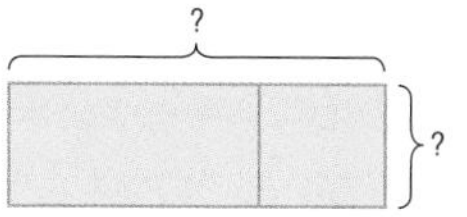

d. ANALYTICAL What pattern does this verify? **$(a + b)(a - b) = a^2 - b^2$**

H.O.T. Problems Use Higher-Order Thinking Skills

57. WHICH ONE DOESN'T BELONG? Which expression does not belong? Explain. **See margin.**

$(2c - d)(2c - d)$	$(2c + d)(2c - d)$	$(2c + d)(2c + d)$	$(c + d)(c + d)$

58. CHALLENGE Does a pattern exist for the cube of the sum $(a + b)^3$?

a. Investigate this question by finding the product $(a + b)(a + b)(a + b)$. **58a. $a^3 + 3a^2b + 3ab^2 + b^3$**

b. Use the pattern you discovered in part a to find $(x + 2)^3$. **$x^3 + 6x^2 + 12x + 8$**

c. Draw a diagram of a geometric model for the cube of a sum. **$(a + b)^3$**

d. What is the pattern for the cube of a difference, $(a - b)^3$? **$a^3 - 3a^2b + 3ab^2 - b^3$**

59. REASONING Find c that makes $25x^2 - 90x + c$ a perfect square trinomial. **81**

60. OPEN ENDED Write two binomials with a product that is a binomial. Then write two binomials with a product that is not a binomial.

61. WRITING IN MATH Describe how to square the sum of two quantities, square the difference of two quantities, and how to find the product of a sum of two quantities and a difference of two quantities. **See margin.**

49. $c^3 + 3c^2d + 3cd^2 + d^3$
50. $8a^3 - 12a^2b + 6ab^2 - b^3$
51. $f^3 + f^2g - fg^2 - g^3$
52. $k^3 - k^2m - km^2 + m^3$
53. $n^3 - n^2p - np^2 + p^3$
54. $q^3 + q^2r - qr^2 - r^3$

58c. Sample answer:

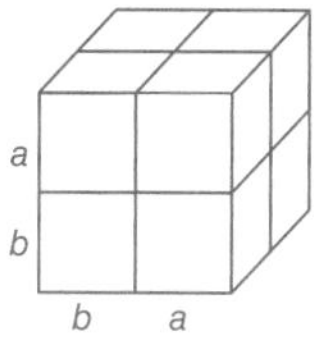

60. Sample answer: $(x - 2)(x + 2) = x^2 - 4$ and $(x - 2) \cdot (x - 2) = x^2 - 4x + 4$

Multiple Representations In Exercise 56, students use algebra and a physical model to represent the difference of two squares.

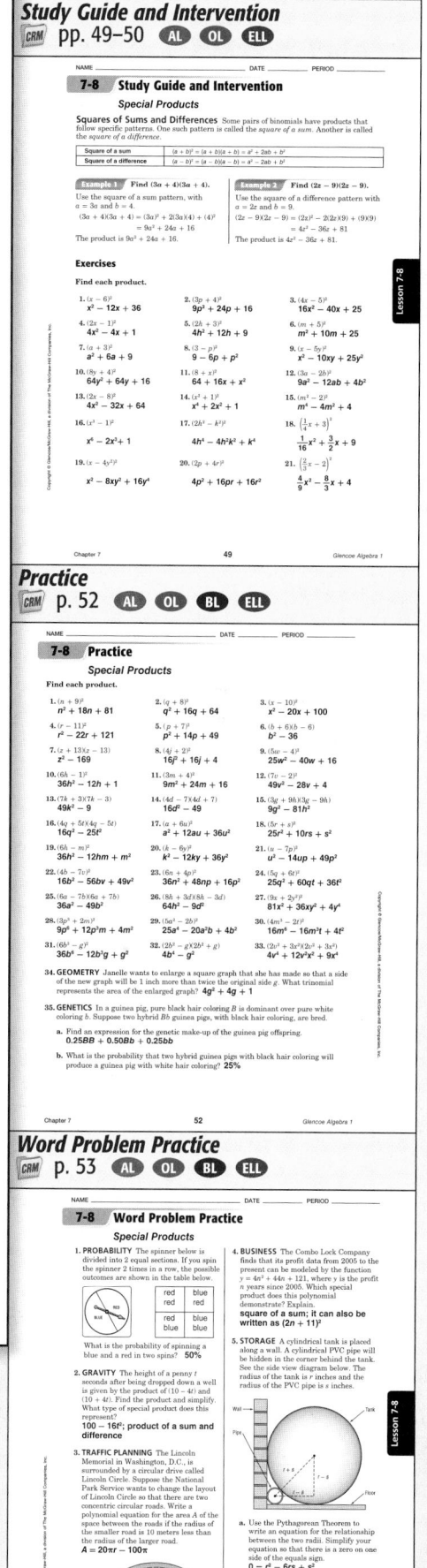

Enrichment
CRM p. 54 OL BL

NAME ______ DATE ______ PERIOD ______

7-8 Enrichment

Sums and Differences of Cubes

Recall the formulas for finding some special products:

Perfect-square trinomials: $(a + b)^2 = a^2 + 2ab + b^2$ or $(a - b)^2 = a^2 - 2ab + b^2$

Difference of two squares: $(a + b)(a - b) = a^2 - b^2$

A pattern also exists for finding the cube of a sum $(a + b)^3$.

1. Find the product of $(a + b)(a + b)(a + b)$. **$a^3 + 3a^2b + 3ab^2 + b^3$**
2. Use the pattern from Exercise 1 to evaluate $(x + 2)^3$. **$x^3 + 6x^2 + 12x + 8$**
3. Based on your answer to Exercise 1, predict the pattern for the cube of a difference $(a - b)^3$. **$a^3 - 3a^2b + 3ab^2 - b^3$**
4. Find the product of $(a - b)(a - b)(a - b)$ and compare it to your answer for Exercise 3. **$a^3 - 3a^2b + 3ab^2 - b^3$**
5. Use the pattern from Exercise 4 to evaluate $(x - 4)^3$. **... 48x – 64**

Study Guide and Intervention
CRM pp. 49–50 AL OL ELL

NAME ______ DATE ______ PERIOD ______

7-8 Study Guide and Intervention

Special Products

Squares of Sums and Differences Some pairs of binomials have products that follow specific patterns. One such pattern is called the *square of a sum*. Another is called the *square of a difference*.

Square of a sum	$(a + b)^2 = (a + b)(a + b) = a^2 + 2ab + b^2$
Square of a difference	$(a - b)^2 = (a - b)(a - b) = a^2 - 2ab + b^2$

Example 1 Find $(3a + 4)(3a + 4)$.

Use the square of a sum pattern, with $a = 3a$ and $b = 4$.

$(3a + 4)(3a + 4) = (3a)^2 + 2(3a)(4) + (4)^2 = 9a^2 + 24a + 16$

The product is $9a^2 + 24a + 16$.

Example 2 Find $(2z - 9)(2z - 9)$.

Use the square of a difference pattern with $a = 2z$ and $b = 9$.

$(2z - 9)(2z - 9) = (2z)^2 - 2(2z)(9) + (9)(9) = 4z^2 - 36z + 81$

The product is $4z^2 - 36z + 81$.

Exercises

Find each product.

1. $(x - 6)^2$ **$x^2 - 12x + 36$**
2. $(3p + 4)^2$ **$9p^2 + 24p + 16$**
3. $(4x - 5)^2$ **$16x^2 - 40x + 25$**
4. $(2x - 1)^2$ **$4x^2 - 4x + 1$**
5. $(2h + 3)^2$ **$4h^2 + 12h + 9$**
6. $(m + 5)^2$ **$m^2 + 10m + 25$**
7. $(a + 3)^2$ **$a^2 + 6a + 9$**
8. $(3 - p)^2$ **$9 - 6p + p^2$**
9. $(x - 5y)^2$ **$x^2 - 10xy + 25y^2$**
10. $(8y + 4)^2$ **$64y^2 + 64y + 16$**
11. $(8 + x)^2$ **$64 + 16x + x^2$**
12. $(3a - 2b)^2$ **$9a^2 - 12ab + 4b^2$**
13. $(2x - 8)^2$ **$4x^2 - 32x + 64$**
14. $(x^2 + 1)^2$ **$x^4 + 2x^2 + 1$**
15. $(m^2 - 2)^2$ **$m^4 - 4m^2 + 4$**
16. $(x^3 - 1)^2$ **$x^6 - 2x^3 + 1$**
17. $(2h^2 - k^2)^2$ **$4h^4 - 4h^2k^2 + k^4$**
18. $\left(\frac{1}{4}x + 3\right)^2$ **$\frac{1}{16}x^2 + \frac{3}{2}x + 9$**
19. $(x - 4y^2)^2$ **$x^2 - 8xy^2 + 16y^4$**
20. $(2p + 4r)^2$ **$4p^2 + 16pr + 16r^2$**
21. $\left(\frac{2}{3}x - 2\right)^2$ **$\frac{4}{9}x^2 - \frac{8}{3}x + 4$**

Lesson 7-8

Chapter 7 49 Glencoe Algebra 1

Practice
CRM p. 52 AL OL BL ELL

NAME ______ DATE ______ PERIOD ______

7-8 Practice

Special Products

Find each product.

1. $(n + 9)^2$ **$n^2 + 18n + 81$**
2. $(q + 8)^2$ **$q^2 + 16q + 64$**
3. $(x - 10)^2$ **$x^2 - 20x + 100$**
4. $(r - 11)^2$ **$r^2 - 22r + 121$**
5. $(p + 7)^2$ **$p^2 + 14p + 49$**
6. $(b + 6)(b - 6)$ **$b^2 - 36$**
7. $(z + 13)(z - 13)$ **$z^2 - 169$**
8. $(4j + 2)^2$ **$16j^2 + 16j + 4$**
9. $(5w - 4)^2$ **$25w^2 - 40w + 16$**
10. $(6h - 1)^2$ **$36h^2 - 12h + 1$**
11. $(3m + 4)^2$ **$9m^2 + 24m + 16$**
12. $(7v - 2)^2$ **$49v^2 - 28v + 4$**
13. $(7k + 3)(7k - 3)$ **$49k^2 - 9$**
14. $(4d - 7)(4d + 7)$ **$16d^2 - 49$**
15. $(3g + 9h)(3g - 9h)$ **$9g^2 - 81h^2$**
16. $(4q + 5t)(4q - 5t)$ **$16q^2 - 25t^2$**
17. $(a + 6u)^2$ **$a^2 + 12au + 36u^2$**
18. $(5r + s)^2$ **$25r^2 + 10rs + s^2$**
19. $(6h - m)^2$ **$36h^2 - 12hm + m^2$**
20. $(k - 6y)^2$ **$k^2 - 12ky + 36y^2$**
21. $(u - 7p)^2$ **$u^2 - 14up + 49p^2$**
22. $(4b - 7v)^2$ **$16b^2 - 56bv + 49v^2$**
23. $(6n + 4p)^2$ **$36n^2 + 48np + 16p^2$**
24. $(5q + 6t)^2$ **$25q^2 + 60qt + 36t^2$**
25. $(6a - 7b)(6a + 7b)$ **$36a^2 - 49b^2$**
26. $(8h + 3d)(8h - 3d)$ **$64h^2 - 9d^2$**
27. $(9x + 2y^2)^2$ **$81x^2 + 36xy^2 + 4y^4$**
28. $(3p^3 + 2m)^2$ **$9p^6 + 12p^3m + 4m^2$**
29. $(5a^2 - 2b)^2$ **$25a^4 - 20a^2b + 4b^2$**
30. $(4m^3 - 2t)^2$ **$16m^6 - 16m^3t + 4t^2$**
31. $(6b^3 - g)^2$ **$36b^6 - 12b^3g + g^2$**
32. $(2b^2 - g)(2b^2 + g)$ **$4b^4 - g^2$**
33. $(2v^2 + 3x^2)(2v^2 + 3x^2)$ **$4v^4 + 12v^2x^2 + 9x^4$**

34. **GEOMETRY** Janelle wants to enlarge a square graph that she has made so that a side of the new graph will be 1 inch more than twice the original side g. What trinomial represents the area of the enlarged graph? **$4g^2 + 4g + 1$**

35. **GENETICS** In a guinea pig, pure black hair coloring B is dominant over pure white coloring b. Suppose two hybrid Bb guinea pigs, with black hair coloring, are bred.

a. Find an expression for the genetic make-up of the guinea pig offspring. **$0.25BB + 0.50Bb + 0.25bb$**

b. What is the probability that two hybrid guinea pigs with black hair coloring will produce a guinea pig with white hair coloring? **25%**

Chapter 7 52 Glencoe Algebra 1

Word Problem Practice
CRM p. 53 AL OL BL ELL

NAME ______ DATE ______ PERIOD ______

7-8 Word Problem Practice

Special Products

1. **PROBABILITY** The spinner below is divided into 2 equal sections. If you spin the spinner 2 times in a row, the possible outcomes are shown in the table below.

red red	blue red
red blue	blue blue

What is the probability of spinning a blue and a red in two spins? **50%**

2. **GRAVITY** The height of a penny t seconds after being dropped down a well is given by the product of $(10 - 4t)$ and $(10 + 4t)$. Find the product and simplify. What type of special product does this represent? **$100 - 16t^2$; product of a sum and difference**

3. **TRAFFIC PLANNING** The Lincoln Memorial in Washington, D.C., is surrounded by a circular drive called Lincoln Circle. Suppose the National Park Service wants to change the layout of Lincoln Circle so that there are two concentric circular roads. Write a polynomial equation for the area A of the space between the roads if the radius of the smaller road is 10 meters less than the radius of the larger road. **$A = 20\pi r - 100\pi$**

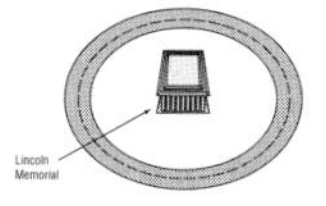

4. **BUSINESS** The Combo Lock Company finds that its profit data from 2005 to the present can be modeled by the function $y = 4n^2 + 44n + 121$, where y is the profit n years since 2005. Which special product does this polynomial demonstrate? Explain. **square of a sum; it can also be written as $(2n + 11)^2$**

5. **STORAGE** A cylindrical tank is placed along a wall. A cylindrical PVC pipe will be hidden in the corner behind the tank. See the side view diagram below. The radius of the tank is r inches and the radius of the PVC pipe is s inches.

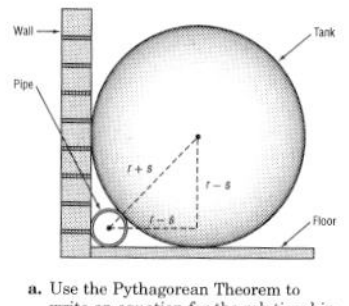

a. Use the Pythagorean Theorem to write an equation for the relationship between the two radii. Simplify your equation so that there is a zero on one side of the equals sign. **$0 = r^2 - 6rs + s^2$**

b. Write a polynomial equation you could solve to find the radius s of the PVC pipe if the radius of the tank is 20 inches. **$0 = s^2 - 120s + 400$**

Lesson 7-8

Chapter 7 53 Glencoe Algebra 1

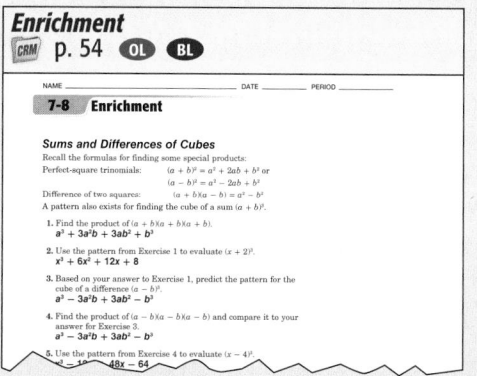

4 ASSESS

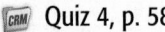

Ticket Out the Door Make several copies each of five squares of sums that need to be multiplied. Give one expression to each student. As the students leave the room, ask them to tell you the products of the expressions.

Formative Assessment

Check for student understanding of concepts in Lessons 7-7 and 7-8.

CRM Quiz 4, p. 58

PSAE PRACTICE 9.11.05, 6.11.05, 8.11.02, 8.11.21

62. GRIDDED RESPONSE In the right triangle, $\overline{DB}$ bisects $\angle B$. What is the measure of $\angle ADB$ in degrees? 85

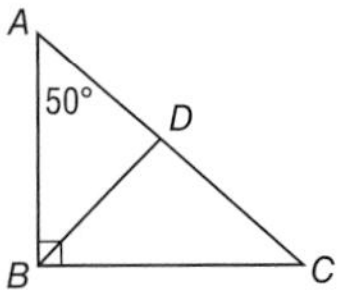

63. What is the product of $(2a - 3)$ and $(2a - 3)$? D

A $4a^2 + 12a + 9$
B $4a^2 + 9$
C $4a^2 - 12a - 9$
D $4a^2 - 12a + 9$

64. Myron can drive 4 miles in m minutes. At this rate, how many minutes will it take him to drive 19 miles? G

F $76m$
G $\frac{19m}{4}$
H $\frac{4m}{19}$
J $\frac{4}{19m}$

65. What property is illustrated by the equation $2x + 0 = 2x$? C

A Commutative Property of Addition
B Additive Inverse Property
C Additive Identity Property
D Associative Property of Addition

Spiral Review

Find each product. (Lesson 7-7)

66. $(y - 4)(y - 2)$ $y^2 - 6y + 8$
67. $(2c - 1)(c + 3)$ $2c^2 + 5c - 3$
68. $(d - 9)(d + 5)$ $d^2 - 4d - 45$
69. $(4h - 3)(2h - 7)$ $8h^2 - 34h + 21$
70. $(3x + 5)(2x + 3)$ $6x^2 + 19x + 15$
71. $(5m + 4)(8m + 3)$ $40m^2 + 47m + 12$

Simplify. (Lesson 7-6)

72. $x(2x - 7) + 5x$ $2x^2 - 2x$
73. $c(c - 8) + 2c(c + 3)$ $3c^2 - 2c$
74. $8y(-3y + 7) - 11y^2$ $-35y^2 + 56y$
75. $-2d(5d) - 3d(d + 6)$ $-13d^2 - 18d$
76. $5m(2m^3 + m^2 + 8) + 4m$ $10m^4 + 5m^3 + 44m$
77. $3p(6p - 4) + 2\left(\frac{1}{2}p^2 - 3p\right)$ $19p^2 - 18p$

Use substitution to solve each system of equations. (Lesson 6-2)

78. $4c = 3d + 3$, $c = d - 1$ (6, 7)
79. $c - 5d = 2$, $2c + d = 4$ (2, 0)
80. $5r - t = 5$, $-4r + 5t = 17$ (2, 5)

81. BIOLOGY Each type of fish thrives in a specific range of temperatures. The best temperatures for sharks range from 18°C to 22°C, inclusive. Write a compound inequality to represent temperatures where sharks will not thrive. (Lesson 6-2) $t < 18$ or $t > 22$

Write an equation of the line that passes through each pair of points. (Lesson 4-2)

82. (1, 1), (7, 4) $y = \frac{1}{2}x + \frac{1}{2}$
83. (5, 7), (0, 6) $y = \frac{1}{5}x + 6$
84. (5, 1), (8, −2) $y = -x + 6$

85. COFFEE A coffee store wants to create a mix using two coffees. How many pounds of coffee A should be mixed with 9 pounds of coffee B to get a mixture that can sell for \$6.95 per pound? (Lesson 2-9) 15 lb

Skills Review

Find the prime factorization of each number. (Concepts and Skills Bank Lesson 3)

86. 40 $2^3 \cdot 5$
87. 120 $2^3 \cdot 3 \cdot 5$
88. 900 $2^2 \cdot 3^2 \cdot 5^2$
89. 165 $3 \cdot 5 \cdot 11$

Differentiated Instruction OL BL

Extension A diagram of the Gwennap Pit is shown here. Tell students the historical Gwennap Pit, an outdoor amphitheater in southern England, consists of a circular stage surrounded by circular levels used for seating. Each seating level is about 1 meter wide. Suppose the radius of the stage is s meters.

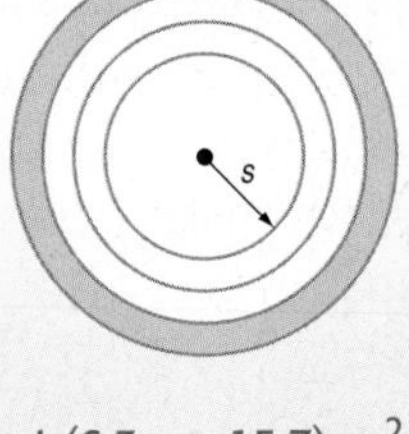

a. Find binomial representations for the radii of the second and third seating levels. $s + 2, s + 3$

b. Find the area of the shaded region representing the third seating level. about $(6.3s + 15.7)\ m^2$

CHAPTER 7 Study Guide and Review

IL Math Online glencoe.com
- STUDY TO GO
- Vocabulary Review

Chapter Summary

Key Concepts

For any nonzero real numbers a and b and any integers m, n, and p, the following are true.

Multiplying Monomials (Lesson 7-1)

- Product of Powers: $a^m \cdot a^n = a^{m+n}$
- Power of a Power: $(a^m)^n = a^{m \cdot n}$
- Power of a Product: $(ab)^m = a^m b^m$

Dividing Monomials (Lesson 7-2)

- Quotient of Powers: $\frac{a^m}{a^p} = a^{m-p}$
- Power of a Quotient: $\left(\frac{a}{b}\right)^m = \frac{a^m}{b^m}$
- Zero Exponent: $a^0 = 1$
- Negative Exponent: $a^{-n} = \frac{1}{a^n}$ and $\frac{1}{a^{-n}} = a^n$

Scientific Notation (Lesson 7-3)

- A number is in scientific notation if it is in the form $a \times 10^n$, where $1 \le a < 10$.
- To write in standard form:
  - If $n > 0$, move the decimal n places right.
  - If $n < 0$, move the decimal n places left.

Operations with Polynomials (Lessons 7-5 through 7-8)

- To add or subtract polynomials, add or subtract like terms. To multiply polynomials, use the Distributive Property.
- Special products: $(a + b)^2 = a^2 + 2ab + b^2$

  $(a - b)^2 = a^2 - 2ab + b^2$

  $(a + b)(a - b) = a^2 - b^2$

FOLDABLES® Study Organizer

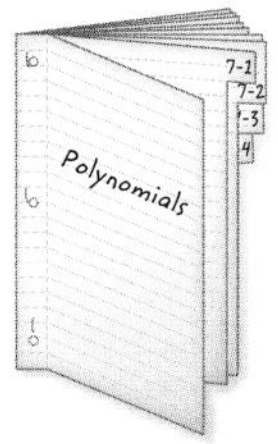

Be sure the Key Concepts are noted in your Foldable.

Key Vocabulary

binomial (p. 424)

constant (p. 401)

degree of a monomial (p. 424)

degree of a polynomial (p. 424)

FOIL method (p. 448)

leading coefficient (p. 425)

monomial (p. 401)

order of magnitude (p. 411)

polynomial (p. 424)

quadratic expression (p. 448)

scientific notation (p. 416)

standard form of a polynomial (p. 425)

trinomial (p. 424)

Vocabulary Check

Choose a term from the Key Vocabulary list above that best describes each expression or equation.

1. $x^2 + 1$ binomial
2. $5^0 = 1$ zero exponent
3. $x^2 - 3x + 2$ trinomial
4. $(xy^3)(x^2y^4) = x^3y^7$ product of powers
5. $(a^7)^3 = a^{21}$ power of a power
6. $5^{-2} = \frac{1}{5^2}$ negative exponent
7. 6.2×10^5 scientific notation
8. $(x + 2)(x - 5) = x^2 - 3x - 10$ FOIL method
9. $x^3 + 2x^2 - 3x - 1$ polynomial
10. $7xy^4$ monomial

CHAPTER 7 Study Guide and Review

Formative Assessment

Key Vocabulary The page reference after each word denotes where that term was first introduced. If students have difficulty answering questions 1–10, remind them that they can use these page references to refresh their memories about the vocabulary terms.

Summative Assessment

CRM Vocabulary Test, p. 60

IL Math Online glencoe.com

Vocabulary PuzzleMaker improves students' mathematics vocabulary using four puzzle formats—crossword, scramble, word search using a word list, and word search using clues. Students can work online or from a printed worksheet.

FOLDABLES® Study Organizer

Dinah Zike's Foldables®

Have students look through the chapter to make sure they have included examples in their Foldables for each lesson of the chapter.

Suggest that students keep their Foldables handy while completing the Study Guide and Review pages. Point out that their Foldables can serve as a quick review when studying for the chapter test.

Lesson-by-Lesson Review

Intervention If the given examples are not sufficient to review the topics covered by the questions, remind students that the page references tell them where to review that topic in their textbook.

Two-Day Option Have students complete the Lesson-by-Lesson Review on pp. 460–462. Then you can use ExamView® Assessment Suite to customize another review worksheet that practices all the objectives of this chapter or only the objectives on which your students need more help.

Differentiated Instruction

Super DVD: Mindjogger Videoquizzes
Use this DVD as an alternative format of review for the test.

CHAPTER 7 Study Guide and Review

Lesson-by-Lesson Review

7-1 Multiplying Monomials (pp. 401–407)

7.A.4b, 8.A.4b

Simplify each expression.

11. $x \cdot x^3 \cdot x^5$ **x^9**
12. $(2xy)(-3x^2y^5)$ **$-6x^3y^6$**
13. $(-4ab^4)(-5a^5b^2)$ **$20a^6b^6$**
14. $(6x^3y^2)^2$ **$36x^6y^4$**
15. $[(2r^3t)^3]^2$ **$64r^{18}t^6$**
16. $(-2u^3)(5u)$ **$-10u^4$**
17. $(2x^2)^3(x^3)^3$ **$8x^{15}$**
18. $\frac{1}{2}(2x^3)^3$ **$4x^9$**
19. **GEOMETRY** Use the formula $V = \pi r^2 h$ to find the volume of the cylinder. **$45\pi x^4$**

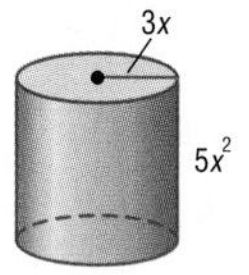

EXAMPLE 1

Simplify $(5x^2y^3)(2x^4y)$.

$(5x^2y^3)(2x^4y)$

$= (5 \cdot 2)(x^2 \cdot x^4)(y^3 \cdot y)$ — Commutative Property

$= 10x^6y^4$ — Product of Powers

EXAMPLE 2

Simplify $(3a^2b^4)^3$.

$(3a^2b^4)^3 = 3^3(a^2)^3(b^4)^3$ — Power of a Product

$= 27a^6b^{12}$ — Simplify.

7-2 Dividing Monomials (pp. 408–415)

8.A.4b

Simplify each expression. Assume that no denominator equals zero.

20. $\frac{(3x)^0}{2a}$ **$\frac{1}{2a}$**
21. $\left(\frac{3xy^3}{2z}\right)^3$ **$\left(\frac{27x^3y^9}{8z^3}\right)$**
22. $\frac{12y^{-4}}{3y^{-5}}$ **$4y$**
23. $a^{-3}b^0c^6$ **$\frac{c^6}{a^3}$**
24. $\frac{-15x^7y^8z^4}{-45x^3y^5z^3}$ **$\frac{x^4y^3z}{3}$**
25. $\frac{(3x^{-1})^{-2}}{(3x^2)^{-2}}$ **x^6**
26. $\left(\frac{6xy^{11}z^9}{48x^6yz^{-7}}\right)^0$ **1**
27. $\left(\frac{12}{2}\right)\left(\frac{x}{y^5}\right)\left(\frac{y^4}{x^4}\right)$ **$\frac{6}{yx^3}$**
28. **GEOMETRY** The area of a rectangle is $25x^2y^4$ square feet. The width of the rectangle is $5xy$ feet. What is the length of the rectangle? **$5xy^3$ ft**

EXAMPLE 3

Simplify $\frac{2k^4m^3}{4k^2m}$. Assume that no denominator equals zero.

$\frac{2k^4m^3}{4k^2m} = \left(\frac{2}{4}\right)\left(\frac{k^4}{k^2}\right)\left(\frac{m^3}{m}\right)$ — Group powers with the same base.

$= \left(\frac{1}{2}\right)k^{4-2}m^{3-1}$ — Quotient of Powers

$= \frac{k^2m^2}{2}$ — Simplify.

EXAMPLE 4

Simplify $\frac{t^4uv^{-2}}{t^{-3}u^7}$. Assume that no denominator equals zero.

$\frac{t^4uv^{-2}}{t^{-3}u^7} = \left(\frac{t^4}{t^{-3}}\right)\left(\frac{u}{u^7}\right)(v^{-2})$ — Group the powers with the same base.

$= (t^{4+3})(u^{1-7})(v^{-2})$ — Quotient of Powers

$= t^7u^{-6}v^{-2}$ — Simplify.

$= \frac{t^7}{u^6v^2}$ — Simplify.

MIXED PROBLEM SOLVING
For mixed problem-solving practice, see page 851.

7-3 Scientific Notation (pp. 416–422)

7.A.4b

Express each number in scientific notation.

29. 2,300,000 2.3×10^6 **30.** 0.0000543 5.43×10^{-5}

31. ASTRONOMY Earth has a diameter of about 8000 miles. Jupiter has a diameter of about 88,000 miles. Write in scientific notation the ratio of Earth's diameter to Jupiter's diameter. about 9.1×10^{-2}

EXAMPLE 5

Express 300,000,000 in scientific notation.

Step 1 300,000,000 ⟶ 3.00000000

Step 2 The decimal point moved 8 places to the left, so $n = 8$.

Step 3 $300{,}000{,}000 = 3 \times 10^8$

7-4 Polynomials (pp. 424–429)

7.A.4b, 8.C.4b

Write each polynomial in standard form.

32. $x + 2 + 3x^2$ $3x^2 + x + 2$ **33.** $1 - x^4$ $-x^4 + 1$

34. $2 + 3x + x^2$ $x^2 + 3x + 2$ **35.** $3x^5 - 2 + 6x - 2x^2 + x^3$ $3x^5 + x^3 - 2x^2 + 6x - 2$

36. GEOMETRY Write a polynomial that represents the perimeter of the figure. $8x^4 + 3x^3 + 6x^2 + 15x + 2$

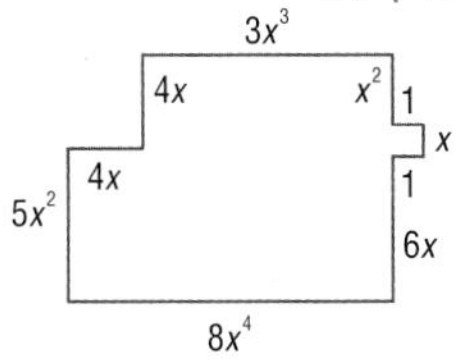

EXAMPLE 6

Write $3 - x^2 + 4x$ in standard form.

Step 1 Find the degree of each term.

3: degree 0

$-x^2$: degree 2

$4x$: degree 1

Step 2 Write the terms in descending order of degree.

$3 - x^2 + 4x = -x^2 + 4x + 3$

7-5 Adding and Subtracting Polynomials (pp. 433–438)

8.C.4b

Find each sum or difference.

37. $(x^3 + 2) + (-3x^3 - 5)$ $-2x^3 - 3$

38. $a^2 + 5a - 3 - (2a^2 - 4a + 3)$ $-a^2 + 9a - 6$

39. $(4x - 3x^2 + 5) + (2x^2 - 5x + 1)$ $-x^2 - x + 6$

40. $(6ab + 3b^2) - (3ab - 2b^2)$ $3ab + 5b^2$

41. PICTURE FRAMES Jean is framing a painting that is a rectangle. What is the perimeter of the frame? $4x^2 + 4x + 8$

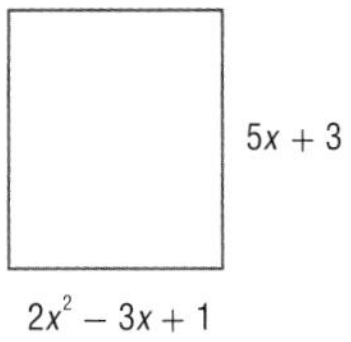

EXAMPLE 7

Find $(8r^2 + 3r) - (10r^2 - 5)$.

$(8r^2 + 3r) - (10r^2 - 5)$

$= (8r^2 + 3r) + (-10r^2 + 5)$ **Use the additive inverse.**

$= (8r^2 - 10r^2) + 3r + 5$ **Group like terms.**

$= -2r^2 + 3r + 5$ **Add like terms.**

Chapter 7 Study Guide and Review 461

Problem Solving Review

For additional practice in problem solving for Chapter 7, see the Mixed Problem Solving Appendix, p. 851, in the Student Handbook section.

Anticipation Guide

Have students complete the Chapter 7 Anticipation Guide and discuss how their responses have changed now that they have completed Chapter 7.

7-6 Multiplying a Polynomial by a Monomial (pp. 439–444)

8.A.4b

Solve each equation.

42. $x^2(x + 2) = x(x^2 + 2x + 1)$ **0**

43. $2x(x + 3) = 2(x^2 + 3)$ **1**

44. $2(4w + w^2) - 6 = 2w(w - 4) + 10$ **1**

45. $6k(k + 2) = 6(k^2 + 4)$ **2**

46. GEOMETRY Find the area of the rectangle. $3x^3 + 3x^2 - 21x$

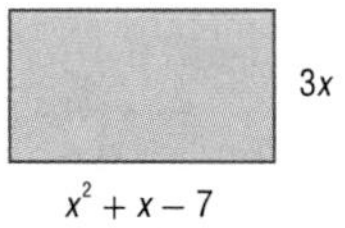

EXAMPLE 8

Solve $m(2m - 5) + m = 2m(m - 6) + 16$.

$$m(2m - 5) + m = 2m(m - 6) + 16$$
$$2m^2 - 5m + m = 2m^2 - 12m + 16$$
$$2m^2 - 4m = 2m^2 - 12m + 16$$
$$-4m = -12m + 16$$
$$8m = 16$$
$$m = 2$$

7-7 Multiplying Polynomials (pp. 447–452)

8.A.4b

Find each product.

47. $(x - 3)(x + 7)$ $x^2 + 4x - 21$

48. $(3a - 2)(6a + 5)$ $18a^2 + 3a - 10$

49. $(3r - 7t)(2r + 5t)$ $6r^2 + rt - 35t^2$

50. $(2x + 5)(5x + 2)$ $10x^2 + 29x + 10$

51. PARKING LOT The parking lot shown is to be paved. What is the area to be paved? $10x^2 + 7x - 12$

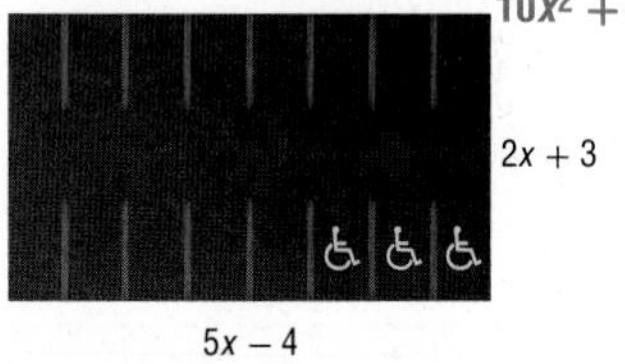

EXAMPLE 9

Find $(6x - 5)(x + 4)$.

$(6x - 5)(x + 4)$

F O I L

$= (6x)(x) + (6x)(4) + (-5)(x) + (-5)(4)$

$= 6x^2 + 24x - 5x - 20$ **Multiply.**

$= 6x^2 + 19x - 20$ **Combine like terms.**

7-8 Special Products (pp. 453–458)

8.A.4b

Find each product. See margin

52. $(x + 5)(x - 5)$ $x^2 - 25$

53. $(3x - 2)^2$ $9x^2 - 12x + 4$

54. $(5x + 4)^2$ $25x^2 + 40x + 16$

55. $(2x - 3)(2x + 3)$ $4x^2 - 9$

56. $(2r + 5t)^2$ $4r^2 + 20rt + 25t^2$

57. $(3m - 2)(3m + 2)$ $9m^2 - 4$

58. GEOMETRY Write an expression to represent the area of the shaded region. $3x^2 - 21$

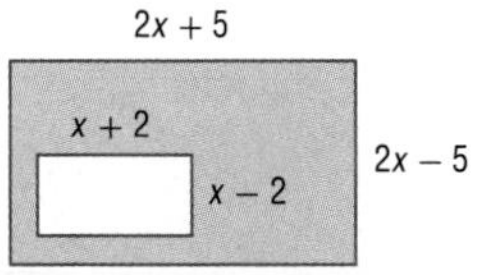

EXAMPLE 10

Find $(x - 7)^2$.

$(a - b)^2 = a^2 - 2ab + b^2$ **Square of a Difference**

$(x - 7)^2 = x^2 - 2(x)(7) + (-7)^2$ **$a = x$ and $b = 7$**

$= x^2 - 14x + 49$ **Simplify.**

EXAMPLE 11

Find $(5a - 4)(5a + 4)$.

$(a + b)(a - b) = a^2 - b^2$ **Product of a Sum and Difference**

$(5a - 4)(5a + 4) = (5a)^2 - (4)^2$ **$a = 5a$ and $b = 4$**

$= 25a^2 - 16$ **Simplify.**

IL Math Online glencoe.com
Chapter Test

Simplify each expression.

1. $(x^2)(7x^8)$ $7x^{10}$
2. $(5a^7bc^2)(-6a^2bc^5)$ $-30a^9b^2c^7$
3. **MULTIPLE CHOICE** Express the volume of the solid as a monomial. **A**

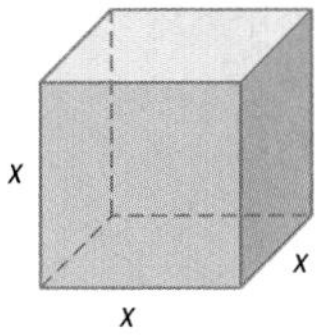

A x^3 C $6x^3$

B $6x$ D x^6

Simplify each expression. Assume that no denominator equals 0.

4. $\frac{x^6y^8}{x^2}$ x^4y^8
5. $\left(\frac{2a^4b^3}{c^6}\right)^0$ 1
6. $\frac{2xy^{-7}}{8x}$ $\frac{1}{4y^7}$

Express each number in scientific notation.

(Lesson 7-3)

7. 0.00021 2.1×10^{-4}
8. 58,000 5.8×10^4

Express each number in standard form.

9. 2.9×10^{-5} 0.000029
10. 9.1×10^6 9,100,000

Evaluate each product or quotient. Express the results in scientific notation.

11. $(2.5 \times 10^3)(3 \times 10^4)$ 7.5×10^7
12. $\frac{8.8 \times 10^2}{4 \times 10^{-4}}$ 2.2×10^6
13. **ASTRONOMY** The average distance from Mercury to the Sun is 35,980,000 miles. Express this distance in scientific notation. 3.598×10^7

Find each sum or difference.

14. $(x + 5) + (x^2 - 3x + 7)$ $x^2 - 2x + 12$
15. $(7m - 8n^2 + 3n) - (-2n^2 + 4m - 3n)$ $3m - 6n^2 + 6n$
16. **MULTIPLE CHOICE** Antonia is carpeting two of the rooms in her house. The dimensions are shown. What is the total area to be carpeted? **G**

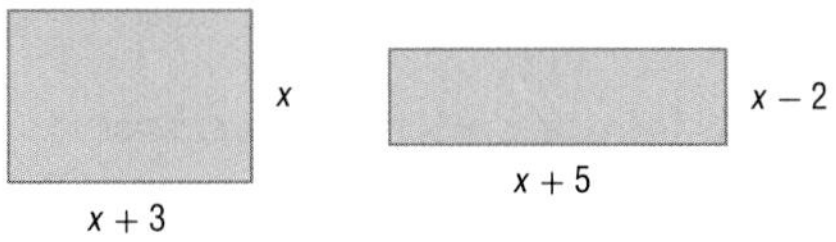

F $x^2 + 3x$ H $x^2 + 3x - 5$

G $2x^2 + 6x - 10$ J $8x + 12$

Find each product.

17. $a(a^2 + 2a - 10)$ $a^3 + 2a^2 - 10a$
18. $(2a - 5)(3a + 5)$ $6a^2 - 5a - 25$
19. $(x - 3)(x^2 + 5x - 6)$ $x^3 + 2x^2 - 21x + 18$
20. $(x + 3)^2$ $x^2 + 6x + 9$
21. $(2b - 5)(2b + 5)$ $4b^2 - 25$
22. **GEOMETRY** A rectangular prism has dimensions x, $x + 3$, and $2x + 5$.
    a. Find the volume of the prism in terms of x. $2x^3 + 11x^2 + 15x$
    b. Choose two values for x. How do the volumes compare? **See students' work.**

Solve each equation.

23. $5(t^2 - 3t + 2) = t(5t - 2)$ $\frac{10}{13}$
24. $3x(x + 2) = 3(x^2 - 2)$ -1
25. **FINANCIAL LITERACY** Money invested in a certificate of deposit (CD) earns interest once per year. Suppose you invest \$4000 in a 2-year CD.
    a. If the interest rate is 5% per year, the expression $4000(1 + 0.05)^2$ can be evaluated to find the total amount of money after two years. Explain the numbers in this expression. **See margin.**
    b. Find the amount at the end of two years. **\$4410**
    c. Suppose you invest \$10,000 in a CD for 4 years at an annual rate of 6.25%. What is the total amount of money you will have after 4 years? **about \$12,744**

CHAPTER 7 Practice Test

ExamView Assessment Suite Customize and create multiple versions of your chapter tests and their answer keys. All of the questions from the leveled chapter tests in the *Chapter 7 Resource Masters* are also available on ExamView Assessment Suite.

Additional Answer

25a. 4000 is the amount of the investment, 1 will add the amount of the investment to the interest, 0.05 is the interest rate as a decimal, and 2 is the number of the years of the investment.

Intervention Planner

Tier 1 On Level	Tier 2 Strategic Intervention approaching grade level	Tier 3 Intensive Intervention 2 or more grades below level
If students miss about 25% of the exercises or less,	**If** students miss about 50% of the exercises,	**If** students miss about 75% of the exercises,
Then choose a resource: **SE** Lessons 7-1, 7-2, 7-3, 7-4, 7-5, 7-6, 7-7, and 7-8 **CRM** Skills Practice, pp. 7, 13, 19, 25, 32, 38, 44, and 51 **TE** Chapter Project, p. 398 IL Math Online Self-Check Quiz	**Then** choose a resource: **CRM** Study Guide and Intervention, Chapter 7, pp. 5, 11, 17, 23, 30, 36, 42, and 49 IL Math Online Extra Examples, Personal Tutor, Homework Help	**Then** use *Math Triumphs, Alg. 1* IL Math Online Extra Examples, Personal Tutor, Homework Help, Review Vocabulary

1 FOCUS

Objective Use the strategy of using a scientific calculator to solve standardized test problems.

2 TEACH

Scaffolding Questions

Ask:

- For which types of math problems have you used a scientific calculator? Answers will vary.
- Are there any types of math problems in which you find that it is faster or easier to *not* use a scientific calculator? Answers will vary.
- Are you more likely or less likely to make calculation errors when using a scientific calculator? Explain. Sample answer: You are less likely to make a calculation error, but you could still make errors if you enter the numbers incorrectly, or use formulas incorrectly, or round incorrectly.

CHAPTER 7 Preparing for Standardized Tests

Using a Scientific Calculator

Scientific calculators are powerful problem-solving tools. There are times when using a scientific calculator can be used to make computations faster and easier, such as computations with very large numbers. However, there are times when using a scientific calculator is necessary, like the estimation of irrational numbers.

Strategies for Using a Scientific Calculator

Step 1

Familiarize yourself with the various functions of a scientific calculator as well as when they should be used:

- **Exponents** scientific notation, calculating with large or small numbers
- **Pi** solving circle problems, like circumference and area
- **Square roots** distance on a coordinate plane, Pythagorean theorem
- **Graphs** analyzing paired data in a scatter plot, graphing functions, finding roots of equations

Step 2

Use your scientific or graphing calculator to solve the problem.

- Remember to work as efficiently as possible. Some steps may be done mentally or by hand, while others should be completed using your calculator.
- If time permits, check your answer.

EXAMPLE

Read the problem. Identify what you need to know. Then use the information in the problem to solve.

The distance from the Sun to Jupiter is approximately 7.786×10^{11} meters. If the speed of light is about 3×10^{8} meters per second, how long does it take for light from the Sun to reach Jupiter? Round to the nearest minute.

A about 43 minutes	**C** about 1876 minutes
B about 51 minutes	**D** about 2595 minutes

464 Chapter 7 Polynomials

Read the problem carefully. You are given the approximate distance from the Sun to Jupiter as well as the speed of light. Both quantities are given in scientific notation. You are asked to find how many minutes it takes for light from the Sun to reach Jupiter. Use the relationship distance = rate × time to find the amount of time.

$d = r \times t$

$\frac{d}{r} = t$

To find the amount of time, divide the distance by the rate. Notice, however, that the units for time will be seconds.

$\frac{7.786 \times 10^{11} \text{ m}}{3 \times 10^{8} \text{ m/s}} = t$ seconds

Use a scientific calculator to quickly find the quotient. On most scientific calculators, the EE key is used to enter numbers in scientific notation.

KEYSTROKES: (7.786 [2nd] [EE] 11) / (3 [2nd] [EE] 8)

The result is 2595.33333333 seconds. To convert this number to minutes, use your calculator to divide the result by 60. This gives an answer of about 43.2555 minutes. The answer is A.

Additional Example

Light travels at about 9.46×10^{12} kilometers per year. The star Altair is about 1.5136×10^{14} kilometers from Earth. About many months would it take light to travel from Earth to Altair? B

A about 1920 months

B about 192 months

C about 160 months

D about 16 months

3 ASSESS

Use Exercise 1–4 to assess students' understanding.

Exercises

Read each problem. Identify what you need to know. Then use the information in the problem to solve.

1. Since its creation 5 years ago, approximately 2.504×10^7 items have been sold or traded on a popular online website. What is the average daily number of items sold or traded over the 5-year period? B

A about 9640 items per day

B about 13,720 items per day

C about 1,025,000 items per day

D about 5,008,000 items per day

2. Evaluate $\sqrt{ab}$ if $a = 121$ and $b = 23$. J

F about 5.26

G about 9.90

H about 12

J about 52.75

3. The population of the United States is about 3.034×10^8 people. The land area of the country is about 3.54×10^6 square miles. What is the average *population density* (number of people per square mile) of the United States? D

A about 136.3 people per square mile

B about 112.5 people per square mile

C about 94.3 people per square mile

D about 85.7 people per square mile

4. Eleece is making a cover for the marching band's bass drum. The drum has a diameter of 20 inches. Estimate the area of the face of the bass drum. J

F 31.41 square inches

G 62.83 square inches

H 78.54 square inches

J 314.16 square inches

Diagnose Student Errors

Survey students' responses for each item. Class trends may indicate common errors and misconceptions.

1. A forgot to multiply by $\frac{1}{2}$
B forgot to multiply by $\frac{1}{2}$ and multiplied instead of added exponents
C multiplied instead of added exponents
D correct
E added coefficients

2. F forgot to raise $\frac{2}{3}$ to the power of 3 and added instead of multiplied exponents
G correct
H added instead of multiplied exponents
J forgot to raise $\frac{2}{3}$ to the power of 3
K only cubed numbers

3. A correct
B slope is reciprocal, but not opposite sign
C slope is opposite, but not opposite reciprocal
D same slope; this is a parellel line
E slope should be the reciprocal

4. F added two sides instead of four
G added two sides instead of four and made addition error when adding *x* terms
H correct
J added two sides only when adding *x* terms and constants
K added like terms incorrectly

5. A correct
B added coefficients in the first terms of the two expressions and then subtracted the coefficients in the second two terms
C added instead of subtracted $7a^2$ and $3a^2$ and -2 and 5
D guess
E added like terms incorrectly

Multiple Choice

Read each question. Then fill in the correct answer on the answer document provided by your teacher or on a sheet of paper.

1. Express the area of the triangle below as a monomial. D

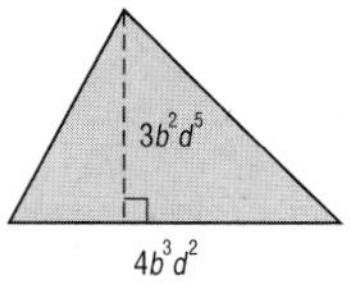

A $12b^5d^7$
B $12b^6d^{10}$
C $6b^6d^{10}$
D $6b^5d^7$
E $7b^5d^7$

2. Simplify the following expression. G

$$\left(\frac{2w^2z^5}{3y^4}\right)^3$$

F $\frac{2w^5z^8}{3y^7}$
G $\frac{8w^6z^{15}}{27y^{12}}$
H $\frac{8w^5z^8}{27y^7}$
J $\frac{2w^6z^{15}}{3y^{12}}$
K $\frac{8w^2z^5}{27y^4}$

3. Which equation of a line is perpendicular to $y = \frac{3}{5}x - 3$? A

A $y = -\frac{5}{3}x + 2$
B $y = \frac{5}{3}x - 2$
C $y = -\frac{3}{5}x + 2$
D $y = \frac{3}{5}x - 2$
E $y = -\frac{3}{5}x - 3$

Test-Taking Tip

Question 2 Use the laws of exponents to simplify the expression. Remember, to find the power of a power, multiply the exponents.

4. Express the perimeter of the rectangle below as a polynomial. H

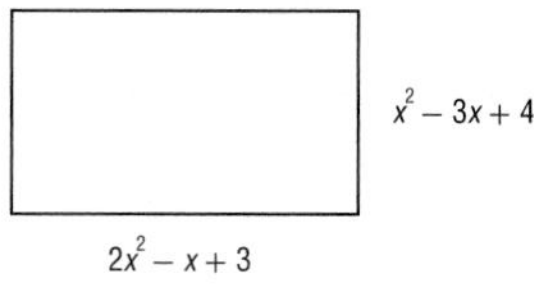

F $3x^2 - 4x + 7$
G $3x^2 + x + 7$
H $6x^2 - 8x + 14$
J $6x^2 - 4x + 7$
K $6x^2 + 4x + 7$

5. Subtract the polynomials below. A

$(7a^2 + 6a - 2) - (-4a^3 + 3a^2 + 5)$

A $4a^3 + 4a^2 + 6a - 7$
B $11a^2 + 3a - 7$
C $4a^3 + 10a^2 + 6a + 3$
D $4a^3 + 7a^3 - 3a$
E $11a^2 + 9a - 7$

6. Which inequality is shown in the graph? K

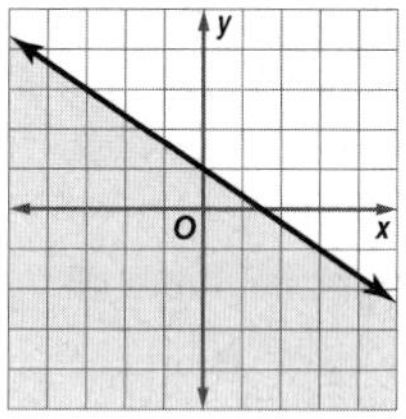

F $y \le -\frac{2}{3}x - 1$
G $y \le -\frac{3}{4}x - 1$
H $y \ge -\frac{3}{2}x + 1$
J $y \le -\frac{3}{4}x + 1$
K $y \le -\frac{2}{3}x + 1$

6. F boundary has wrong intercept
G boundary has wrong slope and intercept
H boundary has wrong intercept
J boundary has wrong intercept
K correct

Short Response/Gridded Response

7. Mickey has 180 feet of fencing that she wants to use to enclose a play area for her puppy. She will use her house as one of the sides of the region.

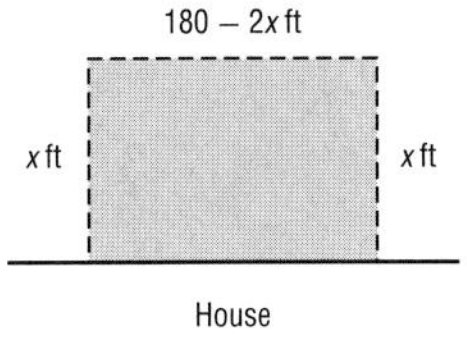

a. If she makes the play area x feet deep as shown in the figure, write a polynomial in standard form to represent the area of the region. **$-2x^2 + 180x$**

b. How many square feet of area will the puppy have to play in if Mickey makes it 40 feet deep? **4000 ft²**

8. Identify the expression below that does not belong with the other two. Explain. **See margin.**

$(3m - 2n)(3m + 2n)$

$(3m + 2n)(3m + 2n)$

$(3m + 2n)(3m - 2n)$

9. What is the solution to the following system of equations? Show your work. **no solution**

$$\begin{cases} y = 6x - 1 \\ y = 6x + 4 \end{cases}$$

10. GRIDDED RESPONSE At a family fun center, the Wilson and Sanchez families each bought video game tokens and batting cage tokens as shown in the table.

Family	Wilson	Sanchez
Number of Video Game Tokens	25	30
Number of Batting Cage Tokens	8	6
Total Cost	\$26.50	\$25.50

What is the cost in dollars of a batting cage token at the family fun center? **1.75**

Extended Response

Record your answers on a sheet of paper. Show your work.

11. The table below shows the distances from the Sun to Mercury, Earth, Mars, and Saturn. Use the data to answer each question.

Planet	Distance from Sun (km)
Mercury	5.79×10^7
Earth	1.50×10^8
Mars	2.28×10^8
Saturn	1.43×10^9

a. Of the planets listed, which one is the closest to the Sun? **Mercury**

b. About how many times as far from the Sun is Mars as Earth? **about 1.52 times farther**

Need Extra Help?											
If you missed Question...	1	2	3	4	5	6	7	8	9	10	11
Go to Lesson or Page...	7-1	7-2	4-4	7-5	7-5	5-6	7-6	7-8	6-1	6-4	7-3
IL Assessment Objectives	8.11.02	8.11.01	8.11.09	7.11.03	8.11.01	8.11.16	8.11.01	8.11.01	8.11.17	8.11.17	8.11.19

Formative Assessment

You can use these two pages to benchmark student progress.

CRM Standardized Test Practice, pp. 74–76

Answer Sheet Practice

Have students simulate taking a standardized test by recording their answers on a practice recording sheet.

CRM Student Recording Sheet, p. 55

Chapter Resource Master

CRM p. 55

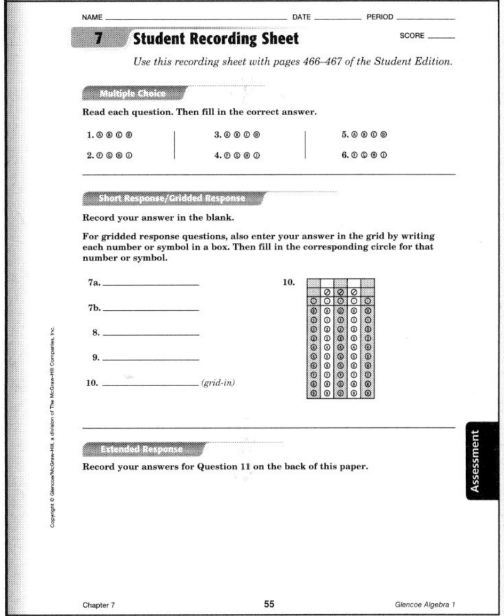
NAME ______ DATE ______ PERIOD ______

7 **Student Recording Sheet** SCORE ______

Use this recording sheet with pages 466–467 of the Student Edition.

Multiple Choice

Read each question. Then fill in the correct answer.

1. Ⓐ Ⓑ Ⓒ Ⓓ
2. Ⓕ Ⓖ Ⓗ Ⓙ
3. Ⓐ Ⓑ Ⓒ Ⓓ
4. Ⓕ Ⓖ Ⓗ Ⓙ
5. Ⓐ Ⓑ Ⓒ Ⓓ
6. Ⓕ Ⓖ Ⓗ Ⓙ

Short Response/Gridded Response

Record your answer in the blank.

For gridded response questions, also enter your answer in the grid by writing each number or symbol in a box. Then fill in the corresponding circle for that number or symbol.

7a. ______

7b. ______

8. ______

9. ______

10. ______ *(grid-in)*

Extended Response

Record your answers for Question 11 on the back of this paper.

Assessment

Copyright © Glencoe/McGraw-Hill, a division of The McGraw-Hill Companies, Inc.

Chapter 7 55 *Glencoe Algebra 1*

ExamView Assessment Suite — Create practice worksheets or tests that align to your state's standards, as well as TIMSS and NAEP tests.

Homework Option

Get Ready for Chapter 8 Assign students the exercises on p. 469 as homework to assess whether they possess the prerequisite skills needed for the next chapter.

Page 406, Lesson 7-1

65b.

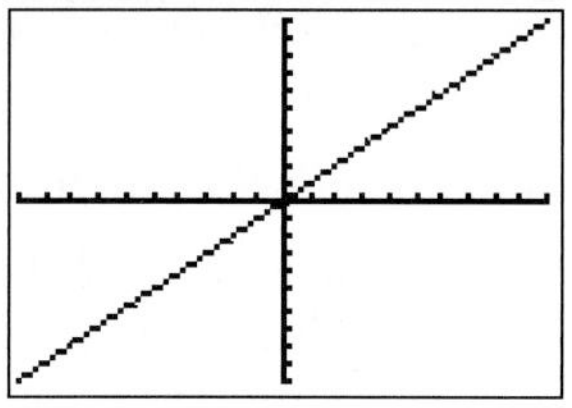

[−10, 10] scl: 1 by
[−10, 10] scl: 1

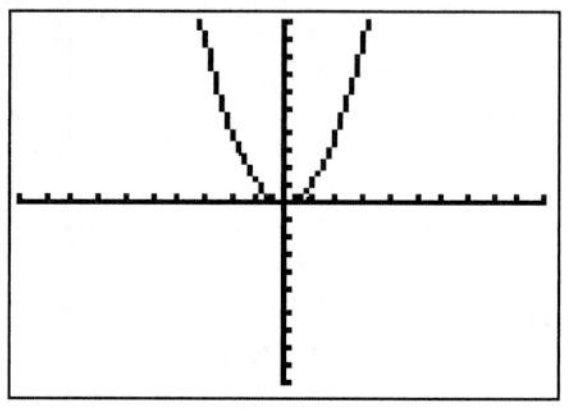

[−10, 10] scl: 1 by
[−10, 10] scl: 1

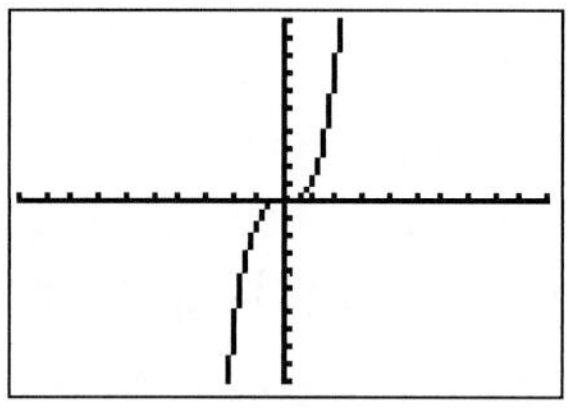

[−10, 10] scl: 1 by
[−10, 10] scl: 1

65d. If the power of x is 1, the equation or its related expression is linear. Otherwise, it is nonlinear.

Page 415, Lesson 7-2

71.

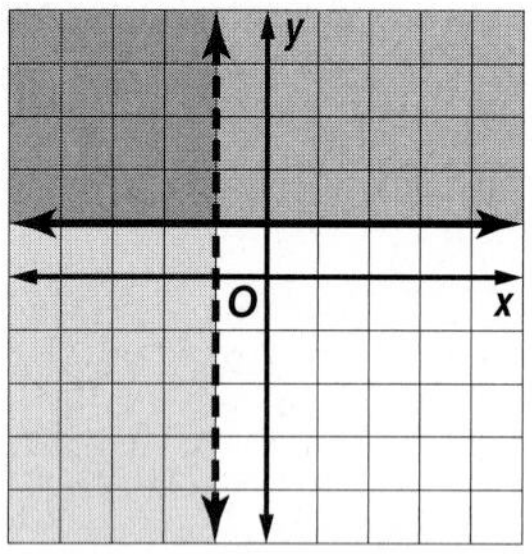

72.

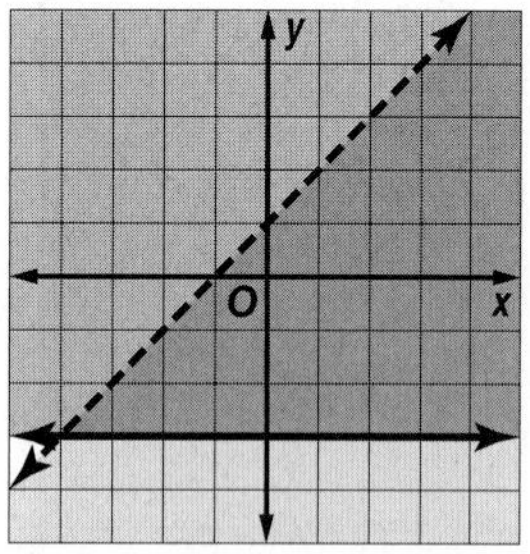

73.

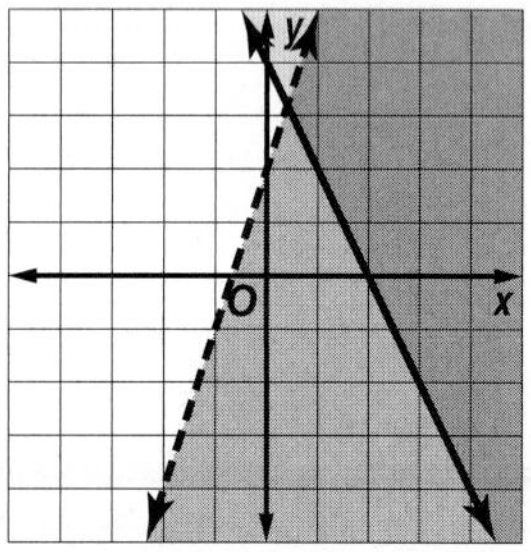

74.

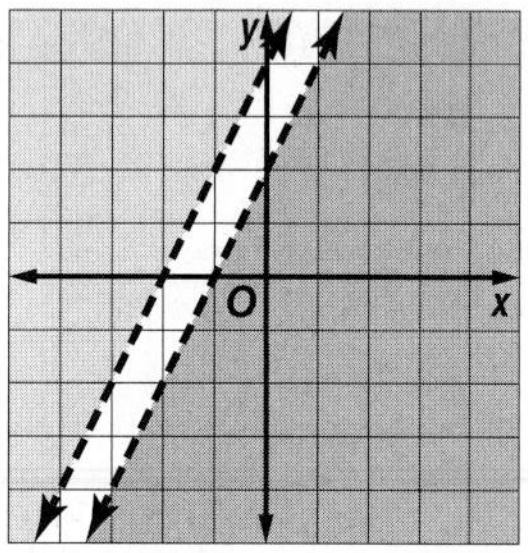

no solution

Page 428, Lesson 7-4

51a. Sample answer:

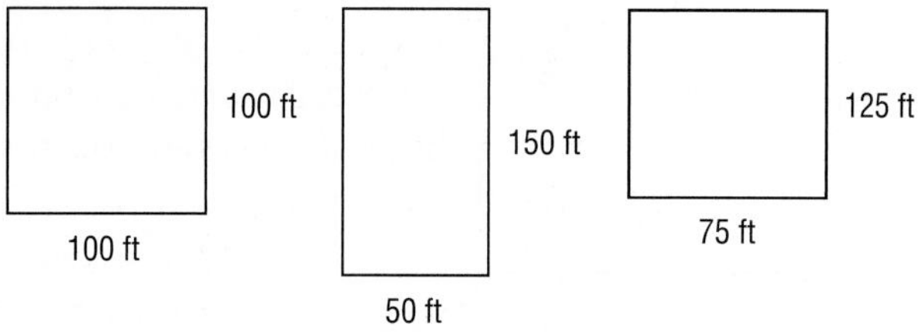

51c.

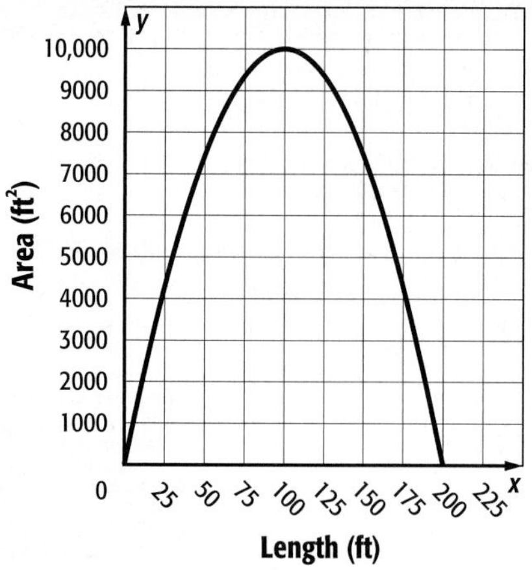

The largest possible area is 10,000 square feet.

Page 432, Explore 7-5

4. Method from Activity 2:

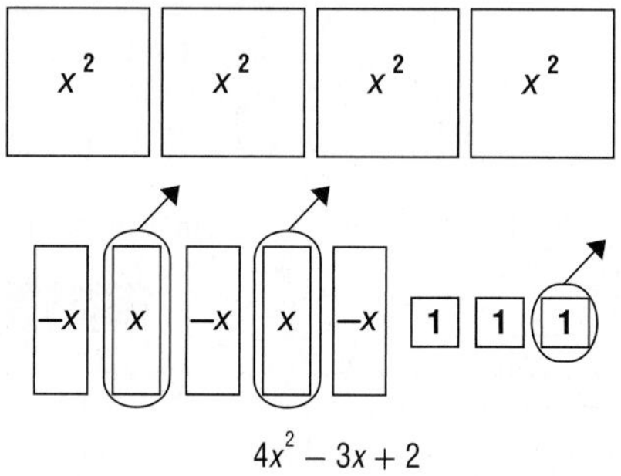

You need to add zero pairs so that you can move 2 green x-tiles and 1 yellow 1-tile.

Method from Activity 3:

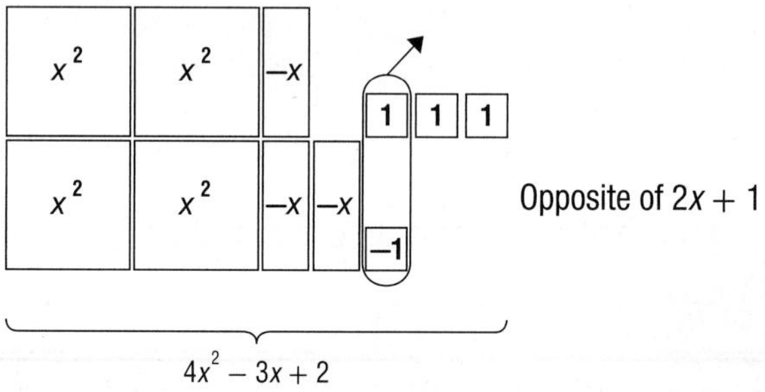

You remove all zero pairs to find the difference in simplest form.

Page 446, Explore 7-7

7.

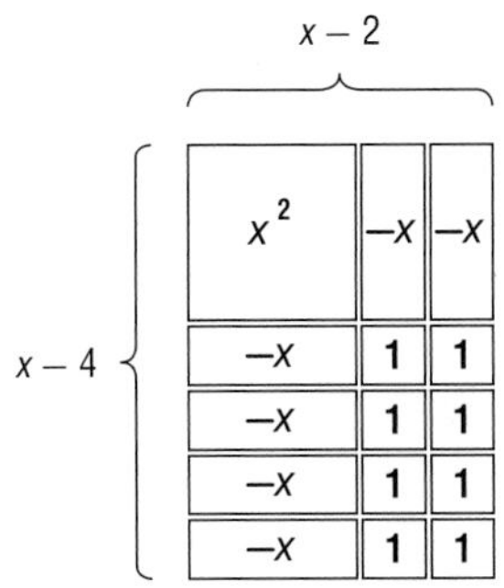

8.

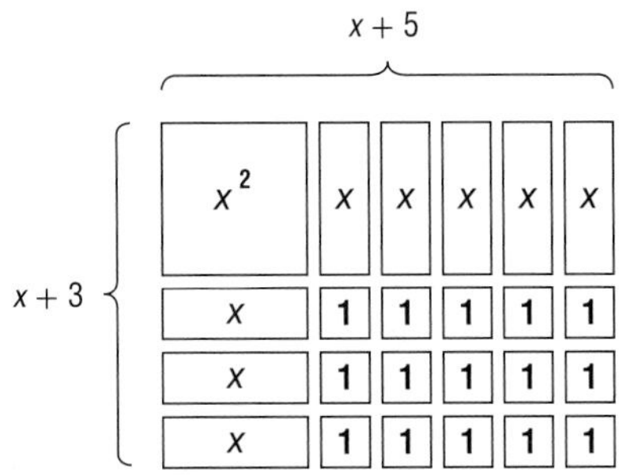

Page 451, Lesson 7-7

44b. The first term of the square of a sum is the first term of the sum squared. The middle term of the sum is two times the first term of the sum multiplied by the last term of the sum. The third term of the square of the sum is the last term of the sum squared.

49. The Distributive Property can be used with a vertical or horizontal format by distributing, multiplying, and combining like terms. The FOIL method is used with a horizontal format. You multiply the first, outer, inner, and last terms of the binomials and then combine like terms. A rectangular method can also be used by writing the terms of the polynomials along the top and left side of a rectangle and then multiplying the terms and combining like terms.

Chapter Planner

Diagnostic Assessment
Quick Check, p. 469

	Lesson 8-1 Pacing: 1 day	Explore 8-2 Pacing: 0.5 day	Lesson 8-2 Pacing: 1.5 days	Explore 8-3 Pacing: 0.5 day
Title	**Monomials and Factoring**	**Algebra Lab: Factoring Using the Distributive Property**	**Using Distributive Property**	**Algebra Lab: Factoring Trinomials**
Objectives	• Factor monomials. • Find the greatest common factors of monomials.	• Use algebra tiles to model using the Distributive Property to factor binomials.	• Use the Distributive Property to factor polynomials. • Solve quadratic equations of the form $ax^2 + bx = 0$.	• Use algebra tiles to model factoring trinomials.
Key Vocabulary	factored form greatest common factor (GCF)		factoring factoring by grouping Zero Product Property	
ILS	8.A.4b	8.B.4a	7.B.4, 8.C.4b	8.B.4a
Multiple Representations	p. 473		p. 481	
Lesson Resources	**Chapter 8 Resource Masters** • Study Guide and Intervention, pp. 5–6 AL OL ELL • Skills Practice, p. 7 AL OL ELL • Practice, p. 8 AL OL BL ELL • Word Problem Practice, p. 9 AL OL BL ELL • Enrichment, p. 10 OL BL **Transparencies** • 5-Minute Check Transparency 8-1 AL OL BL ELL **Additional Print Resources** • *Study Notebook* AL OL BL ELL	**Materials** • algebra tiles • product mats **Additional Print Resources** • *Teaching Algebra with Manipulatives,* pp. 10, 11, 17, 131 AL OL ELL	**Chapter 8 Resource Masters** • Study Guide and Intervention, pp. 11–12 AL OL ELL • Skills Practice, p. 13 AL OL ELL • Practice, p. 14 AL OL BL ELL • Word Problem Practice, p. 15 AL OL BL ELL • Enrichment, p. 16 OL BL • Quiz 1, p. 45 AL OL BL ELL **Transparencies** • 5-Minute Check Transparency 8-2 AL OL BL ELL **Additional Print Resources** • *Study Notebook* AL OL BL ELL • *Teaching Algebra with Manipulatives,* pp. 132–133 AL OL ELL	**Materials** • algebra tiles • product mats **Additional Print Resources** • *Teaching Algebra with Manipulatives,* pp. 10, 11, 17, 134 AL OL ELL
Technology for Every Lesson	IL Math Online glencoe.com • Extra Examples • Personal Tutor • Self-Check Quizzes • Homework Help	CD/DVD Resources IWB INTERACTIVE WHITEBOARD READY IWB StudentWorks Plus IWB Interactive Classroom IWB Diagnostic and Assessment Planner		• TeacherWorks Plus • eSolutions Manual Plus • ExamView Assessment Suite
Math in Motion	Animation	Animation		Animation
Differentiated Instruction	p. 474		pp. 478, 482	

KEY: AL Approaching Level OL On Level BL Beyond Level ELL English Learners

Factoring and Quadratic Equations

Suggested Pacing			
Time Periods	Instruction	Review & Assessment	Total
45-minute	9	2	11
90-minute	4	1	5

Lesson 8-3 Pacing: 1.5 days	Lesson 8-4 Pacing: 2 days	Lesson 8-5 Pacing: 1 day	Lesson 8-6 Pacing: 1 day
Quadratic Equations: $x^2 + bx + c = 0$	**Quadratic Equations: $ax^2 + bx + c = 0$**	**Quadratic Equations: Differences of Squares**	**Quadratic Equations: Perfect Squares**
• Factor trinomials of the form $x^2 + bx + c$. • Solve equations of the form $x^2 + bx + c = 0$.	• Factor trinomials of the form $ax^2 + bx + c$. • Solve equations of the form $ax^2 + bx + c = 0$.	• Factor binomials that are the difference of squares. • Use the difference of squares to solve equations.	• Factor perfect square trinomials. • Solve equations involving perfect squares.
quadratic equation	prime polynomial	difference of two squares	perfect square trinomial
8.A.4b, 8.D.4	8.A.4b, 8.D.4	8.A.4b, 8.D.4	8.A.4b, 8.D.4
p. 490	p. 497	p. 503	
Chapter 8 Resource Masters • Study Guide and Intervention, pp. 17–18 AL OL ELL • Skills Practice, p. 19 AL OL ELL • Practice, p. 20 AL OL BL ELL • Word Problem Practice, p. 21 AL OL BL ELL • Enrichment, p. 22 OL BL • Quiz 2, p. 45 AL OL BL ELL **Transparencies** • 5-Minute Check Transparency 8-3 AL OL BL ELL **Additional Print Resources** • *Study Notebook* AL OL BL ELL	**Chapter 8 Resource Masters** • Study Guide and Intervention, pp. 23–24 AL OL ELL • Skills Practice, p. 25 AL OL ELL • Practice, p. 26 AL OL BL ELL • Word Problem Practice, p. 27 AL OL BL ELL • Enrichment, p. 28 OL BL • Graphing Calculator Activity, p. 29 OL • Quiz 3, p. 46 AL OL BL ELL **Transparencies** • 5-Minute Check Transparency 8-4 AL OL BL ELL **Additional Print Resources** • *Study Notebook* AL OL BL ELL • *Teaching Algebra with Manipulatives,* pp. 135–139 AL OL ELL	**Chapter 8 Resource Masters** • Study Guide and Intervention, pp. 30–31 AL OL ELL • Skills Practice, p. 32 AL OL ELL • Practice, p. 33 AL OL BL ELL • Word Problem Practice, p. 34 AL OL BL ELL • Enrichment, p. 35 OL BL • Spreadsheet Activity, p. 36 OL **Transparencies** • 5-Minute Check Transparency 8-5 AL OL BL ELL **Additional Print Resources** • *Study Notebook* AL OL BL ELL • *Teaching Algebra with Manipulatives,* pp. 140–141 AL OL ELL	**Chapter 8 Resource Masters** • Study Guide and Intervention, pp. 37–38 AL OL ELL • Skills Practice, p. 39 AL OL ELL • Practice, p. 40 AL OL BL ELL • Word Problem Practice, p. 41 AL OL BL ELL • Enrichment, p. 42 OL BL • Quiz 4, p. 46 AL OL BL ELL **Transparencies** • 5-Minute Check Transparency 8-6 AL OL BL ELL **Additional Print Resources** • *Study Notebook* AL OL BL ELL • *Teaching Algebra with Manipulatives,* pp. 142–146 AL OL ELL
	IL Math Online glencoe.com • Extra Examples • Self-Check Quizzes • Personal Tutor • Homework Help	**CD/DVD Resources** IWB INTERACTIVE WHITEBOARD READY IWB StudentWorks Plus IWB Interactive Classroom IWB Diagnostic and Assessment Planner	• TeacherWorks Plus • eSolutions Manual Plus • ExamView Assessment Suite
		Animation	Interactive Lab
pp. 486, 488	pp. 494, 498	pp. 501, 504	pp. 506, 512

Formative Assessment
Mid-Chapter Quiz, p. 492

Summative Assessment
- Study Guide and Review, p. 513
- Practice Test, p. 517

CHAPTER 8

Assessment and Intervention

SE = Student Edition, **TE** = Teacher Edition, **CRM** = Chapter Resource Masters

	Diagnosis	Prescription
Diagnostic Assessment	**Beginning Chapter 8**	
	Get Ready for Chapter 8 **SE**, p. 469	Response to Intervention **TE**, p. 469
	Beginning Every Lesson	
	Then, Now, Why? **SE** 5-Minute Check Transparencies	Chapter 0 **SE**, pp. P1–P45 Concepts and Skills Bank **SE**, pp. 857–867 *Quick Review Math Handbook*
Formative Assessment	**During/After Every Lesson**	
	Check Your Progress **SE**, every example Check Your Understanding **SE** H.O.T. Problems **SE** Spiral Review **SE** Additional Examples **TE** Watch Out! **TE** Step 4, Assess **TE** Chapter 8 Quizzes **CRM**, pp. 45–46 Self-Check Quizzes glencoe.com	**Tier 1 Intervention** Concepts and Skills Bank **SE**, pp. 857–867 Skills Practice **CRM**, Ch. 1–8 glencoe.com **Tier 2 Intervention** Differentiated Instruction **TE** Differentiated Homework Options **TE** Study Guide and Intervention Masters **CRM**, Ch. 1–8 *Quick Review Math Handbook* **Tier 3 Intervention** *Math Triumphs, Alg. 1*
	Mid-Chapter	
	Mid-Chapter Quiz **SE**, p. 492 Mid-Chapter Test **CRM**, p. 47 ExamView Assessment Suite	**Tier 1 Intervention** Concepts and Skills Bank **SE**, pp. 857–867 Skills Practice **CRM**, Ch. 1–8 glencoe.com **Tier 2 Intervention** Study Guide and Intervention Masters **CRM**, Ch. 1–8 *Quick Review Math Handbook* **Tier 3 Intervention** *Math Triumphs, Alg. 1*
	Before Chapter Test	
	Chapter Study Guide and Review **SE**, pp. 513–516 Practice Test **SE**, p. 517 Standardized Test Practice **SE**, pp. 518–521 Chapter Test glencoe.com Standardized Test Practice glencoe.com Vocabulary Review glencoe.com ExamView Assessment Suite	**Tier 1 Intervention** Concepts and Skills Bank **SE**, pp. 857–867 Skills Practice **CRM**, Ch. 1–8 glencoe.com **Tier 2 Intervention** Study Guide and Intervention Masters **CRM**, Ch. 1–8 *Quick Review Math Handbook* **Tier 3 Intervention** *Math Triumphs, Alg. 1*
Summative Assessment	**After Chapter 8**	
	Multiple-Choice Tests, Forms 1, 2A, 2B **CRM**, pp. 49–54 Free-Response Tests, Forms 2C, 2D, 3 **CRM**, pp. 55–60 Vocabulary Test **CRM**, p. 48 Extended Response Test **CRM**, p. 61 Standardized Test Practice **CRM**, pp. 62–64 ExamView Assessment Suite	Study Guide and Intervention Masters **CRM**, Ch. 1–8 *Quick Review Math Handbook* glencoe.com

Differentiated Instruction

Option 1 Reaching All Learners AL OL BL ELL

VISUAL/SPATIAL As students learn the rules for factoring trinomials, encourage them to use algebra tiles to confirm their results. Students should soon realize that the greater the values of b and c in the trinomials, the more cumbersome the algebra tiles become, which should then reinforce the importance of learning to factor using the methods in the text.

AUDITORY Ask groups to create a mnemonic device that will help them remember how to factor one of the types of trinomials studied in this chapter. Then write an example of a trinomial on the board and have a volunteer say his or her mnemonic device as he or she factors the trinomial.

Option 2 Approaching Level AL

In large print, write a number and each step of its prime factorization (using the factor tree-method) on sticky notes. Each number in the steps should be on a separate note. On other notes draw some arrows. Stick the notes randomly on the board. Ask volunteers to arrange the factor and arrow notes so that they show the prime factorization of the number.

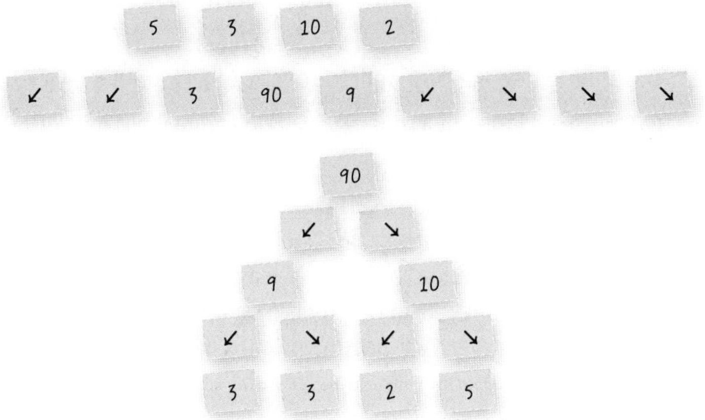

Option 3 English Learners ELL

Factoring integers is a very visual skill, whether it is done by writing out factors in a line or by using a factor tree. Have students describe one of the methods of factoring in their own words, without actually writing out the factors as an example. Alternatively, have students write a description of how to factor, using an example as a guide.

Option 4 Beyond Level BL

Tell students that some polynomials are prime when considering the set of integers, but can be factored when the set of real numbers is considered. For example, $x^2 - 7$ is a prime polynomial. However, it can be factored if the set of real numbers is considered. That is, $x^2 - 7 = (x + \sqrt{7})(x - \sqrt{7})$. Ask students to factor other prime polynomials such as $3x^2 - 2$ when the set of real numbers is considered. $(x\sqrt{3} + \sqrt{2})(x\sqrt{3} - \sqrt{2})$

Focus on Mathematical Content

Vertical Alignment

Before Chapter 8

Related Topics before Grade 8

- write prime factorizations using exponents
- identify the greatest common factor of a set of positive integers

Previous Topics from Algebra 1

- use the Distributive Property to simplify algebraic expressions

Chapter 8

Related Topics from Algebra 1

- factor as necessary in problem situations
- solve quadratic equations using concrete models, tables, graphs, and algebraic methods

After Chapter 8

Preparation for Algebra 2

- use tools including factoring to simplify expressions and to transform and solve equations
- determine reasonable domain and range values of quadratic functions
- analyze situations involving quadratic functions and formulate quadratic equations to solve problems
- solve quadratic equations using graphs, tables, and algebraic methods

Lesson-by-Lesson Preview

8-1 Monomials and Factoring

A prime number is a whole number greater than 1 that has only two factors: 1 and itself. The prime factorization of a whole number expresses the number as the product of its prime factors. Monomials can also be written in factored form.

- To factor a monomial completely, express it as the product of prime numbers and variables, where no variable has an exponent greater than 1. For example, x^4 in factored form is $x \cdot x \cdot x \cdot x$.
- The greatest common factor (GCF) of two or more whole numbers can be found by using their prime factorizations. The GCF of two or more monomials is the product of their common factors when each monomial is completely factored.
- If the GCF of two or more monomials is 1, then the two monomials are said to be *relatively prime*.

8-2 Using the Distributive Property

The Distributive Property is used to find the product of a monomial and a polynomial. Reverse the process to factor a polynomial whose terms have a GCF. To factor a polynomial,

- First, find the GCF of all its terms.
- Then, rewrite each term as the product of the GCF and its remaining factors.
- Finally, use the Distributive Property to factor out the GCF.

Or, use factoring by grouping if the polynomial has four or more terms.

Factoring can be used to solve some equations containing polynomials. According to the Zero Product Property, if the product of two factors is 0, then at least one of the factors must be 0. The Zero Product Property can be used to solve equations that can be written in the form $ab = 0$. Each factor is set equal to 0 and the resulting equations are solved.

8-3 Quadratic Equations: $x^2 + bx + c = 0$

Two binomials can be multiplied using the FOIL method (Lesson 7-7). By reversing the process, some trinomials of the form $x^2 + bx + c$ can be factored into two binomials.

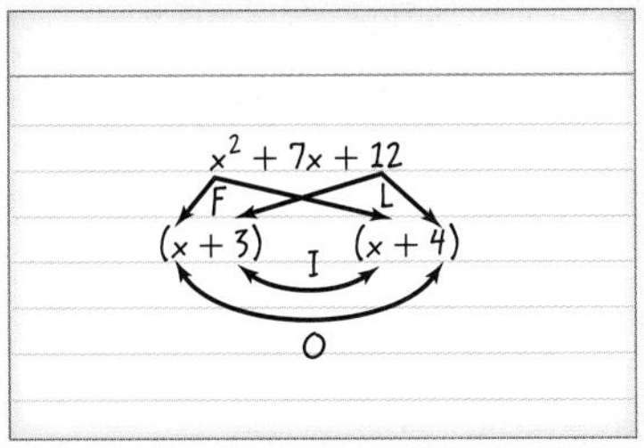

- To factor a trinomial of the form $x^2 + bx + c$, find two integers, m and p, whose sum is b and whose product is c. The factors of the trinomial are the two binomials $(x + m)$ and $(x + p)$, when $b = m + p$ and $c = mp$.
- Determining whether m and p are positive or negative depends on b and c. If b is negative and c is negative, then m and p must have different signs.
- First, factor the trinomial. Then set each factor equal to 0. Solve the resulting equations. Check all solutions in the original equation.

8-4 Quadratic Equations: $ax^2 + bx + c = 0$

In this lesson the trinomials are of the form $ax^2 + bx + c$ with $a \neq 1$. To factor $ax^2 + bx + c$,

- first factor out the GCF of the terms,
- then, if the new trinomial has $a = 1$, use the method learned in Lesson 8-3 to complete the factorization.
- If, in the new trinomial, a still does not equal 1, then find two factors, m and p, such that $ac = mp$ and $b = m + p$. Rewrite the trinomial, replacing bx with $mx + px$, forming the polynomial $ax^2 + mx + px + c$. In this form, the grouping technique used in Lesson 8-2 can be used to factor the polynomial into two binomial factors.
- Any polynomial that cannot be factored is a prime polynomial.
- Equations of the form $ax^2 + bx + c = 0$ can be solved by using the method above to factor the trinomial and then applying the Zero Product Property.

8-5 Quadratic Equations: Differences of Squares

To factor the difference of squares, find a (the square root of the first term) and b (the square root of the last term). The two binomial factors are the sum of the square roots and difference of the square roots. In the factored form, $a^2 - b^2 = (a + b)(a - b)$.

If the terms of the original expression have a GCF, factor it out before applying any other factoring technique.

8-6 Quadratic Equations: Perfect Squares

Products that result from squaring a binomial, $a^2 + 2ab + b^2$ or $a^2 - 2ab + b^2$, are known as *perfect square trinomials*.

Three conditions must be satisfied for a trinomial to be a perfect square trinomial.

- The first term must be a perfect square.
- The last term must be a perfect square.
- The middle term must be twice the product of the square roots of the first and last terms.

To factor a perfect square trinomial with a plus sign before the middle term, use the pattern $a^2 + 2ab + b^2 = (a + b)^2$.

To factor a perfect square trinomial with a minus sign before the middle term, use the pattern $a^2 - 2ab + b^2 = (a - b)^2$.

The Square Root Property can be used to solve any equation that is in the form $x^2 = n$, where $n \geq 0$, or that can be written in that form. This property lets you take the square root of each side of the equation as long as both $\sqrt{n}$ and $-\sqrt{n}$ are considered.

McGraw Hill Professional Development

Targeted professional development has been articulated throughout *Algebra 1*. More quality, customized professional development is available from McGraw-Hill Professional Development. Visit glencoe.com for details on each product.

- **Online Lessons** emphasize the strategies and techniques used to teach Algebra 1. Includes streaming video, interactive pages, and online tools.
- **Video Workshops** allow mentors, coaches, or leadership personnel to facilitate on-site workshops on educational strategies in mathematics and mathematical concepts.
- **MHPD Online** (www.mhpdonline.com) offers online professional development with video clips of instructional strategies, links, student activities, and news and issues in education.
- **Teaching Today** (teachingtoday.glencoe.com) gives secondary teachers practical strategies and materials that inspire excellence and innovation in teaching.

Chapter 8 Notes

Chapter Project

Awesome Landscape Architects

Students use what they have learned about finding a GCF and writing and solving equations to design a landscape for a backyard.

- Tell students that they are going to create a landscape design on a piece of grid paper that represents a homeowner's property. Have them use the scale that one square on their paper is equal to one square unit.
- Tell students to draw a rectangular house in an upper corner of their grid paper with a width that is 8 units shorter than its length and that covers an area of 240 $units^2$.
- Tell students that there is an existing patio connected to the house that is 10 units by 8 units. The owner wants to increase both dimensions by the same number of units so that the area of the increased patio is 224 $units^2$. What are the dimensions of the new patio?
- Tell students the owner wants a pond in the shape of a triangle with an area of 36 $units^2$. The base and height are to be whole numbers but not prime numbers.
- Tell students the owner wants a rectangular vegetable garden that covers an area of 36 $units^2$ and has a 26-unit fence around it to keep animals out.
- Ask students to make the owner's backyard beautiful and useful by designing and drawing flowerbeds, walkways, and other details.

Chapter 8 Factoring and Quadratic Equations

Then

In Chapter 7, you multiplied monomials and polynomials.

Now

In Chapter 8, you will:

- Factor monomials.
- Factor trinomials.
- Factor differences of squares.
- Solve quadratic equations.

IL Learning Standards

8.A.4b Represent mathematical patterns and describe their properties using variables and mathematical symbols.
8.D.4 Formulate and solve quadratic equations algebraically and using graphs, tables, calculators and computers.

Why?

ARCHITECTURE Quadratic equations can be used to model the shape of architectural structures such as the tallest memorial in the United States, the Gateway Arch in St. Louis, Missouri.

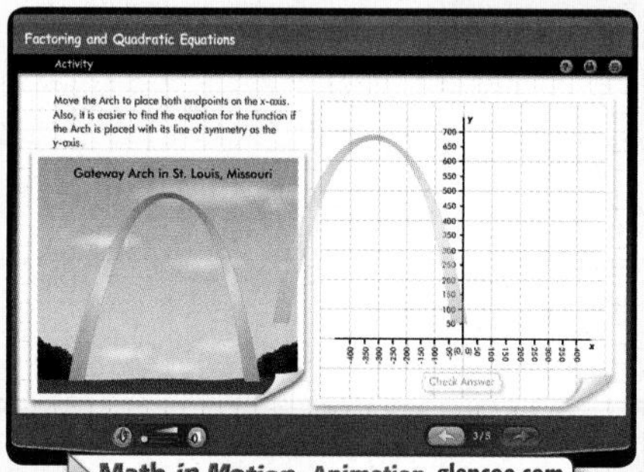

Math *in Motion*, Animation glencoe.com

Key Vocabulary Introduce the key vocabulary in the chapter using the routine below.

Define: The greatest common factor (GCF) is the product of the prime factors common to two or more integers.

Example: 2 • 2 • 3, or 12, is the greatest common factor of 48 and 60.

Ask: What is 48 divided by 12? 4 What is 60 divided by 12? 5

Get Ready for Chapter 8

Diagnose Readiness You have two options for checking Prerequisite Skills.

Text Option Take the Quick Check below. Refer to the Quick Review for help.

QuickCheck

(Used in Lessons 8-2 through 8-6)
Rewrite each expression using the Distributive Property. Then simplify. (Lesson 1-4)

1. $a(a + 5)$ **2.** $2(3 + x)$

3. $n(n - 3n^2 + 2)$ **4.** $-6(x^2 - 5x + 6)$

5. FINANCIAL LITERACY Five friends will pay \$9 per ticket, \$3 per drink, and \$6 per popcorn at the movies. Write an expression that could be used to determine the cost for them to go to the movies. **5(9 + 3 + 6); \$90**

(Used in Lessons 8-3 and 8-4)
Find each product. (Lesson 7-7)

6. $(x + 2)(x - 5)$ $x^2 - 3x - 10$

7. $(x + 4)(x - 1)$ $x^2 + 3x - 4$

8. $(2a - 3)(5a + 4)$ $10a^2 - 7a - 12$

9. $(3x - 4)(x + 5)$ $3x^2 + 11x - 20$

10. $(x + 4)(x + 7)$ $x^2 + 11x + 28$

11. $(6a - 2b)(9a + b)$ $54a^2 - 12ab - 2b^2$

12. TABLECLOTH The dimensions of a tablecloth are represented by a width of $2x + 3$ and a length of $x + 1$. Find an expression for the area of the tablecloth. $2x^2 + 5x + 3$

(Used in Lessons 8-5 and 8-6)
Find each product. (Lesson 7-8)

13. $(3 - a)^2$ $9 - 6a + a^2$

14. $(x + 5)^2$ $x^2 + 10x + 25$

15. $(3x - 2y)^2$ $9x^2 - 12xy + 4y^2$

16. $(2x + 5y)(2x - 5y)$ $4x^2 - 25y^2$

17. PHOTOGRAPHY A photo is $x + 6$ inches by $x - 6$ inches. What is the area of the photo? $x^2 - 36$ in^2

QuickReview

EXAMPLE 1

Rewrite $6x(-3x - 5x - 5x^2 + x^3)$ using the Distributive Property. Then simplify.

$6x(-3x - 5x - 5x^2 + x^3)$

$= 6x(-3x) + 6x(-5x) + 6x(-5x^2) + 6x(x^3)$

$= -18x^2 - 30x^2 - 30x^3 + 6x^4$

$= -48x^2 - 30x^3 + 6x^4$

1. $a(a) + a(5)$; $a^2 + 5a$
2. $2(3) + 2(x)$; $6 + 2x$

EXAMPLE 2

Find $(x + 3)(2x - 1)$.

$(x + 3)(2x - 1)$	Original expression
$= x(2x) + x(-1) + 3(2x) + 3(-1)$	FOIL method
$= 2x^2 - x + 6x - 3$	Multiply.
$= 2x^2 + 5x - 3$	Combine like terms.

3. $n(n) + n(-3n^2) + n(2)$; $n^2 - 3n^3 + 2n$
4. $-6(x^2) + (-6)(-5x) + (-6)(6)$; $-6x^2 + 30x - 36$

EXAMPLE 3

Find $(y + 8)^2$.

$(a + b)^2 = a^2 + 2ab + b^2$	Square of a sum
$(y + 8)^2 = (y)^2 + 2(y)(8) + 8^2$	$a = y, b = 8$
$= y^2 + 16y + 64$	Simplify.

Online Option IL Math Online Take a self-check Chapter Readiness Quiz at glencoe.com.

Get Ready for Chapter 8

Response to Intervention (RtI)

Use the *Quick Check* results and the Intervention Planner chart to help you determine your Response to Intervention. The If-Then statements in the chart below help you decide the appropriate tier of RtI and suggest intervention resources for each tier.

Intervention Planner

Tier 1 — On Level

If students miss about 25% of the exercises or less,

Then choose a resource:

SE Concepts and Skills Bank, p. 859
Lessons 1-4, 7-7, and 7-8

CRM Skills Practice, Chapter 1, p. 26, Chapter 7, pp. 44 and 51

IL Math Online Self-Check Quiz

Tier 2 — Strategic Intervention approaching grade level

If students miss about 50% of the exercises,

Then choose a resource:

CRM Study Guide and Intervention, Chapter 1, p. 24, Chapter 7, pp. 42 and 49

Quick Review Math Handbook

IL Math Online Extra Examples, Personal Tutor, Homework Help

Tier 3 — Intensive Intervention 2 or more grades below level

If students miss about 75% of the exercises,

Then use *Math Triumphs, Alg. 1*

IL Math Online Extra Examples, Personal Tutor, Homework Help, Review Vocabulary

FOLDABLES® Study Organizer

Dinah Zike's Foldables®

Focus Students write about factoring and quadratic equations as these concepts are presented in the lessons of this chapter.

Teach Have students make and label their Foldables as illustrated. Suggest that students use their Foldables to take notes, record concepts, and define terms. They can also use them to record the direction and progress of learning, to describe positive and negative experiences during learning, to write about personal associations and experiences, and to list examples of ways in which this new knowledge has or will be used in their daily lives.

When to Use It Encourage students to add to their Foldables as they work through the chapter and to use them to review for the chapter test.

Differentiated Instruction

CRM Student-Built Glossary, pp. 1–2 Students should complete the chart by providing a definition of each term and an example as they progress through Chapter 8. This study tool can also be used to review for the chapter test.

Get Started on Chapter 8

You will learn several new concepts, skills, and vocabulary terms as you study Chapter 8. To get ready, identify important terms and organize your resources. You may wish to refer to **Chapter 0** to review prerequisite skills.

FOLDABLES® Study Organizer

Factoring and Quadratic Equations Make this Foldable to help you organize your Chapter 8 notes about factoring and quadratic equations. Begin with four sheets of grid paper.

1. **Fold** in half along the width. On the first two sheets, cut 5 centimeters along the fold at the ends. On the second two sheets cut in the center, stopping 5 centimeters from the ends.

First Sheets Second Sheets

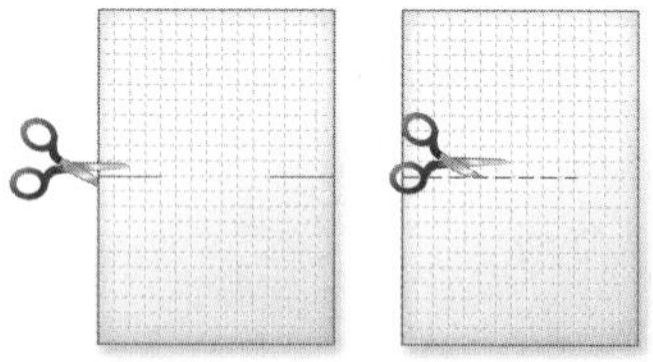

2. **Insert** the first sheets through the second sheets and align the folds. Label the front Chapter 8, Factoring and Quadratic Equations. Label the pages with lesson numbers and the last page with vocabulary.

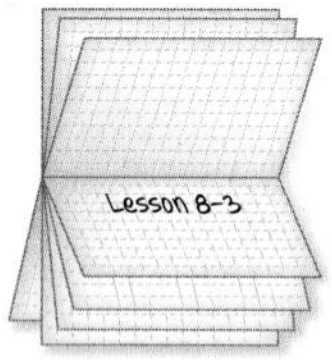

IL Math Online glencoe.com

- Study the chapter online
- Explore **Math in Motion**
- Get extra help from your own **Personal Tutor**
- Use **Extra Examples** for additional help
- Take a **Self-Check Quiz**
- **Review Vocabulary** in fun ways

New Vocabulary

English		Español
factored form	p. 471	forma reducida
greatest common factor (GCF)	p. 471	máximo común divisor (MCD)
factoring	p. 476	factorización
factoring by grouping	p. 477	factorización por agrupamiento
Zero Product Property	p. 478	propiedad del producto de cero
quadratic equation	p. 488	ecuación cuadrática
prime polynomial	p. 495	polinomio primo
difference of two squares	p. 499	diferencia de cuadrados
perfect square trinomial	p. 505	trinomio cuadrado perfecto
Square Root Property	p. 508	Propiedad de la raíz cuadrada

Review Vocabulary

absolute value • p. 103 • valor absoluto the absolute value of any number n is the distance the number is from zero on a number line and is written $|n|$

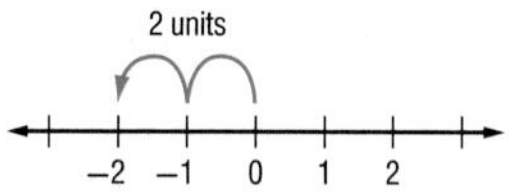

The absolute value of −2 is 2 because it is 2 units from 0.

perfect square • p. P7 • cuadrado perfecto a number with a square root that is a rational number

prime number • p. 861 • numero primo a whole number, greater than 1, with the only factor being 1 and itself

Multilingual eGlossary glencoe.com

8-1 Monomials and Factoring

Why?

Susie is making beaded bracelets for extra money. She has 60 gemstone beads and 15 glass beads. She wants each bracelet to have only one type of bead and all of the bracelets to have the same number of beads. Susie needs to determine the *greatest common factor* of 60 and 15.

Then
You multiplied monomials and divided a polynomial by a monomial. (Lesson 7-1 and 7-2)

Now
- Factor monomials.
- Find the greatest common factors of monomials.

IL Learning Standards
8.A.4b Represent mathematical patterns and describe their properties using variables and mathematical symbols.

New Vocabulary
factored form
greatest common factor (GCF)

IL Math Online
glencoe.com
- Extra Examples
- Personal Tutor
- Self-Check Quiz
- Homework Help
- Math in Motion

Factor Monomials Factoring a monomial is similar to factoring a whole number. A monomial is in **factored form** when it is expressed as the product of prime numbers and variables, and no variable has an exponent greater than 1.

EXAMPLE 1 Monomial in Factored Form

Factor $-20x^3y^2$ completely.

$-20x^3y^2 = -1 \cdot 20x^3y^2$ — Express -20 as $-1 \cdot 20$.
$= -1 \cdot 2 \cdot 10 \cdot x \cdot x \cdot x \cdot y \cdot y$ — $20 = 2 \cdot 10$, $x^3 = x \cdot x \cdot x$, and $y^2 = y \cdot y$
$= -1 \cdot 2 \cdot 2 \cdot 5 \cdot x \cdot x \cdot x \cdot y \cdot y$ — $10 = 2 \cdot 5$

Thus, $-20x^3y^2$ in factored form is $-1 \cdot 2 \cdot 2 \cdot 5 \cdot x \cdot x \cdot x \cdot y \cdot y$.

Check Your Progress

Factor each monomial completely.

1A. $34x^4y^3$ **1B.** $-52a^2b$

1A. $2 \cdot 17 \cdot x \cdot x \cdot x \cdot x \cdot y \cdot y \cdot y$
1B. $-1 \cdot 2 \cdot 2 \cdot 13 \cdot a \cdot a \cdot b$

Personal Tutor glencoe.com

Greatest Common Factor Two or more whole numbers may have some common prime factors. The product of the common prime factors is called their greatest common factor. The **greatest common factor (GCF)** is the greatest number that is a factor of both original numbers. The GCF of two or more monomials can be found in a similar way.

EXAMPLE 2 GCF of a Set of Monomials

Find the GCF of $12a^2b^2c$ and $18ab^3$.

$12a^2b^2c = (2) \cdot 2 \cdot (3) \cdot (a) \cdot a \cdot (b) \cdot (b) \cdot c$ — Factor each number, and write all powers of variables as products.

$18ab^3 = (2) \cdot (3) \cdot 3 \cdot (a) \cdot (b) \cdot (b) \cdot b$ — Circle the common prime factors.

The GCF of $12a^2b^2c$ and $18ab^2$ is $2 \cdot 3 \cdot a \cdot b \cdot b$ or $6ab^2$.

Check Your Progress

Find the GCF of each pair of monomials.

2A. $6xy^3$, $18yz$ $6y$ **2B.** $11a^2b$, $21ab^2$ ab **2C.** $30q^3r^2t$, $50q^2rt$ $10q^2rt$

Personal Tutor glencoe.com

8-1 Lesson Notes

1 FOCUS

Vertical Alignment

Before Lesson 8-1
Multiply monomials and divide a polynomial by a monomial.

Lesson 8-1
Factor monomials.
Find the greatest common factors of monomials.

After Lesson 8-1
Factor polynomials.

2 TEACH

Scaffolding Questions

Have students read the *Why?* section of the lesson.

Ask:
- What is a prime number? A prime number is any whole number greater than 1 whose only factors are one and itself.
- What is the prime factorization of 60? of 15? $60 = 2^2 \cdot 3 \cdot 5$; $15 = 3 \cdot 5$
- What are the common prime factors of 60 and 15? 3, 5
- What is the GCF of 60 and 15? 15
- How many and what kind of bracelets can Susie make? 5 bracelets; 4 gemstone, 1 glass

Lesson 8-1 Resources

Resource	Approaching-Level	On-Level	Beyond-Level	English Learners
Teacher Edition	• Differentiated Instruction, p. 474			
Chapter Resource Masters	• Study Guide and Intervention, pp. 5–6 • Skills Practice, p. 7 • Practice, p. 8 • Word Problem Practice, p. 9	• Study Guide and Intervention, pp. 5–6 • Skills Practice, p. 7 • Practice, p. 8 • Word Problem Practice, p. 9 • Enrichment, p. 10	• Practice, p. 8 • Word Problem Practice, p. 9 • Enrichment, p. 10	• Study Guide and Intervention, pp. 5–6 • Skills Practice, p. 7 • Practice, p. 8
Transparencies	• 5-Minute Check Transparency 8-1	• 5-Minute Check Transparency 8-1	• 5-Minute Check Transparency 8-1	• 5-Minute Check Transparency 8-1
Other	• Study Notebook	• Study Notebook	• Study Notebook	• Study Notebook

Real-World EXAMPLE 3 Find a GCF

FLOWERS **A florist has 20 roses and 30 tulips to make bouquets. What is the greatest number of identical bouquets she can make without having any flowers left over? How many of each kind of flower will be in each bouquet?**

Find the GCF of 20 and 30.

$20 = 2^2 \cdot 5$ **Write the prime factorization of each number.**

$30 = 2 \cdot 3 \cdot 5$ **The common prime factors are 2 and 5 or 10.**

The GCF of 20 and 30 is 10. So, the florist can make 10 bouquets. Since $2 \times 10 = 20$ and $3 \times 10 = 30$, each bouquet will have 2 roses and 3 tulips.

Math *in Motion*, Animation glencoe.com

Check Your Progress

3. What is the greatest possible value for the widths of two rectangles if their areas are 84 square inches and 70 square inches, respectively, and the length and width are whole numbers? **14 in.**

Personal Tutor glencoe.com

Check Your Understanding

Example 1 p. 471

Factor each monomial completely.

1. $12g^2h^4$ $2 \cdot 2 \cdot 3 \cdot g \cdot g \cdot h \cdot h \cdot h \cdot h$

2. $-38rp^2t^2$ $-1 \cdot 2 \cdot 19 \cdot r \cdot p \cdot p \cdot t \cdot t$

3. $-17x^3y^2z$ $-1 \cdot 17 \cdot x \cdot x \cdot x \cdot y \cdot y \cdot z$

4. $23ab^3$ $23 \cdot a \cdot b \cdot b \cdot b$

Examples 2 and 3 pp. 471–472

Find the GCF of each pair of monomials.

5. $24cd^3, 48c^2d$ **24cd**

6. $7gh, 11mp$ **1**

7. $8x^2y^5, 31xy^3$ xy^3

8. $10ab, 25a$ **5a**

9. **GEOMETRY** The areas of two rectangles are 15 square inches and 16 square inches. The length and width of both figures are whole numbers. If the rectangles have the same width, what is the greatest possible value for their widths? **1 in.**

Practice and Problem Solving

= **Step-by-Step Solutions** begin on page R12.
Extra Practice begins on page 815.

Example 1 p. 471

Factor each monomial completely. **10–15. See margin.**

10. $95xy^2$

11. $-35a^3c^2$

12. $42g^3h^3$

13. $81n^5p$

14. $-100q^4r$

15. $121abc^3$

Examples 2 and 3 pp. 471–472

Find the GCF of each set of monomials.

16. $25x^3, 45x^4, 65x^2$ $5x^2$

17. $26z^2, 32z, 44z^4$ **2z**

18. $30gh^2, 42g^2h, 66g$ **6g**

19. $12qr, 8r^2, 16rt$ **4r**

20. $42a^2b, 6a^2, 18a^3$ $6a^2$

21. $15r^2t, 35t^2, 70rt$ **5t**

22. **BAKING** Delsin wants to package the same number of cookies in each bag, and each bag should have every type of cookie. If he puts the greatest possible number of cookies in each bag, how many bags can he make?

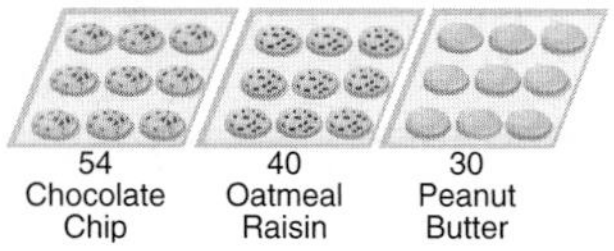

22. 2 bags each with 15 peanut butter cookies, 20 oatmeal raisin cookies, and 27 chocolate chip cookies

Factor Monomials

Example 1 shows how to factor a monomial completely.

Formative Assessment

Use the Check Your Progress exercises after each Example to determine students' understanding of concepts.

Additional Example

1 Factor $18x^2y^3$ completely.
$2 \cdot 3 \cdot 3 \cdot x \cdot x \cdot y \cdot y \cdot y$

Additional Examples also in Interactive Classroom PowerPoint® Presentations

IWB INTERACTIVE WHITEBOARD READY

Greatest Common Factor

Example 2 shows how to find the GCF of a set of monomials. **Example 3** shows how to use the GCF to solve a real-world problem.

Additional Examples

2 Find the GCF of $27a^2b$ and $15ab^2c$. The GCF is $3ab$.

3 **GEOMETRY** The lengths of the sides of a triangle are $12wz^2$, $8wz$, and $16w^2z$. Find the GCF of the three lengths. The GCF is $4wz$.

3 PRACTICE

Formative Assessment

Use Exercises 1–9 to check for understanding.

Use the chart at the bottom of this page to customize assignments for your students.

Multiple Representations In Exercise 28, students use a diagram and number theory to find the prime factorization of a number.

Differentiated Homework Options

Level	Assignment	Two-Day Option	
AL Basic	10–22, 30–31, 33–60	11–21 odd, 35–38	10–22 even, 30–31, 33–34, 39–60
OL Core	11–21 odd, 23–28, 30–31, 33–60	10–22, 35–38	23–28, 30–31, 33–34, 39–60
BL Advanced	23–54, (optional: 55–60)		

Real-World Link

About 77% of 18- to 25-year-olds say their favorite way to watch a movie at home is watching a DVD or video, while only 17% say they watch movies that are on television.

Source: 2006 Gen Next Survey

23. GEOMETRY The area of a triangle is 28 square inches. What are possible whole-number dimensions for the base and height of the triangle? **See Ch. 8 Answer Appendix.**

24. MUSIC In what ways can Clara organize her 36 CDs so that she has the same number of CDs on each shelf, at least 4 per shelf, and at least 2 shelves of CDs? **See Ch. 8 Answer Appendix.**

25. MOVIES In what ways can Shannon arrange her 80 DVDs so that she has at least 4 shelves of DVDS, the same number on each shelf, and at least 5 on each shelf?

26. VOLUNTEER Denzell is donating packages of school supplies to an elementary school where he volunteers. He bought 200 pencils, 150 glue sticks, and 120 folders. How many packages can Denzell make using an equal number of each item? How many items of each type will each package contain?

27. NUMBER THEORY *Twin primes* are two consecutive odd numbers that are prime. The first two pairs of twin primes are 3 and 5 and 5 and 7. List the next five pairs. **11, 13; 17, 19; 29, 31; 41, 43; 59, 61**

28. MULTIPLE REPRESENTATIONS In this problem, you will investigate a method of factoring a number.

```
3|12
 2|4
  2|2
   |1
```

So, the prime factorization of 12 is $2^2 \cdot 3$.

a. ANALYTICAL Copy the ladder diagram shown at the right six times and record six whole numbers, two of which are prime, in the top right portion of the diagrams. **See students' work.**

b. ANALYTICAL Choose a prime factor of one of your numbers. Record the factor on the left of the number in the diagram. Divide the two numbers. Keep dividing by prime factors until the quotient is 1. Add to or subtract boxes from the diagram as necessary. Repeat this process with all of your numbers. **See students' work.**

c. VERBAL What is the prime factorization of your six numbers? **See students' work.**

H.O.T. Problems

Use Higher-Order Thinking Skills

29. CHALLENGE Find the least pair of numbers that satisfies the following conditions. The GCF of the numbers is 11. One number is even and the other number is odd. One number is not a multiple of the other. **22 and 33**

30. REASONING The *least common multiple* (LCM) of two or more numbers is the least number that is a multiple of each number. Compare and contrast the GCF and LCM of two or more numbers.

31. REASONING Determine whether the following statement is *true* or *false*. Provide an example or counterexample. **See Ch. 8 Answer Appendix.**

Two monomials always have a greatest common factor that is not equal to 1.

32. CHALLENGE Two or more integers or monomials with a GCF of 1 are said to be *relatively prime*. Copy and complete the chart to determine which pairs of monomials are relatively prime. **$15a^2bc^3$, $22d^3fg^2$**

Monomial	Prime Factorization
$15a^2bc^3$	$3 \cdot 5 \cdot a^2bc^3$
$6b^3c^3d$	$2 \cdot 3 \cdot b^3c^3d$
$12cd^2f$	$2^2 \cdot 3 \cdot cd^2f$
$22d^3fg^2$	$2 \cdot 11 \cdot d^3fg^2$
$30f^2gh^2$	$2 \cdot 3 \cdot 5 \cdot f^2gh^2$

33. OPEN ENDED Name three monomials with a GCF of $6y^3$. Explain your answer. **See Ch. 8 Answer Appendix.**

34. WRITING IN MATH Define *prime factorization* in your own words. Explain how to find the prime factorization of a monomial, and how a prime factorization helps you determine the GCF of two or more monomials. **See Ch. 8 Answer Appendix.**

25. 5 DVDs on 16 shelves, 8 DVDs on 10 shelves, 16 DVDs on 5 shelves, 10 DVDs on 8 shelves, or 20 DVDs on 4 shelves

26. 10 packages; Each package will contain 20 pencils, 15 glue sticks, and 12 folders.

30. The GCF and LCM are both found using the factors of the numbers. The greatest common factor only uses the factors the numbers have in common, while the least common multiple uses all of the factors.

Additional Answers

10. $5 \cdot 19 \cdot x \cdot y \cdot y$

11. $-1 \cdot 5 \cdot 7 \cdot a \cdot a \cdot a \cdot c \cdot c$

12. $2 \cdot 3 \cdot 7 \cdot g \cdot g \cdot g \cdot h \cdot h \cdot h$

13. $3 \cdot 3 \cdot 3 \cdot 3 \cdot n \cdot n \cdot n \cdot n \cdot n \cdot p$

14. $-1 \cdot 2 \cdot 2 \cdot 5 \cdot 5 \cdot q \cdot q \cdot q \cdot q \cdot r$

15. $11 \cdot 11 \cdot a \cdot b \cdot c \cdot c \cdot c$

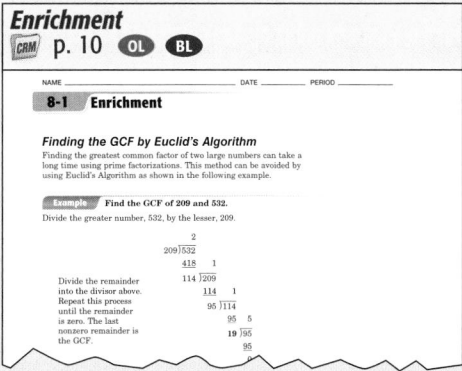

Enrichment
CRM p. 10 OL BL

NAME ______ DATE ______ PERIOD ______

8-1 Enrichment

Finding the GCF by Euclid's Algorithm

Finding the greatest common factor of two large numbers can take a long time using prime factorizations. This method can be avoided by using Euclid's Algorithm as shown in the following example.

Example Find the GCF of 209 and 532.

Divide the greater number, 532, by the lesser, 209.

```
      2
209)532
    418   1
    114)209
        114   1
         95)114
             95   5
          19)95
             95
              0
```

Divide the remainder into the divisor above. Repeat this process until the remainder is zero. The last nonzero remainder is the GCF.

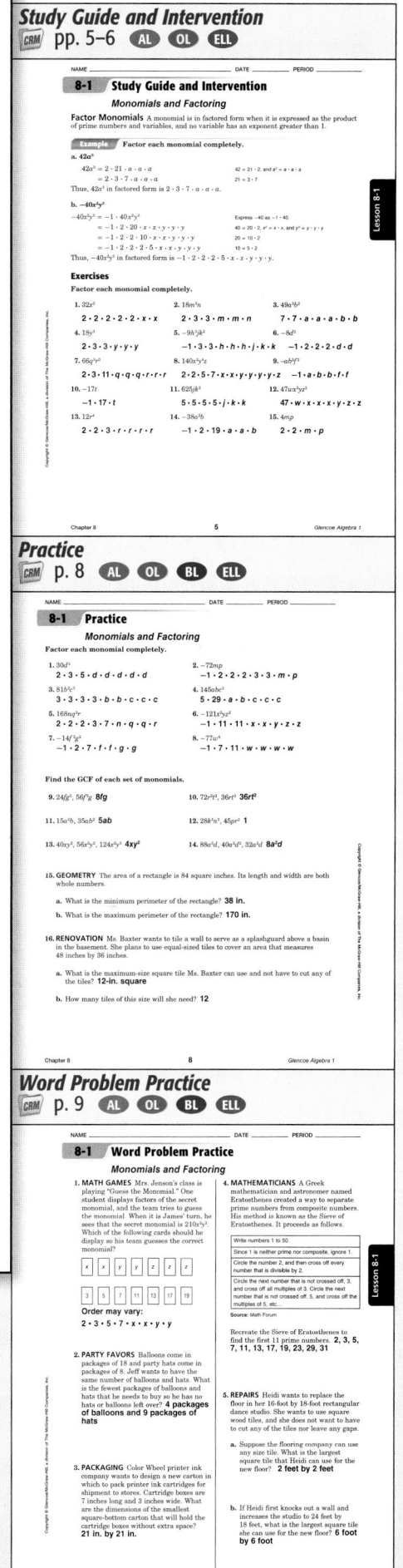

Study Guide and Intervention
CRM pp. 5–6 AL OL ELL

NAME ______ DATE ______ PERIOD ______

8-1 Study Guide and Intervention

Monomials and Factoring

Factor Monomials A monomial is in factored form when it is expressed as the product of prime numbers and variables, and no variable has an exponent greater than 1.

Example Factor each monomial completely.

a. $42a^3$

$42a^3 = 2 \cdot 21 \cdot a \cdot a \cdot a$ — $42 = 21 \cdot 2$, and $a^3 = a \cdot a \cdot a$

$= 2 \cdot 3 \cdot 7 \cdot a \cdot a \cdot a$ — $21 = 3 \cdot 7$

Thus, $42a^3$ in factored form is $2 \cdot 3 \cdot 7 \cdot a \cdot a \cdot a$.

b. $-40x^2y^3$

$-40x^2y^3 = -1 \cdot 40x^2y^3$ — Express -40 as $-1 \cdot 40$.

$= -1 \cdot 2 \cdot 20 \cdot x \cdot x \cdot y \cdot y \cdot y$ — $40 = 20 \cdot 2$, $x^2 = x \cdot x$, and $y^3 = y \cdot y \cdot y$

$= -1 \cdot 2 \cdot 2 \cdot 10 \cdot x \cdot x \cdot y \cdot y \cdot y$ — $20 = 10 \cdot 2$

$= -1 \cdot 2 \cdot 2 \cdot 2 \cdot 5 \cdot x \cdot x \cdot y \cdot y \cdot y$ — $10 = 5 \cdot 2$

Thus, $-40x^2y^3$ in factored form is $-1 \cdot 2 \cdot 2 \cdot 2 \cdot 5 \cdot x \cdot x \cdot y \cdot y \cdot y$.

Exercises

Factor each monomial completely.

1. $32x^2$ **$2 \cdot 2 \cdot 2 \cdot 2 \cdot 2 \cdot x \cdot x$**
2. $18m^2n$ **$2 \cdot 3 \cdot 3 \cdot m \cdot m \cdot n$**
3. $49a^3b^2$ **$7 \cdot 7 \cdot a \cdot a \cdot a \cdot b \cdot b$**
4. $18y^3$ **$2 \cdot 3 \cdot 3 \cdot y \cdot y \cdot y$**
5. $-9h^3jk^2$ **$-1 \cdot 3 \cdot 3 \cdot h \cdot h \cdot h \cdot j \cdot k \cdot k$**
6. $-8d^2$ **$-1 \cdot 2 \cdot 2 \cdot 2 \cdot d \cdot d$**
7. $66q^3r^3$ **$2 \cdot 3 \cdot 11 \cdot q \cdot q \cdot q \cdot r \cdot r \cdot r$**
8. $140x^2y^4z$ **$2 \cdot 2 \cdot 5 \cdot 7 \cdot x \cdot x \cdot y \cdot y \cdot y \cdot y \cdot z$**
9. $-ab^2f^2$ **$-1 \cdot a \cdot b \cdot b \cdot f \cdot f$**
10. $-17t$ **$-1 \cdot 17 \cdot t$**
11. $625jk^2$ **$5 \cdot 5 \cdot 5 \cdot 5 \cdot j \cdot k \cdot k$**
12. $47wx^3yz^2$ **$47 \cdot w \cdot x \cdot x \cdot x \cdot y \cdot z \cdot z$**
13. $12r^4$ **$2 \cdot 2 \cdot 3 \cdot r \cdot r \cdot r \cdot r$**
14. $-38a^2b$ **$-1 \cdot 2 \cdot 19 \cdot a \cdot a \cdot b$**
15. $4mp$ **$2 \cdot 2 \cdot m \cdot p$**

Lesson 8-1

Chapter 8 5 Glencoe Algebra 1

Practice
CRM p. 8 AL OL BL ELL

NAME ______ DATE ______ PERIOD ______

8-1 Practice

Monomials and Factoring

Factor each monomial completely.

1. $30d^5$ **$2 \cdot 3 \cdot 5 \cdot d \cdot d \cdot d \cdot d \cdot d$**
2. $-72mp$ **$-1 \cdot 2 \cdot 2 \cdot 2 \cdot 3 \cdot 3 \cdot m \cdot p$**
3. $81b^2c^3$ **$3 \cdot 3 \cdot 3 \cdot 3 \cdot b \cdot b \cdot c \cdot c \cdot c$**
4. $145abc^3$ **$5 \cdot 29 \cdot a \cdot b \cdot c \cdot c \cdot c$**
5. $168nq^2r$ **$2 \cdot 2 \cdot 2 \cdot 3 \cdot 7 \cdot n \cdot q \cdot q \cdot r$**
6. $-121x^2yz^2$ **$-1 \cdot 11 \cdot 11 \cdot x \cdot x \cdot y \cdot z \cdot z$**
7. $-14f^2g^2$ **$-1 \cdot 2 \cdot 7 \cdot f \cdot f \cdot g \cdot g$**
8. $-77w^4$ **$-1 \cdot 7 \cdot 11 \cdot w \cdot w \cdot w \cdot w$**

Find the GCF of each set of monomials.

9. $24fg^5$, $56f^3g$ **$8fg$**
10. $72r^2t^2$, $36rt^3$ **$36rt^2$**
11. $15a^2b$, $35ab^2$ **$5ab$**
12. $28k^3n^2$, $45pr^2$ **1**
13. $40xy^2$, $56x^3y^2$, $124x^2y^3$ **$4xy^2$**
14. $88a^3d$, $40a^2d^2$, $32a^2d$ **$8a^2d$**

15. **GEOMETRY** The area of a rectangle is 84 square inches. Its length and width are both whole numbers.
   a. What is the minimum perimeter of the rectangle? **38 in.**
   b. What is the maximum perimeter of the rectangle? **170 in.**

16. **RENOVATION** Ms. Baxter wants to tile a wall to serve as a splashguard above a basin in the basement. She plans to use equal-sized tiles to cover an area that measures 48 inches by 36 inches.
   a. What is the maximum-size square tile Ms. Baxter can use and not have to cut any of the tiles? **12-in. square**
   b. How many tiles of this size will she need? **12**

Chapter 8 8 Glencoe Algebra 1

Word Problem Practice
CRM p. 9 AL OL BL ELL

NAME ______ DATE ______ PERIOD ______

8-1 Word Problem Practice

Monomials and Factoring

1. **MATH GAMES** Mrs. Jenson's class is playing "Guess the Monomial." One student displays factors of the secret monomial, and the team tries to guess the monomial. When it is James' turn, he sees that the secret monomial is $210x^2y^2$. Which of the following cards should he display so his team guesses the correct monomial?

   x x y y z z z

   3 5 7 11 13 17 19

   Order may vary: $2 \cdot 3 \cdot 5 \cdot 7 \cdot x \cdot x \cdot y \cdot y$

2. **PARTY FAVORS** Balloons come in packages of 18 and party hats come in packages of 8. Jeff wants to have the same number of balloons and hats. What is the fewest packages of balloons and hats that he needs to buy so he has no hats or balloons left over? **4 packages of balloons and 9 packages of hats**

3. **PACKAGING** Color Wheel printer ink company wants to design a new carton in which to pack printer ink cartridges for shipment to stores. Cartridge boxes are 7 inches long and 3 inches wide. What are the dimensions of the smallest square-bottom carton that will hold the cartridge boxes without extra space? **21 in. by 21 in.**

4. **MATHEMATICIANS** A Greek mathematician and astronomer named Eratosthenes created a way to separate prime numbers from composite numbers. His method is known as the Sieve of Eratosthenes. It proceeds as follows.

Write numbers 1 to 50.
Since 1 is neither prime nor composite, ignore 1.
Circle the number 2, and then cross off every number that is divisible by 2.
Circle the next number that is not crossed off, 3, and cross off all multiples of 3. Circle the next number that is not crossed off, 5, and cross off the multiples of 5, etc...

   Source: Math Forum

   Recreate the Sieve of Eratosthenes to find the first 11 prime numbers. **2, 3, 5, 7, 11, 13, 17, 19, 23, 29, 31**

5. **REPAIRS** Heidi wants to replace the floor in her 16-foot by 18-foot rectangular dance studio. She wants to use square wood tiles, and she does not want to have to cut any of the tiles nor leave any gaps.
   a. Suppose the flooring company can use any size tile. What is the largest square tile that Heidi can use for the new floor? **2 feet by 2 feet**
   b. If Heidi first knocks out a wall and increases the studio to 24 feet by 18 feet, what is the largest square tile she can use for the new floor? **6 foot by 6 foot**

Lesson 8-1

Chapter 8 9 Glencoe Algebra 1

Differentiated Instruction BL

Extension Ask students to find the greatest common factor of $5x^8(x+1)^7$ and $9x^3(x-1)$. x^3

4 ASSESS

Ticket Out the Door Make several copies each of five different sets of monomials. Give one set to each student. As the students leave the room, ask them to tell you the GCF of their monomials.

TEACH with TECH

INTERACTIVE WHITEBOARD Have students randomly name two monomials. Then show students how to find the GCF of these monomials. After listing the prime factorizations, highlight the common factors. Then drag these common factors to form the prime factorization of the GCF.

Additional Answers

38.
$$\begin{array}{r} \\ \text{High} \\ \text{Low} \end{array}\begin{array}{c} \begin{array}{ccccc} \text{Mon} & \text{Tue} & \text{Wed} & \text{Thu} & \text{Fri} \end{array} \\ \left[\begin{array}{ccccc} 92 & 87 & 85 & 88 & 90 \\ 68 & 64 & 62 & 65 & 66 \end{array}\right] \end{array}$$

54. $T = 50 + 5w$

Money Saved

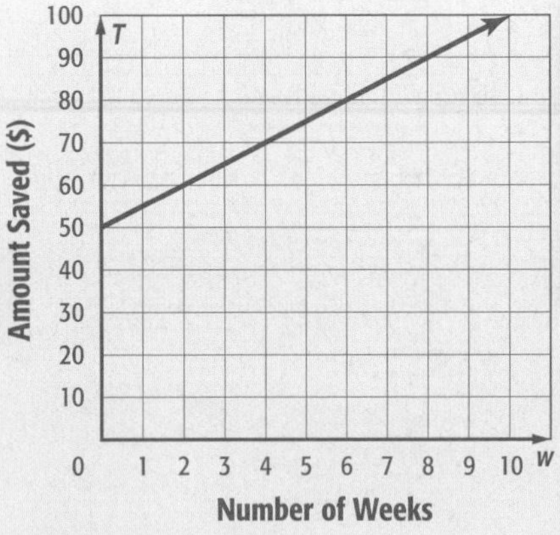

PSAE PRACTICE 10.11.01, 6.11.13, 8.11.07, 6.11.03

35. Abigail surveyed 320 of her classmates about what type of movie they prefer. The results of the survey are shown below. What percent of her classmates enjoyed action movies? **A**

Type of Movie	Number of Responses
comedy	160
drama	25
science fiction	55
action	80

A 25% C 75%
B 50% D 95%

36. What is the value of c in the equation $4c - 27 = 19 + 2c$? **H**

F −4
G 4
H 23
J 46

37. Which equation best represents a line parallel to the line shown below? **B**

A $y = 2x + 4$
B $y = -2x - 5$
C $y = \frac{1}{2}x - 6$
D $y = -\frac{1}{2}x + 3$

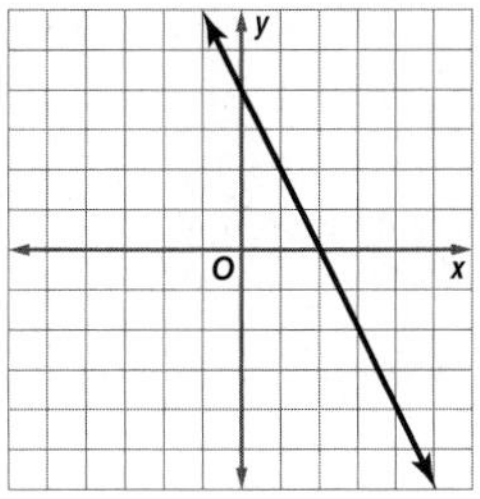

38. SHORT RESPONSE The table shows a five-day forecast indicating high (H) and low (L) temperatures. Organize the temperatures in a matrix. **See margin.**

	Mon	Tue	Wed	Thurs	Fri
H	92	87	85	88	90
L	68	64	62	65	66

Spiral Review

Find each product. (Lesson 7-8)

39. $(a-4)^2$ $a^2 - 8a + 16$
40. $(c+6)^2$ $c^2 + 12c + 36$
41. $(z-5)^2$ $z^2 - 10z + 25$
42. $(n-3)(n+3)$ $n^2 - 9$
43. $(y+2)^2$ $y^2 + 4y + 4$
44. $(d-7)(d+7)$ $d^2 - 49$

Find each product. (Lesson 7-7)

45. $(2m-3)(m+4)$ $2m^2 + 5m - 12$
46. $(h-2)(3h-5)$ $3h^2 - 11h + 10$
47. $(t+2)(t+9)$ $t^2 + 11t + 18$
48. $(8r-1)(r-6)$ $8r^2 - 49r + 6$
49. $(p+3q)(p+3q)$ $p^2 + 6pq + 9q^2$
50. $(n-4)(n+2)(n+1)$ $n^3 - n^2 - 10n - 8$

Write an augmented matrix to solve each system of equations. (Lesson 6-7)

51. $y = 2x + 3$, $y = 4x - 1$ (2, 7)
52. $8x + 2y = 13$, $4x + y = 11$ no solution
53. $-x + \frac{1}{3}y = 5$, $2x + 3y = 1$ (−4, 3)

54. FINANCIAL LITERACY Suppose you have already saved $50 toward the cost of a new television. You plan to save $5 more each week. Write and graph an equation for the total amount T that you will have w weeks from now. (Lesson 4-1) **See margin.**

Skills Review

Use the Distributive Property to rewrite each expression. (Lesson 1-4)

55. $2(4x-7)$ $8x - 14$
56. $\frac{1}{2}d(2d+6)$ $d^2 + 3d$
57. $-h(6h-1)$ $-6h^2 + h$
58. $9m - 9p$ $9(m-p)$
59. $5y - 10$ $5(y-2)$
60. $3z - 6x$ $3(z-2x)$

Differentiated Instruction AL

If students have trouble identifying prime factors,

Then have them make a sieve of Eratosthenes. Use a 10 × 10 grid with numbers 1–100 on it. Cross out 1, circle 2, cross out all multiples of 2 greater than 2. Circle 3; cross out all multiples of 3 greater than 3. Continue with the next uncrossed number until all multiples have been eliminated. The circled numbers are the prime numbers less than 100.

474 Chapter 8 Factoring and Quadratic Equations

EXPLORE
8-2 Algebra Lab
Factoring Using the Distributive Property

IL Math Online glencoe.com
Math *in Motion*, Animation

IL Learning Standards **8.B.4a** Represent algebraic concepts with physical materials, words, diagrams, tables, graphs, equations and inequalities and use appropriate technology.

When two or more numbers are multiplied, these numbers are *factors* of the product. Sometimes you know the product of binomials and are asked to find the factors. This is called factoring. You can use algebra tiles and a product mat to factor binomials.

ACTIVITY 1 Use algebra tiles to factor $2x - 8$.

Step 1 Model $2x - 8$.

Step 2 Arrange the tiles into a rectangle. The total area of the rectangle represents the product, and its length and width represent the factors.

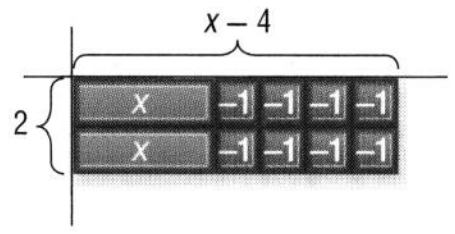

The rectangle has a width of 2 and a length of $x - 4$. Therefore, $2x - 8 = 2(x - 4)$.

ACTIVITY 2 Use algebra tiles to factor $x^2 + 3x$.

Step 1 Model $x^2 + 3x$.

Step 2 Arrange the tiles into a rectangle.

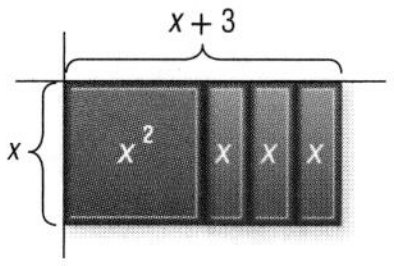

The rectangle has a width of x and a length of $x + 3$. Therefore, $x^2 + 3x = x(x + 3)$.

Model and Analyze

Use algebra tiles to factor each binomial.

1. $4x + 12$ **$4(x + 3)$**
2. $4x - 6$ **$2(2x - 3)$**
3. $3x^2 + 4x$ **$x(3x + 4)$**
4. $10 - 2x$ **$2(5 - x)$**

Determine whether each binomial can be factored. Justify your answer with a drawing.

5. $6x - 9$
6. $5x - 4$
7. $4x^2 + 7$
8. $x^2 + 3x$

5–8. See Ch. 8 Answer Appendix.

9. WRITING IN MATH Write a paragraph that explains how you can use algebra tiles to determine whether a binomial can be factored. Include an example of one binomial that can be factored and one that cannot.

9. Sample answer: Binomials can be factored if they can be represented by a rectangle. Examples: $3x + 3$ can be factored and $3x + 2$ cannot be factored.

EXPLORE
8-2 Lesson Notes

1 FOCUS

Objective Use algebra tiles to model using the Distributive Property to factor binomials.

Materials for Each Student

- algebra tiles and product mats

Easy to Make Manipulatives

Teaching Algebra with Manipulatives
Templates for:
- algebra tiles, pp. 10–11
- product mat, p. 17

2 TEACH

Working in Cooperative Groups

Put students in groups of two or three, mixing abilities. Have groups complete Activities 1 and 2 and Exercises 1–4.

- For Exercises 1–4, students should recognize that they must arrange the tiles into a rectangle with a width greater than 1 in order to find the factors of the polynomial.
- Point out that the area of the rectangle represents the polynomial, and the length and width represent the factors of the polynomial.

Practice Have students complete Exercises 5–9.

- For Exercises 5–9, emphasize that if a binomial can only be modeled with a width of 1, it cannot be factored.

3 Assess

Formative Assessment

Use Exercise 3 to assess whether students can use algebra tiles to factor a binomial.

From Concrete to Abstract

Write $x^2 + 5x$ on the board. Have students factor the binomial without using tiles. If they answer incorrectly, have them use their tiles to help them find their errors.

8-2 Lesson Notes

1 FOCUS

Vertical Alignment

Before Lesson 8-2
Find the GCF of a set of monomials.

Lesson 8-2
Use the Distributive Property to factor polynomials.
Solve quadratic equations of the form $ax^2 + bx = 0$.

After Lesson 8-2
Solve equations of the form $ax^2 + bx + c = 0$.

2 TEACH

Scaffolding Questions

Have students read the *Why?* section of the lesson.

Ask:

- What is the formula for the area of a rectangle? $A = \ell \times w$
- What do you multiply w by to get $1.6w^2 + 6w$? $1.6w + 6$
- What is the area for Ms. Cole's store expressed as a monomial times a polynomial? $w(1.6w + 6)$
- What is the area when $w = 50$? 4300 ft^2

8-2 Using the Distributive Property

Then
You found the GCF of a set of monomials. (Lesson 8-1)

Now
- Use the Distributive Property to factor polynomials.
- Solve equations of the form $ax^2 + bx = 0$.

IL Learning Standards

7.B.4 Estimate and measure the magnitude and directions of physical quantities using rulers, protractors and other scientific instruments including timers, calculators and computers.
8.C.4b Apply algebraic properties and procedures with matrices, vectors, functions and sequences using data found in business, industry and consumer situations.

New Vocabulary
factoring
factoring by grouping
Zero Product Property

IL Math Online
glencoe.com
- Extra Examples
- Personal Tutor
- Self-Check Quiz
- Homework Help

Why?

The cost of rent for Ms. Cole's store is determined by the square footage of the space. The area of the store can be modeled by the equation $A = 1.6w^2 + 6w$, where w is the width of the store in feet. We can use factoring and the Zero Product Property to find possible dimensions of the store.

Use the Distributive Property to Factor In Chapter 7, the Distributive Property was used to multiply a monomial by a polynomial.

$$5z(4z + 7) = 5z(4z) + 5z(7)$$
$$= 20z^2 + 35z$$

You can work backward to express a polynomial as a product of a monomial factor and a polynomial factor.

$$1.6w^2 + 6w = 1.6w(w) + 6(w)$$
$$= w(1.6w + 6)$$

So, $5z(4z + 7)$ is the *factored form* of $20z^2 + 35z$. **Factoring** a polynomial involves finding the *completely* factored form.

EXAMPLE 1 Use the Distributive Property

Use the Distributive Property to factor each polynomial.

a. $\mathbf{27y^2 + 18y}$

Find the GCF of each term.

$27y^2 = 3 \cdot 3 \cdot 3 \cdot y \cdot y$ — **Factor each term.**
$18y = 2 \cdot 3 \cdot 3 \cdot y$ — **Circle common factors.**
$\text{GCF} = 3 \cdot 3 \cdot y$ or $9y$

Write each term as the product of the GCF and the remaining factors. Use the Distributive Property to *factor out* the GCF.

$27y^2 + 18y = 9y(3y) + 9y(2)$ — **Rewrite each term using the GCF.**
$= 9y(3y + 2)$ — **Distributive Property**

b. $\mathbf{-4a^2b - 8ab^2 + 2ab}$

$-4a^2b = -1 \cdot 2 \cdot 2 \cdot a \cdot a \cdot b$ — **Factor each term.**
$-8ab^2 = -1 \cdot 2 \cdot 2 \cdot 2 \cdot a \cdot b \cdot b$ — **Circle common factors.**
$2ab = 2 \cdot a \cdot b$
$\text{GCF} = 2 \cdot a \cdot b$ or $2ab$

$-4a^2b - 8ab^2 + 2ab = 2ab(-2a) - 2ab(4b) + 2ab(1)$ — **Rewrite each term using the GCF.**
$= 2ab(-2a - 4b + 1)$ — **Distributive Property**

Check Your Progress

1A. $15w - 3v$ $\mathbf{3(5w - v)}$

1B. $7u^2t^2 + 21ut^2 - ut$ $\mathbf{ut(7ut + 21t - 1)}$

Personal Tutor glencoe.com

Lesson 8-2 Resources

Resource	Approaching-Level	On-Level	Beyond-Level	English Learners
Teacher Edition	• Differentiated Instruction, p. 478	• Differentiated Instruction, p. 478	• Differentiated Instruction, p. 482	
Chapter Resource Masters	• Study Guide and Intervention, pp. 11–12 • Skills Practice, p. 13 • Practice, p. 14 • Word Problem Practice, p. 15	• Study Guide and Intervention, pp. 11–12 • Skills Practice, p. 13 • Practice, p. 14 • Word Problem Practice, p. 15 • Enrichment, p. 16	• Practice, p. 14 • Word Problem Practice, p. 15 • Enrichment, p. 16	• Study Guide and Intervention, pp. 11–12 • Skills Practice, p. 13 • Practice, p. 14
Transparencies	• 5-Minute Check Transparency 8-2	• 5-Minute Check Transparency 8-2	• 5-Minute Check Transparency 8-2	• 5-Minute Check Transparency 8-2
Other	• Study Notebook • Teaching Algebra with Manipulatives	• Study Notebook • Teaching Algebra with Manipulatives	• Study Notebook	• Study Notebook • Teaching Algebra with Manipulatives

Using the Distributive Property to factor polynomials with four or more terms is called **factoring by grouping** because terms are put into groups and then factored. The Distributive Property is then applied to a common binomial factor.

Key Concept — Factoring by Grouping (For Your FOLDABLE)

Words A polynomial can be factored by grouping only if all of the following conditions exist.

- There are four or more terms.
- Terms have common factors that can be grouped together.
- There are two common factors that are identical or additive inverses of each other.

Symbols $ax + bx + ay + by = (ax + bx) + (ay + by)$
$= x(a + b) + y(a + b)$
$= (x + y)(a + b)$

EXAMPLE 2 Factor by Grouping

Factor $4qr + 8r + 3q + 6$.

$4qr + 8r + 3q + 6$	**Original expression**
$= (4qr + 8r) + (3q + 6)$	**Group terms with common factors.**
$= 4r(q + 2) + 3(q + 2)$	**Factor the GCF from each group.**

Notice that $(q + 2)$ is common in both groups, so it becomes the GCF.

$= (4r + 3)(q + 2)$	**Distributive Property**

Check Your Progress

Factor each polynomial.

2A. $rn + 5n - r - 5$ $(r + 5)(n - 1)$ **2B.** $3np + 15p - 4n - 20$ $(n + 5)(3p - 4)$

Personal Tutor glencoe.com

It can be helpful to recognize when binomials are additive inverses of each other. For example $6 - a = -1(a - 6)$.

StudyTip

Check To check your factored answers, multiply your factors out. You should get your original expression as a result.

EXAMPLE 3 Factor by Grouping with Additive Inverses

Factor $2mk - 12m + 42 - 7k$.

$2mk - 12m + 42 - 7k$	
$= (2mk - 12m) + (42 - 7k)$	**Group terms with common factors.**
$= 2m(k - 6) + 7(6 - k)$	**Factor the GCF from each group.**
$= 2m(k - 6) + 7[(-1)(k - 6)]$	**$6 - k = -1(k - 6)$**
$= 2m(k - 6) - 7(k - 6)$	**Associative Property**
$= (2m - 7)(k - 6)$	**Distributive Property**

Check Your Progress **3A.** $(-c + 4)(2d - 1)$ or $(c - 4)(1 - 2d)$

Factor each polynomial. **3B.** $(p + 9)(3 - 2p)$ or $(-p - 9)(2p - 3)$

3A. $c - 2cd + 8d - 4$ **3B.** $3p - 2p^2 - 18p + 27$

Personal Tutor glencoe.com

Use the Distributive Property to Factor

Example 1 shows how to use the Distributive Property to factor a polynomial. **Example 2** shows how to use grouping to factor a polynomial. **Example 3** shows how to use grouping with additive inverses to factor a polynomial.

Formative Assessment

Use the Check Your Progress exercises after each Example to determine students' understanding of concepts.

Additional Examples

1 Use the Distributive Property to factor each polynomial.

a. $15x + 25x^2$ $5x(3 + 5x)$

b. $12xy + 24xy^2 - 30x^2y^4$ $6xy(2 + 4y - 5xy^3)$

2 Factor $2xy + 7x - 2y - 7$. $(x - 1)(2y + 7)$

3 Factor $15a - 3ab + 4b - 20$. $(-3a + 4)(b - 5)$ or $(3a - 4)(5 - b)$

Additional Examples also in Interactive Classroom PowerPoint® Presentations

IWB INTERACTIVE WHITEBOARD READY

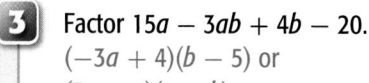

Focus on Mathematical Content

Greatest Common Factor Factoring using the Distributive Property requires expressing a polynomial as the product of the greatest common monomial factor of the polynomial's terms and a polynomial factor. To find the nonmonomial factor, each term of the polynomial is divided by the common monomial factor.

Tips for New Teachers

Reasoning Sometimes students find the monomial that is the GCF of the terms of the polynomial but do not know how to get the other polynomial factor. One way to find the remaining factor is to divide each term of the polynomial by the GCF. Tell students to check their answers by multiplying their factors using the Distributive Property.

TEACH with TECH

VIDEO RECORDING Separate the class into groups and have each group create a video showing how to factor by grouping. Assign a different expression to each group, and share each group's video with the class.

Solve Equations by Factoring

Example 4 shows how to solve two different quadratic equations–one in factored form and one that must be factored. **Example 5** shows how to solve a real-world problem using the Zero Product Property.

Additional Example

4 Solve each equation. Check your solutions.

a. $(x - 2)(4x - 1) = 0$ $2, \frac{1}{4}$

b. $4y = 12y^2$ $0, \frac{1}{3}$

Focus on Mathematical Content

Zero Product Property Quadratic equations can be solved by using the Zero Product Property: If the product of two factors is zero, then one of the factors is zero. To solve equations using this property, write the equation with the terms in factored form on one side of the equation and zero on the other side. Each factor is then set equal to zero, and the resulting equations are solved to arrive at the solutions.

Solve Equations by Factoring Some equations can be solved by factoring. Consider the following.

$3(0) = 0$ $\quad 0(2 - 2) = 0$ $\quad -312(0) = 0$ $\quad 0(0.25) = 0$

Notice that in each case, at least one of the factors is 0. These examples are demonstrations of the **Zero Product Property**.

Key Concept — Zero Product Property (For Your FOLDABLE)

Words If the product of two factors is 0, then at least one of the factors must be 0.

Symbols For any real numbers a and b, if $ab = 0$, then $a = 0$, $b = 0$, or both a and b equal zero.

Recall from Lesson 3-2 that a solution or root of an equation is any value that makes the equation true.

Watch Out!

Unknown Value It may be tempting to solve an equation by dividing each side by the variable. However, the variable has an unknown value, so you may be dividing by 0, which is undefined.

EXAMPLE 4 Solve Equations

Solve each equation. Check your solutions.

a. $(2d + 6)(3d - 15) = 0$

$(2d + 6)(3d - 15) = 0$		Original equation
$2d + 6 = 0$ or	$3d - 15 = 0$	Zero Product Property
$2d = -6$	$3d = 15$	Solve each equation.
$d = -3$	$d = 5$	Divide.

The roots are −3 and 5.

CHECK Substitute −3 and 5 for d in the original equation.

$(2d + 6)(3d - 15) = 0$	$(2d + 6)(3d - 15) = 0$
$[2(-3) + 6][3(-3) - 15] \stackrel{?}{=} 0$	$[2(5) + 6][3(5) - 15] \stackrel{?}{=} 0$
$(-6 + 6)(-9 - 15) \stackrel{?}{=} 0$	$(10 + 6)(15 - 15) \stackrel{?}{=} 0$
$(0)(-24) \stackrel{?}{=} 0$	$16(0) \stackrel{?}{=} 0$
$0 = 0$ ✓	$0 = 0$ ✓

b. $c^2 = 3c$

$c^2 = 3c$	Original equation
$c^2 - 3c = 0$	Subtract $3c$ from each side to get 0 on one side of the equation.
$c(c - 3) = 0$	Factor by using the GCF to get the form $ab = 0$.
$c = 0$ or $c - 3 = 0$	Zero Product Property
$c = 3$	Solve each equation.
The roots are 0 and 3.	Check by substituting 0 and 3 for c.

Check Your Progress

4A. $3n(n + 2) = 0$ **0, −2** **4B.** $8b^2 - 40b = 0$ **0, 5** **4C.** $x^2 = -10x$ **0, −10**

Personal Tutor glencoe.com

Differentiated Instruction (AL OL)

If students have trouble solving quadratic equations like Example 4b,

Then you may wish to allow students to use algebra tiles. They can use the methods from Explore 8-2 to factor the quadratic to solve the equation.

Real-World EXAMPLE 5 Use Factoring

AGILITY Penny is a Labrador Retriever who competes with her trainer in the agility course. Within the course, Penny must leap over a hurdle. Penny's jump can be modeled by the equation $h = -16t^2 + 20t$, where h is the height of the leap in inches at t seconds. Find the values of t when $h = 0$.

$h = -16t^2 + 20t$	**Original equation**
$0 = -16t^2 + 20t$	**Substitution, $h = 0$**
$0 = 4t(-4t + 5)$	**Factor by using the GCF.**
$4t = 0$ or $-4t + 5 = 0$	**Zero Product Property**
$t = 0$ $\quad -4t = -5$	**Solve each equation.**
$t = \frac{5}{4}$ or 1.25	**Divide each side by −4.**

Penny's height is 0 inches at 0 seconds and 1.25 seconds into the jump.

Check Your Progress

5. **KANGAROOS** The hop of a kangaroo can be modeled by $h = 24t - 16t^2$ where h represents the height of the hop in meters and t is the time in seconds. Find the values of t when $h = 0$. **0, 1.5**

Personal Tutor glencoe.com

Real-World Link

Dog agility tests a person's skills as a trainer and handler. Competitors race through an obstacle course that includes hurdles, tunnels, a see-saw, and line poles.

Source: United States Dog Agility Association

Check Your Understanding

Example 1 p. 476

Use the Distributive Property to factor each polynomial.

1. $21b - 15a$ **$3(7b - 5a)$**
2. $14c^2 + 2c$ **$2c(7c + 1)$**
3. $10g^2h^2 + 9gh^2 - g^2h$ **$gh(10gh + 9h - g)$**
4. $12jk^2 + 6j^2k + 2j^2k^2$ **$2jk(6k + 3j + jk)$**

Examples 2 and 3 p. 477

Factor each polynomial.

5. $np + 2n + 8p + 16$ **$(n + 8)(p + 2)$**
6. $xy - 7x + 7y - 49$ **$(x + 7)(y - 7)$**
7. $3bc - 2b - 10 + 15c$ **$(b + 5)(3c - 2)$**
8. $9fg - 45f - 7g + 35$ **$(9f - 7)(g - 5)$**

Example 4 p. 478

Solve each equation. Check your solutions.

9. $3k(k + 10) = 0$ **0, −10**
10. $(4m + 2)(3m - 9) = 0$ **$-\frac{1}{2}$, 3**
11. $20p^2 - 15p = 0$ **0, $\frac{3}{4}$**
12. $r^2 = 14r$ **0, 14**

Example 5 p. 479

13. **SPIDERS** Jumping spiders can commonly be found in homes and barns throughout the United States. A jumping spider's jump can be modeled by the equation $h = 33.3t - 16t^2$, where t represents the time in seconds and h is the height in feet.
    a. When is the spider's height at 0 feet? **0, 2.08125**
    b. What is the spider's height after 1 second? after 2 seconds? **17.3 ft, 2.6 ft**
14. **ROCKETS** At a Fourth of July celebration, a rocket is launched straight up with an initial velocity of 125 feet per second. The height h of the rocket in feet above sea level is modeled by the formula $h = 125t - 16t^2$, where t is the time in seconds after the rocket is launched.
    a. What is the height of the rocket when it returns to the ground? **0 ft**
    b. Let $h = 0$ in the equation and solve for t. **0, 7.8125**
    c. How many seconds will it take for the rocket to return to the ground? **about 7.8 s**

Additional Example

5 **FOOTBALL** A football is kicked into the air. The height of the football can be modeled by the equation $h = -16x^2 + 16x$, where h is the height reached by the ball after x seconds. Find the values of x when $h = 0$.
0 seconds, 1 second

3 PRACTICE

Formative Assessment

Use Exercises 1-14 to check for understanding.

Use the chart at the bottom of the next page to customize assignments for your students.

Exercise Alert

Grid Paper For Exercise 47, students will need grid paper.

Multiple Representations In Exercise 51, students use a diagram and analysis to factor an algebraic expression.

Additional Answers

47a.

x	0	1	2	3	4
y	0	9	12	9	0

47b.

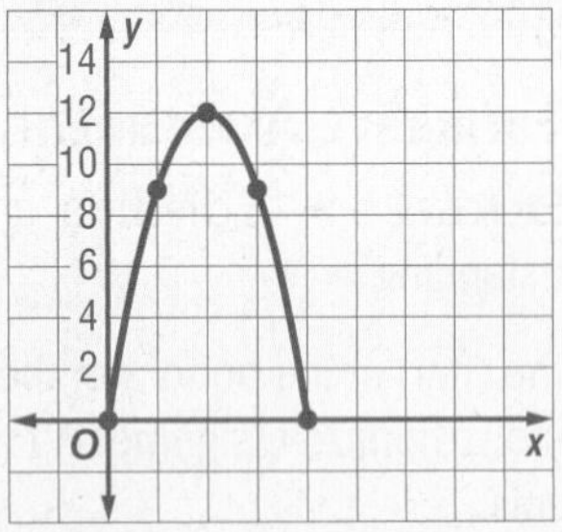

51b.

x^2	$+3x$
$-2x$	-6

51c.

	x	$+3$
x	x^2	$+3x$
-2	$-2x$	-6

$(x + 3)(x - 2)$

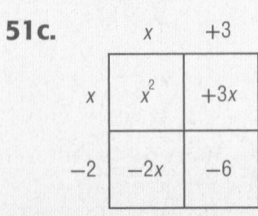

53. If $a = 0$ and $b = 0$, then all real numbers are solutions. If $a \neq 0$, then the solutions are $-\frac{b}{a}$ and $\frac{b}{a}$.

56. Rewrite the equation to have zero on one side of the equals sign. Then factor the other side. Set each factor equal to zero, and then solve each equation.

Practice and Problem Solving

= **Step-by-Step Solutions** begin on page R12.
Extra Practice begins on page 815.

Example 1 p. 476

Use the Distributive Property to factor each polynomial.

15. $16t - 40y$ $8(2t - 5y)$

16. $30v + 50x$ $10(3v + 5x)$

17. $2k^2 + 4k$ $2k(k + 2)$

18. $5z^2 + 10z$ $5z(z + 2)$

19. $4a^2b^2 + 2a^2b - 10ab^2$ $2ab(2ab + a - 5b)$

20. $5c^2v - 15c^2v^2 + 5c^2v^3$ $5c^2v(1 - 3v + v^2)$

Examples 2 and 3 p. 477

Factor each polynomial.

21. $fg - 5g + 4f - 20$ $(g + 4)(f - 5)$

22. $a^2 - 4a - 24 + 6a$ $(a - 4)(a + 6)$

23. $hj - 2h + 5j - 10$ $(h + 5)(j - 2)$

24. $xy - 2x - 2 + y$ $(x + 1)(y - 2)$

25. $45pq - 27q - 50p + 30$

26. $24ty - 18t + 4y - 3$ $(6t + 1)(4y - 3)$

27. $3dt - 21d + 35 - 5t$ $(3d - 5)(t - 7)$

28. $8r^2 + 12r$ $4r(2r + 3)$

29. $21th - 3t - 35h + 5$ $(3t - 5)(7h - 1)$

30. $vp + 12v + 8p + 96$ $(v + 8)(p + 12)$

31. $5br - 25b + 2r - 10$ $(r - 5)(5b + 2)$

32. $2nu - 8u + 3n - 12$ $(2u + 3)(n - 4)$

33. $5gf^2 + g^2f + 15gf$ $gf(5f + g + 15)$

34. $rp - 9r + 9p - 81$ $(r + 9)(p - 9)$

35. $27cd^2 - 18c^2d^2 + 3cd$

36. $18r^3t^2 + 12r^2t^2 - 6r^2t$

37. $48tu - 90t + 32u - 60$

38. $16gh + 24g - 2h - 3$ $(8g - 1)(2h + 3)$

25. $(9q - 10)(5p - 3)$
35. $3cd(9d - 6cd + 1)$
36. $6r^2t(3rt + 2t - 1)$
37. $2(8u - 15)(3t + 2)$

Example 4 p. 478

Solve each equation. Check your solutions.

39. $3b(9b - 27) = 0$ $0, 3$

40. $2n(3n + 3) = 0$ $0, -1$

41. $(8z + 4)(5z + 10) = 0$ $-\frac{1}{2}, -2$

42. $(7x + 3)(2x - 6) = 0$ $-\frac{3}{7}, 3$

43. $b^2 = -3b$ $0, -3$

44. $a^2 = 4a$ $0, 4$

Example 5 p. 479

45. GEOMETRY Use the drawing at the right.

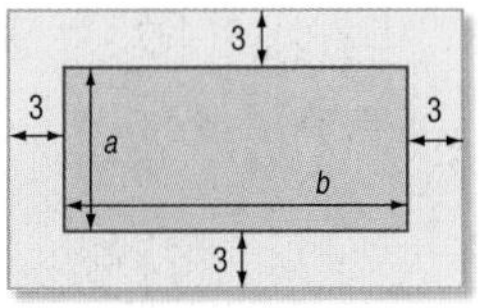

a. Write an expression in factored form to represent the area of the blue section. ab

b. Write an expression in factored form to represent the area of the region formed by the outer edge. $(a + 6)(b + 6)$

c. Write an expression in factored form to represent the orange region. $6(a + b + 6)$

46. FIREWORKS A ten-inch fireworks shell is fired from ground level. The height of the shell in feet is given by the formula $h = 263t - 16t^2$, where t is the time in seconds after launch.

a. Write the expression that represents the height in factored form. $t(263 - 16t)$

b. At what time will the height be 0? Is this answer practical? Explain.

c. What is the height of the shell 8 seconds and 10 seconds after being fired?

d. At 10 seconds, is the shell rising or falling?

46b. 0 and 16.4375 seconds; Yes, the shell starts at ground level and is in the air for 16.4375 seconds before landing on the ground again.
46c. 1080 ft; 1030 ft
46d. The shell has begun to fall.

47. ARCHITECTURE The frame of a doorway is an arch that can be modeled by the graph of the equation $y = -3x^2 + 12x$, where x and y are measured in feet. On a coordinate plane, the floor is represented by the x-axis. **a–b. See margin.**

a. Make a table of values for the height of the arch if $x = 0, 1, 2, 3$, and 4 feet.

b. Plot the points from the table on a coordinate plane and connect the points to form a smooth curve to represent the arch.

c. How high is the doorway? 12 ft

Differentiated Homework Options

Level	Assignment		Two-Day Option	
AL Basic	15–45, 52, 54–86	15–45 odd, 57–60	16–44 even, 52, 54–56, 61–86
OL Core	15–45 odd, 46–52, 54–86	15–45, 57–60	46–52, 54–56, 61–86
BL Advanced	46–80, (optional: 81–86)		

Real-World Link

The Xtreme Skyflyer at Virginia's Kings Dominion uses a free-fall/cable swing to hoist people about 160 feet in the air. Then the riders experience a free-fall followed by a period of swinging back and forth.

Source: Theme Park Insider

48. RIDES Suppose the height of a rider after being dropped can be modeled by $h = -16t^2 - 96t + 160$, where h is the height in feet and t is time in seconds.

a. Write an expression to represent the height in factored form. **$16(-t^2 - 6t + 10)$**

b. From what height is the rider initially dropped? **160 ft**

c. At what height will the rider be after 3 seconds of falling? Is this possible? Explain.

49 ARCHERY The height h in feet of an arrow can be modeled by the equation $h = 64t - 16t^2$, where t is time in seconds. Ignoring the height of the archer, how long after the arrow is released does it hit the ground? **4 s**

50. TENNIS A tennis player hits a tennis ball upward with an initial velocity of 80 feet per second. The height h in feet of the tennis ball can be modeled by the equation $h = 80t - 16t^2$, where t is time in seconds. Ignoring the height of the tennis player, how long does it take the ball to hit the ground? **5 s**

51. MULTIPLE REPRESENTATIONS In this problem, you will explore the *box method* of factoring. To factor $x^2 + x - 6$, write the first term in the top left-hand corner of the box, and then write the last term in the lower right-hand corner.

	?	?
?	x^2	?
?	?	-6

a. **ANALYTICAL** Determine which two factors have a product of -6 and a sum of 1. **3 and −2**

b. **SYMBOLIC** Write each factor in an empty square in the box. Include the positive or negative sign and variable. **See margin.**

c. **ANALYTICAL** Find the factor for each row and column of the box. What are the factors of $x^2 + x - 6$? **See margin.**

d. **VERBAL** Describe how you would use the box method to factor $x^2 - 3x - 40$.

48c. -272 ft; No, the rider cannot be a negative number of feet in the air.

51d. Sample answer: Place x^2 in the top left-hand corner and place -40 in the lower right-hand corner. Then determine which two factors have a product of -40 and a sum of -3. Then place these factors in the box. Then find the factor of each row and column. The factors will be listed on the very top and far left of the box.

55. Sample answer: $a = 0$ or $a = b$ for any real values of a and b.

H.O.T. Problems

Use Higher-Order Thinking Skills

52. FIND THE ERROR Hernando and Rachel are solving $2m^2 = 4m$. Is either of them correct? Explain your reasoning. **Rachel; the equation first must have 0 on one side.**

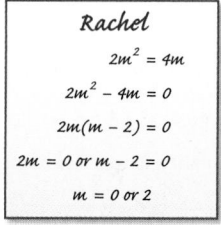

Hernando

$2m^2 = 4m$

$\frac{2m^2}{m} = \frac{4m^2}{2m}$

$2m = 2$

$m = 1$

Rachel

$2m^2 = 4m$

$2m^2 - 4m = 0$

$2m(m - 2) = 0$

$2m = 0$ or $m - 2 = 0$

$m = 0$ or 2

53. CHALLENGE Given the equation $(ax + b)(ax - b) = 0$, solve for x. What do we know about the values of a and b? **See margin.**

54. OPEN ENDED Write a four-term polynomial that can be factored by grouping. Then factor the polynomial. **Sample answers: $x^2 + 2xy + 3x + 6y$, $(x + 3)(x + 2y)$**

55. REASONING Given the equation $c = a^2 - ab$, for what values of a and b does $c = 0$?

56. WRITING IN MATH Explain how to solve a quadratic equation by using the Zero Product Property. **See margin.**

Watch Out!

Find the Error For Exercise 52, remind students that the quickest way to check a solution is to substitute the value back into the original equation.

Study Guide and Intervention

CRM pp. 11–12 AL OL ELL

NAME ______ DATE ______ PERIOD ______

8-2 Study Guide and Intervention

Using the Distributive Property

Use the Distributive Property to Factor The Distributive Property has been used to multiply a polynomial by a monomial. It can also be used to express a polynomial in factored form. Compare the two columns in the table below.

Multiplying	Factoring
$3(a + b) = 3a + 3b$	$3a + 3b = 3(a + b)$
$x(y - z) = xy - xz$	$xy - xz = x(y - z)$
$6y(2x + 1) = 6y(2x) + 6y(1) = 12xy + 6y$	$12xy + 6y = 6y(2x) + 6y(1) = 6y(2x + 1)$

Example 1 Use the Distributive Property to factor $12mp + 80m^2$.

Find the GCF of $12mp$ and $80m^2$.

$12mp = 2 \cdot 2 \cdot 3 \cdot m \cdot p$

$80m^2 = 2 \cdot 2 \cdot 2 \cdot 2 \cdot 5 \cdot m \cdot m$

GCF $= 2 \cdot 2 \cdot m$ or $4m$

Write each term as the product of the GCF and its remaining factors.

$12mp + 80m^2 = 4m(3 \cdot p) + 4m(2 \cdot 2 \cdot 5 \cdot m)$
$= 4m(3p) + 4m(20m)$
$= 4m(3p + 20m)$

Thus $12mp + 80m^2 = 4m(3p + 20m)$.

Example 2 Factor $6ax + 3ay + 2bx + by$ by grouping.

$6ax + 3ay + 2bx + by$
$= (6ax + 3ay) + (2bx + by)$
$= 3a(2x + y) + b(2x + y)$
$= (3a + b)(2x + y)$

Check using the FOIL method.

$(3a + b)(2x + y)$
$= 3a(2x) + (3a)(y) + (b)(2x) + (b)(y)$
$= 6ax + 3ay + 2bx + by$ ✓

Exercises

Factor each polynomial.

1. $24x + 48y$ **$24(x + 2y)$**
2. $30mp^2 + m^2p - 6p$ **$p(30mp + m^2 - 6)$**
3. $q^4 - 18q^3 + 22q$ **$q(q^3 - 18q^2 + 22)$**
4. $9x^2 - 3x$ **$3x(3x - 1)$**
5. $4m + 6p - 8mp$ **$2(2m + 3p - 4mp)$**
6. $45r^3 - 15r^2$ **$15r^2(3r - 1)$**
7. $14t^3 - 42t^5 - 49t^4$ **$7t^3(2 - 6t^2 - 7t)$**
8. $55p^2 - 11p^4 + 44p^5$ **$11p^2(5 - p^2 + 4p^3)$**
9. $14y^3 - 28y^2 + y$ **$y(14y^2 - 28y + 1)$**
10. $4x + 12x^2 + 16x^3$ **$4x(1 + 3x + 4x^2)$**
11. $4a^2b + 28ab^2 + 7ab$ **$ab(4a + 28b + 7)$**
12. $6y + 12x - 8z$ **$2(3y + 6x - 4z)$**
13. $x^2 + 2x + x + 2$ **$(x + 1)(x + 2)$**
14. $6y^2 - 4y + 3y - 2$ **$(2y + 1)(3y - 2)$**
15. $4m^2 + 4mp + 3mp + 3p^2$ **$(4m + 3p)(m + p)$**
16. $12ax + 3xz + 4ay + yz$ **$(3x + y)(4a + z)$**
17. $12a^2 + 3a - 8a - 2$ **$(4a + 1)(3a - 2)$**
18. $xa + ya + x + y$ **$(x + y)(a + 1)$**

Chapter 8 11 Glencoe Algebra 1

Lesson 8-2

Practice

CRM p. 14 AL OL BL ELL

NAME ______ DATE ______ PERIOD ______

8-2 Practice

Using the Distributive Property

Factor each polynomial.

1. $64 - 40ab$ **$8(8 - 5ab)$**
2. $4d^2 + 16$ **$4(d^2 + 4)$**
3. $6r^2t - 3rt^2$ **$3rt(2r - t)$**
4. $15ad + 30a^2d^2$ **$15ad(1 + 2ad)$**
5. $32a^2 + 24b^2$ **$8(4a^2 + 3b^2)$**
6. $36xy^2 - 48x^2y$ **$12xy(3y - 4x)$**
7. $30x^3y + 35x^2y^2$ **$5x^2y(6x + 7y)$**
8. $9a^3d^2 - 6ad^3$ **$3ad^2(3a^2 - 2d)$**
9. $75b^2g^3 + 60bg^3$ **$15bg^3(5b + 4)$**
10. $8p^2r^2 - 24pr^3 + 16pr$ **$8pr(pr - 3r^2 + 2)$**
11. $5x^3y^2 + 10x^2y + 25x$ **$5x(x^2y^2 + 2xy + 5)$**
12. $9ax^3 + 18bx^2 + 24cx$ **$3x(3ax^2 + 6bx + 8c)$**
13. $x^2 + 4x + 2x + 8$ **$(x + 2)(x + 4)$**
14. $2a^2 + 3a + 6a + 9$ **$(a + 3)(2a + 3)$**
15. $4b^2 - 12b + 2b - 6$ **$(4b + 2)(b - 3)$**
16. $6xy - 8x + 15y - 20$ **$(2x + 5)(3y - 4)$**
17. $-6mp + 4m + 18p - 12$ **$(-2m + 6)(3p - 2)$**
18. $12a^2 - 15ab - 16a + 20b$ **$(3a - 4)(4a - 5b)$**

Solve each equation. Check your solutions.

19. $x(x - 32) = 0$ **$\{0, 32\}$**
20. $4b(b + 4) = 0$ **$\{-4, 0\}$**
21. $(y - 3)(y + 2) = 0$ **$\{-2, 3\}$**
22. $(a + 6)(3a - 7) = 0$ **$\{-6, \frac{7}{3}\}$**
23. $(2y + 5)(y - 4) = 0$ **$\{-\frac{5}{2}, 4\}$**
24. $(4y + 8)(3y - 4) = 0$ **$\{-2, \frac{4}{3}\}$**
25. $2z^2 + 20z = 0$ **$\{-10, 0\}$**
26. $8p^2 - 4p = 0$ **$\{0, \frac{1}{2}\}$**
27. $9x^2 = 27x$ **$\{0, 3\}$**
28. $18x^2 = 15x$ **$\{0, \frac{5}{6}\}$**
29. $14x^2 = -21x$ **$\{-\frac{3}{2}, 0\}$**
30. $8x^2 = -26x$ **$\{-\frac{13}{4}, 0\}$**

31. **LANDSCAPING** A landscaping company has been commissioned to design a triangular flower bed for a mall entrance. The final dimensions of the flower bed have not been determined, but the company knows that the height will be two feet less than the base. The area of the flower bed can be represented by the equation $A = \frac{1}{2}b^2 - b$.

a. Write this equation in factored form. **$A = b\left(\frac{1}{2}b - 1\right)$**

b. Suppose the base of the flower bed is 16 feet. What will be its area? **112 ft²**

32. **PHYSICAL SCIENCE** Mr. Alim's science class launched a toy rocket from ground level with an initial upward velocity of 60 feet per second. The height h of the rocket in feet above the ground after t seconds is modeled by the equation $h = 60t - 16t^2$. How long was the rocket in the air before it returned to the ground? **3.75 s**

Chapter 8 14 Glencoe Algebra 1

Word Problem Practice

CRM p. 15 AL OL BL ELL

NAME ______ DATE ______ PERIOD ______

8-2 Word Problem Practice

Using the Distributive Property

1. **PHYSICS** According to legend, Galileo dropped objects of different weights from the so-called "leaning tower" of Pisa while developing his formula for free falling objects. The relationship that he discovered was that the distance d an object falls after t seconds is given by $d = 16t^2$ (ignoring air resistance). This relationship can be found in the equation $h = 4t - 16t^2$, where h is the height of an object thrown upward from ground level at a rate of 32 feet per second. Solve the equation for $h = 0$. **$t = 0.25$ and 0**

2. **SWIMMING POOL** The area A of a rectangular swimming pool is given by the equation $A = 12w - w^2$, where w is the width of one side. Write an expression for the other side of the pool. **$12 - w$**

3. **CONSTRUCTION** Unique Building Company is constructing a triangular roof truss for a building. The workers assemble the truss with the dimensions shown on the diagram below. Using the Pythagorean Theorem, find the length of the sides of the truss. **3 yd, 4 yd, 5 yd**

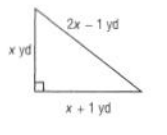

4. **VERTICAL JUMP** Your vertical jump height is measured by subtracting your standing reach height from the height of the highest point you can reach by jumping without taking a running start. Typically, NBA players have vertical jump heights of up to 34 inches. If an NBA player jumps this high, his height h in inches above his standing reach height after t seconds can be modeled by the equation $h = 162t - 192t^2$. Solve the equation for $h = 0$ and interpret the solution. Round your answer to the nearest hundredth.

$t = 0$ and $t \approx 0.844$; The player lands after about 0.84 seconds.

5. **PETS** Conner tosses a dog treat upward with an initial velocity of 13.7 meters per second. The height of the treat above the dog's mouth h in meters after t seconds is given by the equation.

$$h = 13.7t - 4.9t^2$$

a. Assuming the dog doesn't jump, after how many seconds does the dog catch the treat? **2.795**

b. The dog treat reaches its maximum height halfway between when it was thrown and when it was caught. What is its maximum height? **9.6 m**

c. How fast would Connor have to throw the dog treat in order to make it fly through the air for 6 seconds? **at 29.4 m/s**

Chapter 8 15 Glencoe Algebra 1

Lesson 8-2

Enrichment

CRM p. 16 OL BL

NAME ______ DATE ______ PERIOD ______

8-2 Enrichment

Linear Combinations

The greatest common factor, GCF, of two numbers can be written as a linear combination of the two numbers. A linear combination is an expression of the form $Ax + By$.

Example Write the greatest common factor of 52 and 36 as a linear combination.

First, use the Euclidean Algorithm to find the greatest common factor of the two numbers.

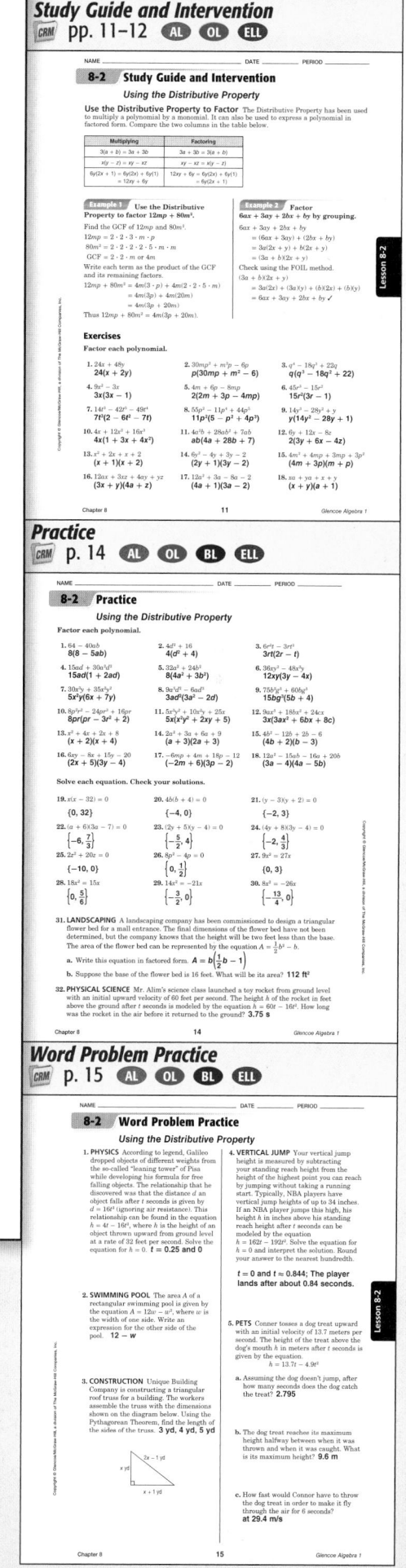

$36\overline{)52}$ quotient 1, subtract 36 — Divide the greater number by the lesser number.

$16\overline{)36}$ original divisor; quotient 2, subtract 32 — Then divide using the remainder as the new divisor.

$4\overline{)16}$ second divisor; quotient 4, subtract 16, remainder 0 — Divide again. Stop dividing.

Last divisor used is the GCF. In this case, 4 is the GCF for 36 and 52.

…write 4 … linear combination of … d 52, it need… be written as:

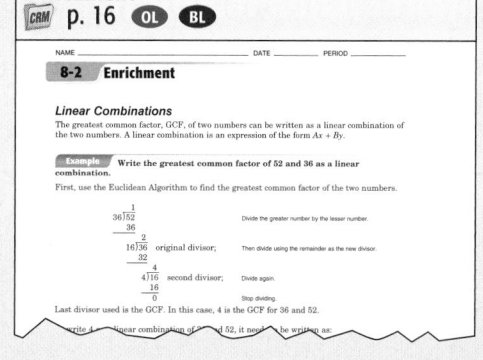

4 ASSESS

Yesterday's News Have students write how yesterday's concept of finding the GCF of a set of monomials helped them with today's new material.

Formative Assessment

Check for student understanding of concepts in Lessons 8-1 and 8-2.

CRM Quiz 1, p. 45

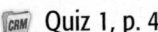

PSAE PRACTICE 8.11.18, 10.11.07, 7.11.03, 8.11.14

57. Which is a factor of $6z^2 - 3z - 2 + 4z$? **D**

A $2z + 1$ C $z + 2$
B $3z - 2$ D $2z - 1$

58. PROBABILITY Hailey has 10 blocks: 2 red, 4 blue, 3 yellow, and 1 green. What is the probability that a randomly chosen block will be either red or yellow? **H**

F $\frac{3}{10}$ H $\frac{1}{2}$
G $\frac{1}{5}$ J $\frac{7}{10}$

59. GRIDDED RESPONSE Cho is making a 140-inch by 160-inch quilt with quilt squares that measure 8 inches on each side. How many will be needed to make the quilt? **350**

60. GEOMETRY The area of the right triangle shown below is $5h$ square centimeters. What is the height of the triangle? **D**

A 2 cm
B 5 cm
C 8 cm
D 10 cm

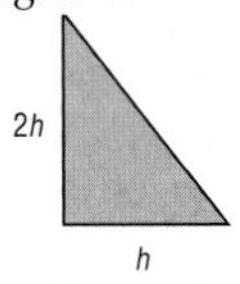

Spiral Review

Find the GCF of each set of monomials. (Lesson 8-1)

61. 15, 25 **5** **62.** 40, 100 **20** **63.** $16x, 24x^2$ **$8x$**

64. $30a^2, 50ab^2$ **$10a$** **65.** $8c^2d^3, 16c^3d$ **$8c^2d$** **66.** $4y, 18y^2, 6y^3$ **$2y$**

67. GENETICS Brown genes *B* are dominant over blue genes *b*. A person with genes *BB* or *Bb* has brown eyes. Someone with genes *bb* has blue eyes. Elisa has brown eyes with *Bb* genes, and Bob has blue eyes. Write an expression for the possible eye coloring of Elisa and Bob's children. Determine the probability that their child would have blue eyes. (Lesson 7-8) **$0.5Bb + 0.5b^2$; $\frac{1}{2}$**

Simplify. (Lesson 7-1)

68. $(ab^4)(ab^2)$ **a^2b^6** **69.** $(p^5r^4)(p^2r)$ **p^7r^5** **70.** $(-7c^3d^4)(4cd^3)$ **$-28c^4d^7$**

71. $(9xy^7)^2$ **$81x^2y^{14}$** **72.** $\left[(3^2)^4\right]^2$ **43,046,721** **73.** $\left[(4^2)^3\right]^2$ **16,777,216**

74. BASKETBALL In basketball, a free throw is 1 point and a field goal is either 2 or 3 points. In a season, Tim Duncan of the San Antonio Spurs scored a total of 1342 points. The total number of 2-point field goals and 3-point field goals was 517, and he made 305 of the 455 free throws that he attempted. Find the number of 2-point field goals and 3-point field goals Duncan made that season. (Lesson 6-4)

74. 514 2-point field goals; 3 3-point field goals

Solve each inequality. Check your solution. (Lesson 5-3)

75. $3y - 4 > -37$ **$\{y \mid y > -11\}$** **76.** $-5q + 9 > 24$ **$\{q \mid q < -3\}$** **77.** $-2k + 12 < 30$ **$\{k \mid k > -9\}$**

78. $5q + 7 \leq 3(q + 1)$ **$\{q \mid q \leq -2\}$** **79.** $\frac{z}{4} + 7 \geq -5$ **$\{z \mid z \geq -48\}$** **80.** $8c - (c - 5) > c + 17$ **$\{c \mid c > 2\}$**

Skills Review

Find each product. (Lesson 7-7)

81. $(a + 2)(a + 5)$ **$a^2 + 7a + 10$** **82.** $(d + 4)(d + 10)$ **$d^2 + 14d + 40$** **83.** $(z - 1)(z - 8)$ **$z^2 - 9z + 8$**

84. $(c + 9)(c - 3)$ **$c^2 + 6c - 27$** **85.** $(x - 7)(x - 6)$ **$x^2 - 13x + 42$** **86.** $(g - 2)(g + 11)$ **$g^2 + 9g - 22$**

Differentiated Instruction BL

Extension Write the following polynomial on the board: $c^2xy - c^3 - x^2y + cx$. Ask students to factor it by grouping.
$(c^2 - x)(xy - c)$, or $(x - c^2)(c - xy)$

482 Chapter 8 Factoring and Quadratic Equations

EXPLORE 8-3 Algebra Lab

Factoring Trinomials

IL Math Online glencoe.com
Math *in Motion*, Animation

IL Learning Standards **8.B.4a** Represent algebraic concepts with physical materials, words, diagrams, tables, graphs, equations and inequalities and use appropriate technology.

You can use algebra tiles to factor trinomials. If a polynomial represents the area of a rectangle formed by algebra tiles, then the rectangle's length and width are *factors* of the area. If a rectangle cannot be formed to represent the trinomial, then the trinomial is not factorable.

ACTIVITY 1 Factor $x^2 + bx + c$

Use algebra tiles to factor $x^2 + 4x + 3$.

Step 1 Model $x^2 + 4x + 3$.

Step 2 Place the x^2-tile at the corner of the product mat. Arrange the 1-tiles into a rectangular array. Because 3 is prime, the 3 tiles can be arranged in a rectangle in one way, a 1-by-3 rectangle.

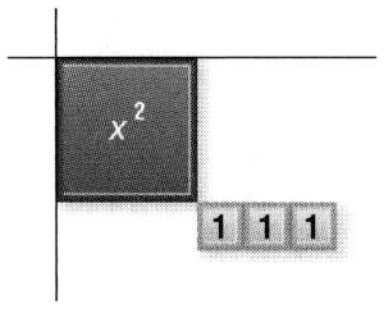

Step 3 Complete the rectangle with the x-tiles.

The rectangle has a width of $x + 1$ and a length of $x + 3$.

Therefore, $x^2 + 4x + 3 = (x + 1)(x + 3)$.

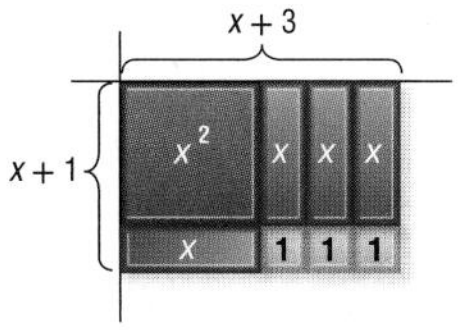

ACTIVITY 2 Factor $x^2 + bx + c$

Use algebra tiles to factor $x^2 + 8x + 12$.

Step 1 Model $x^2 + 8x + 12$.

Step 2 Place the x^2-tile at the corner of the product mat. Arrange the 1-tiles into a rectangular array. Since $12 = 3 \times 4$, try a 3-by-4 rectangle. Try to complete the rectangle. Notice that there is an extra x-tile.

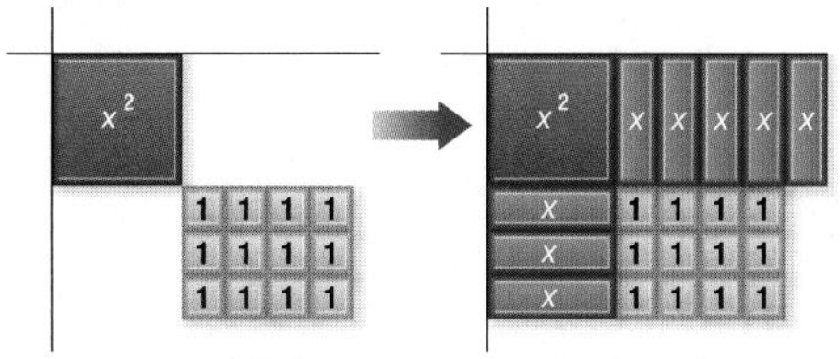

Step 3 Arrange the 1-tiles into a 2-by-6 rectangular array. This time you can complete the rectangle with the x-tiles.

The rectangle has a width of $x + 2$ and a length of $x + 6$.

Therefore, $x^2 + 8x + 12 = (x + 2)(x + 6)$.

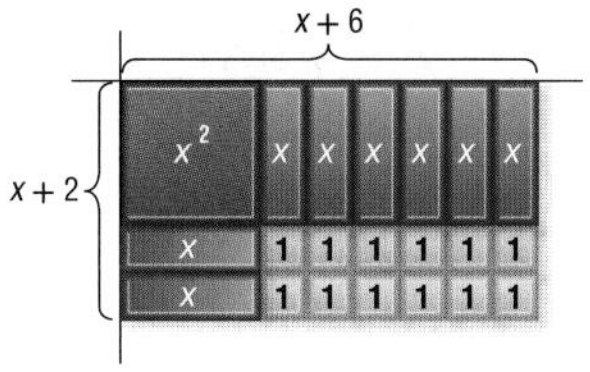

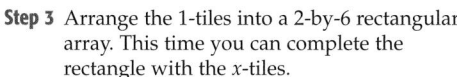

(continued on the next page)

EXPLORE 8-3

Lesson Notes

1 FOCUS

Objective Use algebra tiles to model factoring trinomials.

Materials for Each Group

- algebra tiles
- product mat

Easy to Make Manipulatives

Teaching Algebra with Manipulatives
Templates for:

- algebra tiles, pp. 10–11
- product mat, p. 17

Tips for New Teachers

You may want to remind students that the area of the rectangle represents the polynomial, and the length and width of the rectangle represent the factors of the polynomial.

2 TEACH

Working in Cooperative Groups

Place students in groups of two or three, mixing abilities. Have groups complete Activities 1–4.

- Ask students to name the shape they must form with the tiles in order to factor a polynomial. rectangle
- In Activity 1, remind students to read the width of the tiles along the edge of the rectangle. The x^2-tiles have a width of x and the x-tiles have a width of one.
- For Activity 2, encourage students to try several different arrangements until they can form a rectangle. While the x^2-tile should be in the corner, there is more than one correct way to arrange the tiles into a rectangle.

Explore 8-3 Algebra Lab: Factoring Trinomials 483

- As students work through Activity 3, remind them to pay close attention to the sign of each tile.
- As students work through Activity 4, remind them to be careful to add one x-tile and one $-x$-tile when they add a zero pair.

Practice Have students complete Exercises 1–13.

3 Assess

Formative Assessment

Use Exercises 7 and 8 to assess whether students can use algebra tiles to factor trinomials.

From Concrete to Abstract

After students complete Exercises 1–8, ask them whether they noticed a correlation between the need to use zero pairs to factor the trinomial and the appearance of the resulting factors. Sample answer: When zero pairs are used, the signs of the constant terms of the factors are opposite. When zero pairs are not used, the signs of the constant terms of factors are the same.

Extending the Concept

Ask students what they notice about the sum of the constant terms in the factors of the trinomials in Exercises 1–8. Sample answer: Their sum equals the coefficient of the middle term of the trinomial.

ACTIVITY 3 Factor $x^2 - bx + c$

Use algebra tiles to factor $x^2 - 5x + 6$.

Step 1 Model $x^2 - 5x + 6$.

Step 2 Place the x^2-tile at the corner of the product mat. Arrange the 1-tiles into a 2-by-3 rectangular array as shown.

Step 3 Complete the rectangle with the x-tiles. The rectangle has a width of $x - 2$ and a length of $x - 3$.

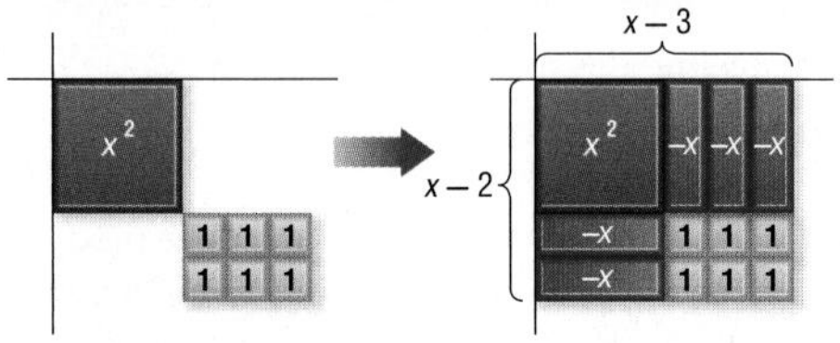

Therefore, $x^2 - 5x + 6 = (x - 2)(x - 3)$.

ACTIVITY 4 Factor $x^2 - bx - c$

Use algebra tiles to factor $x^2 - 4x - 5$.

Step 1 Model $x^2 - 4x - 5$.

Step 2 Place the x^2-tile at the corner of the product mat. Arrange the 1-tiles into a 1-by-5 rectangular array as shown.

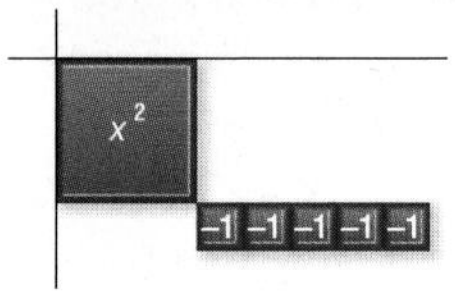

Step 3 Place the x-tile as shown. Recall that you can add zero pairs without changing the value of the polynomial. In this case, add a zero pair of x-tiles.

The rectangle has a width of $x + 1$ and a length of $x - 5$.

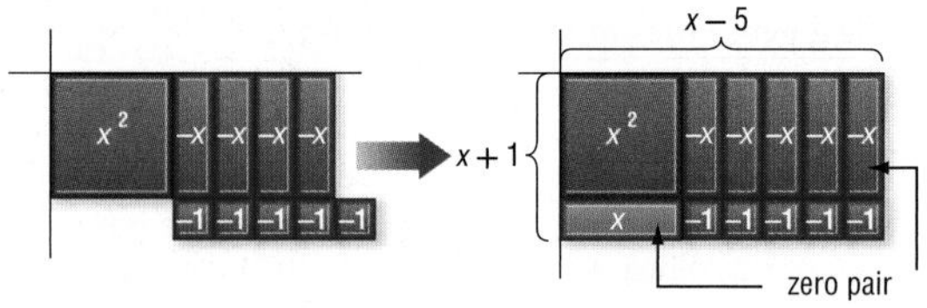

Therefore, $x^2 - 4x - 5 = (x + 1)(x - 5)$.

Model and Analyze

13. Trinomials can be factored if they can be represented by a rectangle. Sample answers: $x^2 + 4x + 4$ can be factored, and $x^2 + 6x + 4$ cannot be factored.

Use algebra tiles to factor each trinomial. 1–8. See margin.

1. $x^2 + 3x + 2$	**2.** $x^2 + 6x + 8$	**3.** $x^2 + 3x - 4$	**4.** $x^2 - 7x + 12$
5. $x^2 + 7x + 10$	**6.** $x^2 - 2x + 1$	**7.** $x^2 + x - 12$	**8.** $x^2 - 8x + 15$

Tell whether each trinomial can be factored. Justify your answer with a drawing.

9. $x^2 + 3x + 6$	**10.** $x^2 - 5x - 6$	**11.** $x^2 - x - 4$	**12.** $x^2 - 4$

9–12. See Ch. 8 Answer Appendix.

13. WRITING IN MATH How can you use algebra tiles to determine whether a trinomial can be factored?

Additional Answers

1. $(x + 1)(x + 2)$
2. $(x + 2)(x + 4)$
3. $(x - 1)(x + 4)$
4. $(x - 3)(x - 4)$
5. $(x + 2)(x + 5)$
6. $(x - 1)(x - 1)$
7. $(x + 4)(x - 3)$
8. $(x - 3)(x - 5)$

8-3 Quadratic Equations: $x^2 + bx + c = 0$

Then

You multiplied binomials by using the FOIL method. (Lesson 7-7)

Now

- Factor trinomials of the form $x^2 + bx + c$.
- Solve equations of the form $x^2 + bx + c = 0$.

IL Learning Standards

8.A.4b Represent mathematical patterns and describe their properties using variables and mathematical symbols.
8.D.4 Formulate and solve linear and **quadratic equations** and linear inequalities **algebraically** and investigate nonlinear inequalities using graphs, tables, calculators and computers.

New Vocabulary

quadratic equation

IL Math Online

glencoe.com

- Extra Examples
- Personal Tutor
- Self-Check Quiz
- Homework Help

Why?

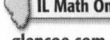

Diana is having a rectangular in-ground swimming pool installed and she wants to include a 24-foot fence around the pool. The pool requires a space of 36 square feet. What dimensions should the pool have?

To solve this problem, the landscape architect needs to find two numbers that have a product of 36 and a sum of 12, half the perimeter of the pool.

Factor $x^2 + bx + c$ In Lesson 7-7, you learned how to multiply two binomials by using the FOIL method. Each of the binomials was a factor of the product. The pattern for multiplying two binomials can be used to factor certain types of trinomials.

$$(x + 3)(x + 4) = x^2 + 4x + 3x + 3 \cdot 4 \quad \text{Use the FOIL method.}$$
$$= x^2 + (4 + 3)x + 3 \cdot 4 \quad \text{Distributive Property}$$
$$= x^2 + 7x + 12 \quad \text{Simplify.}$$

Notice that the coefficient of the middle term, $7x$, is the sum of 3 and 4, and the last term, 12, is the product of 3 and 4.

Observe the following pattern in this multiplication.

$$(x + 3)(x + 4) = x^2 + (4 + 3)x + (3 \cdot 4)$$
$$(x + m)(x + p) = x^2 + (p + m)x + mp \quad \text{Let } 3 = m \text{ and } 4 = p.$$
$$= x^2 + \underbrace{(m + p)x}_{bx} + \underbrace{mp}_{c} \quad \text{Commutative } (+)$$
$$x^2 + bx + c \quad b = m + p \text{ and } c = mp$$

Notice that the coefficient of the middle term is the sum of m and p, and the last term is the product of m and p. This pattern can be used to factor trinomials of the form $x^2 + bx + c$.

Key Concept Factoring $x^2 + bx + c$ — For Your FOLDABLE

Words To factor trinomials in the form $x^2 + bx + c$, find two integers, m and p, with a sum of b and a product of c. Then write $x^2 + bx + c$ as $(x + m)(x + p)$.

Symbols $x^2 + bx + c = (x + m)(x + p)$ when $m + p = b$ and $mp = c$

Example $x^2 + 6x + 8 = (x + 2)(x + 4)$, because $2 + 4 = 6$ and $2 \cdot 4 = 8$.

When c is positive, its factors have the same signs. Both of the factors are positive or negative based upon the sign of b. If b is positive, the factors are positive. If b is negative, the factors are negative.

8-3 Lesson Notes

1 FOCUS

Vertical Alignment

Before Lesson 8-3
Multiply binomials by using the FOIL method.

Lesson 8-3
Factor trinomials of the form $x^2 + bx + c$.
Solve equations of the form $x^2 + bx + c = 0$.

After Lesson 8-3
Factor trinomials into two binomials.

2 TEACH

Scaffolding Questions

Have students read the *Why?* section of the lesson.

Ask:

- Why do you need to find two numbers whose product is 36 to find the dimensions of the pool? The pool is a rectangle, so the area is equal to the length times the width. Since the pool's area is 36 ft^2, the length and width must be two numbers with a product of 36.

(continued on the next page)

Lesson 8-3 Resources

Resource	Approaching-Level	On-Level	Beyond-Level	English Learners
Teacher Edition	• Differentiated Instruction, p. 486	• Differentiated Instruction, pp. 486, 488	• Differentiated Instruction, p. 488	
Chapter Resource Masters	• Study Guide and Intervention, pp. 17–18 • Skills Practice, p. 19 • Practice, p. 20 • Word Problem Practice, p. 21	• Study Guide and Intervention, pp. 17–18 • Skills Practice, p. 19 • Practice, p. 20 • Word Problem Practice, p. 21 • Enrichment, p. 22	• Practice, p. 20 • Word Problem Practice, p. 21 • Enrichment, p. 22	• Study Guide and Intervention, pp. 17–18 • Skills Practice, p. 19 • Practice, p. 20
Transparencies	• 5-Minute Check Transparency 8-3	• 5-Minute Check Transparency 8-3	• 5-Minute Check Transparency 8-3	• 5-Minute Check Transparency 8-3
Other	• Study Notebook	• Study Notebook	• Study Notebook	• Study Notebook

- What two integers have a product of 36? 1 and 36; 2 and 18; 3 and 12; 4 and 9; 6 and 6
- Which pair has a sum of 12? 6 and 6
- What are the dimensions of the pool? 6 ft by 6 ft

Factor $x^2 + bx + c$

Examples 1–3 show how to factor trinomials of the form $x^2 + bx + c$, when b and c are positive, when b is negative and c is positive, and when c is negative.

Formative Assessment

Use the Check Your Progress exercises after each example to determine students' understanding of concepts.

Additional Examples

1 Factor $x^2 + 7x + 12$. $(x + 3)(x + 4)$

2 Factor $x^2 - 12x + 27$. $(x - 3)(x - 9)$

Additional Examples also in Interactive Classroom PowerPoint® Presentations

IWB INTERACTIVE WHITEBOARD READY

Watch Out!

Preventing Errors If students use a graphing calculator to check their factoring, make sure they clear all other functions from the [Y=] list and clear all other drawings from the draw menu. Caution students that while two graphs may appear to coincide in the standard viewing window, they may not. Suggest that students use the [Table] feature to verify identical y-values.

Tips for New Teachers

Calculators Have students change the line type on the graph of the second equation so they can see it as it is graphed on the first graph.

Problem-Solving Tip

Guess and Check When factoring a trinomial, make an educated guess, check for reasonableness, and then adjust the guess until the correct answer is found.

EXAMPLE 1 b and c Are Positive

Factor $x^2 + 9x + 20$.

In this trinomial, $b = 9$ and $c = 20$. Since c is positive and b is positive, you need to find two positive factors with a sum of 9 and a product of 20. Make an organized list of the factors of 20, and look for the pair of factors with a sum of 9.

Factors of 20	Sum of Factors
1, 20	21
2, 10	12
4, 5	9

The correct factors are 4 and 5.

$$x^2 + 9x + 20 = (x + m)(x + p) \quad \text{Write the pattern.}$$
$$= (x + 4)(x + 5) \quad m = 4 \text{ and } p = 5$$

CHECK You can check this result by multiplying the two factors. The product should be equal to the original expression.

$$(x + 4)(x + 5) = x^2 + 5x + 4x + 20 \quad \text{FOIL Method}$$
$$= x^2 + 9x + 20 \checkmark \quad \text{Simplify.}$$

Check Your Progress Factor each polynomial.

1A. $d^2 + 11x + 24$ $(d + 3)(d + 8)$ **1B.** $9 + 10t + t^2$ $(t + 9)(t + 1)$

Personal Tutor glencoe.com

When factoring a trinomial in which b is negative and c is positive, use what you know about the product of binomials to narrow the list of possible factors.

StudyTip

Finding Factors Once the correct factors are found, it is not necessary to test any other factors. In Example 2, −2 and −6 are the correct factors, so −3 and −4 do not need to be tested.

EXAMPLE 2 b Is Negative and c Is Positive

Factor $x^2 - 8x + 12$.

In this trinomial, $b = -8$ and $c = 12$. Since c is positive and b is negative, you need to find two negative factors with a sum of −8 and a product of 12.

Factors of 12	Sum of Factors
−1, −12	−13
−2, −6	−8
−3, −4	−7

The correct factors are −2 and −6.

$$x^2 - 8x + 12 = (x + m)(x + p) \quad \text{Write the pattern.}$$
$$= (x - 2)(x - 6) \quad m = -2 \text{ and } p = -6$$

CHECK Graph $y = x^2 - 8x + 12$ and $y = (x - 2)(x - 6)$ on the same screen. Since only one graph appears, the two graphs must coincide. Therefore, the trinomial has been factored correctly. ✓

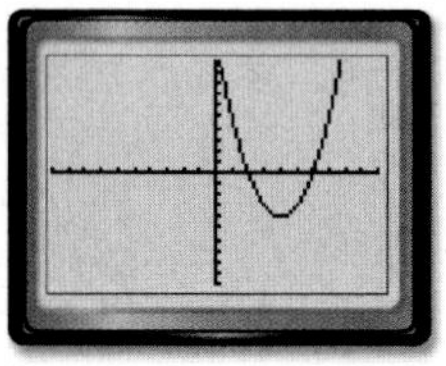

[−10, 10] scl: 1 by [−10, 10] scl: 1

Check Your Progress Factor each polynomial.

2A. $21 - 22m + m^2$ $(m - 1)(m - 21)$ **2B.** $w^2 - 11w + 28$ $(w - 7)(w - 4)$

Personal Tutor glencoe.com

Differentiated Instruction AL OL

If the concept of factoring trinomials seems somewhat abstract to some students,

Then whenever you introduce abstract concepts, it is a good idea to reinforce them with concrete examples. After introducing factoring trinomials, refer students to the lesson-opener problem. Ask students to describe any similarities they notice between finding the dimensions of the pool and factoring a trinomial. Some students may benefit from modeling some problems using algebra tiles. They can then use this method to solve quadratic equations.

486 Chapter 8 Factoring and Quadratic Equations

Review Vocabulary

absolute value the distance a number is from zero on a number line, written $|n|$ (Lesson 0-2)

When c is negative, its factors have opposite signs. To determine which factor is positive and which is negative, look at the sign of b. The factor with the greater absolute value has the same sign as b.

EXAMPLE 3 c is Negative

Factor each polynomial.

a. $x^2 + 2x - 15$

In this trinomial, $b = 2$ and $c = -15$. Since c is negative, the factors m and p have opposite signs. So either m or p is negative, but not both. Since b is positive, the factor with the greater absolute value is also positive.

List the factors of -15, where one factor of each pair is negative. Look for the pair of factors with a sum of 2.

Factors of −15	Sum of Factors
−1, 15	14
−3, 5	2

The correct factors are −3 and 5.

$x^2 + 2x - 15 = (x + m)(x + p)$ **Write the pattern.**

$= (x - 3)(x + 5)$ **$m = -3$ and $p = 5$**

CHECK $(x - 3)(x + 5) = x^2 + 5x - 3x - 15$ **FOIL Method**

$= x^2 + 2x - 15$ ✓ **Simplify.**

b. $x^2 - 7x - 18$

In this trinomial, $b = -7$ and $c = -18$. Either m or p is negative, but not both. Since b is negative, the factor with the greater absolute value is also negative.

List the factors of -18, where one factor of each pair is negative. Look for the pair of factors with a sum of -7.

Factors of −18	Sum of Factors
1, −18	−17
2, −9	−7
3, −6	−3

The correct factors are 2 and −9.

$x^2 - 7x - 18 = (x + m)(x + p)$ **Write the pattern.**

$= (x + 2)(x - 9)$ **$m = 2$ and $p = -9$**

CHECK Graph $y = x^2 - 7x - 18$ and $y = (x + 2)(x - 9)$ on the same screen.

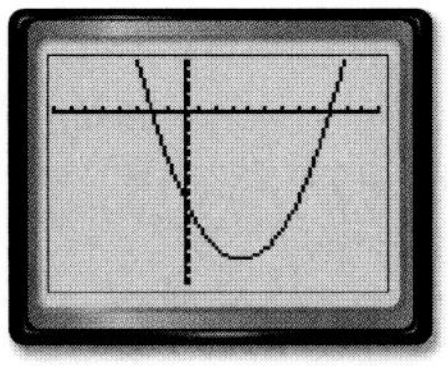

[−10, 15] scl: 1 by [−40, 20] scl: 1

The graphs coincide. Therefore, the trinomial has been factored correctly. ✓

Check Your Progress

3A. $y^2 + 13y - 48$ $(y - 3)(y + 16)$

3B. $r^2 - 2r - 24$ $(r + 4)(r - 6)$

Personal Tutor glencoe.com

Additional Example

3 Factor each polynomial.

a. $x^2 + 3x - 18$
$(x + 6)(x - 3)$

b. $x^2 - x - 20$
$(x - 5)(x + 4)$

Focus on Mathematical Content

Factoring Trinomials A trinomial of the form $x^2 + bx + c$ may or may not be factorable into binomial factors. If the trinomial is factorable, then the factors of c must be two integers, m and p, such that $m + p = b$ and $mp = c$.

TEACH with TECH

WEB PAGE Develop a class Web page about how to factor different types of trinomials. Update the page with information from the most recent lesson, such as notes from class, video clips, and additional resources.

Lesson 8-3 Quadratic Equations: $x^2 + bx + c = 0$ **487**

Solve Equations by Factoring

Example 4 shows how to solve an equation of the form $x^2 + bx + c = 0$ by factoring. **Example 5** shows how to solve a real-world problem by factoring.

Additional Examples

4 Solve $x^2 + 2x = 15$. Check your solutions. $-5, 3$

5 **ARCHITECTURE** Marion wants to build a new art studio that has three times the area of her old studio by increasing the length and width of the old studio by the same amount. What should be the dimensions of the new studio?

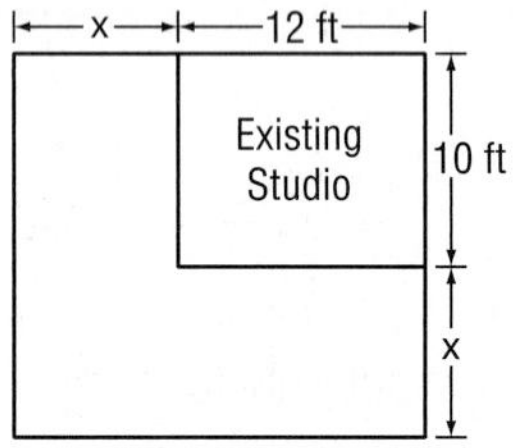

The dimensions of the new studio should be 18 ft by 20 ft.

Watch Out!

Common Errors Students often are not careful when rewriting equations so that one side equals zero. Remind them that they must perform the same operation on both sides of the equation and pay attention to the signs in the resulting equation.

Solve Equations by Factoring A **quadratic equation** can be written in the standard form $ax^2 + bx + c = 0$, where $a \neq 0$. Some equations of the form $x^2 + bx + c = 0$ can be solved by factoring and then using the Zero Product Property.

EXAMPLE 4 Solve an Equation by Factoring

Solve $x^2 + 6x = 27$. Check your solutions.

$x^2 + 6x = 27$	**Original equation**
$x^2 + 6x - 27 = 0$	**Subtract 27 from each side.**
$(x - 3)(x + 9) = 0$	**Factor.**
$x - 3 = 0$ or $x + 9 = 0$	**Zero Product Property**
$x = 3$ $\quad$ $x = -9$	**Solve each equation.**

The roots are 3 and -9.

CHECK Substitute 3 and -9 for x in the original equation.

$$x^2 + 6x = 27 \qquad\qquad x^2 + 6x = 27$$
$$(3)^2 + 6(3) \stackrel{?}{=} 27 \qquad\qquad (-9)^2 + 6(-9) \stackrel{?}{=} 27$$
$$9 + 18 \stackrel{?}{=} 27 \qquad\qquad 81 - 54 \stackrel{?}{=} 27$$
$$27 = 27 \checkmark \qquad\qquad 27 = 27 \checkmark$$

Check Your Progress **Solve each equation. Check your solutions.**

4A. $z^2 - 3z = 70$ $-7, 10$ $\qquad$ **4B.** $x^2 + 3x - 18 = 0$ $3, -6$

Personal Tutor glencoe.com

Factoring can be useful when solving real-world problems.

Real-World Link

A company that produces event signs recommends foamcore boards for event signs that will be used only once. For signs used more than once, use a stronger type of foamcore board.

Source: MegaPrint Inc.

Real-World EXAMPLE 5 Solve a Problem by Factoring

DESIGN Ling is designing a poster. The top of the poster is 4 inches long and the rest of the poster is 2 inches longer than the width. If the poster requires 616 square inches of poster board, find the width w of the poster.

Understand You want to find the width of the poster.

Plan Since the poster is a rectangle, width • length = area.

Solve Let w = the width of the poster.
The length is $w + 2 + 4$ or $w + 6$.

$w(w + 6) = 616$	**Write the equation.**
$w^2 + 6w = 616$	**Multiply.**
$w^2 + 6w - 616 = 0$	**Subtract 616 from each side.**
$(w + 28)(w - 22) = 0$	**Factor.**
$w + 28 = 0$ or $w - 22 = 0$	**Zero Product Property**
$w = -28$ $\quad$ $w = 22$	**Solve each equation.**

Since dimensions cannot be negative, the width is 22 inches.

Check If the width is 22 inches, then the area of the poster is $22 \cdot (22 + 6)$ or 616 square inches, which is the amount the poster requires. ✓

Check Your Progress

5. GEOMETRY The height of a parallelogram is 18 centimeters less than its base. If the area is 175 square centimeters, what is its height? 7 cm

Personal Tutor glencoe.com

Differentiated Instruction

OL BL

Extension Write the trinomials $x^2 + x - 6$ and $x^2 - x - 6$ on the board. Ask students to compare the two trinomials. How are the trinomials related? How are their factors related? The trinomials are the same except for the sign of the middle term. When factored, $x^2 + x - 6$ is $(x + 3)(x - 2)$, while $x^2 - x - 6$ is $(x - 3)(x + 2)$. The factors have opposite signs in the constant term.

Check Your Understanding

Examples 1–3 pp. 486–487

Factor each polynomial.

1. $x^2 + 14x + 24$ **$(x + 2)(x + 12)$**

2. $y^2 - 7y - 30$ **$(y - 10)(y + 3)$**

3. $n^2 + 4n - 21$ **$(n + 7)(n - 3)$**

4. $m^2 - 15m + 50$ **$(m - 5)(m - 10)$**

Example 4 p. 488

Solve each equation. Check your solutions.

5. $x^2 - 4x - 21 = 0$ **$-3, 7$**

6. $n^2 - 3n + 2 = 0$ **1, 2**

7. $x^2 - 15x + 54 = 0$ **6, 9**

8. $x^2 + 12x = -32$ **$-4, -8$**

9. $x^2 - x - 72 = 0$ **$-8, 9$**

10. $x^2 - 10x = -24$ **4, 6**

Example 5 p. 488

11. **FRAMING** Tina bought a frame for a photo, but the photo is too big for the frame. Tina needs to reduce the width and length of the photo by the same amount. The area of the photo should be reduced to half the original area. If the original photo is 12 inches by 16 inches, what will be the dimensions of the smaller photo? **8 in. by 12 in.**

Practice and Problem Solving

= **Step-by-Step Solutions** begin on page R12.
Extra Practice begins on page 815.

Examples 1–3 pp. 486–487

Factor each polynomial.

12. $x^2 + 17x + 42$ **$(x + 3)(x + 14)$**

13. $y^2 - 17y + 72$ **$(y - 9)(y - 8)$**

14. $a^2 + 8a - 48$ **$(a - 4)(a + 12)$**

15. $n^2 - 2n - 35$ **$(n - 7)(n + 5)$**

16. $44 + 15h + h^2$ **$(h + 4)(h + 11)$**

17. $40 - 22x + x^2$ **$(x - 2)(x - 20)$**

18. $-24 - 10x + x^2$ **$(x + 2)(x - 12)$**

19. $-42 - m + m^2$ **$(m + 6)(m - 7)$**

Example 4 p. 488

Solve each equation. Check your solutions.

20. $x^2 - 7x + 12 = 0$ **3, 4**

21. $y^2 + y = 20$ **$4, -5$**

22. $x^2 - 6x = 27$ **$-3, 9$**

23. $a^2 + 11a = -18$ **$-2, -9$**

24. $c^2 + 10c + 9 = 0$ **$-1, -9$**

25. $x^2 - 18x = -32$ **2, 16**

26. $n^2 - 120 = 7n$ **$-8, 15$**

27. $d^2 + 56 = -18d$ **$-4, -14$**

28. $y^2 - 90 = 13y$ **$-5, 18$**

29. $h^2 + 48 = 16h$ **4, 12**

Example 5 p. 488

30. **GEOMETRY** A triangle has an area of 36 square feet. If the height of the triangle is 6 feet more than its base, what are its height and base? **12 ft, 6 ft**

31. **GEOMETRY** A rectangle has an area represented by $x^2 - 4x - 12$ square feet. If the length is $x + 2$ feet, what is the width of the rectangle? **$(x - 6)$ ft**

B

32. **SOCCER** The width of a high school soccer field is 45 yards shorter than its length.

a. Define a variable, and write an expression for the area of the field.

b. The area of the field is 9000 square yards. Find the dimensions. **75 yd by 120 yd**

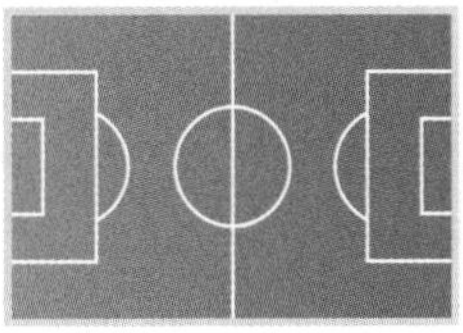

$\ell - 45$

ℓ

32a. Let ℓ = length, A = area of the field, $\ell(\ell - 45) = A$.

Factor each polynomial.

33. $q^2 + 11qr + 18r^2$ **$(q + 2r)(q + 9r)$**

34. $x^2 - 14xy - 51y^2$ **$(x + 3y)(x - 17y)$**

35. $x^2 - 6xy + 5y^2$ **$(x - y)(x - 5y)$**

36. $a^2 + 10ab - 39b^2$ **$(a + 13b)(a - 3b)$**

3 PRACTICE

Formative Assessment

Use Exercises 1-11 to check for understanding.

Use the chart at the bottom of this page to customize assignments for your students.

Watch Out!

Student Misconceptions For Exercises 1–4, students may need to be reminded that the order in which they record the factors does not matter. So, $(x + m)(x + n)$ and $(x + n)(x + m)$ are both correct.

Exercise Alert

Formula For Exercise 30, students will need to know that the formula for the area of a triangle is $A = \frac{1}{2}bh$.

Differentiated Homework Options

Level	Assignment	Two-Day Option	
AL Basic	12–31, 41, 46–47, 49–68	13–31 odd, 50–53	12–30 even, 41, 46–47, 49, 54–68
OL Core	13–31 odd, 32, 33, 35, 37, 39–41, 46–47, 49–68	12–31, 50–53	32–41, 46–47, 49, 54–68
BL Advanced	32–65, (optional: 66–68)		

Study Guide and Intervention
CRM pp. 17–18 AL OL ELL

NAME ______ DATE ______ PERIOD ______

8-3 Study Guide and Intervention

Quadratic Equations: $x^2 + bx + c = 0$

Factor $x^2 + bx + c$ To factor a trinomial of the form $x^2 + bx + c$, find two integers, m and p, whose sum is equal to b and whose product is equal to c.

Factoring $x^2 + bx + c$	$x^2 + bx + c = (x + m)(x + p)$, where $m + p = b$ and $mp = c$.

Example 1 Factor each polynomial.

a. $x^2 + 7x + 10$

In this trinomial, $b = 7$ and $c = 10$.

Factors of 10	Sum of Factors
1, 10	11
2, 5	7

Since $2 + 5 = 7$ and $2 \cdot 5 = 10$, let $m = 2$ and $p = 5$.

$x^2 + 7x + 10 = (x + 5)(x + 2)$

b. $x^2 - 8x + 7$

In this trinomial, $b = -8$ and $c = 7$.

Notice that $m + p$ is negative and mp is positive, so m and p are both negative. Since $-7 + (-1) = -8$ and $(-7)(-1) = 7$, $m = -7$ and $p = -1$.

$x^2 - 8x + 7 = (x - 7)(x - 1)$

Example 2 Factor $x^2 + 6x - 16$.

In this trinomial, $b = 6$ and $c = -16$. This means $m + p$ is positive and mp is negative. Make a list of the factors of -16, where one factor of each pair is positive.

Factors of −16	Sum of Factors
1, −16	−15
−1, 16	15
2, −8	−6
−2, 8	6

Therefore, $m = -2$ and $p = 8$.

$x^2 + 6x - 16 = (x - 2)(x + 8)$

Lesson 8-3

Exercises

Factor each polynomial.

1. $x^2 + 4x + 3$ **(x + 3)(x + 1)**
2. $m^2 + 12m + 32$ **(m + 4)(m + 8)**
3. $r^2 - 3r + 2$ **(r − 2)(r − 1)**
4. $x^2 - x - 6$ **(x − 3)(x + 2)**
5. $x^2 - 4x - 21$ **(x − 7)(x + 3)**
6. $x^2 - 22x + 121$ **(x − 11)(x − 11)**
7. $t^2 - 4t - 12$ **(t + 2)(t − 6)**
8. $p^2 - 16p + 64$ **(p − 8)(p − 8)**
9. $9 - 10x + x^2$ **(9 − x)(1 − x)**
10. $x^2 + 6x + 5$ **(x + 5)(x + 1)**
11. $a^2 + 8a - 9$ **(a − 1)(a + 9)**
12. $y^2 - 7y - 8$ **(y − 8)(y + 1)**
13. $x^2 - 2x - 3$ **(x − 3)(x + 1)**
14. $y^2 + 14y + 13$ **(y + 1)(y + 13)**
15. $m^2 + 9m + 20$ **(m + 4)(m + 5)**
16. $x^2 + 12x + 20$ **(x + 10)(x + 2)**
17. $a^2 - 14a + 24$ **(a − 2)(a − 12)**
18. $18 + 11y + y^2$ **(9 + y)(2 + y)**
19. $x^2 + 2xy + y^2$ **(x + y)(x + y)**
20. $a^2 - 4ab + 4b^2$ **(a − 2b)(a − 2b)**
21. $x^2 + 6xy - 7y^2$ **(x + 7y)(x − y)**

Chapter 8 17 Glencoe Algebra 1

Practice
CRM p. 20 AL OL BL ELL

NAME ______ DATE ______ PERIOD ______

8-3 Practice

Quadratic Equations: $x^2 + bx + c = 0$

Factor each polynomial.

1. $a^2 + 10a + 24$ **(a + 4)(a + 6)**
2. $h^2 + 12h + 27$ **(h + 3)(h + 9)**
3. $x^2 + 14x + 33$ **(x + 11)(x + 3)**
4. $g^2 - 2g - 63$ **(g + 7)(g − 9)**
5. $w^2 + w - 56$ **(w + 8)(w − 7)**
6. $y^2 + 4y - 60$ **(y + 10)(y − 6)**
7. $b^2 + 4b - 32$ **(b − 4)(b + 8)**
8. $n^2 - 3n - 28$ **(n − 7)(n + 4)**
9. $t^2 + 4t - 45$ **(t − 5)(t + 9)**
10. $z^2 - 11z + 30$ **(z − 6)(z − 5)**
11. $d^2 - 16d + 63$ **(d − 9)(d − 7)**
12. $x^2 - 11x + 24$ **(x − 3)(x − 8)**
13. $q^2 - q - 56$ **(q − 8)(q + 7)**
14. $x^2 - 6x - 55$ **(x + 5)(x − 11)**
15. $32 + 18r + r^2$ **(r + 16)(r + 2)**
16. $48 - 16g + g^2$ **(g − 12)(g − 4)**
17. $j^2 - 9jk - 10k^2$ **(j − 10k)(j + k)**
18. $m^2 - mv - 56v^2$ **(m − 8v)(m + 7v)**

Solve each equation. Check the solutions.

19. $x^2 + 17x + 42 = 0$ **{−14, −3}**
20. $p^2 + 5p - 84 = 0$ **{−12, 7}**
21. $k^2 + 3k - 54 = 0$ **{−9, 6}**
22. $b^2 - 12b - 64 = 0$ **{−4, 16}**
23. $n^2 + 4n = 32$ **{−8, 4}**
24. $h^2 - 17h = -60$ **{5, 12}**
25. $t^2 - 26t = 56$ **{−2, 28}**
26. $z^2 - 14z = 72$ **{−4, 18}**
27. $y^2 - 84 = 5y$ **{−7, 12}**
28. $80 + a^2 = 18a$ **{8, 10}**
29. $u^2 = 16u + 36$ **{−2, 18}**
30. $17r + r^2 = -52$ **{−13, −4}**

31. Find all values of k so that the trinomial $x^2 + kx - 35$ can be factored using integers. **−34, −2, 2, 34**

32. **CONSTRUCTION** A construction company is planning to pour concrete for a driveway. The length of the driveway is 16 feet longer than its width w.

a. Write an expression for the area of the driveway. **w(w + 16) ft²**

b. Find the dimensions of the driveway if it has an area of 260 square feet. **10 ft by 26 ft**

32. **WEB DESIGN** Janeel has a 10-inch by 12-inch photograph. She wants to scan the photograph, then reduce the result by the same amount in each dimension to post on her Web site. Janeel wants the area of the image to be one eighth that of the original photograph.

a. Write an equation to represent the area of the reduced image. **(10 − x)(12 − x) = 15, or x² − 22x + 105 = 0**

b. Find the dimensions of the reduced image. **3 in. by 5 in.**

Chapter 8 20 Glencoe Algebra 1

Word Problem Practice
CRM p. 21 AL OL BL ELL

NAME ______ DATE ______ PERIOD ______

8-3 Word Problem Practice

Quadratic Equations: $x^2 + bx + c = 0$

1. **COMPACT DISCS** A standard jewel case for a compact disc has a width 2 cm greater than its length. The area for the front cover is 168 square centimeters. The first two steps to finding the value of x are shown below. Solve the equation and find the length of the case.

$$Length \times width = area$$
$$x(x + 2) = 168$$
$$x^2 + 2x - 168 = 0$$

−14 or 12; 12 cm

2. **MATH GAMES** Fiona and Greg play a number guessing game. Greg gives Fiona this hint about his two secret numbers, "The product of the two consecutive positive integers that I am thinking of is 11 more than their sum." What are Greg's numbers? **4 and 5**

3. **BRIDGE ENGINEERING** A car driving over a suspension bridge is supported by a cable hanging between the ends of the bridge. Since its shape is parabolic, it can be modeled by a quadratic equation. The height above the road bed of a bridge's cable h (in inches) measured at distance d (in yards) from the first tower is given by the equation $h = d^2 - 36d + 324$.

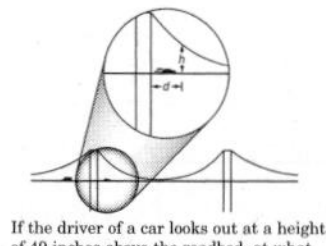

If the driver of a car looks out at a height of 49 inches above the roadbed, at what distance(s) from the tower will the driver's eyes be at the same height as the cable? **at 11 and 25 yds from the first tower**

4. **PHYSICAL SCIENCE** The boiling point of water depends on altitude. The following equation approximates the number of degrees D below 212°F at which water will boil at altitude h.

$$D^2 + 520D = H$$

In Denver, Colorado, the altitude is approximately 5300 feet above sea level. At approximately what temperature does water boil in Denver? **D = 10° drop. The boiling point is about 202°F.**

5. **MONUMENTS** Susan is designing a pyramidal stone monument for a local park. The design specifications tell her that the height needs to be 9 feet, the width of the base must be 5 feet less than the length, and the volume should be 150 cubic feet. Recall that the volume of a pyramid is given by $V = \frac{1}{3}Bh$, where B is the area of the base and h is the height.

a. Write and solve an equation to find the width of the base of the monument. **$150 = \frac{1}{3}w(w + 5) \cdot 9$ or $3w^2 + 15w - 150 = 0$; $w = \{5, -10\}$**

b. Interpret each answer in terms of the situation. **w = 5: the width of the pyramid is 5 feet; w = −10: negative length doesn't make sense in the situation.**

Lesson 8-3

Chapter 8 21 Glencoe Algebra 1

Real-World Link

Australian Libby Trickett has set the world record three times for the 100 meter freestyle event. In the 2008 Beijing Olympics, she won the silver medal for the event.

Source: *Fox Sports*

37. **SWIMMING** The length of a rectangular swimming pool is 20 feet greater than its width. The area of the pool is 525 square feet.

a. Define a variable and write an equation for the area of the pool. **Sample answer: Let w = width; (w + 20)w = 525.**

b. Solve the equation. **−35, 15**

c. Interpret the solutions. Do both solutions make sense? Explain.

37c. The solution of 15 means that the width is 15 ft. The solution −35 does not make sense because length cannot be negative.

GEOMETRY Find an expression for the perimeter of a rectangle with the given area.

38. $A = x^2 + 24x - 81$ **4x + 48**

39. $A = x^2 + 13x - 90$ **4x + 26**

40. **MULTIPLE REPRESENTATIONS** In this problem, you will explore factoring when the leading coefficient is not 1.

a. **TABULAR** Copy and complete the table below. **See margin.**

Product of Two Binomials	$ax^2 + mx + px + c$	$ax^2 + bx + c$	$m \times p$	$a \times c$
$(2x + 3)(x + 4)$	$2x^2 + 8x + 3x + 12$	$2x^2 + 11x + 12$	24	24
$(x + 1)(3x + 5)$	**$3x^2 + 5x + 3x + 5$**	**$3x^2 + 8x + 5$**	**15**	**15**
$(2x - 1)(4x + 1)$	**$8x^2 + 2x - 4x - 1$**	**$8x^2 - 2x - 1$**	**−8**	**−8**
$(3x + 5)(4x - 2)$	**$12x^2 - 6x + 20x - 10$**	**$12x^2 + 14x - 10$**	**−120**	**−120**

b. **ANALYTICAL** How are m and p related to a and c? **mp = ac**

c. **ANALYTICAL** How are m and p related to b? **m + p = b**

d. **VERBAL** Describe a process you can use for factoring a polynomial of the form $ax^2 + bx + c$. **Look for two integers, m and p, for which mp = ac and m + p = b.**

H.O.T. Problems
Use Higher-Order Thinking Skills

41. **FIND THE ERROR** Jerome and Charles have factored $x^2 + 6x - 16$. Is either of them correct? Explain your reasoning.

Jerome	Charles
$x^2 + 6x - 16 = (x + 2)(x - 8)$	$x^2 + 6x - 16 = (x - 2)(x + 8)$

41. Charles; Jerome's answer once multiplied is x² − 6x − 16. The middle term should be positive.

CHALLENGE Find all values of k so that each polynomial can be factored using integers.

42. $x^2 + kx - 19$ **−18, 18**

43. $x^2 + kx + 14$ **−15, −9, 9, 15**

44. $x^2 - 8x + k, k > 0$ **7, 12, 15, 16**

45. $x^2 - 5x + k, k > 0$ **4, 6**

46. **REASONING** For any factorable trinomial, $x^2 + bx + c$, will the absolute value of b *sometimes*, *always*, or *never* be less than the absolute value of c? Explain. **See margin.**

47. **OPEN ENDED** Give an example of a trinomial that can be factored using the factoring techniques presented in this lesson. Then factor the trinomial. **x² + 19x − 20; (x − 1)(x + 20)**

48. **CHALLENGE** Factor $(4y - 5)^2 + 3(4y - 5) - 70$.

48. (4y − 5)² + 3(4y − 5) − 70 = [(4y − 5) + 10] • [(4y − 5) − 7] = (4y + 5)(4y − 12) = 4(4y + 5)(y − 3)

49. **WRITING IN MATH** Explain how to factor trinomials of the form $x^2 + bx + c$ and how to determine the signs of the factors of c. **See margin.**

Enrichment
CRM p. 22 OL BL

NAME ______ DATE ______ PERIOD ______

8-3 Enrichment

Puzzling Primes

A prime number has only two factors, itself and 1. The number 6 is not prime because it has 2 and 3 as factors; 5 and 7 are prime. The number 1 is not considered to be prime.

1. Use a calculator to help you find the 25 prime numbers less than 100. **2, 3, 5, 7, 11, 13, 17, 19, 23, 29, 31, 37 41, 43, 47, 53, 59, 61, 67, 71, 73, 79, 83, 89, 97**

Prime numbers have interested mathematicians for centuries. They have tried to find expressions that will give all the prime numbers, or only prime numbers. In the 1700s, Euler discovered that the trinomial $x^2 + x + 41$ will yield prime numbers for values of x from 0 through 39.

2. Find the prime numbers generated by Euler's formula for x from 0 through 7. **41, 43, 47, 53, 61, 71, 83, 97**

Multiple Representations In Exercise 40, students use information organized in a table and algebra to factor polynomials.

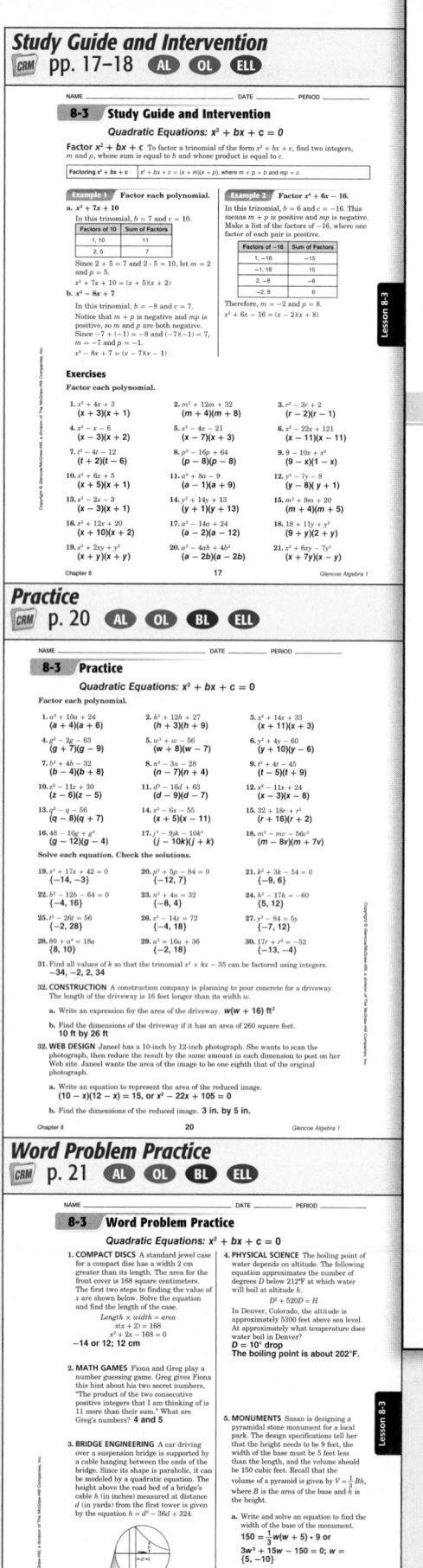

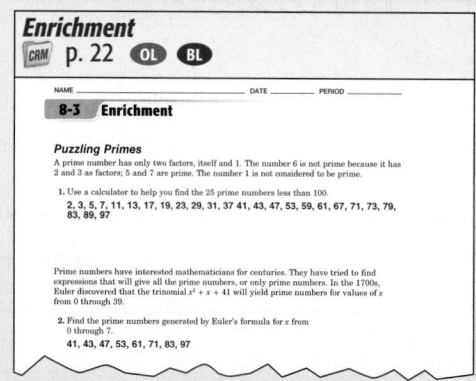

PSAE PRACTICE 8.11.12, 9.11.07, 8.11.02

50. Which inequality is shown in the graph below? **C**

A $y \leq -\frac{3}{4}x + 3$

B $y < -\frac{3}{4}x + 3$

C $y > -\frac{3}{4}x + 3$

D $y \geq -\frac{3}{4}x + 3$

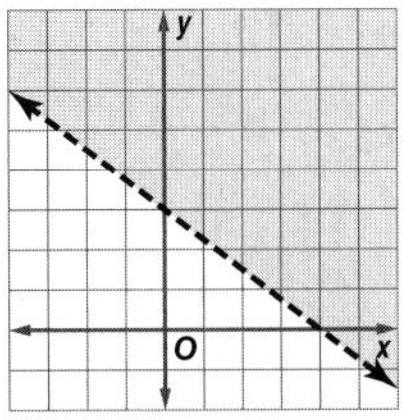

51. SHORT RESPONSE Olivia must earn more than \$254 from selling candy bars in order to go on a trip with the National Honor Society. If each candy bar is sold for \$1.25, what is the fewest candy bars she must sell? **204**

52. GEOMETRY Which expression represents the length of the rectangle? **H**

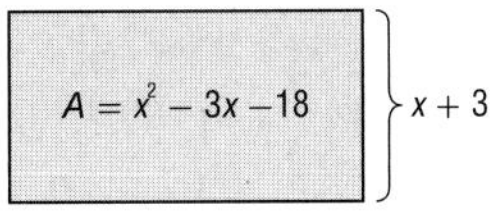

F $x + 5$

G $x + 6$

H $x - 6$

J $x - 5$

53. The difference of 21 and a number n is 6. Which equation shows the relationship? **A**

A $21 - n = 6$ C $21n = 6$

B $21 + n = 6$ D $6n = -21$

Spiral Review

Factor each polynomial. (Lesson 8-2) **56.** $2mp(m^2p - 8p + 4)$

54. $10a^2 + 40a$ **$10a(a + 4)$**

55. $11x + 44x^2y$ **$11x(1 + 4xy)$**

56. $2m^3p^2 - 16mp^2 + 8mp$

57. $2ax + 6xc + ba + 3bc$ **$(2x + b)(a + 3c)$**

58. $8ac - 2ad + 4bc - bd$ **$(2a + b)(4c - d)$**

59. $x^2 - xy - xy + y^2$ **$(x - y)(x - y)$**

60. FLOORING Emma is replacing her dining room floor, which is 10 feet by 12 feet. The flooring comes in pieces 1 foot by 1 foot, 2 foot by 2 foot, 3 foot by 3 foot, and 2 foot by 3 foot. Without cutting the pieces, which of the four sizes of flooring can Emma use? Explain. (Lesson 8-1) **1 by 1, 2 by 2, and 2 by 3; The 3-foot squares will not cover the 10-foot dimension without cutting.**

Perform the indicated matrix operations. If an operation cannot be performed, write *impossible*. (Lesson 6-6)

61. $\begin{bmatrix} 10 & 0 & 8 \\ 2 & -5 & -7 \end{bmatrix} + \begin{bmatrix} 2 & -9 & 4 \\ -1 & 2 & -3 \end{bmatrix}$ **$\begin{bmatrix} 12 & -9 & 12 \\ 1 & -3 & -10 \end{bmatrix}$**

62. $\begin{bmatrix} 7 & 3 & 1 \\ 9 & -2 & -4 \\ 4 & -8 & 7 \end{bmatrix} - \begin{bmatrix} -7 & 4 & 2 \\ 6 & 3 & -3 \\ 11 & -16 & 5 \end{bmatrix}$ **$\begin{bmatrix} 14 & -1 & -1 \\ 3 & -5 & -1 \\ -7 & 8 & 2 \end{bmatrix}$**

63. $\begin{bmatrix} 25 \\ -8 \\ -23 \end{bmatrix} + \begin{bmatrix} -9 & 21 & -2 & 7 \end{bmatrix}$ **impossible**

64. $3\begin{bmatrix} -5 & 3 \\ 4 & 0 \\ -1 & 8 \end{bmatrix}$ **$\begin{bmatrix} -15 & 9 \\ 12 & 0 \\ -3 & 24 \end{bmatrix}$**

65. LANDSCAPING Kendrick is planning a circular flower garden with a low fence around the border. He has 38 feet of fence. What is the radius of the largest garden he can make? (*Hint:* $C = 2\pi r$) (Lesson 5-2) **about 6 ft**

Skills Review

Factor each polynomial. (Lesson 8-2) **66.** $(2m + r)(3x - 2)$ **67.** $(3x - 4)(a - 2b)$ **68.** $2(d^2 + f)(g + 2h)$

66. $6mx - 4m + 3rx - 2r$

67. $3ax - 6bx + 8b - 4a$

68. $2d^2g + 2fg + 4d^2h + 4fh$

Watch Out!

Find the Error For Exercise 41, remind students that they can check the correctness of the factors by multiplying them to see if the result is the original polynomial. They could also use their graphing calculators for the procedure in Example 2.

4 ASSESS

Crystal Ball Tell students that the next lesson they will study is titled *Quadratic Equations*: $ax^2 + bx + c = 0$. Ask them to write how they think what they learned today will connect with the next lesson.

Formative Assessment

Check for student understanding of concepts in Lesson 8-3.

CRM Quiz 2, p. 45

Additional Answers

46. Sometimes; Sample answer: The trinomial $x^2 + 10x + 9 = (x + 1)(x + 9)$ and $10 > 9$. The trinomial $x^2 + 7x + 10 = (x + 2)(x + 5)$ and $7 < 10$.

49. Sample answer: Find factors m and n such that $m + n = b$ and $mn = c$. If b and c are positive, then m and n are positive. If b is negative and c is positive, then m and n are negative. When c is negative, m and n have different signs and the factor with the greatest absolute value has the same sign as b.

CHAPTER 8 Mid-Chapter Quiz

Formative Assessment

Use the Mid-Chapter Quiz to assess students' progress in the first half of the chapter.

For problems answered incorrectly, have students review the lessons indicated in parentheses.

ExamView Assessment Suite — Customize and create multiple versions of your Mid-Chapter Quiz and their answer keys.

FOLDABLES Follow-Up

Before students complete the Mid-Chapter Quiz, encourage them to review the information for Lessons 8-1 through 8-3 in their Foldables.

Additional Answer

9. 2 shelves of 12 pairs, 3 shelves of 8 pairs, 4 shelves of 6 pairs, 6 shelves of 4 pairs

CHAPTER 8 Mid-Chapter Quiz

Lessons 8-1 through 8-3

IL Learning Standards: 8.B.4a, 8.D.4

Factor each monomial completely. (Lesson 8-1)

1. $16x^3y^2$ **$2 \cdot 2 \cdot 2 \cdot 2 \cdot x \cdot x \cdot x \cdot y \cdot y$**
2. $35ab^4$ **$5 \cdot 7 \cdot a \cdot b \cdot b \cdot b \cdot b$**
3. $-20m^5n^2$ **$-1 \cdot 2 \cdot 2 \cdot 5 \cdot m \cdot m \cdot m \cdot m \cdot m \cdot n \cdot n$**
4. $-13xy^3$ **$-1 \cdot 13 \cdot x \cdot y \cdot y \cdot y$**
5. **ROOM DESIGN** The area of a rectangular room is 120 square feet. What are the possible whole-number dimensions for the length and width of the room? (Lesson 8-1) **1×120, 2×60, 3×40, 4×30, 5×24, 6×20, 8×15, 10×12**

Find the GCF of each set of monomials. (Lesson 8-1)

6. $10a, 20a^2, 25a$ **$5a$**
7. $13c, 25d$ **1**
8. $21ab, 35a, 56ab^3$ **$7a$**
9. **FASHION** A sales clerk is organizing 24 pairs of shoes for a sales display. In what ways can she organize the shoes so that she has the same number of shoes on each shelf, at least 4 pairs of shoes per shelf, and at least 2 shelves of shoes? **See margin.**

Use the Distributive Property to factor each polynomial. (Lesson 8-2)

10. $3xy - 9x$ **$3x(y - 3)$**
11. $6ab + 12ab^2 + 18b$ **$6b(a + 2ab + 3)$**
12. **MULTIPLE CHOICE** The area of the rectangle is $3x^2 + 6x - 12$ square units. What is the width of the rectangle? (Lesson 8-2) **B**

$x^2 + 2x - 4$

A 2 units

B 3 units

C 4 units

D 6 units

Factor each polynomial. (Lesson 8-2)

13. $5h + 40g$ **$5(h + 8g)$**
14. $3x^2 + 6x + x + 2$ **$(3x + 1)(x + 2)$**
15. $5a^2 - 25a - a + 5$ **$(5a - 1)(a - 5)$**

Solve each equation. Check your solutions. (Lesson 8-2)

16. $2x(x - 5) = 0$ **0, 5**
17. $6p^2 - 3p = 0$ **$0, \frac{1}{2}$**
18. $a^2 = 15a$ **0, 15**
19. **ARCHITECTURE** The curve of the archway under a bridge can be modeled by the equation $y = -\frac{1}{5}x^2 + 6x$, where x and y are measured in feet. Copy and complete the table for each value of x. (Lesson 8-2)

x	y
0	**0**
10	**40**
15	**45**
20	**40**
30	**0**

Factor each polynomial. (Lesson 8-3)

20. $x^2 - 4x - 21$ **$(x - 7)(x + 3)$**
21. $x^2 - 10x + 24$ **$(x - 6)(x - 4)$**
22. $x^2 + 4x - 21$ **$(x + 7)(x - 3)$**

Solve each equation. Check your solutions. (Lesson 8-3)

23. $x^2 - 5x = 14$ **$-2, 7$**
24. $x^2 - 3x - 18 = 0$ **$-3, 6$**
25. $24 + x^2 = 10x$ **4, 6**
26. **MULTIPLE CHOICE** A rectangle has a length that is 2 inches longer than its width. The area of the rectangle is 48 square inches. What is the length of the rectangle? (Lesson 8-3) **G**

F 48 in.

G 8 in.

H 6 in.

J 2 in.

Intervention Planner

Tier 1 — On Level

If students miss about 25% of the exercises or less,

Then choose a resource:

- **SE** Lessons 8-1, 8–2, and 8–3
- **CRM** Skills Practice, pp. 7, 13, and 19
- **TE** Chapter Project, p. 468

IL Math Online Self-Check Quiz

Tier 2 — Strategic Intervention approaching grade level

If students miss about 50% of the exercises,

Then choose a resource:

- **CRM** Study Guide and Intervention, Chapter 8, p. 5, 11, and 17

Quick Review Math Handbook

IL Math Online Extra Examples, Personal Tutor, Homework Help

Tier 3 — Intensive Intervention 2 or more grades below level

If students miss about 75% of the exercises,

Then use *Math Triumphs, Alg. 1*

IL Math Online Extra Examples, Personal Tutor, Homework Help, Review Vocabulary

8-4 Quadratic Equations: $ax^2 + bx + c = 0$

Then

You factored trinomials of the form $x^2 + bx + c$. (Lesson 8-3)

Now

- Factor trinomials of the form $ax^2 + bx + c$.
- Solve equations of the form $ax^2 + bx + c = 0$.

IL Learning Standards

8.A.4b Represent mathematical patterns and describe their properties using variables and mathematical symbols.
8.D.4 Formulate and solve linear and **quadratic equations** and linear inequalities **algebraically** and investigate nonlinear inequalities using graphs, tables, calculators and computers. *Also addresses 7.B.4.*

New Vocabulary

prime polynomial

IL Math Online

glencoe.com

- Extra Examples
- Personal Tutor
- Self-Check Quiz
- Homework Help

Why?

At amusement parks around the country, the paths of riders can be modeled by the expression $16t^2 - 5t + 120$.

Factoring this expression can help the ride operators determine how long a rider rides on the initial swing.

Factor $ax^2 + bx + c$ In the last lesson, you factored quadratic expressions of the form $ax^2 + bx + c$, where $a = 1$. In this lesson, you will apply the factoring methods to quadratic expressions in which a is not 1.

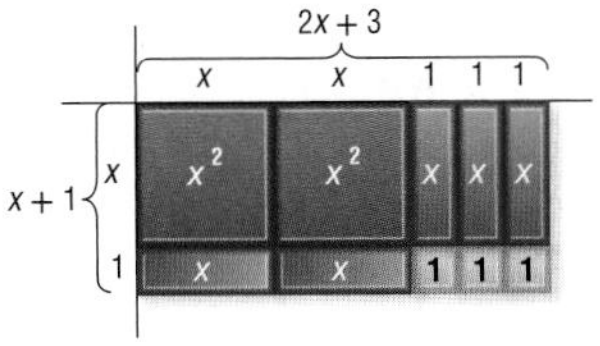

The dimensions of the rectangle formed by the algebra tiles are the factors of $2x^2 + 5x + 3$. The factors of $2x^2 + 5x + 3$ are $x + 1$ and $2x + 3$.

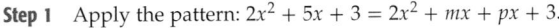

You can also use the method of factoring by grouping to solve this expression.

Step 1 Apply the pattern: $2x^2 + 5x + 3 = 2x^2 + mx + px + 3$.

Step 2 Find two numbers that have a product of $2 \cdot 3$ or 6 and a sum of 5.

Factors of 6	Sum of Factors
1, 6	7
2, 3	5

Step 3 Use grouping to find the factors.

$2x^2 + 5x + 3 = 2x^2 + mx + px + 3$ — **Write the pattern.**
$= 2x^2 + 2x + 3x + 3$ — **$m = 2$ and $p = 3$**
$= (2x^2 + 2x) + (3x + 3)$ — **Group terms with common factors.**
$= 2x(x + 1) + 3(x + 1)$ — **Factor the GCF.**
$= (2x + 3)(x + 1)$ — **$x + 1$ is the common factor.**

Therefore, $2x^2 + 5x + 3 = (2x + 3)(x + 1)$.

Key Concept — Factoring $ax^2 + bx + c$ — *For Your FOLDABLE*

Words To factor trinomials of the form $ax^2 + bx + c$, find two integers, m and p, with a sum of b and a product of ac. Then write $ax^2 + bx + c$ as $ax^2 + mx + px + c$, and factor by grouping.

Example $5x^2 - 13x + 6 = 5x^2 - 10x - 3x + 6$ — $m = -10$ and $p = -3$
$= 5x(x - 2) + (-3)(x - 2)$
$= (5x - 3)(x - 2)$

8-4 Lesson Notes

1 FOCUS

Vertical Alignment

Before Lesson 8-4
Factor trinomials of the form $x^2 + bx + c$.

Lesson 8-4
Factor trinomials of the form $ax^2 + bx + c$.
Solve equations of the form $ax^2 + bx + c = 0$.

After Lesson 8-4
Factor binomials that are the difference of squares.

2 TEACH

Scaffolding Questions

Have students read the *Why?* section of the lesson.

Ask:

- How is the trinomial $16t^2 - 5t + 120$ different from those you learned how to factor in Lesson 8-3? The coefficient of the t^2 term of the trinomial is an integer greater than 1, while the coefficients of the x^2 terms of the trinomials in Lesson 8-3 were always 1.
- What trinomial does the product of $(3x + 1)(2x + 5)$ give? $6x^2 + 17x + 5$

(continued on the next page)

Lesson 8-4 Resources

Resource	Approaching-Level	On-Level	Beyond-Level	English Learners
Teacher Edition	• Differentiated Instruction, p. 494	• Differentiated Instruction, p. 498	• Differentiated Instruction, p. 498	
Chapter Resource Masters	• Study Guide and Intervention, pp. 23–24 • Skills Practice, p. 25 • Practice, p. 26 • Word Problem Practice, p. 27 • Graphing Calculator Activity, p. 29	• Study Guide and Intervention, pp. 23–24 • Skills Practice, p. 25 • Practice, p. 26 • Word Problem Practice, p. 27 • Enrichment, p. 28 • Graphing Calculator Activity, p. 29	• Practice, p. 26 • Word Problem Practice, p. 27 • Enrichment, p. 28 • Graphing Calculator Activity, p. 29	• Study Guide and Intervention, pp. 23–24 • Skills Practice, p. 25 • Practice, p. 26 • Graphing Calculator Activity, p. 29
Transparencies	• 5-Minute Check Transparency 8-4	• 5-Minute Check Transparency 8-4	• 5-Minute Check Transparency 8-4	• 5-Minute Check Transparency 8-4
Other	• Study Notebook • Teaching Algebra with Manipulatives	• Study Notebook • Teaching Algebra with Manipulatives	• Study Notebook	• Study Notebook • Teaching Algebra with Manipulatives

- How does the coefficient of the x^2 term relate to the coefficients of the x term in each factor? The coefficient of the x^2 term equals their product. $3 \times 2 = 6$

Factor $ax^2 + bx + c$

Example 1 shows how to factor a trinomial of the form $ax^2 + bx + c$. **Example 2** shows how to factor a trinomial of the form $ax^2 - bx + c$. **Example 3** shows how to determine whether a polynomial is prime.

Formative Assessment

Use the Check Your Progress exercises after each example to determine students' understanding of concepts.

Additional Examples

1 Factor each trinomial.

a. $5x^2 + 27x + 10$
$(5x + 2)(x + 5)$

b. $4x^2 + 24x + 32$
$4(x + 2)(x + 4)$

2 Factor $24x^2 - 22x + 3$.
$(4x - 3)(6x - 1)$

Additional Examples also in Interactive Classroom PowerPoint® Presentations

IWB INTERACTIVE WHITEBOARD READY

Watch Out!

Preventing Errors Many students forget to include the GCF that they factored from the trinomial. Remind students to put the GCF in front of the other two factors.

StudyTip

Greatest Common Factor Always look for a GCF of the terms of a polynomial before you factor.

EXAMPLE 1 Factor $ax^2 + bx + c$

Factor each trinomial.

a. $7x^2 + 29x + 4$

In this trinomial, $a = 7$, $b = 29$, and $c = 4$. You need to find two numbers with a sum of 29 and a product of $7 \cdot 4$ or 28. Make a list of the factors of 28 and look for the pair of factors with the sum of 29.

Factors of 28	Sum of Factors
1, 28	29

The correct factors are 1 and 28.

$7x^2 + 29x + 4 = 7x^2 + mx + px + 4$ — **Write the pattern.**
$= 7x^2 + 1x + 28x + 4$ — **$m = 1$ and $p = 28$**
$= (7x^2 + 1x) + (28x + 4)$ — **Group terms with common factors.**
$= x(7x + 1) + 4(7x + 1)$ — **Factor the GCF.**
$= (x + 4)(7x + 1)$ — **$7x + 1$ is the common factor.**

b. $3x^2 + 15x + 18$

The GCF of the terms $3x^2$, $15x$, and 18 is 3. Factor this first.

$3x^2 + 15x + 18 = 3(x^2 + 5x + 6)$ — **Distributive Property**
$= 3(x + 3)(x + 2)$ — **Find two factors of 6 with a sum of 5.**

Check Your Progress

1A. $5x^2 + 13x + 6$ $(5x + 3)(x + 2)$ **1B.** $6x^2 + 22x - 8$ $2(3x - 1)(x + 4)$

Personal Tutor glencoe.com

Sometimes the coefficient of the x-term is negative.

EXAMPLE 2 Factor $ax^2 - bx + c$

Factor $3x^2 - 17x + 20$.

In this trinomial, $a = 3$, $b = -17$, and $c = 20$. Since b is negative, $m + p$ will be negative. Since c is positive, mp will be positive.

To determine m and p, list the negative factors of ac or 60. The sum of m and p should be -17.

Factors of 60	Sum of Factors
−2, −30	−32
−3, −20	−23
−4, −15	−19
−5, −12	−17

The correct factors are −5 and −12.

$3x^2 - 17x + 20 = 3x^2 - 12x - 5x + 20$ — **$m = -12$ and $p = -5$**
$= (3x^2 - 12x) + (-5x + 20)$ — **Group terms with common factors.**
$= 3x(x - 4) + (-5)(x - 4)$ — **Factor the GCF.**
$= (3x - 5)(x - 4)$ — **Distributive Property**

Check Your Progress

2A. $2n^2 - n - 1$ $(n - 1)(2n + 1)$ **2B.** $10y^2 - 35y + 30$ $5(2y - 3)(y - 2)$

Personal Tutor glencoe.com

Differentiated Instruction AL

If some students have trouble factoring polynomials,

Then place students in groups to factor polynomials such as those in Example 1. Depending on the number of factors and number of students in each group, have each student find one or two factors for mn. By dividing the labor, students should be able to find the factors for mn that sum to $m + n$ quickly. Once they have found the factors, have students complete the factoring as a group.

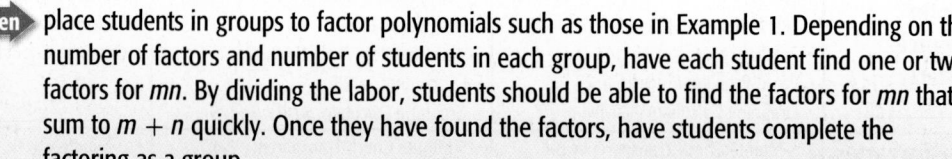

A polynomial that cannot be written as a product of two polynomials with integral coefficients is called a **prime polynomial**.

EXAMPLE 3 Determine Whether a Polynomial is Prime

Factor $4x^2 - 3x + 5$, if possible. If the polynomial cannot be factored using integers, write *prime*.

In this trinomial, $a = 4$, $b = -3$, and $c = 5$. Since b is negative, $m + p$ is negative. Since c is positive, mp is positive. So, m and p are both negative. Next, list the factors of 20. Look for the pair with a sum of -3.

Factors of 20	Sum of Factors
$-20, -1$	-21
$-4, -5$	-9
$-2, -10$	-12

There are no factors with a sum of -3. So the quadratic expression cannot be factored using integers. Therefore, $4x^2 - 3x + 5$ is prime.

Check Your Progress

Factor each polynomial, if possible. If the polynomial cannot be factored using integers, write *prime*.

3A. $4r^2 - r + 7$ prime

3B. $2x^2 + 3x - 5$ $(2x + 5)(x - 1)$

Personal Tutor glencoe.com

Real-World Link

Cheetahs are the fastest land animals in the world, reaching speeds of up to 70 mph. It can accelerate from 0 to 40 mph in 3 strides. It takes just seconds for the cheetah to reach the full speed of 70 mph.

Source: Cheetah Conservation Fund

Solve Equations by Factoring A model for the height of a projectile is given by $h = -16t^2 + vt + h_0$, where h is the height in feet, t is the time in seconds, v is the initial velocity in feet per second, and h_0 is the initial height in feet. Equations of the form $ax^2 + bx + c = 0$ can be solved by factoring and by using the Zero Product Property.

Real-World EXAMPLE 4 Solve Equations by Factoring

WILDLIFE **Suppose a cheetah pouncing on an antelope leaps with an initial velocity of 49 feet per second. How long is the cheetah in the air if it lands on the antelope's hind quarter, 3 feet from the ground?**

$h = -16t^2 + vt + h_0$	Equation for height
$3 = -16t^2 + 49t + 0$	$h = 3$, $v = 49$, and $s = 0$
$0 = -16t^2 + 49t - 3$	Subtract 3 from each side.
$0 = 16t^2 - 49t + 3$	Multiply each side by -1.
$0 = (16t - 1)(t - 3)$	Factor $16t^2 - 49t + 3$.
$16t - 1 = 0$ or $t - 3 = 0$	Zero Product Property
$16t = 1$ $\quad t = 3$	Solve each equation.
$t = \frac{1}{16}$	

The solutions are $\frac{1}{16}$ and 3 seconds. It takes the cheetah $\frac{1}{16}$ second to reach a height of 3 feet on his way up. It takes the cheetah 3 seconds to reach a height of 3 feet on his way down. So, the cheetah is in the air 3 seconds before he catches the antelope.

Check Your Progress

4. PHYSICAL SCIENCE A person throws a ball upward from a 506-foot tall building. The ball's height h in feet after t seconds is given by the equation $h = -16t^2 + 48t + 506$. The ball lands on a balcony that is 218 feet above the ground. How many seconds was it in the air? 6 s

Personal Tutor glencoe.com

Watch Out!

Keep the −1 Do not forget to carry the −1 that was factored out through the rest of the steps or multiply both sides by −1.

Watch Out!

Preventing Errors Make sure students list all possible factors of mn, including both positive and negative factors, before they decide the polynomial is prime.

Additional Example

3 Factor $3x^2 + 7x - 5$. If the polynomial cannot be factored using integers, write *prime*. prime

Solve Equations by Factoring

Example 4 shows how to solve a real-world problem by writing an equation of the form $ax^2 + bx + c = 0$ and then solving it.

Additional Example

4 **MODEL ROCKETS** Mr. Nguyen's science class built a model rocket. They launched the rocket outside. It cleared the top of a 60-foot high pole and then landed in a nearby tree. If the launch pad was 2 feet above the ground, the initial velocity of the rocket was 64 feet per second, and the rocket landed 30 feet above the ground, how long was the rocket in flight? Use the equation $h = -16t^2 + vt + h_0$. about 3.5 seconds

Focus on Mathematical Content

Factoring $ax^2 + bx + c$ To factor trinomials by grouping where x^2 has a coefficient other than 1, express the trinomial as four terms, $ax^2 + mx + nx + c$, where $m + n = b$ and $mn = ac$. Make a table of possible factors for mn and the sum of these factors for b. Replace a, m, n, and c with their values. Group terms with common factors. Factor out the GCF from each grouping, then factor using the Distributive Property.

TEACH with TECH

INTERACTIVE WHITEBOARD Create a template that shows the multiplication of two binomials, such as $(\square \pm \square)(\square \pm \square)$. Demonstrate finding the factors of a quadratic expression. Drag each factor into the spaces until the correct one is found.

3 PRACTICE

Formative Assessment

Use Exercises 1–9 to check for understanding.

Use the chart at the bottom of this page to customize assignments for your students.

Exercise Alert

Scissors For Exercise 39, students will need a pair of scissors.

Multiple Representations In Exercise 39, students use a concrete model and algebraic reasoning to represent the difference of two squares.

Additional Answers

41. $(12x + 20y)$ in.; The area of the square equals $(3x + 5y) \cdot (3x + 5y)$ in^2, so the length of one side is $(3x + 5y)$ in. The perimeter is $4(3x + 5y)$ or $(12x + 20y)$ in.

43. Sample answer: $10x^2 + x - 3 = 0$; The polynomial factors into $(2x - 1)(5x + 3) = 0$, so the solutions are $\frac{1}{2}$ and $-\frac{3}{5}$.

Check Your Understanding

Examples 1–3 pp. 494–495

Factor each polynomial, if possible. If the polynomial cannot be factored using integers, write *prime*.

1. $3x^2 + 17x + 10$ **$(3x + 2)(x + 5)$**

2. $2x^2 + 22x + 56$ **$2(x + 4)(x + 7)$**

3. $5x^2 - 3x + 4$ **prime**

4. $3x^2 - 11x - 20$ **$(3x + 4)(x - 5)$**

Example 4 p. 495

Solve each equation. Check your solutions.

5. $2x^2 + 9x + 9 = 0$ **$-\frac{3}{2}, -3$**

6. $3x^2 + 17x + 20 = 0$ **$-\frac{5}{3}, -4$**

7. $3x^2 - 10x + 8 = 0$ **$\frac{4}{3}, 2$**

8. $2x^2 - 17x + 30 = 0$ **$\frac{5}{2}, 6$**

9. DISCUS Ken throws the discus at a school meet.

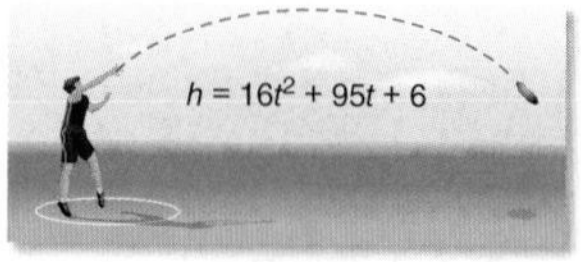

a. What is the initial height of the discus? **6 ft**

b. After how many seconds does the discus hit the ground? **6 seconds**

Practice and Problem Solving

● = **Step-by-Step Solutions** begin on page R12.
Extra Practice begins on page 815.

Examples 1–3 pp. 494–495

10. $(5x + 4)(x + 6)$
11. $(2x + 3)(x + 8)$
12. $2(2x + 1)(x + 5)$
13. $2(2x + 5)(x + 7)$
14. $(2x + 3)(x - 3)$
15. $(4x - 5)(x - 2)$

Factor each polynomial, if possible. If the polynomial cannot be factored using integers, write *prime*.

10. $5x^2 + 34x + 24$

11. $2x^2 + 19x + 24$

12. $4x^2 + 22x + 10$

13. $4x^2 + 38x + 70$

14. $2x^2 - 3x - 9$

15. $4x^2 - 13x + 10$

16. $2x^2 + 3x + 6$ **prime**

17. $5x^2 + 3x + 4$ **prime**

18. $12x^2 + 69x + 45$

19. $4x^2 - 5x + 7$ **prime**

20. $5x^2 + 23x + 24$ **$(5x + 8)(x + 3)$**

21. $3x^2 - 8x + 15$ **prime**

Example 4 p. 495

18. $3(4x + 3)(x + 5)$
29c. Less; sample answer: It starts closer to the ground so the shot will not have as far to fall.

22. SHOT PUT An athlete throws a shot put with an initial velocity of 29 feet per second and from an initial height of 6 feet.

a. Write an equation that models the height of the shot put in feet with respect to time in seconds. **$h = -16t^2 + 29t + 6$**

b. After how many seconds will the shot put hit the ground? **2 seconds**

Solve each equation. Check your solutions.

23. $2x^2 + 9x - 18 = 0$ **$\frac{3}{2}, -6$**

24. $4x^2 + 17x + 15 = 0$ **$-\frac{5}{4}, -3$**

25. $-3x^2 + 26x = 16$ **$\frac{2}{3}, 8$**

26. $-2x^2 + 13x = 15$ **$\frac{3}{2}, 5$**

27. $-3x^2 + 5x = -2$ **$-\frac{1}{3}, 2$**

28. $-4x^2 + 19x = -30$ **$-\frac{5}{4}, 6$**

B

29. BASKETBALL When Jerald shoots a free throw, the ball is 6 feet from the floor and has an initial velocity of 20 feet per second. The hoop is 10 feet from the floor.

a. Use the vertical motion model to determine an equation that models Jerald's free throw. **$10 = -16t^2 + 20t + 6$**

b. How long is the basketball in the air before it reaches the hoop? **1 second**

c. Raymond shoots a free throw that is 5 foot 9 inches from the floor with the same initial velocity. Will the ball be in the air more or less time? Explain.

30. DIVING Ben dives from a 10-foot platform. The equation $h = -16t^2 + 27t + 10$ models the dive. How long will it take Ben to reach the water? **2 seconds**

Differentiated Homework Options

Level	Assignment	Two-Day Option	
AL Basic	10–28, 40–41, 43–74	11–27 odd, 45–48	10–28 even, 40–41, 43–44, 49–74
OL Core	11–27 odd, 29–31, 33–37 odd, 39–41, 43–74	10–28, 45–48	29–41, 43–44, 49–74
BL Advanced	29–68, (optional: 69–74)		

31. **NUMBER THEORY** Six times the square of a number x plus 11 times the number equals 2. What are possible values of x? **-2 or $\frac{1}{6}$**

Factor each polynomial, if possible. If the polynomial cannot be factored using integers, write *prime*.

32. $-6x^2 - 23x - 20$	**33.** $-4x^2 - 15x - 14$	**34.** $-5x^2 + 18x + 8$
35. $-6x^2 + 31x - 35$	**36.** $-4x^2 + 5x - 12$	**37.** $-12x^2 + x + 20$

38. **URBAN PLANNING** The city has commissioned the building of a new park. The area of the park can be expressed as $660x^2 + 524x + 85$. Factor this expression to find binomials with integer coefficients that represent possible dimensions of the park. If $x = 8$, what is the perimeter of the park? **$(22x + 5)(30x + 17)$; 876 units**

Real-World Career

Urban Planner
Urban planners design the layout of an area. They take into consideration the available land and geographical and environmental factors to design an area that benefits the community the most. City planners have a bachelor's degree in planning and almost half have a master's degree.

39. **MULTIPLE REPRESENTATIONS** In this problem, you will explore factoring a special type of polynomial.

a. **GEOMETRIC** Draw a square and label the sides a. Within this square, draw a smaller square that shares a vertex with the first square. Label the sides b. What are the areas of the two squares? **a^2 and b^2**

b. **GEOMETRIC** Cut and remove the small square. What is the area of the remaining region? **$a^2 - b^2$**

c. **ANALYTICAL** Draw a diagonal line between the inside corner and outside corner of the figure, and cut along this line to make two congruent pieces. Then rearrange the two pieces to form a rectangle. What are the dimensions?

d. **ANALYTICAL** Write the area of the rectangle as the product of two binomials. **$(a - b)(a + b)$**

e. **VERBAL** Complete this statement: $a^2 - b^2 = \ldots$ Why is this statement true? **$(a - b)(a + b)$; the figure with area $a^2 - b^2$ and the rectangle with area $(a - b)(a + b)$ have the same area, so $a^2 - b^2 = (a - b)(a + b)$.**

32. $-(2x + 5)(3x + 4)$
33. $-(x + 2)(4x + 7)$
34. $-(x - 4)(5x + 2)$
35. $-(2x - 7)(3x - 5)$
36. prime
37. $-(3x - 4)(4x + 5)$
39c. width: $a - b$, length: $a + b$
40. Samantha; sample answer: She rewrote the equation to have zero on one side. Then she factored and used the Zero Product Property.
44. Sample answer: Find two numbers, m and n, with a product of ac and a sum of b.

H.O.T. Problems

Use Higher-Order Thinking Skills

40. **FIND THE ERROR** Zachary and Samantha are solving $6x^2 - x = 12$. Is either of them correct? Explain your reasoning.

Zachary	Samantha
$6x^2 - x = 12$	$6x^2 - x = 12$
$x(6x - 1) = 12$	$6x^2 - x - 12 = 0$
$x = 12$ or $6x - 1 = 12$	$(2x - 3)(3x + 4) = 0$
$6x = 13$	$2x - 3 = 0$ or $3x + 4 = 0$
$x = \frac{13}{6}$	$x = \frac{3}{2}$ $\quad x = -\frac{4}{3}$

41. **REASONING** A square has an area of $9x^2 + 30xy + 25y^2$ square inches. The dimensions are binomials with positive integer coefficients. What is the perimeter of the square? Explain. **See margin.**

42. **CHALLENGE** Find all values of k so that $2x^2 + kx + 12$ can be factored as two binomials using integers. **$\pm25, \pm14, \pm11, \pm10$**

43. **OPEN ENDED** Write a quadratic equation with integer coefficients that has $\frac{1}{2}$ and $-\frac{3}{5}$ as solutions. Explain your reasoning. **See margin.**

44. **WRITING IN MATH** Explain how to determine which values should be chosen for m and n when factoring a polynomial of the form $ax^2 + bx + c$.

Study Guide and Intervention

CRM pp. 23–24 AL OL ELL

NAME ______ DATE ______ PERIOD ______

8-4 Study Guide and Intervention

Quadratic Equations: $ax^2 + bx + c = 0$

Factor $ax^2 + bx + c$ To factor a trinomial of the form $ax^2 + bx + c$, find two integers, m and p whose product is equal to ac and whose sum is equal to b. If there are no integers that satisfy these requirements, the polynomial is called a **prime polynomial**.

Example 1 Factor $2x^2 + 15x + 18$.

In this example, $a = 2$, $b = 15$, and $c = 18$. You need to find two numbers that have a sum of 15 and a product of $2 \cdot 18$ or 36. Make a list of the factors of 36 and look for the pair of factors with a sum of 15.

Factors of 36	Sum of Factors
1, 36	37
2, 18	20
3, 12	15

Use the pattern $ax^2 + mx + px + c$, with $a = 2$, $m = 3$, $p = 12$, and $c = 18$.

$2x^2 + 15x + 18 = 2x^2 + 3x + 12x + 18$
$= (2x^2 + 3x) + (12x + 18)$
$= x(2x + 3) + 6(2x + 3)$
$= (x + 6)(2x + 3)$

Therefore, $2x^2 + 15x + 18 = (x + 6)(2x + 3)$.

Example 2 Factor $3x^2 - 3x - 18$.

Note that the GCF of the terms $3x^2$, $3x$, and 18 is 3. First factor out this GCF.

$3x^2 - 3x - 18 = 3(x^2 - x - 6)$.

Now factor $x^2 - x - 6$. Since $a = 1$, find the two factors of -6 with a sum of -1.

Factors of −6	Sum of Factors
1, −6	−5
−1, 6	5
−2, 3	1
2, −3	−1

Now use the pattern $(x + m)(x + p)$ with $m = 2$ and $p = -3$.

$x^2 - x - 6 = (x + 2)(x - 3)$

The complete factorization is $3x^2 - 3x - 18 = 3(x + 2)(x - 3)$.

Exercises

Factor each polynomial, if possible. If the polynomial cannot be factored using integers, write *prime*.

1. $2x^2 - 3x - 2$ **$(2x + 1)(x - 2)$**	2. $3m^2 - 8m - 3$ **$(3m + 1)(m - 3)$**	3. $16r^2 - 8r + 1$ **$(4r - 1)(4r - 1)$**
4. $6x^2 + 5x - 6$ **$(2x + 3)(3x - 2)$**	5. $3x^2 + 2x - 8$ **$(3x - 4)(x + 2)$**	6. $18x^2 - 27x - 5$ **$(3x - 5)(6x + 1)$**
7. $2a^2 + 5a + 3$ **$(2a + 3)(a + 1)$**	8. $18y^2 + 9y - 5$ **$(6y + 5)(3y - 1)$**	9. $-4t^2 + 19t - 21$ **$(4t - 7)(3 - t)$**
10. $8x^2 - 4x - 24$ **$2(2x - 4)(2x + 3)$**	11. $28p^2 + 60p - 25$ **$(2p + 5)(14p - 5)$**	12. $48x^2 + 22x - 15$ **$(6x + 5)(8x - 3)$**
13. $3y^2 - 6y - 24$ **$3(y + 2)(y - 4)$**	14. $4x^2 + 26x - 48$ **$2(x + 8)(2x - 3)$**	15. $8m^2 - 44m + 48$ **$4(2m - 3)(m - 4)$**
16. $6x^2 - 7x + 18$ **prime**	17. $2a^2 - 14a + 18$ **$2(a^2 - 7a + 9)$**	18. $18 + 11y + 2y^2$ **prime**

Lesson 8-4

Chapter 8 23 *Glencoe Algebra 1*

Practice

CRM p. 26 AL OL BL ELL

NAME ______ DATE ______ PERIOD ______

8-4 Practice

Quadratic Equations: $ax^2 + bx + c = 0$

Factor each polynomial, if possible. If the polynomial cannot be factored using integers, write *prime*.

1. $2b^2 + 10b + 12$ **$2(b + 2)(b + 3)$**	2. $3g^2 + 8g + 4$ **$(3g + 2)(g + 2)$**	3. $4x^2 + 4x - 3$ **$(2x + 3)(2x - 1)$**
4. $8b^2 - 5b - 10$ **prime**	5. $6m^2 + 7m - 3$ **$(3m - 1)(2m + 3)$**	6. $10d^2 + 17d - 20$ **$(5d - 4)(2d + 5)$**
7. $6a^2 - 17a + 12$ **$(3a - 4)(2a - 3)$**	8. $8w^2 - 18w + 9$ **$(4w - 3)(2w - 3)$**	9. $10x^2 - 9x + 6$ **prime**
10. $15n^2 - n - 28$ **$(5n - 7)(3n + 4)$**	11. $10x^2 + 21x - 10$ **$(2x + 5)(5x - 2)$**	12. $9r^2 + 15r + 6$ **$3(3r + 2)(r + 1)$**
13. $12y^2 - 4y - 5$ **$(2y + 1)(6y - 5)$**	14. $14k^2 - 9k - 18$ **$(2k - 3)(7k + 6)$**	15. $8z^2 + 20z - 48$ **$4(z + 4)(2z - 3)$**
16. $12q^2 + 34q - 28$ **$2(3q - 2)(2q + 7)$**	17. $18h^2 + 15h - 18$ **$3(2h + 3)(3h - 2)$**	18. $12p^2 - 22p - 20$ **$2(3p + 2)(2p - 5)$**

Solve each equation. Check the solutions.

19. $3h^2 + 2h - 16 = 0$ **$\{-\frac{8}{3}, 2\}$**	20. $15n^2 - n = 2$ **$\{-\frac{1}{3}, \frac{2}{5}\}$**	21. $8q^2 - 10q + 3 = 0$ **$\{\frac{1}{2}, \frac{3}{4}\}$**
22. $6b^2 - 5b = 4$ **$\{-\frac{1}{2}, \frac{4}{3}\}$**	23. $10r^2 - 21r = -4r + 6$ **$\{-\frac{3}{10}, 2\}$**	24. $10g^2 + 10 = 29g$ **$\{\frac{2}{5}, \frac{5}{2}\}$**
25. $6y^2 = -7y - 2$ **$\{-\frac{2}{3}, -\frac{1}{2}\}$**	26. $9z^2 = -6z + 15$ **$\{-\frac{5}{3}, 1\}$**	27. $12k^2 + 15k = 16k + 20$ **$\{-\frac{5}{4}, \frac{4}{3}\}$**
28. $12x^2 - 1 = -x$ **$\{-\frac{1}{3}, \frac{1}{4}\}$**	29. $8a^2 - 16a = 6a - 12$ **$\{\frac{3}{4}, 2\}$**	30. $18a^2 + 10a = -11a + 4$ **$\{-\frac{4}{3}, \frac{1}{6}\}$**

31. **DIVING** Lauren dove into a swimming pool from a 15-foot-high diving board with an initial upward velocity of 8 feet per second. Find the time t in seconds it took Lauren to enter the water. Use the model for vertical motion given by the equation $h = -16t^2 + vt + s$, where h is height in feet, t is time in seconds, v is the initial upward velocity in feet per second, and s is the initial height in feet. (*Hint:* Let $h = 0$ represent the surface of the pool.) **1.25 s**

32. **BASEBALL** Brad tossed a baseball in the air from a height of 6 feet with an initial upward velocity of 14 feet per second. Enrique caught the ball on its way down at a point 4 feet above the ground. How long was the ball in the air before Enrique caught it? Use the model of vertical motion from Exercise 31. **1 s**

Chapter 8 26 *Glencoe Algebra 1*

Word Problem Practice

CRM p. 27 AL OL BL ELL

NAME ______ DATE ______ PERIOD ______

8-4 Word Problem Practice

Quadratic Equations: $ax^2 + bx + c = 0$

1. **BREAK EVEN** Breaking even occurs when the revenues for a business equal the cost. A local children's museum studied their costs (wages, electricity, etc.) and revenues from paid admission. They found that their break-even time is given by the equation $2h^2 - 2h - 24 = 0$, where h is the number of hours the museum is open per day. How many hours must the museum be open per day to reach the break even point? **4 hours**

2. **CARPENTRY** Miko wants to build a toy box for her sister. It is to be 2 feet high, and the width is to be 3 feet less than its length. If it needs to hold a volume of 80 cubic feet, find the length and width of the box. **length = 8 ft; width = 5 ft**

3. **FURNITURE** The student council wants to purchase a table for the school lobby. The table comes in a variety of dimensions, but for every table, the length is 1 meter greater than twice the width. The student council has budgeted for a table top with an area of exactly 3 square meters.

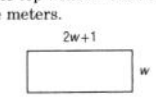

Find the width and length of the table they can purchase. **width = 1 m; length = 3 m**

4. **LADDERS** A ladder is resting against a wall. The top of the ladder touches the wall at a height of 15 feet, and the length of the ladder is one foot more than twice its distance from the wall. Find the distance from the wall to the bottom of the ladder. (*Hint:* Use the Pythagorean Theorem to solve the problem.) **8 ft**

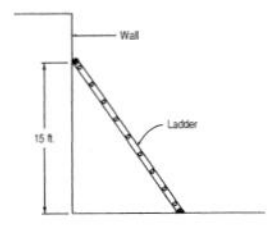

5. **FARMING** Mr. Hensley has a total of 480 square feet of sheet metal with which he would like to construct a cylindrical tank for storing grain. The local zoning law limits the height of the tank to 13.5 feet. Recall that a formula for the surface area of a bottomless cylinder with radius r and height h is

$$A = \pi r^2 + 2\pi rh.$$

a. Write a quadratic equation (set equal to zero) to represent the information. **$0 = \pi r^2 + 27\pi r - 480$**

b. Using 3 as an approximation for π, solve the equation for r. **$\{5, -32\}$**

c. What radius should Mr. Hensley use for his tank? **5 ft**

Lesson 8-4

Chapter 8 27 *Glencoe Algebra 1*

Watch Out!

Find the Error For Exercise 40, tell students to think about the first step in solving an equation by factoring: *put the equation in standard form.* This clue should immediately tell them which student is correct. You may also remind students that although at least one factor in a zero product must be a zero, no such principle holds for any other number.

Enrichment

CRM p. 28 OL BL

NAME ______ DATE ______ PERIOD ______

8-4 Enrichment

Area Models for Quadratic Trinomials

After you have factored a quadratic trinomial, you can use the factors to draw geometric models of the trinomial.

$x^2 + 5x - 6 = (x - 1)(x + 6)$

To draw a rectangular model, the value 2 was used for x so that the shorter side would have a length of 1. Then the drawing was done in centimeters. So, the area of the rectangle is $x^2 + 5x - 6$.

To draw a right triangle model, recall that the area of a triangle is one-half the base times the height. So, one of the sides must be twice as long as the shorter side of the rectangular model.

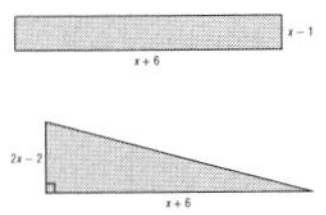

$x^2 + 5x - 6 = (x - 1)(x + 6)$
$= \frac{1}{2}(2x - 2)(x + 6)$

The area of the right triangle is also $x^2 + 5x - 6$.

Factor each trinomial. Then follow the directions to draw each model of the trinomial.

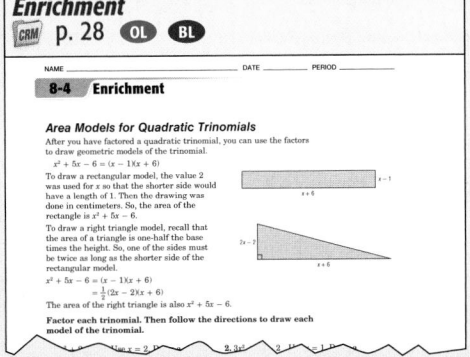

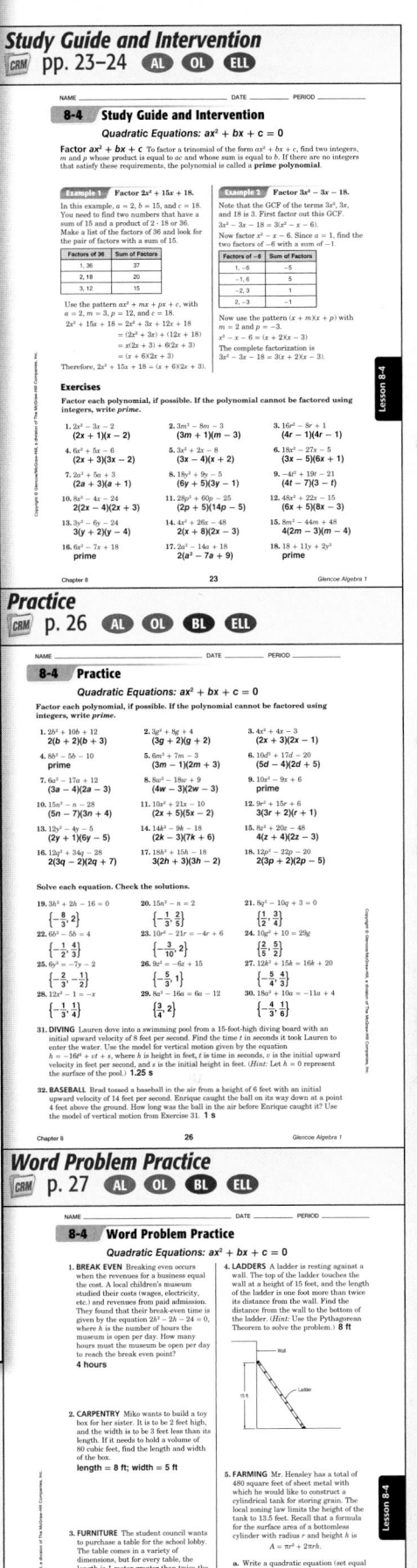

4 ASSESS

Yesterday's News Have students write how yesterday's lesson on quadratic equations helped them with today's lesson on quadratic equations.

Additional Answers

61.

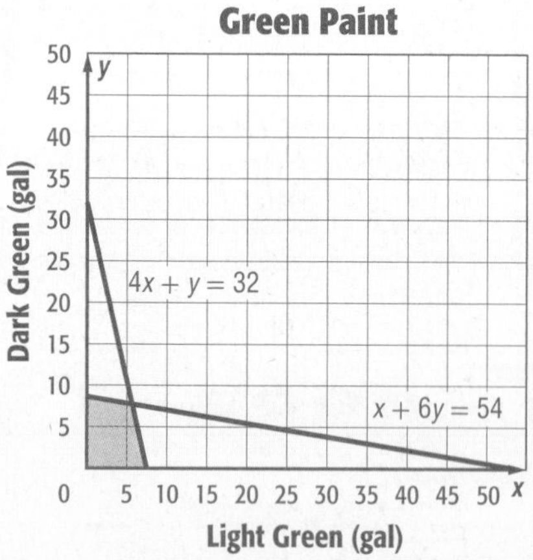

Sample answers: 2 light, 8 dark; 6 light, 8 dark; 7 light, 4 dark

62. $\{k \mid 10 < k \leq 16\}$

63. $\{d \mid d \leq 5 \text{ or } d > 7\}$

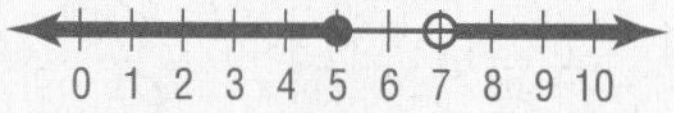

64. $\{x \mid 3 < x < 9\}$

65. $\varnothing$

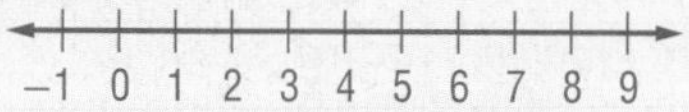

66. $\{h \mid h < -1\}$

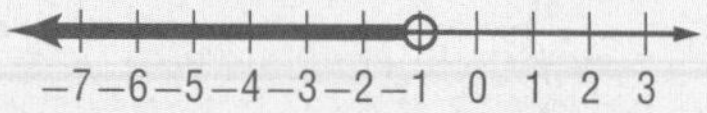

67. $\{y \mid 3 < y < 6\}$

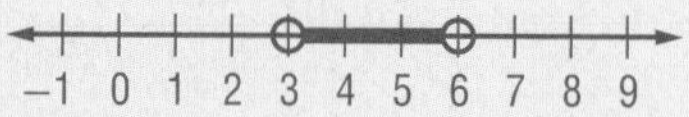

PSAE PRACTICE 8.11.14, 6.11.05, 8.11.18, 6.11.01

45. GRIDDED RESPONSE Savannah has two sisters. One sister is 8 years older than her and the other sister is 2 years younger than her. The product of Savannah's sisters' ages is 56. How old is Savannah? **6**

46. What is the product of $\frac{2}{3}a^3b^5$ and $\frac{3}{5}a^5b^2$? **A**

A $\frac{2}{5}a^8b^7$

B $\frac{2}{5}a^2b^3$

C $\frac{2}{5}a^8b^3$

D $\frac{2}{5}a^2b^7$

47. What is the solution set of $x^2 + 2x - 24 = 0$? **J**

F $\{-4, 6\}$ H $\{-3, 8\}$

G $\{3, -8\}$ J $\{4, -6\}$

48. Which is the solution set of $x \geq -2$? **C**

A 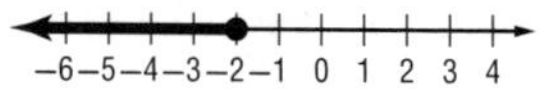

B 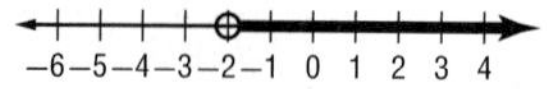

C 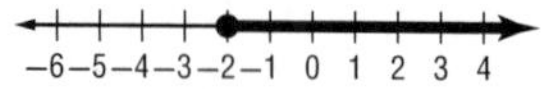

D 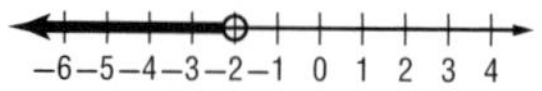

Spiral Review

Factor each polynomial. (Lesson 8-3)

49. $x^2 - 9x + 14$ $(x - 2)(x - 7)$

50. $n^2 - 8n + 15$ $(n - 3)(n - 5)$

51. $x^2 - 5x - 24$ $(x + 3)(x - 8)$

52. $z^2 + 15z + 36$ $(z + 12)(z + 3)$

53. $r^2 + 3r - 40$ $(r + 8)(r - 5)$

54. $v^2 + 16v + 63$ $(v + 9)(v + 7)$

Solve each equation. Check your solutions. (Lesson 8-2)

55. $a(a - 9) = 0$ **0, 9**

56. $(2y + 6)(y - 1) = 0$ **−3, 1**

57. $10x^2 - 20x = 0$ **0, 2**

58. $8b^2 - 12b = 0$ **0, 1.5**

59. $15a^2 = 60a$ **0, 4**

60. $33x^2 = -22x$ $-\frac{2}{3}, 0$

61. ART A painter has 32 units of yellow dye and 54 units of blue dye to make two shades of green. The units needed to make a gallon of light green and a gallon of dark green are shown. Make a graph showing the numbers of gallons of the two greens she can make, and list three possible solutions. (Lesson 6-8) **See margin.**

Color	Units of Yellow Dye	Units of Blue Dye
light green	4	1
dark green	1	6

Solve each compound inequality. Then graph the solution set. (Lesson 5-4) **62–67. See margin.**

62. $k + 2 > 12$ and $k + 2 \leq 18$

63. $d - 4 > 3$ or $d - 4 \leq 1$

64. $3 < 2x - 3 < 15$

65. $3t - 7 \geq 5$ and $2t + 6 \leq 12$

66. $h - 10 < -21$ or $h + 3 < 2$

67. $4 < 2y - 2 < 10$

68. FINANCIAL LITERACY A home security company provides security systems for $5 per week, plus an installation fee. The total cost for installation and 12 weeks of service is $210. Write the point-slope form of an equation to find the total fee y for any number of weeks x. What is the installation fee? (Lesson 4-3) $y - 210 = 5(x - 12)$; **$150**

Skills Review

Find the principal square root of each number. (Lesson 0-2)

69. 16 **4**

70. 36 **6**

71. 64 **8**

72. 81 **9**

73. 121 **11**

74. 100 **10**

Differentiated Instruction OL BL

Extension Have students write a quadratic equation in the form $ax^2 + bx + c = 0$. Tell them that a, b, and c must be integers, and the solutions to the equation must be $\frac{1}{2}$ and 4. Sample answer: $2x^2 - 9x + 4 = 0$

498 Chapter 8 Factoring and Quadratic Equations

8-5 Quadratic Equations: Differences of Squares

Then
You factored trinomials into two binomials. (Lesson 8-3, 8-4)

Now
- Factor binomials that are the difference of squares.
- Use the difference of squares to solve equations.

IL Learning Standards

8.A.4b Represent mathematical patterns and describe their properties using variables and mathematical symbols. **8.D.4 Formulate and solve** linear and **quadratic equations** and linear inequalities **algebraically** and investigate nonlinear inequalities using graphs, tables, calculators and computers. *Also addresses 8.C.4b.*

New Vocabulary
difference of two squares

IL Math Online

glencoe.com
- Extra Examples
- Personal Tutor
- Self-Check Quiz
- Homework Help
- Math in Motion

Why?

Computer graphics designers use a combination of art and mathematics skills to design images and videos. They use equations to form shapes and lines on computers. Factoring can help to determine the dimensions and shapes of the figures.

Factor Differences of Squares Recall that in Lesson 7-8, you learned about the product of the sum and difference of two quantities. This resulting product is referred to as the **difference of two squares**. So, the factored form of the difference of squares is called the product of the sum and difference of the two quantities.

Key Concept Difference of Squares — For Your FOLDABLE

Symbols $a^2 - b^2 = (a + b)(a - b)$ or $(a - b)(a + b)$

Examples $x^2 - 25 = (x + 5)(x - 5)$ or $(x - 5)(x + 5)$

$t^2 - 64 = (t + 8)(t - 8)$ or $(t - 8)(t + 8)$

EXAMPLE 1 Factor Differences of Squares

Factor each polynomial.

a. $16h^2 - 9a^2$

$16h^2 - 9a^2 = (4h)^2 - (3a)^2$ — Write in the form of $a^2 - b^2$.

$= (4h + 3a)(4h - 3a)$ — Factor the difference of squares.

b. $121 - 4b^2$

$121 - 4b^2 = (11)^2 - (2b)^2$ — Write in the form of $a^2 - b^2$.

$= (11 - 2b)(11 + 2b)$ — Factor the difference of squares.

c. $27g^3 - 3g$

Because the terms have a common factor, factor out the GCF first. Then proceed with other factoring techniques.

$27g^3 - 3g = 3g(9g^2 - 1)$ — Factor out the GCF of $3g$.

$= 3g[(3g)^2 - (1)^2]$ — Write in the form $a^2 - b^2$.

$= 3g(3g - 1)(3g + 1)$ — Factor the difference of squares.

Check Your Progress

1A. $81 - c^2$ $(9 + c)(9 - c)$

1B. $64g^2 - h^2$ $(8g + h)(8g - h)$

1C. $9x^3 - 4x$ $x(3x + 2)(3x - 2)$

1D. $-4y^3 + 9y$ $-y(2y + 3)(2y - 3)$

Personal Tutor glencoe.com

8-5 Lesson Notes

1 FOCUS

Vertical Alignment

Before Lesson 8-5
Factor trinomials into two binomials.

Lesson 8-5
Factor binomials that are the difference of squares.
Use the difference of squares to solve equations.

After Lesson 8-5
Factor perfect square trinomials.

2 TEACH

Scaffolding Questions
Have students read the *Why?* section of the lesson.

Ask:
- Find $(x + 3)(x - 3)$. $x^2 - 9$
- Find $(x - 6)(x + 6)$. $x^2 - 36$
- Find $(a - b)(a + b)$. $a^2 - b^2$

TEACH with TECH
INTERACTIVE WHITEBOARD Use the template from the previous lesson to demonstrate why the difference of squares is factorable, but the difference of sums is not.

Lesson 8-5 Resources

Resource	Approaching-Level	On-Level	Beyond-Level	English Learners
Teacher Edition		• Differentiated Instruction, pp. 501, 504	• Differentiated Instruction, pp. 501, 504	
Chapter Resource Masters	• Study Guide and Intervention, pp. 30–31 • Skills Practice, p. 32 • Practice, p. 33 • Word Problem Practice, p. 34 • Spreadsheet Activity, p. 36	• Study Guide and Intervention, pp. 30–31 • Skills Practice, p. 32 • Practice, p. 33 • Word Problem Practice, p. 34 • Enrichment, p. 35 • Spreadsheet Activity, p. 36	• Practice, p. 33 • Word Problem Practice, p. 34 • Enrichment, p. 35 • Spreadsheet Activity, p. 36	• Study Guide and Intervention, pp. 30–31 • Skills Practice, p. 32 • Practice, p. 33 • Spreadsheet Activity, p. 36
Transparencies	• 5-Minute Check Transparency 8-5	• 5-Minute Check Transparency 8-5	• 5-Minute Check Transparency 8-5	• 5-Minute Check Transparency 8-5
Other	• Study Notebook • Teaching Algebra with Manipulatives	• Study Notebook • Teaching Algebra with Manipulatives	• Study Notebook	• Study Notebook • Teaching Algebra with Manipulatives

Factor Differences of Squares

Example 1 shows how to factor the differences of squares. **Examples 2** and **3** show how to apply a factoring technique more than once to factor a polynomial completely.

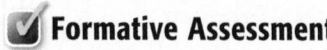

Formative Assessment

Use the Check Your Progress exercises after each example to determine students' understanding of concepts.

Additional Examples

1 Factor each polynomial.

a. $m^2 - 64$ $(m + 8)(m - 8)$

b. $16y^2 - 81z^2$
$(4y + 9z)(4y - 9z)$

c. $3b^3 - 27b$
$3b(b + 3)(b - 3)$

2 Factor each polynomial.

a. $y^4 - 625$
$(y^2 + 25)(y + 5)(y - 5)$

b. $256 - n^4$
$(16 + n^2)(4 - n)(4 + n)$

3 Factor each polynomial.

a. $9x^5 - 36x$
$9x(x^2 - 2)(x^2 + 2)$

b. $6x^3 + 30x^2 - 24x - 120$
$6(x + 2)(x - 2)(x + 5)$

Additional Examples also in Interactive Classroom PowerPoint® Presentations

IWB INTERACTIVE WHITEBOARD READY

Watch Out!

Sum of Squares The sum of squares, $a^2 + b^2$, does not factor into $(a + b)(a + b)$. The sum of squares is a prime polynomial and cannot be factored.

Math *in Motion*, Animation glencoe.com

To factor a polynomial completely, a technique may need to be applied more than once. This also applies to the difference of squares pattern.

EXAMPLE 2 Apply a Technique More than Once

Factor each polynomial.

a. $b^4 - 16$

$b^4 - 16 = (b^2)^2 - (4)^2$	**Write $b^4 - 16$ in $a^2 - b^2$ form.**
$= (b^2 + 4)(b^2 - 4)$	**Factor the difference of squares.**

Notice that the factor $b^2 - 4$ is also the difference of squares.

$= (b^2 + 4)(b^2 - 2^2)$	**Write $b^2 - 4$ in $a^2 - b^2$ form.**
$= (b^2 + 4)(b + 2)(b - 2)$	**Factor the difference of squares.**

b. $625 - x^4$

$625 - x^4 = (25)^2 - (x^2)^2$	**Write $625 - x^4$ in $a^2 - b^2$ form.**
$= (25 + x^2)(25 - x^2)$	**Factor the difference of squares.**
$= (25 + x^2)(5^2 - x^2)$	**Write $25 - x^2$ in $a^2 - b^2$ form.**
$= (25 + x^2)(5 - x)(5 + x)$	**Factor the difference of squares.**

Check Your Progress

Factor each polynomial.

2A. $y^4 - 1$ $(y^2 + 1)(y + 1)(y - 1)$

2B. $4a^4 - b^4$ $(2a^2 + b^2)(2a^2 - b^2)$

2C. $81 - x^4$ $(3 - x)(3 + x)(9 + x^2)$

2D. $16y^4 - 1$ $(4y^2 + 1)(2y - 1)(2y + 1)$

Personal Tutor glencoe.com

Sometimes more than one factoring technique needs to be applied to ensure that a polynomial is factored completely.

EXAMPLE 3 Apply Different Techniques

Factor each polynomial.

a. $5x^5 - 45x$

$5x^5 - 45x = 5x(x^4 - 9)$	**Factor out GCF.**
$= 5x[(x^2)^2 - (3)^2]$	**Write $x^4 - 9$ in the form $a^2 - b^2$.**
$= 5x(x^2 - 3)(x^2 + 3)$	**Factor the difference of squares.**

Notice that the factor $x^2 - 3$ is not the difference of squares because 3 is not a perfect square.

b. $7x^3 + 21x^2 - 7x - 21$

$7x^3 + 21x^2 - 7x - 21$	**Original expression**
$= 7(x^3 + 3x^2 - x - 3)$	**Factor out GCF.**
$= 7[(x^3 + 3x^2) - (x + 3)]$	**Group terms with common factors.**
$= 7[x^2(x + 3) - 1(x + 3)]$	**Factor each grouping.**
$= 7(x + 3)(x^2 - 1)$	**$x + 3$ is the common factor.**
$= 7(x + 3)(x + 1)(x - 1)$	**Factor the difference of squares.**

Check Your Progress

Factor each polynomial.

3A. $2y^4 - 50$ $2(y^2 - 5)(y^2 + 5)$

3B. $6x^4 - 96$ $6(x - 2)(x + 2)(x^2 + 4)$

3C. $2m^3 + m^2 - 50m - 25$ $(2m + 1)(m + 5)(m - 5)$

3D. $r^3 + 6r^2 + 11r + 66$ $(r^2 + 11)(r + 6)$

Personal Tutor glencoe.com

Watch Out!

Preventing Errors Students should always check their factoring by multiplying the factors using the FOIL method.

Focus on Mathematical Content

Factoring Differences of Squares The binomial $a^2 - b^2$ is the difference of two squares, a^2 and b^2. One of the binomial factors, $(a + b)$, is the sum of the principal square roots of a^2 and b^2, and the other binomial factor, $(a - b)$, is the difference of their principal square roots.

500 Chapter 8 Factoring and Quadratic Equations

Solve Equations by Factoring After factoring, you can apply the Zero Product Property to an equation that is written as the product of factors set equal to 0.

PSAE EXAMPLE 4 8.11.06

In the equation $y = x^2 - \frac{9}{16}$, which is a value of x when $y = 0$?

A $-\frac{9}{4}$ B 0 C $\frac{3}{4}$ D $\frac{9}{4}$

Read the Test Item

Replace y with 0 and then solve.

Solve the Test Item

$y = x^2 - \frac{9}{16}$	**Original equation**
$0 = x^2 - \frac{9}{16}$	**Replace y with 0.**
$0 = x^2 - \left(\frac{3}{4}\right)^2$	**Write in the form $a^2 - b^2$.**
$0 = \left(x + \frac{3}{4}\right)\left(x - \frac{3}{4}\right)$	**Factor the difference of squares.**
$0 = x + \frac{3}{4}$ or $0 = x - \frac{3}{4}$	**Zero Product Property**
$x = -\frac{3}{4}$ $x = \frac{3}{4}$	The correct answer is C.

Test-Taking Tip

Use Another Method Another method that can be used to solve this equation is to substitute each answer choice into the equation.

Check Your Progress

4. Which are the solutions of $18x^3 = 50x$? **H**

F $0, \frac{5}{3}$ G $-\frac{5}{3}, \frac{5}{3}$ H $-\frac{5}{3}, \frac{5}{3}, 0$ J $-\frac{5}{3}, \frac{5}{3}, 1$

Personal Tutor glencoe.com

Check Your Understanding

Examples 1–3 pp. 499–500

Factor each polynomial.

1. $x^2 - 9$ **$(x + 3)(x - 3)$**
2. $4a^2 - 25$ **$(2a + 5)(2a - 5)$**
3. $9m^2 - 144$ **$9(m + 4)(m - 4)$**
4. $2p^3 - 162p$ **$2p(p + 9)(p - 9)$**
5. $u^4 - 81$ **$(u + 3)(u - 3)(u^2 + 9)$**
6. $2d^4 - 32f^4$ **$2(d^2 + 4f^2)(d + 2f)(d - 2f)$**
7. $20r^4 - 45n^4$ **$5(2r^2 - 3n^2)(2r^2 + 3n^2)$**
8. $256n^4 - c^4$ **$(16n^2 + c^2)(4n + c)(4n - c)$**
9. $2c^3 + 3c^2 - 2c - 3$ **9. $(c + 1)(c - 1)(2c + 3)$**
10. $f^3 - 4f^2 - 9f + 36$ **$(f + 3)(f - 3)(f - 4)$**
11. $3t^3 + 2t^2 - 48t - 32$ **11. $(t + 4)(t - 4)(3t + 2)$**
12. $w^3 - 3w^2 - 9w + 27$ **12. $(w - 3)(w + 3)(w - 3)$**

Example 4 p. 501

EXTENDED RESPONSE After an accident, skid marks may result from sudden breaking. The formula $\frac{1}{24}s^2 = d$ approximates a vehicle's speed s in miles per hour given the length d in feet of the skid marks on dry concrete.

13. If skid marks on dry concrete are 54 feet long, how fast was the car traveling when the brakes were applied? **36 mph**
14. If the skid marks on dry concrete are 150 feet long, how fast was the car traveling when the brakes were applied? **60 mph**

Watch Out!

Preventing Errors Students should notice that after the GCF has been factored out and the difference of squares factoring technique has been applied once, one of the factors should be prime.

Solve Equations by Factoring

Example 4 shows how to answer a multiple-choice test item on solving equations by factoring.

Additional Example

4 Standardized Test Practice In the equation $y = q^2 - \frac{4}{25}$, which is a value of q when $y = 0$? **D**

A $\frac{2}{25}$ B $\frac{4}{25}$ C 0 D $-\frac{2}{5}$

Tips for New Teachers

Sense-Making Students may not be used to thinking of fractions as perfect squares. Remind them that if both the numerator and denominator are perfect squares, then the fraction is a perfect square.

Differentiated Instruction OL BL

Visual/Spatial Learners Draw the geometric model shown below on the board. Ask students to use their own paper square and scissors to make the model for a^2 when the b^2 square is removed. Then ask students to explain how their models show that $(a - b)(a + b) = a^2 - b^2$.

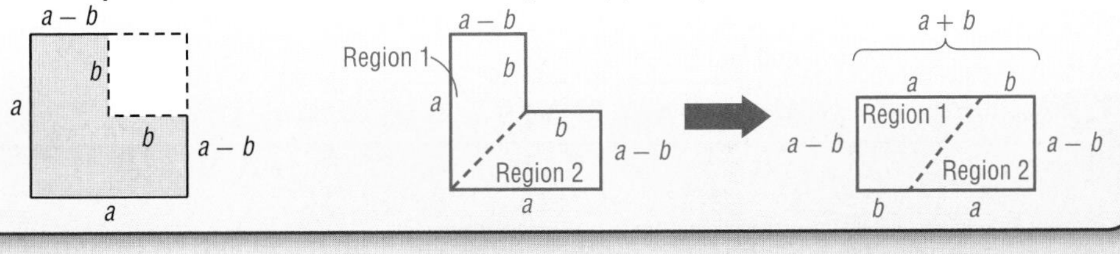

3 PRACTICE

Formative Assessment

Use Exercises 1–14 to check for understanding.

Use the chart at the bottom of this page to customize assignments for your students.

Exercise Alert

Graphing Calculator For Exercise 45, students will need a graphing calculator.

Multiple Representations In Exercise 56, students use algebra and information organized in a table to explore the format of a perfect-square trinomial.

Additional Answers

25. $7(h^2 + p^2)(h + p)(h - p)$
26. $(c + 7)(c - 7)(3c + 2)$
27. $6k^2(h^2 + 3k)(h^2 - 3k)$
28. $5a(a + 2)(a - 2)$
29. $(f + 8)(f - 8)(f + 2)$
30. $3r(r + 8)(r - 8)$
31. $10q(q + 11)(q - 11)$
32. $3x(n^2 + 3x)(n^2 - 3x)$
33. $p^3r(r + 1)(r - 1)(r^2 + 1)$
34. $8c(c + 1)(c - 1)$
35. $(r + 10)(r - 10)(r - 5)$
36. $(t + 1)(t - 1)(3t - 7)$
37. $(a + 7)(a - 7)$
38. $(m + 3)(m - 3)(4m + 9)$
39. $3(m^4 + 81)$
40. $(x + 5)(x - 5)(3x + 1)$
41. $2(a + 4)(a - 4)(6a + 1)$
42. $x(x + 6)(x - 6)(x + 6)$
43. $3(m + 5)(m - 5)(5m + 4)$

Practice and Problem Solving

● = Step-by-Step Solutions begin on page R12. Extra Practice begins on page 815.

Examples 1–3 pp. 499–500

Factor each polynomial. **25–43. See margin.**

15. $(q + 11)(q - 11)$
16. $(r^2 + k^2)(r + k) \bullet (r - k)$
17. $6(n^2 + 1)(n + 1) \bullet (n - 1)$
18. $(w^2 + 25)(w + 5) \bullet (w - 5)$
19. $(r + 3t)(r - 3t)$
20. $2(c + 4d)(c - 4d)$
21. $h(h + 10)(h - 10)$
22. $(h^2 + 16)(h + 4) \bullet (h - 4)$
23. $(x + 9)(x - 9) \bullet (2x - 1)$
24. $(x + 2y)(x - 2y)$

15. $q^2 - 121$	**16.** $r^4 - k^4$	**17.** $6n^4 - 6$
18. $w^4 - 625$	**19.** $r^2 - 9t^2$	**20.** $2c^2 - 32d^2$
21. $h^3 - 100h$	**22.** $h^4 - 256$	**23.** $2x^3 - x^2 - 162x + 81$
24. $x^2 - 4y^2$	**25.** $7h^4 - 7p^4$	**26.** $3c^3 + 2c^2 - 147c - 98$
27. $6k^2h^4 - 54k^4$	**28.** $5a^3 - 20a$	**29.** $f^3 + 2f^2 - 64f - 128$
30. $3r^3 - 192r$	**31.** $10q^3 - 1210q$	**32.** $3xn^4 - 27x^3$
33. $p^3r^5 - p^3r$	**34.** $8c^3 - 8c$	**35.** $r^3 - 5r^2 - 100r + 500$

36. $3t^3 - 7t^2 - 3t + 7$	**37.** $a^2 - 49$
38. $4m^3 + 9m^2 - 36m - 81$	**39.** $3m^4 + 243$
40. $3x^3 + x^2 - 75x - 25$	**41.** $12a^3 + 2a^2 - 192a - 32$
42. $x^4 + 6x^3 - 36x^2 - 216x$	**43.** $15m^3 + 12m^2 - 375m - 300$

Example 4 p. 501

44. GEOMETRY The drawing at the right is a square with a square cut out of it.

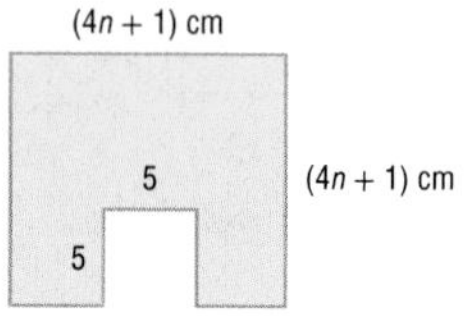

a. Write an expression that represents the area of the shaded region. **$(4n + 1)^2 - 5^2$**

b. Find the dimensions of a rectangle with the same area as the shaded region in the drawing. Assume that the dimensions of the rectangle must be represented by binomials with integral coefficients. **$(4n + 6)$ by $(4n - 4)$**

45. DECORATIONS An arch decorated with balloons was used to decorate the gym for the spring dance. The shape of the arch can be modeled by the equation $y = -0.5x^2 + 4.5x$, where x and y are measured in feet and the x-axis represents the floor. **a. $-0.5x(x - 9)$**

a. Write the expression that represents the height of the arch in factored form.

b. How far apart are the two points where the arch touches the floor? **9 ft**

c. Graph this equation on your calculator. What is the highest point of the arch? **10.125 ft**

46. DECKS Zelda is building a deck in her backyard. The plans for the deck show that it is to be 24 feet by 24 feet. Zelda wants to reduce one dimension by a number of feet and increase the other dimension by the same number of feet. If the area of the reduced deck is 512 square feet, what are the dimensions of the deck? **16 ft by 32 ft**

Real-World Link

Teens were asked "If you were given $20 today, what would you most likely spend it on?" Of the teens surveyed, 32% would spend it on a music CD.

Source: *USA TODAY*

47. SALES The sales of a particular CD can be modeled by the equation $S = -25m^2 + 125m$, where S is the number of CDs sold in thousands, and m is the number of months that it is on the market.

a. In what month should the music store expect the CD to stop selling? **5**

b. In what month will CD sales peak? **2.5**

c. How many copies will the CD sell at its peak? **156,250**

Differentiated Homework Options

Level	Assignment	Two-Day Option	
AL Basic	15–44, 57, 60–87	15–43 odd, 64–67	16–44 even, 57, 60–63, 68–87
OL Core	15–43 odd, 44–47, 49–55 odd, 56–57, 60–87	15–44, 64–67	45–57, 60–63, 68–87
BL Advanced	45–81, (optional: 82–87)		

StudyTip

Solving an Equation By Factoring Remember to get 0 on one side of the equation before factoring.

Solve each equation by factoring. Check your solutions.

48. $36w^2 = 121$ $\frac{11}{6}, -\frac{11}{6}$

49. $100 = 25x^2$ $2, -2$

50. $64x^2 - 1 = 0$ $\frac{1}{8}, -\frac{1}{8}$

51. $4y^2 - \frac{9}{16} = 0$ $\frac{3}{8}, -\frac{3}{8}$

52. $\frac{1}{4}b^2 = 16$ $-8, 8$

53. $81 - \frac{1}{25}x^2 = 0$ $-45, 45$

54. $9d^2 - 81 = 0$ $3, -3$

55. $4a^2 = \frac{9}{64}$ $\frac{3}{16}, -\frac{3}{16}$

56. MULTIPLE REPRESENTATIONS In this problem, you will investigate perfect square trinomials.

a. **TABULAR** Copy and complete the table below by factoring each polynomial. Then write the first and last terms of the given polynomials as perfect squares.

Polynomial	Factored Polynomial	First Term	Last Term	Middle Term
$4x^2 + 12x + 9$	$(2x + 3)(2x + 3)$	$4x^2 = (2x)^2$	$9 = 3^2$	$12x = 2 \cdot 2x \cdot 3$
$9x^2 - 24x + 16$	$(3x - 4)(3x - 4)$	$9x^2 = (3x)^2$	$16 = 4^2$	$-24x = -2 \cdot 3x \cdot 4$
$4x^2 - 20x + 25$	$(2x - 5)(2x - 5)$	$4x^2 = (2x)^2$	$25 = 5^2$	$-20x = -2 \cdot 2x \cdot 5$
$16x^2 + 24x + 9$	$(4x + 3)(4x + 3)$	$16x^2 = (4x)^2$	$9 = 3^2$	$24x = 2 \cdot 4x \cdot 3$
$25x^2 + 20x + 4$	$(5x + 2)(5x + 2)$	$25x^2 = (5x)^2$	$4 = 2^2$	$20x = 2 \cdot 5x \cdot 2$

b. **ANALYTICAL** Write the middle term of each polynomial using the square roots of the perfect squares of the first and last terms. See table.

c. **ALGEBRAIC** Write the pattern for a perfect square trinomial.

d. **VERBAL** What conditions must be met for a trinomial to be classified as a perfect square trinomial? The first and last terms must be perfect squares and the middle term must be 2 times the square roots of the first and last terms.

H.O.T. Problems
Use Higher-Order Thinking Skills

57. FIND THE ERROR Elizabeth and Lorenzo are factoring an expression. Is either of them correct? Explain your reasoning.

Elizabeth	Lorenzo
$16x^4 - 25y^2 =$	$16x^4 - 25y^2 =$
$(4x - 5y)(4x + 5y)$	$(4x^2 - 5y)(4x^2 + 5y)$

58. CHALLENGE Factor and simplify $9 - (k + 3)^2$, a difference of squares. $[3 + (k + 3)][3 - (k + 3)] = (k + 6)(-k) = -k^2 - 6k$

59. CHALLENGE Factor $x^{16} - 81$. $(x^4 - 3)(x^4 + 3)(x^8 + 9)$

60. REASONING Write and factor a binomial that is the difference of two perfect squares and that has a greatest common factor of $5mk$.

61. REASONING Determine whether the following statement is *true* or *false*. Give an example or counterexample to justify your answer. false; $a^2 + b^2$

All binomials that have a perfect square in each of the two terms can be factored.

62. OPEN ENDED Write a binomial in which the difference of squares pattern must be repeated to factor it completely. Then factor the binomial.

63. WRITING IN MATH Describe why the difference of squares pattern has no middle term with a variable.

56c. $(a + b)(a + b) = a^2 + 2ab + b^2$ and $(a - b)(a - b) = a^2 - 2ab + b^2$

57. Lorenzo; sample answer: Checking Elizabeth's answer gives us $16x^2 - 25y^2$. The exponent on x in the final product should be 4.

60. Sample answer: $5mka^2 - 5mkb^2 = 5mk(a^2 - b^2) = 5mk(a - b)(a + b)$

62. Sample answer: $x^4 - 16$; $(x - 2)(x + 2)(x^2 + 4)$

63. When the difference of squares pattern is multiplied together using the FOIL method, the outer and inner terms are opposites of each other. When these terms are added together, the sum is zero.

Study Guide and Intervention
CRM pp. 30–31 AL OL ELL

NAME ____________ DATE ________ PERIOD ________

8-5 Study Guide and Intervention

Quadratic Equations: Differences of Squares

Factor Differences of Squares The binomial expression $a^2 - b^2$ is called the **difference of two squares**. The following pattern shows how to factor the difference of squares.

Difference of Squares	$a^2 - b^2 = (a - b)(a + b) = (a + b)(a - b)$.

Example 1 Factor each polynomial.

a. $n^2 - 64$

$n^2 - 64$
$= n^2 - 8^2$ Write in the form $a^2 - b^2$.
$= (n + 8)(n - 8)$ Factor.

b. $4m^2 - 81n^2$

$4m^2 - 81n^2$
$= (2m)^2 - (9n)^2$ Write in the form $a^2 - b^2$.
$= (2m - 9n)(2m + 9n)$ Factor.

Example 2 Factor each polynomial.

a. $50a^2 - 72$

$50a^2 - 72$
$= 2(25a^2 - 36)$ Find the GCF.
$= 2[(5a)^2 - 6^2]$ $25a^2 = 5a \cdot 5a$ and $36 = 6 \cdot 6$
$= 2(5a + 6)(5a - 6)$ Factor the difference of squares.

b. $4x^4 + 8x^3 - 4x^2 - 8x$

$4x^4 + 8x^3 - 4x^2 - 8x$ Original polynomial
$= 4x(x^3 + 2x^2 - x - 2)$ Find the GCF.
$= 4x[(x^3 + 2x^2) - (x + 2)]$ Group terms.
$= 4x[x^2(x + 2) - 1(x + 2)]$ Find the GCF.
$= 4x[(x^2 - 1)(x + 2)]$ Factor by grouping.
$= 4x[(x - 1)(x + 1)(x + 2)]$ Factor the difference of squares.

Exercises

Factor each polynomial.

1. $x^2 - 81$ $(x + 9)(x - 9)$
2. $m^2 - 100$ $(m + 10)(m - 10)$
3. $16n^2 - 25$ $(4n - 5)(4n + 5)$
4. $36x^2 - 100y^2$ $(6x + 10y)(6x - 10y)$
5. $49x^2 - 36$ $(7x + 6)(7x - 6)$
6. $16a^2 - 9b^2$ $(4a - 3b)(4a + 3b)$
7. $225b^2 - a^2$ $(15b - a)(15b + a)$
8. $72p^2 - 50$ $2(6p + 5)(6p - 5)$
9. $-2 + 2x^2$ $2(x - 1)(x + 1)$
10. $-81 + a^4$ $(a - 3)(a + 3)(a^2 + 9)$
11. $6 - 54a^2$ $6(1 + 3a)(1 - 3a)$
12. $8y^2 - 200$ $8(y + 5)(y - 5)$
13. $4x^3 - 100x$ $4x(x + 5)(x - 5)$
14. $2y^4 - 32y^2$ $2y^2(y + 4)(y - 4)$
15. $8m^3 - 128m$ $8m(m + 4)(m - 4)$
16. $4x^2 - 25$ $(2x + 5)(2x - 5)$
17. $2a^3 - 98ab^2$ $2a(a - 7b)(a + 7b)$
18. $18y^2 - 72y^4$ $18y^2(1 - 2y)(1 + 2y)$
19. $169x^3 - x$ $x(13x + 1)(13x - 1)$
20. $3a^4 - 3a^2$ $3a^2(a + 1)(a - 1)$
21. $3x^4 + 6x^3 - 3x^2 - 6x$ $3x(x - 1)(x + 1)(x + 2)$

Chapter 8 30 *Glencoe Algebra 1*

Practice
CRM p. 33 AL OL BL ELL

NAME ____________ DATE ________ PERIOD ________

8-5 Practice

Quadratic Equations: Differences of Squares

Factor each polynomial, if possible. If the polynomial cannot be factored, write *prime*.

1. $k^2 - 100$ $(k + 10)(k - 10)$
2. $81 - r^2$ $(9 + r)(9 - r)$
3. $16p^2 - 36$ $(4p + 6)(4p - 6)$
4. $4x^2 + 25$ prime
5. $144 - 9f^2$ $(12 + 3f)(12 - 3f)$
6. $36g^2 - 49h^2$ $(6g + 7h)(6g - 7h)$
7. $121m^2 - 144p^2$ $(11m - 12p)(11m + 12p)$
8. $32 - 8y^2$ $8(2 - y)(2 + y)$
9. $24a^2 - 54b^2$ $6(2a - 3b)(2a + 3b)$
10. $32t^2 - 18u^2$ $2(4t - 3u)(4t + 3u)$
11. $9d^2 - 32$ prime
12. $36z^3 - 9z$ $9z(2z + 1)(2z - 1)$
13. $45q^3 - 20q$ $5q(3q + 2)(3q - 2)$
14. $100b^3 - 36b$ $4b(5b + 3)(5b - 3)$
15. $3t^4 - 48t^2$ $3t^2(t + 4)(t - 4)$

Solve each equation by factoring. Check your solutions.

16. $4y^2 = 81$ $\{\pm\frac{9}{2}\}$
17. $64p^2 = 9$ $\{\pm\frac{3}{8}\}$
18. $98b^2 - 50 = 0$ $\{\pm\frac{5}{7}\}$
19. $32 - 162k^2 = 0$ $\{\pm\frac{4}{9}\}$
20. $t^2 - \frac{64}{121} = 0$ $\{\pm\frac{8}{11}\}$
21. $\frac{16}{49} - v^2 = 0$ $\{\pm\frac{4}{7}\}$
22. $\frac{1}{36}x^2 - 25 = 0$ $\{\pm 30\}$
23. $27h^3 = 48h$ $\{\pm\frac{4}{3}, 0\}$
24. $75g^3 = 147g$ $\{\pm\frac{7}{5}, 0\}$

25. **EROSION** A rock breaks loose from a cliff and plunges toward the ground 400 feet below. The distance d that the rock falls in t seconds is given by the equation $d = 16t^2$. How long does it take the rock to hit the ground? **5 s**

26. **FORENSICS** Mr. Cooper contested a speeding ticket given to him after he applied his brakes and skidded to a halt to avoid hitting another car. In traffic court, he argued that the length of the skid marks on the pavement, 150 feet, proved that he was driving under the posted speed limit of 65 miles per hour. The ticket cited his speed at 70 miles per hour. Use the formula $\frac{1}{24}s^2 = d$, where s is the speed of the car and d is the length of the skid marks, to determine Mr. Cooper's speed when he applied the brakes. Was Mr. Cooper correct in claiming that he was not speeding when he applied the brakes? **60 mph; yes**

Chapter 8 33 *Glencoe Algebra 1*

Lesson 8-5

Word Problem Practice
CRM p. 34 AL OL BL ELL

NAME ____________ DATE ________ PERIOD ________

8-5 Word Problem Practice

Quadratic Equations: Differences of Squares

1. **LOTTERY** A state lottery commission analyzes the ticket purchasing patterns of its citizens. The following expression is developed to help officials calculate the likely number of people who will buy tickets for a certain size jackpot.

$81a^2 - 36b^2$

Factor the expression completely. **9(3a + 2b) (3a − 2b)**

2. **OPTICS** A reflector on the inside of a certain flashlight is a parabola given by the equation $y = x^2 - 25$. Find the points where the reflector meets the lens by finding the values of x when $y = 0$. **5, −5**

3. **ARCHITECTURE** The drawing shows a triangular roof truss with a base measuring the same as its height. The area of the truss is 98 square meters.

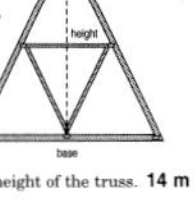

Find the height of the truss. **14 m**

4. **BALLOONING** The function $f(t) = -16t^2 + 576$ represents the height of a freely falling ballast bag that starts from rest on a balloon 576 feet above the ground. After how many seconds t does the ballast bag hit the ground? **after 6 seconds**

5. **DECORATING** Marvin wants to purchase a rectangular rug. It has an area of 80 square feet. He cannot remember the length and width, but he remembers that the length was 8 more than some number and the width was 8 less than that same number.

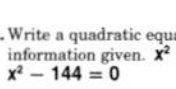

a. Write a quadratic equation using the information given. **$x^2 - 64 = 80$ or $x^2 - 144 = 0$**

b. What are the length and width of the rug? **20 ft and 4 ft**

Chapter 8 34 *Glencoe Algebra 1*

Watch Out!

Find the Error For Exercise 57, make sure students can explain what Elizabeth did wrong. Stress that her error is a common one. Ask students what they can do to avoid making the same mistake themselves.

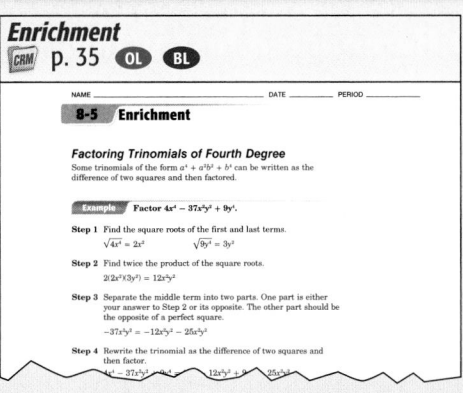

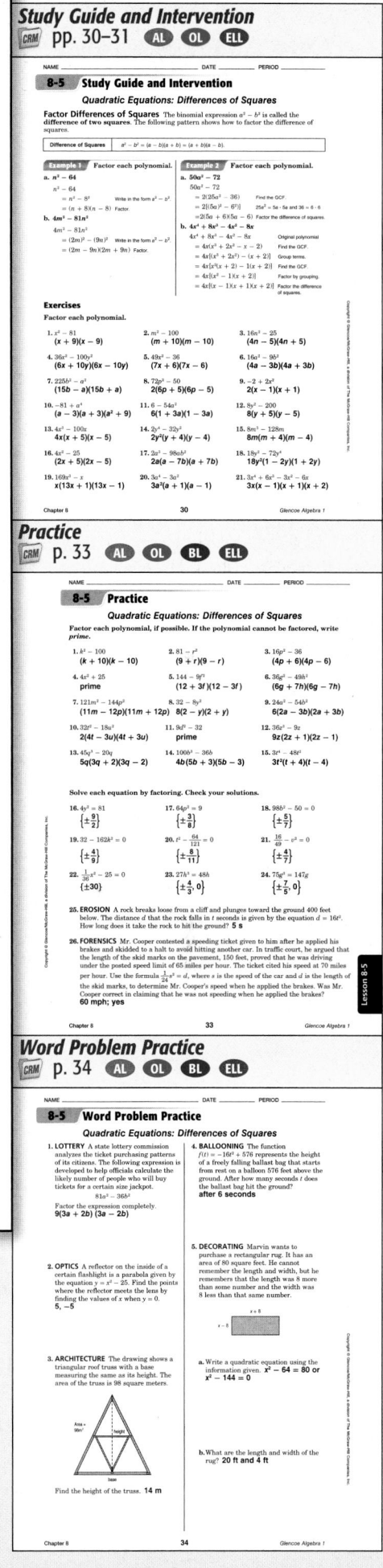

Enrichment
CRM p. 35 OL BL

NAME ____________ DATE ________ PERIOD ________

8-5 Enrichment

Factoring Trinomials of Fourth Degree

Some trinomials of the form $a^4 + a^2b^2 + b^4$ can be written as the difference of two squares and then factored.

Example Factor $4x^4 - 37x^2y^2 + 9y^4$.

Step 1 Find the square roots of the first and last terms.
$\sqrt{4x^4} = 2x^2$ $\sqrt{9y^4} = 3y^2$

Step 2 Find twice the product of the square roots.
$2(2x^2)(3y^2) = 12x^2y^2$

Step 3 Separate the middle term into two parts. One part is either your answer to Step 2 or its opposite. The other part should be the opposite of a perfect square.
$-37x^2y^2 = -12x^2y^2 - 25x^2y^2$

Step 4 Rewrite the trinomial as the difference of two squares and then factor.

4 ASSESS

Ticket Out the Door Have students write the factors of $18x^2 - 50$. $2(3x + 5)(3x - 5)$

Formative Assessment

Check for student understanding of concepts in Lessons 8-4 and 8-5.

CRM Quiz 3, p. 46

Additional Answers

75. $\{t \mid t \geq 4\}$

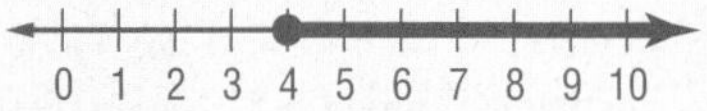

76. $\{d \mid d \leq 2\}$

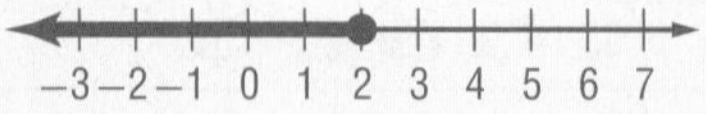

77. $\{k \mid k > 4\}$

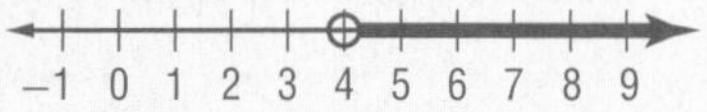

78. $\{g \mid g > 2\}$

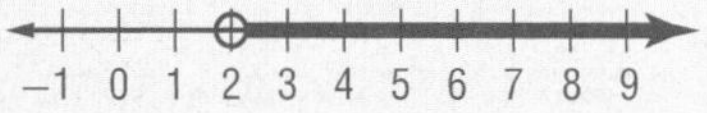

79. $\{m \mid m \geq 3\}$

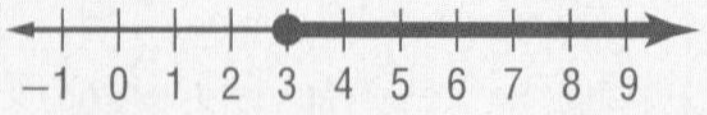

80. $\{y \mid y > -8\}$

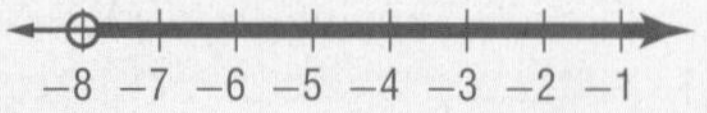

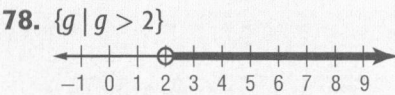

PSAE PRACTICE 8.11.18, 8.11.11, 8.11.06

64. One of the roots of $2x^2 + 13x = 24$ is -8. What is the other root? **B**

A $-\frac{3}{2}$ C $\frac{2}{3}$

B $\frac{3}{2}$ D $-\frac{2}{3}$

65. Which of the following is the sum of both solutions of the equation $x^2 + 3x = 54$? **G**

F -21 H 3

G -3 J 21

66. What are the x-intercepts of the graph of $y = -3x^2 + 7x + 20$? **C**

A $\frac{5}{3}, -4$ C $-\frac{5}{3}, 4$

B $-\frac{5}{3}, -4$ D $\frac{5}{3}, 4$

67. EXTENDED RESPONSE Two cars leave Cleveland at the same time from different parts of the city and both drive to Cincinnati. The distance in miles of the cars from the center of Cleveland can be represented by the two equations below, where t represents the time in hours. **Car A, because it is traveling at 65 mph, and Car B is traveling at 60 mph.**

Car A: $65t + 15$ Car B: $60t + 25$

a. Which car is faster? Explain.

b. Find an expression that models the distance between the two cars. $5t - 10$

c. How far apart are the cars after $2\frac{1}{2}$ hours? **2.5 mi**

Spiral Review

Factor each trinomial, if possible. If the trinomial cannot be factored using integers, write *prime*. (Lesson 8-4)

68. $5x^2 - 17x + 14$ $(5x - 7)(x - 2)$ **69.** $5a^2 - 3a + 15$ **prime** **70.** $10x^2 - 20xy + 10y^2$ $10(x - y)(x - y)$

Solve each equation. Check your solutions. (Lesson 8-3)

71. $n^2 - 9n = -18$ $\{3, 6\}$ **72.** $10 + a^2 = -7a$ $\{-5, -2\}$ **73.** $22x - x^2 = 96$ $\{6, 16\}$

74. SAVINGS Victoria and Trey each want to buy a scooter. In how many weeks will Victoria and Trey have saved the same amount of money, and how much will each of them have saved? (Lesson 6-1) **3 wk; $40**

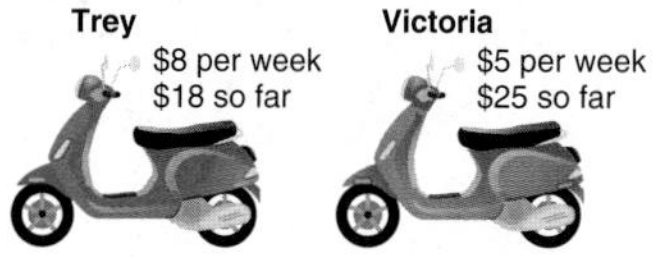

Solve each inequality. Graph the solution set on a number line. (Lesson 5-1) **75–80. See margin.**

75. $t + 14 \geq 18$ **76.** $d + 5 \leq 7$ **77.** $-5 + k > -1$

78. $5 < 3 + g$ **79.** $2 \leq -1 + m$ **80.** $2y > -8 + y$

81. FITNESS Silvia is beginning an exercise program that calls for 20 minutes of walking each day for the first week. Each week thereafter, she has to increase her daily walking for a week by 7 minutes. In which week will she first walk over an hour a day? (Lesson 3-5) **the seventh week**

Skills Review

Find each product. (Lesson 7-8)

82. $(x - 6)^2$ $x^2 - 12x + 36$ **83.** $(x - 2)(x - 2)$ $x^2 - 4x + 4$ **84.** $(x + 3)(x + 3)$ $x^2 + 6x + 9$

85. $(2x - 5)^2$ $4x^2 - 20x + 25$ **86.** $(6x - 1)^2$ $36x^2 - 12x + 1$ **87.** $(4x + 5)(4x + 5)$ $16x^2 + 40x + 25$

Differentiated Instruction OL BL

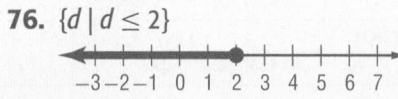

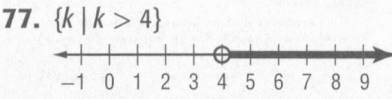

Extension Have students solve the equation $x^3 - 4x = 12 - 3x^2$ by factoring. Ask them to check their solutions. $-3, -2, 2$

8-6 Quadratic Equations: Perfect Squares

Then
You found the product of a sum and difference. (Lesson 7-8)

Now
- Factor perfect square trinomials.
- Solve equations involving perfect squares.

IL Learning Standards
8.A.4b Represent mathematical patterns and describe their properties using variables and mathematical symbols. **8.D.4 Formulate and solve** linear and **quadratic equations** and linear inequalities **algebraically** and investigate nonlinear inequalities using graphs, tables, calculators and computers. *Also addresses 7.A.4b and 7.B.4.*

New Vocabulary
perfect square trinomial

IL Math Online
glencoe.com
- Extra Examples
- Personal Tutor
- Self-Check Quiz
- Homework Help
- Math in Motion

Why?

In a vacuum, a feather and a piano would fall at the same speed, or velocity. To find about how long it takes an object to hit the ground if it is dropped from an initial height of h_0 feet above ground, you would need to solve the equation $0 = -16t^2 + h_0$, where t is time in seconds after the object is dropped.

Factor Perfect Square Trinomials In Lesson 7-8, you learned the patterns for the products of the binomials $(a + b)^2$ and $(a - b)^2$. Recall that these are special products that follow specific patterns.

$$(a + b)^2 = (a + b)(a + b) = a^2 + ab + ab + b^2 = a^2 + 2ab + b^2$$

$$(a - b)^2 = (a - b)(a - b) = a^2 - ab - ab + b^2 = a^2 - 2ab + b^2$$

These products are called **perfect square trinomials**, because they are the squares of binomials. The above patterns can help you factor perfect square trinomials.

For a trinomial to be factorable as a perfect square, the first and last terms must be perfect squares and the middle term must be two times the square roots of the first and last terms.

The trinomial $16x^2 + 24x + 9$ is a perfect square trinomial, as illustrated below.

$$16x^2 + 24x + 9$$

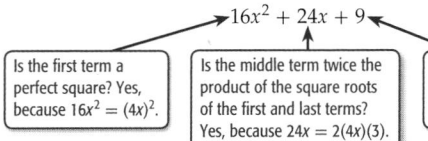

- Is the first term a perfect square? Yes, because $16x^2 = (4x)^2$.
- Is the middle term twice the product of the square roots of the first and last terms? Yes, because $24x = 2(4x)(3)$.
- Is the last term a perfect square? Yes, because $9 = 3^2$.

Key Concept — Factoring Perfect Square Trinomials — For Your FOLDABLE

Symbols $a^2 + 2ab + b^2 = (a + b)(a + b) = (a + b)^2$

$a^2 - 2ab + b^2 = (a - b)(a - b) = (a - b)^2$

Examples $x^2 + 8x + 16 = (x + 4)(x + 4)$ or $(x + 4)^2$

$x^2 - 6x + 9 = (x - 3)(x - 3)$ or $(x - 3)^2$

8-6 Lesson Notes

1 FOCUS

Vertical Alignment

Before Lesson 8-6
Find the product of the sum and difference of two quantities.

Lesson 8-6
Factor perfect square trinomials. Solve equations involving perfect squares.

After Lesson 8-6
Solve quadratic equations by using the quadratic formula.

2 TEACH

Scaffolding Questions

Have students read the *Why?* section of the lesson.

Ask:
- If the initial height is 64 feet, what equation would you write to determine how long it takes an object to hit the ground? $0 = -16t^2 + 64$
- Solve the equation for t. $-16(t - 2)(t + 2) = 0$; 2 seconds
- How could you use the definition of square root to solve the equation? $0 = -16t^2 + 64$; $-64 = -16t^2$; $4 = t^2$; $t = \pm\sqrt{4}$ or ± 2; Since a negative answer is not reasonable in this situation, the solution is $t = 2$.

Lesson 8-6 Resources

Resource	Approaching-Level	On-Level	Beyond-Level	English Learners
Teacher Edition	• Differentiated Instruction, p. 506	• Differentiated Instruction, pp. 506, 512	• Differentiated Instruction, p. 512	
Chapter Resource Masters	• Study Guide and Intervention, pp. 37–38 • Skills Practice, p. 39 • Practice, p. 40 • Word Problem Practice, p. 41	• Study Guide and Intervention, pp. 37–38 • Skills Practice, p. 39 • Practice, p. 40 • Word Problem Practice, p. 41 • Enrichment, p. 42	• Practice, p. 40 • Word Problem Practice, p. 41 • Enrichment, p. 42	• Study Guide and Intervention, pp. 37–38 • Skills Practice, p. 39 • Practice, p. 40
Transparencies	• 5-Minute Check Transparency 8-6	• 5-Minute Check Transparency 8-6	• 5-Minute Check Transparency 8-6	• 5-Minute Check Transparency 8-6
Other	• Study Notebook • Teaching Algebra with Manipulatives	• Study Notebook • Teaching Algebra with Manipulatives	• Study Notebook	• Study Notebook • Teaching Algebra with Manipulatives

Factor Perfect Square Trinomials

Example 1 shows how to determine whether a trinomial is a perfect square trinomial and, if it is, how to factor it. **Example 2** shows how to use various factoring methods to factor a polynomial completely.

Formative Assessment

Use the Check Your Progress exercises after each example to determine students' understanding of concepts.

Additional Example

1 Determine whether each trinomial is a perfect square trinomial. Write *yes* or *no*. If it is a perfect square, factor it.

a. $25x^2 - 30x + 9$ yes; $(5x - 3)^2$

b. $49y^2 + 42y + 36$ *no*

Additional Examples also in Interactive Classroom PowerPoint® Presentations

IWB INTERACTIVE WHITEBOARD READY

Watch Out!

Preventing Errors Students should be reminded to look closely at the coefficient of the second term of a perfect square trinomial. Its sign determines whether the factors are in the form $(a + b)$ or $(a - b)$.

TEACH with TECH

BLOG On your secure classroom blog have students create a blog entry explaining the inverse relationship between squaring a binomial and factoring a perfect square trinomial.

StudyTip

Recognizing Perfect Square Trinomials If the constant term of the trinomial is negative, the trinomial is not a perfect square trinomial, so it is not necessary to check the other conditions.

EXAMPLE 1 Recognize and Factor Perfect Square Trinomials

Determine whether each trinomial is a perfect square trinomial. Write *yes* or *no*. If so, factor it.

a. $4y^2 + 12y + 9$

1. Is the first term a perfect square? Yes, $4y^2 = (2y)^2$.
2. Is the last term a perfect square? Yes, $9 = 3^2$.
3. Is the middle term equal to $2(2y)(3)$? Yes, $12y = 2(2y)(3)$

Since all three conditions are satisfied, $4y^2 + 12y + 9$ is a perfect square trinomial.

$4y^2 + 12y + 9 = (2y)^2 + 2(2y)(3) + 3^2$ **Write as $a^2 + 2ab + b^2$.**

$= (2y + 3)^2$ **Factor using the pattern.**

b. $9x^2 - 6x + 4$

1. Is the first term a perfect square? Yes, $9x^2 = (3x)^2$.
2. Is the last term a perfect square? Yes, $4 = 2^2$.
3. Is the middle term equal to $-2(3x)(2)$? No, $-6x \neq -2(3x)(2)$.

Since the middle term does not satisfy the required condition, $9x^2 - 6x + 4$ is not a perfect square trinomial.

Check Your Progress

1A. $9y^2 + 24y + 16$ yes; $(3y + 4)(3y + 4)$ **1B.** $2a^2 + 10a + 25$ no

Personal Tutor glencoe.com

A polynomial is completely factored when it is written as a product of prime polynomials. More than one method might be needed to factor a polynomial completely. When completely factoring a polynomial, the Concept Summary can help you decide where to start.

Remember, if the polynomial does not fit any pattern or cannot be factored, the polynomial is prime.

Concept Summary Factoring Methods — For Your FOLDABLE

Steps		Number of Terms	Examples
Step 1	Factor out the GCF.	any	$4x^3 + 2x^2 - 6x = 2x(2x^2 + x - 3)$
Step 2	Check for a difference of squares or a perfect square trinomial.	2 or 3	$9x^2 - 16 = (3x + 4)(3x - 4)$ $16x^2 + 24x + 9 = (4x + 3)^2$
Step 3	Apply the factoring patterns for $x^2 + bx + c$ or $ax^2 + bx + c$ (general trinomials), or factor by grouping.	3 or 4	$x^2 - 8x + 12 = (x - 2)(x - 6)$ $2x^2 + 13x + 6 = (2x + 1)(x + 6)$ $12y^2 + 9y + 8y + 6$ $= (12y^2 + 9y) + (8y + 6)$ $= 3y(4y + 3) + 2(4y + 3)$ $= (4y + 3)(3y + 2)$

EXAMPLE 2 Factor Completely

Factor each polynomial, if possible. If the polynomial cannot be factored, write *prime*.

a. $5x^2 - 80$

Step 1 The GCF of $5x^2$ and -80 is 5, so factor it out.

Step 2 Since there are two terms, check for a difference of squares.

$5x^2 - 80 = 5(x^2 - 16)$	**5 is the GCF of the terms.**
$= 5(x^2 - 4^2)$	**$x^2 = x \cdot x$ and $16 = 4 \cdot 4$**
$= 5(x - 4)(x + 4)$	**Factor the difference of squares.**

b. $9x^2 - 6x - 35$

Step 1 The GCF of $9x^2$, $-6x$, and -35 is 1.

Step 2 Since 35 is not a perfect square, this is not a perfect square trinomial.

Step 3 Factor using the pattern $ax^2 + bx + c$. Are there two numbers with a product of $9(-35)$ or -315 and a sum of -6? Yes, the product of 15 and -21 is -315, and the sum is -6.

$9x^2 - 6x - 35 = 9x^2 + mx + nx - 35$	**Write the pattern.**
$= 9x^2 + 15x - 21x - 35$	**$m = 15$ and $n = -21$**
$= (9x^2 + 15x) + (-21x - 35)$	**Group terms with common factors.**
$= 3x(3x + 5) - 7(3x + 5)$	**Factor out the GCF from each grouping.**
$= (3x + 5)(3x - 7)$	**$3x + 5$ is the common factor.**

StudyTip

Check Your Answer You can check your answer by:
- Using the FOIL method.
- Using the Distributive Property.
- Graphing the original expression and factored expression and comparing the graphs.

If the product of the factors does not match the original expression exactly, the answer is incorrect.

Check Your Progress

2A. $2x^2 - 32$ $2(x - 4)(x + 4)$ **2B.** $12x^2 + 5x - 25$ $(4x - 5)(3x + 5)$

Personal Tutor glencoe.com

Solve Equations with Perfect Squares When solving equations involving repeated factors, it is only necessary to set one of the repeated factors equal to zero.

EXAMPLE 3 Solve Equations with Repeated Factors

Solve $9x^2 - 48x = -64$.

$9x^2 - 48x = -64$	**Original equation**
$9x^2 - 48x + 64 = 0$	**Add 64 to each side.**
$(3x)^2 - 2(3x)(8) + (8)^2 = 0$	**Recognize $9x^2 - 48x + 64$ as a perfect square trinomial.**
$(3x - 8)^2 = 0$	**Factor the perfect square trinomial.**
$(3x - 8)(3x - 8) = 0$	**Write $(3x - 8)^2$ as two factors.**
$3x - 8 = 0$	**Set the repeated factor equal to zero.**
$3x = 8$	**Add 8 to each side.**
$x = \frac{8}{3}$	**Divide each side by 3.**

Check Your Progress

Solve each equation. Check your solutions.

3A. $a^2 + 12a + 36 = 0$ -6 **3B.** $y^2 - \frac{4}{3}y + \frac{4}{9} = 0$ $\frac{2}{3}$

Personal Tutor glencoe.com

Watch Out!

Common Errors Students often fail to factor polynomials completely. Point out that $4x^2 - 36$ is a difference of squares and can be factored as $(2x - 6)(2x + 6)$, but remind students that a polynomial is not considered completely factored if the terms of any of its factors have a GCF greater than 1.

Student Misconceptions Students have been taught that second-degree equations will have two solutions, so they may be confused when an equation involving a perfect square trinomial has only one solution. Explain that perfect square trinomials have a repeated factor, so that both solutions are the same number. Thus, only one solution is listed.

Additional Example

2 Factor each polynomial if possible. If the polynomial cannot be factored, write *prime*.

a. $6x^2 - 96$ $6(x + 4)(x - 4)$

b. $16y^2 + 8y - 15$ $(4y + 5)(4y - 3)$

Solve Equations with Perfect Squares

Example 3 shows how to solve equations with repeated factors. **Examples 4** and **5** show how to solve equations using the Square Root Property.

Additional Example

3 Solve $4x^2 + 36x = -81$. $-\frac{9}{2}$

Focus on Mathematical Content

Factor Perfect Square Trinomials Once a trinomial has been determined to be a perfect square trinomial, it can be factored into two identical binomials or expressed as a binomial squared. The binomial factors are the sum or difference, depending on the sign of the middle term of the trinomial, of the principal square roots of the first term and last term of the trinomial.

Additional Example

4 Solve each equation. Check the solutions.

a. $(b - 7)^2 = 36$ 1, 13

b. $(x + 9)^2 = 8$ $-9 \pm 2\sqrt{2}$

Tips for New Teachers

Solutions to Second-Degree Equations If students do not understand how a second-degree equation can have only one solution, suggest that they graph a perfect square trinomial on a graphing calculator. The graph will immediately reveal how this is possible. The vertex of the graph of a perfect square trinomial equation lies on the x-axis, and therefore the equation has only one solution.

You have solved equations like $x^2 - 16 = 0$ by factoring. You can also use the definition of a square root to solve the equation.

$x^2 - 16 = 0$	Original equation
$x^2 = 16$	Add 16 to each side.
$x = \pm\sqrt{16}$	Take the square root of each side.

ReadingMath

Square Root Solutions $\pm\sqrt{16}$ is read as *plus or minus the square root of 16.*

Remember that there are two square roots of 16, namely 4 and −4. Therefore, the solution set is {−4, 4}. You can express this as {±4}.

Key Concept — Square Root Property

For Your FOLDABLE

Words To solve a quadratic equation in the form $x^2 = n$, take the square root of each side.

Symbols For any number $n \geq 0$, if $x^2 = n$, then $x = \pm\sqrt{n}$.

Example $x^2 = 25$

$x = \pm\sqrt{25}$ or ± 5

In the equation $x^2 = n$, if n is not a perfect square, you need to approximate the square root. Use a calculator to find an approximation. If n is a perfect square, you will have an exact answer.

EXAMPLE 4 Use the Square Root Property

Solve each equation. Check your solutions.

a. $(y - 6)^2 = 81$

$(y - 6)^2 = 81$	Original equation
$y - 6 = \pm\sqrt{81}$	Square Root Property
$y - 6 = \pm 9$	$81 = 9 \cdot 9$
$y = 6 \pm 9$	Add 6 to each side.
$y = 6 + 9$ or $y = 6 - 9$	Separate into two equations.
$= 15$ $\quad = -3$	Simplify.
The roots are 15 and −3.	Check in the original equation.

b. $(x + 6)^2 = 12$

$(x + 6)^2 = 12$	Original equation
$x + 6 = \pm\sqrt{12}$	Square Root Property
$x = -6 \pm \sqrt{12}$	Subtract 6 from each side.

The roots are $-6 \pm \sqrt{12}$ or $-6 + \sqrt{12}$ and $-6 - \sqrt{12}$.

Using a calculator, $-6 + \sqrt{12} \approx -2.54$ and $-6 - \sqrt{12} \approx -9.46$.

Math *in Motion,* Interactive Lab glencoe.com

Check Your Progress

4A. $(a - 10)^2 = 121$ 21, −1

4B. $(z + 3)^2 = 26$ $-3 \pm \sqrt{26}$ or about 2.1 and −8.1

Personal Tutor glencoe.com

508 Chapter 8 Factoring and Quadratic Equations

Math History Link

Galileo Galilei (1564–1642)
Galileo was the first person to prove that objects of different weights fall at the same velocity by dropping two objects of different weights from the top of the Leaning Tower of Pisa in 1589.

Real-World EXAMPLE 5 Solve an Equation

PHYSICAL SCIENCE During an experiment, a ball is dropped from a height of 205 feet. The formula $h = -16t^2 + h_0$ can be used to approximate the number of seconds t it takes for the ball to reach height h from an initial height of h_0 in feet. Find the time it takes the ball to reach the ground.

At ground level, $h = 0$ and the initial height is 205, so $h_0 = 205$.

$h = -16t^2 + h_0$	**Original Formula**
$0 = -16t^2 + 205$	**Replace h with 0 and h_0 with 205.**
$-205 = -16t^2$	**Subtract 205 from each side.**
$12.8125 = t^2$	**Divide each side by −16.**
$\pm 3.6 \approx t$	**Use the Square Root Property.**

Since a negative number does not make sense in this situation, the solution is 3.6. It takes about 3.6 seconds for the ball to reach the ground.

Check Your Progress

5. Find the time it takes a ball to reach the ground if it is dropped from a bridge that is half as high as the one described above. about 2.5 seconds

Personal Tutor glencoe.com

Check Your Understanding

Example 1 p. 506
Determine whether each trinomial is a perfect square trinomial. Write *yes* or *no*. If so, factor it.

1. $25x^2 + 60x + 36$ yes; $(5x + 6)^2$
2. $6x^2 + 30x + 36$ no

Example 2 p. 507
Factor each polynomial, if possible. If the polynomial cannot be factored, write *prime*.

3. $2x^2 - x - 28$ $(x - 4)(2x + 7)$
4. $6x^2 - 34x + 48$ $2(x - 3)(3x - 8)$
5. $4x^2 + 64$ $4(x^2 + 16)$
6. $4x^2 + 9x - 16$ prime

Examples 3 and 4 pp. 507–508
Solve each equation. Check your solutions.

7. $4x^2 = 36$ ± 3
8. $25a^2 - 40a = -16$ $\frac{4}{5}$
9. $64y^2 - 48y + 18 = 9$ $\frac{3}{8}$
10. $(z + 5)^2 = 47$ $-5 \pm \sqrt{47}$ or about −11.86 and 1.86

Example 5 p. 509
11. PAINT While painting his bedroom, Nick drops his paintbrush off his ladder from a height of 6 feet. Use the formula $h = -16t^2 + h_0$ to approximate the number of seconds it takes for the paintbrush to hit the floor. 0.6 second

Practice and Problem Solving

● = **Step-by-Step Solutions** begin on page R12.
Extra Practice begins on page 815.

Example 1 p. 506
Determine whether each trinomial is a perfect square trinomial. Write *yes* or *no*. If so, factor it.

12. $4x^2 - 42x + 110$ no
13. $16x^2 - 56x + 49$ yes; $(4x - 7)^2$
14. $81x^2 - 90x + 25$ yes; $(9x - 5)^2$
15. $x^2 + 26x + 168$ no

Additional Example

5 **PHYSICAL SCIENCE** A book falls from a shelf that is 5 feet above the floor. A model for the height h in feet if an object dropped from an initial height of h_0 feet is $h = -16t^2 + h_0$, where t is the time in seconds after the object is dropped. Use this model to determine approximately how long it took for the book to reach the ground. 0.56 s

Tips for New Teachers

Formulas Students are naturally curious about *why* certain formulas work. Encourage this curiosity and ask students to develop a way to test the formula $h = -16t^2 + h_0$ from Example 5. What assumptions must be made for the formula to hold true?

3 PRACTICE

Formative Assessment

Use Exercises 1–11 to check for understanding.

Use the chart at the bottom of this page to customize assignments for your students.

Watch Out!

Factoring Remind students that any of the factoring methods they have studied thus far can be used in the exercises.

Differentiated Homework Options

Level	Assignment	Two-Day Option	
AL Basic	12–47, 53, 55–85	13–47 odd, 61–64	12–46 even, 53, 55–60, 65–85
OL Core	13–47 odd, 48–53, 55–85	12–47, 61–64	48–53, 55–60, 65–85
BL Advanced	48–79, (optional: 80–85)		

Watch Out!

Find the Error For Exercise 53, point out to students that they must always take a final look at the factors to be sure they are all factored completely.

Additional Answers

57. First look for a GCF in all the terms and factor the GCF out of all the terms. Then, if the polynomial has two terms, check if the terms are the differences of squares and factor if so. If the polynomial has three terms, check if the polynomial if a perfect square polynomial and factor if so. If the polynomial has four or more terms, factor by grouping. If the polynomial does not have a GCF and cannot be factored, the polynomial is a prime polynomial.

59. Sample answer: $x^4 - 1$; 1, −1

60. Determine if the first and last terms are perfect squares. Then determine if the middle term must be equal to ±2 times the principal square roots of the first and last terms. If these three criteria are met, the trinomial is a perfect square trinomial.

Example 2 p. 507

Factor each polynomial, if possible. If the polynomial cannot be factored, write *prime*. 21. $2m(2m - 7)(3m + 5)$

16. $24d^2 + 39d - 18$ $3(8d - 3)(d + 2)$
17. $8x^2 + 10x - 21$ prime
18. $2b^2 + 12b - 24$ $2(b^2 + 6b - 12)$
19. $8y^2 - 200z^2$ $8(y - 5z)(y + 5z)$
20. $16a^2 - 121b^2$ $(4a - 11b)(4a + 11b)$
21. $12m^3 - 22m^2 - 70m$
22. $8c^2 - 88c + 242$ $2(2c - 11)^2$
23. $12x^2 - 84x + 147$ $3(2x - 7)^2$
24. $w^4 - w^2$ $w^2(w - 1)(w + 1)$
25. $12p^3 - 3p$ $3p(2p + 1)(2p - 1)$
26. $16q^3 - 48q^2 + 36q$ $4q(2q - 3)^2$
27. $4t^3 + 10t^2 - 84t$ $2t(t + 6)(2t - 7)$
28. $x^3 + 2x^2y - 4x - 8y$
29. $2a^2b^2 - 2a^2 - 2ab^3 + 2ab$
30. $2r^3 - r^2 - 72r + 36$
31. $3k^3 - 24k^2 + 48k$ $3k(k - 4)(k - 4)$
32. $4c^4d - 10c^3d + 4c^2d^3 - 10cd^3$ $2cd(c^2 + d^2)(2c - 5)$
33. $g^2 + 2g - 3h^2 + 4h$ prime

30. $(r - 6)(r + 6)(2r - 1)$
28. $(x + 2y)(x - 2)(x + 2)$
29. $2a(a - b)(b + 1)(b - 1)$

Examples 3 and 4 pp. 507–508

Solve each equation. Check the solutions.

34. $4m^2 - 24m + 36 = 0$ 3
35. $(y - 4)^2 = 7$ $4 \pm \sqrt{7}$
36. $a^2 + \frac{10}{7}a + \frac{25}{49} = 0$ $-\frac{5}{7}$
37. $x^2 - \frac{3}{2}x + \frac{9}{16} = 0$ $\frac{3}{4}$
38. $x^2 + 8x + 16 = 25$ 1, −9
39. $5x^2 - 60x = -180$ 6
40. $4x^2 = 80x - 400$ 10
41. $9 - 54x = -81x^2$ $\frac{1}{3}$
42. $4c^2 + 4c + 1 = 15$ $\frac{-1 \pm \sqrt{15}}{2}$
43. $x^2 - 16x + 64 = 6$ $8 \pm \sqrt{6}$

44. **PHYSICAL SCIENCE** For an experiment in physics class, a water balloon is dropped from the window of the school building. The window is 40 feet high. How long does it take until the balloon hits the ground? Round to the nearest hundredth. 1.58 seconds

45. **SCREENS** The area A in square feet of a projected picture on a movie screen can be modeled by the equation $A = 0.25d^2$, where d represents the distance from a projector to a movie screen. At what distance will the projected picture have an area of 100 square feet? 20 ft

48b. 8 in. high by 14 in. long by 6 in. wide
49a. $w^3 + 14w^2 + 48w$
49b. 4 in. wide by 10 in. long by 12 in. high

Example 5 p. 509

46. **GEOMETRY** The area of a square is represented by $9x^2 - 42x + 49$. Find the length of each side. $|3x - 7|$

47. **GEOMETRY** The area of a square is represented by $16x^2 + 40x + 25$. Find the length of each side. $|4x + 5|$

Real-World Link

The Shedd Aquarium in Chicago, Illinois, is home to over 1500 species of fish and mammals.

Source: *Chicago Traveler*

48. **ELECTION** For the student council elections, Franco is building the voting box shown with a volume of 672 cubic inches.

a. Write a polynomial that represents the volume of the box. $h^3 + 4h^2 - 12h$

b. What are the dimensions of the voting box?

49. **AQUARIUM** Dexter has a fish tank shaped like a rectangular prism. It has a volume of 480 cubic inches. The height of the tank is 8 inches taller than the width, and the length of the tank is 6 inches longer than the width.

a. Write a polynomial that represents the volume of the fish tank.

b. What are the dimensions of the fish tank?

510 Chapter 8 Factoring and Quadratic Equations

Real-World Link

In 2005, 219,000 above-ground swimming pools were sold. This brought the total number of above-ground swimming pools in the United States to 3.6 million.

Source: Association of Pool & Spa Professionals

50. GEOMETRY The volume of a rectangular prism is represented by the expression $8y^3 + 40y^2 + 50y$. Find the possible dimensions of the prism if the dimensions are represented by polynomials with integer coefficients. **Sample answer: $2y$, $2y + 5$, $2y + 5$**

51. POOLS Ichiro wants to buy an above-ground swimming pool for his yard. Model A is 42 inches deep and holds 1750 cubic feet of water. The length of the rectangular pool is 5 feet more than the width.

a. What is the surface area of the water? **500 ft²**

b. What are the dimensions of the pool? **20 ft by 25 ft by 42 in.**

c. Model B pool holds twice as much water as Model A. What are some possible dimensions for this pool? **Sample answer: 20 ft by 50 ft by 42 in.**

d. Model C has length and width that are both twice as long as Model A, but the height is the same. What is the ratio of the volume of Model A to Model C? **1:4**

52. GEOMETRY Use the rectangular prism at the right.

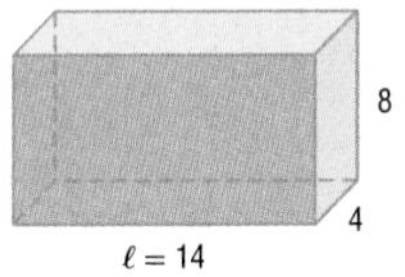

a. Write an expression for the height and width of the prism in terms of the length, ℓ.

b. Write a polynomial for the volume of the prism in terms of the length.

H.O.T. Problems

Use **H**igher-**O**rder **T**hinking Skills

53. FIND THE ERROR Debbie and Adriano are factoring the expression $x^8 - x^4$ completely. Is either of them correct? Explain your reasoning.

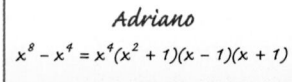

Debbie	Adriano
$x^8 - x^4 = x^4(x^2 + 1)(x^2 - 1)$	$x^8 - x^4 = x^4(x^2 + 1)(x - 1)(x + 1)$

54. CHALLENGE Factor $x^{n+6} + x^{n+2} + x^n$ completely. **$x^n(x^6 + x^2 + 1)$**

55. OPEN ENDED Write a perfect square trinomial equation in which the coefficient of the middle term is negative and the last term is a fraction. Solve the equation.

56. REASONING Find a counterexample to the following statement.

A polynomial equation of degree three always has three real solutions.

57. WRITING IN MATH Explain how to factor a polynomial completely. **See margin.**

58. WHICH ONE DOESN'T BELONG? Identify the trinomial that does not belong. Explain.

$4x^2 - 36x + 81$	$25x^2 + 10x + 1$	$4x^2 + 10x + 4$	$9x^2 - 24x + 16$

59. OPEN ENDED Write a binomial that can be factored using the difference of two squares twice. Set your binomial equal to zero and solve the equation. **See margin.**

60. WRITING IN MATH Explain how to determine whether a trinomial is a perfect square trinomial. **See margin.**

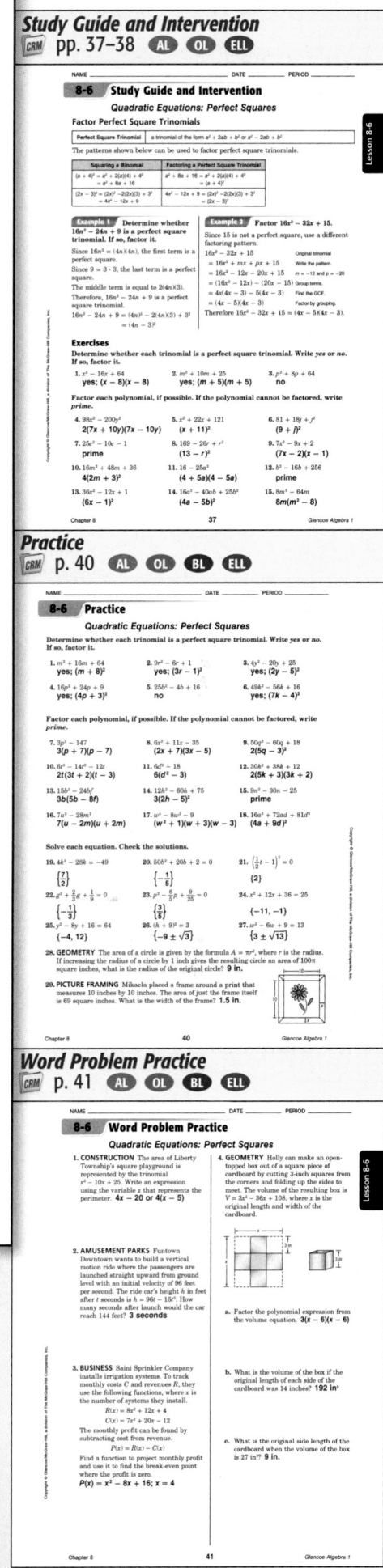

52a. height $= \ell - 6$; width $= \ell - 10$

52b. $V = \ell^3 - 16\ell^2 + 60\ell$

53. Adriano; Debbie did not factor the expression completely.

55. Sample answer: $x^2 - 3x + \frac{9}{4} = 0$; $\left\{\frac{3}{2}\right\}$

56. Sample answer: The equation $x^3 + x^2 + x + 1 = 0$ only has one solution. The polynomial factors to $(x^2 + 1)(x + 1)$ and setting those factors equal to zero gives us only one solution $x = -1$ since $x^2 + 1$ has no real solutions.

58. $4x^2 + 10x + 4$ because it is the only expression that is not a perfect square trinomial.

Study Guide and Intervention

CRM pp. 37–38 AL OL ELL

NAME ______ DATE ______ PERIOD ______

8-6 Study Guide and Intervention

Quadratic Equations: Perfect Squares

Factor Perfect Square Trinomials

Perfect Square Trinomial	a trinomial of the form $a^2 + 2ab + b^2$ or $a^2 - 2ab + b^2$

The patterns shown below can be used to factor perfect square trinomials.

Squaring a Binomial	Factoring a Perfect Square Trinomial
$(a + 4)^2 = a^2 + 2(a)(4) + 4^2$ $= a^2 + 8a + 16$	$a^2 + 8a + 16 = a^2 + 2(a)(4) + 4^2$ $= (a + 4)^2$
$(2x - 3)^2 = (2x)^2 - 2(2x)(3) + 3^2$ $= 4x^2 - 12x + 9$	$4x^2 - 12x + 9 = (2x)^2 - 2(2x)(3) + 3^2$ $= (2x - 3)^2$

Example 1 Determine whether $16n^2 - 24n + 9$ is a perfect square trinomial. If so, factor it.

Since $16n^2 = (4n)(4n)$, the first term is a perfect square.

Since $9 = 3 \cdot 3$, the last term is a perfect square.

The middle term is equal to $2(4n)(3)$.

Therefore, $16n^2 - 24n + 9$ is a perfect square trinomial.

$16n^2 - 24n + 9 = (4n)^2 - 2(4n)(3) + 3^2$
$= (4n - 3)^2$

Example 2 Factor $16x^2 - 32x + 15$.

Since 15 is not a perfect square, use a different factoring pattern.

$16x^2 - 32x + 15$ — Original trinomial
$= 16x^2 + mx + px + 15$ — Write the pattern.
$= 16x^2 - 12x - 20x + 15$ — $m = -12$ and $p = -20$
$= (16x^2 - 12x) - (20x - 15)$ — Group terms.
$= 4x(4x - 3) - 5(4x - 3)$ — Find the GCF.
$= (4x - 5)(4x - 3)$ — Factor by grouping.

Therefore $16x^2 - 32x + 15 = (4x - 5)(4x - 3)$.

Exercises

Determine whether each trinomial is a perfect square trinomial. Write *yes* or *no*. If so, factor it.

1. $x^2 - 16x + 64$ **yes; $(x - 8)(x - 8)$**
2. $m^2 + 10m + 25$ **yes; $(m + 5)(m + 5)$**
3. $p^2 + 8p + 64$ **no**

Factor each polynomial, if possible. If the polynomial cannot be factored, write *prime*.

4. $98x^2 - 200y^2$ **$2(7x + 10y)(7x - 10y)$**
5. $x^2 + 22x + 121$ **$(x + 11)^2$**
6. $81 + 18j + j^2$ **$(9 + j)^2$**
7. $25c^2 - 10c - 1$ **prime**
8. $169 - 26r + r^2$ **$(13 - r)^2$**
9. $7x^2 - 9x + 2$ **$(7x - 2)(x - 1)$**
10. $16m^2 + 48m + 36$ **$4(2m + 3)^2$**
11. $16 - 25a^2$ **$(4 + 5a)(4 - 5a)$**
12. $b^2 - 16b + 256$ **prime**
13. $36x^2 - 12x + 1$ **$(6x - 1)^2$**
14. $16a^2 - 40ab + 25b^2$ **$(4a - 5b)^2$**
15. $8m^3 - 64m$ **$8m(m^2 - 8)$**

Chapter 8 37 Glencoe Algebra 1

Lesson 8-6

Practice

CRM p. 40 AL OL BL ELL

NAME ______ DATE ______ PERIOD ______

8-6 Practice

Quadratic Equations: Perfect Squares

Determine whether each trinomial is a perfect square trinomial. Write *yes* or *no*. If so, factor it.

1. $m^2 + 16m + 64$ **yes; $(m + 8)^2$**
2. $9r^2 - 6r + 1$ **yes; $(3r - 1)^2$**
3. $4y^2 - 20y + 25$ **yes; $(2y - 5)^2$**
4. $16p^2 + 24p + 9$ **yes; $(4p + 3)^2$**
5. $25b^2 - 4b + 16$ **no**
6. $49k^2 - 56k + 16$ **yes; $(7k - 4)^2$**

Factor each polynomial, if possible. If the polynomial cannot be factored, write *prime*.

7. $3p^2 - 147$ **$3(p + 7)(p - 7)$**
8. $6x^2 + 11x - 35$ **$(2x + 7)(3x - 5)$**
9. $50q^2 - 60q + 18$ **$2(5q - 3)^2$**
10. $6t^3 - 14t^2 - 12t$ **$2t(3t + 2)(t - 3)$**
11. $6d^2 - 18$ **$6(d^2 - 3)$**
12. $30k^2 + 38k + 12$ **$2(5k + 3)(3k + 2)$**
13. $15b^2 - 24bf$ **$3b(5b - 8f)$**
14. $12h^2 - 60h + 75$ **$3(2h - 5)^2$**
15. $9n^2 - 30n - 25$ **prime**
16. $7u^2 - 28m^2$ **$7(u - 2m)(u + 2m)$**
17. $w^4 - 8w^2 - 9$ **$(w^2 + 1)(w + 3)(w - 3)$**
18. $16a^2 + 72ad + 81d^2$ **$(4a + 9d)^2$**

Solve each equation. Check the solutions.

19. $4k^2 - 28k = -49$ **$\left\{\frac{7}{2}\right\}$**
20. $50b^2 + 20b + 2 = 0$ **$\left\{-\frac{1}{5}\right\}$**
21. $\left(\frac{1}{2}t - 1\right)^2 = 0$ **$\{2\}$**
22. $g^2 + \frac{2}{3}g + \frac{1}{9} = 0$ **$\left\{-\frac{1}{3}\right\}$**
23. $p^2 - \frac{6}{5}p + \frac{9}{25} = 0$ **$\left\{\frac{3}{5}\right\}$**
24. $x^2 + 12x + 36 = 25$ **$\{-11, -1\}$**
25. $y^2 - 8y + 16 = 64$ **$\{-4, 12\}$**
26. $(h + 9)^2 = 3$ **$\{-9 \pm \sqrt{3}\}$**
27. $w^2 - 6w + 9 = 13$ **$\{3 \pm \sqrt{13}\}$**

28. **GEOMETRY** The area of a circle is given by the formula $A = \pi r^2$, where r is the radius. If increasing the radius of a circle by 1 inch gives the resulting circle an area of 100π square inches, what is the radius of the original circle? **9 in.**

29. **PICTURE FRAMING** Mikaela placed a frame around a print that measures 10 inches by 10 inches. The area of just the frame itself is 69 square inches. What is the width of the frame? **1.5 in.**

Chapter 8 40 Glencoe Algebra 1

Word Problem Practice

CRM p. 41 AL OL BL ELL

NAME ______ DATE ______ PERIOD ______

8-6 Word Problem Practice

Quadratic Equations: Perfect Squares

1. **CONSTRUCTION** The area of Liberty Township's square playground is represented by the trinomial $x^2 - 10x + 25$. Write an expression using the variable x that represents the perimeter. **$4x - 20$ or $4(x - 5)$**

2. **AMUSEMENT PARKS** Funtown Downtown wants to build a vertical motion ride where the passengers are launched straight upward from ground level with an initial velocity of 96 feet per second. The ride car's height h in feet after t seconds is $h = 96t - 16t^2$. How many seconds after launch would the car reach 144 feet? **3 seconds**

3. **BUSINESS** Saini Sprinkler Company installs irrigation systems. To track monthly costs C and revenues R, they use the following functions, where x is the number of systems they install.

$R(x) = 8x^2 + 12x + 4$

$C(x) = 7x^2 + 20x - 12$

The monthly profit can be found by subtracting cost from revenue.

$P(x) = R(x) - C(x)$

Find a function to project monthly profit and use it to find the break-even point where the profit is zero.
$P(x) = x^2 - 8x + 16$; $x = 4$

4. **GEOMETRY** Holly can make an open-topped box out of a square piece of cardboard by cutting 3-inch squares from the corners and folding up the sides to meet. The volume of the resulting box is $V = 3x^2 - 36x + 108$, where x is the original length and width of the cardboard.

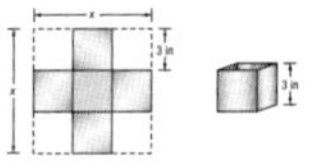

a. Factor the polynomial expression from the volume equation. **$3(x - 6)(x - 6)$**

b. What is the volume of the box if the original length of each side of the cardboard was 14 inches? **192 in³**

c. What is the original side length of the cardboard when the volume of the box is 27 in³? **9 in.**

Chapter 8 41 Glencoe Algebra 1

Lesson 8-6

Enrichment

CRM p. 42 OL BL

NAME ______ DATE ______ PERIOD ______

8-6 Enrichment

Squaring Numbers: A Shortcut

A shortcut helps you to square a positive two-digit number ending in 5. The method is developed using the idea that a two-digit number may be expressed as $10t + u$. Suppose $u = 5$.

$(10t + 5)^2 = (10t + 5)(10t + 5)$
$= 100t^2 + 50t + 50t + 25$
$= 100t^2 + 100t + 25$
$(10t + 5)^2 = 100t(t + 1) + 25$

In words, this formula says that the square of a two-digit number ending in 5 has $t(t + 1)$ in the hundreds place. Then 2 is the tens digit and 5 is the units digit.

Example Using the formula for $(10t + 5)^2$, find 85^2.

$85^2 = 100 \cdot 8 \cdot (8 + 1) + 25$
$= 7200 + 25$
$= 7225$ — Shortcut: First think $8 \cdot 9 = 72$. Then write 25.

Thus, to square a number, such as 85, you can write the product of the

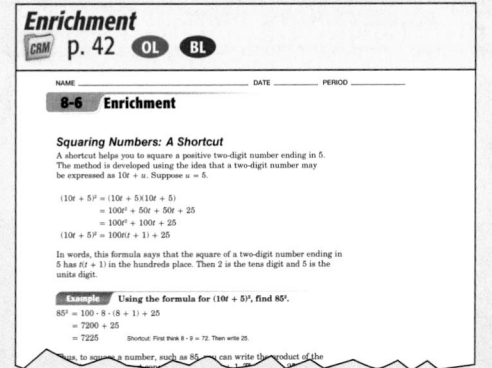

4 ASSESS

Name the Math Have each student tell a partner or write how to determine if a trinomial is a perfect square trinomial.

Formative Assessment

Check for student understanding of concepts in Lesson 8-6.

CRM Quiz 4, p. 46

PSAE PRACTICE 8.11.18, 8.11.07, 8.11.17, 7.11.03

61. What is the solution set for the equation $(x-3)^2 = 25$? **B**

A $\{-8, 2\}$ C $\{4, 14\}$
B $\{-2, 8\}$ D $\{-4, 14\}$

62. SHORT RESPONSE Write an equation in slope-intercept form for the graph shown below. $y = -2x - 4$

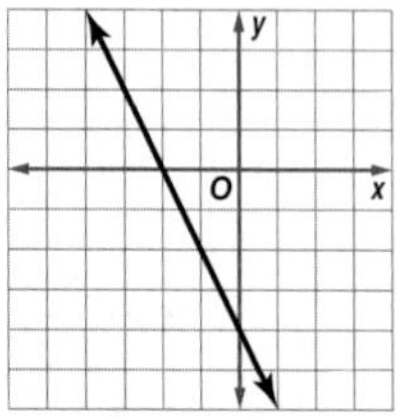

63. At an amphitheater, the price of 2 lawn seats and 2 pavilion seats is \$120. The price of 3 lawn seats and 4 pavilion seats is \$225. How much do lawn and pavilion seats cost? **H**

F \$20 and \$41.25
G \$10 and \$50
H \$15 and \$45
J \$30 and \$30

64. GEOMETRY The circumference of a circle is $\frac{6\pi}{5}$ units. What is the area of the circle? **C**

A $\frac{3\pi}{5}$ units^2 C $\frac{9\pi}{25}$ units^2
B $\frac{12\pi}{5}$ units^2 D $\frac{30\pi}{25}$ units^2

Spiral Review

Factor each polynomial, if possible. If the polynomial cannot be factored, write *prime*. (Lesson 8-5)

65. $x^2 - 16$ $(x-4)(x+4)$
66. $4x^2 - 81y^2$ $(2x-9y)(2x+9y)$
67. $1 - 100p^2$ $(1-10p)(1+10p)$
68. $3a^2 - 20$ prime
69. $25n^2 - 1$ $(5n-1)(5n+1)$
70. $36 - 9c^2$ $9(2-c)(2+c)$

Solve each equation. Check your solutions. (Lesson 8-4)

71. $4x^2 - 8x - 32 = 0$ $\{-2, 4\}$
72. $6x^2 - 48x + 90 = 0$ $\{3, 5\}$
73. $14x^2 + 14x = 28$ $\{-2, 1\}$
74. $2x^2 - 10x = 48$ $\{-3, 8\}$
75. $5x^2 - 25x = -30$ $\{2, 3\}$
76. $8x^2 - 16x = 192$ $\{-4, 6\}$

SOUND The intensity of sound can be measured in watts per square meter. The table gives the watts per square meter for some common sounds. (Lesson 7-2)

Watts Per Square Meter	Common Sounds
10^{-11}	rustling leaves
10^{-10}	whisper
10^{-6}	normal conversation
10^{-5}	busy street traffic
10^{-4}	vacuum cleaner
10^{-1}	front rows of rock concert
10^{1}	threshold of pain
10^{2}	military jet takeoff

77. How many times more intense is the sound from busy street traffic than sound from normal conversation? 10^1 or 10

78. Which sound is 10,000 times as loud as a busy street traffic? front rows of rock concert

79. How does the intensity of a whisper compare to that of normal conversation? $\frac{1}{10{,}000}$

Skills Review

Find the slope of the line that passes through each pair of points. (Lesson 3-3)

80. $(5, 7), (-2, -3)$ $\frac{10}{7}$
81. $(2, -1), (5, -3)$ $-\frac{2}{3}$
82. $(-4, -1), (-3, -3)$ -2
83. $(-3, -4), (5, -1)$ $\frac{3}{8}$
84. $(-2, 3), (8, 3)$ 0
85. $(-5, 4), (-5, -1)$ undefined

Differentiated Instruction OL BL

Extension Write the following polynomial on the board for students to factor completely:

$(m-p)m^2 - 2m(m-p) + (m-p)$
$(m-p)(m-1)(m-1)$ or $(m-p)(m-1)^2$

IL Math Online glencoe.com
• STUDY TO GO
• Vocabulary Review

Chapter Summary

Key Concepts

Monomials and Factoring (Lesson 8-1)

- The greatest common factor (GCF) of two or more monomials is the product of their common prime factors.

Factoring Using the Distributive Property (Lesson 8-2)

- Using the Distributive Property to factor polynomials with four or more terms is called factoring by grouping.
  $ax + bx + ay + by = x(a + b) + y(a + b)$
  $= (a + b)(x + y)$
- Factoring can be used to solve some equations. According to the Zero Product Property, for any real numbers a and b, if $ab = 0$, then either $a = 0$, $b = 0$, or both a and b equal zero.

Factoring Trinomials and Differences of Squares (Lessons 8-3 through 8-5)

- To factor $x^2 + bx + c$, find m and p with a sum of b and a product of c. Then write $x^2 + bx + c$ as $(x + m)(x + p)$.
- To factor $ax^2 + bx + c$, find m and p with a sum of b and a product of ac. Then write as $ax^2 + mx + px + c$ and factor by grouping.
- $a^2 - b^2 = (a - b)(a + b)$

Perfect Squares and Factoring (Lesson 8-6)

- For a trinomial to be a perfect square, the first and last terms must be perfect squares, and the middle term must be twice the product of the square roots of the first and last terms.
- For any number $n \geq 0$, if $x^2 = n$, then $x = \pm\sqrt{n}$.

FOLDABLES® Study Organizer

Be sure the Key Concepts are noted in your Foldable.

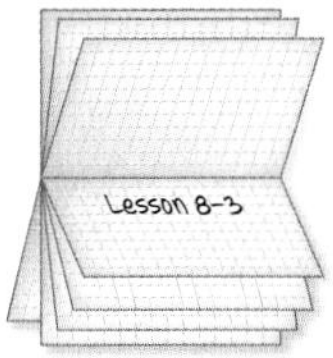

Key Vocabulary

difference of two squares (p. 499)
factored form (p. 471)
factoring (p. 476)
factoring by grouping (p. 477)
greatest common factor (GCF) (p. 471)
perfect square trinomial (p. 505)
prime polynomial (p. 495)
quadratic equation (p. 488)
Square Root Property (p. 508)
Zero Product Property (p. 478)

Vocabulary Check

State whether each sentence is *true* or *false*. If *false*, replace the underlined phrase or expression to make a true sentence.

1. $\underline{x^2 + 5x + 6}$ is an example of a prime polynomial. **false; sample answer: $x^2 + 5x + 7$**
2. $\underline{(x + 5)(x - 5)}$ is the factorization of a difference of squares. **true**
3. $\underline{5x}$ is the greatest common factor of $10x$ and $15xy^2$. **true**
4. $\underline{(x + 5)(x - 2)}$ is the factored form of $x^2 - 3x - 10$. **false; $(x - 5)(x + 2)$**
5. Expressions with four or more unlike terms can sometimes be <u>factored by grouping</u>. **true**
6. The Zero Product Property states that if <u>$ab = 1$, then a or b is 1</u>. **false; $ab = 0$, then a or b is 0, or both a and b are 0.**
7. $x^2 - 12x + 36$ is an example of a <u>perfect square trinomial</u>. **true**
8. $\underline{x - 2 = 0}$ is a quadratic equation. **false; sample answer: $x^2 - 2x + -24 = 0$**
9. $x^2 - 16$ is an example of a <u>perfect square trinomial</u>. **false; difference of squares**
10. The greatest common factor of $8x$ and $4x^2$ is $\underline{4x}$. **true**

CHAPTER 8 Study Guide and Review

Formative Assessment

Key Vocabulary The page references after each word denote where that term was first introduced. If students have difficulty answering questions 1–10, remind them that they can use these page references to refresh their memories about the vocabulary.

Summative Assessment

CRM Vocabulary Test, p. 48

IL Math Online glencoe.com

Vocabulary PuzzleMaker improves students' mathematics vocabulary using four puzzle formats—crossword, scramble, word search using a word list, and word search using clues. Students can work online or from a printed worksheet.

FOLDABLES® Study Organizer

Dinah Zike's Foldables®

Have students look through the chapter to make sure they have included examples in their Foldables for each lesson of the chapter.

Suggest that students keep their Foldables handy while completing the Study Guide and Review pages. Point out that their Foldables can serve as a quick review when studying for the chapter test.

Lesson-by-Lesson Review

Intervention If the given examples are not sufficient to review the topics covered by the questions, remind students that the page references tell them where to review that topic in their textbooks.

Two-Day Option Have students complete the Lesson-by-Lesson Review on pp. 514–516. Then you can use ExamView® Assessment Suite to customize another review worksheet that practices all the objectives of this chapter or only the objectives on which your students need more help.

Differentiated Instruction

Super DVD: Mindjogger Videoquizzes
Use this DVD as an alternative format of review for the test.

CHAPTER 8 Study Guide and Review

Lesson-by-Lesson Review

8-1 Monomials and Factoring (pp. 471–474)

8.A.4b

Factor each monomial completely.

11. $28x^3$ $2 \cdot 2 \cdot 7 \cdot x \cdot x \cdot x$
12. $-33x^2y^3$ $-1 \cdot 3 \cdot 11 \cdot x \cdot x \cdot y \cdot y \cdot y$
13. $68cd^3$ $2 \cdot 2 \cdot 17 \cdot c \cdot d \cdot d \cdot d$
14. $120mq$ $2 \cdot 2 \cdot 2 \cdot 3 \cdot 5 \cdot m \cdot q$

Find the greatest common factor of each set of monomials.

15. $22b, 33c$ 11
16. $21xy, 28x^2y, 42xy^2$ $7xy$
17. $6ab, 24ab^4$ $6ab$
18. $10ab, 30a, 40a^2b$ $10a$

19. **HOME IMPROVEMENT** A landscape architect is designing a stone path 36 inches wide and 120 inches long. What is the maximum size square stone that can be used so that none of the stones have to be cut? 12 by 12

EXAMPLE 1

Factor $24a^2b^3$ completely.

$24a^2b^3 = 4 \cdot 6 \cdot a \cdot a \cdot b \cdot b \cdot b$

$= 2 \cdot 2 \cdot 2 \cdot 3 \cdot a \cdot a \cdot b \cdot b \cdot b$

EXAMPLE 2

Find the greatest common factor of $12xy$ and $8xy^2$.

$12xy = (2) \cdot (2) \cdot 3 \cdot (x) \cdot (y)$

$8xy^2 = (2) \cdot (2) \cdot 2 \cdot (x) \cdot (y) \cdot y$

Factor each monomial. Circle the common prime factors.

The greatest common factor is $2 \cdot 2 \cdot x \cdot y$ or $4xy$.

8-2 Using the Distributive Property (pp. 476–482)

7.B.4, 8.C.4b

Use the Distributive Property to factor each polynomial.

20. $12x + 24y$ $12(x + 2y)$
21. $14x^2y - 21xy + 35xy^2$ $7xy(2x - 3 + 5y)$
22. $8xy - 16x^3y + 10y$ $2y(4x - 8x^3 + 5)$
23. $a^2 - 4ac + ab - 4bc$ $(a + b)(a - 4c)$
24. $2x^2 - 3xz - 2xy + 3yz$ $(2x - 3z)(x - y)$
25. $24am - 9an + 40bm - 15bn$ $(3a + 5b)(8m - 3n)$

Solve each equation. Check your solutions.

26. $x(3x - 6) = 0$ 0, 2
27. $6x^2 = 12x$ 0, 2
28. $x^2 = 3x$ 0, 3
29. $3x^2 = 5x$ $0, \frac{5}{3}$

30. **GEOMETRY** The area of the rectangle shown is $x^3 - 2x^2 + 5x$ square units. What is the length? $x^2 - 2x + 5$

EXAMPLE 3

Factor $12y^2 + 9y + 8y + 6$.

$12y^2 + 9y + 8y + 6$

$= (12y^2 + 9y) + (8y + 6)$ **Group terms with common factors.**

$= 3y(4y + 3) + 2(4y + 3)$ **Factor the GCF from each group.**

$= (4y + 3)(3y + 2)$ **Distributive Property**

EXAMPLE 4

Solve $x^2 - 6x = 0$. Check your solutions.

Write the equation so that it is of the form $ab = 0$.

$x^2 - 6x = 0$ **Original equation**

$x(x - 6) = 0$ **Factor by using the GCF.**

$x = 0$ or $x - 6 = 0$ **Zero Product Property**

$x = 6$ **Solve.**

The roots are 0 and 6. Check by substituting 0 and 6 for x in the original equation.

MIXED PROBLEM SOLVING
For mixed problem-solving practice, see page 852.

8-3 Quadratic Equations: $x^2 + bx + c = 0$ (pp. 485–491)

8.A.4b, 8.D.4

Factor each trinomial.

31. $x^2 - 8x + 15$ **32.** $x^2 + 9x + 20$

33. $x^2 - 5x - 6$ **34.** $x^2 + 3x - 18$

Solve each equation. Check your solutions.

35. $x^2 + 5x - 50 = 0$ $-10, 5$

36. $x^2 - 6x + 8 = 0$ $2, 4$

37. $x^2 + 12x + 32 = 0$ $-8, -4$

38. $x^2 - 2x - 48 = 0$ $-6, 8$

39. $x^2 + 11x + 10 = 0$ $-10, -1$

31. $(x - 5)(x - 3)$
32. $(x + 5)(x + 4)$
33. $(x - 6)(x + 1)$
34. $(x + 6)(x - 3)$

40. ART An artist is working on a painting that is 3 inches longer than it is wide. The area of the painting is 154 square inches. What is the length of the painting? 14 in.

EXAMPLE 5

Factor $x^2 + 10x + 21$

$b = 10$ and $c = 21$, so $m + p$ is positive and mp is positive. Therefore, m and p must both be positive. List the positive factors of 21, and look for the pair of factors with a sum of 10.

Factors of 21	Sum of 10
1, 21	22
3, 7	10

The correct factors are 3 and 7.

$x^2 + 10x + 21 = (x + m)(x + p)$ **Write the pattern.**

$= (x + 3)(x + 7)$ **$m = 3$ and $p = 7$**

8-4 Quadratic Equations: $ax^2 + bx + c = 0$ (pp. 493–498)

8.A.4b, 8.D.4

Factor each trinomial, if possible. If the trinomial cannot be factored, write *prime*.

41. $12x^2 + 22x - 14$ $2(2x - 1)(3x + 7)$

42. $2y^2 - 9y + 3$ prime

43. $3x^2 - 6x - 45$ $3(x - 5)(x + 3)$

44. $2a^2 + 13a - 24$ $(2a - 3)(a + 8)$

Solve each equation. Check your solutions.

45. $40x^2 + 2x = 24$ $\frac{3}{4}, -\frac{4}{5}$

46. $2x^2 - 3x - 20 = 0$ $4, -\frac{5}{2}$

47. $-16t^2 + 36t - 8 = 0$ $2, \frac{1}{4}$

48. $6x^2 - 7x - 5 = 0$ $\frac{5}{3}, -\frac{1}{2}$

49. GEOMETRY The area of the rectangle shown is $6x^2 + 11x - 7$ square units. What is the width of the rectangle? $3x + 7$

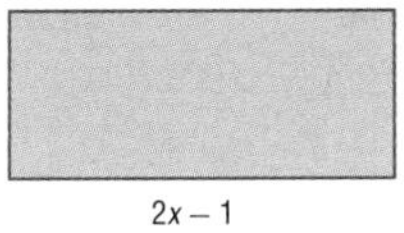

EXAMPLE 6

Factor $12a^2 + 17a + 6$

$a = 12$, $b = 17$, and $c = 6$. Since b is positive, $m + p$ is positive. Since c is positive, mp is positive. So, m and p are both positive. List the factors of 12(6) or 72, where both factors are positive.

Factors of 72	Sum of 17
1, 72	73
2, 36	38
3, 24	27
4, 18	22
6, 12	18
8, 9	17

The correct factors are 8 and 9.

$$\begin{aligned} 12a^2 + 17a + 6 &= 12a^2 + ma + pa + 6 \\ &= 12a^2 + 8a + 9a + 6 \\ &= (12a^2 + 8a) + (9a + 6) \\ &= 4a(3a + 2) + 3(3a + 2) \\ &= (3a + 2)(4a + 3) \end{aligned}$$

So, $12a^2 + 17a + 6 = (3a + 2)(4a + 3)$.

Chapter 8 Study Guide and Review **515**

Problem Solving Review

For additional practice in problem solving for Chapter 8, see the Mixed Problem Solving Appendix, p. 852, in the Student Handbook section.

Anticipation Guide

Have students complete the Chapter 8 Anticipation Guide and discuss how their responses have changed now that they have completed Chapter 8.

CHAPTER 8 Study Guide and Review

8-5 Quadratic Equations: Differences of Squares (pp. 499–504)

8.A.4b, 8.D.4

Factor each polynomial.

50. $y^2 - 81$ $(y + 9)(y - 9)$

51. $64 - 25x^2$ $(8 + 5x)(8 - 5x)$

52. $16a^2 - 21b^2$ prime

53. $3x^2 - 3$ $3(x + 1)(x - 1)$

Solve each equation by factoring. Check your solutions.

54. $a^2 - 25 = 0$ 5, −5

55. $9x^2 - 25 = 0$ $\frac{5}{3}, -\frac{5}{3}$

56. $81 - y^2 = 0$ −9, 9

57. $x^2 - 5 = 20$ −5, 5

58. **EROSION** A boulder falls down a mountain into water 64 feet below. The distance d that the boulder falls in t seconds is given by the equation $d = 16t^2$. How long does it take the boulder to hit the water? 2 seconds

EXAMPLE 7

Solve $x^2 - 4 = 12$ by factoring.

$x^2 - 4 = 12$	Original equation
$x^2 - 16 = 0$	Subtract 12 from each side.
$x^2 - (4)^2 = 0$	$16 = 4^2$
$(x + 4)(x - 4) = 0$	Factor the difference of squares.
$x + 4 = 0$ or $x - 4 = 0$	Zero Product Property
$x = -4$ $\quad$ $x = 4$	Solve each equation.

The solutions are −4 and 4.

8-6 Quadratic Equations: Perfect Squares (pp. 505–512)

8.A.4b, 8.D.4

Factor each polynomial, if possible. If the polynomial cannot be factored write *prime*.

59. $x^2 + 12x + 36$ $(x + 6)^2$

60. $x^2 + 5x + 25$ prime

61. $9y^2 - 12y + 4$ $(3y - 2)^2$

62. $4 - 28a + 49a^2$ $(2 - 7a)^2$

63. $x^4 - 1$ $(x^2 + 1)(x + 1)(x - 1)$

64. $x^4 - 16x^2$ $x^2(x + 4)(x - 4)$

Solve each equation. Check your solutions.

65. $(x - 5)^2 = 121$ 16, −6

66. $4c^2 + 4c + 1 = 9$ 1, −2

67. $4y^2 = 64$ −4, 4

68. $16d^2 + 40d + 25 = 9$ $-2, -\frac{1}{2}$

69. **LANDSCAPING** A sidewalk of equal width is being built around a square yard. What is the width of the sidewalk? 2.5 ft

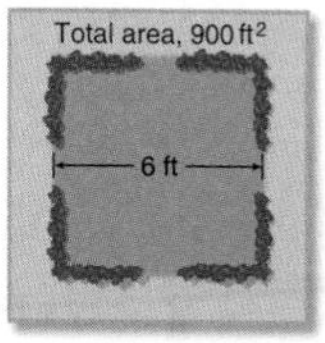

EXAMPLE 8

Solve $(x - 9)^2 = 144$.

$(x - 9)^2 = 144$	Original equation
$x - 9 = \pm\sqrt{144}$	Square Root Property
$x - 9 = \pm 12$	$144 = 12 \cdot 12$
$x = 9 \pm 12$	Add 9 to each side.
$x = 9 + 12$ or $x = 9 - 12$	Zero Product Property
$x = 21$ $\quad$ $x = -3$	Solve.

CHECK

$(x - 9)^2 = 144$	$(x - 9)^2 = 144$
$(21 - 9)^2 \stackrel{?}{=} 144$	$(-3 - 9)^2 \stackrel{?}{=} 144$
$(12)^2 \stackrel{?}{=} 144$	$(-12)^2 \stackrel{?}{=} 144$
$144 = 144$ ✓	$144 = 144$ ✓

CHAPTER 8

Practice Test

IL Math Online glencoe.com Chapter Test

Factor each monomial completely.

1. $25x^2y^4$ $5 \cdot 5 \cdot x \cdot x \cdot y \cdot y \cdot y \cdot y$
2. $17ab^2$ $17 \cdot a \cdot b \cdot b$
3. $-18c^5d^3$ $-1 \cdot 2 \cdot 3 \cdot 3 \cdot c \cdot c \cdot c \cdot c \cdot c \cdot d \cdot d \cdot d$
4. **GARDENING** Conrado is planting 140 pumpkins in a rectangular arrangement in his garden. In what ways can he arrange them so that he has at least 4 rows of pumpkins, the same number of pumpkins in each row, and at least 6 pumpkins in each row? See margin.

Find the greatest common factor of each set of monomials.

5. $2a, 8a^2, 16a^3$ $2a$
6. $7c, 24d$ 1
7. $50g^2h, 120gh^2$ $10gh$
8. $8q^2r^2, 36qr$ $4qr$
9. **MULTIPLE CHOICE** The area of the rectangle shown below is $2x^2 - x - 15$ square units. What is the width of the rectangle? C

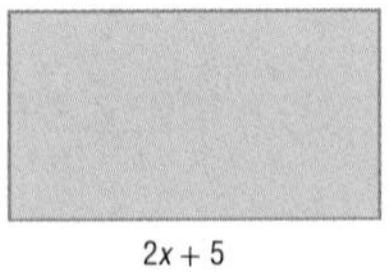

A $x - 5$

B $x + 3$

C $x - 3$

D $2x - 3$

Use the Distributive Property to factor each polynomial.

10. $5xy - 10x$ $5x(y - 2)$
11. $7ab + 14ab^2 + 21a^2b$ $7ab(1 + 2b + 3a)$

Factor each polynomial.

12. $4x^2 + 8x + x + 2$ $(4x + 1)(x + 2)$
13. $10a^2 - 50a - a + 5$ $(10a - 1)(a - 5)$

Solve each equation. Check your solutions.

14. $y(y - 14) = 0$ 0, 14
15. $3x(x + 6) = 0$ 0, −6
16. $a^2 = 12a$ 0, 12
17. **MULTIPLE CHOICE** Chantel is carpeting a room that has an area of $x^2 - 100$ square feet. If the width of the room is $x - 10$ feet, what is the length of the room? G

F $x - 10$ ft

G $x + 10$ ft

H $x - 100$ ft

J 10 ft

Factor each trinomial.

18. $x^2 + 7x + 6$ $(x + 6)(x + 1)$
19. $x^2 - 3x - 28$ $(x - 7)(x + 4)$
20. $10x^2 - x - 3$ $(5x - 3)(2x + 1)$
21. $15x^2 + 7x - 2$ $(3x + 2)(5x - 1)$
22. $x^2 - 25$ $(x + 5)(x - 5)$
23. $4x^2 - 81$ $(2x + 9)(2x - 9)$
24. $9x^2 - 12x + 4$ $(3x - 2)(3x - 2)$
25. $16x^2 + 40x + 25$ $(4x + 5)(4x + 5)$

Solve each equation. Check your solutions.

26. $x^2 - 4x = 21$ $-3, 7$
27. $x^2 - 2x - 24 = 0$ $-4, 6$
28. $6x^2 - 5x - 6 = 0$ $-\frac{2}{3}, \frac{3}{2}$
29. $2x^2 - 13x + 20 = 0$ $4, \frac{5}{2}$
30. **MULTIPLE CHOICE** Which choice is a factor of $x^4 - 1$ when it is factored completely? B

A $x^2 - 1$

B $x - 1$

C x

D 1

CHAPTER 8

Practice Test

ExamView Assessment Suite Customize and create multiple versions of your chapter tests and their answer keys. All of the questions from the leveled chapter tests in the *Chapter 8 Resource Masters* are also available on ExamView® Assessment Suite.

Additional Answer

4. 4 rows of 35 pumpkins, 5 rows of 28 pumpkins, 7 rows of 20 pumpkins, 10 rows of 14 pumpkins, 20 rows of 7 pumpkins, 14 rows of 10 pumpkins

Intervention Planner

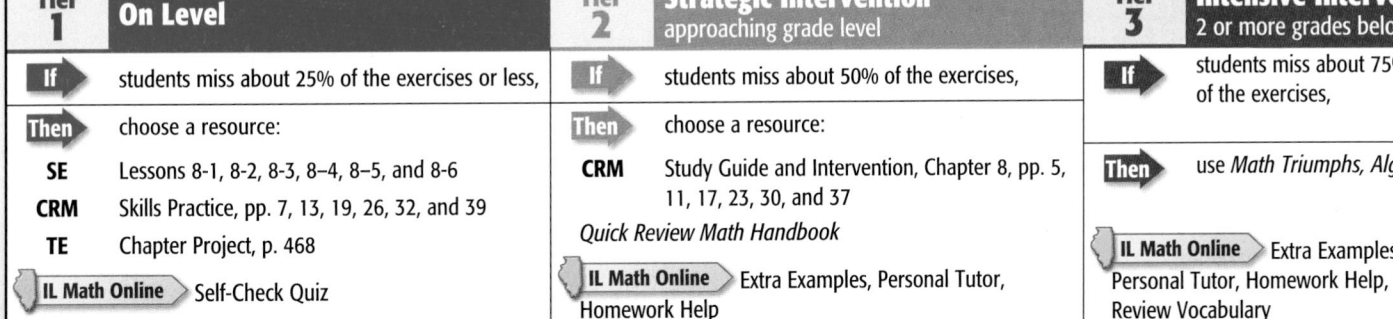

Tier 1 On Level	Tier 2 Strategic Intervention approaching grade level	Tier 3 Intensive Intervention 2 or more grades below level
If students miss about 25% of the exercises or less,	**If** students miss about 50% of the exercises,	**If** students miss about 75% of the exercises,
Then choose a resource: **SE** Lessons 8-1, 8-2, 8-3, 8–4, 8–5, and 8-6 **CRM** Skills Practice, pp. 7, 13, 19, 26, 32, and 39 **TE** Chapter Project, p. 468 IL Math Online Self-Check Quiz	**Then** choose a resource: **CRM** Study Guide and Intervention, Chapter 8, pp. 5, 11, 17, 23, 30, and 37 *Quick Review Math Handbook* IL Math Online Extra Examples, Personal Tutor, Homework Help	**Then** use *Math Triumphs, Alg. 1* IL Math Online Extra Examples, Personal Tutor, Homework Help, Review Vocabulary

1 FOCUS

Objective Use strategies for solving multi-step standardized test problems.

2 TEACH

Scaffolding Questions

Ask:

- Have you ever had to write a research paper or complete some other school project? Answers will vary.
- Did you write the entire paper or complete the project in one session? Or did you use a number of steps to complete the job? Answers will vary.
- Could you have completed the steps in a different order? Could you have used a different set of steps? Answers will vary.

CHAPTER 8 Preparing for Standardized Tests

Solve Multi-Step Problems

Some problems that you will encounter on standardized tests require you to solve multiple parts in order to come up with the final solution. Use this lesson to practice these types of problems.

Strategies for Solving Multi-Step Problems

Step 1

Read the problem statement carefully.

Ask yourself:

- What am I being asked to solve? What information is given?
- Are there any intermediate steps that need to be completed before I can solve the problem?

Step 2

Organize your approach.

- List the steps you will need to complete in order to solve the problem.
- Remember that there may be more than one possible way to solve the problem.

Step 3

Solve and check.

- Work as efficiently as possible to complete each step and solve.
- If time permits, check your answer.

EXAMPLE

Read the problem. Identify what you need to know. Then use the information in the problem to solve.

A florist has 80 roses, 50 tulips, and 20 lilies that he wants to use to create bouquets. He wants to create the maximum number of bouquets possible and use all of the flowers. Each bouquet should have the same number of each type of flower. How many roses will be in each bouquet?

A 4 roses **C** 10 roses

B 8 roses **D** 15 roses

Read the problem carefully. You are given the number of roses, tulips, and lilies and told that bouquets will be made using the same number of flowers in each. You need to find the number of roses that will be in each bouquet.

Step 1 Find the GCF of the number of roses, tulips, and lilies.

Step 2 Use the GCF to determine how many bouquets will be made.

Step 3 Divide the total number of roses by the number of bouquets.

Step 1 Write the prime factorization of each number of flowers to find the GCF.

$80 = \mathbf{2} \cdot 2 \cdot 2 \cdot 2 \cdot \mathbf{5}$

$50 = \mathbf{2} \cdot \mathbf{5} \cdot 5$

$20 = \mathbf{2} \cdot 2 \cdot \mathbf{5}$

$\text{GCF} = 2 \cdot 5 = 10$

Step 2 The GCF of the number of roses, tulips, and lilies tells you how many bouquets can be made because each bouquet will contain the same number of flowers. So, the florist can make a total of 10 bouquets.

Step 3 Divide the number of roses by the number of bouquets to find the number of roses in each bouquet.

$\frac{80}{10} = 8$

So, there will be 8 roses in each bouquet. The answer is B.

Exercises

Read each problem. Identify what you need to know. Then use the information in the problem to solve.

1. Which of the following values is not a solution to $x^3 - 3x^2 - 25x + 75 = 0$? C

A $x = 5$

B $x = 3$

C $x = -3$

D $x = -5$

2. There are 12 teachers, 90 students, and 36 parent volunteers going on a field trip. Mrs. Bartholomew wants to divide everyone into equal groups with the same number of teachers, students, and parents in each group. If she makes as many groups as possible, how many students will be in each group? J

F 6

G 9

H 12

J 15

3. What is the area of the square? D

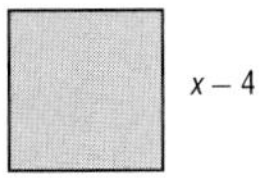

A $x^2 + 16$

B $4x - 16$

C $x^2 - 8x - 16$

D $x^2 - 8x + 16$

4. Students are selling magazines to raise money for a field trip. They make $2.75 for each magazine they sell. If they want to raise $600, what is the least amount of magazines they need to sell? J

F 121

G 177

H 202

J 219

Additional Example

A geologist is preparing rock boxes for students. She has 90 igneous, 75 metamorphic, and 120 sedimentary rocks. She wants to make the maximum number of boxes possible and use all of the rocks. Each box should have the same number of each type of rock. How many metamorphic rocks will be in each box? A

A 5 metamorphic rocks

B 6 metamorphic rocks

C 8 metamorphic rocks

D 15 metamorphic rocks

3 ASSESS

Use Exercises 1–4 to assess students' understanding.

Diagnose Student Errors

Survey students' responses for each item. Class trends may indicate common errors and misconceptions.

1. A found greatest number of chocolate chip cookies in 3 baskets
B guess
C correct
D guess
E guess

2. F found least instead of greatest number of cookies
G correct
H guess
J guess
K guess

3. A guess
B transposed *m* and *n*
C transposed 3 and 5
D correct
E guess

4. F correct
G error in sign: should be 8 instead of −8
H calculation error or guess
J calculation error or guess
K calculator error

5. A can be factored: $(5x + 4)(x + 6)$
B can be factored: $2(2x + 1)(x + 5)$
C can be factored: $2(2x + 5)(x + 7)$
D correct
E can be factored

6. F chose a factor
G chose a factor
H chose a factor
J chose a factor
K correct

7. A correct
B chose one of the dimensions
C chose one of the dimensions
D chose one of the dimensions
E guess

8. F chose factors that would give y^2 and 20, but $-12y$ instead of $-9y$
G correct
H chose factors that would give $-9y$, but 14 instead of 20
J guess
K 3 and 6 not factors of 20

9. A confused negative exponent with negative number
B misunderstood concept of scientific notation
C misunderstood concept of scientific notation
D correct
E guess

PSAE Practice

Cumulative, Chapters 1 through 8

Multiple Choice

Read each question. Then fill in the correct answer on the answer document provided by your teacher or on a sheet of paper.

1. A baker wants to put the same number of each type of cookie into each basket, and each basket should have each type of cookie. If she puts the greatest possible number of cookies in each basket, how many baskets can she make? **C**

Type of Cookie	Number
Chocolate Chip	54
Peanut Butter	45
Oatmeal Raisin	36
Sugar	60

A 18
B 16
C 12
D 10
E 6

2. Refer to the information given in Exercise 1. How many of each cookie type will be in each basket? **G**

F 2
G 3
H 4
J 6
K 10

3. Factor the polynomial $mn + 5m - 3n - 15$. **D**

A $(mn - 3)(5)$
B $(m - 5)(n + 3)$
C $(n - 3)(m + 5)$
D $(m - 3)(n + 5)$
E $mn(1 + 5n - 3m) - 15$

4. Which of the following is a solution to $x^2 + 6x - 112 = 0$? **F**

F −14
G −8
H 6
J 12
K 18

5. Which of the following polynomials is prime? **D**

A $5x^2 + 34x + 24$
B $4x^2 + 22x + 10$
C $4x^2 + 38x + 70$
D $5x^2 + 3x + 4$
E $5x^3 + 10x - 5$

6. Which of the following is not a factor of the polynomial $45a^2 - 80b^2$? **K**

F 5
G $3a - 4b$
H $15a - 20b$
J $3a + 4b$
K $2a - 5b$

7. A rectangular gift box has dimensions that can be represented as shown in the figure. The volume of the box is $56w$ cubic inches. Which of the following is a dimension of the box? **B**

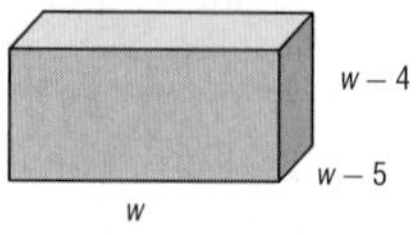

A 6 in.
B 7 in.
C 10 in.
D 11 in.
E 20 in.

8. Factor the polynomial $y^2 - 9y + 20$. **G**

F $(y - 2)(y - 10)$
G $(y - 4)(y - 5)$
H $(y - 3)(y - 8)$
J $(y - 5)(y - 2)$
K $(y - 3)(y - 6)$

9. Which of the following numbers is less than zero? **D**

A 1.03×10^{-21}
B 7.5×10^{2}
C 8.21543×10^{10}
D none of the above
E all of the above

Test-TakingTip

Question 4 If time permits, be sure to check your answer. Substitute it into the equation to see if you get a true number sentence.

520 Chapter 8 Factoring and Quadratic Equations

Short Response/Gridded Response

Record your answers on the answer sheet provided by your teacher or on a sheet of paper.

10. **GRIDDED RESPONSE** Mr. Branson bought a total of 9 tickets to the zoo. He bought children tickets at the rate of $6.50 and adult tickets for $9.25 each. If he spent $69.50 altogether, how many adult tickets did Mr. Branson purchase? **4**

11. What is the domain of the following relation? $\{(2, -1), (4, 3), (7, 6)\}$ **{2, 4, 7}**

12. Lawrence just added 15 more songs to his MP3 player, making the total number of songs more than 84. Draw a number line that represents the original number of songs he had on his MP3 player. **See margin.**

13. Carlos bought a rare painting in 1995 for $14,200. By 2003, the painting was worth $17,120. Write an equation in slope-intercept form that represents the value V of the painting after t years. $V(t) = 365t + 14{,}200$

14. The equation $h = -16t^2 + 40t + 3$ models the height h in feet of a soccer ball after t seconds. What is the height of the ball after 2 seconds? **19 ft**

15. Marcel spent $24.50 on peanuts and walnuts for a party. He bought 1.5 pounds more peanuts than walnuts. How many pounds of peanuts and walnuts did he buy? **3.5 lbs of peanuts and 2 lbs of walnuts**

Product	Price per pound
Peanuts p	$3.80
Cashews c	$6.90
Walnuts w	$5.60

16. **GRIDDED RESPONSE** The amount of money that Humberto earns varies directly as the number of hours that he works as shown in the graph. How much money will he earn for working 40 hours next week? Express your answer in dollars. **600**

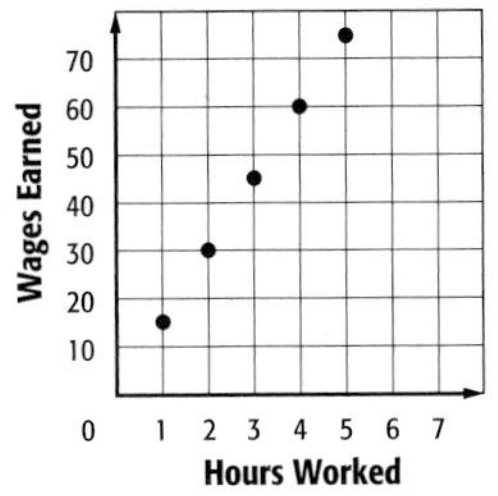

Extended Response

Record your answers on a sheet of paper. Show your work.

17. The height in feet of a model rocket t seconds after being launched into the air is given by the function $h(t) = -16t^2 + 200t$.
    a. Write the expression that shows the height of the rocket in factored form. $h(t) = t(-16t + 200)$
    b. At what time(s) is the height of the rocket equal to zero feet above the ground? Describe the real world meaning of your answer. **See margin.**
    c. What is the greatest height reached by the model rocket? When does this occur? **625 ft; at $t = 6.25$ seconds**

Need Extra Help?																	
If you missed Question...	1	2	3	4	5	6	7	8	9	10	11	12	13	14	15	16	17
Go to Lesson or Page...	8-1	8-1	8-2	8-3	8-4	8-5	8-6	8-3	7-3	6-5	1-6	5-1	4-2	8-4	2-9	3-4	8-2
IL Assessment Objectives	6.11.06	6.11.06	8.11.01	8.11.18	6.11.06	8.11.01	8.11.06	8.11.01	6.11.02	8.11.17	8.11.11	8.11.16	8.11.14	8.11.06	8.11.17	6.11.19	8.11.01

Formative Assessment

You can use these two pages to benchmark student progress.

CRM Standardized Test Practice, pp. 62–64

Answer Sheet Practice

Have students simulate taking a standardized test by recording their answers on practice recording sheets.

CRM Student Recording Sheet, p. 43

Chapter Resource Master
CRM p. 43

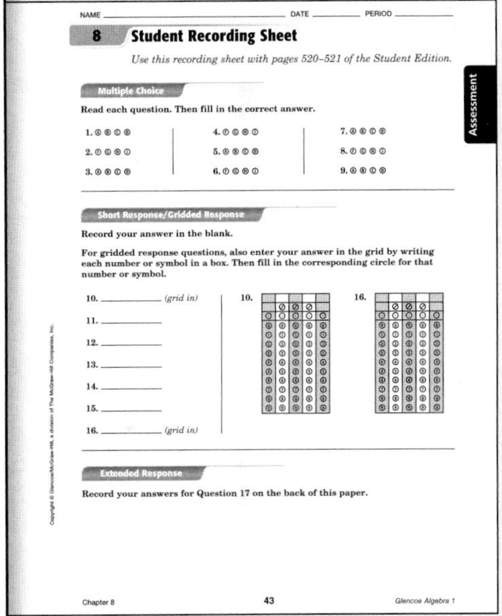
NAME ______ DATE ______ PERIOD ______

8 **Student Recording Sheet**

Use this recording sheet with pages 520–521 of the Student Edition.

Multiple Choice

Read each question. Then fill in the correct answer.

1. Ⓐ Ⓑ Ⓒ Ⓓ 4. Ⓕ Ⓖ Ⓗ Ⓙ 7. Ⓐ Ⓑ Ⓒ Ⓓ
2. Ⓕ Ⓖ Ⓗ Ⓙ 5. Ⓐ Ⓑ Ⓒ Ⓓ 8. Ⓕ Ⓖ Ⓗ Ⓙ
3. Ⓐ Ⓑ Ⓒ Ⓓ 6. Ⓕ Ⓖ Ⓗ Ⓙ 9. Ⓐ Ⓑ Ⓒ Ⓓ

Short Response/Gridded Response

Record your answer in the blank.

For gridded response questions, also enter your answer in the grid by writing each number or symbol in a box. Then fill in the corresponding circle for that number or symbol.

10. ______ (grid in)
11. ______
12. ______
13. ______
14. ______
15. ______
16. ______ (grid in)

10. [grid] 16. [grid]

Extended Response

Record your answers for Question 17 on the back of this paper.

Assessment

Copyright © Glencoe/McGraw-Hill, a division of The McGraw-Hill Companies, Inc.

Chapter 8 43 Glencoe Algebra 1

ExamView Assessment Suite Create practice worksheets or tests that align to your state's standards, as well as TIMSS and NAEP tests.

Homework Option

Get Ready for Chapter 9 Assign students the exercises on p. 523 as homework to assess whether they possess the prerequisite skills needed for the next chapter.

Additional Answers

12.
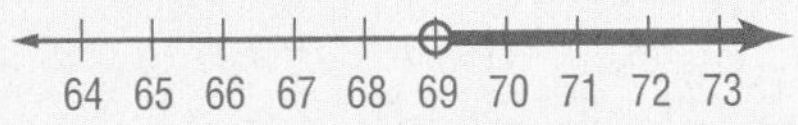

17b. $t = 0$, 12.5 seconds; Sample answer: The rocket is on the ground at launch and takes 12.5 seconds to land again after its flight.

Page 473, Lesson 8-1

23. height 1 in., base 56 in.; height 2 in., base 28 in.; height 4 in., base 14 in.; height 28 in., base 2 in.; height 14 in., base 4 in.; height 7 in., base 8 in.; height 56 in., base 1 in.; height 8 in., base 7 in.

24. 2 shelves of 18 CDs, 3 shelves of 12 CDs, 4 shelves of 9 CDs, 6 shelves of 6 CDs, 9 shelves of 4 CDs,

31. False; sample answer: The monomials $99x^5y^{11}z^{30}$ and $101abc$ have a GCF of 1.

33. Sample answer: $6y^3$, $12y^4$, $18y^5$; 6 is the greatest numerical factor that all three monomials have in common, and y^3 is the highest power of y that they all have in common.

34. A prime factorization of a number lists the prime factors of the number. There are three methods. The first method is to find the least prime factors. Keep dividing the number by the smallest prime until all primes are found. Second a factor tree can be used. Start by choosing any two factors of the number. Then keep finding factors until each branch ends in a prime factor. The primes can be circled to keep track of the primes. Lastly, a ladder diagram can be used. Start by dividing the number by a prime factor. Keep dividing by prime factors until the quotient is 1.

Page 475, Explore 8-2

5. yes

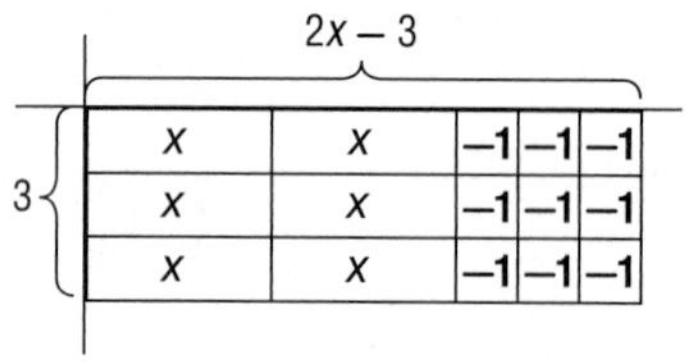

6. no

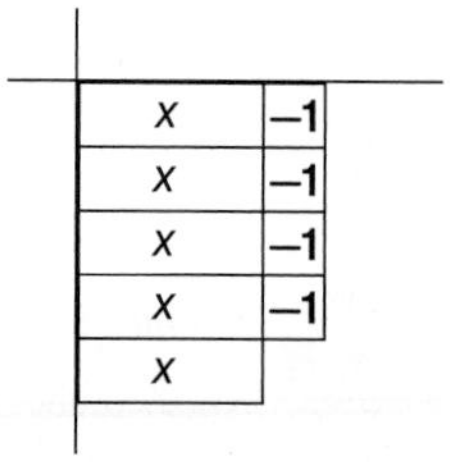

7. no

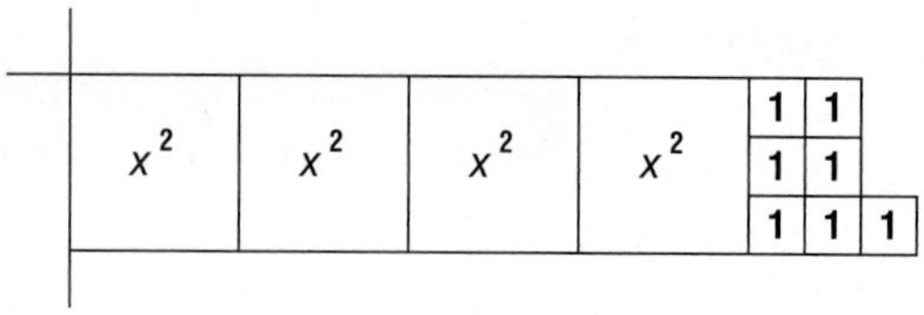

8. yes

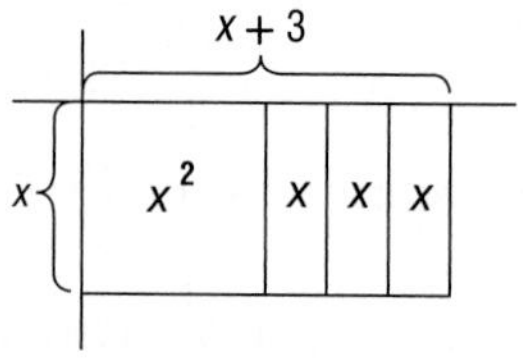

Page 484, Explore 8-3

9. no

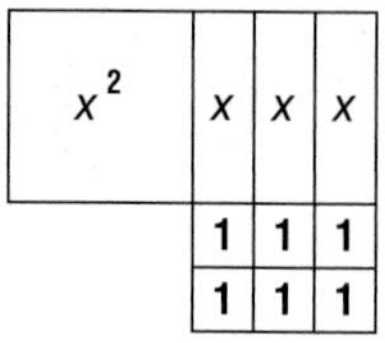

10. yes

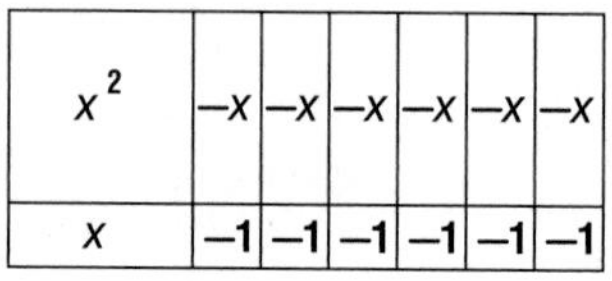

11. no

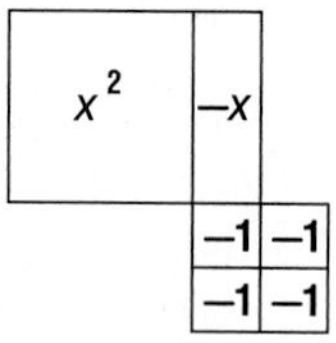

12. yes

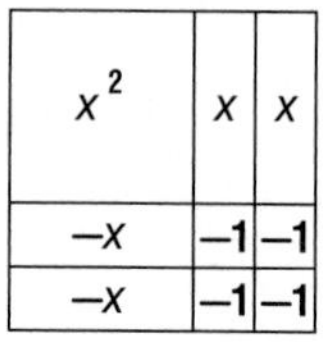

NOTES

CHAPTER 9 Chapter Planner

Diagnostic Assessment
Quick Check, p. 523

	Lesson 9-1 Pacing: 2 days	Extend 9-1 Pacing: 0.5 day	Lesson 9-2 Pacing: 1 day
Title	**Graphing Quadratic Functions**	**Algebra Lab: Rate of Change of a Quadratic Function**	**Solving Quadratic Equations by Graphing**
Objectives	• Analyze the characteristics of the graphs of quadratic functions. • Graph quadratic functions.	• Use a given quadratic function to investigate the rate of change of a quadratic function.	• Solve quadratic equations by graphing. • Estimate solutions of quadratic equations by graphing.
Key Vocabulary	nonlinear functions quadratic function standard form parabola axis of symmetry vertex minimum maximum symmetry		double root
ILS	7.B.4, 8.B.4b	8.A.4b	7.B.4, 8.D.4
Multiple Representations	p. 534		p. 541
Lesson Resources	**Chapter 9 Resource Masters** • Study Guide and Intervention, pp. 5–6 AL OL ELL • Skills Practice, p. 7 AL OL ELL • Practice, p. 8 AL OL BL ELL • Word Problem Practice, p. 9 AL OL BL ELL • Enrichment, p. 10 OL BL **Transparencies** • 5-Minute Check Transparency 9-1 AL OL BL ELL **Additional Print Resources** • Study Notebook AL OL BL ELL • *Teaching Algebra with Manipulatives,* p. 150 AL OL ELL	**Materials** • grid paper **Additional Print Resources** • *Teaching Algebra with Manipulatives,* pp. 1, 151 AL OL ELL	**Chapter 9 Resource Masters** • Study Guide and Intervention, pp. 11–t12 AL OL ELL • Skills Practice, p. 13 AL OL ELL • Practice, p. 14 AL OL BL ELL • Word Problem Practice, p. 15 AL OL BL ELL • Enrichment, p. 16 OL BL **Transparencies** • 5-Minute Check Transparency 9-2 AL OL BL ELL **Additional Print Resources** • Study Notebook AL OL BL ELL
Technology for Every Lesson	IL Math Online glencoe.com • Extra Examples • Self-Check Quizzes • Personal Tutor • Homework Help	**CD/DVD Resources** IWB INTERACTIVE WHITEBOARD READY IWB StudentWorks Plus IWB Interactive Classroom IWB Diagnostic and Assessment Planner	• TeacherWorks Plus • eSolutions Manual Plus • ExamView Assessment Suite
Math in Motion		Animation	Animation
Differentiated Instruction	pp. 529, 535		p. 542

KEY: AL Approaching Level OL On Level BL Beyond Level ELL English Learners

Suggested Pacing			
Time Periods	Instruction	Review & Assessment	Total
45-minute	13	2	15
90-minute	8	1	9

Quadratic and Exponential Functions

Extend 9-2 Pacing: 0.5 day	**Lesson 9-3** Pacing: 1 day	**Extend 9-3** Pacing: 0.5 day	**Lesson 9-4** Pacing: 1 day
Graphing Technology Lab: Quadratic Inequalities	**Transformations of Quadratic Functions**	**Graphing Technology Lab: Systems of Linear and Quadratic Equations**	**Solving Quadratic Equations by Completing the Square**
• Use a graphing calculator to investigate quadratic inequalities.	• Apply translations of quadratic functions. • Apply dilations and reflections to quadratic functions.	• Use a graphing calculator to solve a system of one linear and one quadratic equation.	• Complete the square to write perfect square trinomials. • Solve quadratic equations by completing the square.
	transformation translation dilation reflection		completing the square
8.D.4	8.B.4b, 8.C.4a	Preparation for 8.D.5	8.D.4
	p. 548		p. 556
Materials • TI-83/84 Plus or other graphing calculator	**Chapter 9 Resource Masters** • Study Guide and Intervention, pp. 17–18 AL OL ELL • Skills Practice, p. 19 AL OL ELL • Practice, p. 20 AL OL BL ELL • Word Problem Practice, p. 21 AL OL BL ELL • Enrichment, p. 22 OL BL • Quiz 1, p. 63 AL OL BL ELL **Transparencies** • 5-Minute Check Transparency 9-3 AL OL BL ELL **Additional Print Resources** • Study Notebook AL OL BL ELL	**Materials** • TI-83/84 Plus or other graphing calculator	**Chapter 9 Resource Masters** • Study Guide and Intervention, pp. 23–24 AL OL ELL • Skills Practice, p. 25 AL OL ELL • Practice, p. 26 AL OL BL ELL • Word Problem Practice, p. 27 AL OL BL ELL • Enrichment, p. 28 OL BL **Transparencies** • 5-Minute Check Transparency 9-4 AL OL BL ELL **Additional Print Resources** • Study Notebook AL OL BL ELL • *Teaching Algebra with Manipulatives,* pp. 153–154 AL OL ELL
	IL Math Online glencoe.com • Extra Examples • Self-Check Quizzes • Personal Tutor • Homework Help	**CD/DVD Resources** IWB INTERACTIVE WHITEBOARD READY IWB StudentWorks Plus IWB Interactive Classroom IWB Diagnostic and Assessment Planner	• TeacherWorks Plus • eSolutions Manual Plus • ExamView Assessment Suite
	Animation		Animation
	pp. 545, 549		pp. 554, 557

Chapter Planner

	Lesson 9-5 Pacing: 1 day	Extend 9-5 Pacing: 0.5 day	Lesson 9-6 Pacing: 1 day
Title	**Solving Quadratic Equations by Using the Quadratic Formula**	**Graphing Technology Lab: Cubic Functions**	**Exponential Functions**
Objectives	• Solve quadratic equations by using the Quadratic Formula. • Use the discriminant to determine the number of solutions to a quadratic equation.	• Use a graphing calculator to graph cubic equations and find their solutions.	• Graph exponential functions. • Identify data that display exponential behavior.
Key Vocabulary	Quadratic Formula discriminant	cubic equation	exponential function
ILS	8.C.4b, 8.D.4		8.A.4b, 8.C.4b
Multiple Representations	p. 563		
Lesson Resources	**Chapter 9 Resource Masters** • Study Guide and Intervention, pp. 29–30 AL OL ELL • Skills Practice, p. 31 AL OL ELL • Practice, p. 32 AL OL BL ELL • Word Problem Practice, p. 33 AL OL BL ELL • Enrichment, p. 34 OL BL • Quiz 2, p. 63 AL OL BL ELL **Transparencies** • 5-Minute Check Transparency 9-5 AL OL BL ELL **Additional Print Resources** • Study Notebook AL OL BL ELL	**Materials** • TI-83/84 Plus or other graphing calculator	**Chapter 9 Resource Masters** • Study Guide and Intervention, pp. 35–36 AL OL ELL • Skills Practice, p. 37 AL OL ELL • Practice, p. 38 AL OL BL ELL • Word Problem Practice, p. 39 AL OL BL ELL • Enrichment, p. 40 OL BL **Transparencies** • 5-Minute Check Transparency 9-4 AL OL BL ELL **Additional Print Resources** • Study Notebook AL OL BL ELL • *Teaching Algebra with Manipulatives*, p. 155 AL OL BL
Technology for Every Lesson	**IL Math Online** glencoe.com • Extra Examples • Self-Check Quizzes • Personal Tutor • Homework Help	**CD/DVD Resources** IWB INTERACTIVE WHITEBOARD READY IWB StudentWorks Plus IWB Interactive Classroom IWB Diagnostic and Assessment Planner	• TeacherWorks Plus • eSolutions Manual Plus • ExamView Assessment Suite
Math in Motion			
Differentiated Instruction	pp. 561, 564		pp. 569, 572

Formative Assessment
Mid-Chapter Quiz, p. 566

KEY: AL Approaching Level OL On Level BL Beyond Level ELL English Learners

Lesson 9-7 Pacing: 1 day	Lesson 9-8 Pacing: 1 day	Lesson 9-9 Pacing: 1 day	Extend 9-9 Pacing: 1 day
Growth and Decay	**Geometric Sequences as Exponential Functions**	**Analyzing Functions with Successive Differences**	**Graphing Technology Lab: Curve Fitting**
• Solve problems involving exponential growth. • Solve problems involving exponential decay.	• Identify and generate geometric sequences. • Relate geometric sequences to exponential functions.	• Identify linear, quadratic, and exponential functions from given data. • Write equations that model data.	• Use a graphing calculator to find an appropriate regression equation for a set of data.
exponential growth compound interest exponential decay	geometric sequence common ratio		
8.C.4b	8.A.4b, 8.C.4b	8.A.4b, 8.C.4b	Preparation for 8.D.5
Chapter 9 Resource Masters • Study Guide and Intervention, pp. 41–42 AL OL ELL • Skills Practice, p. 43 AL OL ELL • Practice, p. 44 AL OL BL ELL • Word Problem Practice, p. 45 AL OL BL ELL • Enrichment, p. 46 OL BL • Spreadsheet Activity, p. 47 OL • Quiz 3, p. 64 OL **Transparencies** • 5-Minute Check Transparency 9-7 AL OL BL ELL **Additional Print Resources** • Study Notebook AL OL BL ELL	**Chapter 9 Resource Masters** • Study Guide and Intervention, pp. 48–49 AL OL ELL • Skills Practice, p. 50 AL OL ELL • Practice, p. 51 AL OL BL ELL • Word Problem Practice, p. 52 AL OL BL ELL • Enrichment, p. 53 OL BL • Quiz 4, p. 64 AL OL BL ELL **Transparencies** • 5-Minute Check Transparency 9-8 AL OL BL ELL **Additional Print Resources** • Study Notebook AL OL BL ELL	**Chapter 9 Resource Masters** • Study Guide and Intervention, pp. 54–55 AL OL ELL • Skills Practice, p. 56 AL OL ELL • Practice, p. 57 AL OL BL ELL • Word Problem Practice, p. 58 AL OL BL ELL • Enrichment, p. 59 OL BL • Quiz 4, p. 64 AL OL BL ELL **Transparencies** • 5-Minute Check Transparency 9-9 AL OL BL ELL **Additional Print Resources** • Study Notebook AL OL BL ELL	**Materials** • TI-83/84 Plus or other graphing calculator
	IL Math Online glencoe.com • Extra Examples • Self-Check Quizzes • Personal Tutor • Homework Help	**CD/DVD Resources** IWB INTERACTIVE WHITEBOARD READY IWB StudentWorks Plus IWB Interactive Classroom IWB Diagnostic and Assessment Planner	• TeacherWorks Plus • eSolutions Manual Plus • ExamView Assessment Suite
p. 577	pp. 580, 583	pp. 586, 589	

Summative Assessment
- Study Guide and Review, pp. 592–596
- Practice Test, p. 597

CHAPTER 9 Assessment and Intervention

SE = Student Edition, **TE** = Teacher Edition, **CRM** = Chapter Resource Masters

	Diagnosis	Prescription
Diagnostic Assessment	**Beginning Chapter 9**	
	Get Ready for Chapter 9 **SE,** p. 523	Response to Intervention **TE**, p. 523
	Beginning Every Lesson	
	Then, Now, Why? **SE** 5-Minute Check Transparencies	Chapter 0 **SE**, pp. P1 through P45 Concepts and Skills Bank **SE**, pp. 857–867 *Quick Review Math Handbook*
Formative Assessment	**During/After Every Lesson**	
	Check Your Progress **SE**, every example Check Your Understanding **SE** H.O.T. Problems **SE** Spiral Review **SE** Additional Examples **TE** Watch Out! **SE** Step 4, Assess **TE** Chapter 9 Quizzes **CRM**, pp. 63–64 Self-Check Quizzes glencoe.com	**Tier 1 Intervention** Concepts and Skills Bank **SE**, pp. 857–867 Skills Practice **CRM**, Ch. 1–9 glencoe.com **Tier 2 Intervention** Differentiated Instruction **TE** Study Guide and Intervention Masters **CRM**, Ch. 1–9 *Quick Review Math Handbook* **Tier 3 Intervention** *Math Triumphs, Alg. 1*
	Mid-Chapter	
	Mid-Chapter Quiz **SE**, p. 566 Mid-Chapter Test **CRM**, p. 65 ExamView Assessment Suite	**Tier 1 Intervention** Concepts and Skills Bank **SE**, pp. 857–867 Skills Practice **CRM**, Ch. 1–9 glencoe.com **Tier 2 Intervention** Study Guide and Intervention Masters **CRM**, Ch. 1–9 *Quick Review Math Handbook* **Tier 3 Intervention** *Math Triumphs, Alg. 1*
	Before Chapter Test	
	Chapter Study Guide and Review **SE**, pp. 592–596 Practice Test **SE**, p. 597 Standardized Test Practice **SE**, pp. 598–601 Chapter Test glencoe.com Standardized Test Practice glencoe.com Vocabulary Review glencoe.com ExamView Assessment Suite	**Tier 1 Intervention** Concepts and Skills Bank **SE**, pp. 857–867 Skills Practice **CRM**, Ch. 1–9 glencoe.com **Tier 2 Intervention** Study Guide and Intervention Masters **CRM**, Ch. 1–9 *Quick Review Math Handbook* **Tier 3 Intervention** *Math Triumphs, Alg. 1*
Summative Assessment	**After Chapter 9**	
	Multiple-Choice Tests, Forms 1, 2A, 2B **CRM**, pp. 67–72 Free-Response Tests, Forms 2C, 2D, 3 **CRM**, pp. 73–78 Vocabulary Test **CRM**, p. 66 Extended Response Test **CRM**, p. 79 Standardized Test Practice **CRM**, pp. 80–82 ExamView Assessment Suite	Study Guide and Intervention Masters **CRM**, Ch. 1–9 *Quick Review Math Handbook* glencoe.com

Differentiated Instruction

Option 1 Reaching All Learners AL OL BL ELL

INTERPERSONAL Place students in small groups. Since there are several tasks involved in graphing quadratic functions, have the group members decide which tasks they should each complete in order to graph a given function. For example, one member can be responsible for finding the equation for the axis of symmetry, another can substitute values in order to determine points on the graph, and a third member can graph the points and draw the curve of the parabola.

SOCIAL Make three large columns on the chalkboard. Label the columns: "Two Real Roots," "One Real Root," and "No Real Roots." Ask volunteers to write a quadratic equation for each of the columns. Ask the class to use the discriminant to check whether the volunteers were correct. Then, use the quadratic formula to find the roots of those equations that have real roots.

Option 2 Approaching Level AL

Use a bent pipe cleaner and a coordinate grid on an overhead transparency to model the graph of an exponential function. Ask students to identify the y-intercept and to describe what happens to the y-values as the x-values increase. Repeat for the graphs of other exponential functions.

Option 3 English Learners ELL

Have students describe how to solve a quadratic equation by graphing, as if they were teaching the procedure. Make sure students include any tips or hints that they use when they solve by graphing.

Option 4 Beyond Level BL

Drop a tennis ball while standing in the front of the classroom. Ask students to describe how the bouncing ball can be modeled by a geometric sequence. Have students write an example of a sequence that might model the bouncing ball. Then, ask students to design their own physical models of a geometric sequence.

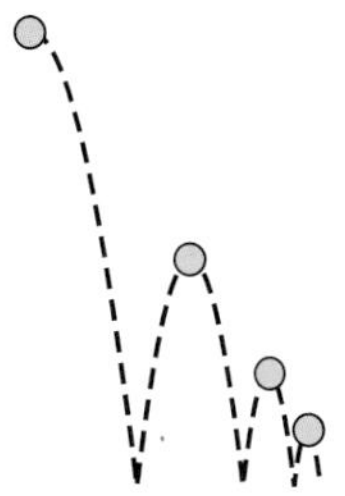

Focus on Mathematical Content

Vertical Alignment

Vertical Alignment

Related Topics before Grade 8

- approximate the value of irrational numbers as they arise from problem situations

Previous Topics from Algebra 1

- simplify numerical expressions involving order of operations and exponents
- find specific function values
- simplify polynomial expressions and factor as necessary in problem situations
- analyze graphs of quadratic functions and draw conclusions

Chapter 9

Related Topics from Algebra 1

- identify and sketch the general forms of quadratic parent functions
- analyze graphs of quadratic functions and draw conclusions
- make connections among the solutions (roots) of quadratic equations, the zeros of their related functions, and the horizontal intercepts of the graph of the function
- solve quadratic equations using concrete models, tables, graphs, and algebraic methods
- use characteristics of the quadratic parent function to sketch the related graphs
- analyze data and represent situations involving exponential growth and decay using tables, graphs, or algebraic methods
- analyze functions with successive differences and ratios

After Chapter 9

Preparation for Algebra 2

- relate representations of quadratic functions, such as algebraic, tabular, graphical, and verbal descriptions
- determine a quadratic function from its roots or a graph
- determine solutions of exponential equations using graphs, tables, and algebraic methods

Lesson-by-Lesson Preview

9-1 Graphing Quadratic Functions

The standard form of a quadratic function is $y = ax^2 + bx + c$, where $a \neq 0$.

- If a is positive, the parabola opens upward and the vertex is the minimum of the function.
- If a is negative, the parabola opens downward and the vertex is the maximum of the function.

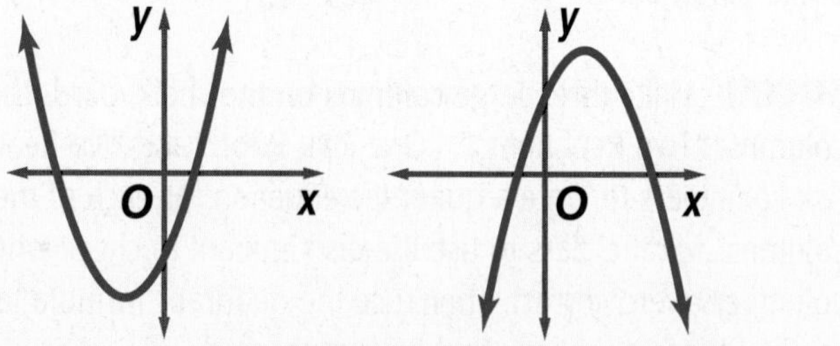

The line that divides a parabola into two congruent halves is called the *axis of symmetry*. The equation for the axis of symmetry for the graph of $y = ax^2 + bx + c$ is $x = \frac{-b}{2a}$.

9-2 Solving Quadratic Equations by Graphing

The solutions of a quadratic equation are called *roots*. All quadratic equations have two roots. The roots are as follows:

- two real roots–when the parabola crosses the x-axis at two distinct points,
- a double real root–when the vertex of the parabola is on the x-axis, or
- two imaginary roots–when the parabola does not intersect the x-axis.

9-3 Transformations of Quadratic Functions

A family of functions is a group of functions with graphs that share the same basic characteristics. The parent graph, which is the graph of the *parent function*, is the simplest of the graphs in a family. All other functions in the family are *transformations* of the graph of the parent function.

Three types of transformations performed on the parent function of the family of quadratics, $f(x) = x^2$, are

- *translation*–moves the parent figure up, down, left, or right,
- *vertical stretches*–shrinks or enlarges a parent figure proportionally,
- *reflection*–flips a figure over a line.

9-4 Solving Quadratic Equations by Completing the Square

If the quadratic expression on one side of the equation, in the form $ax^2 + bx + c = n$, is a perfect square and $n \geq 0$, the equation can be solved by taking the square root of each side. However, since few quadratic expressions are perfect squares, a method called *completing the square* may be used.

To solve an equation of the form $x^2 + bx + c = 0$ by completing the square, isolate the x^2 and bx terms on one side of the equation. Find half of b and square it. Then add this amount to each side of the equation. Solve by factoring and taking the square root of each side, if the right side is a nonnegative number. If the coefficient of x^2 is not 1, divide each term by the coefficient before completing the square.

9-5 Solving Quadratic Equations by Using the Quadratic Formula

A quadratic equation in the standard form $ax^2 + bx + c = 0$, where $a \neq 0$, can be solved using the Quadratic Formula. The coefficients a and b and the constant c are substituted in the formula $x = \dfrac{-b \pm \sqrt{b^2 - 4ac}}{2a}$. The expression is then simplified to find the solutions. The expression under the radical sign, $b^2 - 4ac$, is called the *discriminant*. The discriminant can be used to determine the number of real solutions of a quadratic equation.

9-6 Exponential Functions

Exponential functions are nonlinear and nonquadratic. An exponential function has a variable as an exponent and can be described by an equation of the form $y = ab^x$, where $a \neq 0$, $b > 0$, and $b \neq 1$.

- When $a > 0$ and $b > 1$, y-values change little for small values of x, but increase quickly as the values of x become greater. The graph rises from its left to its right.
- When $a > 0$ and $0 < b < 1$, y-values decrease as x increases. The graph falls as the x-values increase.

9-7 Growth and Decay

- Exponential growth can be modeled using the general equation $y = a(1 + r)^t$, where y is the final amount, a is the initial amount, r is the rate of change expressed as a decimal ($r > 0$), and t is time. An application of exponential growth is compound interest.
- Exponential decay can be modeled using the general equation $y = a(1 - r)^t$. An application of exponential decay is depreciation.

9-8 Geometric Sequences as Exponential Functions

In a geometric sequence, each term after the first is found by multiplying the previous term by the same nonzero constant r called the common ratio. Given several consecutive terms of a geometric sequence,

- r can be found by dividing any term by its previous term,
- successive terms can be found by multiplying the previous term by r, and
- the nth term, a_n, of a sequence, whose first term is a_1 ($a_1 \neq 0$) can be generated using the formula $a_n = a_1 \cdot r^{n-1}$, where n is any positive integer.

9-9 Analyzing Functions with Successive Differences

Linear, quadratic, and exponential functions can be used to model data. To determine which of these three types of functions (if any) represents a set of data,

- observe a pattern in the graph of a set of data,
- observe one of these patterns in the data: *linear function*: the first differences of the y-values are all equal; *quadratic function*: the first differences are not all equal, but the second differences are; and *exponential function*: the ratios of successive y-values are all equal.

McGraw Hill Professional Development

Targeted professional development has been articulated throughout *Algebra 1*. More quality, customized professional development is available from McGraw-Hill Professional Development. Visit glencoe.com for details on each product.

- **Online Lessons** emphasize the strategies and techniques used to teach Algebra 1. Includes streaming video, interactive pages, and online tools.
- **Video Workshops** allow mentors, coaches, or leadership personnel to facilitate on-site workshops on educational strategies in mathematics and mathematical concepts.
- **MHPD Online** (www.mhpdonline.com) offers online professional development with video clips of instructional strategies, links, student activities, and news and issues in education.
- **Teaching Today** (teachingtoday.glencoe.com) gives secondary teachers practical strategies and materials that inspire excellence and innovation in teaching.

CHAPTER 9 Notes

Chapter Project

Finance Fun

Students use what they have learned about exponential growth and decay, compound interest, and geometric sequences to work with the cost of buying a car.

- Have students research the price of a car they like. Tell them that there are various ways to pay for the car. Have them research and write about different plans car dealers offer to finance a car. For this project have students use both of the following ways.
- Suppose they save for the car. Tell students to imagine that the day they were born, \$1000 was placed in a savings account for them. This account has an interest rate of 6% that is compounded monthly. Have students write and graph an equation to represent the growth of this account. Ask students to determine what age they will be when they have saved enough money to purchase the car.
- Suppose they use a payment plan. Tell students that on this payment plan their first payment is half the cost of the car. The next payment is half of the remaining cost of the car. Payments continue in this way until there is less than \$1 to be paid. Have students write and graph an equation for this. Have students find how much the *n*th payment will be, then have them find how much the 10th payment will be.

Tell students that once they purchase their car and drive it off the car dealer's lot, the car starts to lose value or depreciate. Have students find the definitions of retail and wholesale costs for cars. Have students use a 15% depreciation rate for their car to write and graph an equation that represents the depreciation of their chosen car. Have them find the car's worth after a year.

Key Vocabulary Introduce the key vocabulary in the chapter using the routine below.

Define: The axis of symmetry is the vertical line containing the vertex of a parabola.

Ask: How many equal parts of a parabola does an axis of symmetry create? two

Example:

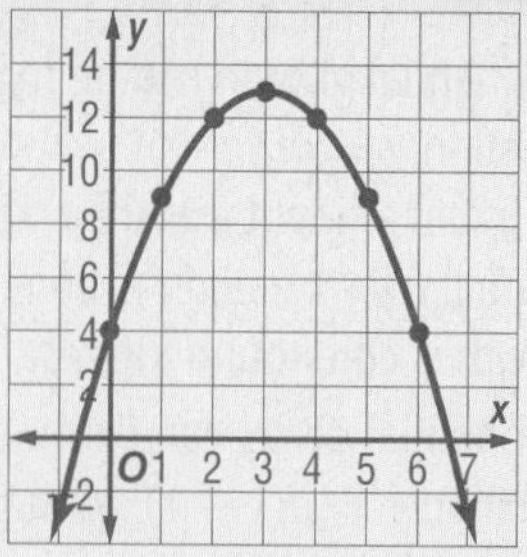

CHAPTER 9 Quadratic and Exponential Functions

Then

In Chapter 8, you solved quadratic equations by factoring and by using the Square Root Property.

Now

In Chapter 9, you will:

- Solve quadratic equations by graphing, completing the square, and using the Quadratic Formula.
- Graph exponential functions.
- Identify geometric sequences.

IL Learning Standards

8.B.4b Use basic quadratic functions to describe numerical relationships.
8.D.4 Formulate and solve quadratic equations algebraically and investigate nonlinear inequalities using graphs, tables, calculators and computers.

Why?

FINANCE The value of a certain company's stock can be modeled by the function $f(x) = x^2 - 12x + 75$. By graphing this quadratic function, we can make an educated guess as to how the stock will perform in the near future.

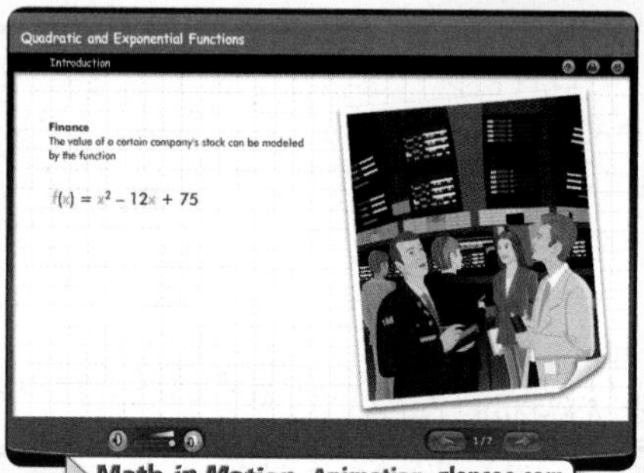

Math *in Motion,* Animation glencoe.com

522 Chapter 9 Quadratic and Exponential Functions

Get Ready for Chapter 9

Diagnose Readiness You have two options for checking Prerequisite Skills.

Text Option Take the Quick Check below. Refer to the Quick Review for help.

QuickCheck

(Used in Lesson 9-1)

Use a table of values to graph each equation. (Lesson 3-1) 1–7. See Ch. 9 Answer Appendix.

1. $y = x + 3$ **2.** $y = 2x + 2$

3. $y = -2x - 3$ **4.** $y = 0.5x - 1$

5. $4x - 3y = 12$ **6.** $3y = 6 + 9x$

7. **SAVINGS** Jack has $100 to buy a game system. He plans to save $10 each week. Graph an equation to show the total amount T Jack will have in w weeks.

Determine whether each trinomial is a perfect square trinomial. Write *yes* or *no*. If so, factor it. (Lesson 8-6) (Used in Lesson 9-4)

8. $a^2 + 12a + 36$ yes; $(a + 6)^2$ **9.** $x^2 + 5x + 25$ no

10. $x^2 - 12x + 32$ no **11.** $x^2 + 20x + 100$ yes; $(x + 10)^2$

12. $4x^2 + 28x + 49$ yes; $(2x + 7)^2$ **13.** $k^2 - 16k + 64$ yes; $(k - 8)^2$

14. $a^2 - 22a + 121$ yes; $(a - 11)^2$ **15.** $5t^2 - 12t + 25$ no

(Used in Lessons 9-7 and 9-8)

Find the next three terms of each arithmetic sequence. (Lessons 3-5)

16. 16, 4, −8, −20, … −32, −44, −56 **17.** 2, 10, 18, 26, … 34, 42, 50

18. −5, −2, 1, 4, … 7, 10, 13 **19.** 3, 5, 7, 9, … 11, 13, 15

20. **GEOMETRY** Write a formula that can be used to find the perimeter of a figure containing n squares. $P = 2n + 2$

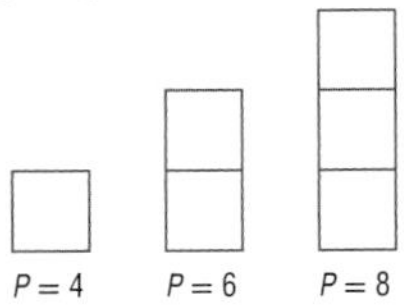

QuickReview

EXAMPLE 1

Use a table of values to graph $y = 3x + 1$.

x	$y = 3x + 1$	y
−1	3(−1) + 1	−2
0	3(0) + 1	1
1	3(1) + 1	4
2	3(2) + 1	7

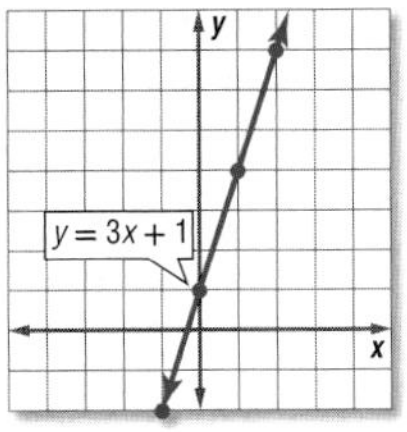

EXAMPLE 2

Determine whether $x^2 - 10x + 25$ is a perfect square trinomial. Write *yes* or *no*. If so, factor it.

1. Is the first term a perfect square? yes

2. Is the last term a perfect square? yes

3. Is the middle term equal to $-2(1x)(5)$? yes

$x^2 - 10x + 25 = (x - 5)^2$

EXAMPLE 3

Find the next three terms of the arithmetic sequence 5, 9, 13, 17, … .

Find the common difference by subtracting a term from the next term.

$$9 - 5 = 4$$

Add to find the next three terms.

$17 + 4 = 21,\ 21 + 4 = 25,\ 25 + 4 = 29$

The next three terms are 21, 25, 29.

Online Option IL Math Online Take a self-check Chapter Readiness Quiz at glencoe.com.

Response to Intervention (RtI)

Use the *Quick Check* results and the Intervention Planner chart to help you determine your Response to Intervention. The If-Then statements in the chart below help you decide the appropriate tier of RtI and suggest intervention resources for each tier.

Intervention Planner

Tier 1 On Level

If students miss about 25% of the exercises or less,

Then choose a resource:

SE Lessons 3-1, 3-5, and 8-6

CRM Skills Practice, Chapter 3, pp. 7 and 32, Chapter 8, p. 39

IL Math Online Self-Check Quiz

Tier 2 Strategic Intervention approaching grade level

If students miss about 50% of the exercises,

Then choose a resource:

CRM Study Guide and Intervention, Chapter 3, pp. 5 and 30, Chapter 8, p. 37

Quick Review Math Handbook

IL Math Online Extra Examples, Personal Tutor, Homework Help

Tier 3 Intensive Intervention 2 or more grades below level

If students miss about 75% of the exercises,

Then use *Math Triumphs, Alg. 1*

IL Math Online Extra Examples, Personal Tutor, Homework Help, Review Vocabulary

CHAPTER 9 Notes

FOLDABLES® Study Organizer

Dinah Zike's Foldables®

Focus Students write about the characteristics of quadratic functions as they are presented in the lessons of this chapter.

Teach Have students make and label their Foldables as illustrated. Students should use the appropriate section to fill in examples of each characteristic listed. Under each example have students write a brief explanation as to how that characteristic relates to the other three concepts in the Foldable.

When to Use It Encourage students to add to their Foldables as they work through the chapter and to use them to review for the chapter test.

Differentiated Instruction

CRM Student-Built Glossary, pp. 1–2 Students should complete the chart by providing a definition of each term and an example as they progress through Chapter 9. This study tool can also be used to review for the chapter test.

Get Started on Chapter 9

You will learn several new concepts, skills, and vocabulary terms as you study Chapter 9. To get ready, identify important terms and organize your resources. You may wish to refer to **Chapter 0** to review prerequisite skills.

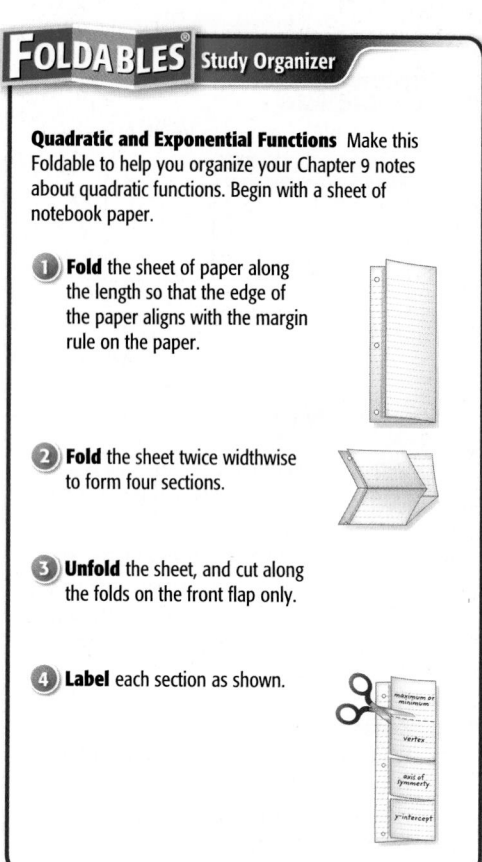

FOLDABLES® Study Organizer

Quadratic and Exponential Functions Make this Foldable to help you organize your Chapter 9 notes about quadratic functions. Begin with a sheet of notebook paper.

1. **Fold** the sheet of paper along the length so that the edge of the paper aligns with the margin rule on the paper.

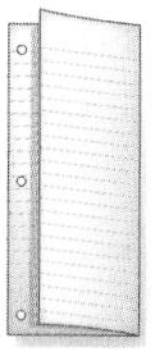

2. **Fold** the sheet twice widthwise to form four sections.

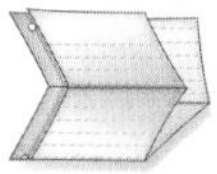

3. **Unfold** the sheet, and cut along the folds on the front flap only.

4. **Label** each section as shown.

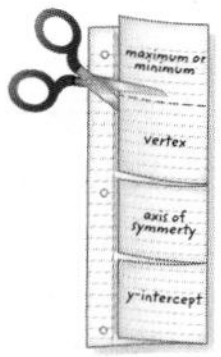

New Vocabulary

English		Español
axis of symmetry	p. 525	eje de simetría
maximum	p. 525	máximo
minimum	p. 525	mínimo
nonlinear function	p. 525	función no lineal
parabola	p. 525	parábola
quadratic function	p. 525	función cuadrática
vertex	p. 525	vértice
double root	p. 538	doble raíz
transformation	p. 544	transformación
completing the square	p. 552	completar el cuadrado
Quadratic Formula	p. 558	Formula cuadrática
discriminant	p. 561	discriminante
exponential function	p. 567	función exponencial
compound interest	p. 574	interés es compuesta
common ratio	p. 578	proporción común
geometric sequence	p. 578	secuencia geométrica

Review Vocabulary

domain • p. 38 • dominio all the possible values of the independent variable, x

leading coefficient • p. 425 • coeficiente delantero the coefficient of the first term of a polynomial written in standard form

range • p. 38 • rango all the possible values of the dependent variable, y

In the function represented by the table, the domain is {0, 2, 4, 6}, and the range is {3, 5, 7, 9}.

x	y
0	3
2	5
4	7
6	9

Multilingual eGlossary glencoe.com

IL Math Online glencoe.com

- Study the chapter online
- Explore **Math in Motion**
- Get extra help from your own **Personal Tutor**
- Use **Extra Examples** for additional help
- Take a **Self-Check Quiz**
- **Review Vocabulary** in fun ways

Additional Answer (Page 525, Check Your Progress)

1.

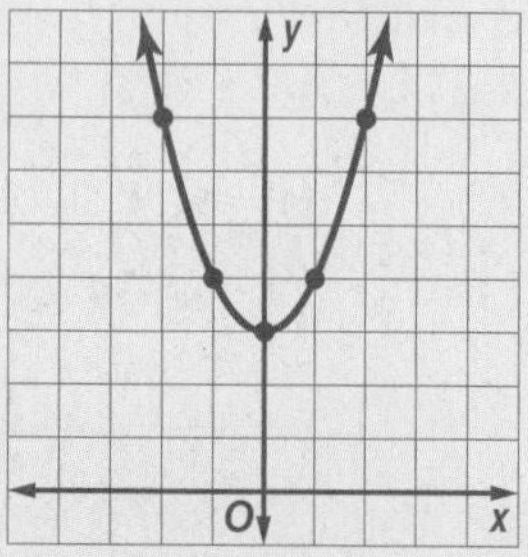

D = {all real numbers},
$R = \{y \mid y \geq 3\}$

x	y
−2	7
−1	4
0	3
1	4
2	7

Graphing Quadratic Functions

Then

You graphed linear functions. (Lesson 3-2)

Now

- Analyze the characteristics of graphs of quadratic functions.
- Graph quadratic functions.

IL Learning Standards

7.B.4 Estimate and measure the magnitude and directions of physical quantities using rulers, protractors and other scientific instruments including timers, calculators and computers.
8.B.4b **Use the basic functions of** absolute value, square root, linear, **quadratic** and step **to describe numerical relationships**.

New Vocabulary

nonlinear function
quadratic function
standard form
parabola
axis of symmetry
vertex
minimum
maximum
symmetry

IL Math Online

glencoe.com

- Extra Examples
- Personal Tutor
- Self-Check Quiz
- Homework Help

Why?

The Innovention Fountain in Epcot's Futureworld in Orlando, Florida, is an elaborate display of water, light, and music. The sprayers shoot water in shapes that can be modeled by quadratic equations. You can use the graph of this equation to show the path of the water.

Characteristics of Quadratic Functions You have studied linear functions. There are also **nonlinear functions** with graphs of other shapes. **Quadratic functions** are nonlinear and can be written in the form $f(x) = ax^2 + bx + c$, where $a \neq 0$. This form is called the **standard form** of a quadratic function.

The shape of the graph of a quadratic function is called a **parabola**. Parabolas are symmetric about a central line called the **axis of symmetry**. The axis of symmetry intersects a parabola at only one point, called the **vertex**.

Key Concept Quadratic Functions — For Your FOLDABLE

Parent Function:	$f(x) = x^2$
Standard Form:	$f(x) = ax^2 + bx + c$
Type of Graph:	parabola
Axis of Symmetry:	$x = -\frac{b}{2a}$
y-intercept:	c

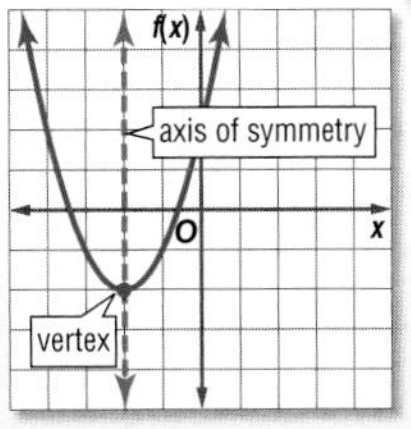

When $a > 0$, the graph of $y = ax^2 + bx + c$ opens upward. The lowest point on the graph is the **minimum**. When $a < 0$, the graph of $y = ax^2 + bx + c$ opens downward. The highest point on the graph is the **maximum**. The maximum or minimum is the vertex.

EXAMPLE 1 Graph a Parabola

Use a table of values to graph $y = 3x^2 + 6x - 4$. State the domain and range.

x	y
1	5
0	−4
−1	−7
−2	−4
−3	5

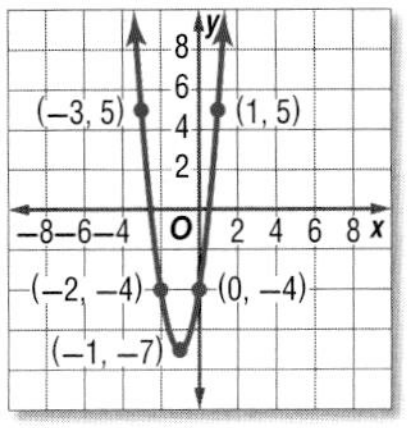

Graph the ordered pairs, and connect them to create a smooth curve. The parabola extends to infinity. The domain is all real numbers. The range is $\{y \mid y \geq -7\}$, because −7 is the minimum.

Check Your Progress See margin.

1. Use a table of values to graph $y = x^2 + 3$. State the domain and range.

Personal Tutor glencoe.com

9-1 Lesson Notes

1 FOCUS

Vertical Alignment

Before Lesson 9-1
Graph linear functions.

Lesson 9-1
Analyze the characteristics of graphs of quadratic functions.
Graph quadratic functions.

After Lesson 9-1
Apply translations, dilations, and reflections to quadratic functions.

2 TEACH

Scaffolding Questions

Have students read the *Why?* section of the lesson.

Ask:

- Is $y = -8x^2 - 49x - 75$ a linear equation? Explain. No; it has an x^2-term.
- Is the path of the water a line? No
- How would you describe the shape the water makes when it is shot from the sprayer? Sample answer: a symmetrical curve called a parabola

TEACH with TECH

INTERACTIVE WHITEBOARD Drag a coordinate grid on the board. Use this throughout the lesson as you work through examples graphing quadratic functions.

Lesson 9-1 Resources

Resource	Approaching-Level	On-Level	Beyond-Level	English Learners
Teacher Edition	• Differentiated Instruction, p. 529	• Differentiated Instruction, pp. 529, 535	• Differentiated Instruction, p. 535	
Chapter Resource Masters	• Study Guide and Intervention, pp. 5–6 • Skills Practice, p. 7 • Practice, p. 8 • Word Problem Practice, p. 9	• Study Guide and Intervention, pp. 5–6 • Skills Practice, p. 7 • Practice, p. 8 • Word Problem Practice, p. 9 • Enrichment, p. 10	• Practice, p. 8 • Word Problem Practice, p. 9 • Enrichment, p. 10	• Study Guide and Intervention, pp. 5–6 • Skills Practice, p. 7 • Practice, p. 8 • Word Problem Practice, p. 9
Transparencies	• 5-Minute Check Transparency 9-1	• 5-Minute Check Transparency 9-1	• 5-Minute Check Transparency 9-1	• 5-Minute Check Transparency 9-1
Other	• Study Notebook • Teaching Algebra with Manipulatives	• Study Notebook • Teaching Algebra with Manipulatives	• Study Notebook	• Study Notebook • Teaching Algebra with Manipulatives

Characteristics of Quadratic Functions

Example 1 shows how to use a table of values to graph a quadratic function.

Formative Assessment

Use the Check Your Progress exercises after each example to determine students' understanding of concepts.

Additional Example

1 Use a table of values to graph $y = x^2 - x - 2$. State the domain and range.

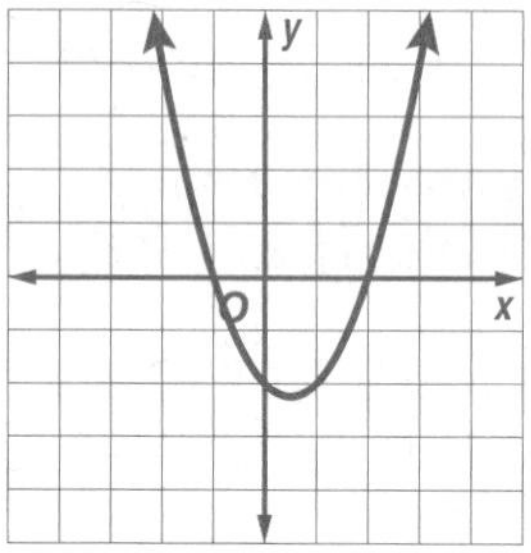

domain: all real numbers; range $\left\{y \mid y \geq -2\frac{1}{4}\right\}$

Additional Examples also in Interactive Classroom PowerPoint® Presentations

IWB INTERACTIVE WHITEBOARD READY

Symmetry and Vertices

Example 2 shows how to find the vertex, an equation for the axis of symmetry, and the y-intercept of a parabola from a graph. **Example 3** shows how to find the vertex, the equation of the axis of symmetry, and the y-intercept from an equation. **Example 4** shows how to determine whether the function has a maximum or minimum value, and how to find these values.

Review Vocabulary

Domain and Range The domain is the set of all of the possible values of the independent variable x. The range is the set of all of the possible values of the dependent variable y.

Figures that possess **symmetry** are those in which each half of the figure matches exactly.

A parabola is symmetric about the axis of symmetry. Every point on the parabola to the left of the axis of symmetry has a corresponding point on the other half.

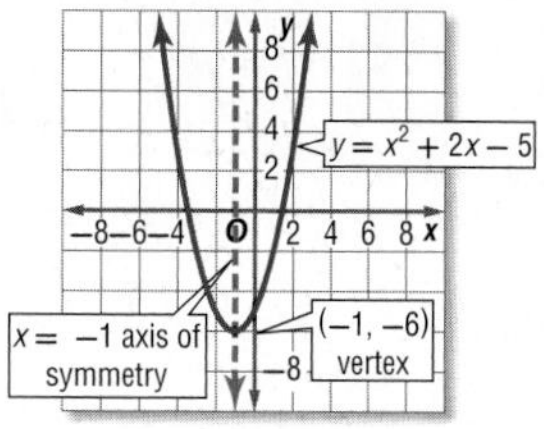

When identifying characteristics from a graph, it is often easiest to locate the vertex first. It is either the maximum or minimum point of the graph.

EXAMPLE 2 Identify Characteristics from Graphs

Find the vertex, the equation of the axis of symmetry, and the y-intercept of each graph.

a.

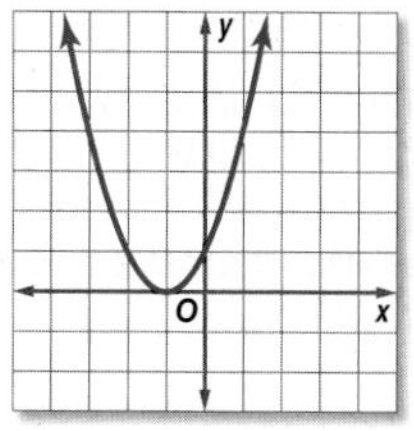

Step 1 Find the vertex.
Because the parabola opens upward, the vertex is located at the minimum point of the parabola. It is located at $(-1, 0)$.

Step 2 Find the axis of symmetry.
The axis of symmetry is the line that goes through the vertex and divides the parabola into congruent halves. It is located at $x = -1$.

Step 3 Find the y-intercept.
The y-intercept is the point where the graph intersects the y-axis. It is located at $(0, -1)$, so the y-intercept is -1.

b.

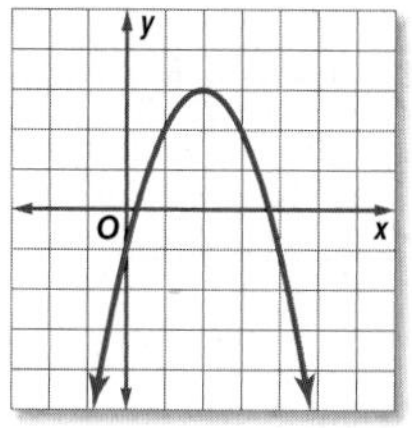

Step 1 Find the vertex.
The parabola opens downward, so the vertex is located at its maximum point, $(2, 3)$.

Step 2 Find the axis of symmetry.
The axis of symmetry is located at $x = 2$.

Step 3 Find the y-intercept.
The y-intercept is where the parabola crosses the y-axis. It is located at $(0, -1)$, so the y-intercept is -1.

Check Your Progress

2A.

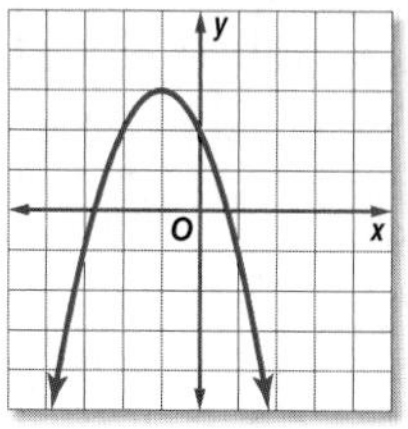

2B.

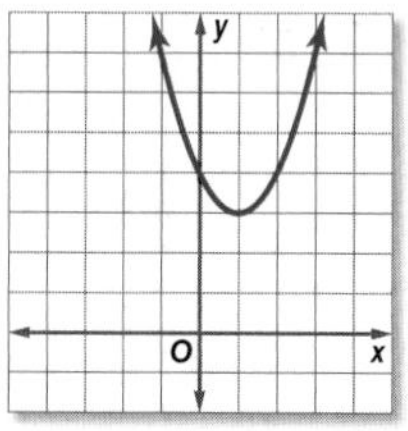

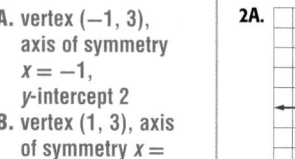

2A. vertex $(-1, 3)$, axis of symmetry $x = -1$, y-intercept 2
2B. vertex $(1, 3)$, axis of symmetry $x = 1$, y-intercept 4

Personal Tutor glencoe.com

526 Chapter 9 Quadratic and Exponential Functions

StudyTip

Function Characteristics When identifying characteristics of a function, it is often easiest to locate the axis of symmetry first.

EXAMPLE 3 Identify Characteristics from Functions

Find the vertex, the equation of the axis of symmetry, and the y-intercept of each function.

a. $y = 2x^2 + 4x - 3$

$x = -\frac{b}{2a}$	**Formula for the equation of the axis of symmetry**
$x = -\frac{4}{2 \cdot 2}$	**$a = 2$ and $b = 4$**
$x = -1$	**Simplify.**

The equation for the axis of symmetry is $x = -1$.

To find the vertex, use the value you found for the axis of symmetry as the x-coordinate of the vertex. To find the y-coordinate, substitute that value for x in the original equation.

$y = 2x^2 + 4x - 3$	**Original equation**
$= 2(-1)^2 + 4(-1) - 3$	**$x = -1$**
$= -5$	**Simplify.**

The vertex is at $(-1, -5)$.

The y-intercept always occurs at $(0, c)$. So, the y-intercept is -3.

b. $y = -x^2 + 6x + 4$

$x = -\frac{b}{2a}$	**Formula for the equation of the axis of symmetry**
$x = -\frac{6}{2(-1)}$	**$a = -1$ and $b = 6$**
$x = 3$	**Simplify.**

The equation of the axis of symmetry is $x = 3$.

$y = -x^2 + 6x + 4$	**Original equation**
$= -(3)^2 + 6(3) + 4$	**$x = 3$**
$= 13$	**Simplify.**

The vertex is at $(3, 13)$.

The y-intercept is 4.

StudyTip

***y*-intercept** The y-coordinate of the y-intercept is also the constant term (c) of the quadratic function in standard form.

Check Your Progress

3A. $y = -3x^2 + 6x - 5$

3B. $y = 2x^2 + 2x + 2$

Personal Tutor glencoe.com

3A. vertex $(1, -2)$, axis of symmetry $x = 1$, y-intercept -5

3B. vertex $\left(-\frac{1}{2}, \frac{3}{2}\right)$, axis of symmetry $x = -\frac{1}{2}$, y-intercept 2

There are general differences between linear functions and quadratic functions.

	Linear Functions	Quadratic Functions
Standard Form	$y = ax + b$	$y = ax^2 + bx + c; a \neq 0$
Degree	1; Notice that all of the variables are to the first power.	2; Notice that the independent variable, x, is squared in the first term. The coefficient a can not equal 0, or the equation would be linear.
Example	$y = 2x + 6$	$y = 3x^2 + 5x - 4$
Graph	line	parabola

Next you will learn how to identify whether the parabola opens up or down and whether the vertex is a maximum or a minimum point.

Additional Examples

2 Find the vertex, the equation of the axis of symmetry, and y-intercept.

a.

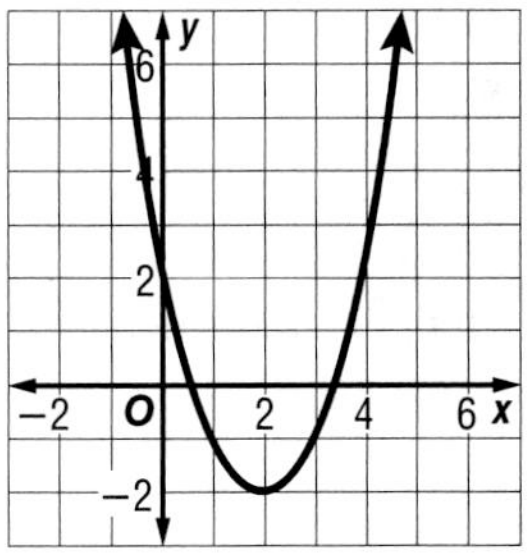

vertex: $(2, -2)$; axis of symmetry: $x = 2$; y-intercept: $(0, 2)$

b.

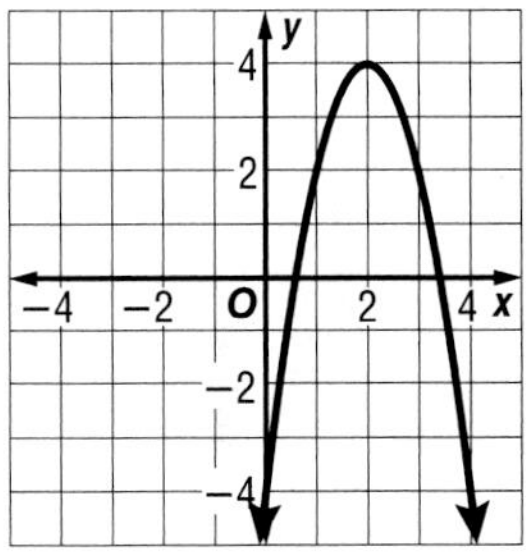

vertex: $(2, 4)$; axis of symmetry: $x = 2$; y-intercept: $(0, -4)$

3 Find the vertex, the equation of the axis of symmetry, and y-intercept.

a. $y = -2x^2 - 8x - 2$
$(-2, 6)$, $x = -2$, -2

b. $y = 3x^2 + 6x - 2$
$(-1, -5)$, $x = -1$, -2

Additional Example

4 Consider $f(x) = -x^2 - 2x - 2$.

a. Determine whether the function has a maximum or a minimum value. maximum

b. State the maximum or minimum value of the function. -1

c. State the domain and range of the function. domain: all real numbers; range: $\{y \mid y \leq -1\}$

Graph Quadratic Functions

Examples 5 shows how to use the characteristics of a quadratic function to graph the function. **Example 6** shows how to analyze the graph of a quadratic function to solve real-world problems.

Key Concept — Maximum and Minimum Values

For Your FOLDABLE

Words The graph of $f(x) = ax^2 + bx + c$, where $a \neq 0$:

- opens upward and has a minimum value when $a > 0$, and
- opens downward and has a maximum value when $a < 0$.
- The range of a quadratic function is all real numbers greater than or equal to the minimum, or all real numbers less than or equal to the maximum.

Examples a is positive.

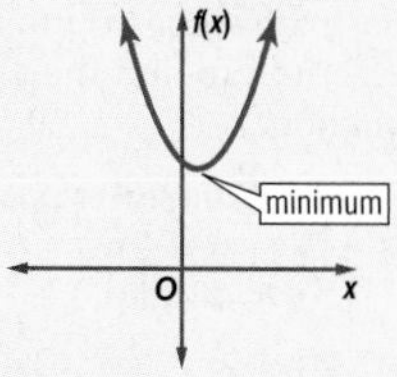

a is negative.

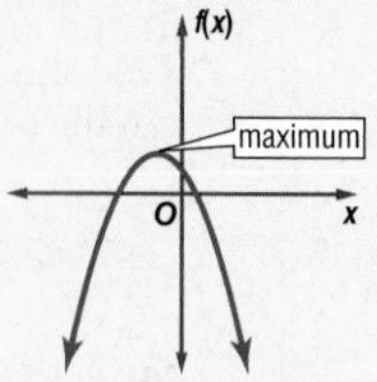

Watch Out!

Minimum and Maximum Values Don't forget to find both coordinates of the vertex (x, y). The minimum or maximum value is the y-coordinate.

EXAMPLE 4 Maximum and Minimum Values

Consider $f(x) = -2x^2 - 4x + 6$.

a. Determine whether the function has a *maximum* or *minimum* value.

For $f(x) = -2x^2 - 4x + 6$, $a = -2$, $b = -4$, and $c = 6$.
Because a is negative the graph opens down, so the function has a maximum value.

b. State the maximum or minimum value of the function.

The maximum value is the y-coordinate of the vertex.
The x-coordinate of the vertex is $\frac{-b}{2a}$ or $\frac{4}{2(-2)}$ or -1.

$f(x) = -2x^2 - 4x + 6$ **Original function**
$f(-1) = -2(-1)^2 - 4(-1) + 6$ **$x = -1$**
$f(-1) = 8$ **Simplify.**

The maximum value is 8.

c. State the domain and range of the function.

The domain is all real numbers. The range is all real numbers less than or equal to the maximum value, or $\{y \mid y \leq 8\}$.

Check Your Progress

Consider $g(x) = 2x^2 - 4x - 1$.

4A. Determine whether the function has a *maximum* or *minimum* value. minimum

4B. State the maximum or minimum value. -3

4C. State the domain and range of the function.

4C. D = all real numbers, R = $\{y \mid y \geq -3\}$

Personal Tutor glencoe.com

Focus on Mathematical Content

Vertex The maximum or minimum point of a parabola is called the *vertex*. When a quadratic function is written in standard form $y = ax^2 + bx + c$, and a is positive, the parabola opens upward, and the vertex is a minimum. When a is negative, the parabola opens downward, and the vertex is a maximum.

Math *in Motion*, Animation glencoe.com

Graph Quadratic Functions You have learned how to find several important characteristics of quadratic functions.

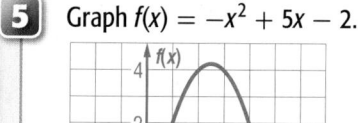

Key Concept **Graph Quadratic Functions** For Your FOLDABLE

Step 1 Find the equation of the axis of symmetry.

Step 2 Find the vertex, and determine whether it is a maximum or minimum.

Step 3 Find the *y*-intercept.

Step 4 Use symmetry to find additional points on the graph, if necessary.

Step 5 Connect the points with a smooth curve.

EXAMPLE 5 **Graph Quadratic Functions**

Graph $f(x) = x^2 + 4x + 3$.

Step 1 Find the equation of the axis of symmetry.

$x = \frac{-b}{2a}$ **Formula for the equation of the axis of symmetry**

$x = \frac{-4}{2 \cdot 1}$ **$a = 1$ and $b = 4$**

$x = -2$ **Simplify.**

Step 2 Find the vertex, and determine whether it is a maximum or minimum.

$y = x^2 + 4x + 3$ **Original equation**

$= (-2)^2 + 4(-2) + 3$ **$x = -2$**

$= -1$ **Simplify.**

The vertex lies at $(-2, -1)$. Because a is positive the graph opens up, and the vertex is a minimum.

Step 3 Find the y-intercept.

$y = x^2 + 4x + 3$ **Original equation**

$= (0)^2 + 4(0) + 3$ **$x = 0$**

$= 3$ **Simplify.**

The y-intercept is 3.

Step 4 The axis of symmetry divides the parabola into two equal parts. So if there is a point on one side, there is a corresponding point on the other side that is the same distance from the axis of symmetry and has the same y-value.

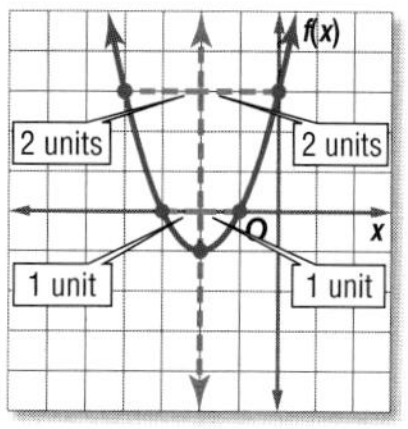

Step 5 Connect the points with a smooth curve.

Check Your Progress

Graph each function.

5A. $f(x) = -2x^2 + 2x - 1$

5B. $f(x) = 3x^2 - 6x + 2$

Personal Tutor glencoe.com

StudyTip

Symmetry and Points When locating points that are on opposite sides of the axis of symmetry, they are not only the same distance to the left and right of the axis of symmetry. They are also the same number of spaces up or down from the vertex.

5A.

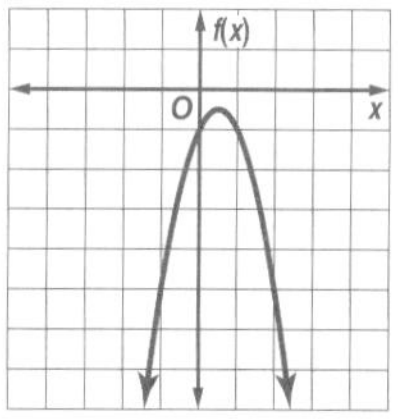

5B.

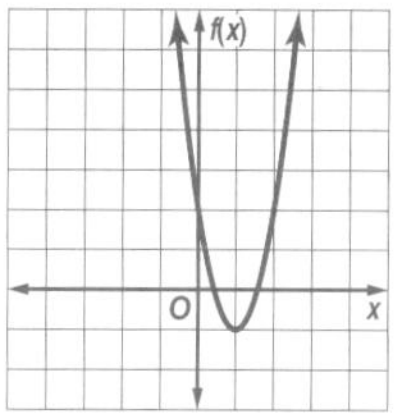

Watch Out!

Preventing Errors Tell students that their sketches of parabolas do not have to be perfect. However, students should not "connect the dots" with straight lines. The important thing is for the curve to pass through the graphed ordered pairs.

Symmetry and Graphing

When students use symmetry to graph parabolas, they only need to find a few points and then reflect those points across the line of symmetry. You may want to suggest that students occasionally check their reflected points by substituting them into the original equation.

Additional Example

5 Graph $f(x) = -x^2 + 5x - 2$.

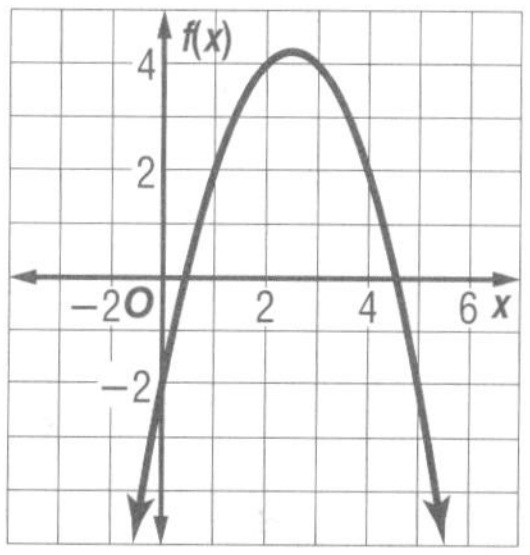

Differentiated Instruction

AL OL

If students need a visual to understand the concept of a vertex and an axis of symmetry,

Then ask students to make a table of values and graph $y = x^2 + 6x + 8$ on grid paper. Have students hold their paper up to the light and fold their parabola in half so that the two sides match exactly. Have students use the crease on their unfolded paper to locate the vertex, axis of symmetry, and minimum value. $(-3, -1)$; $x = -3$; -1

Lesson 9-1 Graphing Quadratic Functions **529**

Additional Example

6 **ARCHERY** Ben shoots an arrow. The height of the arrow can be modeled by $y = -16x^2 + 100x + 4$, where y represents the height in feet of the arrow x seconds after it is shot into the air.

a. Graph the height of the arrow.

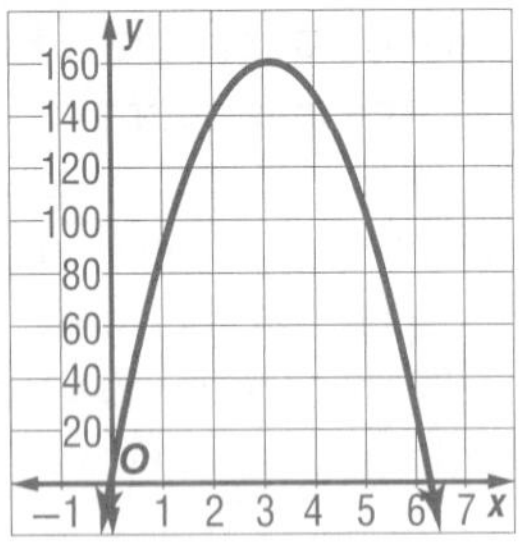

b. At what height was the arrow shot? 4 feet

c. What is the maximum height of the arrow? $160\frac{1}{4}$ feet

You have used what you know about quadratic functions, parabolas, and symmetry to create graphs. You can analyze these graphs to solve real-world problems.

Real-World EXAMPLE 6 Use a Graph of a Quadratic Function

SCHOOL SPIRIT The cheerleaders at Lake High School launch T-shirts into the crowd every time the Lakers score a touchdown. The height of the T-shirt can be modeled by the function $h(x) = -16x^2 + 48x + 6$, where $h(x)$ represents the height in feet of the T-shirt after x seconds.

a. Graph the function.

$x = -\frac{b}{2a}$ — **Equation of the axis of symmetry**

$x = -\frac{48}{2(-16)}$ or $\frac{3}{2}$ — **$a = -16$ and $b = 48$**

The equation of the axis of symmetry is $x = \frac{3}{2}$. Thus, the x-coordinate for the vertex is $\frac{3}{2}$.

$y = -16x^2 + 48x + 6$	**Original equation**
$= -16\left(\frac{3}{2}\right)^2 + 48\left(\frac{3}{2}\right) + 6$	$x = \frac{3}{2}$
$= -16\left(\frac{9}{4}\right) + 48\left(\frac{3}{2}\right) + 6$	$\left(\frac{3}{2}\right)^2 = \frac{9}{4}$
$= -36 + 72 + 6$ or 42	**Simplify.**

The vertex is at $\left(\frac{3}{2}, 42\right)$.

Let's find another point. Choose an x-value of 0 and substitute. Our new point is at (0, 6). The point paired with it on the other side of the axis of symmetry is (3, 6).

Repeat this and choose an x-value of 1 to get (1, 38) and its corresponding point (2, 38). Connect these points and create a smooth curve.

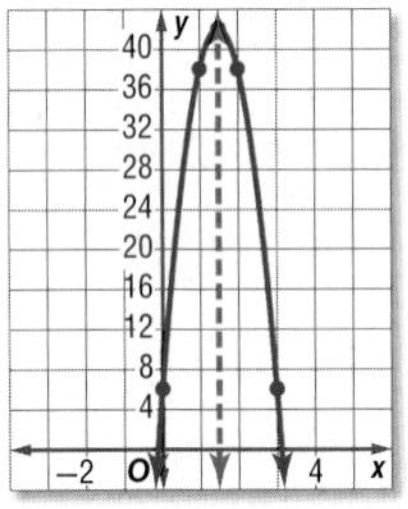

Real-World Link

About 1 in 17 high school seniors playing football will go on to play football at an NCAA school.

Source: National Collegiate Athletic Association

b. At what height was the T-shirt launched?
The T-shirt is launched when time equals 0, or at the y-intercept. So, the T-shirt was launched 6 feet from the ground.

c. What is the maximum height of the T-shirt? When was the maximum height reached?
The maximum height of the T-shirt occurs at the vertex. So the T-shirt reaches a maximum height of 42 feet. The time was $\frac{3}{2}$ or 1.5 seconds after launch.

Check Your Progress

6. TRACK Emilio is competing in the javelin throw. The height of the javelin can be modeled by the equation $y = -16x^2 + 64x + 6$, where y represents the height in feet of the javelin after x seconds.

A. Graph the path of the javelin.

B. At what height is the javelin thrown? **6 ft**

C. What is the maximum height of the javelin? **70 ft**

6A.

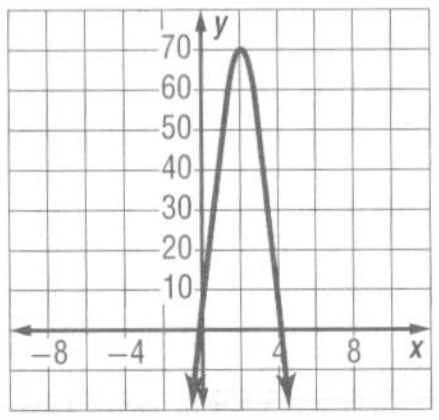

Personal Tutor glencoe.com

Additional Answers

13a. maximum

13b. 1

13c. D = {all real numbers}; R = $\{y \mid y \leq 1\}$

14a. maximum

14b. 3

14c. D = {all real numbers}; R = $\{y \mid y \leq 3\}$

15a. maximum

15b. 6

15c. D = {all real numbers}; R = $\{y \mid y \leq 6\}$

16a. maximum

16b. 2

16c. D = {all real numbers}; R = $\{y \mid y \leq 2\}$

17.

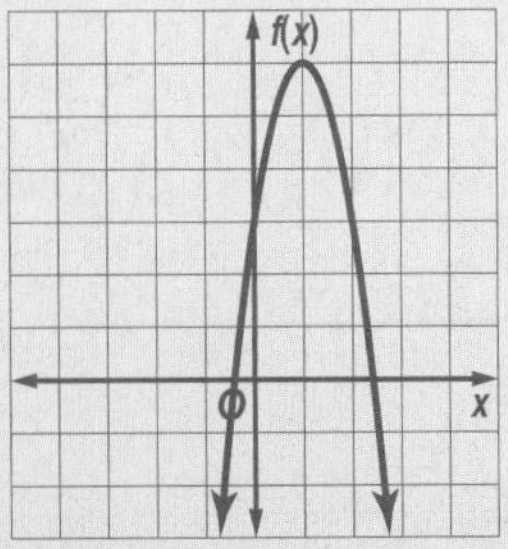

18.

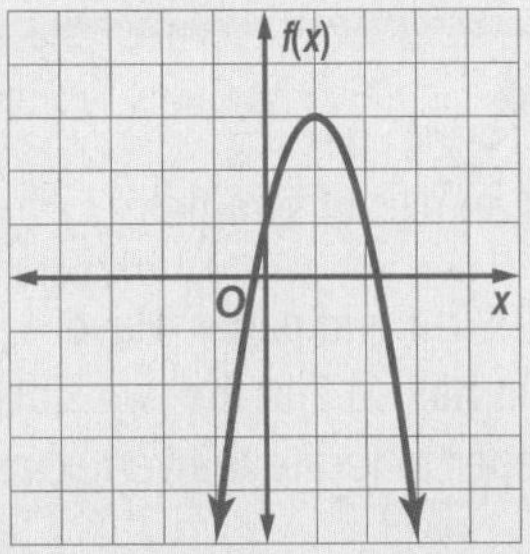

19.

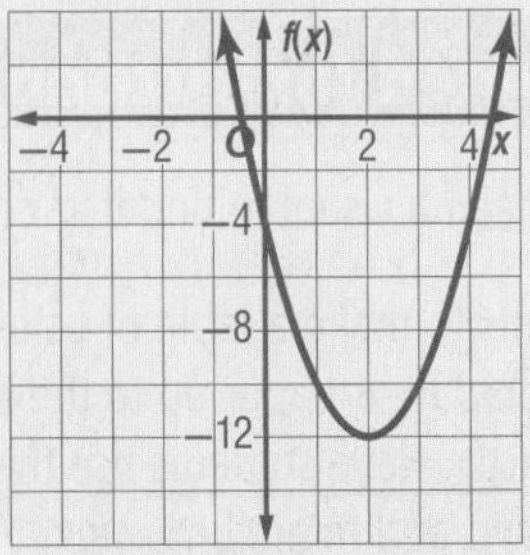

Check Your Understanding

1–4. See Ch. 9 Answer Appendix.

Example 1 p. 525 Use a table of values to graph each equation. State the domain and range.

1. $y = 2x^2 + 4x - 6$
2. $y = x^2 + 2x - 1$
3. $y = x^2 - 6x - 3$
4. $y = 3x^2 - 6x - 5$

Example 2 p. 526 Find the vertex, the equation of the axis of symmetry, and the y-intercept of each graph.

5.
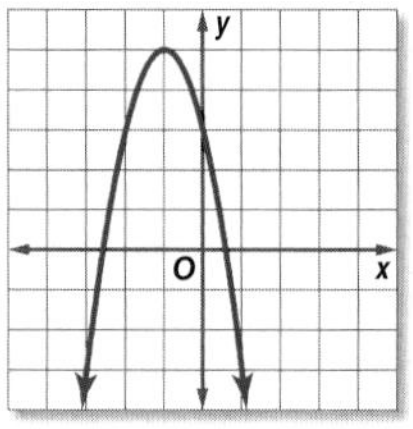

6.
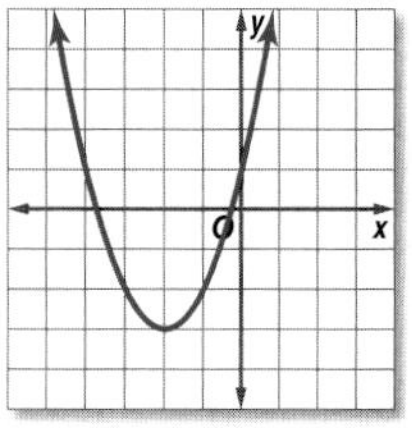

7.
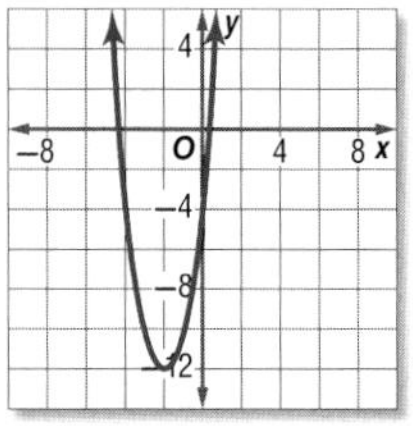

8.
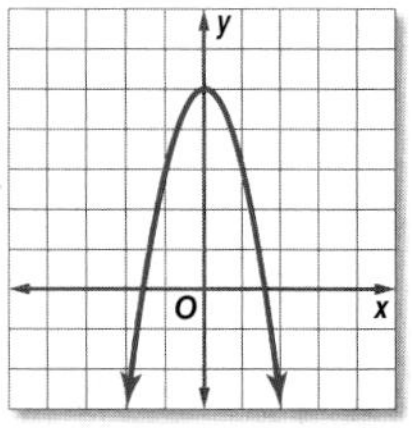

Example 3 p. 527 Find the vertex, the equation of the axis of symmetry, and the y-intercept of the graph of each function.

9. $y = -3x^2 + 6x - 1$
10. $y = -x^2 + 2x + 1$
11. $y = x^2 - 4x + 5$
12. $y = 4x^2 - 8x + 9$

Example 4 p. 528 Consider each function. 13–16. See margin.

a. Determine whether the function has *maximum* or *minimum* value.

b. State the maximum or minimum value.

c. What are the domain and range of the function?

13. $y = -x^2 + 4x - 3$
14. $y = -x^2 - 2x + 2$
15. $y = -3x^2 + 6x + 3$
16. $y = -2x^2 + 8x - 6$

Example 5 p. 529 Graph each function. 17–20. See margin.

17. $f(x) = -3x^2 + 6x + 3$
18. $f(x) = -2x^2 + 4x + 1$
19. $f(x) = 2x^2 - 8x - 4$
20. $f(x) = 3x^2 - 6x - 1$

Example 6 p. 530

21. **JUGGLING** A juggler is tossing a ball into the air. The height of the ball in feet can be modeled by the equation $y = -16x^2 + 16x + 5$, where y represents the height of the ball at x seconds.

 a. Graph this equation. See margin.

 b. At what height is the ball thrown? 5 ft

 c. What is the maximum height of the ball? 9 ft

5. vertex (−1, 5), axis of symmetry $x = -1$, y-intercept 3
6. vertex (−2, −3), axis of symmetry $x = -2$, y-intercept 1
7. vertex (−2, −12), axis of symmetry $x = -2$, y-intercept −4
8. vertex (0, 5), axis of symmetry $x = 0$, y-intercept 5
9. vertex (1, 2), axis of symmetry $x = 1$, y-intercept −1
10. vertex (1, 2), axis of symmetry $x = 1$, y-intercept 1
11. vertex (2, 1), axis of symmetry $x = 2$, y-intercept 5
12. vertex (1, 5), axis of symmetry $x = 1$, y-intercept 9

3 PRACTICE

Formative Assessment

Use Exercises 1–21 to check for understanding.

Use the chart at the bottom of this page to customize assignments for your students.

Exercise Alert

Grid Paper For Exercises 1–4, 17–27, 52–58, 63, and 68 students will need grid paper.

Additional Answers

20.
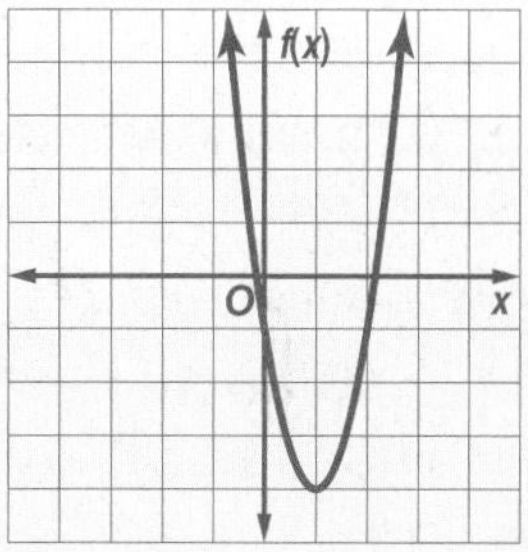

21a.
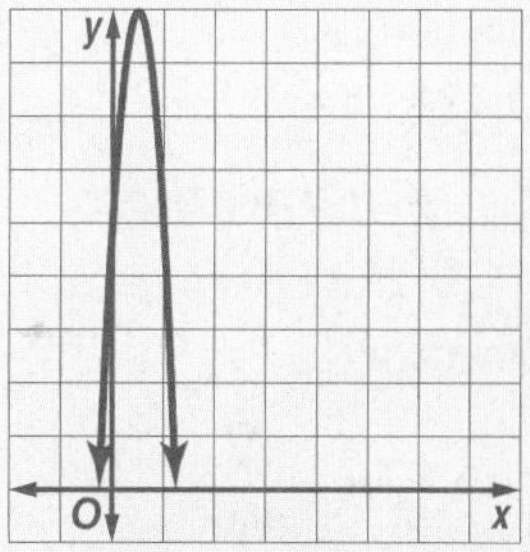

Differentiated Homework Options

Level	Assignment	Two-Day Option	
AL Basic	22–58, 68–69, 71–95	23–57 odd, 75–78	22–58 even, 68–69, 71–74, 79–95
OL Core	23–63 odd, 64–69, 71–95	22–58, 75–78	59–69, 71–74, 79–95
BL Advanced	59–92, (optional: 93—95)		

Additional Answers

34. vertex (−4, −6), axis of symmetry $x = -4$, y-intercept 10

35. vertex (−3, −8), axis of symmetry $x = -3$, y-intercept 10

36. vertex (−1, 10), axis of symmetry $x = -1$, y-intercept 7

37. vertex (−3, 4), axis of symmetry $x = -3$, y-intercept −5

38. vertex (−2, −10), axis of symmetry $x = -2$, y-intercept 10

39. vertex (2, −14), axis of symmetry $x = 2$, y-intercept 14

40. vertex (3, −12), axis of symmetry $x = 3$, y-intercept 6

41. vertex (1, −15), axis of symmetry $x = 1$, y-intercept −18

42. vertex (5, 12), axis of symmetry $x = 5$, y-intercept −13

43a. maximum

43b. 9

43c. D = {all real numbers}, R = $\{y \mid y \leq 9\}$

44a. minimum

44b. −9

44c. D = {all real numbers}, R = $\{y \mid y \geq -9\}$

45a. minimum

45b. −48

45c. D = {all real numbers}, R = $\{y \mid y \geq -48\}$

46a. maximum

46b. 50

46c. D = {all real numbers}, R = $\{y \mid y \leq 50\}$

47a. maximum

47b. 33

47c. D = {all real numbers}, R = $\{y \mid y \leq 33\}$

48a. minimum

48b. −56

48c. D = {all real numbers}, R = $\{y \mid y \geq -56\}$

49a. maximum

49b. 4

49c. D = {all real numbers}, R = $\{y \mid y \leq 4\}$

50a. minimum

50b. 4

50c. D = {all real numbers}, R = $\{y \mid y \geq 4\}$

51a. maximum

51b. 3

51c. D = {all real numbers}, R = $\{y \mid y \leq 3\}$

Practice and Problem Solving

● = **Step-by-Step Solutions** begin on page R12.
Extra Practice begins on page 815.

22–27. See Ch. 9 Answer Appendix.

Example 1 p. 525

Use a table of values to graph each equation. State the domain and range.

22. $y = x^2 + 4x + 6$ **23.** $y = 2x^2 + 4x + 7$ **24.** $y = 2x^2 - 8x - 5$

25. $y = 3x^2 + 12x + 5$ **26.** $y = 3x^2 - 6x - 2$ **27.** $y = x^2 - 2x - 1$

Example 2 p. 526

Find the vertex, the equation of the axis of symmetry, and the y-intercept of each graph.

28. vertex (−3, −6), axis of symmetry $x = -3$, y-intercept 3
29. vertex (0, 1), axis of symmetry $x = 0$, y-intercept 1
30. vertex (−1, 5), axis of symmetry $x = -1$, y-intercept 4
31. vertex (1, 1), axis of symmetry $x = 1$, y-intercept 4
32. vertex (0, −4), axis of symmetry $x = 0$, y-intercept −4
33. vertex (0, 0), axis of symmetry $x = 0$, y-intercept 0

28.

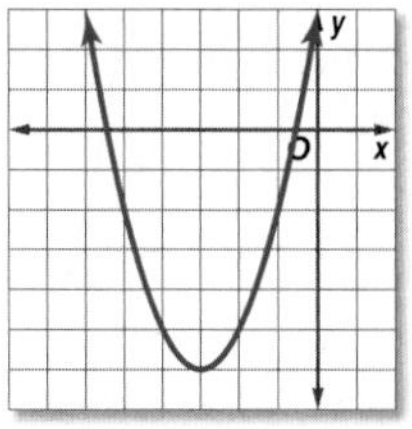

29.

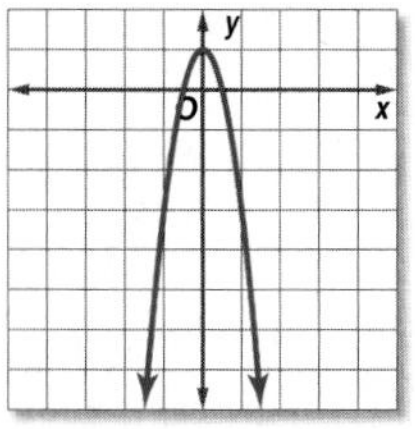

30.

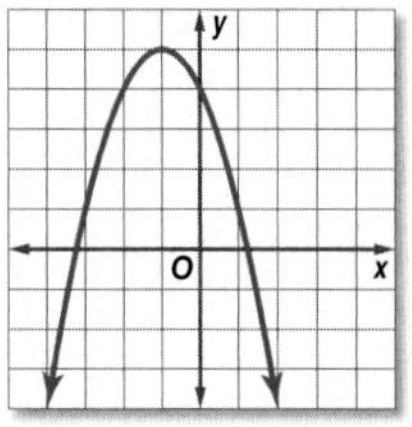

31.

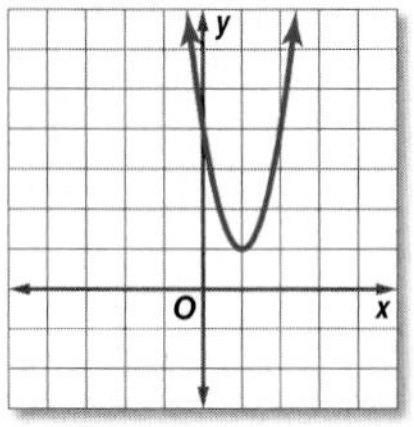

32.

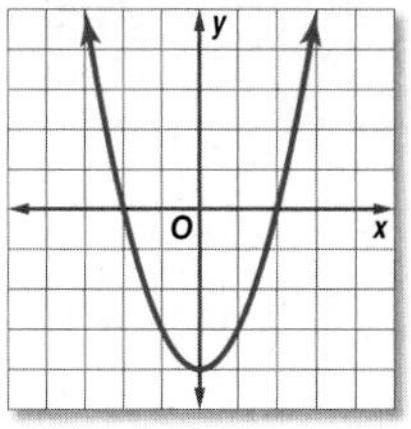

33.

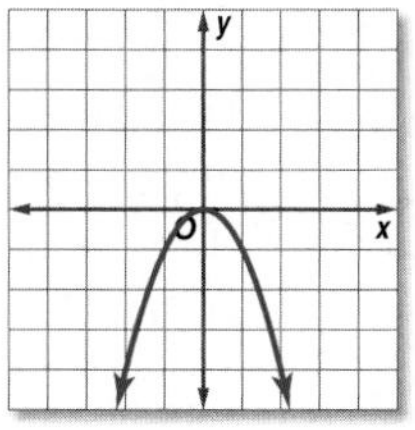

Example 3 p. 527

Find the vertex, the equation of the axis of symmetry, and the y-intercept of each function. **34–42. See margin.**

34. $y = x^2 + 8x + 10$ **35** $y = 2x^2 + 12x + 10$ **36.** $y = -3x^2 - 6x + 7$

37. $y = -x^2 - 6x - 5$ **38.** $y = 5x^2 + 20x + 10$ **39.** $y = 7x^2 - 28x + 14$

40. $y = 2x^2 - 12x + 6$ **41.** $y = -3x^2 + 6x - 18$ **42.** $y = -x^2 + 10x - 13$

Example 4 p. 528

Consider each function. **43–51. See margin.**

a. Determine whether the function has a *maximum* or *minimum* value.
b. State the maximum or minimum value.
c. What are the domain and range of the function?

43. $y = -2x^2 - 8x + 1$ **44.** $y = x^2 + 4x - 5$ **45.** $y = 3x^2 + 18x - 21$

46. $y = -2x^2 - 16x + 18$ **47.** $y = -x^2 - 14x - 16$ **48.** $y = 4x^2 + 40x + 44$

49. $y = -x^2 - 6x - 5$ **50.** $y = 2x^2 + 4x + 6$ **51.** $y = -3x^2 - 12x - 9$

Example 5 p. 529

Graph each function. **52–57. See Ch. 9 Answer Appendix.**

52. $y = -3x^2 + 6x - 4$ **53.** $y = -2x^2 - 4x - 3$ **54.** $y = -2x^2 - 8x + 2$

55. $y = x^2 + 6x - 6$ **56.** $y = x^2 - 2x + 2$ **57.** $y = 3x^2 - 12x + 5$

58a.

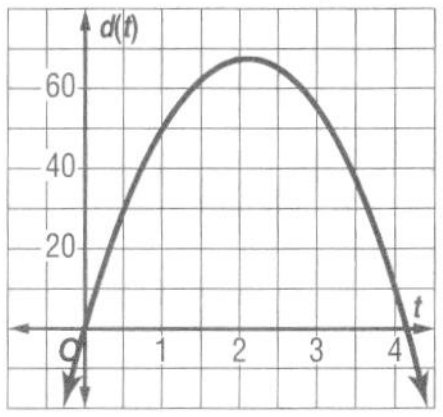

Example 6 p. 530

58. BOATING Miranda has her boat docked on the west side of Casper Point. She is boating over to the Casper Marina. The distance traveled by Miranda over time can be modeled by the equation $d = -16t^2 + 66t$, where d is the number of feet she travels in t minutes.

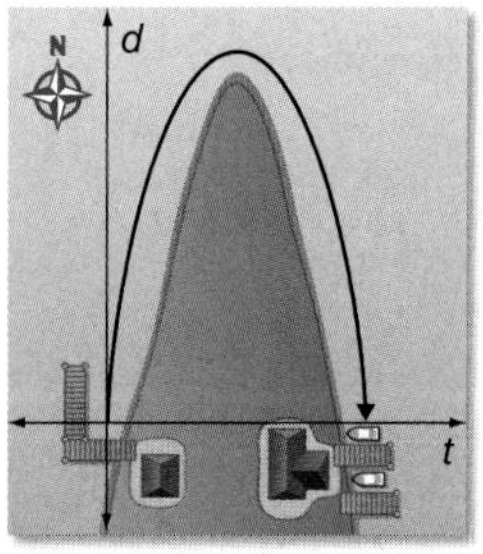

a. Graph this equation.

b. What is the maximum number of feet north that she traveled? **≈68 ft**

c. How long did it take her to reach Casper Marina? **≈4 min**

63a.

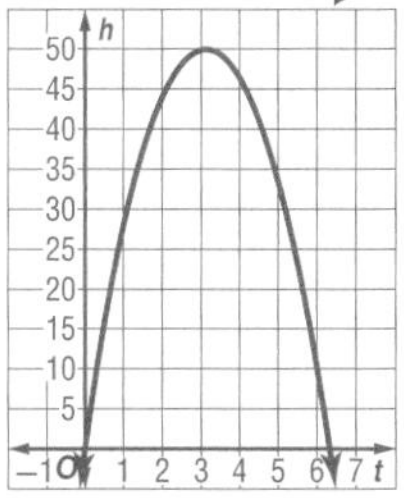

B

GRAPHING CALCULATOR Graph each equation. Use the TRACE feature to find the vertex on the graph. Round to the nearest thousandth if necessary. **59–62. See Ch. 9 Answer Appendix for graphs.**

59. $y = 4x^2 + 10x + 6$ **(−1.25, −0.25)**

60. $y = 8x^2 - 8x + 8$ **(−3.1, −2.55)**

61. $y = -5x^2 - 3x - 8$ **(−0.3, −7.55)**

62. $y = -7x^2 + 12x - 10$ **(0.857, −4.857)**

63. GOLF The average amateur golfer can hit a ball with an initial velocity of 31.3 meters per second. If the ball is hit straight up, the height can be modeled by the equation $h = -4.9t^2 + 31.3t$, where h is the height of the ball, in meters, after t seconds. **63e. $D = \{t \mid 0 \leq t \leq 6.4\}$; $R = \{h \mid 0 \leq h \leq 50.0\}$**

a. Graph this equation.

b. At what height is the ball hit? **0 m**

c. What is the maximum height of the ball? **≈50.0 m**

d. How long did it take for the ball to hit the ground? **≈6.4 s**

e. State a reasonable range and domain for this situation.

Real-World Link

School fundraisers provide revenue for extracurricular activities that are not part of a school budget.

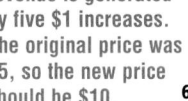

64. FUNDRAISING The marching band is selling poinsettias to buy new uniforms. Last year the band charged \$5 each, and they sold 150. They want to increase the price this year, and they expect to lose 10 sales for each \$1 increase. The sales revenue R, in dollars, generated by selling the poinsettias is predicted by the function $R = (5 + p)(150 - 10p)$, where p is the number of \$1 price increases.

a. Write the function in standard form. **$R = -10p^2 + 100p + 750$**

b. Find the maximum value of the function. **1000**

c. At what price should the poinsettias be sold to generate the most sales revenue? Explain your reasoning.

64c. \$10; Sample answer: The maximum revenue is generated by five \$1 increases. The original price was \$5, so the new price should be \$10.

65. FOOTBALL A football is kicked up from ground level at an initial upward velocity of 90 feet per second. The equation $h = -16t^2 + 90t$ gives the height h of the football after t seconds.

a. What is the height of the ball after one second? **74 ft**

b. When is the ball 126 feet high? **2.625 seconds and 3 seconds**

c. When is the height of the ball 0 feet? What do these points represent in the context of the situation? **See Ch. 9 Answer Appendix.**

66. REASONING Let $f(x) = x^2 - 9$.

C

a. What is the domain of $f(x)$? **{all real numbers}**

b. What is the range of $f(x)$? **$\{f(x) \mid f(x) \geq -9\}$**

c. For what values of x is $f(x)$ negative? **$\{x \mid -3 < x < 3\}$**

d. When x is a real number, what are the domain and range of $f(x) = \sqrt{x^2 - 9}$?

66d. $D = \{x \mid x \leq -3$ or $x \geq 3\}$, $R = \{y \mid y \geq 0\}$

Study Guide and Intervention
CRM pp. 5–6 AL OL ELL

NAME ______ DATE ______ PERIOD ______

9-1 Study Guide and Intervention

Graphing Quadratic Functions

Characteristics of Quadratic Functions

Quadratic Function	a function described by an equation of the form $f(x) = ax^2 + bx + c$, where $a \neq 0$	Example: $y = 2x^2 + 3x + 8$

The parent graph of the family of quadratic fuctions is $y = x^2$. Graphs of quadratic functions have a general shape called a **parabola**. A parabola opens upward and has a **minimum point** when the value of a is positive, and a parabola opens downward and has a **maximum point** when the value of a is negative.

Example 1

a. Use a table of values to graph $y = x^2 - 4x + 1$.

x	y
−1	6
0	1
1	−2
2	−3
3	−2
4	1

Graph the ordered pairs in the table and connect them with a smooth curve.

b. What are the domain and range of this function?
The domain (the x-values) is all real numbers. The range (the y-values) is all real numbers greater than or equal to −3, which is the minimum.

Example 2

a. Use a table of values to graph $y = -x^2 - 6x - 7$.

x	y
−6	−7
−5	−2
−4	1
−3	2
−2	1
−1	−2
0	−7

Graph the ordered pairs in the table and connect them with a smooth curve.

b. What are the domain and range of this function?
The domain (the x-values is all real numbers. The range (the y-values) is all real numbers less than or equal to 2, which is the maximum.

Exercises

Use a table of values to graph each function. Determine the domain and range.

1. $y = x^2 + 2$ **D: {x|x is a real number.} R: {y|y ≥ 2}**

2. $y = -x^2 - 4$ **D: {x|x is a real number.} R: {y|y ≤ −4}**

3. $y = x^2 - 3x + 2$ **D: {x|x is a real number.} R: $\{y \mid y \geq -\frac{1}{4}\}$**

Chapter 9 5 Glencoe Algebra 1

Lesson 9-1

Practice
CRM p. 8 AL OL BL ELL

NAME ______ DATE ______ PERIOD ______

9-1 Practice

Graphing Quadratic Functions

Use a table of values to graph each function. Determine the domain and range.

1. $y = -x^2 + 2$ **D: {x| all reals} R: {y|y ≤ 2}**

2. $y = x^2 - 6x + 3$ **D: {x| all reals} R: {y|y ≥ −6}**

3. $y = -2x^2 - 8x - 5$ **D: {x| all reals} R: {y|y ≤ 3}**

Find the vertex, the equation of the axis of symmetry, and the y-intercept.

4. $y = x^2 - 9$ **(0, −9); x = 0; (0, −9)**

5. $y = -2x^2 + 8x - 5$ **(2, 3); x = 2; (0, −5)**

6. $y = 4x^2 - 4x + 1$ **(0.5, 0); x = 0.5; (0, 1)**

Consider each equation. Determine whether the function has a *maximum* or a *minimum* value. State the maximum or minimum value. What are the domain and range of the function?

7. $y = 5x^2 - 2x + 2$ **min; (0.2, 1.8); D: {x| all reals}, R: {y|y ≥ 1.8}**

8. $y = -x^2 + 5x - 10$ **max; (2.5, −3.75); D: {x| all reals}, R: {y|y ≤ −3.75}**

9. $y = \frac{3}{2}x^2 + 4x - 9$ **min; $(-1\frac{1}{3}, -11\frac{2}{3})$; D: {x| all reals}, R: $\{y \mid y \geq -11\frac{2}{3}\}$**

Graph each function.

10. $f(x) = -x^2 + 3$

11. $f(x) = -2x^2 + 8x - 3$

12. $f(x) = 2x^2 + 8x + 1$

13. **BASEBALL** A player hits a baseball into the outfield. The equation $h = -0.005x^2 + x + 3$ gives the path of the ball, where h is the height and x is the horizontal distance the ball travels.

a. What is the equation of the axis of symmetry? **x = 100**

b. What is the maximum height reached by the baseball? **53 ft**

c. An outfielder catches the ball three feet above the ground. How far has the ball traveled horizontally when the outfielder catches it? **200 ft**

Chapter 9 8 Glencoe Algebra 1

Word Problem Practice
CRM p. 9 AL OL BL ELL

NAME ______ DATE ______ PERIOD ______

9-1 Word Problem Practice

Graphing Quadratic Functions

1. **OLYMPICS** Olympics were held in 1896 and have been held every four years (except 1916, 1940, and 1944). The winning height y in men's pole vault at any number Olympiad x can be approximated by the equation $y = 0.37x^2 + 4.3x + 126$. Complete the table to estimate the pole vault heights in each of the Olympic Games. Round your answers to the nearest tenth.

Year	Olympiad (x)	Height (y inches)
1896	1	**130.7**
1900	2	**136.1**
1924	7	**174.2**
1936	10	**206.0**
1964	15	**273.8**
2008	26	**487.9**

Source: National Security Agency

2. **PHYSICS** Mrs. Capwell's physics class investigates what happens when a ball is given an initial push, rolls up, and then back down an inclined plane. The class finds that $y = -x^2 + 6x$ accurately predicts the ball's position y after rolling x seconds. On the graph of the equation, what would be the y value when $x = 4$? **8**

3. **ARCHITECTURE** A hotel's main entrance is in the shape of a parabolic arch. The equation $y = -x^2 + 10x$ models the arch height y for any distance x from one side of the arch. Use a graph to determine its maximum height. **25 ft**

4. **SOFTBALL** Olympic softball gold medalist Michele Smith pitches a curveball with a speed of 64 feet per second. If she throws the ball straight upward at this speed, the ball's height h (in feet) after t seconds is given by $h = -16t^2 + 64t$. Find the coordinates of the vertex of the graph of the ball's height and interpret its meaning. **(2, 64); After 2 seconds, the ball reaches its highest point, 64 ft above the ground.**

5. **GEOMETRY** Teddy is building the rectangular deck shown below.

x + 6
x − 2

a. Write the equation representing the area of the deck. **y = (x − 2)(x + 6) or y = x² + 4x − 12**

b. What is the equation of the axis of symmetry? **x = −2**

c. Graph the equation and label its vertex. **(−2, −16)**

Chapter 9 9 Glencoe Algebra 1

Lesson 9-1

Enrichment
CRM p. 10 OL BL

NAME ______ DATE ______ PERIOD ______

9-1 Enrichment

Graphing Cubic Functions

A **cubic function** is a polynomial written in the form of $f(x) = ax^3 + bx^2 + cx + n$, where $a \neq 0$. Cubic functions do not have absolute minimum and maximum values like quadratic functions do, but they can have a **local minimum** and a **local maximum** point.

Parent Function: $f(x) = x^3$
Domain: all real numbers
Range: all real numbers

Example Use a table of values to graph $y = x^3 + 3x^2 - 1$. Then use the graph to estimate the locations of the local minimum and local maximum points.

x	−3	−2	−1	0	1
y	−1	2	1	−1	2

Graph the ordered pairs, and connect them to create a smooth curve. The "S" shape extends to infinity in the positive y direction and to

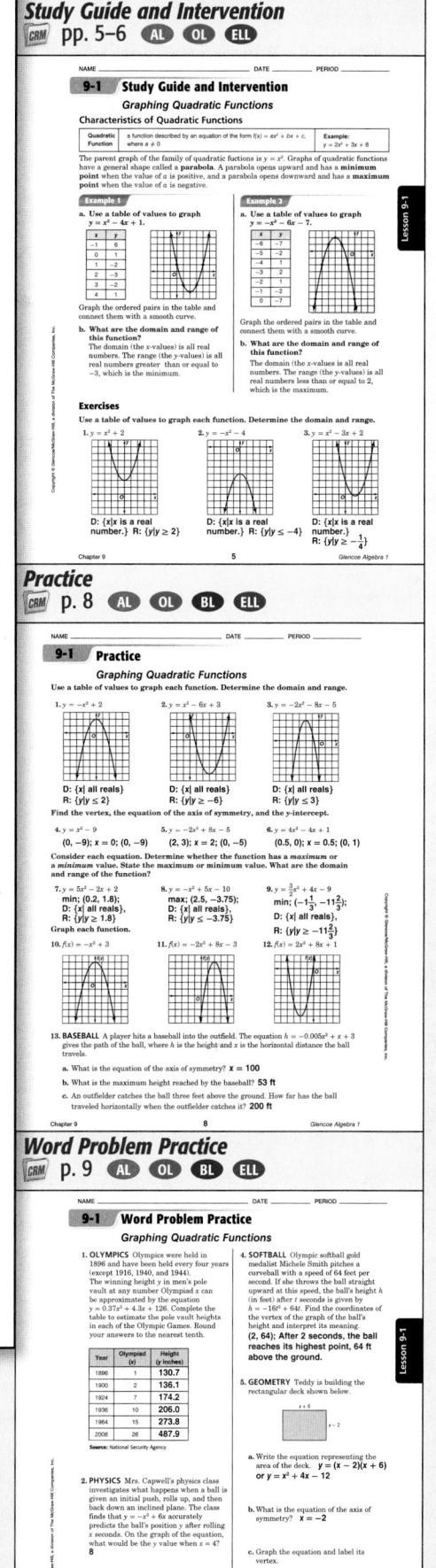

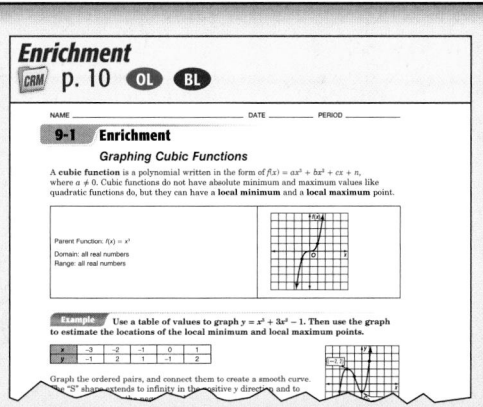

Multiple Representations In Exercise 67, students use a graphing calculator, information organized in a table, and algebraic analysis to solve quadratic equations.

Watch Out!

Find the Error For Exercise 69, suggest students identify the values for a, b, and c, being careful to include the signs of the values. Have them substitute those values into $x = -\frac{b}{2a}$, using parentheses as necessary.

StudyTip

Zeros The number of zeros is equal to the degree of the related function.

68. Sample answer: $y = 4x^2 + 3x + 5$; Write the equation of the axis of symmetry, $x = -\frac{b}{2a}$. From the equation, $b = 3$ and $2a = 8$, so $a = 4$. Substitute these values for a and b into the equation $y = ax^2 + bx + c$.

71. (−1, 9); Sample answer: I graphed the points given, and sketched the parabola that goes through them. I counted the spaces over and up from the vertex and did the same on the opposite side of the line $x = 2$.

72. Sample answer: A football is kicked during a game. The vertex gives the maximum height of the ball.

73. Sample answer: The function $y = -x^2 - 4$ has a vertex at (0, −4), but it is a maximum.

74. Sample answer: Find a and b from the standard form. The axis of symmetry is $x = -\frac{b}{2a}$. This will also give you the x-coordinate of the vertex. To find the y-coordinate, substitute the x-value into the original equation.

67. **MULTIPLE REPRESENTATIONS** In this problem, you will investigate solving quadratic equations using tables.

a. **ALGEBRAIC** Determine the related function for each equation. Copy and complete the table below. See margin.

Equation	Related Function	Zeros	y-Values
$x^2 - x = 12$	?	?	?
$x^2 + 8x = 9$	?	?	?
$x^2 = 14x - 24$	?	?	?
$x^2 + 16x = -28$	?	?	?

b. **GRAPHICAL** Graph each related function with a graphing calculator. See margin.

c. **ANALYTICAL** Use the table feature on your calculator to determine the zeros of each related function. Record the zeros in the table above. Also record the values of the function one unit less than and one unit more than each zero. See margin.

d. **VERBAL** Compare the signs of the function values for x-values just before and just after a zero. What happens to the sign of the function value before and after a zero?
The function values have opposite signs just before and just after a zero.

H.O.T. Problems Use Higher-Order Thinking Skills

68. **OPEN ENDED** Write and graph a quadratic function for which the graph has the axis of symmetry $x = -\frac{3}{8}$. Summarize your steps.

69. **FIND THE ERROR** Chase and Jade are finding the axis of symmetry of a parabola. Is either of them correct? Explain your reasoning. See margin.

Chase	Jade
$y = -x^2 - 4x + 6$	$y = -x^2 - 4x + 6$
$x = -\frac{b}{2a}$	$x = -\frac{b}{2a}$
$x = -\frac{4}{2(-1)}$	$x = -\frac{-4}{2(-1)}$
$x = 2$	$x = -2$

70. **CHALLENGE** Using the axis of symmetry and one x-intercept, write an equation for the graph shown. See margin.

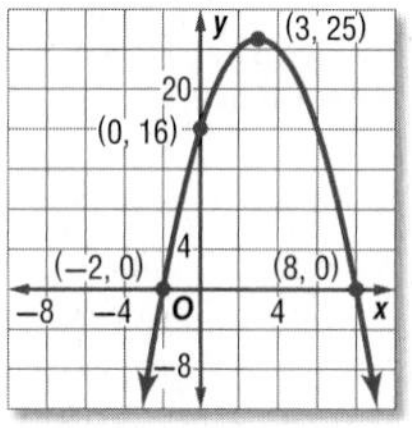

71. **REASONING** The graph of a quadratic function has a vertex at (2, 0). One point on the graph is (5, 9). Find another point on the graph. Explain how you found it.

72. **OPEN ENDED** Describe a real-world situation that involves a quadratic equation. Explain what the vertex represents.

73. **REASONING** Provide a counterexample to the following statement. *The vertex of a parabola is always the minimum of the graph.*

74. **WRITING IN MATH** Explain how to find the axis of symmetry from an equation for a quadratic function. What other characteristics of the graph can you derive from the equation? Explain.

Additional Answers

67a, 67c.

Equation	Related Function	Zeros	y-values
$x^2 - x = 12$	$y = x^2 - x - 12$	−3, 4	−3: 8, −6; 4: −6, 8
$x^2 + 8x = 9$	$y = x^2 + 8x - 9$	−9, 1	−9: 11, −9; 1: −9, 11
$x^2 = 14x - 24$	$y = x^2 - 14x + 24$	2, 12	2: 11, −9; 12: −9, 11
$x^2 + 16x = -28$	$y = x^2 + 16x + 28$	−14, −2	−14: 13, −11: −2: −11, 13

PSAE PRACTICE 8.11.07, 7.11.04, , 8.11.11, 6.11.10

75. Which of the following is an equation for the line that passes through $(2, -5)$ and is perpendicular to $2x + 4y = 8$? **C**

A $y = 2x + 10$ C $y = 2x - 9$
B $y = -\frac{1}{2}x - 4$ D $y = -2x - 1$

76. GEOMETRY The area of the circle is 36π square units. If the radius is doubled, what is the area of the new circle? **G**

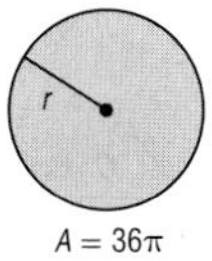

$A = 36\pi$

F 72π units^2 H 1296π units^2
G 144π units^2 J 9π units^2

77. What is the range of the function $f(x) = -4x^2 - \frac{1}{2}$? **D**

A $\left\{\text{all integers less than or equal to } \frac{1}{2}\right\}$
B {all nonnegative integers}
C {all real numbers}
D $\left\{\text{all real numbers less than or equal to } -\frac{1}{2}\right\}$

78. SHORT RESPONSE Dylan delivers newspapers for extra money. He starts delivering the newspapers at 3:15 P.M. and finishes at 5:05 P.M. How long does it take Dylan to complete his route? **1 hour 50 min**

Spiral Review

Determine whether each trinomial is a perfect square trinomial. Write *yes* or *no*. If so, factor it. (Lesson 8-6)

79. $4x^2 + 4x + 1$ **yes; $(2x + 1)^2$**
80. $4x^2 - 20x + 25$ **yes; $(2x - 5)^2$**
81. $9x^2 + 8x + 16$ **no**

Factor each polynomial if possible. If the polynomial cannot be factored, write *prime*. (Lesson 8-5)

82. $n^2 - 16$ **$(n - 4)(n + 4)$**
83. $x^2 + 25$ **prime**
84. $9 - 4a^2$ **$(3 - 2a)(3 + 2a)$**

Find each product. (Lesson 7-7)

85. $(b - 7)(b + 3)$ **$b^2 - 4b - 21$**
86. $(c - 6)(c - 5)$ **$c^2 - 11c + 30$**
87. $(2x - 1)(x + 9)$ **$2x^2 + 17x - 9$**

88. MULTIPLE BIRTHS The number of quadruplet births Q in the United States in recent years can be modeled by $Q = -0.5t^3 + 11.7t^2 - 21.5t + 218.6$, where t represents the number of years since 1992. For what values of t does this model no longer allow for realistic predictions? Explain your reasoning. (Lesson 7-4)
88. Sample answer: For $t \geq 23$; if $t \geq 23$, then the value of Q is negative.

Use elimination to solve each system of equations. (Lesson 6-4)

89. $2x + y = 5$, $3x - 2y = 4$ **(2, 1)**
90. $4x - 3y = 12$, $x + 2y = 14$ **(6, 4)**
91. $2x - 3y = 2$, $5x + 4y = 28$ **(4, 2)**

92. HEALTH About 20% of the time you sleep is spent in rapid eye movement (REM), which is associated with dreaming. If an adult sleeps 7 to 8 hours, how much time is spent in REM sleep? (Lesson 5-4) **between 1.4 and 1.6 hours, inclusive**

Skills Review

Find the x-intercept of the graph of each equation. (Lesson 3-1)

93. $x + 2y = 10$ **10**
94. $2x - 3y = 12$ **6**
95. $3x - y = -18$ **−6**

Differentiated Instruction OL BL

Extension Tell students that a fireworks rocket is designed to explode at its highest point. The height is given by the equation $h = -4.9t^2 + 34.2t + 1.6$, where h is the rocket's height in meters after t seconds. At what time and height will the rocket explode? The rocket will explode after about 3.5 seconds at a height of approximately 61 meters.

4 ASSESS

Ticket Out the Door Make several copies each of the five graphs of quadratic functions. Give one graph to each student. As the students leave the room, ask them to tell you the coordinates of the parabolas' vertices and to identify them as maximums or minimums.

Additional Answers

67b.

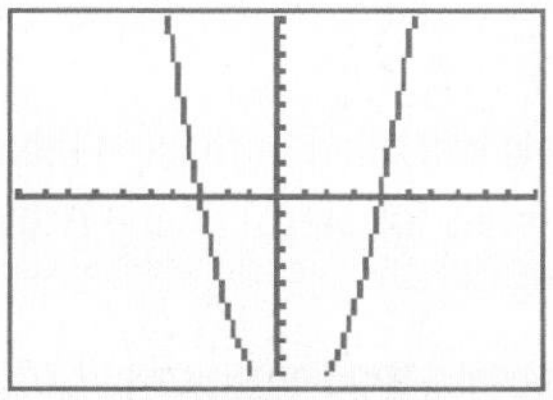

[−10, 10] scl: 1 by [−10, 10] scl: 1
$y = x^2 - x - 12$

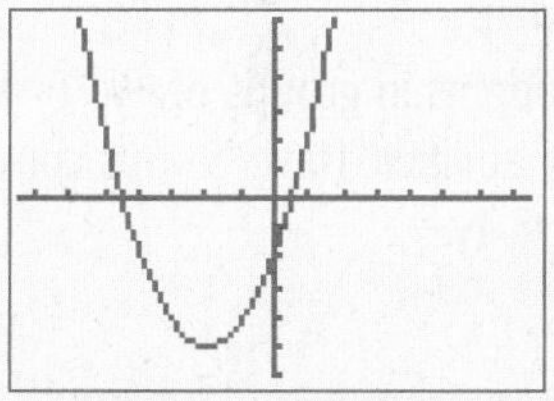

[−15, 15] scl: 2 by [−30, 30] scl: 5
$y = x^2 + 8x - 9$

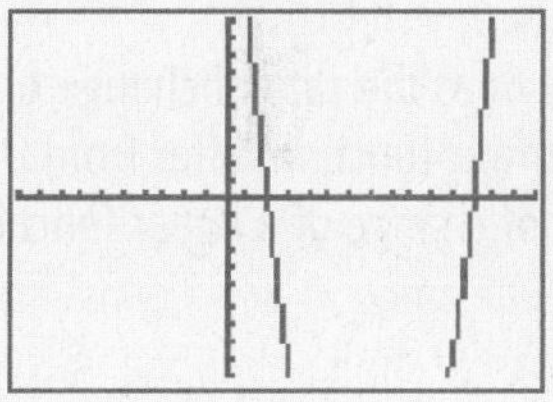

[−10, 15] scl: 1 by [−10, 10] scl: 1
$y = x^2 - 14x + 24$

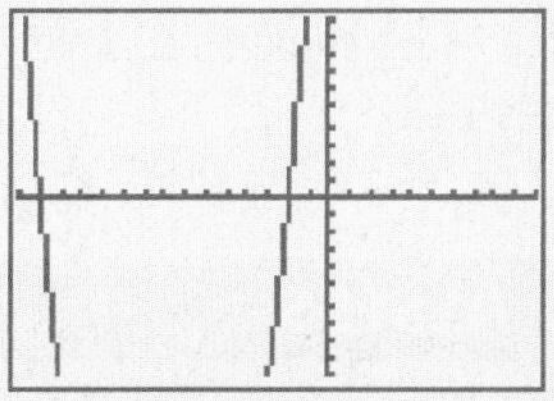

[−15, 10] scl: 1 by [−10, 10] scl: 1
$y = x^2 + 16x + 28$

69. Jade; Chase forgot the negative sign with the −4.

70. Sample answer: $y = -x^2 + 6x + 16$

EXTEND 9-1

Lesson Notes

1 FOCUS

Objective Use a given quadratic function to investigate the rate of change of a quadratic function.

Materials for Each Student

- grid paper

Teaching Tip

Students will need to make a table with 19 columns for Step 1 of the Activity.

2 TEACH

Working in Cooperative Groups

Put students in groups of two or three, mixing abilities. Have groups complete the Activity.

Ask:

- What maximum and minimum x- and y-axis values do you need when drawing the coordinate system for the function in the Activity?
  x: 0 to 9, y: 0 to 324
- How does the rate of change of a quadratic function differ from the rate of change of a linear function?
  A linear function has a constant rate of change, so it never changes sign. The rate of change of a quadratic function is positive on some intervals and negative on others.

Practice Have students complete Exercises 1–4.

3 ASSESS

Formative Assessment

Use Exercises 1–3 to assess whether students understand the rate of change in a quadratic function.

EXTEND 9-1

Algebra Lab: Rate of Change of a Quadratic Function

IL Math Online glencoe.com
Math *in Motion,* Animation

Objective
You will use percentiles to represent data.

IL Learning Standards

8.A.4b Represent mathematical patterns and describe their properties using variables and mathematical symbols. *Also addresses 7.B.4.*

A model rocket is launched from the ground with an upward velocity of 144 feet per second. The function $y = -16x^2 + 144x$ models the height y of the rocket in feet after x seconds. Using this function, we can investigate the rate of change of a quadratic function.

ACTIVITY

Step 1 Copy the table below.

x	0	0.5	1.0	1.5	…	9.0
y	0					
Rate of Change	–					

Step 2 Find the value of y for each value of x from 0 through 9.

Step 3 Graph the ordered pairs (x, y) on grid paper. Connect the points with a smooth curve. Notice that the function *increases* when $0 < x < 4.5$ and *decreases* when $4.5 < x < 9$.

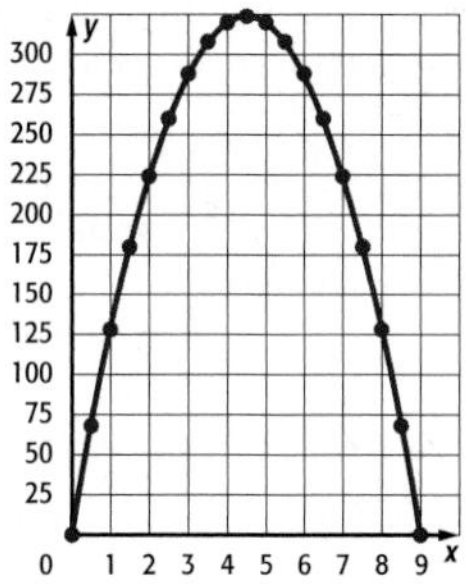

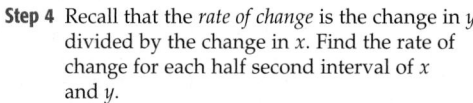

Step 4 Recall that the *rate of change* is the change in y divided by the change in x. Find the rate of change for each half second interval of x and y.

Exercises

Use the quadratic function $y = x^2$. **1–4. See Ch. 9 Answer Appendix.**

1. Make a table, similar to the one in the Activity, for the function using $x = -4, -3, -2, -1, 0, 1, 2, 3$, and 4. Find the values of y for each x-value.
2. Graph the ordered pairs on grid paper. Connect the points with a smooth curve. Describe where the function is increasing and where it is decreasing.
3. Find the rate of change for each column starting with $x = -3$. Compare the rates of change when the function is increasing and when it is decreasing.
4. **CHALLENGE** If an object is dropped from 100 feet in the air and air resistance is ignored, the object will fall at a rate that can be modeled by the equation $f(x) = -16x^2 + 100$, where $f(x)$ represents the object's height in feet after x seconds. Make a table like that in Exercise 1, selecting appropriate values for x. Fill in the x-values, the y-values, and rates of change. Compare the rates of change. Describe any patterns that you see.

From Concrete to Abstract

Have students examine the situation in the Activity. Ask students how the equation and its rate of change will be affected if the model rocket is launched from the ground with an upward velocity of 44 meters per second.
The equation (with rounded coefficients) will be $h = -5t^2 + 44t$. Since a meter is about 3.3 times as long as a foot, the coefficients in the equation for feet per second are divided by 3.3. The variables are not affected. The rates of change will change accordingly.

Solving Quadratic Equations by Graphing

Then

You solved quadratic equations by factoring. (Lesson 8-3)

Now

- Solve quadratic equations by graphing.
- Estimate solutions of quadratic equations by graphing.

IL Learning Standards

7.B.4 Estimate and measure the magnitude and directions of physical quantities using rulers, protractors and other scientific instruments including timers, calculators and computers.
8.D.4 Formulate and solve linear and **quadratic equations** and linear inequalities **algebraically** and investigate nonlinear inequalities using graphs, tables, calculators and computers.

New Vocabulary

double root

IL Math Online

glencoe.com

- Extra Examples
- Personal Tutor
- Self-Check Quiz
- Homework Help
- Math in Motion

Why?

Dorton Arena at the state fairgrounds in Raleigh, North Carolina, has a shape created by two intersecting parabolas. The shape of one of the parabolas can be modeled by the equation $y = -x^2 + 127x$, where x represents the width of the parabola in feet, and y represents the length of the parabola in feet.

The x-intercepts of the graph of this function can be used to determine the distance between the points where the parabola meets the ground.

Solve by Graphing A quadratic equation can be written in the standard form $ax^2 + bc + c = 0$, where $a \neq 0$. To write a quadratic function as an equation, replace y or $f(x)$ with 0. Recall that the solutions or roots of an equation can be identified by finding the x-intercepts of the related graph. Quadratic equations may have two, one, or no solutions.

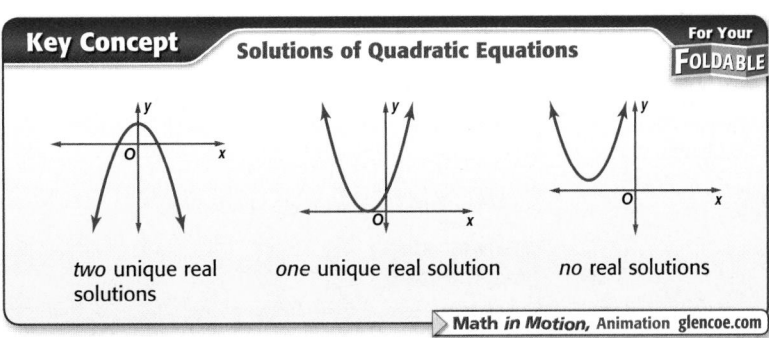

Key Concept Solutions of Quadratic Equations — For Your FOLDABLE

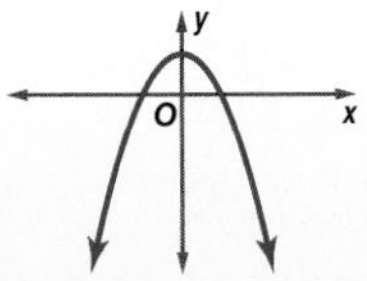

two unique real solutions

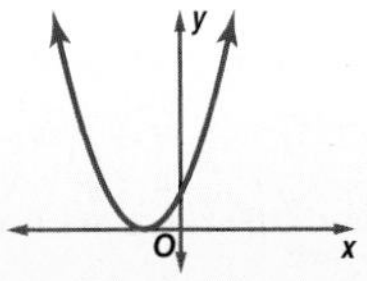

one unique real solution

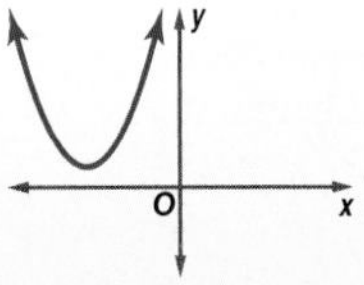

no real solutions

Math *in Motion*, Animation glencoe.com

EXAMPLE 1 Two Roots

Solve $x^2 - 2x - 8 = 0$ by graphing.

Graph the related function $f(x) = x^2 - 2x - 8$.

The x-intercepts of the graph appear to be at -2 and 4, so the solutions are -2 and 4.

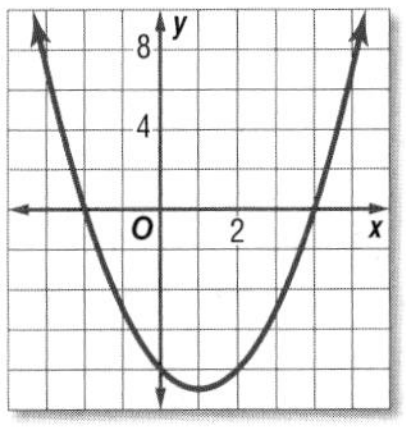

CHECK Check each solution in the original equation.

$x^2 - 2x - 8 = 0$	**Original equation**	$x^2 - 2x - 8 = 0$
$(-2)^2 - 2(-2) - 8 \stackrel{?}{=} 0$	**$x = -2$ or $x = 4$**	$(4)^2 - 2(4) - 8 \stackrel{?}{=} 0$
$0 = 0$ ✓	**Simplify.**	$0 = 0$ ✓

1A–1B. See Ch. 9 Answer Appendix for graphs.

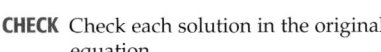

Check Your Progress Solve each equation by graphing.

1A. $-x^2 - 3x + 18 = 0$ **3, −6**

1B. $x^2 - 4x + 3 = 0$ **1, 3**

Personal Tutor glencoe.com

9-2 Lesson Notes

1 FOCUS

Vertical Alignment

Before Lesson 9-2
Solve quadratic equations by factoring.

Lesson 9-2
Solve quadratic equations by graphing.
Estimate solutions of quadratic equations by graphing.

After Lesson 9-2
Identify quadratic functions from given data.

2 TEACH

Scaffolding Questions

Have students read the *Why?* section of the lesson.

Ask:

- If the x-intercepts represent where the parabola meets the ground, what represents the ground? the x-axis
- What are the x-intercepts of the graph of the equation? 0, 127
- What is the equation of the axis of symmetry? $x = 63.5$
- What is the distance between the points where the parabola meets the ground? 127 feet

Lesson 9-2 Resources

Resource	Approaching-Level	On-Level	Beyond-Level	English Learners
Teacher Edition	• Differentiated Instruction, p. 538	• Differentiated Instruction, p. 538	• Differentiated Instruction, p. 542	
Chapter Resource Masters	• Study Guide and Intervention, pp. 11–12 • Skills Practice, p. 13 • Practice, p. 14 • Word Problem Practice, p. 15	• Study Guide and Intervention, pp. 11–12 • Skills Practice, p. 13 • Practice, p. 14 • Word Problem Practice, p. 15 • Enrichment, p. 16	• Practice, p. 14 • Word Problem Practice, p. 15 • Enrichment, p. 16	• Study Guide and Intervention, pp. 11–12 • Skills Practice, p. 13 • Practice, p. 14 • Word Problem Practice, p. 15
Transparencies	• 5-Minute Check Transparency	• 5-Minute Check Transparency	• 5-Minute Check Transparency	• 5-Minute Check Transparency
Other	• Study Notebook	• Study Notebook	• Study Notebook	• Study Notebook

Solve By Graphing

Example 1 shows how to use a graph to find the two roots of a quadratic equation. **Example 2** shows how to use graphing to find the double root of a quadratic equation. **Example 3** shows how to use a graph to identify a quadratic equation that has no real number solutions.

Formative Assessment

Use the Check Your Progress exercises after each example to determine students' understanding of concepts.

Additional Examples

1 Solve $x^2 - 3x - 10 = 0$ by graphing. $-2, 5$

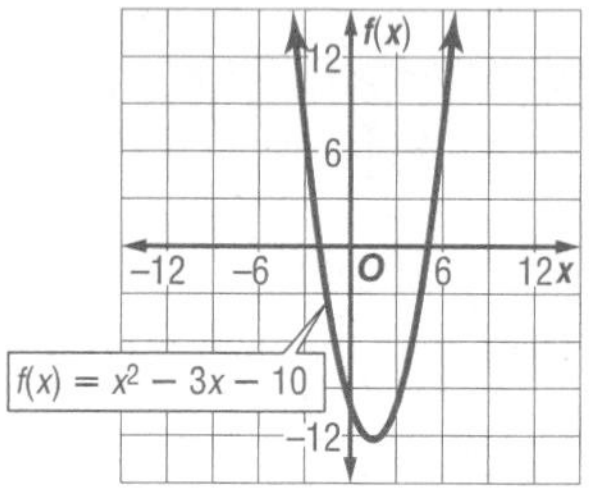

2 Solve $x^2 + 8x = -16$ by graphing. -4

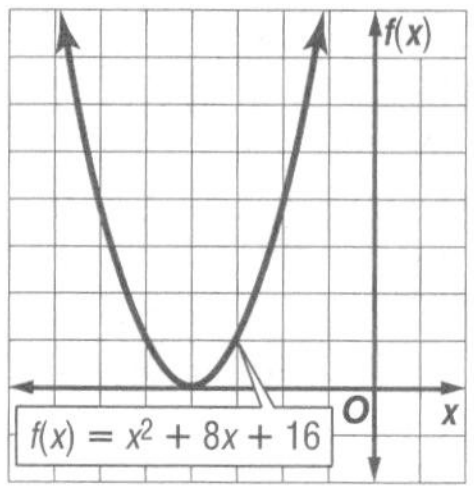

3 Solve $x^2 + 2x + 3 = 0$ by graphing. $\varnothing$

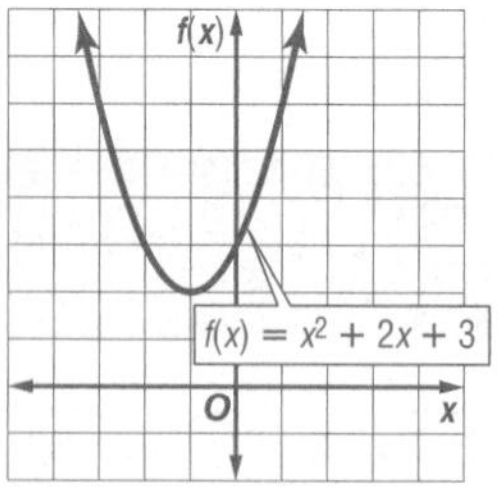

Additional Examples also in Interactive Classroom PowerPoint® Presentations

IWB INTERACTIVE WHITEBOARD READY

The solutions in Example 1 were two distinct numbers. Sometimes the two roots are the same number, called a **double root**.

EXAMPLE 2 Double Root

Solve $x^2 - 6x = -9$ by graphing.

Step 1 Rewrite the equation in standard form.

$x^2 - 6x = -9$ **Original equation**

$x^2 - 6x + 9 = 0$ **Add 9 to each side.**

Step 2 Graph the related function $f(x) = x^2 - 6x + 9$.

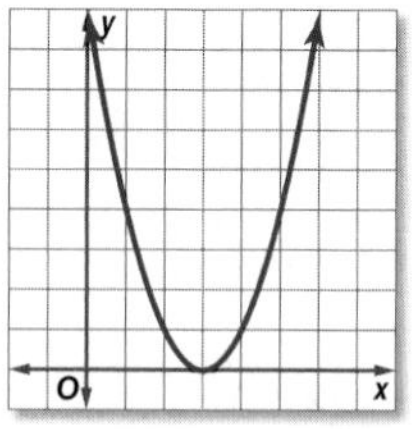

Step 3 Locate the x-intercepts of the graph. Notice that the vertex of the parabola is the only x-intercept. Therefore, there is only one solution, 3.

CHECK Solve by factoring.

$x^2 - 6x + 9 = 0$ **Original equation**

$(x - 3)(x - 3) = 0$ **Factor.**

$x - 3 = 0$ or $x - 3 = 0$ **Zero Product Property**

$x = 3$ $\quad x = 3$ **Add 3 to each side.**

The only solution is 3.

Watch Out!

Exact Solutions Solutions found from the graph of an equation may appear to be exact. Check them in the original equation to be sure.

Check Your Progress

Solve each equation by graphing. 2A–2B. See Ch. 9 Answer Appendix for graphs.

2A. $x^2 + 25 = 10x$ 5 **2B.** $x^2 = -8x - 16$ -4

Personal Tutor glencoe.com

Sometimes the roots are not real numbers.

EXAMPLE 3 No Real Roots

Solve $2x^2 - 3x + 5 = 0$ by graphing.

Step 1 Rewrite the equation in standard form.

This equation is written in standard form.

Step 2 Graph the related function $f(x) = 2x^2 - 3x + 5$.

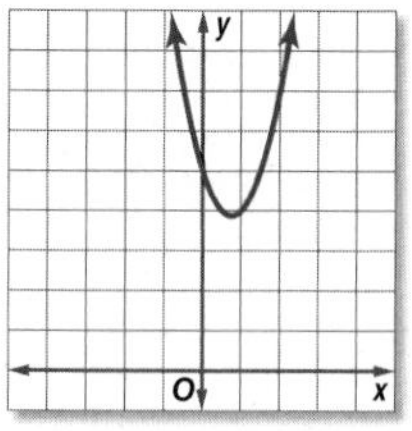

Step 3 Locate the x-intercepts of the graph. This graph has no x-intercepts. Therefore, this equation has no real number solutions. The solution set is $\varnothing$.

CHECK Solve by factoring.

There are no factors of 10 that have a sum of -3, so the expression is not factorable. Thus, the equation has no real number solutions.

Check Your Progress

Solve each equation by graphing. 3A–3B. See Ch. 9 Answer Appendix for graphs.

3A. $-x^2 - 3x = 5$ $\varnothing$ **3B.** $-2x^2 - 8 = 6x$ $\varnothing$

Personal Tutor glencoe.com

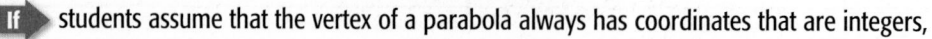

Differentiated Instruction AL OL

If students assume that the vertex of a parabola always has coordinates that are integers,

Then point out that in Example 3, the y-value for the vertex of the graph is greater than 3 and somewhat less than 4.

StudyTip

Location of Zeros Since quadratic functions are continuous, there must be a zero between two x-values for which the corresponding y-values have opposite signs.

Estimate Solutions The real roots found thus far have been integers. However, the roots of quadratic equations are usually not integers. In these cases, use estimation to approximate the roots of the equation.

EXAMPLE 4 Approximate Roots with a Table

Solve $x^2 + 6x + 6 = 0$ by graphing. If integral roots cannot be found, estimate the roots to the nearest tenth.

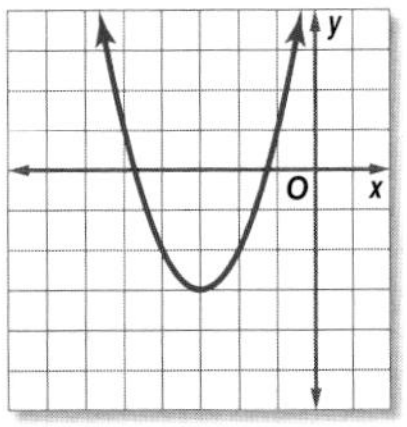

Graph the related function $f(x) = x^2 + 6x + 6$.

The x-intercepts are located between -5 and -4 and between -2 and -1.

Make a table using an increment of 0.1 for the x-values located between -5 and -4 and between -2 and -1.

Look for a change in the signs of the function values. The function value that is closest to zero is the best approximation for a zero of the function.

x	−4.9	−4.8	−4.7	−4.6	−4.5	−4.4	−4.3	−4.2	−4.1
y	0.61	0.24	−0.11	−0.44	−0.75	−1.04	−1.31	−1.56	−1.79

x	−1.9	−1.8	−1.7	−1.6	−1.5	−1.4	−1.3	−1.2	−1.1
y	−1.79	−1.56	−1.31	−1.04	−0.75	−0.44	−0.11	0.24	0.61

For each table, the function value that is closest to zero when the sign changes is -0.11. Thus, the roots are approximately -4.7 and -1.3.

Check Your Progress

4. Solve $2x^2 + 6x - 3 = 0$ by graphing. If integral roots cannot be found, estimate the roots to the nearest tenth. **0.4, −3.4**

Personal Tutor glencoe.com

Approximating the x-intercepts of graphs is helpful for real-world applications.

Real-World Link

The game of soccer, called "football" outside of North America, began in 1863 in Britain when the Football Association was founded. Soccer is played on every continent of the world.

Source: Sports Know How

Real-World EXAMPLE 5 Approximate Roots with a Calculator

SOCCER A goalie kicks a soccer ball with an upward velocity of 65 feet per second, and her foot meets the ball 1 foot off the ground. The quadratic function $h = -16t^2 + 65t + 1$ represents the height of the ball h in feet after t seconds. Approximately how long is the ball in the air?

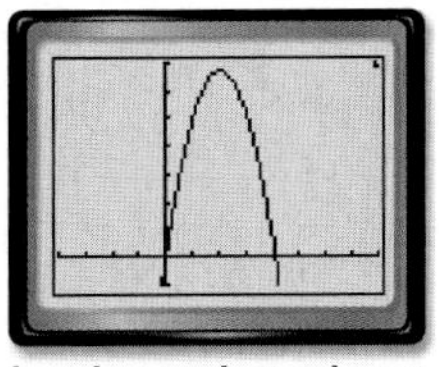

[−4, 7] scl: 1 by [−10, 70] scl: 10

You need to find the roots of the equation $-16t^2 + 65t + 1 = 0$. Use a graphing calculator to graph the related function $f(x) = -16t^2 + 65t + 1$.

The positive x-intercept of the graph is approximately 4. Therefore, the ball is in the air for approximately 4 seconds.

Check Your Progress

5. If the goalie kicks the soccer ball with an upward velocity of 55 feet per second and his foot meets the ball 2 feet off the ground, approximately how long is the ball in the air? **3.5 seconds**

Personal Tutor glencoe.com

Estimate Solutions

Example 4 shows how to use graphing and a table of values to estimate roots of a quadratic equation when integral roots cannot be found. **Example 5** shows how to estimate a solution to a real-world problem involving quadratic equations.

Additional Examples

4 Solve $x^2 - 4x + 2 = 0$ by graphing. If integral roots cannot be found, estimate the roots to the nearest tenth. 0.6, 3.4

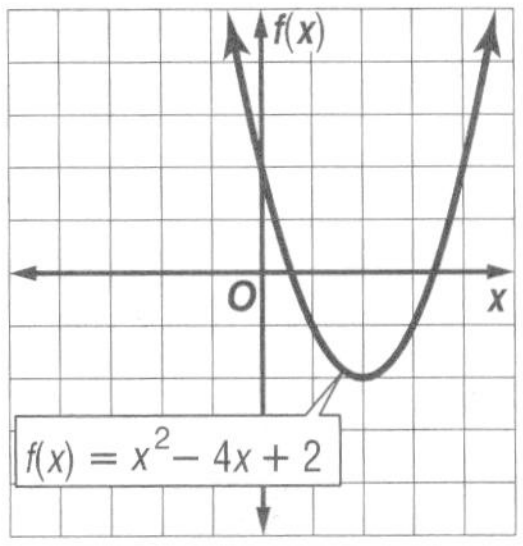

5 **MODEL ROCKETS** Consuela built a model rocket for her science project. The equation $h = -16t^2 + 250t$ models the flight of the rocket launched from ground level at a velocity of 250 feet per second, where h is the height of the rocket in feet after t seconds. Approximately how long was Consuela's rocket in the air? 15.6 seconds

Tips for New Teachers

A graphing calculator is a powerful tool for solving quadratic equations by graphing or using tables. You may wish to discuss these techniques with students.

TEACH with TECH

PORTABLE MEDIA PLAYER Load images of graphs of quadratic functions onto your class web page for students to download to their portable media players. For each graph, have students find the zeros of the function.

Focus on Mathematical Content

No Real Roots Creating a table of values before graphing a function helps to reveal whether a function has no x-intercepts. If all y-values of a function are positive, first decreasing then increasing, or if all are negative, first increasing then decreasing, the graph of the function does not cross the x-axis, and there are no real roots.

Double Root When there are two identical factors for the trinomial in a quadratic equation, there is only one root, called a *double root*. If either the greatest or least y-value in the range is 0, then the vertex is on the x-axis and the solution is a double root.

3 PRACTICE

Formative Assessment

Use Exercises 1–9 to check for understanding.

Use the chart at the bottom of this page to customize assignments for students.

Exercise Alert

Grid Paper For Exercises 1–8, 10–27, 38, 51–56, and 71–76, students will need grid paper.

Multiple Representations In Exercise 38, students use graphing and analysis to compare related quadratic functions.

Additional Answers

41. Iku; sample answer: The zeros of a quadratic function are the x-intercepts of the graph. Since the graph does not intersect the x-axis, there are no x-intercepts and no real zeros.

42. Sample answer: A tennis ball being hit in the air; an equation is $h = -16t^2 + 25t + 2$. The ball is in the air for about 1.6 seconds.

43. Sometimes; for (1, 3), the y-value is greater than 2, but for (1, −1), it is less than 2.

45. 1.5 and −1.5; Sample answer: Make a table of values for x from −2.0 to 2.0. Use increments of 0.1.

46. First graph the related function. Then determine between which two integers the graph crosses the x-axis. Make a table going by tenths of the values between the integers. Locate where the function value changes signs. The x-value for which the function value is closest to zero is the best approximation of the root of the equation.

Check Your Understanding

Examples 1–3 pp. 537–538

Solve each equation by graphing. 1–4. See Ch. 9 Answer Appendix for graphs.

1. $x^2 + 3x - 10 = 0$ 2, −5

2. $2x^2 - 8x = 0$ 0, 4

3. $x^2 + 4x = -4$ −2

4. $x^2 + 12 = -8x$ −6, −2

Example 4 p. 539

Solve each equation by graphing. If integral roots cannot be found, estimate the roots to the nearest tenth. 5–8. See Ch. 9 Answer Appendix for graphs.

5. $-x^2 - 5x + 1 = 0$ −5.2, 0.2

6. $-9 = x^2$ no solutions

7. $x^2 = 25$ 5, −5

8. $x^2 - 8x = -9$ 6.6, 1.4

Example 5 p. 539

9. SCIENCE FAIR Ricky built a model rocket. Its flight can be modeled by the equation shown, where h is the height of the rocket in feet after t seconds. About how long was Ricky's rocket in the air? about 8.4 seconds

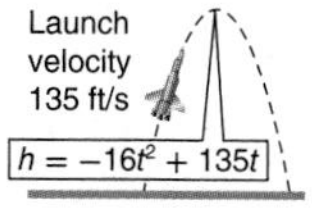

Practice and Problem Solving

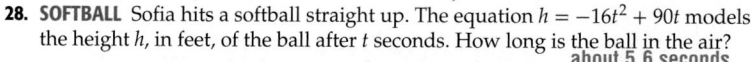

● = Step-by-Step Solutions begin on page R12.
Extra Practice begins on page 815.

Examples 1–3 pp. 537–538

Solve each equation by graphing. 10–21. See Ch. 9 Answer Appendix for graphs.

10. $x^2 + 7x + 14 = 0$ $\varnothing$

11. $x^2 + 2x - 24 = 0$ 4, −6

12. $x^2 - 16x + 64 = 0$ 8

13. $x^2 - 5x + 12 = 0$ $\varnothing$

14. $x^2 + 14x = -49$ −7

15. $x^2 = 2x - 1$ 1

16. $x^2 - 10x = -16$ 2, 8

17. $-2x^2 - 8x = 13$ $\varnothing$

18. $2x^2 - 16x = -30$ 3, 5

19. $2x^2 = -24x - 72$ −6

20. $-3x^2 + 2x = 15$ $\varnothing$

21. $x^2 = -2x + 80$ 8, −10

Example 4 p. 539

Solve each equation by graphing. If integral roots cannot be found, estimate the roots to the nearest tenth. 22–27. See Ch. 9 Answer Appendix for graphs.

22. $x^2 + 2x - 9 = 0$ 2.2, −4.2

23. $x^2 - 4x = 20$ 6.9, −2.9

24. $x^2 + 3x = 18$ 3, −6

25. $2x^2 - 9x = -8$ 3.3, 1.2

26. $3x^2 = -2x + 7$ 1.2, −1.9

27. $5x = 25 - x^2$ 3.1, −8.1

Example 5 p. 539

28. SOFTBALL Sofia hits a softball straight up. The equation $h = -16t^2 + 90t$ models the height h, in feet, of the ball after t seconds. How long is the ball in the air? about 5.6 seconds

B

29. RIDES A skyrocket roller coaster takes riders straight up and then returns straight down. The equation $h = -16t^2 + 185t$ models the height h, in feet, of the coaster after t seconds. How long is it until the coaster returns to the bottom? about 11.6 seconds

Use factoring to determine how many times the graph of each function intersects the x-axis. Identify each zero.

30. $y = x^2 - 8x + 16$ 1; 4

31. $y = x^2 + 3x + 4$ 0; no real roots

32. $y = x^2 + 2x - 24$ 2; −6, 4

33. $y = x^2 + 12x + 32$ 2; −4, −8

34. NUMBER THEORY Use a quadratic equation to find two numbers that have a sum of 9 and a product of 20. 4, 5

35. NUMBER THEORY Use a quadratic equation to find two numbers that have a sum of 1 and a product of −12. −3, 4

36. GOLF The height of a golf ball in the air can be modeled by the equation $h = -16t^2 + 60t + 3$, where h is the height in feet of the ball after t seconds.

a. How long was the ball in the air? about 3.8 seconds

b. What is the ball's maximum height? about 59 ft

c. When will the ball reach its maximum height? 1.9 seconds

Differentiated Homework Options

Level	Assignment	Two-Day Option	
AL Basic	10–28, 41–43, 46–76	11–27 odd, 47–50	10–28 even, 41–43, 46, 51–76
OL Core	11–33 odd, 34–43, 46–76	10–28, 47–50	29–43, 46, 51–76
BL Advanced	29–70, (optional: 71–76)		

540 Chapter 9 Quadratic and Exponential Functions

37. **SNOWBOARDING** Stefanie is in a snowboarding competition. The equation $h = -16t^2 + 30t + 10$ models Stefanie's height h, in feet, in the air after t seconds.

a. How long is Stefanie in the air? **about 2.2 seconds**

b. When will Stefanie reach a height of 15 feet? **about 1.7 seconds and 0.2 seconds**

c. To earn bonus points in the competition, you must reach a height of 20 feet. Will Stefanie earn bonus points? **Yes; Stefanie's maximum height is about 24 ft.**

Real-World Link

In the 1998 Winter Games in Japan, snowboarding became an Olympic event for the first time. A total of four competitions were held that were divided into two categories: men's and women's halfpipe and men's and women's giant slalom.

Source: About, Inc.

38. **MULTIPLE REPRESENTATIONS** In this problem, you will explore how to further interpret the relationship between quadratic functions and graphs. **a, c. See Ch. 9 Answer Appendix.**

a. **GRAPHICAL** Graph $y = x^2$.

b. **ANALYTICAL** Name the vertex and two other points on the graph.

c. **GRAPHICAL** Graph $y = x^2 + 2$, $y = x^2 + 4$, and $y = x^2 + 6$ on the same coordinate plane as the previous graph.

d. **ANALYTICAL** Name the vertex and two points from each of these graphs that have the same x-coordinates as the first graph.

e. **ANALYTICAL** What conclusion can you draw from this?

GRAPHING CALCULATOR **Approximate the zeros of each cubic function by graphing. If integral zeros cannot be found, estimate the zeros to the nearest tenth.**

39. $f(x) = x^3 - 3x^2 - 6x + 8$ **−2, 1, 4**

40. $g(x) = x^3 - 4x^2 + 5x - 12$ **3.5**

H.O.T. Problems

Use Higher-Order Thinking Skills

38b. (0, 0); Sample answers: (1, 1), (−1, 1)

38d. $y = x^2 + 2$: (0, 2), (1, 3), (−1, 3); $y = x^2 + 4$: (0, 4), (1, 5), (−1, 5); $y = x^2 + 6$: (0, 6), (1, 7), (−1, 7)

38e. Sample answer: The graphs of $y = x^2 + 2$, $y = x^2 + 4$, and $y = x^2 + 6$ can be obtained by moving the graph of $y = x^2$ straight up 2 units, 4 units, and 6 units, respectively.

41. **FIND THE ERROR** Iku and Zachary are finding the number of real zeros of the function graphed at the right. Iku says that the function has no real zeros because there are no x-intercepts. Zachary says that the function has one real zero because the graph has a y-intercept. Is either of them correct? Explain your reasoning. **See margin.**

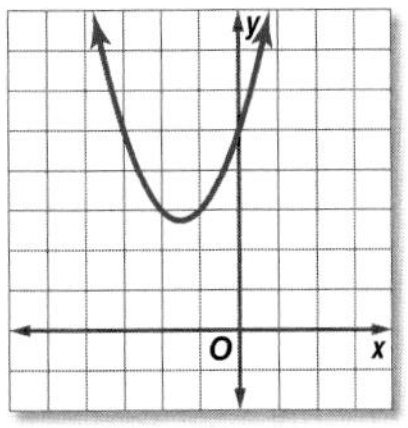

42. **OPEN ENDED** Describe a real-world situation in which a thrown object travels in the air. Write an equation that models the height of the object with respect to time, and determine how long the object travels in the air. **See margin.**

43. **REASONING** The graph shown is that of a *quadratic inequality*. Analyze the graph, and determine whether the y-value of a solution of the inequality is *sometimes*, *always*, or *never* greater than 2. Explain. **See margin.**

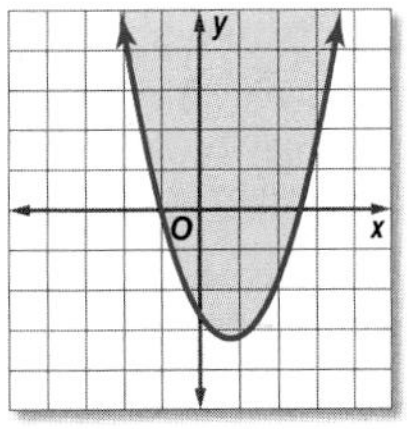

44. **CHALLENGE** Write a quadratic equation that has the roots described.

a. one double root **Sample answer: $x^2 + 8x + 16 = 0$**

b. one rational (nonintegral) root and one integral root

c. two distinct integral roots that are additive opposites.

44b. Sample answer: $2x^2 - 23x + 45 = 0$

44c. Sample answer: $x^2 - 4 = 0$

45. **CHALLENGE** Find the roots of $x^2 = 2.25$ without using a calculator. Explain your strategy. **See margin.**

46. **WRITING IN MATH** Explain how to approximate the roots of a quadratic equation when the roots are not integers. **See margin.**

Study Guide and Intervention

CRM pp. 11–12 AL OL ELL

NAME ______ DATE ______ PERIOD ______

9-2 Study Guide and Intervention

Solving Quadratic Equations by Graphing

Solve by Graphing

Quadratic Equation	an equation of the form $ax^2 + bx + c = 0$, where $a \neq 0$

The solutions of a quadratic equation are called the **roots** of the equation. The roots of a quadratic equation can be found by graphing the related quadratic function $f(x) = ax^2 + bx + c$ and finding the x-intercepts or **zeros** of the function.

Example 1 Solve $x^2 + 4x + 3 = 0$ by graphing.

Graph the related function $f(x) = x^2 + 4x + 3$. The equation of the axis of symmetry is $x = -\frac{4}{2(1)}$ or −2. The vertex is at (−2, −1). Graph the vertex and several other points on either side of the axis of symmetry.

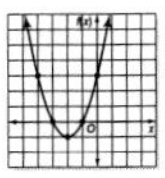

To solve $x^2 + 4x + 3 = 0$, you need to know where the value of $f(x) = 0$. This occurs at the x-intercepts, −3 and −1.

The solutions are −3 and −1.

Example 2 Solve $x^2 - 6x + 9 = 0$ by graphing.

Graph the related function $f(x) = x^2 - 6x + 9$. The equation of the axis of symmetry is $x = \frac{6}{2(1)}$ or 3. The vertex is at (3, 0). Graph the vertex and several other points on either side of the axis of symmetry.

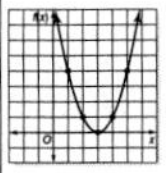

To solve $x^2 - 6x + 9 = 0$, you need to know where $f(x) = 0$. The vertex of the parabola is the x-intercept. Thus, the only solution is 3.

Exercises

Solve each equation by graphing.

1. $x^2 + 7x + 12 = 0$
2. $x^2 - x - 12 = 0$
3. $x^2 - 4x + 5 = 0$

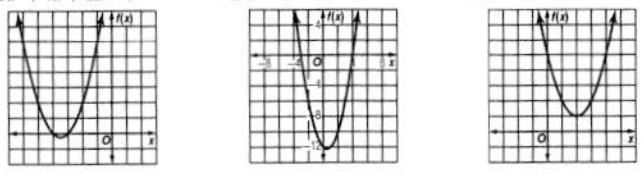

1. **−3, −4**
2. **4, −3**
3. **no real roots**

Chapter 9 11 Glencoe Algebra 1

Lesson 9-2

Practice

CRM p. 14 AL OL BL ELL

NAME ______ DATE ______ PERIOD ______

9-2 Practice

Solving Quadratic Equations by Graphing

Solve each equation by graphing.

1. $x^2 - 5x + 6 = 0$ **2, 3**
2. $w^2 + 6w + 9 = 0$ **−3**
3. $b^2 - 3b + 4 = 0$ **∅**

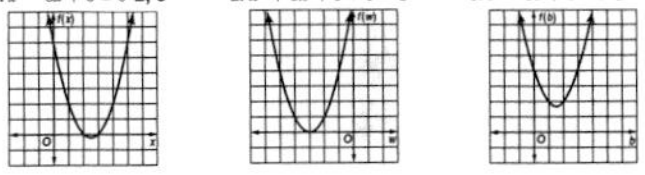

Solve each equation by graphing. If integral roots cannot be found, estimate the roots to the nearest tenth.

4. $p^2 + 4p = 3$
5. $2m^2 + 5 = 10m$
6. $2v^2 + 8v = -7$

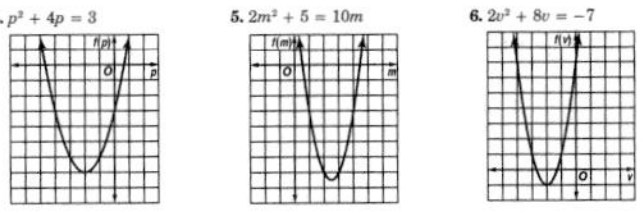

4. **−4.6, 0.6**
5. **0.6, 4.4**
6. **−2.7, −1.3**

7. **NUMBER THEORY** Two numbers have a sum of 2 and a product of −8. The quadratic equation $-n^2 + 2n + 8 = 0$ can be used to determine the two numbers.

a. Graph the related function $f(n) = -n^2 + 2n + 8$ and determine its x-intercepts. **−2, 4**

b. What are the two numbers? **−2 and 4**

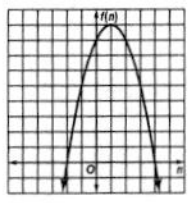

8. **DESIGN** A footbridge is suspended from a parabolic support. The function $h(x) = -\frac{1}{25}x^2 + 9$ represents the height in feet of the support above the walkway, where $x = 0$ represents the midpoint of the bridge.

a. Graph the function and determine its x-intercepts. **−15, 15**

b. What is the length of the walkway between the two supports? **30 ft**

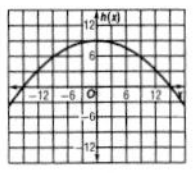

Chapter 9 14 Glencoe Algebra 1

Word Problem Practice

CRM p. 15 AL OL BL ELL

NAME ______ DATE ______ PERIOD ______

9-2 Word Problem Practice

Solving Quadratic Equations by Graphing

1. **FARMING** In order for Ray to decide how much fertilizer to apply to his corn crop this year, he reviews records from previous years. He finds that his crop yield y depends on the amount of fertilizer he applies to his fields x according to the equation $y = -x^2 + 4x + 12$. Graph the function, and find the point at which Ray gets the highest yield possible.

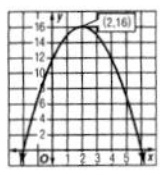

2. **LIGHT** Ayzha and Jeremy hold a flashlight so that the light falls on a piece of graph paper in the shape of a parabola. Ayzha and Jeremy sketch the shape of the parabola and find that the equation $y = x^2 - 3x - 10$ matches the shape of the light beam. Determine the roots of the function. **−2 and 5**

3. **FRAMING** A rectangular photograph is 7 inches long and 6 inches wide. The photograph is framed using material x inches wide. If the area of the frame and photograph combined is 156 square inches, what is the width of the framing material? **3 in.**

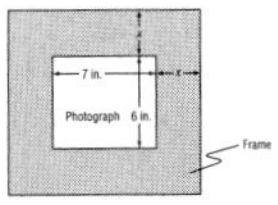

4. **WRAPPING PAPER** Can a rectangular piece of wrapping paper with an area of 81 square inches have a perimeter of 60 inches? (*Hint:* Let length = 30 − w.) Explain. **Solving the equation $(30 - w)w = 81$ gives $w = 3$ or 27. A 3 in. by 27 in. sheet of paper would work.**

5. **ENGINEERING** The shape of a satellite dish is often parabolic because of the reflective qualities of parabolas. Suppose a particular satellite dish is modeled by the following equation.

$$0.5x^2 = 2 + y$$

a. Approximate the solution by graphing. **−2 and 2**

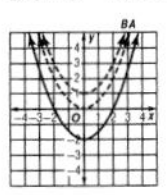

b. On the coordinate plane above, translate the parabola so that there is only one root. Label this curve A. **See students' work.**

c. Translate the parabola so that there are no roots. Label this curve B. **See students' work.**

Chapter 9 15 Glencoe Algebra 1

Lesson 9-2

Watch Out!

Find the Error For Exercise 41, ask students to recall that the solutions or roots of an equation can be identified by finding the x-intercepts or zeros of the related function.

Enrichment

CRM p. 16 OL BL

NAME ______ DATE ______ PERIOD ______

9-2 Enrichment

Parabolas Through Three Given Points

If you know two points on a straight line, you can find the equation of the line. To find the equation of a parabola, you need three points on the curve.

Here is how to approximate an equation of the parabola through the points (0, −2), (3, 0), and (5, 2).

Use the general equation $y = ax^2 + bx + c$. By substituting the given values for x and y, you get three equations.

(0, −2): $-2 = c$

(3, 0): $0 = 9a + 3b + c$

(5, 2): $2 = 25a + 5b + c$

First, substitute −2 for c in the second and third equations.
Then solve those two equations as you would any system of two equations.
Multiply the second equation by 5 and the third equation by −3.

$0 = 9a + 3b - 2$ Multiply by 5. $0 = 45a + 15b - 10$

$2 = 25a + 5b - 2$ Multiply by −3. $-6 = -75a - 15b + 6$

$-6 = -30a \quad - 4$

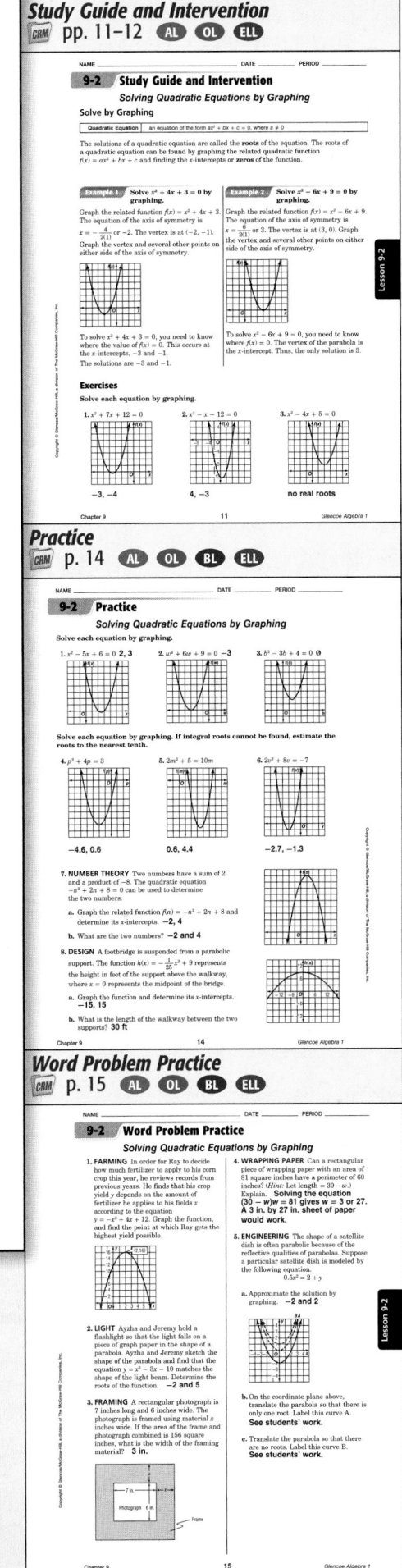

$a = \frac{1}{15}$

4 ASSESS

Yesterday's News Ask students to write two ways in which learning to graph quadratic functions in the previous lesson helped them to solve quadratic equations in this lesson.

Additional Answer

49.

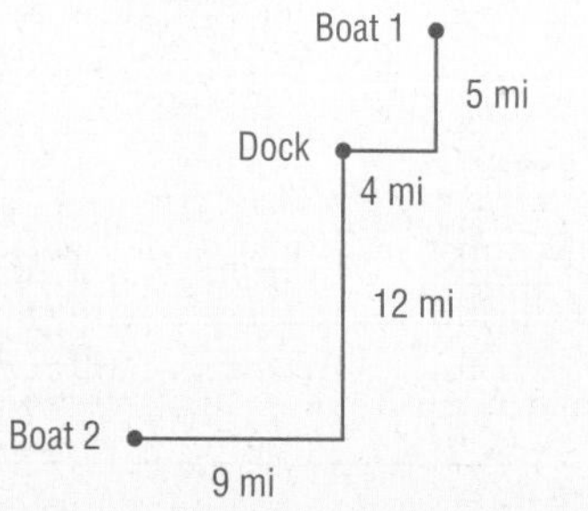

about 21.4 mi

PSAE PRACTICE 6.11.18, 6.11.01, 9.11.01, 8.11.22

47. Adrahan earned 50 out of 80 points on a test. What percentage did Adrahan score on the test? **A**

A 62.5%
B 6.25%
C 1.6%
D 16%

48. Ernesto needs to loosen a bolt. He needs a wrench that is smaller than a $\frac{7}{8}$-inch wrench, but larger than a $\frac{3}{4}$-inch wrench. Which of the following sizes should Ernesto use? **H**

F $\frac{11}{16}$ inch
G $\frac{5}{8}$ inch
H $\frac{13}{16}$ inch
J $\frac{3}{8}$ inch

49. EXTENDED RESPONSE Two boats leave a dock. One boat travels 4 miles east and then 5 miles north. The second boat travels 12 miles south and 9 miles west. Draw a diagram that represents the paths traveled by the boats. How far apart are the boats in miles? **See margin.**

50. The formula $s = \frac{1}{2}at^2$ represents the distance s in meters that a free-falling object will fall near a planet or the Moon in a given time t in seconds. Solve the formula for a, the acceleration due to gravity. **D**

A $a = \frac{1}{2}t^2 - s$
B $a = 2s - t^2$
C $a = s - \frac{1}{2}t^2$
D $a = \frac{2s}{t^2}$

Spiral Review

Write the equation of the axis of symmetry, and find the coordinates of the vertex of the graph of each function. Identify the vertex as a maximum or minimum. Then graph the function. (Lesson 9-1) **51–56. See Ch. 9 Answer Appendix.**

51. $y = 3x^2$
52. $y = -4x^2 - 5$
53. $y = -x^2 + 4x - 7$
54. $y = x^2 - 6x - 8$
55. $y = 3x^2 + 2x + 1$
56. $y = -4x^2 - 8x + 5$

Solve each equation. Check the solutions. (Lesson 8-6)

57. $2x^2 = 32$ **−4, 4**
58. $(x - 4)^2 = 25$ **−1, 9**
59. $4x^2 - 4x + 1 = 16$ **$-\frac{3}{2}, \frac{5}{2}$**
60. $2x^2 + 16x = -32$ **−4**
61. $(x + 3)^2 = 5$ **$-3 \pm \sqrt{5}$**
62. $4x^2 - 12x = -9$ **$\frac{3}{2}$**

Find each sum or difference. (Lesson 7-5)

65. $-3b^4 + 2b^3 - 9b^2 + 13$
66. $6h^4 + 2h^3 + h^2 + 5$

63. $(3n^2 - 3) + (4 + 4n^2)$ **$7n^2 + 1$**
64. $(2d^2 - 7d - 3) - (4d^2 + 7)$ **$-2d^2 - 7d - 10$**
65. $(2b^3 - 4b^2 + 4) - (3b^4 + 5b^2 - 9)$
66. $(8 - 4h^2 + 6h^4) + (5h^2 - 3 + 2h^3)$

67. GEOMETRY Supplementary angles are two angles with measures that have a sum of 180°. For the supplementary angles in the figure, the measure of the larger angle is 24° greater than the measure of the smaller angle. Write and solve a system of equations to find these measures. (Lesson 6-5)
$x + y = 180$; $x = y + 24$; 102°, 78°

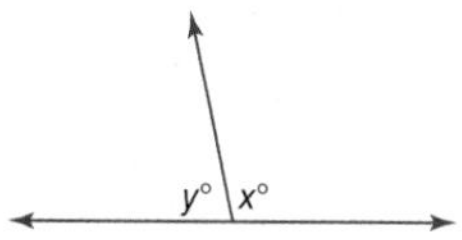

Write an equation in point-slope form for the line that passes through each point with the given slope. (Lesson 4-3)

68. $(2, 5), m = 3$ **$y - 5 = 3(x - 2)$**
69. $(-3, 6), m = -7$ **$y - 6 = -7(x + 3)$**
70. $(-1, -2), m = -\frac{1}{2}$ **$y + 2 = -\frac{1}{2}(x + 1)$**

Skills Review

Graph each function. (Lesson 9-1) **71–76. See Ch. 9 Answer Appendix.**

71. $y = x^2 + 5$
72. $y = x^2 - 8$
73. $y = 2x^2 - 7$
74. $y = -x^2 + 2$
75. $y = -0.5x^2 - 3$
76. $y = (-x)^2 + 1$

Differentiated Instruction BL

Extension Tell students that in a computer golf game, the function $y = -0.002x^2 + 0.22x$ models the path of a golf ball, where y is the height of the ball and x is the horizontal distance in yards the ball has traveled. The green lies uphill from the tee, 90 yards away horizontally, atop a hill that has a steady incline of 1 yard per 10 yards of distance. Ask, "Will the ball reach the green without hitting the ground first? Explain your answer." No; the ball will land on the slope when it is 60 yards horizontally from the tee.

542 Chapter 9 Quadratic and Exponential Functions

Graphing Technology Lab: Quadratic Inequalities

IL Math Online glencoe.com
- Other Calculator Keystrokes
- Graphing Technology Personal Tutor

IL Learning Standards **8.D.4** Formulate and solve linear and quadratic equations and linear inequalities algebraically and **investigate nonlinear inequalities using graphs, tables, calculators and computers.**

Recall that the graph of a linear inequality consists of the boundary and the shaded half plane. The solution set of the inequality lies in the shaded region of the graph. Graphing quadratic inequalities is similar to graphing linear inequalities.

ACTIVITY 1 Shade Inside a Parabola

Graph $y \geq x^2 - 5x + 4$ in the standard viewing window.

First, clear all functions from the Y= list.

To graph $y \geq x^2 - 5x + 4$, enter the equation in the Y= list. Then use the left arrow to select =. Press [ENTER] until shading above the line is selected.

KEYSTROKES: [◀] [◀] [ENTER] [ENTER] [▶] [▶] [X,T,θ,n] [x^2] [−] 5 [X,T,θ,n] [+] 4 [GRAPH]

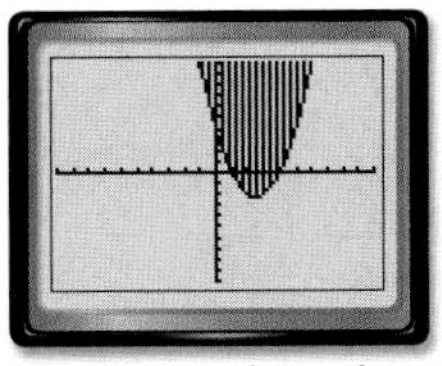

[−10, 10] scl: 1 by [−10, 10] scl: 1

All ordered pairs for which y is *greater than or equal* to $x^2 - 5x + 4$ lie *above or on* the line and are solutions.

A similar procedure will be used to graph an inequality in which the shading is outside of the parabola.

ACTIVITY 2 Shade Outside a Parabola

Graph $y - 4 \leq x^2 - 5x$ in the standard viewing window.

First, clear the graph that is displayed.

KEYSTROKES: [Y=] [CLEAR]

Then rewrite $y - 4 \leq x^2 - 5x$ as $y \leq x^2 - 5x + 4$, and graph it.

KEYSTROKES: [◀] [◀] [ENTER] [ENTER] [ENTER] [▶] [▶] [X,T,θ,n] [x^2] [−] 5 [X,T,θ,n] [+] 4 [GRAPH]

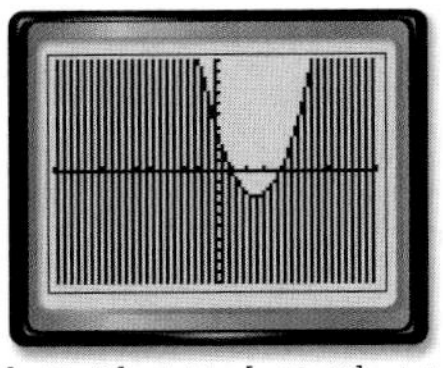

[−10, 10] scl: 1 by [−10, 10] scl: 1

All ordered pairs for which y is *less than or equal* to $x^2 - 5x + 4$ lie *below or on* the line and are solutions.

Exercises

1. Compare and contrast the two graphs shown above.
2. Graph $y - 2x + 6 \geq 5x^2$ in the standard viewing window. Name three solutions of the inequality. (0, −6), (1, 1), (2, 18)
3. Graph $y - 6x \leq -x^2 - 3$ in the standard viewing window. Name three solutions of the inequality. (0, −3), (1, 2), (2, 5)

1. The graph of $y \geq x^2 - 5x + 4$ is a parabola with the inside shaded. The graph of $y \leq x^2 - 5x + 4$ is a parabola with the outside shaded.

Lesson Notes

1 FOCUS

Objective Use a graphing calculator to investigate quadratic inequalities.

Materials for Each Student

- TI-83/84 Plus or other graphing calculator

Teaching Tip

Remind students that the [x^2] key squares the quantity but does not enter [x^2] into an equation. To enter $5x^2$, press 5 [X,T,θ,n] [x^2].

2 TEACH

Working in Cooperative Groups

Put students in groups of two or three, mixing abilities. Have groups complete the Activities and Exercise 1.

Ask:

- Where are the solutions for the inequalities? all ordered pairs in the shaded area of the graph, including the graph of the related function itself
- How many solutions does each inequality have? infinite number
- Are any of the solutions to the first graph the same as for the second graph? yes, the solutions that lie on the graph of the function itself

Practice Have students complete Exercises 2 and 3.

3 ASSESS

Formative Assessment

Use Exercise 3 to assess whether students understand how to use a graphing calculator to solve an inequality.

From Concrete to Abstract

Have students examine the graph they made for the first inequality in the Activity. Then have them explain how the solution set to this inequality is the same as, or different from, the solution set for $y > x^2 - 5x + 4$. The solution set for $y > x^2 - 5x + 4$ does not include the values on the graph of the related function, while the solution set for $y \geq x^2 - 5x + 4$ does.

9-3 Lesson Notes

1 FOCUS

Vertical Alignment

Before Lesson 9-3
Graph quadratic functions by using the vertex and axis of symmetry.

Lesson 9-3
Apply translations of quadratic functions.
Apply vertical stretches and reflections to quadratic functions.

After Lesson 9-3
Write equations that model data.

2 TEACH

Scaffolding Questions

Have students read the *Why?* section of the lesson.

Ask:

- What is the vertex of each parabola? blue: (0, 1); red: (0, 4)
- What do we know about the coefficient of the x^2 term for the equations of these graphs? They are both positive.
- What is the axis of symmetry for these two graphs? the *y*-axis
- What do we know about the *b* value in the equations for these graphs? Since $-\frac{b}{2a} = 0$, we know then that *b* must equal 0 for both.

9-3 Transformations of Quadratic Functions

Then
You graphed quadratic functions by using the vertex and axis of symmetry. (Lesson 9-1)

Now
- Apply translations to quadratic functions.
- Apply dilations and reflections to quadratic functions.

IL Learning Standards
8.B.4b Use the basic functions of absolute value, square root, linear, **quadratic** and step **to describe numerical relationships.**
8.C.4a Analyze and report the effects of changing coefficients, exponents and other parameters on functions and their graphs.

New Vocabulary
transformation
translation
dilation
reflection

IL Math Online
glencoe.com
- Extra Examples
- Personal Tutor
- Self-Check Quiz
- Homework Help
- Math in Motion

Why?

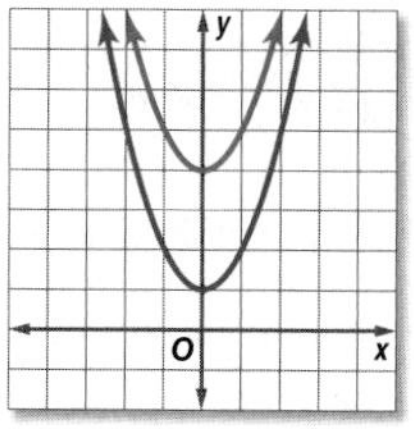

The graphs of the parabolas shown at the right are the same size and shape, but notice that the vertex of the red parabola is higher on the *y*-axis than the vertex of the blue parabola. Shifting a parabola up and down is an example of a transformation.

Translations A **transformation** changes the position or size of a figure. One type of transformation, a **translation**, moves a figure up, down, left, or right. When a constant *c* is added to or subtracted from the parent function, the graph of the resulting function $f(x) \pm c$ is the graph of the parent function translated up or down.

The parent function of the family of quadratics is $f(x) = x^2$. All other quadratic functions have graphs that are transformations of the graph of $f(x) = x^2$.

Key Concept Vertical Translations — For Your FOLDABLE

The graph of $g(x) = x^2 + c$ is the graph of $f(x) = x^2$ translated vertically.

If $c > 0$, the graph of $f(x) = x^2$ is translated $|c|$ units **up**.

If $c < 0$, the graph of $f(x) = x^2$ is translated $|c|$ units **down**.

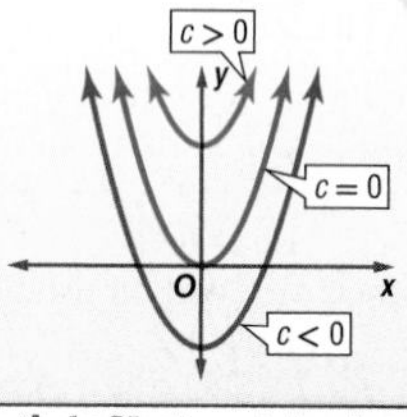

Math *in Motion*, Animation glencoe.com

EXAMPLE 1 Describe and Graph Translations

Describe how the graph of each function is related to the graph of $f(x) = x^2$.

a. $h(x) = x^2 + 3$
The value of *c* is 3, and $3 > 0$. Therefore, the graph of $y = x^2 + 3$ is a translation of the graph of $y = x^2$ up 3 units.

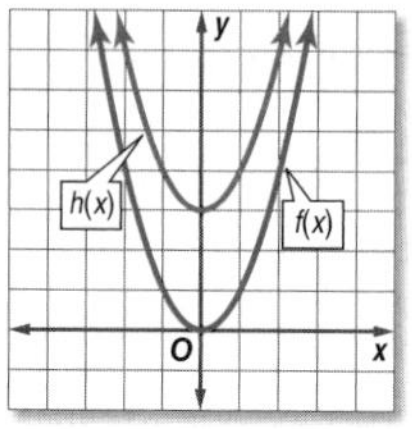

b. $g(x) = x^2 - 4$
The value of *c* is −4, and $-4 < 0$. Therefore, the graph of $y = x^2 - 4$ is a translation of the graph of $y = x^2$ down 4 units.

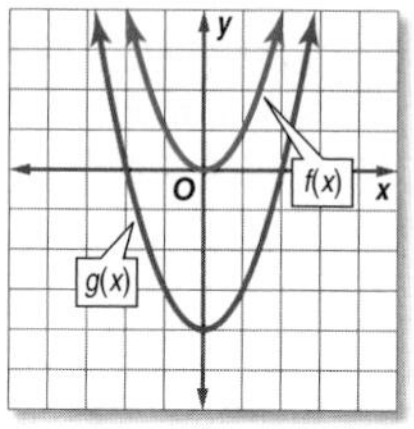

Check Your Progress

1A. $f(x) = x^2 - 7$ translated down 7 **1B.** $g(x) = 5 + x^2$ translated up 5 **1C.** $h(x) = -5 + x^2$ translated down 5 **1D.** $f(x) = x^2 + 1$ translated up 1

Personal Tutor glencoe.com

Lesson 9-3 Resources

Resource	Approaching-Level	On-Level	Beyond-Level	English Learners
Teacher Edition	• Differentiated Instruction, p. 545	• Differentiated Instruction, pp. 545, 549	• Differentiated Instruction, p. 549	
Chapter Resource Masters	• Study Guide and Intervention, pp. 17–18 • Skills Practice, p. 19 • Practice, p. 20 • Word Problem Practice, p. 21	• Study Guide and Intervention, pp. 17–18 • Skills Practice, p. 19 • Practice, p. 20 • Word Problem Practice, p. 21 • Enrichment, p. 22	• Practice, p. 20 • Word Problem Practice, p. 21 • Enrichment, p. 22	• Study Guide and Intervention, pp. 17–18 • Skills Practice, p. 19 • Practice, p. 20 • Word Problem Practice, p. 21
Transparencies	• 5-Minute Check Transparency 9-3	• 5-Minute Check Transparency 9-3	• 5-Minute Check Transparency 9-3	• 5-Minute Check Transparency 9-3
Other	• Study Notebook	• Study Notebook	• Study Notebook	• Study Notebook

Dilations and Reflections Another type of transformation is a dilation. A **dilation** makes the graph narrower than the parent graph or wider than the parent graph. When the parent function $f(x) = x^2$ is multiplied by a constant a, the graph of the resulting function $f(x) = ax^2$ is either stretched or compressed vertically.

Key Concept — Dilations

For Your FOLDABLE

The graph of $g(x) = ax^2$ stretches or compresses the graph of $f(x) = x^2$ vertically.

If $|a| > 1$, the graph of $f(x) = x^2$ is stretched vertically.

If $0 < |a| < 1$, the graph of $f(x) = x^2$ is compressed vertically.

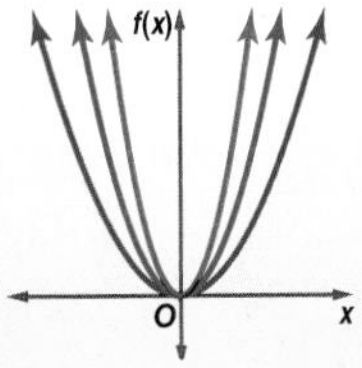

StudyTip

Compress or Stretch When the graph of a quadratic function is stretched vertically, the shape of the graph is narrower than that of the parent function. When it is compressed vertically, the graph is wider than the parent function.

EXAMPLE 2 Describe and Graph Dilations

Describe how the graph of each function is related to the graph of $f(x) = x^2$.

a. $h(x) = \frac{1}{2}x^2$

The function can be written $h(x) = ax^2$, where $a = \frac{1}{2}$. Since $0 < \frac{1}{2} < 1$, the graph of $y = \frac{1}{2}x^2$ is a dilation of the graph of $y = x^2$ that is compressed vertically.

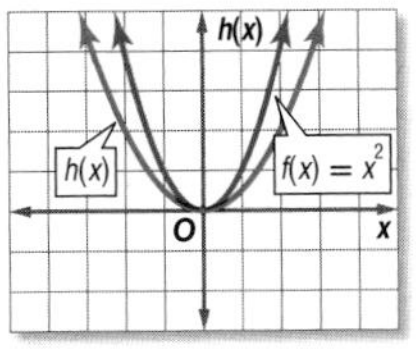

b. $g(x) = 3x^2 + 2$

The function $g(x) = ax^2 + c$, where $a = 3$ and $c = 2$. Since $2 > 0$ and $3 > 1$, the graph of $y = 3x^2 + 2$ translates the graph $y = x^2$ up 2 units and stretches it vertically.

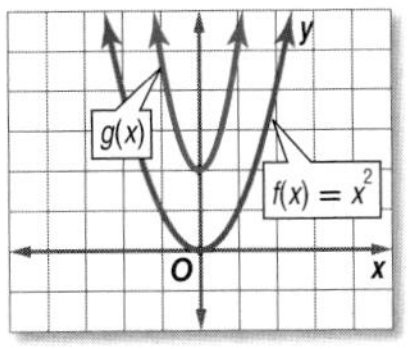

Check Your Progress

2A. $j(x) = 2x^2$ **2B.** $h(x) = 5x^2 - 2$ **2C.** $g(x) = \frac{1}{3}x^2 + 2$

Personal Tutor glencoe.com

2A. stretched vertically
2B. stretched vertically and translated down
2C. compressed vertically and translated up

A **reflection** flips a figure across a line. When $f(x) = x^2$ or the variable x is multiplied by -1, the graph is reflected across the x- or y-axis.

StudyTip

Reflection A reflection of $f(x) = x^2$ across the y-axis results in the same function, because $f(-x) = (-x)^2 = x^2$.

Key Concept — Reflections

For Your FOLDABLE

The graph of $-f(x)$ is the reflection of the graph of $f(x) = x^2$ across the x-axis.

The graph of $f(-x)$ is the reflection of the graph of $f(x) = x^2$ across the y-axis.

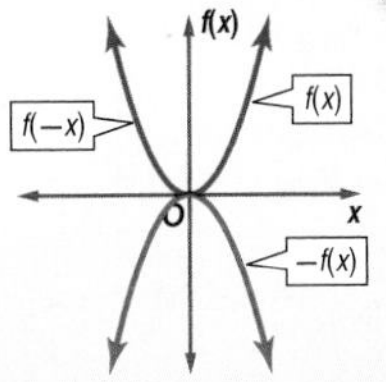

Translations

Example 1 shows how to describe the graph of a quadratic function of the form $f(x) = x^2 + c$ based on its relationship to the parent function $f(x) = x^2$.

Formative Assessment

Use the Check Your Progress exercises after each example to determine students' understanding of concepts.

Additional Example

1 Describe how the graph of each function is related to the graph of $f(x) = x^2$.

a. $h(x) = 10 + x^2$ translated up 10 units

b. $g(x) = x^2 - 8$ translated down 8 units

Dilations and Reflections

Example 2 shows how to describe the graph of a quadratic function of the form $f(x) = ax^2$ based on its relationship to the parent function $f(x) = x^2$. **Example 3** shows how to describe the graph of a quadratic function of the form $f(x) = -ax^2 + c$ based on its relationship to the parent function $f(x) = x^2$. **Example 4** shows how to choose the equation that correlates to a function shown in a graph.

Additional Example

2 Describe how the graph of each function is related to the graph of $f(x) = x^2$.

a. $d(x) = \frac{1}{3}x^2$ The graph of $y = \frac{1}{3}x^2$ is a vertical compression of the graph of $f(x) = x^2$.

b. $m(x) = 2x^2 + 1$ The graph of $y = 2x^2 + 1$ is stretched vertically and then translated up 1 unit.

Differentiated Instruction (AL OL)

If students need help comparing and contrasting a function's graph and its parent function's graph,

Then have students write and graph three different functions on the same coordinate plane. Using a red pencil, on this same coordinate plane, have students graph the parent function $f(x) = x^2$. Finally, have students create observation notebooks in which to record their thoughts on how each function's graph is similar to or different from the parent function's graph.

Additional Examples

3 Describe how the graph of $g(x) = -3x^2 + 1$ is related to the graph of $f(x) = x^2$. The graph of $g(x) = -3x^2 + 1$ is reflected across the x-axis, stretched by a factor of 3, and translated up 1 unit.

4 **STANDARDIZED TEST PRACTICE** Which is an equation for the function shown in the graph? A

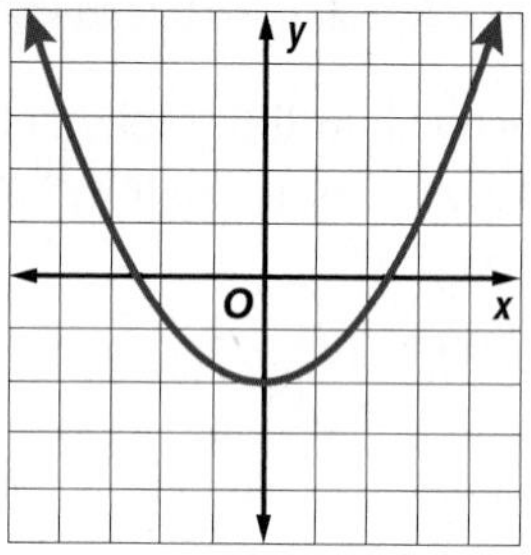

A $y = \frac{1}{3}x^2 - 2$
B $y = 3x^2 + 2$
C $y = -\frac{1}{3}x^2 + 2$
D $y = -3x^2 - 2$

Additional Examples also in Interactive Classroom PowerPoint® Presentations

IWB INTERACTIVE WHITEBOARD READY

Focus on Mathematical Content

Quadratic Functions Each constant in the quadratic function $f(x) = ax^2 + c$ has meaning when compared to its parent function $f(x) = x^2$. The value of $|a|$ in the function either compresses or expands (dilates) the graph of the parent function. When the value of a is negative, the graph of the parent function is flipped (reflected) over the x-axis. The value of c in the function moves (translates) the graph of the parent function c units up or down.

Watch Out!

Transformations The graph of $f(x) = -ax^2$ can result in two transformations of the graph of $f(x) = x^2$: a reflection across the x-axis if $a > 0$ and either a compression or expansion depending on the absolute value of a.

3A. reflected across the y-axis, compressed, and translated down

3B. reflected across the x-axis, expanded, and translated up

EXAMPLE 3 Describe and Graph Reflections

Describe how the graph of $g(x) = -2x^2 - 3$ is related to the graph of $f(x) = x^2$.

Three separate transformations are occurring. The negative sign of the coefficient of x^2 causes a reflection across the x-axis. Then a dilation occurs and finally a translation down 3 units.

So the graph of $y = -2x^2 - 3$ is reflected across the x-axis, compressed, and translated down 3 units.

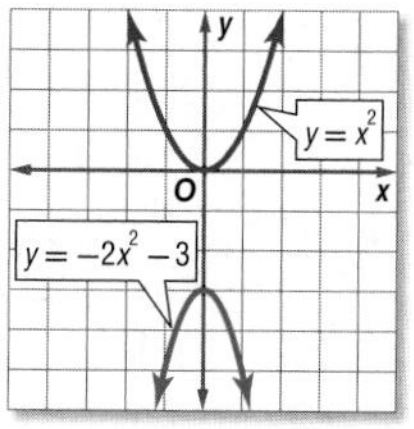

Check Your Progress

Describe how the graph of each function is related to the graph of $f(x) = x^2$.

3A. $h(x) = 2(-x)^2 - 9$

3B. $g(x) = -\frac{1}{5}x^2 + 3$

Personal Tutor glencoe.com

You can use what you know about the characteristics of graphs of quadratic equations to match an equation with a graph.

PSAE EXAMPLE 4 8.11.08

Which is an equation for the function shown in the graph?

A $y = \frac{1}{2}x^2 - 5$ C $y = -\frac{1}{2}x^2 + 5$
B $y = -2x^2 - 5$ D $y = 2x^2 + 5$

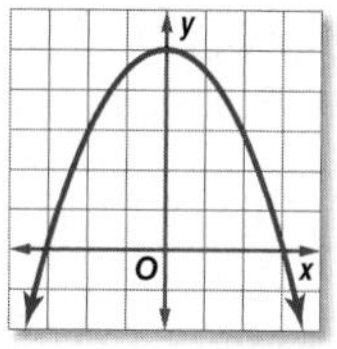

Read the Test Item

You are given the graph of a parabola. You need to find an equation of the graph.

Solve the Test Item

Notice that the graph opens downward. Therefore, the graph of $y = x^2$ has been reflected across the x-axis. The leading coefficient should be negative, so eliminate choices A and D.

The parabola is translated up 5 units, so $c = 5$. Look at the equations. Only choices C and D have $c = 5$. The answer is C.

Review Vocabulary

leading coefficient the coefficient of the first term of a polynomial written in standard form (Lesson 7-4)

Check Your Progress

4. Which is the graph of $y = -3x^2 + 1$? H

F
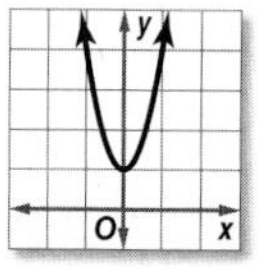

G
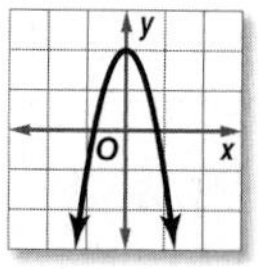

H
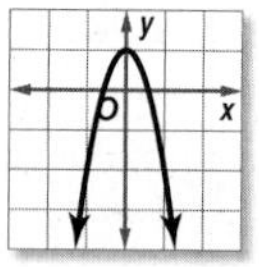

J
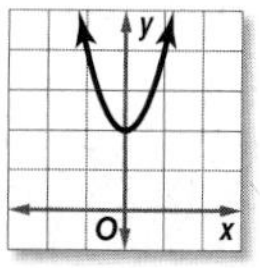

Personal Tutor glencoe.com

TEACH with TECH

INTERACTIVE WHITEBOARD Drag a coordinate grid onto the board. Sketch the graph of a quadratic function on the board and give students the equation of the graph. Drag the parabola to another location on the board and have students find the new equation. Discussing similarities and differences.

Additional Answers

1. translated down
2. compressed vertically
3. reflected across the x-axis, translated up
4. translated up
5. reflected across the x-axis, stretched vertically
6. reflected across the x-axis, translated down

Check Your Understanding

1–6. See margin.

Examples 1–3 pp. 544–546

Describe how the graph of each function is related to the graph of $f(x) = x^2$.

1. $g(x) = x^2 - 11$
2. $h(x) = \frac{1}{2}x^2$
3. $h(x) = -x^2 + 8$
4. $g(x) = x^2 + 6$
5. $g(x) = -4x^2$
6. $h(x) = -x^2 - 2$

Example 4 p. 546

7. **MULTIPLE CHOICE** Which is an equation for the function shown in the graph? C

A $g(x) = \frac{1}{5}x^2 + 2$

B $g(x) = -5x^2 - 2$

C $g(x) = \frac{1}{5}x^2 - 2$

D $g(x) = -\frac{1}{5}x^2 - 2$

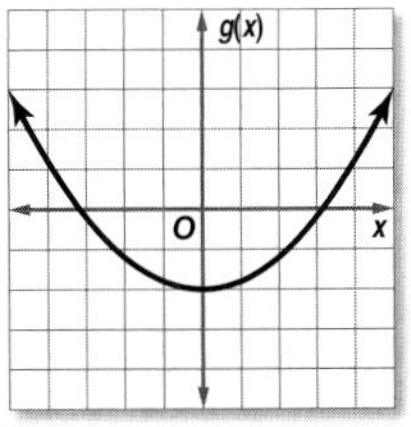

Practice and Problem Solving

● = **Step-by-Step Solutions** begin on page R12.
Extra Practice begins on page 815.

Examples 1–3 pp. 544–546

8–17. See margin.

Describe how the graph of each function is related to the graph of $f(x) = x^2$.

8. $g(x) = -10 + x^2$
9. $h(x) = -7 - x^2$
10. $g(x) = 2x^2 + 8$
11. $h(x) = 6 + \frac{2}{3}x^2$
12. $g(x) = -5 - \frac{4}{3}x^2$
13. $h(x) = 3 + \frac{5}{2}x^2$
14. $g(x) = 0.25x^2 - 1.1$
15. $h(x) = 1.35x^2 + 2.6$
16. $g(x) = \frac{3}{4}x^2 + \frac{5}{6}$
17. $h(x) = 1.01x^2 - 6.5$

Example 4 p. 546

Match each equation to its graph.

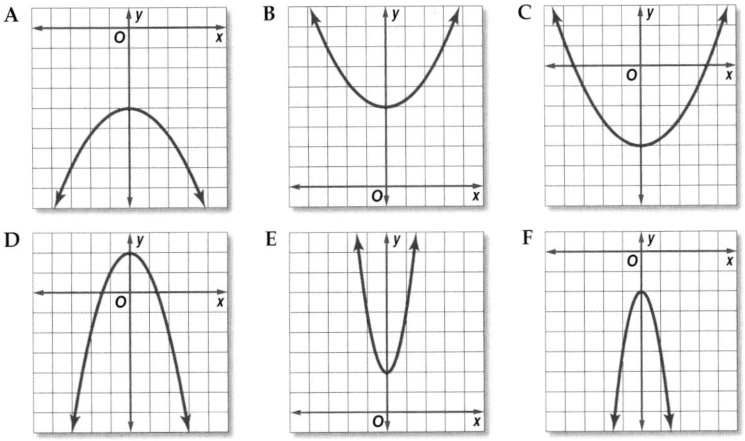

18. $y = \frac{1}{3}x^2 - 4$ C
19. $y = -\frac{1}{3}x^2 - 4$ A
20. $y = \frac{1}{3}x^2 + 4$ B
21. $y = -3x^2 - 2$ F
22. $y = -x^2 + 2$ D
23. $y = 3x^2 + 2$ E

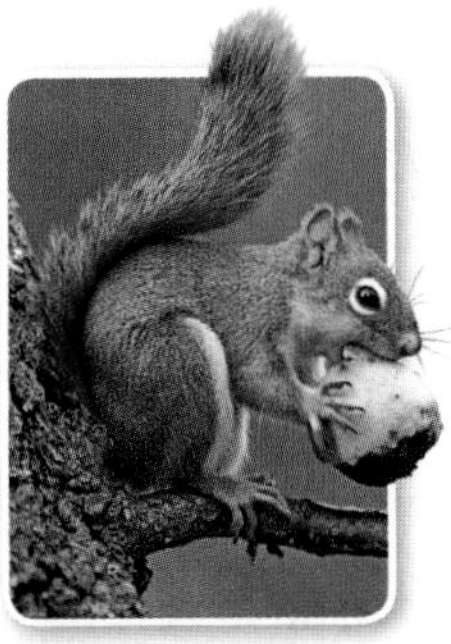

Real-World Link

There are over 365 species of squirrels or squirrel-like mammals in the world. The three most common are the flying squirrel, the tree squirrel, and the ground squirrel.

Source: The Squirrel Place

24. **SQUIRRELS** A squirrel 12 feet above the ground drops an acorn from a tree. The function $h = -16t^2 + 12$ models the height of the acorn above the ground in feet after t seconds. Graph the function and compare this graph to the graph of its parent function. The graph is stretched vertically, reflected across the x-axis, and translated up. See Ch. 9 Answer Appendix for graph.

Differentiated Homework Options

Level	Assignment	Two-Day Option	
AL Basic	8–24, 35, 37–62	9–23 odd, 40–43	8–24 even, 35, 37–39, 44–62
OL Core	9–33 odd, 30, 34, 35, 37–62	8–24, 40–43	25–35, 37–39, 44–62
BL Advanced	25–56, (optional: 57–62)		

Tips for New Teachers

Width of the Parabola Students often mistake a greater value for $|a|$ to imply a wider parabola. Suggest that students think of the value of a in $y = ax^2 + c$ the same way they thought of the value of the slope m in $y = mx + b$. A greater value for m means a steeper line. A greater value for $|a|$ means that the sides of the parabola are steeper.

3 PRACTICE

Formative Assessment

Use Exercises 1–7 to check for understanding.

Use the chart at the bottom of this page to customize assignments for your students.

Exercise Alert

Grid Paper For Exercises 24, 44–49, and 52–54, students will need grid paper.

Additional Answers

8. translated down
9. reflected across the x-axis, translated down
10. stretched vertically, translated up
11. compressed vertically, translated up
12. reflected across the x-axis, stretched vertically, translated down
13. stretched vertically, translated up
14. compressed vertically, translated down
15. stretched vertically, translated up
16. compressed vertically, translated up
17. stretched vertically, translated down

B List the functions in order from the most stretched vertically to the least compressed graph. **27. h(x), g(x), f(x) 28. f(x), h(x), g(x)**

25. $g(x) = 2x^2, h(x) = \frac{1}{2}x^2$ **g(x), h(x)**

26. $g(x) = -3x^2, h(x) = \frac{2}{3}x^2$ **g(x), h(x)**

27. $g(x) = -4x^2, h(x) = 6x^2, f(x) = 0.3x^2$

28. $g(x) = -x^2, h(x) = \frac{5}{3}x^2, f(x) = -4.5x^2$

29a. $h = -16t^2 + 20{,}000$ and $h = -16t^2 + 30{,}000$

29. ROCKS A rock drops from a cliff 20,000 inches above the ground. Another rock drops from a cliff 30,000 inches above the ground.

a. Write two functions that model the heights h of the rocks after t seconds.

b. Which rock will reach the ground first? **See margin.**

Real-World Link

This fountain is in the East Concourse of Midfield Terminal in Detroit, Michigan. The streams are choreographed to create feelings ranging from tranquil to energetic.

Source: The WET Design

30. SPRINKLERS The path of water from a sprinkler can be modeled by quadratic functions. The following functions model paths for three different sprinklers.

Sprinkler A: $y = -0.35x^2 + 3.5$ Sprinkler B: $y = -0.21x^2 + 1.7$

Sprinkler C: $y = -0.08x^2 + 2.4$

a. Which sprinkler will send water the farthest? Explain. **Sprinkler C because the graph is compressed vertically the most.**

b. Which sprinkler will send water the highest? Explain. **b. Sprinkler A because it is translated up the most.**

c. Which sprinkler will produce the narrowest path? Explain. **Sprinkler A because it is expanded the least.**

Describe the transformations to obtain the graph of $g(x)$ from the graph of $f(x)$.

31. $f(x) = x^2 + 3$, $g(x) = x^2 - 2$

32. $f(x) = x^2 - 4$, $g(x) = x^2 + 7$

33. $f(x) = -6x^2$, $g(x) = -3x^2$

31. Translate the graph of f(x) down.

32. Translate the graph of f(x) up.

33. Compress vertically the graph of f(x).

34c. The graph of $y = (x - 7)^2$ will be translated 7 units to the right and the graph of $y = (x + 4)^2$ will be translated 4 units to the left.

34. MULTIPLE REPRESENTATIONS In this problem, you will investigate another type of transformation using your graphing calculator. **C**

a. **GRAPHICAL** Graph the following family of equations: $y = x^2$, $y = (x - 2)^2$, $y = (x - 4)^2$, $y = (x + 3)^2$, and $y = (x + 5)^2$ on the same screen. Describe how the graphs of the functions are related to the graph of $f(x) = x^2$. **See margin.**

b. **ALGEBRAIC** Write a concept for quadratic functions, similar to the concept for vertical translations, to describe the effect of a value being added to or subtracted from x inside the parentheses. **See margin.**

c. **ANALYTICAL** Predict where the graphs of $y = (x - 7)^2$ and $y = (x + 4)^2$ will be located. Verify your answer by graphing each equation. **See margin for graph.**

H.O.T. Problems

Use **H**igher-**O**rder **T**hinking Skills

35. REASONING Are the following statements *sometimes*, *always*, or *never* true? Explain. **See Ch. 9 Answer Appendix.**

a. The graph of $y = x^2 + c$ has its vertex at the origin.

b. The graphs of $y = ax^2$ and of $y = -ax^2$ are the same width.

c. The graph of $y = x^2 + c$ opens downward.

36. CHALLENGE Write a function of the form $y = ax^2 + c$ with a graph that passes through the points (−2, 3) and (4, 15). $y = x^2 - 1$

37. REASONING Determine whether all quadratic functions that are reflected across the y-axis produce the same graph. Explain your answer. **See margin.**

38. OPEN ENDED Write a quadratic function that opens downward and is wider than the parent graph. **Sample answer:** $f(x) = -\frac{1}{2}x^2$

39. WRITING IN MATH Describe how the values of a and c affect the graphical and tabular representations for the functions $y = ax^2$, $y = x^2 + c$, and $y = ax^2 + c$. **See Ch. 9 Answer Appendix.**

Study Guide and Intervention
CRM pp. 17–18 AL OL ELL

NAME ______ DATE ______ PERIOD ______

9-3 Study Guide and Intervention
Transformations of Quadratic Functions

Translations A **translation** is a change in the position of a figure either up, down, or diagonal. When a constant c is added to or subtracted from the parent function, the resulting function $f(x) \pm c$ is a translation of the graph up or down.

The graph of $f(x) = x^2 + c$ translates the graph of $f(x) = x^2$ vertically.
If $c > 0$, the graph of $f(x) = x^2$ is translated $\lvert c \rvert$ units up.
If $c < 0$, the graph of $f(x) = x^2$ is translated $\lvert c \rvert$ units down.

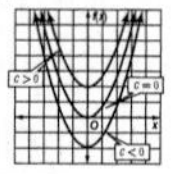

Example Describe how the graph of each function is related to the graph of $f(x) = x^2$.

a. $g(x) = x^2 + 4$
The function can be written as $f(x) = x^2 + c$. The value of c is 4, and $4 > 0$. Therefore, the graph of $g(x) = x^2 + 4$ is a translation of the graph of $f(x) = x^2$ up 4 units.

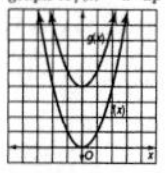

b. $h(x) = x^2 - 3$
The function can be written as $f(x) = x^2 + c$. The value of c is −3, and $-3 < 0$. Therefore, the graph of $g(x) = x^2 - 3$ is a translation of the graph of $f(x) = x^2$ down 3 units.

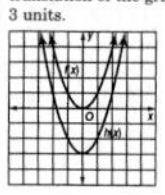

Lesson 9-2

Exercises

Describe how the graph of each function is related to the graph of $f(x) = x^2$.

1. $g(x) = x^2 + 1$ **Translation of $f(x) = x^2$ up 1 unit.**
2. $h(x) = x^2 - 6$ **Translation of $f(x) = x^2$ down 6 units.**
3. $g(x) = x^2 - 1$ **Translation of $f(x) = x^2$ down 1 unit.**
4. $h(x) = 20 + x^2$ **Translation of $f(x) = x^2$ up 20 units.**
5. $g(x) = -2 + x^2$ **Translation of $f(x) = x^2$ down 2 units.**
6. $h(x) = -\frac{1}{2} + x^2$ **Translation of $f(x) = x^2$ down $\frac{1}{2}$ unit.**
7. $g(x) = x^2 + \frac{8}{9}$ **Translation of $f(x) = x^2$ up $\frac{8}{9}$ unit.**
8. $h(x) = x^2 - 0.3$ **Translation of $f(x) = x^2$ down 0.3 unit.**
9. $g(x) = x^2 - 4$ **Translation of $f(x) = x^2$ down 4 units.**

Chapter 9 17 Glencoe Algebra 1

Practice
CRM p. 20 AL OL BL ELL

NAME ______ DATE ______ PERIOD ______

9-3 Practice
Transformations of Quadratic Functions

Describe how the graph of each function is related to the graph of $f(x) = x^2$.

1. $g(x) = 10 + x^2$ **Translation of $y = x^2$ up 10 units.**
2. $h(x) = -\frac{2}{5} + x^2$ **Translation of $y = x^2$ down $\frac{2}{5}$ unit.**
3. $g(x) = 9 - x^2$ **Reflection of $y = x^2$ across the x-axis translated up 9 units.**
4. $h(x) = 2x^2 + 2$ **Compression of $y = x^2$ narrower than the graph of $f(x) = x^2$ translated up 2 units.**
5. $g(x) = -\frac{3}{4}x^2 - \frac{1}{2}$ **Dilation of $y = x^2$ wider than the graph of $f(x) = x^2$, reflected over the x-axis, translated down $\frac{1}{2}$ unit.**
6. $h(x) = 4 - 3x^2$ **Compression of $y = x^2$ narrower than the graph of $f(x) = x^2$, reflected over the x-axis translated up 4 units.**

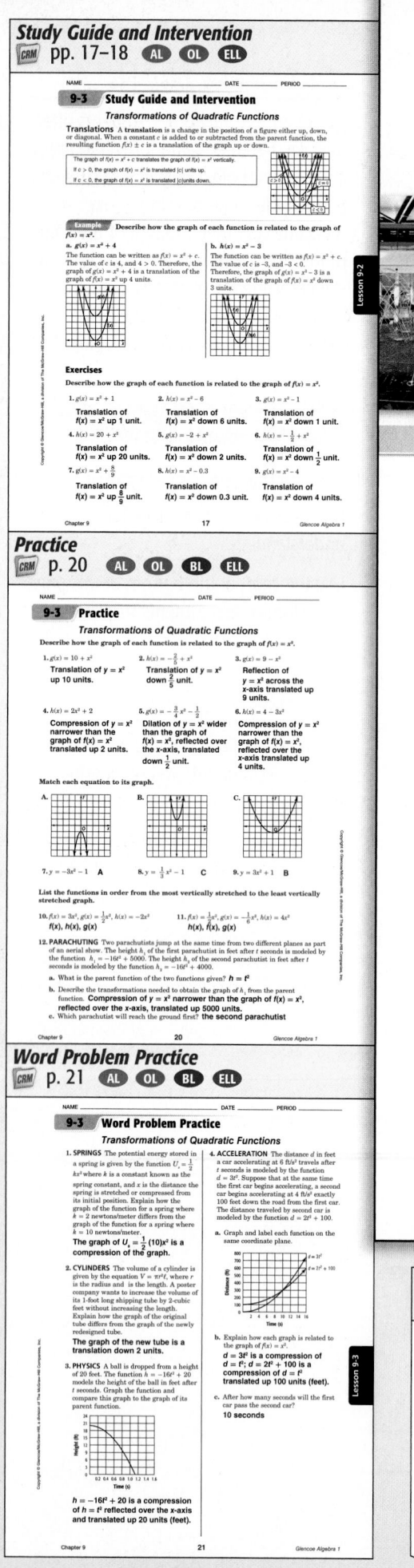

Match each equation to its graph.

A.
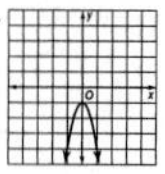
B.
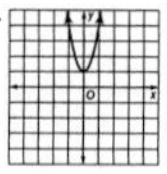
C.
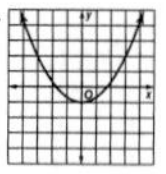

7. $y = -3x^2 - 1$ **A**
8. $y = \frac{1}{3}x^2 - 1$ **C**
9. $y = 3x^2 + 1$ **B**

List the functions in order from the most vertically stretched to the least vertically stretched graph.

10. $f(x) = 3x^2, g(x) = \frac{1}{2}x^2, h(x) = -2x^2$ **f(x), h(x), g(x)**
11. $f(x) = \frac{1}{2}x^2, g(x) = -\frac{1}{6}x^2, h(x) = 4x^2$ **h(x), f(x), g(x)**

12. **PARACHUTING** Two parachutists jump at the same time from two different planes as part of an aerial show. The height h_1 of the first parachutist in feet after t seconds is modeled by the function $h_1 = -16t^2 + 5000$. The height h_2 of the second parachutist in feet after t seconds is modeled by the function $h_2 = -16t^2 + 4000$.

a. What is the parent function of the two functions given? $h = t^2$

b. Describe the transformations needed to obtain the graph of h_1 from the parent function. **Compression of $y = x^2$ narrower than the graph of $f(x) = x^2$, reflected over the x-axis, translated up 5000 units.**

c. Which parachutist will reach the ground first? **the second parachutist**

Chapter 9 20 Glencoe Algebra 1

Word Problem Practice
CRM p. 21 AL OL BL ELL

NAME ______ DATE ______ PERIOD ______

9-3 Word Problem Practice
Transformations of Quadratic Functions

1. **SPRINGS** The potential energy stored in a spring is given by the function $U_s = \frac{1}{2}kx^2$ where k is a constant known as the spring constant, and x is the distance the spring is stretched or compressed from its initial position. Explain how the graph of the function for a spring where $k = 2$ newtons/meter differs from the graph of the function for a spring where $k = 10$ newtons/meter.
The graph of $U_s = \frac{1}{2}(10)x^2$ is a compression of the graph.

2. **CYLINDERS** The volume of a cylinder is given by the equation $V = \pi r^2 \ell$, where r is the radius and is the length. A poster company wants to increase the volume of its 1-foot long shipping tube by 2-cubic feet without increasing the length. Explain how the graph of the original tube differs from the graph of the newly redesigned tube.
The graph of the new tube is a translation down 2 units.

3. **PHYSICS** A ball is dropped from a height of 20 feet. The function $h = -16t^2 + 20$ models the height of the ball in feet after t seconds. Graph the function and compare this graph to the graph of its parent function.

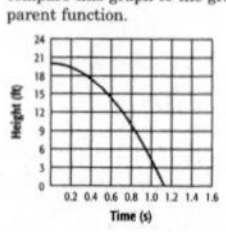

$h = -16t^2 + 20$ is a compression of $h = t^2$ reflected over the x-axis and translated up 20 units (feet).

4. **ACCELERATION** The distance d in feet a car accelerating at 6 ft/s² travels after t seconds is modeled by the function $d = 3t^2$. Suppose that at the same time the first car begins accelerating, a second car begins accelerating at 4 ft/s² exactly 100 feet down the road from the first car. The distance traveled by second car is modeled by the function $d = 2t^2 + 100$.

a. Graph and label each function on the same coordinate plane.

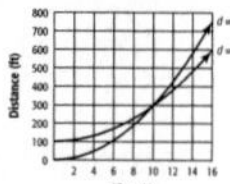

b. Explain how each graph is related to the graph of $f(x) = x^2$.
$d = 3t^2$ is a compression of $d = t^2$; $d = 2t^2 + 100$ is a compression of $d = t^2$ translated up 100 units (feet).

c. After how many seconds will the first car pass the second car?
10 seconds

Lesson 9-3

Chapter 9 21 Glencoe Algebra 1

Enrichment
CRM p. 22 OL BL

NAME ______ DATE ______ PERIOD ______

9-3 Enrichment

Translating Quadratic Graphs

When a figure is moved to a new position without undergoing any rotation, then the figure is said to have been **translated** to that position.

The graph of a quadratic equation in the form $y = (x - b)^2 + c$ is a translation of the graph of $y = x^2$.

Start with $y = x^2$.

Slide to the right 4 units.
$y = (x - 4)^2$

Then slide up 3 units.
$y = (x - 4)^2 + 3$

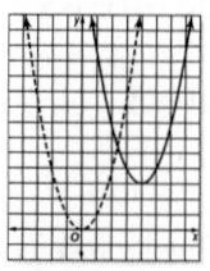

These equations have the form $y = (x - b)^2$. Graph each equation.

1. $y = (x - 1)^2$
2. $y = (x - 3)^2$
3. $y = (x + 2)^2$

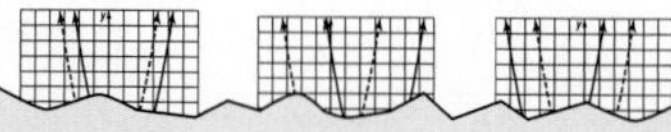

Multiple Representations In Exercise 34, students use a graphing calculator and algebraic analysis to compare graphs of related quadratic functions.

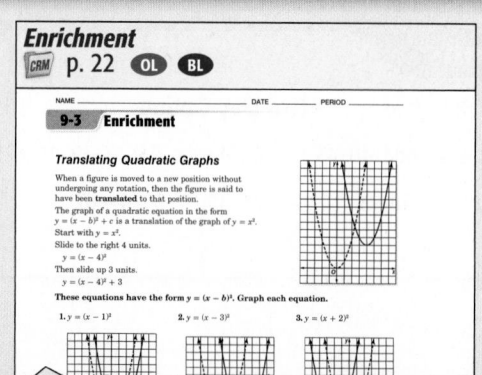

PSAE PRACTICE 8.11.14, 8.11.11, 7.11.02, 6.11.17

40. SHORT RESPONSE A plumber charges a flat fee of \$55 and \$30 for each hour of work. Write a function that represents the total charge C, in terms of the number of hours h worked. $C = 55 + 30h$

41. Which *best* describes the graph of $y = 2x^2$? D

A a line with a y-intercept of (0, 2) and an x-intercept at the origin

B a parabola with a minimum point at (0, 0) and that is twice as wide as the graph of $y = x^2$ when $y = 2$

C a parabola with a maximum point at (0, 0) and that is half as wide as the graph of $y = x^2$ when $y = 2$

D a parabola with a minimum point at (0, 0) and that is half as wide as the graph of $y = x^2$ when $y = 2$

42. Candace is 5 feet tall. If 1 inch is about 2.54 centimeters, how tall is Candace to the nearest centimeter? J

F 123 cm H 13 cm

G 26 cm J 152 cm

43. While in England, Imani spent 49.60 British pounds on a pair of jeans. If this is equivalent to \$100 in U.S. currency, how many British pounds would Imani have spent on a sweater that cost \$60? B

A 8.26 pounds

B 29.76 pounds

C 2976 pounds

D 19.84 pounds

Spiral Review

Solve each equation by graphing. (Lesson 9-2) **44–49. See Ch. 9 Answer Appendix for graphs.**

44. $x^2 + 6 = 0$ $\varnothing$ **45.** $x^2 - 10x = -24$ 4, 6 **46.** $x^2 + 5x + 4 = 0$ 4, −1

47. $2x^2 - x = 3$ $-1, \frac{3}{2}$ **48.** $2x^2 - x = 15$ $-\frac{5}{2}, 3$ **49.** $12x^2 = -11x + 15$ $-\frac{5}{3}, \frac{3}{4}$

Find the vertex, the equation of the axis of symmetry, and the y-intercept of each graph. (Lesson 9-1) **50.** (0, 4); $x = 0$; 4 **51.** (2, 2); $x = 2$; 6 **52.** (−2, 6); $x = -2$; 2

50.

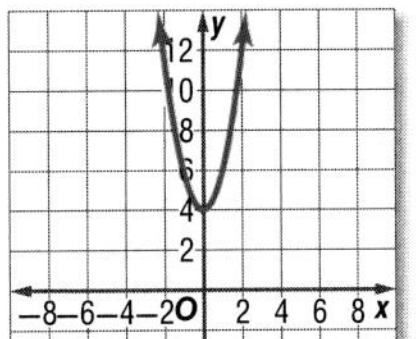

51.

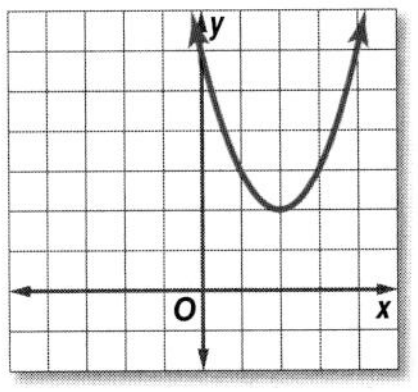

52.

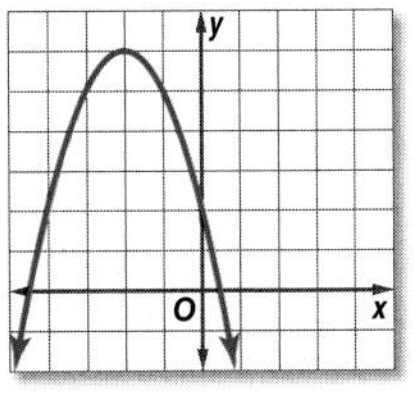

53. CLASS TRIP Mr. Wong's American History class will take taxis from their hotel in Washington, D.C., to the Lincoln Memorial. The fare is \$2.75 for the first mile and \$1.25 for each additional mile. If the distance is m miles and t taxis are needed, write an expression for the cost to transport the group. (Lesson 7-6) $2.75t + 1.25(m - 1)$

Solve each inequality. Check your solution. (Lesson 5-3)

54. $-3t + 6 \le -3$ $\{t \mid t \ge 3\}$ **55.** $59 > -5 - 8f$ $\{f \mid f > -8\}$ **56.** $-2 - \frac{d}{5} < 23$ $\{d \mid d > -125\}$

Skills Check

Determine whether each trinomial is a perfect square trinomial. If so, factor it. (Lesson 8-6)

57. $16x^2 - 24x + 9$ $(4x - 3)^2$ **58.** $9x^2 + 6x + 1$ $(3x + 1)^2$ **59.** $25x^2 - 60x + 36$ $(5x - 6)^2$

60. $x^2 - 8x + 81$ no **61.** $36x^2 - 84x + 49$ $(6x - 7)^2$ **62.** $4x^2 - 3x + 9$ no

4 ASSESS

Ticket Out the Door Write five different quadratic functions of the form $f(x) = ax^2 + c$ on pieces of paper. Give each student one. Have students tell you how the graph of each function is related to the graph of $y = x^2$ as they walk out the door.

Formative Assessment

Check for student understanding of Lessons 9-1 through 9-3.

CRM Quiz 1, p. 63

Additional Answers

29b. The rock from the 20,000-in. cliff will reach the ground first.

34a.

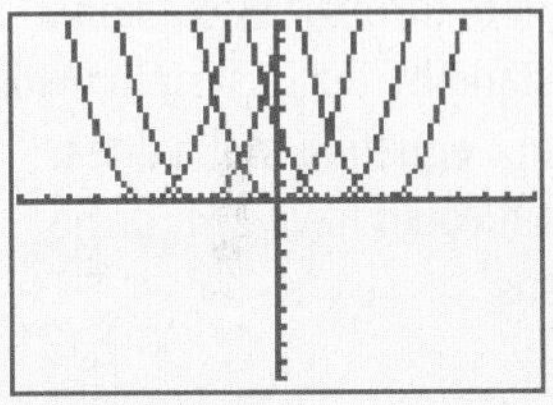

[−10, 10] scl:1 by [−10, 10] scl:1

The graphs are translated right or left depending on the value being added to or subtracted on the inside of the parentheses.

34b. The graph of $f(x) = (x + c)^2$ translates the graph of $f(x) = x^2$ horizontally. If $c > 0$, the graph of $f(x) = x^2$ is translated $|c|$ left. If $c < 0$, the graph of $f(x) = x^2$ is translated $|c|$ units right.

34c.

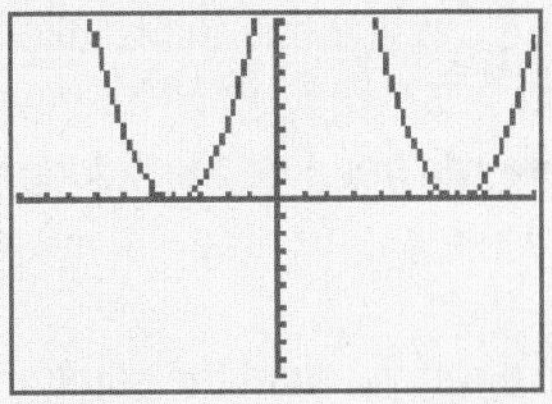

[−10, 10] scl:1 by [−10, 10] scl:1

37. Sample answer: Not all reflections over the y-axis produce the same graph. If the vertex of the original graph is not on the y-axis, the graph will not have the y-axis as its axis of symmetry and its reflection across the y-axis will be a different parabola.

Differentiated Instruction OL BL

Extension All of the functions graphed and analyzed in this lesson had their vertex located on the y-axis. Ask students to graph $y = (x - 3)^2 + 2$ and then tell how the graph is related to the graph of $y = x^2$. It is a parabola that is moved 3 units to the right and 2 units up.

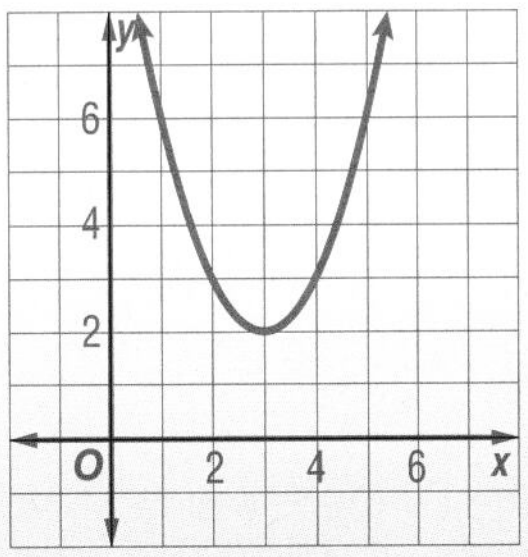

EXTEND 9-3

Lesson Notes

1 FOCUS

Objective Use a graphing calculator to solve a system of one linear and one quadratic equation.

Materials for Each Group

- TI-83/84 Plus or other graphing calculator

Teaching Tip

Remind students that a solution to a system of equations is an ordered pair that satisfies both equations. Ask them how that looks on a graph of a system. Lead them through discussion to an understanding that a system involving a quadratic equation and a linear equation could have 2, 1, or no solutions.

2 TEACH

Working in Cooperative Groups

Pair students with different abilities. Have students work through Activities 1–3 and Exercises 1–3.

Activity 1

Ask:

- Where can you find the solutions for $y = x - 3$? They all lie on the line.
- Where can you find the solutions for $y = x^2 - x - 6$? They all lie on the parabola.
- Where can you find the solutions for the system of equations: $y = x^2 - x - 6$ and $y = x - 3$? They are found where the two graphs intersect.
- How many times does the graph of the line intersect the graph of the parabola? two
- How many solutions are there to the system? two

EXTEND 9-3

Graphing Technology Lab

Systems of Linear and Quadratic Equations

IL Math Online glencoe.com
- Other Calculator Keystrokes
- Graphing Technology Personal Tutor

IL Learning Standards — **Preparation for 8.D.5 Formulate and solve nonlinear** equations and **systems** including problems involving inverse variation and exponential and logarithmic growth and decay.

You can use a graphing calculator to solve systems involving linear and quadratic equations.

ACTIVITY 1

Use a graphing calculator to solve the system of equations.

$$y = x^2 - x - 6$$
$$y = x - 3$$

Step 1 Enter each equation in the Y= list. Enter the quadratic equation as Y1 and the linear equation as Y2.

KEYSTROKES: [X,T,θ,n] [x^2] [−] [X,T,θ,n] [−] 6 [ENTER] [X,T,θ,n] [−] 3

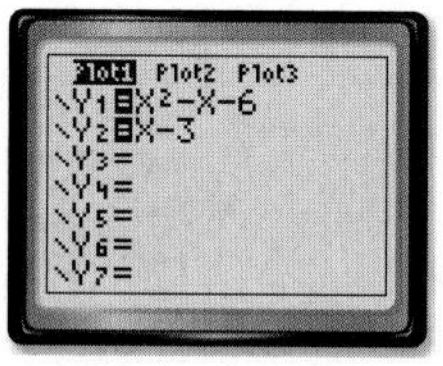

Step 2 Graph the system. **KEYSTROKE:** [Graph]

The solutions of the system are the intersection points. The graphs intersect at two points. So, there are two solutions.

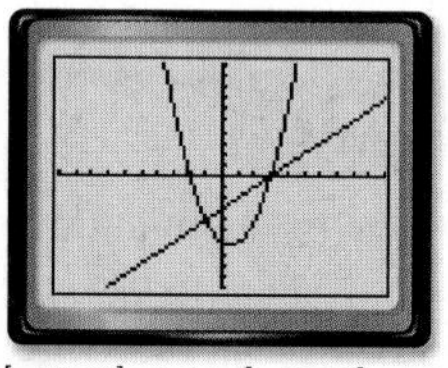

[−10, 10] scl: 1 by [−10, 10] scl: 1

Step 3 Find the first intersection of the graphs by using the CALC menu.

KEYSTROKES: [2nd] [CALC] 5

On the screen, notice the question "First Curve?" The cursor should be on the parabola. Press [ENTER].

Notice that the question changes to "Second curve?" and the cursor jumps to the line. Press [ENTER].

Use the arrow keys to move the cursor as close as possible to the intersection point in Quadrant III. Press [ENTER] again.

The intersection is the point at (−1, −4).

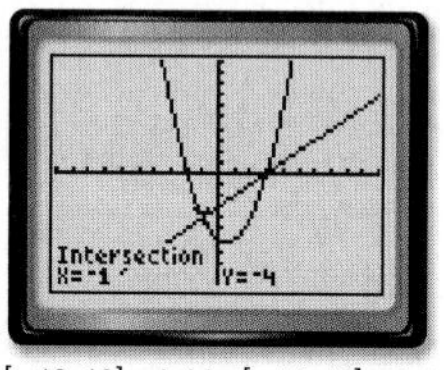

[−10, 10] scl: 1 by [−10, 10] scl: 1

Step 4 Move the cursor to the second intersection. Find the second intersection by repeating Step 3.

The intersection is at (3, 0).

Therefore, the solutions of the system of equations are (–1, –4) and (3, 0).

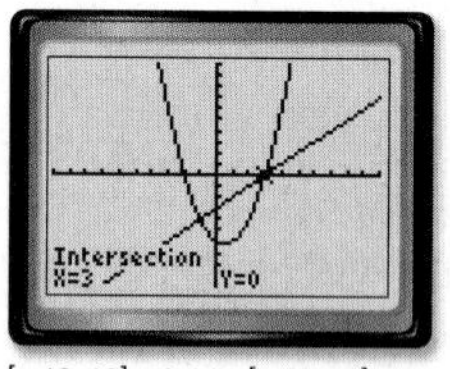

[−10, 10] scl: 1 by [−10, 10] scl: 1

ACTIVITY 2

Use a graphing calculator to solve the system of equations.

$y = x^2 - 8x + 19$
$y = 2x - 6$

Step 1 Enter each equation in the Y= list.
Enter the quadratic equation as Y1 and the linear equation as Y2.

Step 2 Graph the system.
In this case, the graphs of the equations intersect at only one point. Therefore, there is only one solution of this system of equations.

Step 3 Find the intersection of the graphs of the equations.
The intersection is the point at about (5, 4).
Thus, the solution of the system of equations is about (5, 4).

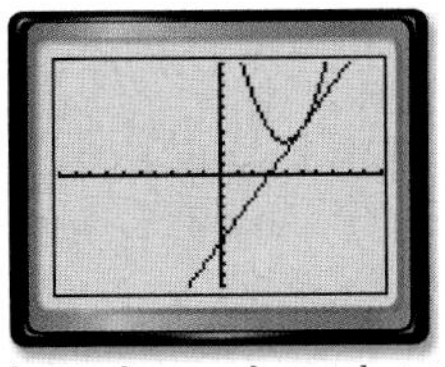

[−10, 10] scl: 1 by [−10, 10] scl: 1

ACTIVITY 3

Use a graphing calculator to solve the system of equations.

$y = -x^2 - 4x - 6$
$y = -\frac{1}{3}x + 4$

Step 1 Enter each equation in the Y= list.
Enter the quadratic equation as Y1 and the linear equation as Y2.

Step 2 Graph the system.
The graphs of the equations do not intersect. Thus, this system of equations has no solution.

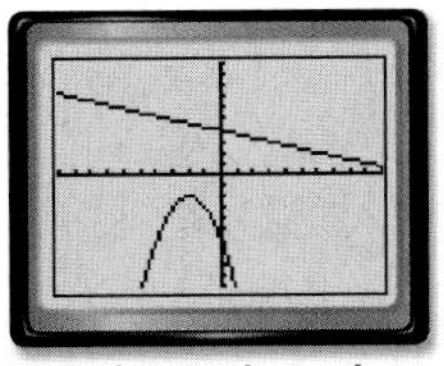

[−10, 10] scl: 1 by [−10, 10] scl: 1

Exercises

Use factoring to solve each system of equations. Then use a graphing calculator to check your solutions.

1. $y = x^2 + 7x + 12$, $y = 2x + 8$ (−1, 6), (−4, 0)
2. $y = x^2 - x - 20$, $y = 3x + 12$ (−4, 0), (8, 36)
3. $y = 3x^2 - x - 2$, $y = -2x + 2$ (1, 0), $\left(-1\frac{1}{3}, 4\frac{2}{3}\right)$

Use a graphing calculator to solve each system of equations.

4. $y = x^2$, $y = 2x$ (0, 0), (2, 4)
5. $y = -x^2 - 6x - 3$, $y = 6$ (−3, 6)
6. $y = -x^2 + 4$, $y = \frac{1}{2}x + 5$ no solution
7. $y = x^2 + 5x + 4$, $y = -x - 8$ no solution
8. $y = \frac{1}{2}x^2 - 4$, $y = 3x + 4$ (−2, −2), (8, 28)
9. $y = x^2$, $y = -2x - 1$ (−1, 1)

Extending the Concept

Ask students how many solutions are possible for a system that includes a quadratic equation and two linear equations that are not dependent. One solution or none is possible since there is, at most, one solution to a system of non-dependent linear equations.

Activity 2

Ask:

- How many times does the graph of the line intersect the graph of the parabola? one
- How many solutions are there to the system? one

Activity 3

Ask:

- How many times does the graph of the line intersect the graph of the parabola? none
- How many solutions are there to the system? none
- How many times could the graph of a line intersect the graph of a parabola? The two graphs could intersect in one point, two points, or no points.

Practice Have students complete Exercises 4–9 independently.

3 ASSESS

Formative Assessment

Use Exercises 4–9 to assess whether students are able to solve systems of equations using a graphing calculator.

From Concrete to Abstract

Have students explain what must occur for there to be no solutions to a system of a linear and a quadratic equation. For no solutions, the graph of the linear equation must be either above the vertex of the quadratic graph if the graph opens downward, or below the vertex if the graph opens upward.

Extend 9-3 Graphing Technology Lab: Systems of Linear and Quadratic Equations 551

9-4 Lesson Notes

1 FOCUS

Vertical Alignment

Before Lesson 9-4
Solve quadratic equations by using the square root property.

Lesson 9-4
Complete the square to write perfect square trinomials.
Solve quadratic equations by competing the square.

After Lesson 9-4
Solve quadratic equations using the Quadratic Formula.

2 TEACH

Scaffolding Questions

Have students read the *Why?* section of the lesson.

Ask:

- Look at the equation. Is 25 a perfect square? yes
- Is $-16t^2 + 20t + 12$ a perfect square? no
- Can you solve the equation by taking the square root of each side of the equation? no

TEACH with TECH

INTERACTIVE WHITEBOARD As you teach students to complete the square, save each example as a notes page. Then send your notes to students.

9-4 Solving Quadratic Equations by Completing the Square

Then
You solved quadratic equations by using the square root property. (Lesson 8-6)

Now
- Complete the square to write perfect square trinomials.
- Solve quadratic equations by completing the square.

IL Learning Standards
8.D.4 Formulate and solve linear and **quadratic equations** and linear inequalities **algebraically** and investigate nonlinear inequalities using graphs, tables, calculators and computers.

New Vocabulary
completing the square

IL Math Online
glencoe.com
- Extra Examples
- Personal Tutor
- Self-Check Quiz
- Homework Help
- Math in Motion

Why?

In competitions, skateboarders may launch themselves from a half pipe into the air to perform tricks. The equation $h = -16t^2 + 20t + 12$ can be used to model their height, in feet, after t seconds.

To find how long a skateboarder is in the air if he is 25 feet above the half pipe, you can solve $25 = -16t^2 + 20t + 12$ by using a method called completing the square.

Complete the Square In Lesson 8-6, you solved equations by taking the square root of each side. This method worked only because the expression on the left-hand side was a perfect square. In perfect square trinomials in which the leading coefficient is 1, there is a relationship between the coefficient of the x-term and the constant term.

$$(x + 5)^2 = x^2 + 2(5)(x) + 5^2$$
$$= x^2 + 10x + 25$$

Notice that $\left(\frac{10}{2}\right)^2 = 25$. To get the constant term, divide the coefficient of the x-term by 2 and square the result. Any quadratic expression in the form $x^2 + bx$ can be made into a perfect square by using a method called **completing the square**.

Key Concept — Completing the Square

For Your FOLDABLE

Words To complete the square for any quadratic expression of the form $x^2 + bx$, follow the steps below.

Step 1 Find one half of b, the coefficient of x.

Step 2 Square the result in Step 1.

Step 3 Add the result of Step 2 to $x^2 + bx$.

Symbols $x^2 + bx + \left(\frac{b}{2}\right)^2 = \left(x + \frac{b}{2}\right)^2$

Math *in Motion*, Animation glencoe.com

EXAMPLE 1 Complete the Square

Find the value of c that makes $x^2 + 4x + c$ a perfect square trinomial.

Method 1 Use algebra tiles.

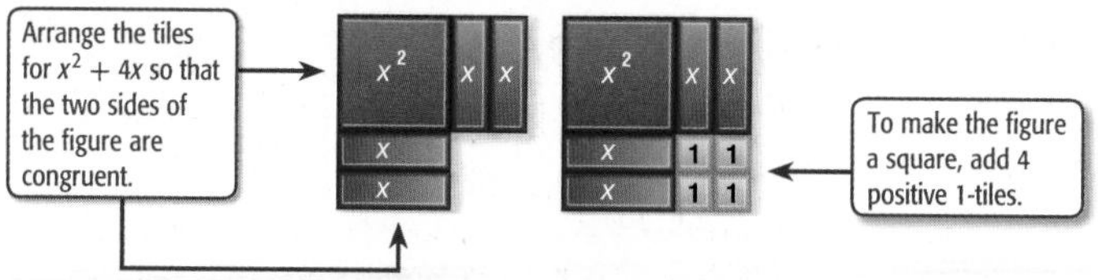

Lesson 9-4 Resources

Resource	Approaching-Level	On-Level	Beyond-Level	English Learners
Teacher Edition	• Differentiated Instruction, p. 554	• Differentiated Instruction, p. 554	• Differentiated Instruction, p. 557	
Chapter Resource Masters	• Study Guide and Intervention, pp. 23–24 • Skills Practice, p. 25 • Practice, p. 26 • Word Problem Practice, p. 27	• Study Guide and Intervention, pp. 23–24 • Skills Practice, p. 25 • Practice, p. 26 • Word Problem Practice, p. 27 • Enrichment, p. 28	• Practice, p. 26 • Word Problem Practice, p. 27 • Enrichment, p. 28	• Study Guide and Intervention, pp. 23–24 • Skills Practice, p. 25 • Practice, p. 26 • Word Problem Practice, p. 27
Transparencies	• 5-Minute Check Transparency 9-4	• 5-Minute Check Transparency 9-4	• 5-Minute Check Transparency 9-4	• 5-Minute Check Transparency 9-4
Other	• Study Notebook • Teaching Algebra with Manipulatives	• Study Notebook • Teaching Algebra with Manipulatives	• Study Notebook	• Study Notebook • Teaching Algebra with Manipulatives

StudyTip

Algorithms An algorithm is a series of steps for carrying out a procedure or solving a problem.

Method 2 Use complete the square algorithm.

Step 1 Find $\frac{1}{2}$ of 4. $\frac{4}{2} = 2$

Step 2 Square the result in Step 1. $2^2 = 4$

Step 3 Add the result of Step 2 to $x^2 + 4x$. $x^2 + 4x + 4$

Thus, $c = 4$. Notice that $x^2 + 4x + 4 = (x + 2)^2$.

Check Your Progress

1. Find the value of c that makes $r^2 - 8r + c$ a perfect square trinomial. 16

Personal Tutor glencoe.com

Solve Equations by Completing the Square You can complete the square to solve quadratic equations. First, you must isolate the x^2- and bx-terms.

EXAMPLE 2 Solve an Equation by Completing the Square

Solve $x^2 - 6x + 12 = 19$ by completing the square.

$x^2 - 6x + 12 = 19$	Original equation
$x^2 - 6x = 7$	Subtract 12 from each side.
$x^2 - 6x + 9 = 7 + 9$	Since $\left(\frac{-6}{2}\right)^2 = 9$, add 9 to each side.
$(x - 3)^2 = 16$	Factor $x^2 - 6x + 9$.
$x - 3 = \pm 4$	Take the square root of each side.
$x = 3 \pm 4$	Add 3 to each side.
$x = 3 + 4$ or $x = 3 - 4$	Separate the solutions.
$= 7$ $= -1$	The solutions are 7 and -1.

Check Your Progress

2. Solve $x^2 - 12x + 3 = 8$ by completing the square. about -0.4, 12.4

Personal Tutor glencoe.com

To solve a quadratic equation in which the leading coefficient is not 1, divide each term by the coefficient. Then isolate the x^2- and x-terms and complete the square.

Watch Out!

Leading Coefficient Remember that the leading coefficient has to be 1 before you can complete the square.

EXAMPLE 3 Equation with $a \neq 1$

Solve $-2x^2 + 8x - 18 = 0$ by completing the square.

$-2x^2 + 8x - 18 = 0$	Original equation
$\frac{-2x^2 + 8x - 18}{-2} = \frac{0}{-2}$	Divide each side by -2.
$x^2 - 4x + 9 = 0$	Simplify.
$x^2 - 4x = -9$	Subtract 9 from each side.
$x^2 - 4x + 4 = -9 + 4$	Since $\left(\frac{-4}{2}\right)^2 = 4$, add 4 to each side.
$(x - 2)^2 = -5$	Factor $x^2 - 4x + 4$.

No real number has a negative square. So, this equation has no real solutions.

Check Your Progress

3. Solve $3x^2 - 9x - 3 = 21$ by completing the square. about -1.7, 4.7

Personal Tutor glencoe.com

Complete the Square

Example 1 shows how to make any binomial of the form $x^2 + bx$ a perfect square by completing the square.

Formative Assessment

Use Check Your Progress exercises after each example to determine students' understanding of concepts.

Additional Example

1. Find the value of c that makes $x^2 - 12x + c$ a perfect square trinomial. 36

Additional Examples also in Interactive Classroom PowerPoint® Presentations

IWB INTERACTIVE WHITEBOARD READY

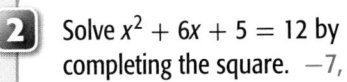

Solve by Completing the Square

Example 2 shows how to solve a quadratic equation by completing the square. **Example 3** shows how to solve a quadratic equation in which a does not equal 1. **Example 4** shows how to use completing the square to solve real-world problems.

Tips for New Teachers

Reasoning Students should always check their solutions by graphing the related function or by substituting the solutions into the original equation. For instance, tell students that in Example 2, substituting 7 and -1 into $x^2 - 6x + 12$ should produce 19.

Additional Examples

2. Solve $x^2 + 6x + 5 = 12$ by completing the square. -7, 1

3. Solve $-2x^2 + 36x - 10 = 24$ by completing the square. 17, 1

Additional Example

4 **CANOEING** Suppose the rate of flow of an 80-foot-wide river is given by the equation $r = -0.01x^2 + 0.8x$, where r is the rate in miles per hour and x is the distance from the shore in feet. Joacquim does not want to paddle his canoe against a current that is faster than 5 miles per hour. At what distance from the river bank must he paddle in order to avoid a current of 5 miles per hour? up to 7 ft from either bank **Note:** The solutions of the equation are about 7 feet and about 73 feet. Since the river is 80 feet wide, $80 - 73 = 7$. Both ranges are within 7 feet of one bank or the other.

Tips for New Teachers

Student Misconceptions Tell students not to throw out negative solutions to real-world problems. Remind them that they must first examine the problem to see if the solution fits the situation.

3 PRACTICE

Formative Assessment

Use Exercises 1–9 to check for understanding.

Use the chart on the bottom of the next page to customize assignments for your students.

Real-World Link

The oldest public high school rivalry takes place between Wellesley High School and Needham Heights High School in Massachusetts. The first football game between them took place on Thanksgiving morning in 1882 in Needham.

Source: USA Football

Real-World EXAMPLE 4 Solve a Problem by Completing the Square

JERSEYS The senior class at Bay High School buys jerseys to wear to the football games. The cost of the jerseys can be modeled by the equation $C = 0.1x^2 + 2.4x + 25$, where C is the amount it costs to buy x jerseys. How many jerseys can they purchase for $430?

The seniors have $430, so set the equation equal to 430 and complete the square.

$0.1x^2 + 2.4x + 25 = 430$	Original equation
$\frac{0.1x^2 + 2.4x + 25}{0.1} = \frac{430}{0.1}$	Divide each side by 0.1.
$x^2 + 24x + 250 = 4300$	Simplify.
$x^2 + 24x + 250 - 250 = 4300 - 250$	Subtract 250 from each side.
$x^2 + 24x = 4050$	Simplify.
$x^2 + 24x + 144 = 4050 + 144$	Since $\left(\frac{24}{2}\right)^2 = 144$, add 144 to each side.
$x^2 + 24x + 144 = 4194$	Simplify.
$(x + 12)^2 = 4194$	Factor $x^2 + 24x + 144$.
$x + 12 = \pm\sqrt{4194}$	Take the square root of each side.
$x = -12 \pm\sqrt{4194}$	Subtract 12 from each side.

Use a calculator to approximate each value of x.

$x = -12 + \sqrt{4194}$ or $x = -12 - \sqrt{4194}$ Separate the solutions.
≈ 52.7 ≈ -76.7 Evaluate.

Since you cannot buy a negative number of jerseys, the negative solution is not reasonable. The seniors can afford to buy 52 jerseys.

Check Your Progress

4. If the senior class were able to raise $620, how many jerseys could they buy? 66 jerseys

Personal Tutor glencoe.com

Check Your Understanding

Example 1 pp. 552–553

Find the value of c that makes each trinomial a perfect square.

1. $x^2 - 18x + c$ 81
2. $x^2 + 22x + c$ 121
3. $x^2 + 9x + c$ $\frac{81}{4}$
4. $x^2 - 7x + c$ $\frac{49}{4}$

Examples 2 and 3 p. 553

Solve each equation by completing the square. Round to the nearest tenth if necessary.

5. $x^2 + 4x = 6$ −5.2, 1.2
6. $x^2 - 8x = -9$ 1.4, 6.6
7. $4x^2 + 9x - 1 = 0$ −2.4, 0.1
8. $-2x^2 + 10x + 22 = 4$ −1.4, 6.4

Example 4 p. 554

9. CONSTRUCTION Collin is building a deck on the back of his family's house. He has enough lumber for the deck to be 144 square feet. The length should be 10 feet more than its width. What should the dimensions of the deck be? 8 ft by 18 ft

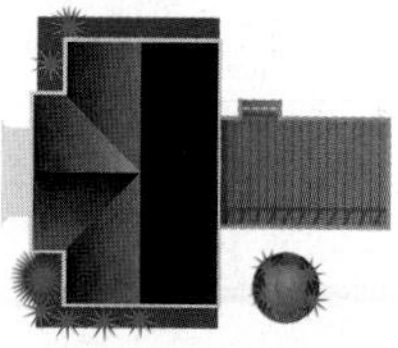

Differentiated Instruction AL OL

Kinesthetic Learners Some students may benefit from using algebra tiles to complete the square when solving quadratic equations like those in Examples 2 and 3. Have students use an equation mat. Remind them to add or remove the same number of tiles to or from each side of the mat.

Practice and Problem Solving

● = **Step-by-Step Solutions** begin on page R12.
Extra Practice begins on page 815.

Example 1 pp. 552–553

Find the value of c that makes each trinomial a perfect square.

10. $x^2 + 26x + c$ 169
11. $x^2 - 24x + c$ 144
12. $x^2 - 19x + c$ $\frac{361}{4}$
13. $x^2 + 17x + c$ $\frac{289}{4}$
14. $x^2 + 5x + c$ $\frac{25}{4}$
15. $x^2 - 13x + c$ $\frac{169}{4}$
16. $x^2 - 22x + c$ 121
17. $x^2 - 15x + c$ $\frac{225}{4}$
18. $x^2 + 24x + c$ 144

Examples 2 and 3 p. 553

Solve each equation by completing the square. Round to the nearest tenth if necessary.

19. $x^2 + 6x - 16 = 0$ −8, 2
20. $x^2 - 2x - 14 = 0$ −2.9, 4.9
21. $x^2 - 8x - 1 = 8$ −1, 9
22. $x^2 + 3x + 21 = 22$ −3.3, 0.3
23. $x^2 - 11x + 3 = 5$ −0.2, 11.2
24. $5x^2 - 10x = 23$ −1.4, 3.4
25. $2x^2 - 2x + 7 = 5$ ∅
26. $3x^2 + 12x + 81 = 15$ ∅
27. $4x^2 + 6x = 12$ −2.6, 1.1
28. $4x^2 + 5 = 10x$ 0.7, 1.8
29. $-2x^2 + 10x = -14$ −1.1, 6.1
30. $-3x^2 - 12 = 14x$ −3.5, −1.1

Example 4 p. 554

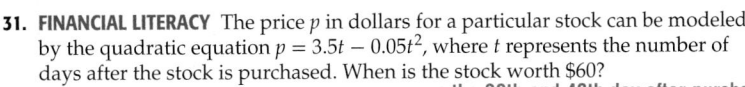

Real-World Link

According to a Junior Achievement survey, 25% of 13- and 14-year-olds own stocks in their own name. Most got their shares as gifts.

Source: *Money Magazine*

31. **FINANCIAL LITERACY** The price p in dollars for a particular stock can be modeled by the quadratic equation $p = 3.5t - 0.05t^2$, where t represents the number of days after the stock is purchased. When is the stock worth \$60? on the 30th and 40th day after purchase

GEOMETRY Find the value of x for each figure. Round to the nearest tenth if necessary.

32. $A = 45 \text{ in}^2$ 6.3

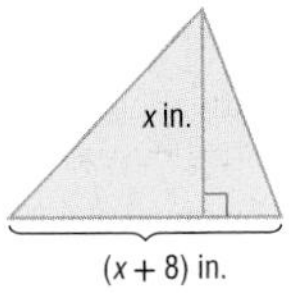

33. $A = 110 \text{ ft}^2$ 5.3

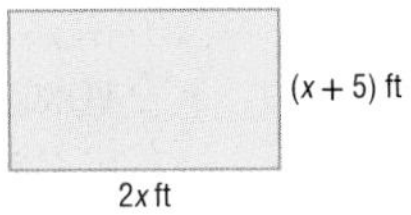

34. **NUMBER THEORY** The product of two consecutive even integers is 224. Find the integers. 14 and 16; −14 and −16

35. **NUMBER THEORY** The product of two consecutive negative odd integers is 483. Find the integers. −21 and −23

36. **GEOMETRY** Find the area of the triangle below. 216 m²

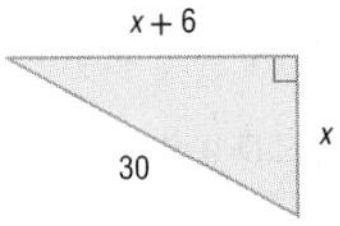

B **Solve each equation by completing the square. Round to the nearest tenth if necessary.**

37. $0.2x^2 - 0.2x - 0.4 = 0$ −1, 2
38. $0.5x^2 = 2x - 0.3$ 0.2, 3.8
39. $2x^2 - \frac{11}{5}x = -\frac{3}{10}$ 0.2, 0.9
40. $\frac{2}{3}x^2 - \frac{4}{3}x = \frac{5}{6}$ −0.5, 2.5
41. $\frac{1}{4}x^2 + 2x = \frac{3}{8}$ −8.2, 0.2
42. $\frac{2}{5}x^2 + 2x = \frac{1}{5}$ −5.1, 0.1

Watch Out!

Preventing Errors For Exercises 19–30, remind students that the amount that they add to one side of the equation to complete the square must also be added to the other side of the equation.

Formula For Exercises 32 and 36, students will need to know the formula for the area of a triangle, $A = \frac{1}{2}bh$.

Focus on Mathematical Content

Irrational Solutions Completing the square to solve a quadratic equation does not mean that the solutions will be integers. If the equation already has a nonzero constant term, it is likely that after completing the square, the constant will not be a perfect square, and the solutions will be irrational.

Differentiated Homework Options

Level	Assignment	Two-Day Option	
AL Basic	10–36, 49–81	11–35 odd, 53–56	10–36 even, 49–52, 57–81
OL Core	11–43 odd, 44–47, 49–81	10–36, 53–56	37–47, 49–52, 57–81
BL Advanced	37–75, (optional: 76–81)		

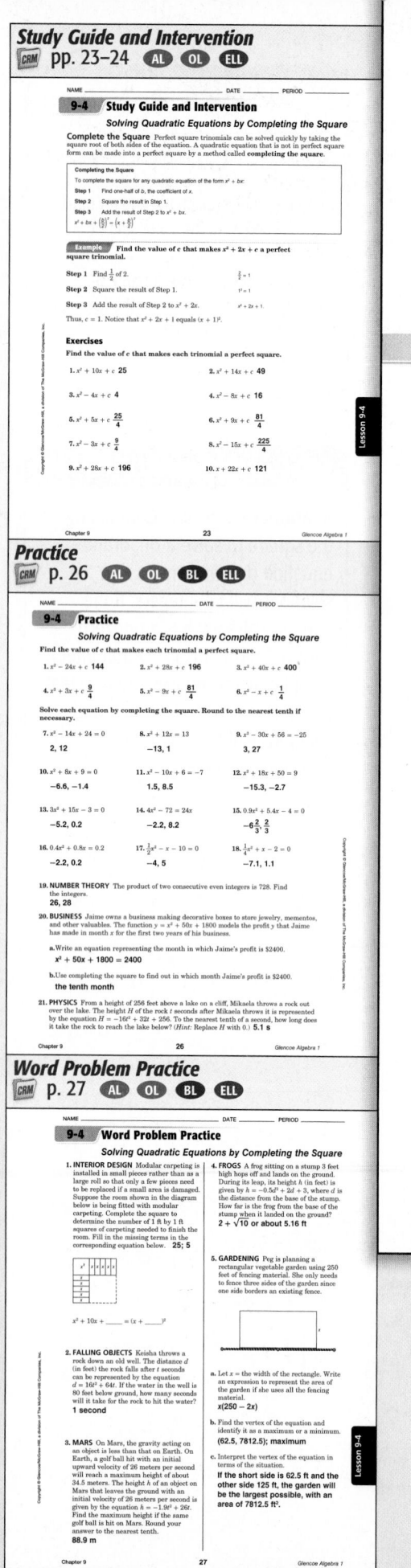

Study Guide and Intervention
CRM pp. 23–24 AL OL ELL

NAME ________ DATE ________ PERIOD ________

9-4 Study Guide and Intervention

Solving Quadratic Equations by Completing the Square

Complete the Square Perfect square trinomials can be solved quickly by taking the square root of both sides of the equation. A quadratic equation that is not in perfect square form can be made into a perfect square by a method called **completing the square**.

Completing the Square

To complete the square for any quadratic equation of the form $x^2 + bx$:

Step 1 Find one-half of b, the coefficient of x.

Step 2 Square the result in Step 1.

Step 3 Add the result of Step 2 to $x^2 + bx$.

$x^2 + bx + \left(\frac{b}{2}\right)^2 = \left(x + \frac{b}{2}\right)^2$

Example **Find the value of c that makes $x^2 + 2x + c$ a perfect square trinomial.**

Step 1 Find $\frac{1}{2}$ of 2. $\frac{2}{2} = 1$

Step 2 Square the result of Step 1. $1^2 = 1$

Step 3 Add the result of Step 2 to $x^2 + 2x$. $x^2 + 2x + 1$

Thus, $c = 1$. Notice that $x^2 + 2x + 1$ equals $(x + 1)^2$.

Exercises

Find the value of c that makes each trinomial a perfect square.

1. $x^2 + 10x + c$ **25**
2. $x^2 + 14x + c$ **49**
3. $x^2 - 4x + c$ **4**
4. $x^2 - 8x + c$ **16**
5. $x^2 + 5x + c$ $\frac{25}{4}$
6. $x^2 + 9x + c$ $\frac{81}{4}$
7. $x^2 - 3x + c$ $\frac{9}{4}$
8. $x^2 - 15x + c$ $\frac{225}{4}$
9. $x^2 + 28x + c$ **196**
10. $x + 22x + c$ **121**

Lesson 9-4

Chapter 9 23 Glencoe Algebra 1

Practice
CRM p. 26 AL OL BL ELL

NAME ________ DATE ________ PERIOD ________

9-4 Practice

Solving Quadratic Equations by Completing the Square

Find the value of c that makes each trinomial a perfect square.

1. $x^2 - 24x + c$ **144**
2. $x^2 + 28x + c$ **196**
3. $x^2 + 40x + c$ **400**
4. $x^2 + 3x + c$ $\frac{9}{4}$
5. $x^2 - 9x + c$ $\frac{81}{4}$
6. $x^2 - x + c$ $\frac{1}{4}$

Solve each equation by completing the square. Round to the nearest tenth if necessary.

7. $x^2 - 14x + 24 = 0$ **2, 12**
8. $x^2 + 12x = 13$ **−13, 1**
9. $x^2 - 30x + 56 = -25$ **3, 27**
10. $x^2 + 8x + 9 = 0$ **−6.6, −1.4**
11. $x^2 - 10x + 6 = -7$ **1.5, 8.5**
12. $x^2 + 18x + 50 = 9$ **−15.3, −2.7**
13. $3x^2 + 15x - 3 = 0$ **−5.2, 0.2**
14. $4x^2 - 72 = 24x$ **−2.2, 8.2**
15. $0.9x^2 + 5.4x - 4 = 0$ $-6\frac{2}{3}, \frac{2}{3}$
16. $0.4x^2 + 0.8x = 0.2$ **−2.2, 0.2**
17. $\frac{1}{2}x^2 - x - 10 = 0$ **−4, 5**
18. $\frac{1}{4}x^2 + x - 2 = 0$ **−7.1, 1.1**

19. **NUMBER THEORY** The product of two consecutive even integers is 728. Find the integers. **26, 28**

20. **BUSINESS** Jaime owns a business making decorative boxes to store jewelry, mementos, and other valuables. The function $y = x^2 + 50x + 1800$ models the profit y that Jaime has made in month x for the first two years of his business.

a. Write an equation representing the month in which Jaime's profit is $2400. **$x^2 + 50x + 1800 = 2400$**

b. Use completing the square to find out in which month Jaime's profit is $2400. **the tenth month**

21. **PHYSICS** From a height of 256 feet above a lake on a cliff, Mikaela throws a rock out over the lake. The height H of the rock t seconds after Mikaela throws it is represented by the equation $H = -16t^2 + 32t + 256$. To the nearest tenth of a second, how long does it take the rock to reach the lake below? (*Hint:* Replace H with 0.) **5.1 s**

Chapter 9 26 Glencoe Algebra 1

Word Problem Practice
CRM p. 27 AL OL BL ELL

NAME ________ DATE ________ PERIOD ________

9-4 Word Problem Practice

Solving Quadratic Equations by Completing the Square

1. **INTERIOR DESIGN** Modular carpeting is installed in small pieces rather than as a large roll so that only a few pieces need to be replaced if a small area is damaged. Suppose the room shown in the diagram below is being fitted with modular carpeting. Complete the square to determine the number of 1 ft by 1 ft squares of carpeting needed to finish the room. Fill in the missing terms in the corresponding equation below. **25; 5**

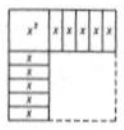

$x^2 + 10x +$ ____ $= (x +$ ____$)^2$

2. **FALLING OBJECTS** Keisha throws a rock down an old well. The distance d (in feet) the rock falls after t seconds can be represented by the equation $d = 16t^2 + 64t$. If the water in the well is 80 feet below ground, how many seconds will it take for the rock to hit the water? **1 second**

3. **MARS** On Mars, the gravity acting on an object is less than that on Earth. On Earth, a golf ball hit with an initial upward velocity of 26 meters per second will reach a maximum height of about 34.5 meters. The height h of an object on Mars that leaves the ground with an initial velocity of 26 meters per second is given by the equation $h = -1.9t^2 + 26t$. Find the maximum height if the same golf ball is hit on Mars. Round your answer to the nearest tenth. **88.9 m**

4. **FROGS** A frog sitting on a stump 3 feet high hops off and lands on the ground. During its leap, its height h (in feet) is given by $h = -0.5d^2 + 2d + 3$, where d is the distance from the base of the stump. How far is the frog from the base of the stump when it landed on the ground? **$2 + \sqrt{10}$ or about 5.16 ft**

5. **GARDENING** Peg is planning a rectangular vegetable garden using 250 feet of fencing material. She only needs to fence three sides of the garden since one side borders an existing fence.

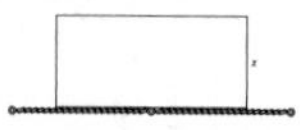

a. Let x = the width of the rectangle. Write an expression to represent the area of the garden if she uses all the fencing material. **$x(250 - 2x)$**

b. Find the vertex of the equation and identify it as a maximum or a minimum. **(62.5, 7812.5); maximum**

c. Interpret the vertex of the equation in terms of the situation. **If the short side is 62.5 ft and the other side 125 ft, the garden will be the largest possible, with an area of 7812.5 ft².**

Lesson 9-4

Chapter 9 27 Glencoe Algebra 1

Real-World Link

The National Aeronautics and Space Administration (NASA) began operations on October 1, 1958. NASA employs about 8000 people and has an annual budget of $100 million.

Source: NASA

43c. Sample answer: Yes; the acceleration due to gravity is much greater on Earth than on Mars, so the time to reach the ground should be much less.

47c. If $b^2 - 4ac$ is negative, the equation has no solutions. If $b^2 - 4ac$ is zero, the equation has one solution. If $b^2 - 4ac$ is positive, the equation has 2 solutions.

47d. 0 because $b^2 - 4ac$ is negative. The equation has no real solutions because taking the square root of a negative number does not produce a real number.

43. **ASTRONOMY** The height of an object t seconds after it is dropped is given by the equation $h = -\frac{1}{2}gt^2 + h_0$, where h_0 is the initial height and g is the acceleration due to gravity. The acceleration due to gravity near the surface of Mars is 3.73 m/s², while on Earth it is 9.8 m/s². Suppose an object is dropped from an initial height of 120 meters above the surface of each planet.
   a. On which planet would the object reach the ground first? **Earth**
   b. How long would it take the object to reach the ground on each planet? Round each answer to the nearest tenth. **Earth: 4.9 seconds, Mars: 8.0 seconds**
   c. Do the times that it takes the object to reach the ground seem reasonable? Explain your reasoning.

44. Find all values of c that make $x^2 + cx + 100$ a perfect square trinomial. **−20 and 20**

45. Find all values of c that make $x^2 + cx + 225$ a perfect square trinomial. **−30 and 30**

46. **PAINTING** Before she begins painting a picture, Donna stretches her canvas over a wood frame. The frame has a length of 60 inches and a width of 4 inches. She has enough canvas to cover 480 square inches. Donna decides to increase the dimensions of the frame. If the increase in the length is 10 times the increase in the width, what will the dimensions of the frame be? **6 in. by 80 in.**

47. **MULTIPLE REPRESENTATIONS** In this problem, you will investigate a property of quadratic equations.
   a. **TABULAR** Copy the table shown and complete the second column.
   b. **ALGEBRAIC** Set each trinomial equal to zero, and solve the equation by completing the square. Complete the last column of the table with the number of roots of each equation.

Trinomial	$b^2 - 4ac$	Number of Roots
$x^2 - 8x + 16$	0	1
$2x^2 - 11x + 3$	97	2
$3x^2 + 6x + 9$	−72	0
$x^2 - 2x + 7$	−24	0
$x^2 + 10x + 25$	0	1
$x^2 + 3x - 12$	57	2

   c. **VERBAL** Compare the number of roots of each equation to the result in the $b^2 - 4ac$ column. Is there a relationship between these values? If so, describe it.
   d. **ANALYTICAL** Predict how many solutions $2x^2 - 9x + 15 = 0$ will have. Verify your prediction by solving the equation.

H.O.T. Problems

Use Higher-Order Thinking Skills **48–52. See margin.**

48. **CHALLENGE** Given $y = ax^2 + bx + c$ with $a \neq 0$, derive the equation for the axis of symmetry by completing the square and rewriting the equation in the form $y = a(x - h)^2 + k$.

49. **REASONING** Determine the number of solutions $x^2 + bx = c$ has if $c < -\left(\frac{b}{2}\right)^2$. Explain.

50. **WHICH ONE DOESN'T BELONG?** Identify the expression that does not belong with the other three. Explain your reasoning.

$n^2 - n + \frac{1}{4}$	$n^2 + n + \frac{1}{4}$	$n^2 - \frac{2}{3}n + \frac{1}{9}$	$n^2 + \frac{1}{3}n + \frac{1}{9}$

51. **OPEN ENDED** Write a quadratic equation for which the only solution is 4.

52. **WRITING IN MATH** Compare and contrast the following strategies for solving $x^2 - 5x - 7 = 0$: completing the square, graphing, and factoring.

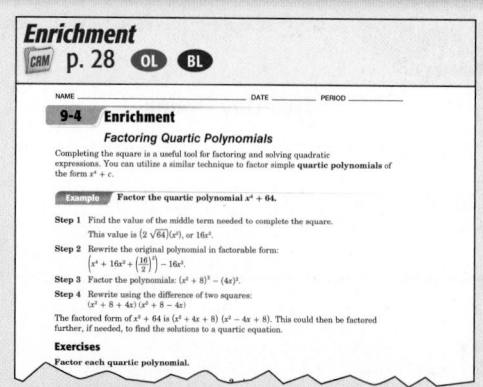

Enrichment
CRM p. 28 OL BL

NAME ________ DATE ________ PERIOD ________

9-4 Enrichment

Factoring Quartic Polynomials

Completing the square is a useful tool for factoring and solving quadratic expressions. You can utilize a similar technique to factor simple **quartic polynomials** of the form $x^4 + c$.

Example **Factor the quartic polynomial $x^4 + 64$.**

Step 1 Find the value of the middle term needed to complete the square. This value is $(2\sqrt{64})(x^2)$, or $16x^2$.

Step 2 Rewrite the original polynomial in factorable form: $\left(x^4 + 16x^2 + \left(\frac{16}{2}\right)^2\right) - 16x^2$.

Step 3 Factor the polynomials: $(x^2 + 8)^2 - (4x)^2$.

Step 4 Rewrite using the difference of two squares: $(x^2 + 8 + 4x)(x^2 + 8 - 4x)$

The factored form of $x^2 + 64$ is $(x^2 + 4x + 8)(x^2 - 4x + 8)$. This could then be factored further, if needed, to find the solutions to a quartic equation.

Exercises

Factor each quartic polynomial.

Multiple Representations In Exercise 47, students use information organized in a table, algebraic equations, and analysis to relate the value of the discriminant in a quadratic equation with the number of real roots of the equation.

PSAE PRACTICE 7.11.03, 10.11.07, 8.11.14, 8.11.16

53. The length of a rectangle is 3 times its width. The area of the rectangle is 75 square feet. Find the length of the rectangle in feet. **B**

A 25 B 15 C 10 D 5

54. PROBABILITY At a festival, winners of a game draw a token for a prize. There is one token for each prize. The prizes include 9 movie passes, 8 stuffed animals, 5 hats, 10 jump ropes, and 4 glow necklaces. What is the probability that the first person to draw a token will win a movie pass? **H**

F $\frac{9}{61}$ G $\frac{1}{9}$ H $\frac{1}{4}$ J $\frac{1}{36}$

55. GRIDDED RESPONSE The population of a town can be modeled by $P = 22{,}000 + 125t$, where P represents the population and t represents the number of years from 2000. How many years after 2000 will the population be 26,000? **32**

56. Percy delivers pizzas for Pizza King. He is paid \$6 an hour plus \$2.50 for each pizza he delivers. Percy earned \$280 last week. If he worked a total of 30 hours, how many pizzas did he deliver? **C**

A 250 pizzas
B 184 pizzas
C 40 pizzas
D 34 pizzas

Spiral Review

Describe how the graph of each function is related to the graph of $f(x) = x^2$. (Lesson 9-3) **57–62. See Ch. 9 Answer Appendix.**

57. $g(x) = -12 + x^2$ **58.** $h(x) = 2 - x^2$ **59.** $g(x) = 2x^2 + 5$

60. $h(x) = -6 + \frac{2}{3}x^2$ **61.** $g(x) = 6 + \frac{4}{3}x^2$ **62.** $h(x) = -1 - \frac{3}{2}x^2$

63. RIDES A popular amusement park ride whisks riders to the top of a 250-foot tower and drops them. A function for the height of a rider is $h = -16t^2 + 250$, where h is the height and t is the time in seconds. The ride stops the descent of the rider 40 feet above the ground. Write an equation that models the drop of the rider. How long does it take to fall from 250 feet to 40 feet? (Lesson 9-2) **$40 = -16t^2 + 250$; about 3.6 s**

Simplify. Assume that no denominator is equal to zero. (Lesson 7-2)

64. $\frac{a^6}{a^3}$ a^3 **65.** $\frac{4^7}{4^5}$ 16 **66.** $\frac{c^3d^4}{cd^7}$ $\frac{c^2}{d^3}$

67. $\left(\frac{4h^{-2}g}{2g^5}\right)^0$ 1 **68.** $\frac{5q^{-2}t^6}{10q^2t^{-4}}$ $\frac{t^{10}}{2q^4}$ **69.** $b^3(m^{-3})(b^{-6})$ $\frac{1}{m^3b^3}$

Solve each open sentence. (Lesson 5-5)

70. $|y - 2| > 7$ $\{y \mid y > 9 \text{ or } y < -5\}$ **71.** $|z + 5| < 3$ $\{z \mid -8 < z < -2\}$ **72.** $|2b + 7| \leq -6$ $\varnothing$

73. $|3 - 2y| \geq 8$ $\{y \mid y \geq 5.5 \text{ or } y \leq -2.5\}$ **74.** $|9 - 4m| < -1$ $\varnothing$ **75.** $|5c - 2| \leq 13$ $\{c \mid -2.2 \leq c \leq 3\}$

Skills Check

Evaluate $\sqrt{b^2 - 4ac}$ for each set of values. Round to the nearest tenth if necessary. (Lesson 1-2)

76. $a = 2, b = -5, c = 2$ ± 3 **77.** $a = 1, b = 12, c = 11$ ± 10 **78.** $a = -9, b = 10, c = -1$ ± 8

79. $a = 1, b = 7, c = -3$ ± 7.8 **80.** $a = 2, b = -4, c = -6$ ± 8 **81.** $a = 3, b = 1, c = 2$ not a real number

Differentiated Instruction BL

Extension Have students solve $\frac{1}{3}x^2 - \frac{7}{6}x + \frac{1}{2} = 0$ by completing the square. Ask them how this strategy compares to factoring and graphing. $\frac{1}{2}$, 3; the equation can be solved more easily by factoring. Graphing may not produce an exact answer.

4 ASSESS

Name the Math Ask students what mathematical procedures they would use to solve a quadratic equation by completing the square.

Additional Answers

48. $y = ax^2 + bx + c$

$y = a\left(x^2 + \frac{b}{a}x\right) + c$

$y = a\left[x^2 + \frac{b}{a}x + \left(\frac{b}{2a}\right)^2\right] + c - a\left(\frac{b}{2a}\right)^2$

$y = a\left[x - \left(-\frac{b}{2a}\right)^2\right] + \frac{4ac - b^2}{4a}$

This last equation has the form $y = a(x - h)^2 + k$, where $h = -\frac{b}{2a}$ and $k = \frac{4ac - b^2}{4a}$. So, the axis of symmetry is $x = -\frac{b}{2a}$.

49. None; Sample answer: If you add $\left(\frac{b}{2}\right)^2$ to each side of the equation and each side of the inequality, you get $x^2 + bx + \left(\frac{b}{2}\right)^2 = c + \left(\frac{b}{2}\right)^2$ and $c + \left(\frac{b}{2}\right)^2 < 0$. Since the left side of the last equation is a perfect square, it cannot equal the negative number $c + \left(\frac{b}{2}\right)^2$. So, there are no real solutions.

50. $n^2 + \frac{1}{3}n + \frac{1}{9}$; It is the only trinomial that is not a perfect square.

51. Sample answer: $x^2 - 8x + 16 = 0$

52. Sample answer: Because the leading coefficient is 1, completing the square is simpler. Graphing the related function may be done with a graphing calculator and using the trace option. However, this is only good for estimation. Factoring is not possible.

9-5 Lesson Notes

1 FOCUS

Vertical Alignment

Before Lesson 9-5
Solve quadratic equations by completing the square.

Lesson 9-5
Solve quadratic equations by using the Quadratic Formula.
Use the discriminant to determine the number of solutions of a quadratic equation.

After Lesson 9-5
Use the Quotient Property of Square Roots to derive the Quadratic Formula.

2 TEACH

Scaffolding Questions

Have students read the *Why?* section of the lesson.

Ask:

- What equation would you need to solve to find the age of a woman whose systolic blood pressure is 120? $120 = 0.01a^2 + 0.05a + 107$
- Write this equation in standard form. $0 = 0.01a^2 + 0.05a - 13$
- What are the values for *a*, *b*, and *c*? $a = 0.01, b = 0.05, c = -13$

(continued on the next page)

9-5 Solving Quadratic Equations by Using the Quadratic Formula

Then
You solved quadratic equations by completing the square. (Lesson 9-4)

Now
- Solve quadratic equations by using the Quadratic Formula.
- Use the discriminant to determine the number of solutions of a quadratic equation.

IL Learning Standards

8.C.4b Apply algebraic properties and procedures with matrices, vectors, functions and sequences using data found in business, industry and consumer situations.
8.D.4 Formulate and solve linear and **quadratic equations** and linear inequalities **algebraically** and investigate nonlinear inequalities using graphs, tables, calculators and computers. *Also addresses 8.A.4b.*

New Vocabulary
Quadratic Formula
discriminant

IL Math Online
glencoe.com
- Extra Examples
- Personal Tutor
- Self-Check Quiz
- Homework Help
- Math in Motion

Why?

For adult women, the normal systolic blood pressure P in millimeters of mercury (mm Hg) can be modeled by $P = 0.01a^2 + 0.05a + 107$, where a is age in years. This equation can be used to approximate the age of a woman with a certain systolic blood pressure. However, it would be difficult to solve by factoring, graphing, or completing the square.

Quadratic Formula Completing the square of the quadratic equation $ax^2 + bx + c = 0$ produces a formula that allows you to find the solutions of *any* quadratic equation that is written in standard form. This formula is called the **Quadratic Formula**.

Key Concept **The Quadratic Formula** *For Your FOLDABLE*

The solutions of a quadratic equation $ax^2 + bx + c = 0$, where $a \neq 0$, are given by the Quadratic Formula.

$$x = \frac{-b \pm \sqrt{b^2 - 4ac}}{2a}$$

You will derive this formula in Lesson 10-2.

EXAMPLE 1 Use the Quadratic Formula

Solve $x^2 - 12x = -20$ by using the Quadratic Formula.

Step 1 Rewrite the equation in standard form.

$x^2 - 12x = -20$ — **Original equation**
$x^2 - 12x + 20 = 0$ — **Add 20 to each side.**

Step 2 Apply the Quadratic Formula.

$x = \frac{-b \pm \sqrt{b^2 - 4ac}}{2a}$ — **Quadratic Formula**
$= \frac{-(-12) \pm \sqrt{(-12)^2 - 4(1)(20)}}{2(1)}$ — **$a = 1$, $b = -12$, and $c = 20$**
$= \frac{12 \pm \sqrt{144 - 80}}{2}$ — **Multiply.**
$= \frac{12 \pm \sqrt{64}}{2}$ or $\frac{12 \pm 8}{2}$ — **Subtract and take the square root.**
$x = \frac{12 - 8}{2}$ or $x = \frac{12 + 8}{2}$ — **Separate the solutions.**
$= 2 \qquad = 10$ — **Simplify.**

The solutions are 2 and 10.

Check Your Progress

1. Solve $2x^2 + 9x = 18$ by using the Quadratic Formula. $-6, \frac{3}{2}$

Personal Tutor glencoe.com

Lesson 9-5 Resources

Resource	Approaching-Level	On-Level	Beyond-Level	English Learners
Teacher Edition	• Differentiated Instruction, p. 561	• Differentiated Instruction, pp. 561, 564	• Differentiated Instruction, pp. 561, 564	• Differentiated Instruction, p. 561
Chapter Resource Masters	• Study Guide and Intervention, pp. 29–30 • Skills Practice, p. 31 • Practice, p. 32 • Word Problem Practice, p. 33	• Study Guide and Intervention, pp. 29–30 • Skills Practice, p. 31 • Practice, p. 32 • Word Problem Practice, p. 33 • Enrichment, p. 34	• Practice, p. 32 • Word Problem Practice, p. 33 • Enrichment, p. 34	• Study Guide and Intervention, pp. 29–30 • Skills Practice, p. 31 • Practice, p. 32 • Word Problem Practice, p. 33
Transparencies	• 5-Minute Check Transparency 9-5	• 5-Minute Check Transparency 9-5	• 5-Minute Check Transparency 9-5	• 5-Minute Check Transparency 9-5
Other	• Study Notebook	• Study Notebook	• Study Notebook	• Study Notebook

The solutions of quadratic equations are not always integers.

EXAMPLE 2 **Use the Quadratic Formula**

Solve each equation by using the Quadratic Formula. Round to the nearest tenth if necessary.

a. $3x^2 + 5x - 12 = 0$

For this equation, $a = 3$, $b = 5$, and $c = -12$.

$x = \frac{-b \pm \sqrt{b^2 - 4ac}}{2a}$ — Quadratic Formula

$= \frac{-(5) \pm \sqrt{(5)^2 - 4(3)(-12)}}{2(3)}$ — $a = 3$, $b = 5$, and $c = -12$

$= \frac{-5 \pm \sqrt{25 + 144}}{6}$ — Multiply.

$= \frac{-5 \pm \sqrt{169}}{6}$ or $\frac{-5 \pm 13}{6}$ — Add and simplify.

$x = \frac{-5 - 13}{6}$ or $x = \frac{-5 + 13}{6}$ — Separate the solutions.

$= -3$ $\quad = \frac{4}{3}$ — Simplify.

The solutions are -3 and $\frac{4}{3}$.

b. $10x^2 - 5x = 25$

Step 1 Rewrite the equation in standard form.

$10x^2 - 5x = 25$ — Original equation

$10x^2 - 5x - 25 = 0$ — Subtract 25 from each side.

Step 2 Apply the Quadratic Formula.

$x = \frac{-b \pm \sqrt{b^2 - 4ac}}{2a}$ — Quadratic Formula

$= \frac{-(-5) \pm \sqrt{(-5)^2 - 4(10)(-25)}}{2(10)}$ — $a = 10$, $b = -5$, and $c = -25$

$= \frac{5 \pm \sqrt{25 + 1000}}{20}$ — Multiply.

$= \frac{5 \pm \sqrt{1025}}{20}$ — Add.

$= \frac{5 - \sqrt{1025}}{20}$ or $\frac{5 + \sqrt{1025}}{20}$ — Separate the solutions.

≈ -1.4 $\quad \approx 1.9$ — Simplify.

The solutions are about -1.4 and 1.9.

StudyTip

Exact Answers In Example 2, the number $\sqrt{1025}$ is irrational, so the calculator can only give you an approximation of its value. So, the exact answer in Example 2 is $\frac{5 \pm \sqrt{1025}}{20}$. The numbers -1.4 and 1.9 are approximations.

Check Your Progress

2A. $4x^2 - 24x + 35 = 0$ $\frac{7}{2}, \frac{5}{2}$

2B. $3x^2 - 2x - 9 = 0$ **2.1, −1.4**

Personal Tutor glencoe.com

You can solve quadratic equations by using many different methods. No one way is always best.

- Why would the equation be difficult to solve using factoring or completing the square? The decimal values of the coefficients may make using the methods difficult, if not impossible.

Quadratic Formula

Examples 1 and 2 show how to use the Quadratic Formula to solve quadratic equations with integral and non-integral roots. **Example 3** shows how to solve a quadratic equation using four different methods.

Formative Assessment

Use the Check Your Progress exercises after each example to determine students' understanding of concepts.

Additional Examples

1 Solve $x^2 - 2x = 35$ by using the Quadratic Formula. $-5, 7$

2 Solve each equation by using the Quadratic Formula. Round to the nearest tenth if necessary.

a. $2x^2 - 2x - 5 = 0$ $2.2, -1.2$

b. $5x^2 - 8x = 4$ $2, -0.4$

Additional Examples also in Interactive Classroom PowerPoint® Presentations

IWB INTERACTIVE WHITEBOARD READY

Watch Out!

Preventing Errors Some students may notice that the trinomial in Example 1 can be factored. Explain that an equation that could be factored was used to demonstrate that the Quadratic Formula produces the correct solutions. Tell students that if they see an easier way (such as factoring) to solve a quadratic equation, they should use the easier method.

Focus on Mathematical Content

The Quadratic Formula Even though the Quadratic Formula may not be the easiest way to solve some quadratic equations, it always works. To derive the formula, solve $ax^2 + bx + c = 0$ by completing the square. The derivation is shown in Lesson 10-2 when students learn about simplifying radical expressions.

TEACH with TECH

AUDIO RECORDING Have students work in groups to record a rap or rhythmic phrase to help students remember the quadratic formula. These can be repeated as a review before beginning problems, a quiz, or a test.

Tips for New Teachers

Using the Quadratic Formula Tell students that when they use the Quadratic Formula, it is best to simplify one step at a time. For example, students should first simplify under the radical sign, then find the square root, then simplify the numerator and denominator, and finally perform the division. Skipping steps may introduce errors.

Additional Example

3 Solve $3x^2 - 5x = 12$. $3, -\frac{4}{3}$

EXAMPLE 3 Solve Quadratic Equations Using Different Methods

Solve $x^2 - 4x = 12$.

Method 1 Graphing

Rewrite the equation in standard form.

$x^2 - 4x = 12$ **Original equation**

$x^2 - 4x - 12 = 0$ **Subtract 12 from each side.**

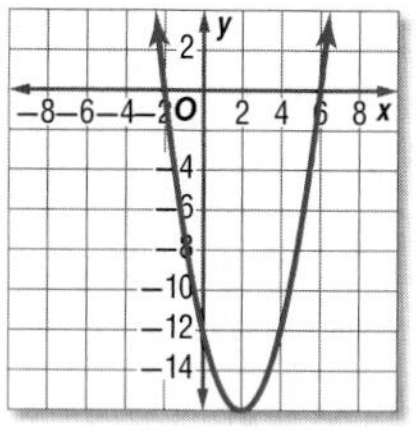

Graph the related function $f(x) = x^2 - 4x - 12$.
Locate the x-intercepts of the graph.
The solutions are −2 and 6.

Method 2 Factoring

$x^2 - 4x = 12$	**Original equation**
$x^2 - 4x - 12 = 0$	**Subtract 12 from each side.**
$(x - 6)(x + 2) = 0$	**Factor.**
$x - 6 = 0$ or $x + 2 = 0$	**Zero Product Property**
$x = 6$ $\quad$ $x = -2$	**Solve for *x*.**

Method 3 Completing the Square

The equation is in the correct form to complete the square, since the leading coefficient is 1 and the x^2 and x terms are isolated.

$x^2 - 4x = 12$	**Original equation**
$x^2 - 4x + 4 = 12 + 4$	**Since $\left(\frac{-4}{2}\right)^2 = 4$, add 4 to each side.**
$(x - 2)^2 = 16$	**Factor $x^2 - 4x + 4$.**
$x - 2 = \pm 4$	**Take the square root of each side.**
$x = 2 \pm 4$	**Add 2 to each side.**
$x = 2 + 4$ or $x = 2 - 4$	**Separate the solutions.**
$= 6$ $\quad$ $= -2$	**Simplify.**

> **Watch Out!**
>
> **Solutions** No matter what method is used to solve a quadratic equation, all of the methods should produce the same solution(s).

Method 4 Quadratic Formula

From Method 1, the standard form of the equation is $x^2 - 4x - 12 = 0$.

$x = \frac{-b \pm \sqrt{b^2 - 4ac}}{2a}$	**Quadratic Formula**
$= \frac{-(-4) \pm \sqrt{(-4)^2 - 4(1)(-12)}}{2(1)}$	**$a = 1$, $b = -4$, and $c = -12$**
$= \frac{4 \pm \sqrt{16 + 48}}{2}$	**Multiply.**
$= \frac{4 \pm \sqrt{64}}{2}$ or $\frac{4 \pm 8}{2}$	**Add and simplify.**
$x = \frac{4 - 8}{2}$ or $x = \frac{4 + 8}{2}$	**Separate the solutions.**
$= -2$ $\quad$ $= 6$	**Simplify.**

Check Your Progress

Solve each equation.

3A. $2x^2 - 17x + 8 = 0$ $8, \frac{1}{2}$

3B. $4x^2 - 4x - 11 = 0$ about 2.2, −1.2

Personal Tutor glencoe.com

560 Chapter 9 Quadratic and Exponential Functions

Concept Summary — Solving Quadratic Equations

For Your FOLDABLE

Method	When to Use
Factoring	Use when the constant term is 0 or if the factors are easily determined. Not all equations are factorable.
Graphing	Use when an approximate solution is sufficient.
Using Square Roots	Use when an equation can be written in the form $x^2 = n$. Can only be used if the equation has no x-term.
Completing the Square	Can be used for any equation $ax^2 + bx + c = 0$, but is simplest to apply when b is even and $a = 1$.
Quadratic Formula	Can be used for any equation $ax^2 + bx + c = 0$.

The Discriminant In the Quadratic Formula, the expression under the radical sign, $b^2 - 4ac$, is called the **discriminant**. The discriminant can be used to determine the number of real solutions of a quadratic equation.

Key Concept — Using the Discriminant

For Your FOLDABLE

Equation	$x^2 + 2x + 5 = 0$	$x^2 + 10x + 25 = 0$	$2x^2 - 7x + 2 = 0$
Discriminant	$b^2 - 4ac = -16$ negative	$b^2 - 4ac = 0$ zero	$b^2 - 4ac = 33$ positive
Graph of Related Function	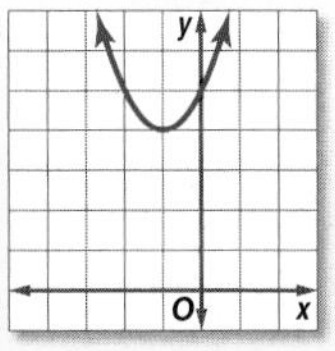 0 x-intercepts	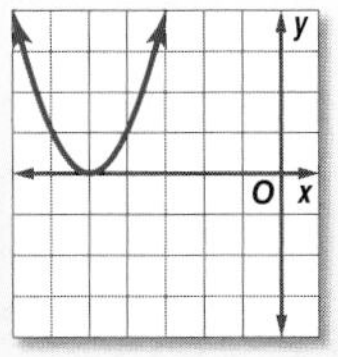 1 x-intercept	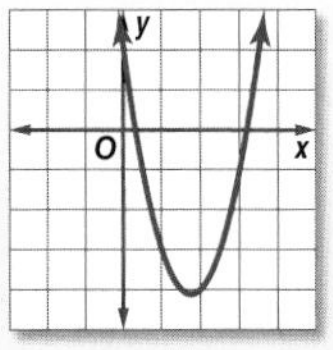 2 x-intercepts
Real Solutions	0	1	2

StudyTip

Discriminant Recall that when the left side of the standard form of an equation is a perfect square trinomial, there is only one solution. Therefore, the discriminant of a perfect square trinomial will always be zero.

EXAMPLE 4 Use the Discriminant

State the value of the discriminant of $4x^2 + 5x = -3$. Then determine the number of real solutions of the equation.

Step 1 Rewrite in standard form. $4x^2 - 5x = -3 \longrightarrow 4x^2 - 5x + 3 = 0$

Step 2 Find the discriminant.

$b^2 - 4ac = (-5)^2 - 4(4)(3)$ — $a = 4$, $b = -5$, and $c = 3$

$= -23$ — Simplify.

Since the discriminant is negative, the equation has no real solutions.

Check Your Progress 4A. 1; two real solutions 4B. 0; one real solution

4A. $2x^2 + 11x + 15 = 0$ **4B.** $9x^2 - 30x + 25 = 0$

Personal Tutor glencoe.com

Tips for New Teachers

Sense-Making While the chart on this page offers suggestions for when to use each method, do not hold students to using all methods. Some students do not yet have the mathematical maturity to analyze each equation and determine the best method to use to save time.

The Discriminant

Example 4 shows how to use the discriminant to determine the number of real solutions for a quadratic equation.

Additional Example

4 State the value of the discriminant of $3x^2 + 10x = 12$. Then determine the number of real solutions of the equation. 244; 2 real solutions

Watch Out!

Preventing Errors Remind students to be careful to include any negative signs when finding the discriminant. One missed negative sign can turn the discriminant from positive to negative and yield an incorrect result.

Differentiated Instruction

AL OL BL ELL

If you think students would benefit from being creative in this lesson,

Then have students come up with a riddle, poem, or some other mnemonic device to help them remember the Quadratic Formula and how to use the discriminant to determine the number of real solutions. Ask students to share with the class.

Lesson 9-5 Solving Quadratic Equations by Using the Quadratic Formula 561

3 PRACTICE

Formative Assessment

Use Exercises 1–15 to check for understanding.

Use the chart at the bottom of this page to customize assignments for students.

Exercise Alert

Grid Paper For Exercise 50, students will need grid paper.

Additional Answers

35. −0.07; no real solution

36. −135; no real solutions

37. 12.64; two real solutions

38. 0; one real solution

39. 0; one real solution

40. 18.25; two real solutions

41b. Sample answer: No; the parabola has a maximum at about 66, meaning only 66% of the population would ever have high-speed Internet.

42. No; sample answer: Hannah was traveling at about 61 mph, so she was not speeding.

50b. **Bacteria**

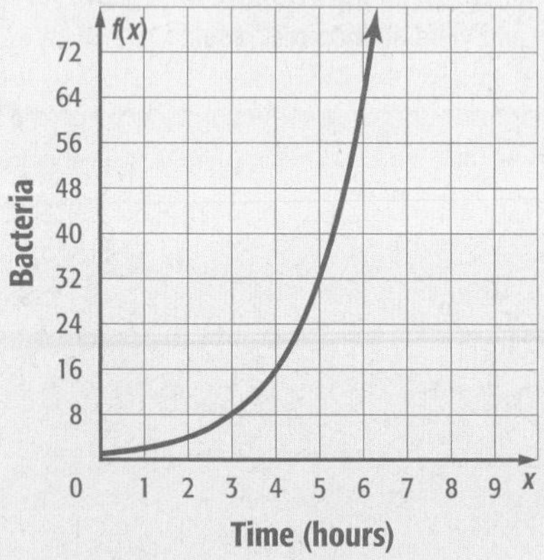

The graph is neither linear nor quadratic.

57. Sample answer: positive discriminant: $f(x) = x^2 - 4$, negative discriminant: $f(x) = x^2 + 4$, zero discriminant: $f(x) = x^2 - 8x + 16$

Check Your Understanding

Examples 1 and 2 pp. 558–559

Solve each equation by using the Quadratic Formula. Round to the nearest tenth if necessary.

1. $x^2 - 2x - 15 = 0$ **−3, 5**
2. $x^2 - 10x + 16 = 0$ **2, 8**
3. $x^2 - 8x = -10$ **6.4, 1.6**
4. $x^2 + 3x = 12$ **2.3, −5.3**
5. $10x^2 - 31x + 15 = 0$ **0.6, 2.5**
6. $5x^2 + 5 = -13x$ **−0.5, −2.1**

Example 3 p. 560

Solve each equation. State which method you used.

7. $2x^2 + 11x - 6 = 0$ **$-6, \frac{1}{2}$; factoring**
8. $2x^2 - 3x - 6 = 0$ **2.6, −1.1; Quadratic formula**
9. $9x^2 = 25$ **$\pm\frac{5}{3}$; completing the square**
10. $x^2 - 9x = -19$ **5.6, 3.4; Quadratic formula**

Example 4 p. 561

State the value of the discriminant for each equation. Then determine the number of real solutions of the equation.

11. $x^2 - 9x + 21 = 0$ **−3; no real solutions**
12. $2x^2 - 11x + 10 = 0$ **41; two real solutions**
13. $9x^2 + 24x = -16$ **0; one real solution**
14. $3x^2 - x = 8$ **97; two real solutions**

15. TRAMPOLINE Eva is jumping on a trampoline. Her height h in feet can be modeled by the equation $h = -16t^2 + 2.4t + 6$, where t is time in seconds. Use the discriminant to determine if Eva will ever reach a height of 20 feet. Explain.

15. The discriminant is −890.24, so the equation has no solutions. Thus, Eva will not reach a height of 20 feet.

Practice and Problem Solving

● = **Step-by-Step Solutions** begin on page R12. **Extra Practice** begins on page 815.

Examples 1 and 2 pp. 558–559

Solve each equation by using the Quadratic Formula. Round to the nearest tenth if necessary.

16. $4x^2 + 5x - 6 = 0$ **$-2, \frac{3}{4}$**
17. $x^2 + 16 = 0$ **∅**
18. $6x^2 - 12x + 1 = 0$ **1.9, 0.1**
19. $5x^2 - 8x = 6$ **2.2, −0.6**
20. $2x^2 - 5x = -7$ **∅**
21. $5x^2 + 21x = -18$ **$-3, -\frac{6}{5}$**
22. $81x^2 = 9$ **$\pm\frac{1}{3}$**
23. $8x^2 + 12x = 8$ **0.5, −2**
24. $4x^2 = -16x - 16$ **−2**
25. $10x^2 = -7x + 6$ **0.5, −1.2**
26. $-3x^2 = 8x - 12$ **1.1, −3.7**
27. $2x^2 = 12x - 18$ **3**

28. AMUSEMENT PARKS The Demon Drop at Cedar Point in Ohio takes riders to the top of a tower and drops them 60 feet. A function that approximates this ride is $h = -16t^2 + 64t - 60$, where h is the height in feet and t is the time in seconds. About how many seconds does it take for riders to drop from 60 feet to 0 feet? **about 2.5 seconds**

Example 3 p. 560

Solve each equation. State which method you used.

29. $2x^2 - 8x = 12$ **−1.2, 5.2**
30. $3x^2 - 24x = -36$ **2, 6**
31. $x^2 - 3x = 10$ **−2, 5**
32. $4x^2 + 100 = 0$ **∅**
33. $x^2 = -7x - 5$ **−6.2, −0.8**
34. $12 - 12x = -3x^2$ **2**

Example 4 p. 561

State the value of the discriminant for each equation. Then determine the number of real solutions of the equation. **35–40. See margin.**

35. $0.2x^2 - 1.5x + 2.9 = 0$
36. $2x^2 - 5x + 20 = 0$
37. $x^2 - \frac{4}{5}x = 3$
38. $0.5x^2 - 2x = -2$
39. $2.25x^2 - 3x = -1$
40. $2x^2 = \frac{5}{2}x + \frac{3}{2}$

41. INTERNET The percent of U.S. households with high-speed Internet h can be estimated by $h = -0.2n^2 + 7.2n + 1.5$, where n is the number of years since 1990.

a. Use the Quadratic Formula to determine when 20% of the population will have high-speed Internet. **in 1993 and 2023**

b. Is a quadratic equation a good model for this information? Explain. **See margin.**

Differentiated Homework Options

Level	Assignment	Two-Day Option	
AL Basic	16–41, 52–77	17–41 odd, 59–62	16–40 even, 52–58, 63–77
OL Core	17–41 odd, 42, 43–49 odd, 52–77	16–41, 59–62	42–50, 52–58, 63–77
BL Advanced	42–71, (optional: 72–77)		

42. TRAFFIC The equation $d = 0.05v^2 + 1.1v$ models the distance d in feet it takes a car traveling at a speed of v miles per hour to come to a complete stop. The speed limit on some highways is 65 miles per hour. If Hannah's car stopped after 250 feet, was she speeding? Explain your reasoning. **See margin.**

Without graphing, determine the number of x-intercepts of the graph of the related function for each equation.

43. $4.25x + 3 = -3x^2$ **0**

44. $x^2 + \frac{2}{25} = \frac{3}{5}x$ **2**

45. $0.25x^2 + x = -1$ **1**

Solve each equation by using the Quadratic Formula. Round to the nearest tenth if necessary. **46. −3.7, 0.2** **47. −1.4, 2.1**

46. $-2x^2 - 7x = -1.5$

47. $2.3x^2 - 1.4x = 6.8$

48. $x^2 - 2x = 5$ **3.4, −1.4**

Real-World Link

The risk of motor vehicle crashes is higher among 16- to 19-year-olds than any other age group. Per mile driven, 16- to 19-year-olds are four times more likely than older drivers to crash.

Source: Centers for Disease Control and Prevention

49. POSTER Bartolo is making a poster for the dance. He wants to cover three fourths of the area with text.

a. Write an equation for the area of the section with text. **$(20 - 2x)(25 - 7x) = 375$**

b. Solve the equation by using the Quadratic Formula. **about 12.9, 0.7**

c. What should be the margins of the poster? **about 0.7 in. on the sides, 2.8 in. on the top, and 2.1 in. on the bottom**

50. **MULTIPLE REPRESENTATIONS** In this problem, you will investigate *exponential* functions.

a. **TABULAR** Copy and complete the table.

b. **GRAPHICAL** Construct a graph from the information given in the table using the points (time, number of bacteria). Is the graph linear or quadratic? **See margin.**

c. **ANALYTICAL** What happens to the number of bacteria after every hour? Write a function that models the pattern in the table. **The number of bacteria doubles every hour; $f(x) = 2^x$.**

Time (hours)	Number of Bacteria
0	$1 = 2^0$
1	$2 = 2^1$
2	$4 = 2^2$
3	$8 = 2^3$
4	$16 = 2^4$
5	$32 = 2^5$
6	$64 = 2^6$

H.O.T. Problems

Use Higher-Order Thinking Skills

51. CHALLENGE Find all values of k such that $2x^2 - 3x + 5k = 0$ has two solutions. **$k < \frac{9}{40}$**

52. REASONING Use factoring techniques to determine the number of real zeros of $f(x) = x^2 - 8x + 16$. Compare this method to using the discriminant.

52. Sample answer: The polynomial can be factored to get $f(x) = (x - 4)^2$, so the only real zero is 4. The discriminant is 0, so there is 1 real zero. The discriminant tells us how many real zeros there are. Factoring tells us what they are.

REASONING Determine whether there are *two*, *one*, or *no* real solutions.

53. The graph of a quadratic function does not have an x-intercept. **none**

54. The graph of a quadratic function is tangent at the x-axis. **one**

55. The graph of a quadratic function intersects the x-axis twice. **two**

56. Both a and b are greater than 0 and c is less than 0 in a quadratic equation. **two**

57. OPEN ENDED Write a quadratic function that has a positive discriminant, one with a negative discriminant, and one with a zero discriminant. **See margin.**

58. WRITING IN MATH Describe the advantages and disadvantages of each method of solving quadratic equations. Which method do you prefer, and why? **See Ch. 9 Answer Appendix.**

Multiple Representations

In Exercise 50, students use a table of values, a graph in the coordinate plane, and analysis to illustrate an exponential function.

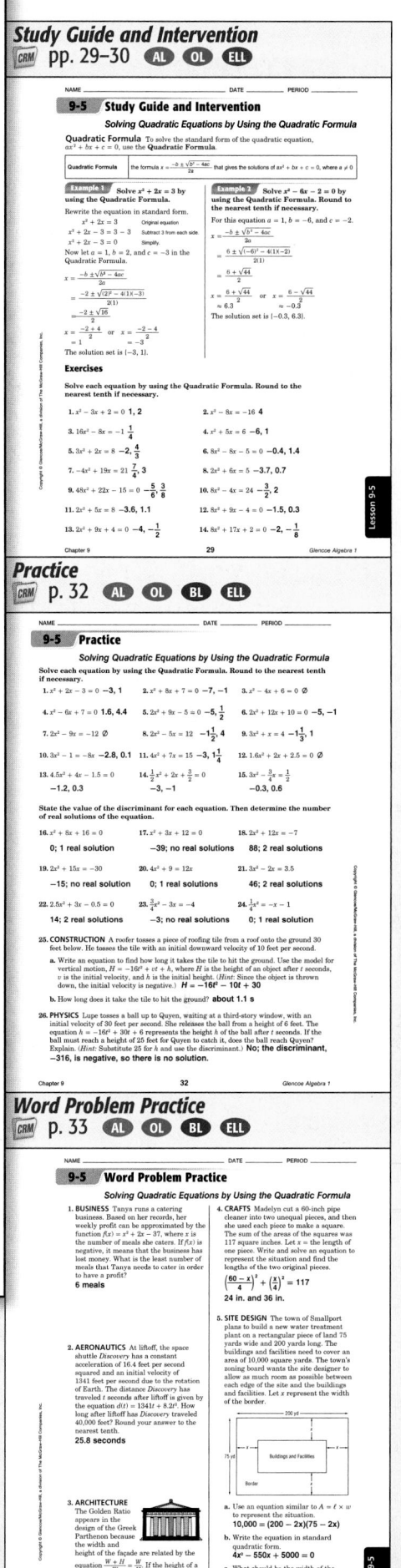

Study Guide and Intervention

CRM pp. 29–30 AL OL ELL

NAME ______ DATE ______ PERIOD ______

9-5 Study Guide and Intervention

Solving Quadratic Equations by Using the Quadratic Formula

Quadratic Formula To solve the standard form of the quadratic equation, $ax^2 + bx + c = 0$, use the **Quadratic Formula**.

Quadratic Formula	the formula $x = \frac{-b \pm \sqrt{b^2 - 4ac}}{2a}$ that gives the solutions of $ax^2 + bx + c = 0$, where $a \neq 0$

Example 1 **Solve $x^2 + 2x = 3$ by using the Quadratic Formula.**

Rewrite the equation in standard form.

$x^2 + 2x = 3$ Original equation

$x^2 + 2x - 3 = 3 - 3$ Subtract 3 from each side.

$x^2 + 2x - 3 = 0$ Simplify.

Now let $a = 1$, $b = 2$, and $c = -3$ in the Quadratic Formula.

$x = \frac{-b \pm \sqrt{b^2 - 4ac}}{2a}$

$= \frac{-2 \pm \sqrt{(2)^2 - 4(1)(-3)}}{2(1)}$

$= \frac{-2 \pm \sqrt{16}}{2}$

$x = \frac{-2 + 4}{2}$ or $x = \frac{-2 - 4}{2}$

$= 1$ $= -3$

The solution set is $\{-3, 1\}$.

Example 2 **Solve $x^2 - 6x - 2 = 0$ by using the Quadratic Formula. Round to the nearest tenth if necessary.**

For this equation $a = 1$, $b = -6$, and $c = -2$.

$x = \frac{-b \pm \sqrt{b^2 - 4ac}}{2a}$

$= \frac{6 \pm \sqrt{(-6)^2 - 4(1)(-2)}}{2(1)}$

$= \frac{6 + \sqrt{44}}{2}$

$x = \frac{6 + \sqrt{44}}{2}$ or $x = \frac{6 - \sqrt{44}}{2}$

≈ 6.3 ≈ -0.3

The solution set is $\{-0.3, 6.3\}$.

Exercises

Solve each equation by using the Quadratic Formula. Round to the nearest tenth if necessary.

1. $x^2 - 3x + 2 = 0$ **1, 2**
2. $x^2 - 8x = -16$ **4**
3. $16x^2 - 8x = -1$ **$\frac{1}{4}$**
4. $x^2 + 5x = 6$ **−6, 1**
5. $3x^2 + 2x = 8$ **$-2, \frac{4}{3}$**
6. $8x^2 - 8x - 5 = 0$ **−0.4, 1.4**
7. $-4x^2 + 19x = 21$ **$\frac{7}{4}, 3$**
8. $2x^2 + 6x = 5$ **−3.7, 0.7**
9. $48x^2 + 22x - 15 = 0$ **$-\frac{5}{6}, \frac{3}{8}$**
10. $8x^2 - 4x = 24$ **$-\frac{3}{2}, 2$**
11. $2x^2 + 5x = 8$ **−3.6, 1.1**
12. $8x^2 + 9x - 4 = 0$ **−1.5, 0.3**
13. $2x^2 + 9x + 4 = 0$ **$-4, -\frac{1}{2}$**
14. $8x^2 + 17x + 2 = 0$ **$-2, -\frac{1}{8}$**

Lesson 9-5

Chapter 9 29 Glencoe Algebra 1

Practice

CRM p. 32 AL OL BL ELL

NAME ______ DATE ______ PERIOD ______

9-5 Practice

Solving Quadratic Equations by Using the Quadratic Formula

Solve each equation by using the Quadratic Formula. Round to the nearest tenth if necessary.

1. $x^2 + 2x - 3 = 0$ **−3, 1**
2. $x^2 + 8x + 7 = 0$ **−7, −1**
3. $x^2 - 4x + 6 = 0$ **∅**
4. $x^2 - 6x + 7 = 0$ **1.6, 4.4**
5. $2x^2 + 9x - 5 = 0$ **$-5, \frac{1}{2}$**
6. $2x^2 + 12x + 10 = 0$ **−5, −1**
7. $2x^2 - 9x = -12$ **∅**
8. $2x^2 - 5x = 12$ **$-1\frac{1}{2}, 4$**
9. $3x^2 + x = 4$ **$-1\frac{1}{3}, 1$**
10. $3x^2 - 1 = -8x$ **−2.8, 0.1**
11. $4x^2 + 7x = 15$ **$-3, 1\frac{1}{4}$**
12. $1.6x^2 + 2x + 2.5 = 0$ **∅**
13. $4.5x^2 + 4x - 1.5 = 0$ **−1.2, 0.3**
14. $\frac{1}{2}x^2 + 2x + \frac{3}{2} = 0$ **−3, −1**
15. $3x^2 - \frac{3}{4}x = \frac{1}{2}$ **−0.3, 0.6**

State the value of the discriminant for each equation. Then determine the number of real solutions of the equation.

16. $x^2 + 8x + 16 = 0$ **0; 1 real solution**
17. $x^2 + 3x + 12 = 0$ **−39; no real solutions**
18. $2x^2 + 12x = -7$ **88; 2 real solutions**
19. $2x^2 + 15x = -30$ **−15; no real solution**
20. $4x^2 + 9 = 12x$ **0; 1 real solutions**
21. $3x^2 - 2x = 3.5$ **46; 2 real solutions**
22. $2.5x^2 + 3x - 0.5 = 0$ **14; 2 real solutions**
23. $\frac{3}{4}x^2 - 3x = -4$ **−3; no real solutions**
24. $\frac{1}{4}x^2 = -x - 1$ **0; 1 real solution**

25. **CONSTRUCTION** A roofer tosses a piece of roofing tile from a roof onto the ground 30 feet below. He tosses the tile with an initial downward velocity of 10 feet per second.

a. Write an equation to find how long it takes the tile to hit the ground. Use the model for vertical motion, $H = -16t^2 + vt + h$, where H is the height of an object after t seconds, v is the initial velocity, and h is the initial height. (*Hint*: Since the object is thrown down, the initial velocity is negative.) **$H = -16t^2 - 10t + 30$**

b. How long does it take the tile to hit the ground? **about 1.1 s**

26. **PHYSICS** Lupe tosses a ball up to Quyen, waiting at a third-story window, with an initial velocity of 30 feet per second. She releases the ball from a height of 6 feet. The equation $h = -16t^2 + 30t + 6$ represents the height h of the ball after t seconds. If the ball must reach a height of 25 feet for Quyen to catch it, does the ball reach Quyen? Explain. (*Hint:* Substitute 25 for h and use the discriminant.) **No; the discriminant, −316, is negative, so there is no solution.**

Chapter 9 32 Glencoe Algebra 1

Word Problem Practice

CRM p. 33 AL OL BL ELL

NAME ______ DATE ______ PERIOD ______

9-5 Word Problem Practice

Solving Quadratic Equations by Using the Quadratic Formula

1. **BUSINESS** Tanya runs a catering business. Based on her records, her weekly profit can be approximated by the function $f(x) = x^2 + 2x - 37$, where x is the number of meals she caters. If $f(x)$ is negative, it means that the business has lost money. What is the least number of meals that Tanya needs to cater in order to have a profit? **6 meals**

2. **AERONAUTICS** At liftoff, the space shuttle *Discovery* has a constant acceleration of 16.4 feet per second squared and an initial velocity of 1341 feet per second due to the rotation of Earth. The distance *Discovery* has traveled t seconds after liftoff is given by the equation $d(t) = 1341t + 8.2t^2$. How long after liftoff has *Discovery* traveled 40,000 feet? Round your answer to the nearest tenth. **25.8 seconds**

3. **ARCHITECTURE** The Golden Ratio appears in the design of the Greek Parthenon because the width and height of the façade are related by the equation $\frac{W + H}{W} = \frac{W}{H}$. If the height of a model of the Parthenon is 16 inches, what is its width? Round your answer to the nearest tenth. **25.9 in.**

4. **CRAFTS** Madelyn cut a 60-inch pipe cleaner into two unequal pieces, and then she used each piece to make a square. The sum of the areas of the squares was 117 square inches. Let x = the length of one piece. Write and solve an equation to represent the situation and find the lengths of the two original pieces. **$\left(\frac{60 - x}{4}\right)^2 + \left(\frac{x}{4}\right)^2 = 117$** **24 in. and 36 in.**

5. **SITE DESIGN** The town of Smallport plans to build a new water treatment plant on a rectangular piece of land 75 yards wide and 200 yards long. The buildings and facilities need to cover an area of 10,000 square yards. The town's zoning board wants the site designer to allow as much room as possible between each edge of the site and the buildings and facilities. Let x represent the width of the border.

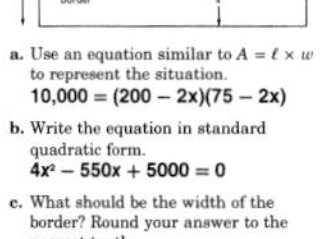

a. Use an equation similar to $A = \ell \times w$ to represent the situation. **$10{,}000 = (200 - 2x)(75 - 2x)$**

b. Write the equation in standard quadratic form. **$4x^2 - 550x + 5000 = 0$**

c. What should be the width of the border? Round your answer to the nearest tenth. **9.8 yd**

Lesson 9-5

Chapter 9 33 Glencoe Algebra 1

Enrichment

CRM p. 34 OL BL

NAME ______ DATE ______ PERIOD ______

9-5 Enrichment

Golden Rectangles

A **golden rectangle** has the property that its sides satisfy the following proportion. $\frac{a + b}{a} = \frac{a}{b}$

Two quadratic equations can be written from the proportion. These are sometimes called **golden quadratic** equations.

1. In the proportion, let $a = 1$. Use cross-multiplication to write a quadratic equation. **$b^2 + b - 1 = 0$**

2. Solve the equation in Exercise 1 for b. **$b = \frac{-1 \pm \sqrt{5}}{2}$**

3. In the proportion, let $b = 1$. Write a quadratic equation in a. **$a^2 - a - 1 = 0$**

4. Solve the equation in Exercise 3 for a. **$a = \frac{1 \pm \sqrt{5}}{2}$**

5. Explain why $\frac{1}{2}(\sqrt{5} + 1)$ and $\frac{1}{2}(\sqrt{5} - 1)$ are called golden ratios. **They are the ratios of the sides in a golden rectangle. The first is the ratio**

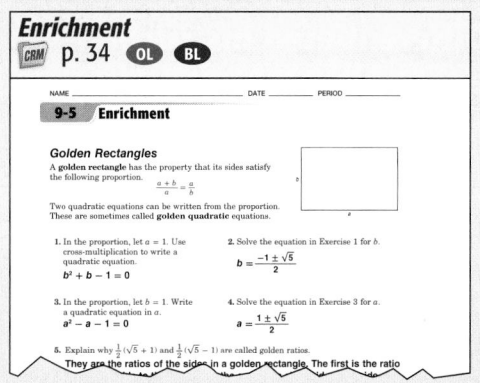

4 ASSESS

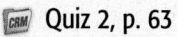

Ticket Out the Door Make several copies each of five quadratic equations. Give one equation to each student. As students leave the room, ask each of them to tell you the discriminant of the equation and the number of real solutions.

Formative Assessment

Check for student understanding of Lessons 9-4 and 9-5.

CRM Quiz 2, p. 63

Additional Answer

71.

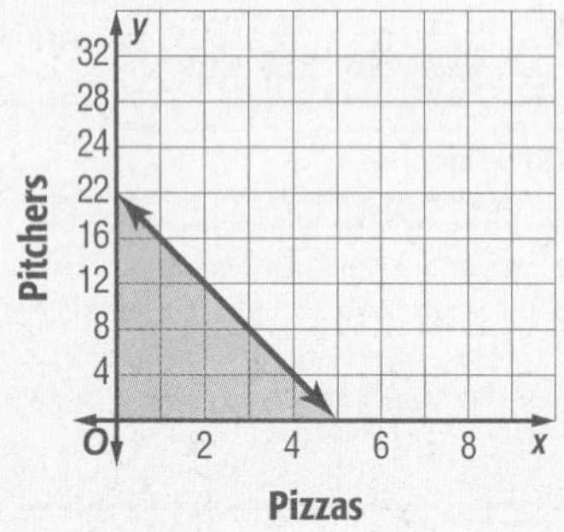

PSAE PRACTICE 8.11.02, 9.11.05, 8.11.08, 8.11.18

59. If n is an even integer, which expression represents the product of three consecutive even integers? **D**

A $n(n + 1)(n + 2)$

B $(n + 1)(n + 2)(n + 3)$

C $3n + 2$

D $n(n + 2)(n + 4)$

60. **SHORT RESPONSE** The triangle shown is an isosceles triangle. What is the value of x? **58 or 64**

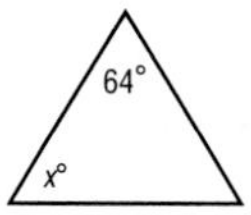

61. Which statement best describes the graph of $x = 5$? **G**

F It is parallel to the x-axis.

G It is parallel to the y-axis.

H It passes through the point (2, 5).

J It has a y-intercept of 5.

62. What are the solutions of the quadratic equation $6h^2 + 6h = 72$? **A**

A 3 or −4

B −3 or 4

C no solution

D 12 or −48

Spiral Review

Solve each equation by completing the square. Round to the nearest tenth if necessary. (Lesson 9-4)

63. $6x^2 - 17x + 12 = 0$ **$\frac{4}{3}, \frac{3}{2}$**

64. $x^2 - 9x = -12$ **1.6, 7.4**

65. $4x^2 = 20x - 25$ **$\frac{5}{2}$**

Describe the transformations needed to obtain the graph of $g(x)$ from the graph of $f(x)$. (Lesson 9-3)

66. $f(x) = 4x^2$, $g(x) = 2x^2$ **Compress vertically.**

67. $f(x) = x^2 + 5$, $g(x) = x^2 - 1$ **Translate down 6.**

68. $f(x) = x^2 - 6$, $g(x) = x^2 + 3$ **Translate up 9.**

Determine whether each graph shows a *positive correlation*, a *negative correlation*, or *no correlation*. If there is a positive or negative correlation, describe its meaning in the situation. (Lesson 4-4)

69. Electronic Tax Returns

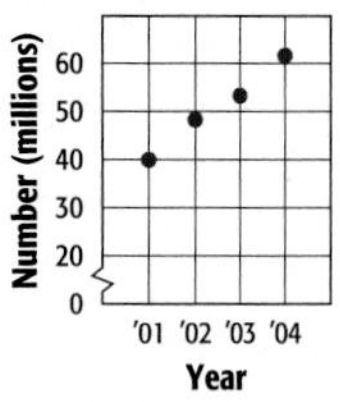

Positive; as time goes on, more people use electronic tax returns.

70. Atlantic Hurricanes

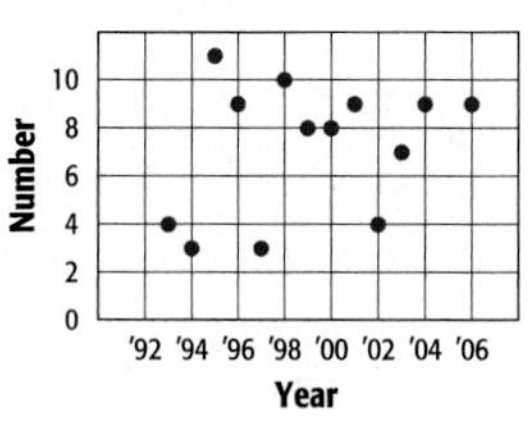

no correlation

71. **ENTERTAINMENT** Coach Washington wants to take her softball team out for pizza and soft drinks after the last game of the season. A large pizza costs \$12 and a pitcher of a soft drink costs \$3. She does not want to spend more than \$60. Write an inequality that represents this situation and graph the solution set. (Lesson 5-6)
$12x + 3y \leq 60$; See margin for graph.

Skills Check

Evaluate $a(b^x)$ for each of the given values. (Lesson 1-2)

72. $a = 1, b = 2, x = 4$ **16**

73. $a = 4, b = 1, x = 7$ **4**

74. $a = 5, b = 3, x = 0$ **5**

75. $a = 0, b = 6, x = 8$ **0**

76. $a = -2, b = 3, x = 1$ **−6**

77. $a = -3, b = 5, x = 2$ **−75**

Differentiated Instruction OL BL

Extension Since students are much more likely to retain a concept that they have researched and explained, ask them to research the derivation of the Quadratic Formula and to write short paragraphs showing and explaining the derivation.

564 Chapter 9 Quadratic and Exponential Functions

EXTEND 9-5 Graphing Technology Lab
Cubic Functions

IL Math Online > glencoe.com
- Other Calculator Keystrokes
- Graphing Technology Personal Tutor

You have studied linear functions and monomials. Some functions can be defined by the sums of monomials. One function that can be defined this way is a cubic function. A **cubic equation** has the form $ax^3 + bx^2 + cx + d = 0$, where $a \neq 0$. All cubic equations have at least one but no more than three real roots.

ACTIVITY

Solve $x^3 - 6x^2 + 3x + 10 = 0$ by graphing.

Step 1 Enter the related function in the Y= list.

KEYSTROKES: [Y=] [X,T,θ,n] [^] 3 [−] 6 [X,T,θ,n] [x^2] [+] 3 [X,T,θ,n] [+] 10

Step 2 Graph the function in the standard viewing window.

KEYSTROKES: [Zoom] 6

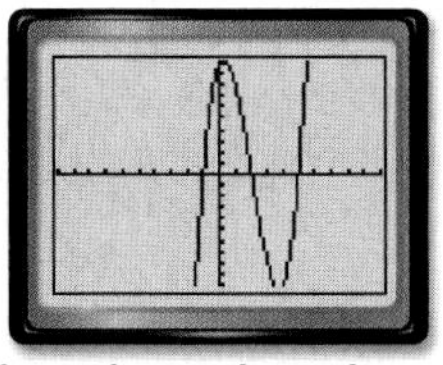
[−10, 10] scl: 1 by [−10, 10] scl: 1

Step 3 Find the zeros of the function by determining where the graph crosses the x-axis. Notice that this graph crosses the x-axis three times. Therefore, there are 3 real solutions for the equation.

KEYSTROKES: [2nd] [CALC] 2

Press the left arrow to move to the left of the intercept closest to the origin.

Press [ENTER].

Press the right arrow to move to the right of the intercept. Do not go past another intercept. Press [ENTER].

Notice the arrows above the intercept. The intercept you are finding should be between these two arrows.

Press the left arrow to move as close as possible to the intercept. Press [ENTER].

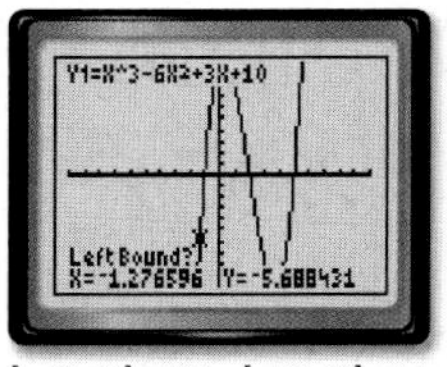

[−10, 10] scl:1 by [−10, 10] scl:1

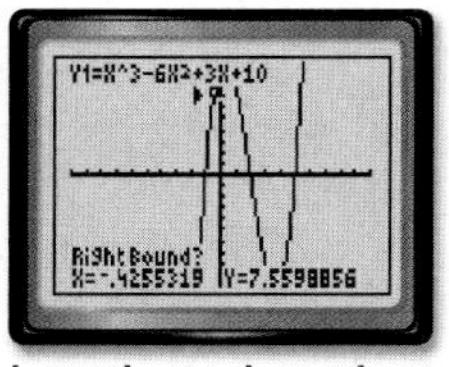

[−10, 10] scl:1 by [−10, 10] scl:1

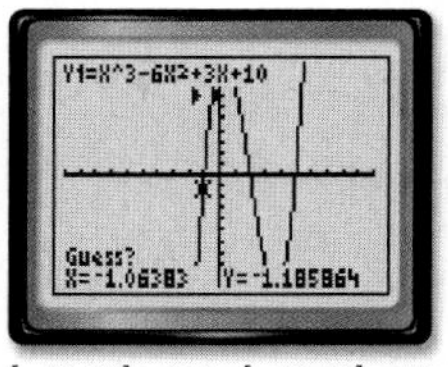

[−10, 10] scl:1 by [−10, 10] scl:1

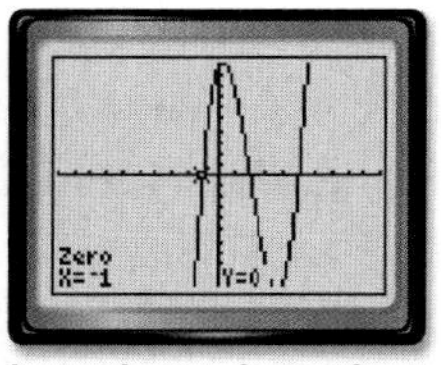

[−10, 10] scl:1 by [−10, 10] scl:1

One root is $x = -1$.

Step 4 Repeat Step 3 for each additional root.

The solutions for $x^3 - 6x^2 + 3x + 10 = 0$ are $x = -1, 2$, and 5.

Exercises

Solve each equation by graphing. 1–4. See Ch. 9 Answer Appendix for graphs.

1. $x^3 - 4x^2 - 9x + 36 = 0$ −3, 3, 4
2. $x^3 - 6x^2 - 6x - 7 = 0$ 7
3. $x^3 + x^2 + x - 3 = 0$ 1
4. $x^3 - 5x^2 - 2x + 24 = 0$ −2, 3, 4

EXTEND 9-5 Lesson Notes

1 FOCUS

Objective Use a graphing calculator to find solutions of cubic equations.

Materials for Each Student
- TI-83/84 Plus or other graphing calculator

Teaching Tip
Tell students that solutions to a cubic equation, as with quadratic equations, are found where the graph of the function crosses the x-axis. If students try to find a root where the graph crosses the y-axis, other than at (0, 0), they may see this message on their calculator screen: ERR: NO SIGN CHANGE. This means that to the left and to the right of each root, the values for y must have a sign change from − to +, or + to −. If there is no sign change, then there is no root between the two bounds chosen by the student.

2 TEACH

Working in Cooperative Groups
Put students in groups of two or three, mixing abilities. Have groups complete the Activity and Exercises 1 and 2.

Ask:
- If $a = 0$ in $ax^3 + bx^2 + cx + d = 0$, what type of equation do you have? quadratic if $b \neq 0$
- How does the graph of a cubic function compare to a graph of a quadratic function? A quadratic function can intersect the x-axis 0, 1, or 2 times, and the ends of the graph go in the same direction. A cubic function can intersect the x-axis 1, 2, or 3 times, and the ends of the graph go in opposite directions.

Practice Have students complete Exercises 3 and 4.

3 ASSESS

Formative Assessment
Use Exercise 4 to assess whether students understand how to use a graphing calculator to find the solutions of a cubic equation.

From Concrete to Abstract
The solutions to some quadratic equations can be found by factoring. Have students use this concept and the solutions to the equation in the Activity to determine the factors of the cubic expression $x^3 - 6x^2 + 3x + 10$.
$(x + 1)(x - 2)(x - 5)$

✓ Formative Assessment

Use the Mid-Chapter Quiz to assess students' progress in the first half of the chapter.

For problems answered incorrectly, have students review the lessons indicated in parentheses.

ExamView Assessment Suite Customize and create multiple versions of your Mid-Chapter Test and their answer keys.

FOLDABLES Follow-Up

Before students complete the Mid-Chapter Quiz, encourage them to review the information for Lessons 9-1 through 9-5 in their Foldables.

Additional Answer

7. 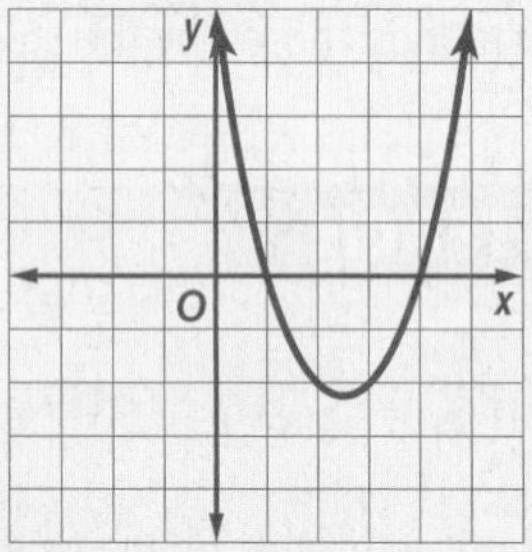

CHAPTER 9 Mid-Chapter Quiz

Lessons 9-1 through 9-5

IL Learning Standards
8.B.4b, 8.D.4

Use a table of values to graph each equation. State the domain and range. (Lesson 9-1) **1–4. See Ch. 9 Answer Appendix.**

1. $y = x^2 + 3x + 1$
2. $y = 2x^2 - 4x + 3$
3. $y = -x^2 - 3x - 3$
4. $y = -3x^2 - x + 1$

Consider $y = x^2 - 5x + 4$. (Lesson 9-1)

5. Write the equation of the axis of symmetry. **$x = 2.5$**
6. Find the coordinates of the vertex. Is it a maximum or minimum point? **(2.5, −2.25); minimum**
7. Graph the function. **See margin.**
8. **SOCCER** A soccer ball is kicked from ground level with an initial upward velocity of 90 feet per second. The equation $h = -16t^2 + 90t$ gives the height h of the ball after t seconds. (Lesson 9-1)
   a. What is the height of the ball after one second? **74 ft**
   b. How many seconds will it take for the ball to reach its maximum height? **2.8125 s**
   c. When is the height of the ball 0 feet? What do these points represent in this situation? **$t = 0$, $t = 5.625$; Before the ball is kicked, and when the ball hits the ground after the kick.**

Solve each equation by graphing. If integral roots cannot be found, estimate the roots to the nearest tenth. (Lesson 9-2)

9. $x^2 + 5x + 6 = 0$ **−3, −2**
10. $x^2 + 8 = -6x$ **−4, −2**
11. $-x^2 + 3x - 1 = 0$ **0.4, 2.6**
12. $x^2 = 12$ **−3.5, 3.5**
13. **BASEBALL** Juan hits a baseball. The equation $h = -16t^2 + 120t$ models the height h, in feet, of the ball after t seconds. How long is the ball in the air? (Lesson 9-2) **7.5 seconds**
14. **CONSTRUCTION** Christopher is repairing the roof on a shed. He accidentally dropped a box of nails from a height of 14 feet. This is represented by the equation $h = -16t^2 + 14$, where h is the height in feet and t is the time in seconds. Describe how the graph is related to $h = t^2$. (Lesson 9-3) **compressed vertically and shifted up 14 units**

Describe how the graph of each function is related to the graph of $f(x) = x^2$. (Lesson 9-3)

15. $g(x) = x^2 + 3$ **shifted up 3 units**
16. $h(x) = 2x^2$ **compressed**
17. $g(x) = x^2 - 6$ **shifted down 6 units**
18. **MULTIPLE CHOICE** Which is an equation for the function shown in the graph? (Lesson 9-3) **D**

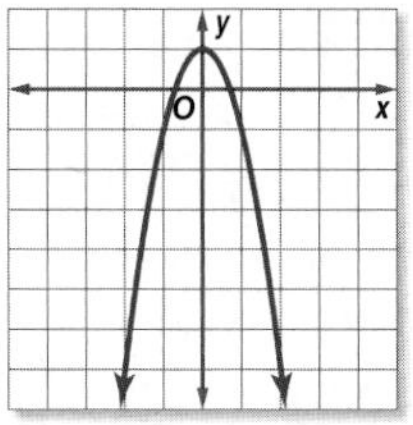

A $y = -2x^2$
B $y = 2x^2 + 1$
C $y = x^2 - 1$
D $y = -2x^2 + 1$

Solve each equation by completing the square. Round to the nearest tenth. (Lesson 9-4)

19. $x^2 + 4x + 2 = 0$ **−3.4, −0.6**
20. $x^2 - 2x - 10 = 0$ **−2.3, 4.3**
21. $2x^2 + 4x - 5 = 7$ **−3.6, 1.6**

Solve each equation by using the Quadratic Formula. Round to the nearest tenth if necessary. (Lesson 9-5)

22. $x^2 - 3x - 18 = 0$ **−3, 6**
23. $x^2 - 10x = -24$ **4, 6**
24. $2x^2 + 5x - 3 = 0$ **$\frac{1}{2}$, −3**
25. **PARTIES** Della's parents are throwing a Sweet 16 party for her. At 10:00, a ball will slide 25 feet down a pole and light up. A function that models the drop is $h = -t^2 + 5t + 25$, where h is height in feet of the ball after t seconds. How many seconds will it take for the ball to reach the bottom of the pole? (Lesson 9-5) **≈8.5 s**

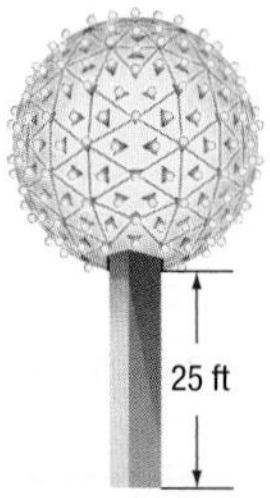

Intervention Planner

Tier 1 On Level	Tier 2 Strategic Intervention approaching grade level	Tier 3 Intensive Intervention 2 or more grades below level
If students miss about 25% of the exercises or less,	**If** students miss about 50% of the exercises,	**If** students miss about 75% of the exercises,
Then choose a resource: **SE** Lessons 9-1, 9-2, 9–3, 9–4, and 9-5 **CRM** Skills Practice, pp. 7, 13, 19, 25, and 31 **TE** Chapter Project, p. 522 **IL Math Online** Self-Check Quiz	**Then** choose a resource: **CRM** Study Guide and Intervention, Chapter 9, pp. 5, 11, 17, 23, and 29 *Quick Review Math Handbook* **IL Math Online** Extra Examples, Personal Tutor, Homework Help	**Then** use *Math Triumphs, Alg. 1* **IL Math Online** Extra Examples, Personal Tutor, Homework Help, Review Vocabulary

Exponential Functions

Then

You simplified numerical expressions involving exponents. (Lesson 1-2)

Now

- Graph exponential functions.
- Identify data that display exponential behavior.

IL Learning Standards

8.A.4b Represent mathematical patterns and describe their properties using variables and mathematical symbols.
8.C.4b Apply algebraic properties and procedures with matrices, vectors, functions and sequences using data found in business, industry and consumer situations.

New Vocabulary
exponential function

IL Math Online

glencoe.com
- Extra Examples
- Personal Tutor
- Self-Check Quiz
- Homework Help

Why?

Tarantulas can appear scary with their large hairy bodies and legs, but they are harmless to humans. The graph shows a tarantula spider population that increases over time. Notice that the graph is neither linear nor quadratic.

The graph represents the function $y = 3(2)^x$. This is an example of an *exponential* function.

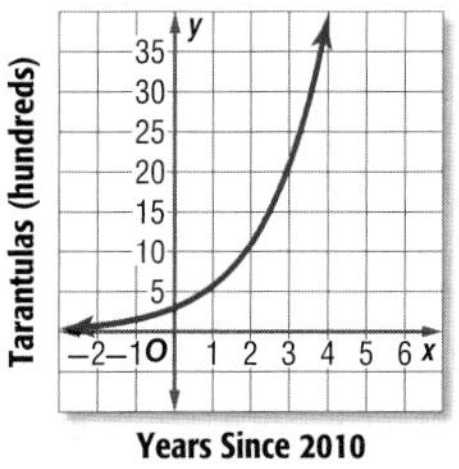

Graph Exponential Functions An **exponential function** is a function of the form $y = ab^x$, where $a \neq 0$, $b > 0$, and $b \neq 1$. Notice that the base is a constant and the exponent is a variable. Exponential functions are nonlinear and nonquadratic functions.

Key Concept — Exponential Function

For Your FOLDABLE

Words An exponential function is a function that can be described by an equation of the form $y = ab^x$, where $a \neq 0$, $b > 0$, and $b \neq 1$.

Examples $y = 2(3)^x$ $y = 4^x$ $y = \left(\frac{1}{2}\right)^x$

EXAMPLE 1 Graph with $a > 0$ and $b > 1$

a. Graph $y = 3^x$. Find the y-intercept, and state the domain and range.

x	3^x	y
−2	3^{-2}	$\frac{1}{9}$
−1	3^{-1}	$\frac{1}{3}$
0	3^0	1
1	3^1	3
2	3^2	9

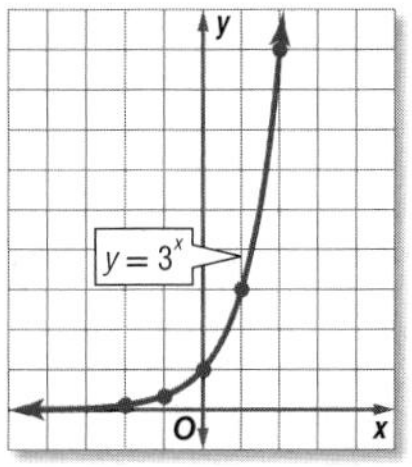

Graph the ordered pairs, and connect the points with a smooth curve.
The graph crosses the y-axis at 1, so the y-intercept is 1.
The domain is all real numbers, and the range is all positive real numbers.

b. Use the graph to approximate the value of $3^{0.7}$.

The graph represents all real values of x and their corresponding values of y for $y = 3^x$. So, when $x = 0.7$, y is about 2. Use a calculator to confirm this value: $3^{0.7} \approx 2.157669$.

Check Your Progress

1A. Graph $y = 7^x$. Find the y-intercept, and state the domain and range. See Ch. 9 Answer Appendix.

1B. Use the graph to approximate the value of $y = 7^{0.5}$ to the nearest tenth. Use a calculator to confirm the value. 2.6

Personal Tutor glencoe.com

9-6 Lesson Notes

1 FOCUS

Vertical Alignment

Before Lesson 9-6
Simplify numerical expressions involving exponents.

Lesson 9-6
Graph exponential functions.
Identify data that display exponential behavior.

After Lesson 9-6
Solve problems involving exponential growth and decay.

2 TEACH

Scaffolding Questions

Have students read the *Why?* section of the lesson.

Ask:

- How is the exponent in this equation different from the exponent in a quadratic equation? It changes as the value of x changes.
- What is the value of y when $x = 0$? $y = 3$
- Can the value of y ever be 0? no

Lesson 9-6 Resources

Resource	Approaching-Level	On-Level	Beyond-Level	English Learners
Teacher Edition		• Differentiated Instruction, pp. 569, 572	• Differentiated Instruction, pp. 569, 572	
Chapter Resource Masters	• Study Guide and Intervention, pp. 35–36 • Skills Practice, p. 37 • Practice, p. 38 • Word Problem Practice, p. 39	• Study Guide and Intervention, pp. 35–36 • Skills Practice, p. 37 • Practice, p. 38 • Word Problem Practice, p. 39 • Enrichment, p. 40	• Practice, p. 38 • Word Problem Practice, p. 39 • Enrichment, p. 40	• Study Guide and Intervention, pp. 35–36 • Skills Practice, p. 37 • Practice, p. 38 • Word Problem Practice, p. 39
Transparencies	• 5-Minute Check Transparency 9-6	• 5-Minute Check Transparency 9-6	• 5-Minute Check Transparency 9-6	• 5-Minute Check Transparency 9-6
Other	• Study Notebook • Teaching Algebra with Manipulatives	• Study Notebook • Teaching Algebra with Manipulatives	• Study Notebook	• Study Notebook • Teaching Algebra with Manipulatives

Graph Exponential Functions

Example 1 shows how to graph an exponential function when $a > 0$ and $b > 1$. **Example 2** shows how to graph an exponential function when $a > 0$ and $0 < b < 1$. **Example 3** shows how to use an exponential function to solve a real-world problem.

Formative Assessment

Use the Check Your Progress exercises after each example to determine students' understanding of concepts.

Additional Examples

1 **a.** Graph $y = 4^x$. Find the y-intercept and state the domain and range.
y-intercept: 1, D = {all real numbers}, R = {all positive numbers}

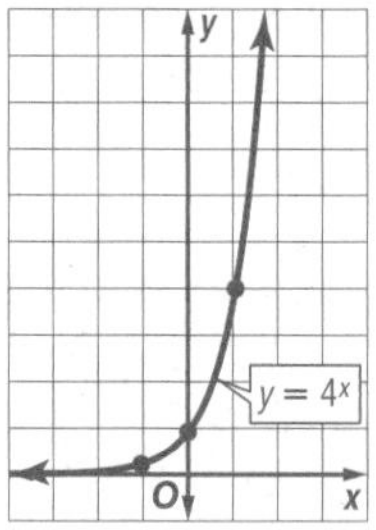

b. Use the graph to approximate the value of $4^{1.5}$. ≈ 8

2 **a.** Graph $y = \left(\frac{1}{4}\right)^x$. Find the y-intercept and state the domain and range.
y-intercept: 1, D = {all real numbers}, R = {all positive numbers}

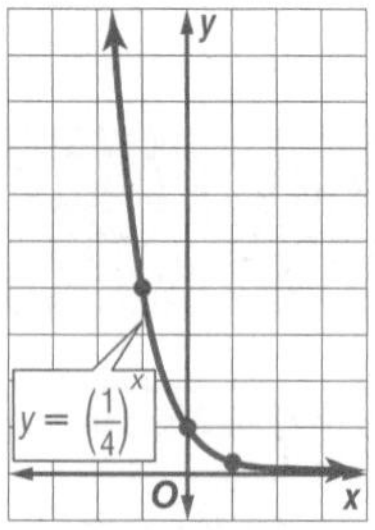

b. Use the graph to approximate the value of $\left(\frac{1}{4}\right)^{-1.5}$. 8

The graphs of functions of the form $y = ab^x$, where $a > 0$ and $b > 1$, all have the same shape as the graph in Example 1. The greater the base or b-value, the faster the graph rises as you move from left to right on the graph. The graphs of functions of the form $y = ab^x$, where $a > 0$ and $0 < b < 1$, also have the same general shape.

StudyTip

$a < 0$ If the value of a is less than 0, the graph will be reflected across the x-axis.

EXAMPLE 2 Graph with $a > 0$ and $0 < b < 1$

a. Graph $y = \left(\frac{1}{3}\right)^x$. Find the y-intercept, and state the domain and range.

x	$\left(\frac{1}{3}\right)^x$	y
−2	$\left(\frac{1}{3}\right)^{-2}$	9
0	$\left(\frac{1}{3}\right)^0$	1
2	$\left(\frac{1}{3}\right)^2$	$\frac{1}{9}$

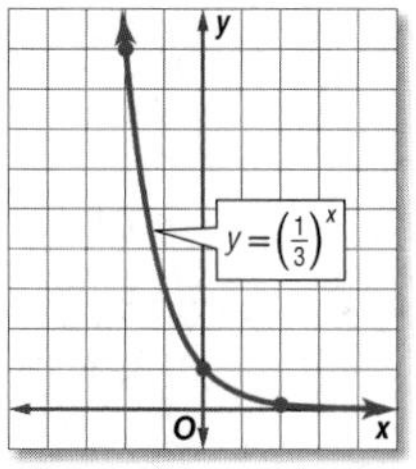

The y-intercept is 1. The domain is all real numbers, and the range is all positive real numbers. Notice that as x increases, the y-values decrease less rapidly.

b. Use the graph to approximate the value of $\left(\frac{1}{3}\right)^{-1.5}$.

When $x = -1.5$, the value of y is about 5. Use a calculator to confirm this value:

KEYSTROKES: [( ] 1 [÷] 3 [ )] [^] −1.5 [ENTER] 5.196152.

2A.

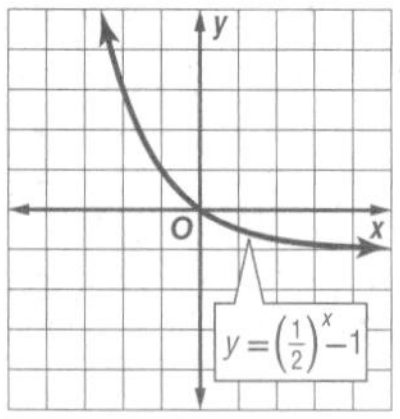

(0, 0); D = {all real numbers}; R = {y | y > −1}

Check Your Progress

2A. Graph $y = \left(\frac{1}{2}\right)^x - 1$. Find the y-intercept, and state the domain and range.

2B. Use the graph to approximate the value of $\left(\frac{1}{2}\right)^{-2.5} - 1$ to the nearest tenth. Use a calculator to confirm the value. $\left(\frac{1}{2}\right)^{-2.5} - 1 \approx 4.7$

Personal Tutor glencoe.com

Real-World Link

The United States is the largest soda consumer in the world. In a recent year, the United States accounted for one third of the world's total soda consumption.

Source: Worldwatch Institute

Exponential functions occur in many real world situations.

Real-World EXAMPLE 3 Use Exponential Functions to Solve Problems

SODA The consumption of soda has increased each year since 2000. The function $C = 179(1.029)^t$ models the amount of soda consumed in the world, where C is the amount consumed in billions of liters and t is the number of years since 2000.

a. Graph the function. What values of C and t are meaningful in the context of the problem?

Since t represents time, $t > 0$. At $t = 0$, the consumption is 179 billion liters. Therefore, in the context of this problem, $C > 179$ is meaningful.

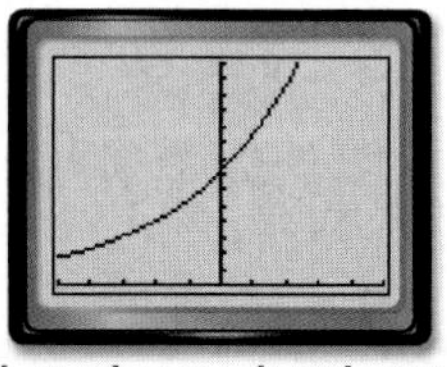

[−50, 50] scl: 10 by [0, 350] scl: 25

Watch Out!

Student Misconceptions Make sure students understand that the graphs of exponential functions never actually touch the x-axis. It is acceptable for hand-drawn graphs to show the graph just above and about parallel to the x-axis as long as students understand that the graph gets infinitely close to the axis without touching it.

TEACH with TECH

INTERACTIVE WHITEBOARD Create a template for a table of values, and drag a coordinate grid onto the board. Write a function and have students complete the table of values. Then have students draw the graph of the function.

b. How much soda was consumed in 2005?

$C = 179(1.029)^t$ **Original equation**

$= 179(1.029)^5$ **$t = 5$**

≈ 206.5 **Use a calculator.**

The world soda consumption in 2005 was approximately 206.5 billion liters.

Check Your Progress

3. A certain bacteria population doubles every 20 minutes. Beginning with 10 cells in a culture, the population can be represented by the function $B = 10(2)^t$, where B is the number of bacteria cells and t is the time in 20 minute increments. How many will there be after 2 hours? **640**

Personal Tutor glencoe.com

Identify Exponential Behavior Recall from Lesson 3-3 that linear functions have a constant rate of change. Exponential functions do not have constant rates of change, but they do have constant ratios.

EXAMPLE 4 Identify Exponential Behavior

Determine whether the set of data shown below displays exponential behavior. Write *yes* or *no*. Explain why or why not.

x	0	5	10	15	20	25
y	64	32	16	8	4	2

Method 1 Look for a pattern.

The domain values are at regular intervals of 5. Look for a common factor among the range values.

64 32 16 8 4 2

$\times\frac{1}{2}$ $\times\frac{1}{2}$ $\times\frac{1}{2}$ $\times\frac{1}{2}$ $\times\frac{1}{2}$

The range values differ by the common factor of $\frac{1}{2}$.

Since the domain values are at regular intervals and the range values differ by a positive common factor, the data are probably exponential. Its equation may involve $\left(\frac{1}{2}\right)^x$.

Method 2 Graph the data.

Plot the points and connect them with a smooth curve. The graph shows a rapidly decreasing value of y as x increases. This is a characteristic of exponential behavior in which the base is between 0 and 1.

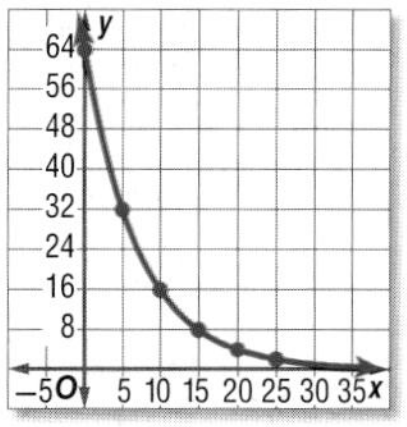

Check Your Progress

4. Determine whether the set of data shown below displays exponential behavior. Write *yes* or *no*. Explain why or why not.

x	0	3	6	9	12	15
y	12	16	20	24	28	32

Personal Tutor glencoe.com

Problem-Solving Tip

Make an Organized List Making an organized list of x-values and corresponding y-values is helpful in graphing the function. It can also help you identify patterns in the data.

4. No; the domain values are at regular intervals, but the range values have a common difference of 4.

Study Tip

Checking Answers The graph of an exponential function may resemble part of the graph of a quadratic function. Be sure to check for a pattern as well as to look at a graph.

Focus on Mathematical Content

Graphs of Exponential Functions An equation of the form $y = a^x$, where a is greater than zero but not equal to 1, is an exponential equation. When $a > 1$, y increases as x increases. The greater the value of a, the more rapidly y increases. When $0 < a < 1$, y decreases as x increases. The smaller the value of a, the more rapidly the function decreases.

Additional Example

3 **DEPRECIATION** Some people say that the value of a new car decreases as soon as it is driven off the lot. The function $V = 25{,}000 \cdot 0.82^t$ models the depreciation in the value of a new car that originally cost \$25,000. V represents the value of the car and t represents the time in years from the time of purchase.

a. Graph the function. What values of V and t are meaningful in the context of the problem?

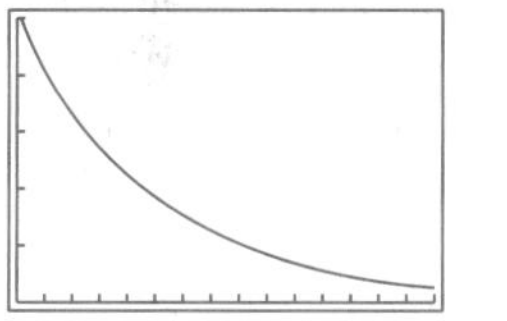

[0, 15] scl: 1 by [0, 25,000] scl: 500
Only values of $V \leq 25{,}000$ and $t \geq 0$ are meaningful.

b. What is the car's value after five years? about \$9270

Additional Examples also in Interactive Classroom PowerPoint® Presentations

IWB INTERACTIVE WHITEBOARD READY

Differentiated Instruction

OL BL

Logical Learners Ask students to write a comparison of an exponential function to a quadratic function and to a linear function.

Identify Exponential Behavior

Example 4 shows how to determine whether a set of data displays exponential behavior.

Additional Example

4 Determine whether the set of data shown below displays exponential behavior. Write *yes* or *no*. Explain why or why not.

x	0	10	20	30
y	10	25	62.5	156.25

The domain values are at regular intervals, and the range values have a common factor of 2.5, so the set is probably exponential. Also, the graph shows rapidly increasing values of y as x increases.

3 PRACTICE

Formative Assessment

Use Exercises 1–9 to check for understanding.

Use the chart at the bottom of this page to customize assignments for your students.

Exercise Alert

Grid Paper For Exercises 1–6 and 10–20, students will need grid paper.

Additional Answers

21. No; the domain values are at regular intervals, but the range values do not have a positive common factor.

22. No; the domain values are at regular intervals, but the range values have a common difference of 5.

23. Yes; the domain values are at regular intervals, and the range values have a common factor of 2.

24. Yes; the domain values are at regular intervals, and the range values have a common factor of 0.4.

Check Your Understanding

Examples 1 and 2 pp. 567–568

Graph each function. Find the y-intercept and state the domain and range. Then use the graph to determine the approximate value of the given expression to the nearest tenth. Use a calculator to confirm the value. 1–6. See Ch. 9 Answer Appendix.

1. $y = 2^x; 2^{1.5}$

2. $y = -5^x; -5^{0.5}$

3. $y = -\left(\frac{1}{5}\right)^x; -\left(\frac{1}{5}\right)^{-0.5}$

4. $y = 3\left(\frac{1}{4}\right)^x; 3\left(\frac{1}{4}\right)^{0.5}$

Graph each function. Find the y-intercept, and state the domain and range.

5. $f(x) = 6^x + 3$

6. $f(x) = 2 - 2^x$

Example 3 pp. 568–569

7. **BIOLOGY** The function $f(t) = 100(1.05)^t$ models the growth of a fruit fly population, where $f(t)$ is the number of flies and t is time in days.

a. What values for the domain and range are reasonable in the context of this situation? Explain.

b. After two weeks, approximately how many flies are in this population? about 198 fruit flies

7a. D = {$d \mid d \geq 0$}, the number of days is greater than or equal to 0; R = {$y \mid y \geq 100$}, the number of fruit flies is greater than or equal to 100.

Example 4 p. 569

Determine whether the set of data shown below displays exponential behavior. Write *yes* or *no*. Explain why or why not.

8.

x	1	2	3	4	5	6
y	−4	−2	0	2	4	6

9.

x	2	4	6	8	10	12
y	1	4	16	64	256	1024

8. No; the domain values are at regular intervals, but the range values have a common difference of 2.

9. Yes; the domain values are at regular intervals, and the range values have a common factor of 4.

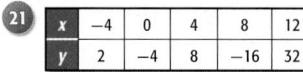

Practice and Problem Solving

= **Step-by-Step Solutions** begin on page R12. **Extra Practice** begins on page 815.

Examples 1 and 2 pp. 567–568

Graph each function. Find the y-intercept and state the domain and range. Then use the graph to determine the approximate value of the given expression to the nearest tenth. Use a calculator to confirm the value. 10–15. See Ch. 9 Answer Appendix.

10. $y = 2 \cdot 8^x, 2(8)^{-0.5}$

11. $y = 2 \cdot \left(\frac{1}{6}\right)^x; 2\left(\frac{1}{6}\right)^{1.5}$

12. $y = \left(\frac{1}{12}\right)^x; \left(\frac{1}{12}\right)^{0.5}$

13. $y = -3 \cdot 9^x, -3(9)^{-0.5}$

14. $y = -4 \cdot 10^x, -4(10)^{-0.5}$

15. $y = 3 \cdot 11^x, 3(11)^{-0.2}$

Graph each function. Find the y-intercept and state the domain and range.

16. $y = 4^x + 3$

17. $y = \frac{1}{2}(2^x - 8)$

18. $y = 5(3^x) + 1$

19. $y = -2(3^x) + 5$

16–19. See Ch. 9 Answer Appendix.

Example 3 pp. 568–569

20. **BIOLOGY** A population of bacteria in a culture increases according to the model $p = 300(2.7)^{0.02t}$, where t is the number of hours and $t = 0$ corresponds to 9:00 A.M.

a. Use this model to estimate the number of bacteria at 11 A.M. about 312

b. Graph the function and name the p-intercept. Describe what the p-intercept represents, and describe a reasonable domain and range for this situation. See Ch. 9 Answer Appendix.

Example 4 p. 569

Determine whether the set of data shown below displays exponential behavior. Write *yes* or *no*. Explain why or why not. 21–24. See margin.

21.

x	−4	0	4	8	12
y	2	−4	8	−16	32

22.

x	−6	−3	0	3
y	5	10	15	20

23.

x	−8	−6	−4	−2
y	0.25	0.5	1	2

24.

x	20	30	40	50	60
y	1	0.4	0.16	0.064	0.0256

Differentiated Homework Options

Level	Assignment	Two-Day Option	
AL Basic	10–24, 42–68	11–23 odd, 46–49	10–24 even, 42–45, 50–68
OL Core	11–39 odd, 26, 40, 42–68	10–24, 46–49	25–40, 42–45, 50–68
BL Advanced	25–62, (optional: 63–68)		

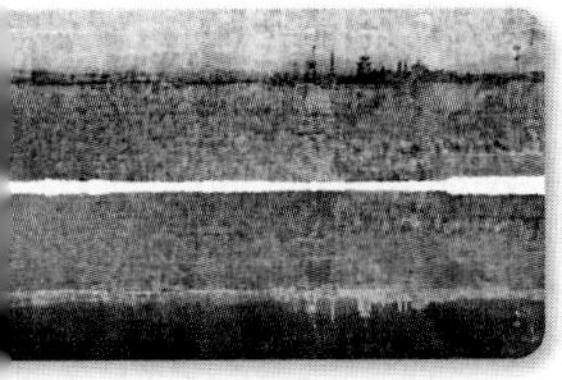

Real-World Link

The world's largest photograph, named The Great Picture, was created by a group of photographers known as The Legacy Project. The photograph has an area of 3375 square feet.

Source: Photoshop Support

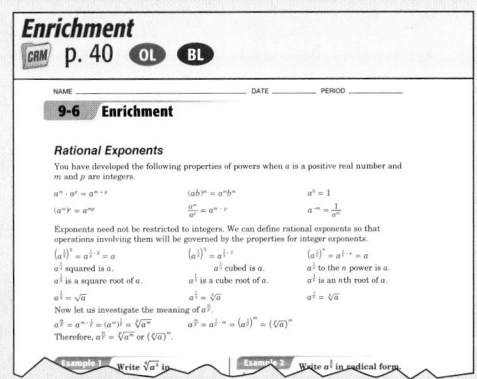

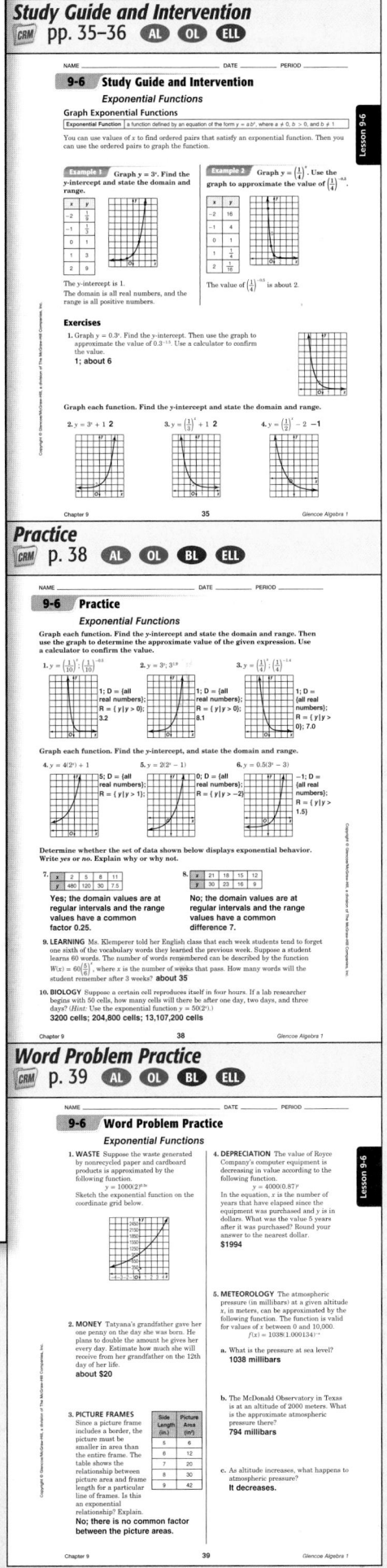

25. **PHOTOGRAPHY** Jameka is enlarging a photograph to make a poster for school. She will enlarge the picture repeatedly at 150%. The function $P = 1.5^x$ models the new size of the picture being enlarged, where x is the number of enlargements. How many times as big is the picture after 4 enlargements? **about 506% bigger than the original**

26. **FINANCIAL LITERACY** Daniel invested \$500 into a savings account. The equation $A = 500(1.005)^{12t}$ models the value of Daniel's investment A after t years. How much will Daniel's investment be worth in 8 years? **about \$807.07**

Identify each function as *linear*, *quadratic*, or *exponential*.

27. 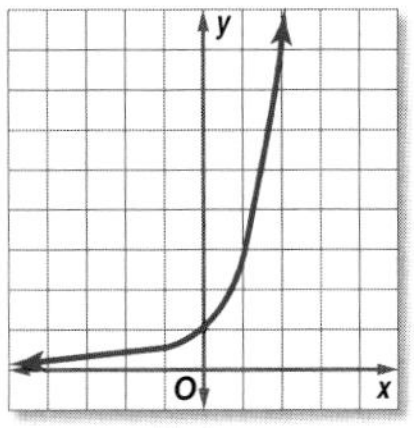
exponential

28. 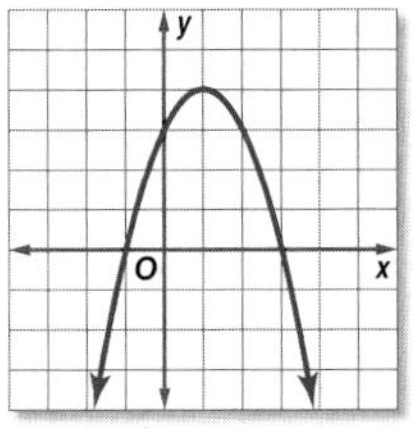
quadratic

29. 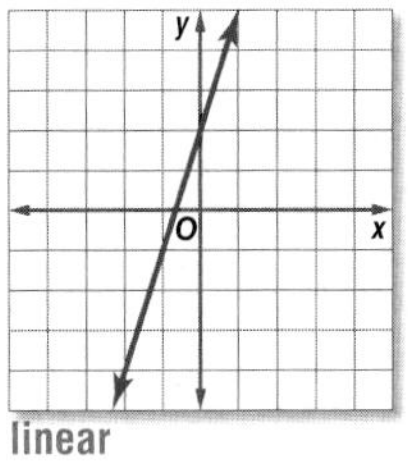
linear

30. $y = 4^x$ **exponential**
31. $y = 2x(x - 1)$ **quadratic**
32. $5x + y = 8$ **linear**

33. **GRADUATION** The number of graduates at a high school has increased by a factor of 1.055 every year since 2001. In 2001, 110 students graduated. The function $N = 110(1.055)^t$ models N, the number of students expected to graduate t years after 2001. How many students will graduate in 2012? **about 198 students**

Describe the graph of each equation as a transformation of the graph of $y = 2^x$.

34. $y = 2^x + 6$
35. $y = 3(2)^x$
36. $y = -\frac{1}{4}(2)^x$
37. $y = -3 + 2^x$
38. $y = \left(\frac{1}{2}\right)^x$
39. $y = -5(2)^x$

40. **DEER** The deer population at a national park doubles every year. In 2000, there were 25 deer in the park. The function $N = 25(2)^t$ models the number of deer N in the park t years after 2000. What will the deer population be in 2015? **819,200**

34. a translation 6 units up
35. a vertical stretch by a factor of 3
36. a reflection over the x-axis and a vertical compression
37. a translation down 3 units
38. a reflection over the y-axis
39. a vertical stretch by a factor of 5 and a reflection over the x-axis.
42. Never; the graph never crosses the x-axis because the powers of b are always positive and $a \neq 0$. Thus, ab^x is never 0.

H.O.T. Problems

Use Higher-Order Thinking Skills

41. **CHALLENGE** Write an exponential function for which the graph passes through the points at (0, 3) and (1, 6). $f(x) = 3(2)^x$

42. **REASONING** Determine whether the graph of $y = ab^x$, where $a \neq 0$, $b > 0$, and $b \neq 1$, *sometimes*, *always*, or *never* has an x-intercept. Explain your reasoning.

43. **OPEN ENDED** Find an exponential function that represents a real-world situation, and graph the function. Analyze the graph. **See Ch. 9 Answer Appendix.**

44. **REASONING** Compare and contrast a function of the form $y = ab^x + c$, where $a \neq 0$, $b > 0$, and $b \neq 1$ and a quadratic function of the form $y = ax^2 + c$. **See Ch. 9 Answer Appendix.**

45. **WRITING IN MATH** Explain how to determine whether a set of data displays exponential behavior. **See Ch. 9 Answer Appendix.**

Study Guide and Intervention

CRM pp. 35–36 AL OL ELL

NAME ______ DATE ______ PERIOD ______

9-6 Study Guide and Intervention

Exponential Functions

Graph Exponential Functions

Exponential Function	a function defined by an equation of the form $y = ab^x$, where $a \neq 0$, $b > 0$, and $b \neq 1$

You can use values of x to find ordered pairs that satisfy an exponential function. Then you can use the ordered pairs to graph the function.

Example 1 Graph $y = 3^x$. Find the y-intercept and state the domain and range.

x	y
−2	$\frac{1}{9}$
−1	$\frac{1}{3}$
0	1
1	3
2	9

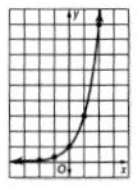

The y-intercept is 1.
The domain is all real numbers, and the range is all positive numbers.

Example 2 Graph $y = \left(\frac{1}{4}\right)^x$. Use the graph to approximate the value of $\left(\frac{1}{4}\right)^{-0.5}$.

x	y
−2	16
−1	4
0	1
1	$\frac{1}{4}$
2	$\frac{1}{16}$

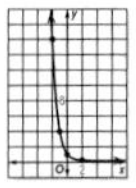

The value of $\left(\frac{1}{4}\right)^{-0.5}$ is about 2.

Exercises

1. Graph $y = 0.3^x$. Find the y-intercept. Then use the graph to approximate the value of $0.3^{-1.5}$. Use a calculator to confirm the value. **1; about 6**

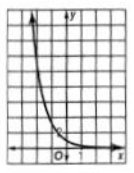

Graph each function. Find the y-intercept and state the domain and range.

2. $y = 3^x + 1$ **2**
3. $y = \left(\frac{1}{3}\right)^x + 1$ **2**
4. $y = \left(\frac{1}{2}\right)^x - 2$ **−1**

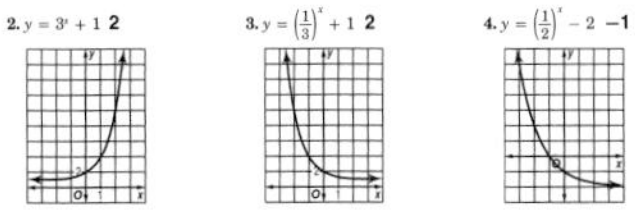

Lesson 9-6

Practice

CRM p. 38 AL OL BL ELL

NAME ______ DATE ______ PERIOD ______

9-6 Practice

Exponential Functions

Graph each function. Find the y-intercept and state the domain and range. Then use the graph to determine the approximate value of the given expression. Use a calculator to confirm the value.

1. $y = \left(\frac{1}{10}\right)^x$; $\left(\frac{1}{10}\right)^{-0.5}$ **1; D = {all real numbers}; R = { y | y > 0}; 3.2**
2. $y = 3^x$; $3^{1.9}$ **1; D = {all real numbers}; R = { y | y > 0}; 8.1**
3. $y = \left(\frac{1}{4}\right)^x$; $\left(\frac{1}{4}\right)^{-1.4}$ **1; D = {all real numbers}; R = { y | y > 0}; 7.0**

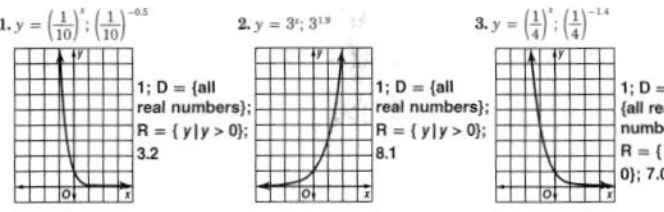

Graph each function. Find the y-intercept, and state the domain and range.

4. $y = 4(2^x) + 1$ **5; D = {all real numbers}; R = { y | y > 1};**
5. $y = 2(2^x - 1)$ **0; D = {all real numbers}; R = { y | y > −2}**
6. $y = 0.5(3^x - 3)$ **−1; D = {all real numbers}; R = { y | y > 1.5}**

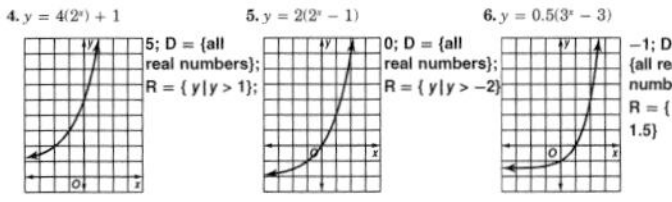

Determine whether the set of data shown below displays exponential behavior. Write *yes* or *no*. Explain why or why not.

7.

x	2	5	8	11
y	480	120	30	7.5

Yes; the domain values are at regular intervals and the range values have a common factor 0.25.

8.

x	21	18	15	12
y	30	23	16	9

No; the domain values are at regular intervals and the range values have a common difference 7.

9. **LEARNING** Ms. Klemperer told her English class that each week students tend to forget one sixth of the vocabulary words they learned the previous week. Suppose a student learns 60 words. The number of words remembered can be described by the function $W(x) = 60\left(\frac{5}{6}\right)^x$, where x is the number of weeks that pass. How many words will the student remember after 3 weeks? **about 35**

10. **BIOLOGY** Suppose a certain cell reproduces itself in four hours. If a lab researcher begins with 50 cells, how many cells will there be after one day, two days, and three days? (*Hint:* Use the exponential function $y = 50(2^x)$.) **3200 cells; 204,800 cells; 13,107,200 cells**

Word Problem Practice

CRM p. 39 AL OL BL ELL

NAME ______ DATE ______ PERIOD ______

9-6 Word Problem Practice

Exponential Functions

1. **WASTE** Suppose the waste generated by nonrecycled paper and cardboard products is approximated by the following function.
$$y = 1000(2)^{0.3x}$$
Sketch the exponential function on the coordinate grid below.

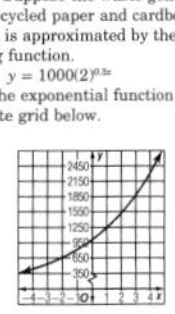

2. **MONEY** Tatyana's grandfather gave her one penny on the day she was born. He plans to double the amount he gives her every day. Estimate how much she will receive from her grandfather on the 12th day of her life. **about \$20**

3. **PICTURE FRAMES** Since a picture frame includes a border, the picture must be smaller in area than the entire frame. The table shows the relationship between picture area and frame length for a particular line of frames. Is this an exponential relationship? Explain.

Side Length (in.)	Picture Area (in²)
5	6
6	12
7	20
8	30
9	42

No; there is no common factor between the picture areas.

4. **DEPRECIATION** The value of Royce Company's computer equipment is decreasing in value according to the following function.
$$y = 4000(0.87)^x$$
In the equation, x is the number of years that have elapsed since the equipment was purchased and y is in dollars. What was the value 5 years after it was purchased? Round your answer to the nearest dollar. **\$1994**

5. **METEOROLOGY** The atmospheric pressure (in millibars) at a given altitude x, in meters, can be approximated by the following function. The function is valid for values of x between 0 and 10,000.
$$f(x) = 1038(1.000134)^{-x}$$
a. What is the pressure at sea level? **1038 millibars**
b. The McDonald Observatory in Texas is at an altitude of 2000 meters. What is the approximate atmospheric pressure there? **794 millibars**
c. As altitude increases, what happens to atmospheric pressure? **It decreases.**

Lesson 9-6

Enrichment

CRM p. 40 OL BL

NAME ______ DATE ______ PERIOD ______

9-6 Enrichment

Rational Exponents

You have developed the following properties of powers when a is a positive real number and m and p are integers.

$a^m \cdot a^p = a^{m+p}$ $(ab)^m = a^m b^m$ $a^0 = 1$

$(a^m)^p = a^{mp}$ $\frac{a^m}{a^p} = a^{m-p}$ $a^{-m} = \frac{1}{a^m}$

Exponents need not be restricted to integers. We can define rational exponents so that operations involving them will be governed by the properties for integer exponents.

$\left(a^{\frac{1}{2}}\right)^2 = a^{\frac{1}{2} \cdot 2} = a$ $\left(a^{\frac{1}{3}}\right)^3 = a^{\frac{1}{3} \cdot 3}$ $\left(a^{\frac{1}{n}}\right)^n = a^{\frac{1}{n} \cdot n} = a$

$a^{\frac{1}{2}}$ squared is a. $a^{\frac{1}{3}}$ cubed is a. $a^{\frac{1}{n}}$ to the n power is a.

$a^{\frac{1}{2}}$ is a square root of a. $a^{\frac{1}{3}}$ is a cube root of a. $a^{\frac{1}{n}}$ is an nth root of a.

$a^{\frac{1}{2}} = \sqrt{a}$ $a^{\frac{1}{3}} = \sqrt[3]{a}$ $a^{\frac{1}{n}} = \sqrt[n]{a}$

Now let us investigate the meaning of $a^{\frac{m}{p}}$.

$a^{\frac{m}{p}} = a^{m \cdot \frac{1}{p}} = (a^m)^{\frac{1}{p}} = \sqrt[p]{a^m}$ $a^{\frac{m}{p}} = a^{\frac{1}{p} \cdot m} = \left(a^{\frac{1}{p}}\right)^m = (\sqrt[p]{a})^m$

Therefore, $a^{\frac{m}{p}} = \sqrt[p]{a^m}$ or $(\sqrt[p]{a})^m$.

Example 1 Write $\sqrt[4]{a^3}$ in

Example 2 Write $a^{\frac{2}{3}}$ in radical form.

4 ASSESS

Crystal Ball Ask students to write how they think exponential functions will connect with the next lesson, which involves real-world growth and decay problems.

PSAE PRACTICE 8.11.11, 8.11.19, 7.11.03, 8.11.22

46. SHORT RESPONSE What are the zeros of the function graphed below? **2 and 4**

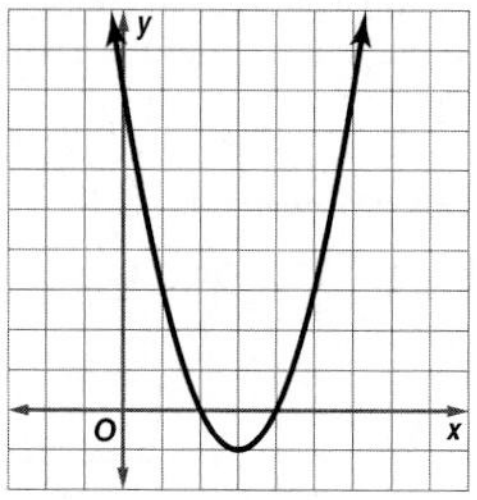

47. Hinto invested \$300 into a savings account. The equation $A = 300(1.005)^{12t}$ models the amount in Hinto's account A after t years. How much will be in Hinto's account after 7 years? **B**

A \$25,326
B \$456.11
C \$385.01
D \$301.52

48. GEOMETRY Ayana placed a circular piece of paper on a square picture as shown below. If the picture extends 4 inches beyond the circle on each side, what is the perimeter of the square picture? **J**

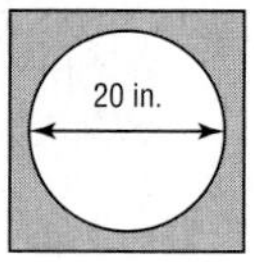

F 64 in.
G 80 in.
H 94 in.
J 112 in.

49. Which of the following shows $4x^2 - 8x - 12$ factored completely? **A**

A $4(x - 3)(x + 1)$
B $4(x + 3)(x - 1)$
C $(4x + 12)(x - 1)$
D $(x - 3)(4x + 4)$

Spiral Review

Solve each equation by using the Quadratic Formula. Round to the nearest tenth if necessary. (Lesson 9-5)

50. $6x^2 - 3x - 30 = 0$ **−2, 2.5**
51. $4x^2 + 18x = 10$ **−5, 0.5**
52. $2x^2 + 6x = 7$ **−3.9, 0.9**

Solve each equation by taking the square root of each side. Round to the nearest tenth if necessary. (Lesson 9-4)

53. $x^2 = 25$ **±5**
54. $x^2 + 6x + 9 = 16$ **−7, 1**
55. $x^2 - 14x + 49 = 15$ **3.1, 10.9**

Evaluate each product. Express the results in both scientific notation and standard form. (Lesson 7-3) **56. 8.93×10^8, 893,000,000 57. 2.52×10^2, 252 58. 2.432×10^{-11}, 0.00000000002432**

56. $(1.9 \times 10^2)(4.7 \times 10^6)$
57. $(4.5 \times 10^{-3})(5.6 \times 10^4)$
58. $(3.8 \times 10^{-4})(6.4 \times 10^{-8})$

59. DEMOLITION DERBY When a car hits an object, the damage is measured by the collision impact. For a certain car the collision impact I is given by $I = 2v^2$, where v represents the speed in kilometers per minute. What is the collision impact if the speed of the car is 4 kilometers per minute? (Lesson 7-1) **32 km²/min²**

Use elimination to solve each system of equations. (Lesson 6-3)

60. $x + y = -3$, $x - y = 1$ **(−1, −2)**
61. $3a + b = 5$, $2a + b = 10$ **(−5, 20)**
62. $3x - 5y = 16$, $-3x + 2y = -10$ **(2, −2)**

Skills Review

Find the next three terms of each arithmetic sequence. (Lesson 3-5)

63. 1, 3, 5, 7, ... **9, 11, 13**
64. −6, −4, −2, 0, ... **2, 4, 6**
65. 6.5, 9, 11.5, 14, ... **16.5, 19, 21.5**
66. 10, 3, −4, −11, ... **−18, −25, −32**
67. $\frac{1}{2}, \frac{5}{4}, 2, \frac{11}{4}, \ldots$ **$\frac{7}{2}, \frac{17}{4}, 5$**
68. $1, \frac{3}{4}, \frac{1}{2}, \frac{1}{4}, \ldots$ **$0, -\frac{1}{4}, -\frac{1}{2}$**

Differentiated Instruction

OL BL

Extension Give students this scenario: a wise man asked his ruler to provide rice for his people. The wise man asked the ruler to give him 2 grains of rice for the first square on a chess board, 4 grains for the second, and so on, doubling the amount of rice with each square of the board.

Ask:

- How many grains of rice will the wise man receive for the sixty-fourth square on the chessboard? 2^{64} or about 1.84×10^{19} grains
- If one pound of rice has approximately 24,000 grains, how many tons of rice will the wise man receive on the last day? (Hint: 1 ton = 2000 pounds) about 3.84×10^{11} tons

572 Chapter 9 Quadratic and Exponential Functions

9-7 Growth and Decay

Then

You analyzed exponential functions. (Lesson 9-6)

Now

- Solve problems involving exponential growth.
- Solve problems involving exponential decay.

IL Learning Standards

8.C.4b Apply algebraic properties and procedures with matrices, vectors, functions and sequences using data found in business, industry and consumer situations.

New Vocabulary

exponential growth
compound interest
exponential decay

IL Math Online

glencoe.com

- Extra Examples
- Personal Tutor
- Self-Check Quiz
- Homework Help

Why?

The number of Weblogs or blogs increased at a monthly rate of about 13.7% over 21 months. The average number of blogs per month can be modeled by $y = 1.1(1 + 0.137)^t$ or $y = 1.1(1.137)^t$, where y represents the total number of blogs in millions and t is the number of months since November 2003.

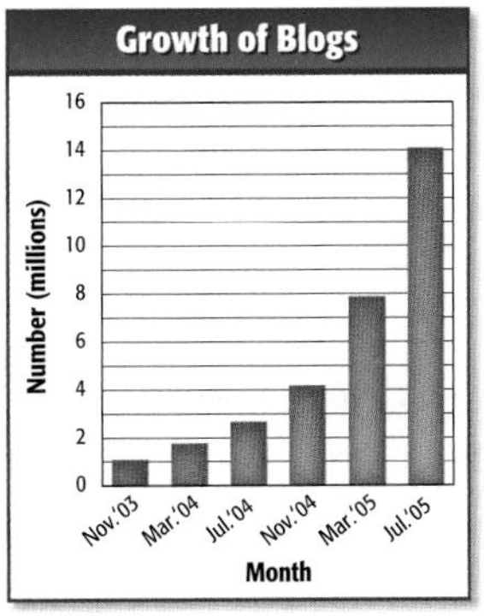

Exponential Growth The equation for the number of blogs is in the form $y = a(1 + r)^t$. This is the general equation for **exponential growth**.

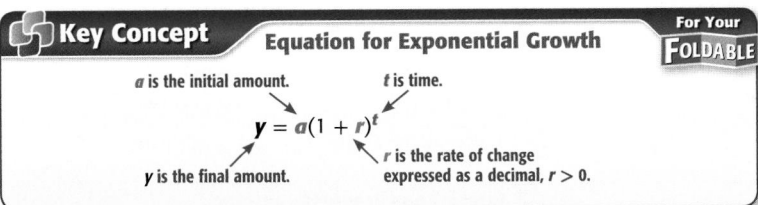

Key Concept — Equation for Exponential Growth

For Your FOLDABLE

$$y = a(1 + r)^t$$

- a is the initial amount.
- t is time.
- y is the final amount.
- r is the rate of change expressed as a decimal, $r > 0$.

Real-World EXAMPLE 1 — Exponential Growth

CONTEST A radio station is sponsoring a contest. The prize begins as a $100 gift card. Once a day, the disc jockey announces a name, and the person has 15 minutes to call. If the person does not call within the allotted time, the prize increases by 2.5%.

a. Write an equation to represent the amount of the gift card in dollars after t days with no winners.

$y = a(1 + r)^t$ — Equation for exponential growth

$y = 100(1 + 0.025)^t$ — $a = 100$ and $r = 2.5\%$ or 0.025

$y = 100(1.025)^t$ — Simplify.

In the equation $y = 100(1.025)^t$, y is the amount of the gift card and t is the number of days since the contest began.

b. How much will the gift card be worth if no one wins after 10 days?

$y = 100(1.025)^t$ — Equation for amount of gift card

$= 100(1.025)^{10}$ — $t = 10$

≈ 128.01 — Use a calculator.

In 10 days, the gift card will be worth $128.01.

Check Your Progress

1. TUITION A college's tuition has risen 5% each year since 2000. If the tuition in 2000 was $10,850, write an equation for the amount of the tuition t years after 2000. Predict the cost of tuition for this college in 2015.
$y = 10{,}850(1.05)^t$; about $22,556.37

Personal Tutor glencoe.com

9-7 Lesson Notes

1 FOCUS

Vertical Alignment

Before Lesson 9-7
Analyze exponential functions.

Lesson 9-7
Solve problems involving exponential growth.
Solve problems involving exponential decay.

After Lesson 9-7
Solve problems involving inverse variation.

2 TEACH

Scaffolding Questions

Have students read the *Why?* section of lesson.

Ask:

- Looking at the equation, how do you know the function is not linear? Time, represented as t, is an exponent so the function is not linear.
- Use the equation to predict the average number of blogs in millions in the 8th month. about 3 million
- Would you describe the average number of blogs per month as growing or decaying? growing

Lesson 9-7 Resources

Resource	Approaching-Level	On-Level	Beyond-Level	English Learners
Teacher Edition		• Differentiated Instruction, p. 577	• Differentiated Instruction, p. 577	
Chapter Resource Masters	• Study Guide and Intervention, pp. 41–42 • Skills Practice, p. 43 • Practice, p. 44 • Word Problem Practice, p. 45	• Study Guide and Intervention, pp. 41–42 • Skills Practice, p. 43 • Practice, p. 44 • Word Problem Practice, p. 45 • Enrichment, p. 46 • Spreadsheet Activity, p. 47	• Practice, p. 44 • Word Problem Practice, p. 45 • Enrichment, p. 46	• Study Guide and Intervention, pp. 41–42 • Skills Practice, p. 43 • Practice, p. 44 • Word Problem Practice, p. 45
Transparencies	• 5-Minute Check Transparency 9-7	• 5-Minute Check Transparency 9-7	• 5-Minute Check Transparency 9-7	• 5-Minute Check Transparency 9-7
Other	• Study Notebook	• Study Notebook	• Study Notebook	• Study Notebook

Exponential Growth

Example 1 shows how to solve a real-world problem involving exponential growth. **Example 2** shows how to solve a real-world problem involving compound interest.

Formative Assessment

Use the Check Your Progress exercises after each example to determine students' understanding of concepts.

Additional Examples

1 **POPULATION** In 2008 the town of Flat Creek had a population of about 280,000 and a growth rate of 0.85% per year.

a. Write an equation to represent the population of Flat Creek since 2008. $y = 280{,}000\ (1.0085)^t$

b. According to the equation, what will be the population of Flat Creek in the year 2018? about 304,731

2 **COLLEGE** When Jing May was born, her grandparents invested \$1000 in a fixed rate savings account at a rate of 7% compounded annually. Jing May will receive the money when she turns 18 to help with her college expenses. What amount of money will Jing May receive from the investment? She will receive about \$3380.

Additional Examples also in Interactive Classroom PowerPoint® Presentations

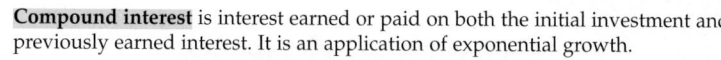

IWB INTERACTIVE WHITEBOARD READY

Real-World Career

Financial advisors help people plan their financial futures. A good financial advisor has mathematical, problem-solving, and communication skills. A bachelor's degree is strongly preferred but not required.

Compound interest is interest earned or paid on both the initial investment and previously earned interest. It is an application of exponential growth.

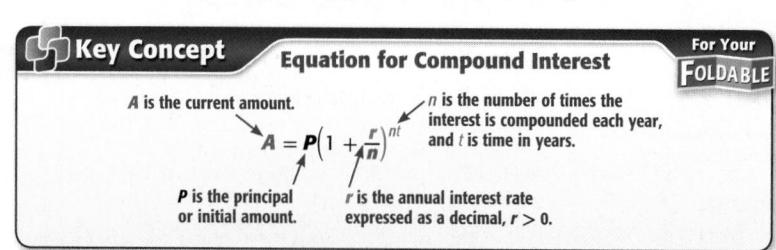

Key Concept — **Equation for Compound Interest** — For Your FOLDABLE

$$A = P\left(1 + \frac{r}{n}\right)^{nt}$$

- *A* is the current amount.
- *P* is the principal or initial amount.
- *r* is the annual interest rate expressed as a decimal, $r > 0$.
- *n* is the number of times the interest is compounded each year, and *t* is time in years.

Real-World EXAMPLE 2 Compound Interest

FINANCE Maria's parents invested \$14,000 at 6% per year compounded monthly. How much money will there be in the account after 10 years?

$A = P\left(1 + \frac{r}{n}\right)^{nt}$	Compound interest equation
$= 14{,}000\left(1 + \frac{0.06}{12}\right)^{12(10)}$	$P = 14{,}000$, $r = 6\%$ or 0.06, $n = 12$, and $t = 10$
$= 14{,}000(1.005)^{120}$	Simplify.
$\approx 25{,}471.55$	Use a calculator.

There will be about \$25,471.55 in 10 years.

Check Your Progress

2. FINANCE Determine the amount of an investment if \$300 is invested at an interest rate of 3.5% compounded monthly for 22 years. about \$647.20

Personal Tutor glencoe.com

Exponential Decay In **exponential decay**, the original amount decreases by the same percent over a period of time. A variation of the growth equation can be used as the general equation for exponential decay.

StudyTip

Growth and Decay Since *r* is added to 1, the value inside the parentheses will be greater than 1 for exponential growth functions. For exponential decay functions, this value will be less than 1 since *r* is subtracted from 1.

Key Concept — **Equation for Exponential Decay** — For Your FOLDABLE

$$y = a(1 - r)^t$$

- *a* is the initial amount.
- *t* is time.
- *y* is the final amount.
- *r* is the rate of decay expressed as a decimal, $0 < r < 1$.

Real-World EXAMPLE 3 Exponential Decay

SWIMMING A fully inflated child's raft for a pool is losing 6.6% of its air every day. The raft originally contained 4500 cubic inches of air.

a. Write an equation to represent the loss of air.

$y = a(1 - r)^t$	Equation for exponential decay
$= 4500(1 - 0.066)^t$	$a = 4500$ and $r = 6.6\%$ or 0.066
$= 4500(0.934)^t$	Simplify.

$y = 4500(0.934)^t$, where y is the air in the raft in cubic inches after t days.

Focus on Mathematical Content

Compound Interest In contrast to simple interest, compound interest is applied to the original principal and any previously earned interest. There are four ways to increase the amount in a compound-interest account: the investor can increase the initial principal, increase the annual interest rate, increase the number of compoundings per year, or increase the time that the money is in the account.

Exponential Decay

Example 3 shows how to solve a real-world problem involving exponential decay.

574 Chapter 9 Quadratic and Exponential Functions

b. Estimate the amount of air in the raft after 7 days.

$y = 4500(0.934)^t$ — **Equation for air loss**

$= 4500(0.934)^7$ — $t = 7$

≈ 2790 — **Use a calculator.**

The amount of air in the raft after 7 days will be about 2790 cubic inches.

Check Your Progress

3. POPULATION The population of Campbell County, Kentucky, has been decreasing at an average rate of about 0.3% per year. In 2000, its population was 88,647. Write an equation to represent the population since 2000. If the trend continues, predict the population in 2010.
$y = 88{,}647(1 - 0.003)^t$; about 86,023

Personal Tutor glencoe.com

Check Your Understanding

Example 1 p. 573

1. SALARY Ms. Acosta received a job as a teacher with a starting salary of $34,000. According to her contract, she will receive a 1.5% increase in her salary every year. How much will Ms. Acosta earn in 7 years? about $37,734.73

Example 2 p. 574

2. MONEY Paul invested $400 into an account with a 5.5% interest rate compounded monthly. How much will Paul's investment be worth in 8 years? about $620.46

Example 3 p. 574

3. ENROLLMENT In 2000, 2200 students attended Polaris High School. The enrollment has been declining 2% annually.

a. Write an equation for the enrollment of Polaris High School t years after 2000.

b. If this trend continues, how many students will be enrolled in 2015?

3a. $y = 2200(0.98)^t$
3b. about 1624

Practice and Problem Solving

= **Step-by-Step Solutions** begin on page R12.
Extra Practice begins on page 815.

Example 1 p. 573

4. MEMBERSHIPS The Work-Out Gym sold 550 memberships in 2001. Since then the number of memberships sold has increased 3% annually.

a. Write an equation for the number of memberships sold at Work-Out Gym t years after 2001. $y = 550(1.03)^t$

b. If this trend continues, predict how many memberships the gym will sell in 2020. about 964

5. COMPUTERS The number of people who own computers has increased 23.2% annually since 1990. If half a million people owned a computer in 1990, predict how many people will own a computer in 2015. about 92,095,349

6. COINS Camilo purchased a rare coin from a dealer for $300. The value of the coin increases 5% each year. Determine the value of the coin in 5 years. about $382.88

Example 2 p. 574

7. INVESTMENTS Theo invested $6600 at an interest rate of 4.5% compounded monthly. Determine the value of his investment in 4 years. about $7898.97

8. FINANCE Paige invested $1200 at an interest rate of 5.75% compounded quarterly. Determine the value of her investment in 7 years. about $1789.54

9. SAVINGS Brooke is saving money for a trip to the Bahamas that costs $295.99. She puts $150 into a savings account that pays 7.25% interest compounded quarterly. Will she have enough money in the account after 4 years? Explain.

9. Sample answer: No; she will have about $199.94 in the account in 4 years.

10. INVESTMENTS Jin's investment of $4500 has been losing its value at a rate of 2.5% each year. What will his investment be worth in 5 years? about $3964.93

Differentiated Homework Options

Level	Assignment	Two-Day Option	
AL Basic	4–12, 16, 18–44	5–11 odd, 21–24	4–12 even, 16, 18–20, 25–44
OL Core	5–11 odd, 13–16, 18–44	4–12, 21–24	13–16, 18–20, 25–44
BL Advanced	13–41, (optional: 42–44)		

Additional Example

3 CHARITY During an economic recession, a charitable organization found that its donations dropped by 1.1% per year. Before the recession, its donations were $390,000.

a. Write an equation to represent the charity's donations since the beginning of the recession.
$A = 390{,}000(0.989)^t$

b. Estimate the amount of the donations 5 years after the start of the recession. about $369,017

Watch Out!

Student Misconceptions Remind students that in growth and decay equations, the amount inside the parentheses will be greater than 1 for growth and less than 1 for decay.

3 PRACTICE

Formative Assessment

Use Exercises 1–3 to check for understanding.

Use the chart at the bottom of this page to customize assignments for your students.

TEACH with TECH

WEB SEARCH Have students search the Web to find the half-life of different radioactive elements. Have them choose three elements, and ask them to calculate the amount of a 500 gram sample that remains after 3 years.

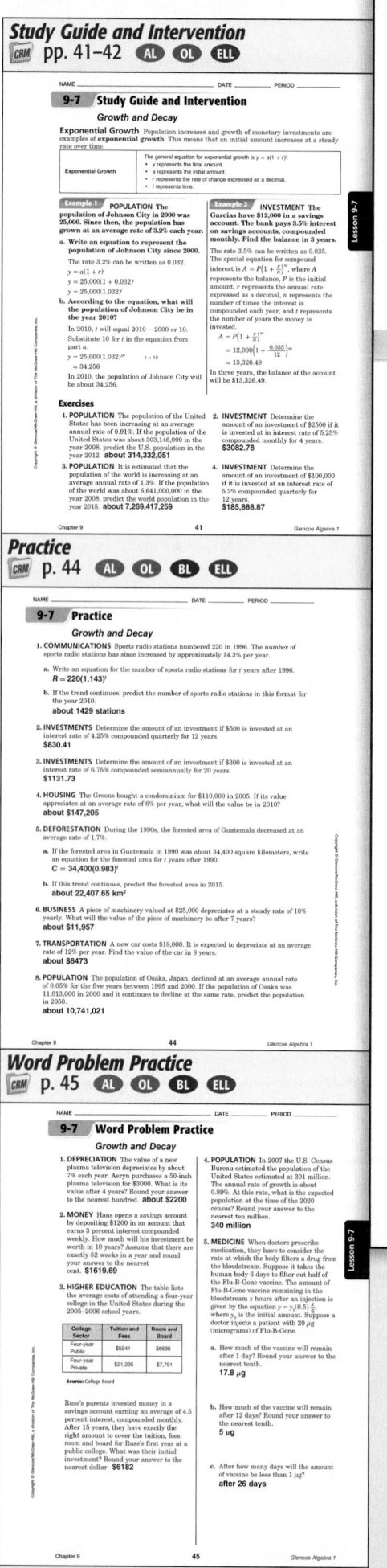

Study Guide and Intervention
CRM pp. 41–42 AL OL ELL

NAME ____________ DATE ________ PERIOD ________

9-7 Study Guide and Intervention
Growth and Decay

Exponential Growth Population increases and growth of monetary investments are examples of **exponential growth**. This means that an initial amount increases at a steady rate over time.

Exponential Growth	The general equation for exponential growth is $y = a(1 + r)^t$. • y represents the final amount. • a represents the initial amount. • r represents the rate of change expressed as a decimal. • t represents time.

Example 1 POPULATION **The population of Johnson City in 2000 was 25,000. Since then, the population has grown at an average rate of 3.2% each year.**

a. **Write an equation to represent the population of Johnson City since 2000.**

The rate 3.2% can be written as 0.032.

$y = a(1 + r)^t$

$y = 25{,}000(1 + 0.032)^t$

$y = 25{,}000(1.032)^t$

b. **According to the equation, what will the population of Johnson City be in the year 2010?**

In 2010, t will equal 2010 − 2000 or 10.

Substitute 10 for t in the equation from part a.

$y = 25{,}000(1.032)^{10}$ $t = 10$

$\approx 34{,}256$

In 2010, the population of Johnson City will be about 34,256.

Example 2 INVESTMENT **The Garcias have $12,000 in a savings account. The bank pays 3.5% interest on savings accounts, compounded monthly. Find the balance in 3 years.**

The rate 3.5% can be written as 0.035. The special equation for compound interest is $A = P\left(1 + \frac{r}{n}\right)^{nt}$, where A represents the balance, P is the initial amount, r represents the annual rate expressed as a decimal, n represents the number of times the interest is compounded each year, and t represents the number of years the money is invested.

$A = P\left(1 + \frac{r}{n}\right)^{nt}$

$= 12{,}000\left(1 + \frac{0.035}{12}\right)^{36}$

$\approx 13{,}326.49$

In three years, the balance of the account will be $13,326.49.

Exercises

1. POPULATION The population of the United States has been increasing at an average annual rate of 0.91%. If the population of the United States was about 303,146,000 in the year 2008, predict the U.S. population in the year 2012. **about 314,332,051**

2. INVESTMENT Determine the amount of an investment of $2500 if it is invested at in interest rate of 5.25% compounded monthly for 4 years. **$3082.78**

3. POPULATION It is estimated that the population of the world is increasing at an average annual rate of 1.3%. If the population of the world was about 6,641,000,000 in the year 2008, predict the world population in the year 2015. **about 7,269,417,259**

4. INVESTMENT Determine the amount of an investment of $100,000 if it is invested at an interest rate of 5.2% compounded quarterly for 12 years. **$185,888.87**

Lesson 9-7

Chapter 9 41 *Glencoe Algebra 1*

Practice
CRM p. 44 AL OL BL ELL

NAME ____________ DATE ________ PERIOD ________

9-7 Practice
Growth and Decay

1. COMMUNICATIONS Sports radio stations numbered 220 in 1996. The number of sports radio stations has since increased by approximately 14.3% per year.

   a. Write an equation for the number of sports radio stations for t years after 1996.
   $R = 220(1.143)^t$

   b. If the trend continues, predict the number of sports radio stations in this format for the year 2010.
   about 1429 stations

2. INVESTMENTS Determine the amount of an investment if $500 is invested at an interest rate of 4.25% compounded quarterly for 12 years.
$830.41

3. INVESTMENTS Determine the amount of an investment if $300 is invested at an interest rate of 6.75% compounded semiannually for 20 years.
$1131.73

4. HOUSING The Greens bought a condominium for $110,000 in 2005. If its value appreciates at an average rate of 6% per year, what will the value be in 2010?
about $147,205

5. DEFORESTATION During the 1990s, the forested area of Guatemala decreased at an average rate of 1.7%.

   a. If the forested area in Guatemala in 1990 was about 34,400 square kilometers, write an equation for the forested area for t years after 1990.
   $C = 34{,}400(0.983)^t$

   b. If this trend continues, predict the forested area in 2015.
   about 22,407.65 km²

6. BUSINESS A piece of machinery valued at $25,000 depreciates at a steady rate of 10% yearly. What will the value of the piece of machinery be after 7 years?
about $11,957

7. TRANSPORTATION A new car costs $18,000. It is expected to depreciate at an average rate of 12% per year. Find the value of the car in 8 years.
about $6473

8. POPULATION The population of Osaka, Japan, declined at an average annual rate of 0.05% for the five years between 1995 and 2000. If the population of Osaka was 11,013,000 in 2000 and it continues to decline at the same rate, predict the population in 2050.
about 10,741,021

Chapter 9 44 *Glencoe Algebra 1*

Word Problem Practice
CRM p. 45 AL OL BL ELL

NAME ____________ DATE ________ PERIOD ________

9-7 Word Problem Practice
Growth and Decay

1. DEPRECIATION The value of a new plasma television depreciates by about 7% each year. Aeryn purchases a 50-inch plasma television for $3000. What is its value after 4 years? Round your answer to the nearest hundred. **about $2200**

2. MONEY Hans opens a savings account by depositing $1200 in an account that earns 3 percent interest compounded weekly. How much will his investment be worth in 10 years? Assume that there are exactly 52 weeks in a year and round your answer to the nearest cent. **$1619.69**

3. HIGHER EDUCATION The table lists the average costs of attending a four-year college in the United States during the 2005–2006 school years.

College Sector	Tuition and Fees	Room and Board
Four-year Public	$5941	$6636
Four-year Private	$21,235	$7,791

Source: College Board

Russ's parents invested money in a savings account earning an average of 4.5 percent interest, compounded monthly. After 15 years, they have exactly the right amount to cover the tuition, fees, room and board for Russ's first year at a public college. What was their initial investment? Round your answer to the nearest dollar. **$6182**

4. POPULATION In 2007 the U.S. Census Bureau estimated the population of the United States estimated at 301 million. The annual rate of growth is about 0.89%. At this rate, what is the expected population at the time of the 2020 census? Round your answer to the nearest ten million.
340 million

5. MEDICINE When doctors prescribe medication, they have to consider the rate at which the body filters a drug from the bloodstream. Suppose it takes the human body 6 days to filter out half of the Flu-B-Gone vaccine. The amount of Flu-B-Gone vaccine remaining in the bloodstream x hours after an injection is given by the equation $y = y_0(0.5)^{\frac{x}{6}}$, where y_0 is the initial amount. Suppose a doctor injects a patient with 20 μg (micrograms) of Flu-B-Gone.

   a. How much of the vaccine will remain after 1 day? Round your answer to the nearest tenth.
   17.8 μg

   b. How much of the vaccine will remain after 12 days? Round your answer to the nearest tenth.
   5 μg

   c. After how many days will the amount of vaccine be less than 1 μg?
   after 26 days

Lesson 9-7

Chapter 9 45 *Glencoe Algebra 1*

Example 3 p. 574

11. **POPULATION** Hawaii has been experiencing a 1.06% annual increase in population. In 2000, the population was 1,211,537. If this trend continues, what will be the population of Hawaii in 2020? **about 1,495,969**

Real-World Link

A car loses 15% to 20% of its value each year. Brand, model, and the condition of the car all contribute to a used car's value. Some brands depreciate much slower than other brands.

Source: Bankrate

12. **CARS** Leonardo purchases a car for $18,995. The car depreciates at a rate of 18% annually. After 6 years, Manuel offers to buy the car for $4500. Should Leonardo sell the car? Explain. **Sample answer: No; the car is worth about $5774.61.**

13. **HOUSING** The median house price in the United States increased an average of 8.6% each year between 2002 and 2004. Assume that this pattern continues. **$I = 221{,}000(1.086)^t$**

    a. Write an equation for the median house price for t years after 2004.

    b. Predict the median house price in 2015. **about $645,922**

Median House Price	
2002	$187,600
2003	$195,000
2004	$221,000

Source: *Real Estate Journal*

14. **ELEMENTS** A radioactive element's half-life is the time it takes for one half of the element's quantity to decay. The half-life of Plutonium-241 is 14.4 years. The number of grams A of Plutonium-241 left after t years can be modeled by $A = p(0.5)^{\frac{t}{14.4}}$, where p is the original amount of the element.

    a. How much of a 0.2-gram sample remains after 72 years? **0.00625 g**

    b. How much of a 5.4-gram sample remains after 1095 days? **≈4.7 g**

15. **FINANCIAL LITERACY** Marta is planning to buy a new car. She will finance $16,000 at an annual interest rate of 7% over a period of 60 months. In the formula, P is the amount of each payment, r is the annual interest rate in decimal form, and t is the time in years of the loan.

$$\text{Amount financed} = P\left[\frac{1-\left(1+\frac{r}{12}\right)^{-12t}}{\frac{r}{12}}\right]$$

    a. Use the formula to find her monthly payment. **$316.82**

    b. Assuming that she does not pay ahead, what will she have paid on the car? **$19,009.20**

H.O.T. Problems
Use Higher-Order Thinking Skills

16. **REASONING** Determine the growth rate (as a percent) of a population that quadruples every year. Explain. **400%; Because 400% written as a number is 4.**

17. **CHALLENGE** Santos invested $1200 into an account with an interest rate of 8% compounded monthly. Use a calculator to approximate how long it will take for Santos' investment to reach $2500. **about 9.2 yr**

18. **REASONING** The amount of water in a container doubles every minute. After 8 minutes, the container is full. After how many minutes was the container half full? Explain.

19. **OPEN ENDED** Create a real-world situation that can be modeled by $y = 200(1.05)^t$.

20. **WRITING IN MATH** Compare and contrast the exponential growth formula and the exponential decay formula.

18. 7; Sample answer: Since the amount of water doubles every minute, the container would be half full a minute before it was full.

19. A population is 200 and increasing at a rate of 5% annually.

20. The exponential growth formula is $y = a(1 + r)^t$, where a is the initial amount, t is time, y is the final amount, and r is the rate of change expressed as a decimal. The exponential decay formula is basically the same except the rate is subtracted from 1 and r represents the rate of decay.

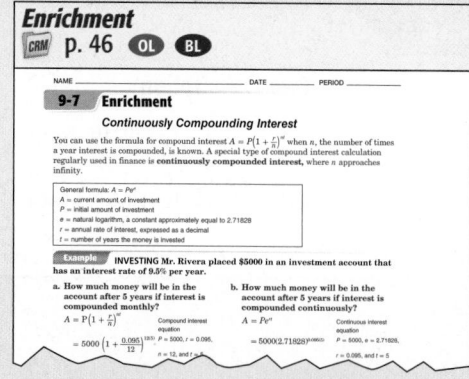

Enrichment
CRM p. 46 OL BL

NAME ____________ DATE ________ PERIOD ________

9-7 Enrichment
Continuously Compounding Interest

You can use the formula for compound interest $A = P\left(1 + \frac{r}{n}\right)^{nt}$ when n, the number of times a year interest is compounded, is known. A special type of compound interest calculation regularly used in finance is **continuously compounded interest,** where n approaches infinity.

General formula: $A = Pe^{rt}$ A = current amount of investment P = initial amount of investment e = natural logarithm, a constant approximately equal to 2.71828 r = annual rate of interest, expressed as a decimal t = number of years the money is invested

Example INVESTING **Mr. Rivera placed $5000 in an investment account that has an interest rate of 9.5% per year.**

a. **How much money will be in the account after 5 years if interest is compounded monthly?**

$A = P\left(1 + \frac{r}{n}\right)^{nt}$ Compound interest equation

$= 5000\left(1 + \frac{0.095}{12}\right)^{12(5)}$ $P = 5000$, $r = 0.095$, $n = 12$, and $t = 5$

b. **How much money will be in the account after 5 years if interest is compounded continuously?**

$A = Pe^{rt}$ Continuous interest equation

$= 5000(2.71828)^{0.095(5)}$ $P = 5000$, $e = 2.71828$, $r = 0.095$, and $t = 5$

PSAE PRACTICE 7.11.03, 8.11.18, 6.11.18

21. GEOMETRY The parallelogram has an area of 35 square inches. Find the height h of the parallelogram. **C**

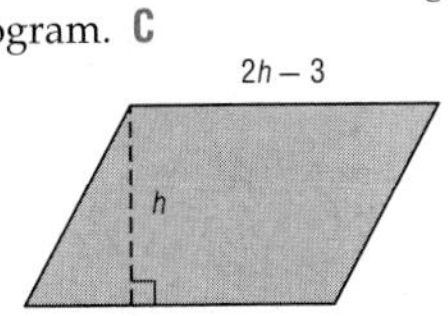

A 3.5 inches
B 4 inches
C 5 inches
D 7 inches

22. What are the roots of $x^2 + 2x = 48$? **H**

F 6 and 8
G −6 and −8
H 6 and −8
J −6 and 8

23. Thi purchased a car for $22,900. The car depreciated at an annual rate of 16%. Which of the following equations models the value of Thi's car after 5 years? **D**

A $A = 22{,}900(1.16)^5$
B $A = 22{,}900(0.16)^5$
C $A = 16(22{,}900)^5$
D $A = 22{,}900(0.84)^5$

24. GRIDDED RESPONSE A deck measures 12 feet by 18 feet. If a painter charges $2.65 per square foot, including tax, how much will it cost in dollars to have the deck painted? **572.4**

Spiral Review

Graph each function. Find the y-intercept and state the domain and range. (Lesson 9-6) **25–27. See margin.**

25. $y = 3^x$
26. $y = \left(\frac{1}{2}\right)^x$
27. $y = 6^x$

Solve each equation by using the Quadratic Formula. Round to the nearest tenth if necessary. (Lesson 9-5)

28. $4x^2 + 15x = 25$ **$-5, \frac{5}{4}$**
29. $3x^2 - 4x = 5$ **−0.8, 2.1**
30. $2x^2 = -2x + 11$ **−2.9, 1.9**
31. $4x^2 + 16x = -16$ **−2**
32. $5x^2 + 5x = 60$ **−4, 3**
33. $2x^2 = 3x + 15$ **−2.1, 3.6**

34. EVENT PLANNING A hall does not charge a rental fee as long as at least $4000 is spent on food. For the prom, the hall charges $28.95 per person for a buffet. How many people must attend the prom to avoid a rental fee for the hall? (Lesson 5-2) **at least 139 people**

Determine whether the graphs of each pair of equations are *parallel*, *perpendicular*, or *neither*. (Lesson 4-4)

35. $y = -2x + 11$, $y + 2x = 23$ **parallel**
36. $3y = 2x + 14$, $-3x - 2y = 2$ **perpendicular**
37. $y = -5x$, $y = 5x - 18$ **neither**

38. AGES The table shows equivalent ages for horses and humans. Write an equation that relates human age to horse age and find the equivalent horse age for a human who is 16 years old. (Lesson 3-4) **$y = 3x$; 5 yr 4 mo**

Horse age (x)	0	1	2	3	4	5
Human age (y)	0	3	6	9	12	15

Find the total price of each item. (Lesson 2-7)

39. umbrella: $14.00, tax: 5.5% **$14.77**
40. sandals: $29.99, tax: 5.75% **$31.71**
41. backpack: $35.00, tax: 7% **$37.45**

Skills Check

Graph each set of ordered pairs. (Lesson 1-6) **42–44. See Ch.9 Answer Appendix.**

42. (3, 0), (0, 1), (−4, −6)
43. (0, −2), (−1, −6), (3, 4)
44. (2, 2), (−2, −3), (−3, −6)

Exercise Alert

Grid Paper For Exercises 25–27, students will need grid paper.

4 ASSESS

Ticket Out the Door Make several copies each of five equations for exponential growth or decay. Give one equation to each student. As students leave the room, ask them to tell you whether their equations are for growth or decay.

Formative Assessment

Check for student understanding of Lessons 9-6 and 9-7.

CRM Quiz 3, p. 64

Additional Answers

25.

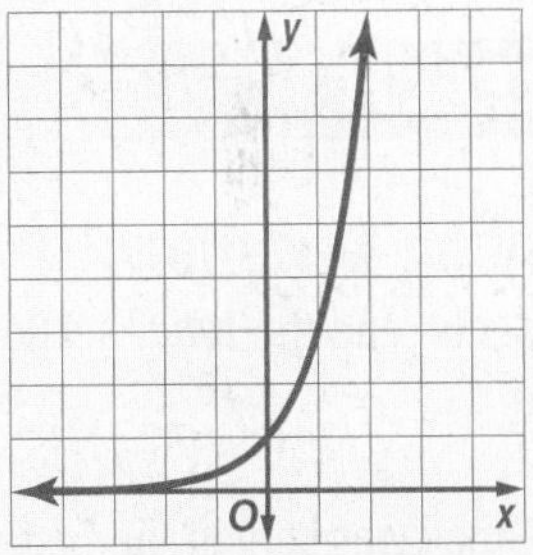

1; D = {all real numbers}; R = {y | y > 0}

26.

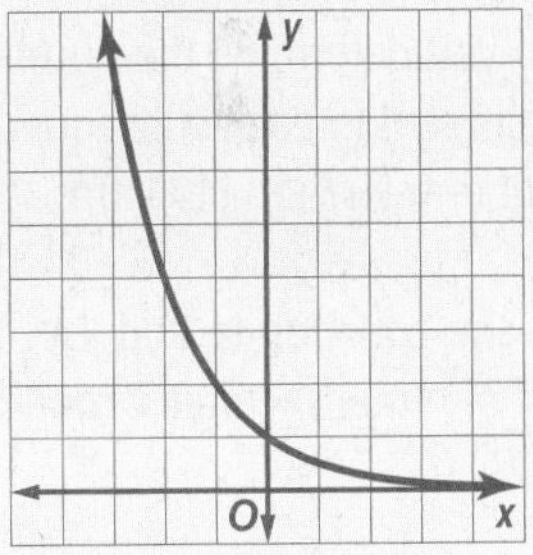

1; D = {all real numbers}; R = {y | y > 0}

27.

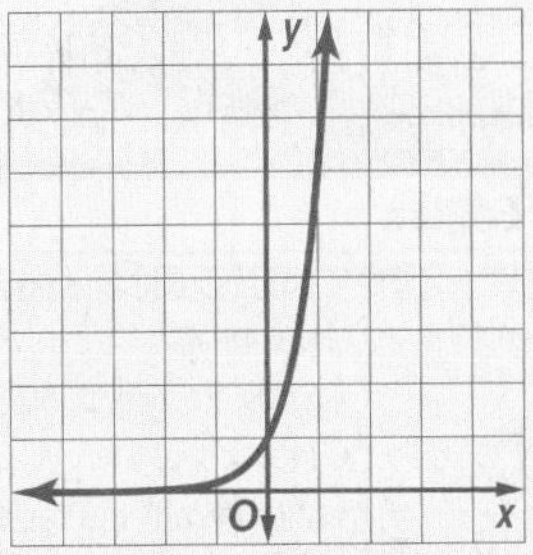

1; D = {all real numbers}; R = {y | y > 0}

Differentiated Instruction OL BL

If you think students need a challenge in this lesson,

Then ask students to write their own exponential growth or decay problems, using data from periodicals or the Internet. Have students share their problems with the class when they are complete.

Lesson 9-7 Growth and Decay 577

9-8 Lesson Notes

1 FOCUS

Vertical Alignment

Before Lesson 9-8
Relate arithmetic sequences to linear functions.

Lesson 9-8
Identify and generate geometric sequences.
Relate geometric sequences to exponential functions.

After Lesson 9-8
Find the geometric mean and the sum of an infinite geometric series.

2 TEACH

Scaffolding Questions

Have students read the *Why?* section of the lesson.

Ask:

- If one e-mail was sent in the first round, how many were sent in the second round? 5 the third round? 25 the fourth round? 125
- How do you determine the number of e-mails sent in each subsequent round of e-mails? Multiply the previous number by 5.
- What is the equation to find the number of e-mails y after x rounds? $y = 5^x$

9-8 Geometric Sequences as Exponential Functions

Then
You related arithmetic sequences to linear functions. (Lesson 3-5)

Now
- Identify and generate geometric sequences.
- Relate geometric sequences to exponential functions.

IL Learning Standards
8.A.4b Represent mathematical patterns and describe their properties using variables and mathematical symbols.
8.C.4b Apply algebraic properties and procedures with matrices, vectors, functions and sequences using data found in business, industry and consumer situations. *Also addresses 7.A.4a.*

New Vocabulary
geometric sequence
common ratio

IL Math Online
glencoe.com
- Extra Examples
- Personal Tutor
- Self-Check Quiz
- Homework Help

Why?

You send a chain e-mail to a friend who forwards the e-mail to five more people. Each of these five people forwards the e-mail to five more people. The number of new e-mails generated forms a geometric sequence.

Recognize Geometric Sequences The first person generates 5 e-mails. If each of these people sends the e-mail to 5 more people, 25 e-mails are generated. If each of the 25 people sends 5 e-mails, 125 e-mails are generated. The sequence of e-mails generated, 1, 5, 25, 125, … is an example of a **geometric sequence**.

In a geometric sequence, the first term is nonzero and each term after the first is found by multiplying the previous term by a nonzero constant r called the **common ratio**. The common ratio can be found by dividing any term by its previous term.

EXAMPLE 1 Identify Geometric Sequences

Determine whether each sequence is *arithmetic, geometric,* or *neither*. Explain.

a. 256, 128, 64, 32, …

Find the ratios of consecutive terms.

256 128 64 32

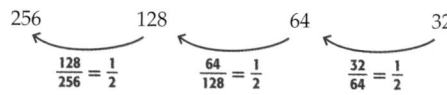

$\frac{128}{256} = \frac{1}{2}$ $\frac{64}{128} = \frac{1}{2}$ $\frac{32}{64} = \frac{1}{2}$

Since the ratios are constant, the sequence is geometric. The common ratio is $\frac{1}{2}$.

b. 4, 9, 12, 18, …

Find the ratios of consecutive terms.

4 9 12 18

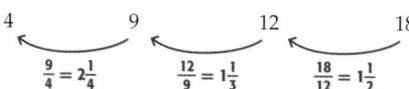

$\frac{9}{4} = 2\frac{1}{4}$ $\frac{12}{9} = 1\frac{1}{3}$ $\frac{18}{12} = 1\frac{1}{2}$

The ratios are not constant, so the sequence is not geometric.

Find the differences of consecutive terms.

4 9 12 18

$9 - 4 = 5$ $12 - 9 = 3$ $18 - 12 = 6$

There is no common difference, so the sequence is not arithmetic. Thus, the sequence is neither geometric nor arithmetic.

Check Your Progress **1A–1C. See margin.**

1A. 1, 3, 9, 27, … **1B.** −20, −15, −10, −5, … **1C.** 2, 8, 14, 22, …

Personal Tutor glencoe.com

Lesson 9-8 Resources

Resource	Approaching-Level	On-Level	Beyond-Level	English Learners
Teacher Edition		• Differentiated Instruction, p. 583	• Differentiated Instruction, p. 583	• Differentiated Instruction, p. 580
Chapter Resource Masters	• Study Guide and Intervention, pp. 48–49 • Skills Practice, p. 50 • Practice, p. 51 • Word Problem Practice, p. 52	• Study Guide and Intervention, pp. 48–49 • Skills Practice, p. 50 • Practice, p. 51 • Word Problem Practice, p. 52 • Enrichment, p. 53	• Practice, p. 51 • Word Problem Practice, p. 52 • Enrichment, p. 53	• Study Guide and Intervention, pp. 48–49 • Skills Practice, p. 50 • Practice, p. 51 • Word Problem Practice, p. 52
Transparencies	• 5-Minute Check Transparency 9-8	• 5-Minute Check Transparency 9-8	• 5-Minute Check Transparency 9-8	• 5-Minute Check Transparency 9-8
Other	• Study Notebook	• Study Notebook	• Study Notebook	• Study Notebook

Once the common ratio is known, more terms of a sequence can be generated. The recursive formula can be rewritten as $a_n = a_1 r^{n-1}$, where n is a counting number and r is the common ratio.

StudyTip

Common Ratio If the terms of a geometric sequence alternate between positive and negative terms or vice versa, the common ratio is negative.

EXAMPLE 2 Find Terms of Geometric Sequences

Find the next three terms in each geometric sequence.

a. 1, −4, 16, −64, ...

Step 1 Find the common ratio.

1   −4   16   −64

$\frac{-4}{1} = -4$ $\frac{16}{-4} = -4$ $\frac{-64}{16} = -4$

Step 2 Multiply each term by the common ratio to find the next three terms.

−64   256   −1024   4096

×(−4)   ×(−4)   ×(−4)

The next three terms are 256, −1024, and 4096.

b. $9, 3, 1, \frac{1}{3} \ldots$

Step 1 Find the common ratio.

9   3   1 $\frac{1}{3}$

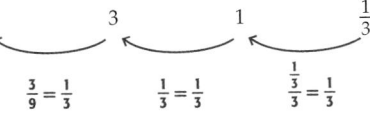

$\frac{3}{9} = \frac{1}{3}$ $\frac{1}{3} = \frac{1}{3}$ $\frac{\frac{1}{3}}{3} = \frac{1}{3}$

The value of r is $\frac{1}{3}$.

Step 2 Multiply each term by the common ratio to find the next three terms.

$\frac{1}{3}$ $\frac{1}{9}$ $\frac{1}{27}$ $\frac{1}{81}$

$\times\frac{1}{3}$ $\times\frac{1}{3}$ $\times\frac{1}{3}$

The next three terms are $\frac{1}{9}$, $\frac{1}{27}$, and $\frac{1}{81}$.

The Granger Collection, New York

Math History Link

Thomas Robert Malthus (1766–1834)
Malthus studied populations and had pessimistic views about the future population of the world. In his work, he stated: "Population increases in a geometric ratio, while the means of subsistence increases in an arithmetic ratio."

Check Your Progress

2A. −3, 15, −75, 375, ...
−1875, 9375, −46,875

2B. 24, 36, 54, 81, ...
121.5, 182.25, 273.375

Personal Tutor glencoe.com

Geometric Sequences and Functions Finding the nth term of a geometric sequence would be tedious if we used the above method. The table below shows a rule for finding the nth term of a geometric sequence.

Position, n	1	2	3	4	...	n
Term, a_n	a_1	$a_1 r$	$a_1 r^2$	$a_1 r^3$	...	$a_1 r^{n-1}$

Notice that the common ratio between the terms is r. The table shows that to get the nth term, you multiply the first term by the common ratio r raised to the power $n - 1$. A geometric sequence can be defined by an exponential function in which n is the independent variable, a_n is the dependent variable, and r is the base. The domain is the counting numbers.

Recognize Geometric Sequences

Example 1 shows how to determine whether a sequence is arithmetic, geometric, or neither. **Example 2** shows how to find additional terms of a geometric sequence.

Formative Assessment

Use the Check Your Progress exercises after each example to determine students' understanding of concepts.

Additional Examples

1 Determine whether each sequence is *arithmetic, geometric,* or *neither*. Explain.

a. 0, 8, 16, 24, 32, ... Arithmetic; the common difference is 8.

b. 64, 48, 36, 27, ... Geometric; the common ratio is $\frac{3}{4}$.

2 Find the next three terms in each geometric sequence.

a. 1, −8, 64, −512, ...
4096; −32,768; 262,144

b. 40, 20, 10, 5, ... $\frac{5}{2}, \frac{5}{4}, \frac{5}{8}$

Additional Examples also in Interactive Classroom PowerPoint® Presentations

IWB INTERACTIVE WHITEBOARD READY

Geometric Sequences and Functions

Example 3 shows how to find the nth term of a geometric sequence. **Example 4** shows how to use real-world data to draw a graph of a geometric sequence.

Additional Answers (Guided Practice)

1A. Geometric; the common ratio is 3.

1B. Arithmetic; the common difference is 5.

1C. Neither; there is no common ratio or common difference.

Focus on Mathematical Content

Common Ratio When finding the common ratio, it is important to set up the ratio in the correct order. For example, in Example 1, had the ratio been set up as $\frac{256}{128}$ instead of $\frac{128}{256}$, an incorrect ratio of 2 would have been found. It should be noted that when a geometric sequence is decreasing, the common ratio must be between 0 and 1.

TEACH with TECH

BLOG On your secure classroom blog have students write a blog entry describing how geometric sequences and exponential functions are related.

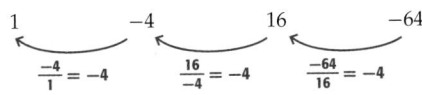

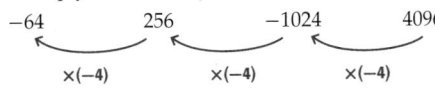

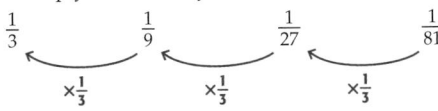

Additional Examples

3 **a.** Write an equation for the nth term of the geometric sequence 1, −2, 4, −8, …
$a_n = 1 \cdot (-2)^{n-1}$

b. Find the 12th term of this sequence. −2048

4 **ART** A 50-pound ice sculpture is melting at a rate in which 80% of its weight remains each hour. Draw a graph to represent how many pounds of the sculpture is left at each hour.

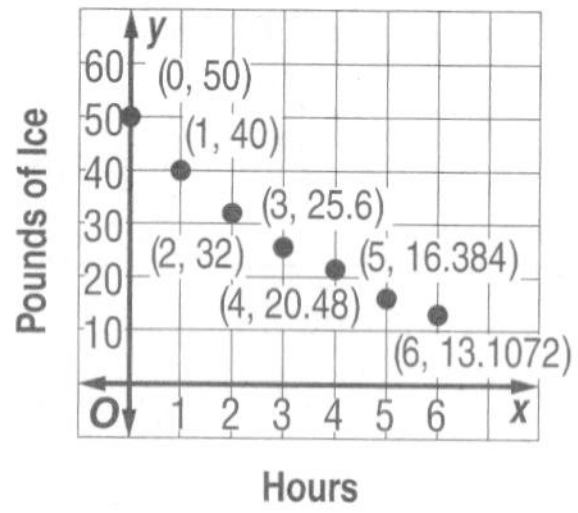

Tips for New Teachers

The Power of r Make sure students raise r to the power $(n - 1)$, in their equations for the nth term of a geometric sequence, instead of n.

Additional Answer (Check Your Progress)

4\.

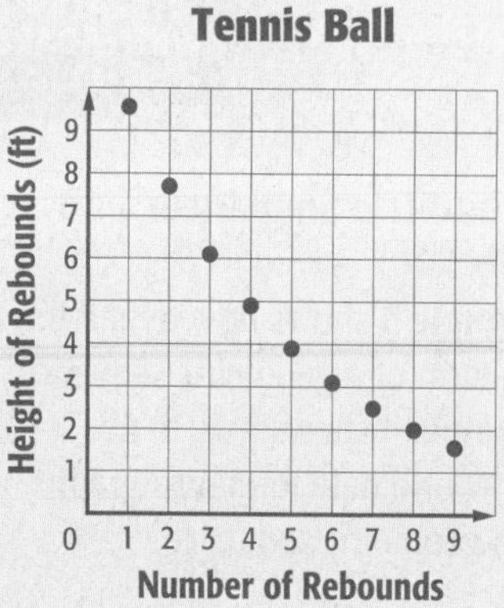

Key Concept — nth term of a Geometric Sequence (For Your FOLDABLE)

The nth term a_n of a geometric sequence with first term a_1 and common ratio r is given by the following formula, where n is any positive integer and $a_1, r \neq 0$.

$$a_n = a_1 r^{n-1}$$

Watch Out!

Negative Common Ratio If the common ratio is negative, as in Example 3, make sure to enclose the common ratio in parentheses. $(-2)^8 \neq -2^8$

EXAMPLE 3 Find the nth Term of a Geometric Sequence

a. Write an equation for the nth term of the sequence −6, 12, −24, 48, … .

The first term of the sequence is −6. So, $a_1 = -6$. Now find the common ratio.

$$-6 \quad 12 \quad -24 \quad 48$$

$\frac{12}{-6} = -2 \qquad \frac{-24}{12} = -2 \qquad \frac{48}{-24} = -2$ The common ratio is −2.

$a_n = a_1 r^{n-1}$ — **Formula for nth term**

$a_n = -6(-2)^{n-1}$ — **$a_1 = -6$ and $r = 2$**

b. Find the ninth term of this sequence.

$a_n = a_1 r^{n-1}$ — **Formula for nth term**

$a_9 = -6(-2)^{9-1}$ — **For the nth term, $n = 9$.**

$= -6(-2)^8$ — **Simplify.**

$= -6(256)$ — **$(-2)^8 = 256$**

$= -1536$

Check Your Progress 3. $a_n = 96 \cdot \left(\frac{1}{2}\right)^{n-1}$; $\frac{3}{16}$

3. Write an equation for the nth term of the geometric sequence 96, 48, 24, 12, … . Then find the tenth term of the sequence.

Personal Tutor glencoe.com

Real-World Link

The first NCAA Division I women's basketball tournament was held in 1982. The University of Tennessee has won the most national titles with 8 titles as of 2008.

Source: NCAA Sports

Real-World EXAMPLE 4 Graph a Geometric Sequence

BASKETBALL The NCAA women's basketball tournament begins with 64 teams. In each round, one half of the teams are left to compete, until only one team remains. Draw a graph to represent how many teams are left in each round.

Compared to the previous rounds, one half of the teams remain. So, $r = \frac{1}{2}$. Therefore, the geometric sequence that models this situation is 64, 32, 16, 8, 4, 2, 1. So in round two, 32 teams compete, in round three 16 teams compete and so forth. Use this information to draw a graph.

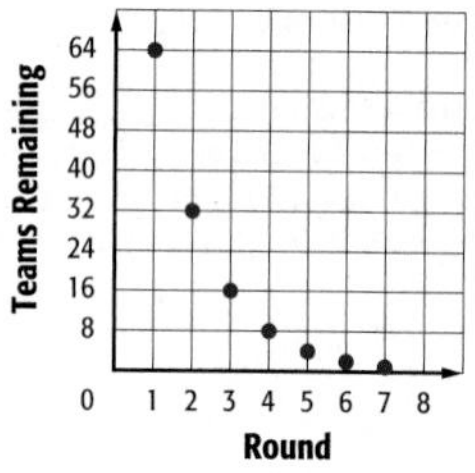

Check Your Progress

4. TENNIS A tennis ball is dropped from a height of 12 feet. Each time the ball bounces back to 80% of the height from which it fell. Draw a graph to represent the height of the ball after each bounce. See margin.

Personal Tutor glencoe.com

Differentiated Instruction ELL

Interpersonal Learners Put students into groups of mixed language and math abilities. Have groups discuss the differences between arithmetic and geometric sequences. Suggest they help each other organize clear, concise, and accurate notes about these and other concepts taught in this lesson.

Check Your Understanding

Example 1 p. 580

1. Geometric; the common ratio is $\frac{1}{5}$.

Determine whether each sequence is *arithmetic, geometric,* or *neither*. Explain.

1. 200, 40, 8, … **2.** 2, 4, 16, … **3.** −6, −3, 0, 3, … **4.** 1, −1, 1, −1, …

Example 2 p. 581

Find the next three terms in each geometric sequence. **5–8. See margin.**

5. 10, 20, 40, 80, … **6.** 100, 50, 25, … **7.** 4, −1, $\frac{1}{4}$, … **8.** −7, 21, −63, …

Example 3 p. 582

Write an equation for the *n*th term of each geometric sequence, and find the indicated term.

2. Neither; there is no common ratio or difference.

3. Arithmetic; the common difference is 3.

4. Geometric; the common ratio is −1.

9. the fifth term of −6, −24, −96, … $a_n = -6 \cdot (4)^{n-1}$; −1536

10. the seventh term of −1, 5, −25, … $a_n = -1 \cdot (-5)^{n-1}$; −15,625

11. the tenth term of 72, 48, 32, … $a_n = 72 \cdot \left(\frac{2}{3}\right)^{n-1}$; $\frac{4096}{2187}$

12. the ninth term of 112, 84, 63, … $a_n = 112 \cdot \left(\frac{3}{4}\right)^{n-1}$; $\frac{45{,}927}{4096}$

Example 4 p. 582

13. EXPERIMENT In a physics class experiment, Diana drops a ball from a height of 16 feet. Each bounce has 70% the height of the previous bounce. Draw a graph to represent the height of the ball after each bounce. **See margin.**

Practice and Problem Solving

● = Step-by-Step Solutions begin on page R12. Extra Practice begins on page 815.

Example 1 p. 580

Determine whether each sequence is *arithmetic, geometric,* or *neither*. Explain. **14–19. See margin.**

14. 4, 1, 2, … **15.** 10, 20, 30, 40, … **16.** 4, 20, 100, …

17. 212, 106, 53, … **18.** −10, −8, −6, −4, … **19.** 5, −10, 20, 40, …

Example 2 p. 581

Find the next three terms in each geometric sequence. **20–25. See margin.**

20. 2, −10, 50, … **21.** 36, 12, 4, … **22.** 4, 12, 36, …

23. 400, 100, 25, … **24.** −6, −42, −294, … **25.** 1024, −128, 16, …

Example 3 p. 582

26. The first term of a geometric series is 1 and the common ratio is 9. What is the 8th term of the sequence? **4,782,969**

27. The first term of a geometric series is 2 and the common ratio is 4. What is the 14th term of the sequence? **134,217,728**

28. What is the 15th term of the geometric series −9, 27, −81, …? **−43,046,721**

29. What is the 10th term of the geometric series 6, −24, 96, …? **−1,572,864**

Example 4 p. 582

30. PENDULUM The first swing of a pendulum is shown. On each swing after that, the arc length is 60% of the length of the previous swing. Draw a graph that represents the arc length after each swing. **See Ch. 9 Answer Appendix.**

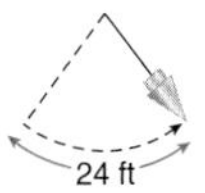

31. Find the eighth term of a geometric sequence for which $a_3 = 81$ and $r = 3$. **19,683**

32. MAPS At an online mapping site, Mr. Mosley notices that when he clicks a spot on the map, the map zooms in on that spot. The magnification increases by 20% each time. **a.** $a_n = 1.2^n$

a. Write a formula for the *n*th term of the geometric sequence that represents the magnification of each zoom level. (*Hint:* The common ratio is not just 0.2.)

b. What is the fourth term of this sequence? What does it represent?

32b. 2.0736; The map will be magnified at approximately 207% of the original size after the fourth click.

Differentiated Homework Options

Level	Assignment	Two-Day Option	
AL Basic	14–31, 39–69	15–31 odd, 43–46	14–30 even, 39–42, 47–69
OL Core	15–31 odd, 32–37, 39–69	14–31, 43–46	32–37, 39–42, 47–69
BL Advanced	32–63, (optional: 64–69)		

3 PRACTICE

Formative Assessment

Use Exercises 1–13 to check for understanding.

Use the chart at the bottom of this page to customize assignments for your students.

Exercise Alert

Grid Paper For Exercises 13, 30, 37, and 58–63, students will need grid paper.

Additional Answers

5. 160, 320, 640

6. 12.5, 6.25, 3.125

7. $-\frac{1}{16}, \frac{1}{64}, -\frac{1}{256}$

8. 189, −567, 1701

13.

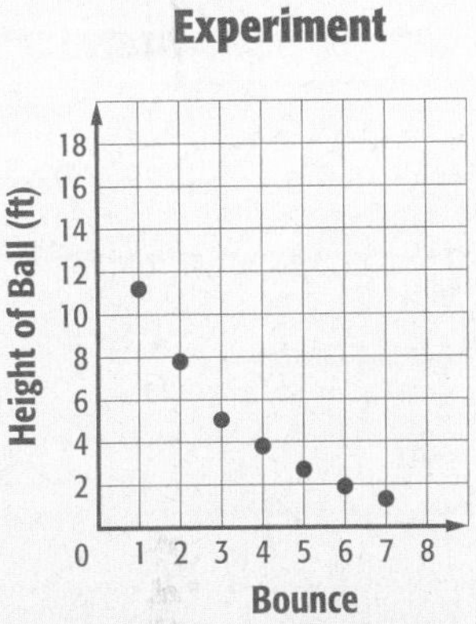

14. Neither; there is no common ratio or difference.

15. Arithmetic; the common difference is 10.

16. Geometric; the common ratio is 5.

17. Geometric; the common ratio is $\frac{1}{2}$.

18. Arithmetic; the common difference is 2.

19. Neither; there is no common ratio or difference.

20. −250, 1250, −6250

21. $\frac{4}{3}, \frac{4}{9}, \frac{4}{27}$

22. 108, 324, 972

23. $\frac{25}{4}, \frac{25}{16}, \frac{25}{64}$

24. −2058; −14,406; −100,842

25. $-2, \frac{1}{4}, -\frac{1}{32}$

Study Guide and Intervention
CRM pp. 48–49 AL OL ELL

NAME ________ DATE ______ PERIOD ______

9-8 Study Guide and Intervention

Geometric Sequences as Exponential Functions

Recognize Geometric Sequences A geometric sequence is a sequence in which each term after the first is found by multiplying the previous term by a nonzero constant r called the **common ratio**. The common ratio can be found by dividing any term by its previous term.

Example 1 Determine whether the sequence is *arithmetic, geometric,* or *neither:* 21, 63, 189, 567, . . .

Find the ratios of the consecutive terms. If the ratios are constant, the sequence is geometric.

21 63 189 567

$\frac{63}{21} = \frac{189}{63} = \frac{567}{189} = 3$

Because the ratios are constant, the sequence is geometric. The common ratio is 3.

Example 2 Find the next three terms in this geometric sequencew: −1215, 405, −135, 45, . . .

Step 1 Find the common ratio.

−1215 405 −135 45

$\frac{405}{-1215} = \frac{-135}{405} = \frac{45}{-135} = \frac{-1}{3}$

The value of r is $-\frac{1}{3}$.

Step 2 Multiply each term by the common ratio to find the next three terms.

45 −15 5 $-\frac{5}{3}$

$\times\left(-\frac{1}{3}\right)$ $\times\left(-\frac{1}{3}\right)$ $\times\left(-\frac{1}{3}\right)$

The next three terms of the sequence are −15, 5, and $-\frac{5}{3}$.

Exercises

Determine whether each sequence is *arithmetic, geometric,* or *neither.* Explain.

1. 1, 2, 4, 8, . . . geometric common ratio = 2;
2. 9, 14, 6, 11, . . . neither no common ratio or difference;
3. $\frac{2}{3}, \frac{1}{3}, \frac{1}{6}, \frac{1}{12}$, . . . geometric common ratio = $\frac{1}{2}$;
4. −2, 5, 12, 19, . . . arithmetic common difference = 7;

Find the next three terms in each geometric sequence.

5. 648, −216, 72, . . . −24, 8, $-2\frac{2}{3}$
6. 25, −5, 1, . . . $\frac{-1}{5}, \frac{1}{25}, \frac{-1}{125}$
7. $\frac{1}{16}, \frac{1}{2}$, 4, . . . 32, 256, 2048
8. 72, 36, 18, . . . 9, $4\frac{1}{2}$, $2\frac{1}{4}$

Chapter 9 48 Glencoe Algebra 1

Practice
CRM p. 51 AL OL BL ELL

NAME ________ DATE ______ PERIOD ______

9-8 Practice

Geometric Sequences as Exponential Functions

Determine whether each sequence is *arithmetic, geometric,* or *neither.* Explain.

1. 1, −5, −11, −17, ... Arithmetic; the common difference is −6.
2. 3, $\frac{3}{2}$, 1, $\frac{3}{4}$, ... Neither; there is no common difference or ratio.
3. 108, 36, 12, 4, ... Geometric; the common ratio is $\frac{1}{3}$.
4. −2, 4, −6, 8, ... Neither; there is no common difference or ratio.

Find the next three terms in each geometric sequence.

5. 64, 16, 4, ... 1; $\frac{1}{4}$; $\frac{1}{16}$
6. 2, −12, 72, ... −432; 2592; −15,552
7. 3750, 750, 150, ... 30; 6; $\frac{6}{5}$
8. 4, 28, 196, ... 1372; 9604; 67,228
9. Write an equation for the nth term of the geometric sequence 896, −448, 224, ... Find the eighth term of this sequence. $a_n = 896\left(-\frac{1}{2}\right)^{n-1}$; −7
10. Write an equation for the nth term of the geometric sequence 3584, 896, 224, ... Find the sixth term of this sequence. $a_n = 3584\left(\frac{1}{4}\right)^{n-1}$; 3.5
11. Find the sixth term of a geometric sequence for which $a_2 = 288$ and $r = \frac{1}{4}$. 1.125
12. Find the eighth term of a geometric sequence for which $a_3 = 35$ and $r = 7$. 588,245
13. PENNIES Thomas is saving pennies in a jar. The first day he saves 3 pennies, the second day 12 pennies, the third day 48 pennies, and so on. How many pennies does Thomas save on the eighth day? 49,152

Lesson 9-8

Chapter 9 51 Glencoe Algebra 1

Word Problem Practice
CRM p. 52 AL OL BL ELL

NAME ________ DATE ______ PERIOD ______

9-8 Word Problem Practice

Geometric Sequences as Exponential Functions

1. **WORLD POPULATION** The CIA estimates the world population is growing at a rate of 1.167% each year. The world population for 2007 was about 6.6 billion.
   a. Write an equation for the world population after n years. (*Hint:* The common ratio is not just 0.01167.) $a_n = 6{,}600{,}000{,}000 \cdot 1.01167^{n-1}$
   b. What will the estimated world population be in 2017? about 7.4 billion
2. **MUSEUMS** The table shows the annual visitors to a museum in millions. Write an equation for the projected number of visitors after n years.

Year	Visitors (millions)
1	4
2	6
3	9
4	$13\frac{1}{2}$
n	?

$a_n = 4 \cdot \left(\frac{3}{2}\right)^{n-1}$

3. **BANKING** Arnold has a bank account with a beginning balance of $5000. He spends one-fifth of the balance each month. How much money will be in the account after 6 months? $1310.72
4. **POPULATION** The table shows the projected population of the United States through 2050. Does this table show an arithmetic sequence, 2 geometric sequence or neither? Explain.

Year	Projected Population
2000	282,125,000
2010	308,936,000
2020	335,805,000
2030	363,584,000
2040	391,946,000
2050	419,854,000

Source: U.S. Census Bureau

Neither, there is no common ratio or difference.

5. **SAVINGS ACCOUNTS** A bank offers a savings account with a 0.5% return each month.
   a. Write an equation for the balance of a savings account after n months. (*Hint:* The common ratio is not just 0.005.) $a_n = p \cdot 1.005^n$
   b. Given an initial deposit of $500, what will the account balance be after 15 months? $538.84

Chapter 9 52 Glencoe Algebra 1

Real-World Link

The average American 9- to 14-year-old gets $9.15 each week for allowance.

Source: *Money Magazine*

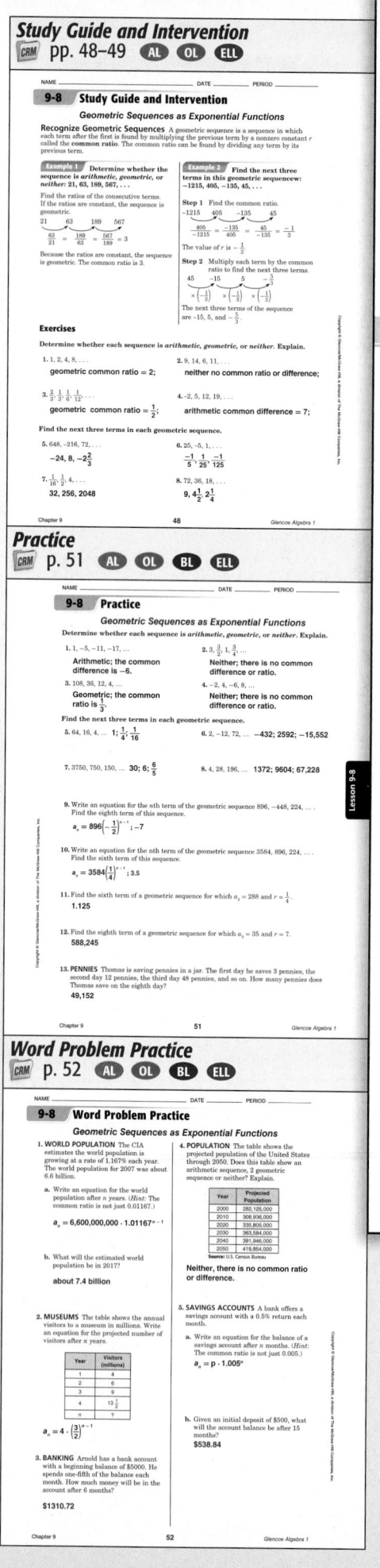

33. **ALLOWANCE** Danielle's parents have offered her two different options to earn her allowance for a 9-week period over the summer. She can either get paid $30 each week or $1 the first week, $2 for the second week, $4 for the third week, and so on. **a. Yes; the common ratio is 2.**
    a. Does the second option form a geometric sequence? Explain.
    b. Which option should Danielle choose? Explain.

34. **SIERPINSKI'S TRIANGLE** Consider the inscribed equilateral triangles at the right. The perimeter of each triangle is one half of the perimeter of the next larger triangle. What is the perimeter of the smallest triangle? **7.5 cm**

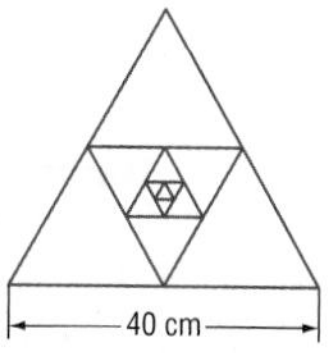

35. If the second term of a geometric sequence is 3 and the third term is 1, find the first and fourth terms of the sequence. **9; $\frac{1}{3}$**

36. If the third term of a geometric sequence is −12 and the fourth term is 24, find the first and fifth terms of the sequence. **−3; −48**

37. **EARTHQUAKES** The Richter scale is used to measure the force of an earthquake. The table shows the increase in magnitude for the values on the Richter scale.

Richter Number (x)	Increase in Magnitude (y)	Rate of Change (slope)
1	1	—
2	10	9
3	100	90
4	1000	900
5	10,000	9000

a. Copy and complete the table. Remember that the rate of change is the change in y divided by the change in x. **b–c. See Ch. 9 Answer Appendix.**
b. Plot the ordered pairs (Richter number, increase in magnitude).
c. Describe the graph that you made of the Richter scale data. Is the rate of change between any two points the same?
d. Write an exponential equation that represents the Richter scale. **$y = 1 \cdot (10)^{x-1}$**

33b. The second option; she would earn $511, which is much more than she would earn with the first option.

38. 1, 1, 1, 1, ...; The common ratio is 1 making it a geometric sequence, but the common difference is 0 making it an arithmetic sequence as well.

40. Sample answer: 1, 4, 9, 16, 25, 36, ...; This is the sequence of squares of counting numbers.

41. 1, $\frac{3}{4}$, $\frac{9}{16}$, ...

H.O.T. Problems
Use Higher-Order Thinking Skills

38. **CHALLENGE** Write a sequence that is both geometric and arithmetic. Explain your answer.

39. **FIND THE ERROR** Haro and Matthew are finding the ninth term of the geometric sequence −5, 10, −20, … . Is either of them correct? Explain your reasoning. **See Ch. 9 Answer Appendix.**

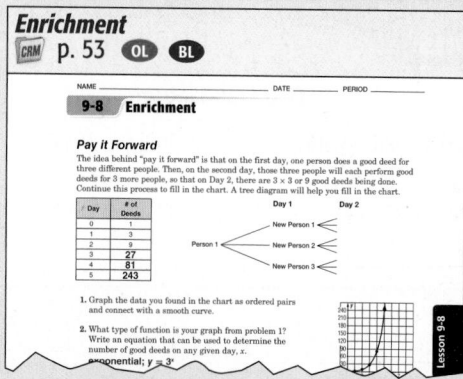

Haro	Matthew
$r = \frac{10}{-5}$ or −2	$r = \frac{10}{-5}$ or −2
$a_9 = -5(-2)^{9-1}$	$a_9 = -5 \cdot (-2)^{9-1}$
$= -5(512)$	$= -5 \cdot -256$
$= -2560$	$= 1280$

40. **REASONING** Write a sequence of numbers that form a pattern but are neither arithmetic nor geometric. Explain the pattern.

41. **OPEN ENDED** Write a geometric sequence that has a common ratio of $\frac{3}{4}$.

42. **WRITING IN MATH** Summarize how to find a specific term of a geometric sequence. **See Ch. 9 Answer Appendix.**

Enrichment
CRM p. 53 OL BL

NAME ________ DATE ______ PERIOD ______

9-8 Enrichment

Pay it Forward

The idea behind "pay it forward" is that on the first day, one person does a good deed for three different people. Then, on the second day, those three people will each perform good deeds for 3 more people, so that on Day 2, there are 3 × 3 or 9 good deeds being done. Continue this process to fill in the chart. A tree diagram will help you fill in the chart.

Day	# of Deeds
0	1
1	3
2	9
3	27
4	81
5	243

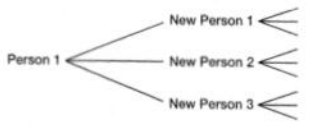

1. Graph the data you found in the chart as ordered pairs and connect with a smooth curve.

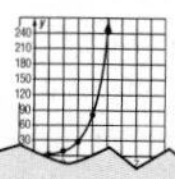

2. What type of function is your graph from problem 1? Write an equation that can be used to determine the number of good deeds on any given day, x. exponential; $y = 3^x$

Lesson 9-8

Watch Out!

Find the Error For Exercise 39, help students see that how a problem is input to a calculator affects the answer. Ask students to explain what Haro and Matthew each did wrong.

PSAE PRACTICE 8.11.04, 8.11.19, 8.11.17, 9.11.05

43. Find the eleventh term of the sequence 3, −6, 12, −24, … . **B**

A 1024
B 3072
C 33
D −6144

44. What is the total amount of the investment shown in the table below if interest is compounded monthly? **H**

Principal	\$500
Length of Investment	4 years
Annual Interest Rate	5.25%

F \$613.56
G \$616.00
H \$616.56
J \$718.75

45. SHORT RESPONSE Gloria has \$6.50 in quarters and dimes. If she has 35 coins in total, how many of each coin does she have? **15 dimes and 20 quarters**

46. A sidewalk is being built along the inside edges of all four sides of a rectangular lawn. The lawn is 32 feet long and 24 feet wide. The remaining lawn will have an area of 425 square feet. How wide will the sidewalk be? **A**

A 3.5 feet
B 17 feet
C 24.5 feet
D 25 feet

Spiral Review

Find the next three terms in each geometric sequence. (Lesson 9-7) **47–52. See margin.**

47. 2, 6, 18, 54, …
48. −5, −10, −20, −40, …
49. $1, -\frac{1}{2}, \frac{1}{4}, -\frac{1}{8}, \ldots$
50. −3, 1.5, −0.75, 0.375, …
51. 1, 0.6, 0.36, 0.216, …
52. 4, 6, 9, 13.5, …

Graph each function. Find the y-intercept and state the domain and range. (Lesson 9-6) **53–55. See margin.**

53. $y = \left(\frac{1}{4}\right)^x - 5$
54. $y = 2(4)^x$
55. $y = \frac{1}{2}(3^x)$

56. LANDSCAPING A blue spruce grows an average of 6 inches per year. A hemlock grows an average of 4 inches per year. If a blue spruce is 4 feet tall and a hemlock is 6 feet tall, write a system of equations to represent their growth. Find and interpret the solution in the context of the situation. (Lesson 6-2) **See Ch. 9 Answer Appendix.**

57. MONEY City Bank requires a minimum balance of \$1500 to maintain free checking services. If Mr. Hayashi is going to write checks for the amounts listed in the table, how much money should he start with in order to have free checking? (Lesson 5-1) **at least \$3747**

Check	Amount
750	\$1300
751	\$947

Write an equation in slope-intercept form of the line with the given slope and y-intercept. (Lesson 4-1) **58–63. See Ch. 9 Answer Appendix.**

58. slope: 4, y-intercept: 2
59. slope: −3, y-intercept: $-\frac{2}{3}$
60. slope: $-\frac{1}{4}$, y-intercept: −5
61. slope: $\frac{1}{2}$, y-intercept: −9
62. slope: $-\frac{2}{5}$, y-intercept: $\frac{3}{4}$
63. slope: −6, y-intercept: −7

Skills Check

Evaluate $a(1 + r)^t$ to the nearest hundredth for each of the given values. (Lesson 1-2)

64. $a = 20, r = 0.25, t = 5$ **61.04**
65. $a = 1000, r = 0.65, t = 4$ **7412.01**
66. $a = 200, r = 0.35, t = 8$ **2206.48**
67. $a = 60, r = 0.2, t = 10$ **371.50**
68. $a = 8, r = 0.5, t = 2$ **18**
69. $a = 500, r = 0.55, t = 12$ **96,150.24**

Differentiated Instruction

OL BL

Extension Often sequences of numbers do not appear, on first calculations, to have a pattern. Sometimes the differences between terms themselves create a sequence that can be used to determine the next term in the original sequence. Ask students to determine the 6th term in the sequence 4, 7, 14, 25, 40, …. Have them also explain how they found the term.

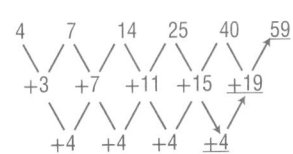

4 7 14 25 40 59
+3 +7 +11 +15 +19
+4 +4 +4 +4

4 ASSESS

Name the Math Give each student one of five different geometric sequences. Ask students to explain how to find the common ratio for their sequence.

Additional Answers

47. 162, 486, 1458

48. −80, −160, −320

49. $\frac{1}{16}, -\frac{1}{32}, \frac{1}{64}$

50. −0.1875, 0.09375, −0.046875

51. 0.1296, 0.07776, 0.046656

52. 20.25, 30.375, 45.5625

53.

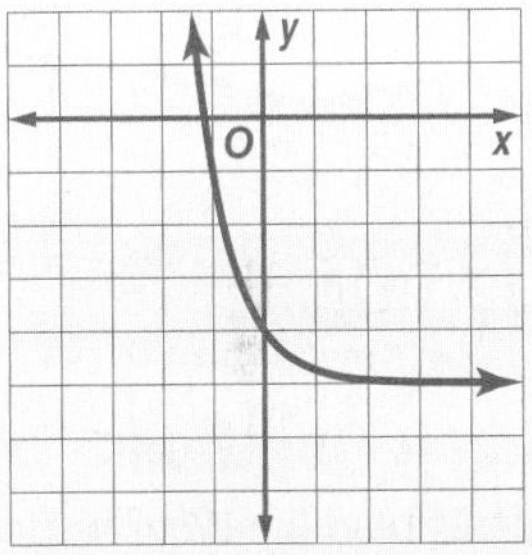

−4; D = {all real numbers}; R = {y|y > −5}

54.

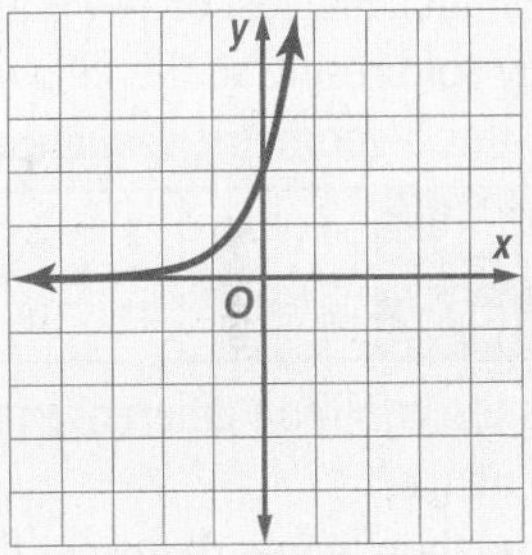

2; D = {all real numbers}; R = {y|y > 0}

55.

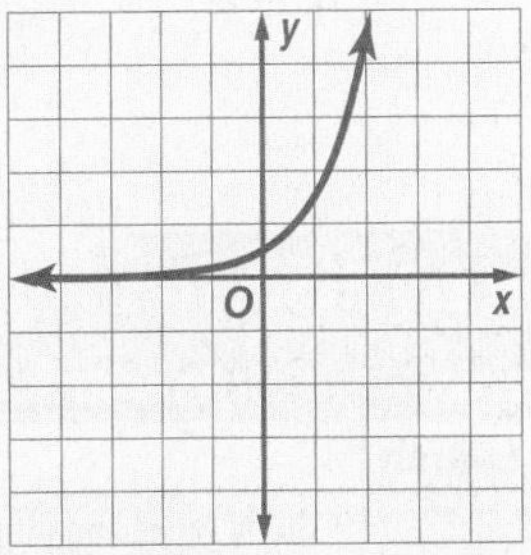

$\frac{1}{2}$; D = {all real numbers}; R = {y|y > 0}

9-9 Lesson Notes

1 FOCUS

Vertical Alignment

Before Lesson 9-9
Graph linear, quadratic, and exponential functions.

Lesson 9-9
Identify linear, quadratic, and exponential functions from given data.
Write equations that model that data.

After Lesson 9-9
Graph and solve direct variation equations.

2 TEACH

Scaffolding Questions

Have students read the *Why?* section of the lesson.

Ask:

- If the data for the cost of 1–4 pounds of candy sold results in the following data, is this a geometric sequence? no

pounds	1	2	3	4
price (in $)	4	8	12	16

- What is the common difference for this sequence? 4
- What equation would represent this function? $y = 4x$, where x = number of pounds and y = price

9-9 Analyzing Functions with Successive Differences

Then
You graphed linear, quadratic, and exponential functions.
(Lessons 3-2, 9-1, 9-6)

Now
- Identify linear, quadratic, and exponential functions from given data.
- Write equations that model data.

IL Learning Standards
8.A.4b Represent mathematical patterns and describe their properties using variables and mathematical symbols.
8.C.4b Apply algebraic properties and procedures with matrices, vectors, functions and **sequences using data found in business, industry and consumer situations.**

IL Math Online
glencoe.com
- Extra Examples
- Personal Tutor
- Self-Check Quiz
- Homework Help

Why?

Every year the golf team sells candy to raise money for charity. By knowing what type of function models the sales of the candy, they can determine the best price of the candy.

Identify Functions You can use linear functions, quadratic functions, and exponential functions to model data. The general forms of the equations and a graph of each function type are listed below.

Concept Summary — Linear and Nonlinear Functions (For Your FOLDABLE)

Linear Function
$y = mx + b$

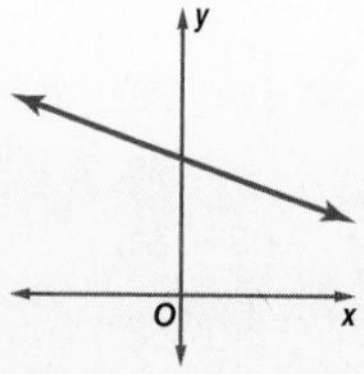

Quadratic Function
$y = ax^2 + bx + c$

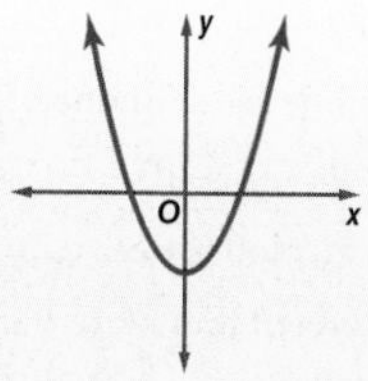

Exponential Function
$y = ab^x$, when $b > 0$

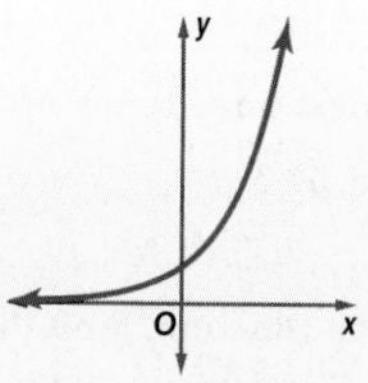

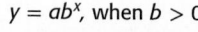

EXAMPLE 1 Choose a Model Using Graphs

Graph each set of ordered pairs. Determine whether the ordered pairs represent a *linear* function, a *quadratic* function, or an *exponential* function.

a. $\{(-2, 5), (-1, 2), (0, 1), (1, 2), (2, 5)\}$

The ordered pairs appear to represent a quadratic function.

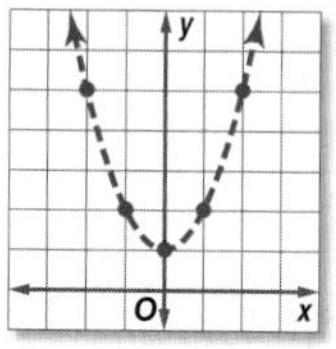

b. $\left\{\left(-2, \frac{1}{4}\right), \left(-1, \frac{1}{2}\right), (0, 1), (1, 2), (2, 4)\right\}$

The ordered pairs appear to represent an exponential function.

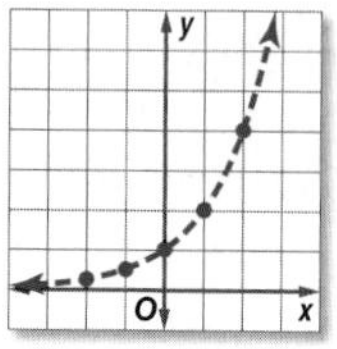

Check Your Progress

1A. $(-2, -3), (-1, -1), (0, 1), (1, 3)$ linear **1B.** $(-1, 0.25), (0, 1), (1, 4), (2, 16)$ exponential

Personal Tutor glencoe.com

Lesson 9-9 Resources

Resource	Approaching-Level	On-Level	Beyond-Level	English Learners
Teacher Edition		• Differentiated Instruction, p. 589	• Differentiated Instruction, p. 589	• Differentiated Instruction, p. 586
Chapter Resource Masters	• Study Guide and Intervention, pp. 54–55 • Skills Practice, p. 56 • Practice, p. 57 • Word Problem Practice, p. 58	• Study Guide and Intervention, pp. 54–55 • Skills Practice, p. 56 • Practice, p. 57 • Word Problem Practice, p. 58 • Enrichment, p. 59	• Practice, p. 57 • Word Problem Practice, p. 58 • Enrichment, p. 59	• Study Guide and Intervention, pp. 54–55 • Skills Practice, p. 56 • Practice, p. 57 • World Problem Practice, p. 58
Transparencies	• 5-Minute Check Transparency 9-9	• 5-Minute Check Transparency 9-9	• 5-Minute Check Transparency 9-9	• 5-Minute Check Transparency 9-9
Other	• Study Notebook	• Study Notebook	• Study Notebook	• Study Notebook

Another way to determine which model best describes data is to use patterns. The differences of successive y-values are called *first differences*. The differences of successive first differences are called *second differences*.

- If the differences of successive y-values are all equal, the data represent a linear function.
- If the second differences are all equal, but the first differences are not equal, the data represent a quadratic function.
- If the ratios of successive y-values are all equal and $r \neq 1$, the data represent an exponential function.

Watch Out!

x-Values Before you check for successive differences or ratios, make sure the x-values are increasing by the same amount.

EXAMPLE 2 Choose a Model Using Differences or Ratios

Look for a pattern in each table of values to determine which kind of model best describes the data.

a.

x	−2	−1	0	1	2
y	−8	−3	2	7	12

First differences: −8, −3, 2, 7, 12 → **5**, **5**, **5**, **5**

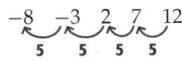

Since the first differences are all equal, the table of values represents a linear function.

b.

x	−1	0	1	2	3
y	8	4	2	1	0.5

First differences: 8, 4, 2, 1, 0.5 → **−4**, **−2**, **−1**, **−0.5**

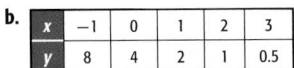

The first differences are not all equal. So, the table of values does not represent a linear function. Find the second differences and compare.

First differences: −4, −2, −1, −0.5

Second differences: **2**, **1**, **0.5**

The second differences are not all equal. So, the table of values does not represent a quadratic function. Find the ratios of the y-values and compare.

8, 4, 2, 1, 0.5

Ratios: $\frac{4}{8} = \frac{1}{2}$, $\frac{2}{4} = \frac{1}{2}$, $\frac{1}{2}$, $\frac{0.5}{1} = \frac{1}{2}$

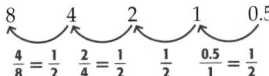

The ratios of successive y-values are equal. Therefore, the table of values can be modeled by an exponential function.

Check Your Progress

2A.

x	−3	−2	−1	0	1
y	−3	−7	−9	−9	−7

quadratic

2B.

x	−2	−1	0	1	2
y	−18	−13	−8	−3	2

linear

Personal Tutor glencoe.com

Write Equations Once you find the model that best describes the data, you can write an equation for the function. For a quadratic function in this lesson, the equation will have the form $y = ax^2$.

Identify Functions

Example 1 shows how to use a graph of a set of ordered pairs to determine whether the data represents a linear, quadratic, or exponential function. **Example 2** shows how to look for a pattern in a table of values to determine whether the data represents a linear, quadratic, or exponential function.

Formative Assessment

Use the Check Your Progress exercises after each example to determine students' understanding of concepts.

Additional Example

1 Graph each set of ordered pairs. Determine whether the ordered pairs represent a *linear*, *quadratic*, or *exponential* function.

a. (1, 2), (2, 5), (3, 6), (4, 5), (5, 2) quadratic

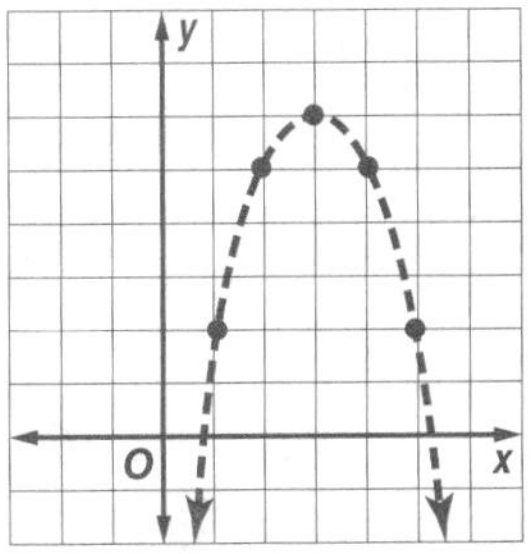

b. $(-1, 6), (0, 2), \left(1, \frac{2}{3}\right), \left(2, \frac{2}{9}\right)$ exponential

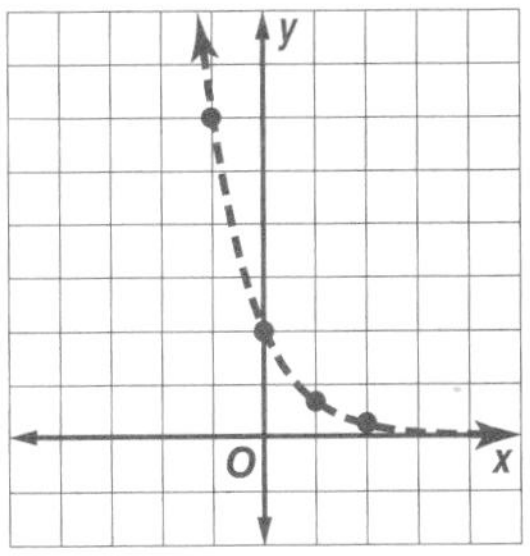

Focus on Mathematical Content

Patterns in Data For the table of values to be useful in determining which model best describes a set of data, the x-values must increase or decrease by a constant amount. If they do not, then the methods shown on this page cannot be used.

TEACH with TECH

VIDEO RECORDING Create a short video introduction to show at the beginning of class, and then work through additional examples with the class.

Write Equations

Example 3 shows how to write an equation for a function modeled by a set of data. **Example 4** shows how to write a function that models real-world data.

Additional Examples

2 Look for a pattern in each table of values to determine which kind of model best describes the data.

a.

x	-2	-1	0	1	2
y	-1	1	3	5	7

linear

b.

x	-2	-1	0	1	2
y	36	12	4	$\frac{4}{3}$	$\frac{4}{9}$

exponential

3 Determine which model best describes the data. Then write an equation for the function that models the data.

x	0	1	2	3	4
y	-1	-8	-64	-512	-4096

exponential, $y = -(8)^x$

4 **KARATE** The table shows the number of children enrolled in a beginner's karate class for four consecutive years. Determine which model best represents the data. Then write a function that models that data.

Time (years)	0	1	2	3	4
Number enrolled	8	11	14	17	20

linear, $y = 3x + 8$

Additional Examples also in Interactive Classroom PowerPoint® Presentations

IWB INTERACTIVE WHITEBOARD READY

EXAMPLE 3 Write an Equation

Determine which kind of model best describes the data. Then write an equation for the function that models the data.

x	-4	-3	-2	-1	0
y	32	18	8	2	0

Step 1 Determine which model fits the data.

32 18 8 2 0

First differences: -14 -10 -6 -2

Second differences: 4 4 4

Since the second differences are equal, a quadratic function models the data.

Step 2 Write an equation for the function that models the data.

The equation has the form $y = ax^2$. Find the value of a by choosing one of the ordered pairs from the table of values. Let's use $(-1, 2)$.

$y = ax^2$ — **Equation for quadratic function**

$2 = a(-1)^2$ — **$x = -1$ and $y = 2$**

$2 = a$ — An equation that models the data is $y = 2x^2$.

Watch Out!

Finding a In Example 3, the point (0, 0) cannot be used to find the value of a. You will have to divide each side by 0, giving you an undefined value for a.

Check Your Progress

3A.

x	-2	-1	0	1	2
y	11	7	3	-1	-5

linear; $y = -4x + 3$

3B.

x	-3	-2	-1	0	1
y	0.375	0.75	1.5	3	6

exponential; $y = 3(2)^x$

Personal Tutor glencoe.com

Real-World EXAMPLE 4 Write an Equation for a Real-World Situation

BOOK CLUB **The table shows the number of book club members for four consecutive years. Determine which model best represents the data. Then write a function that models the data.**

Time (years)	0	1	2	3	4
Members	5	10	20	40	80

Understand We need to find a model for the data, and then write a function.

Plan Find a pattern using successive differences or ratios. Then use the general form of the equation to write a function.

Solve The constant ratio is 2. This is the value of the base. An exponential function of the form $y = ab^x$ models the data.

$y = ab^x$ — **Equation for exponential function**

$5 = a(2)^0$ — **$x = 0$, $y = 5$, and $b = 2$**

$5 = a$ — The equation that models the data is $y = 5 \cdot 2^x$.

Check You used (0, 5) to write the function. Verify that every other ordered pair satisfies the equation.

Real-World Link

A poll by the National Education Association found that 87% of all teens polled found reading relaxing, 85% viewed reading as rewarding, and 79% found reading exciting.

Source: *American Demographics*

Check Your Progress

4. ADVERTISING The table shows the cost of placing an ad in a newspaper. Determine a model that best represents the data and write a function that models the data. linear; $C = 2.1n + 4$

No. of Lines	5	6	7	8
Total Cost ($)	14.50	16.60	18.70	20.80

Personal Tutor glencoe.com

Differentiated Instruction

ELL

Verbal/Linguistic Learners Have students write a list of tips to help someone determine which model best describes a set of data and to write an equation for the function.

Tips for New Teachers

Checking the Equation Encourage students to verify that the ordered pairs satisfy the written equation.

Check Your Understanding

Example 1 p. 586

Graph each set of ordered pairs. Determine whether the ordered pairs represent a *linear* function, a *quadratic* function, or an *exponential* function. **1–4. See margin.**

1. $(-2, 8), (-1, 5), (0, 2), (1, -1)$
2. $(-3, 7), (-2, 3), (-1, 1), (0, 1), (1, 3)$
3. $(-3, 8), (-2, 4), (-1, 2), (0, 1), (1, 0.5)$
4. $(0, 2), (1, 2.5), (2, 3), (3, 3.5)$

Example 2 p. 587

Look for a pattern in each table of values to determine which kind of model best describes the data.

5.

x	0	1	2	3	4
y	5	8	17	32	53

quadratic

6.

x	−3	−2	−1	0
y	−6.75	−7.5	−8.25	−9

linear

7.

x	−1	0	1	2	3
y	3	6	12	24	48

exponential

8.

x	3	4	5	6	7
y	−1.5	0	2.5	6	10.5

quadratic

Example 3 p. 588

Determine which kind of model best describes the data. Then write an equation for the function that models the data.

9. exponential; $y = 3 \cdot 3^x$
10. quadratic; $y = 5x^2$
11. linear; $y = \frac{1}{2}x + \frac{5}{2}$
12. linear; $y = \frac{1}{4}x - 1$

9.

x	−1	0	1	2	3
y	1	3	9	27	81

10.

x	−5	−4	−3	−2	−1
y	125	80	45	20	5

11.

x	−3	−2	−1	0	1
y	1	1.5	2	2.5	3

12.

x	−1	0	1	2
y	−1.25	−1	−0.75	−0.5

Examples 4 p. 588

13. **PLANTS** The table shows the height of a plant for four consecutive weeks. Determine which kind of function best models the height. Then write a function that models the data. **linear; $y = 0.5x + 3$**

Week	0	1	2	3	4
Height (in.)	3	3.5	4	4.5	5

Practice and Problem Solving

● = **Step-by-Step Solutions** begin on page R12. **Extra Practice** begins on page 815.

Example 1 p. 586

14–19. See Ch. 9 Answer Appendix.

Graph each set of ordered pairs. Determine whether the ordered pairs represent a *linear* function, a *quadratic* function, or an *exponential* function.

14. $(-1, 1), (0, -2), (1, -3), (2, -2), (3, 1)$
15. $(1, 2.75), (2, 2.5), (3, 2.25), (4, 2)$
16. $(-3, 0.25), (-2, 0.5), (-1, 1), (0, 2)$
17. $(-3, -11), (-2, -5), (-1, -3), (0, -5)$
18. $(-2, 6), (-1, 1), (0, -4), (1, -9)$
19. $(-1, 8), (0, 2), (1, 0.5), (2, 0.125)$

Examples 2 and 3 pp. 587–588

Look for a pattern in each table of values to determine which kind of model best describes the data. Then write an equation for the function that models the data.

20.

x	−3	−2	−1	0
y	−8.8	−8.6	−8.4	−8.2

linear; $y = 0.2x - 8.2$

21.

x	−2	−1	0	1	2
y	10	2.5	0	2.5	10

quadratic; $y = 2.5x^2$

22.

x	−1	0	1	2	3
y	0.75	3	12	48	192

exponential; $y = 3 \cdot 4^x$

23.

x	−2	−1	0	1	2
y	0.008	0.04	0.2	1	5

exponential; $y = 0.2 \cdot 5^x$

24.

x	0	1	2	3	4
y	0	4.2	16.8	37.8	67.2

quadratic; $y = 4.2x^2$

25.

x	−3	−2	−1	0	1
y	14.75	9.75	4.75	−0.25	−5.25

linear; $y = -5x - 0.25$

Differentiated Homework Options

Level	Assignment	Two-Day Option	
AL Basic	14–26, 32–62	15–25 odd, 36–39	14–26 even, 32–35, 40–62
OL Core	15–25 odd, 27–30, 32–62	14–26, 36–39	27–30, 32–35, 40–62
BL Advanced	27–59, (optional: 60–62)		

3 PRACTICE

Formative Assessment

Use Exercises 1–13 to check for understanding.

Use the chart at the bottom of this page to customize assignments for your students.

Exercise Alert

Grid Paper For Exercises 1–4, 14–19, 27, and 60–62, students will need grid paper.

Additional Answers

1.

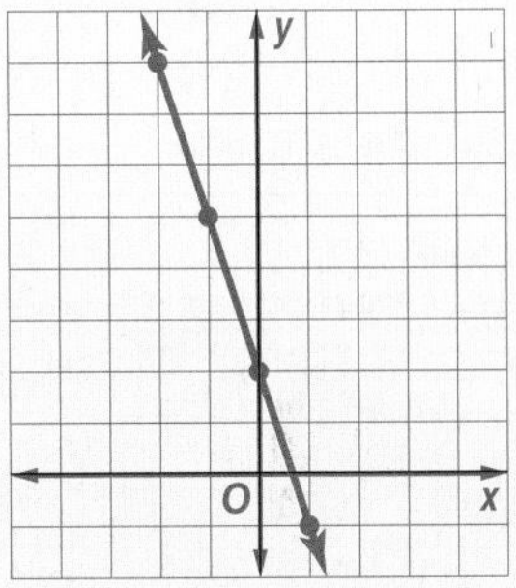

linear

2.

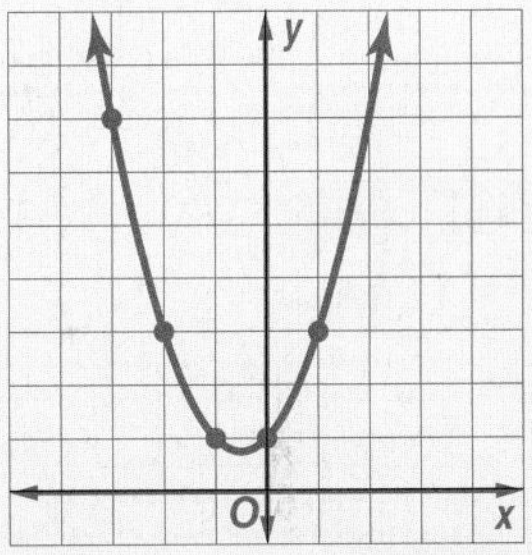

quadratic

3.

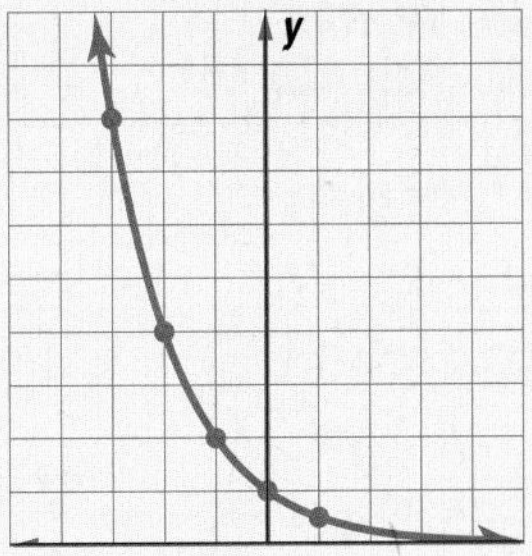

exponential

4.

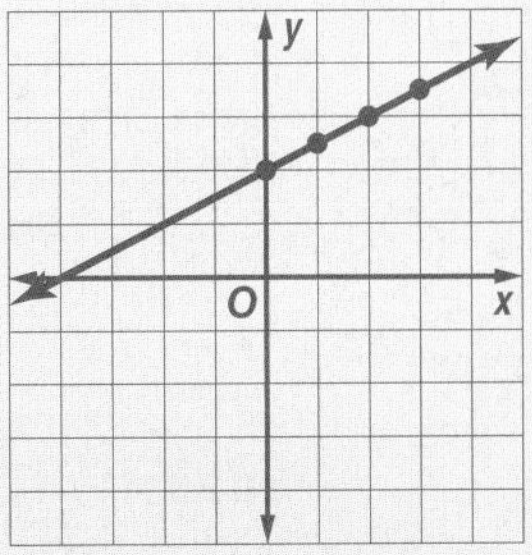

linear

Study Guide and Intervention

CRM pp. 54–55 AL OL ELL

NAME ______________ DATE ________ PERIOD ________

9-9 Study Guide and Intervention

Analyzing Functions with Successive Differences and Ratios

Identify Functions Linear functions, quadratic functions, and exponential functions can all be used to model data. The general forms of the equations are listed at the right.

Linear Function	$y = mx + b$
Quadratic Function	$y = ax^2 + bx + c$
Exponential Function	$y = ab^x$

You can also identify data as linear, quadratic, or exponential based on patterns of behavior of their y-values.

Example 1 **Graph the set of ordered pairs {(–3, 2), (–2, –1), (–1, –2), (0, –1), (1, 2)}. Determine whether the ordered pairs represent a *linear* function, a *quadratic* function, or an *exponential* function.**

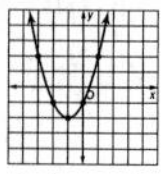

The ordered pairs appear to represent a quadratic function.

Example 2 **Look for a pattern in the table to determine which model best describes the data.**

x	–2	–1	0	1	2
y	4	2	1	0.5	0.25

Start by comparing the first differences.

$4 \xrightarrow{-2} 2 \xrightarrow{-1} 1 \xrightarrow{-0.5} 0.5 \xrightarrow{-0.25} 0.25$

The first differences are not all equal. The table does not represent a linear function. Find the second differences and compare.

$-2 \xrightarrow{+1} -1 \xrightarrow{+0.5} -0.5 \xrightarrow{+0.25} -0.25$

The table does not represent a quadratic function. Find the ratios of the y-values.

$4 \xrightarrow{\times 0.5} 2 \xrightarrow{\times 0.5} 1 \xrightarrow{\times 0.5} 0.5 \xrightarrow{\times 0.5} 0.25$

The ratios are equal. Therefore, the table can be modeled by an exponential function.

Exercises

Graph each set of ordered pairs. Determine whether the ordered pairs represent a *linear* function, a *quadratic* function, or an *exponential* function.

1. (0, –1), (1, 1), (2, 3), (3, 5)

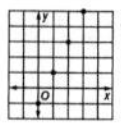

linear

2. (–3, –1), (–2, –4), (–1, –5), (0, –4), (1, –1)

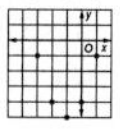

quadratic

Look for a pattern in each table to determine which model best describes the data.

3.

x	–2	–1	0	1	2
y	6	5	4	3	2

linear

4.

x	–2	–1	0	1	2
y	6.25	2.5	1	0.4	0.16

exponential

Chapter 9 54 Glencoe Algebra 1

Practice

CRM p. 57 AL OL BL ELL

NAME ______________ DATE ________ PERIOD ________

9-9 Practice

Analyzing Functions with Successive Differences and Ratios

Graph each set of ordered pairs. Determine whether the ordered pairs represent a *linear* function, a *quadratic* function, or an *exponential* function.

1. (4, 0.5), (3, 1.5), (2, 2.5), (1, 3.5), (0, 4.5)

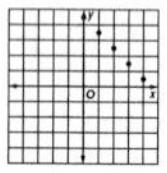

linear

2. $\left(-1, \frac{1}{9}\right), \left(0, \frac{1}{3}\right)$, (1, 1), (2, 3)

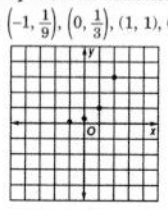

exponential

3. (–4, 4), (–2, 1), (0, 0), (2, 1), (4, 4)

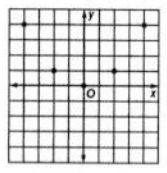

quadratic

4. (–4, 2), (–2, 1), (0, 0), (2, –1), (4, –2)

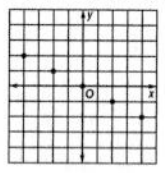

linear

Look for a pattern in each table of values to determine which model best describes the data. Then write an equation for the function that models the data.

5.

x	–3	–1	1	3	5
y	–5	–2	1	4	7

linear; $y = \frac{3}{2}x - \frac{1}{2}$

6.

x	–2	–1	0	1	2
y	0.02	0.2	2	20	200

exponential; $y = 2 \cdot 10^x$

7.

x	–1	0	1	2	3
y	6	0	6	24	54

quadratic; $y = 6x^2$

8.

x	–2	–1	0	1	2
y	18	9	0	–9	–18

linear; $y = -9x$

9. **INSECTS** The local zoo keeps track of the number of dragonflies breeding in their insect exhibit each day.

Day	1	2	3	4	5
Dragonflies	9	18	36	72	144

a. Determine which function best models the data. **exponential**

b. Write an equation for the function that models the data. $y = 9 \cdot 2^x$

c. Use your equation to determine the number of dragonflies that will be breeding after 9 days. **4608 dragonflies**

Chapter 9 57 Glencoe Algebra 1

Lesson 9-9

Word Problem Practice

CRM p. 58 AL OL BL ELL

NAME ______________ DATE ________ PERIOD ________

9-9 Word Problem Practice

Analyzing Functions with Successive Differences and Ratios

1. **WEATHER** The San Mateo weather station records the amount of rainfall since the beginning of a thunderstorm. Data for a storm is recorded as a series of ordered pairs shown below, where the x value is the time in minutes since the start of the storm, and the y value is the amount of rain in inches that has fallen since the start of the storm.

(2, 0.3), (4, 0.6), (6, 0.9), (8, 1.2), (10, 1.5)

Graph the ordered pairs. Determine whether the ordered pairs represent a *linear* function, a *quadratic* function, or an *exponential* function.

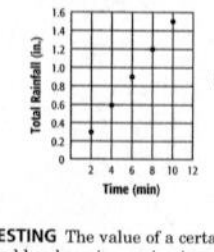

linear

2. **INVESTING** The value of a certain parcel of land has been increasing in value ever since it was purchased. The table shows the value of the land parcel over time.

Year Since Purchasing	0	1	2	3	4
Land Value (thousands $)	$1.05	$2.10	$4.20	$8.40	$16.80

Look for a pattern in the table of values to determine which model best describes the data. Then write an equation for the function that models the data.

exponential; $y = 1.05 \cdot 2^n$

3. **BOATS** The value of a boat typically depreciates over time. The table shows the value of a boat over a period of time.

Years	0	1	2	3	4
Boat Value ($)	8250	6930	5821.20	4889.81	4107.44

Write an equation for the function that models the data. Then use the equation to determine how much the boat is worth after 9 years.

$y = 8250 \cdot (0.84)^x$; **$1717.78**

4. **NUCLEAR WASTE** Radioactive material slowly decays over time. The amount of time needed for an amount of radioactive material to decay to half its initial quantity is known as its half-life. Consider a 20-gram sample of a radioactive isotope.

Half-Lives Elapsed	0	1	2	3	4
Amount of Isotope Remaining (grams)	20	10	5	2.5	1.25

a. Is radioactive decay a *linear* decay, *quadratic* decay, or an *exponential* decay? **exponential**

b. Write an equation to determine how many grams y of a radioactive isotope will be remaining after x half-lives. $y = 20 \cdot (0.5)^x$

c. How many grams of the isotope will remain after 11 half-lives? **0.0098 g**

d. Plutonium-238 is one of the most dangerous waste products of nuclear power plants. If the half-life of plutonium-238 is 87.7 years, how long would it take for a 20-gram sample of plutonium-238 to decay to 0.078 grams? **701.8 years**

Chapter 9 58 Glencoe Algebra 1

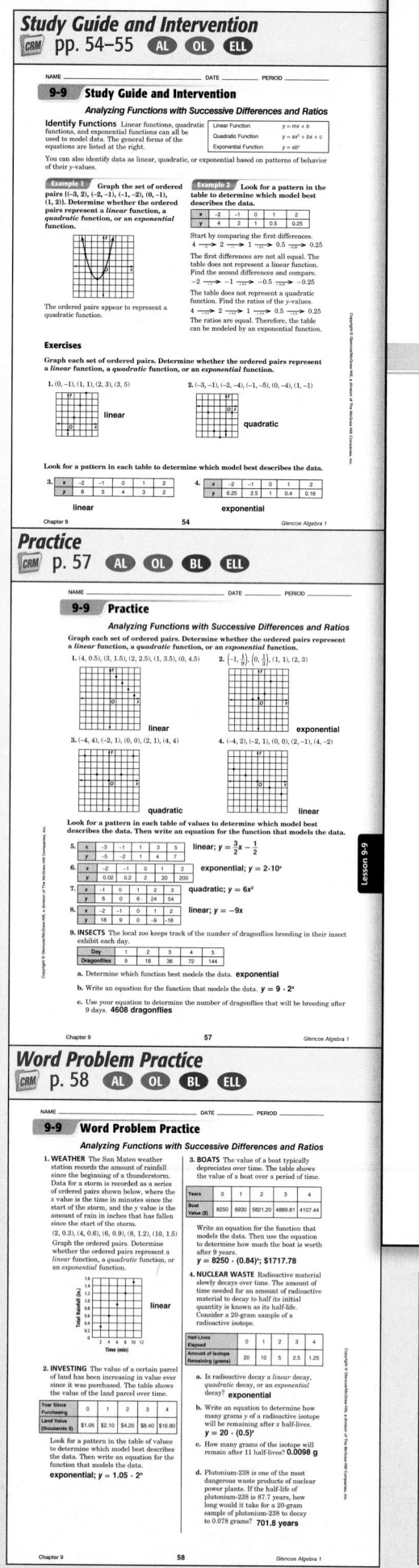

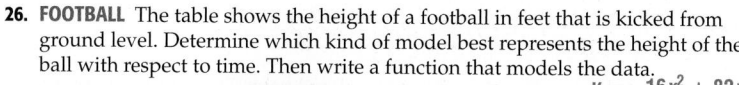

Example 4 p. 588

26. **FOOTBALL** The table shows the height of a football in feet that is kicked from ground level. Determine which kind of model best represents the height of the ball with respect to time. Then write a function that models the data. $y = -16x^2 + 82x$

Time (s)	0	1	2	3	4
Height	0	66	100	102	72

Real-World Link

The top three forms of communication used by teenagers are e-mail, cell phones, and landline telephones.

Source: Harris Interactive

B

27. **LONG DISTANCE** The cost of a long-distance telephone call depends on the length of the call. The table shows the cost for up to 6 minutes.

Length of call (min)	1	2	3	4	5	6
Cost ($)	0.12	0.24	0.36	0.48	0.60	0.72

a. Graph the data and determine which kind of function best models the data. **See margin for graph; linear.**

b. Write an equation for the function that models the data. $y = 0.12x$

c. Use your equation to determine how much a 10-minute call would cost. **$1.20**

28. **DEPRECIATION** The value of a car depreciates over time. The table shows the value of a car over a period of time.

Year	0	1	2	3	4
Value ($)	18,500	15,910	13,682.60	11,767.04	10,119.65

a. Determine which kind of function best models the data. **exponential**

b. Write an equation for the function that models the data. $v = 18{,}500 \cdot (0.86)^t$

c. Use your equation to determine how much the car is worth after 7 years. **$6436.66**

C

29. **BACTERIA** A scientist estimates that a bacteria culture with an initial population of 12 will triple every hour.

a. Make a table to show the bacteria population for the first 4 hours. **See Ch. 9 Answer Appendix.**

b. Which kind of model best represents the data? **exponential**

c. Write a function that models the data. $b = 12 \cdot 3^t$

d. How many bacteria will there be after 8 hours? **78,732**

30. **PRINTING** A printing company charges the fees shown to print flyers. Write a function that models the total cost of the flyers, and determine how much 30 flyers would cost. $C = 0.15f + 25$; **$29.50**

Quick 2 U Printing
Set Up Fee $25
15¢ each flyer

H.O.T. Problems

Use Higher-Order Thinking Skills

31. **CHALLENGE** Write a function that has constant second differences, first differences that are not constant, a y-intercept of –5, and passes through the point at (2, 3). **Sample answer:** $y = 2x^2 - 5$

32. **REASONING** What type of function will have a constant third differences but not constant second differences? Explain.

33. **OPEN ENDED** Write a linear function that has a constant first difference of 4. $y = 4x + 1$

34. **REASONING** If data can be modeled by a quadratic function, what is the relationship between the coefficient of x^2 and the constant second difference?

35. **WRITING IN MATH** Summarize how to determine whether a given set of data is modeled by a *linear* function, a *quadratic* function, or an *exponential* function. **See Ch. 9 Answer Appendix.**

32. Linear functions have a constant first difference and quadratic functions have a constant second difference, so cubic equations would have a constant third difference.

34. The constant second difference is twice the coefficient of x^2.

Enrichment

CRM p. 59 OL BL

NAME ______________ DATE ________ PERIOD ________

9-9 Enrichment

Sierpinski Triangle

Sierpinski Triangle is an example of a fractal that changes exponentially. Start with an equilateral triangle and find the midpoints of each side. Then connect the midpoints to form a smaller triangle. Remove this smaller triangle from the larger one.

Repeat the process to create the next triangle in the sequence. Find the midpoints of the sides of the three remaining triangles and connect them to form smaller triangles to be removed.

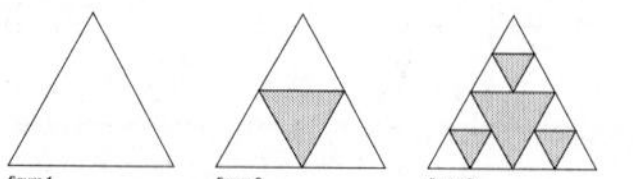

figure 1

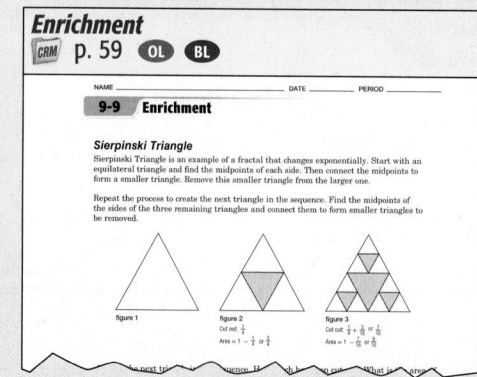

figure 2 Cut out: $\frac{1}{4}$ Area = $1 - \frac{1}{4}$ or $\frac{3}{4}$

figure 3 Cut out: $\frac{1}{4} + \frac{3}{16}$ or $\frac{7}{16}$ Area = $1 - \frac{7}{16}$ or $\frac{9}{16}$

Exercise Alert

Make a Table For Exercise 29, students will need to make a table for the data before choosing the best model or writing the equation that represents the data.

PSAE PRACTICE 8.11.14, 8.11.07, 8.11.06, 7.11.03

36. SHORT RESPONSE Write an equation that models the data in the table. $y = 3 \cdot 2^x$

x	0	1	2	3	4
y	3	6	12	24	48

37. What is the equation of the line below? **A**

A $y = \frac{2}{5}x + 2$

B $y = \frac{2}{5}x - 2$

C $y = \frac{5}{2}x + 2$

D $y = \frac{5}{2}x - 2$

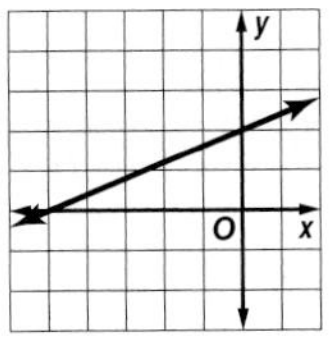

38. The point $(r, -4)$ lies on a line with an equation of $2x + 3y = -8$. Find the value of r. **H**

F −10
G 0
H 2
J 8

39. GEOMETRY The rectangle has an area of 220 square feet. Find the length ℓ. **B**

A 8 feet
B 10 feet
C 22 feet
D 34 feet

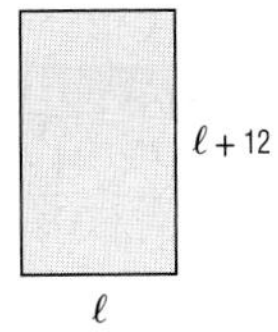

Spiral Review

40. INVESTMENTS Joey's investment of $2500 has been decreasing in value at a rate of 1.5% each year. What will his investment be worth in 5 years? (Lesson 9-8) **$2318.04**

Write an equation for the *n*th term of each geometric sequence, and find the seventh term of each sequence. (Lesson 9-7)

41. 1, 2, 4, 8, … $a_n = 1(2)^{n-1}$; 64

42. −20, −10, −5, … $a_n = -20(0.5)^{n-1}$; −0.3125

43. 4, −12, 36, … $a_n = 4(-3)^{n-1}$; 2916

44. 99, −33, 11, … $a_n = 99\left(\frac{-1}{3}\right)^{n-1}$; $\frac{11}{81}$

45. 22, 44, 88, … $a_n = 22(2)^{n-1}$; 1408

46. $\frac{2}{3}, \frac{1}{3}, \frac{1}{6}, \ldots$ $a_n = \frac{2}{3}\left(\frac{1}{2}\right)^{n-1}$; $\frac{1}{96}$

Find each product. (Lesson 7-8)

47. $(x - 4)^2$ $x^2 - 8x + 16$

48. $(2y + 3)^2$ $4y^2 + 12y + 9$

49. $(4x - 7)^2$ $16x^2 - 56x + 49$

50. $(a - 5)(a + 5)$ $a^2 - 25$

51. $(5x - 6y)(5x + 6y)$ $25x^2 - 36y^2$

52. $(9c - 2d^2)(9c + 2d^2)$ $81c^2 - 4d^4$

53. CANOE RENTAL To rent a canoe, you must pay a daily rate plus $10 per hour. Ilia and her friends rented a canoe for 3 hours and paid $45. Write a linear equation for the cost C of renting the canoe for h hours, and determine how much it cost to rent the canoe for 8 hours. (Lesson 4-2) $C = 10h + 15$; $95

Determine whether each equation is a linear equation. If so, write the equation in standard form. (Lesson 3-1)

54. $3x = 5y$ yes; $3x - 5y = 0$

55. $6 - y = 2x$ yes; $2x + y = 6$

56. $6xy + 3x = 4$ no

57. $y + 5 = 0$ yes; $y = -5$

58. $7y = 2x + 5x$ yes; $x - y = 0$

59. $y = 4x^2 - 1$ no

Skills Review

Graph each function. (Lesson 4-7) **60–62. See margin.**

60. $f(x) = |x - 2|$

61. $g(x) = |3x + 4|$

62. $f(x) = \left|\frac{1}{2}x + 5\right|$

4 ASSESS

Yesterdays News Ask students to write how yesterday's lesson on geometric sequences helped them with today's lesson.

Formative Assessment

Check for student understanding of Lesson 9-9.

CRM Quiz 4, p. 64

Additional Answers

27a.

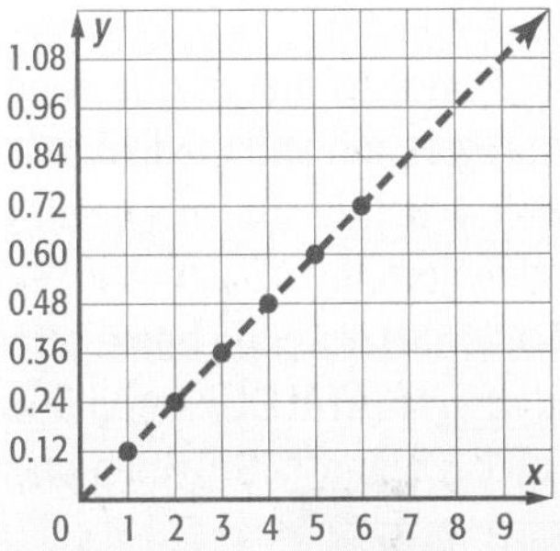

60.

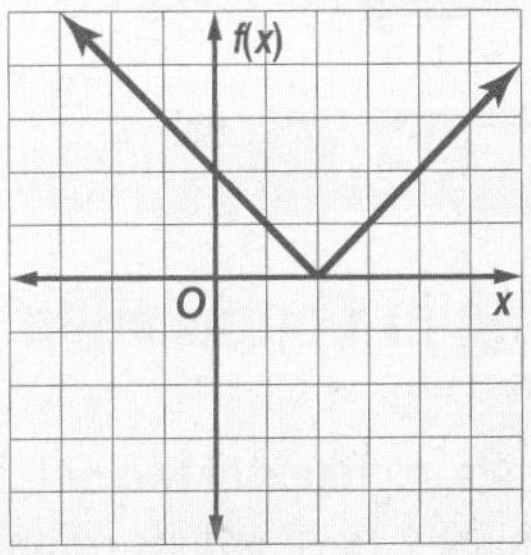

61.

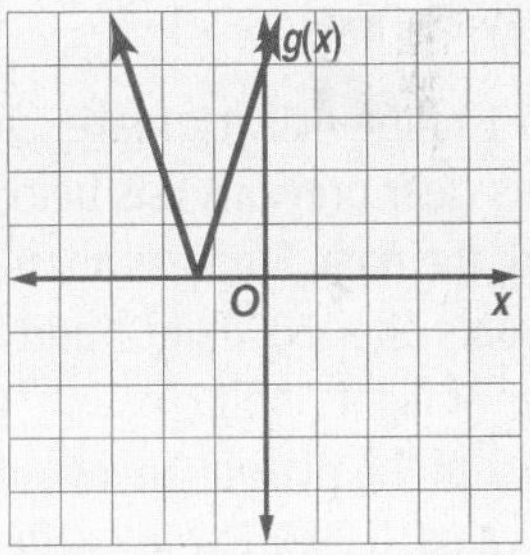

62.

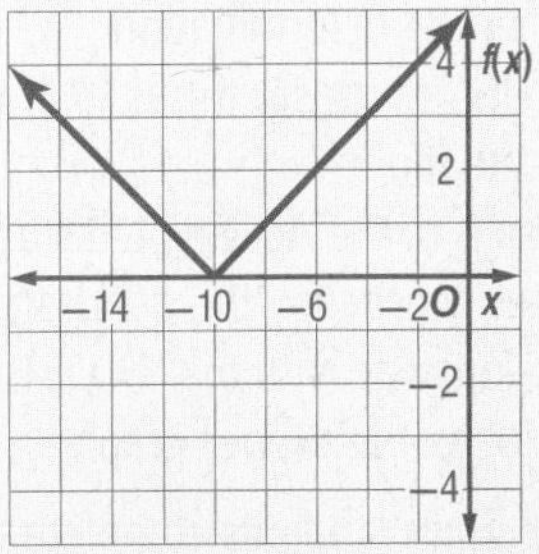

Differentiated Instruction OL BL

Extension Ask students to make a table of values for $y = \sqrt{x}$ and then graph it. Be sure students do not include any negative values for x, because the square root of a negative number is not a real number.

x	0	1	4	9	16	25
y	0	1	2	3	4	5

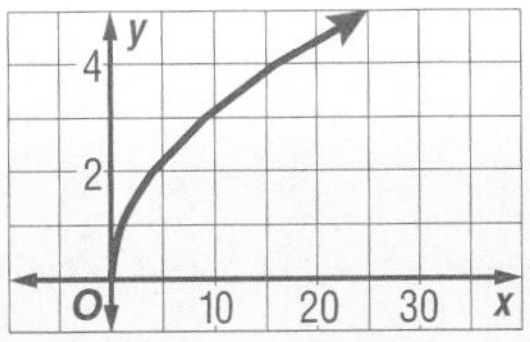

EXTEND 9-9

Lesson Notes

1 FOCUS

Objective Use a graphing calculator to find an appropriate regression equation for a set of data.

Materials for Each Group

- TI-83/84 Plus or other graphing calculator

Teaching Tip

Remind students that they learned about regression and median fit lines in Chapter 4. Before students begin, make sure they turn their Diagnostic setting on. To do this from the home screen, press [2nd] [CATALOG], scroll down and click [DiagnosticOn], then press [ENTER] [ENTER].

2 TEACH

Working in Cooperative Groups

Put students in groups of two or three, mixing abilities. Have groups complete the Activity and Exercises 1–4.

- In Step 1 of the Activity, make sure students clear previous lists before entering the data. Students should enter years after 2000 in L1 and the number of flights in L2.
- In Step 2 of the Activity, point out that the R^2 value, 0.9998751467 is the coefficient of determination. Generally, the closer this is to 1, the better the model.
- For Step 3 of the Activity, tell students that they must copy the quadratic regression exactly to the Y= LIST in order to get the proper graph.

Practice Have students complete Exercise 5.

EXTEND 9-9

Graphing Technology Lab: Curve Fitting

IL Math Online glencoe.com
- Other Calculator Keystrokes
- Graphing Technology Personal Tutor

IL Learning Standards: **Preparation for 8.D.5** Formulate and solve nonlinear equations and systems including problems involving inverse variation and exponential and logarithmic growth and decay.

If there is a constant increase or decrease in data values, there is a linear trend. If the values are increasing or decreasing more and more rapidly, there may be a quadratic or exponential trend.

Linear Trend

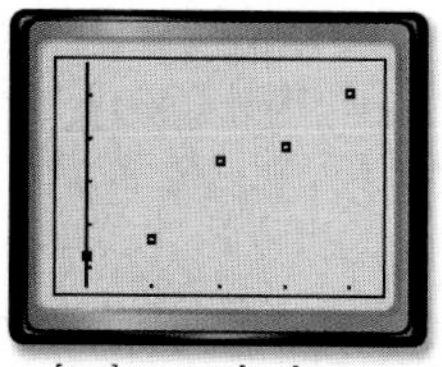

[0, 5] scl: 1 by [0, 6] scl: 1

Quadratic Trend

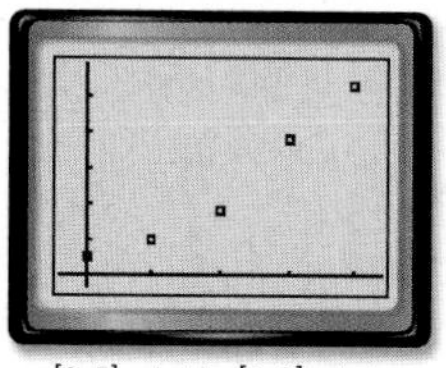

[0, 5] scl: 1 by [0, 6] scl: 1

Exponential Trend

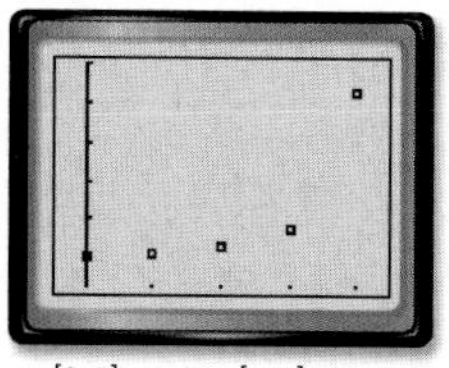

[0, 5] scl: 1 by [0, 6] scl: 1

With a graphing calculator, you can find the appropriate regression equation.

ACTIVITY

CHARTER AIRLINE The table shows the average monthly number of flights made each year by a charter airline that was founded in 2000.

Year	2000	2001	2002	2003	2004	2005	2006	2007
Flights	17	20	24	28	33	38	44	50

Step 1 Make a scatter plot.

- Enter the number of years since 2000 in **L1** and the number of flights in **L2**.

KEYSTROKES: *Review entering a list on page 253.*

- Use **STAT PLOT** to graph the scatter plot.

KEYSTROKES: *Review statistical plots on page 254.*

Use [Zoom] 9 to graph.

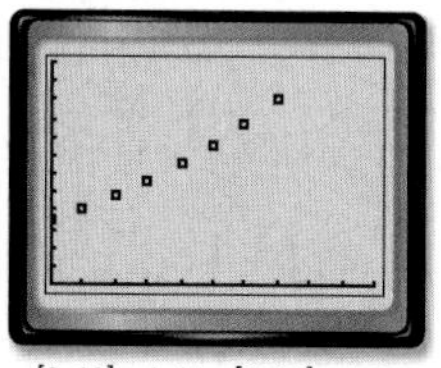

[0, 10] scl: 1 by [0, 60] scl: 5

From the scatter plot we can see that the data may have either a quadratic trend or an exponential trend.

Step 2 Find the regression equation.

We will check both trends by examining their regression equations.

- Select DiagnosticOn from the **CATALOG**.
- Select QuadReg on the [STAT] menu.

KEYSTROKES: [STAT] [▶] 5 [ENTER] [ENTER]

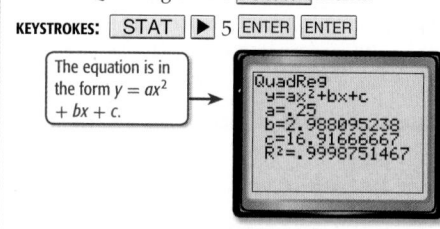

The equation is in the form $y = ax^2 + bx + c$.

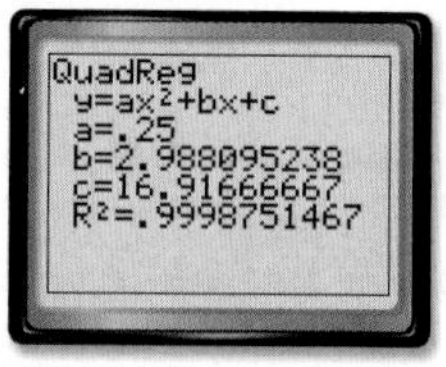

The equation is about $y = 0.25x^2 + 3x + 17$.

R^2 is the **coefficient of determination**. The closer R^2 is to 1, the better the model. To acquire the exponential equation select **ExpReg** on the [STAT] menu. To choose a quadratic or exponential model, fit both and use the one with the R^2 value closer to 1.

Step 3 Graph the quadratic regression equation.

- Copy the equation to the Y= list and graph.

KEYSTROKES: [Y=] [VARS] 5 [▶] [▶] 1 [Zoom] 9

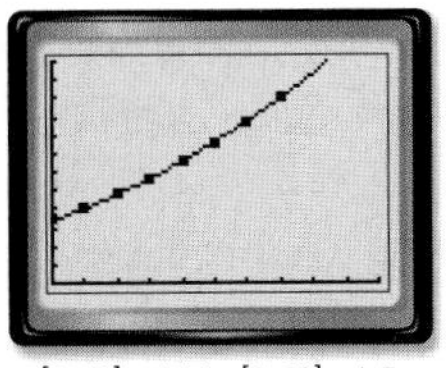

[0, 10] scl: 1 by [0, 60] scl: 5

Step 4 Predict using the equation.

If this trend continues, we can use the graph of our equation to predict the monthly number of flights the airline will make in a specific year. Let's check the year 2020. First adjust the window.

KEYSTROKES: [2nd] [CALC] 1 At x = enter 20 [ENTER].

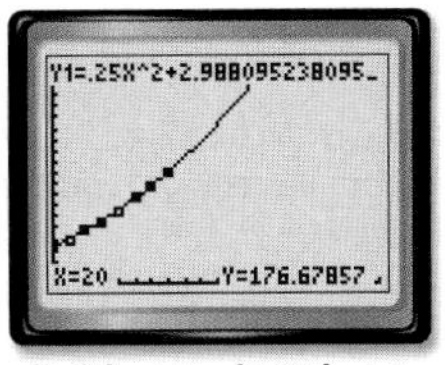

[0, 25] scl: 1 by [0, 200] scl: 5

There will be approximately 177 flights per month if this trend continues.

Exercises

Plot each set of data points. Determine whether to use a *linear, quadratic* or *exponential* regression equation. State the coefficient of determination.

1.

x	y
1	30
2	40
3	50
4	55
5	50
6	40

quadratic; $R^2 \approx 0.969$

2.

x	y
0.0	12.1
0.1	9.6
0.2	6.3
0.3	5.5
0.4	4.8
0.5	1.9

quadratic; $R^2 \approx 0.964$

3.

x	y
0	1.1
2	3.3
4	2.9
6	5.6
8	11.9
10	19.8

quadratic; $R^2 \approx 0.980$

4.

x	y
1	1.67
5	2.59
9	4.37
13	6.12
17	5.48
21	3.12

quadratic; $R^2 \approx 0.840$

5. BAKING **Alyssa baked a cake and is waiting for it to cool so she can ice it. The table shows the temperature of the cake every 5 minutes after Alyssa took it out of the oven.**

Time (min)	Temperature (°F)
0	350
5	244
10	178
15	137
20	112
25	96
30	89

a. Make a scatter plot of the data. See margin.

b. Which regression equation has an R^2 value closest to 1? Is this the equation that best fits the context of the problem? Explain your reasoning. See margin.

c. Find an appropriate regression equation, and state the coefficient of determination. What is the domain and range? $y = (306)(0.96^x)$; $R^2 = 0.957$; $D = \{x \mid x > 0\}$; $R = \{y \mid y > 0\}$

d. Alyssa will ice the cake when it reaches room temperature (70°F). Use the regression equation to predict when she can ice her cake. 32 min

3 ASSESS

Formative Assessment

In Step 4 of the Activity, the quadratic regression estimated that during the 7th month the most passengers flew, about 59 million. Ask students to explain why the estimated number of passengers that flew in the 7th month may not be completely accurate. Sample answer: The quadratic regression equation is a best fit to data points that do not fall on an actual graphed function. There will be differences between actual data points and points that fall on the regression function.

From Concrete to Abstract

Ask:

How do you determine whether to use a linear, quadratic, or exponential regression equation for your data? Sample answer: Make a scatter plot of your data points. If it looks close to a straight line, use a linear regression equation. If the data points follow a curve, fit a quadratic regression equation and an exponential regression equation to your points. The model with the coefficient of determination closest to 1 is the model to use.

Additional Answers

5a.

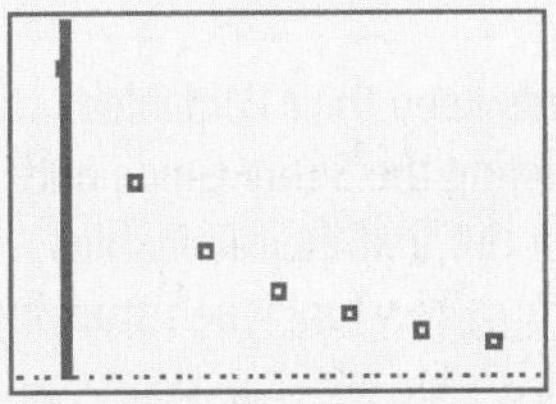

[−5, 35] scl:1 by [0, 400] scl:1

5b. A quadratic equations has an R^2 value closest to 1. However in a quadratic trend, the cake would cool and then heat up again. An exponential regression best fits the context of the problem.

CHAPTER 9 Study Guide and Review

Formative Assessment

Key Vocabulary The page references after each word denote where that term was first introduced. If students have difficulty answering questions 1–10, remind them that they can use these page references to refresh their memories about the vocabulary.

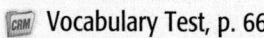

Summative Assessment

CRM Vocabulary Test, p. 66

IL Math Online glencoe.com

Vocabulary PuzzleMaker
improves students' mathematics vocabulary using four puzzle formats–crossword, scramble, word search using a word list, and word search using clues. Students can work online or from a printed worksheet.

CHAPTER 9 Study Guide and Review

IL Math Online glencoe.com
- STUDY TO GO
- Vocabulary Review

Chapter Summary

Key Concepts

Graphing Quadratic Functions (Lesson 9-1)

- A quadratic function can be described by an equation of the form $y = ax^2 + bx + c$, where $a \neq 0$.
- The axis of symmetry for the graph of $y = ax^2 + bx + c$, where $a \neq 0$, is $x = -\frac{b}{2a}$.

Solving Quadratic Equations (Lessons 9-2, 9-4, and 9-5)

- Quadratic equations can be solved by graphing. The solutions are the x-intercepts or zeros of the related quadratic function.
- Quadratic equations can be solved by completing the square. To complete the square for $x^2 + bx$, find $\frac{1}{2}$ of b, square this result, and then add the result to $x^2 + bx$.
- Quadratic equations can be solved by using the Quadratic Formula, $x = \frac{-b \pm \sqrt{b^2 - 4ac}}{2a}$.

Transformations of Quadratic Functions (Lesson 9-3)

- $f(x) = x^2 + c$ translates the graph up or down.
- $f(x) = ax^2$ compresses or expands the graph vertically.

Exponential Functions (Lessons 9-6 and 9-7)

- An exponential function can be described by an equation of the form $y = ab^x$, where $a \neq 0$, $b > 0$ and $b \neq 1$.
- The general equation for exponential growth is $y = a(1 + r)^t$, where $r > 0$, and the general equation for exponential decay is $y = a(1 - r)^t$, where $0 < r < 1$. y represents the final amount, a is the initial amount, r represents the rate of change, and t is the time in years.

FOLDABLES® Study Organizer

Be sure the Key Concepts are noted in your Foldable.

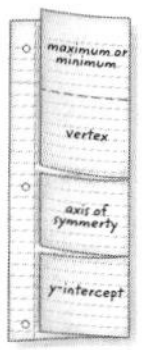

Key Vocabulary

axis of symmetry (p. 525)	**minimum** (p. 525)
common ratio (p. 578)	**nonlinear function** (p. 525)
completing the square (p. 552)	**parabola** (p. 525)
compound interest (p. 574)	**Quadratic Formula** (p. 558)
dilation (p. 545)	**quadratic function** (p. 525)
discriminant (p. 561)	**reflection** (p. 545)
double root (p. 538)	**standard form** (p. 525)
exponential decay (p. 574)	**symmetry** (p. 526)
exponential function (p. 567)	**transformation** (p. 544)
exponential growth (p. 573)	**translation** (p. 544)
geometric sequence (p. 578)	**vertex** (p. 525)
maximum (p. 525)	

Vocabulary Check

State whether each sentence is *true* or *false*. If *false*, replace the underlined term to make a true sentence.

1. The axis of symmetry of a quadratic function can be found by using the equation $x = -\frac{b}{2a}$. **true**
2. The vertex is the maximum or minimum point of a parabola. **true**
3. The graph of a quadratic function is a straight line. **false; parabola**
4. The graph of a quadratic function has a maximum if the coefficient of the x^2 is positive. **false; minimum**
5. A quadratic equation with a graph that has two x-intercepts has one real root. **false; two**
6. The expression $b^2 - 4ac$ is called the discriminant. **true**
7. An example of an exponential function is $y = 3^x$. **true**
8. The exponential growth equation is $y = C(1 - r)^t$. **false; exponential decay**
9. The solutions of a quadratic equation are called roots. **true**
10. The graph of the parent function is translated down to form the graph of $f(x) = x^2 + 5$. **false; translated up 5 units**

FOLDABLES® Study Organizer

Dinah Zike's Foldables®

Have students look through the chapter to make sure they have included examples in their Foldables for each lesson of the chapter.

Suggest that students keep their Foldables handy while completing the Study Guide and Review pages. Point out that their Foldables can serve as a quick review tool when studying for the chapter test.

Lesson-by-Lesson Review

9-1 Graphing Quadratic Functions (pp. 525–535)

7.B.4, 8.B.4b

Consider each equation.

a. Determine whether the function has a *maximum* or *minimum* value.

b. State the maximum or minimum value.

c. What are the domain and range of the function?

11. $y = x^2 - 4x + 4$ **11–14. See margin.**

12. $y = -x^2 + 3x$

13. $y = x^2 - 2x - 3$

14. $y = -x^2 + 2$.

15. **BASEBALL** A baseball is thrown with an upward velocity of 32 feet per second. The equation $h = -16t^2 + 32t$ gives the height of the ball t seconds after it is thrown.

a. Determine whether the function has a *maximum* or *minimum* value. **maximum**

b. State the maximum or minimum value. **16**

c. State a reasonable domain and range for this situation. **D = {t | 0 ≤ t ≤ 2}; R = {h | 0 ≤ h ≤ 16}**

EXAMPLE 1

Consider $f(x) = x^2 + 6x + 5$.

a. Determine whether the function has a *maximum* or *minimum* value.

For $f(x) = x^2 + 6x + 5$, $a = 1$, $b = 6$, and $c = 5$.

Because a is positive, the graph opens up, so the function has a minimum value.

b. State the *minimum* or *maximum* value of the function.

The minimum value is the y-coordinate of the vertex.

The x-coordinate of the vertex is $\frac{-b}{2a}$ or $\frac{-6}{2(1)}$ or -3.

$f(x) = x^2 + 6x + 5$	**Original function**
$f(-3) = (-3)^2 + 6(-3) + 5$	$x = -3$
$f(-3) = -4$	**Simplify.**

The minimum value is -4.

c. State the domain and range of the function.

The domain is all real numbers. The range is all real numbers greater than or equal to the minimum value, or $\{y \mid y \geq -4\}$.

9-2 Solving Quadratic Equations by Graphing (pp. 537–542)

7.B.4, 8.D.4

Solve each equation by graphing. If integral roots cannot be found, estimate the roots to the nearest tenth.

16. $x^2 - 3x - 4 = 0$ **−1, 4**

17. $-x^2 + 6x - 9 = 0$ **3**

18. $x^2 - x - 12 = 0$ **−3, 4**

19. $x^2 + 4x - 3 = 0$ **−4.6, 0.6**

20. $x^2 - 10x = -21$ **3, 7**

21. $6x^2 - 13x = 15$ **−0.8, 3**

22. **NUMBER THEORY** Find two numbers that have a sum of 2 and a product of −15. **−3 and 5**

EXAMPLE 2

Solve $x^2 - x - 6 = 0$ by graphing.

Graph the related function $f(x) = x^2 - x - 6$.

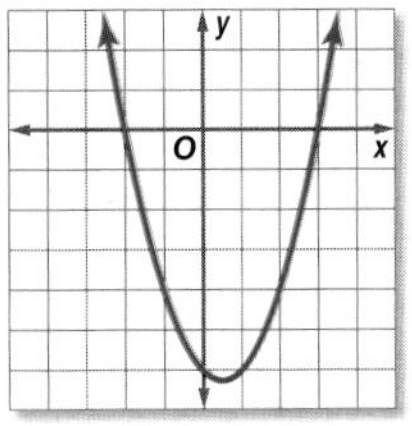

The x-intercepts of the graph appear to be at -2 and 3, so the solutions are -2 and 3.

Lesson-by-Lesson Review

Intervention If the given examples are not sufficient to review the topics covered by the questions, remind students that the page references tell them where to review that topic in their textbook.

Two-Day Option Have students complete the Lesson-by-Lesson Review on pp. 593–596. Then you can use ExamView® Assessment Suite to customize another review worksheet that practices all the objectives of this chapter or only the objectives on which your students need more help.

Differentiated Instruction

Super DVD: MindJogger Videoquizzes Use this DVD as an alternative format of review for the test.

Additional Answers

11a. minimum

11b. 0

11c. D = all real numbers; R = {y | y ≥ 0}

12a. maximum

12b. 2.25

12c. D = all real numbers; R = {y | y ≤ 2.25}

13a. minimum

13b. −4

13c. D = all real numbers; R = {y | y ≥ −4}

14a. maximum

14b. 2

14c. D = all real numbers; R = {y | y ≤ 2}

Additional Answers

23. shifted up 8 units

24. shifted down 3 units

25. vertical stretch

26. vertical stretch and shifted down 18 units

27. vertical compression

28. vertical compression

30. reflected across the x-axis, vertically stretched and shifted up 100 units

CHAPTER 9 Study Guide and Review

9-3 Transformations of Quadratic Functions (pp. 544–549)

8.B.4b, 8.C.4a

Describe how the graph of each function is related to the graph of $f(x) = x^2$. **23–28. See margin.**

23. $f(x) = x^2 + 8$

24. $f(x) = x^2 - 3$

25. $f(x) = 2x^2$

26. $f(x) = 4x^2 - 18$

27. $f(x) = \frac{1}{3}x^2$

28. $f(x) = \frac{1}{4}x^2$

29. Write an equation for the function shown in the graph. **$y = 2x^2 - 3$**

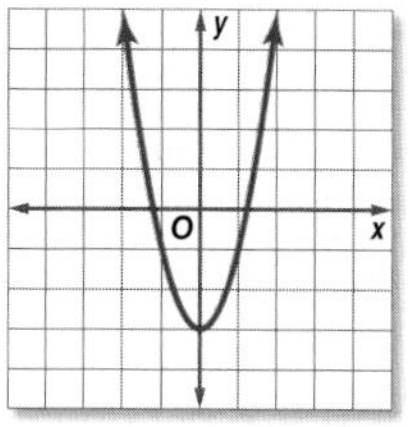

30. PHYSICS A ball is dropped off a cliff that is 100 feet high. The function $h = -16t^2 + 100$ models the height h of the ball after t seconds. Compare the graph of this function to the graph of $h = t^2$. **See margin.**

EXAMPLE 3

Describe how the graph of $f(x) = x^2 - 2$ is related to the graph of $f(x) = x^2$.

The graph of $f(x) = x^2 + c$ represents a translation up or down of the parent graph.

Since $c = -2$, the translation is down.

So, the graph is shifted down from the parent function.

EXAMPLE 4

Write an equation for the function shown in the graph.

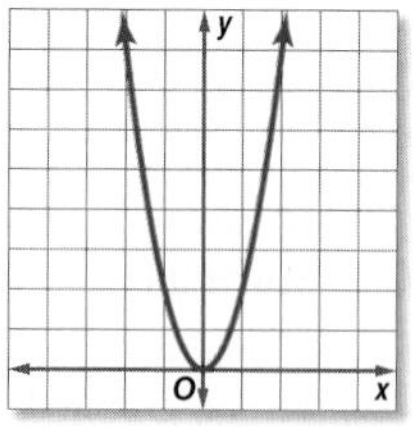

Since the graph opens upward, the leading coefficient must be positive. The parabola has not been translated up or down, so $c = 0$. Since the graph is stretched vertically, it must be of the form of $f(x) = ax^2$ where $a > 1$. The equation for the function is $y = 2x^2$.

9-4 Solving Quadratic Equations by Completing the Square (pp. 552–557)

8.D.4

Solve each equation by completing the square. Round to the nearest tenth if necessary.

31. $x^2 + 6x + 9 = 16$ **1, −7**

32. $-a^2 - 10a + 25 = 25$ **0, −10**

33. $y^2 - 8y + 16 = 36$ **10, −2**

34. $y^2 - 6y + 2 = 0$ **5.6, 0.4**

35. $n^2 - 7n = 5$ **−0.7, 7.7**

36. $-3x^2 + 4 = 0$ **−1.2, 1.2**

37. NUMBER THEORY Find two numbers that have a sum of −2 and a product of −48. **−8, 6**

EXAMPLE 5

Solve $x^2 - 16x + 32 = 0$ by competing the square. Round to the nearest tenth if necessary.

Isolate the x^2- and x-terms. Then complete the square and solve.

$$\begin{aligned} x^2 - 16x + 32 &= 0 \\ x^2 - 16x &= -32 \\ x^2 - 16x + 64 &= -32 + 64 \\ (x - 8)^2 &= 32 \\ x - 8 &= \pm\sqrt{32} \\ x &= 8 \pm\sqrt{32} \\ x &= 8 \pm 4\sqrt{2} \end{aligned}$$

The solutions are about 2.3 and 13.7.

594 Chapter 9 Quadratic and Exponential Functions

MIXED PROBLEM SOLVING
For mixed problem-solving practice, see page 845.

9-5 Solving Quadratic Equations by Using the Quadratic Formula (pp. 558–564)

8.C.4b, 8.D.4

Solve each equation by using the Quadratic Formula. Round to the nearest tenth if necessary.

38. $x^2 - 8x = 20$ **−2, 10**

39. $21x^2 + 5x - 7 = 0$ **−0.7, 0.5**

40. $d^2 - 5d + 6 = 0$ **2, 3**

41. $2f^2 + 7f - 15 = 0$ **−5, 1.5**

42. $2h^2 + 8h + 3 = 3$ **−4, 0**

43. $4x^2 + 4x = 15$ **−2.5, 1.5**

44. GEOMETRY The area of a square can be quadrupled by increasing the side length and width by 4 inches. What is the side length? **4 in.**

EXAMPLE 6

Solve $x^2 + 10x + 9 = 0$ by using the Quadratic Formula.

$x = \frac{-b \pm \sqrt{b^2 - 4ac}}{2a}$ — **Quadratic Formula**

$= \frac{-10 \pm \sqrt{10^2 - 4(1)(9)}}{2(1)}$ — **$a = 1, b = 10, c = 9$**

$= \frac{-10 \pm \sqrt{64}}{2}$ — **Simplify.**

$= \frac{-10 + 8}{2}$ or $\frac{-10 - 8}{2}$ — **Separate the solutions.**

$= -1$ or -9 — **Simplify.**

9-6 Exponential Functions (pp. 567–572)

8.A.4b, 8.C.4b

Graph each function. Find the y-intercept, and state the domain and range. **45–48. See margin.**

45. $y = 2^x$

46. $y = 3^x + 1$

47. $y = 4^x + 2$

48. $y = 2^x - 3$

49. BIOLOGY The population of bacteria in a petri dish increases according to the model $p = 550(2.7)^{0.008t}$, where t is the number of hours and $t = 0$ corresponds to 1:00 P.M. Use this model to estimate the number of bacteria in the dish at 5:00 P.M. **about 568**

EXAMPLE 7

Graph $y = 3^x + 6$. Find the y-intercept, and state the domain and range.

x	$3^x + 6$	y
−3	$3^{-3} + 6$	6.04
−2	$3^{-2} + 6$	6.11
−1	$3^{-1} + 6$	6.33
0	$3^{-0} + 6$	7
1	$3^1 + 6$	9

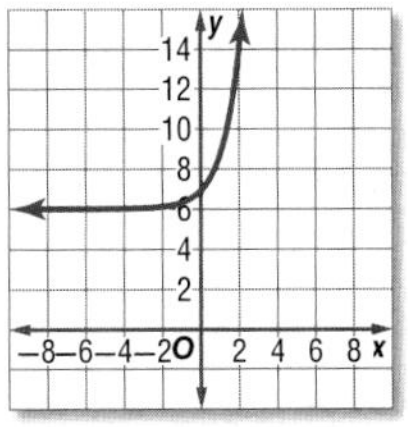

The y-intercept is (0, 7). The domain is all real numbers, and the range is all real numbers greater than 6.

9-7 Growth and Decay (pp. 573–579)

8.C.4b

50. Find the final value of \$2500 invested at an interest rate of 2% compounded monthly for 10 years. **\$3053.00**

51. COMPUTERS Zita's computer is depreciating at a rate of 3% per year. She bought the computer for \$1200.

a. Write an equation to represent this situation. **$y = 1200(1 - 0.03)^t$**

b. What will the computer's value be after 5 years? **\$1030.48**

EXAMPLE 8

Find the final value of \$2000 invested at an interest rate of 3% compounded quarterly for 8 years.

$A = P\left(1 + \frac{r}{n}\right)^{nt}$ — **Compound interest equation**

$= 2000\left(1 + \frac{0.03}{4}\right)^{4(8)}$ — **$P = 2000, r = 0.03, n = 4$, and $t = 8$**

$\approx \$2540.22$ — **Use a calculator.**

There will be about \$2540.22 in 8 years.

Additional Answers

45. y-intercept 1; {D = all real numbers}; R = $\{y \mid y > 0\}$

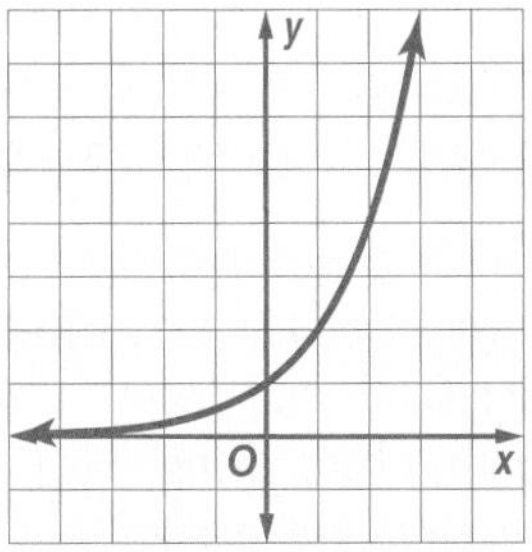

46. y-intercept 2; {D = all real numbers}; R = $\{y \mid y > 1\}$

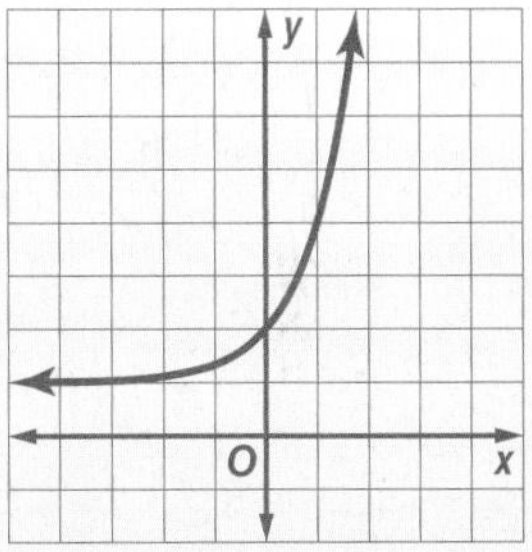

47. y-intercept 3; {D = all real numbers}; R = $\{y \mid y > 2\}$

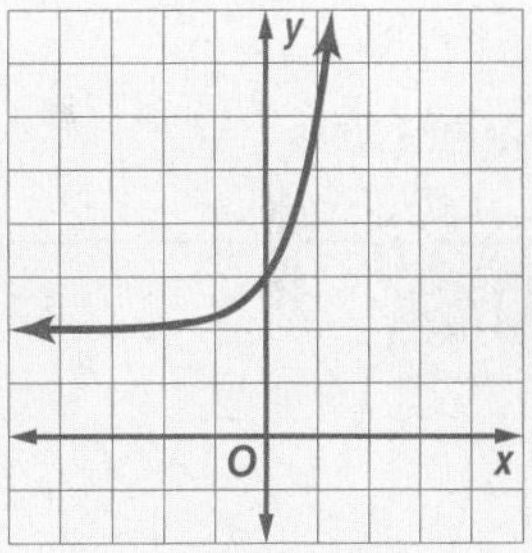

48. y-intercept −2; {D = all real numbers}; R = $\{y \mid y > -3\}$

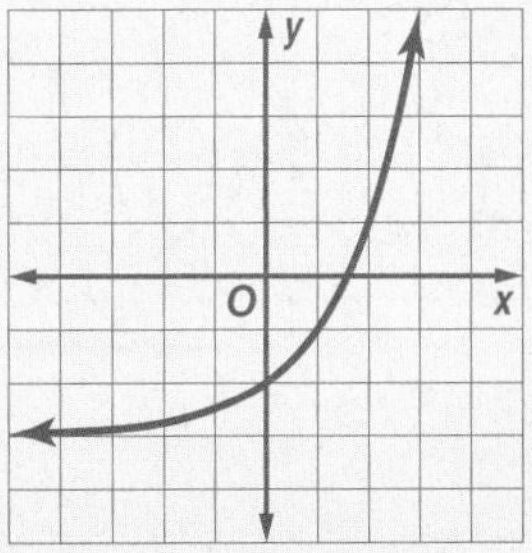

Chapter 9 Study Guide and Review 595

Problem Solving Review

For additional practice in problem solving for Chapter 9, see the Mixed Problem Solving Appendix, p. 853, in the Student Handbook section.

Anticipation Guide

Have students complete the Chapter 9 Anticipation Guide and discuss how their responses have changed now that they have completed Chapter 9.

Additional Answer

58. **Basketball Rebound**

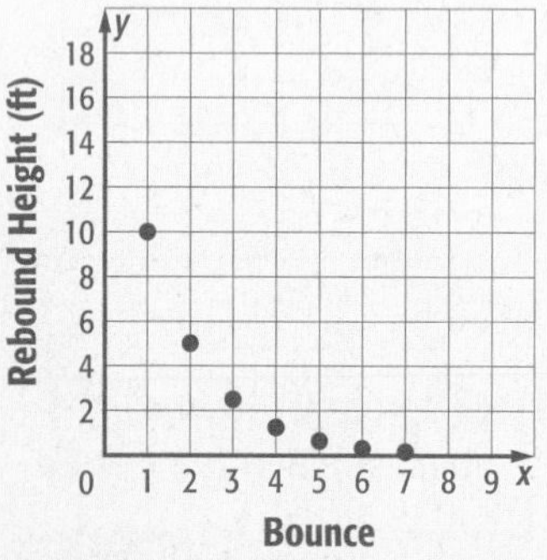

Additional Answers (Practice Test)

1.

x	y
−3	8
−2	5
−1	4
0	5
1	8
2	13

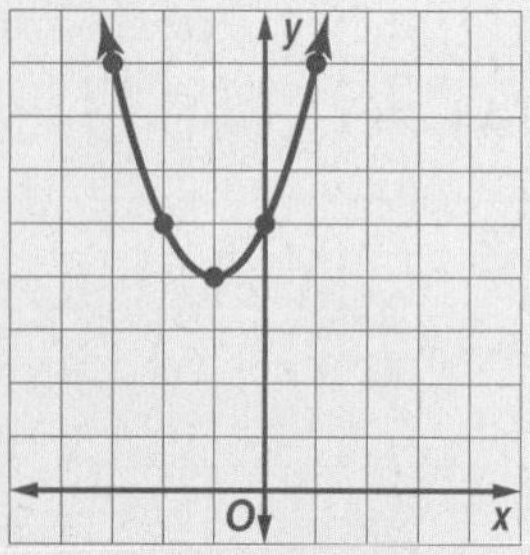

D = {all real numbers};
R = $\{y \mid y \geq 4\}$

CHAPTER 9 Study Guide and Review

9-8 Geometric Sequences as Exponential Functions (pp. 578–583)

8.A.4b, 8.C.4b

Find the next three terms in each geometric sequence.

52. −1, 1, −1, 1, ... **−1, 1, −1**

53. 3, 9, 27, ... **81, 243, 729**

54. 256, 128, 64, ... **32, 16, 8**

Write the equation for the nth term of each geometric sequence.

55. −1, 1, −1, 1, ... $a_n = -1(-1)^{n-1}$

56. 3, 9, 27, ... $a_n = 3(3)^{n-1}$

57. 256, 128, 64, ... $a_n = 256\left(\frac{1}{2}\right)^{n-1}$

58. **SPORTS** A basketball is dropped from a height of 20 feet. It bounces to $\frac{1}{2}$ its height after each bounce. Draw a graph to represent the situation. **See margin.**

EXAMPLE 9

Find the next three terms in the geometric sequence 2, 6, 18, … .

Step 1 Find the common ratio. Each number is 3 times the previous number, so $r = 3$.

Step 2 Multiply each term by the common ratio to find the next three terms.

$18 \times 3 = 54$, $54 \times 3 = 162$, $162 \times 3 = 486$

The next three terms are 54, 162, and 486.

EXAMPLE 10

Write the equation for the nth term of the geometric sequence −3, 12, −48, … .

The common ratio is −4. So $r = -4$.

$a_n = a_1 r^{n-1}$ — Formula for the nth term

$a_n = -3(-4)^{n-1}$ — $a_1 = -3$ and $r = -4$

9-9 Analyzing Functions with Successive Differences (pp. 584–589)

8.A.4b, 8.C.4b

Look for a pattern in each table of values to determine which kind of model best describes the data. Then write an equation for the function that models the data.

59. **quadratic; $y = 3x^2$**

x	0	1	2	3	4
y	0	3	12	27	48

60. **exponential; $y = 2^x$**

x	0	1	2	3	4
y	1	2	4	8	16

61. **quadratic; $y = -x^2$**

x	0	1	2	3	4
y	0	−1	−4	−9	−16

62. **linear; $y = 3x + 3$**

x	0	1	2	3	4
y	3	6	9	12	15

63. **SCHOOL SPIRIT** The table shows the cost to purchase school-spirit posters. Determine which kind of model best describes the data. Then write the equation. **linear; $y = 1.50x + 1$**

No. of posters	2	4	6	8
Cost	4	7	10	13

EXAMPLE 11

Determine which kind of model best describes the data. Then write an equation for the function that models the data.

x	0	1	2	3	4
y	3	4	5	6	7

Step 1 Determine which model fits the data.

First differences: 3 4 5 6 7 → 1 1 1 1

Since the first differences are all equal, a linear function models the data.

Step 2 Write an equation for the function that models the data.

The equation has the form $y = mx + b$.

The slope is 1 and the y-intercept is 3, so the equation is $y = x + 3$.

2.

x	y
−2	15
−1	6
0	1
1	0
2	3
3	10

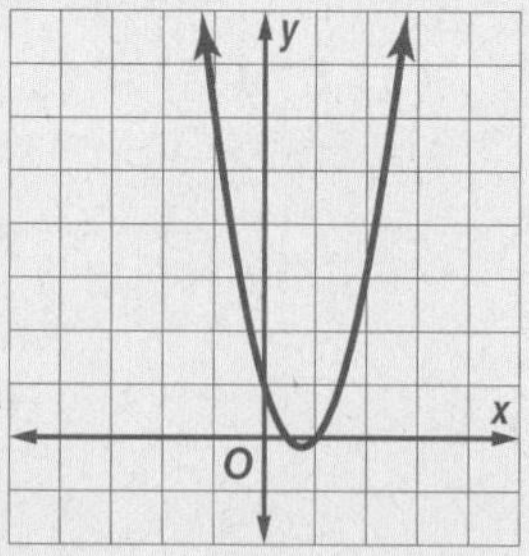

D = {all real numbers};
R = $\{y \mid y \geq -0.125\}$

596 Chapter 9 Quadratic and Exponential Functions

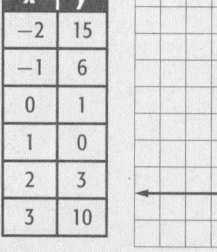

IL Math Online > glencoe.com
Chapter Test

Use a table of values to graph the following functions. State the domain and range. 1–2. See margin.

1. $y = x^2 + 2x + 5$
2. $y = 2x^2 - 3x + 1$

Consider $y = x^2 - 7x + 6$.

3. Determine whether the function has a *maximum* or *minimum* value. minimum
4. State the maximum or minimum value. -6.25
5. What are the domain and range? D = {all real numbers}; R = $\{y \mid y \geq -6.25\}$

Solve each equation by graphing. If integral roots cannot be found, estimate the roots to the nearest tenth.

6. $x^2 + 7x + 10 = 0$ $-5, -2$
7. $x^2 - 5 = -3x$ $-4.2, 1.2$

Describe how the graph of each function is related to the graph of $f(x) = x^2$.

8. $g(x) = x^2 - 5$ shifted down 5 units
9. $g(x) = -3x^2$ reflected over the x-axis, expanded vertically
10. $h(x) = \frac{1}{2}x^2 + 4$ compressed vertically and shifted 4 units up
11. **MULTIPLE CHOICE** Which is an equation for the function shown in the graph? D

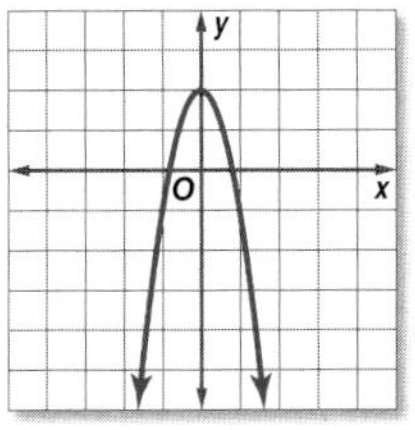

A $y = -3x^2$

B $y = 3x^2 + 1$

C $y = x^2 + 2$

D $y = -3x^2 + 2$

Solve each equation by completing the square.

12. $x^2 + 2x + 5 = 0$ no real solution
13. $x^2 - x - 6 = 0$ $-2, 3$
14. $2x^2 - 36 = -6x$ $-6, 3$

Solve each equation by using the Quadratic Formula. Round to the nearest tenth if necessary.

15. $x^2 - x - 30 = 0$ $-5, 6$
16. $x^2 - 10x = -15$ $1.8, 8.2$
17. $2x^2 + x - 15 = 0$ $2.5, -3$
18. **BASEBALL** Elias hits a baseball into the air. The equation $h = -16t^2 + 60t + 3$ models the height h in feet of the ball after t seconds. How long is the ball in the air? about 3.8 seconds

Graph each function. Find the y-intercept, and state the domain and range. 19–21. See Ch. 9 Answer Appendix.

19. $y = 2(5)^x$
20. $y = -3(11)^x$
21. $y = 3x + 2$

Find the next three terms in each geometric sequence.

22. 2, −6, 18, … $-54, 162, -486$
23. 1000, 500, 250, … 125, 62.5, 31.25
24. 32, 8, 2, … $\frac{1}{2}, \frac{1}{8}, \frac{1}{32}$
25. **MONEY** Lynne invested \$500 into an account with a 6.5% interest rate compounded monthly. How much will Lynne's investment be worth in 10 years? H

F \$600.00 H \$956.09

G \$938.57 J \$957.02

26. **INVESTMENTS** Shelly's investment of \$3000 has been losing value at a rate of 3% each year. What will her investment be worth in 6 years? \$2498.92
27. Graph {(−2, 4), (−1, 1), (0, 0), (1, 1), (2, 4)}. Determine whether the ordered pairs represent a *linear function*, a *quadratic function*, or an *exponential function*. See margin.
28. Look for a pattern in the table to determine which kind of model best describes the data. linear

x	0	1	2	3	4
y	1	3	5	7	9

CHAPTER 9 Practice Test

ExamView Assessment Suite Customize and create multiple versions of your chapter tests and their answer keys. All of the questions from the leveled chapter tests in the *Chapter 9 Resource Masters* are also available on ExamView Assessment Suite.

Additional Answer

27.

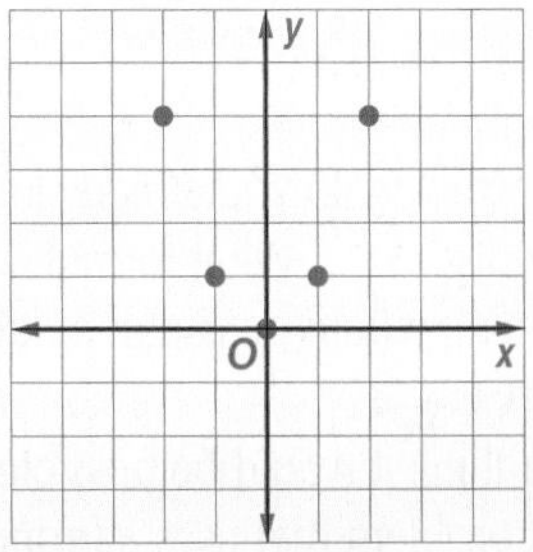

quadratic

Intervention Planner

Tier 1 On Level	Tier 2 Strategic Intervention approaching grade level	Tier 3 Intensive Intervention 2 or more grades below level
If students miss about 25% of the exercises or less,	**If** students miss about 50% of the exercises,	**If** students miss about 75% of the exercises,
Then choose a resource:	**Then** choose a resource:	**Then** use *Math Triumphs, Alg. 1*
SE Lessons 9-1, 9-2, 9-3, 9-4, 9-5, 9-6, 9-7, 9-8, and 9-9 **CRM** Skills Practice, pp. 7, 13, 19, 25, 31, 37, 43, 50, and 56 **TE** Chapter Project, p. 522 IL Math Online > Self-Check Quiz	**CRM** Study Guide and Intervention, Chapter 9, pp. 5, 11, 17, 23, 29, 35, 41, 48, and 54 *Quick Review Math Handbook* IL Math Online > Extra Examples, Personal Tutor, Homework Help	IL Math Online > Extra Examples, Personal Tutor, Homework Help, Review Vocabulary

1 FOCUS

Objective Use the strategy of using a formula to solve standardized test problems.

2 TEACH

Scaffolding Questions

Ask:

- What formulas do you already know? Answers will vary. What formulas do you think it would be useful to know? Answers will vary.
- Do you think it would be possible to solve a problem that uses a formula if you do not know the formula? Explain. Sample answer: If the problem involves something such as perimeter or the volume of a rectangular prism, you could probably solve the problem without the formula, but if the problem involves the Quadratic Formula, you would need to know the formula.

CHAPTER 9 Preparing for Standardized Tests

Use a Formula

A *formula* is an equation that shows a relationship among certain quantities. Many standardized test problems will require using a formula to solve them.

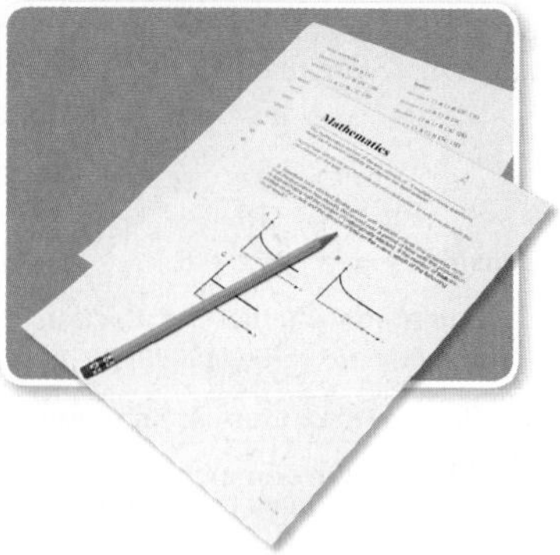

Strategies for Using a Formula

Step 1

Become familiar with common formulas and their uses. You may or may not be given access to a formula sheet to use during the test.

- **If given a formula sheet,** be sure to practice with the formulas on it before taking the test so you know how to apply them.
- **If not given a formula sheet,** study and practice with common formulas such as perimeter, area, and volume formulas, the Distance Formula, the Pythagorean Theorem, the Midpoint Formula, the Quadratic Formula, and others.

Step 2

Choose a formula and solve.

- **Ask Yourself:** What quantities are given in the problem statement?
- **Ask Yourself:** What quantities am I looking for?
- **Ask Yourself:** Is there a formula I know that relates these quantities?
- **Write:** Write the formula out that you have chosen each time.
- **Solve:** Substitute known quantities into the formula and solve for the unknown quantity.
- **Check:** Check your answer if time permits.

EXAMPLE

Read the problem. Identify what you need to know. Then use the information in the problem to solve.

Find the exact roots of the quadratic equation $-2x^2 + 6x + 5 = 0$.

A $\frac{3 \pm \sqrt{17}}{4}$

B $\frac{4 \pm \sqrt{17}}{3}$

C $\frac{3 \pm \sqrt{19}}{2}$

D $\frac{3 \pm \sqrt{19}}{4}$

Read the problem carefully. You are given a quadratic equation and asked to find the exact roots of the equation. Use the **Quadratic Formula** to find the roots.

$-2x^2 + 6x + 5 = 0$	**Original equation**
$a = -2, b = 6, c = 5$	**Identify the coefficients of the equation.**
$x = \frac{-b \pm \sqrt{b^2 - 4ac}}{2a}$	**Quadratic Formula**
$= \frac{-(6) \pm \sqrt{(6)^2 - 4(-2)(5)}}{2(-2)}$	**$a = -2$, $b = 6$, and $c = 5$**
$= \frac{-6 \pm \sqrt{36 - (-40)}}{-4}$	**Simplify.**
$= \frac{-6 \pm \sqrt{76}}{-4}$	**Subtract.**
$= \frac{-6 \pm 2\sqrt{19}}{-4}$	**$\sqrt{76} = \sqrt{4 \cdot 19}$ or $2\sqrt{19}$.**
$= \frac{-2(3 \pm \sqrt{19})}{-2(2)}$	**Factor out −2 from the numerator and denominator.**
$= \frac{3 \pm \sqrt{19}}{2}$	**Simplify.**

The roots of the equation are $\frac{3 + \sqrt{19}}{2}$ and $\frac{3 - \sqrt{19}}{2}$. The correct answer is C.

Exercises

Read each problem. Identify what you need to know. Then use the information in the problem to solve.

1. Find the exact roots of the quadratic equation $x^2 + 5x - 12 = 0$. **A**

A $\frac{-5 \pm \sqrt{73}}{2}$ C $\frac{-3 \pm \sqrt{73}}{4}$

B $\frac{4 \pm \sqrt{61}}{3}$ D $\frac{-1 \pm \sqrt{61}}{2}$

2. The area of a triangle in which the length of the base is 4 centimeters greater than twice the height is 80 square centimeters. What is the length of the base of the triangle? **J**

F −10

G 8

H 16

J 20

3. Find the volume of the figure below. **D**

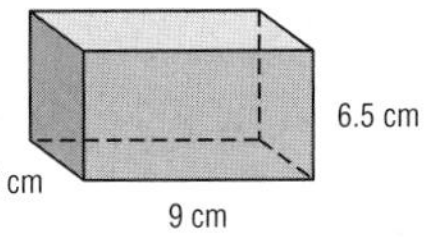

A 18.5 cm^2 C 272 cm^2

B 91 cm^2 D 292.5 cm^2

4. Myron is traveling 263.5 miles at an average rate of 62 miles per hour. How long will it take Myron to complete his trip? **G**

F 5 h 25 min

G 4 h 15 min

H 5 h 10 min

J 4 h 25 min

Additional Example

Find the exact roots of the quadratic equation $2x^2 + 5x - 5 = 0$. **C**

A $\frac{5 \pm \sqrt{65}}{4}$

B $\frac{5 \pm \sqrt{15}}{4}$

C $\frac{-5 \pm \sqrt{65}}{4}$

D $\frac{-5 \pm \sqrt{15}}{4}$

3 ASSESS

Use Exercises 1–4 to assess students' understanding.

Diagnose Student Errors

Survey students' responses for each item. Class trends may indicate common errors and misconceptions.

1. A switched coordinates of y-intercept
B coordinates of y-intercept instead of vertex
C switched x-and y-coordinates
D correct
E guess

2. F switched slope and y-intercept
G chose negative slope and negative y-intercept
H incorrectly chose negative instead of positive y-intercept
J switched slope and y-intercept and incorrectly chose negative instead of positive y-intercept
K correct

3. A correct
B error in simplifying radical and did not factor 2 out of denominator
C error in using quadratic formula or guess
D guess
E error in using quadratic formula or guess

4. F forgot to multiply $-3bc$ by $5bc^2$
G correct
H forgot to multiply coefficients
J multiplied instead of added exponents
K added numbers of first term

5. A incorrectly graphed quadratic equation
B correct
C switched x- and y-coordinates
D incorrectly graphed equation and/or used negative instead of positive coefficient for x^2
E incorrect factors of -15

6. F calculation error for minimum points
G correct
H guess
J calculation error for maximum points
K calculated tickets for platinum

Multiple Choice

Read each question. Then fill in the correct answer on the answer document provided by your teacher or on a sheet of paper.

1. What is the vertex of the parabola graphed below? D

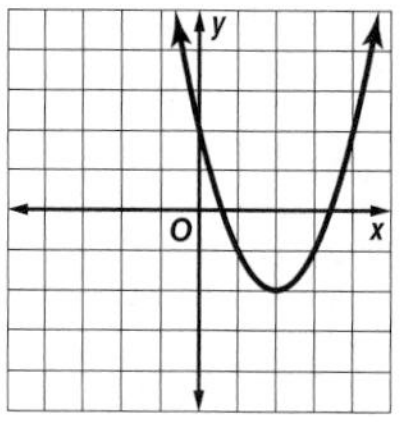

A (2, 0)
B (0, 2)
C (−2, 2)
D (2, −2)
E (3.5, 0)

2. Write an equation in slope-intercept form with a slope of $\frac{9}{10}$ and y-intercept of 3. K

F $y = 3x + \frac{9}{10}$
G $y = -\frac{9}{10}x - 3$
H $y = \frac{9}{10}x - 3$
J $y = 3x - \frac{9}{10}$
K $y = \frac{9}{10}x + 3$

3. Use the Quadratic Formula to find the exact solutions of the equation $2x^2 - 6x + 3 = 0$. A

A $\frac{3 \pm \sqrt{3}}{2}$
B $\frac{3 \pm \sqrt{2}}{4}$
C $\frac{2 \pm \sqrt{5}}{3}$
D $\frac{5 \pm \sqrt{2}}{2}$
E $\frac{-3 \pm \sqrt{6}}{2}$

4. Write an expression for the area of the rectangle below. G

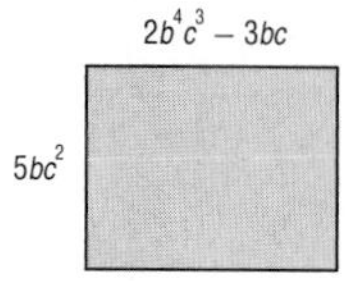

F $10b^5c^5 - 3bc$
G $10b^5c^5 - 15b^2c^3$
H $2b^5c^5 - 3b^2c^3$
J $10b^4c^6 - 15bc^2$
K $7b^5c^5 - 3bc$

5. Solve the quadratic equation below by graphing. B

$$x^2 - 2x - 15 = 0$$

A $-1, 4$
B $-3, 5$
C $3, -5$
D $-1, 5$
E ∅

6. Jason is playing games at a family fun center. So far he has won 38 prize tickets. How many more tickets would he need to win to place him in the gold prize category? G

Number of Tickets	Prize Category
1–20	bronze
21–40	silver
41–60	gold
61–80	platinum

F $2 \leq t \leq 22$
G $3 \leq t \leq 22$
H $1 \leq t \leq 20$
J $3 \leq t \leq 20$
K $22 \leq t \leq 42$

Test-TakingTip

Question 5 If permitted, you can use a graphing calculator to quickly graph an equation and find its roots.

Short Response/Gridded Response

Record your answers on the answer sheet provided by your teacher or on a sheet of paper.

7. **GRIDDED RESPONSE** Misty purchased a car several years ago for $21,459. The value of the car depreciated at a rate of 15% annually. What was the value of the car after 5 years? Round your answer to the nearest whole dollar. **9521**

8. Use the graph of the quadratic equation shown below to answer each question.

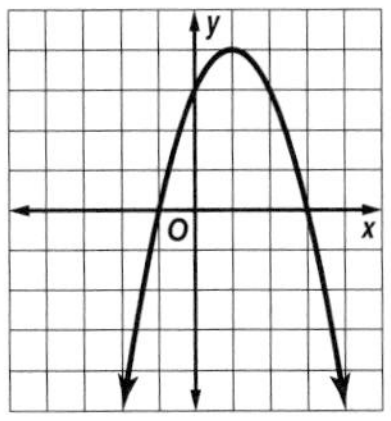

   a. What is the vertex? **(1, 4)**
   b. What is the y-intercept? **(0, 3)**
   c. What is the axis of symmetry? **$x = 1$**
   d. What are the roots of the corresponding quadratic equation? **−1, 3**

9. A school bookstore sells books along with various school supplies including notebooks and pens. The cost of 5 notebooks and 3 pens is $9.75. The cost of 4 notebooks and 6 pens is $10.50.
   a. Write a system of equations to model the situation. **See margin.**
   b. Solve the system of equations. How much does each item cost? **pen: $0.75, notebook: $1.50**

10. The table shows the total cost of renting a canoe for n hours.

Number of Hours (n)	Rental Cost (C)
1	$15
2	$20
3	$25
4	$30

   a. Write a function to represent the situation. **$C(n) = 5n + 10$**
   b. How much would it cost to rent the canoe for 7 hours? **$45**

Extended Response

Record your answers on a sheet of paper. Show your work.

11. Use the equation and its graph to answer each question.

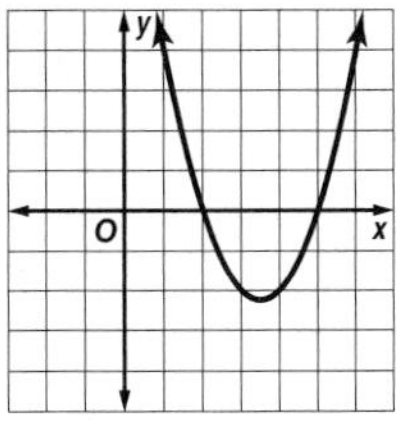

   a. Factor $x^2 - 7x + 10$. **$(x - 2)(x - 5)$**
   b. What are the solutions of $x^2 - 7x + 10 = 0$? **$x = 2, 5$**
   c. What do you notice about the graph of the quadratic equation and where it crosses the x-axis? How do these values compare to the solutions of $x^2 - 7x + 10 = 0$? Explain. **See margin.**

Need Extra Help?											
If you missed Question...	1	2	3	4	5	6	7	8	9	10	11
Go to Lesson or Page...	9-1	4-2	9-5	7-6	9-2	5-1	9-7	9-1	6-4	3-5	8-3
IL Assessment Objectives	8.11.08	8.11.02	8.11.18	8.11.02	8.11.08	8.11.16	6.11.18	8.11.08	8.11.17	8.11.02	8.11.12

Formative Assessment

You can use these two pages to benchmark student progress.

CRM Standardized Test Practice, pp. 80–82

Answer Sheet Practice

Have students simulate taking a standardized test by recording their answers on a practice recording sheet.

CRM Student Recording Sheet, p. 61

Chapter Resource Master
CRM p. 61

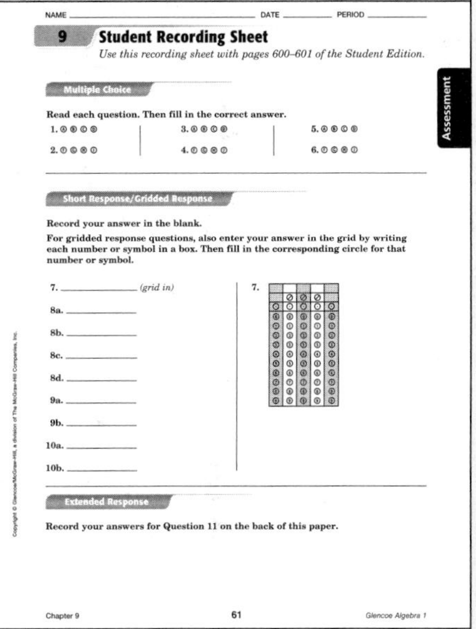
NAME DATE PERIOD

9 **Student Recording Sheet**
Use this recording sheet with pages 600–601 of the Student Edition.

Multiple Choice

Read each question. Then fill in the correct answer.
1. Ⓐ Ⓑ Ⓒ Ⓓ 3. Ⓐ Ⓑ Ⓒ Ⓓ 5. Ⓐ Ⓑ Ⓒ Ⓓ
2. Ⓐ Ⓑ Ⓒ Ⓓ 4. Ⓐ Ⓑ Ⓒ Ⓓ 6. Ⓐ Ⓑ Ⓒ Ⓓ

Short Response/Gridded Response

Record your answer in the blank.
For gridded response questions, also enter your answer in the grid by writing each number or symbol in a box. Then fill in the corresponding circle for that number or symbol.

7. ________ (grid in) 7.
8a. ________
8b. ________
8c. ________
8d. ________
9a. ________
9b. ________
10a. ________
10b. ________

Extended Response

Record your answers for Question 11 on the back of this paper.

Chapter 9 61 Glencoe Algebra 1

Assessment

ExamView Assessment Suite Create practice worksheets or tests that align to your state's standards, as well as TIMSS and NAEP tests.

Additional Answers

9a. $5n + 3p = 9.75$
$4n + 6p = 10.50$

11c. Sample answer: the graph crosses the x-axis at $x = 2$ and $x = 5$. These are the solutions to the equation. On the graph they show what values of x result in $y = 0$.

Homework Option

Get Ready for Chapter 10 Assign students the exercises on p. 603 as homework to assess whether they possess the prerequisite skills needed for the next chapter.

Page 523, Get Ready for Chapter 9

1.
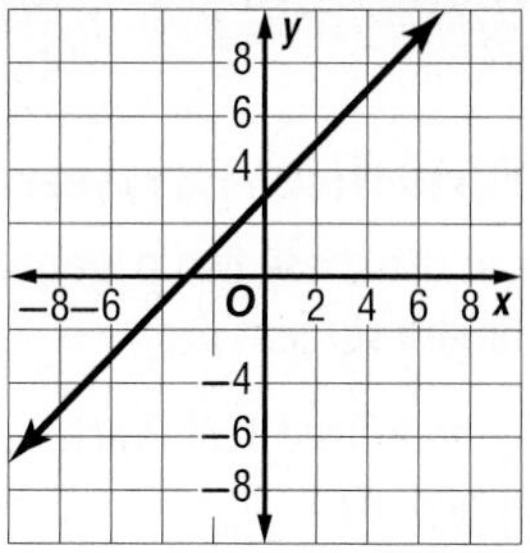

2.
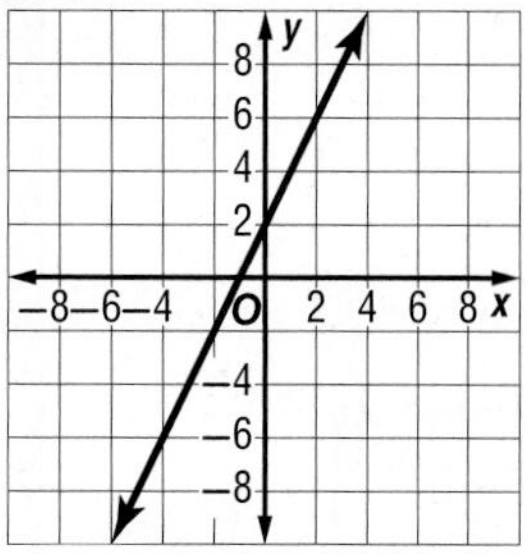

3.
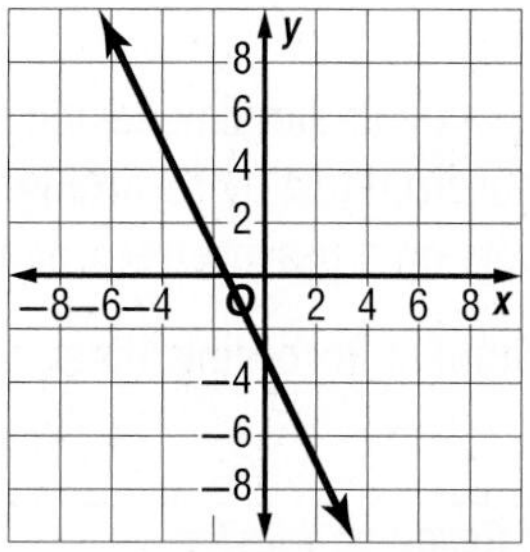

4.
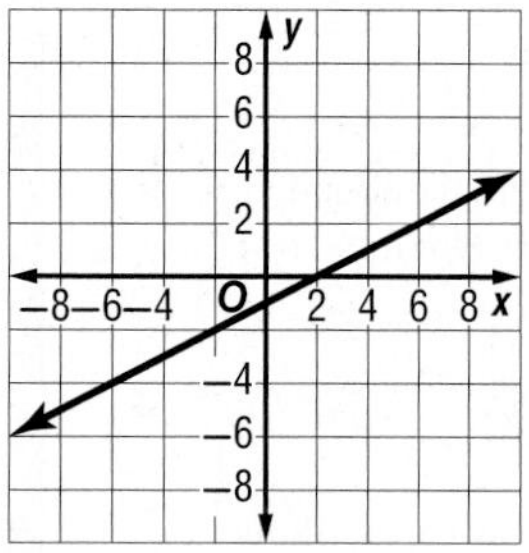

5.
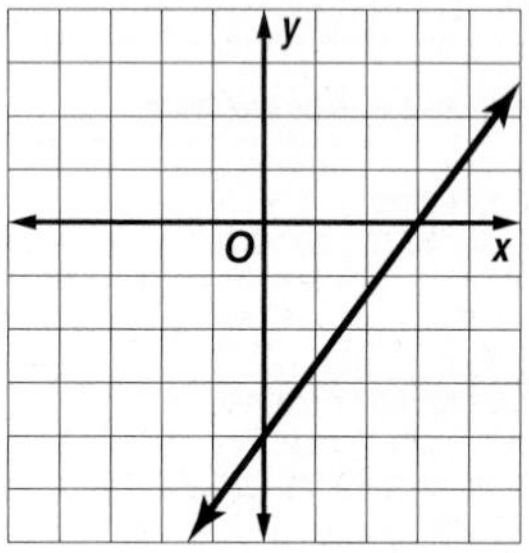

6.
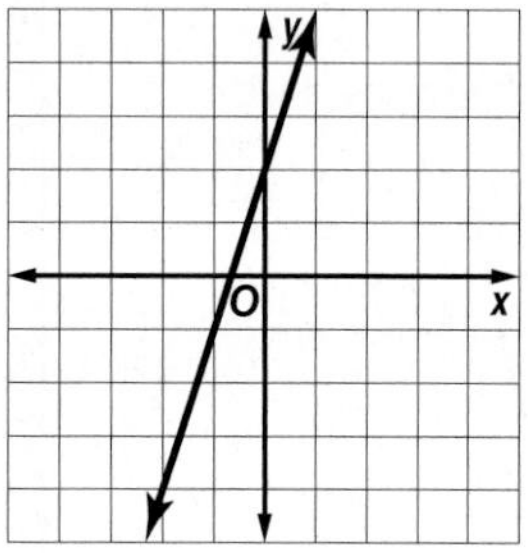

7.
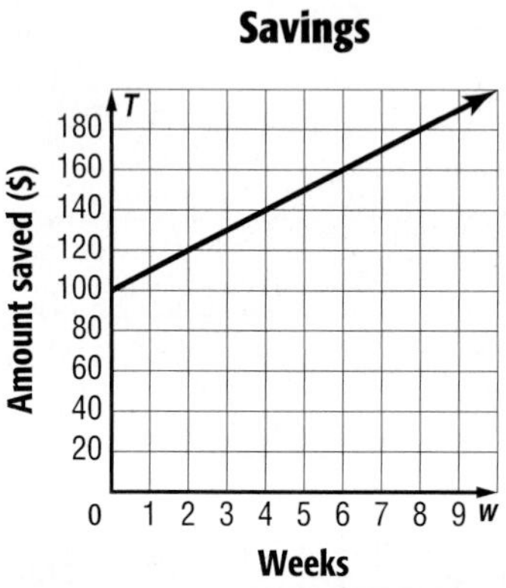

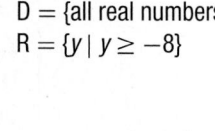

Pages 530–534, Lesson 9-1

1.

x	−3	−2	−1	0	1	2
y	0	−6	−8	−6	0	10

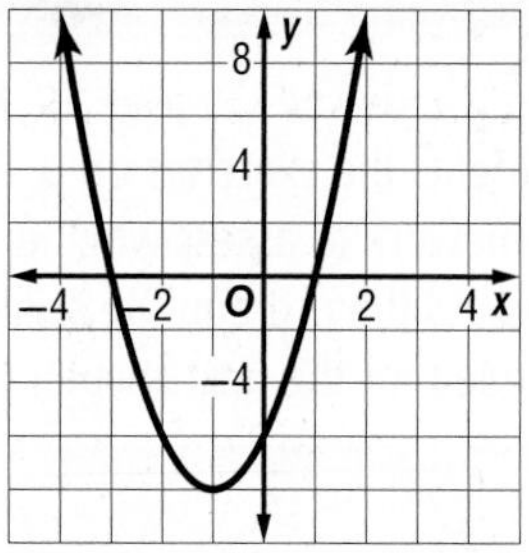

D = {all real numbers}; R = {y | y ≥ −8}

2.

x	−3	−2	−1	0	1	2
y	2	−1	−2	−1	2	7

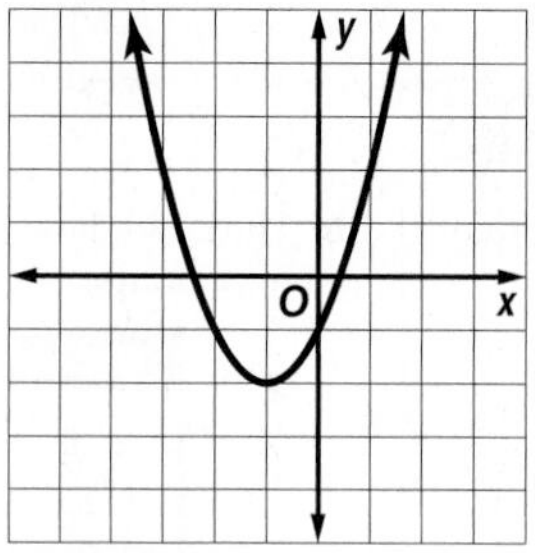

D = {all real numbers}; R = {y | y ≥ −2}

3.

x	y
−1	4
0	−3
1	−8
2	−11
3	−12
4	−11
5	−8
6	−3
7	4

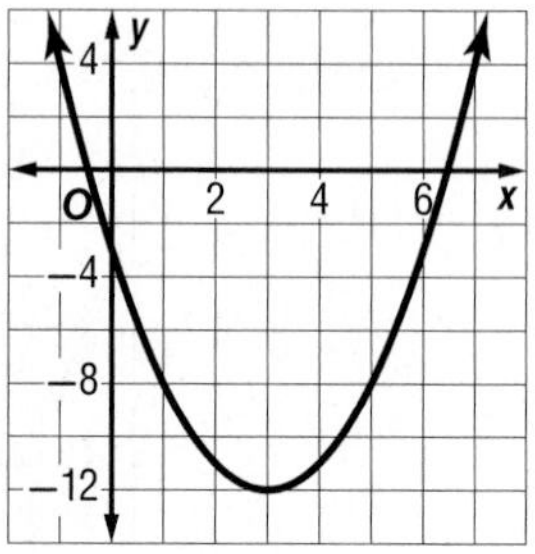

D = {all real numbers}; R = {y | y ≥ −12}

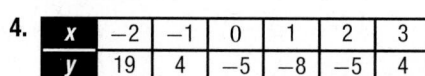

4.

x	−2	−1	0	1	2	3
y	19	4	−5	−8	−5	4

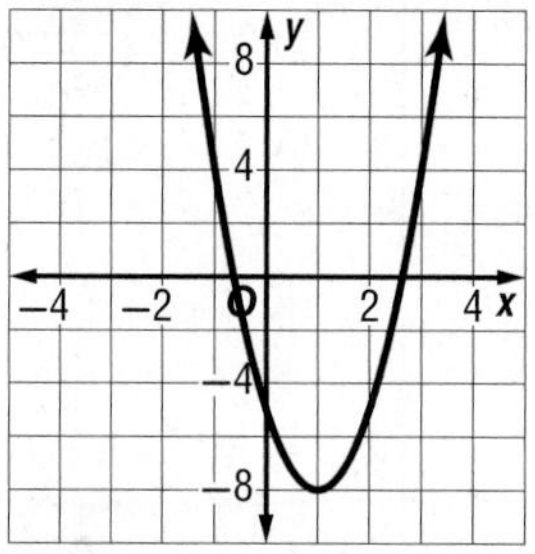

D = {all real numbers}; R = {y | y ≥ −8}

22.

x	−4	−3	−2	−1	0
y	6	3	2	3	6

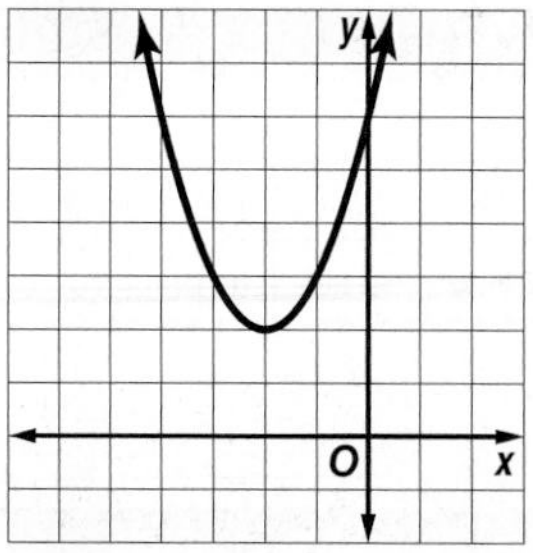

D = {all real numbers}; R = {y | y ≥ 2}

23.

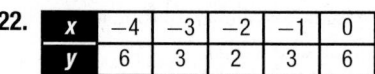

x	−3	−2	−1	0	1
y	13	7	5	7	13

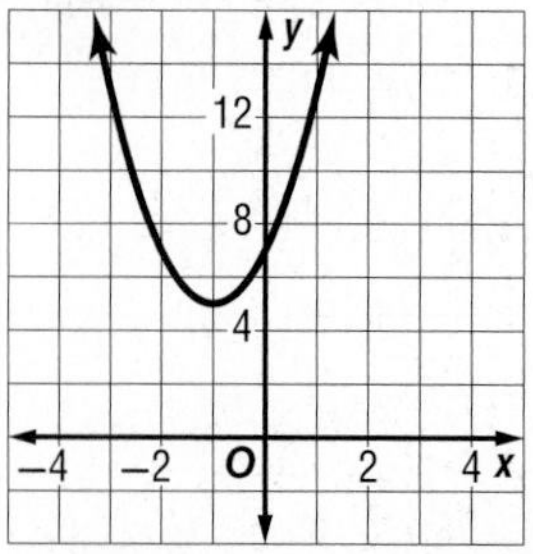

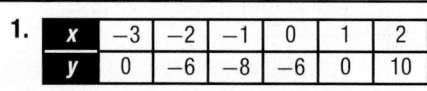

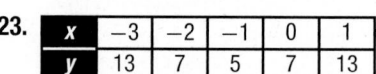

D = {all real numbers}; R = {y | y ≥ 5}

24.

x	4	3	2	1	0
y	−5	−11	−13	−11	−5

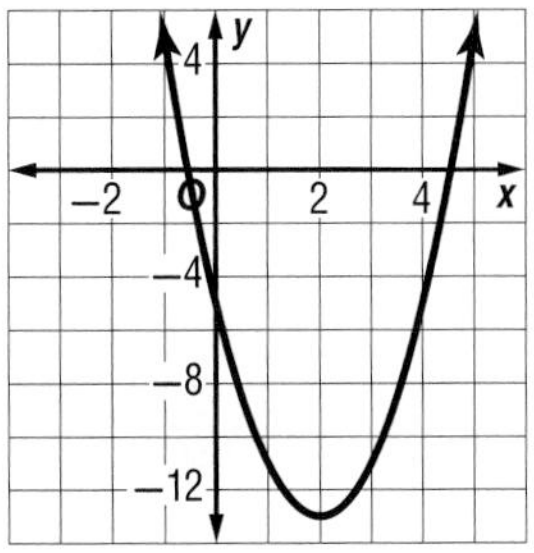

D = {all real numbers};
R = {y | y ≥ −13}

25.

x	0	−1	−2	−3	−4
y	5	−4	−7	−4	5

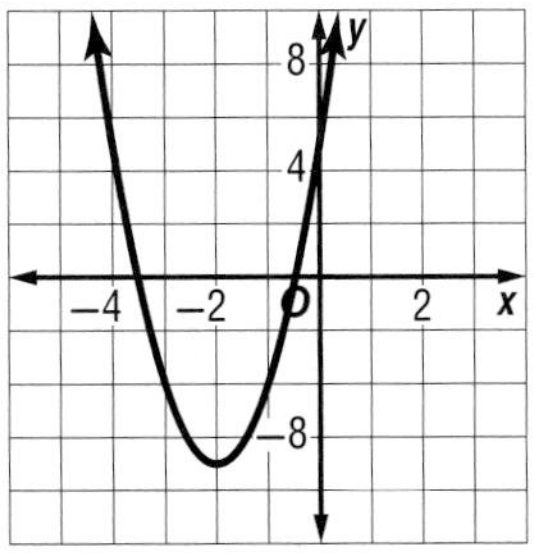

D = {all real numbers};
R = {y | y ≥ −7}

26.

x	3	2	1	0	−1
y	7	−2	−5	−2	7

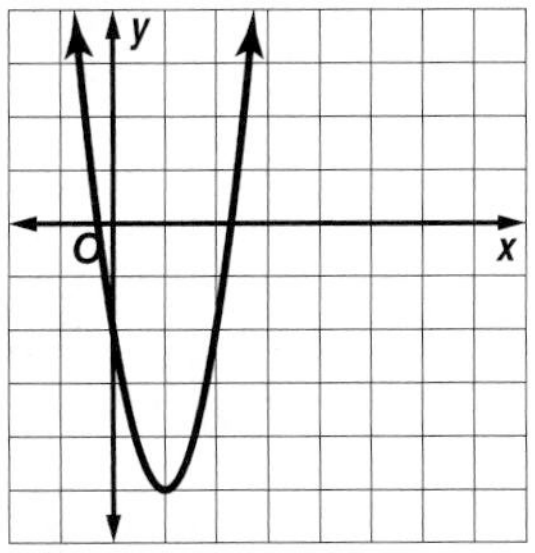

D = {all real numbers};
R = {y | y ≥ −5}

27.

x	3	2	1	0	−1
y	2	−1	−2	−1	2

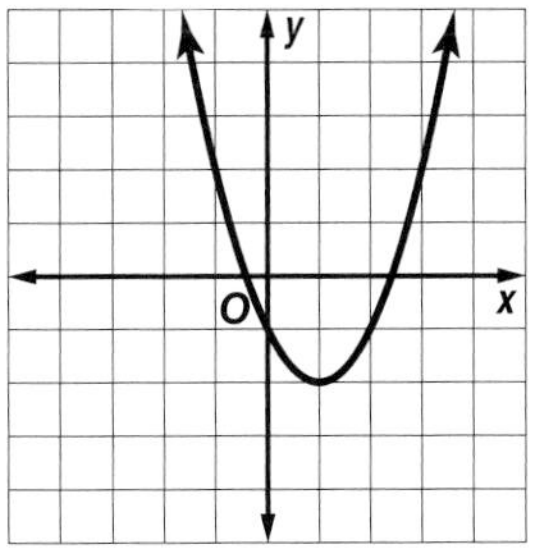

D = {all real numbers};
R = {y | y ≥ −2}

52.

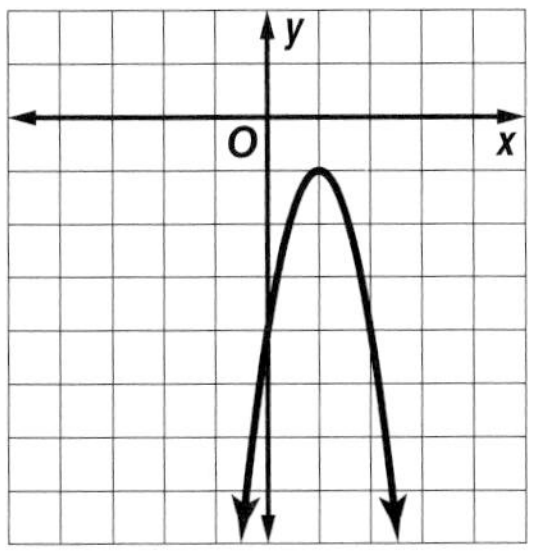

53.

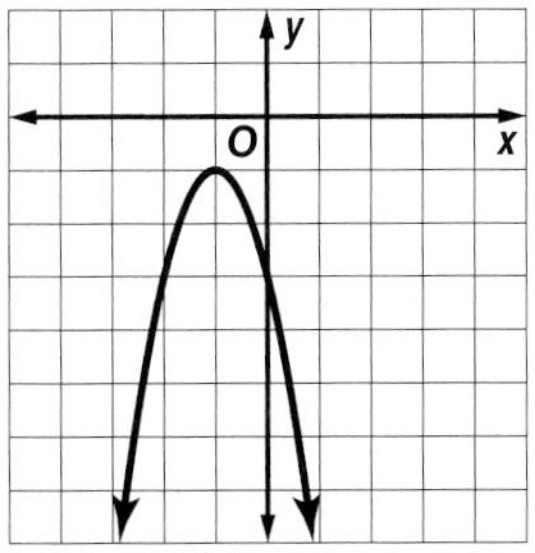

54.

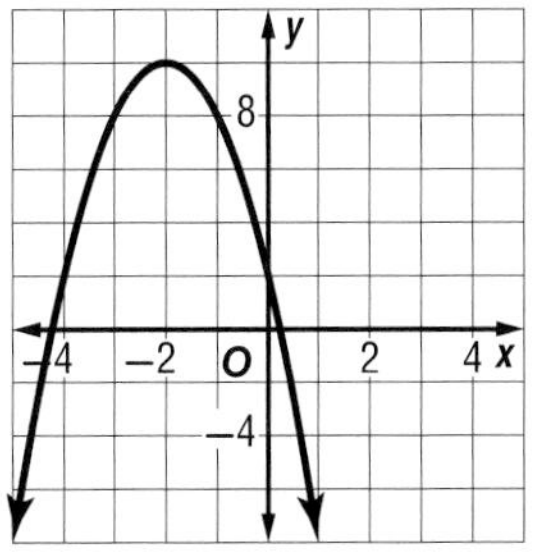

55.

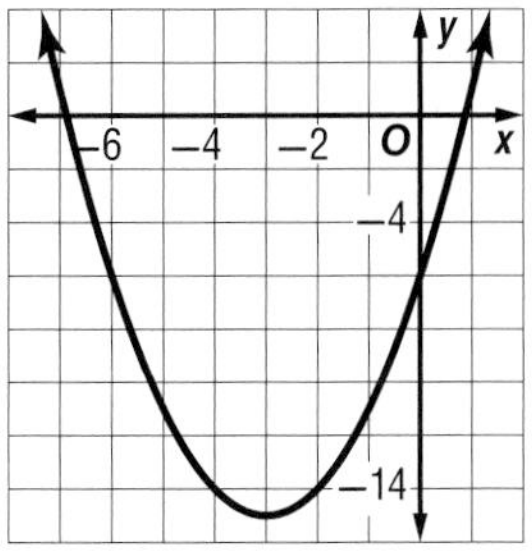

56.

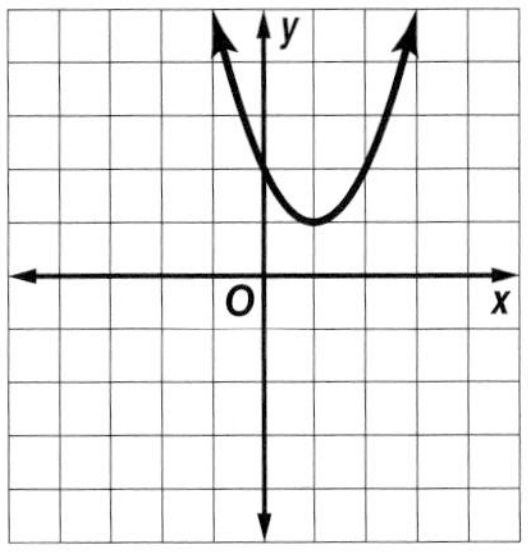

57.

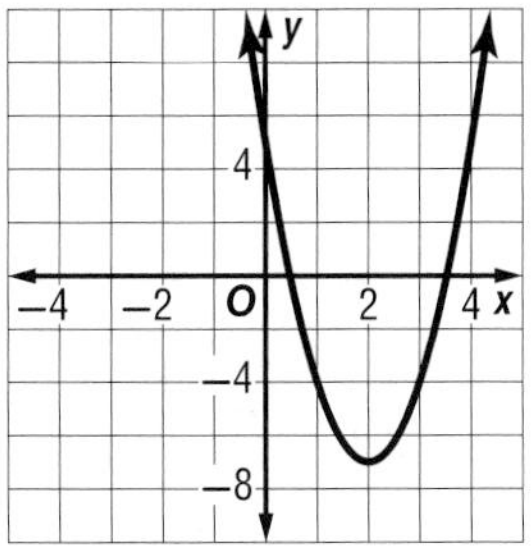

59.

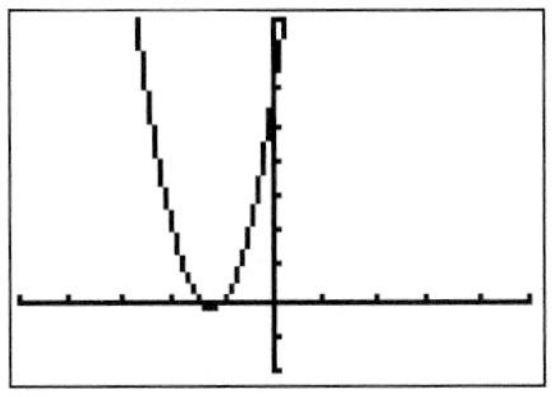

[−5, 5] scl:1 by [−5, 5] scl:1

60.

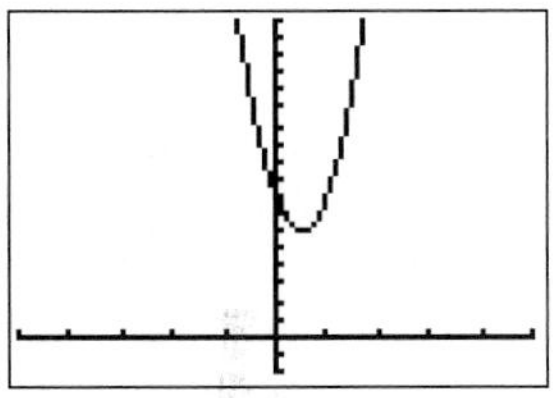

[−5, 5] scl: 1 by [−2, 18] scl: 2

61.

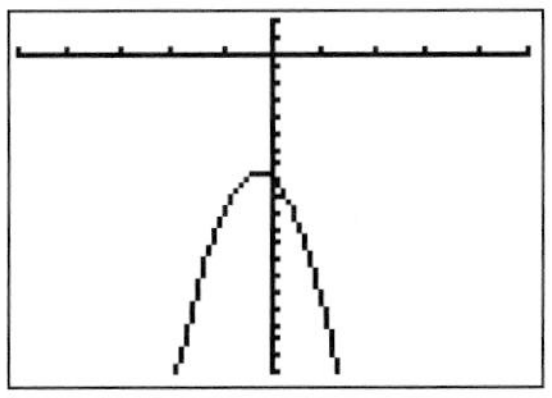

[−5, 5] scl: 1 by [−20, 2] scl: 2

62.

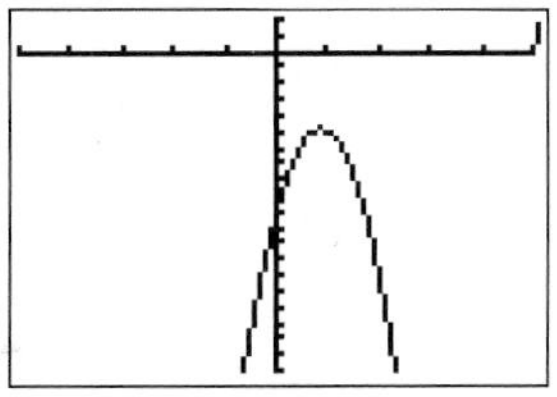

[−5, 5] scl: 1 by [−20, 2] scl: 2

65c. $t = 0$, $t = 5.625$; Before the ball is kicked, and when the ball hits the ground after the kick.

Page 536, Extend 9-1

1.

x	−4	−3	−2	−1	0	1	2	3	4
y	16	9	4	1	0	1	4	9	16

2.

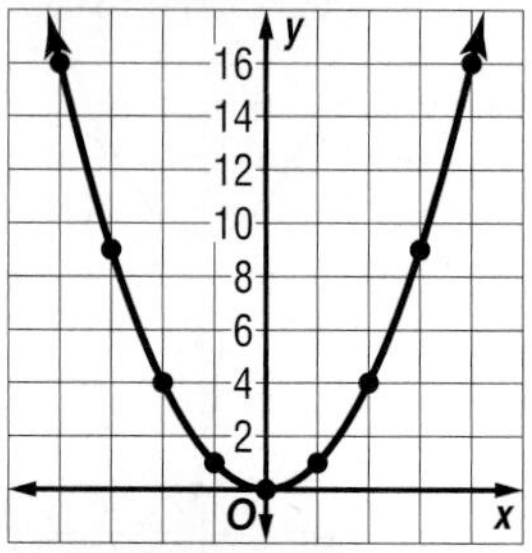

The function is increasing for $x > 0$ and decreasing for $x < 0$.

3.

x	−4	−3	−2	−1	0	1	2	3	4
y	16	9	4	1	0	1	4	9	16
Rate of Change	--	−7	−5	−3	−1	1	3	5	7

Sample answer: The rate of change as the function decreases is the opposite of the rate of change as the function increases.

4.

x	−4	−3	−2	−1	0	1	2	3	4
y	−156	−44	36	84	100	84	36	−44	156
Rate of Change	--	112	80	48	16	−16	−48	−80	−112

Sample answer: The rate of change as the function increases has the same absolute value as when the function decreases.

Pages 537–538, Lesson 9-2 (Guided Practice)

1A. −6, 3

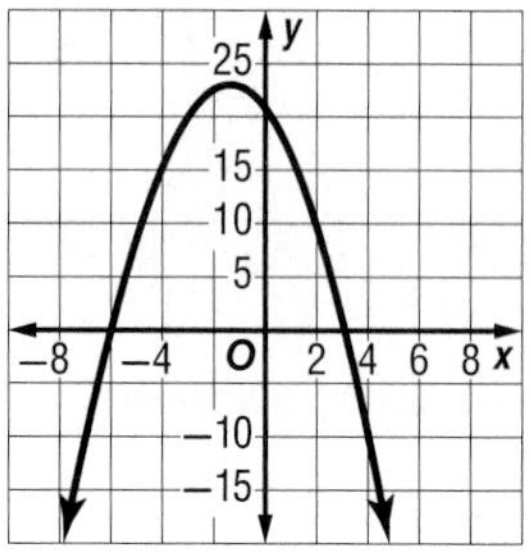

1B. 1, 3

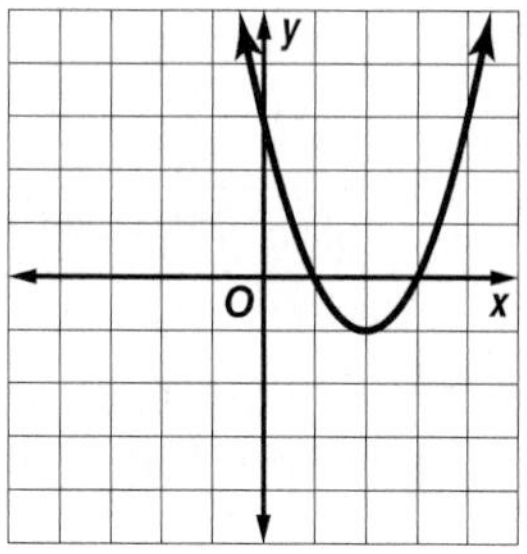

2A.

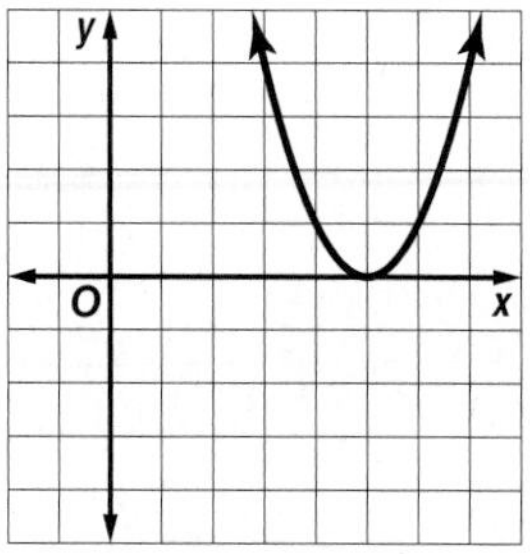

2B.

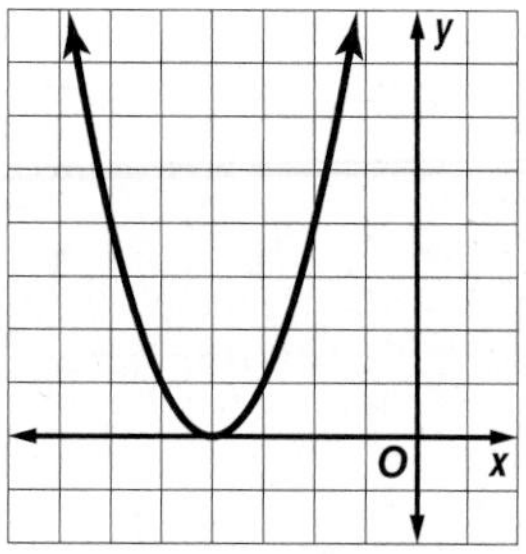

3A.

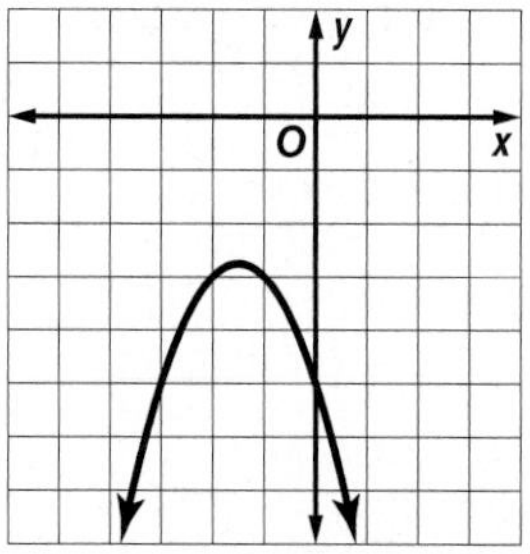

3B.

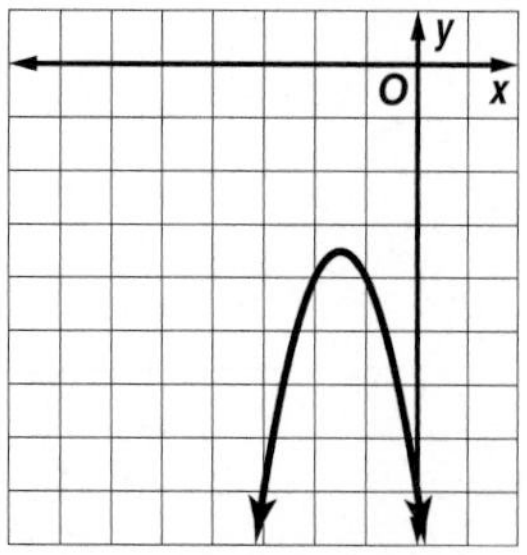

Pages 540–542, Lesson 9-2

1.

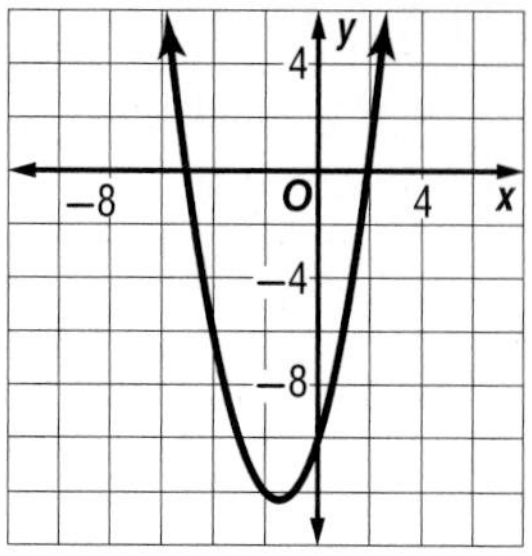

2.

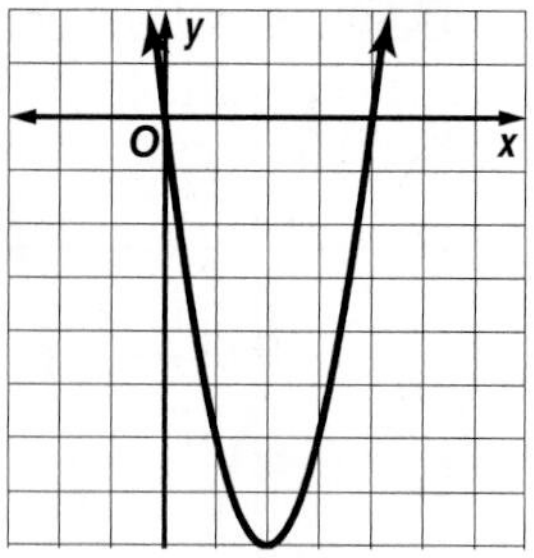

3.

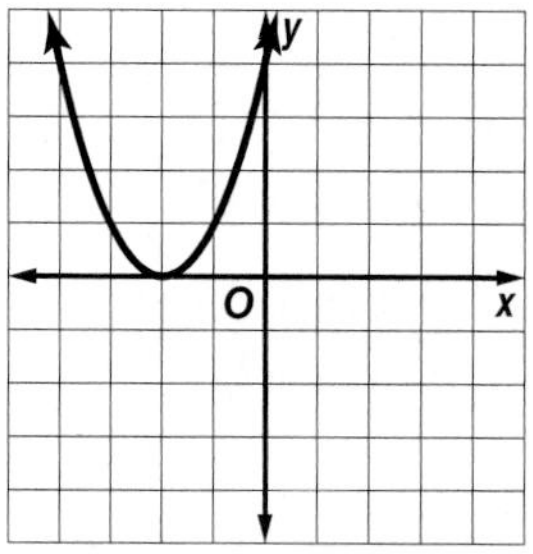

4.

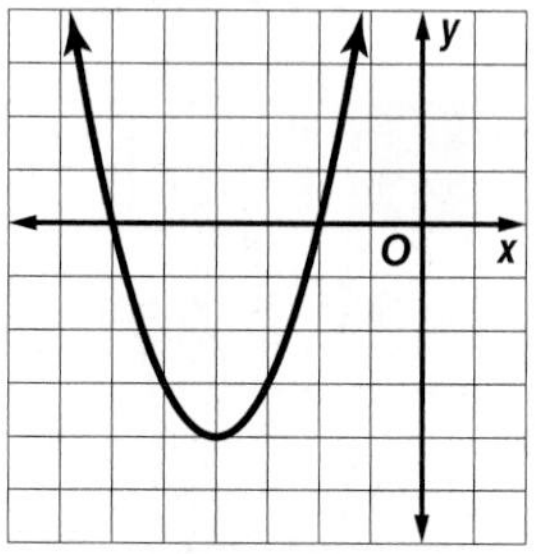

5.

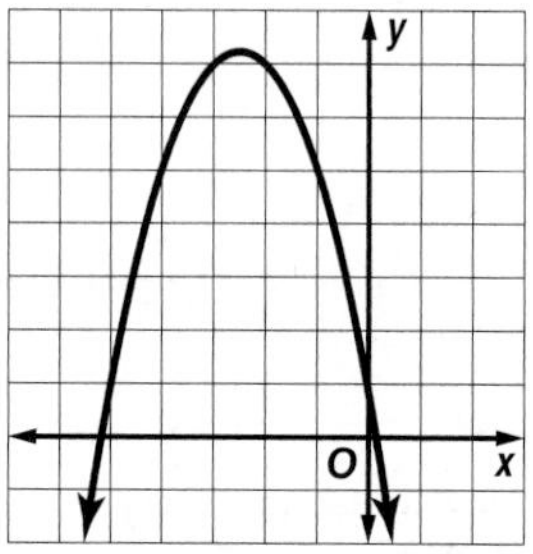

6.

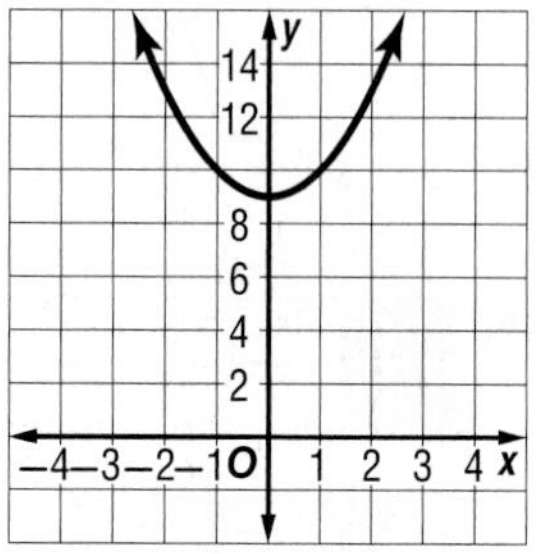

7.

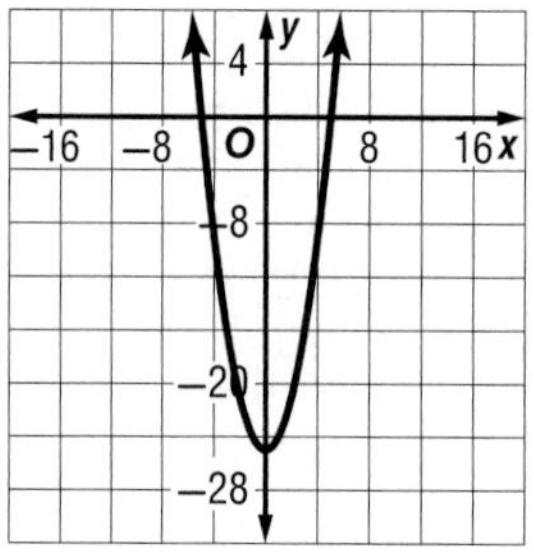

8.

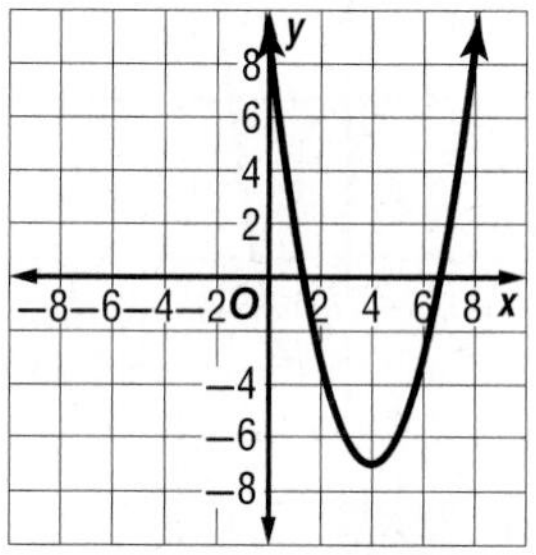

10. no solutions

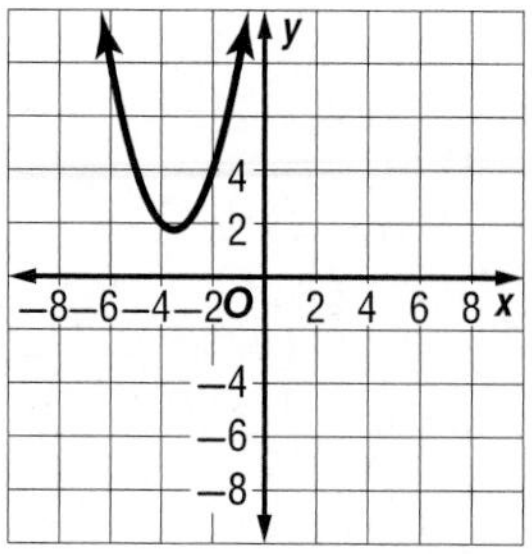

11. −6, 4

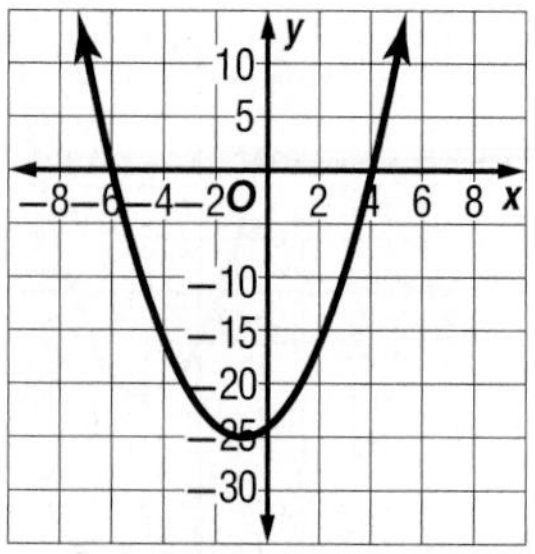

12. 8

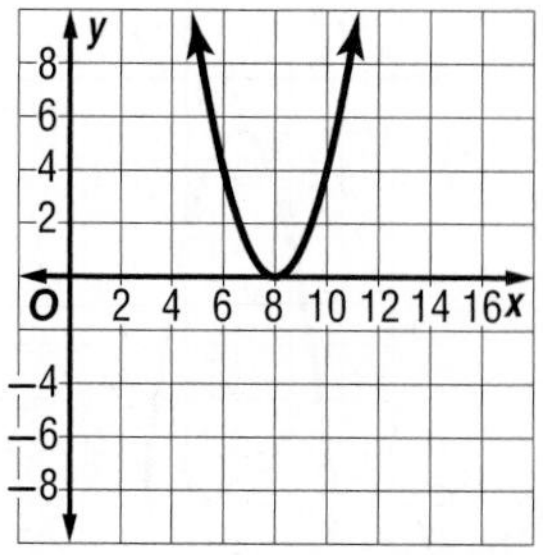

13. no solutions

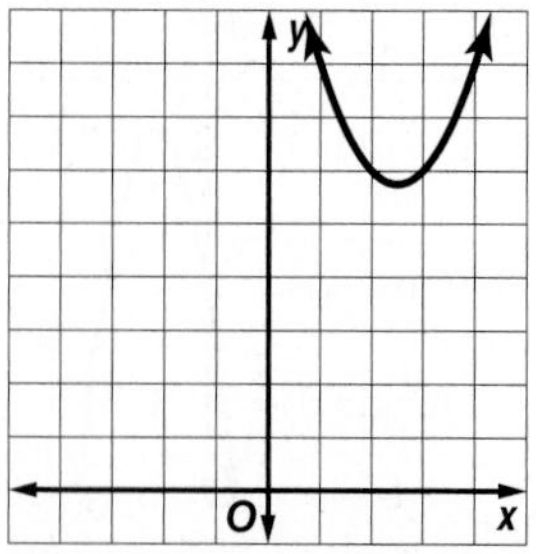

14. −7

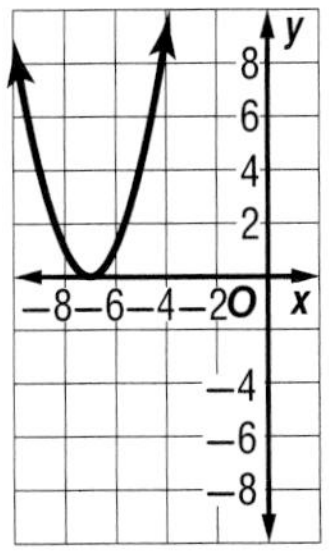

15. 1

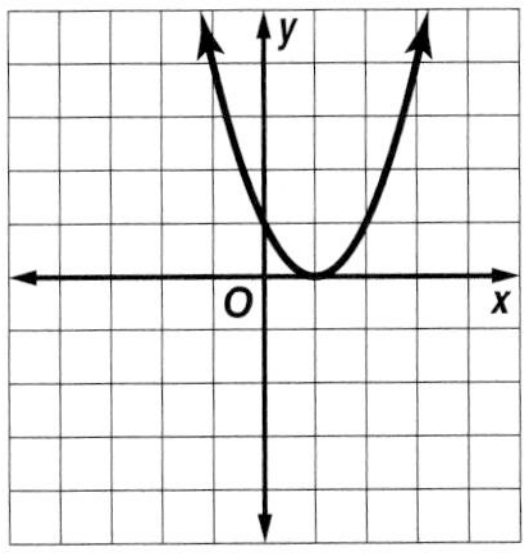

16. 2, 8

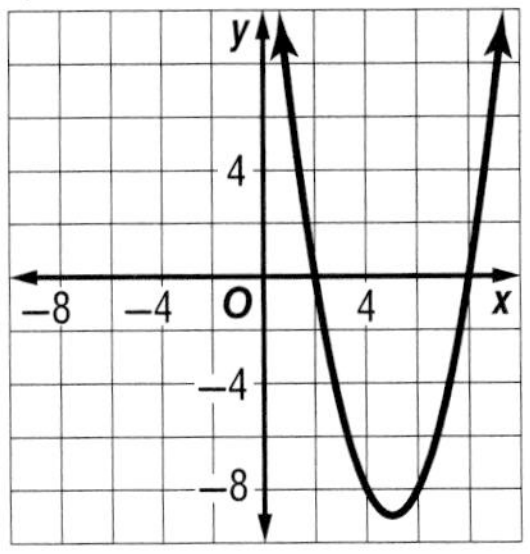

17. no solutions

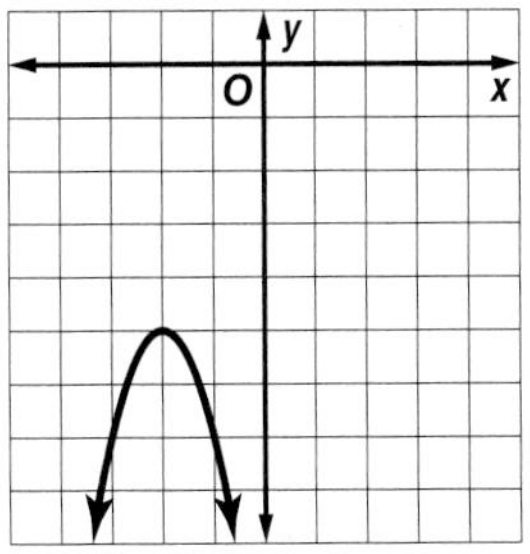

18. 3, 5

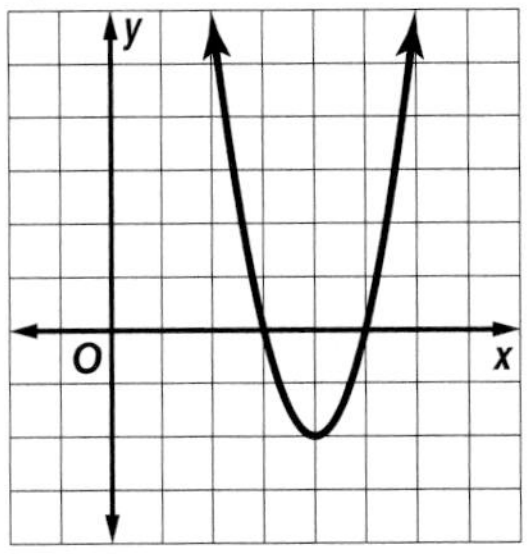

19. −6

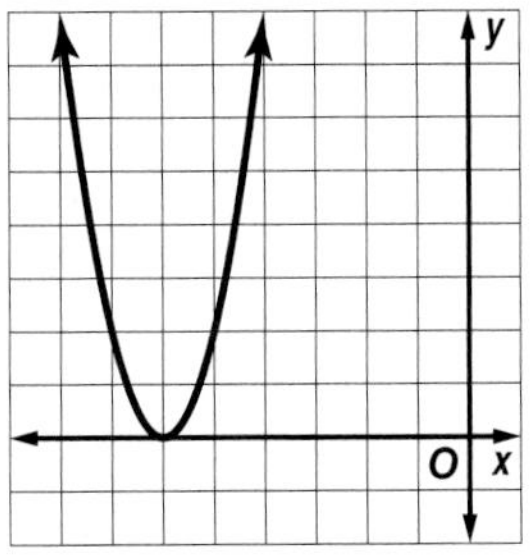

20. no solutions

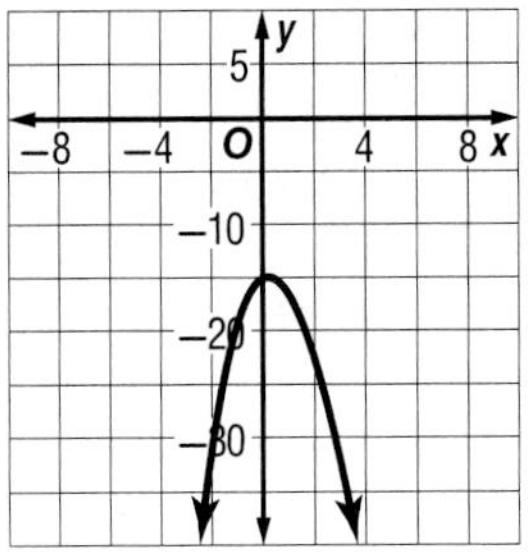

21. −10, 8

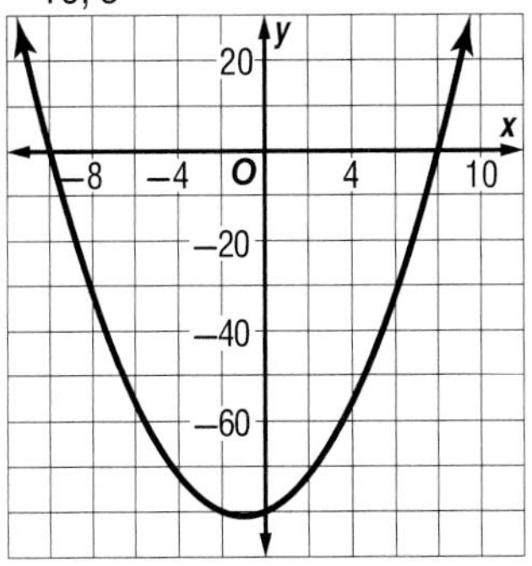

22. about −4.2, 2.2

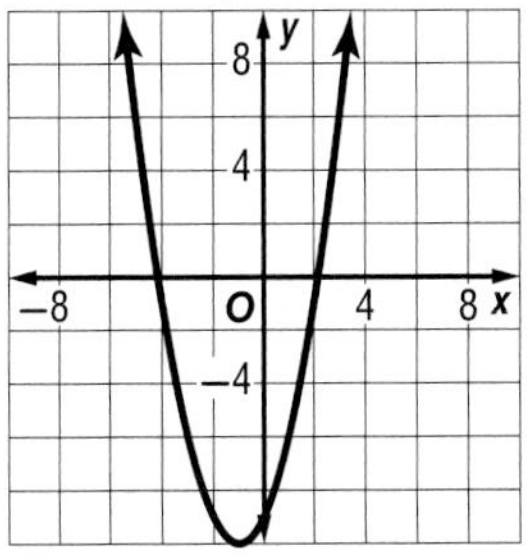

23. about −2.9, 6.9

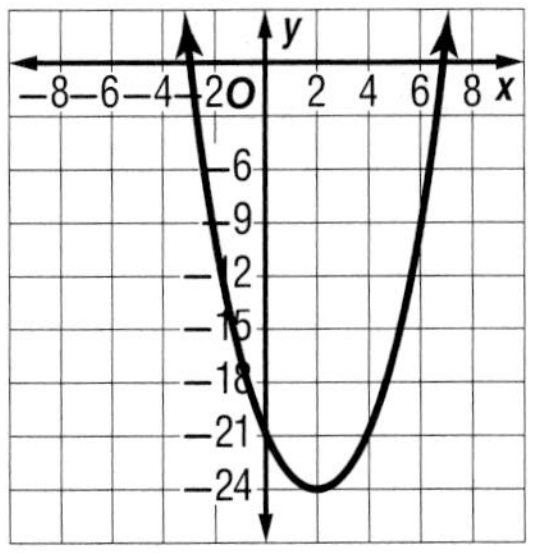

24. −6, 3

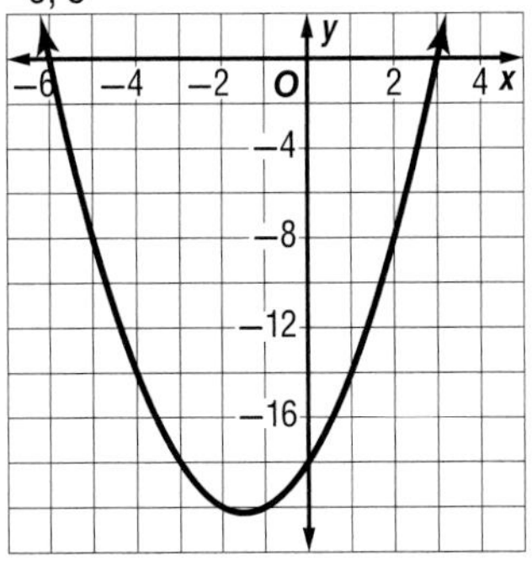

25. about 1.2, 3.3

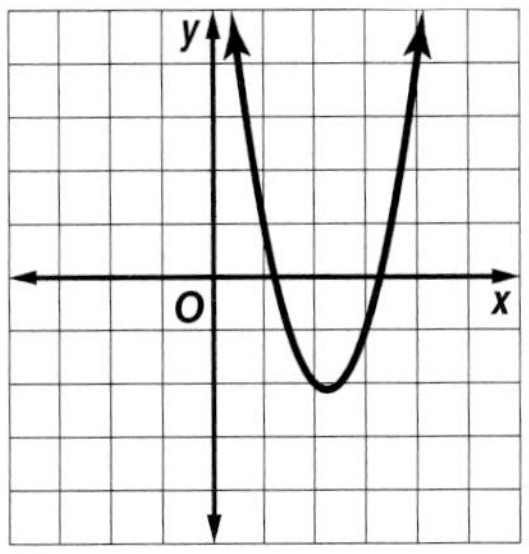

26. about −1.9, 1.2

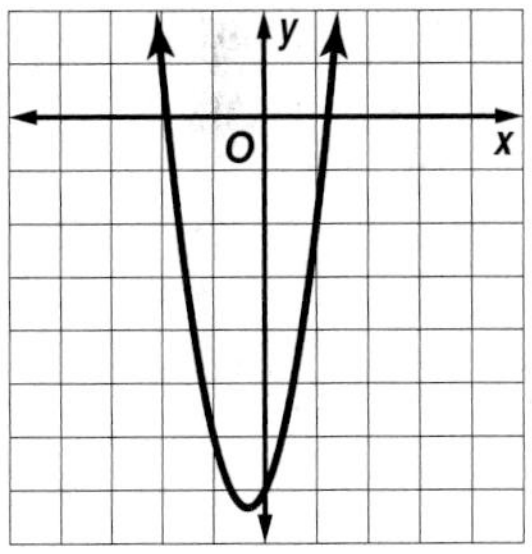

27. about −8.1, 3.1

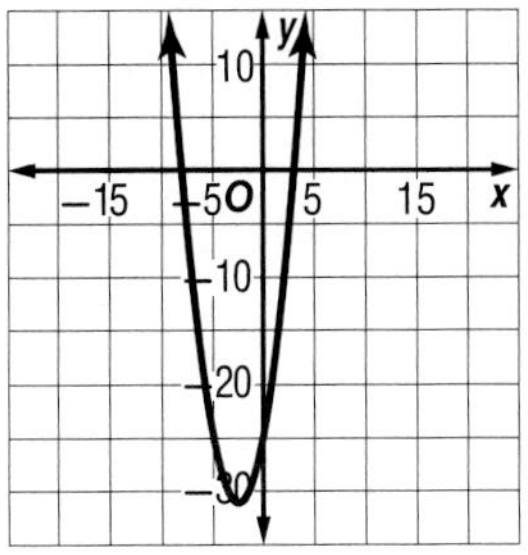

38a.

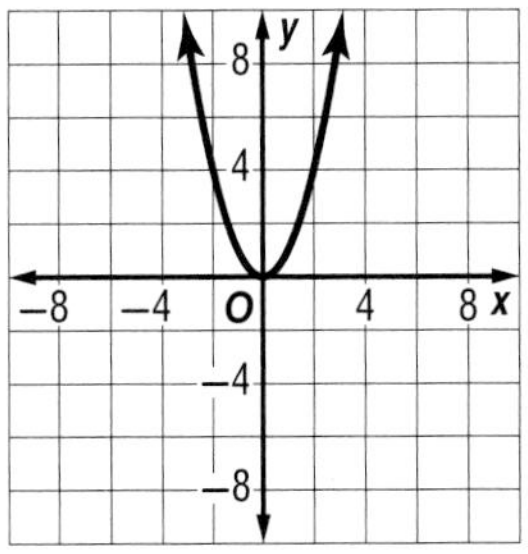

38c.

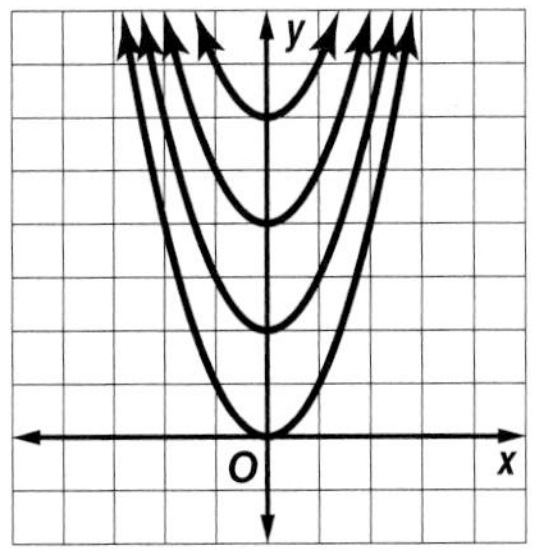

51. $x = 0$; $(0, 0)$; min

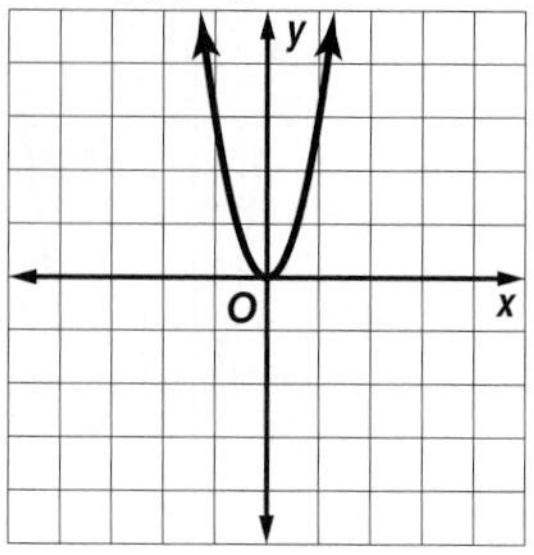

52. $x = 0$; $(0, -5)$; max

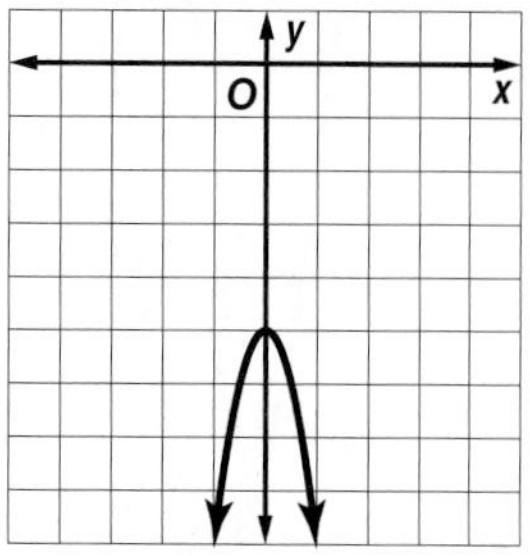

53. $x = 2$; $(2, -3)$; max

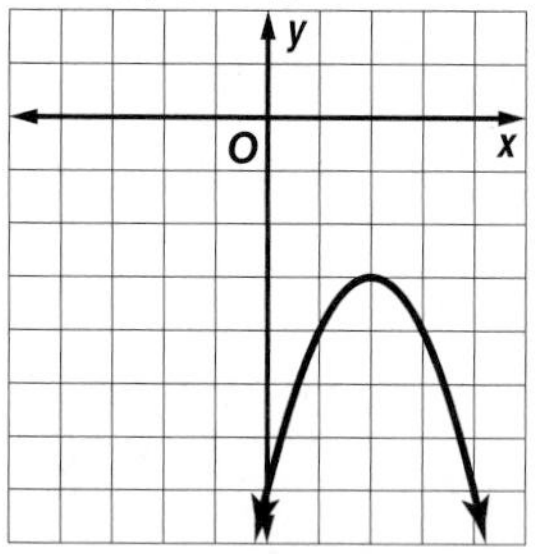

54. $x = 3$; $(3, -17)$; min

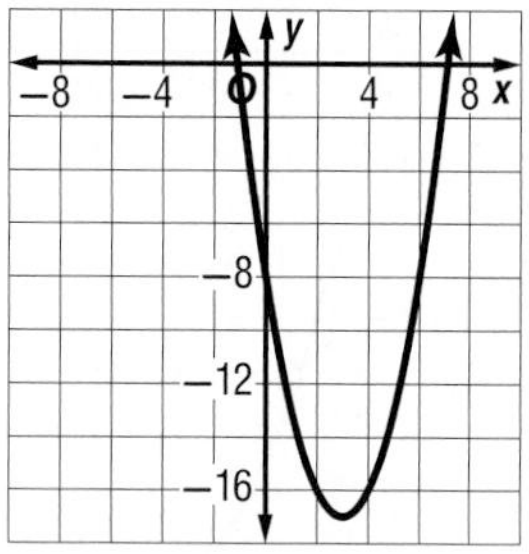

55. $x = -\frac{1}{3}$; $\left(-\frac{1}{3}, \frac{2}{3}\right)$; min

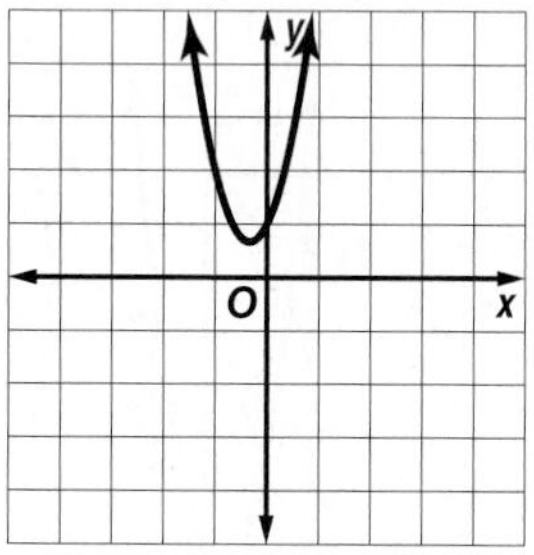

56. $x = -1$, $(-1, 9)$; max

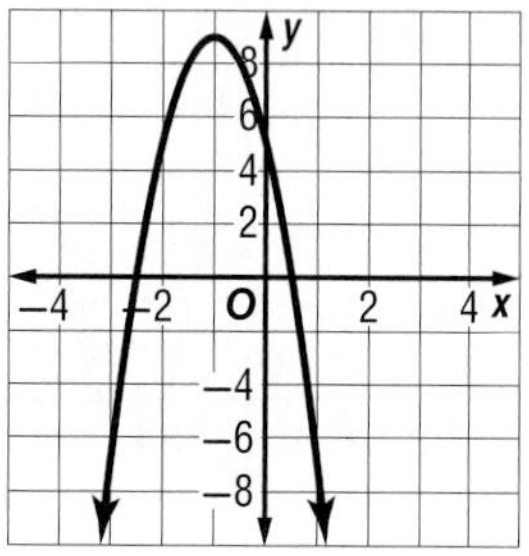

71.

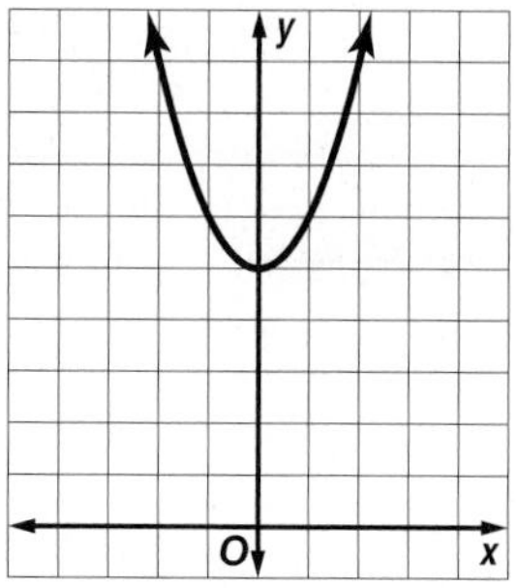

72.

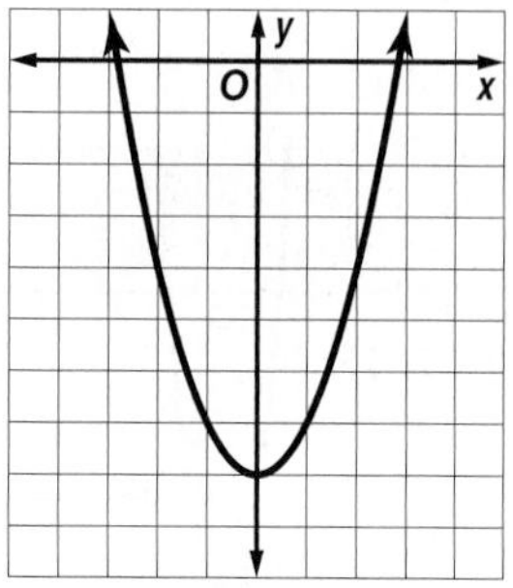

73.

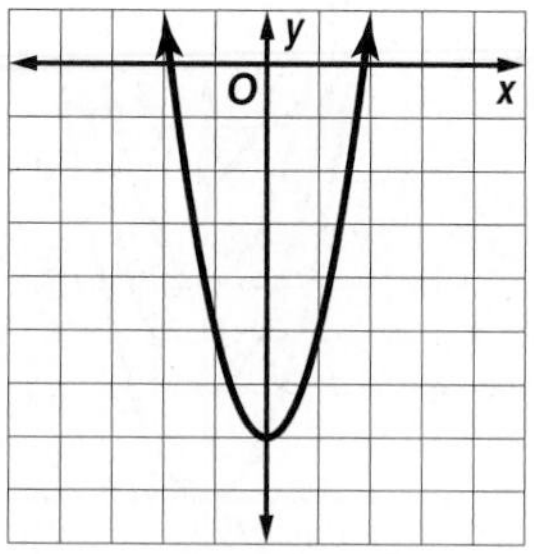

74.

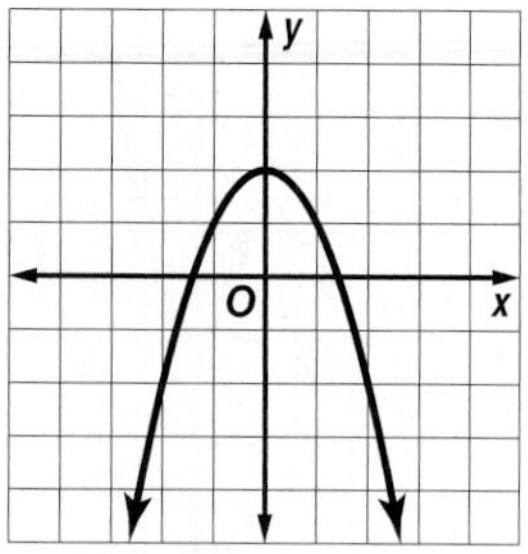

75.

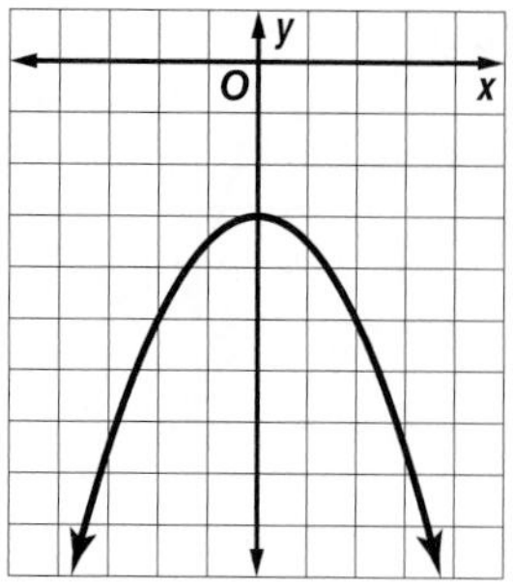

76.

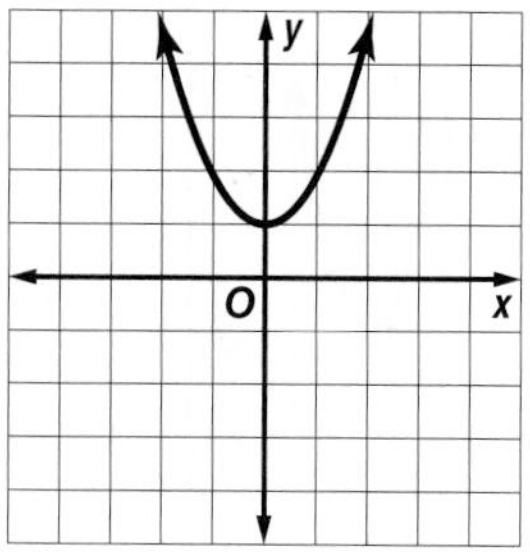

Pages 547–549, Lesson 9-3

24.

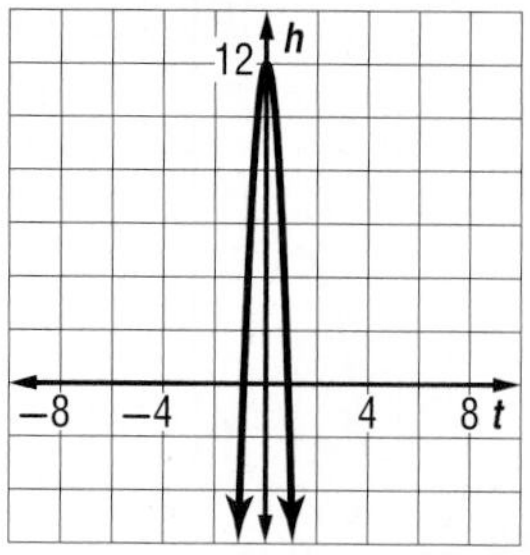

35a. Sometimes; this only occurs if $c = 0$. For any other value, the graph will be translated up or down.

35b. Always; the negative sign only reflects the graph over the *x*-axis. Both graphs are dilated by a factor of *a*.

35c. Never; the coefficient of the x^2-term would have to be negative for the graph to open downward.

39. Sample answer: For $y = ax^2$, the parent graph is stretched vertically if $a > 1$ or compressed vertically if $0 < a < 1$. The *y*-values in the table will all be multiplied by a factor of *a*. For $y = x^2 + c$, the parent graph is translated up if *c* is positive and moved down if *c* is negative. The *y*-values in the table will all have the constant *c* added to them or subtracted from them. For $y = ax^2 + c$, the graph will either be stretched vertically or compressed vertically based upon the value of *a* and then will be translated up or down depending the value of *c*. The *y*-values in the table will be multiplied by a factor of *a* and the constant *c* added to them.

44.

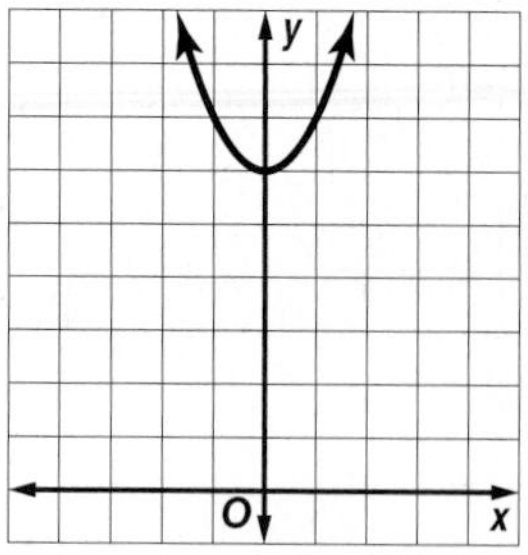

45.

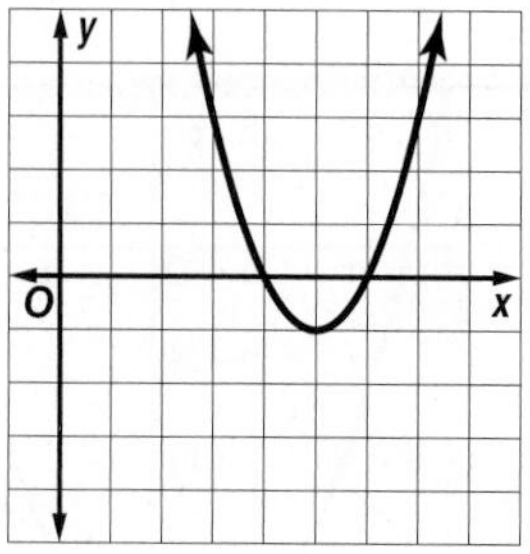

46.

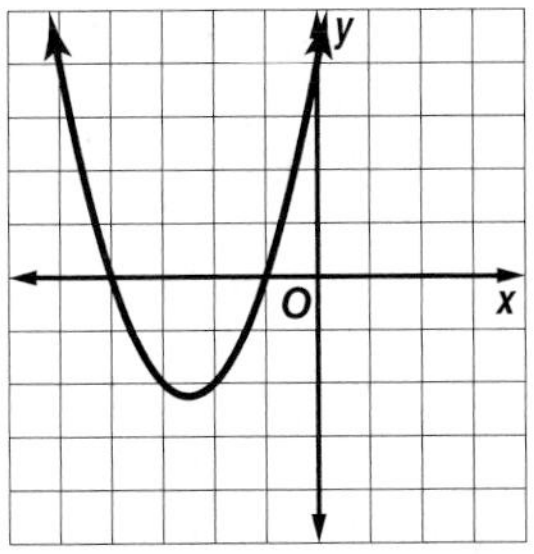

47.

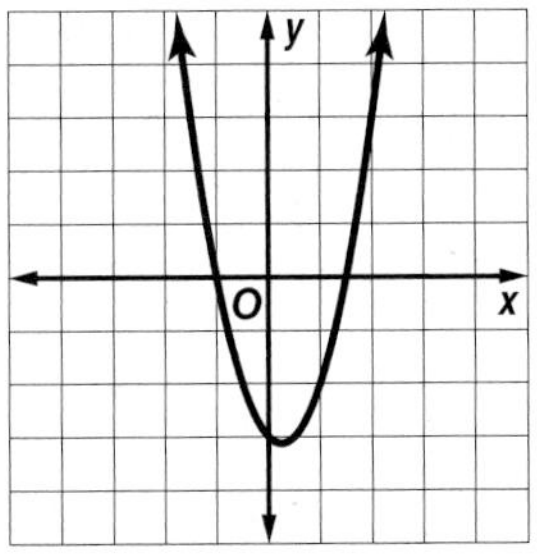

48.

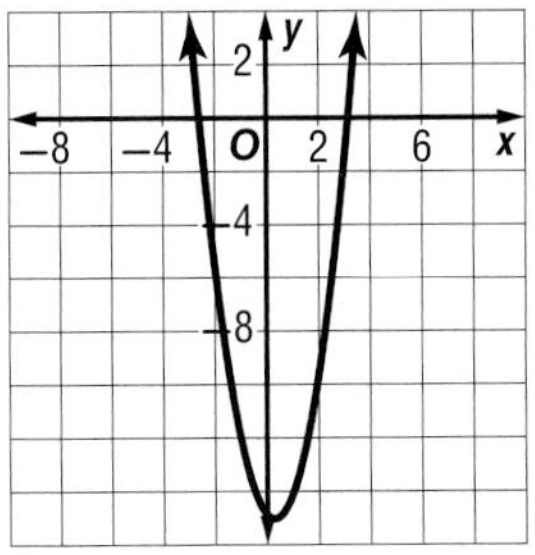

49.

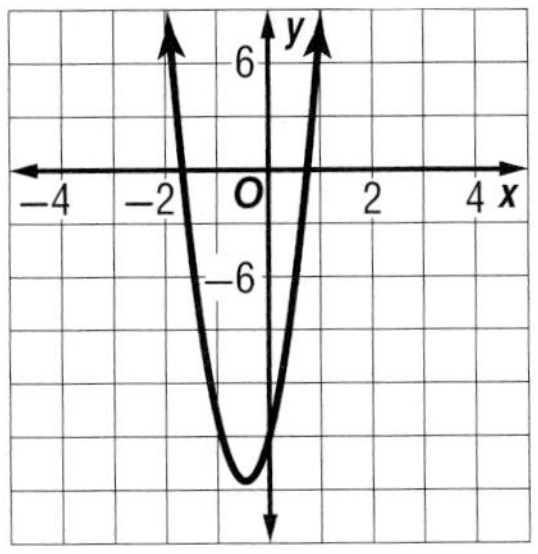

Page 557, Lesson 9-4

57. translated down

58. reflected across the *x*-axis, translated up

59. stretched vertically, translated up

60. compressed vertically, translated down

61. stretched vertically, translated up

62. reflected across the *x*-axis, stretched vertically, translated down

Page 563, Lesson 9-5

58. Sample answer: Factoring is easy if the polynomial is factorable and complicated if it is not. Not all equations are factorable. Graphing only gives approximate answers, but it is easy to see the number of solutions. Using square roots is easy when there is no *x*-term. Completing the square can be used for any quadratic equation and exact solutions can be found, but the leading coefficient has to be 1 and the x^2- and *x*-term must be isolated. It is also easier if the coefficient of the *x*-term is even; if not, the calculations become harder when dealing with fractions. The Quadratic Formula will work for any quadratic equation and exact solutions can be found. This method can be time consuming, especially if an equation is easily factored. See students' preferences.

Page 565, Extend 9-5

1.

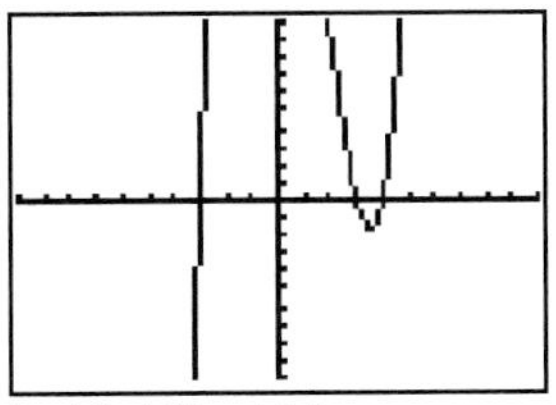

[−10, 10] scl:1 by
[−10, 10] scl:1

2.

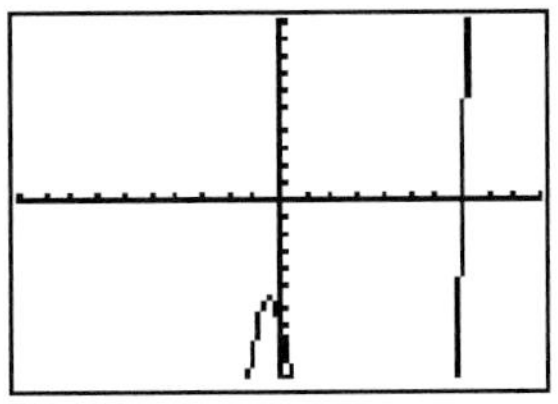

[−10, 10] scl:1 by
[−10, 10] scl:1

3.

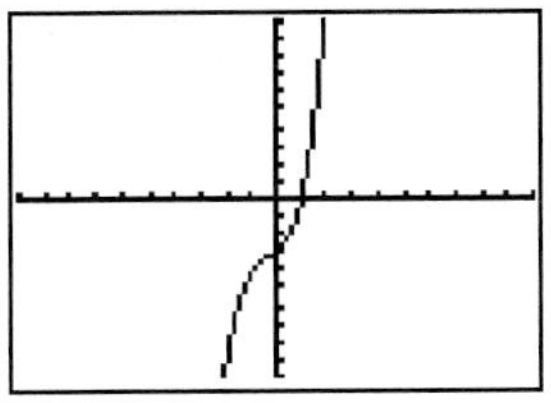

[−10, 10] scl:1 by
[−10, 10] scl:1

4.

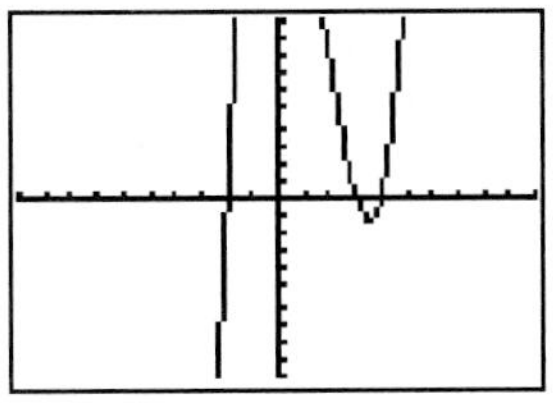

[−10, 10] scl:1 by
[−10, 10] scl:1

Page 566, Mid-Chapter Quiz

1.

x	y
−3	1
−2	−1
−1	−1
0	1
1	5
2	11

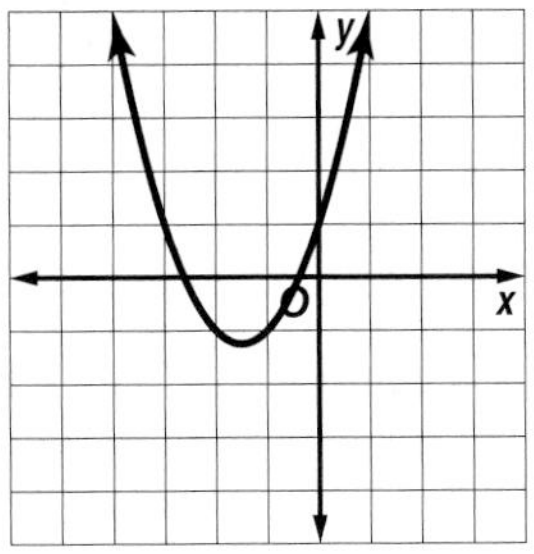

D = {all real numbers}
R = {y | y ≥ −1.25}

2.

x	y
−3	33
−2	19
−1	9
0	3
1	1
2	3
3	9

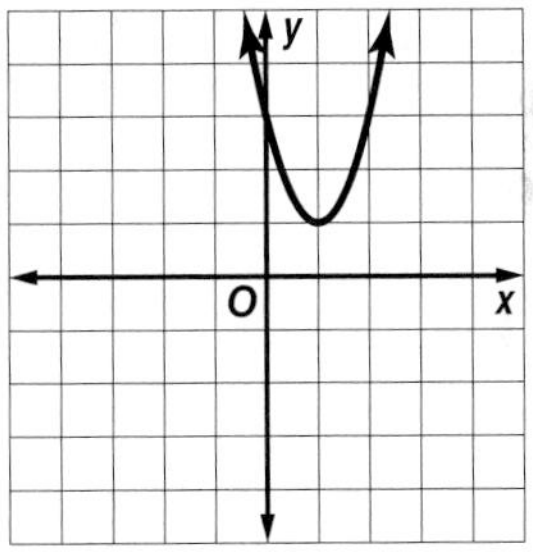

D = {all real numbers}

R = {y | y ≥ 1}

3.

x	y
−3	−3
−2	−1
−1	−1
0	−3
1	−7
2	−13

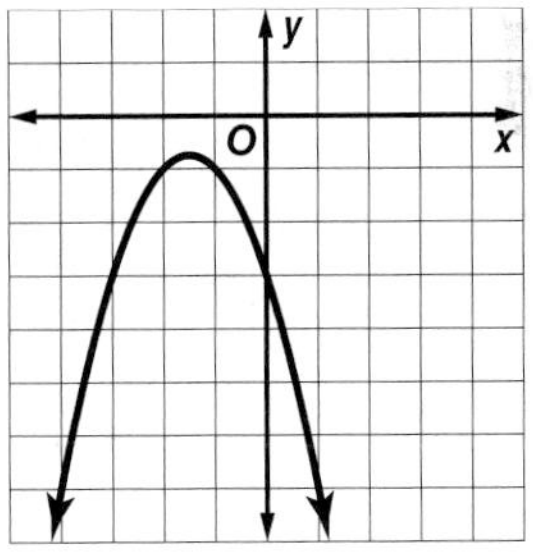

D = {all real numbers}
R = {y | y ≤ −0.75}

4.

x	y
−3	−23
−2	−9
−1	−1
0	1
1	−3
2	−13

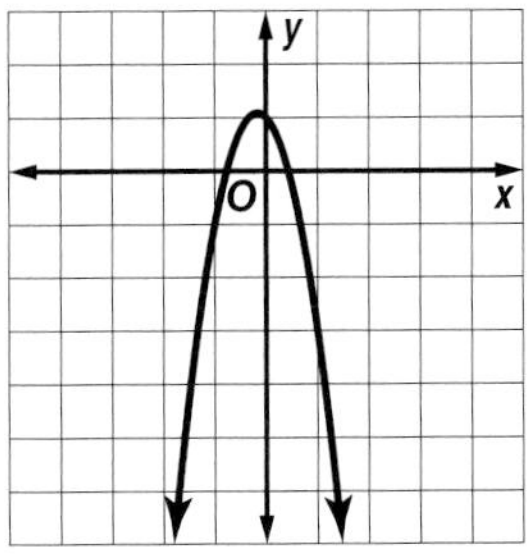

D = {all real numbers}

$R = \left\{y \mid y \leq 1\frac{1}{12}\right\}$

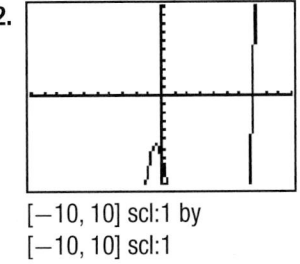

Page 567, Lesson 9-6 Check Your Progress

1A.

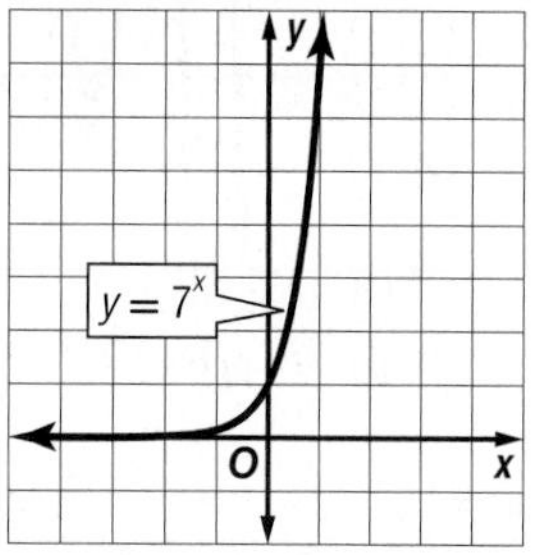

(0, 1); D = {all real numbers}
R = {y | y > 0}

Pages 570–571, Lesson 9-6

1. 1; D = {all real numbers}; R = {y | y > 0}; $2^{1.5} \approx 2.8$

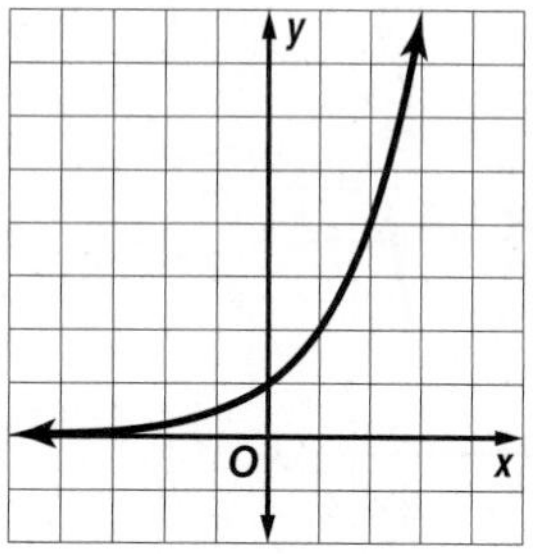

2. −1; D = {all real numbers}; R = {y | y < 0}; $-5^{0.5} \approx -2.2$

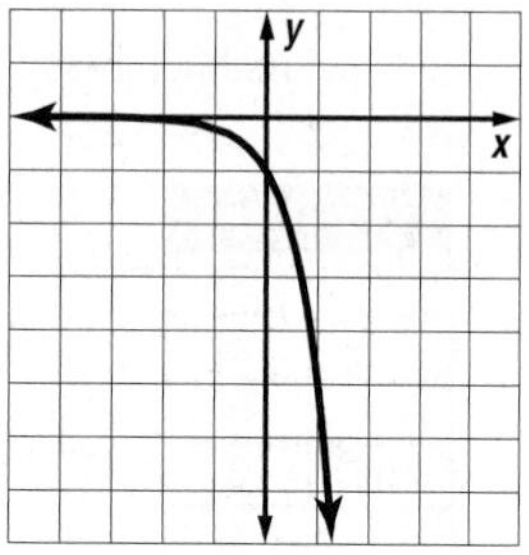

3. −1; D = {all real numbers}; R = {y | y < 0}; $-\left(\frac{1}{5}\right)^{-0.5} \approx -2.2$

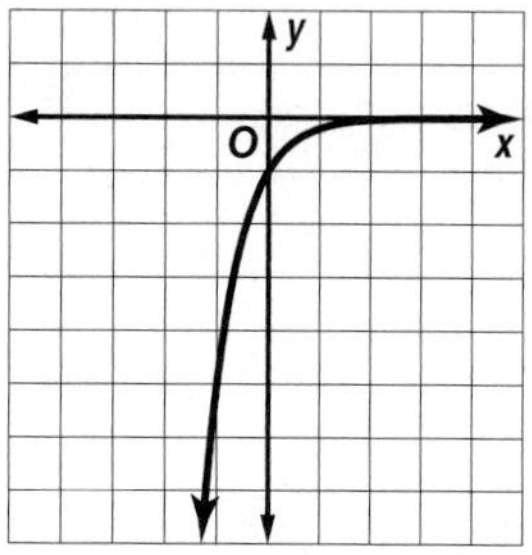

4. 3; D = {all real numbers}; R = {y | y > 0}; $3\left(\frac{1}{4}\right)^{0.5} = 1.5$

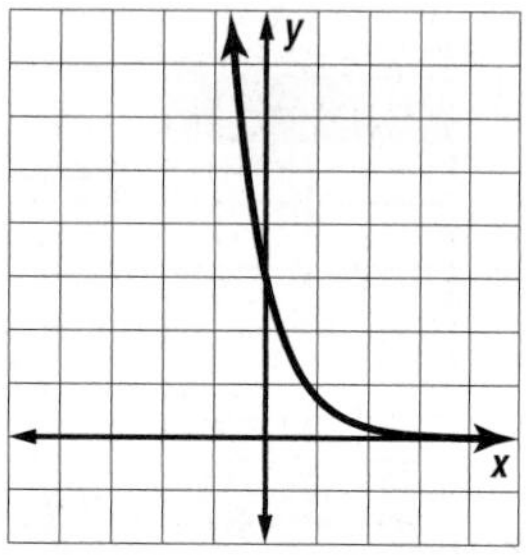

5. 4; D = {all real numbers}; R = {y | y > 3}

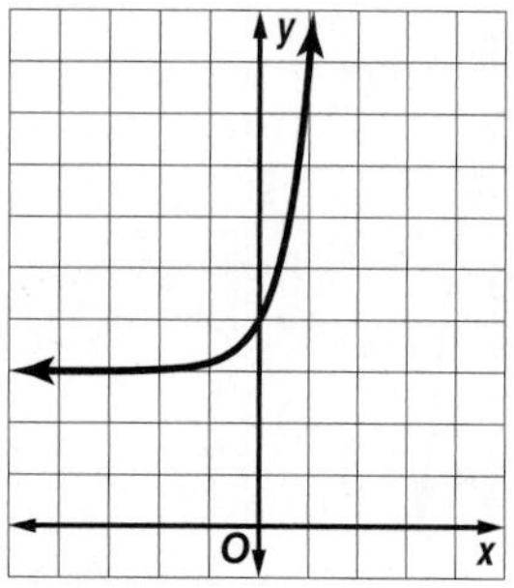

6. 1; D = {all real numbers}; R = {y | y < 2}

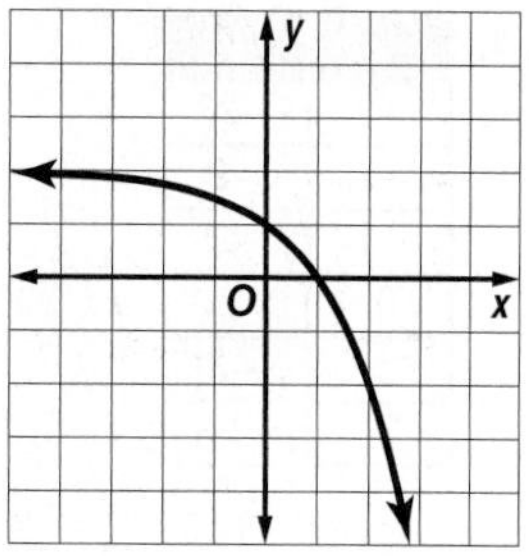

10. 2; D = {all real numbers}; R = {y | y > 0}; $2(8)^{-0.5} \approx 0.7$

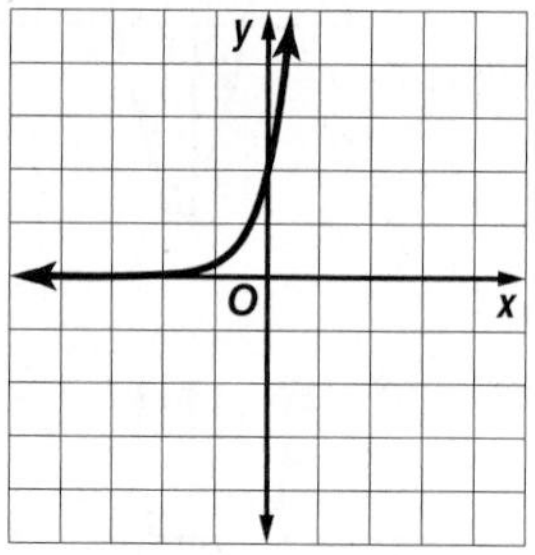

11. 2; D = {all real numbers}; R = {y | y > 0}; $2\left(\frac{1}{6}\right)^{1.5} \approx 0.1$

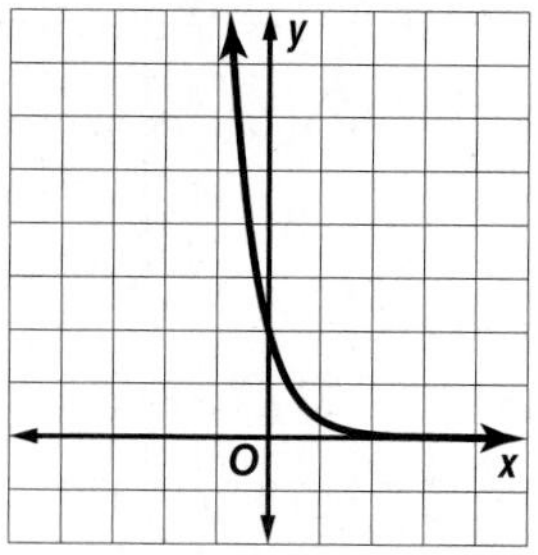

12. 1; D = {all real numbers}; R = {y | y > 0}; $\left(\frac{1}{12}\right)^{0.5} \approx 0.3$

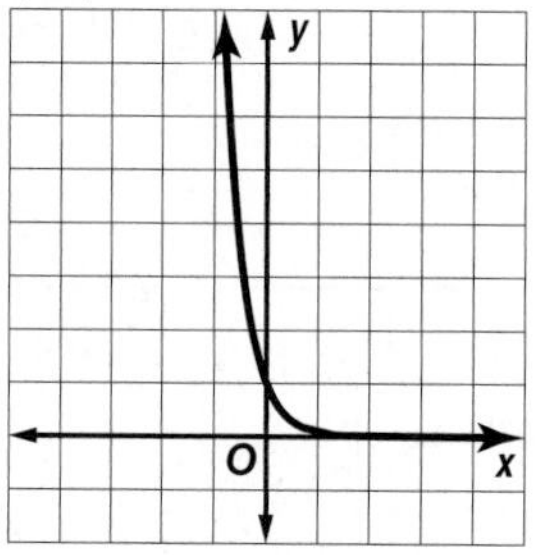

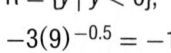

13. −3; D = {all real numbers}; R = {y | y < 0}; $-3(9)^{-0.5} = -1$

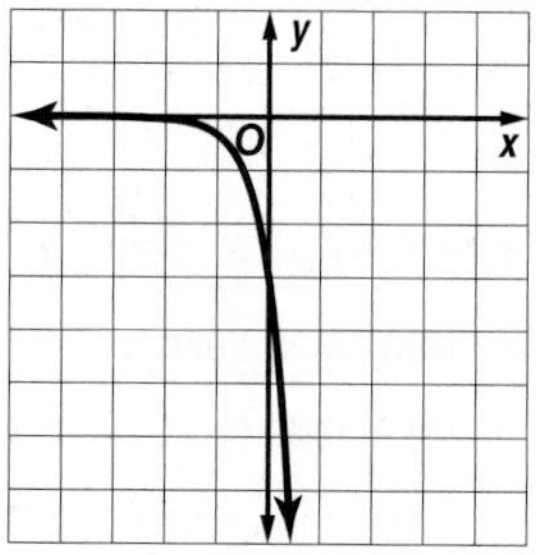

14. −4; D = {all real numbers}; R = {y | y < 0}; $-4(10)^{-0.5} \approx -1.3$

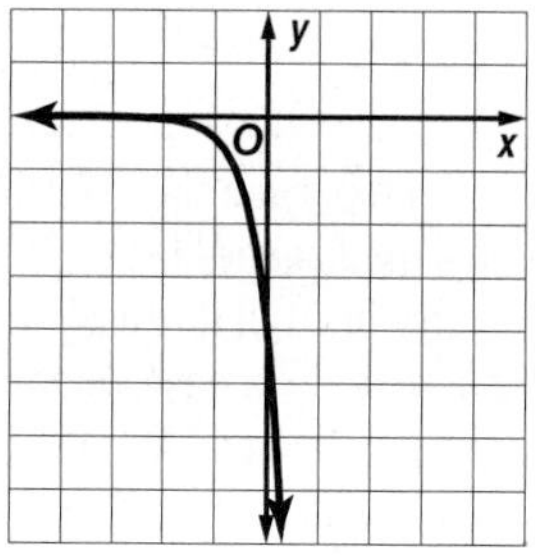

15. 3; D = {all real numbers}; R = {y | y > 0}; $3(11)^{-0.2} \approx 1.9$

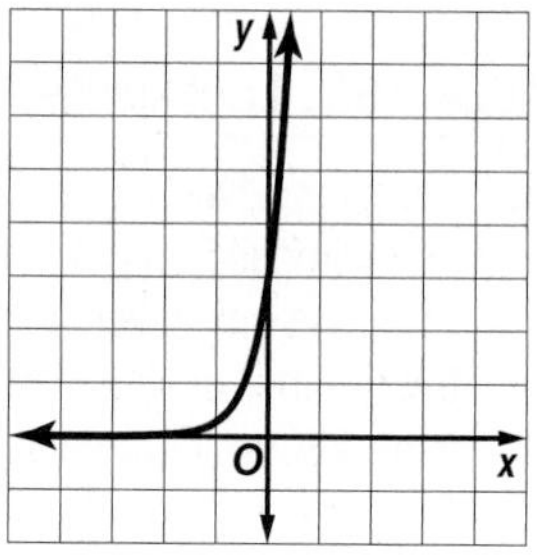

16. The *y*-intercept is 4; D = {all real numbers} R = {y | y > 3}.

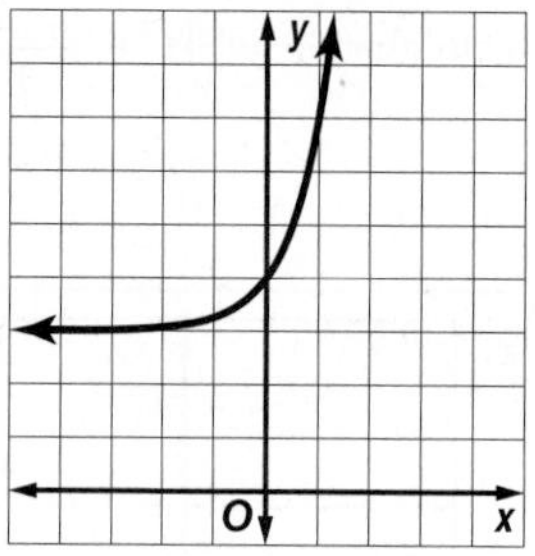

17. The *y*-intercept is −3.5; D = {all real numbers} R = {y | y > −4}.

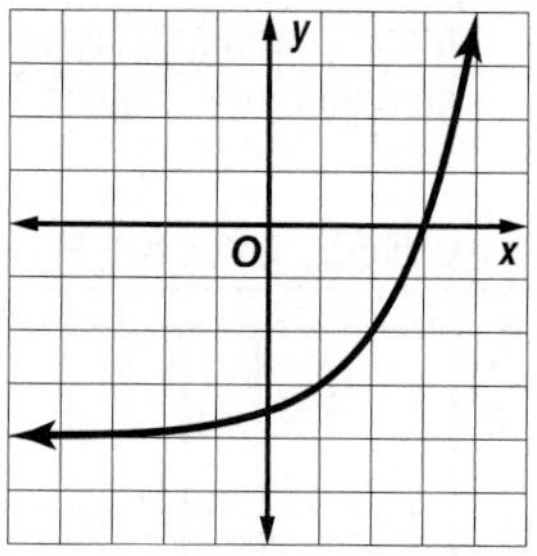

18. The y-intercept is 6;
D = {all real numbers}
R = $\{y \mid y > 1\}$.

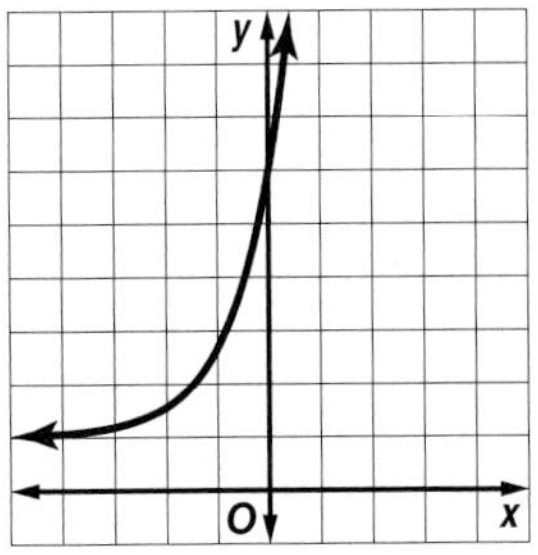

19. The y-intercept is 3;
D = {all real numbers};
R = $\{y \mid y < 5\}$.

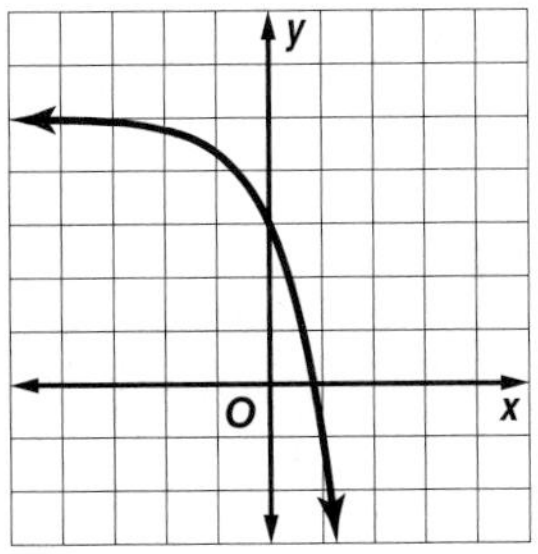

20b.

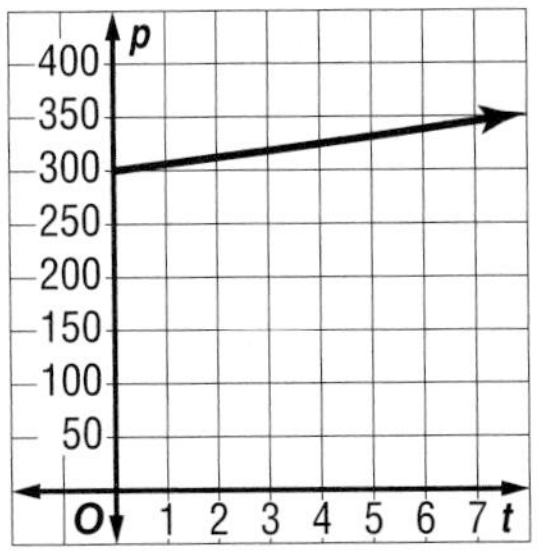

The p-intercept is 300; there are 300 bacteria at 9:00 A.M.;
D = $\{t \mid t \geq 0\}$;
R = $\{p \mid p \geq 300\}$.

43. Sample answer: The number of teams competing in a basketball tournament can be represented by $y = 2^x$, where the number of teams competing is y and the number of rounds is x.

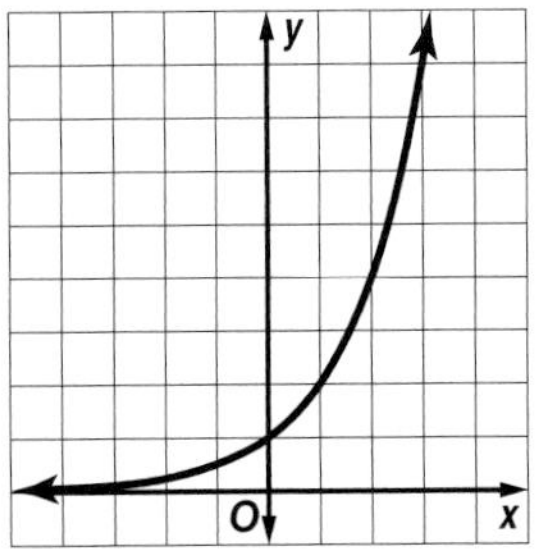

The y-intercept of the graph is 1. The graph increases rapidly for $x > 0$.

44. Sample answer: If $a > 0$, then $y = ab^x + c$ increases as x increases. The quadratic function has a minimum, and it increases as the x-values increase after the minimum value. If $0 < a < 1$, then $y = ab^x + c$ decreases as x increases. If a is < 0, both parent functions will be reflected across the x-axis. The c causes both $y = ab^x$ and $y = ab^2$ to move up or down when $c \neq 0$.

45. Sample answer: First, look for a pattern by making sure that the domain values are at regular intervals and the range values differ by a common factor.

Page 577, Lesson 9-7

42.

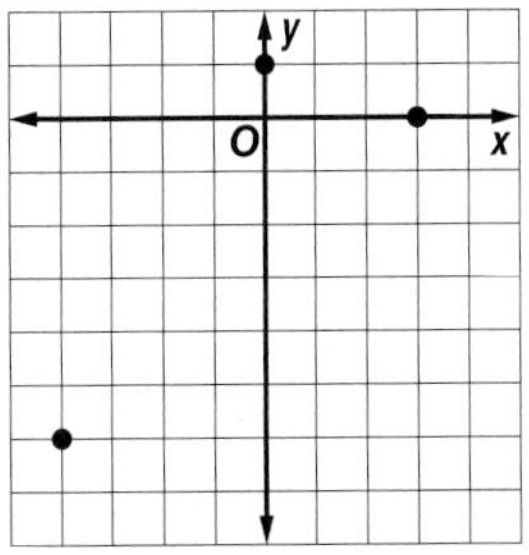

43.

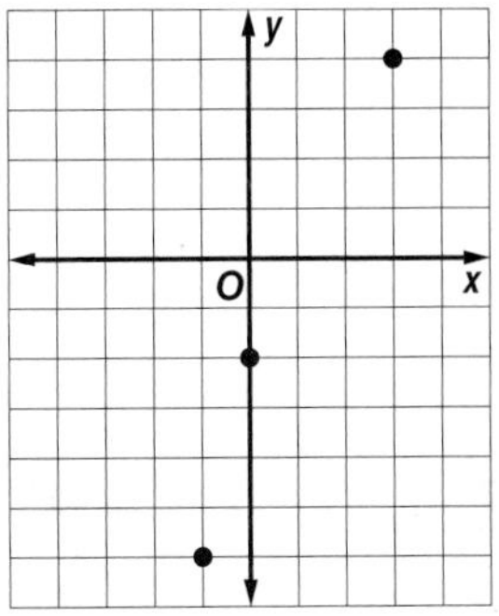

44.

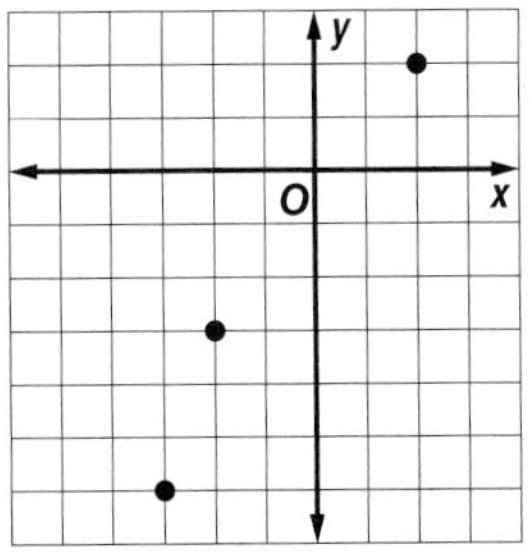

Pages 581–583, Lesson 9-8

30.

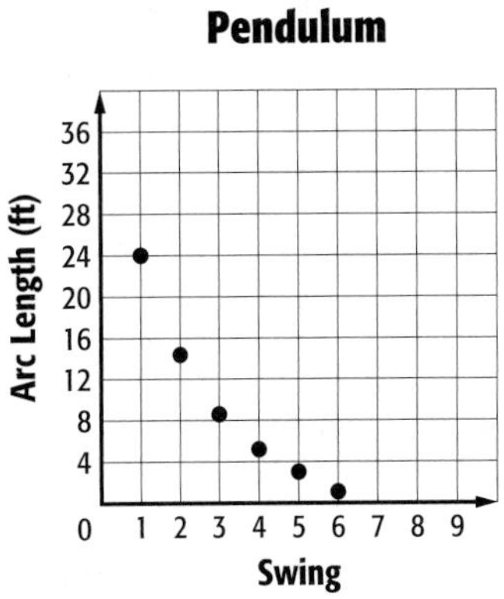

37b.

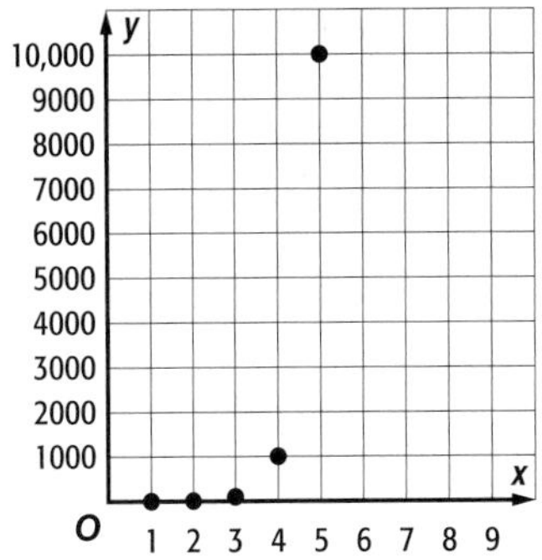

37c. The graph appears to be exponential. The rate of change between any two points does not match any others.

39. Neither; Haro calculated the exponent incorrectly. Matthew did not calculate $(-2)^8$ correctly.

42. Sample answer: First find the common ratio. Then use the formula $a_n = a_1 \bullet r^{n-1}$. Substitute the first term for a_1 and the common ratio for r. Let n be equal to the number of the term you are finding. Then solve the equation.

56. Sample answer. $y = 48 + 6x$, $y = 72 + 4x$; (12, 120) means that in 12 years the trees will be the same height, 120 inches or 10 feet.

58. $y = 4x + 2$

59. $y = -3x - \frac{2}{3}$

60. $y = -\frac{1}{4}x - 5$

61. $y = \frac{1}{2}x - 9$

62. $y = -\frac{2}{5}x + \frac{3}{4}$

63. $y = -6x - 7$

Pages 587–588, Lesson 9-9

14.
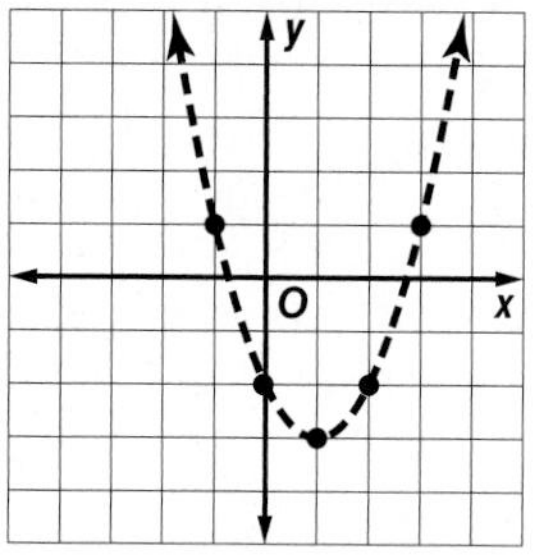
quadratic

15.
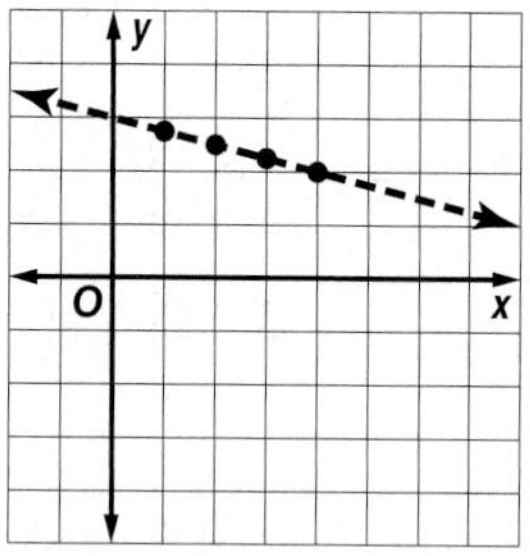
linear

16.
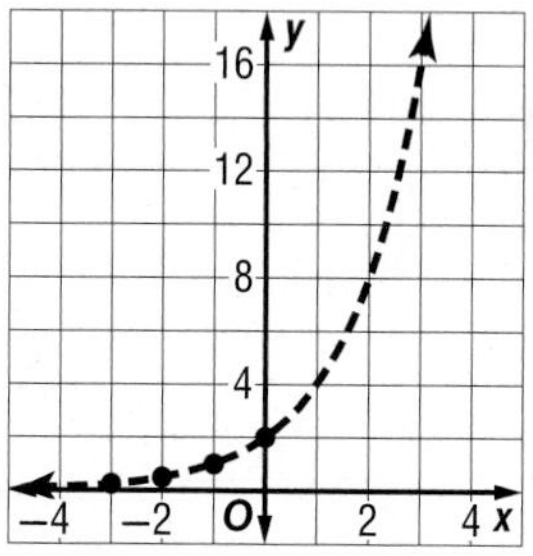

exponential

17.
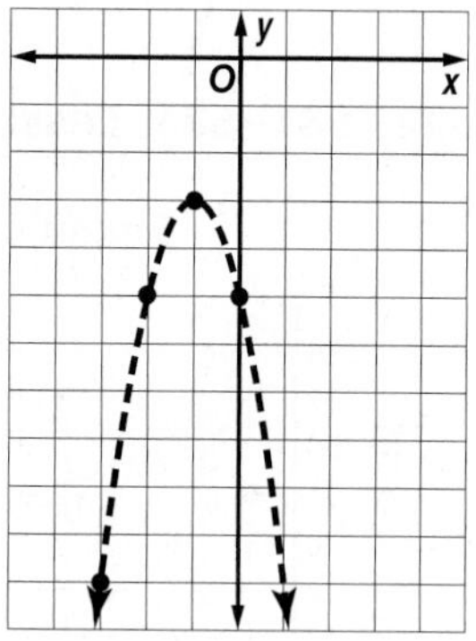
quadratic

18.
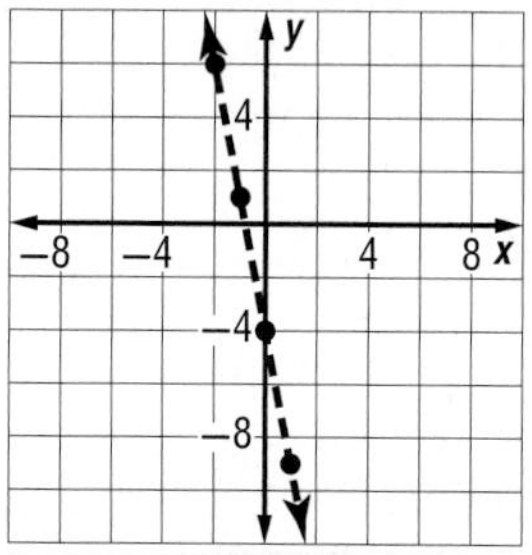

linear

19.
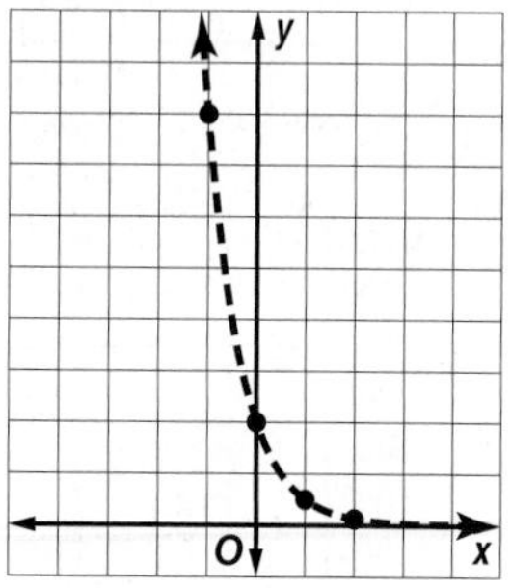
exponential

29a.

Time (hour)	0	1	2	3	4
Amount of Bacteria	12	36	108	324	972

35. The data can be graphed to determine which function best models the data. Also, differences and ratios of the y-values can be used. If the first differences are constant, the data are modeled by a linear function. If the second differences are constant but the first differences are not, the data can be modeled by a quadratic function. If the ratios are constant, then the data can be modeled by an exponential function.

Page 597, Practice Test

19.
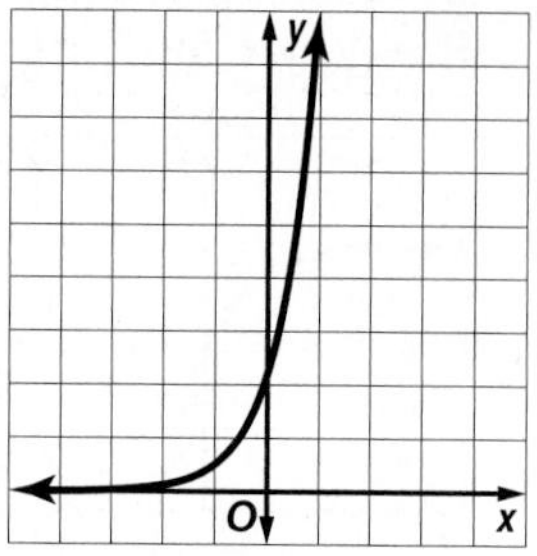
y-intercept = 2
D = {all real numbers}
R = $\{y \mid y > 0\}$

20.
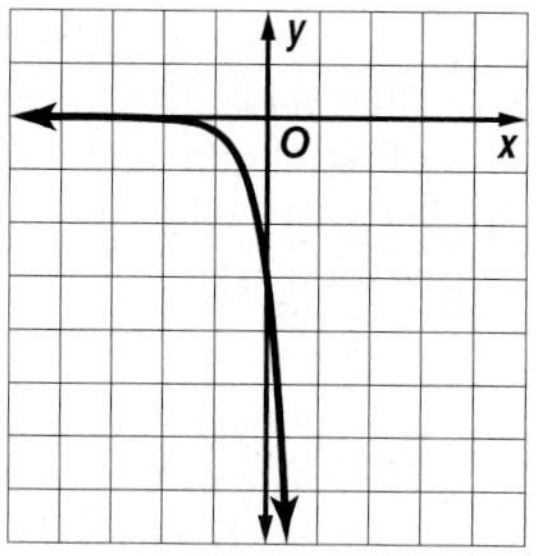
y-intercept = −3
D = {all real numbers}
R = $\{y \mid y < 0\}$

21.
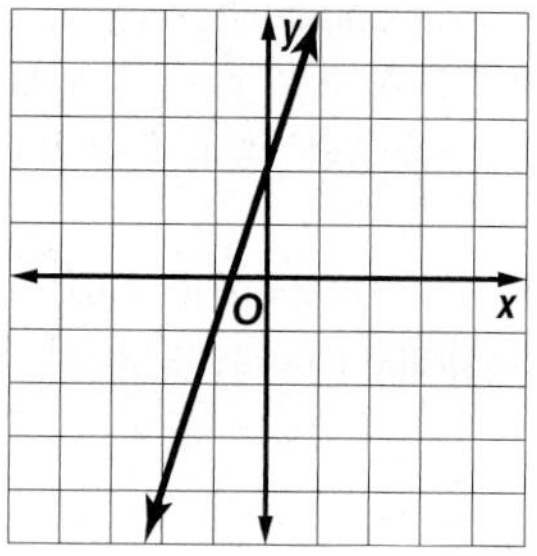
y-intercept = 2
D = {all real numbers}
R = {all real numbers}

NOTES

CHAPTER 10

Chapter Planner

Diagnostic Assessment
Quick Check, p. 603

	Lesson 10-1 Pacing: 1 day	Extend 10-1 Pacing: 0.5 day	Lesson 10-2 Pacing: 1 day
Title	**Square Root Functions**	**Graphing Technology Lab: Graphing Square Root Functions**	**Simplifying Radical Expressions**
Objectives	• Graph and analyze dilations of radical functions. • Graph and analyze reflections and translations of radical functions.	• Use a graphing calculator to investigate the graphs of square root functions.	• Simplify radical expressions by using the Product Property of Square roots. • Simplify radical expressions by using the Quotient Property of Square roots.
Key Vocabulary	square root function radical function radicand		radical expression rationalizing the denominator conjugate
ILS	7.B.4, 8.B.4b	8.B.4b	7.B.4
Multiple Representations	p. 609		
Lesson Resources	**Chapter 10 Resource Masters** • Study Guide and Intervention, pp. 5–6 AL OL ELL • Skills Practice, p. 7 AL OL ELL • Practice, p. 8 AL OL BL ELL • Word Problem Practice, p. 9 AL OL BL ELL • Enrichment, p. 10 OL BL **Transparencies** • 5-Minute Check Transparency 10-1 AL OL BL ELL **Additional Print Resources** • *Study Notebook* AL OL BL ELL	**Materials** • TI–83/84 Plus or other graphing calculator • grid paper	**Chapter 10 Resource Masters** • Study Guide and Intervention, pp. 11–12 AL OL ELL • Skills Practice, p. 13 AL OL ELL • Practice, p. 14 AL OL BL ELL • Word Problem Practice, p. 15 AL OL BL ELL • Enrichment, p. 16 OL BL • Quiz 1, p. 57 AL OL BL ELL **Transparencies** • 5-Minute Check Transparency 10-2 AL OL BL ELL **Additional Print Resources** • *Study Notebook* AL OL BL ELL
Technology for Every Lesson	IL Math Online glencoe.com • Extra Examples • Self-Check Quizzes • Personal Tutor • Homework Help	**CD/DVD Resources** IWB INTERACTIVE WHITEBOARD READY IWB StudentWorks Plus IWB Interactive Classroom IWB Diagnostic and Assessment Planner	• TeacherWorks Plus • eSolutions Manual Plus • ExamView Assessment Suite
Math in Motion			
Differentiated Instruction	pp. 607, 610		pp. 614, 617

KEY: AL Approaching Level OL On Level BL Beyond Level ELL English Learners

Suggested Pacing			
Time Periods	**Instruction**	**Review & Assessment**	**Total**
45-minute	10	2	12
90-minute	6	1	7

Radical Functions and Geometry

Extend 10-2 Pacing: 0.5 day	**Lesson 10-3** Pacing: 1 day	**Lesson 10-4** Pacing: 1 day	**Lesson 10-5** Pacing: 1 day
Graphing Technology Lab: Rational Exponents	**Operations with Radical Expressions**	**Radical Equations**	**The Pythagorean Theorem**
• Use a graphing calculator to explore the meaning of rational exponents.	• Add and subtract radical expressions. • Multiply radical expressions.	• Solve radical equations. • Solve radical equations with extraneous solutions.	• Solve problems by using the Pythagorean Theorem. • Determine whether a triangle is a right triangle.
		radical equations extraneous solutions	hypotenuse legs converse Pythagorean triple
8.B.4a	7.B.4, 8.C.4b	7.A.4b, 8.C.4b	7.A.4b
		p. 627	
Materials • TI–83/84 Plus or other graphing calculator	**Chapter 10 Resource Masters** • Study Guide and Intervention, pp. 17–18 AL OL ELL • Skills Practice, p. 19 AL OL ELL • Practice, p. 20 AL OL BL ELL • Word Problem Practice, p. 21 AL OL BL ELL • Enrichment, p. 22 OL BL **Transparencies** • 5-Minute Check Transparency 10-3 AL OL BL ELL **Additional Print Resources** • *Study Notebook* AL OL BL ELL • *Teaching Algebra with Manipulatives,* p. 158 AL OL ELL	**Chapter 10 Resource Masters** • Study Guide and Intervention, pp. 23–24 AL OL ELL • Skills Practice, p. 25 AL OL ELL • Practice, p. 26 AL OL BL ELL • Word Problem Practice, p. 27 AL OL BL ELL • Enrichment, p. 28 OL BL • Graphing Calculator Acitvity, p. 29 OL • Quiz 2, p. 57 AL OL BL ELL **Transparencies** • 5-Minute Check Transparency 10-4 AL OL BL ELL **Additional Print Resources** • *Study Notebook* AL OL BL ELL	**Chapter 10 Resource Masters** • Study Guide and Intervention, pp. 30–31 AL OL ELL • Skills Practice, p. 32 AL OL ELL • Practice, p. 33 AL OL BL ELL • Word Problem Practice, p. 34 AL OL BL ELL • Enrichment, p. 35 OL BL • Spreadsheet Acitvity, p. 36 OL **Transparencies** • 5-Minute Check Transparency 10-5 AL OL BL ELL **Additional Print Resources** • *Study Notebook* AL OL BL ELL • *Teaching Algebra with Manipulatives,* pp. 159–162 AL OL ELL
	IL Math Online glencoe.com • Extra Examples • Self-Check Quizzes • Personal Tutor	**CD/DVD Resources** IWB INTERACTIVE WHITEBOARD READY IWB StudentWorks Plus IWB Interactive Classroom IWB Diagnostic and Assessment Planner	• TeacherWorks Plus • eSolutions Manual Plus • ExamView Assessment Suite
	pp. 620, 623	pp. 625, 628	pp. 631, 635

Formative Assessment
Mid-Chapter Quiz, p. 629

CHAPTER 10 Chapter Planner

	Lesson 10-6 Pacing: 1 day	Lesson 10-7 Pacing: 1 day	Explore 10-8 Pacing: 0.5 day	Lesson 10-8 Pacing: 1.5 days
Title	**The Distance and Midpoint Formulas**	**Similar Triangles**	**Algebra Lab: Investigating Trigonometric Ratios**	**Trigonometric Ratios**
Objectives	• Find the distance between two points on a coordinate plane. • Find the midpoint between two points on a coordinate plane.	• Determine whether two triangles are similar. • Find the unknown measures of sides of two similar triangles.	• Investigate trigonometric ratios.	• Find trigonometric ratios of angles. • Use trigonometry to solve triangles.
Key Vocabulary	Distance Formula midpoint Midpoint Formula	similar triangles		trigonometry trigonometric ratio sine cosine tangent
ILS	7.A.4b	7.A.4a, 7.C.4a	9.D.4	9.D.4
Multiple Representations		p. 646		p. 654
Lesson Resources	**Chapter 10 Resource Masters** • Study Guide and Intervention, pp. 37–38 AL OL ELL • Skills Practice, p. 39 AL OL ELL • Practice, p. 40 AL OL BL ELL • Word Problem Practice, p. 41 AL OL BL ELL • Enrichment, p. 42 OL BL • Quiz 3, p. 58 AL OL BL ELL **Transparencies** • 5-Minute Check Transparency 10-6 AL OL BL ELL **Additional Print Resources** • *Study Notebook* AL OL BL ELL	**Chapter 10 Resource Masters** • Study Guide and Intervention, pp. 43–44 AL OL ELL • Skills Practice, p. 45 AL OL ELL • Practice, p. 46 AL OL BL ELL • Word Problem Practice, p. 47 AL OL BL ELL • Enrichment, p. 48 OL BL **Transparencies** • 5-Minute Check Transparency 10-7 AL OL BL ELL **Additional Print Resources** • *Study Notebook* AL OL BL ELL • *Teaching Algebra with Manipulatives,* p. 163 AL OL ELL	**Materials** • ruler • protractor • grid paper **Additional Print Resources** • *Teaching Algebra with Manipulatives,* pp. 1, 164 AL OL ELL	**Chapter 10 Resource Masters** • Study Guide and Intervention, pp. 49–50 AL OL ELL • Skills Practice, p. 51 AL OL ELL • Practice, p. 52 AL OL BL ELL • Word Problem Practice, p. 53 AL OL BL ELL • Enrichment, p. 54 OL BL • Quiz 4, p. 58 AL OL BL ELL **Transparencies** • 5-Minute Check Transparency 10-8 AL OL BL ELL **Additional Print Resources** • *Study Notebook* AL OL BL ELL
Technology for Every Lesson	IL Math Online glencoe.com • Extra Examples • Self-Check Quizzes • Personal Tutor • Homework Help	**CD/DVD Resources** IWB INTERACTIVE WHITEBOARD READY IWB StudentWorks Plus IWB Interactive Classroom IWB Diagnostic and Assessment Planner		• TeacherWorks Plus • eSolutions Manual Plus • ExamView Assessment Suite
Math in Motion		Animation, BrainPOP	Animation	
Differentiated Instruction	pp. 637, 641	pp. 644, 647		pp. 650, 655

Summative Assessment
- Study Guide and Review, pp. 656–660
- Practice Test, p. 661

Quick Review Math Handbook*

is Glencoe's mathematical handbook for students and parents.

Hot Words includes a glossary of terms.

Hot Topics consists of two parts:

- explanations of key mathematical concepts
- exercises to check students' understanding.

Lesson	Hot Topics Section	Lesson	Hot Topics Section
10-1	6.7, 7.3	10-5	7.9
10-2	3.2, 6.2	10-6	3.2
10.3	3.2, 3.4	10-7	6.5
10-4	3.1, 3.2	10-8	6.5

**Also available in Spanish*

What the Research Says...

Trafton (1984) states that each lesson should present a sufficient number and range of examples prior to independent practice.

- Numerous detailed examples are provided throughout Chapter 10 to give students models for working with radicals and geometry.
- The additional examples provided in the Teacher Wraparound Edition can be used to help students prepare for their own problem-solving practice.
  Source: Trafton, P.R. (1984). "Toward More Effective, Efficient Instruction in Mathematics." *Elementary School Journal*, 84, Issue 5, pp. 514–528.

Assessment and Intervention

SE = Student Edition, **TE** = Teacher Edition, **CRM** = Chapter Resource Masters

	Diagnosis	Prescription
Diagnostic Assessment	**Beginning Chapter 10**	
	Get Ready for Chapter 10 **SE**, p. 603	Response to Intervention **TE**, p. 603
	Beginning Every Lesson	
	Then, Now, Why? **SE** 5-Minute Check Transparencies	Chapter 0 **SE**, pp. P1 through P45 Concepts and Skills Bank **SE**, pp. 857–867 *Quick Review Math Handbook*
Formative Assessment	**During/After Every Lesson**	
	Check Your Progress **SE**, every example Check Your Understanding **SE** H.O.T. Problems **SE** Spiral Review **SE** Additional Examples **TE** Watch Out! **TE** Step 4, Assess **TE** Chapter 10 Quizzes **CRM**, pp. 57–58 Self-Check Quizzes glencoe.com	**Tier 1 Intervention** Concepts and Skills Bank **SE**, pp. 857–867 Skills Practice **CRM**, Ch. 1–10 glencoe.com **Tier 2 Intervention** Differentiated Instruction **TE** Differentiated Homework Options **TE** Study Guide and Intervention Masters **CRM**, Ch. 1–10 *Quick Review Math Handbook* **Tier 3 Intervention** *Math Triumphs, Alg. 1*
	Mid-Chapter	
	Mid-Chapter Quiz **SE**, p. 629 Mid-Chapter Test **CRM**, p. 59 ExamView Assessment Suite	**Tier 1 Intervention** Concepts and Skills Bank **SE**, pp. 857–867 Skills Practice **CRM**, Ch. 1–10 glencoe.com **Tier 2 Intervention** Study Guide and Intervention Masters **CRM**, Ch. 1–10 *Quick Review Math Handbook* **Tier 3 Intervention** *Math Triumphs, Alg. 1*
	Before Chapter Test	
	Chapter Study Guide and Review **SE**, pp. 656–660 Practice Test **SE**, p. 661 Standardized Test Practice **SE**, pp. 662–665 Chapter Test glencoe.com Standardized Test Practice glencoe.com Vocabulary Review glencoe.com ExamView Assessment Suite	**Tier 1 Intervention** Concepts and Skills Bank **SE**, pp. 857–867 Skills Practice **CRM**, Ch. 1–10 glencoe.com **Tier 2 Intervention** Study Guide and Intervention Masters **CRM**, Ch. 1–10 *Quick Review Math Handbook* **Tier 3 Intervention** *Math Triumphs, Alg. 1*
Summative Assessment	**After Chapter 10**	
	Multiple-Choice Tests, Forms 1, 2A, 2B **CRM**, pp. 61–66 Free-Response Tests, Forms 2C, 2D, 3 **CRM**, pp. 67–72 Vocabulary Test **CRM**, p. 60 Extended Response Test **CRM**, p. 73 Standardized Test Practice **CRM**, pp. 74–76 ExamView Assessment Suite	Study Guide and Intervention Masters **CRM**, Ch. 1–10 *Quick Review Math Handbook* glencoe.com

CHAPTER 10

Differentiated Instruction

Option 1 Reaching All Learners AL OL BL ELL

AUDITORY Discuss with your class the parts of a right triangle that are used to define the sine, cosine, and tangent ratios. As a class, determine which side is opposite and which is adjacent to each of the acute angles of a right triangle. Ask students to refer to the Study Tip on p. 650. Explain how SOH-CAH-TOA (pronounced soa • kuh • TOE • uh) can be used to help them remember the definitions for sine, cosine, and tangent.

VISUAL/SPATIAL Perfect squares can be removed from under a radical sign and written as a square root. For example, because $\sqrt{25} = 5$, $\sqrt{50} = \sqrt{25 \cdot 2} = 5\sqrt{2}$. Suggest that groups make a colorful poster of all the perfect squares from 0 to 400.

LOGICAL One of the conceptually challenging ideas in working with translations of parent graphs is understanding why $y = \sqrt{x - 4}$ moves a graph right (in the positive direction) and $y = \sqrt{x + 4}$ moves a graph left (in the negative direction). Ask students to develop an explanation using examples to show why this happens.

Option 2 Approaching Level AL

On the board, draw several right triangles oriented in different ways. Then have volunteers label the hypotenuse of each triangle. Ask how they know they chose the correct side. The longest side of a right triangle is always the hypotenuse and is always directly opposite the right angle.

Option 3 English Learners ELL

Have students engage in conversations about the Pythagorean Theorem and how it can be used to find a missing side of a right triangle. Provide groups of students with problems similar to Exercises 29 and 31 on p. 633. Have each group provide a solution to their problem that includes diagrams and equations. Then have them present their solution to the entire class.

Option 4 Beyond Level BL

Ask students to choose several square root functions from Lesson 10-1 and graph them on a coordinate grid. Then have students change the equals sign to an inequality. Ask students to modify their graphs so that they now represent the solutions to their square root inequality. For example, the graph of $y = \sqrt{x + 1}$ and $y \geq \sqrt{x + 1}$ is shown below.

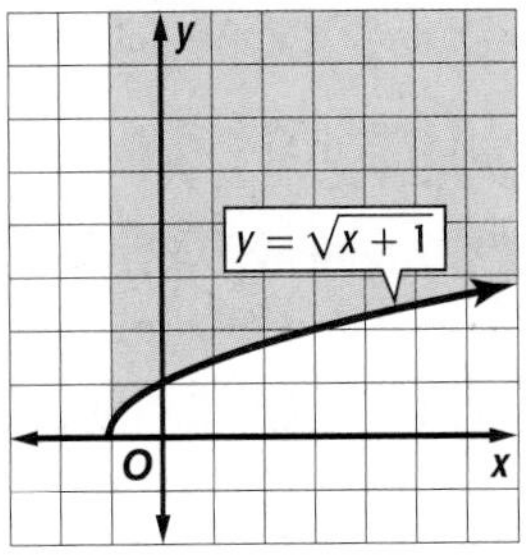

CHAPTER 10 Focus on Mathematical Content

Vertical Alignment

Before Chapter 10

Related Topics before Grade 8

- represent squares and square roots using geometric models
- approximate the values of irrational numbers as they arise from problem situations

Previous Topics from Algebra 1

- use the Distributive Property to simplify algebraic expressions
- solve quadratic equations using algebraic methods
- solve problems involving proportional change

Chapter 10

Related Topics from Algebra 1

- add, subtract, multiply, and simplify radical expressions
- solve radical equations
- use the Pythagorean Theorem, the Distance Formula, the Midpoint Formula, and trigonometric ratios to solve problems
- determine whether two triangles are similar and find the unknown measures of sides of two similar triangles

After Chapter 10

Preparation for Geometry

- use the Pythagorean Theorem
- identify and apply patterns from right triangles to solve meaningful problems
- use formulas for length, slope, and midpoint
- use ratios to solve problems involving similar figures

Preparation for Algebra 2

- formulate equations and inequalities based on square root functions, use a variety of methods to solve them, and analyze the solutions in terms of the situation

Lesson-by-Lesson Preview

10-1 Square Root Functions

A square root function is so named because the function contains a variable inside a square root symbol. The parent function of a square root function is $f(x) = \sqrt{x}$. In order for a square root to be a real number, the radicand cannot be negative. When graphing a square root function, numbers that make the radicand negative must be excluded from the domain of the function. The graph of $y = a\sqrt{x}$ starts at the origin and passes through the point $(1, a)$. If a is positive, the graph is in the first quadrant. If a is negative, the graph is a reflection of the graph of $y = |a|\sqrt{x}$ and lies in the fourth quadrant.

10-2 Simplifying Radical Expressions

When an expression contains a square root, it is called a radical expression. When the radicand, the expression under the square root sign, contains no perfect square factors other than 1, it is said to be in simplest form. Properties of square roots can be used to simplify radical expressions.

- Product Property of Square Roots: For any numbers greater than or equal to 0, the square root of their product is equal to the product of each number's square root. For example, $\sqrt{18} = \sqrt{2 \cdot 3 \cdot 3} = \sqrt{2} \cdot \sqrt{3^2} = 3\sqrt{2}$. Principle square roots are never negative, so absolute value symbols must be used to signify that some results are not negative, for example $\sqrt{x^2} = |x|$.
- Quotient Property of Square Roots: For any number greater than or equal to 0 divided by a number greater than 0, the square root of their quotient is equal to the quotient of each number's square root, for example, $\sqrt{\frac{25}{4}} = \frac{\sqrt{25}}{\sqrt{4}} = \frac{5}{2}$.
- When there is a radical expression in the denominator, the expression is not in simplest form. A process called *rationalizing the denominator* eliminates radicals from a denominator. Since squaring and taking a square root are inverse functions, multiply the numerator and the denominator by the same radical expression so that the radical in the denominator contains a perfect square. For example, $\frac{\sqrt{3}}{\sqrt{5}} = \frac{\sqrt{3}}{\sqrt{5}} \cdot \frac{\sqrt{5}}{\sqrt{5}} = \frac{\sqrt{15}}{5}$.
- If the denominator is an expression containing a radical, multiply by its *conjugate* to rationalize the denominator. For example, if the denominator is in the form $a + \sqrt{b}$, multiply both the numerator and the denominator by $a - \sqrt{b}$.

Radical Functions and Geometry

10-3 Operations with Radical Expressions

- Adding or subtracting expressions with radicals uses the process of combining like terms. For terms to be combined, their radicands must be the same.
- Multiplying two radical expressions with two terms is similar to multiplying binomials. The radicands do not have to be like radicands when multiplying.

10-4 Radical Equations

Equations that contain radicals with variables in the radicands are called *radical equations*. To solve radical equations, the radical must first be isolated on one side of the equation. Then both sides are squared. This will eliminate the radical. Squaring each side sometimes produces *extraneous solutions*, results that are not solutions of the original equation. Be sure to substitute all solutions back into the original equation to check their validity.

10-5 The Pythagorean Theorem

The Pythagorean Theorem states that in a right triangle, the square of the length of the hypotenuse equals the sum of the squares of the lengths of the legs, that is, $c^2 = a^2 + b^2$, where c is the length of the hypotenuse and a and b are the lengths of the legs.

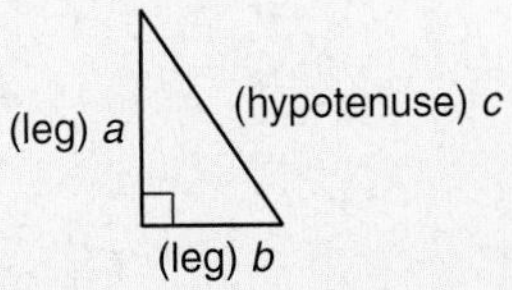

This formula can be used to find the length of any missing side of a right triangle if two sides are known.

Any three nonzero whole numbers that satisfy this equation are known as a *Pythagorean triple*. The triples represent side lengths that always form right triangles. It follows that if three nonzero numbers do not satisfy the Pythagorean Theorem, then a triangle with those lengths will not form a right triangle.

10-6 The Distance and Midpoint Formulas

The Distance Formula, based on the Pythagorean Theorem, can be used to find the distance between two points on a coordinate plane. It states that the distance d between two points with coordinates (x_1, y_1) and (x_2, y_2) is given by $d = \sqrt{(x_2 - x_1)^2 + (y_2 - y_1)^2}$. The *Midpoint Formula*, $M = \left(\frac{x_1 + x_2}{2}, \frac{y_1 + y_2}{2}\right)$, can be used to find the midpoint M of a line segment with endpoints (x_1, y_1) and (x_2, y_2).

10-7 Similar Triangles

Similar triangles are triangles that have the same shape, but are not necessarily the same size.

- All corresponding angles have equal measures.
- All corresponding sides are proportional.

Similar triangles, whose sides have a 1 to 1 ratio of proportionality, have the same size.

To determine whether triangles are similar, check if the corresponding angles have the same measure. If all angle measures cannot be determined, then check the corresponding sides to see if they are proportional.

Proportions can be used to find the lengths of missing sides of similar triangles. You must know the lengths of at least one pair of corresponding sides and the length of the side that corresponds to the missing side's length. Set up the proportion and solve for the missing length.

10-8 Trigonometric Ratios

Trigonometry is the study of relationships among the angles and sides of a right triangle. Ratios comparing the measures of two sides of a right triangle are called *trigonometric ratios*. The three most common trigonometric ratios are sine, cosine, and tangent. These ratios can be used to find the missing side lengths or angle measures. If the lengths of two sides of a right triangle or the length of one side and one acute angle measure are known, then the missing lengths and angle measures can be found. This is referred to as *solving the triangle*.

Professional Development

Targeted professional development has been articulated throughout *Algebra 1*. More quality, customized professional development is available from McGraw-Hill Professional Development. Visit glencoe.com for details on each product.

- **Online Lessons** emphasize the strategies and techniques used to teach Algebra 1. Includes streaming video, interactive pages, and online tools.
- **Video Workshops** allow mentors, coaches, or leadership personnel to facilitate on-site workshops on educational strategies in mathematics and mathematical concepts.
- **MHPD Online** (www.mhpdonline.com) offers online professional development with video clips of instructional strategies, links, student activities, and news and issues in education.
- **Teaching Today** (teachingtoday.glencoe.com) gives secondary teachers practical strategies and materials that inspire excellence and innovation in teaching.

CHAPTER 10 Notes

Chapter Project

Oceans in Motion

Students use what they have learned about indirect measurement, trigonometric ratios, and simplifying radical expressions to work with height and velocity of ocean waves.

- Tell students that tsunamis can have heights as short as 12 inches or as high as 100 feet or more. Ask students if they have any idea how high 100 feet is. Do you think the school's flagpole is 100 feet tall? Let's find out how tall it is.
- Put students into small groups. Ask groups to measure the height, to the nearest inch, of one student in their group. Have groups measure the length of that person's shadow and the flagpole's shadow.
- Have groups write a proportion that compares the heights of the student and the flagpole (x) to the lengths of their shadows. What is the value of x?
- Tell groups that a person is floating in the water, 100 feet from the base of a wave whose height is the same as the height of their school's flagpole. What is the angle, to the nearest degree, that the person must look up to see the top of the wave?
- Tell students that the velocity, V, of a shallow-water wave is equal to $\sqrt{\left(\frac{10 \text{ m}}{\text{sec}^2}\right)d}$, where d is the depth of the water in meters. Ask students to find the velocity of a wave in water as deep as the height of the person they measured in their group. Remind groups to multiply by 0.3048 to convert from feet to meters.

CHAPTER 10 Radical Functions and Geometry

Then

In Chapters 8 and 9, you solved quadratic equations.

Now

In Chapter 10, you will:

- Graph and transform radical functions.
- Simplify, add, subtract, and multiply radical expressions.
- Solve radical equations.
- Use the Pythagorean Theorem.
- Find trigonometric ratios.

IL Learning Standards

7.A.4b Apply formulas in a wide variety of theoretical and practical real-world measurement applications.
8.B.4b Use basic square root functions to describe numerical relationships.

Why?

OCEANS Tsunamis, or large waves, are generated by undersea earthquakes. A radical equation can be used to find the speed of a tsunami in meters per second or the depth of the ocean in meters.

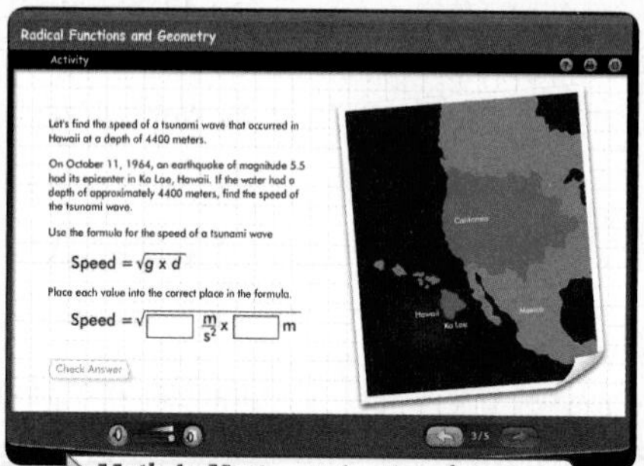

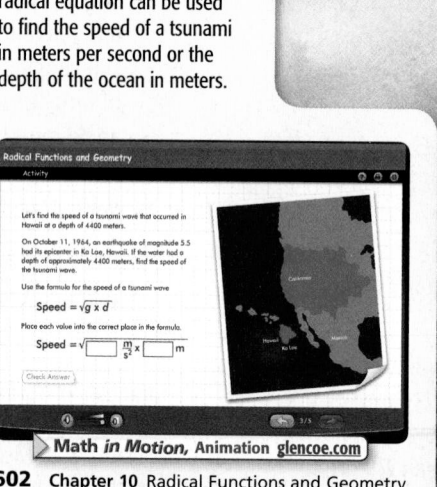

Math *in Motion*, Animation glencoe.com

Key Vocabulary Introduce the key vocabulary in the chapter using the routine below.

Define: A radicand is the expression that is under the radical sign.

Example: $\frac{2ab}{c}$ is the radicand in the expression $\sqrt{\frac{2ab}{c}}$.

Ask: What does the radical sign indicate in regards to the radicand? the square root of the radicand

Get Ready for Chapter 10

Diagnose Readiness You have two options for checking Prerequisite Skills.

Text Option

Take the Quick Check below. Refer to the Quick Review for help.

*Quick*Check

(Used in Lesson 10-2)
Find each square root. If necessary, round to the nearest hundredth. (Lesson 0-2)

1. $\sqrt{82}$ 9.06 **2.** $\sqrt{26}$ 5.10
3. $\sqrt{15}$ 3.87 **4.** $\sqrt{99}$ 9.95

5. SANDBOX Isaac is making a square sandbox with an area of 100 square feet. How long is a side of the sandbox? 10 ft

(Used in Lesson 10-3)
Simplify each expression. (Lesson 1-4)

6. $(21x + 15y) - (9x - 4y)$ $12x + 19y$
7. $13x - 5y + 2y$ $13x - 3y$
8. $(10a - 5b) + (6a + 5b)$ $16a$
9. $6m + 5n + 4 - 3m - 2n + 6$ $3m + 3n + 10$
10. $x + y - 3x - 4y + 2x - 8y$ $-11y$

(Used in Lesson 10-4)
Solve each equation. (Lesson 8-4) 11–14. See margin.

11. $2x^2 - 4x = 0$ **12.** $6x^2 - 5x - 4 = 0$
13. $x^2 - 7x + 10 = 0$ **14.** $2x^2 + 7x - 5 = -1$

15. GEOMETRY The area of the rectangle is 90 square feet. Find x. (Lesson 8-3) 10

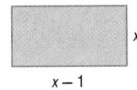

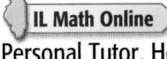

Use cross products to determine whether each pair of ratios forms a proportion. Write *yes* or *no*. (Lesson 2-6) (Used in Lesson 10-7)

16. $\frac{2}{3}$ and $\frac{4}{9}$ no **17.** $\frac{3}{4}$ and $\frac{15}{20}$ yes

18. MAPS On a map, 1 inch = 10 miles. If the distance between cities is 50 miles, how many inches will it be on the map? (Lesson 2-6) 5 in.

*Quick*Review

EXAMPLE 1

Find the square root of $\sqrt{50}$. If necessary, round to the nearest hundredth.

$\sqrt{50} = 7.071067812....$ **Use a calculator.**

To the nearest hundredth, $\sqrt{50} = 7.07$.

EXAMPLE 2

Simplify $3x + 7y - 4x - 8y$.

$3x + 7y - 4x - 8y$
$= (3x - 4x) + (7y - 8y)$ **Combine like terms.**
$= -x - y$ **Simplify.**

EXAMPLE 3

Solve $x^2 - 5x + 6 = 0$.

$x^2 - 5x + 6 = 0$ **Original equation**
$(x - 3)(x - 2) = 0$ **Factor.**
$x - 3 = 0$ or $x - 2 = 0$ **Zero Product Property**
$x = 3$ $x = 2$ **Solve each equation.**

EXAMPLE 4

Use cross products to determine whether $\frac{2}{3}$ and $\frac{8}{12}$ form a proportion.

$\frac{2}{3} \stackrel{?}{=} \frac{8}{12}$ **Write the equation.**
$2(12) \stackrel{?}{=} 3(8)$ **Find the cross products.**
$24 = 24$ ✓ **Simplify.**

They form a proportion.

Online Option

IL Math Online Take a self-check Chapter Readiness Quiz at glencoe.com.

Additional Answers

11. 0, 2
12. $-\frac{1}{2}, \frac{4}{3}$
13. 2, 5
14. $-4, \frac{1}{2}$

Response to Intervention (RtI)

Use the *Quick Check* results and the Intervention Planner chart to help you determine your Response to Intervention. The If-Then statements in the chart below help you decide the appropriate tier of RtI and suggest intervention resources for each tier.

Intervention Planner

Tier 1 — On Level

If students miss about 25% of the exercises or less,

Then choose a resource:

SE Concepts and Skills Bank, p. 862
Lessons 0-2, 1-4, 2-6 and 8-4

CRM Skills Practice, Chapter 1, p. 26, Chapter 2, p. 38, Chapter 8, p. 25

IL Math Online Self-Check Quiz

Tier 2 — Strategic Intervention approaching grade level

If students miss about 50% of the exercises,

Then choose a resource:

CRM Study Guide and Intervention, Chapter 1, p. 24, Chapter 2, p. 36, Chapter 8, p. 23

Quick Review Math Handbook

IL Math Online Extra Examples, Personal Tutor, Homework Help

Tier 3 — Intensive Intervention 2 or more grades below level

If students miss about 75% of the exercises,

Then use *Math Triumphs, Alg. 1*

IL Math Online Extra Examples, Personal Tutor, Homework Help, Review Vocabulary

FOLDABLES® Study Organizer

Dinah Zike's Foldables®

Focus As students read and study this chapter, they show examples and write notes about radical functions and geometry in their booklet.

Teach Have students make and label their Foldables as illustrated. Before beginning, have them skim the chapter and write down any problems from the chapter that they think are challenging on the right-hand page of the problems' corresponding lessons. As students work through the chapter, ascertain that students are able to find the answers to their problems.

When to Use It Encourage students to add to their Foldables as they work through the chapter and to use them to review for the chapter test.

Differentiated Instruction

CRM Student-Built Glossary, pp. 1–2 Students should complete the chart by providing a definition of each term and an example as they progress through Chapter 10. This study tool can also be used to review for the chapter test.

Get Started on Chapter 10

You will learn several new concepts, skills, and vocabulary terms as you study Chapter 10. To get ready, identify important terms and organize your resources. You may wish to refer to **Chapter 0** to review prerequisite skills.

FOLDABLES® Study Organizer

Radical Functions and Geometry Make this Foldable to help you organize your Chapter 10 notes about radical functions and geometry. Begin with four sheets of grid paper.

1. **Fold** in half along the width.

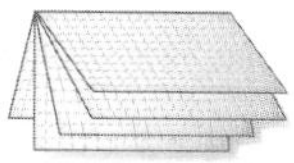

2. **Staple** along the fold.

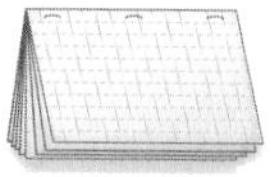

3. **Turn** the fold to the left and write the title of the chapter on the front. On each left-hand page of the booklet, write the title of a lesson from the chapter.

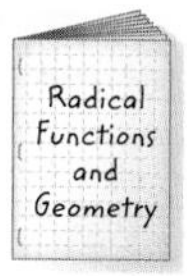

New Vocabulary

English		Español
radicand	• p. 605 •	radicando
radical function	• p. 605 •	función radicales
conjugate	• p. 614 •	conjugado
radical equations	• p. 624 •	ecuaciones radicales
hypotenuse	• p. 630 •	hipotenusa
legs	• p. 630 •	catetos
converse	• p. 631 •	recíproco
midpoint	• p. 638 •	punto medio
similar triangles	• p. 642 •	semejantes
cosine	• p. 649 •	coseno
tangent	• p. 649 •	tangente
trigonometry	• p. 649 •	trigonometría
inverse cosine	• p. 651 •	coseno inverso
inverse sine	• p. 651 •	seno inverso
inverse tangent	• p. 651 •	tangente inverse

Review Vocabulary

FOIL method • p. 448 • metodo FOIL to multiply two binomials, find the sum of the products of the First terms, Outer terms, Inner terms, and Last terms

perfect square • p. P7 • cuadrado perfecto a number with a square root that is a rational number

proportion • p. 111 • proporcion an equation of the form $\frac{a}{b} = \frac{c}{d}$ stating that two ratios are equivalent

$$\frac{a}{b} \times \frac{c}{d}$$
$$ad = bc$$

Multilingual eGlossary glencoe.com

IL Math Online glencoe.com
- Study the chapter online
- Explore **Math in Motion**
- Get extra help from your own **Personal Tutor**
- Use **Extra Examples** for additional help
- Take a **Self-Check Quiz**
- **Review Vocabulary** in fun ways

604 Chapter 10 Radical Functions and Geometry

Additional Answers (Lesson 10-1, Check Your Progress)

1A. $D = \{x \mid x \geq 0\}, R = \{y \mid y \geq 0\}$

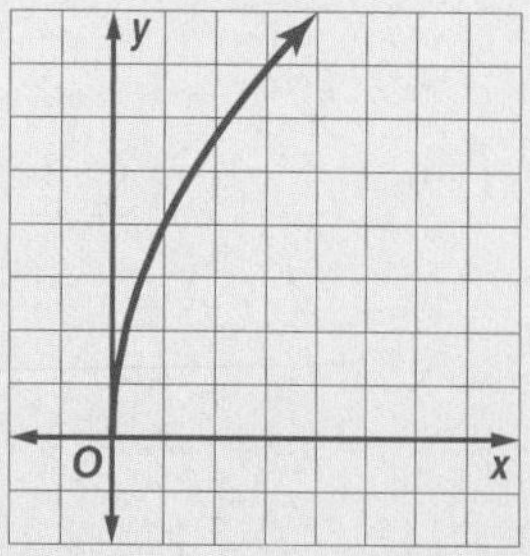

1B. $D = \{x \mid x \geq 0\}, R = \{y \mid y \geq 0\}$

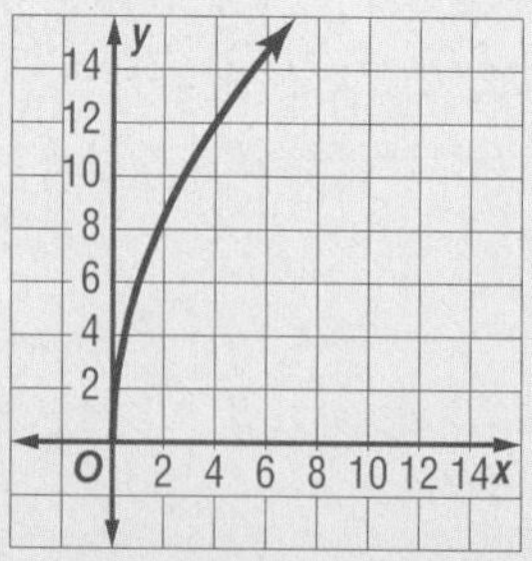

10-1 Square Root Functions

Why?

Scientists use sounds of whales to track their movements. The distance to a whale can be found by relating time to the speed of sound in water.

The speed of sound in water can be described by the *square root function* $c = \sqrt{\frac{E}{d}}$, where E represents the bulk modulus elasticity of the water and d represents the density of the water.

Then
You solved quadratic equations by using the Quadratic Formula. (Lesson 9-5)

Now
- Graph and analyze dilations of radical functions.
- Graph and analyze reflections and translations of radical functions.

IL Learning Standards
7.B.4 Estimate and measure the magnitude and directions of physical quantities using rulers, protractors and other scientific instruments including timers, calculators and computers.
8.B.4b Use the basic functions of absolute value, **square root**, linear, quadratic and step **to describe numerical relationships.**

New Vocabulary
square root function
radical function
radicand

IL Math Online
glencoe.com
- Extra Examples
- Personal Tutor
- Self-Check Quiz
- Homework Help

Dilations of Radical Functions A **square root function** contains the square root of a variable. Square root functions are a type of **radical function**. The expression under the radical sign is called the **radicand**. For a square root to be a real number, the radicand cannot be negative. Values that make the radicand negative are not included in the domain.

Key Concept — Square Root Function (For Your FOLDABLE)

Parent function: $f(x) = \sqrt{x}$
Type of graph: curve
Domain: $\{x \mid x \geq 0\}$
Range: $\{y \mid y \geq 0\}$

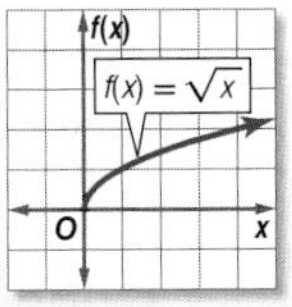

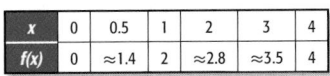

EXAMPLE 1 Dilation of the Square Root Function

Graph $f(x) = 2\sqrt{x}$. State the domain and range.

Step 1 Make a table.

x	0	0.5	1	2	3	4
f(x)	0	≈1.4	2	≈2.8	≈3.5	4

Step 2 Plot points. Draw a smooth curve.

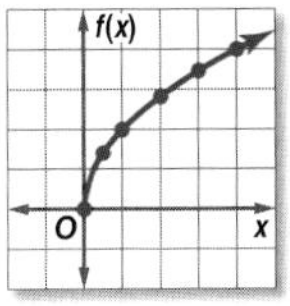

The domain is $\{x \mid x \geq 0\}$, and the range is $\{y \mid y \geq 0\}$.

Check Your Progress **1A–1B. See margin.**

1A. $g(x) = 4\sqrt{x}$ **1B.** $h(x) = 6\sqrt{x}$

Personal Tutor glencoe.com

1 FOCUS

Vertical Alignment

Before Lesson 10-1
Solve quadratic equations by using the Quadratic Formula.

Lesson 10-1
Graph and analyze vertical stretches of radical functions. Graph and analyze reflections and translations of radical functions.

After Lesson 10-1
Solve radical equations.

2 TEACH

Scaffolding Questions

Have students read the *Why?* section of the lesson.

Ask:
- What part of the equation indicates that it is a square root function? the radical symbol, which represents a square root
- If the number under the square root symbol cannot be negative, what must be true about $\frac{E}{d}$? The quotient must be greater than or equal to zero.
- If d is constant and E increases, what happens to c? It increases.

Lesson 10-1 Resources

Resource	Approaching-Level	On-Level	Beyond-Level	English Learners
Teacher Edition		• Differentiated Instruction, pp. 607, 610	• Differentiated Instruction, pp. 607, 610	
Chapter Resource Masters	• Study Guide and Intervention, pp. 5–6 • Skills Practice, p. 7 • Practice, p. 8 • Word Problem Practice, p. 9	• Study Guide and Intervention, pp. 5–6 • Skills Practice, p. 7 • Practice, p. 8 • Word Problem Practice, p. 9 • Enrichment, p. 10	• Practice, p. 8 • Word Problem Practice, p. 9 • Enrichment, p. 10	• Study Guide and Intervention, pp. 5–6 • Skills Practice, p. 7 • Practice, p. 8
Transparencies	• 5-Minute Check Transparency 10-1	• 5-Minute Check Transparency 10-1	• 5-Minute Check Transparency 10-1	• 5-Minute Check Transparency 10-1
Other	• Study Notebook	• Study Notebook	• Study Notebook	• Study Notebook

Dilations of Radical Functions

Example 1 shows how to graph a dilation of a radical function.

Formative Assessment

Use the Check Your Progress exercises after each example to determine students' understanding of concepts.

Additional Example

1 Graph $y = \frac{1}{2}\sqrt{x}$. State the domain and range.
$D = \{x \mid x \geq 0\}; R = \{y \mid y \geq 0\}$

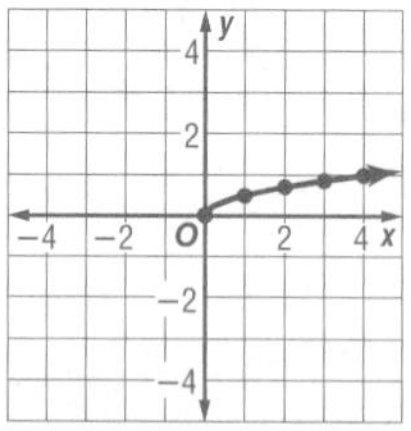

Additional Examples also in Interactive Classroom PowerPoint® Presentations

IWB INTERACTIVE WHITEBOARD READY

Reflections and Translations of Radical Functions

Examples 2 and 3 show how to graph reflections and translations of radical functions. **Example 4** shows how to solve a real-world problem involving a radical function. **Example 5** shows how to graph a radical function that has more than one transformation.

Additional Example

2 Graph $y = -\frac{1}{2}\sqrt{x}$. Compare to the parent graph. State the domain and range. vertical compression of $y = \sqrt{x}$ and reflection over the x-axis; $D = \{x \mid x \geq 0\}; R = \{y \mid y \leq 0\}$

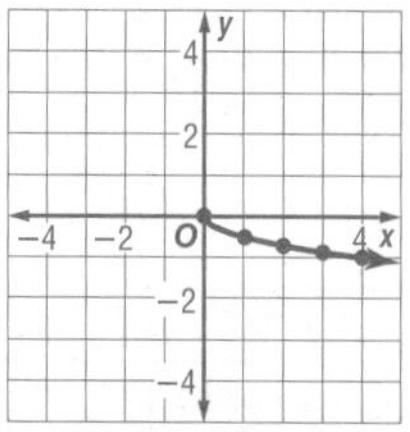

Reflections and Translations of Radical Functions Recall that when the value of a is negative in the quadratic function $f(x) = ax^2$, the graph of the parent function is reflected across the x-axis.

StudyTip

Graphing Radical Functions Choose perfect squares for x-values that will result in coordinates that are easy to plot.

Key Concept Graphing $y = a\sqrt{x + h} + c$ — For Your FOLDABLE

Step 1 Draw the graph of $y = a\sqrt{x}$. The graph starts at the origin and passes through $(1, a)$. If $a > 0$, the graph is in quadrant I. If $a < 0$, the graph is reflected across the x-axis and is in quadrant IV.

Step 2 Translate the graph $|c|$ units up if $c > 0$ and down if $c < 0$.

Step 3 Translate the graph $|h|$ units left if $h > 0$ and right if $h < 0$.

EXAMPLE 2 Reflection of the Square Root Function

Graph $y = -3\sqrt{x}$. Compare to the parent graph. State the domain and range.

Make a table of values. Then plot the points on a coordinate system and draw a smooth curve that connects them.

x	0	0.5	1	4
y	0	≈−2.1	−3	−6

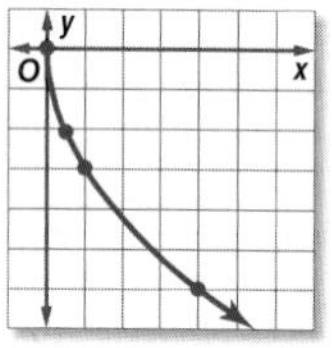

Notice that the graph is in the 4th quadrant. It is obtained by stretching the graph of $y = \sqrt{x}$ vertically and then reflecting across the x-axis. The domain is $\{x \mid x \geq 0\}$, and the range is $\{y \mid y \leq 0\}$.

Check Your Progress 2A–2B. See Ch. 10 Answer Appendix.

2A. $y = -2\sqrt{x}$ **2B.** $y = -4\sqrt{x}$

Personal Tutor glencoe.com

StudyTip

Translating Radical Functions If $c > 0$, a radical function $f(x) = \sqrt{x - c}$ is a horizontal translation c units to the right. $f(x) = \sqrt{x + c}$ is a horizontal translation c units to the left.

EXAMPLE 3 Translation of the Square Root Function

Graph each function. Compare to the parent graph. State the domain and range.

a. $g(x) = \sqrt{x} + 1$

x	0	0.5	1	4	9
y	0	≈1.7	2	3	4

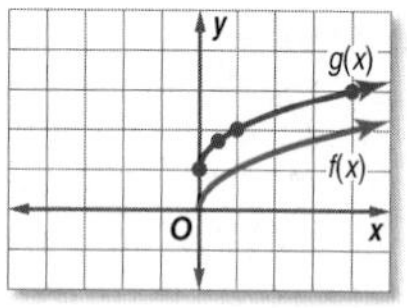

Notice that the values of $g(x)$ are 1 greater than those of $f(x) = \sqrt{x}$. This is a vertical translation 1 unit up from the parent function. The domain is $\{x \mid x \geq 0\}$, and the range is $\{y \mid y \geq 1\}$.

b. $h(x) = \sqrt{x - 2}$

x	2	3	4	6
y	0	1	≈1.4	2

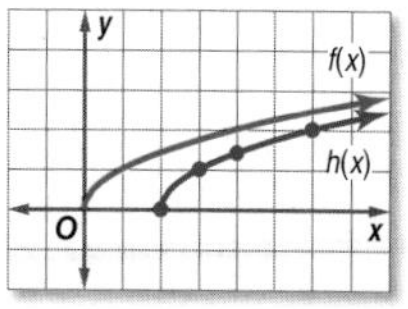

This is a horizontal translation 2 units to the right of the parent function. The domain is $\{x \mid x \geq 2\}$, and the range is $\{y \mid y \geq 0\}$.

Focus on Mathematical Content

Square Root Functions Square root functions are a type of radical function. The square root function $y = \sqrt{x}$ is the inverse function of $y = x^2$ for $x \geq 0$. It can also be represented as $y = x^{\frac{1}{2}}$. To graph a square root function, exclude any values from the domain that result in a negative radicand.

Tips for New Teachers

Sense-Making Show students that the limits on the domain and range of a square root function are also representative of the inital point of the graph of the function, where x is the minimum value in the domain and y is the minimum value in the range.

Check Your Progress 3A–3B. See Ch. 10 Answer Appendix.

3A. $g(x) = \sqrt{x} - 4$ **3B.** $h(x) = \sqrt{x + 3}$

Personal Tutor glencoe.com

Physical phenomena such as motion can be modeled by radical functions. Often these functions are transformations of the parent square root function.

Real-World Link

Approximately 39 million cars cross the Golden Gate Bridge in San Francisco each year.

Source: San Francisco Convention and Visitors Bureau

Real-World EXAMPLE 4 Analyze a Radical Function

BRIDGES The Golden Gate Bridge is about 67 meters above the water. The velocity v of a freely falling object that has fallen h meters is given by $v = \sqrt{2gh}$, where g is the constant 9.8 meters per second squared. Graph the function. If an object is dropped from the bridge, what is its velocity when it hits the water?

Use a graphing calculator to graph the function.

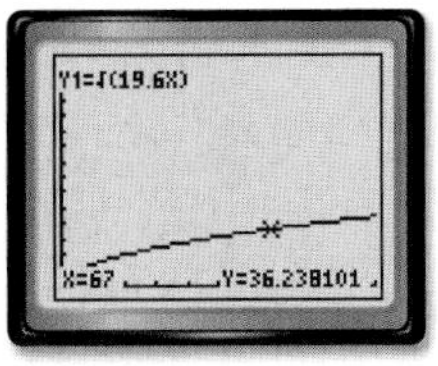

To find the velocity of the object, substitute 67 meters for h.

$v = \sqrt{2gh}$	Original function
$= \sqrt{2(9.8)(67)}$	$g = 9.8$ and $h = 67$
$= \sqrt{1313.2}$	Simplify.
≈ 36.2 m/s	Use a calculator.

The velocity of the object is about 36.2 meters per second after dropping 67 meters.

Check Your Progress

4. Use the graph above to estimate the initial height of an object if it is moving at 20 meters per second when it hits the water. ≈20 m

Personal Tutor glencoe.com

Transformations such as reflections, translations, and dilations can be combined in one equation.

EXAMPLE 5 Transformations of the Square Root Function

Graph $y = -2\sqrt{x} + 1$, and compare to the parent graph. State the domain and range.

x	0	1	4	9
y	1	−1	−3	−5

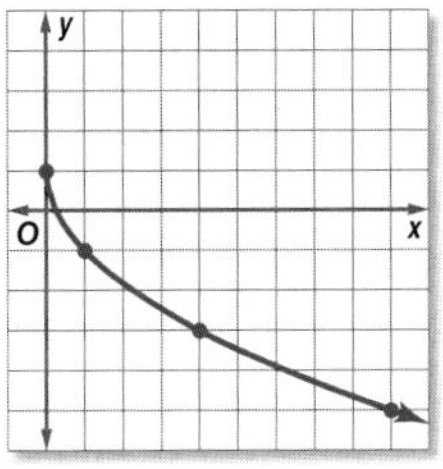

This graph is the result of a vertical stretch of the graph of $y = \sqrt{x}$ followed by a reflection across the x-axis, and then a translation 1 unit up. The domain is $\{x \mid x \geq 0\}$, and the range is $\{y \mid y \leq 1\}$.

Check Your Progress

5A. $y = \frac{1}{2}\sqrt{x} - 1$ **5B.** $y = -2\sqrt{x - 1}$

Personal Tutor glencoe.com

5A. compressed vertically and translated down 1; $D = \{x \mid x \geq 0\}$, $R = \{y \mid y \geq -1\}$

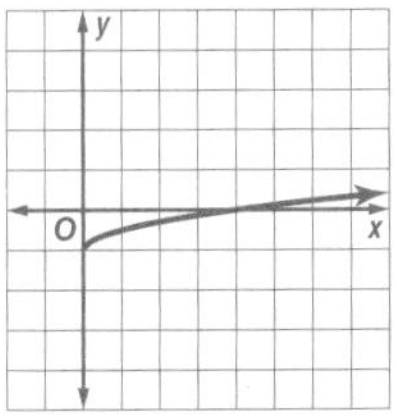

5B. stretched vertically and reflected across the x-axis, and translated right 1; $D = \{x \mid x \geq 1\}$, $R = \{y \mid y \leq 0\}$

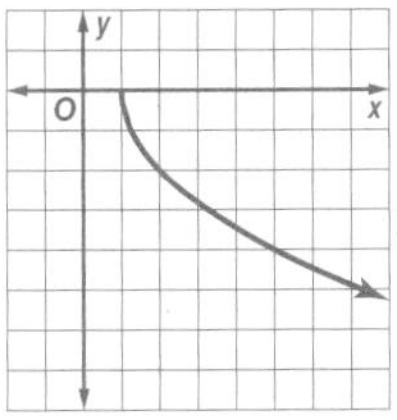

Additional Examples

3 Graph each function. Compare to the parent graph. State the domain and range.

a. $g(x) = \sqrt{x} - 1$ vertical translation of $y = \sqrt{x}$ one unit down; $D = \{x \mid x \geq 0\}$; $R = \{g(x) \mid g(x) \geq -1\}$

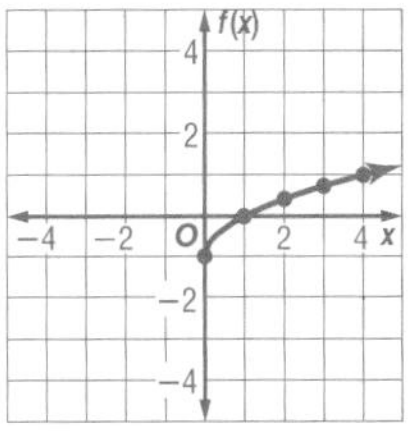

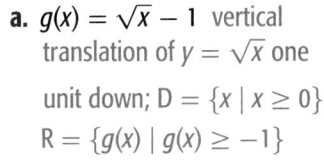

b. $h(x) = \sqrt{x + 1}$ horizontal translation of $y = \sqrt{x}$ one unit left; $D = \{x \mid x \geq -1\}$; $R = \{h(x) \mid h(x) \geq 0\}$

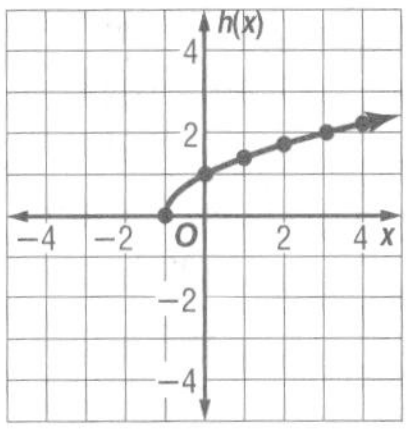

4 **TSUNAMIS** The speed s of a tsunami, in meters per second, is given by the function $s = 3.1\sqrt{d}$, where d is the depth of the ocean water in meters. Graph the function. If a tsunami is traveling in water 26 meters deep, what is its speed? about 15.8 m/s

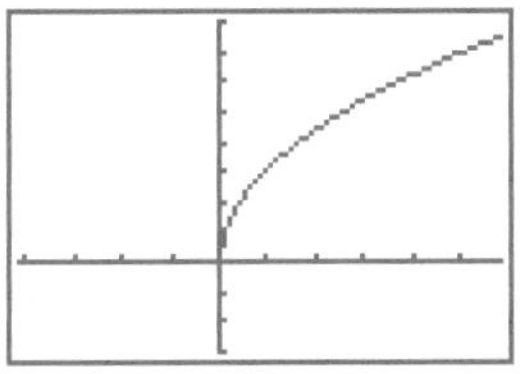

[−5, 5] scl: 1 by [−4, 7] scl: 1

Differentiated Instruction

OL BL

If students demonstrate an understanding of the translations of the graphs of square root functions,

Then have students work in pairs or groups to graph square root functions such as $y = \sqrt{x^2 + 2}$, $y = \sqrt{9 - x^2}$, and $y = \sqrt{x^2 - 2x}$. Have them state the domain and range of the functions and describe the graphs. Ask how they might use a graph of the quadratic in the radicand to find the domain and range of the function.

TEACH with TECH

INTERACTIVE WHITEBOARD Drag a coordinate grid onto the board, and draw a graph of $y = \sqrt{x}$. Write an example of a radical function. Have a student drag the parent to graph to the position created by the example.

Additional Example

5 Graph $y = 3\sqrt{x-2}$ and compare to the parent graph. State the domain and range.
vertical stretch of $y = \sqrt{x}$ translation 2 units right; D = $\{x \mid x \geq 2\}$; R = $\{y \mid y \geq 0\}$

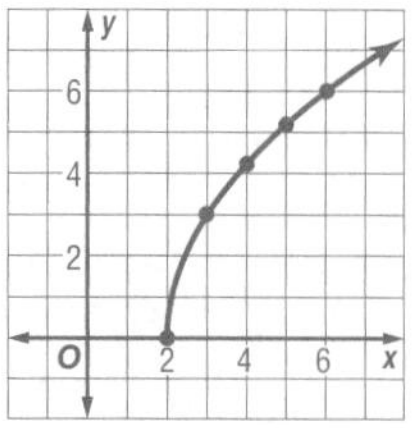

3 PRACTICE

Formative Assessment

Use Exercises 1–13 to check for understanding.

Use the chart at the bottom of this page to customize assignments for your students.

Additional Answers

9.

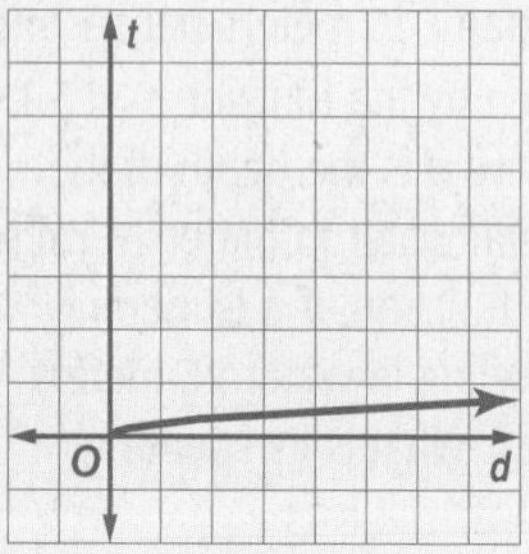

34a.

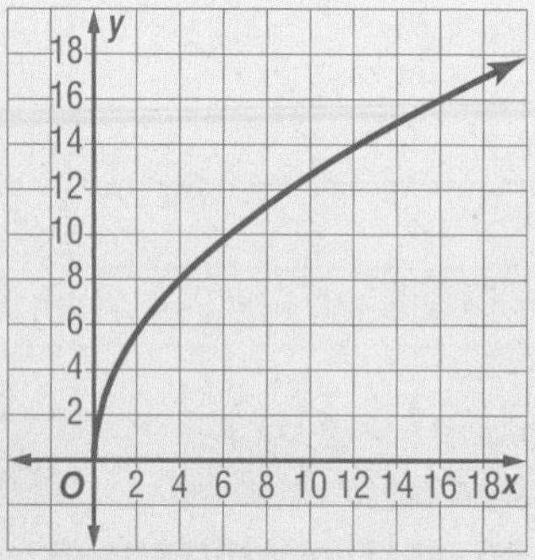

41.

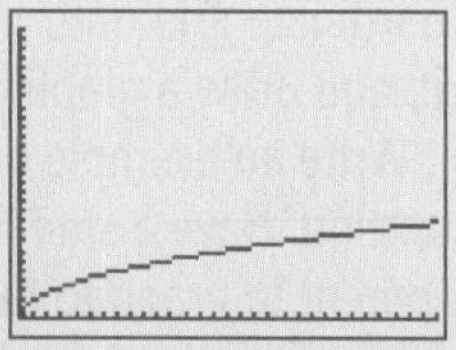

[0, 28] scl: 1 by [0, 28] scl: 1

Check Your Understanding

Examples 1 and 3 pp. 605–606

Graph each function. Compare to the parent graph. State the domain and range. **1–8. See Ch. 10 Answer Appendix.**

1. $y = 3\sqrt{x}$
2. $y = -5\sqrt{x}$
3. $y = \frac{1}{3}\sqrt{x}$
4. $y = -\frac{1}{2}\sqrt{x}$
5. $y = \sqrt{x} + 3$
6. $y = \sqrt{x} - 2$
7. $y = \sqrt{x+2}$
8. $y = \sqrt{x-3}$

Example 4 p. 607

9. See margin for graph.

9. **FREE FALL** The time in seconds that it takes an object to fall a distance d is given by the function $t = \frac{1}{4}\sqrt{d}$ (assuming zero air resistance). Graph the function, and state the domain and range. **D = $\{d \mid d \geq 0\}$, R = $\{t \mid t \geq 0\}$**

Example 5 p. 607

Graph each function, and compare to the parent graph. State the domain and range. **10–13. See Ch. 10 Answer Appendix.**

10. $y = \frac{1}{2}\sqrt{x} + 2$
11. $y = -\frac{1}{4}\sqrt{x} - 1$
12. $y = -2\sqrt{x+1}$
13. $y = 3\sqrt{x-2}$

Practice and Problem Solving

● = **Step-by-Step Solutions** begin on page R12.
Extra Practice begins on page 815.

Examples 1 and 3 pp. 605–606

Graph each function. Compare to the parent graph. State the domain and range. **14–33. See Ch. 10 Answer Appendix.**

14. $y = 5\sqrt{x}$
15. $y = \frac{1}{2}\sqrt{x}$
16. $y = -\frac{1}{3}\sqrt{x}$
17. $y = 7\sqrt{x}$
18. $y = -\frac{1}{4}\sqrt{x}$
19. $y = -\sqrt{x}$
20. $y = -\frac{1}{5}\sqrt{x}$
21. $y = -7\sqrt{x}$
22. $y = \sqrt{x} + 2$
23. $y = \sqrt{x} + 4$
24. $y = \sqrt{x} - 1$
25. $y = \sqrt{x} - 3$
26. $y = \sqrt{x} + 1.5$
27. $y = \sqrt{x} - 2.5$
28. $y = \sqrt{x+4}$
29. $y = \sqrt{x-4}$
30. $y = \sqrt{x+1}$
31. $y = \sqrt{x-0.5}$
32. $y = \sqrt{x+5}$
33. $y = \sqrt{x-1.5}$

Example 4 p. 607

34. **GEOMETRY** The perimeter of a square is given by the function $P = 4\sqrt{A}$, where A is the area of the square.
    a. Graph the function. **See margin.**
    b. Determine the perimeter of a square with an area of 225 m^2. **60 m**
    c. When will the perimeter and the area be the same value?
    When the sides of the square have length 4 m, the perimeter is 16 m.

Example 5 p. 607

Graph each function, and compare to the parent graph. State the domain and range. **35–40. See Ch. 10 Answer Appendix.**

35. $y = -2\sqrt{x} + 2$
36. $y = -3\sqrt{x} - 3$
37. $y = \frac{1}{2}\sqrt{x+2}$
38. $y = -\sqrt{x-1}$
39. $y = \frac{1}{4}\sqrt{x-1} + 2$
40. $y = \frac{1}{2}\sqrt{x-2} + 1$

B

41. **ENERGY** An object has kinetic energy when it is in motion. The velocity in meters per second of an object of mass m kilograms with an energy of E joules is given by the function $v = \sqrt{\frac{2E}{m}}$. Use a graphing calculator to graph the function that represents the velocity of a basketball with a mass of 0.6 kilogram. **See margin.**

Differentiated Homework Options

Level	Assignment	Two-Day Option	
AL Basic	14–40, 47, 49–71	15–39 odd, 53–56	14–40 even, 47, 49–52, 57–71
OL Core	15–39 odd, 41–44, 47, 49–71	14–40, 53–56	41–44, 47, 49–52, 57–71
BL Advanced	41–65, (optional: 66–71)		

Real-World Link

Wind farms harness the kinetic energy of the wind and convert it to usable power. A turbine that is designed to power a house can have a rotor with a diameter of 50 feet.

Source: American Wind Energy Association

42. GEOMETRY The radius of a circle is given by $r = \sqrt{\frac{A}{\pi}}$, where A is the area of the circle.

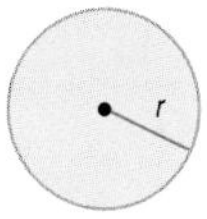

a. Graph the function. **See Ch. 10 Answer Appendix.**

b. Use a graphing calculator to determine the radius of a circle that has an area of 27 in^2. **about 2.9 in.**

43. SPEED OF SOUND The speed of sound in air is determined by the temperature of the air. The speed c in meters per second is given by $c = 331.5\sqrt{1 + \frac{t}{273.15}}$, where t is the temperature of the air in degrees Celsius.

a. Use a graphing calculator to graph the function.

b. How fast does sound travel when the temperature is 55°C? **about 363.3 m/s**

c. How is the speed of sound affected when the temperature increases by 10°?

44. MULTIPLE REPRESENTATIONS In this problem, you will explore the relationship between the graphs of square root functions and parabolas.

a. **GRAPHICAL** Graph $y = x^2$ on a coordinate system.

b. **ALGEBRAIC** Write a piecewise-defined function to describe the graph of $y^2 = x$ in each quadrant.

c. **GRAPHICAL** On the same coordinate system, graph $y = \sqrt{x}$ and $y = -\sqrt{x}$.

d. **GRAPHICAL** On the same coordinate system, graph $y = x$. Plot the points (2, 4), (4, 2), and (1, 1).

e. **ANALYTICAL** Compare the graph of the parabola to the graphs of the square root functions. **c–e. See Ch. 10 Answer Appendix.**

43a.

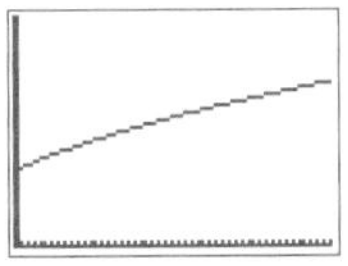

[0, 1000] scl: 20 by [0, 1000] scl: 0.1

43c. When t is 65°C, c is about 368.8 m/s, so a 10-degree increase results in an increase in speed of about 5.5 m/s.

44a.

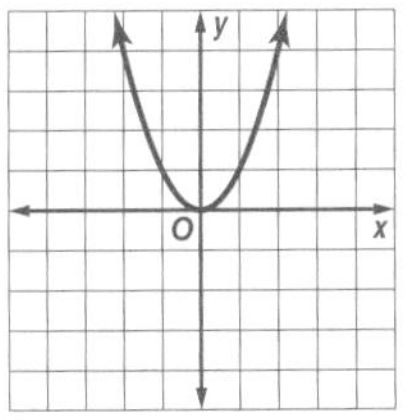

44b. $y = \begin{cases} \sqrt{x} & x \geq 0 \\ -\sqrt{x} & x \geq 0 \end{cases}$

H.O.T. Problems

Use Higher-Order Thinking Skills

45–46. See Ch. 10 Answer Appendix.

CHALLENGE Determine whether each statement is *true* or *false*. Provide an example or counterexample to support your answer. **48. Sample answer: $y = -\sqrt{x - 2} + 5$**

45. Numbers in the domain of a radical function will always be nonnegative.

46. Numbers in the range of a radical function will always be nonnegative.

47. **REASONING** Write a radical function that translates $y = \sqrt{x}$ four units to the right. Graph the function. **$y = \sqrt{x - 4}$; See Ch. 10 Answer Appendix for graph.**

48. **CHALLENGE** Write a radical function with a domain of all real numbers greater than or equal to 2 and a range of all real numbers less than or equal to 5.

49. **WHICH DOES NOT BELONG?** Identify the equation that does not belong. Explain.

$y = 3\sqrt{x}$	$y = 0.7\sqrt{x}$	$y = \sqrt{x} + 3$	$y = \frac{\sqrt{x}}{6}$

See Ch. 10 Answer Appendix.

50. **OPEN ENDED** Write a function that is a reflection, translation, and a dilation of the parent graph $y = \sqrt{x}$. **See Ch. 10 Answer Appendix.**

51. **REASONING** If the range of the function $y = a\sqrt{x}$ is $\{y \mid y \leq 0\}$, what can you conclude about the value of a? Explain your reasoning. **See Ch. 10 Answer Appendix.**

52. **WRITING IN MATH** Compare and contrast the graphs of $f(x) = \sqrt{x} + 2$ and $g(x) = \sqrt{x + 2}$. **See Ch. 10 Answer Appendix.**

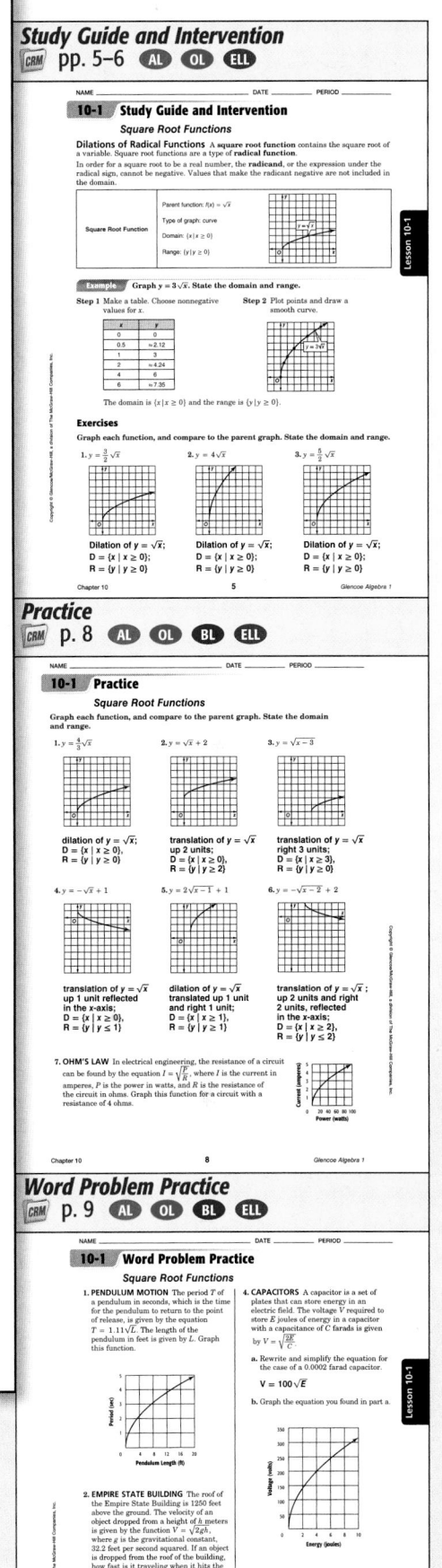

Multiple Representations In Exercise 44, students use graphs and a piecewise-defined function to compare quadratic and square-root functions.

Study Guide and Intervention
CRM pp. 5–6 AL OL ELL

NAME ______ DATE ______ PERIOD ______

10-1 Study Guide and Intervention

Square Root Functions

Dilations of Radical Functions A **square root function** contains the square root of a variable. Square root functions are a type of **radical function**.

In order for a square root to be a real number, the **radicand**, or the expression under the radical sign, cannot be negative. Values that make the radicand negative are not included in the domain.

Square Root Function — Parent function: $f(x) = \sqrt{x}$; Type of graph: curve; Domain: $\{x \mid x \geq 0\}$; Range: $\{y \mid y \geq 0\}$

Example Graph $y = 3\sqrt{x}$. State the domain and range.

Step 1 Make a table. Choose nonnegative values for x.

x	y
0	0
0.5	≈2.12
1	3
2	≈4.24
4	6
6	≈7.35

Step 2 Plot points and draw a smooth curve.

The domain is $\{x \mid x \geq 0\}$ and the range is $\{y \mid y \geq 0\}$.

Exercises

Graph each function, and compare to the parent graph. State the domain and range.

1. $y = \frac{3}{2}\sqrt{x}$ — Dilation of $y = \sqrt{x}$; D = $\{x \mid x \geq 0\}$; R = $\{y \mid y \geq 0\}$
2. $y = 4\sqrt{x}$ — Dilation of $y = \sqrt{x}$; D = $\{x \mid x \geq 0\}$; R = $\{y \mid y \geq 0\}$
3. $y = \frac{5}{2}\sqrt{x}$ — Dilation of $y = \sqrt{x}$; D = $\{x \mid x \geq 0\}$; R = $\{y \mid y \geq 0\}$

Chapter 10 5 Glencoe Algebra 1

Practice
CRM p. 8 AL OL BL ELL

NAME ______ DATE ______ PERIOD ______

10-1 Practice

Square Root Functions

Graph each function, and compare to the parent graph. State the domain and range.

1. $y = \frac{4}{3}\sqrt{x}$ — dilation of $y = \sqrt{x}$; D = $\{x \mid x \geq 0\}$, R = $\{y \mid y \geq 0\}$
2. $y = \sqrt{x} + 2$ — translation of $y = \sqrt{x}$ up 2 units; D = $\{x \mid x \geq 0\}$, R = $\{y \mid y \geq 2\}$
3. $y = \sqrt{x - 3}$ — translation of $y = \sqrt{x}$ right 3 units; D = $\{x \mid x \geq 3\}$, R = $\{y \mid y \geq 0\}$
4. $y = -\sqrt{x} + 1$ — translation of $y = \sqrt{x}$ up 1 unit reflected in the x-axis; D = $\{x \mid x \geq 0\}$, R = $\{y \mid y \leq 1\}$
5. $y = 2\sqrt{x - 1} + 1$ — dilation of $y = \sqrt{x}$ translated up 1 unit and right 1 unit; D = $\{x \mid x \geq 1\}$, R = $\{y \mid y \geq 1\}$
6. $y = -\sqrt{x - 2} + 2$ — translation of $y = \sqrt{x}$; up 2 units and right 2 units, reflected in the x-axis; D = $\{x \mid x \geq 2\}$, R = $\{y \mid y \leq 2\}$

7. **OHM'S LAW** In electrical engineering, the resistance of a circuit can be found by the equation $I = \sqrt{\frac{P}{R}}$, where I is the current in amperes, P is the power in watts, and R is the resistance of the circuit in ohms. Graph this function for a circuit with a resistance of 4 ohms.

Chapter 10 8 Glencoe Algebra 1

Word Problem Practice
CRM p. 9 AL OL BL ELL

NAME ______ DATE ______ PERIOD ______

10-1 Word Problem Practice

Square Root Functions

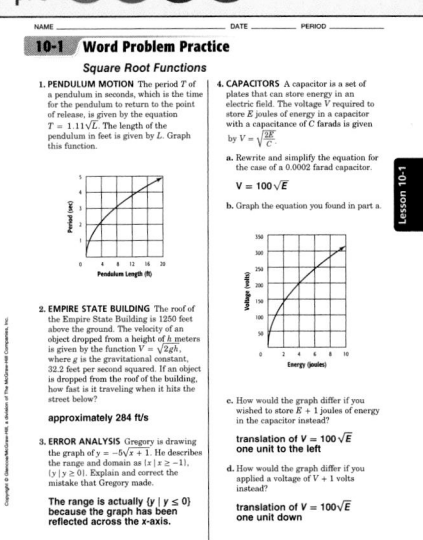

1. **PENDULUM MOTION** The period T of a pendulum in seconds, which is the time for the pendulum to return to the point of release, is given by the equation $T = 1.11\sqrt{L}$. The length of the pendulum in feet is given by L. Graph this function.

2. **EMPIRE STATE BUILDING** The roof of the Empire State Building is 1250 feet above the ground. The velocity of an object dropped from a height of h meters is given by the function $V = \sqrt{2gh}$, where g is the gravitational constant, 32.2 feet per second squared. If an object is dropped from the roof of the building, how fast is it traveling when it hits the street below?
approximately 284 ft/s

3. **ERROR ANALYSIS** Gregory is drawing the graph of $y = -5\sqrt{x} + 1$. He describes the range and domain as $\{x \mid x \geq -1\}$, $\{y \mid y \geq 0\}$. Explain and correct the mistake that Gregory made.
The range is actually $\{y \mid y \leq 0\}$ because the graph has been reflected across the x-axis.

4. **CAPACITORS** A capacitor is a set of plates that can store energy in an electric field. The voltage V required to store E joules of energy in a capacitor with a capacitance of C farads is given by $V = \sqrt{\frac{2E}{C}}$.
a. Rewrite and simplify the equation for the case of a 0.0002 farad capacitor. **$V = 100\sqrt{E}$**
b. Graph the equation you found in part a.
c. How would the graph differ if you wished to store $E + 1$ joules of energy in the capacitor instead? **translation of $V = 100\sqrt{E}$ one unit to the left**
d. How would the graph differ if you applied a voltage of $V + 1$ volts instead? **translation of $V = 100\sqrt{E}$ one unit down**

Chapter 10 9 Glencoe Algebra 1

Enrichment
CRM p. 10 OL BL

NAME ______ DATE ______ PERIOD ______

10-1 Enrichment

Cubic Root Functions

A **cubic root function** contains the cubic root of a variable. The **cubic root** of a number x are the numbers y that satisfy the equation $y \cdot y \cdot y = x$ (or, alternatively, $y = \sqrt[3]{x}$). Unlike square root functions, cubic root functions return real numbers when the radicand is negative.

Example Graph $y = \sqrt[3]{x}$.

Step 1 Make a table.

x	y
−5	−1.71
−3	−1.44
−1	−1
0	0
1	1
3	1.44
5	1.71

Step 2 Plot points and draw a smooth curve.

Exercises

Graph each function, and compare to the parent graph.

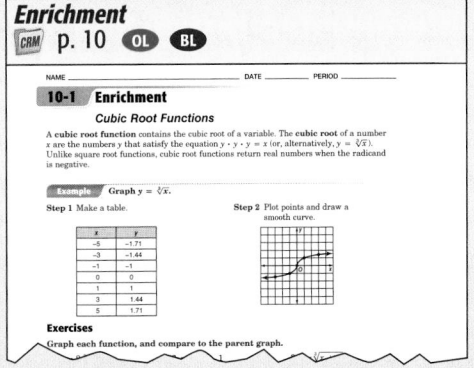

4 ASSESS

Name the Math Give students a square root function such as $y = \sqrt{x - 5}$ and have them explain how to find the domain and range of the function.

Additional Answers

57. 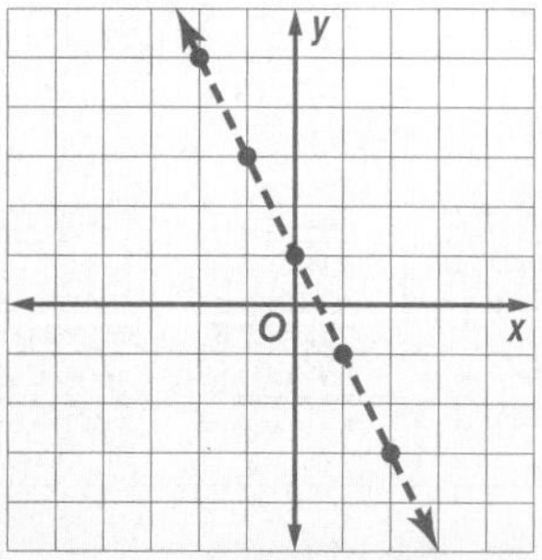

linear

58. 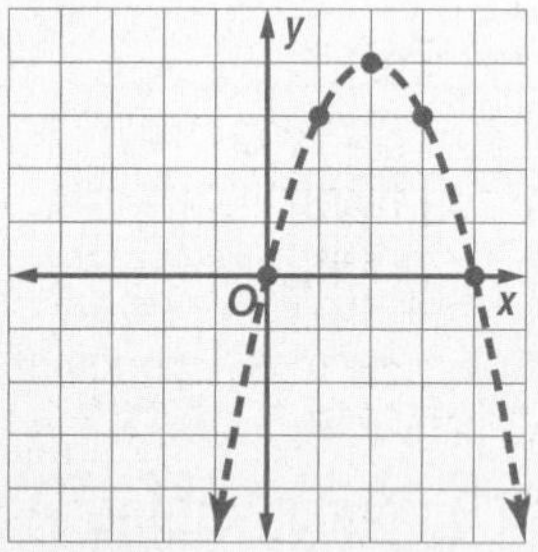

quadratic

59. 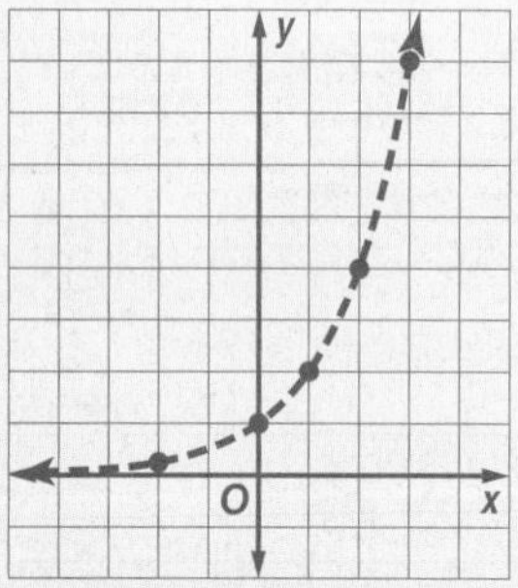

exponential

60. 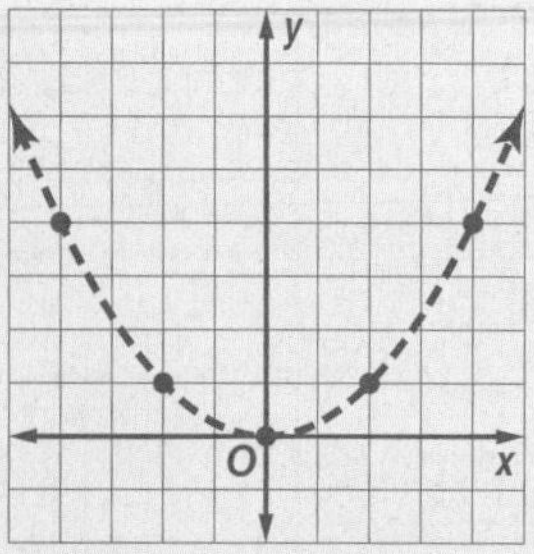

quadratic

PSAE PRACTICE 8.11.08, 8.11.06, 8.11.07, 7.11.03

53. 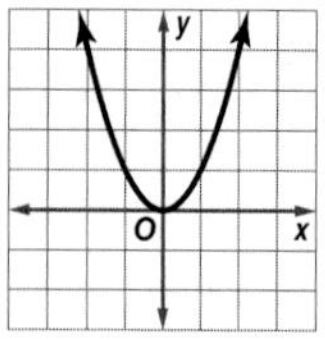

Which function *best* represents the graph? A

A $y = x^2$ C $y = \sqrt{x}$

B $y = 2^x$ D $y = x$

54. The statement "$x < 10$ and $3x - 2 \geq 7$" is true when x is equal to what? H

F 0 H 8

G 2 J 12

55. Which of the following is the equation of a line parallel to $y = -\frac{1}{2}x + 3$ and passing through $(-2, -1)$? D

A $y = \frac{1}{2}x$ C $y = -\frac{1}{2}x + 2$

B $y = 2x + 3$ D $y = -\frac{1}{2}x - 2$

56. SHORT RESPONSE A landscaper needs to mulch 6 rectangular flower beds that are 8 feet by 4 feet and 4 circular flower beds each with a radius of 3 feet. One bag of mulch covers 25 square feet. How many bags of mulch are needed to cover the flower beds?
13 bags of mulch

Spiral Review

Graph each set of ordered pairs. Determine whether the ordered pairs represent a *linear* function, a *quadratic* function, or an *exponential* function. (Lesson 9-9) **57–60. See margin.**

57. $\{(-2, 5), (-1, 3), (0, 1), (1, -1), (2, -3)\}$

58. $\{(0, 0), (1, 3), (2, 4), (3, 3), (4, 0)\}$

59. $\left\{\left(-2, \frac{1}{4}\right), (0, 1), (1, 2), (2, 4), (3, 8)\right\}$

60. $\{(-4, 4), (-2, 1), (0, 0), (2, 1), (4, 4)\}$

Find the next three terms in each geometric sequence. (Lesson 9-8)

61. 5, 20, 80, 320, … 1280, 5120, 20,480

62. $-4, 2, -1, \frac{1}{2}, \ldots$ $-\frac{1}{4}, \frac{1}{8}, -\frac{1}{16}$

63. $\frac{1}{8}, \frac{1}{4}, \frac{1}{2}, 1, \ldots$ 2, 4, 8

64. HEALTH Aida exercises every day by walking and jogging at least 3 miles. Aida walks at a rate of 4 miles per hour and jogs at a rate of 8 miles per hour. Suppose she has exactly one half-hour to exercise today. (Lesson 6-8) **a–b. See Ch. 10 Answer Appendix.**

a. Draw a graph showing the possible amounts of time she can spend walking and jogging.

b. List three possible solutions.

65. NUTRITION Determine whether the graph shows a *positive*, a *negative*, or *no* correlation. If there is a positive or negative correlation, describe its meaning in the situation. (Lesson 4-5)
Positive; as the number of grams of fat increases, the amount of Calories increases.

Fast-Food Choices

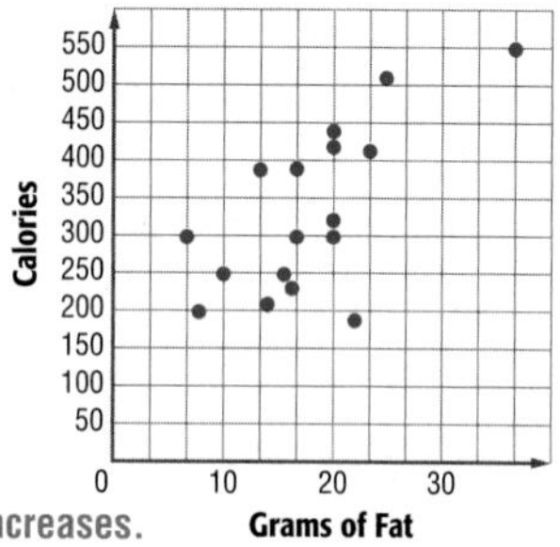

Skills Review

70. 3 • 3 • 5 • 5 • a • a • a • b • b • c

Factor each monomial completely. (Lesson 8-1)

66. $28n^3$ 2 • 2 • 7 • n • n • n

67. $-33a^2b$ −3 • 11 • a • a • b

68. $150rt$ 2 • 3 • 5 • 5 • r • t

69. $-378nq^2r^2$ −2 • 3 • 3 • 3 • 7 • n • q • q • r • r

70. $225a^3b^2c$

71. $-160x^2y^4$ −2 • 2 • 2 • 2 • 2 • 5 • x • x • y • y • y • y

Differentiated Instruction OL BL

Extension Write several square root functions on the board and have students state the domain and range of each. Examples may include $y = \sqrt{3x + 2}$, $y = -5\sqrt{\frac{x + 2}{8}}$, or $y = \sqrt{\frac{1}{x + 2}}$. Encourage students to graph the functions to check the domain and range. $D = \left\{x \mid x \geq -\frac{2}{3}\right\}$; $R = \{y \mid y \geq 0\}$; $D = \{x \mid x \geq -2\}$; $R = \{y \mid y \leq 0\}$; $D = \{x \mid x > -2\}$; $R = \{y \mid y > 0\}$

EXTEND
10-1
Graphing Technology Lab: Graphing Square Root Functions

IL Math Online glencoe.com
- Other Calculator Keystrokes
- Graphing Technology Personal Tutor

IL Learning Standards — **8.B.4b Use the basic functions of** absolute value, **square root**, linear, quadratic and step **to describe numerical relationships.**

For a square root to be a real number, the radicand cannot be negative. When graphing a radical function, determine when the radicand would be negative and exclude those values from the domain.

ACTIVITY 1 Parent Function

Graph $y = \sqrt{x}$.

Enter the equation in the Y= list.

KEYSTROKES: [Y=] [2nd] [√‾] [X,T,θ,n] [ )] [GRAPH]

1A. Examine the graph. What is the domain of the function? $\{x \mid x \geq 0\}$

1B. What is the range of the function? $\{y \mid y \geq 0\}$

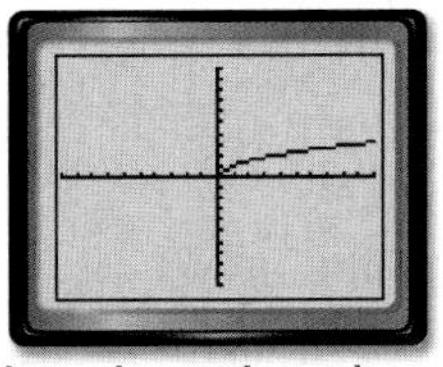

[−10, 10] scl: 1 by [−10, 10] scl: 1

ACTIVITY 2 Translation of Parent Function

Graph $y = \sqrt{x - 2}$.

Enter the equation in the Y= list.

KEYSTROKES: [Y=] [2nd] [√‾] [X,T,θ,n] [−] 2 [ )] [GRAPH]

2A. What are the domain and range of the function? $\{x \mid x \geq 2\}$; $\{y \mid y \geq 0\}$

2B. How does the graph of $y = \sqrt{x - 2}$ compare to the graph of the parent function $y = \sqrt{x}$? It is translated 2 units to the right.

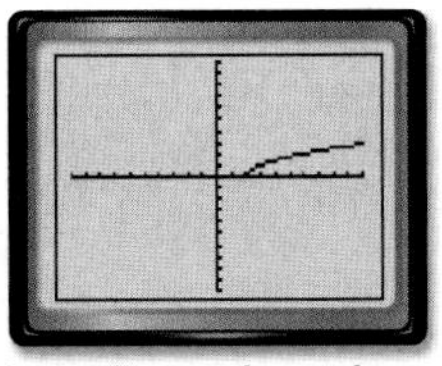

[−10, 10] scl: 1 by [−10, 10] scl: 1

Exercises

Graph each equation, and sketch the graph on your paper. State the domain and range. Describe how the graph differs from that of the parent function $y = \sqrt{x}$. 1–8. See Ch. 10 Answer Appendix.

1. $y = \sqrt{x - 1}$ **2.** $y = \sqrt{x + 3}$ **3.** $y = \sqrt{x} - 2$ **4.** $y = \sqrt{-x}$

5. $y = -\sqrt{x}$ **6.** $y = \sqrt{2x}$ **7.** $y = \sqrt{2 - x}$ **8.** $y = \sqrt{x - 3} + 2$

9. Does $x = y^2$ represent a function? Explain your reasoning.

10. Does $x^2 + y^2 = 4$ determine y as a function of x? Explain.

11. Does $x^2 + y^2 = 2$ determine y as a function of x? Explain.

9. No; you must consider the graph of $y = \sqrt{x}$ and the graph of $y = -\sqrt{x}$. This graph fails the vertical line test.
10. No; there are both positive and negative values of y for most values of x.
11. No; there are both positive and negative values of y for most values of x.

Write a function with a graph that translates $y = \sqrt{x}$ in each way.

12. Shifted 4 units to the left $y = \sqrt{x + 4}$

13. Shifted up 7 units $y = \sqrt{x} + 7$

14. Shifted down 6 units $y = \sqrt{x} - 6$

15. Shifted 5 units to the right and up 3 units $y = \sqrt{x - 5} + 3$

EXTEND
10-1
Lesson Notes

1 FOCUS

Objective Use a graphing calculator to investigate the graphs of square root functions.

Materials for Each Student

- TI-83/84 Plus or other graphing calculator
- grid paper

Teaching Tip

Before starting this lab, familiarize students with the [ZoomFit] option in the [Zoom] menu. This option lets the calculator automatically zoom the viewing window to fit the graph. Suggest that students use this option to get a better view of the shape of the graph of a square root function.

2 TEACH

Working in Cooperative Groups

Have students work in groups of two or three, mixing abilities, to complete Activities 1 and 2.

- Have students use the value operation from the CALCULATE menu to find the value of the function at different x-values. Press [2nd] [CALC] 1 and then enter an x-value. Students should see that the value of the function is the square root of the radicand of the function.

Practice Have students complete Exercises 1–5.

3 ASSESS

Formative Assessment

Use Exercise 8 to assess whether students understand how to graph square root functions and can describe how the graph differs from the parent function.

From Concrete to Abstract

Use Exercise 15 to assess whether students can write a function given a description of the graph of the function.

10-2 Lesson Notes

1 FOCUS

Vertical Alignment

Before Lesson 10-2
Simplify radicals.

Lesson 10-2
Simplify radical expressions by using the Product Property of Square Roots.
Simplify radical expressions by using the Quotient Property of Square Roots.

After Lesson 10-2
Add, subtract, and multiply radical expressions.

2 TEACH

Scaffolding Questions

Have students read the *Why?* section of the lesson.

Ask:

- Which is the radical expression in the equation for the diameter of a steel cable? $\sqrt{\frac{W}{8}}$
- What does the radical sign in the equation mean? You must find the square root of the value under the radical sign.
- Based on what you know about the order of operations, when do you think you should simplify the radical expression? Simplify the expression under the radical sign before finding the square root.

10-2 Simplifying Radical Expressions

Then
You simplified radicals. (Lesson 0-2)

Now
- Simplify radical expressions by using the Product Property of Square Roots.
- Simplify radical expressions by using the Quotient Property of Square Roots.

IL Learning Standards
7.B.4 Estimate and measure the magnitude and directions of physical quantities using rulers, protractors and other scientific instruments including timers, calculators and computers.

New Vocabulary
radical expression
rationalizing the denominator
conjugate

IL Math Online
glencoe.com
- Extra Examples
- Personal Tutor
- Self-Check Quiz
- Homework Help

Why?

The Sunshine Skyway Bridge across Tampa Bay in Florida, is supported by 21 steel cables, each 9 inches in diameter.

To find the diameter a steel cable should have to support a given weight, you can use the equation $d = \sqrt{\frac{w}{8}}$, where d is the diameter of the cable in inches and w is the weight in tons.

Product Property of Square Roots A **radical expression** contains a radical, such as a square root. Recall the expression under the radical sign is called the radicand. A radicand is in simplest form if the following three conditions are true.

- No radicands have perfect square factors other than 1.
- No radicands contain fractions.
- No radicals appear in the denominator of a fraction.

The following property can be used to simplify square roots.

Key Concept | **Product Property of Square Roots** | For Your FOLDABLE

Words For any nonnegative real numbers a and b, the square root of ab is equal to the square root of a times the square root of b.

Symbols $\sqrt{ab} = \sqrt{a} \cdot \sqrt{b}$, if $a \geq 0$ and $b \geq 0$

Examples $\sqrt{4 \cdot 9} = \sqrt{36}$ or 6 $\qquad \sqrt{4 \cdot 9} = \sqrt{4} \cdot \sqrt{9} = 2 \cdot 3$ or 6

EXAMPLE 1 Simplify Square Roots

Simplify $\sqrt{80}$.

$\sqrt{80} = \sqrt{2 \cdot 2 \cdot 2 \cdot 2 \cdot 5}$ — Prime factorization of 80

$= \sqrt{2^2} \cdot \sqrt{2^2} \cdot \sqrt{5}$ — Product Property of Square Roots

$= 2 \cdot 2 \cdot \sqrt{5}$ or $4\sqrt{5}$ — Simplify.

Check Your Progress

1A. $\sqrt{54}$ $3\sqrt{6}$ **1B.** $\sqrt{180}$ $6\sqrt{5}$

Personal Tutor glencoe.com

Lesson 10-2 Resources

Resource	Approaching-Level	On-Level	Beyond-Level	English Learners
Teacher Edition	• Differentiated Instruction, p. 614	• Differentiated Instruction, p. 614	• Differentiated Instruction, p. 617	
Chapter Resource Masters	• Study Guide and Intervention, pp. 11–12 • Skills Practice, p. 13 • Practice, p. 14 • Word Problem Practice, p. 15	• Study Guide and Intervention, pp. 11–12 • Skills Practice, p. 13 • Practice, p. 14 • Word Problem Practice, p. 15 • Enrichment, p. 16	• Practice, p. 14 • Word Problem Practice, p. 15 • Enrichment, p. 16	• Study Guide and Intervention, pp. 11–12 • Skills Practice, p. 13 • Practice, p. 14
Transparencies	• 5-Minute Check Transparency 10–2	• 5-Minute Check Transparency 10–2	• 5-Minute Check Transparency 10–2	• 5-Minute Check Transparency 10–2
Other	• Study Notebook	• Study Notebook	• Study Notebook	• Study Notebook

612 Chapter 10 Radical Functions and Geometry

EXAMPLE 2 Multiply Square Roots

Simplify $\sqrt{2} \cdot \sqrt{14}$.

$\sqrt{2} \cdot \sqrt{14} = \sqrt{2} \cdot \sqrt{2} \cdot \sqrt{7}$ — **Product Property of Square Roots**

$= \sqrt{2^2} \cdot \sqrt{7}$ or $2\sqrt{7}$ — **Product Property of Square Roots**

Check Your Progress

2A. $\sqrt{5} \cdot \sqrt{10}$ $5\sqrt{2}$

2B. $\sqrt{6} \cdot \sqrt{8}$ $4\sqrt{3}$

Personal Tutor glencoe.com

Consider the expression $\sqrt{x^2}$. It may seem that $x = \sqrt{x^2}$, but when finding the principal square root of an expression containing variables, you have to be sure that the result is not negative. Consider $x = -3$.

$\sqrt{x^2} \stackrel{?}{=} x$

$\sqrt{(-3)^2} \stackrel{?}{=} -3$ — **Replace x with -3.**

$\sqrt{9} \stackrel{?}{=} -3$ — **$(-3)^2 = 9$**

$3 \neq -3$ — **$\sqrt{9} = 3$**

Notice in this case, if the right hand side of the equation were $|x|$, the equation would be true. For expressions where the exponent of the variable inside a radical is even and the simplified exponent is odd, you must use absolute value.

$\sqrt{x^2} = |x|$ $\quad \sqrt{x^3} = |x|\sqrt{x}$ $\quad \sqrt{x^4} = x^2$ $\quad \sqrt{x^6} = |x^3|$

EXAMPLE 3 Simplify a Square Root with Variables

Simplify $\sqrt{90x^3y^4z^5}$.

$\sqrt{90x^3y^4z^5} = \sqrt{2 \cdot 3^2 \cdot 5 \cdot x^3 \cdot y^4 \cdot z^5}$ — **Prime factorization**

$= \sqrt{2} \cdot \sqrt{3^2} \cdot \sqrt{5} \cdot \sqrt{x^2} \cdot \sqrt{x} \cdot \sqrt{y^4} \cdot \sqrt{z^4} \cdot \sqrt{z}$ — **Product Property**

$= \sqrt{2} \cdot 3 \cdot \sqrt{5} \cdot |x| \cdot \sqrt{x} \cdot y^2 \cdot z^2 \cdot \sqrt{z}$ — **Simplify.**

$= 3y^2z^2|x|\sqrt{10xz}$ — **Simplify.**

Check Your Progress

3A. $\sqrt{32r^2k^4t^5}$ $4|r|k^2t^2\sqrt{2t}$

3B. $\sqrt{56xy^{10}z^5}$ $2|y^5|z^2\sqrt{14xz}$

Personal Tutor glencoe.com

Quotient Property of Square Roots To divide square roots and simplify radical expressions, you can use the Quotient Property of Square Roots.

ReadingMath

Fractions in the Radicand The expression $\sqrt{\frac{a}{b}}$ is read *the square root of a over b, or the square root of the quantity of a over b.*

Key Concept — Quotient Property of Square Roots

For Your FOLDABLE

Words For any real numbers a and b, where $a \geq 0$ and $b > 0$, the square root of $\frac{a}{b}$ is equal to the square root of a divided by the square root of b.

Symbols $\sqrt{\frac{a}{b}} = \frac{\sqrt{a}}{\sqrt{b}}$

Tips for New Teachers

Intervention In order to simplify square roots with the Product Property of Square Roots, students need to be able to find the prime factorization of the radicand. Take a few minutes to review finding prime factorizations so that students can focus on learning the new concept rather than trying to recall earlier material.

Product Property of Square Roots

Example 1 shows how to simplify a radical expression in which the radicand is not a perfect square. **Example 2** shows how to multiply square roots. **Example 3** shows how to simplify a square root that contains variables.

Formative Assessment

Use the Check Your Progress exercises after each example to determine students' understanding of concepts.

Additional Examples

1. Simplify $\sqrt{52}$. $2\sqrt{13}$
2. Simplify $\sqrt{2} \cdot \sqrt{24}$. $4\sqrt{3}$
3. Simplify $\sqrt{45a^4b^5c^6}$. $3a^2b^2|c^3|\sqrt{5b}$

Additional Examples also in Interactive Classroom PowerPoint® Presentations

IWB INTERACTIVE WHITEBOARD READY

Focus on Mathematical Content

Product Property of Square Roots The Product Property can be used to simplify radical expressions. For all nonnegative numbers, the product of each square root equals the square root of the products.

TEACH with TECH

WIKI On your secure classroom wiki have half of the students show and explain how they simplified a radical expression. Have different students show how to simplify products and quotients of radicals. When all agree, post on the secure classroom website for additional reference.

Quotient Property of Square Roots

Example 4 is a test item that shows how to rationalize the denominator of a radical expression to eliminate radicals from the denominator. **Example 5** shows how to use conjugates to rationalize the denominator of a radical expression.

Focus on Mathematical Content

Quotient Property of Square Roots The Quotient Property can be used to simplify radical expressions. For nonnegative dividends and positive divisors, the square root of a quotient is equal to the quotient of the principal square roots of the numbers.

Additional Examples

4 **STANDARDIZED TEST PRACTICE** Which expression is equivalent to $\frac{\sqrt{3n}}{\sqrt{8}}$? D

A $\frac{\sqrt{3n}}{8}$ C $\frac{\sqrt{6n}}{2}$

B $\frac{\sqrt{3n}}{4}$ D $\frac{\sqrt{6n}}{4}$

5 Simplify $\frac{2}{4-\sqrt{5}}$. $\frac{8+2\sqrt{5}}{11}$

You can use the properties of square roots to **rationalize the denominator** of a fraction with a radical. This involves multiplying the numerator and denominator by a factor that eliminates radicals in the denominator.

Test-Taking Tip

Simplify Look at the radicand to see if it can be simplified first. This may make your computations simpler.

PSAE EXAMPLE 4 6.11.02

Which expression is equivalent to $\sqrt{\frac{35}{15}}$?

A $\frac{5\sqrt{21}}{15}$ B $\frac{\sqrt{21}}{3}$ C $\frac{\sqrt{525}}{15}$ D $\frac{\sqrt{35}}{15}$

Read the Test Item

The radical expression needs to be simplified.

Solve the Test Item

$\sqrt{\frac{35}{15}} = \frac{\sqrt{35}}{\sqrt{15}}$ **Quotient Property of Square Roots**

$= \frac{\sqrt{35}}{\sqrt{15}} \cdot \frac{\sqrt{15}}{\sqrt{15}}$ **Multiply by $\frac{\sqrt{15}}{\sqrt{15}}$.**

$= \frac{\sqrt{525}}{15}$ **Product Property of Square Roots**

$= \frac{\sqrt{3 \cdot 5 \cdot 5 \cdot 7}}{15}$ **Prime factorization**

$= \frac{5\sqrt{21}}{15}$ or $\frac{\sqrt{21}}{3}$ The correct choice is B.

Check Your Progress

4. Simplify $\frac{\sqrt{6y}}{\sqrt{12}}$. $\frac{\sqrt{2y}}{2}$

Personal Tutor glencoe.com

Binomials of the form $a\sqrt{b} + c\sqrt{d}$ and $a\sqrt{b} - c\sqrt{d}$, where a, b, c, and d are rational numbers, are called **conjugates**. For example, $2 + \sqrt{7}$ and $2 - \sqrt{7}$ are conjugates. The product of two conjugates is a rational number and can be found using the pattern for the difference of squares.

EXAMPLE 5 Use Conjugates to Rationalize a Denominator

Simplify $\frac{3}{5+\sqrt{2}}$.

$\frac{3}{5+\sqrt{2}} = \frac{3}{5+\sqrt{2}} \cdot \frac{5-\sqrt{2}}{5-\sqrt{2}}$ **The conjugate of $5+\sqrt{2}$ is $5-\sqrt{2}$.**

$= \frac{3(5-\sqrt{2})}{5^2-(\sqrt{2})^2}$ **$(a-b)(a+b) = a^2 - b^2$**

$= \frac{15-3\sqrt{2}}{25-2}$ or $\frac{15-3\sqrt{2}}{23}$ **$(\sqrt{2})^2 = 2$**

Check Your Progress

Simplify each expression.

5A. $\frac{3}{2+\sqrt{2}}$ $\frac{6-3\sqrt{2}}{2}$ **5B.** $\frac{7}{3-\sqrt{7}}$ $\frac{21+7\sqrt{7}}{2}$

Personal Tutor glencoe.com

Differentiated Instruction AL OL

If students need further practice with conjugates,

Then have students use their calculators to show that using conjugates produces equivalent expressions in Example 5. Have students show that $\frac{3}{5+\sqrt{2}}$, $\frac{3(5-\sqrt{2})}{(5+\sqrt{2})(5-\sqrt{2})}$, and $\frac{15-3\sqrt{2}}{23}$ are equivalent. They should find that each expression is about 0.4677.

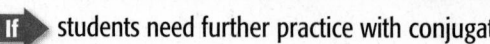

Check Your Understanding

Examples 1–3 pp. 612–613

Simplify each expression.

1. $\sqrt{24}$ $2\sqrt{6}$
2. $3\sqrt{16}$ 12
3. $2\sqrt{25}$ 10
4. $\sqrt{10} \cdot \sqrt{14}$ $2\sqrt{35}$
5. $\sqrt{3} \cdot \sqrt{18}$ $3\sqrt{6}$
6. $3\sqrt{10} \cdot 4\sqrt{10}$ 120
7. $\sqrt{60x^4y^7}$ $2x^2|y^3|\sqrt{15y}$
8. $\sqrt{88m^3p^2r^5}$ $2|m||p|r^2\sqrt{22mr}$
9. $\sqrt{99ab^5c^2}$ $3b^2|c|\sqrt{11ab}$

Example 4 p. 614

10. **MULTIPLE CHOICE** Which expression is equivalent to $\sqrt{\frac{45}{10}}$? D

A $\frac{5\sqrt{2}}{10}$ B $\frac{\sqrt{450}}{10}$ C $\frac{\sqrt{50}}{10}$ D $\frac{3\sqrt{2}}{2}$

Example 5 p. 614

Simplify each expression.

11. $\frac{3}{3+\sqrt{5}}$ $\frac{9-3\sqrt{5}}{4}$
12. $\frac{5}{2-\sqrt{6}}$ $\frac{10+5\sqrt{6}}{-2}$
13. $\frac{2}{1-\sqrt{10}}$ $\frac{2+2\sqrt{10}}{-9}$
14. $\frac{1}{4+\sqrt{12}}$ $\frac{2-\sqrt{3}}{2}$
15. $\frac{4}{6-\sqrt{7}}$ $\frac{24+4\sqrt{7}}{29}$
16. $\frac{6}{5+\sqrt{11}}$ $\frac{15-3\sqrt{11}}{7}$

Practice and Problem Solving

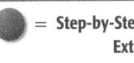

● = Step-by-Step Solutions begin on page R12.
Extra Practice begins on page 815.

Examples 1 and 3 pp. 612–613

Simplify each expression.

17. $\sqrt{52}$ $2\sqrt{13}$
18. $\sqrt{56}$ $2\sqrt{14}$
19. $\sqrt{72}$ $6\sqrt{2}$
20. $3\sqrt{18}$ $9\sqrt{2}$
21. $\sqrt{243}$ $9\sqrt{3}$
22. $\sqrt{245}$ $7\sqrt{5}$
23. $\sqrt{5} \cdot \sqrt{10}$ $5\sqrt{2}$
24. $\sqrt{10} \cdot \sqrt{20}$ $10\sqrt{2}$
25. $3\sqrt{8} \cdot 2\sqrt{7}$ $12\sqrt{14}$
26. $4\sqrt{2} \cdot 5\sqrt{8}$ 80
27. $3\sqrt{25t^2}$ $15|t|$
28. $5\sqrt{81q^5}$ $45q^2\sqrt{q}$
29. $\sqrt{28a^2b^3}$ $2|a||b|\sqrt{7b}$
30. $\sqrt{75qr^3}$ $5|r|\sqrt{3qr}$
31. $7\sqrt{63m^3p}$ $21|m|\sqrt{7mp}$
32. $4\sqrt{66g^2h^4}$ $4|g|h^2\sqrt{66}$
33. $\sqrt{2ab^2} \cdot \sqrt{10a^5b}$
34. $\sqrt{4c^3d^3} \cdot \sqrt{8c^3d}$

33. $2|a^3||b|\sqrt{5b}$
34. $4|c^3||d^2|\sqrt{2}$

35. **ROLLER COASTER** The velocity v of a roller coaster in feet per second at the bottom of a hill can be approximated by $v = \sqrt{64h}$, where h is the height of the hill in feet.
    a. Simplify the equation. $v = 8\sqrt{h}$
    b. Determine the velocity of a roller coaster at the bottom of a 134-foot hill. about 92.6 ft/s

36. **FIREFIGHTING** When fighting a fire, the velocity v of water being pumped into the air is modeled by the function $v = \sqrt{2hg}$, where h represents the maximum height of the water and g represents the acceleration due to gravity (32 ft/s^2).
    a. Solve the function for h. $h = \frac{v^2}{2g}$
    b. The Hollowville Fire Department needs a pump that will propel water 80 feet into the air. Will a pump advertised to project water with a velocity of 70 feet per second meet their needs? Explain. See margin.
    c. The Jackson Fire Department must purchase a pump that will propel water 90 feet into the air. Will a pump that is advertised to project water with a velocity of 77 feet per second meet the fire department's need? Explain. See margin.

Real-World Link

In 1736, Benjamin Franklin founded the first volunteer fire organization, the Union Fire Company, in Philadelphia.

Source: *Firehouse Magazine*

Watch Out!

Preventing Errors Students may not think the simplified form of a fraction containing radicals looks any simpler than the original fraction. Explain that meeting the three conditions for simplifying a radical expression, not the look of the fraction, dictates whether a fraction containing radicals is simplified.

3 PRACTICE

Formative Assessment

Use Exercises 1–16 to check for understanding.

Use the chart at the bottom of this page to customize assignments for your students.

Additional Answers

36b. No; sample answer: The advertised pump will pump water only to a maximum height of about 76.6 feet.

36c. Yes; sample answer: The advertised pump will pump water to a maximum height of about 92.6 feet.

Differentiated Homework Options

Level	Assignment	Two-Day Option	
AL Basic	17–48, 52, 54, 55, 57–90	17–47 odd, 58–61	18–48 even, 52, 54–55, 57, 62–90
OL Core	17–47 odd, 49–52, 54, 55, 57–90	17–48, 58–61	49–52, 54–55, 57, 62–90
BL Advanced	49–84, (optional: 85–90)		

Study Guide and Intervention
CRM pp. 11–12 AL OL ELL

NAME ______________ DATE ________ PERIOD ________

10-2 Study Guide and Intervention
Simplifying Radical Expressions

Product Property of Square Roots The **Product Property of Square Roots** and prime factorization can be used to simplify expressions involving irrational square roots. When you simplify radical expressions with variables, use absolute value to ensure nonnegative results.

Product Property of Square Roots	For any numbers a and b, where $a \ge 0$ and $b \ge 0$, $\sqrt{ab} = \sqrt{a} \cdot \sqrt{b}$.

Example 1 Simplify $\sqrt{180}$.

$\sqrt{180} = \sqrt{2 \cdot 2 \cdot 3 \cdot 3 \cdot 5}$ Prime factorization of 180
$= \sqrt{2^2} \cdot \sqrt{3^2} \cdot \sqrt{5}$ Product Property of Square Roots
$= 2 \cdot 3 \cdot \sqrt{5}$ Simplify.
$= 6\sqrt{5}$ Simplify.

Example 2 Simplify $\sqrt{120a^2 \cdot b^5 \cdot c^4}$.

$\sqrt{120a^2 \cdot b^5 \cdot c^4}$
$= \sqrt{2^3 \cdot 3 \cdot 5 \cdot a^2 \cdot b^5 \cdot c^4}$
$= \sqrt{2^2} \cdot \sqrt{2} \cdot \sqrt{3} \cdot \sqrt{5} \cdot \sqrt{a^2} \cdot \sqrt{b^4 \cdot b} \cdot \sqrt{c^4}$
$= 2 \cdot \sqrt{2} \cdot \sqrt{3} \cdot \sqrt{5} \cdot |a| \cdot b^2 \cdot \sqrt{b} \cdot c^2$
$= 2|a|b^2c^2\sqrt{30b}$

Exercises

Simplify each expression.

1. $\sqrt{28}$ **$2\sqrt{7}$**
2. $\sqrt{68}$ **$2\sqrt{17}$**
3. $\sqrt{60}$ **$2\sqrt{15}$**
4. $\sqrt{75}$ **$5\sqrt{3}$**
5. $\sqrt{162}$ **$9\sqrt{2}$**
6. $\sqrt{3} \cdot \sqrt{6}$ **$3\sqrt{2}$**
7. $\sqrt{2} \cdot \sqrt{5}$ **$\sqrt{10}$**
8. $\sqrt{5} \cdot \sqrt{10}$ **$5\sqrt{2}$**
9. $\sqrt{4a^2}$ **$2|a|$**
10. $\sqrt{9x^4}$ **$3x^2$**
11. $\sqrt{300a^4}$ **$10a^2\sqrt{3}$**
12. $\sqrt{128c^6}$ **$8|c^3|\sqrt{2}$**
13. $4\sqrt{10} \cdot 3\sqrt{6}$ **$24\sqrt{15}$**
14. $\sqrt{3x^2} \cdot 3\sqrt{3x^4}$ **$9|x^3|$**
15. $\sqrt{20a^2b^4}$ **$2|a|b^2\sqrt{5}$**
16. $\sqrt{100x^3y}$ **$10|x|\sqrt{xy}$**
17. $\sqrt{24a^4b^2}$ **$2a^2|b|\sqrt{6}$**
18. $\sqrt{81x^4y^2}$ **$9x^2|y|$**
19. $\sqrt{150a^2b^2c}$ **$5|ab|\sqrt{6c}$**
20. $\sqrt{72a^6b^3c^2}$ **$6|a^3bc|\sqrt{2b}$**
21. $\sqrt{45x^2y^5z^8}$ **$3|x|y^2z^4\sqrt{5y}$**
22. $\sqrt{98x^4y^6z^2}$ **$7x^2|y^3z|\sqrt{2}$**

Lesson 10-2

Practice
CRM p. 14 AL OL BL ELL

NAME ______________ DATE ________ PERIOD ________

10-2 Practice
Simplifying Radical Expressions

Simplify.

1. $\sqrt{24}$ **$2\sqrt{6}$**
2. $\sqrt{60}$ **$2\sqrt{15}$**
3. $\sqrt{108}$ **$6\sqrt{3}$**
4. $\sqrt{8} \cdot \sqrt{6}$ **$4\sqrt{3}$**
5. $\sqrt{7} \cdot \sqrt{14}$ **$7\sqrt{2}$**
6. $3\sqrt{12} \cdot 5\sqrt{6}$ **$90\sqrt{2}$**
7. $4\sqrt{3} \cdot 3\sqrt{18}$ **$36\sqrt{6}$**
8. $\sqrt{27tu^3}$ **$3|u|\sqrt{3tu}$**
9. $\sqrt{50p^5}$ **$5p^2\sqrt{2p}$**
10. $\sqrt{108x^6y^4z^5}$ **$6|x^3|y^2z^2\sqrt{3z}$**
11. $\sqrt{56m^2n^4p^5}$ **$2|m|n^2p^2\sqrt{14p}$**
12. $\frac{\sqrt{8}}{\sqrt{6}}$ **$\frac{2\sqrt{3}}{3}$**
13. $\sqrt{\frac{2}{10}}$ **$\frac{\sqrt{5}}{5}$**
14. $\sqrt{\frac{5}{32}}$ **$\frac{\sqrt{10}}{8}$**
15. $\sqrt{\frac{3}{4}} \cdot \sqrt{\frac{4}{5}}$ **$\frac{\sqrt{15}}{5}$**
16. $\sqrt{\frac{1}{7}} \cdot \sqrt{\frac{7}{11}}$ **$\frac{\sqrt{11}}{11}$**
17. $\frac{\sqrt{3k}}{\sqrt{8}}$ **$\frac{\sqrt{6k}}{4}$**
18. $\sqrt{\frac{18}{x^3}}$ **$\frac{3\sqrt{2x}}{x^2}$**
19. $\sqrt{\frac{4y}{3y^2}}$ **$\frac{2\sqrt{3y}}{3|y|}$**
20. $\sqrt{\frac{9ab}{4ab^4}}$ **$\frac{3\sqrt{b}}{2b^2}$**
21. $\frac{3}{5-\sqrt{2}}$ **$\frac{15+3\sqrt{2}}{23}$**
22. $\frac{8}{3+\sqrt{3}}$ **$\frac{12-4\sqrt{3}}{3}$**
23. $\frac{5}{\sqrt{7}+\sqrt{3}}$ **$\frac{5\sqrt{7}-5\sqrt{3}}{4}$**
24. $\frac{3\sqrt{7}}{-1-\sqrt{27}}$ **$\frac{3\sqrt{7}-9\sqrt{21}}{26}$**

25. **SKY DIVING** When a skydiver jumps from an airplane, the time t it takes to free fall a given distance can be estimated by the formula $t = \sqrt{\frac{2s}{9.8}}$, where t is in seconds and s is in meters. If Julie jumps from an airplane, how long will it take her to free fall 750 meters? **about 12.4 s**

26. **METEOROLOGY** To estimate how long a thunderstorm will last, meteorologists can use the formula $t = \sqrt{\frac{d^3}{216}}$, where t is the time in hours and d is the diameter of the storm in miles.
   a. A thunderstorm is 8 miles in diameter. Estimate how long the storm will last. Give your answer in simplified form and as a decimal. **$\frac{8\sqrt{3}}{9}$ h ≈ 1.5 h**
   b. Will a thunderstorm twice this diameter last twice as long? Explain. **No; it will last about 4.4 h, or nearly 3 times as long.**

Word Problem Practice
CRM p. 15 AL OL BL ELL

NAME ______________ DATE ________ PERIOD ________

10-2 Word Problem Practice
Simplifying Radical Expressions

1. **SPORTS** Jasmine calculated the height of her team's soccer goal to be $\frac{15}{\sqrt{3}}$ feet. Simplify the expression.
$5\sqrt{3}$

2. **NATURE** In 2004, an earthquake below the ocean floor initiated a devastating tsunami in the Indian Ocean. Scientists can approximate the velocity (in feet per second) of a tsunami in water of depth d (in feet) with the formula $V = \sqrt{16d}$. Determine the velocity of a tsunami in 300 feet of water. Write your answer in simplified radical form.
$40\sqrt{3}$ ft/s

3. **AUTOMOBILES** The following formula can be used to find the "zero to sixty" time for a car, or the time it takes for a car to accelerate from a stop to sixty miles per hour.
$$V = \sqrt{\frac{2PT}{M}}$$
V is the velocity (in meters per second).
P is the car's average power (in watts).
M is the mass of the car (in kilograms).
T is the time (in seconds).
Find the time it takes for a 900-kilogram car with an average 60,000 watts of power to accelerate from stop to 26.82 meters per second (60 miles per hour). Round your answer to the nearest tenth.
about 5.4 s

4. **PHYSICAL SCIENCE** When a substance such as water vapor is in its gaseous state, the volume and the velocity of its molecules increase as temperature increases. The average velocity V of a molecule with mass m at temperature T is given by the formula $V = \sqrt{\frac{3kT}{m}}$.
Solve the equation for k.
$k = \frac{mV^2}{3T}$

5. **GEOMETRY** Suppose Emeryville Hospital wants to build a new helipad on which medic rescue helicopters can land. The helipad will be circular and made of fire resistant rubber.

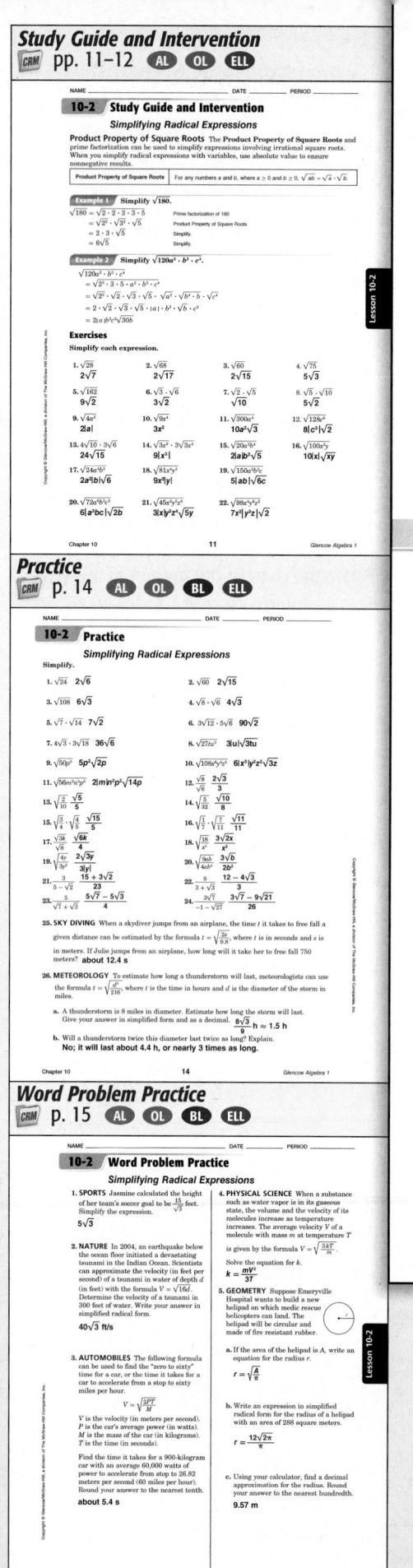

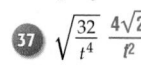

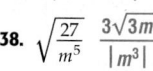

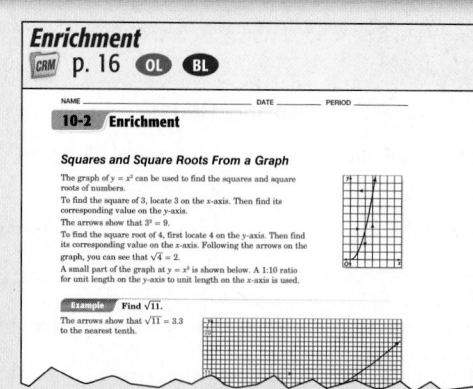

   a. If the area of the helipad is A, write an equation for the radius r.
   $r = \sqrt{\frac{A}{\pi}}$
   b. Write an expression in simplified radical form for the radius of a helipad with an area of 288 square meters.
   $r = \frac{12\sqrt{2\pi}}{\pi}$
   c. Using your calculator, find a decimal approximation for the radius. Round your answer to the nearest hundredth.
   9.57 m

Lesson 10-2

Examples 4 and 5 p. 614

Simplify each expression. **48. $4\sqrt{35} - 6\sqrt{15}$**

37. $\sqrt{\frac{32}{t^4}}$ **$\frac{4\sqrt{2}}{t^2}$**
38. $\sqrt{\frac{27}{m^5}}$ **$\frac{3\sqrt{3m}}{|m^3|}$**
39. $\frac{\sqrt{68ac^3}}{\sqrt{27a^2}}$ **$\frac{2|c|\sqrt{51ac}}{9|a|}$**
40. $\frac{\sqrt{h^3}}{\sqrt{8}}$ **$\frac{h\sqrt{2h}}{4}$**
41. $\sqrt{\frac{3}{16}} \cdot \sqrt{\frac{9}{5}}$ **$\frac{3\sqrt{15}}{20}$**
42. $\sqrt{\frac{7}{2}} \cdot \sqrt{\frac{5}{3}}$ **$\frac{\sqrt{210}}{6}$**
43. $\frac{7}{5+\sqrt{3}}$ **$\frac{35-7\sqrt{3}}{22}$**
44. $\frac{9}{6-\sqrt{8}}$ **$\frac{27+9\sqrt{2}}{14}$**
45. $\frac{3\sqrt{3}}{-2+\sqrt{6}}$ **$\frac{6\sqrt{3}+9\sqrt{2}}{2}$**
46. $\frac{3}{\sqrt{7}-\sqrt{2}}$ **$\frac{3\sqrt{7}+3\sqrt{2}}{5}$**
47. $\frac{5}{\sqrt{6}+\sqrt{3}}$ **$\frac{5\sqrt{6}-5\sqrt{3}}{3}$**
48. $\frac{2\sqrt{5}}{2\sqrt{7}+3\sqrt{3}}$

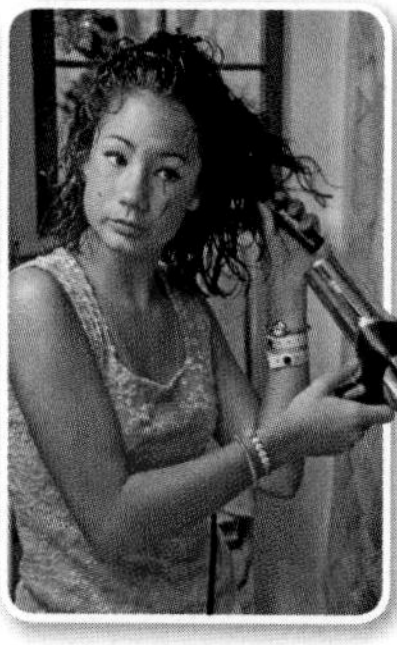

Real-World Link

The first hand-held hair dryer was sold in 1925 and dried hair with 100 watts of heat. Modern hair dryers may have 2000 watts.

Source: *Enotes Encyclopedia*

49. **ELECTRICITY** The amount of current in amperes I that an appliance uses can be calculated using the formula $I = \sqrt{\frac{P}{R}}$, where P is the power in watts and R is the resistance in ohms.
   a. Simplify the formula. **$I = \frac{\sqrt{PR}}{R}$**
   b. How much current does an appliance use if the power used is 75 watts and the resistance is 5 ohms? **about 3.9 amps**

50. **KINETIC ENERGY** The speed v of a ball can be determined by the equation $v = \sqrt{\frac{2k}{m}}$, where k is the kinetic energy and m is the mass of the ball.
   a. Simplify the formula if the mass of the ball is 3 kilograms. **$v = \frac{\sqrt{2km}}{m}$**
   b. If the ball is traveling 7 meters per second, what is the kinetic energy of the ball in Joules? **73.5 Joules**

51. **SUBMARINES** The greatest distance d in miles that a lookout can see on a clear day is modeled by the formula shown. Determine how high the submarine would have to raise its periscope to see a ship, if the submarine is the given distances away from the ship.

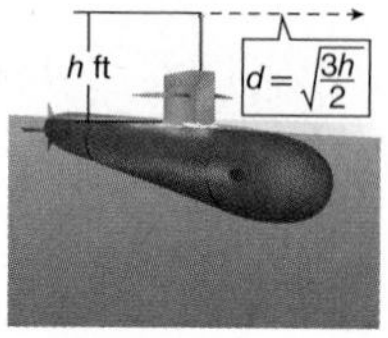

Distance	3	6	9	12	15
Height	**6**	**24**	**54**	**96**	**150**

52. Sample answer: First, take the square root of each side. Then simplify to find that $x = -\frac{4}{5}$ and 8.

55. Sample answer: $1 + \sqrt{2}$ and $1 - \sqrt{2}$; $(1 + \sqrt{2}) \cdot (1 - \sqrt{2}) = 1 - 2 = -1$

H.O.T. Problems
Use **H**igher-**O**rder **T**hinking Skills

52. **REASONING** Explain how to solve $(3x - 2)^2 = (2x + 6)^2$.

53. **CHALLENGE** Solve $|y^3| = \frac{1}{3\sqrt{3}}$ for y. **$\pm\frac{\sqrt{3}}{3}$**

54. 5; $\frac{1}{\sqrt{4(x-4)}} = \frac{1}{2}$

54. **REASONING** Marge takes a number, subtracts 4, multiplies by 4, takes the square root, and takes the reciprocal to get $\frac{1}{2}$. What number did she start with? Write a formula to describe the process.

55. **OPEN ENDED** Write two binomials of the form $a\sqrt{b} + c\sqrt{f}$ and $a\sqrt{b} - c\sqrt{f}$. Then find their product.

56. **CHALLENGE** Use the Quotient Property of Square Roots to derive the Quadratic Formula by solving the quadratic equation $ax^2 + bx + c = 0$. (*Hint*: Begin by completing the square.) **See Ch. 10 Answer Appendix.**

57. **WRITING IN MATH** Summarize how to write a radical expression in simplest form. **See margin.**

Enrichment
CRM p. 16 OL BL

NAME ______________ DATE ________ PERIOD ________

10-2 Enrichment

Squares and Square Roots From a Graph

The graph of $y = x^2$ can be used to find the squares and square roots of numbers.

To find the square of 3, locate 3 on the x-axis. Then find its corresponding value on the y-axis.

The arrows show that $3^2 = 9$.

To find the square root of 4, first locate 4 on the y-axis. Then find its corresponding value on the x-axis. Following the arrows on the graph, you can see that $\sqrt{4} = 2$.

A small part of the graph at $y = x^2$ is shown below. A 1:10 ratio for unit length on the y-axis to unit length on the x-axis is used.

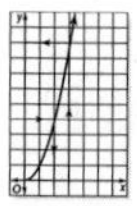

Example Find $\sqrt{11}$.

The arrows show that $\sqrt{11} = 3.3$ to the nearest tenth.

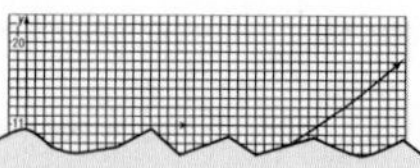

PSAE PRACTICE 8.11.17, 8.11.18, 8.11.01, 6.11.18

58. Jerry's electric bill is $23 less than his natural gas bill. The two bills are a total of $109. Which of the following equations can be used to find the amount of his natural gas bill? **D**

A $g + g = 109$
B $23 + 2g = 109$
C $g - 23 = 109$
D $2g - 23 = 109$

59. Solve $a^2 - 2a + 1 = 25$. **H**

F $-4, -6$
G $4, -6$
H $-4, 6$
J $4, 6$

60. The expression $\sqrt{160x^2y^5}$ is equivalent to which of the following? **C**

A $16|x|y^2\sqrt{10y}$
B $|x|y^2\sqrt{160y}$
C $4|x|y^2\sqrt{10y}$
D $10|x|y^2\sqrt{4y}$

61. GRIDDED RESPONSE Miki earns $10 an hour and 10% commission on sales. If Miki worked 38 hours and had a total sales of $1275 last week, how much did she make? **507.50**

Spiral Review

Graph each function. Compare to the parent graph. State the domain and range. (Lesson 10-1) **62–67. See Ch. 10 Answer Appendix.**

62. $y = 2\sqrt{x} - 1$
63. $y = \frac{1}{2}\sqrt{x}$
64. $y = 2\sqrt{x + 2}$
65. $y = -\sqrt{x + 1}$
66. $y = -3\sqrt{x - 3}$
67. $y = -2\sqrt{x} + 1$

Look for a pattern in each table of values to determine which kind of model best describes the data. (Lesson 9-9)

68.

x	0	1	2	3	4
y	1	3	9	27	81

exponential

69.

x	−3	−2	−1	0	1
y	18	8	2	0	2

quadratic

70.

x	1	2	3	4	5
y	1	3	5	7	9

linear

71. POPULATION The country of Latvia has been experiencing a 1.1% annual decrease in population. In 2005, its population was 2,290,237. If the trend continues, predict Latvia's population in 2015. (Lesson 9-7) **about 2,050,422**

Solve each equation by using the Quadratic Formula. Round to the nearest tenth if necessary. (Lesson 9-5)

72. $x^2 - 25 = 0$ **−5, 5**
73. $r^2 + 25 = 0$ **∅**
74. $4w^2 + 100 = 40w$ **5**
75. $2r^2 + r - 14 = 0$ **−2.9, 2.4**
76. $5v^2 - 7v = 1$ **−0.1, 1.5**
77. $11z^2 - z = 3$ **−0.5, 0.6**

Factor each polynomial, if possible. If the polynomial cannot be factored, write *prime*. (Lesson 8-5) **81. $2(4x^2 + y^2)(2x - y)(2x + y)$ 83. $(x + 3)(x - 3)(x - 3)$**

78. $n^2 - 81$ **$(n - 9)(n + 9)$**
79. $4 - 9a^2$ **$(2 - 3a)(2 + 3a)$**
80. $2x^5 - 98x^3$ **$2x^3(x + 7)(x - 7)$**
81. $32x^4 - 2y^4$
82. $4t^2 - 27$ **prime**
83. $x^3 - 3x^2 - 9x + 27$

84. GARDENING Cleveland is planting 120 jalapeno pepper plants in a rectangular arrangement in his garden. In what ways can he arrange them so that he has at least 4 rows of plants, the same number of plants in each row, and at least 6 plants in each row? (Lesson 8-1) **4 rows of of 30 plants, 5 rows of 24 plants, 6 rows of of 20 plants, 8 rows of 15 plants, 10 rows of 12 plants, 12 rows of 10 plants, 15 rows of 8 plants, or 20 rows of 6 plants**

Skills Review

Write the prime factorization of each number. (Concepts and Skills Bank Lesson 6)

85. 24 **$2^3 \cdot 3$**
86. 88 **$2^3 \cdot 11$**
87. 180 **$2^2 \cdot 3^2 \cdot 5$**
88. 31 **31**
89. 60 **$2^2 \cdot 3 \cdot 5$**
90. 90 **$2 \cdot 3^2 \cdot 5$**

4 ASSESS

Ticket Out the Door Ask students to write radical expressions in which they need to use a conjugate to rationalize the denominators. Have students simplify the expressions.

Formative Assessment

Check for student understanding of concepts in Lessons 10-1 and 10-2.

CRM Quiz 1, p. 57

Additional Answer

57. No radicals can appear in the denominator of a fraction. So, rationalize the denominator to get rid of the radicand in the denominator. Then check if any of the radicands have perfect square factors other than 1. If so, simplify.

Differentiated Instruction BL

Extension Remind students that to undo squaring a number, they take the square root. Write $3^2 = 9$ and $\sqrt{9} = 3$ on the board. Challenge students to determine whether a square root can be written with an exponent. In Extend Lesson 10-2, students will learn that square roots can be expressed as a number with the exponent $\frac{1}{2}$, and that $9^{\frac{1}{2}} = 3$.

1 FOCUS

Objective: Use a graphing calculator to explore the meaning of rational exponents.

Materials for Each Student

- TI-83/84 Plus or other graphing calculator

Teaching Tip

Show students the keystrokes needed to evaluate $16^{\frac{1}{2}}$ and $\sqrt{16}$ on the calculator. Point out that the calculator also has a key for cube roots. To find roots other than square roots and cube roots, tell students to choose the $\sqrt[x]{\ }$ function from the MATH menu.

2 TEACH

Working in Cooperative Groups

Put students in groups of two or three, mixing abilities. Have groups complete the Activity and Exercises 1 and 2.

- Make sure students use parentheses under the radical sign when needed. For example, to calculate $\sqrt[4]{81^3}$, have students enter 4 MATH 5 to select $\sqrt[x]{\ }$ from the MATH menu, and then enter (81 ^ 3) ENTER. Point out that the 4 is entered before pressing MATH.
- For Exercise 2, you may wish to review the property $(a^m)^n = a^{mn}$.

Practice Have students complete Exercises 3–10.

3 ASSESS

Formative Assessment

Use Exercises 4 and 5 to assess whether students can write the roots using a rational exponent.

Graphing Technology Lab
Rational Exponents

IL Math Online glencoe.com
- Other Calculator Keystrokes
- Graphing Technology Personal Tutor

IL Learning Standards **8.B.4a** Represent algebraic concepts with physical materials, words, diagrams, tables, graphs, equations and inequalities and use appropriate technology.

You have studied the properties of exponents that are whole numbers. Some exponents are rational numbers or fractions. You can use a calculator to explore the meaning of rational exponents.

ACTIVITY Rational Exponents

Step 1 Evaluate $16^{\frac{1}{2}}$ and $\sqrt{16}$.
KEYSTROKES: 16 ^ (1 ÷ 2) ENTER
KEYSTROKES: 2nd [√] 16 ENTER
Record the results in a table like the one at the right.

Step 2 Use a calculator to evaluate each expression. Record each result in your table. To find a root other than a square root, choose the $\sqrt[x]{\ }$ function from the MATH menu.

Expression	Value	Expression	Value
$16^{\frac{1}{2}}$	4	$\sqrt{16}$	4
$25^{\frac{1}{2}}$	5	$\sqrt{25}$	5
$64^{\frac{1}{3}}$	4	$\sqrt[3]{64}$	4
$125^{\frac{1}{3}}$	5	$\sqrt[3]{125}$	5
$64^{\frac{2}{3}}$	16	$\sqrt[3]{64^2}$	16
$81^{\frac{3}{4}}$	27	$\sqrt[4]{81^3}$	27

1A. Study the table. What do you observe about the value of an expression of the form $a^{\frac{1}{n}}$? **It is equal to $\sqrt[n]{a}$.**

1B. What do you observe about the value of an expression of the form $a^{\frac{m}{n}}$? **It is equal to $\sqrt[n]{a^m}$.**

Exercises

1. Recall the Power of a Power Property. For any number a and all integers m and n, $(a^m)^n = (a^{m \cdot n})$. Assume that fractional exponents behave as whole number exponents and find the value of $\left(b^{\frac{1}{2}}\right)^2$.

$\left(b^{\frac{1}{2}}\right)^2 = b^{\frac{1}{2} \cdot 2}$ **Power of a Power Property**

$= b^1$ or b **Simplify.**

Thus, $b^{\frac{1}{2}}$ is a number whose square equals b. So it makes sense to define $b^{\frac{1}{2}} = \sqrt{b}$. Use a similar process to define $b^{\frac{1}{n}}$. **See Ch. 10 Answer Appendix.**

2. Define $b^{\frac{m}{n}}$. Justify your answer. **See Ch. 10 Answer Appendix.**

Write each root as an expression using a fractional exponent. Then evaluate the expression.

3. $\sqrt{36}$ **$36^{\frac{1}{2}}$; 6**
4. $\sqrt{121}$ **$121^{\frac{1}{2}}$; 11**
5. $\sqrt[4]{256}$ **$256^{\frac{1}{4}}$; 4**
6. $\sqrt[5]{32}$ **$32^{\frac{1}{5}}$; 2**
7. $\sqrt[3]{8^2}$ **$8^{\frac{2}{3}}$; 4**
8. $\sqrt[4]{1296}$ **$1296^{\frac{1}{4}}$; 6**
9. $\sqrt[4]{16^3}$ **$16^{\frac{3}{4}}$; 8**
10. $\sqrt[3]{8^3}$ **$8^{\frac{3}{3}}$; 8**

From Concrete to Abstract

For Exercise 2, students should be able to show $b^{\frac{m}{n}} = \sqrt[n]{b^m}$. Point out that $b^{\frac{m}{n}} = \sqrt[n]{b^m} = (\sqrt[n]{b})^m$. Demonstrate for students that it is easier to evaluate $\sqrt[n]{b}$ first and then raise $\sqrt[n]{b}$ to the mth power.

10-3 Operations with Radical Expressions

10-3 Lesson Notes

Then
You simplified radical expressions. (Lesson 10-2)

Now
- Add and subtract radical expressions.
- Multiply radical expressions.

IL Learning Standards

7.B.4 Estimate and measure the magnitude and directions of physical quantities using rulers, protractors and other scientific instruments including timers, calculators and computers.
8.C.4b Apply algebraic properties and procedures with matrices, vectors, functions and sequences using data found in business, industry and consumer situations.

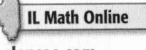

IL Math Online

glencoe.com
- Extra Examples
- Personal Tutor
- Self-Check Quiz
- Homework Help

Why?

Conchita is going to run in her neighborhood to get ready for the soccer season. She plans to run the course that she has laid out three times each day.

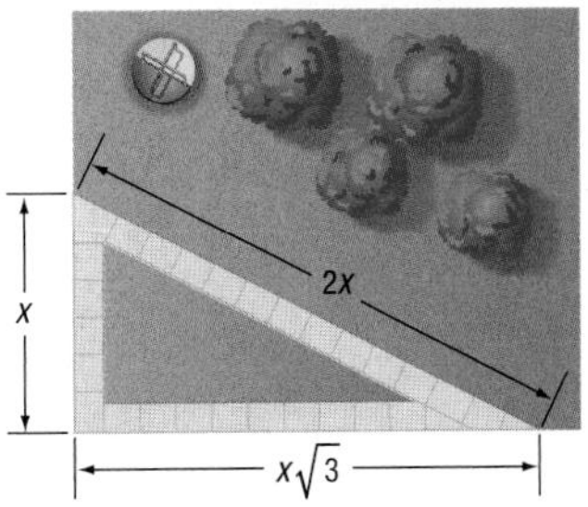

How far does Conchita have to run to complete the course that she laid out?

How far does she run every day?

Add or Subtract Radical Expressions To add or subtract radical expressions, the radicands must be alike in the same way that monomial terms must be alike to add or subtract.

Monomials	Radical Expressions
$4a + 2a = (4 + 2)a$	$4\sqrt{5} + 2\sqrt{5} = (4 + 2)\sqrt{5}$
$= 6a$	$= 6\sqrt{5}$
$9b - 2b = (9 - 2)b$	$9\sqrt{3} - 2\sqrt{3} = (9 - 2)\sqrt{3}$
$= 7b$	$= 7\sqrt{3}$

Notice that when adding and subtracting radical expressions, the radicand does not change. This is the same as when adding or subtracting monomials.

EXAMPLE 1 Add and Subtract Expressions with Like Radicands

Simplify each expression.

a. $5\sqrt{2} + 7\sqrt{2} - 6\sqrt{2}$

$5\sqrt{2} + 7\sqrt{2} - 6\sqrt{2} = (5 + 7 - 6)\sqrt{2}$ — **Distributive Property**

$= 6\sqrt{2}$ — **Simplify.**

b. $10\sqrt{7} + 5\sqrt{11} + 4\sqrt{7} - 6\sqrt{11}$

$10\sqrt{7} + 5\sqrt{11} + 4\sqrt{7} - 6\sqrt{11} = (10 + 4)\sqrt{7} + (5 - 6)\sqrt{11}$ — **Distributive Property**

$= 14\sqrt{7} - \sqrt{11}$ — **Simplify.**

Check Your Progress **1C.** $4\sqrt{3} - 8\sqrt{5}$ **1D.** $-2\sqrt{3} + 6\sqrt{7}$

1A. $3\sqrt{2} - 5\sqrt{2} + 4\sqrt{2}$ $2\sqrt{2}$

1B. $6\sqrt{11} + 2\sqrt{11} - 9\sqrt{11}$ $-\sqrt{11}$

1C. $15\sqrt{3} - 14\sqrt{5} + 6\sqrt{5} - 11\sqrt{3}$

1D. $4\sqrt{3} + 3\sqrt{7} - 6\sqrt{3} + 3\sqrt{7}$

Personal Tutor glencoe.com

Not all radical expressions have like radicands. Simplifying the expressions may make it possible to have like radicands so that they can be added or subtracted.

1 FOCUS

Vertical Alignment

Before Lesson 10-3
Simplify radical expressions.

Lesson 10-3
Add and subtract radical expressions.
Multiply radical expressions.

After Lesson 10-3
Solve radical equations.

2 TEACH

Scaffolding Questions

Have students read the *Why?* section of the lesson.

Ask:
- What expression shows the length of the course? $x + 2x + x\sqrt{3}$
- Which terms in the expression can be combined? Explain. x and $2x$ because they are like terms
  Which term cannot be combined? Explain. $x\sqrt{3}$ because it contains a radical
- What expression shows how far Conchita will run each day? $3(3x + x\sqrt{3})$

Lesson 10-3 Resources

Resource	Approaching-Level	On-Level	Beyond-Level	English Learners
Teacher Edition	• Differentiated Instruction, p. 620	• Differentiated Instruction, pp. 620, 623	• Differentiated Instruction, p. 623	• Differentiated Instruction, p. 620
Chapter Resource Masters	• Study Guide and Intervention, pp. 17–18 • Skills Practice, p. 19 • Practice, p. 20 • Word Problem Practice, p. 21	• Study Guide and Intervention, pp. 17–18 • Skills Practice, p. 19 • Practice, p. 20 • Word Problem Practice, p. 21 • Enrichment, p. 22	• Practice, p. 20 • Word Problem Practice, p. 21 • Enrichment, p. 22	• Study Guide and Intervention, pp. 17–18 • Skills Practice, p. 19 • Practice, p. 20
Transparencies	• 5-Minute Check Transparency 10-3	• 5-Minute Check Transparency 10-3	• 5-Minute Check Transparency 10-3	• 5-Minute Check Transparency 10-3
Other	• Study Notebook • Teaching Algebra with Manipulatives	• Study Notebook • Teaching Algebra with Manipulatives	• Study Notebook	• Study Notebook • Teaching Algebra with Manipulatives

Add or Subtract Radical Expressions

Example 1 shows how to use the Distributive Property to add or subtract like radicands in a radical expression. **Example 2** shows how to simplify the radicals in a radical expression with unlike radicands.

Formative Assessment

Use the Check Your Progress exercises after each example to determine students' understanding of concepts.

Additional Examples

1 Simplify each expression.

a. $6\sqrt{5} + 2\sqrt{5} - 5\sqrt{5}$ $3\sqrt{5}$

b. $7\sqrt{2} + 8\sqrt{11} - 4\sqrt{11} - 6\sqrt{2}$ $\sqrt{2} + 4\sqrt{11}$

2 Simplify $6\sqrt{27} + 8\sqrt{12} + 2\sqrt{75}$. $44\sqrt{3}$

Additional Examples also in Interactive Classroom PowerPoint® Presentations

IWB INTERACTIVE WHITEBOARD READY

Multiply Radical Expressions

Example 3 shows how to multiply radical expressions with different radicands. **Example 4** shows how to multiply radical expressions to find the area of a rectangle.

Additional Example

3 Simplify each expression.

a. $2\sqrt{3} \cdot 4\sqrt{6}$ $24\sqrt{2}$

b. $4\sqrt{2}(3\sqrt{2} + 2\sqrt{6})$ $24 + 16\sqrt{3}$

StudyTip

Simplify First Simplify each radical term first. Then perform the operations needed.

EXAMPLE 2 Add and Subtract Expressions with Unlike Radicands

Simplify $2\sqrt{18} + 2\sqrt{32} + \sqrt{72}$.

$2\sqrt{18} + 2\sqrt{32} + \sqrt{72} = 2(\sqrt{3^2} \cdot \sqrt{2}) + 2(\sqrt{4^2} \cdot \sqrt{2}) + (\sqrt{6^2} \cdot \sqrt{2})$ **Product Property**

$= 2(3\sqrt{2}) + 2(4\sqrt{2}) + (6\sqrt{2})$ **Simplify.**

$= 6\sqrt{2} + 8\sqrt{2} + 6\sqrt{2}$ **Multiply.**

$= 20\sqrt{2}$ **Simplify.**

Check Your Progress

2A. $4\sqrt{54} + 2\sqrt{24}$ $16\sqrt{6}$

2B. $4\sqrt{12} - 6\sqrt{48}$ $-16\sqrt{3}$

2C. $3\sqrt{45} + \sqrt{20} - \sqrt{245}$ $4\sqrt{5}$

2D. $\sqrt{24} - \sqrt{54} + \sqrt{96}$ $3\sqrt{6}$

Personal Tutor glencoe.com

Multiply Radical Expressions Multiplying radical expressions is similar to multiplying monomial algebraic expressions. Let $x \geq 0$.

Monomials	Radical Expressions
$(2x)(3x) = 2 \cdot 3 \cdot x \cdot x$	$(2\sqrt{x})(3\sqrt{x}) = 2 \cdot 3 \cdot \sqrt{x} \cdot \sqrt{x}$
$= 6x^2$	$= 6x$

You can also apply the Distributive Property to radical expressions.

Watch Out!

Multiplying Radicands Make sure that you multiply the radicands when multiplying radical expressions. A common mistake is to add the radicands rather than multiply.

EXAMPLE 3 Multiply Radical Expressions

Simplify each expression.

a. $3\sqrt{2} \cdot 2\sqrt{6}$

$3\sqrt{2} \cdot 2\sqrt{6} = (3 \cdot 2)(\sqrt{2} \cdot \sqrt{6})$ **Associative Property**

$= 6(\sqrt{12})$ **Multiply.**

$= 6(2\sqrt{3})$ **Simplify.**

$= 12\sqrt{3}$ **Multiply.**

b. $3\sqrt{5}(2\sqrt{5} + 5\sqrt{3})$

$3\sqrt{5}(2\sqrt{5} + 5\sqrt{3}) = (3\sqrt{5} \cdot 2\sqrt{5}) + (3\sqrt{5} \cdot 5\sqrt{3})$ **Distributive Property**

$= [(3 \cdot 2)(\sqrt{5} \cdot \sqrt{5})] + [(3 \cdot 5)(\sqrt{5} \cdot \sqrt{3})]$ **Associative Property**

$= [6(\sqrt{25})] + [15(\sqrt{15})]$ **Multiply.**

$= [6(5)] + [15(\sqrt{15})]$ **Simplify.**

$= 30 + 15\sqrt{15}$ **Multiply.**

Check Your Progress

3A. $2\sqrt{6} \cdot 7\sqrt{3}$ $42\sqrt{2}$

3B. $9\sqrt{5} \cdot 11\sqrt{15}$ $495\sqrt{3}$

3C. $3\sqrt{2}(4\sqrt{3} + 6\sqrt{2})$ $12\sqrt{6} + 36$

3D. $5\sqrt{3}(3\sqrt{2} - \sqrt{3})$ $15\sqrt{6} - 15$

Personal Tutor glencoe.com

You can also multiply radical expressions with more than one term in each factor. This is similar to multiplying two algebraic binomials with variables.

Differentiated Instruction

AL OL ELL

If students struggle with the FOIL method in Example 4,

Then have students rewrite the example in five steps to facilitate an understanding of First terms, Outer terms, Inner terms, and Last terms. For example, in Step 1, have students write the original expression, underline the first terms, and then multiply to find the product of the first terms. Students continue this process until they have found the products of all of the terms. Then for the fifth step, have them combine and simplify the results of the previous four steps.

Real-World EXAMPLE 4 Multiply Radical Expressions

GEOMETRY Find the area of the rectangle in simplest form.

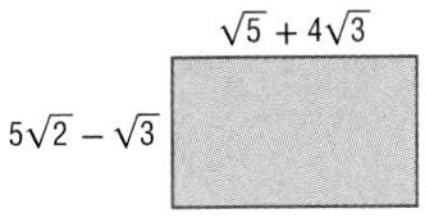

$A = (5\sqrt{2} - \sqrt{3})(\sqrt{5} + 4\sqrt{3})$ $\quad A = \ell \cdot w$

First Terms, Outer Terms, Inner Terms, Last Terms

$= (5\sqrt{2})(\sqrt{5}) + (5\sqrt{2})(4\sqrt{3}) + (-\sqrt{3})(\sqrt{5}) + (-\sqrt{3})(4\sqrt{3})$

$= 5\sqrt{10} + 20\sqrt{6} - \sqrt{15} - 4\sqrt{9}$ **Multiply.**

$= 5\sqrt{10} + 20\sqrt{6} - \sqrt{15} - 12$ **Simplify.**

Review Vocabulary

FOIL Method Multiply two binomials by finding the sum of the products of the First terms, the Outer terms, the Inner terms, and the Last terms. (Lesson 7-7)

Check Your Progress

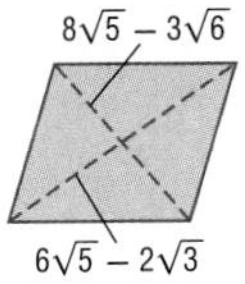

4. **GEOMETRY** The area A of a rhombus can be found using the equation $A = \frac{1}{2}d_1d_2$, where d_1 and d_2 are the lengths of the diagonals. What is the area of the rhombus at the right? $A = 120 - 8\sqrt{15} - 9\sqrt{30} + 9\sqrt{2}$

Personal Tutor glencoe.com

Concept Summary

For Your FOLDABLE

Operations with Radical Expressions

Operation	Symbols	Example
addition, $b \geq 0$	$a\sqrt{b} + c\sqrt{b} = (a + c)\sqrt{b}$ like radicands	$4\sqrt{3} + 6\sqrt{3} = (4 + 6)\sqrt{3} = 10\sqrt{3}$
subtraction, $b \geq 0$	$a\sqrt{b} - c\sqrt{b} = (a - c)\sqrt{b}$ like radicands	$12\sqrt{5} - 8\sqrt{5} = (12 - 8)\sqrt{5} = 4\sqrt{5}$
multiplication, $b \geq 0, g \geq 0$	$a\sqrt{b}(f\sqrt{g}) = af\sqrt{bg}$ Radicands do not have to be like radicands.	$3\sqrt{2}(5\sqrt{7}) = (3 \cdot 5)(\sqrt{2 \cdot 7}) = 15\sqrt{14}$

Check Your Understanding

Examples 1–3 pp. 619–620

Simplify each expression.

1. $3\sqrt{5} + 6\sqrt{5}$ $9\sqrt{5}$
2. $8\sqrt{3} + 5\sqrt{3}$ $13\sqrt{3}$
3. $\sqrt{7} - 6\sqrt{7}$ $-5\sqrt{7}$
4. $10\sqrt{2} - 6\sqrt{2}$ $4\sqrt{2}$
5. $4\sqrt{5} + 2\sqrt{20}$ $8\sqrt{5}$
6. $\sqrt{12} - \sqrt{3}$ $\sqrt{3}$
7. $\sqrt{8} + \sqrt{12} + \sqrt{18}$
8. $\sqrt{27} + 2\sqrt{3} - \sqrt{12}$ $3\sqrt{3}$
9. $9\sqrt{2}(4\sqrt{6})$ $72\sqrt{3}$
10. $4\sqrt{3}(8\sqrt{3})$ 96
11. $\sqrt{3}(\sqrt{7} + 3\sqrt{2})$
12. $\sqrt{5}(\sqrt{2} + 4\sqrt{2})$ $5\sqrt{10}$

7. $5\sqrt{2} + 2\sqrt{3}$
11. $\sqrt{21} + 3\sqrt{6}$

Example 4 p. 621

13. **GEOMETRY** The area A of a triangle can be found by using the formula $A = \frac{1}{2}bh$, where b represents the base and h is the height. What is the area of the triangle at the right? $14.5 + 3\sqrt{15}$

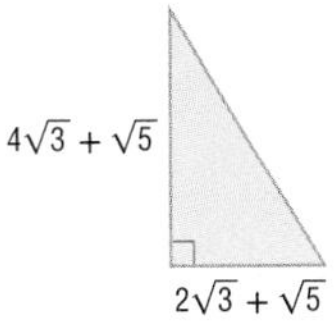

Focus on Mathematical Content

Operations with Radical Expressions Radical expressions can be added or subtracted only if the radicands are the same. Radical expressions can be multiplied whether the radicands are the same or different.

Additional Example

4 **GEOMETRY** Find the area of a rectangle in simplest form with a width of $4\sqrt{6} - 2\sqrt{10}$ and a length of $5\sqrt{3} + 7\sqrt{5}$. $18\sqrt{30} - 10\sqrt{2}$

3 PRACTICE

Formative Assessment

Use Exercises 1–13 to check for understanding.

Use the chart at the bottom of this page to customize assignments for your students.

TEACH with TECH

INTERACTIVE WHITEBOARD Write an expression on the board to add or subtract radical expressions. As you simplify the expression, drag the like terms to group them together. Then combine like terms and simplify the expression.

Differentiated Homework Options

Level	Assignment	Two-Day Option	
AL Basic	14–26, 37–68	15–25 odd, 40–43	14–26 even, 37–39, 44–68
OL Core	15–33 odd, 34, 35, 37–68	14–26, 40–43	27–35, 37–39, 44–68
BL Advanced	27–62, (optional: 63–68)		

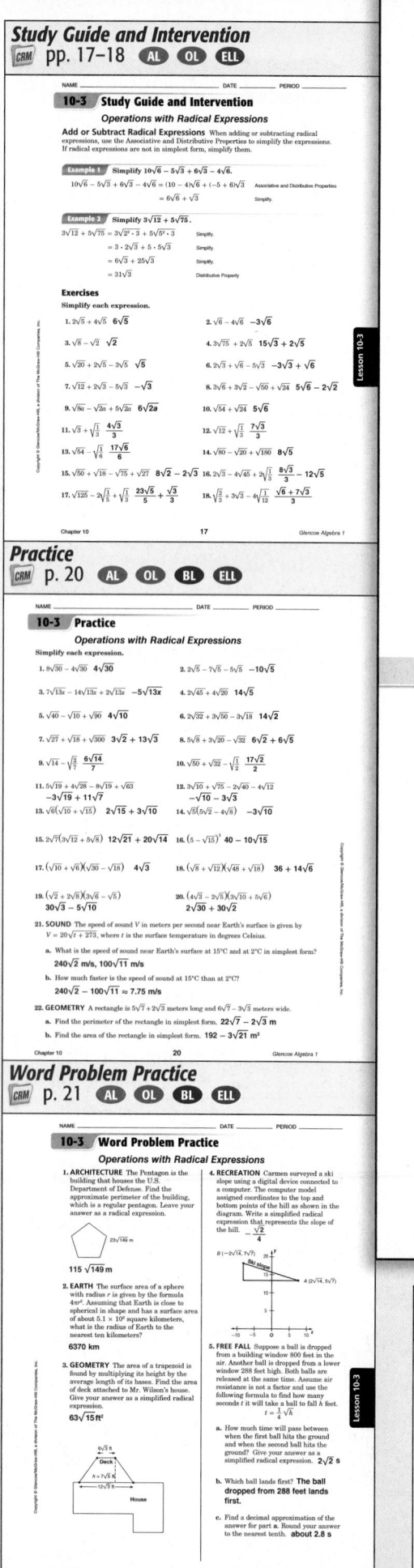

Study Guide and Intervention
CRM pp. 17–18 AL OL ELL

NAME ______ DATE ______ PERIOD ______

10-3 Study Guide and Intervention

Operations with Radical Expressions

Add or Subtract Radical Expressions When adding or subtracting radical expressions, use the Associative and Distributive Properties to simplify the expressions. If radical expressions are not in simplest form, simplify them.

Example 1 Simplify $10\sqrt{6} - 5\sqrt{3} + 6\sqrt{3} - 4\sqrt{6}$.

$10\sqrt{6} - 5\sqrt{3} + 6\sqrt{3} - 4\sqrt{6} = (10 - 4)\sqrt{6} + (-5 + 6)\sqrt{3}$ Associative and Distributive Properties

$= 6\sqrt{6} + \sqrt{3}$ Simplify.

Example 2 Simplify $3\sqrt{12} + 5\sqrt{75}$.

$3\sqrt{12} + 5\sqrt{75} = 3\sqrt{2^2 \cdot 3} + 5\sqrt{5^2 \cdot 3}$ Simplify.

$= 3 \cdot 2\sqrt{3} + 5 \cdot 5\sqrt{3}$ Simplify.

$= 6\sqrt{3} + 25\sqrt{3}$ Simplify.

$= 31\sqrt{3}$ Distributive Property

Exercises

Simplify each expression.

1. $2\sqrt{5} + 4\sqrt{5}$ **$6\sqrt{5}$**
2. $\sqrt{6} - 4\sqrt{6}$ **$-3\sqrt{6}$**
3. $\sqrt{8} - \sqrt{2}$ **$\sqrt{2}$**
4. $3\sqrt{75} + 2\sqrt{5}$ **$15\sqrt{3} + 2\sqrt{5}$**
5. $\sqrt{20} + 2\sqrt{5} - 3\sqrt{5}$ **$\sqrt{5}$**
6. $2\sqrt{3} + \sqrt{6} - 5\sqrt{3}$ **$-3\sqrt{3} + \sqrt{6}$**
7. $\sqrt{12} + 2\sqrt{3} - 5\sqrt{3}$ **$-\sqrt{3}$**
8. $3\sqrt{6} + 3\sqrt{2} - \sqrt{50} + \sqrt{24}$ **$5\sqrt{6} - 2\sqrt{2}$**
9. $\sqrt{8a} - \sqrt{2a} + 5\sqrt{2a}$ **$6\sqrt{2a}$**
10. $\sqrt{54} + \sqrt{24}$ **$5\sqrt{6}$**
11. $\sqrt{3} + \sqrt{\frac{1}{3}}$ **$\frac{4\sqrt{3}}{3}$**
12. $\sqrt{12} + \sqrt{\frac{1}{3}}$ **$\frac{7\sqrt{3}}{3}$**
13. $\sqrt{54} - \sqrt{\frac{1}{6}}$ **$\frac{17\sqrt{6}}{6}$**
14. $\sqrt{80} - \sqrt{20} + \sqrt{180}$ **$8\sqrt{5}$**
15. $\sqrt{50} + \sqrt{18} - \sqrt{75} + \sqrt{27}$ **$8\sqrt{2} - 2\sqrt{3}$**
16. $2\sqrt{3} - 4\sqrt{45} + 2\sqrt{\frac{1}{3}}$ **$\frac{8\sqrt{3}}{3} - 12\sqrt{5}$**
17. $\sqrt{125} - 2\sqrt{\frac{1}{5}} + \sqrt{\frac{1}{3}}$ **$\frac{23\sqrt{5}}{5} + \frac{\sqrt{3}}{3}$**
18. $\sqrt{\frac{2}{3}} + 3\sqrt{3} - 4\sqrt{\frac{1}{12}}$ **$\frac{\sqrt{6} + 7\sqrt{3}}{3}$**

Lesson 10-3

Practice
CRM p. 20 AL OL BL ELL

NAME ______ DATE ______ PERIOD ______

10-3 Practice

Operations with Radical Expressions

Simplify each expression.

1. $8\sqrt{30} - 4\sqrt{30}$ **$4\sqrt{30}$**
2. $2\sqrt{5} - 7\sqrt{5} - 5\sqrt{5}$ **$-10\sqrt{5}$**
3. $7\sqrt{13x} - 14\sqrt{13x} + 2\sqrt{13x}$ **$-5\sqrt{13x}$**
4. $2\sqrt{45} + 4\sqrt{20}$ **$14\sqrt{5}$**
5. $\sqrt{40} - \sqrt{10} + \sqrt{90}$ **$4\sqrt{10}$**
6. $2\sqrt{32} + 3\sqrt{50} - 3\sqrt{18}$ **$14\sqrt{2}$**
7. $\sqrt{27} + \sqrt{18} + \sqrt{300}$ **$3\sqrt{2} + 13\sqrt{3}$**
8. $5\sqrt{8} + 3\sqrt{20} - \sqrt{32}$ **$6\sqrt{2} + 6\sqrt{5}$**
9. $\sqrt{14} - \sqrt{\frac{2}{7}}$ **$\frac{6\sqrt{14}}{7}$**
10. $\sqrt{50} + \sqrt{32} - \sqrt{\frac{1}{2}}$ **$\frac{17\sqrt{2}}{2}$**
11. $5\sqrt{19} + 4\sqrt{28} - 8\sqrt{19} + \sqrt{63}$ **$-3\sqrt{19} + 11\sqrt{7}$**
12. $3\sqrt{10} + \sqrt{75} - 2\sqrt{40} - 4\sqrt{12}$ **$-\sqrt{10} - 3\sqrt{3}$**
13. $\sqrt{6}(\sqrt{10} + \sqrt{15})$ **$2\sqrt{15} + 3\sqrt{10}$**
14. $\sqrt{5}(5\sqrt{2} - 4\sqrt{8})$ **$-3\sqrt{10}$**
15. $2\sqrt{7}(3\sqrt{12} + 5\sqrt{8})$ **$12\sqrt{21} + 20\sqrt{14}$**
16. $(5 - \sqrt{15})^2$ **$40 - 10\sqrt{15}$**
17. $(\sqrt{10} + \sqrt{6})(\sqrt{30} - \sqrt{18})$ **$4\sqrt{3}$**
18. $(\sqrt{8} + \sqrt{12})(\sqrt{48} + \sqrt{18})$ **$36 + 14\sqrt{6}$**
19. $(\sqrt{2} + 2\sqrt{8})(3\sqrt{6} - \sqrt{5})$ **$30\sqrt{3} - 5\sqrt{10}$**
20. $(4\sqrt{3} - 2\sqrt{5})(3\sqrt{10} + 5\sqrt{6})$ **$2\sqrt{30} + 30\sqrt{2}$**
21. **SOUND** The speed of sound V in meters per second near Earth's surface is given by $V = 20\sqrt{t + 273}$, where t is the surface temperature in degrees Celsius.
    a. What is the speed of sound near Earth's surface at 15°C and at 2°C in simplest form? **$240\sqrt{2}$ m/s, $100\sqrt{11}$ m/s**
    b. How much faster is the speed of sound at 15°C than at 2°C? **$240\sqrt{2} - 100\sqrt{11} \approx 7.75$ m/s**
22. **GEOMETRY** A rectangle is $5\sqrt{7} + 2\sqrt{3}$ meters long and $6\sqrt{7} - 3\sqrt{3}$ meters wide.
    a. Find the perimeter of the rectangle in simplest form. **$22\sqrt{7} - 2\sqrt{3}$ m**
    b. Find the area of the rectangle in simplest form. **$192 - 3\sqrt{21}$ m²**

Word Problem Practice
CRM p. 21 AL OL BL ELL

NAME ______ DATE ______ PERIOD ______

10-3 Word Problem Practice

Operations with Radical Expressions

1. **ARCHITECTURE** The Pentagon is the building that houses the U.S. Department of Defense. Find the approximate perimeter of the building, which is a regular pentagon. Leave your answer as a radical expression.

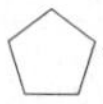

$115\sqrt{149}$ m

2. **EARTH** The surface area of a sphere with radius r is given by the formula $4\pi r^2$. Assuming that Earth is close to spherical in shape and has a surface area of about 5.1×10^8 square kilometers, what is the radius of Earth to the nearest ten kilometers?

6370 km

3. **GEOMETRY** The area of a trapezoid is found by multiplying its height by the average length of its bases. Find the area of deck attached to Mr. Wilson's house. Give your answer as a simplified radical expression.

$63\sqrt{15}$ ft²

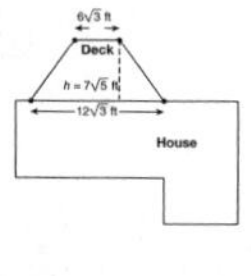

4. **RECREATION** Carmen surveyed a ski slope using a digital device connected to a computer. The computer model assigned coordinates to the top and bottom points of the hill as shown in the diagram. Write a simplified radical expression that represents the slope of the hill. **$-\frac{\sqrt{2}}{4}$**

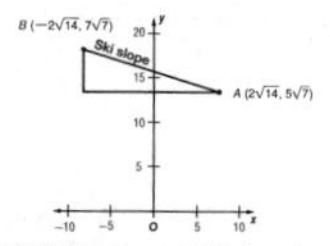

5. **FREE FALL** Suppose a ball is dropped from a building window 800 feet in the air. Another ball is dropped from a lower window 288 feet high. Both balls are released at the same time. Assume air resistance is not a factor and use the following formula to find how many seconds t it will take a ball to fall h feet.

$$t = \frac{1}{4}\sqrt{h}$$

   a. How much time will pass between when the first ball hits the ground and when the second ball hits the ground? Give your answer as a simplified radical expression. **$2\sqrt{2}$ s**
   b. Which ball lands first? **The ball dropped from 288 feet lands first.**
   c. Find a decimal approximation of the answer for part a. Round your answer to the nearest tenth. **about 2.8 s**

Lesson 10-3

Practice and Problem Solving

= Step-by-Step Solutions begin on page R12.
Extra Practice begins on page 815.

Examples 1–3
pp. 619–620

Simplify each expression. **18. $12\sqrt{3} + \sqrt{2}$**

14. $7\sqrt{5} + 4\sqrt{5}$ **$11\sqrt{5}$**
15. $2\sqrt{6} + 9\sqrt{6}$ **$11\sqrt{6}$**
16. $3\sqrt{5} - 2\sqrt{20}$ **$-\sqrt{5}$**
17. $3\sqrt{50} - 3\sqrt{32}$ **$3\sqrt{2}$**
18. $7\sqrt{3} - 2\sqrt{2} + 3\sqrt{2} + 5\sqrt{3}$
19. $\sqrt{5}(\sqrt{2} + 4\sqrt{2})$ **$5\sqrt{10}$**
20. $\sqrt{6}(2\sqrt{10} + 3\sqrt{2})$ **$4\sqrt{15} + 6\sqrt{3}$**
21. $4\sqrt{5}(3\sqrt{5} + 8\sqrt{2})$ **$60 + 32\sqrt{10}$**
22. $5\sqrt{3}(6\sqrt{10} - 6\sqrt{3})$ **$30\sqrt{30} - 90$**
23. $(\sqrt{3} - \sqrt{2})(\sqrt{15} + \sqrt{12})$
24. $(3\sqrt{11} + 3\sqrt{15})(3\sqrt{3} - 2\sqrt{2})$
25. $(5\sqrt{2} + 3\sqrt{5})(2\sqrt{10} - 5)$ **$5\sqrt{5} + 5\sqrt{2}$**

23. $3\sqrt{5} + 6 - \sqrt{30} - 2\sqrt{6}$

24. $9\sqrt{33} - 6\sqrt{22} + 27\sqrt{5} - 6\sqrt{30}$

Example 4
p. 621

26. **GEOMETRY** Find the perimeter and area of a rectangle with a width of $2\sqrt{7} - 2\sqrt{5}$ and a length of $3\sqrt{7} + 3\sqrt{5}$. **$10\sqrt{7} + 2\sqrt{5}$ units; 12 units²**

Simplify each expression. **30. $8\sqrt{5}$**

B 27. $\sqrt{\frac{1}{5}} - \sqrt{5}$ **$\frac{-4\sqrt{5}}{5}$**
28. $\sqrt{\frac{2}{3}} + \sqrt{6}$ **$\frac{4\sqrt{6}}{3}$**
29. $2\sqrt{\frac{1}{2}} + 2\sqrt{2} - \sqrt{8}$ **$\sqrt{2}$**
30. $8\sqrt{\frac{5}{4}} + 3\sqrt{20} - 10\sqrt{\frac{1}{5}}$
31. $(3 - \sqrt{5})^2$ **$14 - 6\sqrt{5}$**
32. $(\sqrt{2} + \sqrt{3})^2$ **$5 + 2\sqrt{6}$**

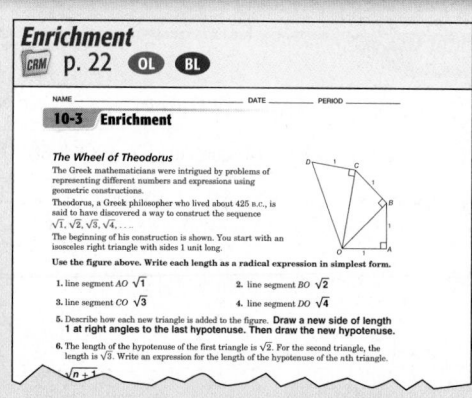

Real-World Link

The Top Thrill Dragster roller coaster at Ohio's Cedar Point is powered by a 10,000 horsepower motor–equivalent to about 10 Formula One racecars.

Source: *National Geographic*

33. **ROLLER COASTERS** The velocity v in feet per second of a roller coaster at the bottom of a hill is related to the vertical drop h in feet and the velocity v_0 of the coaster at the top of the hill by the formula $v_0 = \sqrt{v^2 - 64h}$.
    a. What velocity must a coaster have at the top of a 225-foot hill to achieve a velocity of 120 feet per second at the bottom? **0 ft/s**
    b. Explain why $v_0 = v - 8\sqrt{h}$ is not equivalent to the formula given.

33b. Sample answer: In the formula, we are taking the square root of the difference, not the square root of each term.

34. **FINANCIAL LITERACY** Tadi invests $225 in a savings account. In two years, Tadi has $270 in his account. You can use the formula $r = \sqrt{\frac{v_2}{v_0}} - 1$ to find the average annual interest rate r that the account has earned. The initial investment is v_0, and v_2 is the amount in two years. What was the average annual interest rate that Tadi's account earned? **about 9.5%**

35. **ELECTRICITY** Electricians can calculate the electrical current in amps A by using the formula $A = \frac{\sqrt{w}}{\sqrt{r}}$, where w is the power in watts and r the resistance in ohms. How much electrical current is running through a microwave oven that has 850 watts of power and 5 ohms of resistance? Write the number of amps in simplest radical form, and then estimate the amount of current to the nearest tenth. **$\sqrt{170}$; about 13 amps**

H.O.T. Problems
Use **H**igher-**O**rder **T**hinking Skills

C 36. **CHALLENGE** Determine whether the following statement is *true* or *false*. Provide an example or counterexample to support your answer.

$x + y > \sqrt{x^2 + y^2}$ when $x > 0$ and $y > 0$ **True; $1 + 1 > \sqrt{1 + 1}$ or $2 > \sqrt{2}$.**

37. **REASONING** Let $a, b, c, d,$ and f be rational numbers. Show that if you multiply $a\sqrt{b} + c\sqrt{f}$ and $a\sqrt{b} - c\sqrt{f}$, the product has no radicals. Explain why this occurs. **See margin.**

38. **OPEN ENDED** Write an equation that shows a sum of two radicals with different radicands. Explain how you could combine these terms. **See margin.**

39. **WRITING IN MATH** Describe step by step how to multiply two radical expressions, each with two terms. Write an example to demonstrate your description. **See margin.**

Enrichment
CRM p. 22 OL BL

NAME ______ DATE ______ PERIOD ______

10-3 Enrichment

The Wheel of Theodorus

The Greek mathematicians were intrigued by problems of representing different numbers and expressions using geometric constructions.

Theodorus, a Greek philosopher who lived about 425 B.C., is said to have discovered a way to construct the sequence $\sqrt{1}, \sqrt{2}, \sqrt{3}, \sqrt{4}, \ldots$.

The beginning of his construction is shown. You start with an isosceles right triangle with sides 1 unit long.

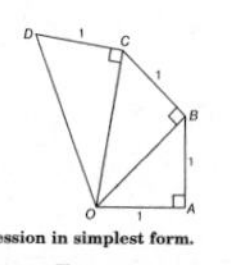

Use the figure above. Write each length as a radical expression in simplest form.

1. line segment AO **$\sqrt{1}$**
2. line segment BO **$\sqrt{2}$**
3. line segment CO **$\sqrt{3}$**
4. line segment DO **$\sqrt{4}$**
5. Describe how each new triangle is added to the figure. **Draw a new side of length 1 at right angles to the last hypotenuse. Then draw the new hypotenuse.**
6. The length of the hypotenuse of the first triangle is $\sqrt{2}$. For the second triangle, the length is $\sqrt{3}$. Write an expression for the length of the hypotenuse of the nth triangle. **$\sqrt{n+1}$**

PSAE PRACTICE 8.11.16, 8.11.14, 8.11.22, 8.11.11

40. SHORT RESPONSE The population of a town is 13,000 and is increasing by about 250 people per year. This can be represented by the equation $p = 13{,}000 + 250y$, where y is the number of years from now and p represents the population. In how many years will the population of the town be 14,500? **6 years**

41. GEOMETRY Which expression represents the sum of the lengths of the 12 edges on this rectangular solid? **C**

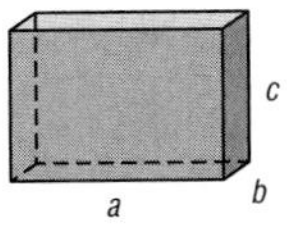

A $2(a + b + c)$
B $3(a + b + c)$
C $4(a + b + c)$
D $12(a + b + c)$

42. Which of the following is equivalent to $8(3 - y) + 5(3 - y)$? **G**

F $39 - y$
G $13(3 - y)$
H $40(30 - y)$
J $13(6 - 2y)$

43. The current I in a simple electrical circuit is given by the formula $I = \frac{V}{R}$, where V is the voltage and R is the resistance of the circuit. If the voltage remains unchanged, what effect will doubling the resistance of the circuit have on the current? **C**

A The current will remain the same.
B The current will double its previous value.
C The current will be half its previous value.
D The current will be two units more than its previous value.

Spiral Review

Simplify. (Lesson 10-2)

44. $\sqrt{18}$ $3\sqrt{2}$
45. $\sqrt{24}$ $2\sqrt{6}$
46. $\sqrt{60}$ $2\sqrt{15}$
47. $\sqrt{50a^3b^5}$ $5|a|b^2\sqrt{2ab}$
48. $\sqrt{169x^4y^7}$ $13|x^2||y^3|\sqrt{y}$
49. $\sqrt{63c^3d^4f^5}$ $3|c|d^2f^2\sqrt{7cf}$

Graph each function. Compare to the parent graph. State the domain and range. (Lesson 10-1) **50–55. See Ch. 10 Answer Appendix.**

50. $y = 2\sqrt{x}$
51. $y = -3\sqrt{x}$
52. $y = \sqrt{x + 1}$
53. $y = \sqrt{x - 4}$
54. $y = \sqrt{x} + 3$
55. $y = \sqrt{x} - 2$

56. FINANCIAL LITERACY Determine the value of an investment if \$400 is invested at an interest rate of 7.25% compounded quarterly for 7 years. (Lesson 9-7) **\$661.44**

Factor each trinomial. (Lesson 8-2)

57. $x^2 + 12x + 27$ $(x + 3)(x + 9)$
58. $y^2 + 13y + 30$ $(y + 10)(y + 3)$
59. $p^2 - 17p + 72$ $(p - 8)(p - 9)$
60. $x^2 + 6x - 7$ $(x - 1)(x + 7)$
61. $y^2 - y - 42$ $(y - 7)(y + 6)$
62. $-72 + 6w + w^2$ $(w + 12)(w - 6)$

Skills Review

Solve each equation. Round each solution to the nearest tenth, if necessary. (Lesson 2-3)

63. $-4c - 1.2 = 0.8$ -0.5
64. $-2.6q - 33.7 = 84.1$ -45.3
65. $0.3m + 4 = 9.6$ 18.7
66. $-10 - \frac{n}{5} = 6$ -80
67. $\frac{-4h - (-5)}{-7} = 13$ 24
68. $3.6t + 6 - 2.5t = 8$ 1.8

4 ASSESS

Crystal Ball Ask students to write how they think what they learned today about adding, subtracting, and multiplying radical expressions will connect with the next lesson on radical equations.

Additional Answers

37. $(a\sqrt{b} + c\sqrt{f})(a\sqrt{b} - c\sqrt{f}) = a^2\sqrt{b^2} - ac\sqrt{bf} + ac\sqrt{bf} - c^2\sqrt{f^2} = a^2b - c^2f$; Sample answer: This pattern is the difference of squares.

38. Sample answer: $\sqrt{12} + \sqrt{27} = 5\sqrt{3}$; When you simplify $\sqrt{12}$, you get $2\sqrt{3}$. When you simplify $\sqrt{27}$, you get $3\sqrt{3}$. Because $2\sqrt{3}$ and $3\sqrt{3}$ have the same radicand, you can add them.

39. Sample answer: You can use the FOIL method. You multiply the first terms within the parentheses. Then you multiply the outer terms within the parentheses. Then you would multiply the inner terms within the parentheses. And, then you would multiply the last terms within each parentheses. Combine any like terms and simplify any radicals. For example, $(\sqrt{2} + \sqrt{3})(\sqrt{5} + \sqrt{7}) = \sqrt{10} + \sqrt{14} + \sqrt{15} + \sqrt{21}$.

Differentiated Instruction OL BL

Extension Write $\sqrt{6} + \sqrt{3} = \sqrt{9} = 3$ and $\sqrt{40} = \sqrt{36} + \sqrt{4} = 8$ on the board. Ask students to explain the errors. You cannot add radical expressions unless they can be written with the same radicand, and you cannot write the square root of a sum as the sum of the square roots.

10-4 Lesson Notes

1 FOCUS

Vertical Alignment

Before Lesson 10-4
Add, subtract, and multiply radical expressions.

Lesson 10-4
Solve radical equations.
Solve radical equations with extraneous solutions.

After Lesson 10-4
Apply radical equations to trigonometry.

2 TEACH

Scaffolding Questions

Have students read the *Why?* section of the lesson.

- If you know the value for h, what do you need to isolate to solve the equation? $\sqrt{\ell}$
- How can you isolate it? Divide each side by 1.34.
- How can you remove the radical sign? Square each side of the equation.

10-4 Radical Equations

Then
You added, subtracted, and multiplied radical expressions. (Lesson 10-3)

Now
- Solve radical equations.
- Solve radical equations with extraneous solutions.

IL Learning Standards

7.A.4b Apply formulas in a wide variety of theoretical and practical real-world measurement applications involving perimeter, area, volume, angle, time, temperature, mass, speed, distance, density and monetary values.
8.C.4b Apply algebraic properties and procedures with matrices, vectors, functions and sequences using data found in business, industry and consumer situations. *Also addresses 7.B.4.*

New Vocabulary
radical equations
extraneous solutions

IL Math Online
glencoe.com
- Extra Examples
- Personal Tutor
- Self-Check Quiz
- Homework Help

Why?

The waterline length of a sailboat is the length of the line made by the water's edge when the boat is full. A sailboat's hull speed is the fastest speed that it can travel.

You can estimate hull speed h by using the formula $h = 1.34\sqrt{\ell}$, where ℓ is the length of the sailboat's waterline.

Radical Equations Equations that contain variables in the radicand, like $h = 1.34\sqrt{\ell}$, are called **radical equations**. To solve, isolate the desired variable on one side of the equation first. Then square each side of the equation to eliminate the radical.

Key Concept Power Property of Equality — For Your FOLDABLE

Words If you square both sides of a true equation, the resulting equation is still true.

Symbols If $a = b$, then $a^2 = b^2$.

Example If $\sqrt{x} = 4$, then $(\sqrt{x})^2 = 4^2$.

Real-World EXAMPLE 1 Variable as a Radicand

SAILING Idris and Sebastian are sailing in a friend's sailboat. They measure the hull speed at 9 nautical miles per hour. Find the length of the sailboat's waterline. Round to the nearest foot.

Understand You know how fast the boat will travel and that it relates to the length.

Plan The boat travels at 9 nautical miles per hour. The formula for hull speed is $h = 1.34\sqrt{\ell}$.

Solve

$h = 1.34\sqrt{\ell}$	Formula for hull speed
$9 = 1.34\sqrt{\ell}$	Substitute 9 for h.
$\frac{9}{1.34} = \frac{1.34\sqrt{\ell}}{1.34}$	Divide each side by 1.34.
$6.72 \approx \sqrt{\ell}$	Simplify.
$(6.72)^2 \approx (\sqrt{\ell})^2$	Square each side of the equation.
$45.16 \approx \ell$	Simplify.

The sailboat's waterline length is about 45 feet.

Check Check by substituting the estimate into the original formula.

$h = 1.34\sqrt{\ell}$	Formula for hull speed
$9 \stackrel{?}{=} 1.34\sqrt{45}$	$h = 9$ and $\ell = 45$
$9 \approx 8.98899327$ ✓	Multiply.

Lesson 10-4 Resources

Resource	Approaching-Level	On-Level	Beyond-Level	English Learners
Teacher Edition		• Differentiated Instruction, p. 625	• Differentiated Instruction, pp. 625, 628	
Chapter Resource Masters	• Study Guide and Intervention, pp. 23–24 • Skills Practice, p. 25 • Practice, p. 26 • Word Problem Practice, p. 27 • Graphing Calculator, p. 29	• Study Guide and Intervention, pp. 23–24 • Skills Practice, p. 25 • Practice, p. 26 • Word Problem Practice, p. 27 • Enrichment, p. 28 • Graphing Calculator, p. 29	• Practice, p. 26 • Word Problem Practice, p. 27 • Enrichment, p. 28 • Graphing Calculator, p. 29	• Study Guide and Intervention, pp. 23–24 • Skills Practice, p. 25 • Practice, p. 26 • Graphing Calculator, p. 29
Transparencies	• 5-Minute Check Transparency 10-4	• 5-Minute Check Transparency 10-4	• 5-Minute Check Transparency 10-4	• 5-Minute Check Transparency 10-4
Other	• Study Notebook	• Study Notebook	• Study Notebook	• Study Notebook

Check Your Progress

1. DRIVING The equation $v = \sqrt{2.5r}$ represents the maximum velocity that a car can travel safely on an unbanked curve when v is the maximum velocity in miles per hour and r is the radius of the turn in feet. If a road is designed for a maximum speed of 65 miles per hour, what is the radius of the turn? **1690 ft**

Personal Tutor glencoe.com

To solve a radical equation, isolate the radical first. Then square both sides of the equation.

Watch Out!

Squaring Each Side Remember that when you square each side of the equation, you must square the entire side of the equation, even if there is more than one term on the side.

EXAMPLE 2 Expression as a Radicand

Solve $\sqrt{a+5} + 7 = 12$.

$\sqrt{a+5} + 7 = 12$	Original equation
$\sqrt{a+5} = 5$	Subtract 7 from each side.
$(\sqrt{a+5})^2 = 5^2$	Square each side.
$a + 5 = 25$	Simplify.
$a = 20$	Subtract 5 from each side.

Check Your Progress Solve each equation.

2A. $\sqrt{c-3} - 2 = 4$ **39** **2B.** $4 + \sqrt{h+1} = 14$ **99**

Personal Tutor glencoe.com

Extraneous Solutions Squaring each side of an equation sometimes produces a solution that is not a solution of the original equation. These are called **extraneous solutions**. Therefore, you must check all solutions in the original equation.

StudyTip

Extraneous Solutions When checking solutions for extraneous solutions, we are only interested in principal roots.

EXAMPLE 3 Variable on Each Side

Solve $\sqrt{k+1} = k - 1$. Check your solution.

$\sqrt{k+1} = k - 1$	Original equation
$(\sqrt{k+1})^2 = (k-1)^2$	Square each side.
$k + 1 = k^2 - 2k + 1$	Simplify.
$0 = k^2 - 3k$	Subtract k and 1 from each side.
$0 = k(k-3)$	Factor.
$k = 0$ or $k - 3 = 0$	Zero Product Property
$k = 3$	Solve.

CHECK $\sqrt{k+1} = k - 1$	Original equation	$\sqrt{k+1} = k - 1$	Original equation
$\sqrt{0+1} \stackrel{?}{=} 0 - 1$	$k = 0$	$\sqrt{3+1} \stackrel{?}{=} 3 - 1$	$k = 3$
$\sqrt{1} \stackrel{?}{=} -1$	Simplify.	$\sqrt{4} \stackrel{?}{=} 2$	Simplify.
$1 \neq -1$ ✗	False	$2 = 2$ ✓	True

Since 0 does not satisfy the original equation, 3 is the only solution.

Check Your Progress

Solve each equation. Check your solution.

3A. $\sqrt{t+5} = t + 3$ **−1** **3B.** $x - 3 = \sqrt{x-1}$ **5**

Personal Tutor glencoe.com

Radical Equations

Example 1 shows how to solve a real-world problem with a variable in the radicand. **Example 2** shows how to solve a radical equation with a radical expression as the radicand.

Formative Assessment

Use the Check Your Progress exercises after each example to determine students' understanding of concepts.

Additional Examples

1 **FREE-FALL HEIGHT** An object is dropped from an unknown height and reaches the ground in 5 seconds. Use the equation $t = \frac{\sqrt{h}}{4}$, where t is time in seconds and h is height in feet, to find the height from which the object was dropped. 400 ft

2 Solve $\sqrt{x-3} + 8 = 15$. 52

Additional Examples also in Interactive Classroom PowerPoint® Presentations

IWB INTERACTIVE WHITEBOARD READY

Extraneous Solutions

Example 3 shows how to determine extraneous solutions when solving a radical equation with a variable on each side of the equal sign.

Additional Example

3 Solve $\sqrt{2-y} = y$. Check your solution. 1

Differentiated Instruction OL BL

If students are familiar with graphing calculators,

Then have students graph the equation in Example 3 to check the solution. Have them subtract $k - 1$ from both sides of the equation and then enter the equation as $Y_1 = \sqrt{x+1} - x + 1$ [GRAPH]. Press [2nd] [CALC] 2 to calculate the zero point or x-intercept of the graph. Move the cursor to the left of the x-intercept for left bound, press [ENTER], and to the right of the x-intercept for right bound and press [ENTER]. Press [ENTER] to give the coordinates of the x-intercept.

Focus on Mathematical Content

Solutions to Radical Equations When solving radical equations, it is always important to check all solutions in the *original* equation, since one or more of the solutions could be extraneous.

Check Your Understanding

Example 1 p. 624

1. GEOMETRY The surface area of a basketball is x square inches. What is the radius of the basketball if the formula for the surface area of a sphere is $SA = 4\pi r^2$? $r = \frac{\sqrt{\pi x}}{2\pi}$

Examples 2 and 3 p. 625

Solve each equation. Check your solution.

2. $\sqrt{10h} + 1 = 21$ **40**

3. $\sqrt{7r + 2} + 3 = 7$ **2**

4. $5 + \sqrt{g - 3} = 6$ **4**

5. $\sqrt{3x - 5} = x - 5$ **10**

6. $\sqrt{2n + 3} = n$ **3**

7. $\sqrt{a - 2} + 4 = a$ **6**

Practice and Problem Solving

● = **Step-by-Step Solutions** begin on page R12.
Extra Practice begins on page 815.

Example 1 p. 624

8. EXERCISE Suppose the function $S = \pi\sqrt{\frac{9.8\ell}{7}}$, where S represents speed in meters per second and ℓ is the leg length of a person in meters, can approximate the maximum speed that a person can run.

a. What is the maximum running speed of a person with a leg length of 1.1 meters to the nearest tenth of a meter? **3.9 m/s**

b. What is the leg length of a person with a running speed of 2.7 meters per second to the nearest tenth of a meter? **0.5 m**

c. As leg length increases, does maximum speed increase or decrease? Explain. **See margin.**

Examples 2 and 3 p. 625

Solve each equation. Check your solution.

9. $\sqrt{a} + 11 = 21$ **100**

10. $\sqrt{t} - 4 = 7$ **121**

11. $\sqrt{n - 3} = 6$ **39**

12. $\sqrt{c + 10} = 4$ **6**

13. $\sqrt{h - 5} = 2\sqrt{3}$ **17**

14. $\sqrt{k + 7} = 3\sqrt{2}$ **11**

15. $y = \sqrt{12 - y}$ **3**

16. $\sqrt{u + 6} = u$ **3**

17. $\sqrt{r + 3} = r - 3$ **6**

18. $\sqrt{1 - 2t} = 1 + t$ **0**

19. $5\sqrt{a - 3} + 4 = 14$ **7**

20. $2\sqrt{x - 11} - 8 = 4$ **47**

Real-World Link

The Giant Swing at Silver Dollar City in Branson, Missouri, swings riders at 45 miles per hour and reaches a height of 7 stories.

Source: Silver Dollar City Amusement Park

21. RIDES The amount of time t, in seconds, that it takes a simple pendulum to **B** complete a full swing is called the *period*. It is given by $t = 2\pi\sqrt{\frac{\ell}{32}}$, where ℓ is the length of the pendulum, in feet.

a. The Giant Swing completes a period in about 8 seconds. About how long is the pendulum's arm? Round to the nearest foot. **52 ft**

b. Does increasing the length of the pendulum increase or decrease the period? Explain. **See margin.**

Solve each equation. Check your solution.

22. $\sqrt{6a - 6} = a + 1$ **no solution**

23. $\sqrt{x^2 + 9x + 15} = x + 5$ **no solution**

24. $6\sqrt{\frac{5k}{4}} - 3 = 0$ $\frac{1}{5}$

25. $\sqrt{\frac{5y}{6}} - 10 = 4$ **235.2**

26. $\sqrt{2a^2 - 121} = a$ **11**

27. $\sqrt{5x^2 - 9} = 2x$ **3**

28. GEOMETRY The formula for the slant height c of a cone is $c = \sqrt{h^2 + r^2}$, where h is the height of the cone and r is the radius of its base. Find the height of the cone if the slant height is 4 and the radius is 2. Round to the nearest tenth. $2\sqrt{3}$ **or** ≈ 3.5

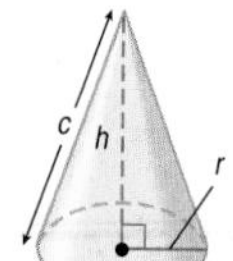

3 PRACTICE

Formative Assessment

Use Exercises 1–7 to check for understanding.

Use the chart at the bottom of this page to customize assignments for your students.

Multiple Representations In Exercise 29, students solve a radical equation algebraically and by use of a graphing calculator and compare the solutions.

Exercise Alert

Graphing For Exercise 29, students will need grid paper.

Watch Out!

Find the Error For Exercise 31, have students carefully check each step in the two solutions to determine whether Jada, Fina, or both made an error. Have them identify the step in which the error was made and the likely cause of the error. Have students discuss ways in which they can avoid similar errors.

Additional Answers

8c. Increases; sample answer: As the leg length increases, the value of the radicand also increases.

21b. Increases; sample answer: If the length is longer, the quotient and square root will be a greater number than before.

29a.

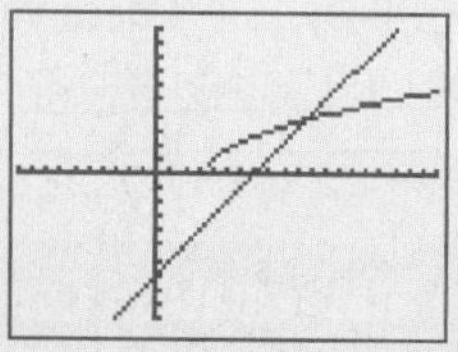

[−10, 20] scl: 1 by [−10, 10] scl: 1

29c.

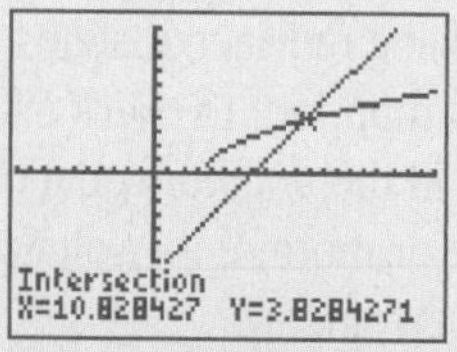

[−10, 20] scl: 1 by [−10, 10] scl: 1

Differentiated Homework Options

Level	Assignment		Two-Day Option	
AL Basic	8–20, 31–35, 37–67		9–19 odd, 38–41	8–20 even, 31–35, 37, 42–67
OL Core	9–27 odd, 28–35, 37–67		8–20, 38–41	21–35, 37, 42–67
BL Advanced	21–61, (optional: 62–67)			

29 **MULTIPLE REPRESENTATIONS** Consider $\sqrt{2x - 7} = x - 7$.

a. **GRAPHICAL** Clear the Y= list. Enter the left side of the equation as $Y1 = \sqrt{2x - 7}$. Enter the right side of the equation as $Y2 = x - 7$. Press GRAPH. **See margin.**

b. **GRAPHICAL** Sketch what is shown on the screen. **See students' work.**

c. **ANALYTICAL** Use the **intersect** feature on the CALC menu to find the point of intersection. **See margin.**

d. **ANALYTICAL** Solve the radical equation algebraically. How does your solution compare to the solution from the graph? **About 10.83; they are the same.**

Real-World Link

Packaging has several objectives, including physical protection, information transmission, marketing, convenience, security, and portion control.

Source: *Packaging World*

30. **PACKAGING** A cylindrical container of chocolate drink mix has a volume of 162 cubic inches. The radius r of the container can be found by using the formula $r = \sqrt{\frac{V}{\pi h}}$, where V is the volume of the container and h is the height.

a. If the radius is 2.5 inches, find the height of the container. Round to the nearest hundredth. **8.25 in.**

b. If the height of the container is 10 inches, find the radius. Round to the nearest hundredth. **2.27 in.**

H.O.T. Problems

Use **H**igher-**O**rder **T**hinking Skills

C

31. **FIND THE ERROR** Jada and Fina solved $\sqrt{6 - b} = \sqrt{b + 10}$. Is either of them correct? Explain. **Jada; Fina had the wrong sign for $2b$ in the fourth step.**

Jada	Fina
$\sqrt{6-b} = \sqrt{b+10}$	$\sqrt{6-b} = \sqrt{b+10}$
$(\sqrt{6-b})^2 = (\sqrt{b+10})^2$	$(\sqrt{6-b})^2 = (\sqrt{b+10})^2$
$6 - b = b + 10$	$6 - b = b + 10$
$-2b = 4$	$2b = 4$
$b = -2$	$b = 2$
Check $\sqrt{6-(-2)} \stackrel{?}{=} \sqrt{(-2)+10}$	Check $\sqrt{6-(2)} \stackrel{?}{=} \sqrt{(2)+10}$
$\sqrt{8} = \sqrt{8}$ ✓	$\sqrt{4} \neq \sqrt{12}$ X
	no solution

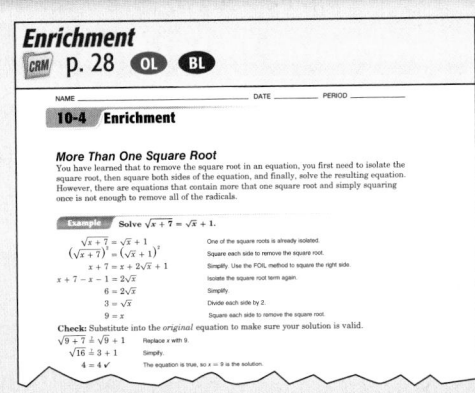

32. **REASONING** Which equation has the same solution set as $\sqrt{4} = \sqrt{x + 2}$? Explain.

A. $\sqrt{4} = \sqrt{x} + \sqrt{2}$ B. $4 = x + 2$ C. $2 - \sqrt{2} = \sqrt{x}$

33. **REASONING** Explain how solving $5 = \sqrt{x} + 1$ is different from solving $5 = \sqrt{x + 1}$.

34. **OPEN ENDED** Write a radical equation with a variable on each side. Then solve the equation. **Sample answer: $\sqrt{2x - 1} = x$; 1**

35. **REASONING** Is the following equation *sometimes*, *always* or *never* true? Explain.

$$\sqrt{(x - 2)^2} = x - 2$$

36. **CHALLENGE** Solve $\sqrt{x + 9} = \sqrt{3} + \sqrt{x}$. **3**

37. **WRITING IN MATH** Write some general rules about how to solve radical equations. Demonstrate your rules by solving a radical equation. **See margin.**

32. The solution of the given equation is 2. Choice B is the only equation that is true when $x = 2$.

33. Sample answer: In the first equation, you have to isolate the radical first by subtracting 1 from each side. Then square each side to find the value of x. In the second equation, the radical is already isolated, so square each side to start. Then subtract 1 from each side to solve for x.

35. Sometimes; the equation is true for $x \geq 2$, but false for $x < 2$.

37. Sample answer: Add or subtract any expressions that are not in the radicand from each side. Multiply or divide any values that are not in the radicand to each side. Square each side of the equation. Solve for the variable as you did previously. See students' examples.

Study Guide and Intervention
CRM pp. 23–24 AL OL ELL

NAME ______ DATE ______ PERIOD ______

10-4 Study Guide and Intervention

Radical Equations

Radical Equations Equations containing radicals with variables in the radicand are called **radical equations**. These can be solved by first using the following steps.

Step 1 Isolate the radical on one side of the equation.
Step 2 Square each side of the equation to eliminate the radical.

Example 1 Solve $16 = \frac{\sqrt{x}}{2}$ for x.

$16 = \frac{\sqrt{x}}{2}$	Original equation
$2(16) = 2\left(\frac{\sqrt{x}}{2}\right)$	Multiply each side by 2.
$32 = \sqrt{x}$	Simplify.
$(32)^2 = (\sqrt{x})^2$	Square each side.
$1024 = x$	Simplify.

The solution is 1024, which checks in the original equation.

Example 2 Solve $\sqrt{4x - 7} + 2 = 7$.

$\sqrt{4x-7} + 2 = 7$	Original equation
$\sqrt{4x-7} + 2 - 2 = 7 - 2$	Subtract 2 from each side.
$\sqrt{4x-7} = 5$	Simplify.
$(\sqrt{4x-7})^2 = 5^2$	Square each side.
$4x - 7 = 25$	Simplify.
$4x - 7 + 7 = 25 + 7$	Add 7 to each side.
$4x = 32$	Simplify.
$x = 8$	Divide each side by 4.

The solution is 8, which checks in the original equation.

Exercises

Solve each equation. Check your solution.

1. $\sqrt{a} = 8$ **64**
2. $\sqrt{a} + 6 = 32$ **676**
3. $2\sqrt{x} = 8$ **16**
4. $7 = \sqrt{26 - n}$ **−23**
5. $\sqrt{-a} = 6$ **−36**
6. $\sqrt{3r^2} = 3$ **$\pm\sqrt{3}$**
7. $2\sqrt{3} = \sqrt{y}$ **12**
8. $2\sqrt{3a} - 2 = 7$ **$6\frac{3}{4}$**
9. $\sqrt{x - 4} = 6$ **40**
10. $\sqrt{2m + 3} = 5$ **11**
11. $\sqrt{3b - 2} + 19 = 24$ **9**
12. $\sqrt{4x - 1} = 3$ **$\frac{5}{2}$**
13. $\sqrt{3r + 2} = 2\sqrt{3}$ **$\frac{10}{3}$**
14. $\sqrt{\frac{x}{2}} = \frac{1}{2}$ **$\frac{1}{2}$**
15. $\sqrt{\frac{x}{8}} = 4$ **128**
16. $\sqrt{6x^2 + 5x} = 2$ **$\frac{1}{2}, -\frac{4}{3}$**
17. $\sqrt{\frac{x}{3}} + 6 = 8$ **12**
18. $2\sqrt{\frac{3x}{5}} + 3 = 11$ **$26\frac{2}{3}$**

Chapter 10 23 Glencoe Algebra 1

Lesson 10-4

Practice
CRM p. 26 AL OL BL ELL

NAME ______ DATE ______ PERIOD ______

10-4 Practice

Radical Equations

Solve each equation. Check your solution.

1. $\sqrt{-b} = 8$ **−64**
2. $4\sqrt{3} = \sqrt{x}$ **48**
3. $2\sqrt{4r} + 3 = 11$ **4**
4. $6 - \sqrt{2y} = -2$ **32**
5. $\sqrt{k + 2} - 3 = 7$ **98**
6. $\sqrt{m - 5} = 4\sqrt{3}$ **53**
7. $\sqrt{6t + 12} = 8\sqrt{6}$ **62**
8. $\sqrt{3j - 11} + 2 = 9$ **20**
9. $\sqrt{2x + 15} + 5 = 18$ **77**
10. $\sqrt{\frac{3d}{5}} - 4 = 2$ **60**
11. $6\sqrt{\frac{3x}{3}} - 3 = 0$ **$\frac{1}{4}$**
12. $6 + \sqrt{\frac{5r}{6}} = -2$ **∅**
13. $y = \sqrt{y + 6}$ **3**
14. $\sqrt{15 - 2x} = x$ **3**
15. $\sqrt{w + 4} = w + 4$ **−4, −3**
16. $\sqrt{17 - k} = k - 5$ **8**
17. $\sqrt{5m - 16} = m - 2$ **4, 5**
18. $\sqrt{24 + 8q} = q + 3$ **−3, 5**
19. $\sqrt{4t + 17} - t - 3 = 0$ **2**
20. $4 - \sqrt{3m + 28} = m$ **−1**
21. $\sqrt{10p + 61} - 7 = p$ **−6, 2**
22. $\sqrt{2x^2 - 9} = x$ **3**

23. **ELECTRICITY** The voltage V in a circuit is given by $V = \sqrt{PR}$, where P is the power in watts and R is the resistance in ohms.

a. If the voltage in a circuit is 120 volts and the circuit produces 1500 watts of power, what is the resistance in the circuit? **9.6 ohms**

b. Suppose an electrician designs a circuit with 110 volts and a resistance of 10 ohms. How much power will the circuit produce? **1210 watts**

24. **FREE FALL** Assuming no air resistance, the time t in seconds that it takes an object to fall h feet can be determined by the equation $t = \frac{\sqrt{h}}{4}$.

a. If a skydiver jumps from an airplane and free falls for 10 seconds before opening the parachute, how many feet does the skydiver fall? **1600 ft**

b. Suppose a second skydiver jumps and free falls for 6 seconds. How many feet does the second skydiver fall? **576 ft**

Chapter 10 26 Glencoe Algebra 1

Word Problem Practice
CRM p. 27 AL OL BL ELL

NAME ______ DATE ______ PERIOD ______

10-4 Word Problem Practice

Radical Equations

1. **SUBMARINES** The distance in miles that the lookout of a submarine can see is approximately $d = 1.22\sqrt{h}$, where h is the height in feet above the surface of the water. How far would a submarine periscope have to be above the water to locate a ship 6 miles away? Round your answer to the nearest tenth. **24.2 ft**

2. **PETS** Find the value of x if the perimeter of a triangular dog pen is 25 meters. **x = 8**

3. **LOGGING** Doyle's log rule estimates the amount of usable lumber (in board feet) that can be milled from a shipment of logs. It is represented by the equation $B = L\left(\frac{d - 4}{4}\right)^2$, where d is the log diameter (in inches) and L is the log length (in feet). Suppose the truck carries 20 logs, each 25 feet long, and that the shipment yields a total of 6000 board feet of lumber. Estimate the diameter of the logs to the nearest inch. Assume that all the logs have uniform length and diameter. **18 in.**

4. **FIREFIGHTING** Fire fighters calculate the flow rate of water out of a particular hydrant by using the following formula.

$$F = 26.9d^2\sqrt{p}$$

F is the flow rate (in gallons per minute), p is the nozzle pressure (in pounds per square inch), and d is the diameter of the hose (in inches). In order to effectively fight a fire, the combined flow rate of two hoses needs to be about 2430 gallons per minute. The diameter of each of the hoses is 3 inches, but the nozzle pressure of one hose is 4 times that of the second hose. What are the nozzle pressures for each hose? Round your answers to the nearest tenth.

11.2 psi and 44.8 psi

5. **GEOMETRY** The lateral surface area s of a right circular cone, not including the base, is represented by the equation $s = \pi r\sqrt{r^2 + h^2}$, where r is the radius of the circular base and h is the height of the cone.

a. If the lateral surface area of a funnel is 127.54 square centimeters and its radius is 3.5 centimeters, find its height to the nearest tenth of a centimeter.

11.1 cm

b. What is the area of the opening (i.e., the base) of the funnel?

38.5 cm²

Chapter 10 27 Glencoe Algebra 1

Lesson 10-4

Enrichment
CRM p. 28 OL BL

NAME ______ DATE ______ PERIOD ______

10-4 Enrichment

More Than One Square Root

You have learned that to remove the square root in an equation, you first need to isolate the square root, then square both sides of the equation, and finally, solve the resulting equation. However, there are equations that contain more that one square root and simply squaring once is not enough to remove all of the radicals.

Example Solve $\sqrt{x + 7} = \sqrt{x} + 1$.

$\sqrt{x+7} = \sqrt{x} + 1$	One of the square roots is already isolated.
$(\sqrt{x+7})^2 = (\sqrt{x} + 1)^2$	Square each side to remove the square root.
$x + 7 = x + 2\sqrt{x} + 1$	Simplify. Use the FOIL method to square the right side.
$x + 7 - x - 1 = 2\sqrt{x}$	Isolate the square root term again.
$6 = 2\sqrt{x}$	Simplify.
$3 = \sqrt{x}$	Divide each side by 2.
$9 = x$	Square each side to remove the square root.

Check: Substitute into the *original* equation to make sure your solution is valid.

$\sqrt{9+7} \stackrel{?}{=} \sqrt{9} + 1$	Replace x with 9.
$\sqrt{16} \stackrel{?}{=} 3 + 1$	Simplify.
$4 = 4$ ✓	The equation is true, so $x = 9$ is the solution.

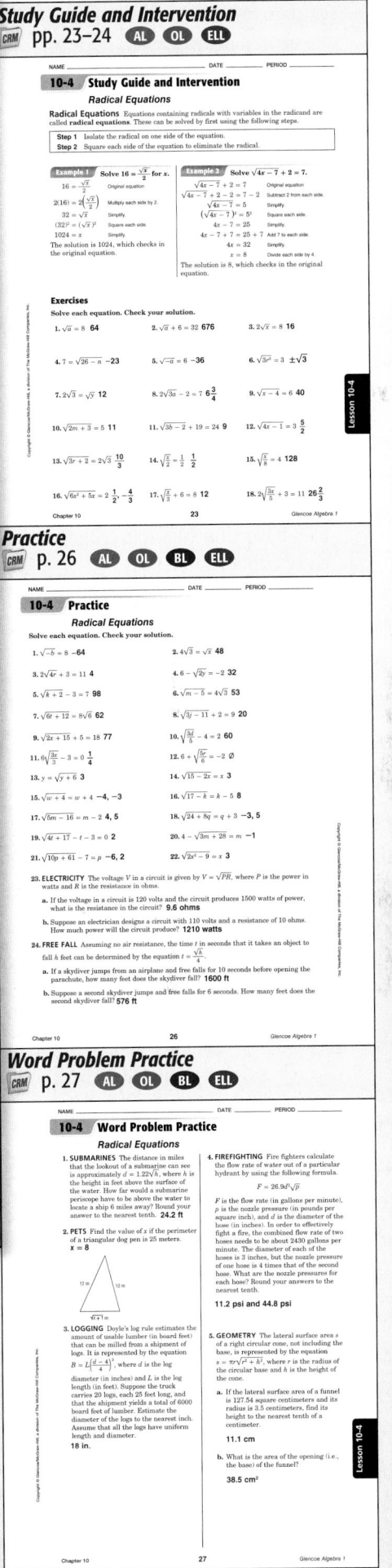

4 ASSESS

Yesterday's News Have students explain how yesterday's lesson on operations with radical expressions helped with today's lesson on radical equations.

Formative Assessment

Check for student understanding of concepts in Lessons 10-3 and 10-4.

CRM Quiz 2, p. 57

TEACH with TECH

BLOG On your secure classroom blog have students write a blog entry about extraneous solutions. Have them explain what extraneous solutions are and how they can check their solutions both graphically and algebraically.

Additional Answers

56. Yes; 12 is a real number and therefore a monomial.

57. Yes; $4x^3$ is the product of a number and three variables.

58. No; $a - 2b$ shows subtraction, not multiplication alone of numbers and variables.

59. No; $4n + 5p$ shows addition, not multiplication alone of numbers and variables.

60. No; $\frac{x}{y^2}$ has a variable in the denominator.

61. Yes; $\frac{1}{5}abc^{14}$ is the product of a number, $\frac{1}{5}$, and several variables.

PSAE PRACTICE 9.11.10, 8.11.06, 8.11.09, 8.11.19

38. SHORT RESPONSE Zack needs to drill a hole at *A*, *B*, *C*, *D*, and *E* on circle *P*.

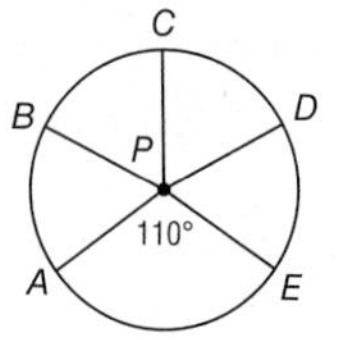

If Zack drills holes so that $m\angle APE = 110°$ and the other four angles are congruent, what is $m\angle CPD$? **62.5°**

39. Which expression is undefined when $w = 3$? **C**

A $\frac{w-3}{w+1}$

B $\frac{w^2-3w}{3w}$

C $\frac{w+1}{w^2-3w}$

D $\frac{3w}{3w^2}$

40. What is the slope of a line that is parallel to the line? **J**

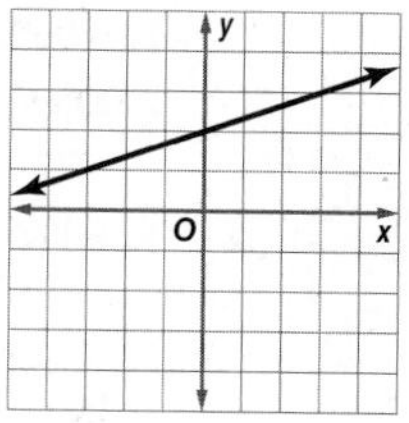

F -3

G $-\frac{1}{3}$

H 3

J $\frac{1}{3}$

41. What are the solutions of $\sqrt{x+3} - 1 = x - 4$? **D**

A 1, 6

B $-1, -6$

C 1

D 6

Spiral Review

42. ELECTRICITY The voltage *V* required for a circuit is given by $V = \sqrt{PR}$, where *P* is the power in watts and *R* is the resistance in ohms. How many more volts are needed to light a 100-watt light bulb than a 75-watt light bulb if the resistance of both is 110 ohms? (Lesson 10-3) **about 14**

Simplify each expression. (Lesson 10-2)

43. $\sqrt{6} \cdot \sqrt{8}$ $4\sqrt{3}$

44. $\sqrt{3} \cdot \sqrt{6}$ $3\sqrt{2}$

45. $7\sqrt{3} \cdot 2\sqrt{6}$ $42\sqrt{2}$

46. $\sqrt{\frac{27}{a^2}}$ $\frac{3\sqrt{3}}{|a|}$

47. $\sqrt{\frac{5c^5}{4d^5}}$ $\frac{c^2\sqrt{5cd}}{2|d^3|}$

48. $\frac{\sqrt{9x^3y}}{\sqrt{16x^2y^2}}$ $\frac{3\sqrt{xy}}{4|y|}$

49. PHYSICAL SCIENCE A projectile is shot straight up from ground level. Its height *h*, in feet, after *t* seconds is given by $h = 96t - 16t^2$. Find the value(s) of *t* when *h* is 96 feet. (Lesson 9-5) **about 1.3 s and 4.7 s**

Factor each trinomial, if possible. If the trinomial cannot be factored using integers, write *prime*. (Lesson 8-4)

50. $2x^2 + 7x + 5$ $(2x + 5)(x + 1)$

51. $6p^2 + 5p - 6$ $(2p + 3)(3p - 2)$

52. $5d^2 + 6d - 8$ $(5d - 4)(d + 2)$

53. $8k^2 - 19k + 9$ **prime**

54. $9g^2 - 12g + 4$ $(3g - 2)(3g - 2)$

55. $2a^2 - 9a - 18$ $(2a + 3)(a - 6)$

Determine whether each expression is a monomial. Write *yes* or *no*. Explain. (Lesson 7-1) **56–61. See margin.**

56. 12

57. $4x^3$

58. $a - 2b$

59. $4n + 5p$

60. $\frac{x}{y^2}$

61. $\frac{1}{5}abc^{14}$

Skills Review

Simplify. (Lesson 1-1)

62. 9^2 **81**

63. 10^6 **1,000,000**

64. 4^5 **1024**

65. $(8v)^2$ $64v^2$

66. $\left(\frac{w^3}{9}\right)^2$ $\frac{w^6}{81}$

67. $(10y^2)^3$ $1000y^6$

Differentiated Instruction

BL

Extension Explain that the *geometric mean* of two positive numbers is the positive square root of their product. Ask students to find a pair of consecutive positive even integers whose geometric mean is $4\sqrt{5}$. Since $4\sqrt{5} = \sqrt{x(x+2)}$, $x = 8$ or -10. Since the two numbers are positive, *x* must equal only 8 and, therefore, $x + 2 = 10$. The two numbers are 8 and 10.

IL Learning Standards
7.A.4b, 8.B.4b

Graph each function. Compare to the parent graph. State the domain and range. (Lesson 10-1) **1–6. See Ch. 10 Answer Appendix.**

1. $y = 2\sqrt{x}$
2. $y = -4\sqrt{x}$
3. $y = \frac{1}{2}\sqrt{x}$
4. $y = \sqrt{x} - 3$
5. $y = \sqrt{x - 1}$
6. $y = 2\sqrt{x - 2}$

7. **GEOMETRY** The length of the side of a square is given by the function $s = \sqrt{A}$, where A is the area of the square. What is the length of the side of a square that has an area of 121 square inches? **B** (Lesson 10-1)

   A 121 inches C 44 inches
   B 11 inches D 10 inches

Simplify each expression. (Lesson 10-2)

8. $2\sqrt{25}$ **10**
9. $\sqrt{12} \cdot \sqrt{8}$ $4\sqrt{6}$
10. $\sqrt{72xy^5z^6}$ $6y^2|z^3|\sqrt{2xy}$
11. $\frac{3}{1 + \sqrt{5}}$ $\frac{3 - 3\sqrt{5}}{-4}$
12. $\frac{1}{5 - \sqrt{7}}$ $\frac{5 + \sqrt{7}}{18}$

13. **SATELLITES** A satellite is launched into orbit 200 kilometers above Earth. The orbital velocity of a satellite is given by the formula $v = \sqrt{\frac{Gm_E}{r}}$. v is velocity in meters per second, G is a given constant, m_E is the mass of Earth, and r is the radius of the satellite's orbit in meters. (Lesson 10-2)

   a. The radius of Earth is 6,380,000 meters. What is the radius of the satellite's orbit in meters? **6,580,000 m**

   b. The mass of Earth is 5.97×10^{24} kilograms, and the constant G is $6.67 \times 10^{-11}\ \text{N} \cdot \frac{\text{m}^2}{\text{kg}^2}$ where N is in Newtons. Use the formula to find the orbital velocity of the satellite in meters per second. **about 7779 m/s**

14. Which expression is equivalent to $\sqrt{\frac{16}{32}}$? (Lesson 10-2) **H**

   F $\frac{1}{2}$
   G 2
   H $\frac{\sqrt{2}}{2}$
   J 4

Simplify each expression. (Lesson 10-3)

15. $3\sqrt{2} + 5\sqrt{2}$ $8\sqrt{2}$
16. $\sqrt{11} - 3\sqrt{11}$ $-2\sqrt{11}$
17. $6\sqrt{2} + 4\sqrt{50}$ $26\sqrt{2}$
18. $\sqrt{27} - \sqrt{48}$ $-\sqrt{3}$
19. $4\sqrt{3}(2\sqrt{6})$ $24\sqrt{2}$
20. $3\sqrt{20}(2\sqrt{5})$ **60**
21. $(\sqrt{5} + \sqrt{7})(\sqrt{20} + \sqrt{3})$ $10 + \sqrt{15} + 2\sqrt{35} + \sqrt{21}$

22. **GEOMETRY** Find the area of the rectangle. (Lesson 10-3) $36\sqrt{5}$

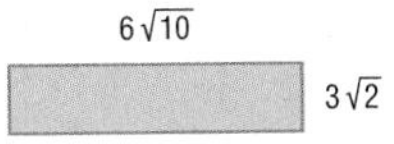

Solve each equation. Check your solution. (Lesson 10-4)

23. $\sqrt{5x} - 1 = 4$ **5**
24. $\sqrt{a - 2} = 6$ **38**
25. $\sqrt{15 - x} = 4$ **−1**
26. $\sqrt{3x^2 - 32} = x$ **4**
27. $\sqrt{2x - 1} = 2x - 7$ **5**
28. $\sqrt{x + 1} + 2 = 4$ **3**

29. **GEOMETRY** The lateral surface area S of a cone can be found by using the formula $S = \pi r\sqrt{r^2 + h^2}$, where r is the radius of the base and h is the height of the cone. Find the height of the cone. (Lesson 10-4) **about 12.5 in.**

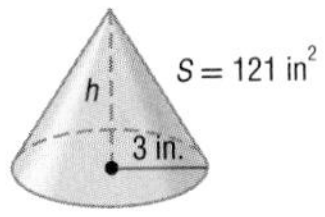

Formative Assessment

Use the Mid-Chapter Quiz to assess students' progress in the first half of the chapter.

For problems answered incorrectly, have students review the lessons indicated in parentheses.

ExamView Assessment Suite — Customize and create multiple versions of your Mid-Chapter Test and their answer keys.

FOLDABLES Follow-Up

Before students complete the Mid-Chapter Quiz, encourage them to review the information for Lessons 10-1 through 10-4 in their Foldables.

Intervention Planner

Tier 1 On Level	Tier 2 Strategic Intervention (approaching grade level)	Tier 3 Intensive Intervention (2 or more grades below level)
If students miss about 25% of the exercises or less,	**If** students miss about 50% of the exercises,	**If** students miss about 75% of the exercises,
Then choose a resource: **SE** Lessons 10-1, 10-2, 10-3, and 10-4 **CRM** Skills Practice, pp. 7, 13, 19, and 25 **TE** Chapter Project, p. 602 **IL Math Online** Self-Check Quiz	**Then** choose a resource: **CRM** Study Guide and Intervention, Chapter 10, pp. 5, 11, 17, and 23 *Quick Review Math Handbook* **IL Math Online** Extra Examples, Personal Tutor, Homework Help	**Then** use *Math Triumphs, Alg. 1* **IL Math Online** Extra Examples, Personal Tutor, Homework Help, Review Vocabulary

10-5 Lesson Notes

1 FOCUS

Vertical Alignment

Before Lesson 10-5
Solve quadratic equations by using the Square Root Property.

Lesson 10-5
Solve problems by using the Pythagorean Theorem.
Determine whether a triangle is a right triangle.

After Lesson 10-5
Use the Distance Formula to find the distance between two points on a coordinate plane.

2 TEACH

Scaffolding Questions

Have students read the *Why?* section of the lesson.

Ask:

- What is the shape of most television screens? rectangles
- Which measurement on a television is longest: the height, the width, or the diagonal? diagonal
- If you draw a triangle to represent the height, width, and diagonal of the television, which side is opposite the right angle? diagonal

10-5 The Pythagorean Theorem

Then

You solved quadratic equations by using the Square Root Property. (Lesson 8-6)

Now

- Solve problems by using the Pythagorean Theorem.
- Determine whether a triangle is a right triangle.

IL Learning Standards

7.A.4b Apply formulas in a wide variety of theoretical and real-world measurement applications involving perimeter, area, volume, angle, time, temperature, mass, speed, distance, density and monetary values.

New Vocabulary

hypotenuse
legs
converse
Pythagorean triple

IL Math Online

glencoe.com

- Extra Examples
- Personal Tutor
- Self-Check Quiz
- Homework Help

Why?

The designer television shown is made of black and white leather just like a real soccer ball. Televisions are measured along the diagonal of the screen. If the height and width of the screen is known, the Pythagorean Theorem can be used to find the measure of the diagonal.

The Pythagorean Theorem In a right triangle, the side opposite the right angle is the **hypotenuse**. This side is always the longest. The other two sides are the **legs**.

Key Concept — The Pythagorean Theorem

For Your FOLDABLE

Words If a triangle is a right triangle, then the square of the length of the hypotenuse is equal to the sum of the squares of the lengths of the legs.

Symbols $c^2 = a^2 + b^2$

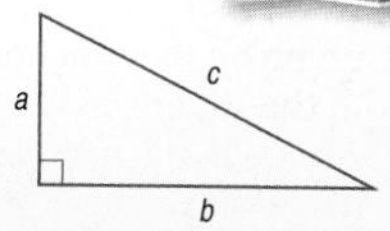

EXAMPLE 1 Find the Length of a Side

Find each missing length. If necessary, round to the nearest hundredth.

a.

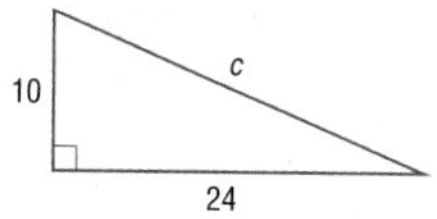

$c^2 = a^2 + b^2$	Pythagorean Theorem
$c^2 = 10^2 + 24^2$	$a = 10$ and $b = 24$
$c^2 = 100 + 576$	Evaluate squares.
$c^2 = 676$	Simplify.
$c = \pm\sqrt{676}$	Take the square root of each side.
$c = \pm 26$	$(\pm 26)^2 = 676$

A length cannot be negative. The missing length is 26 units.

b.

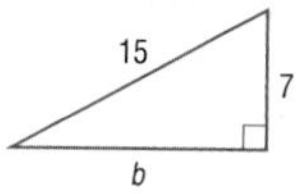

$c^2 = a^2 + b^2$	Pythagorean Theorem
$15^2 = 7^2 + b^2$	$a = 7$ and $c = 15$
$225 = 49 + b^2$	Evaluate squares.
$176 = b^2$	Subtract 49 from each side.
$\pm\sqrt{176} = b$	Take the square root of each side.
$\pm 13.27 \approx b$	Use a calculator to evaluate $\sqrt{176}$.

The missing length is 13.27 units.

Check Your Progress

1A. 10

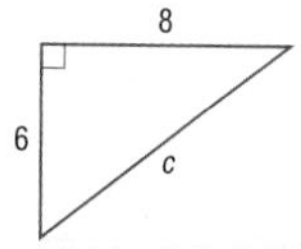

1B. 10.58

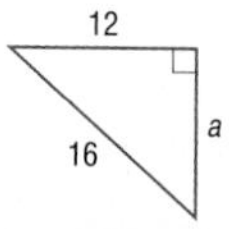

Personal Tutor glencoe.com

Lesson 10-5 Resources

Resource	Approaching-Level	On-Level	Beyond-Level	English Learners
Teacher Edition			• Differentiated Instruction, pp. 631, 635	
Chapter Resource Masters	• Study Guide and Intervention, pp. 30–31 • Skills Practice, p. 32 • Practice, p. 33 • Word Problem Practice, p. 34 • Spreadsheet Activity, p. 36	• Study Guide and Intervention, pp. 30–31 • Skills Practice, p. 32 • Practice, p. 33 • Word Problem Practice, p. 34 • Enrichment, p. 35 • Spreadsheet Activity, p. 36	• Practice, p. 33 • Word Problem Practice, p. 34 • Enrichment, p. 35 • Spreadsheet Activity, p. 36	• Study Guide and Intervention, pp. 30–31 • Skills Practice, p. 32 • Practice, p. 33 • Spreadsheet Activity, p. 36
Transparencies	• 5-Minute Check Transparency 10-5	• 5-Minute Check Transparency 10-5	• 5-Minute Check Transparency 10-5	• 5-Minute Check Transparency 10-5
Other	• Study Notebook • Teaching Algebra with Manipulatives	• Study Notebook • Teaching Algebra with Manipulatives	• Study Notebook	• Study Notebook • Teaching Algebra with Manipulatives

Real-World Link

A keelboat is a sailboat with a weighted keel, a vertical fin at the bottom of the boat. Keels are 20 to 30 inches in length.

Source: United States Sailing Association

Real-World EXAMPLE 2 Find the Length of a Side

SAILING **The sail of a keelboat forms a right triangle as shown. Find the height of the sail.**

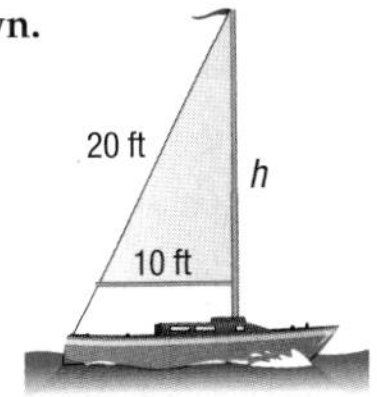

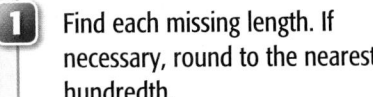

$20^2 = h^2 + 10^2$	Pythagorean Theorem
$400 = h^2 + 100$	Evaluate squares.
$300 = h^2$	Subtract 100 from each side.
$\pm 17.32 \approx h$	Take the square root of each side.
$17.32 \approx h$	Use the positive value.

The sail is approximately 17.32 feet high.

Check Your Progress

2. Suppose the longest side of the sail is 30 feet long and the shortest side is 14 feet long. Find the height of the sail. about 26.53 ft

Personal Tutor glencoe.com

Right Triangles If you exchange the hypothesis and conclusion of an if-then statement, the result is the **converse** of the statement. The converse of the Pythagorean Theorem can be used to determine whether a triangle is a right triangle.

Key Concept Converse of the Pythagorean Theorem — For Your FOLDABLE

If a triangle has side lengths a, b, and c such that $c^2 = a^2 + b^2$, then the triangle is a right triangle. If $c^2 \neq a^2 + b^2$, then the triangle is not a right triangle.

A **Pythagorean triple** is a group of three counting numbers that satisfy the equation $c^2 = a^2 + b^2$, where c is the greatest number. Examples include (3, 4, 5) and (5, 12, 13). Multiples of Pythagorean triples also satisfy the converse of the Pythagorean Theorem, so (6, 8, 10) is also a Pythagorean triple.

EXAMPLE 3 Check for Right Triangles

Determine whether 9, 12, and 16 can be the lengths of the sides of a right triangle.

Since the measure of the longest side is 16, let $c = 16$, $a = 9$, and $b = 12$.

$c^2 = a^2 + b^2$	Pythagorean Theorem
$16^2 \stackrel{?}{=} 9^2 + 12^2$	$a = 9$, $b = 12$, and $c = 16$
$256 \stackrel{?}{=} 81 + 144$	Evaluate squares.
$256 \neq 225$	Add.

Since $c^2 \neq a^2 + b^2$, segments with these measures cannot form a right triangle.

Check Your Progress

Determine whether each set of measures can be the lengths of the sides of a right triangle.

3A. 30, 40, 50 yes; $30^2 + 40^2 = 50^2$

3B. 6, 12, 18 no; $6^2 + 12^2 \neq 18^2$

Personal Tutor glencoe.com

The Pythagorean Theorem

Example 1 shows how to use the Pythagorean Theorem to find the missing length of a side of a right triangle. **Example 2** shows how to use the Pythagorean Theorem to solve a real-world problem.

Formative Assessment

Use the Check Your Progress exercises after each example to determine students' understanding of concepts.

Additional Examples

1 Find each missing length. If necessary, round to the nearest hundredth.

a. 30 units

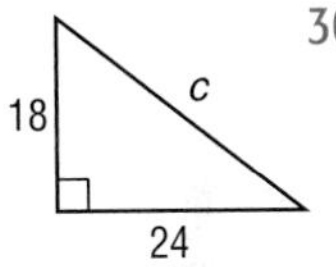

b. 13.23 units

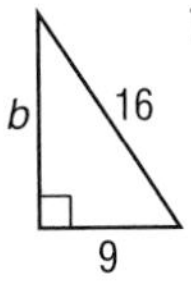

2 **TELEVISION** The diagonal of a television screen is 32 inches. The width of the screen is 21 inches. Find the height of the screen. $\approx$ 24.15 in.

Additional Examples also in Interactive Classroom PowerPoint® Presentations

IWB INTERACTIVE WHITEBOARD READY

Right Triangles

Example 3 shows how to use the converse of the Pythagorean Theorem to determine whether a triangle is a right triangle.

Additional Example

3 Determine whether 7, 12, and 15 can be the lengths of the sides of a right triangle. no; $7^2 + 12^2 \neq 15^2$

Differentiated Instruction BL

If students would benefit from further exploration of Pythagorean triples,

Then have them use manipulatives with equivalent lengths to build triangles with side lengths that form Pythagorean triples. Manipulatives could include algebra tiles, blocks, integer rods, or cubes.

Focus on Mathematical Content

Pythagorean Theorem The Pythagorean Theorem can be used to find the length of a side of a right triangle when the lengths of the other two sides are known. To find the length of a side, rewrite the formula for the Pythagorean Theorem in terms of that side; for example, to find the length of the hypotenuse, solve for c: $c = \sqrt{a^2 + b^2}$.

3 PRACTICE

Formative Assessment

Use Exercises 1–9 to check for understanding.

Use the chart at the bottom of this page to customize assignments for your students.

Watch Out!

Preventing Errors Point out to students that with Pythagorean triples, the greatest value is always the measure of the hypotenuse, and the two lesser values are the measures of the two legs.

Converses Tell students that the converses of theorems are not necessarily true. But the converse of the Pythagorean Theorem is true.

TEACH with TECH

DOCUMENT CAMERA Have students bring in objects, or photos of objects that have right triangles to be displayed (such as a toy boat with a triangular sail). Measure two of the sides and have student use the Pythagorean Theorem to find the length of the third side.

Check Your Understanding

Example 1 p. 630

Find each missing length. If necessary, round to the nearest hundredth.

1. 5
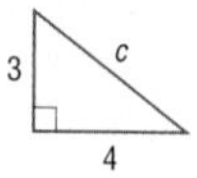

2. 20.62
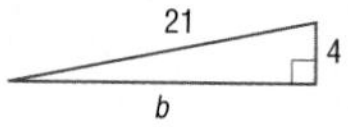

3. 18.03
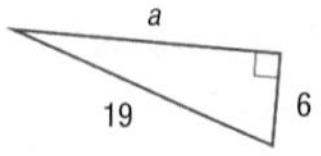

4. 14.42
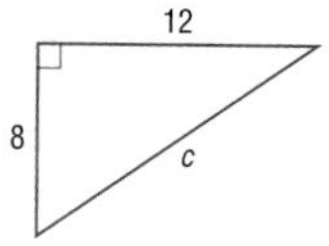

Example 2 p. 631

5. BASEBALL A baseball diamond is a square. The distance between consecutive bases is 90 feet.

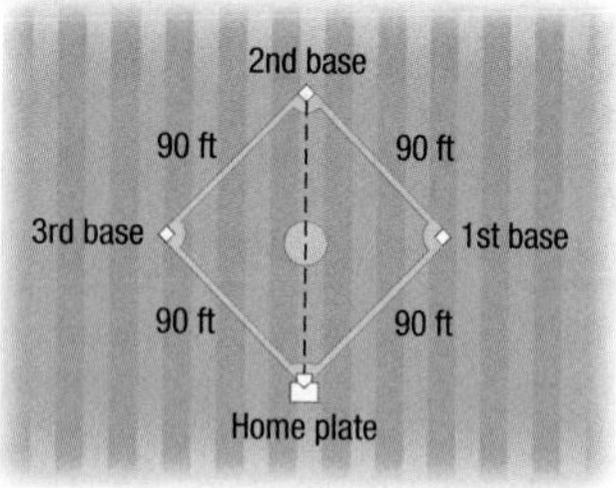

a. How far does a catcher have to throw the ball from home plate to second base? about 127 ft

b. How far does a third baseman have to throw the ball to the first baseman? about 127 ft

c. If the catcher is five feet behind home plate, how far does he have to throw the ball to second base? about 132 ft

Example 3 p. 631

Determine whether each set of measures can be the lengths of the sides of a right triangle.

6. 8, 12, 16 no

7. 28, 45, 53 yes

8. 7, 24, 25 yes

9. 15, 25, 45 no

Practice and Problem Solving

● = **Step-by-Step Solutions** begin on page R12.
Extra Practice begins on page 815.

Example 1 p. 630

Find each missing length. If necessary, round to the nearest hundredth.

10. 15.23
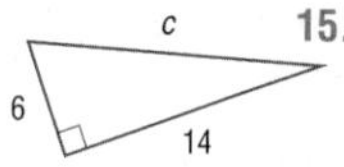

11. 11.83
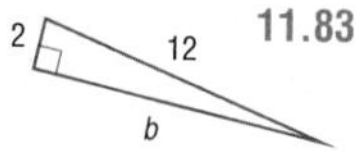

12. 20.27
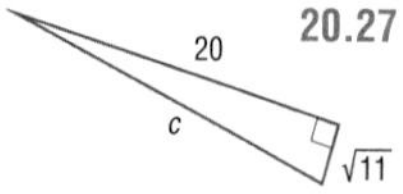

13. 29.66
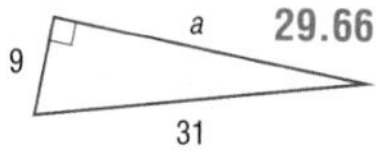

14. 20.49
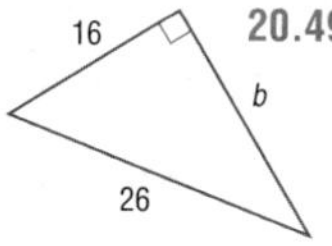

15. 5.29
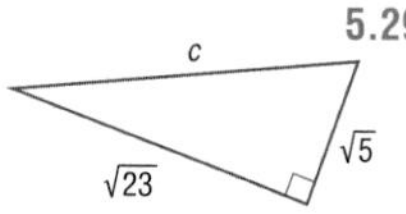

16. 24
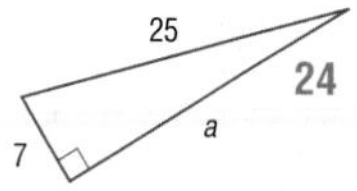

17. 7.21
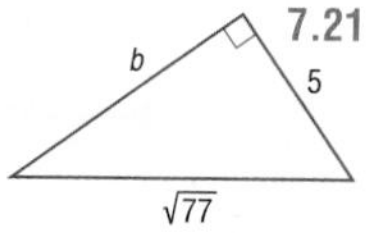

18. 5.66
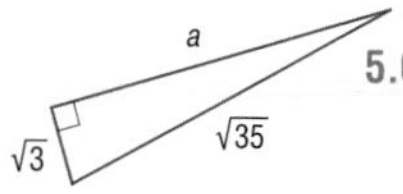

Differentiated Homework Options

Level	Assignment	Two-Day Option	
AL Basic	10–18, 50, 52–88	11–17 odd, 55–58	10–18 even, 50, 52–54, 59–88
OL Core	11–29 odd, 30–41, 43–47 odd, 48–50, 52–88	10–18, 55–58	19–50, 52–54, 59–88
BL Advanced	19–84, (optional: 85–88)		

Example 2 p. 631

19. **TELEVISION** Larry is buying an entertainment stand for his television. The diagonal of his television is 27 inches. The space for the television measures 20 inches by 26 inches. Will Larry's television fit? Explain.

Example 3 p. 631

Determine whether each set of measures can be the lengths of the sides of a right triangle. Then determine whether they form a Pythagorean triple.

19. Yes; sample answer: The diagonal of the space in the TV stand is 32.8 inches, so Larry's TV will fit.

20. 9, 40, 41 yes; yes **21.** 3, $2\sqrt{10}$, $\sqrt{41}$ no; no **22.** 4, $\sqrt{26}$, 12 no; no

23. $\sqrt{5}$, 7, 14 no; no **24.** 8, 31.5, 32.5 yes; no **25.** $\sqrt{65}$, $6\sqrt{2}$, $\sqrt{97}$ no; no

26. 18, 24, 30 yes; yes **27.** 36, 77, 85 yes; yes **28.** 17, 33, 98 no; no

Math History Link

Pythagoras (580–500 B.C.)
Greek mathematician Pythagoras founded the famous Pythagorean school for study of philosophy, mathematics, and natural science.

29. **GEOMETRY** Refer to the triangle at the right.

B **a.** What is *a*? about 20.20 units

b. Find the area of the triangle. about 111.1 units^2

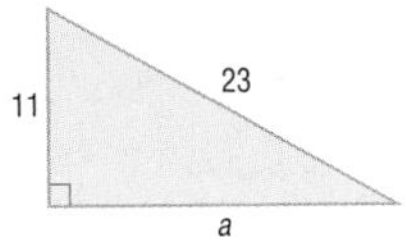

30. **GARDENING** Khaliah wants to plant flowers in a triangular plot. She has three lengths of plastic garden edging that measure 8 feet, 15 feet, and 17 feet. Determine whether these pieces form a right triangle. Explain.

30. Yes; sample answer: $8^2 + 15^2 = 17^2$, so the pieces form a right triangle by the converse of the Pythagorean Theorem.

31. **LADDER** Mr. Takeo is locked out of his house. The only open window is on the second floor. There is a bush along the edge of the house, so he places the neighbor's ladder 10 feet from the house. To the nearest foot, what length of ladder does he need to reach the window? a 30-ft ladder

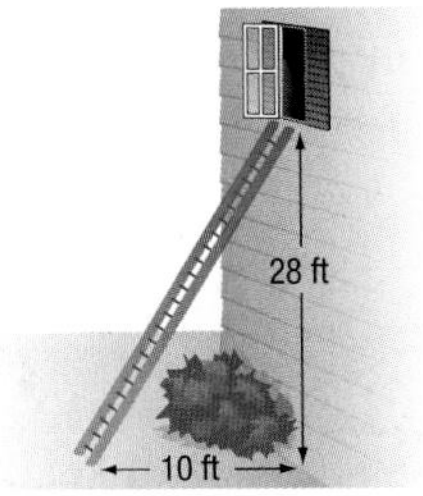

Find the length of the hypotenuse. Round to the nearest hundredth.

32. 12.21

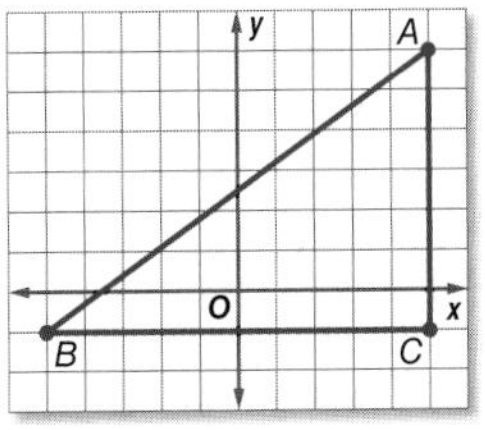

33. 8.06

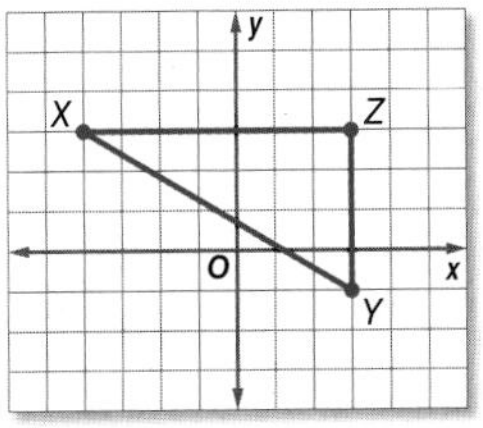

34. **GEOMETRY** A rectangle has a base of 5 feet and a height of 12 feet. What is the length of the diagonal? 13 ft

35. **GEOMETRY** A square has a diagonal with length of 6 meters. Find the length of the sides of the square. about 4.24 m

36. **DOLLHOUSE** Alonso is building a dollhouse for his sister's birthday. The house is 24 inches across and the slanted side is 16 inches long as shown. Find the height of the roof to the nearest tenth of an inch. 10.6 in.

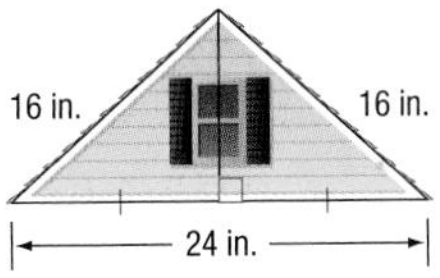

37. **GEOMETRY** Each side of a cube is 5 inches long. Find the length of a diagonal of the cube. $5\sqrt{3}$ in. or about 8.66 in.

Lesson 10-5 The Pythagorean Theorem **633**

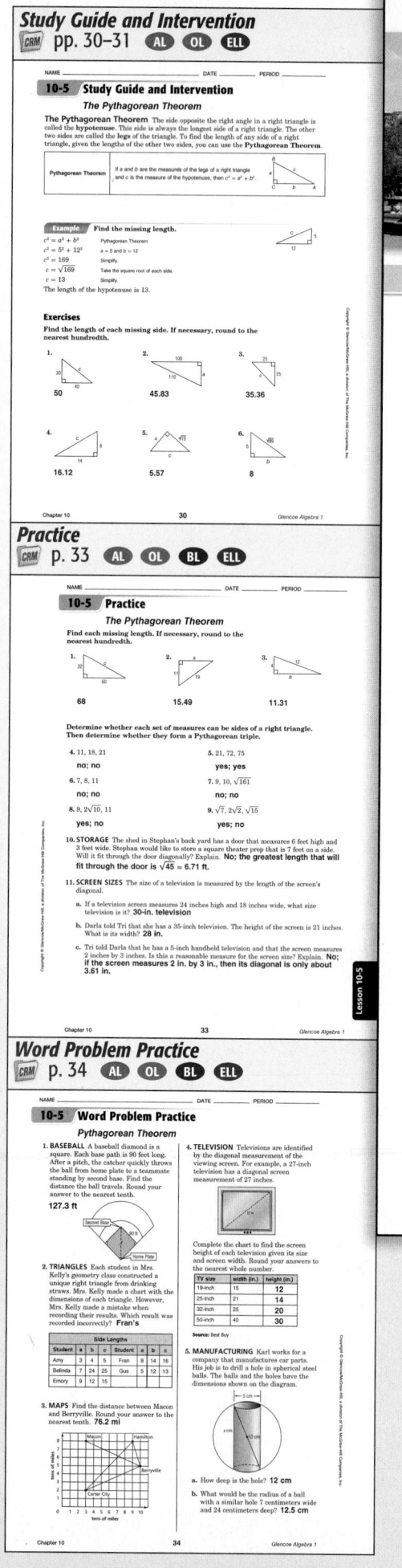

Study Guide and Intervention
CRM pp. 30–31 AL OL ELL

NAME ______ DATE ______ PERIOD ______

10-5 Study Guide and Intervention

The Pythagorean Theorem

The Pythagorean Theorem The side opposite the right angle in a right triangle is called the **hypotenuse**. This side is always the longest side of a right triangle. The other two sides are called the **legs** of the triangle. To find the length of any side of a right triangle, given the lengths of the other two sides, you can use the **Pythagorean Theorem**.

Pythagorean Theorem	If a and b are the measures of the legs of a right triangle and c is the measure of the hypotenuse, then $c^2 = a^2 + b^2$.

Example Find the missing length.

$c^2 = a^2 + b^2$ Pythagorean Theorem
$c^2 = 5^2 + 12^2$ $a = 5$ and $b = 12$
$c^2 = 169$ Simplify.
$c = \sqrt{169}$ Take the square root of each side.
$c = 13$ Simplify.

The length of the hypotenuse is 13.

Exercises

Find the length of each missing side. If necessary, round to the nearest hundredth.

1. 50 2. 45.83 3. 35.36
4. 16.12 5. 5.57 6. 8

Practice
CRM p. 33 AL OL BL ELL

NAME ______ DATE ______ PERIOD ______

10-5 Practice

The Pythagorean Theorem

Find each missing length. If necessary, round to the nearest hundredth.

1. 68 2. 15.49 3. 11.31

Determine whether each set of measures can be sides of a right triangle. Then determine whether they form a Pythagorean triple.

4. 11, 18, 21 **no; no**
5. 21, 72, 75 **yes; yes**
6. 7, 8, 11 **no; no**
7. 9, 10, $\sqrt{161}$ **no; no**
8. 9, $2\sqrt{10}$, 11 **yes; no**
9. $\sqrt{7}$, $2\sqrt{2}$, $\sqrt{15}$ **yes; no**

10. **STORAGE** The shed in Stephan's back yard has a door that measures 6 feet high and 3 feet wide. Stephan would like to store a square theater prop that is 7 feet on a side. Will it fit through the door diagonally? Explain. **No; the greatest length that will fit through the door is $\sqrt{45} \approx 6.71$ ft.**

11. **SCREEN SIZES** The size of a television is measured by the length of the screen's diagonal.
 a. If a television screen measures 24 inches high and 18 inches wide, what size television is it? **30-in. television**
 b. Darla told Tri that she has a 35-inch television. The height of the screen is 21 inches. What is its width? **28 in.**
 c. Tri told Darla that he has a 5-inch handheld television and that the screen measures 2 inches by 3 inches. Is this a reasonable measure for the screen size? Explain. **No; if the screen measures 2 in. by 3 in., then its diagonal is only about 3.61 in.**

Lesson 10-5

Word Problem Practice
CRM p. 34 AL OL BL ELL

NAME ______ DATE ______ PERIOD ______

10-5 Word Problem Practice

Pythagorean Theorem

1. **BASEBALL** A baseball diamond is a square. Each base path is 90 feet long. After a pitch, the catcher quickly throws the ball from home plate to a teammate standing by second base. Find the distance the ball travels. Round your answer to the nearest tenth. **127.3 ft**

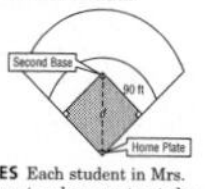

2. **TRIANGLES** Each student in Mrs. Kelly's geometry class constructed a unique right triangle from drinking straws. Mrs. Kelly made a chart with the dimensions of each triangle. However, Mrs. Kelly made a mistake when recording their results. Which result was recorded incorrectly? **Fran's**

Side Lengths							
Student	a	b	c	Student	a	b	c
Amy	3	4	5	Fran	8	14	16
Belinda	7	24	25	Gus	5	12	13
Emory	9	12	15				

3. **MAPS** Find the distance between Macon and Berryville. Round your answer to the nearest tenth. **76.2 mi**

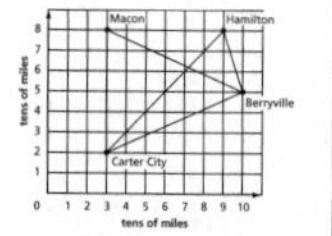

4. **TELEVISION** Televisions are identified by the diagonal measurement of the viewing screen. For example, a 27-inch television has a diagonal screen measurement of 27 inches.

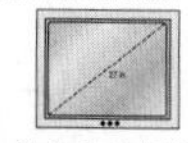

Complete the chart to find the screen height of each television given its size and screen width. Round your answers to the nearest whole number.

TV size	width (in.)	height (in.)
19-inch	15	12
25-inch	21	14
32-inch	25	20
50-inch	40	30

Source: Best Buy

5. **MANUFACTURING** Karl works for a company that manufactures car parts. His job is to drill a hole in spherical steel balls. The balls and the holes have the dimensions shown on the diagram.

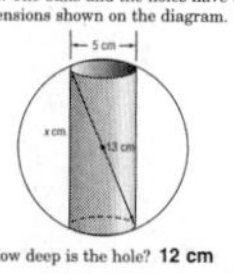

a. How deep is the hole? **12 cm**
b. What would be the radius of a ball with a similar hole 7 centimeters wide and 24 centimeters deep? **12.5 cm**

Real-World Link

The largest town square in the United States is Washington Square Park in New York. The park is 9.75 acres or 39,000 square meters.

Source: *The New York Times*

38. **TOWN SQUARES** The largest town square in the world is Tiananmen Square in Beijing, China, covering 98 acres.
 a. One square mile is 640 acres. Assuming that Tiananmen Square is a square, how many feet long is a side to the nearest foot? **2066 ft**
 b. To the nearest foot, what is the diagonal distance across Tiananmen Square? **2922 ft**

39. **TRUCKS** Violeta needs to construct a ramp to roll a cart of moving boxes from her garage into the back of her truck. How long does the ramp have to be? **about 6.7 ft**

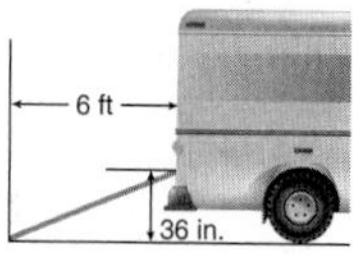

40. **GEOMETRY** A square has an area of 242 square inches. Find the length of a diagonal. **22 in.**

41. **GEOMETRY** A rectangle has a width that is twice as long as its length and an area of 722 square inches. Find the length of a diagonal. **about 42.5 in.**

C **If c is the measure of the hypotenuse of a right triangle, find each missing measure. If necessary, round to the nearest hundredth.**

42. $a = x, b = x + 41, c = 85$
43. $a = 8, b = x, c = x + 2$
44. $a = 12, b = x - 2, c = x$
45. $a = x, b = x + 7, c = 97$
46. $a = x - 47, b = x, c = x + 2$
47. $a = x - 32, b = x - 1, c = x$

42. $a = 36$; $b = 77$
43. $b = 15$; $c = 17$
44. $b = 35$; $c = 37$
45. $a = 65$; $b = 72$
46. $a = 16$; $b = 63$; $c = 65$
47. $a = 9$; $b = 40$; $c = 41$
50. Wyatt; the square of the greatest value should be equal to the sum of the squares of the two smaller values. Since this is the case, the numbers form a Pythagorean triple.

48. **GEOMETRY** A right triangle has one leg that is 8 inches shorter than the other leg. The hypotenuse is 30 inches long. Find the length of each leg. **about 24.83 in. and about 16.83 in.**

49. **GEOMETRY** A rectangle has a diagonal with length 8 centimeters. Its length is 4 centimeters greater than the width. Find the length and width of the rectangle. **about 7.29 cm and about 3.29 cm**

H.O.T. Problems
Use Higher-Order Thinking Skills

50. **FIND THE ERROR** Wyatt and Dario are determining whether 36, 77, and 85 form a Pythagorean triple. Is either of them correct? Explain your reasoning.

Wyatt	Dario
$36^2 + 77^2 \stackrel{?}{=} 85^2$	$36^2 + 85^2 \stackrel{?}{=} 77^2$
$1296 + 5929 \stackrel{?}{=} 7225$	$1296 + 7725 \stackrel{?}{=} 5929$
$7225 = 7225$	$9021 \neq 5929$
yes	no

51. **CHALLENGE** Find the value of x in the figure. $8\sqrt{2}$

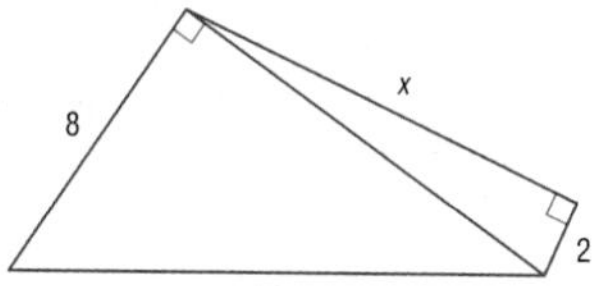

52. **REASONING** Provide a counterexample to the statement.
Any two right triangles with the same hypotenuse have the same area. **See margin.**

53. **OPEN ENDED** Draw a right triangle that has a hypotenuse of $\sqrt{72}$ units. **See margin.**

54. **WRITING IN MATH** Explain how to determine whether segments in three lengths could form a right triangle. **See margin.**

Enrichment
CRM p. 35 OL BL

NAME ______ DATE ______ PERIOD ______

10-5 Enrichment

Pythagorean Triples

Recall the Pythagorean Theorem:
In a right triangle, the square of the length of the hypotenuse is equal to the sum of the squares of the lengths of the legs.

$a^2 + b^2 = c^2$
Note that c is the length of the hypotenuse.

The integers 3, 4, and 5 satisfy the Pythagorean Theorem and can be the lengths of the sides of a right triangle. $3^2 + 4^2 = 5^2$, $9 + 16 = 25$, $25 = 25$

Furthermore, for any positive integer n, the numbers $3n$, $4n$, and $5n$ satisfy the Pythagorean Theorem. For $n = 2$: $6^2 + 8^2 = 10^2$, $36 + 64 = 100$, $100 = 100$

If three numbers satisfy the Pythagorean Theorem, they are called a **Pythagorean triple**. Here is an easy way to find other Pythagorean triples.

The numbers a, b, and c are a Pythagorean triple if $a = m^2 - n^2$, $b = 2mn$, and $c = m^2 + n^2$, where m and n are relatively prime positive integers and $m > n$.

Watch Out!

Find the Error For Exercise 50, students should see that Wyatt and Dario represented the Pythagorean Theorem in two different ways. Ask students to choose the correct representation and explain why it is correct.

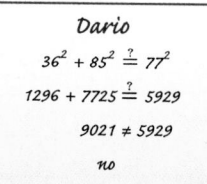

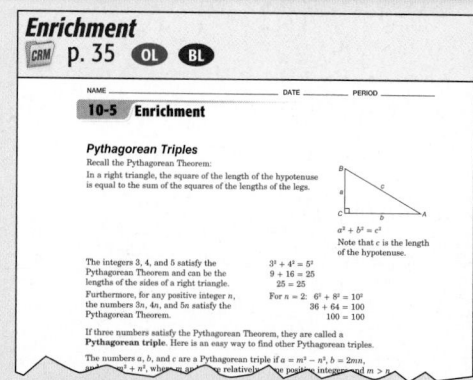

PSAE PRACTICE 9.11.01, 8.11.19, 8.11.02, 8.11.04

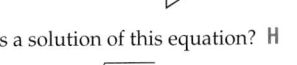

55. GEOMETRY Find the missing length. **C**

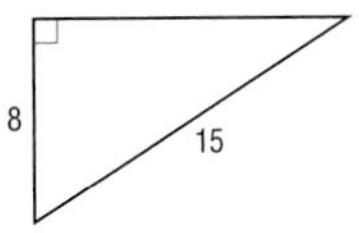

A -17

B $-\sqrt{161}$

C $\sqrt{161}$

D 17

56. What is a solution of this equation? **H**

$$x + 1 = \sqrt{x + 1}$$

F 0, 3

G 3

H 0

J no solutions

57. SHORT RESPONSE A plumber charges \$40 for the first hour of each house call plus \$8 for each additional half hour. If the plumber works for 4 hours, how much does he charge? **\$88**

58. Find the next term in the geometric sequence $4, 3, \frac{9}{4}, \frac{27}{16}, \ldots$. **C**

A $\frac{4}{3}$ B $\frac{81}{64}$ C $\frac{64}{81}$ D $\frac{243}{64}$

Spiral Review

Solve each equation. Check your solution. (Lesson 10-4)

59. $\sqrt{x} = 16$ **256**

60. $\sqrt{4x} = 64$ **1024**

61. $\sqrt{10x} = 10$ **10**

62. $\sqrt{8x} + 1 = 65$ **512**

63. $\sqrt{x + 1} + 2 = 4$ **3**

64. $\sqrt{x - 15} = 3 - \sqrt{x}$ **no real solution**

Simplify each expression. (Lesson 10-3)

65. $2\sqrt{3} + 5\sqrt{3}$ $7\sqrt{3}$

66. $4\sqrt{5} - 2\sqrt{5}$ $2\sqrt{5}$

67. $6\sqrt{7} + 2\sqrt{28}$ $10\sqrt{7}$

68. $\sqrt{18} - 4\sqrt{2}$ $-\sqrt{2}$

69. $3\sqrt{5} - 5\sqrt{3} + 9\sqrt{5}$ $12\sqrt{5} - 5\sqrt{3}$

70. $4\sqrt{3} + 6\sqrt{12}$ $16\sqrt{3}$

71. BUSINESS The amount of money spent at West Outlet Mall continues to increase. The total $T(x)$ in millions of dollars can be estimated by the function $T(x) = 12(1.12)^x$, where x is the number of years after it opened in 2005. Find the amount of sales in 2015, 2016, and 2017. (Lesson 9-6) **about \$37.27 million; about \$41.74 million; about \$46.75 million**

Describe how the graph of each function is related to the graph of $f(x) = x^2$. (Lesson 9-3)

72. $g(x) = x^2 - 8$ **translated down 8**

73. $h(x) = \frac{1}{4}x^2$ **compressed vertically**

74. $h(x) = -x^2 + 5$ **reflected across the x-axis, translated up 5**

75. $g(x) = x^2 + 10$ **translated up 10**

76. $g(x) = -2x^2$ **See margin.**

77. $h(x) = -x^2 - \frac{4}{3}$ **reflected across the x-axis, translated down $\frac{4}{3}$**

78. ROCK CLIMBING While rock climbing, Damaris launches a grappling hook from a height of 6 feet with an initial upward velocity of 56 feet per second. The hook just misses the stone ledge that she wants to scale. As it falls, the hook anchors on a ledge 30 feet above the ground. How long was the hook in the air? (Lesson 8-4) **3 seconds**

Find each product. (Lesson 7-7)

79. $(b + 8)(b + 2)$ $b^2 + 10b + 16$

80. $(x - 4)(x - 9)$ $x^2 - 13x + 36$

81. $(y + 4)(y - 8)$ $y^2 - 4y - 32$

82. $(p + 2)(p - 10)$ $p^2 - 8p - 20$

83. $(2w - 5)(w + 7)$ $2w^2 + 9w - 35$

84. $(8d + 3)(5d + 2)$ $40d^2 + 31d + 6$

Skills Review

Solve each proportion. (Lesson 2-6)

85. $\frac{x}{5} = \frac{12}{3}$ **20**

86. $\frac{12}{x} = \frac{3}{4}$ **16**

87. $\frac{5}{4} = \frac{10}{x}$ **8**

88. $\frac{3}{5} = \frac{12}{x + 8}$ **12**

4 ASSESS

Crystal Ball Have students write how they think today's lesson will connect to tomorrow's lesson on the Distance and Midpoint Formulas.

Additional Answers

52. Sample answer: A right triangle with legs measuring 3 cm and 4 cm has a hypotenuse of 5 cm and an area of 6 cm^2. A right triangle with legs measuring 2 cm and $\sqrt{21}$ cm also has a hypotenuse of 5 cm, but its area is $\sqrt{21}$ cm^2, which is not equivalent to 6 cm^2.

53.

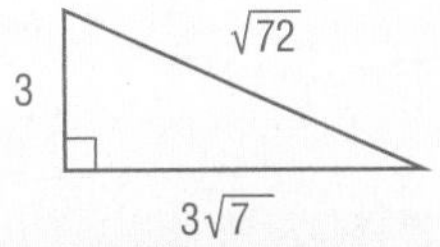

54. Sample answer: From the converse of the Pythagorean Theorem, if $a^2 + b^2 = c^2$, then a, b, and c are the lengths of the side of a right triangle. So, check to see whether the square of the greatest number is equal to the sum of the squares of the other two numbers.

76. reflected across the x-axis, stretched vertically

Differentiated Instruction BL

Extension Tell students that when x equals any odd number, x, $\frac{1}{2}(x^2 - 1)$, and $\frac{1}{2}(x^2 + 1)$ will give them numbers that are Pythagorean triples. Ask students to use the expressions to find a set of Pythagorean triples not given in this lesson. Have students verify that their results are actually Pythagorean triples. Sample answer: $x = 11, 60, 61$; $61^2 = 60^2 + 11^2$, $3721 = 3600 + 121$, $3721 = 3721$

10-6 Lesson Notes

1 FOCUS

Vertical Alignment

Before Lesson 10-6
Use the Pythagorean Theorem.

Lesson 10-6
Find the distance between two points on a coordinate plane.
Find the midpoint between two points on a coordinate plane.

After Lesson 10-6
Apply formulas to real-world and mathematical situations involving similar triangles.

2 TEACH

Scaffolding Questions Have students read the *Why?* section of the lesson.

Ask:

- What must you know in order to use the Pythagorean Theorem to determine the distance between the two points? the lengths of the two legs, so you can find the hypotenuse
- How do you find the vertical distance from Asheville to Huntington? Find the difference in their y-coordinates.
- How do you find the horizontal distance from Asheville to Washington? Find the difference in their x-coordinates.

10-6 The Distance and Midpoint Formulas

Then
You used the Pythagorean Theorem. (Lesson 10-5)

Now
- Find the distance between two points on a coordinate plane.
- Find the midpoint between two points on a coordinate plane.

IL Learning Standards
7.A.4b Apply formulas in a wide variety of theoretical and practical real-world measurement applications involving perimeter, area, volume, angle, time, temperature, mass, speed, **distance**, density and monetary values.

New Vocabulary
Distance Formula
midpoint
Midpoint Formula

IL Math Online
glencoe.com
- Extra Examples
- Personal Tutor
- Self-Check Quiz
- Homework Help

Why?

Rescue helicopters use electronic Global Positioning Systems (GPS) to compute direct distances between two locations.

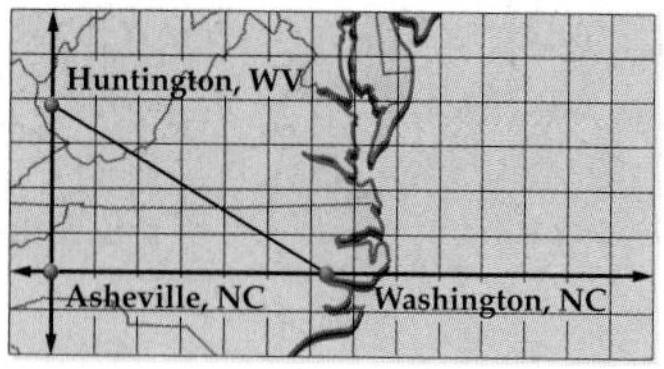

A rescue helicopter can fly 450 miles before it needs to refuel. A person needs to be flown from Washington, North Carolina, to Huntington, West Virginia. Sides of the grid squares are 50 miles long. Asheville, North Carolina, is at the origin, Huntington is at (0, 196), and Washington is at (310, 0). Can the helicopter make the trip without refueling?

Distance Formula The GPS system calculates direct distances by using the **Distance Formula**, which is based on the Pythagorean Theorem.

Key Concept: The Distance Formula

For Your FOLDABLE

Words The distance d between any two points with coordinates (x_1, y_1) and (x_2, y_2) is given by the following formula.

$$d = \sqrt{(x_2 - x_1)^2 + (y_2 - y_1)^2}$$

Model

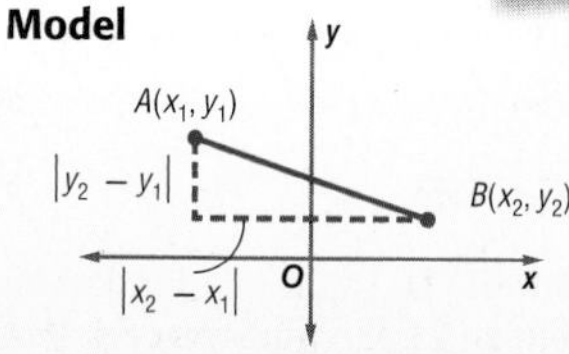

You can use the Distance Formula to find the distance between any two points on a coordinate plane.

EXAMPLE 1 Distance Between Two Points

Find the distance between points at (5, 3) and (1, −2).

$d = \sqrt{(x_2 - x_1)^2 + (y_2 - y_1)^2}$	Distance Formula
$= \sqrt{(1 - 5)^2 + (-2 - 3)^2}$	$(x_1, y_1) = (5, 3)$ and $(x_2, y_2) = (1, -2)$
$= \sqrt{(-4)^2 + (-5)^2}$	Simplify.
$= \sqrt{16 + 25}$	Evaluate squares.
$= \sqrt{41}$ or about 6.4 units	Simplify.

Check Your Progress

Find the distance between points with the given coordinates.

1A. (4, 2) and (−3, −1). $\sqrt{58}$

1B. (−7, −2) and (−5, −8) $2\sqrt{10}$

Personal Tutor glencoe.com

Lesson 10-6 Resources

Resource	Approaching-Level	On-Level	Beyond-Level	English Learners
Teacher Edition	• Differentiated Instruction, p. 637	• Differentiated Instruction, pp. 637, 641	• Differentiated Instruction, p. 641	
Chapter Resource Masters	• Study Guide and Intervention, pp. 37–38 • Skills Practice, p. 39 • Practice, p. 40 • Word Problem Practice, p. 41	• Study Guide and Intervention, pp. 37–38 • Skills Practice, p. 39 • Practice, p. 40 • Word Problem Practice, p. 41 • Enrichment, p. 42	• Practice, p. 40 • Word Problem Practice, p. 41 • Enrichment, p. 42	• Study Guide and Intervention, pp. 37–38 • Skills Practice, p. 39 • Practice, p. 40
Transparencies	• 5-Minute Check Transparency 10-6	• 5-Minute Check Transparency 10-6	• 5-Minute Check Transparency 10-6	• 5-Minute Check Transparency 10-6
Other	• Study Notebook	• Study Notebook	• Study Notebook	• Study Notebook

Real-World Link

About 22% of U.S. residents have a home theater. Technology installations is a $9.6 billion per year business.

Source: *Realty Times*

Real-World EXAMPLE 2 Use the Distance Formula

ENTERTAINMENT The Vaccaro Family is having a home theater system installed. The TV and the seating will be placed in opposite corners of the room. The manufacturer of the TV recommends that for the size of TV that they want, the seating should be placed at least 13 feet away. If each grid square is 1 foot long, is the Vaccaro's room large enough for the TV?

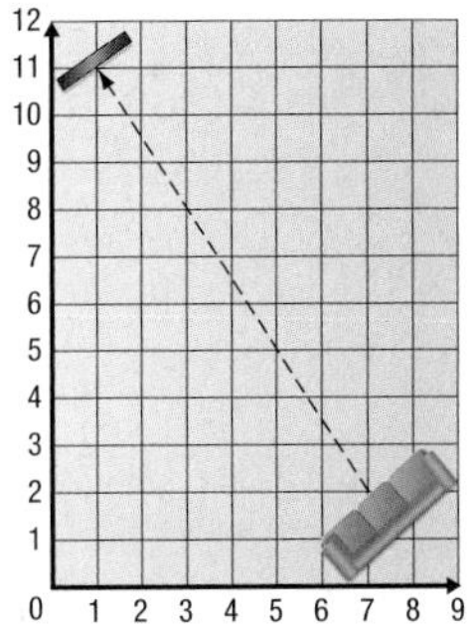

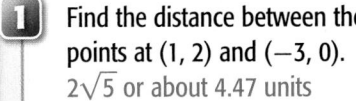

The front of the TV screen is located at (1, 11), and the front of the sofa is located at (7, 2).

$d = \sqrt{(x_2 - x_1)^2 + (y_2 - y_1)^2}$ **Distance Formula**

$= \sqrt{(7 - 1)^2 + (2 - 11)^2}$ **$(x_1, y_1) = (1, 11)$ and $(x_2, y_2) = (7, 2)$**

$= \sqrt{6^2 + (-9)^2}$ **Simplify.**

$= \sqrt{117}$ or about 10.8 feet

No, the room is not large enough for the TV.

Check Your Progress

2. The manufacturer of the speakers recommends that they be placed at least 8 feet from the seating. If one of the speakers is being placed at (0, 9), is the Vaccaros' family room large enough for the speakers? Explain. **Yes; the distance is $7\sqrt{2}$ or about 9.9 ft.**

Personal Tutor glencoe.com

When we know the distance and one of the points, we can use the Distance Formula to find the coordinates of the other point.

StudyTip

Two Possibilities When finding a missing coordinate, there will usually be two possibilities because the point could be the same distance in different directions.

EXAMPLE 3 Find a Missing Coordinate

Find the possible values for a if the distance between points at (4, 7) and $(a, 3)$ are 5 units apart.

$d = \sqrt{(x_2 - x_1)^2 + (y_2 - y_1)^2}$ **Distance Formula**

$5 = \sqrt{(a - 4)^2 + (3 - 7)^2}$ **$(x_1, y_1) = (4, 7)$ and $(x_2, y_2) = (a, 3)$, and $d = 5$**

$5 = \sqrt{(a - 4)^2 + (-4)^2}$ **Simplify.**

$5 = \sqrt{a^2 - 8a + 32}$ **Evaluate squares and simplify.**

$25 = a^2 - 8a + 32$ **Square each side.**

$0 = a^2 - 8a + 7$ **Subtract 25 from each side.**

$0 = (a - 1)(a - 7)$ **Factor.**

$a - 1 = 0$ or $a - 7 = 0$ **Zero Product Property**

$a = 1$ $\quad a = 7$ **Solve each equation.**

Check Your Progress

3. Find the possible values of a if the distance between points at $(2, a)$ and $(-6, 2)$ is 10 units. **$a = 8$ or $a = -4$**

Personal Tutor glencoe.com

Distance Formula

Example 1 shows how to use the Distance Formula to find the distance between two points on a coordinate plane. **Example 2** shows how to use the Distance Formula to solve a real-world problem. **Example 3** shows how to use the Distance Formula to find a missing coordinate.

Formative Assessment

Use the Check Your Progress exercises after each example to determine students' understanding of concepts.

Additional Examples

1 Find the distance between the points at (1, 2) and (−3, 0). $2\sqrt{5}$ or about 4.47 units

2 **BIATHLON** Julianne is sighting in her rifle for an upcoming biathlon competition. Her first shot is 2 inches to the right and 7 inches below the bull's-eye. What is the distance between the bull's-eye and where her first shot hit the target? $\sqrt{53}$ or about 7.28 inches

3 Find the possible values for a if the distance between points at (2, −1) and $(a, -4)$ is 5 units. −2 or 6

Additional Examples also in Interactive Classroom PowerPoint® Presentations

IWB INTERACTIVE WHITEBOARD READY

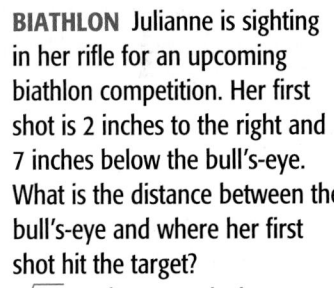

Focus on Mathematical Content

Distance Formula You can use the Distance Formula, $d = \sqrt{(x_2 - x_1)^2 + (y_2 - y_1)^2}$, to find the distance between any two points, (x_1, y_1) and (x_2, y_2), in the coordinate plane. Since the differences are squared, the order in which the points are chosen does not matter.

Differentiated Instruction AL OL

If students need additional practice finding the distance between two points,

Then provide students with a map of your town or city with a coordinate grid superimposed on it, making sure at least one of the landmarks on the map has whole-number coordinates. Have students use the Distance Formula to find the distance between two landmarks on the map.

Midpoint Formula

Example 4 shows how to find the coordinates of the midpoint of a segment given the coordinates of the endpoints.

Additional Example

4 Find the coordinates of the midpoint of the segment with endpoints at (8, −3) and (−4, −1). (2, −2)

3 PRACTICE

Formative Assessment

Use Exercises 1–17 to check for understanding.

Use the chart at the bottom of the next page to customize assignments for your students.

TEACH with TECH

BLOG On your secure classroom blog have students write a blog entry explaining how the distance formula and Pythagorean Theorem are related to each other.

Midpoint Formula The point on the segment that joins two points and is equidistant from the endpoints is called the **midpoint**. You can find the coordinates of the midpoint by using the **Midpoint Formula**.

Key Concept — The Midpoint Formula

For Your FOLDABLE

Words The midpoint M of a line segment with endpoints at (x_1, y_1) and (x_2, y_2) is given by

$$M = \left(\frac{x_1 + x_2}{2}, \frac{y_1 + y_2}{2}\right).$$

Model

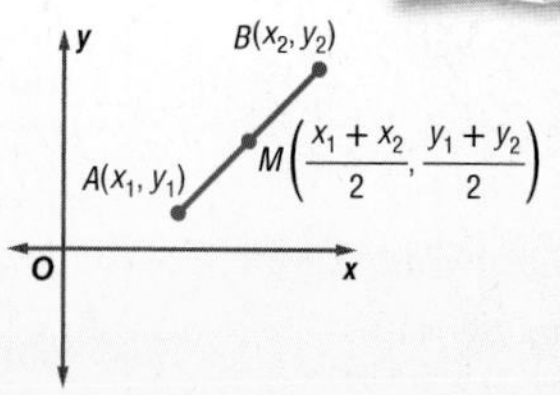

Watch Out!

Midpoint Formula Be careful to add, and not subtract, when using the Midpoint Formula.

EXAMPLE 4 Find the Midpoint

Find the coordinates of the midpoint of the segment with endpoints at (−1, −2) and (3, −4).

$M = \left(\frac{x_1 + x_2}{2}, \frac{y_1 + y_2}{2}\right)$ — Midpoint Formula

$= \left(\frac{-1 + 3}{2}, \frac{-2 + (-4)}{2}\right)$ — $(x_1, y_1) = (-1, -2)$ and $(x_2, y_2) = (3, -4)$

$= \left(\frac{2}{2}, \frac{-6}{2}\right)$ — Simplify the numerators.

$= (1, -3)$ — Simplify.

Check Your Progress

Find the coordinates of the midpoint of the segment with the given endpoints.

4A. (12, 3), (−8, 3) (2, 3) **4B.** (0, 0), (5, 12) $\left(\frac{5}{2}, 6\right)$ **4C.** (6, 8), (3, 4) $\left(\frac{9}{2}, 6\right)$

Personal Tutor glencoe.com

Check Your Understanding

Example 1 p. 636

Find the distance between points with the given coordinates.

1. (6, −2), (12, 8) $2\sqrt{34}$

2. (4, 8), (−3, −6) $7\sqrt{5}$

3. (3, 0), (6, −2) $\sqrt{13}$

4. (−2, −4), (−5, −3) $\sqrt{10}$

Example 2 p. 637

5. GOLF Addison hit a golf ball from a tee to the point at (−3, 12), 12 feet past the hole and 3 feet to the left. The hole is located at the point at (0, 0). Her first putt traveled to the point at (1, 2), 2 feet above the hole and 1 foot to the right.

a. How far did the ball travel on her first putt? $2\sqrt{29}$ or about 10.77 ft

b. How far was her first putt from the cup? $\sqrt{5}$ or about 2.24 ft

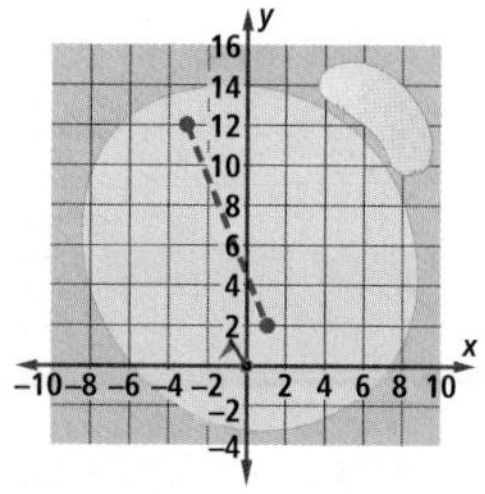

638 Chapter 10 Radical Functions and Geometry

Example 3 p. 637

Find the possible values for a if the points with the given coordinates are the indicated distance apart.

6. $(-5, a), (3, 1); d = \sqrt{89}$ **6 or −4**

7. $(6, a), (5, 0); d = \sqrt{17}$ **−4 or 4**

8. $(5, 8), (a, 2); d = 3\sqrt{5}$ **2 or 8**

9. $(a, 6), (-6, 2); d = 4\sqrt{10}$ **−18 or 6**

Example 4 p. 638

Find the coordinates of the midpoint of the segment with the given endpoints.

10. $(5, -10), (5, 8)$ $(5, -1)$

11. $(2, -2), (6, 2)$ $(4, 0)$

12. $(5, 0), (0, 3)$ $\left(\frac{5}{2}, \frac{3}{2}\right)$

13. $(-4, 1), (3, -1)$ $\left(-\frac{1}{2}, 0\right)$

14. $(3, -17), (2, -8)$ $\left(\frac{5}{2}, -\frac{25}{2}\right)$

15. $(-2, 2), (4, 10)$ $(1, 6)$

16. $(3, 10), (3, 3)$ $\left(3, \frac{13}{2}\right)$

17. $(-17, 8), (-2, 20)$ $\left(-\frac{19}{2}, 14\right)$

Practice and Problem Solving

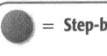

● = **Step-by-Step Solutions** begin on page R12.
Extra Practice begins on page 815.

Example 1 p. 636

Find the distance between points with the given coordinates.

18. $(5, 8), (5, 7)$ 1

19. $(6, -9), (9, -9)$ 3

20. $(3, -3), (7, 2)$ $\sqrt{41}$

21. $(5, 1), (0, 4)$ $\sqrt{34}$

22. $(-5, 2), (4, -2)$ $\sqrt{97}$

23. $(3, 5), (-6, 0)$ $\sqrt{106}$

24. $(-7, 8), (3, 10)$ $2\sqrt{26}$

25. $(-11, 9), (3, -4)$ $\sqrt{365}$

26. $(8, 6), (-13, -2)$ $\sqrt{505}$

27. $(5, 2), (3, -3)$ $\sqrt{29}$

28. $(4, 2), (5, 5)$ $\sqrt{10}$

29. $(-3, 5), (5, -3)$ $8\sqrt{2}$

Example 2 p. 637

30. NAVIGATION Lawana and Ken are meeting at a restaurant in a marina. Ken takes his boat, while Lawana is driving her car. The sides of each grid square on the map represent 1 mile.

a. How far did Ken travel? **10 mi**

b. How far did Lawana travel? $5\sqrt{2}$ **or about 7.07 mi**

c. How many times as great is the distance that Ken traveled as the distance that Lawana traveled? $\sqrt{2}$ **or about 1.41**

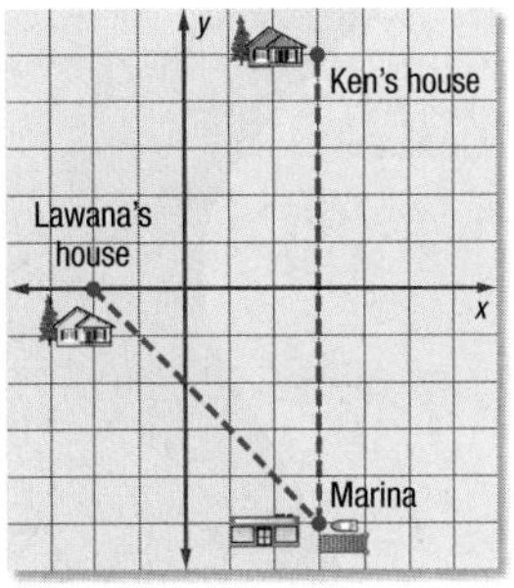

Example 3 p. 637

Find the possible values for a if the points with the given coordinates are the indicated distance apart.

31. $(-9, -2), (a, 5); d = 7$ **−9**

32. $(a, -6), (-5, 2); d = 10$ **−11 or 1**

33. $(a, 0), (3, 1); d = \sqrt{2}$ **2 or 4**

34. $(4, a), (8, 4); d = 2\sqrt{5}$ **2 or 6**

35. $(7, 5), (-9, a); d = 2\sqrt{65}$ **3 or 7**

36. $(-2, a), (6, 1); d = 4\sqrt{5}$ **−3 or 5**

Example 4 p. 638

Find the coordinates of the midpoint of the segment with the given endpoints.

37. $(0, 2), (7, 3)$ $\left(\frac{7}{2}, \frac{5}{2}\right)$

38. $(5, -2), (3, -6)$ $(4, -4)$

39. $(-4, 0), (0, 14)$ $(-2, 7)$

40. $(10, -3), (-8, -5)$ $(1, -4)$

41 $(-5, 5), (3, -3)$ $(-1, 1)$

42. $(-16, -7), (-4, -3)$ $(-10, -5)$

B Find the distance between points with the given coordinates.

43. $(4, 2), \left(6, -\frac{2}{3}\right)$ $\frac{10}{3}$ or $3\frac{1}{3}$

44. $\left(\frac{4}{5}, -1\right), \left(2, -\frac{1}{2}\right)$ $\frac{13}{10}$ or $1\frac{3}{10}$

45. $(4\sqrt{5}, 7), (6\sqrt{5}, 1)$ $2\sqrt{14}$

46. GEOMETRY Triangle ABC has vertices $A(1, 3)$, $B(-2, 5)$, and $C(8, 8)$. Find the perimeter of the triangle. Use a calculator to estimate the perimeter to the nearest tenth. $\sqrt{13} + \sqrt{109} + \sqrt{74}$; **22.6 units**

47. GEOMETRY Quadrilateral $JKLM$ has vertices $J(-3, -4)$, $K(-1, 4)$, $L(4, 5)$, and $M(6, -5)$. Find the perimeter of the quadrilateral to the nearest tenth. $\sqrt{68} + \sqrt{26} + \sqrt{104} + \sqrt{82}$; **32.6 units**

Watch Out!

Student Misconceptions Point out to students that it does not matter which of the two points is designated (x_1, y_1) and (x_2, y_2) when they are finding the distance between two points.

Differentiated Homework Options

Level	Assignment	Two-Day Option	
AL Basic	18–42, 55–75	19–41 odd, 59–62	18–42 even, 55–58, 63–75
OL Core	19–45 odd, 46–51, 53, 55–75	18–42, 59–62	43–53, 55–58, 63–75
BL Advanced	43–69, (optional: 70–75)		

Study Guide and Intervention
CRM pp. 37–38 AL OL ELL

NAME ______ DATE ______ PERIOD ______

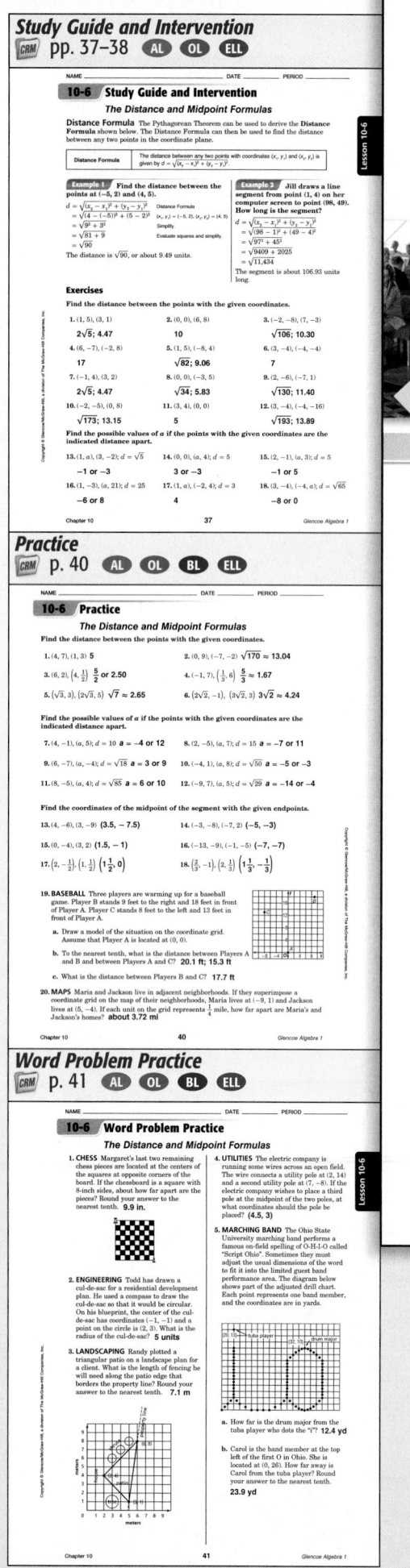

10-6 Study Guide and Intervention
The Distance and Midpoint Formulas

Distance Formula The Pythagorean Theorem can be used to derive the **Distance Formula** shown below. The Distance Formula can then be used to find the distance between any two points in the coordinate plane.

Distance Formula	The distance between any two points with coordinates (x_1, y_1) and (x_2, y_2) is given by $d = \sqrt{(x_2 - x_1)^2 + (y_2 - y_1)^2}$.

Example 1 Find the distance between the points at (−5, 2) and (4, 5).

$d = \sqrt{(x_2 - x_1)^2 + (y_2 - y_1)^2}$ Distance Formula
$= \sqrt{(4 - (-5))^2 + (5 - 2)^2}$ $(x_1, y_1) = (-5, 2), (x_2, y_2) = (4, 5)$
$= \sqrt{9^2 + 3^2}$ Simplify.
$= \sqrt{81 + 9}$ Evaluate squares and simplify.
$= \sqrt{90}$

The distance is $\sqrt{90}$, or about 9.49 units.

Example 2 Jill draws a line segment from point (1, 4) on her computer screen to point (98, 49). How long is the segment?

$d = \sqrt{(x_2 - x_1)^2 + (y_2 - y_1)^2}$
$= \sqrt{(98 - 1)^2 + (49 - 4)^2}$
$= \sqrt{97^2 + 45^2}$
$= \sqrt{9409 + 2025}$
$= \sqrt{11{,}434}$

The segment is about 106.93 units long.

Exercises

Find the distance between the points with the given coordinates.

1. (1, 5), (3, 1) **$2\sqrt{5}$; 4.47**
2. (0, 0), (6, 8) **10**
3. (−2, −8), (7, −3) **$\sqrt{106}$; 10.30**
4. (6, −7), (−2, 8) **17**
5. (1, 5), (−8, 4) **$\sqrt{82}$; 9.06**
6. (3, −4), (−4, −4) **7**
7. (−1, 4), (3, 2) **$2\sqrt{5}$; 4.47**
8. (0, 0), (−3, 5) **$\sqrt{34}$; 5.83**
9. (2, −6), (−7, 1) **$\sqrt{130}$; 11.40**
10. (−2, −5), (0, 8) **$\sqrt{173}$; 13.15**
11. (3, 4), (0, 0) **5**
12. (3, −4), (−4, −16) **$\sqrt{193}$; 13.89**

Find the possible values of *a* if the points with the given coordinates are the indicated distance apart.

13. $(1, a), (3, -2); d = \sqrt{5}$ **−1 or −3**
14. $(0, 0), (a, 4); d = 5$ **3 or −3**
15. $(2, -1), (a, 3); d = 5$ **−1 or 5**
16. $(1, -3), (a, 21); d = 25$ **−6 or 8**
17. $(1, a), (-2, 4); d = 3$ **4**
18. $(3, -4), (-4, a); d = \sqrt{65}$ **−8 or 0**

Lesson 10-6

Chapter 10 37 Glencoe Algebra 1

Practice
CRM p. 40 AL OL BL ELL

NAME ______ DATE ______ PERIOD ______

10-6 Practice
The Distance and Midpoint Formulas

Find the distance between the points with the given coordinates.

1. (4, 7), (1, 3) **5**
2. (0, 9), (−7, −2) **$\sqrt{170} \approx 13.04$**
3. $(6, 2), \left(4, \frac{1}{2}\right)$ **$\frac{5}{2}$ or 2.50**
4. $(-1, 7), \left(\frac{1}{3}, 6\right)$ **$\frac{5}{3} \approx 1.67$**
5. $(\sqrt{3}, 3), (2\sqrt{3}, 5)$ **$\sqrt{7} \approx 2.65$**
6. $(2\sqrt{2}, -1), (3\sqrt{2}, 3)$ **$3\sqrt{2} \approx 4.24$**

Find the possible values of *a* if the points with the given coordinates are the indicated distance apart.

7. $(4, -1), (a, 5); d = 10$ **a = −4 or 12**
8. $(2, -5), (a, 7); d = 15$ **a = −7 or 11**
9. $(6, -7), (a, -4); d = \sqrt{18}$ **a = 3 or 9**
10. $(-4, 1), (a, 8); d = \sqrt{50}$ **a = −5 or −3**
11. $(8, -5), (a, 4); d = \sqrt{85}$ **a = 6 or 10**
12. $(-9, 7), (a, 5); d = \sqrt{29}$ **a = −14 or −4**

Find the coordinates of the midpoint of the segment with the given endpoints.

13. (4, −6), (3, −9) **(3.5, − 7.5)**
14. (−3, −8), (−7, 2) **(−5, −3)**
15. (0, −4), (3, 2) **(1.5, − 1)**
16. (−13, −9), (−1, −5) **(−7, −7)**
17. $\left(2, -\frac{1}{2}\right), \left(1, \frac{1}{2}\right)$ **$\left(1\frac{1}{2}, 0\right)$**
18. $\left(\frac{2}{3}, -1\right), \left(2, \frac{1}{3}\right)$ **$\left(1\frac{1}{3}, -\frac{1}{3}\right)$**

19. **BASEBALL** Three players are warming up for a baseball game. Player B stands 9 feet to the right and 18 feet in front of Player A. Player C stands 8 feet to the left and 13 feet in front of Player A.

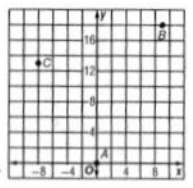

a. Draw a model of the situation on the coordinate grid. Assume that Player A is located at (0, 0).
b. To the nearest tenth, what is the distance between Players A and B and between Players A and C? **20.1 ft; 15.3 ft**
c. What is the distance between Players B and C? **17.7 ft**

20. **MAPS** Maria and Jackson live in adjacent neighborhoods. If they superimpose a coordinate grid on the map of their neighborhoods, Maria lives at (−9, 1) and Jackson lives at (5, −4). If each unit on the grid represents $\frac{1}{4}$ mile, how far apart are Maria's and Jackson's homes? **about 3.72 mi**

Chapter 10 40 Glencoe Algebra 1

Word Problem Practice
CRM p. 41 AL OL BL ELL

NAME ______ DATE ______ PERIOD ______

10-6 Word Problem Practice
The Distance and Midpoint Formulas

1. **CHESS** Margaret's last two remaining chess pieces are located at the centers of the squares at opposite corners of the board. If the chessboard is a square with 8-inch sides, about how far apart are the pieces? Round your answer to the nearest tenth. **9.9 in.**

2. **ENGINEERING** Todd has drawn a cul-de-sac for a residential development plan. He used a compass to draw the cul-de-sac so that it would be circular. On his blueprint, the center of the cul-de-sac has coordinates (−1, −1) and a point on the circle is (2, 3). What is the radius of the cul-de-sac? **5 units**

3. **LANDSCAPING** Randy plotted a triangular patio on a landscape plan for a client. What is the length of fencing he will need along the patio edge that borders the property line? Round your answer to the nearest tenth. **7.1 m**

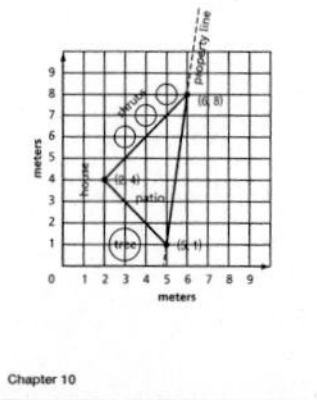

4. **UTILITIES** The electric company is running some wires across an open field. The wire connects a utility pole at (2, 14) and a second utility pole at (7, −8). If the electric company wishes to place a third pole at the midpoint of the two poles, at what coordinates should the pole be placed? **(4.5, 3)**

5. **MARCHING BAND** The Ohio State University marching band performs a famous on-field spelling of O-H-I-O called "Script Ohio". Sometimes they must adjust the usual dimensions of the word to fit it into the limited guest band performance area. The diagram below shows part of the adjusted drill chart. Each point represents one band member, and the coordinates are in yards.

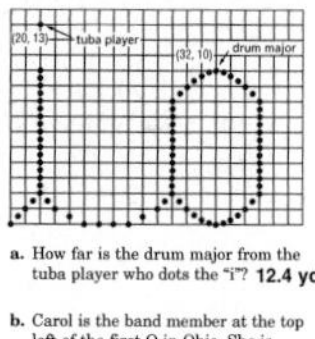

a. How far is the drum major from the tuba player who dots the "i"? **12.4 yd**
b. Carol is the band member at the top left of the first O in Ohio. She is located at (0, 26). How far away is Carol from the tuba player? Round your answer to the nearest tenth. **23.9 yd**

Lesson 10-6

Chapter 10 41 Glencoe Algebra 1

48. **TEMPERATURE** The temperature dropped from 25°F to −8°F over a 12-hour period beginning at 12:00 noon as shown.

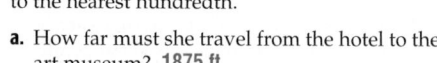

Time	12:00 noon	4:00	8:00	12:00 midnight
Temperature (°F)	25°F	14°F	3°F	−8°F

a. Plot these points on a coordinate plane with time on the *x*-axis and temperature on the *y*-axis. Let *x* represent the number of hours, and let 12:00 noon correspond to $x = 0$. **See margin.**

b. Draw a segment to connect the points. Find the midpoint of this segment. Interpret the meaning of the midpoint in this situation. **See margin for graph; (6, 8.5); at 6:00, the temperature was 8.5°.**

49. **NAVIGATION** Two cruise ships are leaving St. Lucia Island at the same time. One travels 10 miles due east and then 8 miles north. The second ship travels 12 miles due north and then 6 miles west.

a. If St. Lucia is at the origin, how far is the first ship from St. Lucia? **$\sqrt{164}$ or about 12.81 mi**
b. How far is the second ship from St. Lucia? **$\sqrt{180}$ or about 13.42 mi**
c. How far apart are the ships? **$4\sqrt{17}$ or about 16.49 mi**

Real-World Career

Cruise Director
The cruise director is in charge of all onboard entertainment and activities. A professional entertainment background is preferred or 2–5 years experience on board.

50. **TOURING** Sasha is using the GPS system in her car to go from her hotel to the art museum, to a restaurant, and then to the theater. Sides of grid squares represent 500 feet. Round your answers to the nearest hundredth.

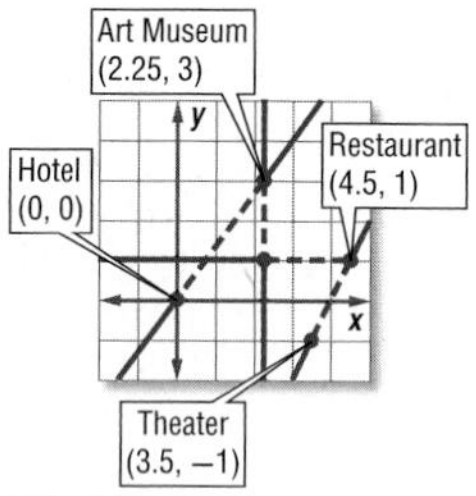

a. How far must she travel from the hotel to the art museum? **1875 ft**
b. What is the distance from the art museum to the restaurant? **1505.20 ft**
c. How far is it from the restaurant to the theater? **1118.03 ft**
d. If Sasha gets a direct distance reading from the theater to her hotel, how far is it? **1820.03 ft**

C **Find the coordinates of the midpoint of the segment with the given endpoints.**

51. (4.25, 2.5), (2.5, −3) **(3.375, −0.25)**
52. $\left(5, -\frac{1}{2}\right), \left(-3, \frac{5}{2}\right)$ **(1,1)**
53. $\left(\frac{2}{5}, -\frac{1}{5}\right), \left(\frac{1}{3}, \frac{5}{2}\right)$ **$\left(\frac{11}{30}, \frac{23}{20}\right)$**

H.O.T. Problems
Use **H**igher-**O**rder **T**hinking Skills

54. **CHALLENGE** $A(-7, 3)$, $B(4, 0)$, and $C(-4, 4)$ are the vertices of a triangle. Discuss two different ways to determine whether $\triangle ABC$ is a right triangle.

54. Sample answer: One way is to find the slope of each side. Then if any pair of the slopes are negative reciprocals, then you have a right triangle. Another way is to find the distance between each pair of points. Then check to see if the converse of the Pythagorean Theorem applies.

55. **REASONING** Explain why there are usually two possible values when looking for a missing coordinate when you are given two sets of coordinates and the distance between the two points. **See margin.**

56. **REASONING** Is the following statement *true* or *false*? Explain your reasoning. **See margin.**
It matters which ordered pair is first when using the Distance Formula.

57. **OPEN ENDED** Plot two points on a coordinate plane and draw the segment between them. Find the coordinates of the midpoint. **See margin.**

58. **WRITING IN MATH** Explain how the Midpoint Formula is related to finding the mean. **See margin.**

Enrichment
CRM p. 42 OL BL

NAME ______ DATE ______ PERIOD ______

10-6 Enrichment

A Space-Saving Method

Two arrangements for cookies on a 32 cm by 40 cm cookie sheet are shown at the right. The cookies have 8-cm diameters after they are baked. The centers of the cookies are on the vertices of squares in the top arrangement. In the other, the centers are on the vertices of equilateral triangles. Which arrangement is more economical? The triangle arrangement is more economical, because it contains one more cookie.

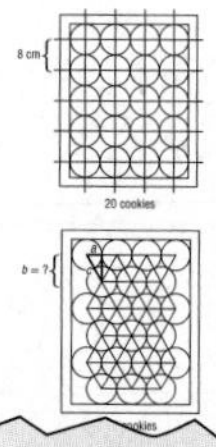

In the square arrangement, rows are placed every 8 cm. At what intervals are rows placed in the triangle arrangement?

Look at the right triangle labeled *a*, *b*, and *c*. A leg *a* of the triangle is the radius of a cookie, or 4 cm. The hypotenuse *c* is the sum of two radii, or 8 cm. Use the Pythagorean theorem to find b, the interval of the rows.

$$c^2 = a^2 + b^2$$
$$8^2 = 4^2 + b^2$$
$$64 - 16 = b^2$$
$$\sqrt{48} = b$$
$$4\sqrt{3} = b$$

Additional Answer

48a–b.

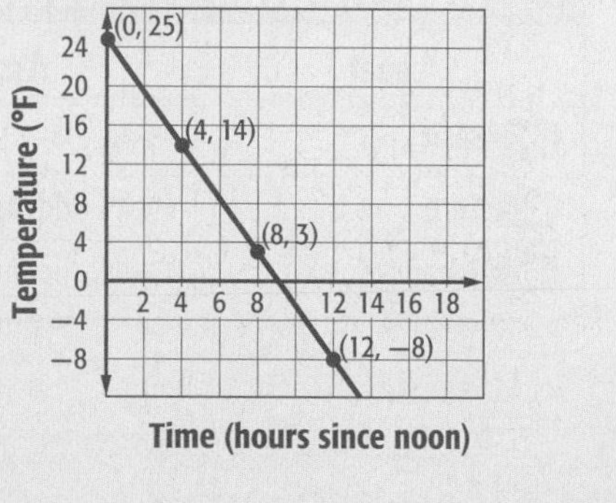

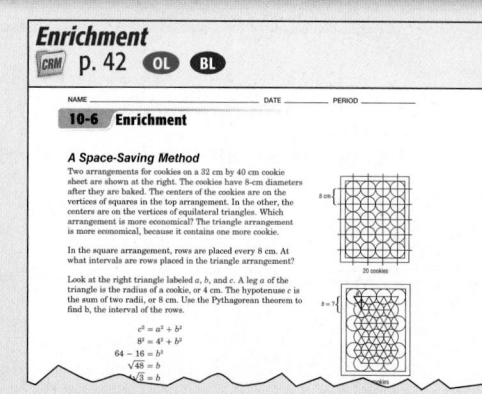

PSAE PRACTICE 6.11.17, 9.11.09

59. SHORT RESPONSE Two sailboats leave Key Largo, Florida, at the same time. One travels east and then north. The other travels south and then west. How far apart are the boats? **15 mi**

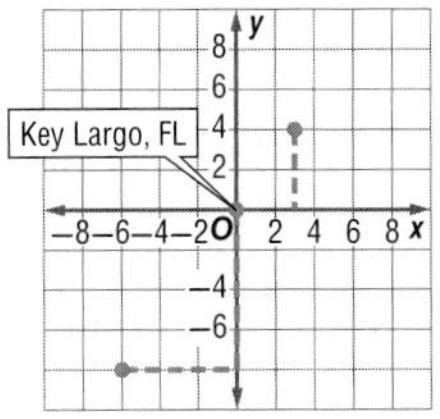

60. While in Tokyo, Callie spent 560 yen for a strand of pearls. The cost of the pearls was equivalent to \$35 in U.S. currency. At the time of Callie's purchase, how many yen were equivalent to \$20 in U.S. currency? **B**

A 109 yen
B 320 yen
C 980 yen
D 2350 yen

61. SHORT RESPONSE L represents a lighthouse and B represents a buoy. A ship is at the midpoint between L and B. Which coordinates best represent the ship's position? **H**

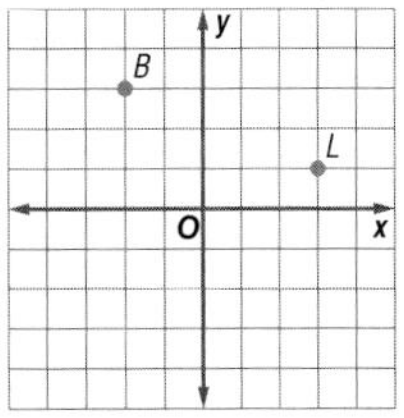

F $\left(2, \frac{1}{2}\right)$ H $\left(\frac{1}{2}, 2\right)$
G $\left(1, \frac{1}{2}\right)$ J $\left(\frac{1}{2}, 5\right)$

62. At a family reunion, Guido cut a slice of cheesecake that was about one sixteenth of the cake. If the entire cheesecake contained 4480 Calories, which is the closest to the number of Calories in Guido's slice? **A**

A 280 C 498
B 373 D 560

Spiral Review

If c is the measure of the hypotenuse of a right triangle, find each missing measure. If necessary, round to the nearest hundredth. (Lesson 10-5)

63. $a = 16, b = 63, c = ?$ **65**
64. $b = 3, a = \sqrt{112}, c = ?$ **11**
65. $c = 14, a = 9, b = ?$ **10.72**
66. $a = 6, b = 3, c = ?$ **6.71**
67. $b = \sqrt{77}, c = 12, a = ?$ **8.19**
68. $a = 4, b = \sqrt{11}, c = ?$ **5.20**

69. AVIATION The relationship between a plane's length L in feet and the pounds P its wings can lift is described by $L = \sqrt{kP}$, where k is the constant of proportionality. Find k for this plane to the nearest hundredth. (Lesson 10-4) **0.06**

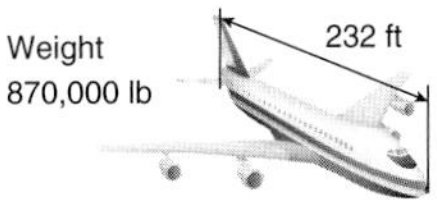

Skills Review

Solve each proportion. If necessary, round to the nearest hundredth. (Lesson 2-6)

70. $\frac{4}{d} = \frac{2}{10}$ **20**
71. $\frac{6}{5} = \frac{f}{15}$ **18**
72. $\frac{20}{28} = \frac{h}{21}$ **15**
73. $\frac{6}{7} = \frac{7}{j}$ **8.17**
74. $\frac{16}{7} = \frac{9}{m}$ **3.94**
75. $\frac{p}{2} = \frac{45}{68}$ **1.32**

4 ASSESS

Ticket Out the Door On a coordinate grid, have students draw line segments that are neither vertical nor horizontal and have endpoints whose coordinates are whole numbers. Have students use the Distance Formula to find the lengths of their line segments.

Formative Assessment

Check for student understanding of concepts in Lessons 10-5 and 10-6.

CRM Quiz 3, p. 58

Additional Answers

55. Sample answer: The Distance Formula requires values to be squared. Once the coordinates and a are substituted into the formula and simplified, the result is a quadratic equation that can result in two possible values for a once solved.

56. False; Sample answer: When you reverse the order of the numbers that you are subtracting, you do get opposite results. However, when you square those results the squares will be the same as before.

57. Sample answer: (0, 2)

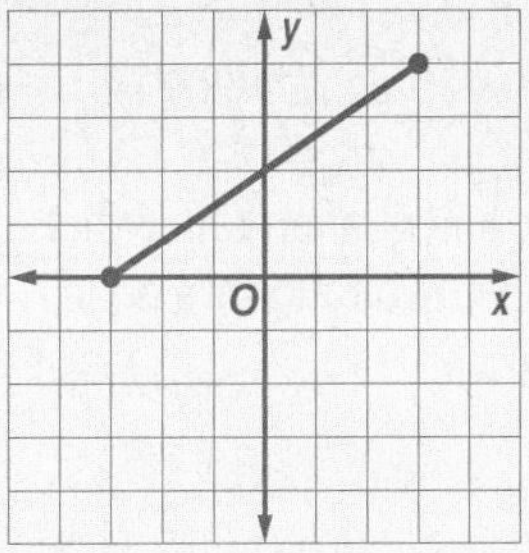

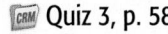

58. Sample answer: To find the mean of two numbers you add them together and divide by 2. To find the coordinate of a midpoint, you add the x-coordinates and divide by 2, then you add the y-coordinates and divide by 2. So, you are finding the means of the x-coordinates and the y-coordinates.

Differentiated Instruction OL BL

Extension Explain that a circle is the set of points in a coordinate plane, all of which are the same distance from a given point. Write $(x - h)^2 + (y - k)^2 = r^2$ on the board. Tell students that in the equation, (h, k) is the center point, (x, y) represents any point on the circle, and r is the length of the radius of the circle. Ask students to compare the equation for a circle to the Distance Formula. Sample answer: The equation of a circle appears to have been derived from the Distance Formula. $(x - h)^2 + (y - k)^2 = r^2$ can be rewritten as $r = \sqrt{(x - h)^2 + (y - k)^2}$, which looks a lot like $d = \sqrt{(x_2 - x_1)^2 + (y_2 - y_1)^2}$.

10-7 Lesson Notes

1 FOCUS

Vertical Alignment

Before Lesson 10-7
Solve proportions.

Lesson 10-7
Determine whether two triangles are similar.
Find the unknown measures of sides of two similar triangles.

After Lesson 10-7
Use trigonometric ratios to solve problems.

2 TEACH

Scaffolding Questions Have students read the *Why?* section of the lesson.

Ask:

- Suppose the measure of the Ferris wheel shadow is five times as long as Simona's shadow. How many times as tall will the Ferris wheel be as Simona? 5 times as high
- How would you describe this idea using ratios? The ratio of the lengths of the shadows is the same as the ratio of the heights of the Ferris wheel and Simona.
- What is an equation called that states that two ratios are equal? a proportion

10-7 Similar Triangles

Then
You solved proportions. (Lesson 2-6)

Now
- Determine whether two triangles are similar.
- Find the unknown measures of sides of two similar triangles.

IL Learning Standards
7.A.4a Apply units and scales to describe and compare numerical data and physical objects.
7.C.4a Make indirect measurements, including heights and distances, using proportions.

New Vocabulary
similar triangles

IL Math Online
glencoe.com
- Extra Examples
- Personal Tutor
- Self-Check Quiz
- Homework Help
- Math in Motion

Why?

Simona needs to measure the height of a Ferris wheel for a class project. Simona can measure her shadow and the shadow of the Ferris wheel. She can then use similar triangles and indirect measurement to find the height of the Ferris wheel.

Similar Triangles **Similar triangles** have the same shape, but not necessarily the same size. The symbol $\sim$ is used to denote that two triangles are similar. The vertices of similar triangles are written in order to show the corresponding parts.

Key Concept — Similar Triangles (For Your FOLDABLE)

Words If two triangles are similar, then the measures of their corresponding angles are equal, and the measures of their corresponding sides are proportional.

Example If $\triangle ABC \sim \triangle DEF$, then $m\angle A = m\angle D$, $m\angle B = m\angle E$, $m\angle C = m\angle F$, and $\frac{AB}{DE} = \frac{BC}{EF} = \frac{AC}{DF} = \frac{1}{2}$.

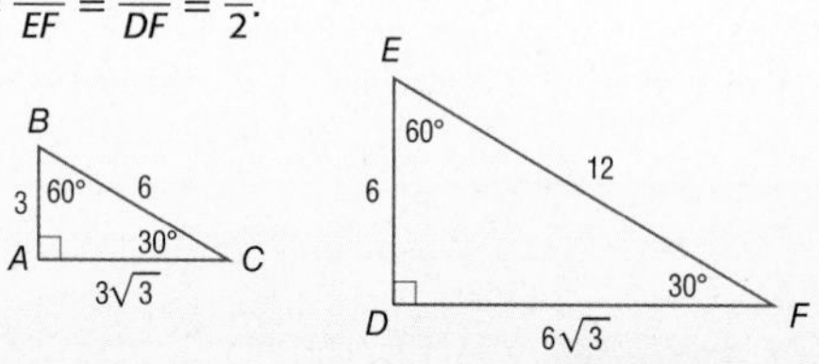

Math *in Motion,* Animation glencoe.com

EXAMPLE 1 Determine Whether Two Triangles are Similar

Determine whether the pair of triangles is similar. Justify your answer.

The measure of $\angle T$ is $180 - (57 + 57)$ or $66°$.

In $\triangle XYZ$, $\angle X$ and $\angle Z$ have the same measure.

Let $x =$ the measure of $\angle X$ and $\angle Z$.

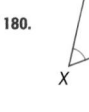

$x + x + 66 = 180$ **Sum of the angle measures is 180.**
$2x = 114$ **Subtract 66 from each side.**
$x = 57$ **Divide each side by 2.**

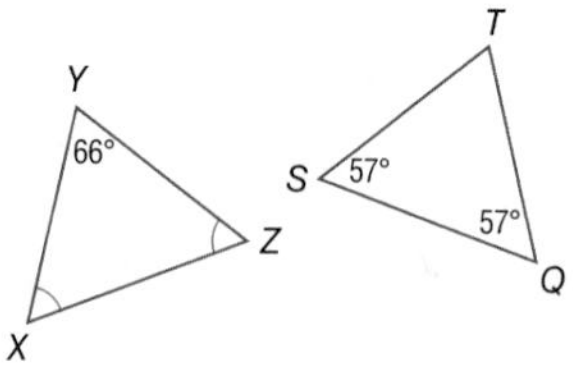

So, $m\angle X = 57°$ and $m\angle Z = 57°$.

Since the corresponding angles have equal measures, $\triangle XYZ \sim \triangle STQ$.

Check Your Progress

1. Determine whether $\triangle ABC$ with $m\angle A = 68°$ and $m\angle B = m\angle C$ is similar to $\triangle DEF$ with $m\angle E = m\angle F = 54°$. Justify your answer. No; the angle measures are not equal.

Personal Tutor glencoe.com

Lesson 10-7 Resources

Resource	Approaching-Level	On-Level	Beyond-Level	English Learners
Teacher Edition		• Differentiated Instruction, pp. 644, 647	• Differentiated Instruction, pp. 644, 647	
Chapter Resource Masters	• Study Guide and Intervention, pp. 43–44 • Skills Practice, p. 45 • Practice, p. 46 • Word Problem Practice, p. 47	• Study Guide and Intervention, pp. 43–44 • Skills Practice, p. 45 • Practice, p. 46 • Word Problem Practice, p. 47 • Enrichment, p. 48	• Practice, p. 46 • Word Problem Practice, p. 47 • Enrichment, p. 48	• Study Guide and Intervention, pp. 43–44 • Skills Practice, p. 45 • Practice, p. 46
Transparencies	• 5-Minute Check Transparency 10-7	• 5-Minute Check Transparency 10-7	• 5-Minute Check Transparency 10-7	• 5-Minute Check Transparency 10-7
Other	• Study Notebook • Teaching Algebra with Manipulatives	• Study Notebook • Teaching Algebra with Manipulatives	• Study Notebook	• Study Notebook • Teaching Algebra with Manipulatives

The ratios of the lengths of the corresponding sides can also be compared to show that two triangles are similar.

ReadingMath

Angle Measures The $m\angle A$ is read as *the measure of angle A.*

EXAMPLE 2 Determine Whether Two Triangles are Similar

Determine whether the pair of triangles is similar. Justify your answer.

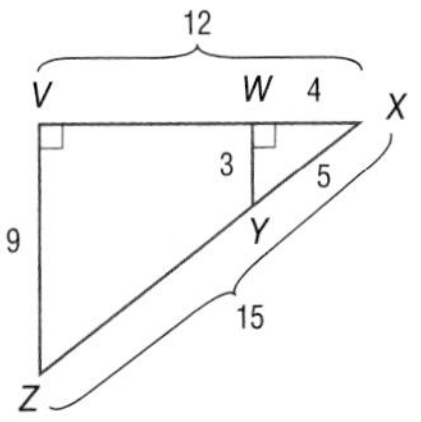

If $\triangle VXZ$ and $\triangle WXY$ are similar, then the measures of their corresponding sides are proportional.

$\frac{VX}{WX} = \frac{12}{4} = 3 \quad \frac{XZ}{XY} = \frac{15}{5} = 3 \quad \frac{VZ}{WY} = \frac{9}{3} = 3$

Since the corresponding sides are proportional, $\triangle VXZ \sim \triangle WXY$.

Check Your Progress

2. Determine whether $\triangle ABC$ with $AB = 6$, $BC = 16$, and $AC = 20$ is similar to $\triangle JKL$ with $JK = 3$, $KL = 8$, and $JL = 9$. Justify your answer.
No; the corresponding sides are not proportional.

Personal Tutor glencoe.com

Find Unknown Measures When some of the measurements of the sides of similar triangles are known, proportions can be used to find the missing measures.

StudyTip

Overlapping Triangles If two triangles overlap, you may want to draw each triangle separately. Make sure the corresponding parts are in the same position and label the corresponding angles and/or sides.

EXAMPLE 3 Find Missing Measures

Find the missing measures for the pair of similar triangles.

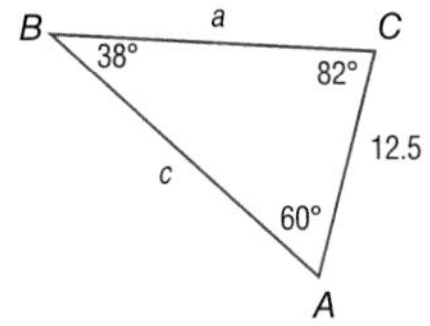

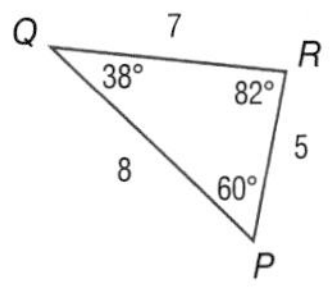

$\frac{AB}{PQ} = \frac{AC}{PR}$	**Corresponding sides of similar triangles are proportional.**	$\frac{BC}{QR} = \frac{AC}{PR}$	**Corresponding sides of similar triangles are proportional.**
$\frac{c}{8} = \frac{12.5}{5}$	**$AB = c$, $AC = 12.5$, $PQ = 8$, $PR = 5$**	$\frac{a}{7} = \frac{12.5}{5}$	**$BC = a$, $AC = 12.5$, $QR = 7$, $PR = 5$**
$5c = 100$	**Find the cross products.**	$5a = 87.5$	**Find the cross products.**
$c = 20$	**Divide each side by 5.**	$a = 17.5$	**Divide each side by 5.**

The missing measures are 20 and 17.5.

Check Your Progress

3A.

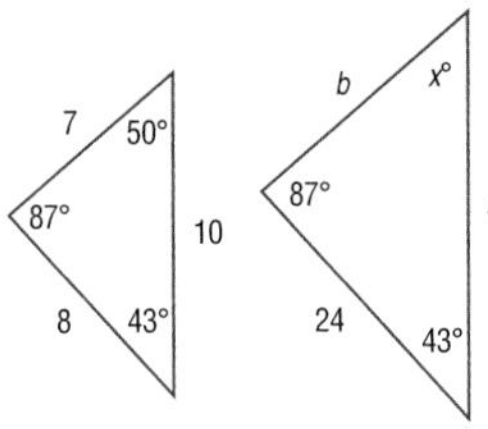

$x = 50°$; $a = 30$; $b = 21$

3B.

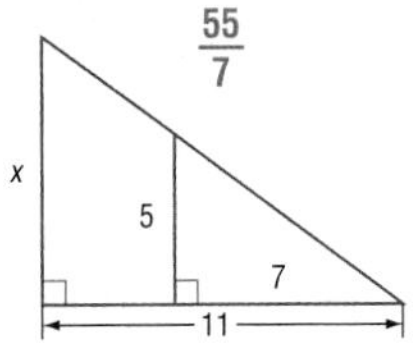

$\frac{55}{7}$

Personal Tutor glencoe.com

Similar Triangles

Example 1 shows how to use angles to determine whether two triangles are similar. **Example 2** shows how to use proportions to determine whether two triangles are similar.

Formative Assessment

Use the Check Your Progress exercises after each example to determine students' understanding of concepts.

Additional Examples

1 Determine whether the pair of triangles is similar. Justify your answer.

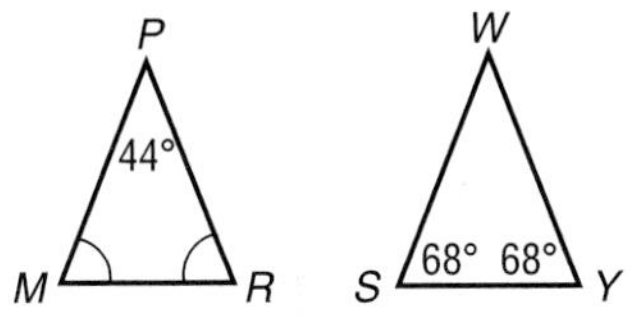

The corresponding angles have equal measures, so the triangles are similar.

2 Determine whether the pair of triangles is similar. Justify your answer.

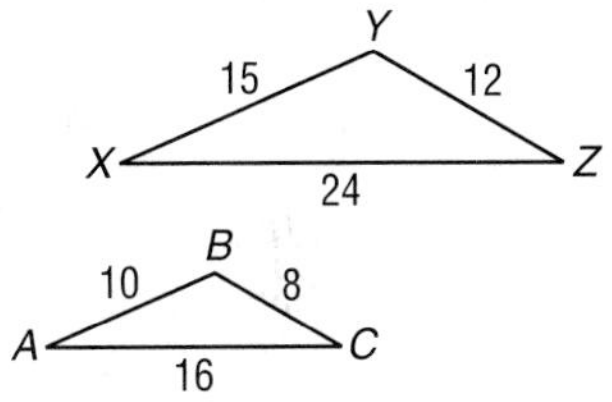

The corresponding sides of the triangles are proportional, so the triangles are similar.

Additional Examples also in Interactive Classroom PowerPoint® Presentations

IWB INTERACTIVE WHITEBOARD READY

Tips for New Teachers

Reading Math In drawings of triangles, arcs are often used to show angles that have equal measures. Angles with one arc have measures that are equal to each other, angles with two arcs have measures that are equal to each other, and so on.

Watch Out!

Preventing Errors Tell students to look closely at all the angles and sides of the two triangles for clues about whether the triangles are similar. In Example 1, the same angles are not marked on both triangles, but there is sufficient information to determine that the angles are congruent.

Find Unknown Measures

Example 3 shows how to use proportions to find the missing measures of the sides of similar triangles. **Example 4** shows how to use similar triangles to solve a real-world problem.

Lesson 10-7 Similar Triangles 643

Focus on Mathematical Content

Similar Triangles Similar triangles have the same shape, but not necessarily the same size. The corresponding sides of similar triangles are proportional, and the corresponding angles are equal in measure.

Additional Examples

3 Find the missing measures for the pair of similar triangles.

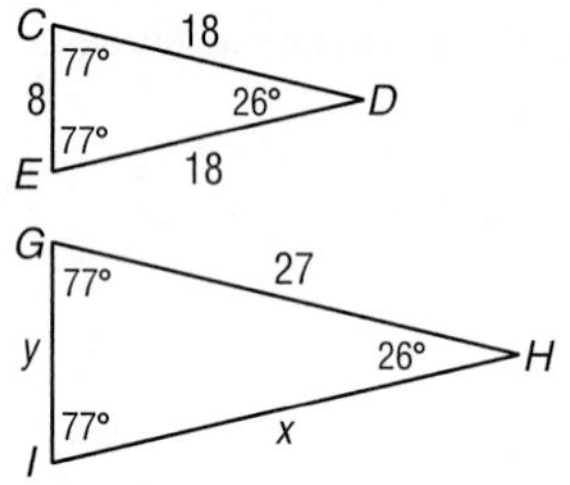

$x = 27; y = 12$

4 **SHADOWS** Ricardo is standing next to the General Sherman Giant Sequoia tree in Sequoia National Park. The shadow of the tree is 22.5 meters, and Ricardo's shadow is 53.6 centimeters. If Ricardo's height is 2 meters, about how tall is the tree? 84 m

3 PRACTICE

Formative Assessment

Use Exercises 1–7 to check for understanding.

Use the chart at the bottom of the next page to customize assignments for your students.

Real-World EXAMPLE 4 Indirect Measurement

SHADOWS Tori is 5 feet 6 inches tall, and her shadow is 2 feet 9 inches long. She is standing next to a flagpole. If the length of the shadow of the flagpole is 12 feet long, how tall is the flagpole?

Math *in Motion*, BrainPOP® glencoe.com

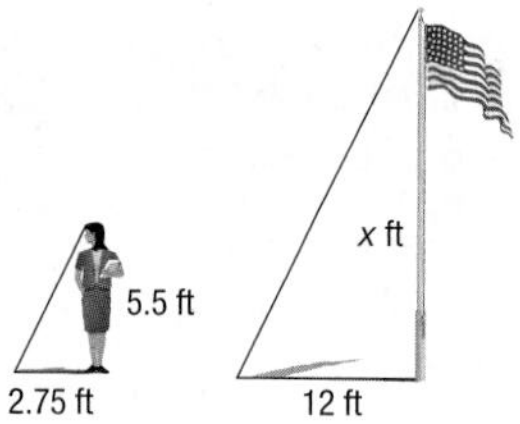

Understand Find the height of the flagpole.

Plan Make a sketch of the situation.

Solve The Sun's rays form similar triangles. Write a proportion that compares the heights of the objects and the lengths of their shadows.

Let x = the height of the flagpole.

height of flagpole → / Tori's height → $\frac{x}{5.5} = \frac{12}{2.75}$ ← length of the flagpole's shadow / ← Tori's shadow

$2.75x = 66$

$x = 24$ The height of the flagpole is 24 feet.

Check $\frac{24}{5.5} \stackrel{?}{=} \frac{12}{2.75}$ **Substitute 24 for *x*.**

$4.36 = 4.36$ ✓

Check Your Progress

4. TENTS The directions for pitching a tent include a scale drawing in which 1 inch represents 4.5 feet. In the drawing, the tent is $1\frac{3}{4}$ inches tall. How tall should the actual tent be? 7.875 ft

Personal Tutor glencoe.com

Check Your Understanding

Examples 1 and 2 pp. 642–643

Determine whether each pair of triangles is similar. Justify your answer.

1.

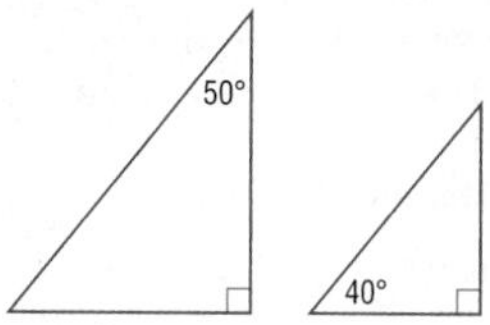

2.

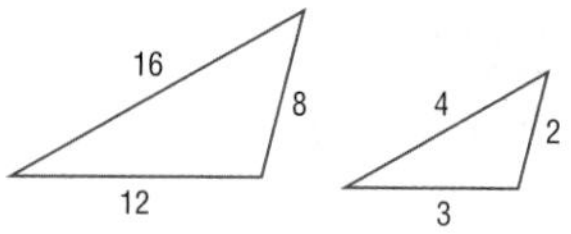

1. Yes; the angle measures are equal.
2. Yes; the sides are proportional.

Example 3 p. 643

Find the missing measures for the pair of similar triangles if $\triangle ABC \sim \triangle XYZ$.

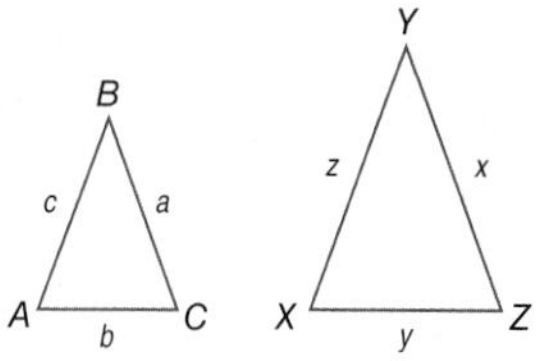

3. $a = 4, b = 6, c = 8, x = 6$ $y = 9; z = 12$

4. $x = 9, y = 15, z = 21, c = 7$ $a = 3; b = 5$

5. $a = 2, b = 5, x = 10, z = 30$ $c = 6; y = 25$

6. $b = 6, c = 10, x = 30, y = 15$ $a = 12; z = 25$

Example 4 p. 644

7. TREES Marla wants to know the height of the tree in her backyard. The tree casts a shadow 8 feet 6 inches long. Marla is 5 feet tall, and her shadow is 2 feet 6 inches long. How tall is the tree? 17 ft

Differentiated Instruction

OL BL

If students have an interest in botany,

Then have students use the method in Example 4 to find the heights of trees that are native to your area. Make sure students record the locations and types of trees along with the heights. Students will need tape measures and should take measurements on a sunny day.

Practice and Problem Solving

● = **Step-by-Step Solutions** begin on page R12.
Extra Practice begins on page 815.

Examples 1 and 2 pp. 642–643

8. No; the angle measures are not equal.
9. No; the sides are not proportional.
10. Yes; the sides are proportional.
11. No; the angle measures are not equal.
12. No; the sides are not proportional.
13. Yes; the angle measures are equal.

Determine whether each pair of triangles is similar. Justify your answer.

8.
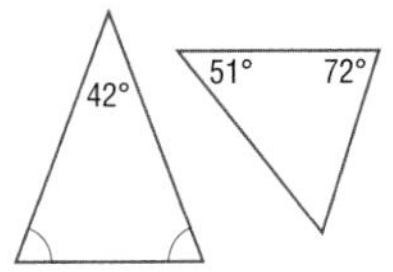

9.
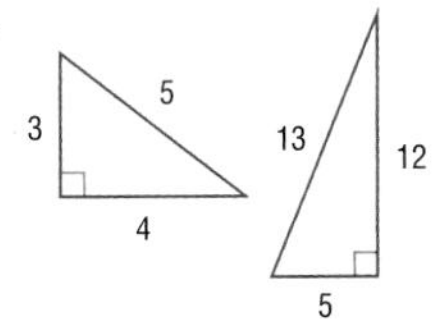

10.
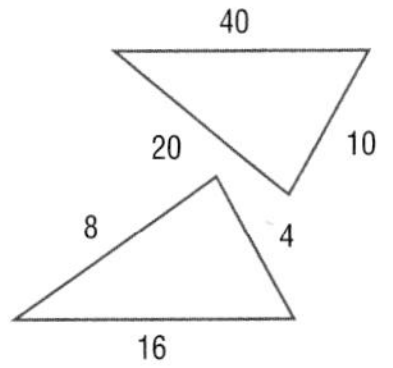

11.
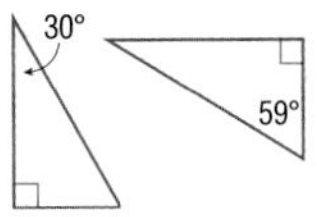

12.
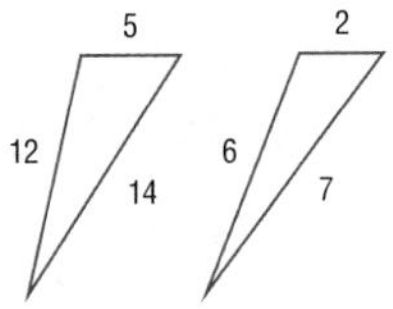

13.
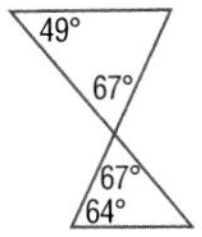

14–19. See margin.

Example 3 p. 643

Find the missing measures for the pair of similar triangles if $\triangle HKM \sim \triangle PTR$.

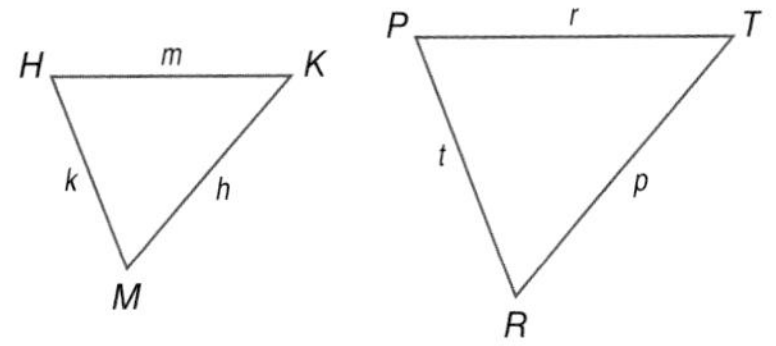

14. $m = 2, k = 7, h = 6, r = 4$

15. $r = 7.5, p = 15, t = 20, h = 6$

16. $m = 3.5, k = 9, t = 13.5, p = 9.75$

17. $m = 1.4, h = 2.8, p = 0.56, t = 0.84$

18. $m = \sqrt{7}, h = 2\sqrt{2}, t = 4\sqrt{3}, r = \sqrt{21}$

19. $m = \sqrt{2}, k = \sqrt{7}, t = \sqrt{14}, p = \sqrt{10}$

Example 4 p. 644

20. TOYS Diecast model cars use a scale of 1 inch : 2 feet of the real vehicle. The original vehicle has a window shaped like a right triangle. If the height of the window on the actual vehicle is 2.5 feet, what will the height of the window be on the model? 1.25 in.

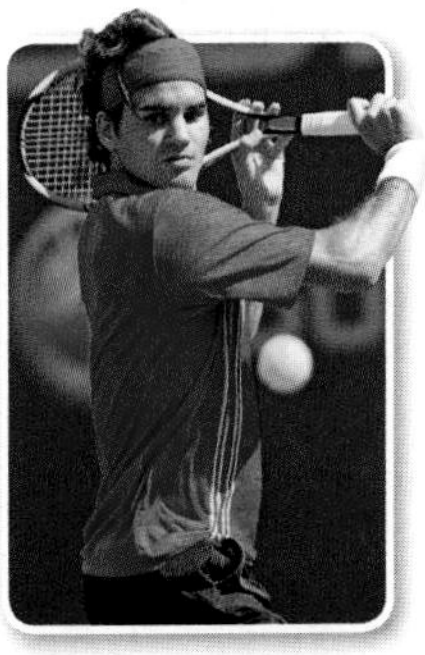

Real-World Link

Roger Federer was the number 1 ranked tennis player for four consecutive years beginning in 2004. He was the first player to reach all four Grand Slam finals in back-to-back years.

Source: ATP Tennis

21. GOLF B Beatriz is playing miniature golf on a hole like the one shown at the right. She wants to putt her ball U so that it will bank at T and travel into the hole at R. Use similar triangles to find where Beatriz's ball should strike the wall. 20 in. from S

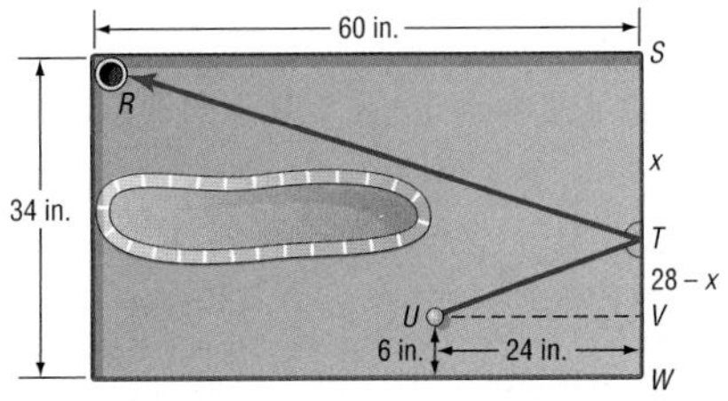

22. MAPS The scale on an Ohio map shows that 2.5 centimeters represents 100 miles. The distance on the map from Cleveland to Cincinnati is 5.5 centimeters. About how many miles apart are the two cities? 220 mi

23. SCHOOL PROJECT For extra credit in his history class, Marquez plans to make a model of the Statue of Liberty in the scale 1 inch : 10 feet. If the height of the actual Statue of Liberty is 151 feet, what will be the height of the model? $15\frac{1}{10}$ in.

24. TENNIS Andy wants to hit the ball just over the net so it will land 16 feet away from the base of the net. If Andy hits the ball 40 feet away from the net, how high does he have to hit the ball? 10.5 ft

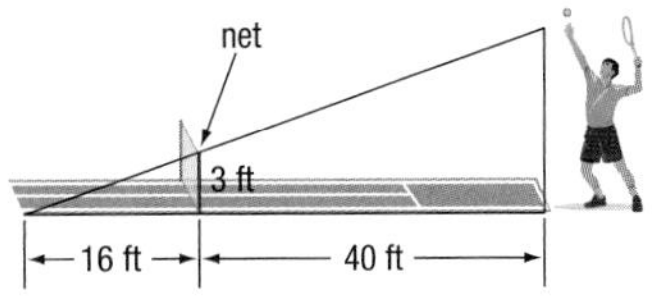

TEACH with TECH

INTERACTIVE WHITEBOARD Use geometry software to draw a triangle and measure its side lengths. Draw a similar triangle and tell students they can measure only one side of the triangle. Drag corresponding sides into pairs. Have them use a proportion to find the lengths of the other sides. Repeat with different triangles.

Additional Answers

14. $p = 12; t = 14$

15. $m = 3; k = 8$

16. $h = 6.5; r = 5.25$

17. $k = 4.2; r = 0.28$

18. $k = 4; p = 2\sqrt{6}$

19. $h = \sqrt{5}; r = 2$

Differentiated Homework Options

Level	Assignment	Two-Day Option	
AL Basic	8–20, 26, 28–59	9–19 odd, 31–34	8–20 even, 26, 28–30, 35–59
OL Core	9–19 odd, 21–26, 28–59	8–20, 31–34	21–26, 28–30, 35–59
BL Advanced	21–54, (optional: 55–59)		

Study Guide and Intervention
CRM pp. 43–44 AL OL ELL

NAME ____________ DATE ______ PERIOD ______

10-7 Study Guide and Intervention

Similar Triangles

Similar Triangles $\triangle RST$ is **similar** to $\triangle XYZ$. The angles of the two triangles have equal measure. They are called **corresponding angles**. The sides opposite the corresponding angles are called **corresponding sides**.

Similar Triangles	If two triangles are similar, then the measures of their corresponding sides are proportional and the measures of their corresponding angles are equal.	$\triangle ABC \sim \triangle DEF$ $\frac{AB}{DE} = \frac{BC}{EF} = \frac{AC}{DF}$

Example 1 Determine whether the pair of triangles is similar. Justify your answer.

Since corresponding angles do not have the equal measures, the triangles are not similar.

Example 2 Determine whether the pair of triangles is similar. Justify your answer.

The measure of $\angle G = 180° - (90° + 45°) = 45°$. The measure of $\angle I = 180° - (45° + 45°) = 90°$. Since corresponding angles have equal measures, $\triangle EFG \sim \triangle HIJ$.

Exercises

Determine whether each pair of triangles is similar. Justify your answer.

1. Yes; corresponding angles have equal measures.
2. No; corresponding angles do not have equal measures.
3. Yes; corresponding angles have equal measures.
4. Yes; corresponding angles have equal measures.
5. Yes; corresponding angles have equal measures.
6. No; corresponding angles do not have equal measures.

Chapter 10 43 Glencoe Algebra 1

Practice
CRM p. 46 AL OL BL ELL

NAME ____________ DATE ______ PERIOD ______

10-7 Practice

Similar Triangles

Determine whether each pair of triangles is similar. Justify your answer.

1. Yes; $\angle Q = \angle T = 90°$; $\angle P = 180° - (90° + 31°) = 59° = \angle S$; $\angle U = 180° - (90° + 59°) = 31° = \angle R$. Since the corresponding angles have equal measures, $\triangle PQR \sim \triangle STU$.

2. No; $\angle C = 180° - (47° + 80°) = 53°$. Since $\triangle FGH$ has a 56° angle, but $\triangle CDE$ does not, corresponding angles do not all have equal measures, and the triangles are not similar.

Find the missing measures for the pair of similar triangles if $\triangle ABC \sim \triangle DEF$.

3. $c = 4, d = 12, e = 16, f = 8$ **$a = 6, b = 8$**
4. $e = 20, a = 24, b = 30, c = 15$ **$d = 16, f = 10$**
5. $a = 10, b = 12, c = 6, d = 4$ **$e = 4.8, f = 2.4$**
6. $a = 4, d = 6, e = 4, f = 3$ **$c = 2, b = \frac{8}{3}$**
7. $b = 15, d = 16, e = 20, f = 10$ **$a = 12, c = \frac{15}{2}$**
8. $a = 16, b = 22, c = 12, f = 8$ **$d = \frac{32}{3}, e = \frac{44}{3}$**
9. $a = \frac{5}{2}, b = 3, f = \frac{11}{2}, e = 7$ **$c = \frac{33}{14}, d = \frac{35}{6}$**
10. $c = 4, d = 6, e = 5.625, f = 12$ **$a = 2, b = 1.875$**

11. **SHADOWS** Suppose you are standing near a building and you want to know its height. The building casts a 66-foot shadow. You cast a 3-foot shadow. If you are 5 feet 6 inches tall, how tall is the building? **121 ft**

12. **MODELS** Truss bridges use triangles in their support beams. Molly made a model of a truss bridge in the scale of 1 inch = 8 feet. If the height of the triangles on the model is 4.5 inches, what is the height of the triangles on the actual bridge? **36 ft**

Chapter 10 46 Glencoe Algebra 1

Word Problem Practice
CRM p. 47 AL OL BL ELL

NAME ____________ DATE ______ PERIOD ______

10-7 Word Problem Practice

Similar Triangles

1. **CRAFTS** Layla is wants to buy a set of similar magnets for her refrigerator door. Layla finds the magnets below for sale at a local shop. Which two are similar? **B and C**

2. **EXHIBITIONS** The world's largest candle was displayed at the 1897 Stockholm Exhibition. Suppose Lars measured the length of the shadow it cast at 11:00 A.M. and found that it was 12 feet. Suppose that immediately after this, he measured to find that a nearby 25-foot tent pole cast a shadow 5 feet long. How tall was the world's largest candle? **60 ft**

3. **LANDMARKS** The Toy and Miniature Museum of Kansas City displays a miniature replica of George Washington's Mount Vernon mansion. The miniature house is 10 feet long, 6 feet wide, 8 feet tall, and has 22 rooms. The scale of the model to the original is one inch to one foot. If the roof gable of the miniature has dimensions as shown on the diagram below, what is the height of the roof gable on the original Mount Vernon mansion? **14 ft**

Source: Mount Vernon

4. **SURVEYING** Surveyors use properties of triangles including similarity and the Pythagorean Theorem to find unknown distances. Use the dimensions on the diagram to find the unknown distance x across the lake. **80 m**

5. **PUZZLES** The figure below shows an ancient Chinese movable puzzle called a tangram. It has 7 pieces that can be reconfigured to produce an endless number of designs and pictures.

Assume that the side length of this tangram square is $\sqrt{2}$ cm. Leave your answers as simplified radical expressions.

a. What are the side lengths of triangles 1 and 2? **1 cm, 1 cm, $\sqrt{2}$ cm**

b. What are the side lengths of triangle 7? **$\frac{\sqrt{2}}{2}$ cm, $\frac{\sqrt{2}}{2}$ cm, 1 cm**

c. What are the side lengths of triangles 3 and 5? **$\frac{1}{2}$ cm, $\frac{1}{2}$ cm, $\frac{\sqrt{2}}{2}$ cm**

Chapter 10 47 Glencoe Algebra 1

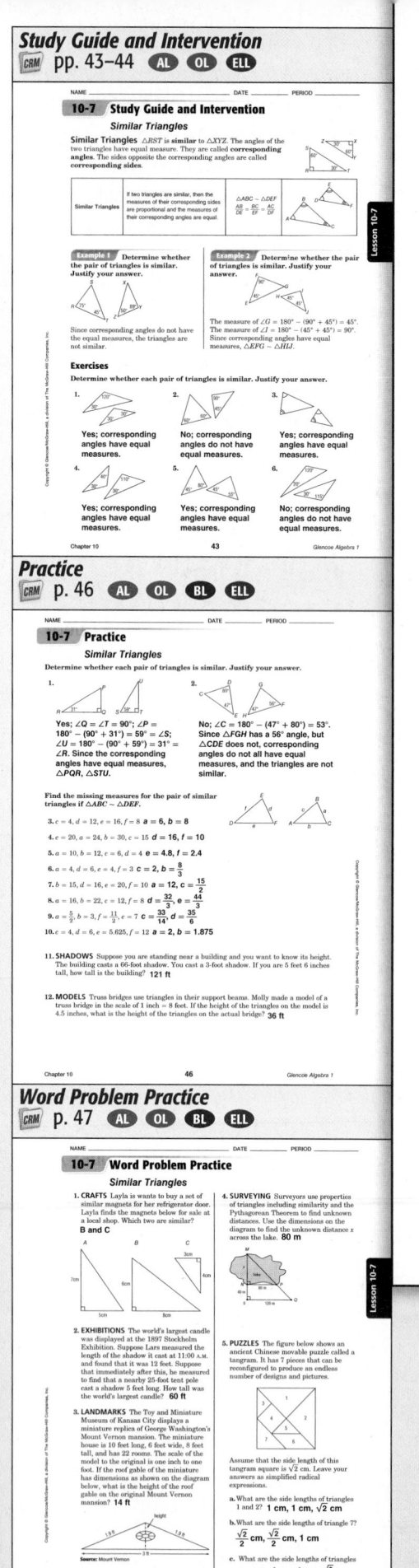

25c. The perimeters are in the same proportion as the side measures of the two similar triangles.

26. Neither; the arcs indicate which angles correspond. So $\triangle XYZ \sim \triangle VUT$.

27. $\triangle XYZ \sim \triangle XZW$, $\triangle XYZ \sim \triangle ZYW$, $\triangle XZW \sim \triangle ZYW$; the triangles are similar to each other because the angle measures are equal.

28. Always, the sides are proportional with a scale factor of 3, which means the triangles are similar and the angles are always congruent.

C 25. **MULTIPLE REPRESENTATIONS** In this problem, you will compare the ratios of corresponding sides and perimeters of similar triangles.

a. **ALGEBRAIC** What is the ratio of the corresponding sides of each pair of similar triangles? Record your results in a table like the one below. **See table below.**

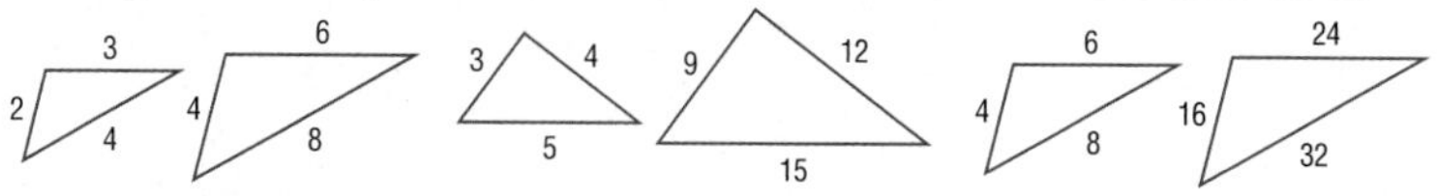

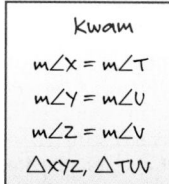

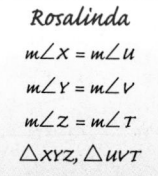

b. **TABULAR** Find the perimeter of each triangle. Then find the ratio of the perimeters for each pair of triangles. Record your results in your table.

Similar Triangles		Ratios of Sides	Perimeters	Ratios of Perimeters
Pair 1	smaller triangle	1:2	9	1:2
	larger triangle		18	
Pair 2	smaller triangle	1:3	12	1:3
	larger triangle		36	
Pair 3	smaller triangle	1:4	18	1:4
	larger triangle		72	

c. **ANALYTICAL** How is the ratio of the perimeters related to the ratio of the lengths of corresponding sides for each pair of triangles?

d. **ANALYTICAL** If the ratio of the lengths of corresponding sides of two similar triangles is 1:6, what would be the ratio of their perimeters? **1:6**

H.O.T. Problems
Use Higher-Order Thinking Skills

26. **FIND THE ERROR** Kwam and Rosalinda are comparing the similar triangles. Is either of them correct? Explain.

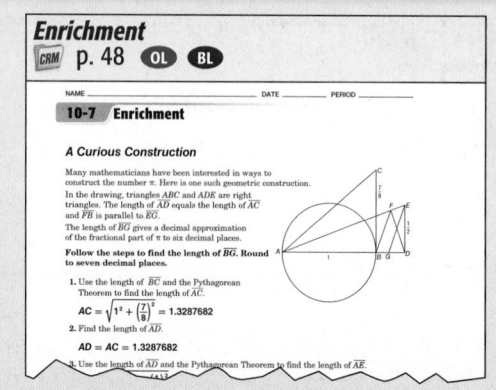

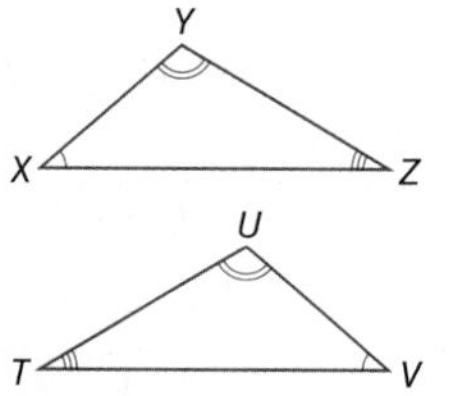

Kwam	Rosalinda
$m\angle X = m\angle T$	$m\angle X = m\angle U$
$m\angle Y = m\angle U$	$m\angle Y = m\angle V$
$m\angle Z = m\angle V$	$m\angle Z = m\angle T$
$\triangle XYZ, \triangle TUV$	$\triangle XYZ, \triangle UVT$

Problem-Solving Tip

Draw a Diagram When a problem involves spatial reasoning, or geometric figures, draw a diagram. For example, in Exercise 27, draw each triangle separately to help determine the answer.

27. **CHALLENGE** Triangle XYZ is similar to the two triangles formed by the line segment from Z perpendicular to $\overline{XY}$, and these two triangles are similar to each other. Write three similarity statements about these triangles. Why are the triangles similar to each other?

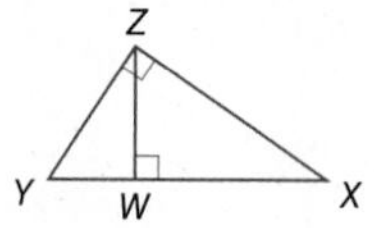

28. **REASONING** Is the statement *sometimes, always,* or *never* true? Explain.

If the measures of the sides of a triangle are multiplied by 3, then the measures of the angles of the enlarged triangle will have the same measures as the angles of the original triangle.

29. **OPEN ENDED** Draw and label a triangle ABC. Then draw and label a similar triangle PQR so that the area of $\triangle PQR$ is four times the area of $\triangle ABC$. Explain your strategy. **See margin.**

30. **WRITING IN MATH** Summarize how to determine whether two triangles are similar to each other and how to find missing measures of similar triangles. **See margin.**

Enrichment
CRM p. 48 OL BL

NAME ____________ DATE ______ PERIOD ______

10-7 Enrichment

A Curious Construction

Many mathematicians have been interested in ways to construct the number π. Here is one such geometric construction.

In the drawing, triangles ABC and ADE are right triangles. The length of $\overline{AD}$ equals the length of $\overline{AC}$ and $\overline{FB}$ is parallel to $\overline{EG}$.

The length of $\overline{BG}$ gives a decimal approximation of the fractional part of π to six decimal places.

Follow the steps to find the length of $\overline{BG}$. Round to seven decimal places.

1. Use the length of $\overline{BC}$ and the Pythagorean Theorem to find the length of $\overline{AC}$.

$AC = \sqrt{1^2 + \left(\frac{7}{8}\right)^2} = 1.3287682$

2. Find the length of $\overline{AD}$.

$AD = AC = 1.3287682$

3. Use the length of $\overline{AD}$ and the Pythagorean Theorem to find the length of $\overline{AE}$.

Multiple Representations In Exercise 25, students use information organized in a table and analysis to relate the side lengths and perimeters of similar triangles.

PSAE PRACTICE 9.11.09, 9.11.12, 8.11.07

31. Find the distance between the points at (2, −4) and (−5, 8). D

A 5
B 7
C $\sqrt{95}$
D $\sqrt{193}$

32. GEOMETRY Find the value of a if the two triangles are similar. F

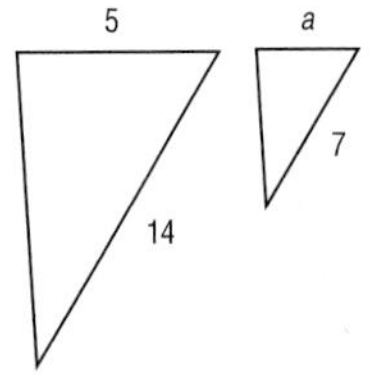

F 2.5 G 10 H 19 J 21

33. Which equation represents a line with a y-intercept of −4 and a slope of 6? A

A $y = 6x - 4$
B $y = -4x + 6$
C $y = -6x - 4$
D $y = 6x + 4$

34. SHORT RESPONSE What are the x- and y-intercepts of the function graphed below? −2 and 4

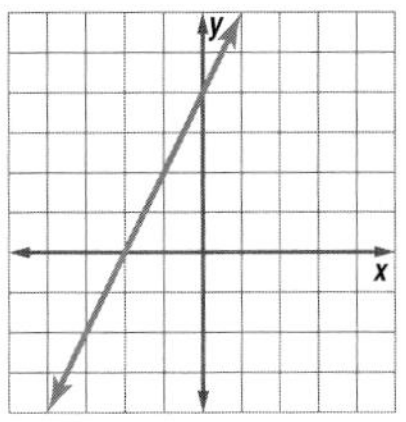

Spiral Review

Find the distance between the points with the given coordinates. (Lesson 10-6)

35. (0, 3), (1, 9) $\sqrt{37}$
36. (−2, 4), (5, 13) $\sqrt{130}$
37. (1, −5), (−1, −5) 2
38. (7, −2), (−2, 4) $\sqrt{117}$
39. (−6, −3), (−1, 2) $5\sqrt{2}$
40. (−4, −3), (−7, −8) $\sqrt{34}$

Determine whether the measures can be the lengths of the sides of a right triangle. (Lesson 10-5)

41. 3, 4, 5 yes
42. 8, 10, 12 no
43. 10, 24, 26 yes
44. 5, 12, 13 yes
45. 6, 9, 14 no
46. 4, 5, 6 no

47. NUTRITION In the function $y = 0.059x^2 - 7.423x + 362.1$, y represents the consumption of bread and cereal in pounds per person in the United States, and x represents the number of years since 1900. If this trend continues, in what future year will the average American consume 300 pounds of bread and cereal? (Lesson 9-4) about 2017

Factor each polynomial, if possible. If the polynomial cannot be factored, write *prime*. (Lesson 8-6)

48. $4k^2 - 100$ $4(k - 5)(k + 5)$
49. $4a^2 - 36b^2$ $4(a - 3b)(a + 3b)$
50. $x^2 + 6x - 9$ prime
51. $50g^2 + 40g + 8$ $2(5g + 2)^2$
52. $9t^3 + 66t^2 - 48t$ $3t(3t - 2)(t + 8)$
53. $20n^2 + 34n + 6$ $2(5n + 1)(2n + 3)$

54. DRIVING Average speed is calculated by dividing distance by time. If the speed limit on an interstate is 65 miles per hour, how far can a person travel legally in $1\frac{1}{2}$ hours? (Lesson 5-2) no more than 97.5 mi

Skills Review

Evaluate if $a = 3$, $b = -2$, and $c = 6$. (Lesson 1-2)

55. $\frac{b}{c}$ $-\frac{1}{3}$
56. $\frac{2ab}{c}$ −2
57. $\frac{ac}{-4b}$ 2.25
58. $\frac{-3ac}{2b}$ 13.5
59. $\frac{-2bc}{a}$ 8

Watch Out!

Find the Error For Exercise 26, remind students to pay close attention to the arcs that denote which angles are congruent.

4 ASSESS

Name the Math Have students write the proportions that can be formed by knowing that $\triangle PQR \sim \triangle RST$.

Additional Answers

29. $\triangle PQR$ has a base that is twice the base and twice the height of $\triangle ABC$. The triangles are similar because their corresponding angles are congruent. The area of $\triangle PQR$ is four times the area of $\triangle ABC$.

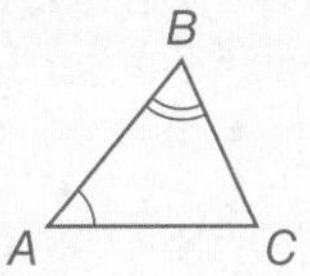

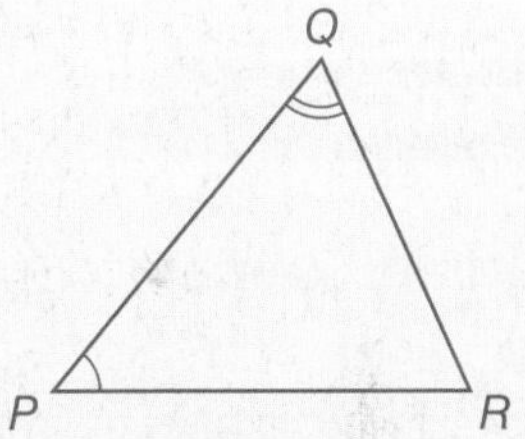

30. Two triangles are similar to each other if their corresponding angles are equal and the measures of their corresponding sides are proportional. If two triangles are similar, then proportions can be solved to find missing measures of sides. If angles are unknown, determine the angle measures of one triangle, and the corresponding angles of the other triangle will have the same angle measures.

Differentiated Instruction

OL BL

Extension Tell students that if two triangles are similar, the ratio of their areas is equal to the square of the ratio of their corresponding sides. Write the following rule on the board: $\frac{A_1}{A_2} = \frac{(s_1)^2}{(s_2)^2}$. Tell students that A_1 is the area of the first triangle, A_2 is the area of the second triangle, s_1 is a side length of the first triangle, and s_2 is the corresponding side length of the second triangle. Ask students to use this proportion to find the ratio of the areas of two triangles with corresponding side lengths that are in the ratio of 2:3. $\frac{A_1}{A_2} = \frac{(2)^2}{(3)^2} = \frac{4}{9}$

EXPLORE **10-8** Lesson Notes

1 FOCUS

Objective Use similar triangles to investigate trigonometric ratios.

Materials for Each Student
- ruler
- protractor
- grid paper

Easy to Make Manipulatives
Teaching Algebra with Manipulatives
Template for:
- grid paper, p. 1

Teaching Tip
Explain to students that even though measurements of side lengths and angles may not be exact, the ratios and angle measures should be close. If not, students should recheck the measurements.

2 TEACH

Working in Cooperative Groups
Have students work in pairs or groups of three to complete the activity. Suggest that they divide the tasks into drawing the triangles, measuring the hypotenuse and angles, and calculating and recording the data. Students should rotate tasks.

Ask:
- Why are the triangles in the activity similar triangles? the ratios of the corresponding sides are the same for all of the triangles
- If you know the ratio of the shortest leg to the longest leg, what angle measures can you find? all angle measures

Practice Have students complete Exercises 1–3.

EXPLORE 10-8 Algebra Lab
Investigating Trigonometric Ratios

IL Math Online glencoe.com
Math *in Motion*, Animation

Objective
Investigate trigonometric ratios.

IL Learning Standards
9.D.4 Analyze and solve problems involving triangles using trigonometric ratios.
Also addresses 8.A.4b.

You can use paper triangles to investigate the ratios of the lengths of sides of right triangles.

Collect the Data

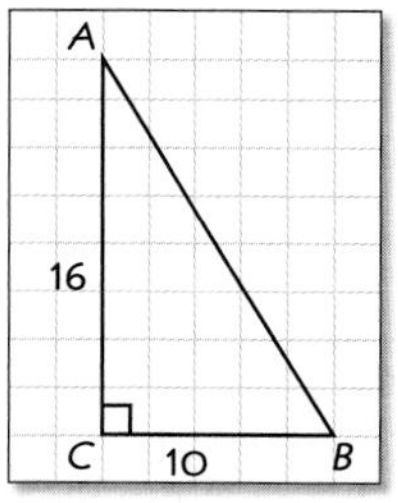

Step 1 Use a ruler and grid paper to draw several right triangles with legs in a ratio of 5:8. Include right triangles with the side lengths listed in the table below and several more right triangles similar to these three. Label the vertices of each triangle as A, B, and C, where C is at the right angle, B is opposite the longest leg, and A is opposite the shortest leg.

Step 2 Copy the table below. Complete the first three columns by measuring the hypotenuse (side $\overline{AB}$) in each right triangle you created and recording its length to the nearest tenth.

Step 3 Calculate and record the ratios in the middle two columns. Round to the nearest hundredth.

Step 4 Use a protractor to carefully measure angles A and B to the nearest degree in each right triangle. Record the angle measures in the table.

Side Lengths			Ratios		Angle Measures		
side BC	side AC	side AB	$\frac{BC}{AC}$	$\frac{BC}{AB}$	angle A	angle B	angle C
2.5	4	4.7	0.63	0.53	32°	58°	90°
5	8	9.4	0.63	0.53	32°	58°	90°
10	16	18.9	0.63	0.53	32°	58°	90°
15	24	28.3	0.63	0.53	32°	58°	90°
20	32	37.7	0.63	0.53	32°	58°	90°
25	40	47.2	0.63	0.53	32°	58°	90°

Sample answers are given in table.

Analyze the Results

1. Examine the measures and ratios in the table. What do you notice? Write a sentence or two to describe any patterns you see.
   All ratios and angle measures are the same for any 5:8 right triangle.

Make a Conjecture

2. For any right triangle similar to the ones you have drawn here, what will be the value of the ratio of the length of the shortest leg to the length of the longest leg? 5:8

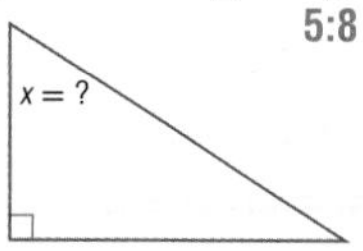

3. If you draw a right triangle and calculate the ratio of the length of the shortest leg to the length of the hypotenuse to be approximately 0.53, what will be the measure of the larger acute angle in the right triangle? 58°

648 Chapter 10 Radical Functions and Geometry

3 Assess

Formative Assessment
Use Exercise 1 to assess whether students understand that similar triangles will have the same ratios for the lengths of the corresponding sides and have the same angle measures.

From Concrete to Abstract
Use Exercise 3 to assess whether students understand that they can use the ratios of the sides of a triangle to find unknown measures, including angle measures.

10-8 Trigonometric Ratios

Then
You used the Pythagorean Theorem (Lesson 10-5)

Now
- Find trigonometric ratios of angles.
- Use trigonometry to solve triangles.

IL Learning Standards
9.D.4 Analyze and solve problems involving triangles using trigonometric ratios.

New Vocabulary
trigonometry
trigonometric ratio
sine
cosine
tangent
solving the triangle

IL Math Online
glencoe.com
- Extra Examples
- Personal Tutor
- Self-Check Quiz
- Homework Help

Why?

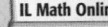

If a road has a percent grade of 8%, this means the road rises or falls 8 feet over a horizontal distance of 100 feet. Trigonometric ratios can be used to determine the angle that the road rises or falls.

Trigonometric Ratios **Trigonometry** is the study of relationships among the angles and sides of triangles. A **trigonometric ratio** is a ratio that compares the side lengths of two sides of a right triangle. The three most common trigonometric ratios, **sine**, **cosine**, and **tangent**, are described below.

Key Concept Trigonometric Ratios — For Your FOLDABLE

Words	Symbols	Model
sine of $\angle A = \dfrac{\text{leg opposite } \angle A}{\text{hypotenuse}}$	$\sin A = \frac{a}{c}$	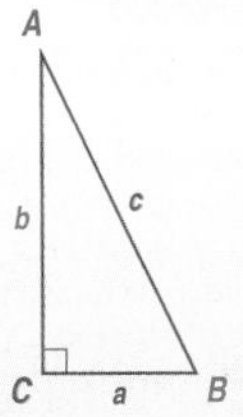
cosine of $\angle A = \dfrac{\text{leg adjacent to } \angle A}{\text{hypotenuse}}$	$\cos A = \frac{b}{c}$	
tangent of $\angle A = \dfrac{\text{leg opposite } \angle A}{\text{leg adjacent to } \angle A}$	$\tan A = \frac{a}{b}$	

Opposite, adjacent, and hypotenuse are abbreviated *opp*, *adj*, and *hyp*, respectively.

EXAMPLE 1 Find Sine, Cosine, and Tangent Ratios

Find the values of the three trigonometric ratios for angle A.

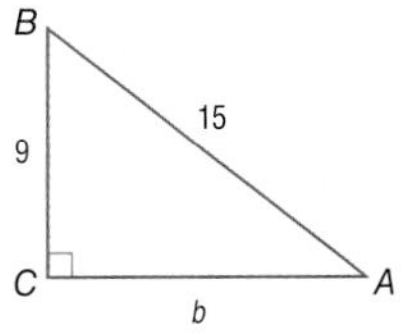

Step 1 Use the Pythagorean Theorem to find AC.

$a^2 + b^2 = c^2$ Pythagorean Theorem

$9^2 + b^2 = 15^2$ $a = 9$ and $c = 15$

$81 + b^2 = 225$ Simplify.

$b^2 = 144$ Subtract 81 from each side.

$b = 12$ Take the square root of each side.

Step 2 Use the side lengths to write the trigonometric ratios.

$\sin A = \frac{\text{opp}}{\text{hyp}} = \frac{9}{15} = \frac{3}{5}$ $\cos A = \frac{\text{adj}}{\text{hyp}} = \frac{12}{15} = \frac{4}{5}$ $\tan A = \frac{\text{opp}}{\text{adj}} = \frac{9}{12} = \frac{3}{4}$

Check Your Progress $\sin B = \frac{4}{5}$; $\cos B = \frac{3}{5}$; $\tan B = \frac{4}{3}$

1. Find the values of the three trigonometric ratios for angle B.

Personal Tutor glencoe.com

10-8 Lesson Notes

1 FOCUS

Vertical Alignment

Before Lesson 10-8
Use the Pythagorean Theorem.

Lesson 10-8
Find trigonometric ratios of angles.
Use trigonometry to solve triangles.

After Lesson 10-8
Use trigonometric ratios to find angles of elevation or depression.

2 TEACH

Scaffolding Questions

Have students read the *Why?* section of the lesson.

Ask:

- Suppose you draw a right triangle to model the 8% grade of the road. which side represents the horizontal distance of 100 feet? longer leg Which side represents the rise of 8 feet? shorter leg
- Which leg is adjacent to the angle at which the road rises or falls? longer leg Which leg is opposite the angle? shorter leg
- Which ratio would you use to find the measure of the angle? the ratio of the leg opposite the angle to the leg adjacent to the angle

Lesson 10-8 Resources

Resource	Approaching-Level	On-Level	Beyond-Level	English Learners
Teacher Edition	• Differentiated Instruction, p. 650	• Differentiated Instruction, pp. 650, 655	• Differentiated Instruction, p. 655	• Differentiated Instruction, p. 650
Chapter Resource Masters	• Study Guide and Intervention, pp. 49–50 • Skills Practice, p. 51 • Practice, p. 52 • Word Problem Practice, p. 53	• Study Guide and Intervention, pp. 49–50 • Skills Practice, p. 51 • Practice, p. 52 • Word Problem Practice, p. 53 • Enrichment, p. 54	• Practice, p. 52 • Word Problem Practice, p. 53 • Enrichment, p. 54	• Study Guide and Intervention, pp. 49–50 • Skills Practice, p. 51 • Practice, p. 52
Transparencies	• 5-Minute Check Transparency 10-8	• 5-Minute Check Transparency 10-8	• 5-Minute Check Transparency 10-8	• 5-Minute Check Transparency 10-8
Other	• Study Notebook	• Study Notebook	• Study Notebook	• Study Notebook

Trigonometric Ratios

Example 1 shows how to find the trigonometric ratios for an angle of a right triangle. **Example 2** shows how to use a calculator to evaluate a trigonometric expression.

Formative Assessment

Use the Check Your Progress exercises after each Example to determine students' understanding of concepts.

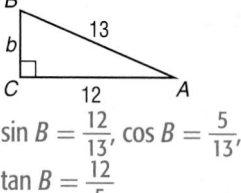

Additional Examples

1 Find the values of the three trigonometric ratios for angle B.

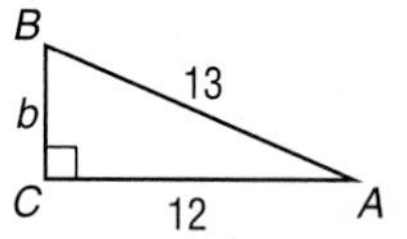

$\sin B = \frac{12}{13}$, $\cos B = \frac{5}{13}$, $\tan B = \frac{12}{5}$

2 Use a calculator to find tan 52° to the nearest ten-thousandth.
1.2799

Additional Examples also in Interactive Classroom PowerPoint® Presentations

IWB INTERACTIVE WHITEBOARD READY

Use Trigonometric Ratios

Example 3 shows how to solve a right triangle. **Example 4** shows how to use trigonometric ratios to solve a real-world problem. **Example 5** shows how to use the inverse of a trigonometric function to find a missing angle measure.

Additional Example

3 Solve the right triangle. Round each side to the nearest tenth.

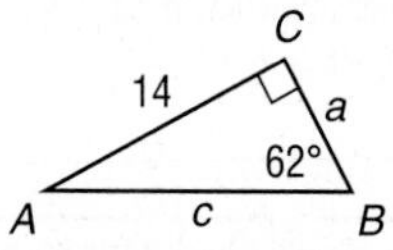

$m\angle A = 28°$; $a \approx 7.4$, $c \approx 15.9$

Watch Out!

Calculator Mode Make sure your graphing calculator is in degree mode.

EXAMPLE 2 Use a Calculator to Evaluate Expressions

Use a calculator to find cos 42° to the nearest ten-thousandth.

KEYSTROKES: [COS] 42 [ )] [ENTER]

Rounded to the nearest ten-thousandth, $\cos 42° \approx 0.7431$.

Check Your Progress

2A. sin 31° **0.5150** **2B.** tan 76° **4.0108** **2C.** cos 55° **0.5736**

Personal Tutor glencoe.com

Use Trigonometric Ratios When you find all unknown measures of the sides and angles of a right triangle, you are **solving the triangle**. You can find the missing measures if you know the measure of two sides of the triangle or the measure of one side and the measure of one acute angle.

StudyTip

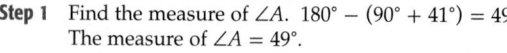

Remembering Trigonometric Ratios SOH-CAH-TOA can be used to help you remember the ratios for sine, cosine, and tangent. Each letter represents a word.

$\sin A = \frac{\text{opp}}{\text{hyp}}$

$\cos A = \frac{\text{adj}}{\text{hyp}}$

$\tan A = \frac{\text{opp}}{\text{adj}}$

EXAMPLE 3 Solve a Triangle

Solve the right triangle. Round each side length to the nearest tenth.

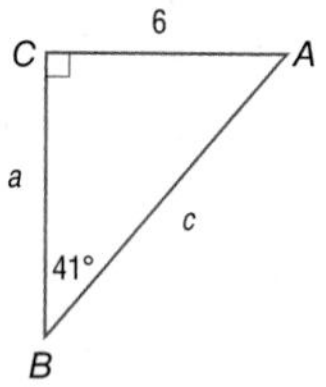

Step 1 Find the measure of $\angle A$. $180° - (90° + 41°) = 49°$
The measure of $\angle A = 49°$.

Step 2 Find a. Since you are given the measure of the side opposite $\angle B$ and are finding the measure of the side adjacent to $\angle B$, use the tangent ratio.

$\tan 41° = \frac{6}{a}$ — **Definition of tangent**

$a \tan 41° = 6$ — **Multiply each side by a.**

$a = \frac{6}{\tan 41°}$ or about 6.9 — **Divide each side by tan 41°. Use a calculator.**

So the measure of a or $\overline{BC}$ is about 6.9.

Step 3 Find c. Since you are given the measure of the side opposite $\angle B$ and are finding the measure of the hypotenuse, use the sine ratio.

$\sin 41° = \frac{6}{c}$ — **Definition of sine**

$c \sin 41° = 6$ — **Multiply each side by c.**

$c = \frac{6}{\sin 41°}$ or about 9.1 — **Divide each side by sin 41°. Use a calculator.**

So the measure of c or $\overline{AB}$ is about 9.1.

Check Your Progress

3A.

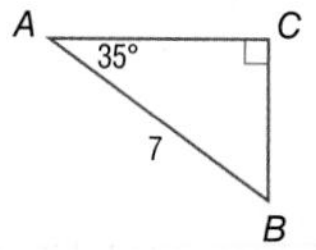

$\angle B = 55°$, $AC \approx 5.7$; $BC \approx 4.0$

3B.

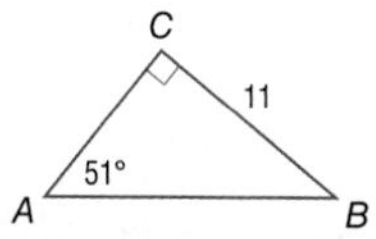

$\angle B = 39°$, $AC \approx 8.9$; $AB \approx 14.2$

Personal Tutor glencoe.com

Differentiated Instruction

AL OL ELL

If students have difficulty remembering the trigonometric ratios,

Then have students work in groups to brainstorm and implement ideas on how to remember them. Prompt students with suggestions such as flash cards, rap verse, or poems. Have groups share their ideas with the class.

Real-World EXAMPLE 4 Find a Missing Side Length

EXERCISE A trainer sets the incline on a treadmill to 10°. The walking surface of the treadmill is 5 feet long. About how many inches is the end of the treadmill from the floor?

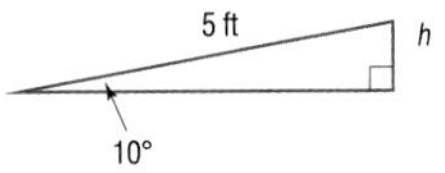

$\sin 10° = \frac{h}{5}$ **Definition of sine**

$5 \cdot \sin 10° = h$ **Multiply each side by 5.**

$0.87 \approx h$ **Use a calculator.**

The value of h is in feet. Multiply 0.87 by 12 to convert feet to inches. The trainer raised the treadmill about 10.4 inches.

Real-World Link

For optimum health, all adults ages 18–65 should get at least 30 minutes of moderately intense activity five days per week.

Source: American Heart Association

Check Your Progress

4. SKATEBOARDING The angle that a skateboarding ramp forms with the ground is 25° and the height of the ramp is 6 feet. Determine the length of the ramp. about 14.2 ft

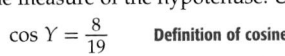

Personal Tutor glencoe.com

A trigonometric function has a rule given by a trigonometric ratio. If you know the sine, cosine, or tangent of an acute angle, you can use the *inverse* of the trigonometric function to find the measure of the angle.

Key Concept Inverse Trigonometric Functions

For Your FOLDABLE

Words	If $\angle A$ is an acute angle and the sine of A is x, then the **inverse sine** of x is the measure of $\angle A$.
Symbols	If $\sin A = x$, then $\sin^{-1} x = m\angle A$.
Words	If $\angle A$ is an acute angle and the cosine of A is x, then the **inverse cosine** of x is the measure of $\angle A$.
Symbols	If $\cos A = x$, then $\cos^{-1} x = m\angle A$.
Words	If $\angle A$ is an acute angle and the tangent of A is x, then the **inverse tangent** of x is the measure of $\angle A$.
Symbols	If $\tan A = x$, then $\tan^{-1} x = m\angle A$.

EXAMPLE 5 Find a Missing Angle Measure

Find $m\angle Y$ to the nearest degree.

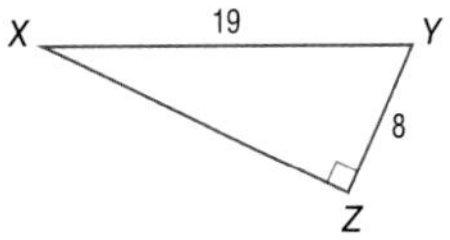

You know the measure of the side adjacent to $\angle Y$ and the measure of the hypotenuse. Use the cosine ratio.

$\cos Y = \frac{8}{19}$ **Definition of cosine**

Use a calculator and the [$\cos^{-1}$] function to find the measure of the angle.

KEYSTROKES: [2nd] [$\cos^{-1}$] 8 [÷] 19 [)] [ENTER] 65.098937 So, $m\angle Y = 65°$.

Check Your Progress

5. Find $m\angle X$ to the nearest degree if $XY = 14$ and $YZ = 5$. 21°

Personal Tutor glencoe.com

Additional Examples

4 **CONVEYOR BELTS** A conveyor belt moves recycled materials from Station A to Station B. The angle the conveyor belt makes with the floor of the first station is 15°. The conveyor belt is 18 feet long. What is the approximate height of the floor of Station B relative to Station A?

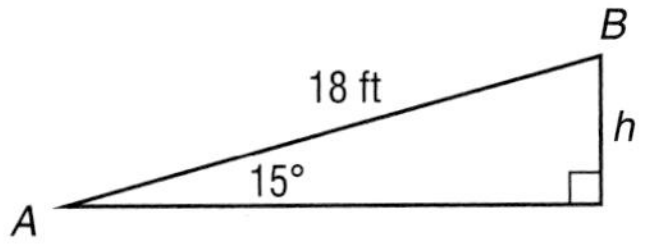

about 4.7 ft

5 Find $m\angle P$ to the nearest degree. 24°

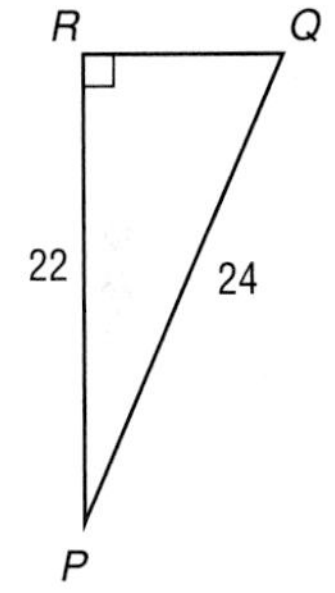

TEACH with TECH

INTERACTIVE WHITEBOARD Draw a right triangle on the board and label each of the side lengths. To write the trigonometric ratios, drag the measurement from the side of the triangle to the ratio.

Focus on Mathematical Content

Trigonometric Ratios The trigonometric ratios include the sine, cosine, and tangent ratios and also the secant, cosecant, and cotangent ratios, which students will use in Algebra 2 and Geometry. The trigonometric ratios give the ratios of the sides of the right triangle in relation to the angles of the triangle. The ratios are used to find missing side lengths. The inverse trigonometric ratios are used to find missing angle measures.

3 PRACTICE

Formative Assessment

Use Exercises 1–17 to check for understanding.

Use the chart at the bottom of the next page to customize assignments for your students

Tips for New Teachers

Reasoning Advise students to be careful not to confuse the notation for inverse trigonometric functions with the notation that is used for negative exponents. For example, $\cos^{-1} x \neq \frac{1}{\cos x}$.

1. $\sin A = \frac{24}{25}$; $\cos A = \frac{7}{25}$; $\tan A = \frac{24}{7}$
2. $\sin A = \frac{3}{5}$; $\cos A = \frac{4}{5}$; $\tan A = \frac{3}{4}$
3. $\sin A = \frac{5}{13}$; $\cos A = \frac{12}{13}$; $\tan A = \frac{5}{12}$
4. $\sin A = \frac{36}{85}$; $\cos A = \frac{77}{85}$; $\tan A = \frac{36}{77}$
9. $m\angle X = 51°$; $XY \approx 4.4$; $YZ \approx 5.4$
10. $m\angle F = 66°$; $DE \approx 31.4$; $EF \approx 34.4$
11. $m\angle Q = 60°$; $RQ \approx 2.9$; $PQ \approx 5.8$
12. $m\angle W = 30°$; $XV \approx 5.2$; $WV \approx 10.4$

Check Your Understanding

Example 1 p. 649 Find the values of the three trigonometric ratios for angle A.

1.

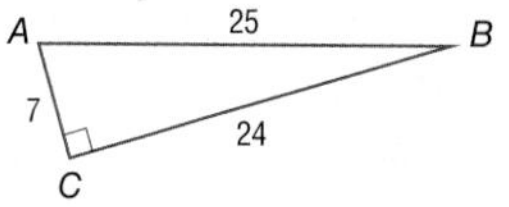

2.

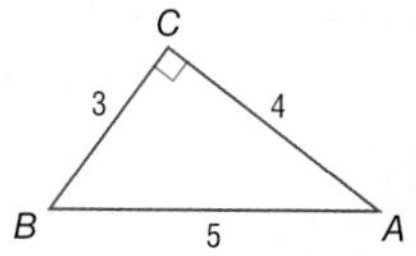

3.

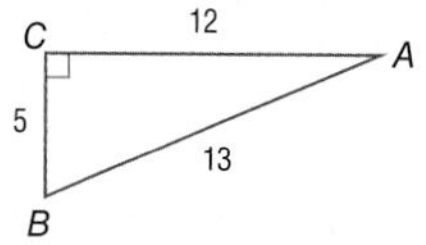

4.

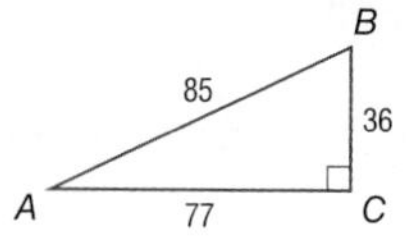

Example 2 p. 650 Use a calculator to find the value of each trigonometric ratio to the nearest ten-thousandth.

5. sin 37° **0.6018** **6.** cos 23° **0.9205** **7.** tan 14° **0.2493** **8.** cos 82° **0.1392**

Example 3 p. 650 Solve each right triangle. Round each side length to the nearest tenth.

9.

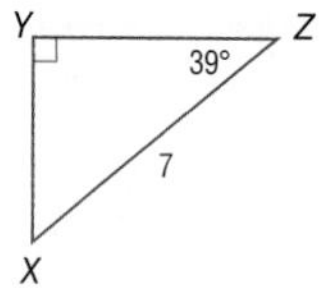

10.

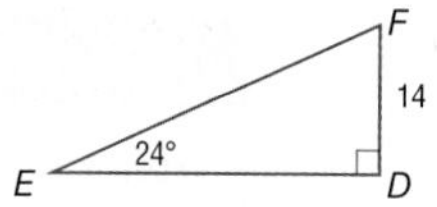

11.

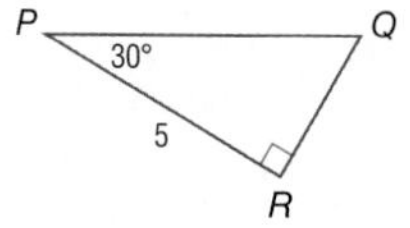

12.

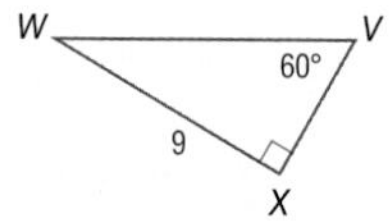

Example 4 p. 651

13. SNOWBOARDING A hill used for snowboarding has a vertical drop of 3500 feet. The angle the run makes with the ground is 18°. Estimate the length of r. **about 11,326.2 ft**

Example 5 p. 651 Find m∠X for each right triangle to the nearest degree.

14. **34°**

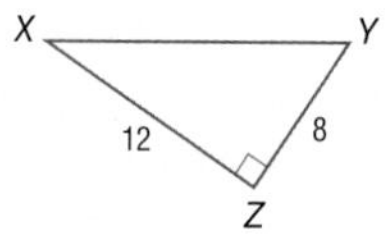

15. **66°**

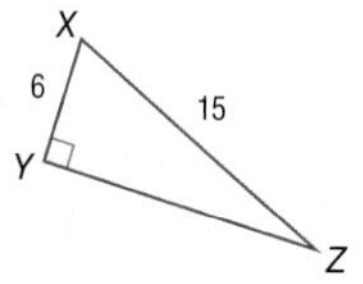

16. **67°**

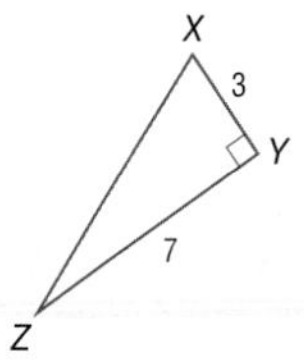

17. **33°**

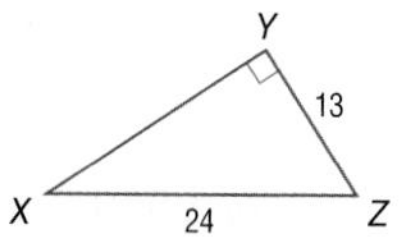

652 Chapter 10 Radical Functions and Geometry

Practice and Problem Solving

= **Step-by-Step Solutions** begin on page R12. **Extra Practice** begins on page 815.

Example 1 p. 649

Find the values of the three trigonometric ratios for angle B. **18–20. See margin.**

18.

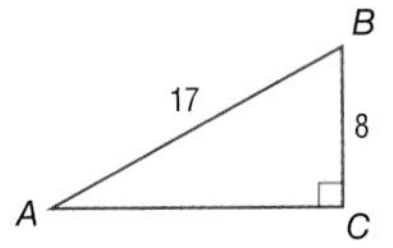

19.

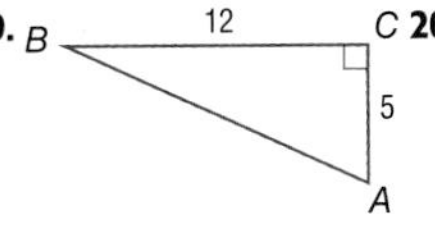

20.

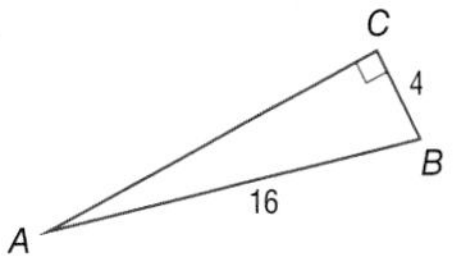

Example 2 p. 650

Use a calculator to find the value of each trigonometric ratio to the nearest ten-thousandth.

21. tan 2° **0.0349** **22.** sin 89° **0.9998** **23.** cos 44° **0.7193** **24.** tan 45° **1**

25. sin 73° **0.9563** **26.** cos 90° **0** **27.** sin 30° **0.5** **28.** tan 60° **1.7321**

Example 3 p. 650

Solve each right triangle. Round each side length to the nearest tenth.

29–34. See margin.

29

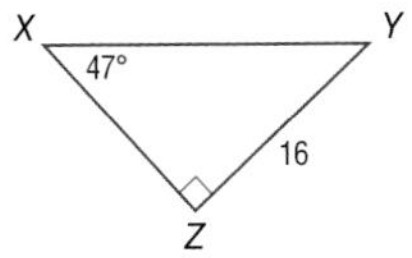

30.

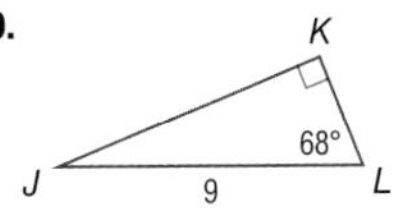

31.

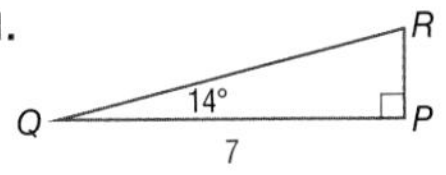

32.

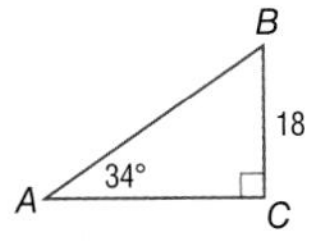

33.

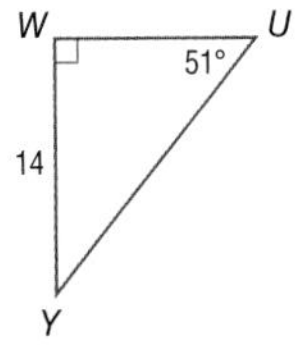

34.

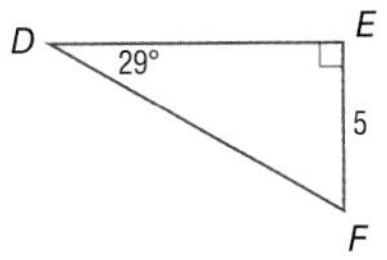

Example 4 p. 651

35. ESCALATORS At a local mall, an escalator is 110 feet long. The angle the escalator makes with the ground is 29°. Find the height reached by the escalator. **about 53 ft**

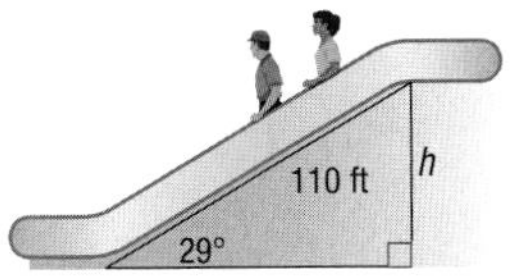

Example 5 p. 651

Find $m\angle J$ for each right triangle to the nearest degree.

36. **25°**

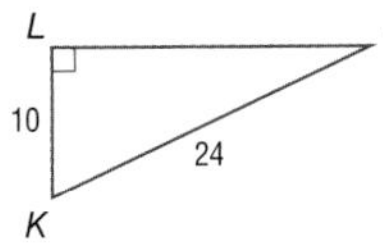

37. **62°**

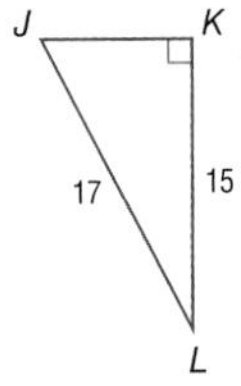

38. **59°**

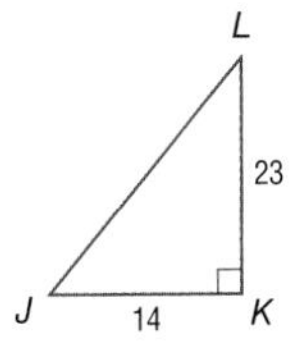

39. **31°**

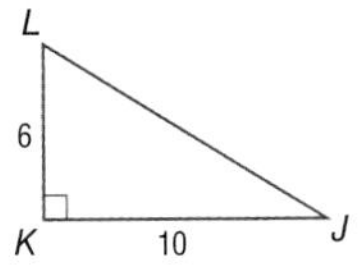

40. **72°**

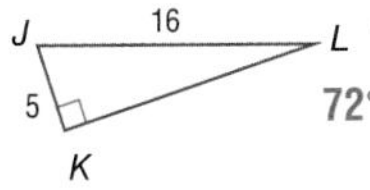

41. **50°**

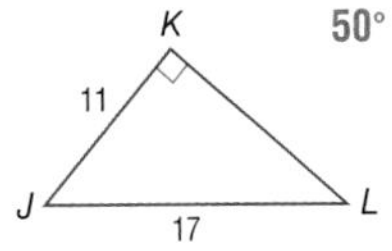

B **42. MONUMENTS** The Lincoln Memorial building measures 204 feet long, 134 feet wide, and 99 feet tall. Chloe is looking at the top of the monument at an angle of 55°. How far away is she standing from the monument? **about 69 ft**

Additional Answers

18. $\sin B = \frac{15}{17}$; $\cos B = \frac{8}{17}$; $\tan B = \frac{15}{8}$

19. $\sin B = \frac{5}{13}$; $\cos B = \frac{12}{13}$; $\tan B = \frac{5}{12}$

20. $\sin B = \frac{\sqrt{15}}{4}$; $\cos B = \frac{1}{4}$; $\tan B = \sqrt{15}$

29. $m\angle Y = 43°$; $XY \approx 21.9$; $XZ \approx 14.9$

30. $m\angle J = 22°$; $JK \approx 8.3$; $KL \approx 3.4$

31. $m\angle R = 76°$; $QR \approx 7.2$; $PR \approx 1.7$

32. $m\angle B = 56°$; $AB \approx 32.2$; $AC \approx 26.7$

33. $m\angle Y = 39°$; $WU \approx 11.3$; $UY \approx 18.0$

34. $m\angle F = 61°$; $DE \approx 9.0$; $DF \approx 10.3$

Differentiated Homework Options

Level	Assignment	Two-Day Option	
AL Basic	18–41, 52–71	19–41 odd, 56–59	18–40 even, 52–55, 60–71
OL Core	19–41 odd, 42–50, 52–71	18–41, 56–59	42–50, 52–55, 60–71
BL Advanced	42–67, (optional: 68–71)		

Study Guide and Intervention

CRM pp. 49–50 AL OL ELL

NAME ______________________ DATE __________ PERIOD __________

10-8 Study Guide and Intervention

Trigonometric Ratios

Trigonometric Ratios Trigonometry is the study of relationships of the angles and the sides of a right triangle. The three most common trigonometric ratios are the **sine**, **cosine**, and **tangent**.

sine of $\angle A = \frac{\text{leg opposite } \angle A}{\text{hypotenuse}}$ sine of $\angle B = \frac{\text{leg opposite } \angle B}{\text{hypotenuse}}$	$\sin A = \frac{a}{c}$ $\sin B = \frac{b}{c}$	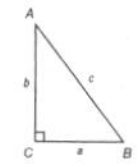
cosine of $\angle A = \frac{\text{leg adjacent to } \angle A}{\text{hypotenuse}}$ cosine of $\angle B = \frac{\text{leg adjacent to } \angle B}{\text{hypotenuse}}$	$\cos A = \frac{b}{c}$ $\cos B = \frac{a}{c}$	
tangent of $\angle A = \frac{\text{leg opposite } \angle A}{\text{leg adjacent to } \angle A}$ tangent of $\angle B = \frac{\text{leg opposite } \angle B}{\text{leg adjacent to } \angle B}$	$\tan A = \frac{a}{b}$ $\tan B = \frac{b}{a}$	

Example Find the values of the three trigonometric ratios for angle *A*.

Step 1 Use the Pythagorean Theorem to find *BC*.

$a^2 + b^2 = c^2$ Pythagorean Theorem

$a^2 + 8^2 = 10^2$ $b = 8$ and $c = 10$

$a^2 + 64 = 100$ Simplify.

$a^2 = 36$ Subtract 64 from both sides.

$a = 6$ Take the square root of each side.

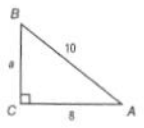

Step 2 Use the side lengths to write the trigonometric ratios.

$\sin A = \frac{\text{opp}}{\text{hyp}} = \frac{6}{10} = \frac{3}{5}$ $\cos A = \frac{\text{adj}}{\text{hyp}} = \frac{8}{10} = \frac{4}{5}$ $\tan A = \frac{\text{opp}}{\text{adj}} = \frac{6}{8} = \frac{3}{4}$

Exercises

Find the values of the three trigonometric ratios for angle *A*.

1. 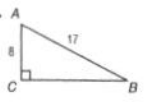

2. 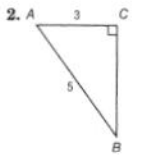

3. 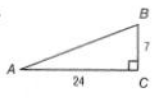

$\sin A = \frac{15}{17}$, $\cos A = \frac{8}{17}$, $\tan A = \frac{15}{8}$

$\sin A = \frac{4}{5}$, $\cos A = \frac{3}{5}$, $\tan A = \frac{4}{3}$

$\sin A = \frac{7}{25}$, $\cos A = \frac{24}{25}$, $\tan A = \frac{7}{24}$

Use a calculator to find the value of each trigonometric ratio to the nearest ten-thousandth.

4. $\sin 40°$ **0.6428** 5. $\cos 25°$ **0.9063** 6. $\tan 85°$ **11.4301**

Chapter 10 49 Glencoe Algebra 1

Lesson 10-8

Practice

CRM p. 52 AL OL BL ELL

NAME ______________________ DATE __________ PERIOD __________

10-8 Practice

Trigonometric Ratios

Find the values of the three trigonometric ratios for angle *A*.

1. 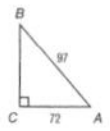

2. 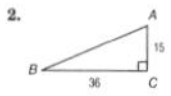

$\sin A = \frac{65}{97}$, $\cos A = \frac{72}{97}$, $\tan A = \frac{65}{72}$

$\sin A = \frac{36}{39}$, $\cos A = \frac{15}{39}$, $\tan A = \frac{36}{15}$

Use a calculator to find the value of each trigonometric ratio to the nearest ten-thousandth.

3. $\tan 26°$ **0.4877** 4. $\sin 53°$ **0.7986** 5. $\cos 81°$ **0.1564**

Solve each right triangle. Round each side length to the nearest tenth.

6. 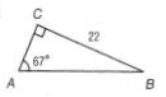

7. 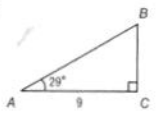

$\angle B = 23°$, $AB = 23.9$, $AC = 9.3$

$\angle A = 61°$, $AB = 10.3$, $BC = 5.0$

Find $m\angle J$ for each right triangle to the nearest degree.

8. 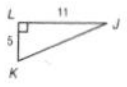

9. 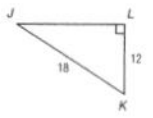

24°

42°

10. **SURVEYING** If point *A* is 54 feet from the tree, and the angle between the ground at point *A* and the top of the tree is 25°, find the height *h* of the tree.

25.2 ft

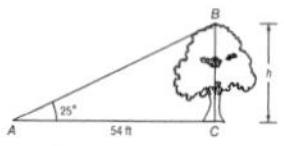

Chapter 10 52 Glencoe Algebra 1

Word Problem Practice

CRM p. 53 AL OL BL ELL

NAME ______________________ DATE __________ PERIOD __________

10-8 Word Problem Practice

Trigonometric Ratios

1. **WASHINGTON MONUMENT** Jeannie is trying to determine the height of the Washington Monument. If point *A* is 765 feet from the monument, and the angle between the ground and the top of the monument at point *A* is 36°, find the height *h* of the monument to the nearest foot. **556 ft**

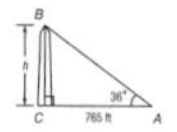

2. **AIRPLANES** A pilot takes off from a runway at an angle of 20° and maintains that angle until it is at its cruising altitude of 2500 feet. What horizontal distance has the plane traveled when it reaches its cruising altitude? **6869 ft**

3. **TRUCK RAMPS** A moving company uses an 11-foot-long ramp to unload furniture from a truck. If the bed of the truck is 3 feet above the ground, what is the angle of incline of the ramp to the nearest degree? **16°**

4. **SPECIAL TRIANGLES** While investigating right triangle *KLM*, Mercedes finds that $\cos M = \sin M$. What is the measure of angle *M*? **45°**

5. **TELEVISIONS** Televisions are commonly sized by measuring their diagonal. A common size for widescreen plasma TVs is 42 inches.

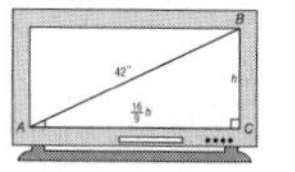

a. A widescreen television has a 16:9 aspect ratio, that is, the screen width is $\frac{16}{9}$ times the screen height. Use the Pythagorean Theorem to write an equation and solve for the height *h* of the television in inches.

$\left(\frac{16}{9}h\right)^2 + h^2 = 42^2$; $h = 20.6$ in.

b. Use the information from part **a** to solve the right triangle.

width = 36.6 in., $\angle A = 29°$, $\angle B = 61°$

c. What would the measure of angle *A* be on a standard television with a 4:3 aspect ratio? **37°**

Chapter 10 53 Glencoe Algebra 1

Lesson 10-8

Real-World Link

The tallest living tree is a redwood called Hyperion. It measures 378.1 feet. There are about 135 redwood trees that are taller than 350 feet.

Source: SFGate

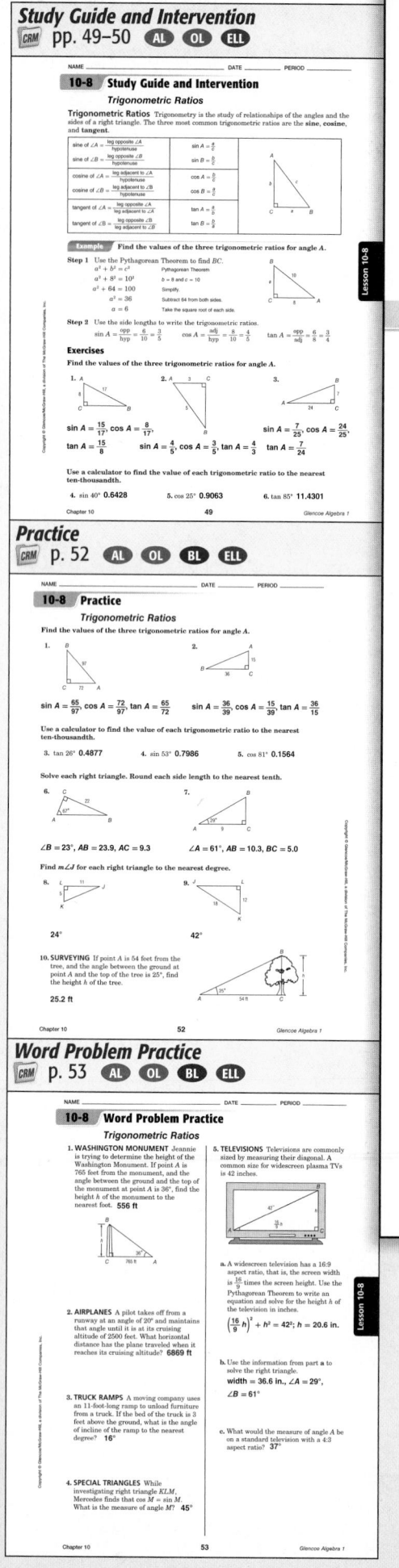

43. **AIRPLANES** Ella looks down at a city from an airplane window. The airplane is 5000 feet in the air, and she looks down at an angle of 8°. Determine the horizontal distance to the city. **about 35,577 ft**

44. **FORESTS** A forest ranger estimates the height of a tree is about 175 feet. If the forest ranger is standing 100 feet from the base of the tree, what is the measure of the angle formed by the ranger and the top of the tree? **about 60°**

Suppose $\angle A$ is an acute angle of right triangle *ABC*. **45–48. See margin.**

45. Find $\sin A$ and $\tan A$ if $\cos A = \frac{3}{4}$.

46. Find $\tan A$ and $\cos A$ if $\sin A = \frac{2}{7}$.

47. Find $\cos A$ and $\tan A$ if $\sin A = \frac{1}{4}$.

48. Find $\sin A$ and $\cos A$ if $\tan A = \frac{5}{3}$.

49. **SUBMARINES** A submarine descends into the ocean at an angle of 10° below the water line and travels 3 miles diagonally. How far beneath the surface of the water has the submarine reached? **about 0.5 mi**

50. **MULTIPLE REPRESENTATIONS** In this problem, you will explore a relationship between the sine and cosine functions.

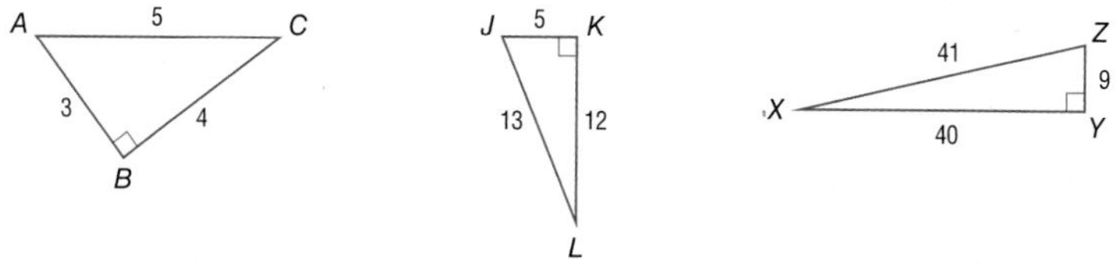

a. **TABULAR** Copy and complete the table using the triangles shown above. **See Ch. 10 Answer Appendix.**

Triangle	Trigonometric Ratios		$\sin^2$	$\cos^2$	$\sin^2 + \cos^2 =$
ABC	$\sin A =$	$\cos A =$	$\sin^2 A =$	$\cos^2 A =$	
	$\sin C =$	$\cos C =$	$\sin^2 C =$	$\cos^2 C =$	
JKL	$\sin J =$	$\cos J =$	$\sin^2 J =$	$\cos^2 J =$	
	$\sin L =$	$\cos L =$	$\sin^2 L =$	$\cos^2 L =$	
XYZ	$\sin X =$	$\cos X =$	$\sin^2 X =$	$\cos^2 X =$	
	$\sin Z =$	$\cos Z =$	$\sin^2 Z =$	$\cos^2 Z =$	

b. **VERBAL** Make a conjecture about the sum of the squares of the sine and cosine functions of an acute angle in a right triangle. **The sum of the squares of the sine and cosine of an acute angle in a right triangle is equal to 1.**

H.O.T. Problems Use Higher-Order Thinking Skills

51. **CHALLENGE** Solve the triangle shown. **$a = 5$; $c = 5$**

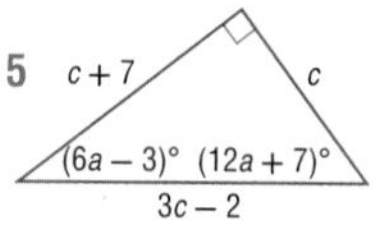

52. **REASONING** Use the definitions of the sine and cosine ratios to define the tangent ratio. **See margin.**

53. **OPEN ENDED** Write a problem that uses the cosine ratio to find the measure of an unknown angle in a triangle. Then solve the problem.

54. **REASONING** The sine and cosine of an acute angle in a right triangle are equal. What can you conclude about the triangle?

55. **WRITING IN MATH** Explain how to use trigonometric ratios to find the missing length of a side of a right triangle given the measure of one acute angle and the length of one side. **See margin.**

53. Sample answer: Find the measure of $\angle A$ in the following triangle; $m\angle A \approx 56°$. See margin for triangle.

54. The triangle is an isosceles right triangle. The legs are equal to each other.

Enrichment

CRM p. 54 OL BL

NAME ______________________ DATE __________ PERIOD __________

10-8 Enrichment

More Trigonometric Ratios

In addition to the sine, cosine, and tangent, there are three other common trigonometric ratios. They are the **secant**, **cosecant**, and **cotangent**.

secant of $\angle A = \frac{\text{hypotenuse}}{\text{leg opposite } \angle A}$ secant of $\angle B = \frac{\text{hypotenuse}}{\text{leg opposite } \angle B}$	$\sec A = \frac{c}{a}$ $\sec B = \frac{c}{b}$	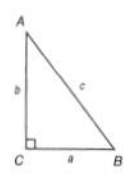
cosecant of $\angle A = \frac{\text{hypotenuse}}{\text{leg adjacent } \angle A}$ cosecant of $\angle B = \frac{\text{hypotenuse}}{\text{leg adjacent } \angle B}$	$\csc A = \frac{c}{b}$ $\csc B = \frac{c}{a}$	
cotangent of $\angle A = \frac{\text{leg adjacent to } \angle A}{\text{leg opposite } \angle A}$ cotangent of $\angle B = \frac{\text{leg adjacent to } \angle B}{\text{leg opposite } \angle B}$	$\cot A = \frac{b}{a}$ $\cot B = \frac{a}{b}$	

Example Find the secant, cosecant, and cotangent of angle *A*.

Use the side lengths to write the trigonometric ratios.

$\sec A = \frac{\text{hyp}}{\text{opp}} = \frac{15}{9} = \frac{5}{3}$ $\csc A = \frac{\text{hyp}}{\text{adj}} = \frac{15}{12} = \frac{5}{4}$

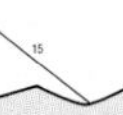

55. Use the angle given and the measure of the known side to set up one of the trigonometric ratios. The sine ratio uses the opposite side and hypotenuse of the triangle. The cosine ratio uses the adjacent side and hypotenuse of the triangle. The tangent ratio uses the opposite and adjacent sides of the triangle. Set up the ratio and solve for the unknown measure.

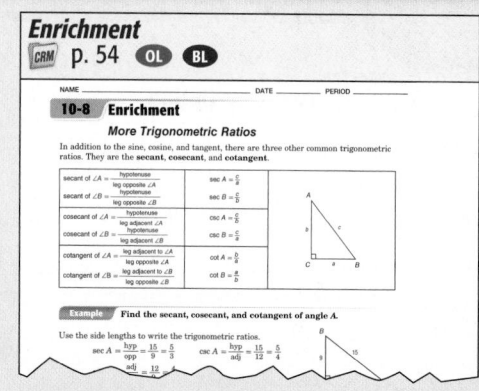

PSAE PRACTICE 10.11.07, 9.11.11, 9.11.01

56. Which graph below represents the solution set for $-2 \le x \le 4$? **A**

A 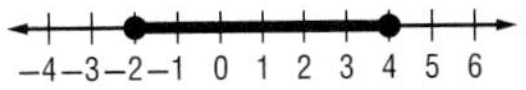

B 

C 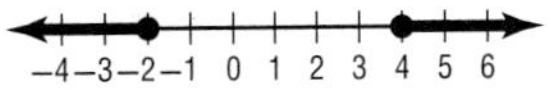

D 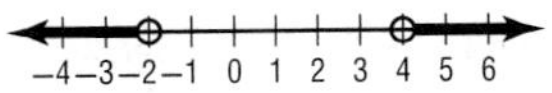

57. PROBABILITY Suppose one chip is chosen from a bin with the chips shown. To the nearest tenth, what is the probability that a green chip is chosen? **F**

Color	Number
yellow	7
blue	9
orange	3
green	5
red	6

F 0.2 H 0.6
G 0.5 J 0.8

58. In the graph, for what value(s) of x is $y = 0$? **D**

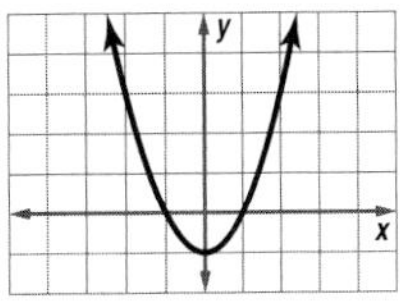

A 0 C 1
B −1 D 1 and −1

59. EXTENDED RESPONSE A 16-foot ladder is placed against the side of a house so that the bottom of the ladder is 8 feet from the base of the house.

a. If the bottom of the ladder is moved closer to the base of the house, does the height reached by the ladder increase or decrease? **increase**

b. What conclusion can you make about the distance between the bottom of the ladder and the base of the house and the height reached by the ladder? **See Ch. 10 Answer Appendix.**

c. How high does the ladder reach if the ladder is 3 feet from the base of the house? **about 15.7 ft**

Spiral Review

For each set of measures given, find the measures of the missing sides if $\triangle ABC \sim \triangle DFH$. (Lesson 10-7)

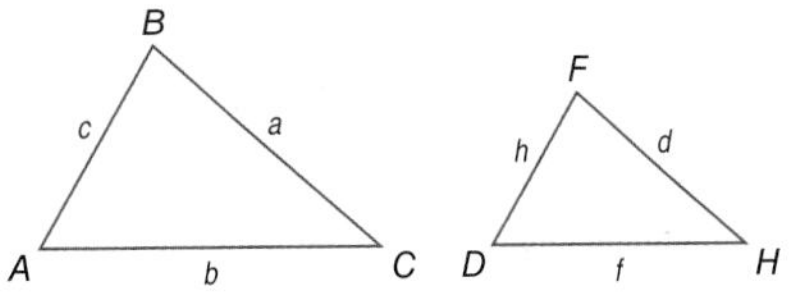

60. $a = 16, b = 12, c = 8, f = 6$ **$h = 4$; $d = 8$**

61. $d = 9, f = 6, h = 4, b = 18$ **$a = 27$; $c = 12$**

62. $a = 36, b = 21, h = 11, f = 14$ **$c = 16.5$; $d = 24$**

63. $c = 22.5, b = 20, h = 9, d = 2$ **$a = 5$; $f = 8$**

Find the coordinates of the midpoint of the segment with the given endpoints. (Lesson 10-6)

64. (5, 3), (11, 9) **(8, 6)** **65.** (8, 2), (6, 4) **(7, 3)** **66.** (−1, 7), (13, −3) **(6, 2)**

67. FINANCIAL LITERACY A salesperson is paid $32,000 a year plus 5% of the amount in sales made. What is the amount of sales needed to have an annual income greater than $45,000? (Lesson 5-3) **The amount of sales must be more than $260,000.**

Skills Review

Solve each proportion. (Lesson 2-6)

68. $\frac{8}{9} = \frac{6}{z}$ **6.75** **69.** $\frac{p}{6} = \frac{4}{3}$ **8** **70.** $\frac{0.3}{r} = \frac{0.9}{1.7}$ **$\frac{17}{30}$** **71.** $\frac{0.6}{1.1} = \frac{y}{8.47}$ **4.62**

Differentiated Instruction OL BL

Extension Have students compute the values of sin *A*, cos *A*, and tan *A* for several values of *A*. Have them make a conjecture about the quotient $\frac{\sin A}{\cos A}$. The value is always tan *A*.

Watch Out!

Preventing Errors For Exercises 42-44, suggest that students draw and label right triangles that fit the descriptions in the exercises. Diagrams help students visualize the situation so that they find the correct measures.

Multiple Representations In Exercise 50, students use diagrams, information organized in a table, and verbal analysis to investigate a relationship between the sine and cosine functions.

4 ASSESS

Yesterday's News Have students write a sentence on how the lesson on the Pythagorean Theorem helped with today's lesson on trigonometric ratios.

Formative Assessment

Check for student understanding of concepts in Lessons 10-7 and 10-8.

CRM Quiz 4, p. 58

Additional Answers

45. $\sin A = \frac{\sqrt{7}}{4}$; $\tan A = \frac{\sqrt{7}}{3}$

46. $\tan A = \frac{2\sqrt{5}}{15}$; $\cos A = \frac{3\sqrt{5}}{7}$

47. $\cos A = \frac{\sqrt{15}}{4}$; $\tan A = \frac{\sqrt{15}}{15}$

48. $\sin A = \frac{5\sqrt{34}}{34}$; $\cos A = \frac{3\sqrt{34}}{34}$

52. $\frac{\sin A}{\cos A} = \frac{\frac{\text{opp}}{\text{hyp}}}{\frac{\text{adj}}{\text{hyp}}}$
$= \frac{\text{opp}}{\text{hyp}} \cdot \frac{\text{hyp}}{\text{adj}}$
$= \frac{\text{opp}}{\text{adj}}$
$= \tan A$

53. 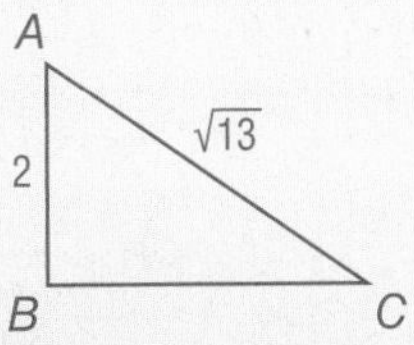

Formative Assessment

Key Vocabulary The page reference after each word denotes where that term was first introduced. If students have difficulty answering questions 1–10, remind them that they can use these page references to refresh their memories about the vocabulary terms.

Summative Assessment

CRM Vocabulary Test, p. 60

IL Math Online glencoe.com

Vocabulary PuzzleMaker improves students' mathematics vocabulary using four puzzle formats–crossword, scramble, word search using a word list, and word search using clues. Students can work online or from a printed worksheet.

Additional Answers

11. translated down 3;
D = $\{x \mid x \geq 0\}$
R = $\{y \mid y \geq 3\}$

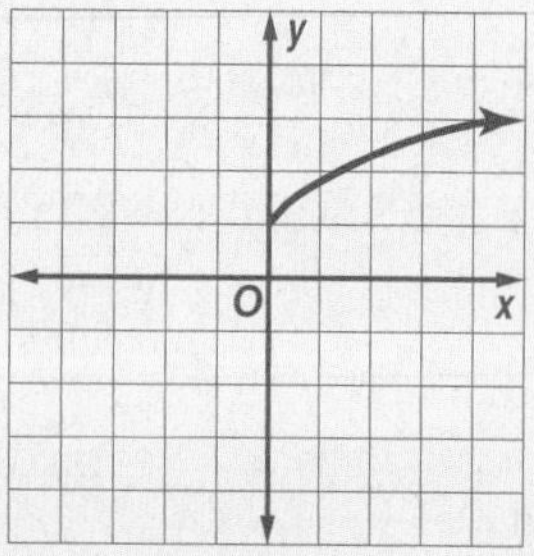

12. translated up 2;
D = $\{x \mid x \geq 0\}$
R = $\{y \mid y \geq -2\}$

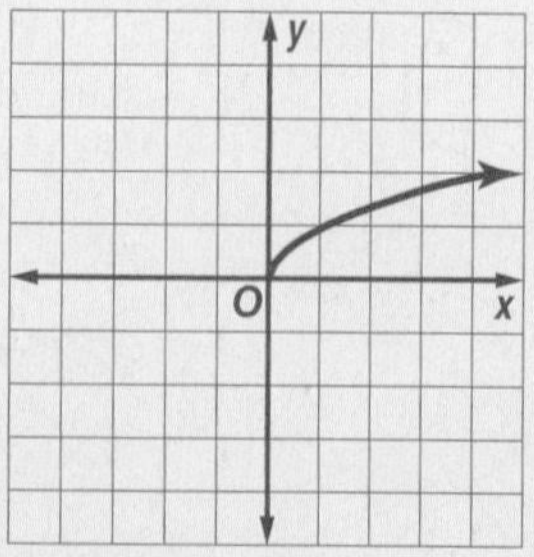

IL Math Online glencoe.com
- STUDY TO GO
- Vocabulary Review

Chapter Summary

Key Concepts

Simplifying Radical Expressions (Lesson 10-2)

- A radical expression is in simplest form when
  - no radicands have perfect square factors other than 1,
  - no radicals contain fractions,
  - and no radicals appear in the denominator of a fraction.

Operations with Radical Expressions and Equations (Lessons 10-3 and 10-4)

- Radical expressions with like radicals can be added or subtracted.
- Use the FOIL method to multiply radical expressions.

Pythagorean Theorem, Distance Formula, and Midpoint Formula (Lessons 10-5 and 10-6)

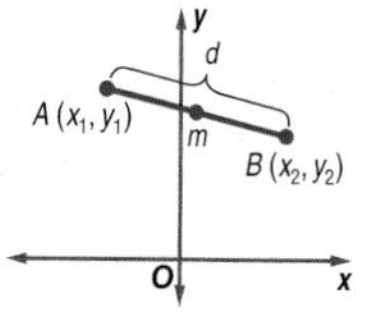

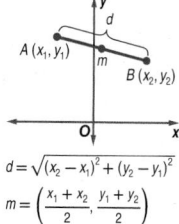

$$d = \sqrt{(x_2 - x_1)^2 + (y_2 - y_1)^2}$$

$$m = \left(\frac{x_1 + x_2}{2}, \frac{y_1 + y_2}{2}\right)$$

Similar Triangles (Lesson 10-7)

- Similar triangles have congruent corresponding angles and proportional corresponding sides.
  If $\triangle ABC \sim \triangle DEF$, then $\frac{AB}{DE} = \frac{BC}{EF} = \frac{AC}{DF}$.

FOLDABLES® Study Organizer

Be sure the Key Concepts are noted in your Foldable.

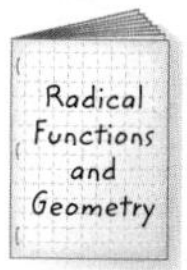

Key Vocabulary

conjugate (p. 614)
converse (p. 631)
cosine (p. 649)
Distance Formula (p. 636)
extraneous solutions (p. 625)
hypotenuse (p. 630)
inverse cosine (p. 651)
inverse sine (p. 651)
inverse tangent (p. 651)
legs (p. 630)
midpoint (p. 638)
Midpoint Formula (p. 638)
Pythagorean triple (p. 631)
radical equations (p. 624)
radical expression (p. 612)
radical function (p. 605)
radicand (p. 605)
rationalizing the denominator (p. 614)
similar triangles (p. 642)
sine (p. 649)
solving the triangle (p. 650)
square root function (p.605)
tangent (p. 649)
trigonometric ratio (p. 649)
trigonometry (p. 649)

Vocabulary Check

State whether each sentence is *true* or *false*. If *false*, replace the underlined word, phrase, expression, or number to make a true sentence.

1. A triangle with sides having measures of 3, 4, and 6 is a right triangle. **false; sample answer: 3, 4, and 5**
2. Two triangles are congruent if corresponding angles are congruent. **false; similar**
3. The expressions $2 + \sqrt{5}$ and $2 - \sqrt{5}$ are conjugates. **true**
4. In the expression $-5\sqrt{2}$, the radicand is 2. **true**
5. The shortest side of a right triangle is the hypotenuse. **false; longest**
6. The cosine of an angle is found by dividing the measure of the side opposite the angle by the hypotenuse. **false; adjacent**
7. The domain of the function $y = \sqrt{x}$ is $\{x \mid x \leq 0\}$. **false; $\{x \mid x \geq 0\}$**
8. After the first step in solving $\sqrt{2x + 4} = x + 5$, you would have $2x + 4 = x^2 + 10x + 25$ **true**
9. The converse of the Pythagorean Theorem is true. **true**
10. The range of the function $y = \sqrt{x}$ is $\{y \mid > 0\}$. **false; $\{y \mid y \geq 0\}$**

FOLDABLES® Study Organizer

Dinah Zike's Foldables®

Have students look through the chapter to make sure they have included examples in their Foldables for each lesson of the chapter.

Suggest that students keep their Foldables handy while completing the Study Guide and Review pages. Point out that their Foldables can serve as a quick review when studying for the chapter test.

Lesson-by-Lesson Review

10-1 Radical Functions (pp. 605–610)

7.B.4, 8.B.4b

Graph each function. Compare to the parent graph. State the domain and range.

11–16. See margin.

11. $y = \sqrt{x} + 3$
12. $y = \sqrt{x} - 2$
13. $y = -5\sqrt{x}$
14. $y = \sqrt{x} - 6$
15. $y = \sqrt{x - 1}$
16. $y = \sqrt{x} + 5$

17. **GEOMETRY** The function $s = \sqrt{A}$ can be used to find the length of a side of a square given its area. Use this function to determine the length of a side of a square with an area of 90 square inches. Round to the nearest tenth if necessary. **9.5 in.**

EXAMPLE 1

Graph $y = -3\sqrt{x}$. Compare to the parent graph. State the domain and range.

Make a table. Choose nonnegative values for x.

x	0	1	2	3	4
y	0	−3	≈−4.2	≈−5.2	−6

Plot points and draw a smooth curve.

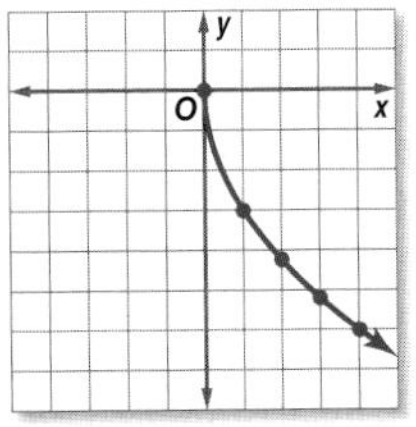

The graph of $y = \sqrt{x}$ is stretched vertically and is reflected across the x-axis.

The domain is $\{x \mid x \geq 0\}$.

The range is $\{y \mid y \leq 0\}$.

10-2 Simplifying Radical Expressions (pp. 612–617)

7.B.4

Simplify.

18. $\sqrt{36x^2y^7}$ **$6|xy^3|\sqrt{y}$**
19. $\sqrt{20ab^3}$ **$2|b|\sqrt{5ab}$**
20. $\sqrt{3} \cdot \sqrt{6}$ **$3\sqrt{2}$**
21. $2\sqrt{3} \cdot 3\sqrt{12}$ **36**
22. $(4 - \sqrt{5})^2$ **$21 - 8\sqrt{5}$**
23. $(1 + \sqrt{2})^2$ **$2\sqrt{2} + 3$**
24. $\sqrt{\frac{50}{a^2}}$ **$\frac{5\sqrt{2}}{|a|}$**
25. $\sqrt{\frac{2}{5}} \cdot \sqrt{\frac{3}{4}}$ **$\frac{\sqrt{30}}{10}$**
26. $\frac{3}{2 - \sqrt{5}}$ **$-6 - 3\sqrt{5}$**
27. $\frac{5}{\sqrt{7} + 6}$ **$\frac{5\sqrt{7} - 30}{-29}$**

28. **WEATHER** To estimate how long a thunderstorm will last, use $t = \sqrt{\frac{d^3}{216}}$, where t is the time in hours and d is the diameter of the storm in miles. A storm is 10 miles in diameter. How long will it last? **about 2.15 hours or 2 hours and 9 minutes**

EXAMPLE 2

Simplify $\frac{2}{4 + \sqrt{3}}$.

$\frac{2}{4 + \sqrt{3}}$

$= \frac{2}{4 + \sqrt{3}} \cdot \frac{4 - \sqrt{3}}{4 - \sqrt{3}}$ **Rationalize the denominator.**

$= \frac{2(4) - 2\sqrt{3}}{4^2 - (\sqrt{3})^2}$ **$(a - b)(a + b) = a^2 - b^2$**

$= \frac{8 - 2\sqrt{3}}{16 - 3}$ **$(\sqrt{3})^2 = 3$**

$= \frac{8 - 2\sqrt{3}}{13}$ **Simplify.**

Lesson-by-Lesson Review

Intervention If the given examples are not sufficient to review the topics covered by the questions, remind students that the page references tell them where to review that topic in their textbooks.

Two-Day Option Have students complete the Lesson-by-Lesson Review on pp. 657–660. Then you can use ExamView® Assessment Suite to customize another review worksheet that practices all the objectives of this chapter or only the objectives on which your students need more help.

Differentiated Instruction

Super DVD: MindJogger Videoquizzes Use this DVD as an alternative format of review for the test.

Additional Answers

13. stretched vertically and reflected across the x-axis; D = $\{x \mid x \geq 0\}$, R = $\{y \mid y \leq 0\}$

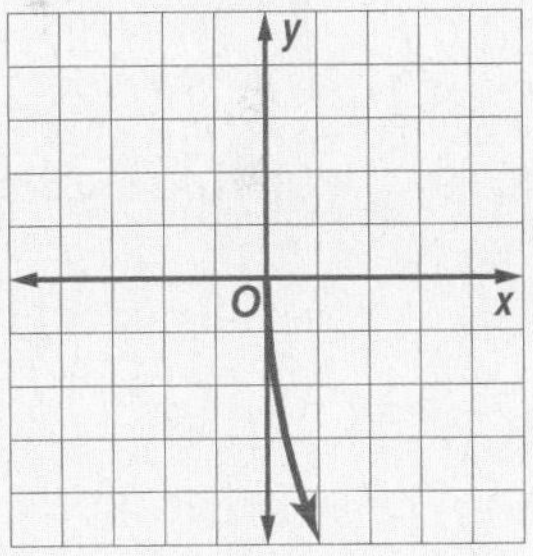

14. translated down 6; D = $\{x \mid x \geq 0\}$, R = $\{y \mid y \geq -6\}$

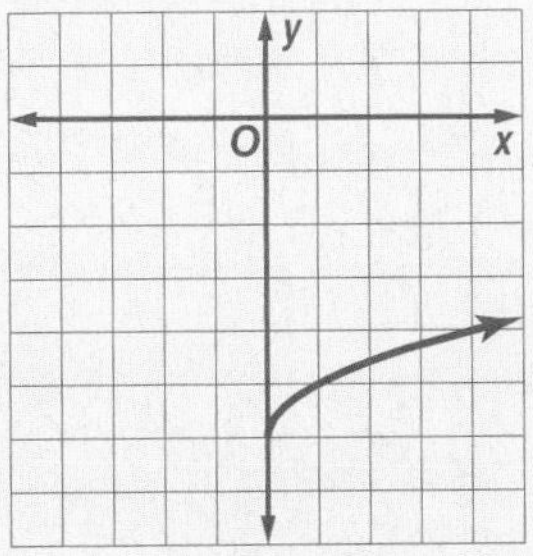

15. translated right 1; D = $\{x \mid x \geq 1\}$, R = $\{y \mid y \geq 0\}$

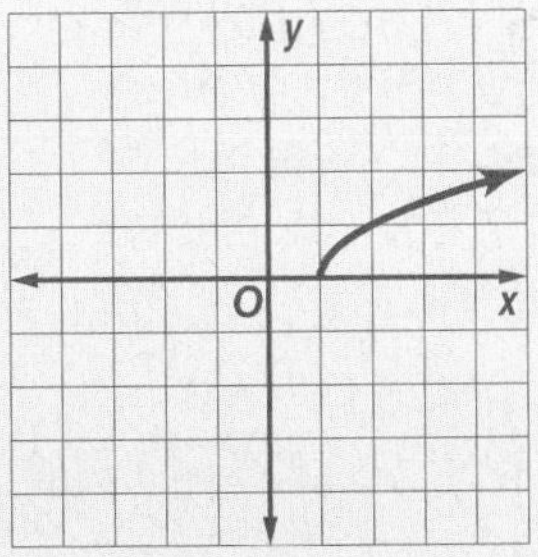

16. translated up 5; D = $\{x \mid x \geq 0\}$, R = $\{y \mid y \geq 5\}$

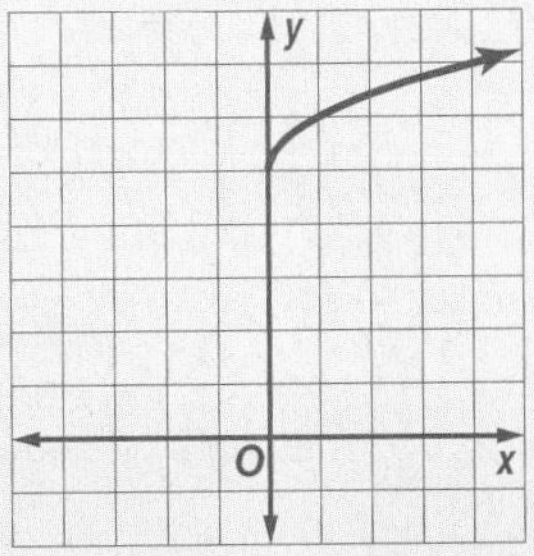

CHAPTER 10 Study Guide and Review

10-3 Operations with Radical Expressions (pp. 619–623)

7.B.4, 8.C.4b

Simplify each expression.

29. $\sqrt{6} - \sqrt{54} + 3\sqrt{12} + 5\sqrt{3}$ $-2\sqrt{6} + 11\sqrt{3}$

30. $2\sqrt{6} - \sqrt{48}$ $2\sqrt{6} - 4\sqrt{3}$

31. $4\sqrt{3x} - 3\sqrt{3x} + 3\sqrt{3x}$ $4\sqrt{3x}$

32. $\sqrt{50} + \sqrt{75}$ $5\sqrt{2} + 5\sqrt{3}$

33. $\sqrt{2}(5 + 3\sqrt{3})$ $5\sqrt{2} + 3\sqrt{6}$

34. $(2\sqrt{3} - \sqrt{5})(\sqrt{10} + 4\sqrt{6})$ $-2\sqrt{30} + 19\sqrt{2}$

35. $(6\sqrt{5} + 2)(4\sqrt{2} + \sqrt{3})$ $24\sqrt{10} + 8\sqrt{2} + 6\sqrt{15} + 2\sqrt{3}$

36. MOTION The velocity of a dropped object when it hits the ground can be found using $v = \sqrt{2gd}$, where v is the velocity in feet per second, g is the acceleration due to gravity, and d is the distance in feet the object drops. Find the speed of a penny when it hits the ground, after being dropped from 984 feet. Use 32 feet per second squared for g. about 250.95 ft/s

EXAMPLE 3

Simplify $2\sqrt{6} - \sqrt{24}$.

$2\sqrt{6} - \sqrt{24} = 2\sqrt{6} - \sqrt{4 \cdot 6}$	Product Property
$= 2\sqrt{6} - 2\sqrt{6}$	Simplify.
$= 0$	Simplify.

EXAMPLE 4

Simplify $(\sqrt{3} - \sqrt{2})(\sqrt{3} + 2\sqrt{2})$.

$(\sqrt{3} - \sqrt{2})(\sqrt{3} + 2\sqrt{2})$

$= (\sqrt{3})(\sqrt{3}) + (\sqrt{3})(2\sqrt{2}) + (-\sqrt{2})(\sqrt{3}) + (\sqrt{2})(2\sqrt{2})$

$= 3 + 2\sqrt{6} - \sqrt{6} + 4$

$= 7 + \sqrt{6}$

10-4 Radical Equations (pp. 624–628)

7.A.4b, 8.C.4b

Solve each equation. Check your solution.

37. $10 + 2\sqrt{x} = 0$ no solution

38. $\sqrt{5 - 4x} - 6 = 7$ -41

39. $\sqrt{a + 4} = 6$ 32

40. $\sqrt{3x} = 2$ $\frac{4}{3}$

41. $\sqrt{x + 4} = x - 8$ 12

42. $\sqrt{3x - 14} + x = 6$ 5

43. FREE FALL Assuming no air resistance, the time t in seconds that it takes an object to fall h feet can be determined by $t = \frac{\sqrt{h}}{4}$. If a skydiver jumps from an airplane and free falls for 10 seconds before opening the parachute, how many feet does she free fall? 1600 ft

EXAMPLE 5

Solve $\sqrt{7x + 4} - 18 = 5$.

$\sqrt{7x + 4} - 18 = 5$	Original equation
$\sqrt{7x + 4} = 23$	Add 18 to each side.
$(\sqrt{7x + 4})^2 = 23^2$	Square each side.
$7x + 4 = 529$	Simplify.
$7x = 525$	Subtract 4 from each side.
$x = 75$	Divide each side by 7.

CHECK	$\sqrt{7x + 4} - 18 = 5$	Original equation
	$\sqrt{7(75) + 4} - 18 \stackrel{?}{=} 5$	$x = 75$
	$\sqrt{525 + 4} - 18 \stackrel{?}{=} 5$	Multiply.
	$\sqrt{529} - 18 \stackrel{?}{=} 5$	Add.
	$23 - 18 \stackrel{?}{=} 5$	Simplify.
	$5 = 5$ ✓	True.

658 Chapter 10 Radical Functions and Geometry

MIXED PROBLEM SOLVING
For mixed problem-solving practice, see page 845.

10-5 The Pythagorean Theorem (pp. 630–635)

7.A.4b

Determine whether each set of measures can be the lengths of the sides of a right triangle.

44. 6, 8, 10 yes
45. 3, 4, 5 yes
46. 12, 16, 21 no
47. 10, 12, 15 no
48. 2, 3, 4 no
49. 7, 24, 25 yes
50. 5, 12, 13 yes
51. 15, 19, 23 no

52. LADDER A ladder is leaning on a building. The base of the ladder is 10 feet from the building, and the ladder reaches up 15 feet on the building. How long is the ladder? 18.0 ft

EXAMPLE 6

Determine whether the set of measures 12, 16, and 20 can be the lengths of the sides of a right triangle.

$a^2 + b^2 = c^2$	**Pythagorean Theorem**
$12^2 + 16^2 \stackrel{?}{=} 20^2$	**$a = 12$, $b = 16$, and $c = 20$**
$144 + 256 \stackrel{?}{=} 400$	**Multiply.**
$400 = 400$ ✓	**Add.**

The measures can be the lengths of the sides of a right triangle.

10-6 The Distance and Midpoint formulas (pp. 636–641)

7.A.4b

Find the distance between points with the given coordinates and the midpoint of the segment with the given endpoints. Round to the nearest hundredth if necessary.

53. $(2, 4), (-3, 4)$ $5; \left(-\frac{1}{2}, 4\right)$

54. $(-1, -3), (3, 5)$ $8.9; (1, 1)$

55. $(-6, 7), (0, 0)$ $9.2; \left(-3, \frac{7}{2}\right)$

56. $(1, 5), (-4, -5)$ $11.2; \left(-\frac{3}{2}, 0\right)$

Find the possible values for a if the points with the given coordinates are the indicated distance apart.

57. $(5, -2), (a, -3); d = \sqrt{170}$ 18 or -8

58. $(1, a), (-3, 2); d = 5$ 5 or -1

59. PLAYGROUND How far apart in feet are the swings from the slide? about 4.1 ft

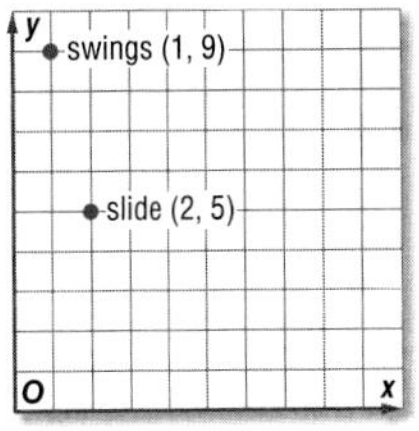

EXAMPLE 7

Find the distance between (−3, 5) and (−5, −3) and the midpoint of the segment with those endpoints. Round to the nearest tenth if necessary.

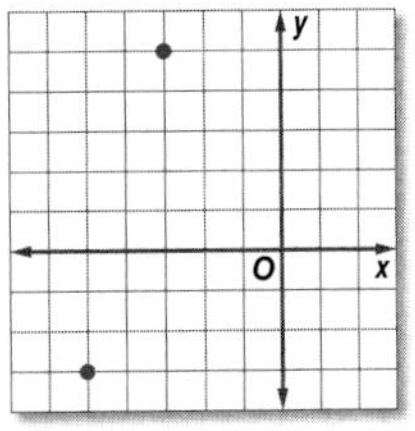

$d = \sqrt{(x_2 - x_1)^2 + (y_2 - y_1)^2}$	**Distance Formula**
$= \sqrt{[-3 - (-5)]^2 + [5 - (-3)]^2}$	**$(x_1, y_1) = (-5, -3)$, $(x_2, y_2) = (-3, 5)$**
$= \sqrt{2^2 + 8^2}$	**Simplify.**
$= \sqrt{4 + 64}$	**Evaluate squares.**
≈ 8.2	**Simplify.**
$M = \left(\frac{-5 + (-3)}{2}, \frac{-3 + 5}{2}\right)$	**Midpoint Formula**
$= (-4, 1)$	**Simplify.**

Chapter 10 Study Guide and Review 659

Problem Solving Review

For additional practice in problem solving for Chapter 10, see the Mixed Problem Solving Appendix, p. 854, in the Student Handbook section.

Anticipation Guide

Have students complete the Chapter 10 Anticipation Guide and discuss how their responses have changed now that they have completed Chapter 10.

Additional Answers

65. $\cos A = \frac{5}{13}$, $\sin A = \frac{12}{13}$, $\tan A = \frac{12}{5}$

66. $\cos A = \frac{3}{5}$, $\sin A = \frac{4}{5}$, $\tan A = \frac{4}{3}$

Additional Answers (Practice Test)

1. reflected across the x-axis; $D = \{x \mid x \geq 0\}$, $R = \{y \mid y \leq 0\}$

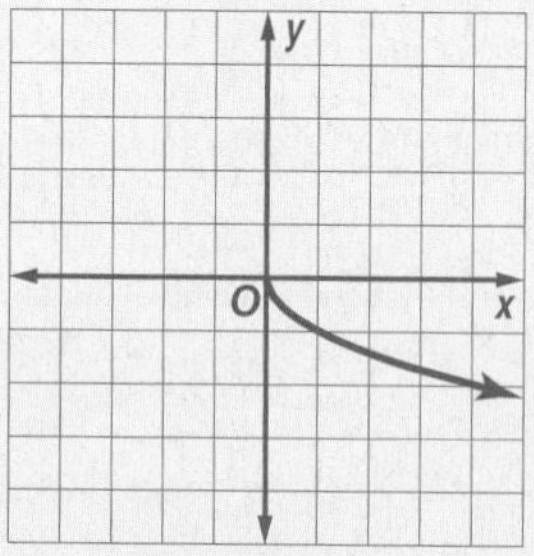

2. compressed vertically; $D = \{x \mid x \geq 0\}$, $R = \{y \mid y \geq 0\}$

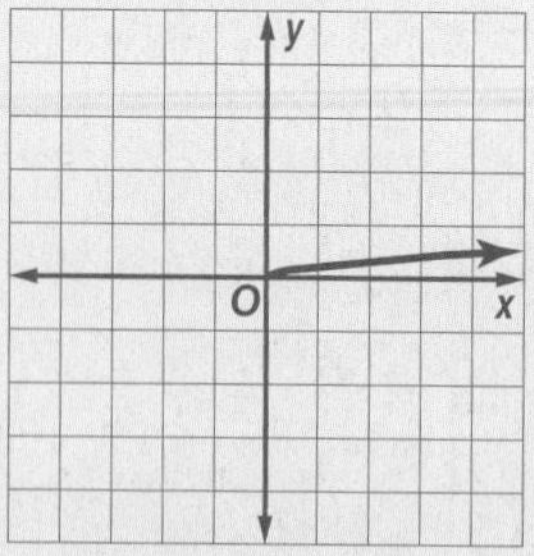

CHAPTER 10 Study Guide and Review

10-7 Similar Triangles (pp. 642–647)

7.A.4a, 7.C.4a

Find the missing measures for the pair of similar triangles if $\triangle ABC \sim \triangle DEF$.

60. $a = 3, b = 4, c = 5, d = 12$ **$e = 16$, $f = 20$**

61. $a = 3, b = 4, c = 5, d = 4.5$ **$e = 6$, $f = 7.5$**

62. $a = 4, b = 8, c = 11, e = 4$ **$d = 2$, $f = 5.5$**

63. $a = 5, b = 7, c = 9, f = 18$ **$d = 10$, $e = 14$**

64. MODELS Kristin is making a model of the artwork shown in the scale of 1 inch = 2 feet. If the height of the artwork is 10 feet, what will the height of the model be? **5 in.**

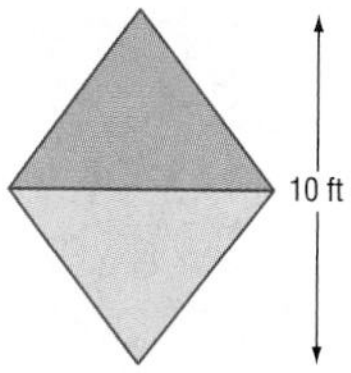

EXAMPLE 8

Find the missing length for the pair of triangles if $\triangle ABC \sim \triangle DFG$.

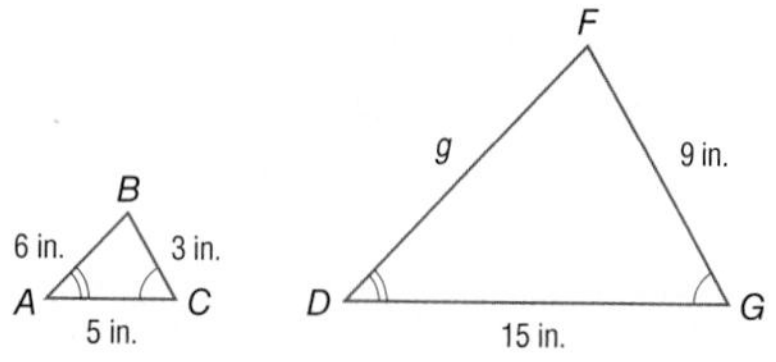

$\frac{AB}{DF} = \frac{BC}{FG}$ **Corresponding sides of similar triangles are proportional.**

$\frac{6}{g} = \frac{3}{9}$ **$AB = 6$, $BC = 3$, $DF = g$, and $FG = 9$**

$18 = g$ **Find the cross products and simplify.**

10-8 Trigonometric Ratios (pp. 649–655)

9.D.4

Find the values of the three trigonometric ratios for angle A. **65–66. See margin.**

65.

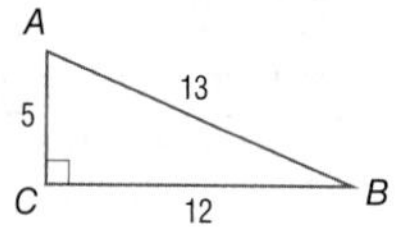

66.

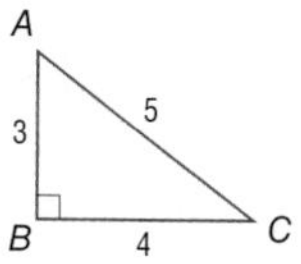

67. RAMPS How long is the ramp? **6 ft**

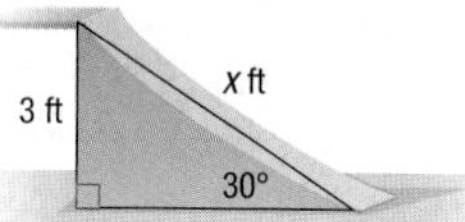

EXAMPLE 9

Find the values of the three trigonometric ratios for angle A.

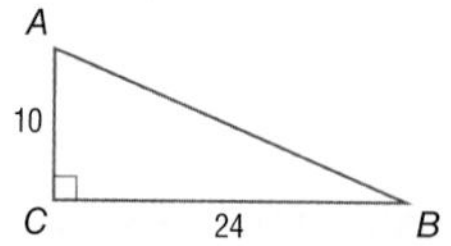

Find the hypotenuse: $c^2 = 10^2 + 24^2$, so $c = 26$.

$\sin A = \frac{\text{leg opposite } \angle A}{\text{hypotenuse}} = \frac{24}{26} = \frac{12}{13}$

$\cos A = \frac{\text{leg adjacent } \angle A}{\text{hypotenuse}} = \frac{10}{26} = \frac{5}{13}$

$\tan A = \frac{\text{leg opposite } \angle A}{\text{leg adjacent } \angle A} = \frac{24}{10} = \frac{12}{5}$

IL Math Online > glencoe.com
Chapter Test

Graph each function, and compare to the parent graph. State the domain and range.

1. $y = -\sqrt{x}$
2. $y = \frac{1}{4}\sqrt{x}$
3. $y = \sqrt{x} + 5$
4. $y = \sqrt{x + 4}$

1–4. See margin.

5. **GEOMETRY** The length of the side of a square is given by the function $s = \sqrt{A}$, where A is the area of the square. What is the perimeter of a square that has an area of 64 square inches? **C**

A 64 inches
B 8 inches
C 32 inches
D 16 inches

Simplify each expression.

6. $5\sqrt{36}$ **30**
7. $\frac{3}{1 - \sqrt{2}}$ **$-3 - 3\sqrt{2}$**
8. $2\sqrt{3} + 7\sqrt{3}$ **$9\sqrt{3}$**
9. $3\sqrt{6}(5\sqrt{2})$ **$30\sqrt{3}$**

10. **GEOMETRY** Find the area of the rectangle. **F**

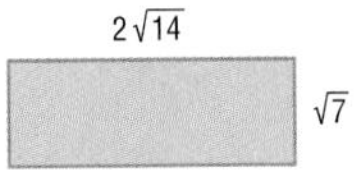

F $14\sqrt{2}$
G 14
H $98\sqrt{2}$
J $7\sqrt{2}$

Solve each equation. Check your solution.

11. $\sqrt{10x} = 20$ **40**
12. $\sqrt{4x - 3} = 6 - x$ **3**

13. **PACKAGING** A cylindrical container of chocolate drink mix has a volume of about 162 in^3. The radius of the container can be found by using the formula $r = \sqrt{\frac{V}{\pi h}}$, where r is the radius and h is the height. If the height is 8.25 inches, find the radius of the container. **about 2.5 in.**

Find each missing length. If necessary, round to the nearest tenth. **14. 10 15. 9.2**

14.

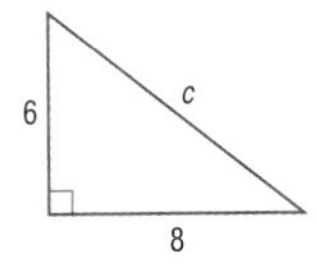

15.

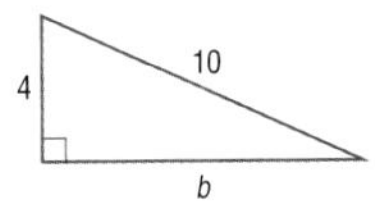

Find the distance between the points with the given coordinates.

16. (2, 3), (3, 5) **$\sqrt{5}$ or ≈ 2.2**
17. (−3, 4), (−2, −3) **$5\sqrt{2}$ or ≈ 7.1**
18. (−1, −1), (3, 2) **5**
19. (−4, −6), (−7, 1) **$\sqrt{58}$ or ≈ 7.6**

Find the coordinates of the midpoint of the segment with the given endpoints.

20. (2, 3), (3, 5) **$\left(\frac{5}{2}, 4\right)$**
21. (−3, 4), (−2, −3) **$\left(-\frac{5}{2}, \frac{1}{2}\right)$**
22. (−1, −1), (3, 2) **$\left(1, \frac{1}{2}\right)$**
23. (−4, −8), (10, −6) **(3, −7)**

24. **PIZZA DELIVERY** The Pizza Place delivers to any location within a radius of 5 miles from the store for free. A delivery person drives 32 blocks north and then 45 blocks east to deliver a pizza. In this city, there are about 6 blocks per half mile.

a. Should there be a charge for delivery? Explain. **No; the distance is about 55 blocks or about 4.6 mi.**

b. Describe two delivery situations that would result in about 5 miles. **See margin.**

25. Find the missing lengths if $\triangle ABC \sim \triangle XYZ$. **$y = 3$; $z = 6$**

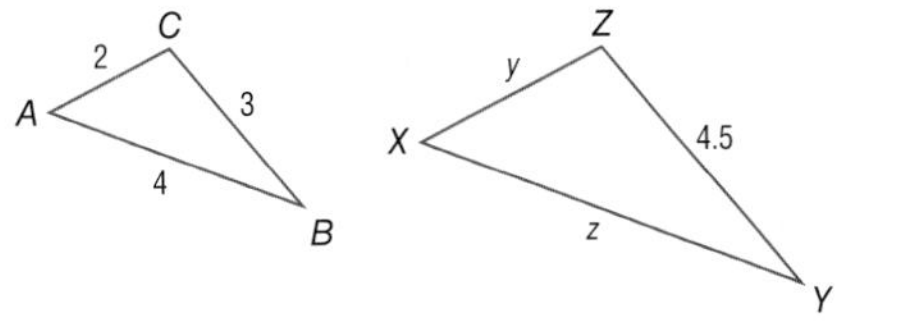

26. Find the values of the three trigonometric ratios for angle A. **$\sin A = \frac{4}{5}$, $\cos A = \frac{3}{5}$, $\tan A = \frac{4}{3}$**

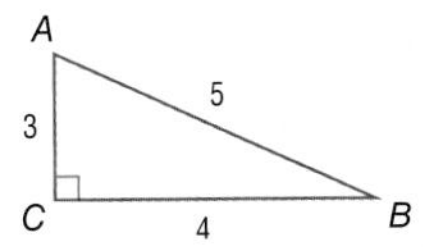

27. Find $m\angle X$ to the nearest degree. **37°**

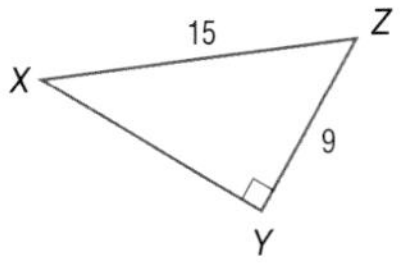

CHAPTER 10 Practice Test

ExamView Assessment Suite Customize and create multiple versions of your chapter test and their answer keys. All of the questions from the leveled chapter tests in the *Chapter 10 Resource Masters* are also available on ExamView® Assessment Suite.

Additional Answers

3. translated up 5; D = {x | x ≥ 0}, R = {y | y ≥ 5}

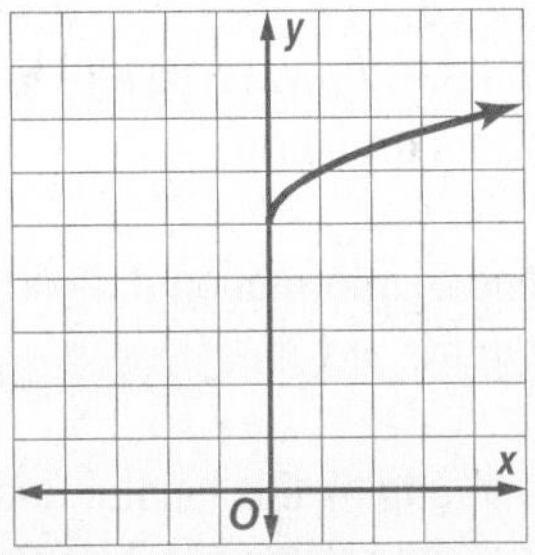

4. translated left 4; D = {x | x ≥ −4}, R = {y | y ≥ 0}

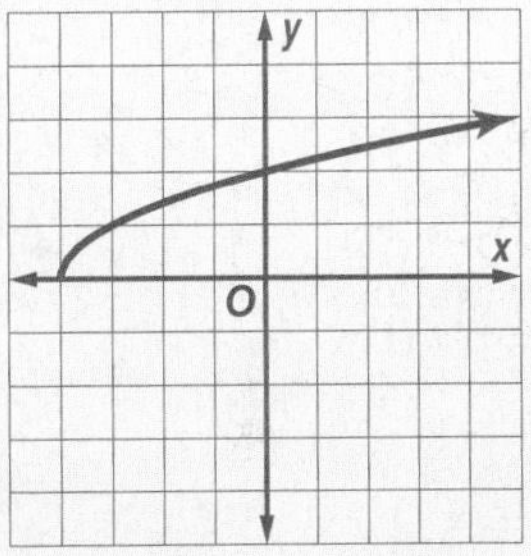

24b. Sample answer: 40 blocks south and 45 blocks west; 38 blocks north and 47 blocks west

Intervention Planner

Tier 1 On Level	Tier 2 Strategic Intervention approaching grade level	Tier 3 Intensive Intervention 2 or more grades below level
If students miss about 25% of the exercises or less,	**If** students miss about 50% of the exercises,	**If** students miss about 75% of the exercises,
Then choose a resource: **SE** Lessons 10-1, 10-2, 10-3, 10-4, 10-5, 10-6, 10-7, and 10-8 **CRM** Skills Practice, pp. 7, 13, 19, 25, 32, 39, 45, and 51 **TE** Chapter Project, p. 602 IL Math Online > Self-Check Quiz	**Then** choose a resource: **CRM** Study Guide and Intervention, Chapter 10, pp. 5, 11, 17, 23, 30, 37, 43, and 49 *Quick Review Math Handbook* IL Math Online > Extra Examples, Personal Tutor, Homework Help	**Then** use *Math Triumphs, Alg. 1* IL Math Online > Extra Examples, Personal Tutor, Homework Help, Review Vocabulary

1 FOCUS

Objective Use the strategy of drawing a picture to solve standardized test problems.

2 TEACH

Scaffolding Questions

Ask:

- Have you ever drawn a picture to help solve a problem? Answers will vary.
- What kind of information did you include in the picture? Answers will vary.
- Why do you think it is helpful to draw pictures when solving problems? Sample answer: It allows you to see relationships in a different way, which makes it easier to solve the problem.

CHAPTER 10 Preparing for Standardized Tests

Draw a Picture

Sometimes it is easier to visualize how to solve a problem if you draw a picture first. You can sketch your picture on scrap paper or in your test booklet (if allowed). Be careful not make any marks on your answer sheet other than your answers.

Strategies for Drawing a Picture

Step 1

Read the problem statement carefully.

Ask yourself:

- What am I being asked to solve?
- What information is given in the problem?
- What is the unknown quantity for which I need to solve?

Step 2

Sketch and label your picture.

- Draw your picture as clearly and accurately as possible.
- Label the picture carefully. Be sure to include all of the information given in the problem statement.

Step 3

Solve the problem.

- Use your picture to help you model the problem situation with an equation. Then solve the equation.
- Check your answer to make sure it is reasonable.

EXAMPLE

Read the problem. Identify what you need to know. Then use the information in the problem to solve. Show your work.

One sunny day, a church steeple casts a shadow that is 24 feet 3 inches long. At the same time, Nicole casts a shadow that is 1 foot 9 inches long. If Nicole is 5 feet 3 inches tall, what is the height of the steeple?

662 Chapter 10 Radical Functions and Geometry

Read the problem statement carefully. You know Nicole's height, her shadow length, and the shadow length of the steeple. You need to find the height of the steeple.

Example of a 2-point response:

Scoring Rubric	
Criteria	**Score**
Full Credit: The answer is correct and a full explanation is provided that shows each step.	2
Partial Credit: • The answer is correct, but the explanation is incomplete. • The answer is incorrect, but the explanation is correct.	1
No Credit: Either an answer is not provided or the answer does not make sense.	0

First convert all measurements to feet.

24 feet 3 inches = $24\frac{3}{12}$ or 24.25 feet

1 foot 9 inches = $1\frac{9}{12}$ or 1.75 feet

5 feet 3 inches = $5\frac{3}{12}$ or 5.25 feet

Use similar triangles to find the height of the church steeple. Draw and label two triangles to represent the situation.

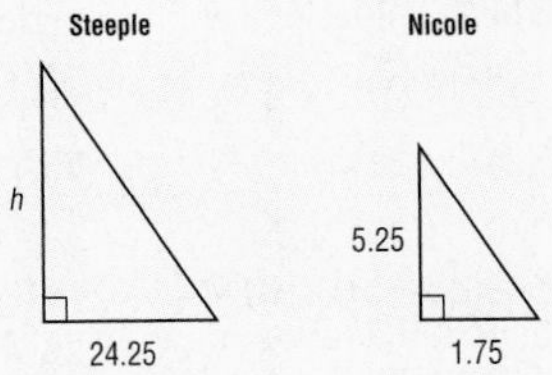

Use the similar triangles to set up and solve a proportion.

$\frac{h}{24.25} = \frac{5.25}{1.75}$

$1.75h = (24.25)(5.25)$

$1.75h = 127.3125$

$h = 72.75$

The height of the church steeple is 72.75 feet or 72 feet 9 inches.

Exercises

Read each problem. Identify what you need to know. Then use the information in the problem to solve. Show your work.

1. A building casts a 15-foot shadow, while a billboard casts a 4.5-foot shadow. If the billboard is 26 feet high, what is the height of the building? Round to the nearest tenth if necessary. **about 86.7 feet**

2. Jamey places a mirror on the ground at a distance of 56 feet from the base of a water tower. When he stands at a distance of 6 feet from the mirror, he can see the top of the water tower in the mirror's reflection and forms a pair of similar triangles. If Jamey is 5 feet 6 inches tall, what is the height of the water tower? Express your answer in feet and inches. **51 feet 4 inches**

Additional Example

SHORT RESPONSE Bradley is standing next to a purple martin birdhouse that is on the ground. The birdhouse casts a shadow that is 2.25 feet long at the same time that Bradley casts a shadow that is 6.5 feet long. Bradley is 6 feet tall. What is the height of the purple martin bird house? Round to the nearest foot.

Sample 2-point response:

Draw and label two triangles to represent the situation.

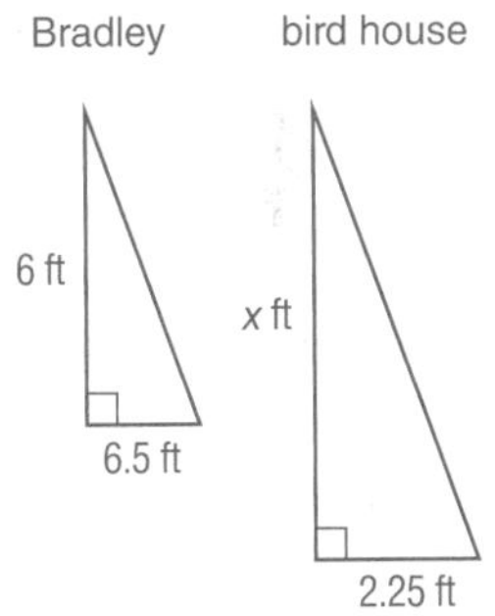

Set up and solve a proportion using the triangles.

$\frac{6}{6.5} = \frac{x}{2.25}$

$6.5x = 13.5$

$x = 2\frac{1}{13}$

The purple martin bird house is about 2 feet high.

3 ASSESS

Use Exercises 1 and 2 to assess students' understanding.

Chapter 10 Preparing for Standardized Tests 663

Diagnose Student Errors

Survey students' responses for each item. Class trends may indicate common errors and misconceptions.

1. A error in units translated up from parent graph
B correct
C incorrectly chose positive instead of negative sign to show graph is reflected over x-axis
D incorrectly chose positive instead of negative sign to show graph is reflected over x-axis and error in units translated up from parent graph
E guess

2. F multiplied numerator by $4+\sqrt{2}$ instead of its conjugate
G incorrectly factored out 2
H correct
J multiplied numerator by $4+\sqrt{2}$ instead of its conjugate and incorrectly factored out 2
K guess

3. A calculation error and added instead of multiplied radicand
B forgot to multiply by $\frac{1}{2}$
C calculation error and added instead of multiplied radicand
D correct
E calculation error

4. F mistakenly divided correct result by 2
G guess
H correct
J guess
K guess

5. A correct
B chose measures that are the sides of a right triangle
C chose measures that are the sides of a right triangle
D chose measures that are the sides of a right triangle
E chose measures that are the sides of a right triangle

6. F error in slope and passes through (4, 0) instead of (4, −4)
G error in slope but passes through (4, −4)
H slope is correct but passes through (0, −4) instead of (4, −4)
J correct
K chose one with negative slope

7. A guess or calculation error
B correct
C guess or calculation error
D guess
E guess or calculation error

CHAPTER 10 PSAE Practice

Cumulative, Chapters 1 through 10

Multiple Choice

Read each question. Then fill in the correct answer on the answer document provided by your teacher on a sheet of paper.

1. What is the equation of the square root function graphed below? B

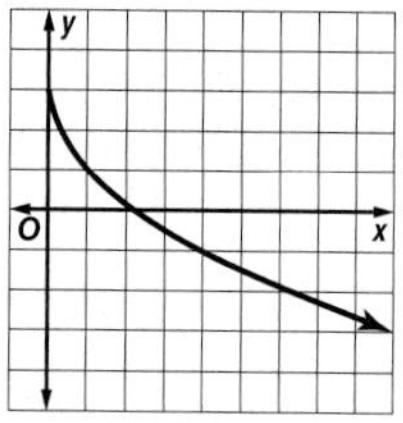

A $y=-2\sqrt{x}+1$
B $y=-2\sqrt{x}+3$
C $y=2\sqrt{x}+3$
D $y=2\sqrt{x}+1$
E $y=\sqrt{x}+2$

2. Simplify $\frac{1}{4+\sqrt{2}}$. H

F $\frac{4+\sqrt{2}}{14}$
G $\frac{2-\sqrt{2}}{7}$
H $\frac{4-\sqrt{2}}{14}$
J $\frac{2+\sqrt{2}}{7}$
K $\frac{-\sqrt{2}}{4}$

3. What is the area of the triangle below? D

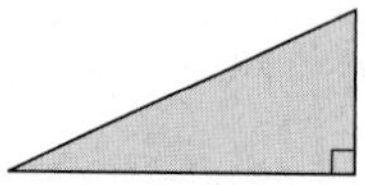

A $3\sqrt{2}+10\sqrt{5}$
B $17+5\sqrt{10}$
C $12\sqrt{2}+8\sqrt{5}$
D $8.5+2.5\sqrt{10}$
E $3\sqrt{2}+\sqrt{5}$

4. The formula for the slant height c of a cone is $c=\sqrt{h^2+r^2}$, where h is the height of the cone and r is the radius of its base. What is the radius of the cone below? Round to the nearest tenth. H

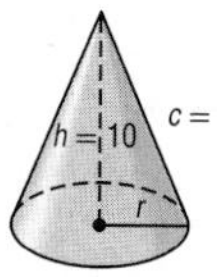

F 4.9
G 6.3
H 9.8
J 10.2
K 16

5. Which of the following sets of measures could not be the sides of a right triangle? A

A (12, 16, 24)
B (24, 45, 51)
C (10, 24, 26)
D (18, 24, 30)
E (15, 20, 25)

6. Which of the following is an equation of the line perpendicular to $4x-2y=6$ and passing through $(4,-4)$? J

F $y=-\frac{3}{4}x+3$
G $y=-\frac{3}{4}x-1$
H $y=-\frac{1}{2}x-4$
J $y=-\frac{1}{2}x-2$
K $y=\frac{1}{2}x-4$

7. The scale on a map shows that 1.5 centimeters is equivalent to 40 miles. If the distance on the map between two cities is 8 centimeters, about how many miles apart are the cities? B

A 178 miles
B 213 miles
C 224 miles
D 275 miles
E 320 miles

Test-Taking Tip

Question 4 Substitute for c and h in the formula. Then solve for r.

CHAPTER 10 PSAE Practice

Short Response/Gridded Response

Record your answers on the answer sheet provided by your teacher or on a sheet of paper.

8. **GRIDDED RESPONSE** How many times does the graph of $y = x^2 - 4x + 10$ cross the x-axis? **0**

9. Factor $2x^4 - 32$ completely.
$2(x-2)(x+2)(x^2+4)$

10. **GRIDDED RESPONSE** In football, a field goal is worth 3 points, and the extra point after a touchdown is worth 1 point. During the 2006 season, John Kasay of the Carolina Panthers scored a total of 100 points for his team by making a total of 52 field goals and extra points. How many field goals did he make? **24**

11. Shannon bought a satellite radio and a subscription to satellite radio. What is the total cost for his first year of service? **$183.87**

Item	Cost
radio	$39.99
subscription	$11.99 per month

12. **GRIDDED RESPONSE** The distance required for a car to stop is directly proportional to the square of its velocity. If a car can stop in 242 meters at 22 kilometers per hour, how many meters are needed to stop at 30 kilometers per hour? **450**

13. The highest point in Kentucky is at an elevation of 4145 feet above sea level. The lowest point in the state is at an elevation of 257 feet above sea level. Write an inequality to describe the possible elevations in Kentucky. **$257 \le x \le 4{,}145$**

14. Simplify the expression below. Show your work. **$\frac{25r^{12}}{4q^6t^{10}}$**

$$\left(\frac{-2r^{-2}q^5t^2}{5r^4q^2t^{-3}}\right)^{-2}$$

15. **GRIDDED RESPONSE** For the first home basketball game, 652 tickets were sold for a total revenue of $5216. If each ticket costs the same, how much is the cost per ticket? State your answer in dollars. **8.00**

Extended Response

Record your answers on a sheet of paper. Show your work.

16. Karen is making a map of her hometown using a coordinate grid. The scale of her map is 1 unit = 2.5 miles.

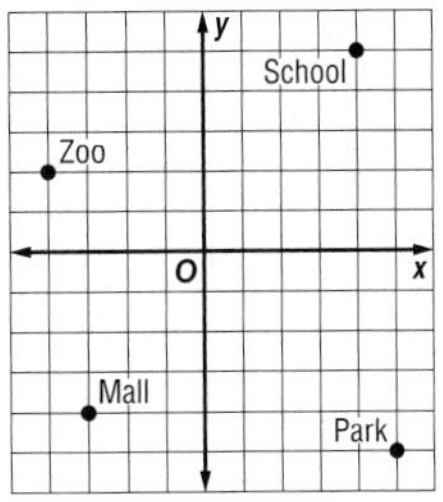

a. What is the actual distance between Karen's school and the park? Round to the nearest tenth of a mile if necessary. **25.1 mi**

b. Suppose Karen's house is located midway between the mall and the school. What coordinates represent her house? Show your work. **(0.5, 0.5)**

Need Extra Help?

If you missed Question...	1	2	3	4	5	6	7	8	9	10	11	12	13	14	15	16
Go to Lesson or Page...	10-1	10-2	10-3	10-4	10-5	4-4	10-7	9-5	8-5	6-4	1-4	3-6	5-4	7-2	2-2	10-6
IL Assessment Objectives	8.11.19	6.11.10	7.11.03	8.11.06	9.11.05	8.11.07	6.11.17	8.11.08	8.11.01	6.11.13	6.11.13	6.11.19	8.11.16	8.11.01	6.11.13	6.11.17

Formative Assessment

You can use these two pages to benchmark student progress.

CRM Standardized Test Practice, pp. 74–76

Answer Sheet Practice

Have students simulate taking a standardized test by recording their answers on a practice recording sheet.

CRM Student Recording Sheet, p. 55

Chapter Resource Master
CRM p. 55

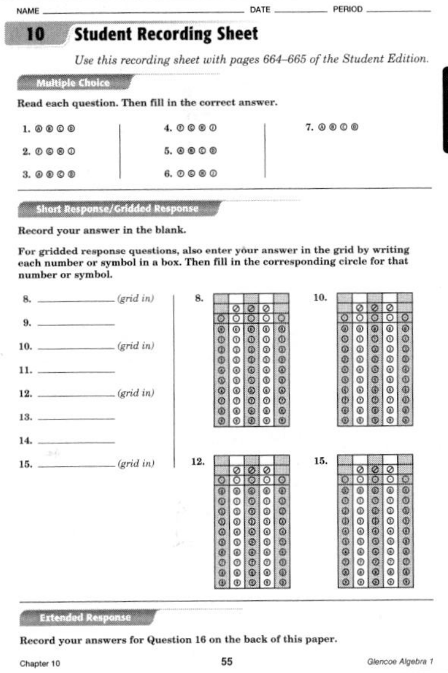

ExamView Assessment Suite Create practice worksheets or tests that align to your state's standards, as well as TIMSS and NAEP tests.

Homework Option

Get Ready for Chapter 11 Assign students the exercises on p. 667 as homework to assess whether they possess the prerequisite skills needed for the next chapter.

Chapters 1–10 PSAE Practice 665

Pages 606–607, Lesson 10-1 (Check Your Progress)

2A. stretched vertically and reflected across the *x*-axis; $D = \{x \mid x \geq 0\}$, $R = \{y \mid y \leq 0\}$

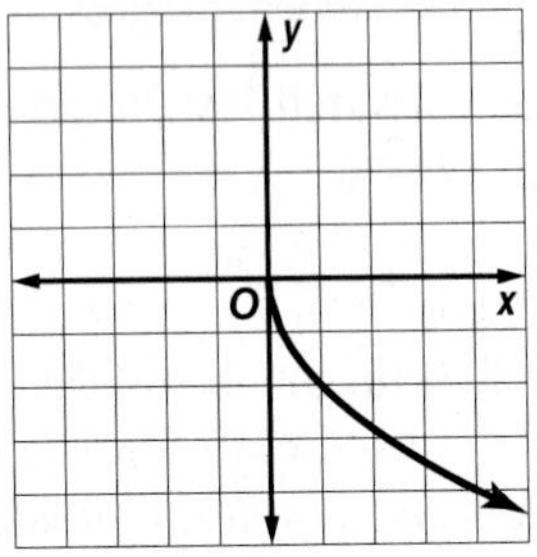

2B. stretched vertically and reflected across the *x*-axis; $D = \{x \mid x \geq 0\}$, $R = \{y \mid y \leq 0\}$

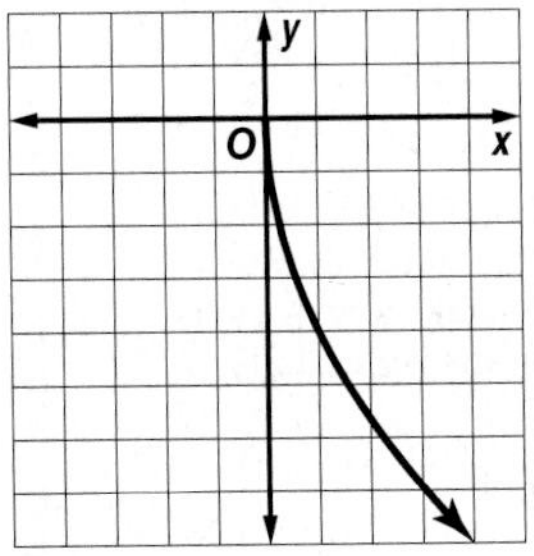

3A. translated down 4; $D = \{x \mid x \geq 0\}$, $R = \{y \mid y \geq -4\}$

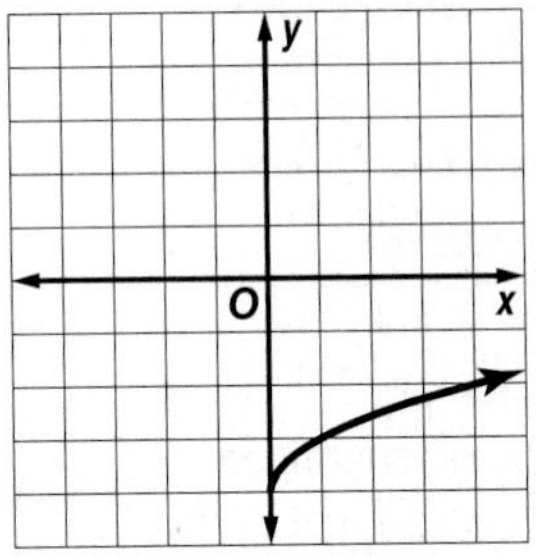

3B. translated left 3; $D = \{x \mid x \geq -3\}$, $R = \{y \mid y \geq 0\}$

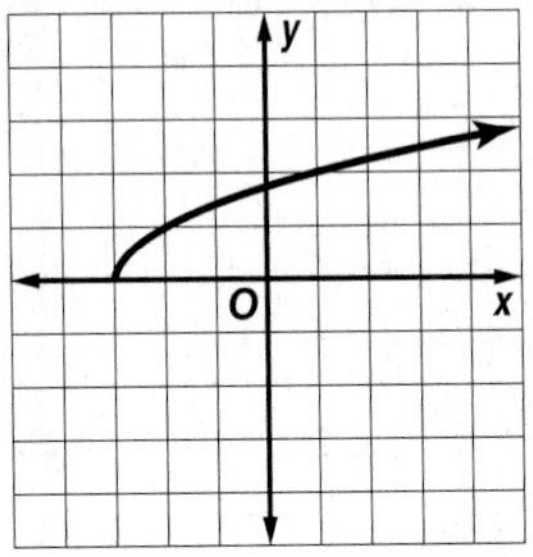

Pages 608–610, Lesson 10-1

1. vertical stretch of $y = \sqrt{x}$; $D = \{x \mid x \geq 0\}$, $R = \{y \mid y \geq 0\}$

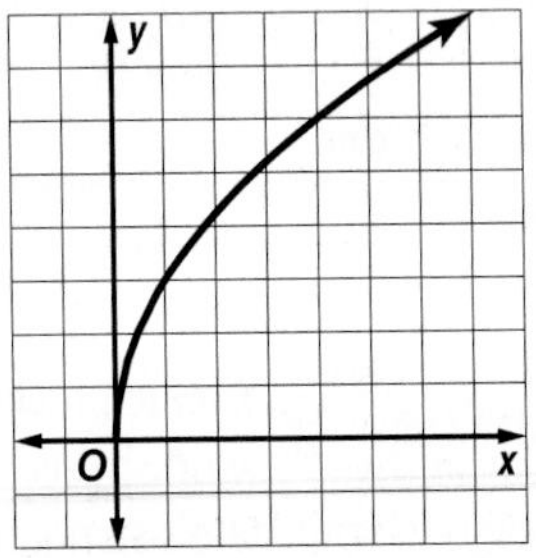

2. vertical stretch of $y = \sqrt{x}$ and a reflection across the *x*-axis; $D = \{x \mid x \leq 0\}$, $R = \{y \mid y \leq 0\}$

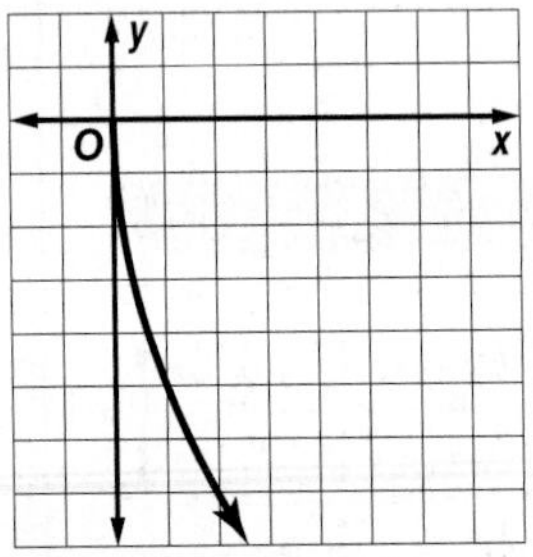

3. vertical compression of $y = \sqrt{x}$; $D = \{x \mid x \geq 0\}$, $R = \{y \mid y \geq 0\}$

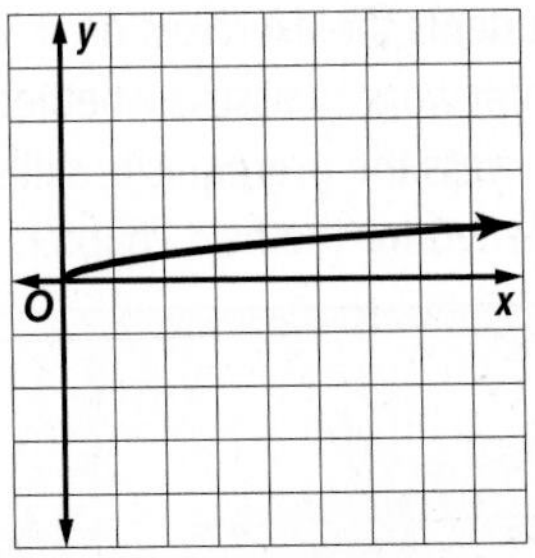

4. vertical compression of $y = \sqrt{x}$ and a reflection across the *x*-axis; $D = \{x \mid x \geq 0\}$; $R = \{y \mid y \leq 0\}$

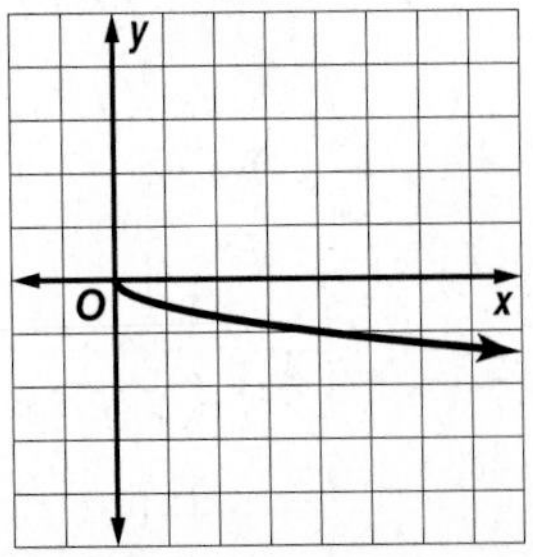

5. translated up 3; $D = \{x \mid x \geq 0\}$, $R = \{y \mid y \geq 3\}$

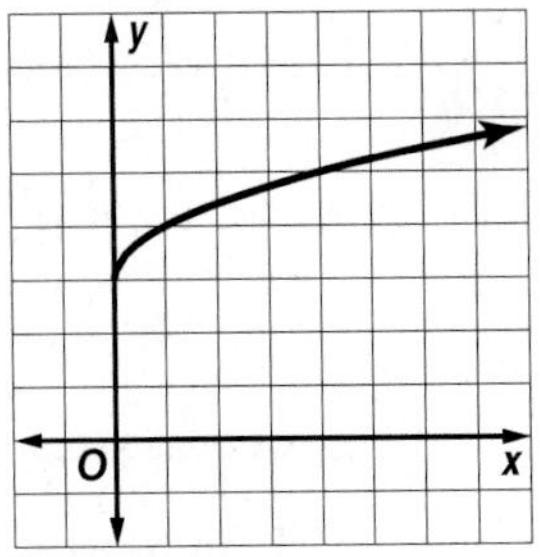

6. translated down 2; $D = \{x \mid x \geq 0\}$, $R = \{y \mid y \geq -2\}$

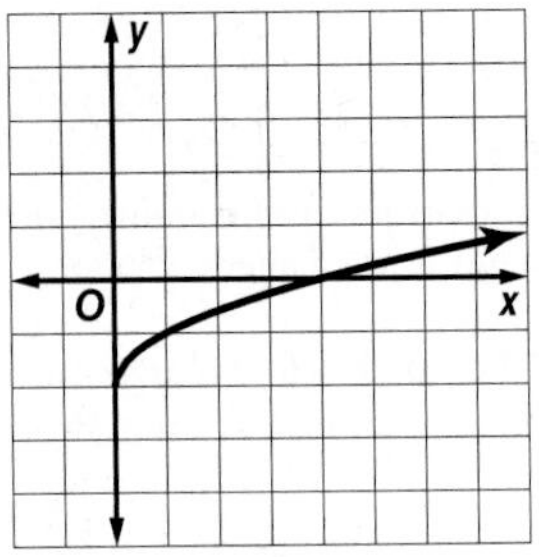

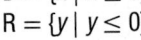

7. translated left 2; $D = \{x \mid x \geq -2\}$, $R = \{y \mid y \geq 0\}$

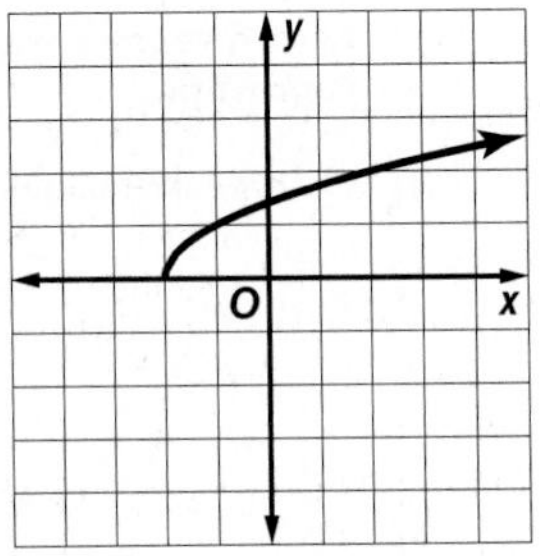

8. translated right 3; $D = \{x \mid x \geq 3\}$, $R = \{y \mid y \geq 0\}$

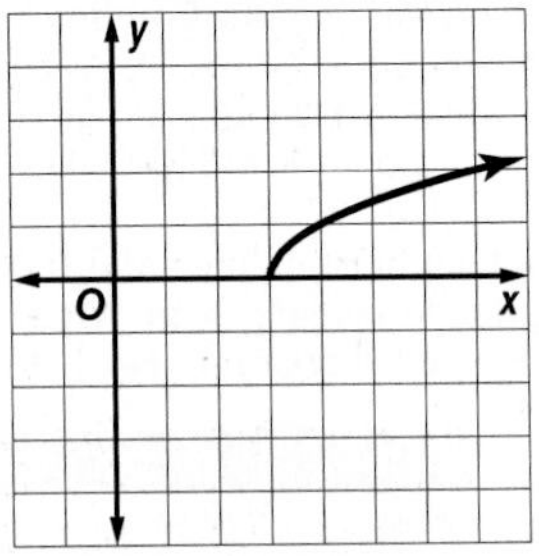

10. vertical compression of $\sqrt{x}$ and translated up 2; $D = \{x \mid x \geq 0\}$, $R = \{y \mid y \geq 2\}$

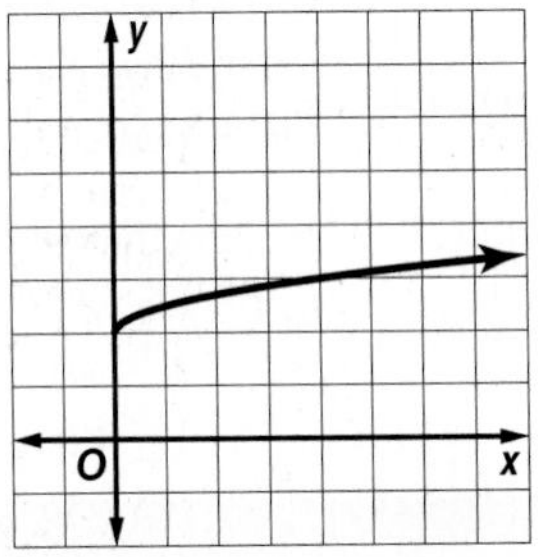

11. vertical compression of $\sqrt{x}$, and reflected across the *x*-axis and translated down 1; $D = \{x \mid x \geq 0\}$, $R = \{y \mid y \leq -1\}$

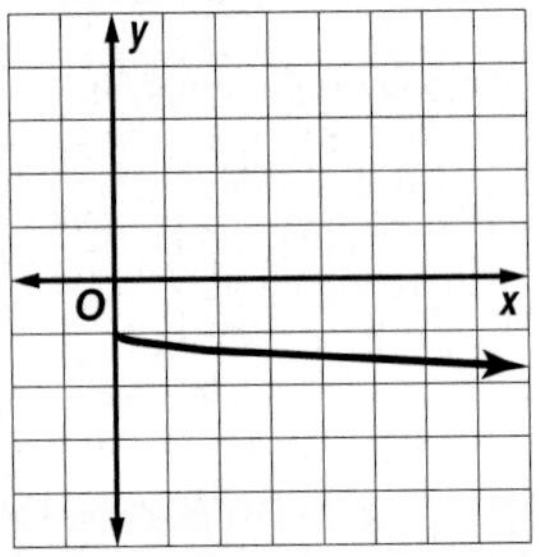

12. translated left 1, vertical stretch and reflected across *x*-axis; $D = \{x \mid x \geq -1\}$, $R = \{y \mid y \leq 0\}$

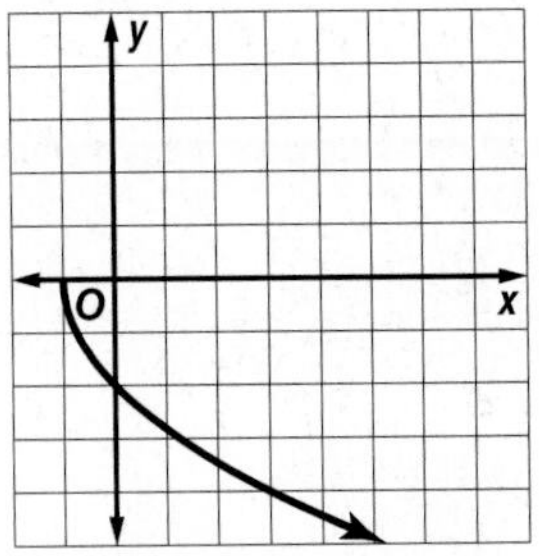

13. translated right 2 and vertical stretch of $\sqrt{x}$; $D = \{x \mid x \geq 2\}$, $R = \{y \mid y \geq 0\}$

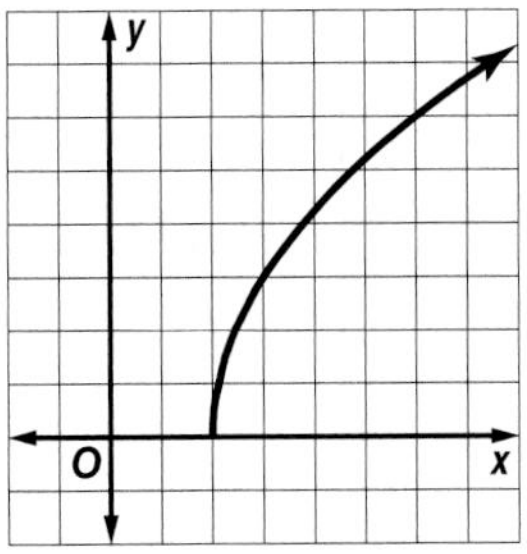

14. vertical stretch of $\sqrt{x}$; $D = \{x \mid x \geq 0\}$, $R = \{y \mid y \geq 0\}$

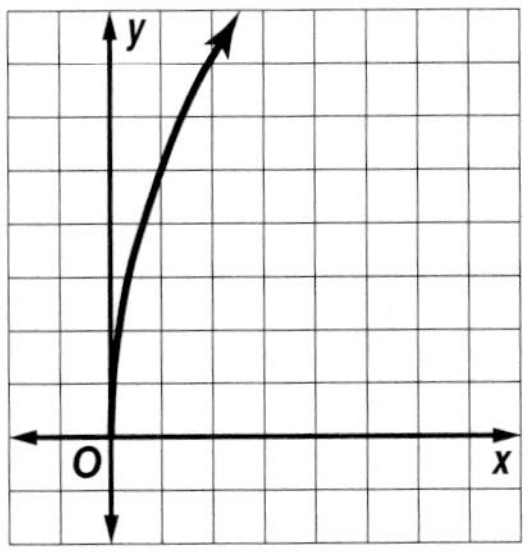

15. vertical compression of $\sqrt{x}$; $D = \{x \mid x \geq 0\}$, $R = \{y \mid y \geq 0\}$

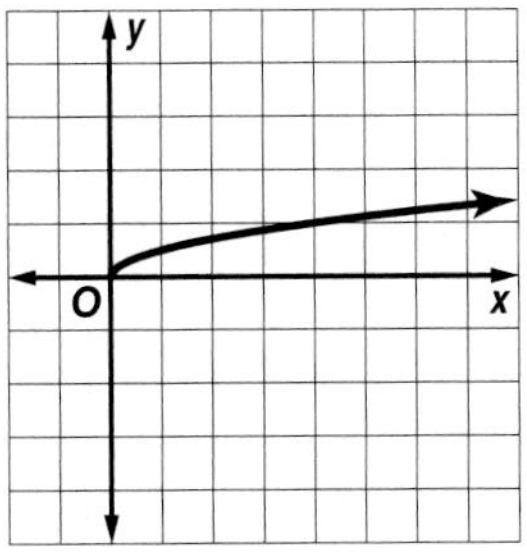

16. vertical compression of $\sqrt{x}$ and reflected across the x-axis; $D = \{x \mid x \geq 0\}$, $R = \{y \mid y \leq 0\}$

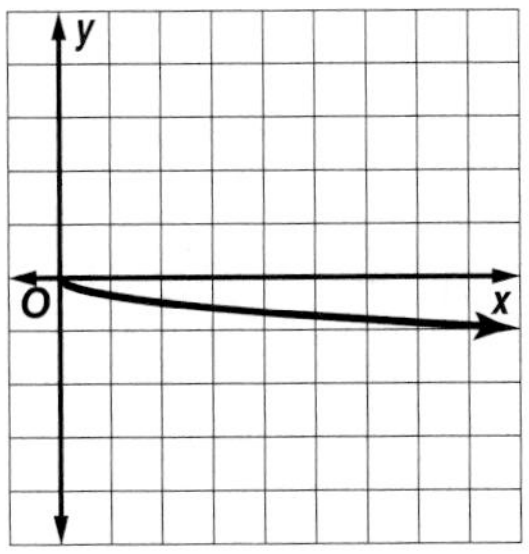

17. vertical stretch of $\sqrt{x}$; $D = \{x \mid x \geq 0\}$, $R = \{y \mid y \geq 0\}$

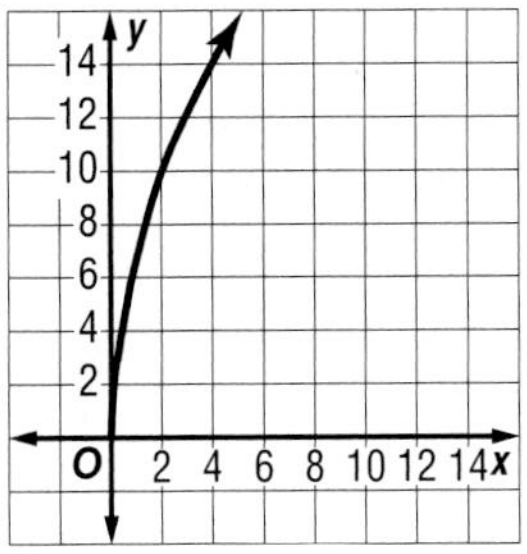

18. vertical compression of $\sqrt{x}$ and reflected across the x-axis; $D = \{x \mid x \geq 0\}$, $R = \{y \mid y \leq 0\}$

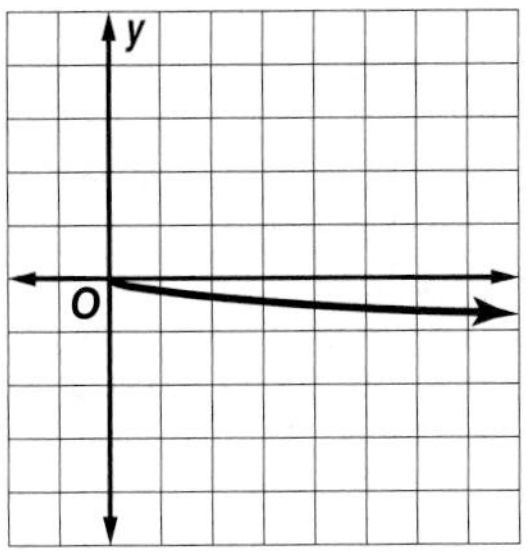

19. reflected across the x-axis; $D = \{x \mid x \geq 0\}$, $R = \{y \mid y \leq 0\}$

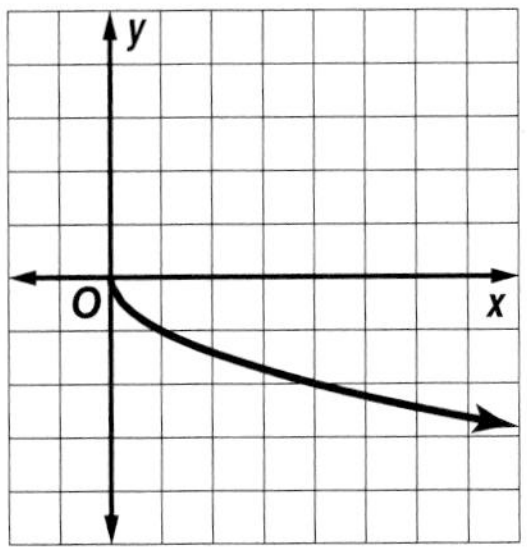

20. vertical compression of $\sqrt{x}$ and reflected across x-axis; $D = \{x \mid x \geq 0\}$, $R = \{y \mid y \leq 0\}$

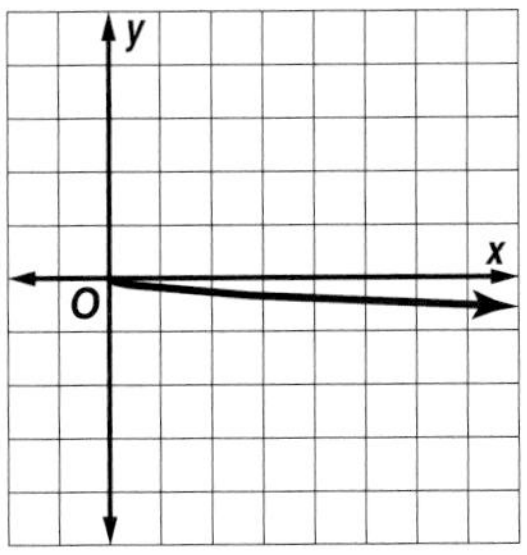

21. vertical stretch of $\sqrt{x}$ and reflected across the x-axis; $D = \{x \mid x \geq 0\}$, $R = \{y \mid y \leq 0\}$

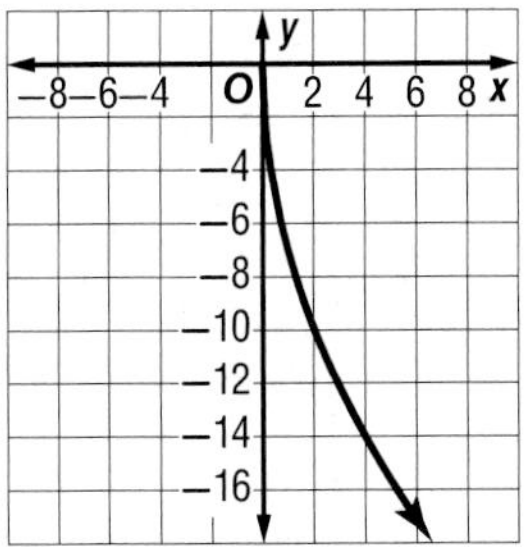

22. translated up 2; $D = \{x \mid x \geq 0\}$, $R = \{y \mid y \geq 2\}$

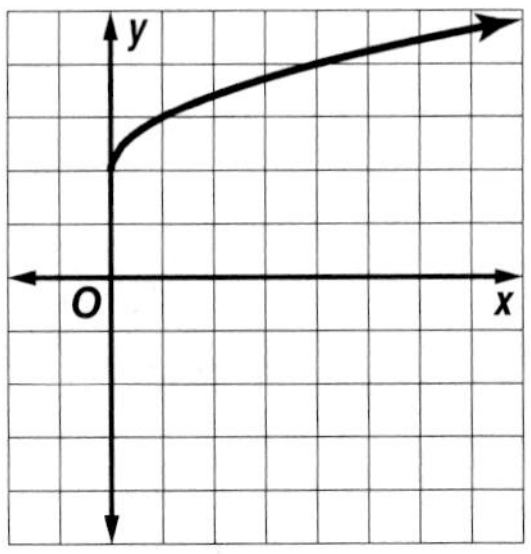

23. translated up 4; $D = \{x \mid x \geq 0\}$, $R = \{y \mid y \geq 4\}$

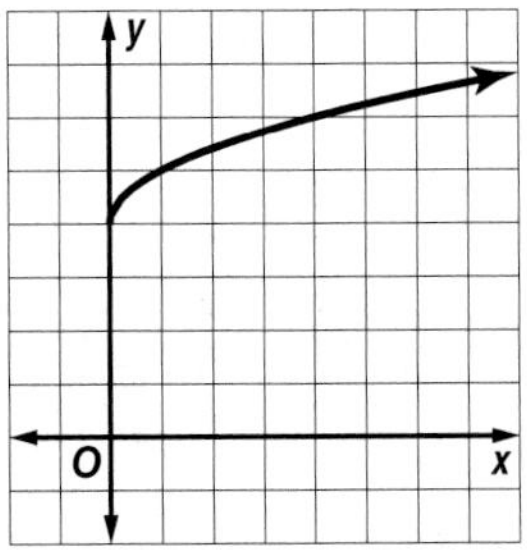

24. translated down 1; $D = \{x \mid x \geq 0\}$, $R = \{y \mid y \geq -1\}$

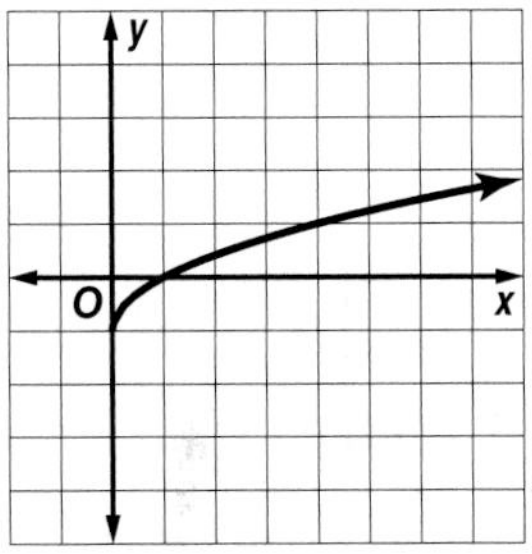

25. translated down 3; $D = \{x \mid x \geq 0\}$, $R = \{y \mid y \geq -3\}$

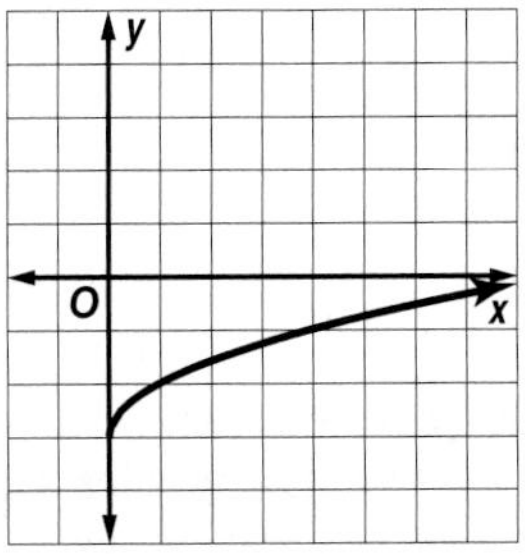

26. translated up 1.5; $D = \{x \mid x \geq 0\}$, $R = \{y \mid y \geq 1.5\}$

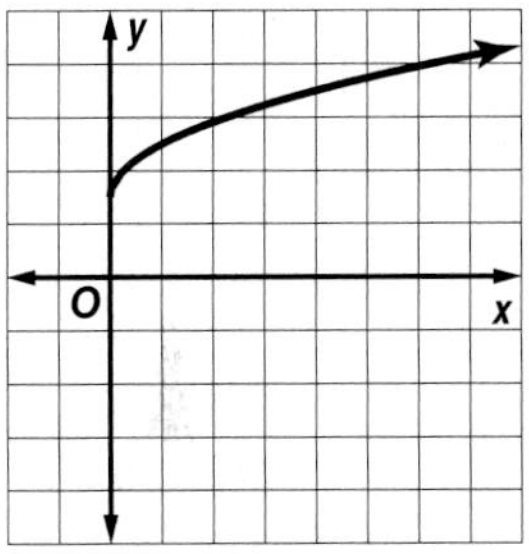

27. translated down 2.5; $D = \{x \mid x \geq 0\}$, $R = \{y \mid y \geq -2.5\}$

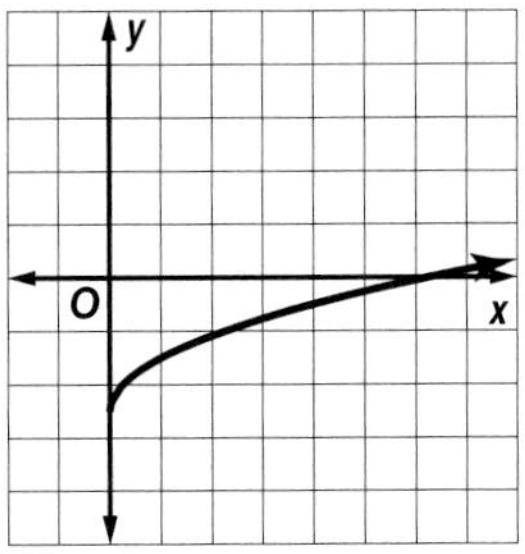

28. translated left 4; $D = \{x \mid x \geq -4\}$, $R = \{y \mid y \geq 0\}$

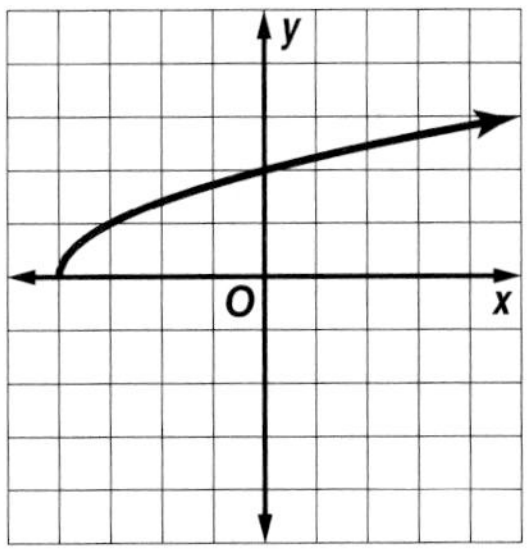

29. translated right 4; D = $\{x \mid x \geq 4\}$, R = $\{y \mid y \geq 0\}$

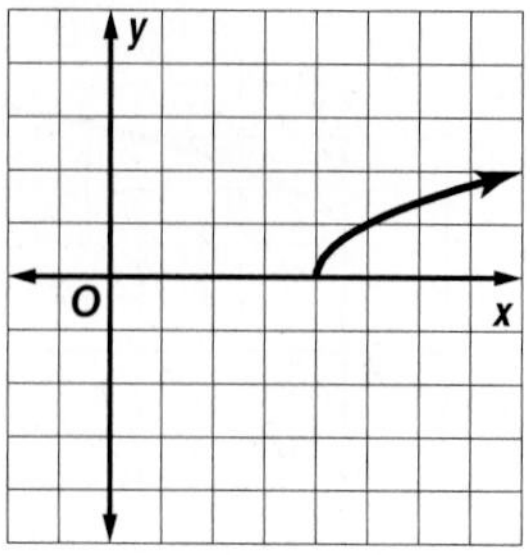

30. translated left 1; D = $\{x \mid x \geq -1\}$, R = $\{y \mid y \geq 0\}$

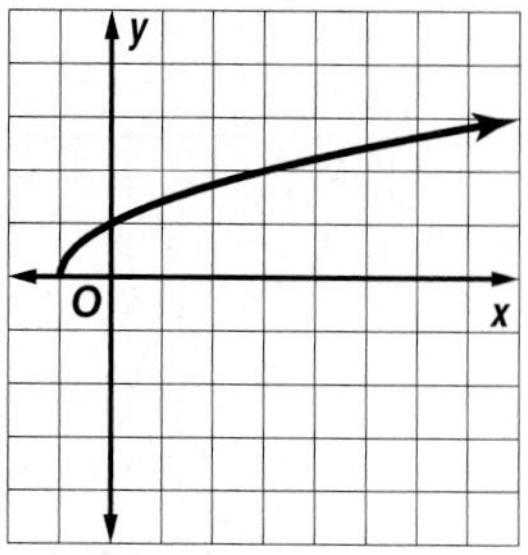

31. translated right 0.5; D = $\{x \mid x \geq 0.5\}$, R = $\{y \mid y \geq 0\}$

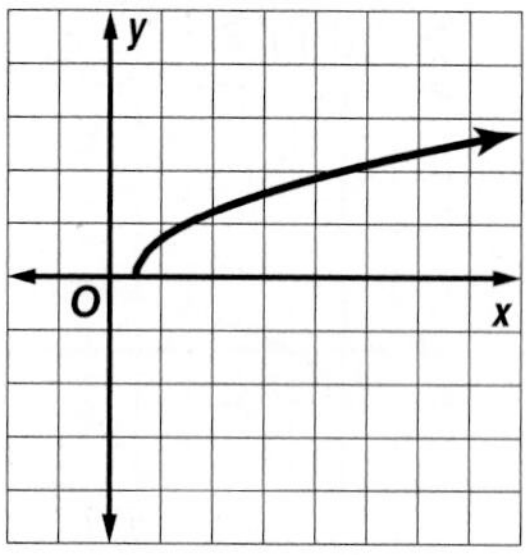

32. translated left 5; D = $\{x \mid x \geq -5\}$, R = $\{y \mid y \geq 0\}$

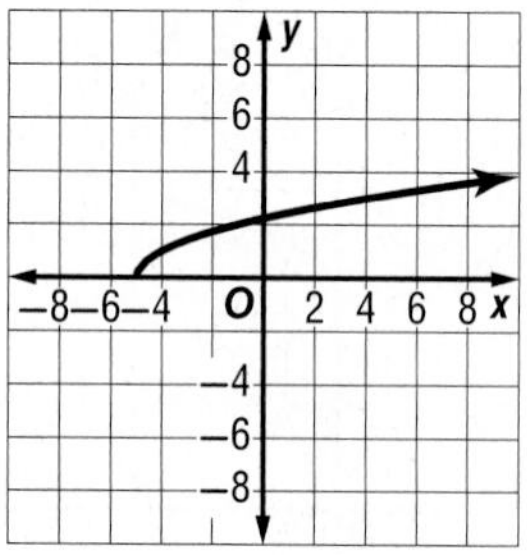

33. translated right 1.5; D = $\{x \mid x \geq 1.5\}$, R = $\{y \mid y \geq 0\}$

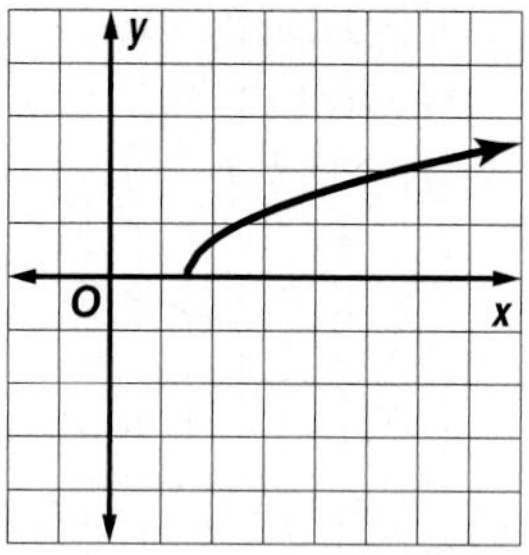

35. vertical stretch of $y = \sqrt{x}$, reflected across the x-axis, and translated up 2; D = $\{x \mid x \geq 0\}$, R = $\{y \mid y \leq 2\}$

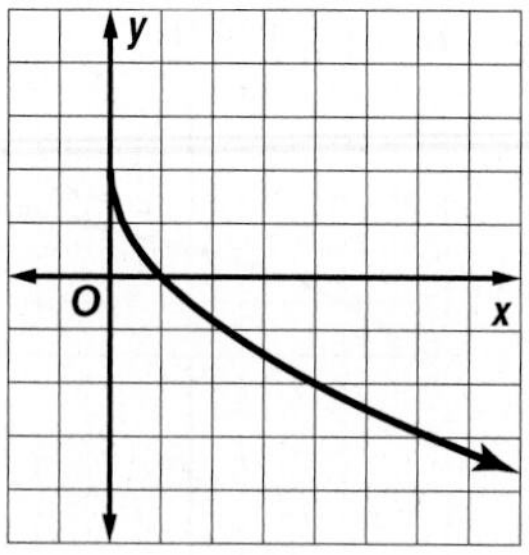

36. vertical stretch of $y = \sqrt{x}$, reflected across the x-axis, and translated down 2; D = $\{x \mid x \geq 0\}$, R = $\{y \mid y \leq -3\}$

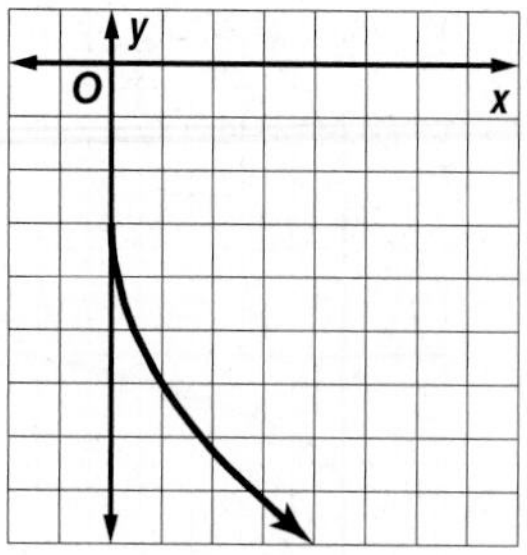

37. vertical compression of $y = \sqrt{x}$ and translated left 2; D = $\{x \mid x \geq -2\}$, R = $\{y \mid y \geq 0\}$

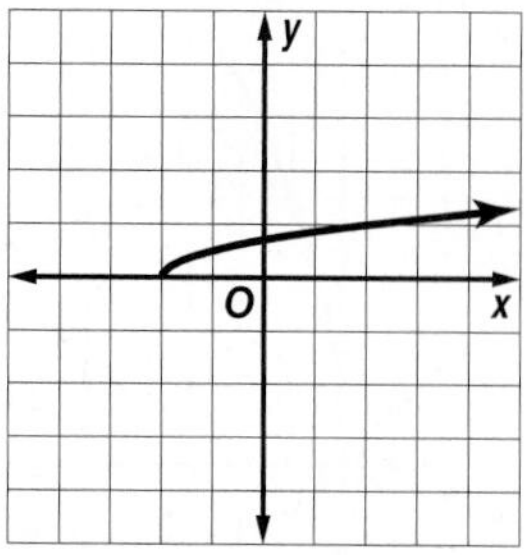

38. reflected across the x-axis and translated right 1; D = $\{x \mid x \geq 1\}$, R = $\{y \mid y \leq 0\}$

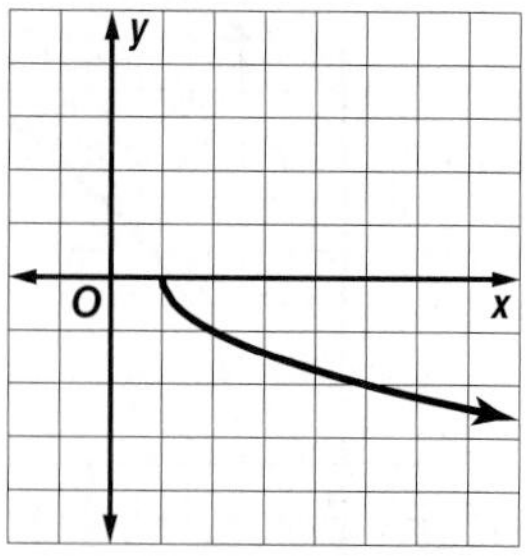

39. vertical compression of $y = \sqrt{x}$ and translated up 2 and right 1; D = $\{x \mid x \geq 1\}$, R = $\{y \mid y \geq 2\}$

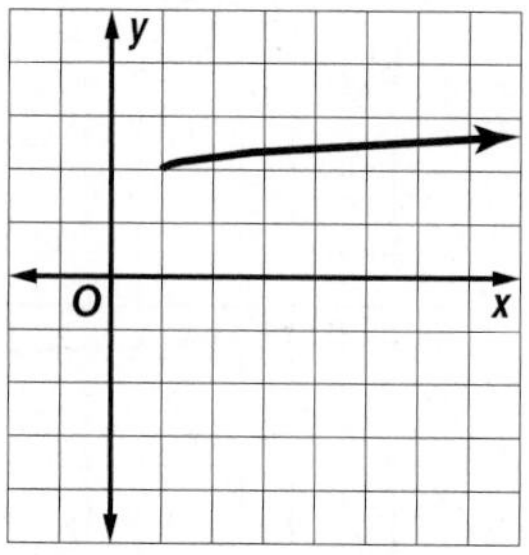

40. vertical compression of $y = \sqrt{x}$ and translated up 1 and right 2; D = $\{x \mid x \geq 2\}$, R = $\{y \mid y \geq 1\}$

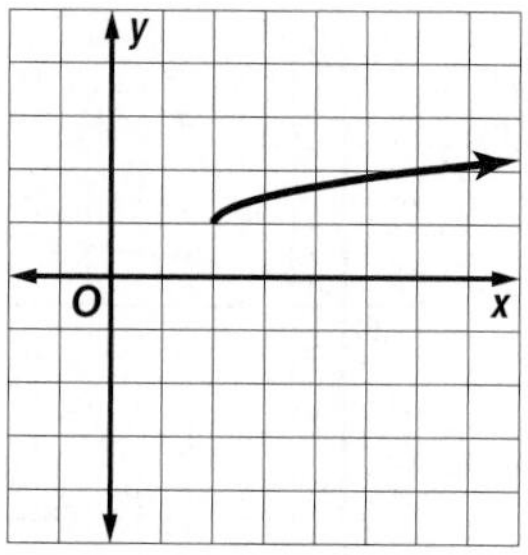

42a.

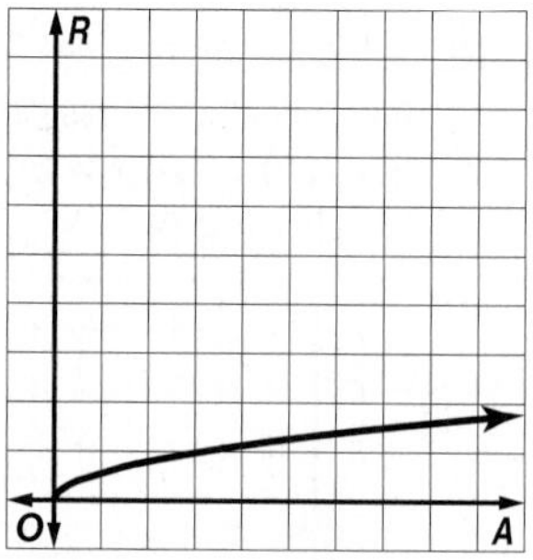

44c.

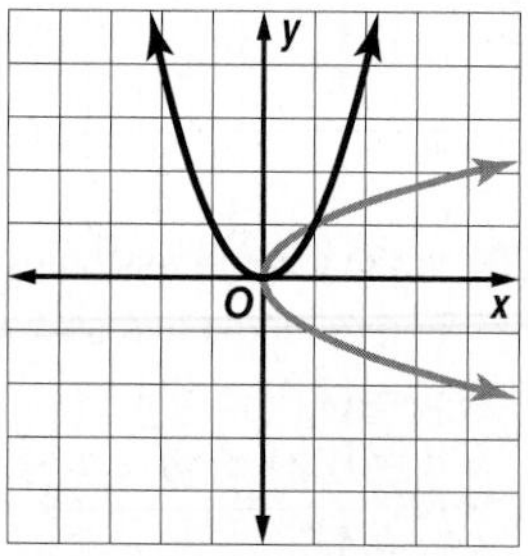

44d.

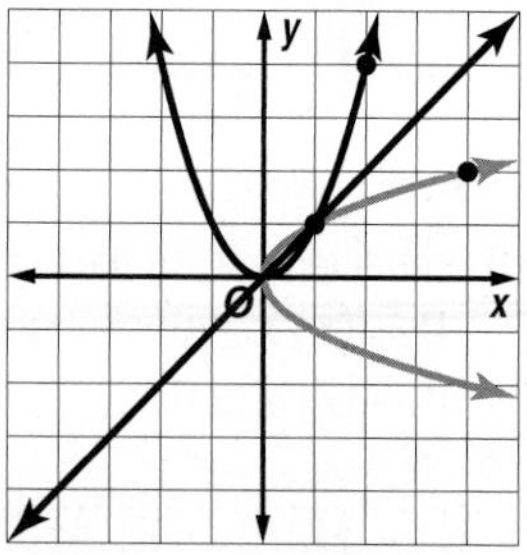

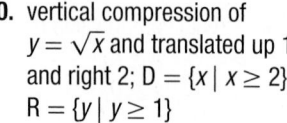

44e. The combined graphs of the square root functions are the same size and shape as the parabola. It is a reflection in the line $y = x$.

45. False; sample answer: The domain of $y = \sqrt{x + 3}$ includes -1, -2, and -3.

46. False; sample answer: -6 and -5 are in the range of $y = \sqrt{x} - 6$.

47.

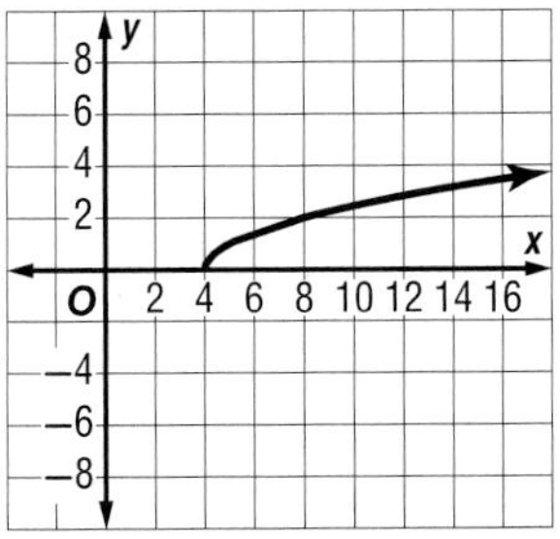

49. $y = \sqrt{x} + 3$; it is a translation of $y = \sqrt{x}$; the other equations represent vertical streches or compressions.

50. Sample answer: $y = -3\sqrt{x - 1}$.

51. The value of a is negative. For the function to have negative y-values, the value of a must be negative.

52. Both functions are translations of the square root function, but $f(x) = \sqrt{x} + 2$ is a translation 2 units up and $g(x) = \sqrt{x + 2}$ is a translation 2 units to the left.

64a.

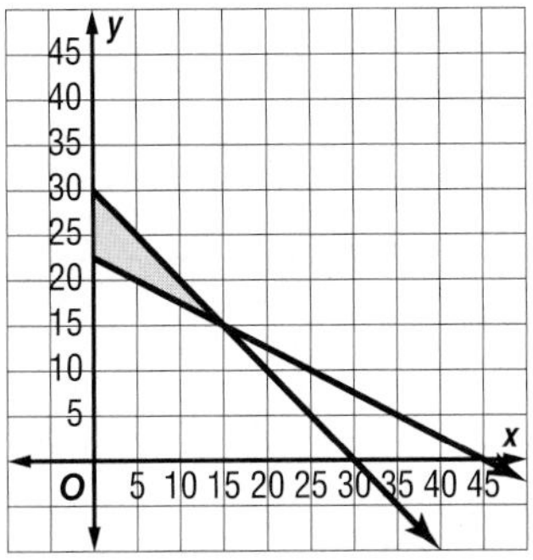

64b. Sample answer: walk: 15 min, jog: 15 min; walk: 10 min, jog: 20 min; walk: 5 min, jog: 25 min

Page 611, Extend 10-1

1. $\{x \mid x \geq 1\}, \{y \mid y \geq 0\}$; moved right 1

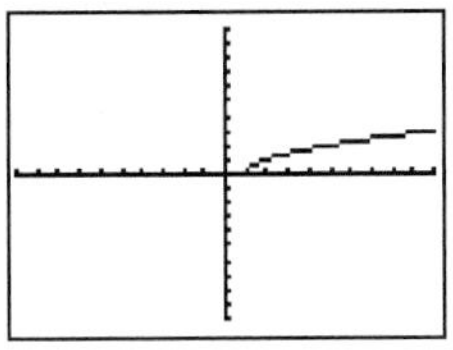

[−10, 10] scl: 1 by
[−10, 10] scl: 1

2. $\{x \mid x \geq -3\}, \{y \mid y \geq 0\}$; moved left 3

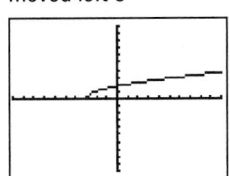

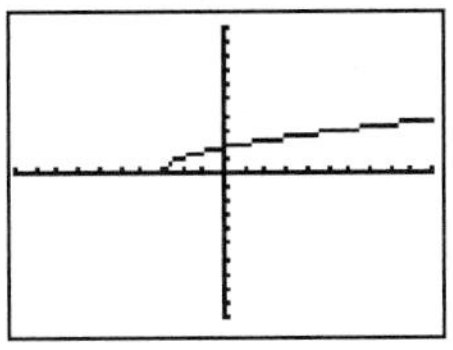

[−10, 10] scl: 1 by
[−10, 10] scl: 1

3. $\{x \mid x \geq 0\}, \{y \mid y \geq -2\}$; moved down 2

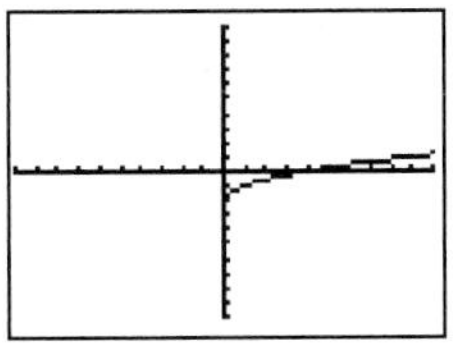

[−10, 10] scl: 1 by
[−10, 10] scl: 1

4. $\{x \mid x \leq 0\}, \{y \mid y \geq 0\}$; reflected over y-axis

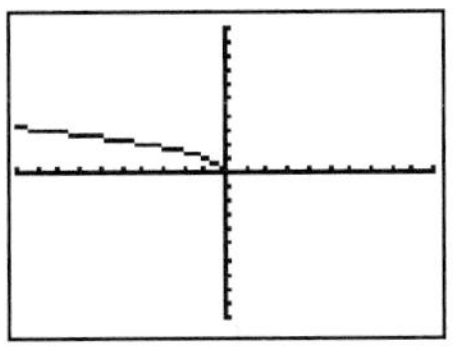

[−10, 10] scl: 1 by
[−10, 10] scl: 1

5. $\{x \mid x \geq 0\}, \{y \mid y \leq 0\}$; reflected across x-axis

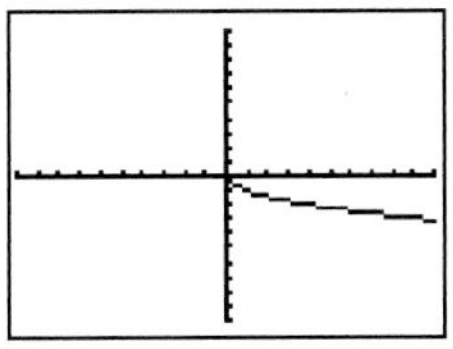

[−10, 10] scl: 1 by
[−10, 10] scl: 1

6. $\{x \mid x \geq 0\}, \{y \mid y \geq 0\}$; vertical stretch of $y = \sqrt{x}$

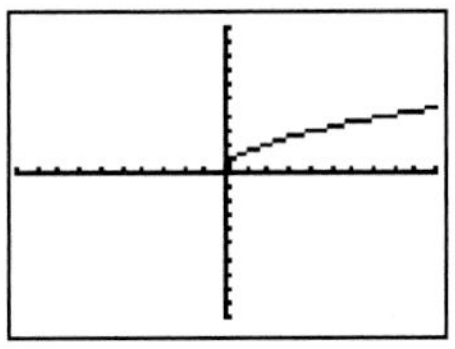

[−10, 10] scl: 1 by
[−10, 10] scl: 1

7. $\{x \mid x \leq 2\}, \{y \mid y \geq 0\}$; moved right 2 and reflected across the y-axis

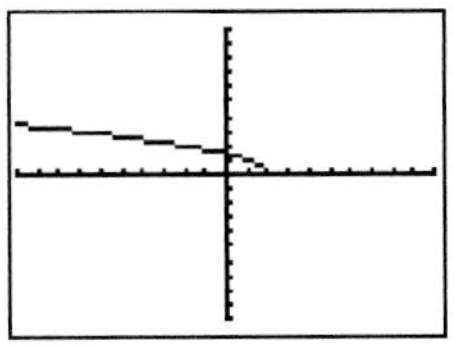

[−10, 10] scl: 1 by
[−10, 10] scl: 1

8. $\{x \mid x \geq 3\}, \{y \mid y \geq 2\}$; moved right 3 and up 2

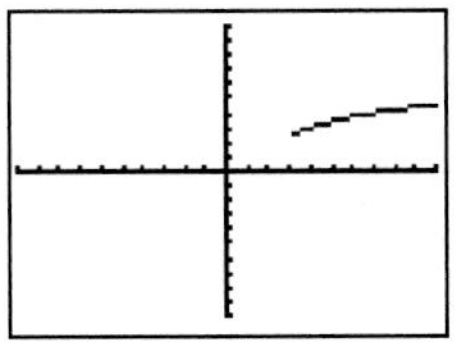

[−10, 10] scl: 1 by
[−10, 10] scl: 1

Pages 616–617, Lesson 10-2

56.

$ax^2 + bx + c = 0$	Original equation
$x^2 + \frac{b}{a}x + \frac{c}{a} = 0$	Divide each side by a.
$x^2 + \frac{b}{a}x = -\frac{c}{a}$	Subtract $\frac{c}{a}$ from each side.
$x^2 + \frac{b}{a}x + \frac{b^2}{4a^2} = -\frac{c}{a} + \frac{b^2}{4a^2}$	Complete the square.
$\left(x + \frac{b}{2a}\right)^2 = \frac{-4ac + b^2}{4a^2}$	Factor $x^2 + \frac{b}{a}x + \frac{b^2}{4a^2}$.
$\left\lvert x + \frac{b}{2a} \right\rvert = \sqrt{\frac{b^2 - 4ac}{4a^2}}$	Take the square root of each side.
$x + \frac{b}{2a} = \pm\sqrt{\frac{b^2 - 4ac}{4a^2}}$	Remove the absolute value symbols and insert $\pm$.
$x + \frac{b}{2a} = \pm\sqrt{\frac{b^2 - 4ac}{4a^2}}$	Quotient Property of Square Roots
$x + \frac{b}{2a} = \pm\sqrt{\frac{b^2 - 4ac}{4a^2}}$	$\sqrt{4a^2} = 2a$
$x = \frac{-b \pm \sqrt{b^2 - 4ac}}{2a}$	Subtract $\frac{b}{2a}$ from each side.

62. vertical stretch of $y = \sqrt{x}$ and translated down 1; $D = \{x \mid x \geq 0\}$, $R = \{y \mid y \geq -1\}$

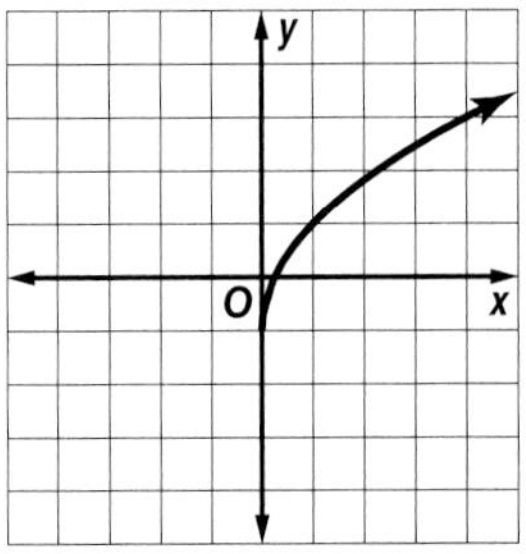

63. vertical compression of $y = \sqrt{x}$, $D = \{x \mid x \geq 0\}$, $R = \{y \mid y \geq 0\}$

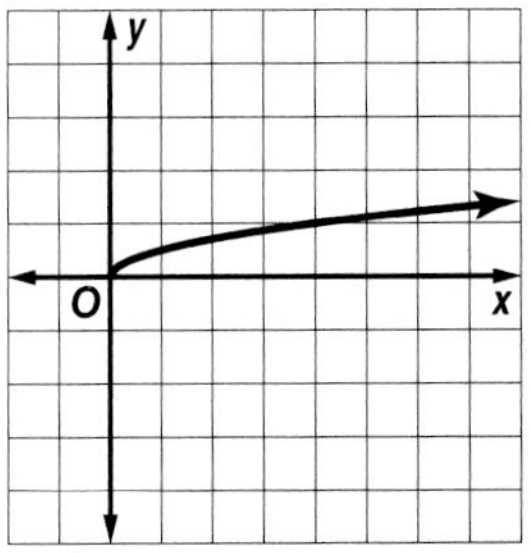

64. stretched vertically and translated left 2; D = $\{x \mid x \geq -2\}$, R = $\{y \mid y \geq 0\}$

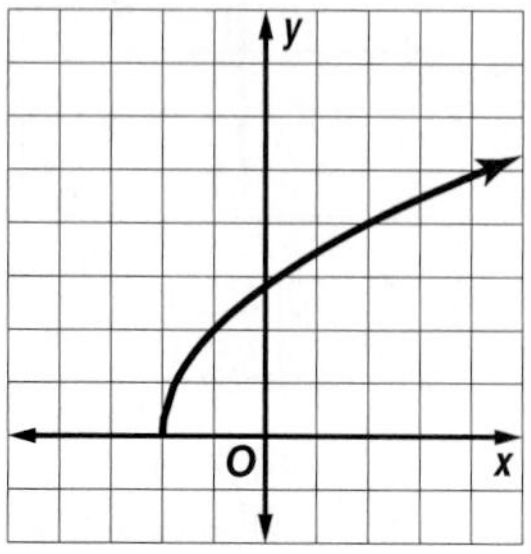

65. reflected across the x-axis and translated left 1; D = $\{x \mid x \geq -1\}$, R = $\{y \mid y \leq 0\}$

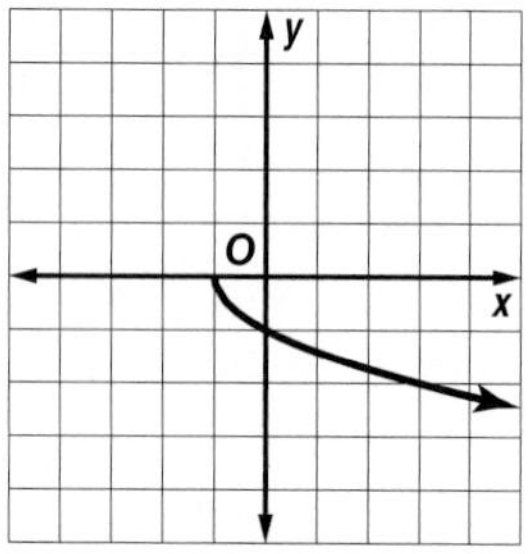

66. stretched vertically, reflected across the x-axis, and translated right 3; D = $\{x \mid x \geq 3\}$, R = $\{y \mid y \leq 0\}$

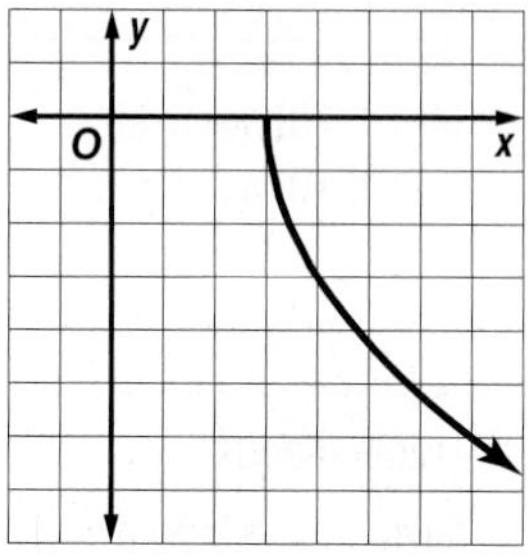

67. stretched vertically, reflected across the x-axis, and translated up 1; D = $\{x \mid x \geq 0\}$, R = $\{y \mid y \leq 1\}$

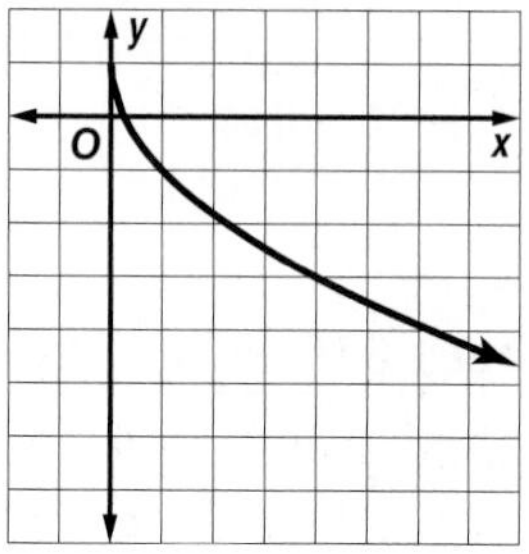

Page 618, Extend 10-2

1. $\left(b^{\frac{1}{n}}\right)^n = b^{\frac{1}{n} \cdot n}$ Power of a Power Property

$= b^1$ or b Simplify.

Therefore, $b^{\frac{1}{n}} = \sqrt[n]{b}$.

2. $b^{\frac{m}{n}} = \sqrt[n]{b^m}$ or $b^{\frac{m}{n}} = \left(\sqrt[n]{b}\right)^m$

$b^{\frac{m}{n}} = \left(b^{\frac{1}{n}}\right)^m$ Power of a Power Property

$= \left(\sqrt[n]{b}\right)^m$ Definition of $b^{\frac{1}{n}}$

or $b^{\frac{m}{n}} = (b^m)^{\frac{1}{n}}$ Power of a Power Property

$= \sqrt[n]{b^m}$ Rational exponents

Page 623, Lesson 10-3

50. stretched vertically; D = $\{x \mid x \geq 0\}$, R = $\{y \mid y \geq 0\}$

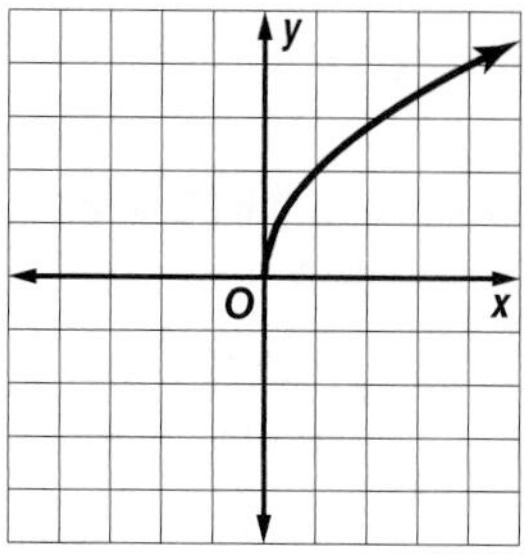

51. stretched vertically, reflected across the x-axis, D = $\{x \mid x \geq 0\}$, R = $\{y \mid y \leq 0\}$

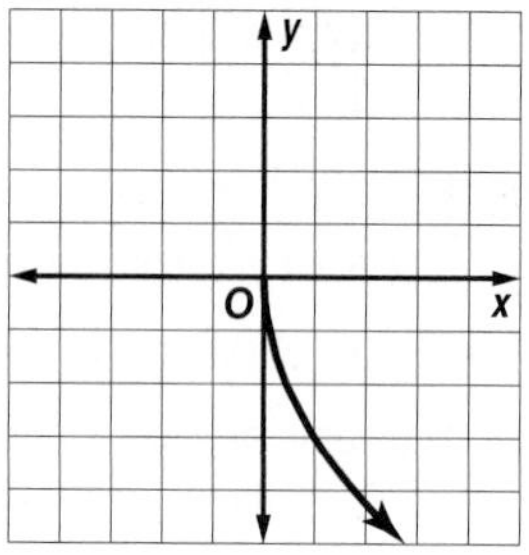

52. translated left 1; D = $\{x \mid x \geq -1\}$, R = $\{y \mid y \geq 0\}$

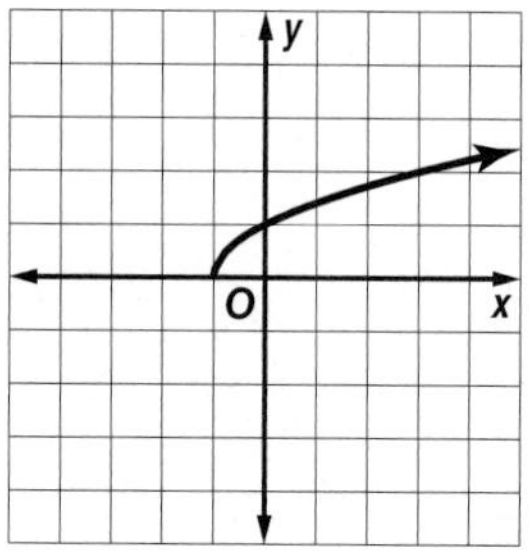

53. translated right 4; D = $\{x \mid x \geq 4\}$, R = $\{y \mid y \geq 0\}$

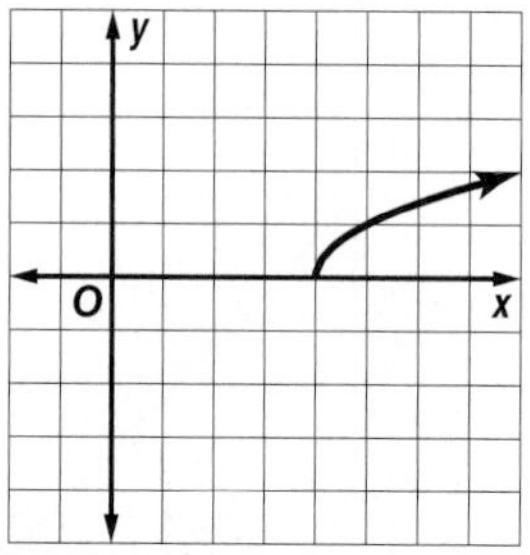

54. translated up 3; D = $\{x \mid x \geq 0\}$, R = $\{y \mid y \geq 3\}$

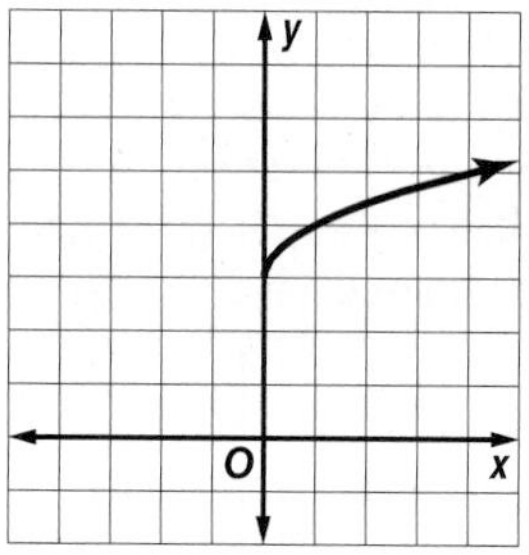

55. translated down 2; D = $\{x \mid x \geq 0\}$, R = $\{y \mid y \geq -2\}$

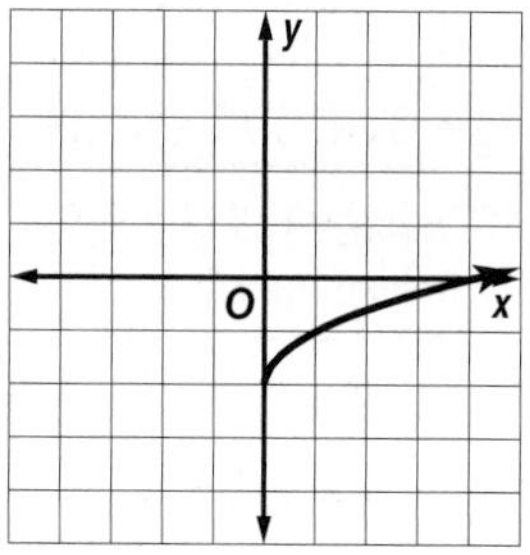

Page 629, Mid-Chapter Quiz

1. stretched vertically; D = $\{x \mid x \geq 0\}$, R = $\{y \mid y \geq 0\}$

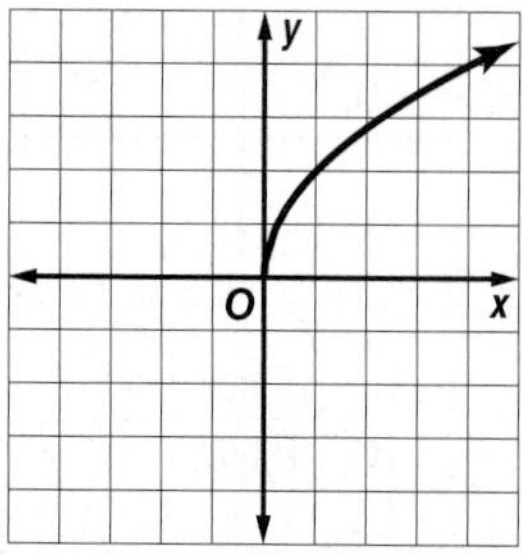

2. vertical stretch of $y = \sqrt{x}$ and reflection across the x-axis D = $\{x \mid x \geq 0\}$, R = $\{y \mid y \leq 0\}$

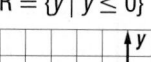

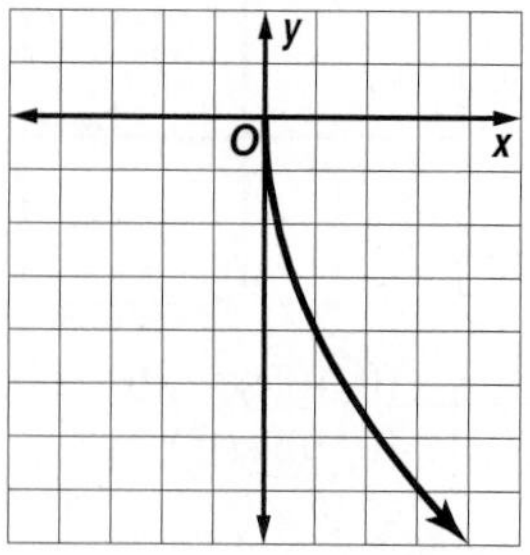

3. compressed vertically;
D = {x | $x \geq 0$},
R = {y | $y \geq 0$}

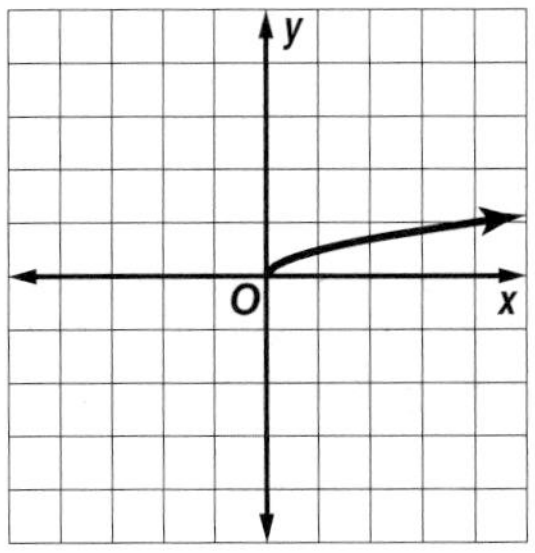

4. translation down 3;
D = {x | $x \geq 0$},
R = {y | $y \geq -3$}

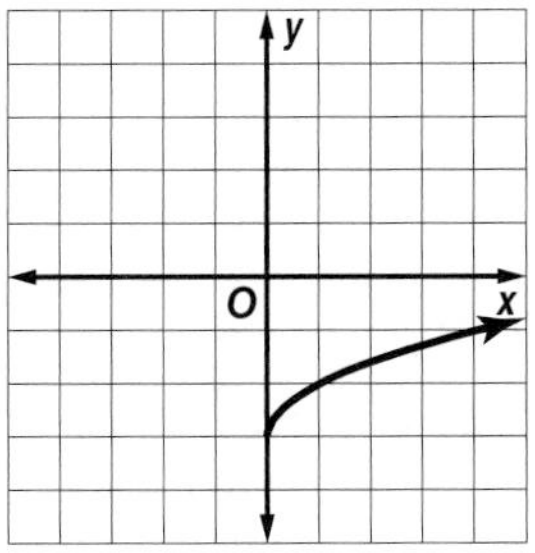

5. translation right 1;
D = {x | $x \geq 1$},
R = {y | $y \geq 0$}

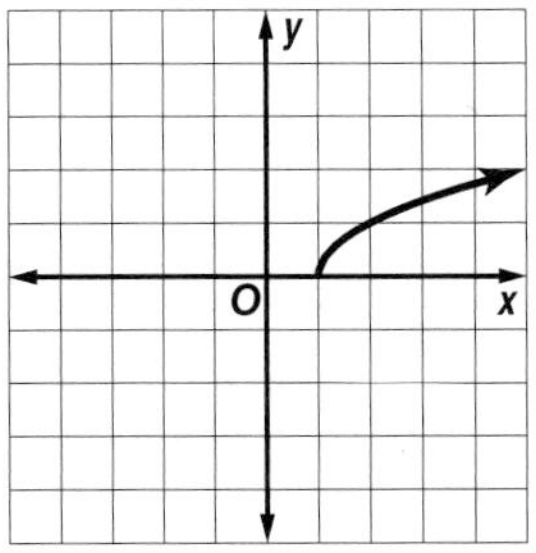

6. stretched vertically and translated right 2;
D = {x | $x \geq 2$},
R = {y | $y \geq 0$}

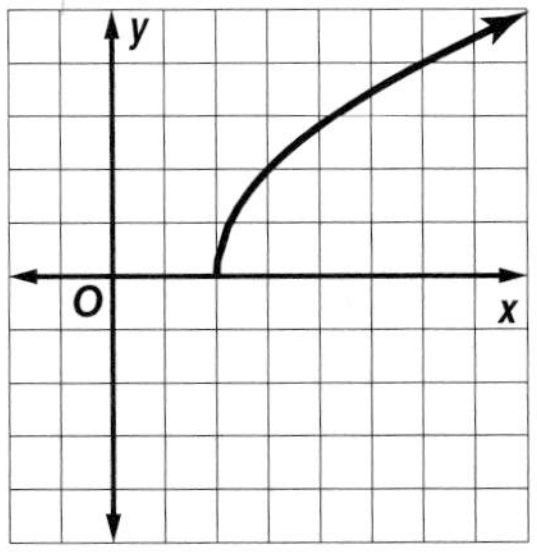

Page 654, Lesson 10-8

50a.

Triangle	Trigonometric Ratios		$\sin^2$	$\cos^2$	$\sin^2 + \cos^2 =$
ABC	$\sin A = \frac{4}{5}$	$\cos A = \frac{3}{5}$	$\sin^2 A = \frac{16}{25}$	$\cos^2 A = \frac{9}{25}$	1
	$\sin C = \frac{3}{5}$	$\cos C = \frac{4}{5}$	$\sin^2 C = \frac{9}{25}$	$\cos^2 C = \frac{16}{25}$	1
JKL	$\sin J = \frac{12}{13}$	$\cos J = \frac{5}{13}$	$\sin^2 J = \frac{144}{169}$	$\cos^2 J = \frac{25}{169}$	1
	$\sin L = \frac{5}{13}$	$\cos L = \frac{12}{13}$	$\sin^2 L = \frac{25}{169}$	$\cos^2 L = \frac{144}{169}$	1
XYZ	$\sin X = \frac{9}{41}$	$\cos X = \frac{40}{41}$	$\sin^2 X = \frac{81}{1681}$	$\cos^2 X = \frac{1600}{1681}$	1
	$\sin Z = \frac{40}{41}$	$\cos Z = \frac{9}{41}$	$\sin^2 Z = \frac{1600}{1681}$	$\cos^2 Z = \frac{81}{1681}$	1

59b. Sample answer: The sum of their squares is 16^2 or 256.

Chapter Planner

Diagnostic Assessment
Quick Check, p. 667

	Explore 11-1 Pacing: 0.5 day	Lesson 11-1 Pacing: 1 day	Explore 11-2 Pacing: 0.5 day
Title	**Graphing Technology Lab: Inverse Variation**	**Inverse Variation**	**Algebra Lab: Reading Rational Expressions**
Objectives	• Collect data to investigate the relationship between volume and pressure.	• Identify and use inverse variations. • Graph inverse variations.	• Read and simplify expressions.
Key Vocabulary		inverse variation product rule	
ILS	8.A.4b	7.B.4	
Multiple Representations			
Lesson Resources	**Materials** • TI–83/84 Plus or other graphing calculator • CBL or other data collection device • syringe • gas pressure sensor	**Chapter 11 Resource Masters** • Study Guide and Intervention, pp. 5–6 AL OL ELL • Skills Practice, p. 7 AL OL ELL • Practice, p. 8 AL OL BL ELL • Word Problem Practice, p. 9 AL OL BL ELL • Enrichment, p. 10 OL BL **Transparencies** • 5-Minute Check Transparency 11-1 AL OL BL ELL **Additional Print Resources** • *Study Notebook* AL OL BL ELL	**Additional Print Resources** • *Teaching Algebra with Manipulatives*, p. 167 AL OL ELL
Technology for Every Lesson	IL Math Online glencoe.com • Extra Examples • Self-Check Quizzes • Personal Tutor • Homework Help	**CD/DVD Resources** IWB INTERACTIVE WHITEBOARD READY IWB StudentWorks Plus IWB Interactive Classroom IWB Diagnostic and Assessment Planner	• TeacherWorks Plus • eSolutions Manual Plus • ExamView Assessment Suite
Math in Motion			Animation
Differentiated Instruction		pp. 673, 676	

KEY: AL Approaching Level OL On Level BL Beyond Level ELL English Learners

Suggested Pacing			
Time Periods	Instruction	Review & Assessment	Total
45-minute	11	2	13
90-minute	7	1	8

Rational Functions and Equations

Lesson 11-2 Pacing: 1 day	Lesson 11-3 Pacing: 1 day	Extend 11-3 Pacing: 0.5 day	Lesson 11-4 Pacing: 1.5 days
Rational Functions	**Simplifying Rational Expressions**	**Graphing Technology Lab: Simplifying Rational Expressions**	**Multiplying and Dividing Rational Expressions**
• Identify excluded values. • Identify and use asymptotes to graph rational functions.	• Identify values excluded from the domain of a rational expression. • Simplify rational expressions.	• Use a graphing calculator to simplify rational expressions, and verify solutions and excluded values.	• Multiply rational expressions. • Divide rational expressions.
rational function excluded value asymptote	rational expression		
8.C.4b	7.A.4b, 7.B.4	8.B.4a	7.A.4b
Chapter 11 Resource Masters • Study Guide and Intervention, pp. 11–12 AL OL ELL • Skills Practice, p. 13 AL OL ELL • Practice, p. 14 AL OL BL ELL • Word Problem Practice, p. 15 AL OL BL ELL • Enrichment, p. 16 OL BL • Quiz 1, p. 57 AL OL BL ELL **Transparencies** • 5-Minute Check Transparency 11-2 AL OL BL ELL **Additional Print Resources** • *Study Notebook* AL OL BL ELL	**Chapter 11 Resource Masters** • Study Guide and Intervention, pp. 17–18 AL OL ELL • Skills Practice, p. 19 AL OL ELL • Practice, p. 20 AL OL BL ELL • Word Problem Practice, p. 21 AL OL BL ELL • Enrichment, p. 22 OL BL **Transparencies** • 5-Minute Check Transparency 11-3 AL OL BL ELL **Additional Print Resources** • *Study Notebook* AL OL BL ELL	**Materials** • TI-83/84 Plus or other graphing calculator	**Chapter 11 Resource Masters** • Study Guide and Intervention, pp. 23–24 AL OL ELL • Skills Practice, Practice, pp. 25–26 AL OL BL ELL • Word Problem Practice, p. 27 AL OL BL ELL • Enrichment, p. 28 OL BL • Spreadsheet Activity, p. 29 AL OL BL ELL • Quiz 2, p. 57 AL OL BL ELL **Transparencies** • 5-Minute Check Transparency 11-4 AL OL BL ELL **Additional Print Resources** • *Study Notebook* AL OL BL ELL
	IL Math Online glencoe.com • Extra Examples • Self-Check Quizzes • Personal Tutor • Homework Help	**CD/DVD Resources** IWB INTERACTIVE WHITEBOARD READY IWB StudentWorks Plus IWB Interactive Classroom IWB Diagnostic and Assessment Planner	• TeacherWorks Plus • eSolutions Manual Plus • ExamView Assessment Suite
	Interactive Lab		
pp. 679, 683	pp. 686, 690		pp. 694, 698

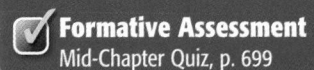

Formative Assessment
Mid-Chapter Quiz, p. 699

Chapter Planner

	Lesson 11-5 Pacing: 1 day	Lesson 11-6 Pacing: 2 days	Lesson 11-7 Pacing: 1 day	Lesson 11-8 Pacing: 1 day
Title	**Dividing Polynomials**	**Adding and Subtracting Rational Expressions**	**Mixed Expressions and Complex Fractions**	**Rational Equations**
Objectives	• Divide a polynomial by a monomial. • Divide a polynomial by a binomial.	• Add and subtract rational expressions with like denominators. • Add and subtract rational expressions with unlike denominators.	• Simplify mixed expressions. • Simplify complex fractions.	• Solve rational equations. • Use rational equations to solve problems.
Key Vocabulary		least common multiple (LCM) least common denominator (LCD)	mixed expression complex fraction	rational equation extraneous solution work and rate problems
ILS	7.A.4b, 8.A.4b	8.A.4b	7.A.4b, 7.B.4	8.C.4b
Multiple Representations	p. 704			
Lesson Resources	**Chapter 11 Resource Masters** • Study Guide and Intervention, pp. 30–31 AL OL ELL • Skills Practice, p. 32 AL OL ELL • Practice, p. 33 AL OL BL ELL • Word Problem Practice, p. 34 AL OL BL ELL • Enrichment, p. 35 OL BL **Transparencies** • 5-Minute Check Transparency 11-5 AL OL BL ELL **Additional Print Resources** • *Study Notebook* AL OL BL ELL • *Teaching Algebra with Manipulatives*, pp. 168–170 AL OL ELL	**Chapter 11 Resource Masters** • Study Guide and Intervention, pp. 36–37 AL OL ELL • Skills Practice, p. 38 AL OL ELL • Practice, p. 39 AL OL BL ELL • Word Problem Practice, p. 40 AL OL BL ELL • Enrichment, p. 41 OL BL • Quiz 3, p. 58 AL OL BL ELL **Transparencies** • 5-Minute Check Transparency 11-6 AL OL BL ELL **Additional Print Resources** • *Study Notebook* AL OL BL ELL	**Chapter 11 Resource Masters** • Study Guide and Intervention, pp. 42–43 AL OL ELL • Skills Practice, p. 44 AL OL ELL • Practice, p. 45 AL OL BL ELL • Word Problem Practice, p. 46 AL OL BL ELL • Enrichment, p. 47 OL BL **Transparencies** • 5-Minute Check Transparency 11-7 AL OL BL ELL **Additional Print Resources** • *Study Notebook* AL OL BL ELL	**Chapter 11 Resource Masters** • Study Guide and Intervention, pp. 48–49 AL OL ELL • Skills Practice, Practice, Word Problem Practice, pp. 50–52 AL OL BL ELL • Enrichment, p. 53 OL BL • Graphing Calculator Activity, p. 54 OL • Quiz 4, p. 58 AL OL BL ELL **Transparencies** • 5-Minute Check Transparency 11-8 AL OL BL ELL **Additional Print Resources** • *Study Notebook* AL OL BL ELL • *Teaching Algebra with Manipulatives*, p. 170 AL OL ELL
Technology for Every Lesson	IL Math Online glencoe.com • Extra Examples • Personal Tutor • Self-Check Quizzes • Homework Help	**CD/DVD Resources** IWB INTERACTIVE WHITEBOARD READY IWB StudentWorks Plus IWB Interactive Classroom IWB Diagnostic and Assessment Planner	• TeacherWorks Plus • eSolutions Manual Plus • ExamView Assessment Suite	
Math in Motion	Animation			Animation
Differentiated Instruction	pp. 701, 705	pp. 709, 713	pp. 716, 719	pp. 723, 726

KEY: AL Approaching Level OL On Level BL Beyond Level ELL English Learners

Summative Assessment
- Study Guide and Review, pp. 727–730
- Practice Test, p. 731

Professional Development

Targeted professional development has been articulated throughout *Algebra 1.* More quality, customized professional development is available from McGraw-Hill Professional Development. Visit glencoe.com for details on each product.

- **Online Lessons** emphasize the strategies and techniques used to teach Algebra 2. Includes streaming video, interactive pages, and online tools.
- **Video Workshops** allow mentors, coaches, or leadership personnel to facilitate on-site workshops on educational strategies in mathematics and mathematical concepts.
- **MHPD Online** (www.mhpdonline.com) offers online professional development with video clips of instructional strategies, links, student activities, and news and issues in education.
- **Teaching Today** (teachingtoday.glencoe.com) gives secondary teachers practical strategies and materials that inspire excellence and innovation in teaching.

What the Research Says...

Collis (1976) describes the use of the reciprocal strategy as involving a relatively complex system. Students often mistakenly apply the simpler inverse strategy when the reciprocal strategy is essential.

- Multiplying by the LCD (Lesson 11-8) is an example of using the reciprocal strategy to solve a rational equation.
- Students frequently make the error of multiplying only one term in a rational equation by the LCD (the inverse strategy). They may need to be reminded that every term must be multiplied by the LCD in order to solve it.

  [Source: Collis, K.F. (1976). "Mathematical Thinking in Children," in Ved P. Varma and Phillip Williams (Eds.) *Piaget, Psychology and Education,* Itasca, IL, F.E. Peacock, pp. 144–154.]

NOTES:

Assessment and Intervention

SE = Student Edition, **TE** = Teacher Edition, **CRM** = Chapter Resource Masters

	Diagnosis	Prescription
Diagnostic Assessment	**Beginning Chapter 11**	
	Get Ready for Chapter 11 **SE**, p. 667	Response to Intervention **TE**, p. 667
	Beginning Every Lesson	
	Then, Now, Why? **SE** 5-Minute Check Transparencies	Chapter 0 **SE**, pp. P1 through P45 Concepts and Skills Bank **SE**, pp. 857–867 *Quick Review Math Handbook*
Formative Assessment	**During/After Every Lesson**	
	Check Your Progress **SE**, every example Check Your Understanding **SE** H.O.T. Problems **SE** Spiral Review **SE** Additional Examples **TE** Watch Out! **TE** Step 4, Assess **TE** Chapter 11 Quizzes **CRM**, pp. 57–58 Self-Check Quizzes glencoe.com	**Tier 1 Intervention** Concepts and Skills Bank **SE**, pp. 857–867 Skills Practice **CRM**, Ch. 1–11 glencoe.com **Tier 2 Intervention** Differentiated Instruction **TE** Study Guide and Intervention Masters **CRM**, Ch. 1–11 *Quick Review Math Handbook* **Tier 3 Intervention** *Math Triumphs, Alg. 1*
	Mid-Chapter	
	Mid-Chapter Quiz **SE**, p. 669 Mid-Chapter Test **CRM**, p. 59 ExamView Assessment Suite	**Tier 1 Intervention** Concepts and Skills Bank **SE**, pp. 857–867 Skills Practice **CRM**, Ch. 1–11 glencoe.com **Tier 2 Intervention** Study Guide and Intervention Masters **CRM**, Ch. 1–11 *Quick Review Math Handbook* **Tier 3 Intervention** *Math Triumphs, Alg. 1*
	Before Chapter Test	
	Chapter Study Guide and Review **SE**, pp. 727–730 Practice Test **SE**, p. 731 Standardized Test Practice **SE**, pp. 732–735 Chapter Test glencoe.com Standardized Test Practice glencoe.com Vocabulary Review glencoe.com ExamView Assessment Suite	**Tier 1 Intervention** Concepts and Skills Bank **SE**, pp. 857–867 Skills Practice **CRM**, Ch. 1–11 glencoe.com **Tier 2 Intervention** Study Guide and Intervention Masters **CRM**, Ch. 1–11 *Quick Review Math Handbook* **Tier 3 Intervention** *Math Triumphs, Alg. 1*
Summative Assessment	**After Chapter 11**	
	Multiple-Choice Tests, Forms 1, 2A, 2B **CRM**, pp. 61–66 Free-Response Tests, Forms 2C, 2D, 3 **CRM**, pp. 67–72 Vocabulary Test **CRM**, p. 60 Extended Response Test **CRM**, p. 73 Standardized Test Practice **CRM**, pp. 74–76 ExamView Assessment Suite	Study Guide and Intervention Masters **CRM**, Ch. 1–11 *Quick Review Math Handbook* glencoe.com

Differentiated Instruction

Option 1 Reaching All Learners AL OL BL ELL

SOCIAL Have students work in groups. Assign each student a polynomial division problem. Tell the students to study their problems for a few minutes to decide on a method for finding the quotient. Then, ask each student to "teach" the group how to find the quotient. Have groups discuss whether the method "taught" is correct.

AUDITORY In pairs or small groups, students work on Exercise 18 on p. 724 and talk about each step of the solution as they show their work. Have them check their solutions and discuss why one of the solutions is extraneous.

KINESTHETIC Average speed r is given by the equation $r = \frac{d}{t}$, where d is the distance traveled and t is the time it takes to travel the distance. Ask students to choose a distance like 50 yards that people are willing to run. Once they have chosen the distance, ask them to create a graph, perform an experiment with the given distance, and then determine whether the graph accurately depicts the performance of their participants. Analyses should be performed to show how the data points relate to the graph.

Option 2 Approaching Level AL

Have students write division problems involving rational expressions on note cards, pieces of scrap paper, or any other item that they can manipulate. Then have students physically "flip" the fractions to multiply by the reciprocal. The act of "flipping" the fractions will help cement the concept in students' minds.

Option 3 English Learners ELL

Place students in small groups. Have students take turns reading example problems to the group. As one student reads, have the other group members record the problem. Then have all members of the group discuss the procedures for solving the problem.

Option 4 Beyond Level BL

Ask students to research a method of dividing polynomials known as synthetic division. Then ask students to compare this method to using the long division method. An example below is shown for $(3x^3 - 5x^2 - 6x - 2) \div (x - 3)$.

Long Division:

$$\begin{array}{r} 3x^2 + 4x + 6 \\ x - 3\overline{)3x^3 - 5x^2 - 6x - 2} \\ \underline{3x^3 - 9x^2} \qquad\qquad \\ 4x^2 - 6x \qquad \\ \underline{4x^2 - 12x} \qquad \\ 6x - 2 \\ \underline{6x - 18} \\ 16 \end{array}$$

Synthetic Division

$$\begin{array}{r|rrrr} 3 & 3 & -5 & -6 & -2 \\ & & 9 & 12 & 18 \\ \hline & 3 & 4 & 6 & 16 \end{array}$$

Focus on Mathematical Content

Vertical Alignment

Before Chapter 11

Related Topics before Pre-Algebra

- identify the greatest common factor of a set of positive integers
- convert measures within the same measurement system

Related Topics from Pre-Algebra

- use appropriate operations to solve problems involving rational numbers

Previous Topics from Algebra 1

- solve problems involving proportional change
- simplify and factor polynomial expressions
- transform and solve equations

Chapter 11

Related Topics from Algebra 1

- analyze data and represent situations involving inverse variation using tables, graphs, or algebraic methods
- identify excluded values from rational expressions and simplify rational expressions
- multiply and divide rational expressions and use dimensional analysis
- divide a polynomial by a monomial or binomial
- add and subtract rational expressions with like and unlike denominators
- solve rational equations and eliminate extraneous roots

After Chapter 11

Preparation for Algebra 2

- use quotients of polynomials to describe the graphs of rational functions
- analyze various representations of rational functions with respect to problem situations
- determine the solutions of rational equations using graphs, tables, and algebraic methods

Lesson-by-Lesson Preview

11-1 Inverse Variation

Some situations in which y increases as x increases are known as *direct variations* (Lesson 3-4). Some situations in which y decreases as x increases, or vice versa, are known as *inverse variations.* Inverse variations can be represented by equations of the form $y = \frac{k}{x}$ or $xy = k$, where $x \neq 0$ and $y \neq 0$. The value of an inverse variation is undefined when $x = 0$.

The *product* rule of inverse variation states that if (x_1, y_1) and (x_2, y_2) are solutions of an inverse variation, then $x_1y_1 = x_2y_2$ because both $x_1y_1 = k$ and $x_2y_2 = k$. The equation $x_1y_1 = x_2y_2$ can be used to solve for missing values of x and y.

11-2 Rational Functions

A rational function is a function of the form $y = \frac{p}{q}$, where the numerator, p, and denominator, q, are both polynomials. Any value that makes the value of q equal to 0 is called an *excluded value* of the rational function and must be excluded from the domain of the function. Depending on the situation represented by a rational function, there may be additional values excluded as well. The graph of a rational function of the form $y = \frac{a}{x - b}$ (where $a \neq 0$), has two asympotes, the line $x = b$ and the line $y = 0$. The graph of the function *appears* to approach these two lines, but in fact, never does.

11-3 Simplifying Rational Expressions

Algebraic fractions that have polynomials for numerators and denominators are called rational expressions. All properties that apply to rational numbers also apply to rational expressions. Because division by 0 is undefined, the polynomial in the denominator cannot be 0.

The numerator and denominator of a simplified rational expression will have no common factors other than 1.

- To simplify rational expressions in which both the numerator and denominator are monomials, divide each by the GCF.
- To simplify rational expressions in which both the numerator and denominator are polynomials, first factor each polynomial and then divide each by the common factors.

11-4 Multiplying and Dividing Rational Expressions

The process of multiplying rational expressions is similar to that of multiplying rational numbers. First, multiply the numerators. Then, multiply the denominators. If either of the rational expressions can be simplified, do so before multiplying.

To divide rational expressions, multiply by the reciprocal of the divisor, just as you would do when dividing rational numbers. Then follow the rules for multiplying rational expressions.

When you multiply or divide fractions or rational expressions that involve units of measure, you can divide by the common units in the same way that you divide by common variables. This process of *dimensional analysis* allows you to convert between units of measure.

11-5 Dividing Polynomials

To divide a polynomial by a monomial, simply divide each term of the polynomial by the monomial.

To divide a polynomial by a binomial, first try to factor the polynomial to see if there is perhaps a common binomial factor. If factoring is not possible, use a division process similar to the one used for dividing whole numbers. Then divide.

Using $(a^3 - 4a) \div (a - 2)$ as an example,

$$\frac{a^3 - 4a}{a - 2} = \frac{a(\cancel{a - 2})(a + 2)}{\cancel{a - 2}} = a^2 + 2a \text{ or}$$

$$\begin{array}{r} a^2 + 2a \\ a - 2\overline{)a^3 + 0a^2 - 4a} \\ \underline{(-)a^3 - 2a^2} \\ 2a^2 - 4a \\ \underline{(-)2a^2 - 4a} \\ 0 \end{array}$$

11-6 Adding and Subtracting Rational Expressions

When adding/subtracting rational expressions with like denominators, add/subtract the numerators and write the sum/difference over the common denominator.

When adding/subtracting rational expressions with unlike denominators, a common denominator must first be found. Use the following steps to add/subtract rational expressions with unlike denominators.

Step 1 Identify the LCD by finding the prime factorization of the denominators. Use each factor the greatest number of times it appears in either of the factorizations.

Step 2 Rewrite each rational expression as an equivalent expression with the LCD as the denominator.

Step 3 Add/subtract.

Step 4 Simplify whenever possible.

11-7 Mixed Expressions and Complex Fractions

A mixed number contains the sum of a whole number and a fraction. Similarly, a *mixed expression* contains the sum of a monomial and a rational expression. To simplify mixed expressions, change them into a single rational expression with the same denominator as the given expression.

A *complex fraction* is a fraction with additional fractions in the numerator, denominator, or both. You can rewrite a complex fraction as a division expression. Divide the numerator of the fraction by the denominator and then write the quotient as a simple fraction.

11-8 Rational Equations

Rational equations are equations that contain rational expressions. If both sides of a rational equation are single fractions, cross products can be used to solve the equation. Or, you can multiply each side of the equation by the LCD of the fractions to eliminate the fractions, and then solve the resulting equation.

When solving a rational equation, more than one solution may result. Always check all solutions in the original equation, as some solutions may be *extraneous solutions.*

CHAPTER 11 Notes

Chapter Project

Super Science Stuff

Students use what they have learned about writing, graphing, and solving rational equations, using dimensional analysis, and solving rate problems to work as a scientist performing an experiment.

- Put students into groups. Have groups create an experiment for which they can measure time x in seconds and distance d in meters. Ask groups to write and graph an equation for the average speed y in the form $y = \frac{d}{x}$. For example, the equation for measuring the seconds it takes to walk 10 meters is $y = \frac{10}{x}$.
- Have group members act out their experiment. Record the x and y values in a table. Are x and y inversely or directly related? Then have each member find his or her average speed in *miles per hour*. Recall that there are 3600 sec/h and about 1609 m/mi.
- Have groups choose the rates, in m/sec, of two students A and B where A's rate is faster than B's. If A starts the experiment $\frac{1}{4}$ second after B, when will A pass B?

CHAPTER 11 Rational Functions and Equations

Then

In Chapter 7, you simplified expressions involving monomials and polynomials.

Now

In Chapter 11, you will:

- Identify and graph inverse variations.
- Identify excluded values of rational functions.
- Multiply, divide, and add rational expressions.
- Divide polynomials.
- Solve rational equations.

IL Learning Standards

7.A.4b Apply formulas in a wide variety of theoretical and practical real-world measurement applications.
8.A.4b Represent mathematical patterns and describe their properties using variables and mathematical symbols.

Why?

HOCKEY The time it will take for a puck hit from the blue line to reach the goal line is given by the rational expression $\frac{64}{x}$, where x is the speed of the puck in feet per seconds. If a player hits the puck at 100 miles per hour, the puck will reach the goal line in 0.34 second.

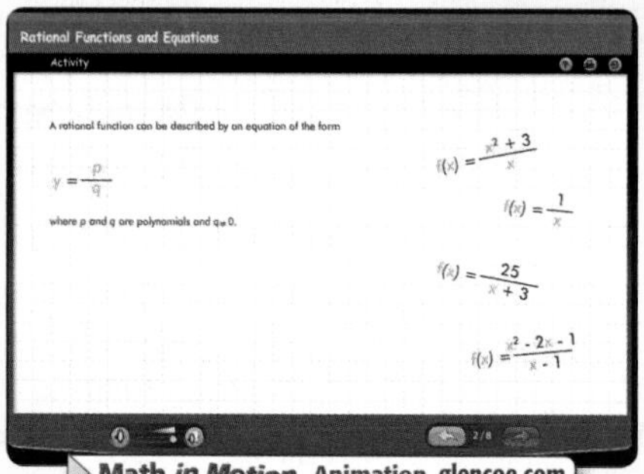

Math *in Motion*, Animation glencoe.com

Key Vocabulary Introduce the key vocabulary in the chapter using the routine below.

Define: A complex fraction is a fraction that has one or more fractions in the numerator or denominator.

Example: $\dfrac{\frac{8}{3}}{\frac{7}{5}}$

Ask: What are the two fractions in this complex fraction? $\frac{8}{3}$ and $\frac{7}{5}$

Get Ready for Chapter 11

Diagnose Readiness You have two options for checking Prerequisite Skills.

Text Option

Take the Quick Check below. Refer to the Quick Review for help.

*Quick*Check

(Used in Lessons 11-1)

Solve each proportion. (Lesson 2-6)

1. $\frac{y}{3} = \frac{8}{9}$ $\frac{8}{3}$
2. $\frac{5}{12} = \frac{x}{36}$ 15
3. $\frac{7}{2} = \frac{y}{3}$ $\frac{21}{2}$
4. $\frac{5}{x} = \frac{10}{4}$ 2
5. **DRAWING** Rosie is making a scale drawing. She is using the scale 1 inch = 3 feet. How many inches will represent 10 feet? $\frac{10}{3}$ or $3\frac{1}{3}$ inches

Find the GCF of each pair of monomials. (Lesson 8-1) (Used in Lessons 11-3)

6. $12ab, 18b$ $6b$
7. $15cd^2, 25c^2d$ $5cd$
8. $60r^2, 45r^3$ $15r^2$
9. $12xy, 16x^2y$ $4xy$
10. **GAMES** Fifty girls and 75 boys attend a sports club. For a game, boys and girls are going to split into groups. The number in each group has to be the same. How large can the groups be? 25

(Used in Lessons 11-4 through 11-9)

Factor each polynomial. (Lessons 8-2 and 8-4)

11. $2x^2 - 4x$
12. $6x^2 - 5x - 4$
13. $6xy + 15x$
14. $2c^2d - 4c^2d^2$

11–14. See margin.

15. **AREA** The area of a rectangle is $x^2 + 5x + 6$. What binomial expressions represent the side lengths of the rectangle? $(x + 3), (x + 2)$

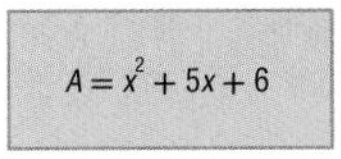

*Quick*Review

EXAMPLE 1

Solve $\frac{3}{5} = \frac{x}{12}$.

$\frac{3}{5} = \frac{x}{12}$	Original equation
$3 \cdot 12 = 5 \cdot x$	Cross products
$36 = 5x$	Simplify.
$\frac{36}{5} = \frac{5x}{5}$	Divide each side by 5.
$\frac{36}{5} = x$	Simplify.

EXAMPLE 2

Find the greatest common factor of 30 and 42.

$2 \cdot 3 \cdot 5$	Prime factorization of 30
$2 \cdot 3 \cdot 7$	Prime factorization of 42
$2 \cdot 3 = 6$	Product of the common factors

The greatest common factor of 30 and 42 is 6.

EXAMPLE 3

Factor $x^2 + 4x - 45$.

In this trinomial, $b = 4$ and $c = -45$. Find factors of -45 with a sum of 4. The correct factors are -5 and 9.

$x^2 + 4x - 45$	Original expression
$= (x + m)(x + p)$	Write the pattern.
$= (x - 5)(x + 9)$	$m = -5$ and $p = 9$

Online Option

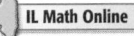

IL Math Online Take a self-check Chapter Readiness Quiz at glencoe.com.

Additional Answers

11. $2x(x - 2)$
12. $(3x - 4)(2x + 1)$
13. $3x(2y + 5)$
14. $2c^2d(1 - 2d)$

Response to Intervention (RtI)

Use the *Quick Check* results and the Intervention Planner chart to help you determine your Response to Intervention. The If-Then statements in the chart below help you decide the appropriate tier of RtI and suggest intervention resources for each tier.

Intervention Planner

Tier 1 — On Level

If students miss about 25% of the exercises or less,

Then choose a resource:

SE Lessons 2-6, 8-1, 8-2, and 8-4

CRM Skills Practice, Chapter 2, p. 38, Chapter 8, pp. 7, 13, 25

IL Math Online Self-Check Quiz

Tier 2 — Strategic Intervention approaching grade level

If students miss about 50% of the exercises,

Then choose a resource:

CRM Study Guide and Intervention, Chapter 2, p. 36, Chapter 8 pp. 5, 11, 23

Quick Review Math Handbook

IL Math Online Extra Examples, Personal Tutor, Homework Help

Tier 3 — Intensive Intervention 2 or more grades below level

If students miss about 75% of the exercises,

Then use *Math Triumphs, Alg. 1*

IL Math Online Extra Examples, Personal Tutor, Homework Help, Review Vocabulary

CHAPTER 11 Notes

FOLDABLES Study Organizer

Dinah Zike's Foldables®

Focus Students write notes about rational expressions and equations as they work through each lesson in this chapter.

Teach Have students make and label their Foldables as illustrated. Ask students to write down the Key Concepts and Concept Summaries in this chapter. Encourage students to reword the information in such a way that someone who did not understand rational functions and equations would understand them after reading what was written.

When to Use It Encourage students to add to their Foldables as they work through the chapter and to use them to review for the chapter test.

Differentiated Instruction

CRM Student-Built Glossary, pp. 1–2 Students should complete the chart by providing a definition of each term and an example as they progress through Chapter 11. This study tool can also be used to review for the chapter test.

Get Started on Chapter 11

You will learn several new concepts, skills, and vocabulary terms as you study Chapter 11. To get ready, identify important terms and organize your resources. You may wish to refer to **Chapter 0** to review prerequisite skills.

FOLDABLES® Study Organizer

Rational Functions and Equations Make this Foldable to help you organize your Chapter 11 notes about rational functions and equations. Begin with 3 sheets of notebook paper.

1. **Take** one sheet of paper and fold in half along the width. Cut 1 inch slits on each side of the paper.

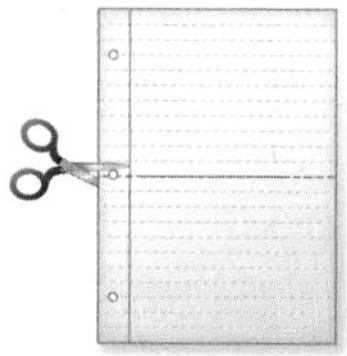

2. **Stack** the two sheets of paper and fold in half along the width. Cut a slit through the center stopping 1 inch from each side.

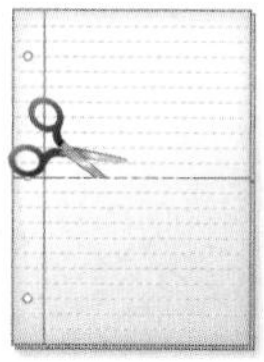

3. **Insert** the first sheet through the second sheets and align the folds to form a booklet. Label the cover with the chapter title.

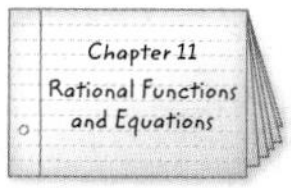

New Vocabulary

English		Español
inverse variation	• p. 670 •	variación inversa
product rule	• p. 671 •	regla del producto
excluded value	• p. 678 •	valores excluidos
rational function	• p. 678 •	función racional
asymptote	• p. 679 •	asíntota
rational expression	• p. 684 •	expresión racional
least common multiple (LCM)	• p. 707 •	mínimo común múltiplo (mcm)
least common denominator (LCD)	• p. 708 •	mínimo común denominador (mcd)
complex fraction	• p. 714 •	fracción compleja
mixed expression	• p. 714 •	expresión mixta
rational equation	• p. 720 •	ecuacion racional
extraneous solutions	• p. 721 •	soluciones extrañas
work problems	• p. 722 •	problemas de trabajo
rate problems	• p. 723 •	problemas de tasas

Review Vocabulary

direct variation • p. 180 • variación directa an equation of the form $y = kx$, where $k \neq 0$

Quotient of Powers • p. 408 • cociente de potencia $\frac{a^m}{a^n} = a^{m-n}$

$$\frac{x^5}{x^3} = \frac{x \cdot x \cdot x \cdot x \cdot x}{x \cdot x \cdot x} = x \cdot x \text{ or } x^2$$

$$\frac{x^5}{x^3} = x^{5-3} \text{ or } x^2$$

Zero Product Property • p. 478 • propiedad del producto de cero if the product of two factors is 0, then at least one of the factors must be 0

Multilingual eGlossary glencoe.com

IL Math Online glencoe.com

- Study the chapter online
- Explore **Math in Motion**
- Get extra help from your own **Personal Tutor**
- Use **Extra Examples** for additional help
- Take a **Self-Check Quiz**
- **Review Vocabulary** in fun ways

Graphing Technology Lab: Inverse Variation

IL Learning Standards **8.A.4b** Represent mathematical patterns and describe their properties using variables and mathematical symbols.

You can use a data collection device to investigate the relationship between volume and pressure.

Set Up The Lab

- Connect a syringe to the gas pressure sensor. Then connect the data collection device to both the sensor and the calculator as shown.
- Start the collection program and select the sensor.

ACTIVITY Collect Data

Step 1 Open the valve between the atmosphere and the syringe. Set the inside ring of the syringe to 20 mL and close the valve. This ensures that the amount of air inside the syringe will be constant throughout the experiment.

Step 2 Press the plunger of the syringe to the 5 mL mark. Wait for the pressure gauge to stop changing, then take the data reading. Enter 5 as the volume in the calculator. The pressure is measured in atmospheres (atm).

Step 3 Repeat step 2, pressing the plunger to 7.5 mL, 10.0 mL, 12.5 mL, 15.0 mL, 17.5 mL, and 20.0 mL. Record the volume from each data reading.

Step 4 After taking the last data reading, use **STAT PLOT** to create a line graph.

Exercises

1. Does the pressure vary directly as the volume? Explain.
2. As the volume changes from 10 to 20 mL, what happens to the pressure?
3. Predict what the pressure of the gas in the syringe would be if the volume increased to 40 mL. **Sample answer: 0.48**
4. Add a column to the data table to find the product of the volume and the pressure for each data reading. What pattern do you observe?
5. **MAKE A CONJECTURE** The relationship between the pressure and volume of a gas is called Boyle's Law. Write an equation relating the volume v in milliliters and pressure p in atmospheres in your experiment. Compare your conjecture to those of two classmates. Formulate mathematical questions about their conjectures. **Sample answer: $pv = 18$; see students' work.**

1. No; the pressure increases as the volume decreases.
2. Sample answer: The pressure decreases by about half.
4. Sample answer: The product is close to constant.

1 FOCUS

Objective Collect data to investigate the relationship between volume and pressure.

Materials for Each Group

- syringe
- gas pressure sensor
- CBL or other data collection device
- TI–83/84 plus or other graphing calculator

Teaching Tip

Before performing the experiment, ask students to think about what they expect to happen. As they push the plunger in the syringe, do they expect it to get harder or easier to push?

2 TEACH

Working in Cooperative Groups

Put students in groups of four or five, mixing abilities, to complete the Activity.

Ask:

- Does the volume of air in the syringe change as you press the plunger? Explain. Yes; the volume decreases.
- Does the air pressure in the syringe change as you press the plunger? Explain. Yes; the pressure increases.
- Does the volume of air in the syringe change as you pull the plunger? Explain. Yes; the volume increases.
- Does the air pressure in the syringe change as you pull the plunger? Explain. Yes; the pressure decreases.

Practice Have students complete Exercises 1–5.

3 ASSESS

Formative Assessment

Use Exercise 5 to assess whether students can determine if there is a relationship between the pressure and volume of gas.

From Concrete to Abstract

Explain that Boyle's Law states that, at constant temperature, the volume of a given mass of gas is inversely proportional to the pressure upon the gas, or $V = k\frac{1}{p}$, where V = volume, p = pressure, and k = a constant. Ask students to explain whether the results of the experiment follow the pattern of Boyle's Law.

11-1 Lesson Notes

1 FOCUS

Vertical Alignment

Before Lesson 11-1
Solve problems involving direct variation.

Lesson 11-1
Identify and use inverse variations.
Graph inverse variations.

After Lesson 11-1
Identify and use rational functions.

2 TEACH

Scaffolding Questions

Have students read the *Why?* section of the lesson.

Ask:

- If a runner has an average pace of 5 miles an hour, how long will it take the runner to run 10 miles? 2 hours
- If a runner has an average pace of 6 miles an hour, how long will it take the runner to run 10 miles? 1 hour 40 min
- In both cases, what number does not change? the distance, 10 miles

11-1 Inverse Variation

Then
You solved problems involving direct variation. (Lesson 3-4)

Now
- Identify and use inverse variations.
- Graph inverse variations.

IL Learning Standards
7.B.4 Estimate and measure the magnitude and directions of physical quantities using rulers, protractors and other scientific instruments including timers, calculators and computers.

New Vocabulary
inverse variation
product rule

IL Math Online
glencoe.com
- Extra Examples
- Personal Tutor
- Self-Check Quiz
- Homework Help

Why?

The time it takes a runner to finish a race is inversely proportional to the average pace of the runner.

Identify and Use Inverse Variations In the situation above, the runner's time decreases as the pace of the runner increases. So, these quantities are *inversely proportional.* An **inverse variation** can be represented by the equation $y = \frac{k}{x}$ or $xy = k$.

Key Concept Inverse Variation — For Your FOLDABLE

y varies inversely as x if there is some nonzero constant k such that $y = \frac{k}{x}$ or $xy = k$, where $x \neq 0$ and $y \neq 0$.

In an inverse variation, the product of two values remains constant. Recall that a relationship of the form $y = kx$ is a *direct variation.* For either a direct or indirect variations, the constant k is called the *constant of variation* or the *constant of proportionality.*

EXAMPLE 1 Identify Inverse and Direct Variations

Determine whether each table or equation represents an *inverse* or a *direct variation.* Explain.

a.

x	y
1	16
2	8
4	4

In an inverse variation, xy equals a constant k. Find xy for each ordered pair in the table.

$1 \cdot 16 = 16$
$2 \cdot 8 = 16$
$4 \cdot 4 = 16$

The product is constant, so the table represents an inverse variation.

b.

x	y
1	3
2	6
3	9

Notice that xy is not constant. So, the table does not represent an indirect variation.

$3 = k(1)$ $\quad 6 = k(2)$ $\quad 9 = k(3)$
$3 = k$ $\quad 3 = k$ $\quad 3 = k$

The table of values represents the direct variation $y = 3x$.

c. $x = 2y$
The equation can be written as $y = \frac{1}{2}x$. Therefore, it represents a direct variation.

d. $2xy = 10$
$2xy = 10$ **Write the equation.**
$xy = 5$ **Divide each side by 2.**
The equation represents an inverse variation.

Check Your Progress

1A.

x	1	2	5
y	10	5	2

Inverse; xy equals a constant.

1B. $-2x = y$ Direct; $-2x = y$ is equivalent to $y = -2x$.

Personal Tutor glencoe.com

Lesson 11-1 Resources

Resource	Approaching-Level	On-Level	Beyond-Level	English Learners
Teacher Edition		• Differentiated Instruction, p. 676	• Differentiated Instruction, pp. 673, 676	
Chapter Resource Masters	• Study Guide and Intervention, pp. 5–6 • Skills Practice, p. 7 • Practice, p. 8 • Word Problem Practice, p. 9	• Study Guide and Intervention, pp. 5–6 • Skills Practice, p. 7 • Practice, p. 8 • Word Problem Practice, p. 9 • Enrichment, p. 10	• Practice, p. 8 • Word Problem Practice, p. 9 • Enrichment, p. 10	• Study Guide and Intervention, pp. 5–6 • Skills Practice, p. 7 • Practice, p. 8 • Word Problem Practice, p. 9
Transparencies	• 5-Minute Check Transparency 11-1	• 5-Minute Check Transparency 11-1	• 5-Minute Check Transparency 11-1	• 5-Minute Check Transparency 11-1
Other	• Study Notebook	• Study Notebook	• Study Notebook	• Study Notebook

ReadingMath

Variation Equations For direct variation equations, you say that *y varies directly* as *x*. For inverse variation equations, you say that *y varies inversely* as *x*.

You can use $xy = k$ to write an inverse variation equation that relates x and y.

EXAMPLE 2 Write an Inverse Variation

Assume that y varies inversely as x. If $y = 18$ when $x = 2$, write an inverse variation equation that relates x and y.

$xy = k$	Inverse variation equation
$2(18) = k$	$x = 2$ and $y = 18$
$36 = k$	Simplify.

The constant of variation is 36. So, an equation that relates x and y is $xy = 36$ or $y = \frac{36}{x}$.

Check Your Progress $xy = -20$ or $y = \frac{-20}{x}$

2. Assume that y varies inversely as x. If $y = 5$ when $x = -4$, write an inverse variation equation that relates x and y.

Personal Tutor glencoe.com

If (x_1, y_1) and (x_2, y_2) are solutions of an inverse variation, then $x_1y_1 = k$ and $x_2y_2 = k$.

$x_1y_1 = k$ and $x_2y_2 = k$	
$x_1y_1 = x_2y_2$	Substitute x_2y_2 for k.

The equation $x_1y_1 = x_2y_2$ is called the **product rule** for inverse variations.

Key Concept Product Rule for Inverse Variations

For Your FOLDABLE

Words If (x_1, y_1) and (x_2, y_2) are solutions of an inverse variation, then the products x_1y_1 and x_2y_2 are equal.

Symbols $x_1y_1 = x_2y_2$ or $\frac{x_1}{x_2} = \frac{y_2}{y_1}$

EXAMPLE 3 Solve for x or y

Assume that y varies inversely as x. If $y = 3$ when $x = 12$, find x when $y = 4$.

$x_1y_1 = x_2y_2$	Product rule for inverse variations
$12 \cdot 3 = x_2 \cdot 4$	$x_1 = 12$, $y_1 = 3$, and $y_2 = 4$
$36 = x_2 \cdot 4$	Simplify.
$\frac{36}{4} = x_2$	Divide each side by 4.
$9 = x_2$	Simplify.

So, when $y = 4$, $x = 9$.

Check Your Progress

3. If y varies inversely as x and $y = 4$ when $x = -8$, find y when $x = -4$. 8

Personal Tutor glencoe.com

The product rule for inverse variations can be used to write an equation to solve real-world problems.

Identify and Use Inverse Variations

Example 1 shows how to identify inverse and direct variations. **Example 2** shows how to write an inverse variation equation to relate x and y. **Example 3** shows how to use the product rule for inverse variations to find a value for x or y. **Example 4** shows how to use the product rule for inverse variations to model a real-world situation.

Formative Assessment

Use the Check Your Progress exercises after each Example to determine students' understanding of concepts.

Additional Examples

1 Determine whether each table or equation represents an *inverse* or a *direct* variation. Explain.

a.

x	6	8	10
y	3	4	5

direct variation; $y = \frac{1}{2}x$

b.

x	1	2	3
y	12	6	4

Inverse variation; xy is a constant.

c. $-2xy = 20$ Inverse variation; xy is a constant.

d. $x = 0.5y$ Direct variation; the equation can be written in the form $y = kx$.

2 Assume that y varies inversely as x. If $y = 5$ when $x = 3$, write an inverse variation equation that relates x and y. $xy = 15$ or $y = \frac{15}{x}$

3 Assume that y varies inversely as x. If $y = 5$ when $x = 12$, find x when $y = 15$. 4

Additional Examples also in Interactive Classroom PowerPoint® Presentations

IWB INTERACTIVE WHITEBOARD READY

TEACH with TECH

INTERACTIVE WHITEBOARD Choose a student to work through an example in front of the class. Give the student an x-value and a y-value. Have the student find the constant of variation given that y varies inversely with x.

Additional Example

4 **PHYSICAL SCIENCE** When two people are balanced on a seesaw, their distances from the center of the seesaw are inversely proportional to their weights. How far should a 105-pound person sit from the center of the seesaw to balance a 63-pound person sitting 3.5 feet from the center? 2.1 ft

Graph Inverse Variations

Example 5 shows how to graph an inverse variation in which there are negative values of x.

Additional Example

5 Graph an inverse variation in which $y = 1$ when $x = 4$.

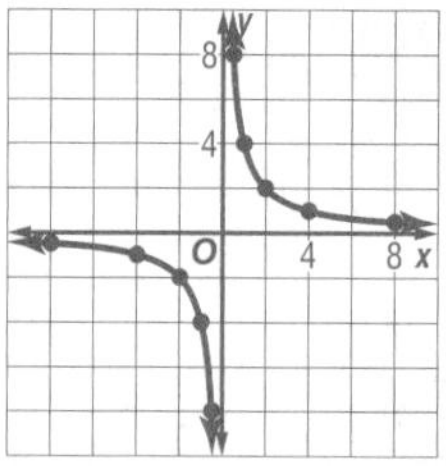

Focus on Mathematical Content

Inverse Variation When the product of two quantities remains constant, the quantities form an inverse variation. As one quantity increases, the other decreases, as long as $k > 0$. The nonzero product of the two quantities xy is called the constant of variation k.

Real-World Link

A standard hockey puck is 1 inch thick and 3 inches in diameter. Its mass is between approximately 156 and 170 grams.

Source: *NHL Rulebook*

Real-World EXAMPLE 4 Use Inverse Variations

PHYSICS The acceleration a of a hockey puck is inversely proportional to its mass m. Suppose a hockey puck with a mass of 164 grams is hit so that it accelerates 122 m/s². Find the acceleration of a 158-gram hockey puck if the same amount of force is applied.

Make a table to organize the information.

Puck	Mass	Acceleration
1	164 g	122 m/s²
2	158 g	a_2

Let $m_1 = 164$, $a_1 = 122$, and $m_2 = 164$. Solve for a_2.

$m_1a_1 = m_2a_2$ **Use the product rule to write an equation.**

$164 \cdot 122 = 158a_2$ **$m_1 = 164$, $a_1 = 122$, and $m_2 = 158$**

$20{,}008 = 158a_2$ **Simplify.**

$126.6 \approx a_2$ **Divide each side by 158 and simplify.**

The 158-gram puck has an acceleration of approximately 126.6 m/s².

Check Your Progress

4. RACING Manuel runs an average of 8 miles per hour and finishes a race in 0.39 hour. Dyani finished the race in 0.35 hour. What was her average pace? about 8.9 mph

Personal Tutor glencoe.com

Graph Inverse Variations The graph of an inverse variation is not a straight line like the graph of a direct variation.

EXAMPLE 5 Graph an Inverse Variation

Graph an inverse variation equation in which $y = 8$ when $x = 3$.

Problem-Solving Tip

Solve a Simpler Problem Sometimes it is necessary to break a problem into parts, solve each part, and then combine them to find the solution to the problem.

Step 1 Write an inverse variation equation.

$xy = k$ **Inverse variation equation**

$3(8) = k$ **$x = 3$, $y = 8$**

$24 = k$ **Simplify.**

The inverse variation equation is $xy = 24$ or $y = \frac{24}{x}$.

Step 2 Choose values for x and y that have a product of 24.

Step 3 Plot each point and draw a smooth curve that connects the points.

x	y
−12	−2
−8	−3
−4	−6
−2	−12
0	undefined
2	12
3	8
6	4
12	2

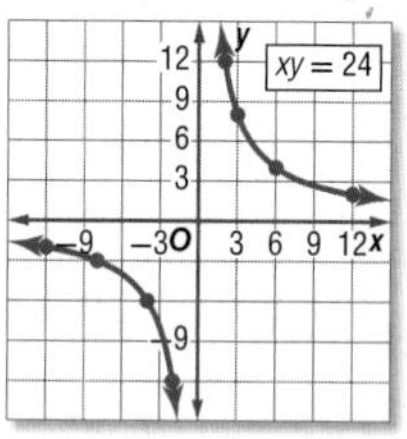

Notice that since y is undefined when $x = 0$, there is no point on the graph when $x = 0$. This graph is called a hyperbola.

5.

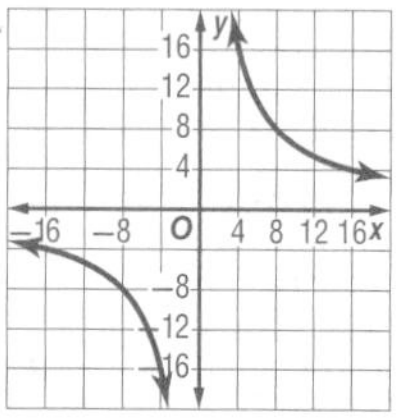

Check Your Progress

5. Graph an inverse variation equation in which $y = 16$ when $x = 4$.

Personal Tutor glencoe.com

Additional Answers

5.

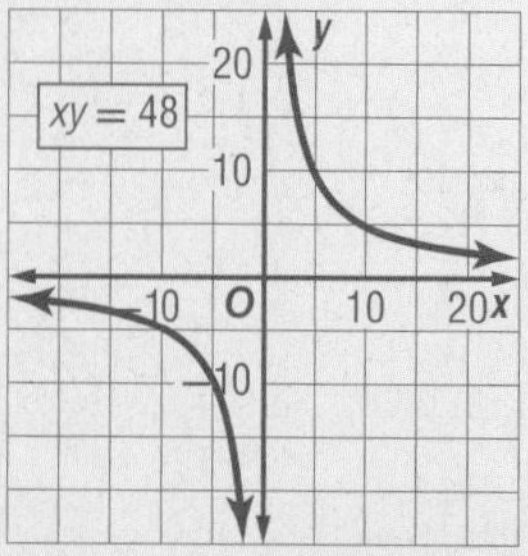

6.

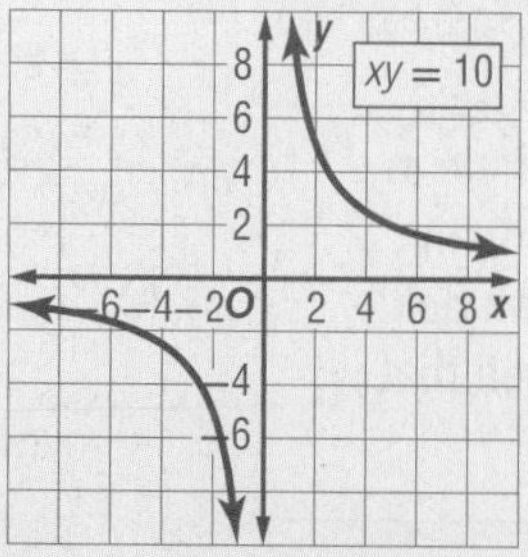

7.

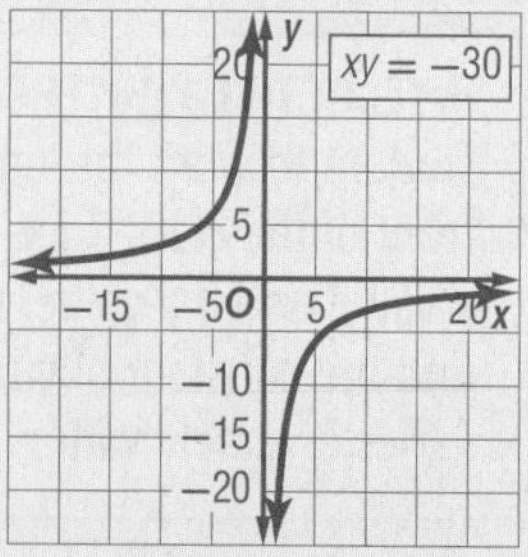

Concept Summary — Direct and Inverse Variations

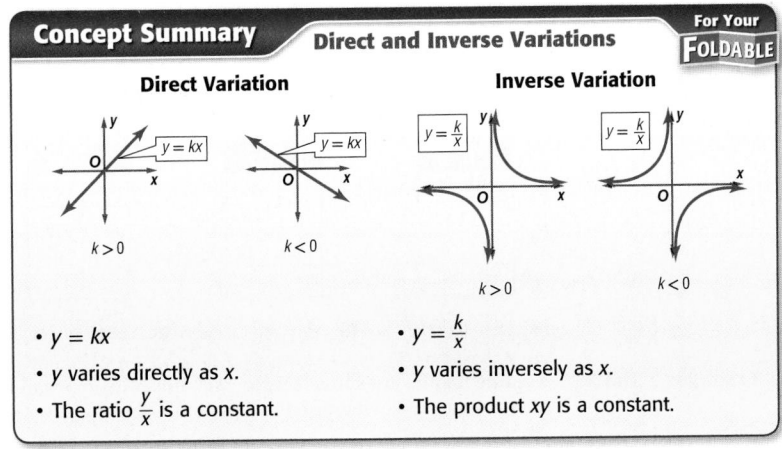

For Your FOLDABLE

Direct Variation

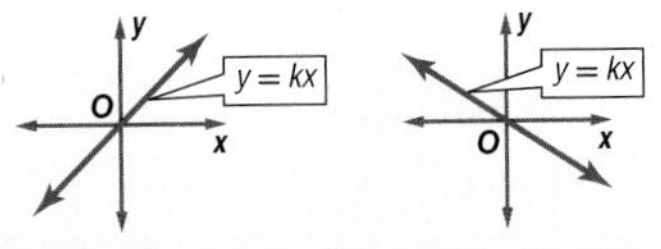

$k > 0$ $k < 0$

Inverse Variation

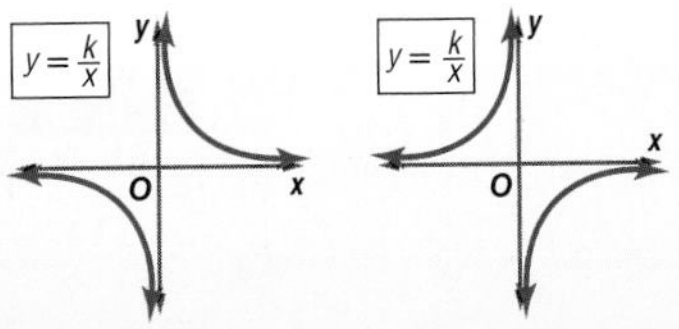

$k > 0$ $k < 0$

- $y = kx$
- y varies directly as x.
- The ratio $\frac{y}{x}$ is a constant.

- $y = \frac{k}{x}$
- y varies inversely as x.
- The product xy is a constant.

Check Your Understanding

Example 1 p. 670

Determine whether each table or equation represents an *inverse* or a *direct* variation. Explain.

1.

x	1	4	8	12
y	2	8	16	24

1. Direct; the data in the table can be represented by the equation $y = 2x$.

2.

x	1	2	3	4
y	24	12	8	6

Inverse; $xy = 24$.

3. $xy = 4$ Inverse; $xy = 4$.

4. $y = \frac{x}{10}$ Direct; $y = \frac{1}{10}x$.

Examples 2 and 5 pp. 671–672

Assume that y varies inversely as x. Write an inverse variation equation that relates x and y. Then graph the equation. 5–8. See margin.

5. $y = 8$ when $x = 6$
6. $y = 2$ when $x = 5$
7. $y = 3$ when $x = -10$
8. $y = -1$ when $x = -12$

Example 3 p. 671

Solve. Assume that y varies inversely as x.

9. If $y = 8$ when $x = 4$, find x when $y = 2$. 16
10. If $y = 7$ when $x = 6$, find y when $x = -21$. -2
11. If $y = -5$ when $x = 9$, find y when $x = 6$. -7.5

Example 4 p. 672

12. **RACING** The time it takes to complete a go-cart race course is inversely proportional to the average speed of the go-cart. One rider has an average speed of 73.3 feet per second and completes the course in 30 seconds. Another rider completes the course in 25 seconds. What was the average speed of the second rider? 87.96 ft/s

13. **OPTOMETRY** When a person does not have clear vision, an optometrist can prescribe lenses to correct the condition. The power P of a lens, in a unit called diopters, is equal to 1 divided by the focal length f, in meters, of the lens.
    a. Graph the inverse variation $P = \frac{1}{f}$. See margin.
    b. Find the powers of lenses with focal lengths +0.2 to −0.4 meters.

13b. 5 to −2.5 diopters

3 PRACTICE

Formative Assessment

Use Exercises 1–13 to check for understanding.

Use the chart at the bottom of the next page to customize assignments for your students.

Exercise Alert

Grid Paper For Exercises 5–8, 13, 22–27, and 51 students will need grid paper.

Additional Answers

8.

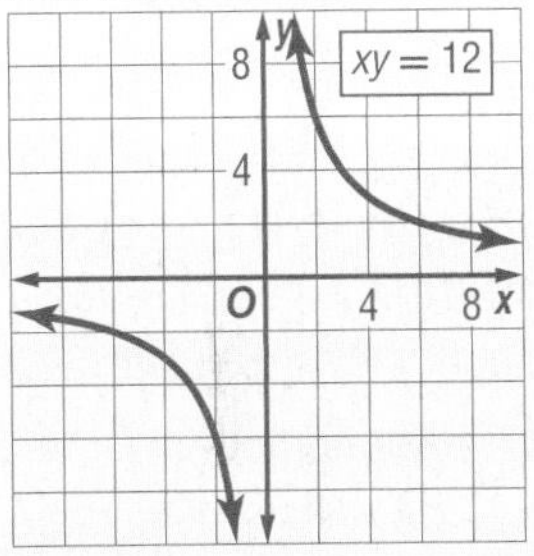

13a.

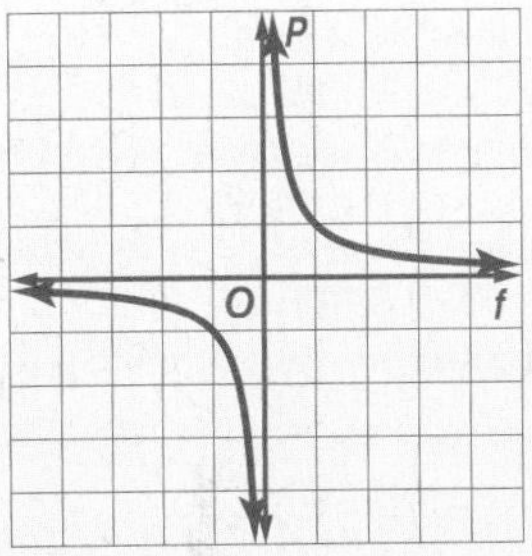

Differentiated Instruction BL

If students need a challenge in this lesson,

Then borrow a fulcrum, lever, and weights from a science teacher to recreate Additional Example 4 or Exercise 44. After some experimentation, ask students to calculate where to place the weights for the lever to balance.

Watch Out!

Find the Error In Exercise 52, point out that a single pair of *x*- and *y*-values could represent either a direct or an inverse variation. In this problem, *x* and *y* vary inversely.

Additional Answers

14. Inverse; $xy = 30$.
15. Direct; $y = -3x$.
16. Direct; $y = -\frac{1}{2}x$.
17. Inverse; $xy = -40$.
18. Direct; $y = 5x$.
19. Inverse; $xy = \frac{1}{4}$.
20. Direct; $y = kx$.
21. Direct; $y = 9x$.
36. Inverse; the cost per wig times the number of wigs equals the total amount they can spend, $20.
37. Direct; the number of lemonades times the cost per lemonade equals the total cost. So the ratio $\frac{\text{total cost}}{\text{number of lemonades}}$ is a constant $1.50.
38. Direct; the number of hours times the rate per hour equals the total pay. The ratio $\frac{\text{total pay}}{\text{number of hours}}$ is a constant $7.
39. Inverse; the number of friends times the number of tokens per person equals the constant 30.
40. Direct; $y = 0.2x$.
41. Inverse; $xy = 21$.
42. Inverse; $xy = 2$.
43. Direct; $y = \frac{1}{2}x$.

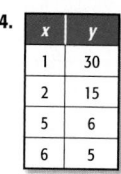

Practice and Problem Solving

● = Step-by-Step Solutions begin on page R12.
Extra Practice begins on page 815.

Example 1 p. 670

Determine whether each table or equation represents an *inverse* or a *direct* variation. Explain. 14–21. See margin.

14.

x	y
1	30
2	15
5	6
6	5

15.

x	y
2	−6
3	−9
4	−12
5	−15

16.

x	y
−4	−2
−2	−1
2	1
4	2

17.

x	y
−5	8
−2	20
4	−10
8	−5

18. $5x - y = 0$ **19.** $xy = \frac{1}{4}$ **20.** $x = 14y$ **21.** $\frac{y}{x} = 9$

Examples 2 and 5 pp. 671–672

Assume that *y* varies inversely as *x*. Write an inverse variation equation that relates *x* and *y*. Then graph the equation. 22–27. See Ch. 11 Answer Appendix.

22. $y = 2$ when $x = 20$ **23.** $y = 18$ when $x = 4$ **24.** $y = -6$ when $x = -3$
25. $y = -4$ when $x = -3$ **26.** $y = -4$ when $x = 16$ **27.** $y = 12$ when $x = -9$

Example 3 p. 671

Solve. Assume that *y* varies inversely as *x*.

28. If $y = 12$ when $x = 3$, find x when $y = 6$. **6**
29. If $y = 5$ when $x = 6$, find x when $y = 2$. **15**
30. If $y = 4$ when $x = 14$, find x when $y = -5$. **−11.2**
31. If $y = 9$ when $x = 9$, find y when $x = -27$. **−3**
32. If $y = 15$ when $x = -2$, find y when $x = 3$. **−10**
33. If $y = -8$ when $x = -12$, find y when $x = 10$. **9.6**

Example 4 p. 672

34. EARTH SCIENCE The water level in a river varies inversely with air temperature. When the air temperature was 90° Fahrenheit, the water level was 11 feet. If the air temperature was 110° Fahrenheit, what was the level of water in the river? **9 ft**

Real-World Link

A medium-sized piano has about 230 strings with a combined tension of 15 to 20 tons. A concert grand piano may have a combined string tension of up to 30 tons.

Source: Piano World

35. MUSIC When under equal tension, the frequency of a vibrating string in a piano varies inversely with the string length. If a string that is 420 millimeters in length vibrates at a frequency of 523 cycles a second, at what frequency will a 707-millimeter string vibrate? **approximately 311 cycles per second**

Determine whether each situation is an example of an *inverse* or a *direct* variation. Justify your reasoning. 36–39. See margin.

36. The drama club can afford to purchase 10 wigs at $2 each or 5 wigs at $4 each.
37. The Spring family buys several lemonades for $1.50 each.
38. Nicole earns $14 for babysitting 2 hours, and $21 for babysitting 3 hours.
B **39.** Thirty video game tokens are divided evenly among a group of friends.

Determine whether each table or graph represents an *inverse* or a *direct* variation. Explain. 40–43. See margin.

40.

x	y
5	1
8	1.6
11	2.2

41.

x	y
−3	−7
−2	−10.5
4	5.25

42.

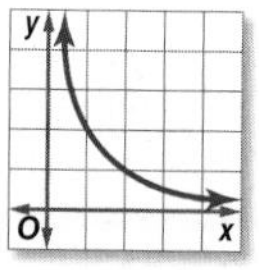

43.

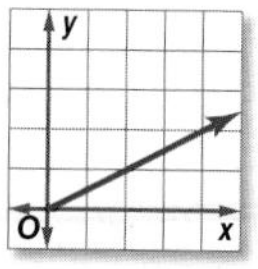

Differentiated Homework Options

Level	Assignment	Two-Day Option	
AL Basic	14–35, 52, 54–78	15–35 odd, 57–60	14–34 even, 52, 54–56, 61–78
OL Core	15–43 odd, 44, 45–49 odd, 50–52, 54–78	14–35, 57–60	36–52, 54–56, 61–78
BL Advanced	36–70, (optional: 71–78)		

44. **PHYSICAL SCIENCE** When two people are balanced on a seesaw, their distances from the center of the seesaw are inversely proportional to their weights. If a 118-pound person sits 1.8 meters from the center of the seesaw, how far should a 125-pound person sit from the center to balance the seesaw? **about 1.7 m**

C **Solve. Assume that y varies inversely as x.**

45. If $y = 9.2$ when $x = 6$, find x when $y = 3$. **18.4**
46. If $y = 3.8$ when $x = 1.5$, find x when $y = 0.3$. **19**
47. If $y = \frac{1}{5}$ when $x = -20$, find y when $x = -\frac{8}{5}$. **2.5**
48. If $y = -6.3$ when $x = \frac{2}{3}$, find y when $x = 8$. **−0.525**

49. **SWIMMING** Logan and Brianna each bought a pool membership. Their average cost per day is inversely proportional to the number of days that they go to the pool. Logan went to the pool 25 days for an average cost per day of $5.60. Brianna went to the pool 35 days. What was her average cost per day? **$4**

50. **PHYSICAL SCIENCE** The amount of force required to do a certain amount of work in moving an object is inversely proportional to the distance that the object is moved. Suppose 90 N of force is required to move an object 10 feet. Find the force needed to move another object 15 feet if the same amount of work is done. **60 N**

51. **DRIVING** Lina must practice driving 40 hours with a parent or guardian before she is allowed to take the test to get her driver's license. She plans to practice the same number of hours each week.
    a. Let h represent the number of hours per week that she practices driving. Make a table showing the number of weeks w that she will need to practice for the following values of h: 1, 2, 4, 5, 8, and 10.
    b. Describe how the number of weeks changes as the number of hours per week increases. **The number of weeks decreases.**
    c. Write and graph an equation that shows the relationship between h and w. **See Ch. 11 Answer Appendix.**

51a.

Hours per Week h	Number of Weeks w
1	40
2	20
4	10
5	8
8	5
10	4

Real-World Link

In 2007, Illinois began the Operation Teen Safe Driving program. The program challenges high schools to compete against each other to develop the most comprehensive and creative safe driving community.

Source: Ford Motor Company

H.O.T. Problems Use Higher-Order Thinking Skills

52. **FIND THE ERROR** Christian and Trevor found an equation such that x and y vary inversely, and $y = 10$ when $x = 5$. Is either of them correct? Explain.

Christian
$k = \frac{y}{x}$
$= \frac{10}{2}$ or 5
$y = 5x$

Trevor
$k = xy$
$= (5)(10)$ or 50
$y = \frac{50}{x}$

52. Trevor; the constant of variation is 5(10) or 50, so the correct equation is $xy = 50$ or $y = \frac{50}{x}$. Christian found an equation for a direct variation.

53. **CHALLENGE** Suppose f varies inversely with g, and g varies inversely with h. What is the relationship between f and h? **direct variation**

54. **REASONING** Does $xy = -k$ represent an inverse variation when $k \neq 0$? Explain. **Yes; the product of x and y is a nonzero constant.**

55. **OPEN ENDED** Give a real-world situation or phenomena that can be modeled by an inverse variation equation. Use the correct terminology to describe your example and explain why this situation is an inverse variation. **See Ch. 11 Answer Appendix.**

56. **WRITING IN MATH** Compare and contrast direct and inverse variation. Include a description of the relationship between slope and the graphs of a direct and inverse variation. **See Ch. 11 Answer Appendix.**

Study Guide and Intervention
CRM pp. 5–6 AL OL ELL

NAME ______ DATE ______ PERIOD ______

11-1 Study Guide and Intervention

Inverse Variation

Identify and Use Inverse Variations An **inverse variation** is an equation in the form of $y = \frac{k}{x}$ or $xy = k$. If two points (x_1, y_1) and (x_2, y_2) are solutions of an inverse variation, then $x_1 \cdot y_1 = k$ and $x_2 \cdot y_2 = k$.

Product Rule f or Inverse Variation	$x_1 \cdot y_1 = x_2 \cdot y_2$

From the product rule, you can form the proportion $\frac{x_1}{x_2} = \frac{y_2}{y_1}$.

Example If y varies inversely as x and y = 12 when x = 4, find x when y = 18.

Method 1 Use the product rule.

$x_1 \cdot y_1 = x_2 \cdot y_2$ Product rule for inverse variation
$4 \cdot 12 = x_2 \cdot 18$ $x_1 = 4, y_1 = 12, y_2 = 18$
$\frac{48}{18} = x_2$ Divide each side by 18.
$\frac{8}{3} = x_2$ Simplify.

Method 2 Use a proportion.

$\frac{x_1}{x_2} = \frac{y_2}{y_1}$ Proportion for inverse variation
$\frac{4}{x_2} = \frac{18}{12}$ $x_1 = 4, y_1 = 12, y_2 = 18$
$48 = 18x_2$ Cross multiply.
$\frac{8}{3} = x_2$ Simplify.

Both methods show that $x_2 = \frac{8}{3}$ when $y = 18$.

Exercises

Determine whether each table or equation represents an *inverse* or a *direct* variation. Explain.

1.

x	y
3	6
5	10
8	16
12	24

direct variation; of the form $y = kx$

2. $y = 6x$ **direct variation; of the form $y = kx$**

3. $xy = 15$ **inverse variation; of the form $xy = k$**

Assume that y varies inversely as x. Write an inverse variation equation that relates x and y. Then solve.

4. If $y = 10$ when $x = 5$, find y when $x = 2$. **$xy = 50$; 25**
5. If $y = 8$ when $x = -2$, find y when $x = 4$. **$xy = -16$; −4**
6. If $y = 100$ when $x = 120$, find x when $y = 20$. **$xy = 12{,}000$; 600**
7. If $y = -16$ when $x = 4$, find x when $y = 32$. **$xy = -64$; −2**
8. If $y = -7.5$ when $x = 25$, find y when $x = 5$. **$xy = -187.5$; −37.5**
9. **DRIVING** The Gerardi family can travel to Oshkosh, Wisconsin, from Chicago, Illinois, in 4 hours if they drive an average of 45 miles per hour. How long would it take them if they increased their average speed to 50 miles per hour? **3.6 h**
10. **GEOMETRY** For a rectangle with given area, the width of the rectangle varies inversely as the length. If the width of the rectangle is 40 meters when the length is 5 meters, find the width of the rectangle when the length is 20 meters. **10 m**

Chapter 11 5 Glencoe Algebra 1

Lesson 11-1

Practice
CRM p. 8 AL BL OL ELL

NAME ______ DATE ______ PERIOD ______

11-1 Practice

Inverse Variation

Determine whether each table or equation represents an *inverse* or a *direct* variation. Explain.

1.

x	y
0.25	40
0.5	20
2	5
8	1.25

inverse; $xy = k$

2.

x	y
−2	8
0	0
2	−8
4	−16

direct; $y = kx$

3. $\frac{y}{x} = -3$ **direct; $y = kx$**

4. $y = \frac{7}{x}$ **inverse; $xy = k$**

Asssume that y varies inversely as x. Write an inverse variation equation that relates x and y. Then graph the equation.

5. $y = -2$ when $x = -12$

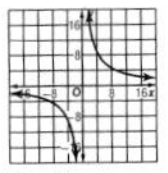

$xy = 24$

6. $y = -6$ when $x = -5$

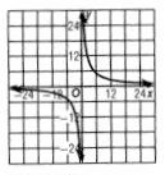

$xy = 30$

7. $y = 2.5$ when $x = 2$

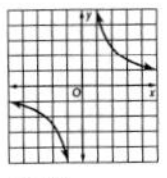

$xy = 5$

Write an inverse variation equation that relates x and y. Assume that y varies inversely as x. Then solve.

8. If $y = 124$ when $x = 12$, find y when $x = -24$. **$xy = 1488$; −62**
9. If $y = -8.5$ when $x = 6$, find y when $x = -2.5$. **$xy = -51$; 20.4**
10. If $y = 3.2$ when $x = -5.5$, find y when $x = 6.4$. **$xy = -17.6$; −2.75**
11. If $y = 0.6$ when $x = 7.5$, find y when $x = -1.25$. **$xy = 4.5$; −3.6**
12. **EMPLOYMENT** The manager of a lumber store schedules 6 employees to take inventory in an 8-hour work period. The manager assumes all employees work at the same rate.
    a. Suppose 2 employees call in sick. How many hours will 4 employees need to take inventory? **12 h**
    b. If the district supervisor calls in and says she needs the inventory finished in 6 hours, how many employees should the manager assign to take inventory? **8**
13. **TRAVEL** Jesse and Joaquin can drive to their grandparents' home in 3 hours if they average 50 miles per hour. Since the road between the homes is winding and mountainous, their parents prefer they average between 40 and 45 miles per hour. How long will it take to drive to the grandparents' home at the reduced speed? **between 3 h 20 min and 3 h 45 min**

Chapter 11 8 Glencoe Algebra 1

Word Problem Practice
CRM p. 9 AL OL OL ELL

NAME ______ DATE ______ PERIOD ______

11-1 Word Problem Practice

Inverse Variation

1. **PHYSICAL SCIENCE** The illumination I produced by a light source varies inversely as the square of the distance d from the source. The illumination produced 5 feet from the light source is 80 foot-candles.

$$Id^2 = k$$
$$80(5)^2 = k$$
$$2000 = k$$

Find the illumination produced 8 feet from the same source.

31.25 foot-candles

2. **MONEY** A formula called the Rule of 72 approximates how fast money will double in a savings account. It is based on the relation that the number of years it takes for money to double varies inversely as the annual interest rate. Use the information in the table to write the Rule of 72 formula. **$yr = 72$**

Years to Double Money	Annual Interest Rate (percent)
18	4
14.4	5
12	6
10.29	7

3. **ELECTRICITY** The resistance, in ohms, of a certain length of electric wire varies inversely as the square of the diameter of the wire. If a wire 0.04 centimeter in diameter has a resistance of 0.60 ohm, what is the resistance of a wire of the same length and material that is 0.08 centimeters in diameter? **0.15 ohm**

4. **BUSINESS** In the manufacturing of a certain digital camera, the cost of producing the camera varies inversely as the number produced. If 15,000 cameras are produced, the cost is $80 per unit. Graph the relationship and label the point that represents the cost per unit to produce 25,000 cameras. **$48**

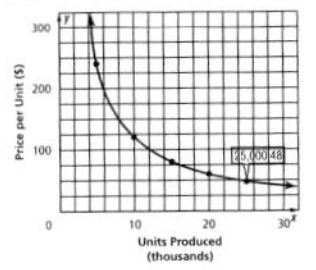

5. **SOUND** The sound produced by a string inside a piano depends on its length. The frequency of a vibrating string varies inversely as its length.
    a. Write an equation that represents the relationship between frequency f and length ℓ. Use k for the constant of variation. **$f \times \ell = k$ or $f = \frac{k}{\ell}$**
    b. If you have two different length strings, which one vibrates more quickly (that is, which string has a greater frequency)? **The shorter string vibrates more quickly than the longer string.**
    c. Suppose a piano string 2 feet long vibrates 300 cycles per second. What would be the frequency of a string 4 feet long? **150 cycles per second**

Chapter 11 9 Glencoe Algebra 1

Lesson 11-1

Enrichment
CRM p. 10 OL BL

NAME ______ DATE ______ PERIOD ______

11-1 Enrichment

Direct or Indirect Variation

Fill in each table below. Then write *inversely*, or *directly* to complete each conclusion.

1.

ℓ	2	4	8	16	32
W	4	4	4	4	4
A	8	16	32	64	128

For a set of rectangles with a width of 4, the area varies **directly** as the length.

2.

Hours	2	4	5	6
Speed	55	55	55	55
Distance	110	220	275	330

For a car traveling at 55 mi/h, the distance covered varies **directly** as the hours driven.

3.

Oat Bran	$\frac{1}{3}$ cup	$\frac{2}{3}$ cup	1 cup
Water	1 cup	2 cup	3 cup
Servings	1	2	3

The number of servings of oat bran varies **directly** as the numb

4.

Hours of Work	128	128	128
People Working	2	4	8
Hours per Person	64	32	16

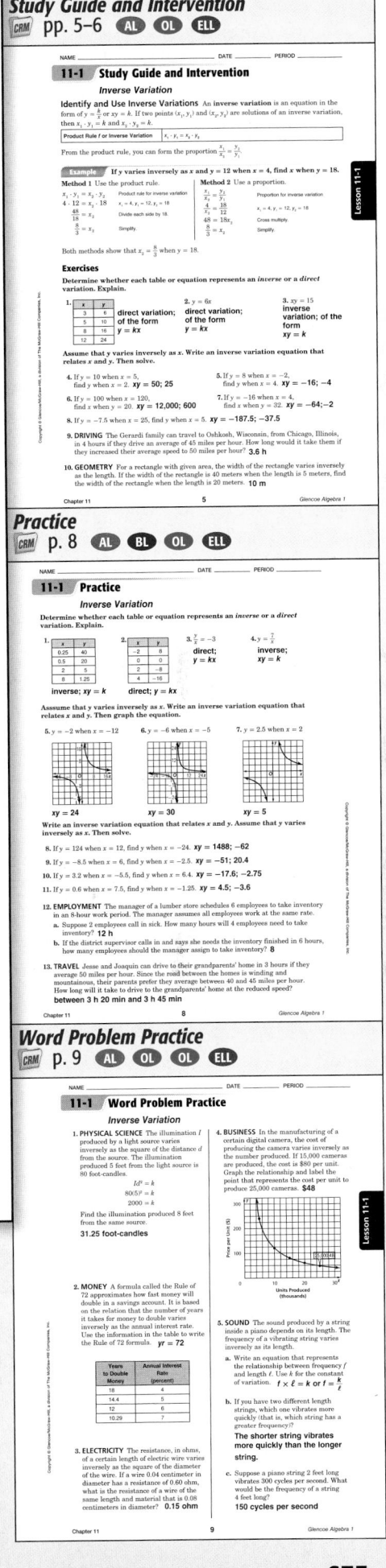

A job requires 128 hours of work. The number of hours each person works

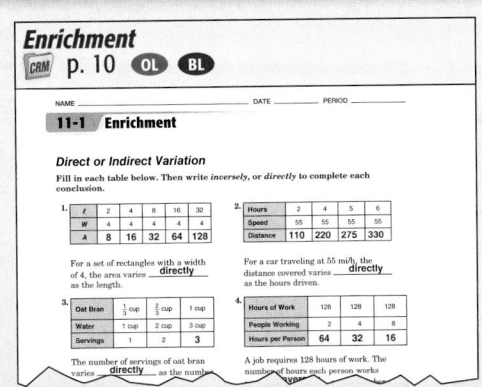

4 ASSESS

Name the Math Prepare two paper bags containing slips of paper: one containing a value for x on each slip, the other a value for y on each slip. Have each student select both an x-value and a y-value and write an inverse variation equation that relates x and y.

Additional Answers (Explore 11-2)

1. Sample answer: the quantity x minus 3 divided by 5
2. Sample answer: $2x$ divided by the quantity x plus 3
3. Sample answer: the quantity c plus 3 divided by the quantity c squared minus 4
4. Sample answer: the quantity b squared minus 9 divided by the quantity b minus 3
5. Sample answer: the quantity n squared plus $2n$ minus 8 divided by the quantity n minus four
6. Sample answer: the quantity h squared minus $6h$ plus 1 divided by the quantity h squared plus h plus 5

PSAE PRACTICE 6.11.19, 10.11.04, 6.11.17, 9.11.05

57. Given a constant force, the acceleration of an object varies inversely with its mass. Assume that a constant force is acting on an object with a mass of 6 pounds resulting in an acceleration of 10 ft/s^2. The same force acts on another object with a mass of 12 pounds. What would be the resulting acceleration? **B**

A 4 ft/s^2 C 6 ft/s^2
B 5 ft/s^2 D 7 ft/s^2

58. Fiona had an average of 56% on her first seven tests. What would she have to make on her eighth test to average 60% on 8 tests? **G**

F 82% H 100%
G 88% J 98%

59. Anthony takes a picture of a 1-meter snake beside a brick wall. When he develops the pictures, the 1-meter snake is 2 centimeters long and the wall is 4.5 centimeters high. What was the actual height of the brick wall? **C**

A 2.25 cm
B 22.5 cm
C 225 cm
D 0.225 cm

60. SHORT RESPONSE Find the area of the rectangle. $x^2 + 15x + 36$ **cm^2**

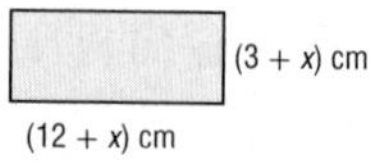

Spiral Review

For each triangle, find sin A, cos A, and tan A to the nearest ten-thousandth. (Lesson 10-8)

61.

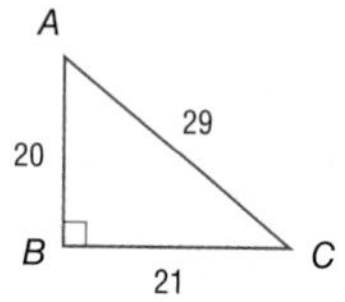

sin $A = 0.7241$, cos $A = 0.6897$, tan $A = 1.05$

62.

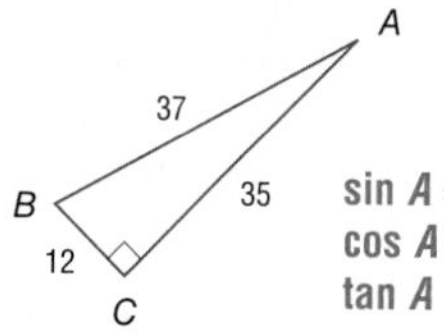

sin $A = 0.3243$, cos $A = 0.9459$, tan $A = 0.3429$

63.

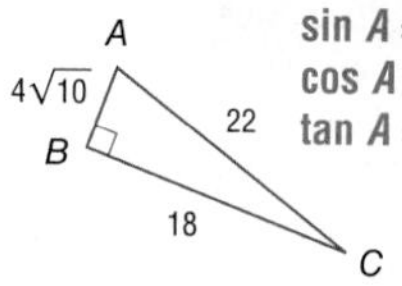

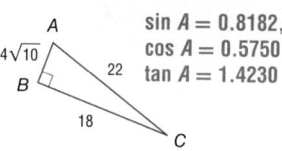

sin $A = 0.8182$, cos $A = 0.5750$, tan $A = 1.4230$

64. CRAFTS Jane is making a stained glass window using several triangular pieces of glass that are similar to the one shown. If two of the sides measure 4 inches, what is the length of the third side? (Lesson 10-7) **$4\sqrt{2}$ in.**

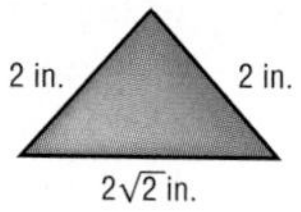

Solve each equation. (Lesson 10-4)

65. $\sqrt{10c} + 2 = 5$ $\frac{9}{10}$

66. $\sqrt{9h + 19} = 9$ $6\frac{8}{9}$

67. $\sqrt{7k + 2} + 2 = 5$ **1**

68. $\sqrt{5r - 1} = r - 5$ **13**

69. $6 + \sqrt{2x + 11} = -x$ **no solution**

70. $4 + \sqrt{4t - 4} = t$ **10**

Skills Review

Simplify. Assume that no denominator is equal to zero. (Lesson 7-2)

71. $\frac{7^8}{7^6}$ **7^2 or 49**

72. $\frac{x^8y^{12}}{x^2y^7}$ **x^6y^5**

73. $\frac{5pq^7}{10p^6q^3}$ **$\frac{q^4}{2p^5}$**

74. $\left(\frac{2c^3d}{7z^2}\right)^3$ **$\frac{8c^9d^3}{343z^6}$**

75. $\left(\frac{4a^2b}{2c^3}\right)^2$ **$\frac{4a^4b^2}{c^6}$**

76. $y^0(y^5)(y^{-9})$ **$\frac{1}{y^4}$**

77. $\frac{(4m^{-3}n^5)^0}{mn}$ **$\frac{1}{mn}$**

78. $\frac{(3x^2y^5)^0}{(21x^5y^2)^0}$ **1**

Differentiated Instruction OL BL

Extension Write $k = 4$ on the board. Ask students to write and graph an inverse variation equation that uses 4 as the constant of variation. $xy = 4$

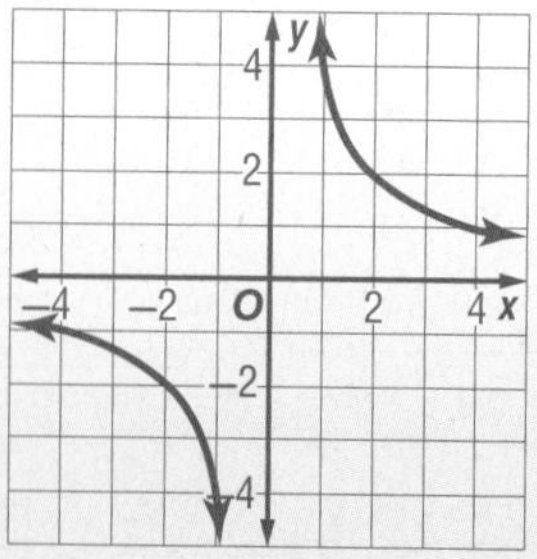

EXPLORE 11-2

Algebra Lab: Reading Rational Expressions

Several concepts need to be applied when reading rational expressions.

A fraction bar acts as a grouping symbol, where the entire numerator is divided by the entire denominator.

ACTIVITY 1

Read the expression $\frac{4y + 6}{14}$.

It is <u>correct</u> to read the expression as *the quantity four y plus six divided by fourteen.*

It is <u>incorrect</u> to read the expression as *four y plus six divided by fourteen or four y divided by fourteen plus six.*

If a fraction consists of two or more terms divided by a monomial or one-term denominator, the denominator divides each term.

ACTIVITY 2

Simplify $\frac{4y + 6}{14}$.

It is <u>correct</u> to write $\frac{4y + 6}{14} = \frac{4y}{14} + \frac{6}{14}$.

$= \frac{2y}{7} + \frac{3}{7}$ or $\frac{2y + 3}{7}$

It is also <u>correct</u> to write $\frac{4y + 6}{14} = \frac{2(2y + 3)}{2 \cdot 7}$

$= \frac{\cancel{2}(2y + 3)}{\cancel{2} \cdot 7}$ or $\frac{2y + 3}{7}$

It is <u>incorrect</u> to write $\frac{4y + 6}{14} = \frac{\overset{2y}{\cancel{4y}} + 6}{\underset{7}{\cancel{14}}} = \frac{2y + 6}{7}$.

Exercises

Write the verbal translation of each rational expression. 1–6. See margin.

1. $\frac{x - 3}{5}$
2. $\frac{2x}{x + 3}$
3. $\frac{c + 3}{c^2 - 4}$
4. $\frac{b^2 - 9}{b - 3}$
5. $\frac{n^2 + 2n - 8}{n - 4}$
6. $\frac{h^2 - 6h + 1}{h^2 + h + 5}$

Simplify each expression.

7. $\frac{2x + 4}{10}$ $\frac{x + 2}{5}$
8. $\frac{4m + 12}{16}$ $\frac{m + 3}{4}$
9. $\frac{2y^2 - 4y}{16y}$ $\frac{y - 2}{8}$
10. $\frac{g - 9}{g^2 - 81}$ $\frac{1}{g + 9}$
11. $\frac{2p - 5}{4p^2 - 20p + 25}$ $\frac{1}{2p - 5}$
12. $\frac{2d - 7}{2d^2 + d - 28}$ $\frac{1}{d + 4}$

From Concrete to Abstract

Ask students why it is not possible to simplify $\frac{x + 3}{6}$ to $\frac{x + 1}{2}$. 3 is not a factor of both the numerator and the denominator.

EXPLORE 11-2 Lesson Notes

1 FOCUS

Objective Read and simplify expressions.

Teaching Tip

Have students describe what they think of when they see a fraction. Some may think of fractions–no matter the value of the numerator or denominator–as numbers that are less than one. Others may think of fractions as division problems. Discuss with them what the different parts of a fraction mean.

2 TEACH

Working in Cooperative Groups

Put students in groups of four or five, mixing abilities, to complete Activities 1 and 2.

Ask:

- How many terms does the numerator in Activity 1 have? 2
- How many terms does the denominator have? 1
- Why do you think it is important to say "the quantity" when reading an expression with more than one term in the numerator? Sample answer: The entire polynomial is divided by the term(s) in the denominator.

Practice Have students complete Exercises 1–12.

3 ASSESS

Formative Assessment

Use Exercises 6 and 12 to assess whether students can read and simplify rational expressions.

11-2 Lesson Notes

1 FOCUS

Vertical Alignment

Before Lesson 11-2
Write inverse variation equations.

Lesson 11-2
Identify excluded values.
Identify and use asymptotes to graph rational functions.

After Lesson 11-2
Use rational equations to solve problems.

2 TEACH

Scaffolding Questions

Have students read the *Why?* section of the lesson.

Ask:

- What does the average number of pages Trina reads each day depend on? the number of days she reads
- What happens to the value of y as x increases? It decreases.
- What values of x are excluded from consideration? x cannot equal 0 or any negative number.

11-2 Rational Functions

Then
You wrote inverse variation equations. (Lesson 11-1)

Now
- Identify excluded values.
- Identify and use asymptotes to graph rational functions.

IL Learning Standards
8.C.4b Apply algebraic properties and procedures with matrices, vectors, functions and sequences using data found in business, industry and consumer situations.

New Vocabulary
rational function
excluded value
asymptote

IL Math Online
glencoe.com
- Extra Examples
- Personal Tutor
- Self-Check Quiz
- Homework Help

Why?

Trina is reading a 300-page book. The average number of pages she reads each day y is given by $y = \frac{300}{x}$, where x is the number of days that she reads.

Identify Excluded Values The function $y = \frac{300}{x}$ is an example of a **rational function**. This function is *nonlinear*.

Key Concept — Rational Functions (For Your FOLDABLE)

Words A rational function can be described by an equation of the form $y = \frac{p}{q}$, where p and q are polynomials and $q \neq 0$.

Parent function:	$f(x) = \frac{1}{x}$
Type of graph:	hyperbola
Domain:	$\{x \mid x \neq 0\}$
Range:	$\{y \mid y \neq 0\}$

Graph

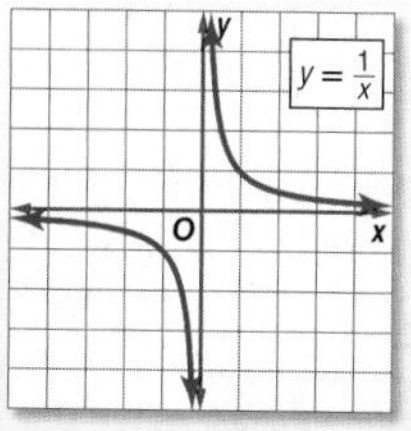

Since division by zero is undefined, any value of a variable that results in a denominator of zero in a rational function is excluded from the domain of the function. These are called **excluded values** for the rational function.

EXAMPLE 1 Find Excluded Values

State the excluded value for each function.

a. $y = -\frac{2}{x}$

The denominator cannot equal 0. So, the excluded value is $x = 0$.

b. $y = \frac{2}{x + 1}$

$x + 1 = 0$ **Set the denominator equal to 0.**
$x = -1$ **Subtract 1 from each side.**

The excluded value is $x = -1$.

c. $y = \frac{5}{4x - 8}$

$4x - 8 = 0$ **Set the denominator equal to 0.**
$4x = 8$ **Add 8 to each side.**
$x = 2$ **Divide each side by 4.**

The excluded value is $x = 2$.

Check Your Progress

1A. $y = \frac{5}{2x}$ $x = 0$ **1B.** $y = \frac{x}{x - 7}$ $x = 7$ **1C.** $y = \frac{4}{3x + 9}$ $x = -3$

Personal Tutor glencoe.com

Lesson 11-2 Resources

Resource	Approaching-Level	On-Level	Beyond-Level	English Learners
Teacher Edition	• Differentiated Instruction, p. 679	• Differentiated Instruction, pp. 679, 683	• Differentiated Instruction, p. 683	• Differentiated Instruction, p. 679
Chapter Resource Masters	• Study Guide and Intervention, pp. 11–12 • Skills Practice, p. 13 • Practice, p. 14 • Word Problem Practice, p. 15	• Study Guide and Intervention, pp. 11–12 • Skills Practice, p. 13 • Practice, p. 14 • Word Problem Practice, p. 15 • Enrichment, p. 16	• Practice, p. 14 • Word Problem Practice, p. 15 • Enrichment, p. 16	• Study Guide and Intervention, pp. 11–12 • Skills Practice, p. 13 • Practice, p. 14 • Word Problem Practice, p. 15
Transparencies	• 5-Minute Check Transparency 11-2	• 5-Minute Check Transparency 11-2	• 5-Minute Check Transparency 11-2	• 5-Minute Check Transparency 11-2
Other	• Study Notebook	• Study Notebook	• Study Notebook	• Study Notebook

Depending on the real-world situation, in addition to excluding x-values that make a denominator zero from the domain of a rational function, additional values might have to be excluded from the domain as well.

Real-World Link

As the temperature of the gas inside a hot air balloon increases, the density of the gas decreases. A hot air balloon rises because the density of the air inside it is less than the density of the air outside.

Source: Goddard Space Flight Center

Real-World EXAMPLE 2 Graph Real-Life Rational Functions

BALLOONS If there are x people in the basket of a hot air balloon, the function $y = \frac{20}{x}$ represents the average number of square feet y per person. Graph this function.

Since the number of people cannot be zero, it is reasonable to exclude negative values and only use positive values for x.

Number of People x	2	4	5	10
Square Feet per Person y	10	5	4	2

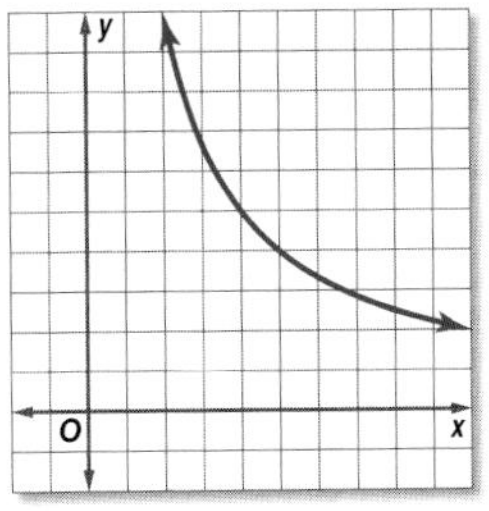

Check Your Progress

2. GEOMETRY A rectangle has an area of 18 square inches. The function $\ell = \frac{18}{w}$ shows the relationship between the length and width. Graph the function. **See Ch. 11 Answer Appendix.**

Personal Tutor glencoe.com

Identify and Use Asymptotes In Example 2, an excluded value is $x = 0$. Notice that the graph approaches the vertical line $x = 0$, but never touches it.

The graph also approaches but never touches the horizontal line $y = 0$. The lines $x = 0$ and $y = 0$ are called *asymptotes*. An **asymptote** is a line that the graph of a function approaches.

StudyTip

Use Asymptotes Asymptotes are helpful for graphing rational functions. However, they are not part of the graph.

Key Concept Asymptotes

For Your FOLDABLE

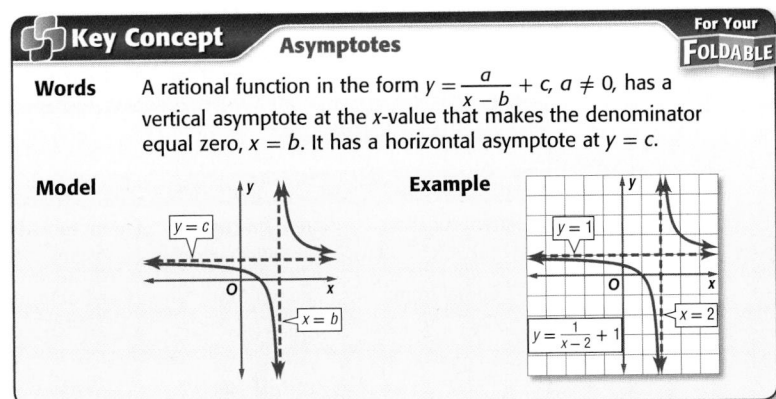

Words A rational function in the form $y = \frac{a}{x-b} + c$, $a \neq 0$, has a vertical asymptote at the x-value that makes the denominator equal zero, $x = b$. It has a horizontal asymptote at $y = c$.

Model

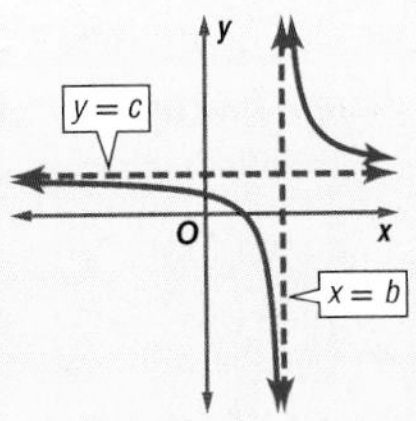

Example

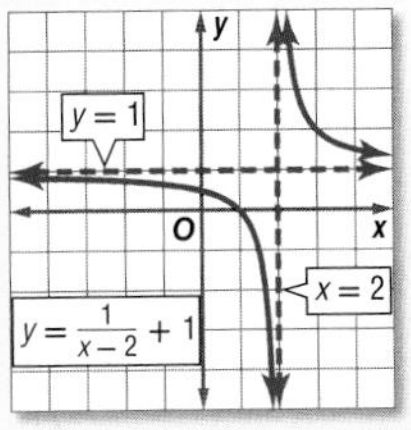

The domain of $y = \frac{a}{x-b} + c$ is all real numbers except $x = b$. The range is all real numbers except $y = c$. Rational functions cannot be traced with a pencil that never leaves the paper, so choose x-values on both sides of the vertical asymptote to graph both portions of the function.

Differentiated Instruction

AL OL ELL

Logical Learners Most students understand that a fraction with a denominator equal to 0 is undefined, thus the vertical asymptote. To help students understand that a horizontal asymptote occurs at $y = c$ in a function in the form $y = \frac{a}{x-b} + c$ (where $a \neq 0$), have students make a table of values for x and y and a graph using the example shown in the Key Concept, $y = \frac{1}{x-2} + 1$. Have students extend the table of values and the graph until they all agree that, as x gets greater and greater, $y = \frac{1}{x-2}$ approaches 0, and y gets closer and closer to 1, the value for c.

Identify Excluded Values

Example 1 shows how to find excluded values for rational functions. **Example 2** shows how to graph real-life rational functions and determine which values should be excluded.

Formative Assessment

Use the Check Your Progress exercises after each example to determine students' understanding of concepts.

Additional Examples

1 State the excluded value for each function.

a. $y = \frac{3}{x}$ $x = 0$

b. $y = \frac{3}{x+2}$ $x = -2$

c. $y = \frac{8}{2x+1}$ $x = -\frac{1}{2}$

2 **TALENT SHOW** If x students will compete in a talent show lasting 100 minutes, the function $y = \frac{100}{x}$ represents the number of minutes available for each act. Graph this function. graph of positive values for $y = \frac{100}{x}$ as shown below, through (10, 10) (5, 20), (20, 5), (25, 4)

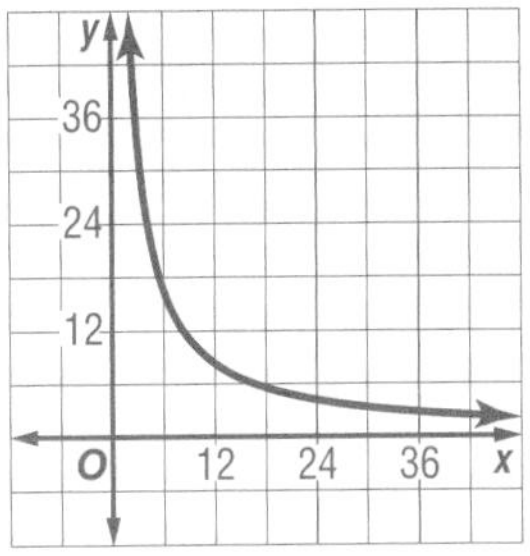

Additional Examples also in Interactive Classroom PowerPoint® Presentations

IWB INTERACTIVE WHITEBOARD READY

Tips for New Teachers

The functions used in Real World Example 2 and Additional Example 2 are discrete, not continuous.

Additional Example

3 Identify the asymptotes for each function. Then graph the function.

a. $y = \frac{3}{x} - 4$ $x = 0; y = -4$

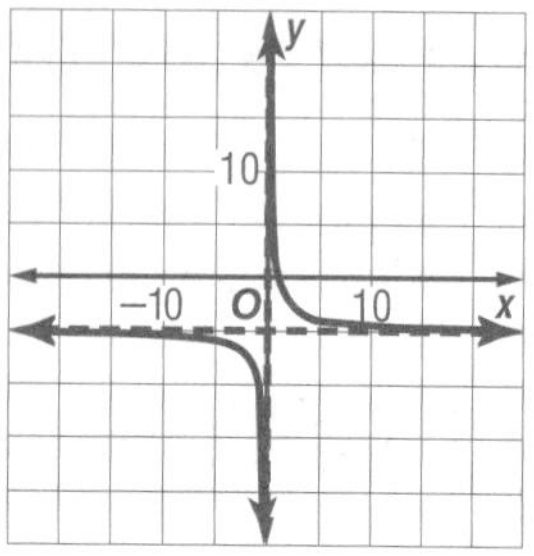

b. $y = \frac{2}{x+2}$ $x = -2; y = 0$

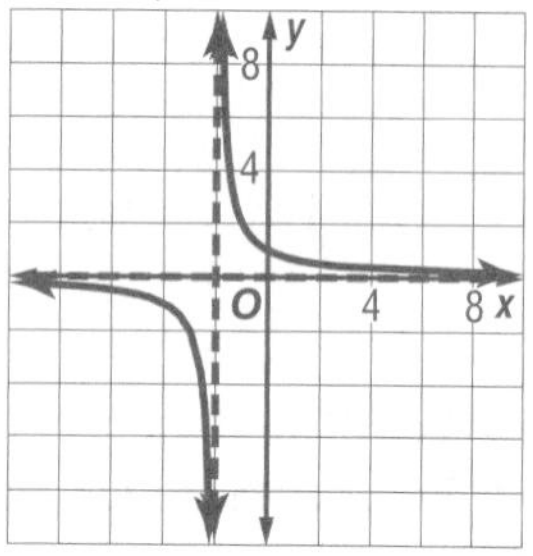

Math History Link

Evelyn Boyd Granville (1924–)
Granville majored in mathematics and physics at Smith College in 1945, where she graduated summa cum laude. She earned an M.A. in mathematics and physics and a Ph.D. in mathematics from Yale University. Granville's doctoral work focused on functional analysis.

EXAMPLE 3 Identify and Use Asymptotes to Graph Functions

Identify the asymptotes of each function. Then graph the function.

a. $y = \frac{2}{x} - 4$

Step 1 Identify and graph the asymptotes using dashed lines.

vertical asymptote: $x = 0$
horizontal asymptote: $y = -4$

Step 2 Make a table of values and plot the points. Then connect them.

x	−2	−1	1	2
y	−5	−6	−2	−3

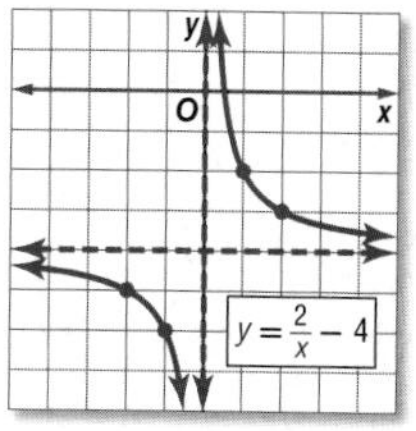

b. $y = \frac{1}{x+1}$

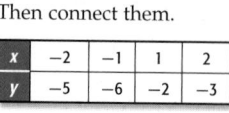

Step 1 To find the vertical asymptote, find the excluded value.

$x + 1 = 0$ **Set the denominator equal to 0.**

$x = -1$ **Subtract 1 from each side.**

vertical asymptote: $x = -1$
horizontal asymptote: $y = 0$

Step 2

x	−3	−2	0	1
y	−0.5	−1	1	0.5

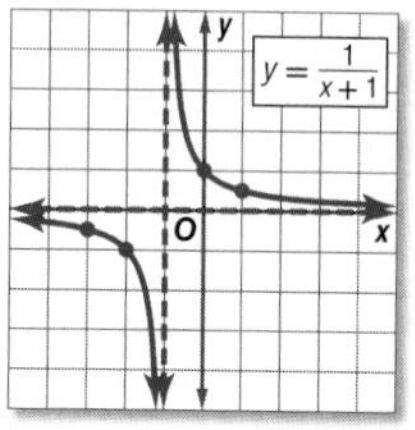

Check Your Progress **3A–3C. See margin.**

3A. $y = -\frac{6}{x}$ **3B.** $y = \frac{1}{x-3}$ **3C.** $y = \frac{2}{x+2} + 1$

Personal Tutor glencoe.com

Four types of nonlinear functions are shown below.

Concept Summary — Families of Functions

For Your FOLDABLE

Quadratic	Exponential	Radical	Rational
Parent function: $y = x^2$	Parent function: varies	Parent function: $y = \sqrt{x}$	Parent function: $y = \frac{1}{x}$
General form: $y = ax^2 + bx + c$	General form: $y = ab^x$	General form: $y = \sqrt{x - b} + c$	General form: $y = \frac{a}{x-b} + c$
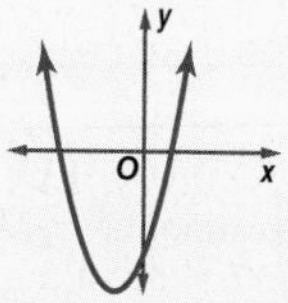	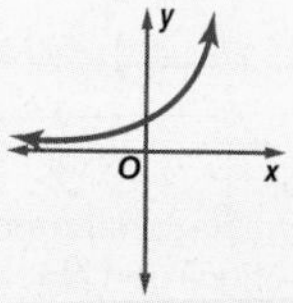	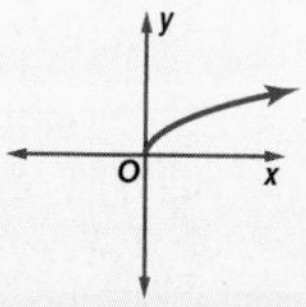	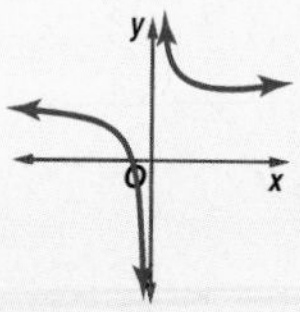

Additional Answers (Check Your Progress)

3A. $x = 0; y = 0$

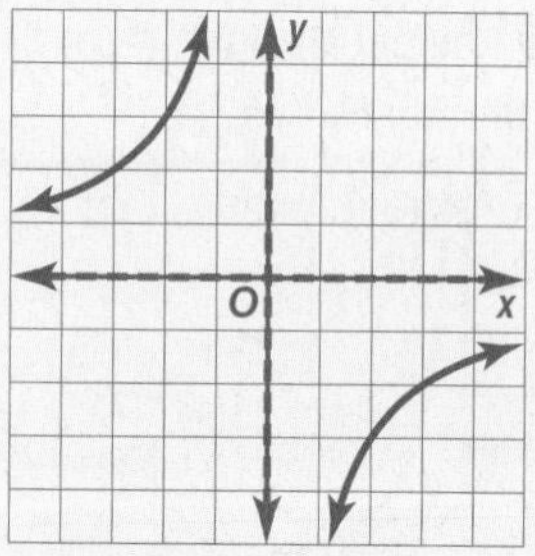

3B. $x = 3; y = 0$

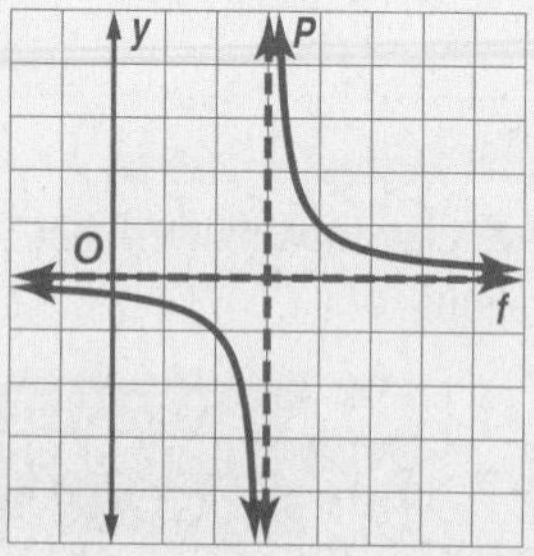

3C. $x = -2; y = 1$

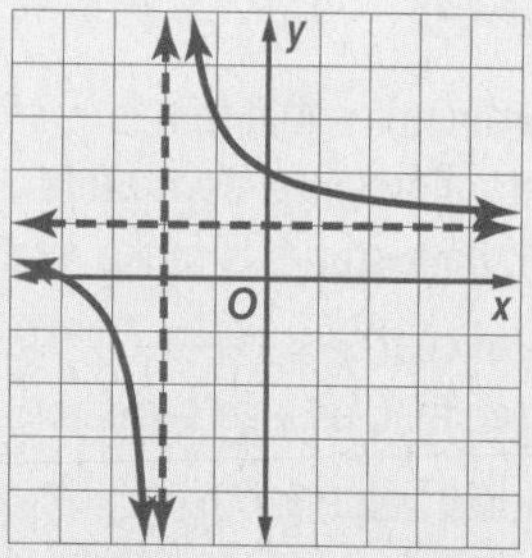

Check Your Understanding

Example 1 p. 678 — State the excluded value for each function.

1. $y = \frac{5}{x}$ $x = 0$
2. $y = \frac{1}{x+3}$ $x = -3$
3. $y = \frac{x+2}{x-1}$ $x = 1$
4. $y = \frac{x}{2x-8}$ $x = 4$

Example 2 p. 679

5. **PARTY PLANNING** The cost of decorations for a party is \$32. This is split among a group of friends. The amount each person pays y is given by $y = \frac{32}{x}$, where x is the number of people. Graph the function. **See margin.**

6–11. See Ch. 11 Answer Appendix.

Example 3 p. 680 — Identify the asymptotes of each function. Then graph the function.

6. $y = \frac{2}{x}$
7. $y = \frac{3}{x} - 1$
8. $y = \frac{1}{x-2}$
9. $y = \frac{-4}{x+2}$
10. $y = \frac{3}{x-1} + 2$
11. $y = \frac{2}{x+1} - 5$

Practice and Problem Solving

● = **Step-by-Step Solutions** begin on page R12. **Extra Practice** begins on page 815.

Example 1 p. 678 — State the excluded value for each function. **14. $x = -2$** **15. $x = -6$**

17. $x = -5$
18. $x = 2$
19. $x = -7$

12. $y = \frac{-1}{x}$ $x = 0$
13. $y = \frac{8}{x-8}$ $x = 8$
14. $y = \frac{x}{x+2}$
15. $y = \frac{4}{x+6}$
16. $y = \frac{x+1}{x-3}$ $x = 3$
17. $y = \frac{2x+5}{x+5}$
18. $y = \frac{7}{5x-10}$
19. $y = \frac{x}{2x+14}$

Example 2 p. 679

20. **ANTELOPES** A pronghorn antelope can run 40 miles without stopping. The average speed is given by $y = \frac{40}{x}$, where x is the time it takes to run the distance.
    a. Graph $y = \frac{40}{x}$. **See margin.**
    b. Describe the asymptotes. **See margin.**
21. **CYCLING** A cyclist rides 10 miles each morning. Her average speed y is given by $y = \frac{10}{x}$, where x is the time it takes her to ride 10 miles. Graph the function. **See margin.**

22–33. See Ch. 11 Answer Appendix.

Example 3 p. 680 — Identify the asymptotes of each function. Then graph the function.

22. $y = \frac{5}{x}$
23. ● $y = \frac{-3}{x}$
24. $y = \frac{2}{x} + 3$
25. $y = \frac{1}{x} - 2$
26. $y = \frac{1}{x+3}$
27. $y = \frac{1}{x-2}$
28. $y = \frac{-2}{x+1}$
29. $y = \frac{4}{x-1}$
30. $y = \frac{1}{x-2} + 1$
31. $y = \frac{3}{x-1} - 2$
32. $y = \frac{2}{x+1} - 4$
33. $y = \frac{-1}{x+4} + 3$

34b. Sample answer: (6, 50); if she reads for 6 days, she will read 50 pages per day.

B

34. **READING** Refer to the application at the beginning of the lesson.
    a. Graph the function. **See Ch. 11 Answer Appendix.**
    b. Choose a point on the graph, and describe what it means in the context of the situation.
35. The graph shows a translation of the graph of $y = \frac{1}{x}$.
    a. Describe the asymptotes. **$x = 3$ and $y = 2$**
    b. Write a function for the graph. **$y = \frac{1}{x-3} + 2$**

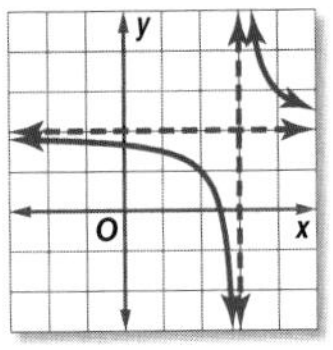

3 PRACTICE

Formative Assessment

Use Exercises 1–11 to check for understanding.

Use the chart at the bottom of this page to customize assignments for your students.

Exercise Alert

Grid Paper For Exercises 5–11, 20–34, 38–40, and 42 students will need grid paper.

TEACH with TECH

VIDEO RECORDING Have students create video recordings showing how to graph a rational function. Have students first describe how to find the horizontal and vertical asymptotes, and then use a table of values to draw the graph.

Additional Answers

5.

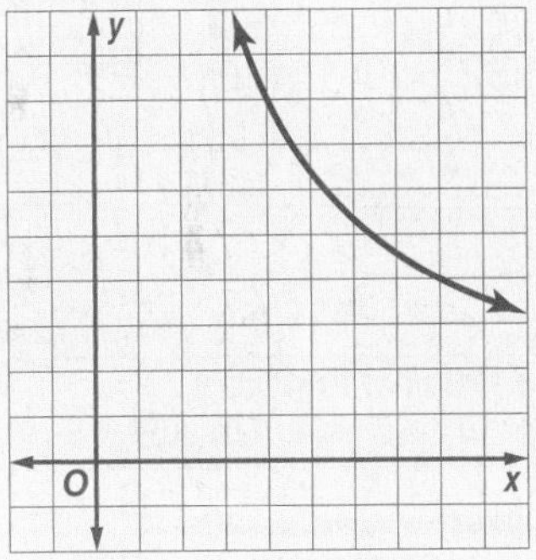

21.

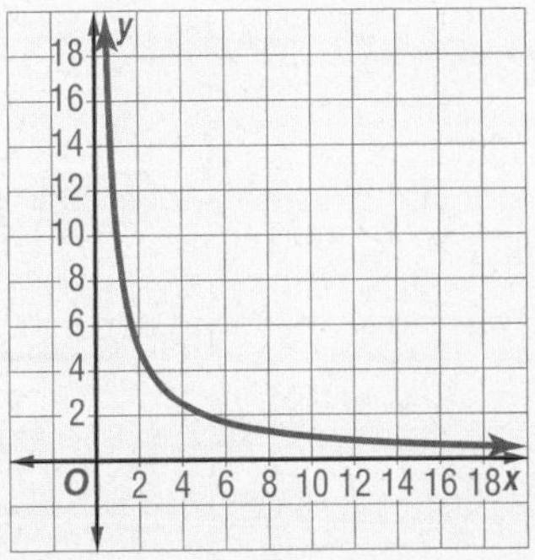

Differentiated Homework Options

Level	Assignment	Two-Day Option	
AL Basic	12–33, 43–77	13–33 odd, 48–51	12–32 even, 43–47, 52–77
OL Core	13–33 odd, 34–37, 39, 41, 43–77	12–33, 48–51	34–41, 43–47, 52–77
BL Advanced	34–65, (optional: 66–77)		

Study Guide and Intervention
CRM pp. 11–12 AL OL ELL

NAME ________ DATE ________ PERIOD ________

11-2 Study Guide and Intervention

Rational Functions

Identify Excluded Values The function $y = \frac{10}{x}$ is an example of a **rational function**. Because division by zero is undefined, any value of a variable that results in a denominator of zero must be excluded from the domain of that variable. These are called **excluded values** of the rational function.

Example State the excluded value for each function.

a. $y = \frac{3}{x}$
The denominator cannot equal zero.
The excluded value is $x = 0$.

b. $y = \frac{4}{x-5}$
$x - 5 = 0$ Set the denominator equal to 0.
$x = 5$ Add 5 to each side.
The excluded value is $x = 5$.

Lesson 11-2

Exercises

State the excluded value for each function.

1. $y = \frac{2}{x}$ **$x = 0$**
2. $y = \frac{1}{x-4}$ **$x = 4$**
3. $y = \frac{x-3}{x+1}$ **$x = -1$**
4. $y = \frac{4}{x-2}$ **$x = 2$**
5. $y = \frac{x}{2x-4}$ **$x = 2$**
6. $y = -\frac{5}{3x}$ **$x = 0$**
7. $y = \frac{3x-2}{x+3}$ **$x = -3$**
8. $y = \frac{x-1}{5x+10}$ **$x = -2$**
9. $y = \frac{x+1}{x}$ **$x = 0$**
10. $y = \frac{x-7}{2x+8}$ **$x = -4$**
11. $y = \frac{x-5}{6x}$ **$x = 0$**
12. $y = \frac{x-2}{x+11}$ **$x = -11$**
13. $y = \frac{7}{3x+21}$ **$x = -7$**
14. $y = \frac{3x-4}{x+4}$ **$x = -4$**
15. $y = \frac{x}{7x-35}$ **$x = 5$**

16. **DINING** Mya and her friends are eating at a restaurant. The total bill of $36 is split among x friends. The amount each person pays y is given by $y = \frac{36}{x}$, where x is the number of people. Graph the function.

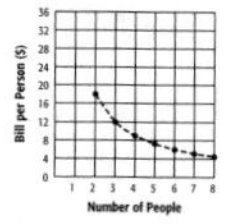

Practice
CRM p. 14 AL OL BL ELL

NAME ________ DATE ________ PERIOD ________

11-2 Practice

Rational Functions

State the excluded value for each function.

1. $y = \frac{-1}{x}$ **$x = 0$**
2. $y = \frac{3}{x+5}$ **$x = -5$**
3. $y = \frac{2x}{x-5}$ **$x = 5$**
4. $y = \frac{x-1}{12x+36}$ **$x = -3$**
5. $y = \frac{x+1}{2x+3}$ **$x = -\frac{3}{2}$**
6. $y = \frac{1}{5x-2}$ **$x = \frac{2}{5}$**

Identify the asymptotes of each function. Then graph the function.

7. $y = \frac{1}{x}$ **$x = 0, y = 0$**
8. $y = \frac{3}{x}$ **$x = 0, y = 0$**
9. $y = \frac{2}{x-1}$ **$x = 1, y = 0$**

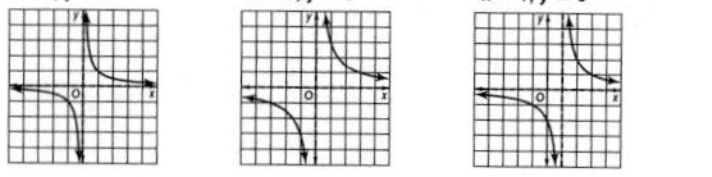

10. $y = \frac{2}{x+2}$ **$x = -2, y = 0$**
11. $y = \frac{1}{x-3} + 2$ **$x = 3, y = 2$**
12. $y = \frac{2}{x+1} - 1$ **$x = -1, y = -1$**

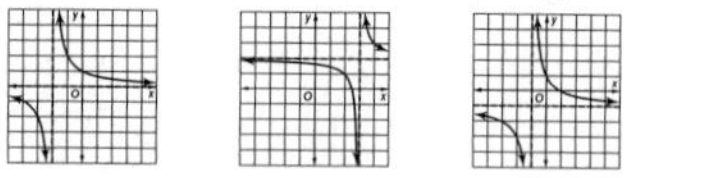

13. **AIR TRAVEL** Denver, Colorado, is located approximately 1000 miles from Indianapolis, Indiana. The average speed of a plane traveling between the two cities is given by $y = \frac{1000}{x}$, where x is the total flight time. Graph the function.

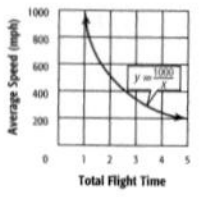

Word Problem Practice
CRM p. 15 AL OL BL ELL

NAME ________ DATE ________ PERIOD ________

11-2 Word Problem Practice

Rational Functions

1. **BULLET TRAINS** The Shinkansen, or Japanese bullet train network, provides high-speed ground transportation throughout Japan. Trains regularly operate at speeds in excess of 200 kilometers per hour. The average speed of a bullet train traveling between Tokyo and Kyoto is given by $y = \frac{515}{x}$, where x is the total travel time in hours. Graph the function.

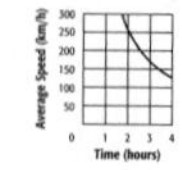

2. **DRIVING** Peter is driving to his grandparents' house 40 miles away. During the trip, Peter makes a 30-minute stop for lunch. The average speed of Peter's trip is given by $y = \frac{40}{x+0.5}$, where x is the total time spent in the car. What are the asymptotes of the function? **$x = -0.5, y = 0$**

3. **ERROR ANALYSIS** Nicolas is graphing the equation $y = \frac{20}{x+3} - 6$ and draws a graph with asymptotes at $y = 3$ and $x = -6$. Explain the error that Nicolas made in his graph. **The asymptotes should be $x = -3, y = -6$.**

4. **USED CARS** While researching cars to purchase online, Ms. Jacobs found that the value of a used car is inversely proportional to the age of the car. The average price of a used car is given by $y = \frac{17{,}900}{x+1.2} + 100$, where x is the age of the car. What are the asymptotes of the function? Explain why $x = 0$ cannot be an asymptote. **$x = -1.2, y = 100$; An asymptote at $x = 0$ would give y, the cost of the car, an infinite value when the car is brand new. The asymptote needs to be located at $x = a$, where $a < 0$.**

5. **FAMILY REUNION** The Gaudet family is holding their annual reunion at Watkins Park. It costs $50 to get a permit to hold the reunion at the park, and the family is spending $8 per person on food. The Gaudets have agreed to split the cost of the event evenly among all those attending.

a. Write an equation showing the cost per person y if x people attend the reunion. **$y = 8 + \frac{50}{x}$**

b. What are the asymptotes of the equation? **$x = 0, y = 8$**

c. Now assume that the family wants to let a long-lost cousin attend for free. Rewrite the equation to find the new cost per paying person y. **$y = 8 + \frac{58}{x-1}$**

d. What are the asymptotes for the new equation? **$x = 1, y = 8$**

Lesson 11-2

Real-World Link

The bird with the longest migration is the arctic tern. The arctic tern flies up to 20,000 miles per year, from the Arctic to the Antarctic and back.

Source: University of Wisconsin

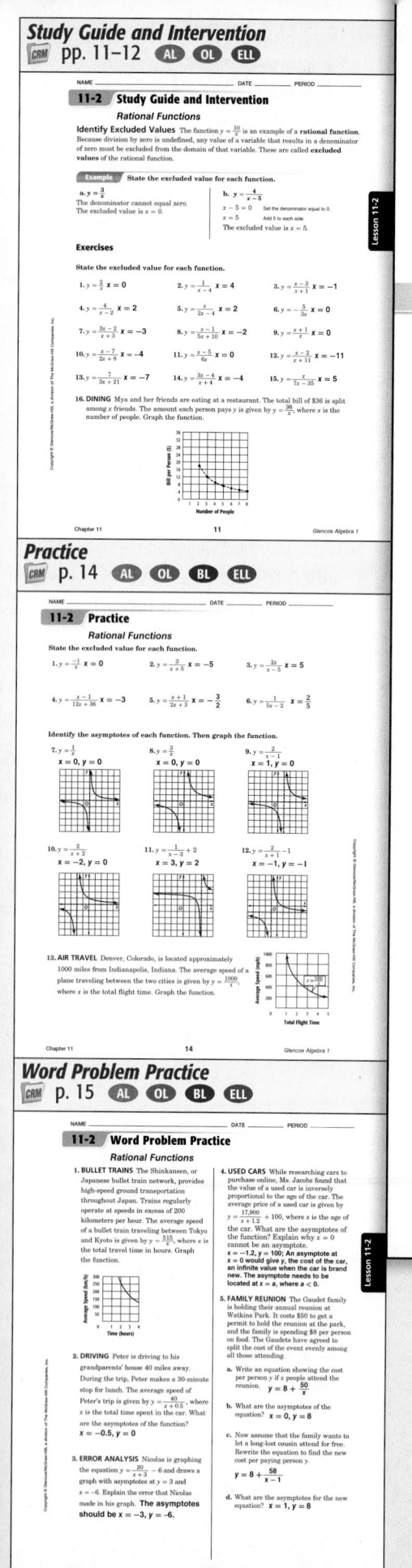

36. **BIRDS** A long-tailed jaeger is a sea bird that can migrate 5000 miles or more each year. The average rate in miles per hour r can be given by the function $r = \frac{5000}{t}$, where t is the time in hours. Use the function to determine the average rate of the bird if it spends 250 hours flying. **20 mi per hour**

37. **CLASS TRIP** The freshmen class is going to a science museum. As part of the trip, each person in the class is also contributing an equal amount of money to name a star.

a. Write a verbal description for the cost per person.

b. Write an equation to represent the total cost y per person if p people go to the museum. **$y = \frac{95}{p} + 8.50$**

c. Use a graphing calculator to graph the equation. **See margin.**

d. Estimate the number of people needed for the total cost of the trip to be about $15. **Sample answer: 15 people**

37a. Sample answer: The total cost of the trip equals the cost of a ticket plus the cost of the star-naming package divided by the number of people.

41a. D = {all positive real numbers}; R = {all positive real numbers}

43. The graph of $y = \frac{1}{x+5} - 2$ is the graph of $y = \frac{1}{x}$ translated 5 units to the left and 2 units down.

45. False; sample answer: The graph of $y = \frac{1}{x}$ has no x- or y-intercepts.

46. Sample answer: The graph of $y = \frac{8}{x} + 1$ is the only one that does not have $y = 0$ as an asymptote.

Graph each function. Identify the asymptotes. **38–40. See Ch. 11 Answer Appendix.**

38. $y = \frac{4x+3}{2x-4}$

39. $y = \frac{x^2}{x^2-1}$

40. $y = \frac{x}{x^2-9}$

41. **GEOMETRY** The equation $h = \frac{2(64)}{b_1 + 8}$ represents the height h of a quadrilateral with an area of 64 square units. The quadrilateral has two opposite sides that are parallel and h units apart; one is b_1 units long and another is 8 units long.

a. Describe a reasonable domain and range for the function.

b. Graph the function in the first quadrant. **See margin.**

c. Use the graph to estimate the value of h when $b_1 = 10$. **about 7 units**

H.O.T. Problems Use Higher-Order Thinking Skills

42. **CHALLENGE** Graph $y = \frac{1}{x^2-4}$. State the domain and the range of the function. **See margin.**

43. **REASONING** Without graphing, describe the transformation that takes place between the graph of $y = \frac{1}{x}$ and the graph of $y = \frac{1}{x+5} - 2$.

44. **OPEN ENDED** Write a rational function if the asymptotes of the graph are at $x = 3$ and $y = 1$. Explain how you found the function. **See Ch. 11 Answer Appendix.**

45. **REASONING** Is the following statement *true* or *false*? If false, give a counterexample.

The graph of a rational function will have at least one intercept.

46. **WHICH ONE DOESN'T BELONG** Identify the function that does not belong with the other three. Explain your reasoning.

$y = \frac{4}{x}$	$y = \frac{6}{x+1}$	$y = \frac{8}{x} + 1$	$y = \frac{10}{2x}$

47. **WRITING IN MATH** Write a rule to find the vertical asymptotes of a rational function. **See Ch. 11 Answer Appendix.**

Enrichment
CRM p. 16 OL BL

NAME ________ DATE ________ PERIOD ________

11-2 Enrichment

Inequalities involving Rational Functions

Inequalities involving rational functions can be graphed much like those involving linear functions.

Example Graph $y \geq \frac{1}{x}$.

Step 1 Plot points and draw a smooth solid curve. Because the inequality involves a greater than or equal to sign, solutions that satisfy $y = \frac{1}{x}$ will be a part of the graph.

Step 2 Plot the asymptotes, $x = 0$ and $y = 0$, as dashed lines.

Step 3 Begin testing values. A value must be tested between each set of lines, including asymptotes.

Region 1 Test (–1, 1). This returns a true value for the inequality.

Region 2 Test (–1, –0.5). This returns a true value for the inequality.

Region 3 Test (–1, –2). This returns a false value for the inequality.

Region 4 Test (1, 2). This returns a true value for the inequality.

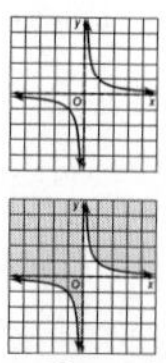

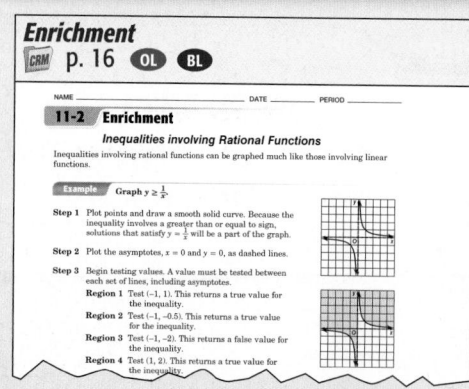

PSAE PRACTICE 8.11.01, 6.11.10, 8.11.03, 9.11.05

48. Simplify $\frac{2a^2d}{3bc} \cdot \frac{9b^2c}{16ad^2}$. **D**

A $\frac{abd}{c}$ C $\frac{6a}{4bd}$

B $\frac{ab}{d}$ D $\frac{3ab}{8d}$

49. SHORT RESPONSE One day Lola ran 100 meters in 15 seconds, 200 meters in 45 seconds, and 200 meters over low hurdles in one and a half minutes. How many more seconds did it take her to run 200 meters over low hurdles than the 200-meter dash? **45 seconds**

50. Scott and Ian started a T-shirt printing business. The total start-up costs were $450. It costs $5.50 to print one T-shirt. Write a rational function $A(x)$ for the average cost of producing x T-shirts. **F**

F $A(x) = \frac{450 + 5.5x}{x}$ H $A(x) = 450x + 5.5$

G $A(x) = \frac{450}{x} + 5.5$ J $A(x) = 450 + 5.5x$

51. GEOMETRY Which of the following is a quadrilateral with exactly one pair of parallel sides? **D**

A parallelogram C square

B rectangle D trapezoid

Spiral Review

52. Yes; sample answer: At 65 mph, the family can travel 220 miles in about 3 hours and 23 minutes, saving them about 37 minutes.

52. TRAVEL The Brooks family can drive to the beach, which is 220 miles away, in 4 hours if they drive 55 miles per hour. Kendra says that they would save at least a half an hour if they were to drive 65 miles per hour. Is Kendra correct? Explain. (Lesson 11-1)

Use a calculator to find the measure of each angle to the nearest degree. (Lesson 10-8)

53. $\sin C = 0.9781$ **78°** **54.** $\tan H = 0.6473$ **33°** **55.** $\cos K = 0.7658$ **40°**

56. $\tan Y = 3.6541$ **75°** **57.** $\cos U = 0.5000$ **60°** **58.** $\sin N = 0.3832$ **23°**

If c is the measure of the hypotenuse of a right triangle, find each missing measure. If necessary round to the nearest hundredth. (Lesson 10-5)

59. $a = 15, b = 60, c = ?$ **61.85** **60.** $a = 17, c = 35, b = ?$ **30.59** **61.** $a = \sqrt{110}, b = 1, c = ?$ **10.54**

62. $a = \sqrt{17}, b = \sqrt{12}, c = ?$ **5.39** **63.** $a = 6, c = 11, b = ?$ **9.22** **64.** $a = 9, b = 6, c = ?$ **10.82**

65. SIGHT The formula $d = \sqrt{\frac{3h}{2}}$ represents the distance d in miles that a person h feet high can see. Irene is standing on a cliff that is 310 feet above sea level. How far can Irene see from the cliff? Write a simplified radical expression and a decimal approximation. (Lesson 10-3) **$\sqrt{465}$ or about 21.56 mi**

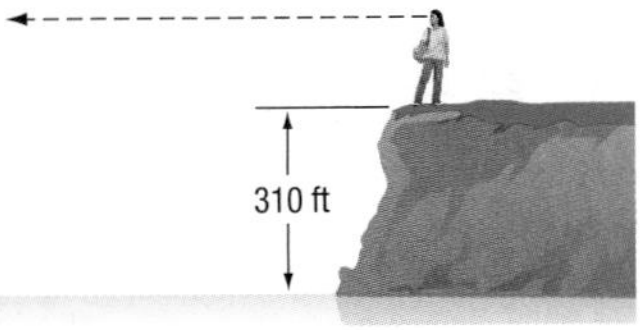

66. $(x + 3)(x + 8)$ **67.** $(w + 16)(w - 3)$ **68.** $(p - 7)(p + 5)$
69. $(3 + a)(24 + a)$ **70.** $(c + 7)(c + 5)$ **71.** $(d - 2)(d - 5)$
72. $(g - 15)(g - 4)$ **73.** $(n + 9)(n - 6)$ **74.** $(5x + 2)(x + 5)$
75. $(4b - 3)(6b + 1)$ **76.** $(4a + 5)(3a - 7)$ **77.** $2(x - 3)(3x + 2)$

Skills Review

Factor each trinomial. (Lessons 8-3 and 8-4)

66. $x^2 + 11x + 24$ **67.** $w^2 + 13w - 48$ **68.** $p^2 - 2p - 35$ **69.** $72 + 27a + a^2$

70. $c^2 + 12c + 35$ **71.** $d^2 - 7d + 10$ **72.** $g^2 - 19g + 60$ **73.** $n^2 + 3n - 54$

74. $5x^2 + 27x + 10$ **75.** $24b^2 - 14b - 3$ **76.** $12a^2 - 13a - 35$ **77.** $6x^2 - 14x - 12$

4 ASSESS

Ticket Out the Door On small pieces of paper, write one of five different rational functions similar to those in this lesson. Give one to each student. As students walk out the door, ask them to tell you the horizontal and vertical asymptotes.

Formative Assessment

Check for student understanding of concepts in Lessons 11-1 and 11-2.

CRM Quiz 1, p. 57

Additional Answers

37c.

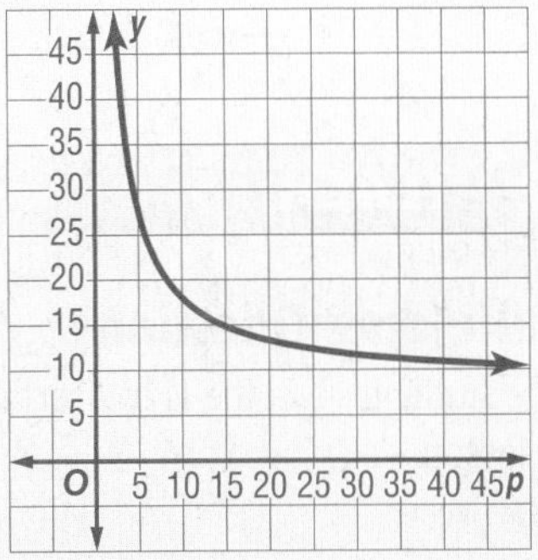

41b.

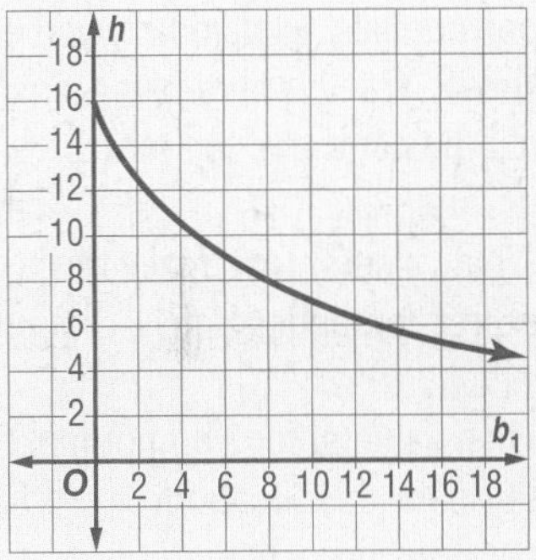

42.

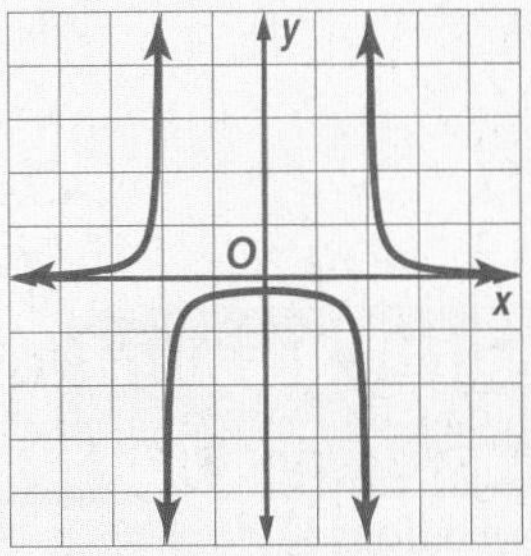

D = all real numbers except $x = -2$ and $x = 2$;
$R = \left\{y \mid y > 0 \text{ or } y \le -\frac{1}{4}\right\}$

Differentiated Instruction OL BL

Extension Ask students to graph the function $y = \frac{x - 1}{x - 1}$. Then ask students to describe the graph. The graph is a horizontal line, $y = 1$, with a hole at (1, 1).

11-3 Lesson Notes

1 FOCUS

Vertical Alignment

Before Lesson 11-3
Simplify expressions involving the quotient of monomials.

Lesson 11-3
Identify values excluded from the domain of a rational expression.
Simplify rational expressions.

After Lesson 11-3
Simplify mixed expressions and complex fractions.

2 TEACH

Scaffolding Questions

Have students read the *Why?* section of the lesson.

Ask:

- Is the given expression a quotient of polynomials? Explain how you know. Yes; the numerator and denominator are one-term polynomials.
- What value(s) for *r* make the expression undefined? *r* cannot equal 0.
- What value(s) for *r* do not make sense for this situation? *r* cannot be a negative value.

11-3 Simplifying Rational Expressions

Then
You simplified expressions involving the quotient of monomials. (Lesson 7-2)

Now

- Identify values excluded from the domain of a rational expression.
- Simplify rational expressions.

IL Learning Standards

7.A.4b Apply formulas in a wide variety of theoretical and practical real-world measurement applications involving perimeter, area, volume, angle, time, temperature, mass, speed, distance, density and monetary values.
7.B.4 Estimate and measure the magnitude and directions of physical quantities using rulers, protractors and other scientific instruments including timers, calculators and computers.

New Vocabulary
rational expression

IL Math Online
glencoe.com

- Extra Examples
- Personal Tutor
- Self-Check Quiz
- Homework Help

Why?

Big-O is a "hubless" Ferris wheel in Tokyo, Japan. The *centripetal force*, or the force acting toward the center, is given by $\frac{mv^2}{r}$, where m is the mass of the Ferris wheel, v is the velocity, and r is the radius.

Identify Excluded Values The expression $\frac{mv^2}{r}$ is an example of a rational expression. A **rational expression** is an algebraic fraction whose numerator and denominator are polynomials. Since division by zero is undefined, the polynomial in the denominator cannot be 0.

EXAMPLE 1 Find Excluded Values

State the excluded values for each rational expression.

a. $\frac{-8}{r^2 - 36}$

Exclude the values for which $r^2 - 36 = 0$.

$r^2 - 36 = 0$ — **The denominator cannot be zero.**

$(r - 6)(r + 6) = 0$ — **Factor.**

$r - 6 = 0$ or $r + 6 = 0$ — **Zero Product Property**

$r = 6$ $\quad$ $r = -6$

Therefore, r cannot equal 6 or -6.

b. $\frac{n^2}{n^2 + 4n - 5}$

Exclude the values for which $n^2 + 4n - 5 = 0$.

$n^2 + 4n - 5 = 0$ — **The denominator cannot be zero.**

$(n - 1)(n + 5) = 0$ — **Factor.**

$n - 1 = 0$ or $n + 5 = 0$ — **Zero Product Property**

$n = 1$ $\quad$ $n = -5$

Therefore, n cannot equal 1 or -5.

Check Your Progress

1A. $\frac{5x}{x^2 - 81}$ **9, −9** $\qquad$ **1B.** $\frac{3a - 2}{a^2 + 6a + 8}$ **−2, −4**

Personal Tutor glencoe.com

Lesson 11-3 Resources

Resource	Approaching-Level	On-Level	Beyond-Level	English Learners
Teacher Edition	• Differentiated Instruction, p. 686	• Differentiated Instruction, p. 686	• Differentiated Instruction, p. 690	• Differentiated Instruction, p. 686
Chapter Resource Masters	• Study Guide and Intervention, pp. 17–18 • Skills Practice, p. 19 • Practice, p. 20 • Word Problem Practice, p. 21	• Study Guide and Intervention, pp. 17–18 • Skills Practice, p. 19 • Practice, p. 20 • Word Problem Practice, p. 21 • Enrichment, p. 22	• Practice, p. 20 • Word Problem Practice, p. 21 • Enrichment, p. 22	• Study Guide and Intervention, pp. 17–18 • Skills Practice, p. 19 • Practice, p. 20 • Word Problem Practice, p. 21
Transparencies	• 5-Minute Check Transparency 11-3	• 5-Minute Check Transparency 11-3	• 5-Minute Check Transparency 11-3	• 5-Minute Check Transparency 11-3
Other	• Study Notebook	• Study Notebook	• Study Notebook	• Study Notebook

Real-World EXAMPLE 2 Use Rational Expressions

GEOMETRY Find the height of a cylinder that has a volume of 821 cubic inches and a radius of 7 inches. Round to the nearest tenth.

Understand You have a rational expression with two variables, V and r.

Plan Substitute 821 for V and 7 for r and simplify.

Solve $\frac{V}{\pi r^2} = \frac{821}{\pi(7)^2}$ **Replace V with 821 and r with 7.**

≈ 5.3 **The height of the cylinder is about 5.3 inches.**

Check Use estimation to determine whether the answer is reasonable.

$\frac{800}{3(50)} \approx 5$ ✓ **The solution is reasonable.**

Check Your Progress

2. Find the height of the cylinder that has a volume of 710 cubic inches and a diameter of 18 inches. 2.8 in.

Personal Tutor glencoe.com

StudyTip

Cylinder The volume of a cylinder is $V = \pi r^2 h$. The height of a cylinder with volume V and radius r is given by $\frac{V}{\pi r^2}$.

Simplify Expressions A rational expression is in simplest form when the numerator and denominator have no common factors except 1. To simplify a rational expression, divide out any common factors of the numerator and denominator.

Key Concept Simplifying Rational Expressions

For Your FOLDABLE

Words Let a, b, and c, be polynomials with $a \neq 0$ and $c \neq 0$.

Symbols $\frac{ba}{ca} = \frac{b \cdot a}{c \cdot a} = \frac{b}{c}$ **Example** $\frac{3x - 9}{4x - 12} = \frac{3(x - 3)}{4(x - 3)} = \frac{3}{4}$

Math *in Motion*, Interactive Lab glencoe.com

PSAE EXAMPLE 3 8.11.01

Which expression is equivalent to $\frac{(-3x^2)(4x^5)}{9x^6}$?

A $\frac{4}{3}x$ B $\frac{4}{3x}$ C $-\frac{4}{3x}$ D $-\frac{4}{3}x$

Read the Test Item The expression represents the product of two monomials and the division of that product by another monomial.

Solve the Test Item

Step 1 Factor the numerator and denominator, using their GCF. $\frac{(3x^6)(-4x)}{(3x^6)(3)}$

Step 2 Simplify. The correct answer is D. $\frac{\cancel{(3x^6)}(-4x)}{\cancel{(3x^6)}(3)}$ or $-\frac{4}{3}x$

Test-TakingTip

Eliminate Possibilities Since there is only one negative factor in the expression in Example 3, the simplified expression should have a negative sign. So, you can eliminate choices A and B.

Check Your Progress

3. Which expression is equivalent to $\frac{16c^2b^4}{8c^3b}$? F

F $\frac{2b^3}{c}$ G $\frac{b^3}{2c}$ H $\frac{1}{2b^3c}$ J $2b^3c$

Personal Tutor glencoe.com

Identify Excluded Values

Example 1 shows how to determine the excluded values for rational expressions. **Example 2** shows how to use rational expressions to solve real-world problems.

Formative Assessment

Use the Check Your Progress exercises after each example to determine students' understanding of concepts

Additional Examples

1 State the excluded value(s) for each expression.

a. $\frac{3b - 2}{b + 7}$ b cannot equal −7.

b. $\frac{5a^2 + 2}{a^2 - a - 12}$ a cannot equal −3 or 4.

c. $y = \frac{8}{2x + 1}$ x cannot equal $-\frac{1}{2}$.

2 **GEOMETRY** Suppose the cylinder in Example 2 has a volume of 770 cubic inches and a diameter of 12 inches. Find the height of the cylinder. Round to the nearest tenth. 6.8 in.

Additional Examples also in Interactive Classroom PowerPoint® Presentations

IWB INTERACTIVE WHITEBOARD READY

Simplify Expressions

Example 3 shows how to simplify a rational expression using the greatest common factor of the numerator and the denominator. **Example 4** shows the importance of finding the excluded values of a rational expression by using the denominator of the original expression rather than that of the simplified expression. **Example 5** shows how to simplify rational expressions containing binomials that are opposites. **Example 6** shows how to find the zeros of a rational function.

Watch Out!

Excluded Values Students may assume that excluded values are determined from the simplified expression. This may or may not be true. Stress that excluded values must *always* be determined from the original denominator.

TEACH with TECH

BLOG On your secure classroom blog, have students write entries explaining why they need to find the excluded values when simplifying a rational expression. Make sure students explain that they need to check the denominator of the *original* expression for values where the denominator is zero.

Additional Examples

3 STANDARDIZED TEST PRACTICE
Which expression is equivalent to $\frac{32x^5y^2}{4xy^7}$? B

A $\frac{8x^5}{y^5}$

B $\frac{8x^4}{y^5}$

C $\frac{8x^6}{y^9}$

D $\frac{24x^4}{y^5}$

4 Simplify $\frac{4x + 16}{x^2 - 5x - 36}$. State the excluded values of x. $\frac{4}{x - 9}$; $x \neq -4$ and $x \neq 9$

5 Simplify $\frac{25 - x^2}{8x - 40}$. State the excluded values of x. $-\frac{5 + x}{8}$; $x \neq 5$

Focus on Mathematical Content

Simplifying Rational Expressions A rational expression is simplified when the numerator and denominator of the expression have no factors in common other than ± 1. Identifying excluded values should be the first step in the simplification process since all restrictions found in a problem should be included in the answer.

Watch Out!

Preventing Errors Refer students to Chapter 8 if they need to review how to factor polynomials.

You can use the same procedure to simplify a rational expression in which the numerator and denominator are polynomials.

EXAMPLE 4 Simplify Rational Expressions

Simplify $\frac{2r + 18}{r^2 + 8r - 9}$. State the excluded values of r.

$\frac{2r + 18}{r^2 + 8r - 9} = \frac{2(r + 9)}{(r + 9)(r - 1)}$ — **Factor.**

$= \frac{2\cancel{(r + 9)}^{1}}{\cancel{(r + 9)}_{1}(r - 1)}$ or $\frac{2}{r - 1}$ — **Divide the numerator and denominator by the GCF, $r + 9$.**

Exclude the values for which $r^2 + 8r - 9$ equals 0.

$r^2 + 8r - 9 = 0$ — **The denominator cannot equal zero.**

$(r + 9)(r - 1) = 0$ — **Factor.**

$r = -9$ or $r = 1$ — **Zero Product Property**

So, $r \neq -9$ and $r \neq 1$.

StudyTip

Excluded Values Determine the excluded values using the *original* expression rather than the simplified expression.

Check Your Progress

Simplify each rational expression. State the excluded values of the variables.

4A. $\frac{n + 3}{n^2 + 10n + 21}$ $\frac{1}{n + 7}$; $-3, -7$

4B. $\frac{y^2 + 9y - 10}{2y + 20}$ $\frac{y - 1}{2}$; -10

Personal Tutor glencoe.com

When simplifying rational expressions, look for binomials that are opposites. For example, $5 - x$ and $x - 5$ are opposites because $5 - x = -1(x - 5)$. So, you can write $\frac{x - 5}{5 - x}$ as $\frac{x - 5}{-1(x - 5)}$.

EXAMPLE 5 Recognize Opposites

Simplify $\frac{36 - t^2}{5t - 30}$. State the excluded values of t.

$\frac{36 - t^2}{5t - 30} = \frac{(6 - t)(6 + t)}{5(t - 6)}$ — **Factor.**

$= \frac{-1(t - 6)(6 + t)}{5(t - 6)}$ — **Rewrite $6 - t$ as $-1(t - 6)$.**

$= \frac{-1\cancel{(t - 6)}^{1}(6 + t)}{5\cancel{(t - 6)}_{1}}$ or $-\frac{6 + t}{5}$ — **Divide out the common factor, $t - 6$.**

Exclude the values for which $5t - 30$ equals 0.

$5t - 30 = 0$ — **The denominator cannot equal zero.**

$5t = 30$ — **Add 30 to each side.**

$t = 6$ — **Zero Product Property**

So, $t \neq 6$.

Check Your Progress

Simplify each expression. State the excluded values of x.

5A. $\frac{12x + 36}{x^2 - x - 12}$ $\frac{12}{x - 4}$; 4 and -3

5B. $\frac{x^2 - 2x - 35}{x^2 - 9x + 14}$ $\frac{x + 5}{x - 2}$; 2 and 7

Personal Tutor glencoe.com

Differentiated Instruction

AL OL ELL

If you think students may benefit from working with a partner,

Then place students in pairs to work through Examples 1, 3, 4, 5, and 6. Have one student factor the numerator, and the other the denominator. Then ask students to jointly find the excluded values and the simplified expression.

StudyTip

Zeros Once simplified, a rational function has zeros at the values that make the numerator 0.

Recall that to find the zeros of a quadratic function, you need to find the values of x when $f(x) = 0$. The zeros of a rational function are found in the same way.

EXAMPLE 6 Rational Functions

Find the zeros of $f(x) = \frac{x^2 + 3x - 18}{x - 3}$.

$f(x) = \frac{x^2 + 3x - 18}{x - 3}$ **Original function**

$0 = \frac{x^2 + 3x - 18}{x - 3}$ **$f(x) = 0$**

$0 = \frac{(x + 6)(x - 3)}{x - 3}$ **Factor.**

$0 = \frac{(x + 6)\cancel{(x - 3)}^{1}}{\cancel{x - 3}_{1}}$ **Divide out common factors.**

$0 = x + 6$ **Simplify.**

When $x = -6$, the numerator becomes 0, so $f(x) = 0$. Therefore, the zero of the function is -6.

Check Your Progress

Find the zeros of each function.

6A. $f(x) = \frac{x^2 + 2x - 15}{x + 1}$ $-5, 3$

6B. $f(x) = \frac{x^2 + 6x + 8}{x^2 + x - 2}$ -4

Personal Tutor glencoe.com

Check Your Understanding

Example 1 p. 684

State the excluded values for each rational expression.

1. $\frac{8}{x^2 - 16}$ $4, -4$

2. $\frac{3m}{m^2 - 6m + 5}$ $1, 5$

Example 2 p. 685

3. **PHYSICAL SCIENCE** A 0.16-kilogram ball attached to a string is being spun in a circle 7.26 meters per second. The expression $\frac{mv^2}{r}$, where m is the mass of the ball, v is the velocity, and r is the radius, can be used to find the force that keeps the ball spinning in a circle. If the circle has a radius of 0.5 meter, find the force that must be exerted to keep the ball spinning. Round to the nearest tenth. 16.9 units of force

Examples 3–5 pp. 685–686

Simplify each expression. State the excluded values of the variables.

4. $\frac{28ab^3}{16a^2b}$ $\frac{7b^2}{4a}$; $a \neq 0$, $b \neq 0$

5. $\frac{(-3r)(10r^4)}{6r^5}$ -5; 0

6. $\frac{5d + 15}{d^2 - d - 12}$ $\frac{5}{d - 4}$; $4, -3$

7. $\frac{x^2 + 11x + 28}{x + 4}$ $x + 7$; -4

8. $\frac{2r - 12}{r^2 - 36}$ $\frac{2}{r + 6}$; $6, -6$

9. $\frac{3y - 27}{81 - y^2}$ $-\frac{3}{9 + y}$; $-9, 9$

Example 6 p. 687

Find the zeros of each function.

10. $f(x) = \frac{x^2 - x - 12}{x - 2}$ $4, -3$

11. $f(x) = \frac{x^2 - x - 6}{x^2 + 8x + 12}$ 3

Additional Example

6 Find the zeros of $f(x) = \frac{x^2 + 8x + 7}{x + 1}$. -7

3 PRACTICE

Formative Assessment

Use Exercises 1–11 to check for understanding.

Use the chart at the bottom of the next page to customize assignments for your students.

Exercise Alert

Formulas For Exercises 17 and 41, students will need to know the formulas for the circumference and area of a circle, the surface area and volume of a rectangular solid, and the surface area and volume of a cylinder.

Watch Out!

Find the Error For Exercise 43, ask students to identify the person who listed the excluded values correctly and also the person who simplified the expression correctly.

Additional Answers

38. $b^3 + 3a - 2a^3$; $a, b \neq 0$

39. $\frac{4x^4 - 5y^2}{y^3}$; $x, y \neq 0$

40. $\frac{1}{3x-1}$; $\frac{1}{3}$, -5

46. Sample answer: $\frac{1}{x^2-4}$; since the excluded values are 2 and -2, the denominator of the rational expression must contain the factors $x - 2$ and $x + 2$.

Practice and Problem Solving

● = Step-by-Step Solutions begin on page R12.
Extra Practice begins on page 815.

Example 1 p. 684

State the excluded values for each rational expression.

12. $\frac{-n}{n^2-49}$ 7, −7

13. $\frac{5x+1}{x^2-1}$ 1, −1

14. $\frac{12a}{a^2-3a-10}$ 5, −2

15. $\frac{k^2-4}{k^2+5k-24}$ 3, −8

Example 2 p. 685

16. **GEOMETRY** The volume of a rectangular prism is $3x^3 + 34x^2 + 72x - 64$. If the height is $x + 4$, what is the area of the base of the prism? $3x^2 + 22x - 16$

17. $\frac{2\pi(5t)}{\pi(5t)^2} = \frac{2}{5t}$; 0

17. **GEOMETRY** Use the circle at the right to write the ratio $\frac{\text{circumference}}{\text{area}}$. Then simplify. State the excluded value of the variable.

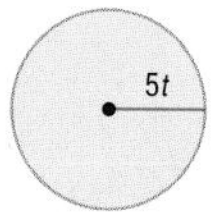

Examples 3–5 pp. 685–686

Simplify each expression. State the excluded values of the variables.

18. $\frac{15x^4y^2}{40x^3y^3}$ $\frac{3x}{8y}$; $x \neq 0, y \neq 0$

19. $\frac{32n^2p}{2n^4p}$ $\frac{16}{n^2}$; $n \neq 0, p \neq 0$

20. $\frac{(4t^3)(2t)}{20t^2}$ $\frac{2t^2}{5}$; 0

21. $\frac{(7c^2)(-6c^3)}{21c^4}$ $-2c$; 0

22. $\frac{4x-24}{x^2-12x+36}$ $\frac{4}{x-6}$; 6

23. $\frac{a^2+3a}{a^2-3a-18}$ $\frac{a}{a-6}$; 6, −3

24. $\frac{n^2+7n-18}{n-2}$ $n + 9$; 2

25. $\frac{x^2+4x-32}{x+8}$ $x - 4$; −8

26. $\frac{x^2-25}{x^2+5x}$ $\frac{x-5}{x}$; 0, −5

27. $\frac{2p^2-14p}{p^2-49}$ $\frac{2p}{p+7}$; 7, −7

28. $\frac{2x-10}{25-x^2}$ $\frac{2}{-(x+5)}$; 5, −5

29. $\frac{64-c^2}{c^2-7c-8}$ $\frac{-(8+c)}{c+1}$; 8, −1

Example 6 p. 687

Find the zeros of each function.

30. $f(x) = \frac{x^2-x-12}{x^2+2x-35}$ −3, 4

31. $f(x) = \frac{x^2+3x-4}{x^2+9x+20}$ 1

32. $f(x) = \frac{2x^2+11x-40}{2x+5}$ $-8, \frac{5}{2}$

33. $f(x) = \frac{3x^2-18x+24}{x-6}$ 2, 4

34. $f(x) = \frac{x^3+x^2-6x}{x-1}$ 0, −3, 2

35. $f(x) = \frac{x^3-4x^2-12x}{x+2}$ 0, 6

38–40. See margin.

B

36. **PYRAMIDS** The perimeter of the base of the Pyramid of the Sun is 4π times the height. The perimeter of the base of the Great Pyramid of Giza is 2π times the height. Write and simplify each ratio comparing the base perimeters. a. about 0.97

Pyramid	Height (ft)
Pyramid of the Sun (Mexico)	233.5
Great Pyramid (Egypt)	481.4

Source: Nexus Network Journal

a. Pyramid of the Sun to the Great Pyramid

b. Great Pyramid to the Pyramid of the Sun about 1.03

Real-World Link

George Ferris built the first Ferris wheel for the World's Columbian Exposition in 1893. It had a diameter of 250 feet.

Source: *The New York Times*

37. **FERRIS WHEELS** Refer to the Real-World Link.

a. To find the speed traveled by a car located on the wheel, you can find the circumference of a circle and divide by the time it takes for one rotation. Write a rational expression for the speed of a car rotating in time t. $\frac{250\pi}{t}$

b. Suppose the first Ferris wheel rotated once every 5 minutes. What was the speed of a car on the circumference in feet per minute? about 157 ft/min

Simplify each expression. State the excluded values of the variables.

38. $\frac{3a^2b^4 + 9a^3b - 6a^5b}{3a^2b}$

39. $\frac{8x^5 - 10xy^2}{2xy^3}$

40. $\frac{x+5}{3x^2+14x-5}$

Differentiated Homework Options

Level	Assignment		Two-Day Option	
AL Basic	12–35, 43, 45–80	13–35 odd, 49–52	12–34 even, 43, 45–48, 53–80
OL Core	13–35 odd, 36, 37, 39, 41–43, 45–80	12–35, 49–52	36–43, 45–48, 53–80
BL Advanced	36–74, (optional: 75–80)		

41. **PACKAGING** To minimize packaging expenses, a company uses packages that have the least surface area to volume ratio. For each figure, write a ratio comparing the surface area to the volume. Then simplify. State the excluded values of the variables.

a. $\frac{2x^2 + 8x^2}{2x^3} = \frac{5}{x}$; 0

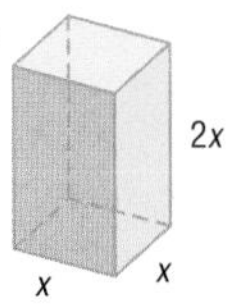

b. $\frac{2\pi a^2 + 2\pi ab}{\pi a^2 b} = \frac{2a + 2b}{ab}$; 0, 0

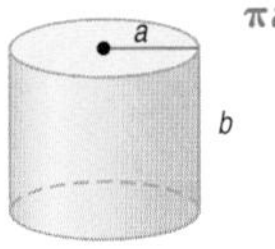

Real-World Link

The ancient Egyptians probably used levers to help them maneuver the giant blocks they used to build the pyramids. An estimated 20,000 to 30,000 workers built the Pyramids at Giza over 80 years.

Source: *National Geographic*

42. **HISTORY** The diagram shows how a lever may have been used to move blocks.

a. The mechanical advantage of a lever is $\frac{L_A}{L_R}$, where L_A is the length of the effort arm and L_R is the length of the resistance arm. Find the mechanical advantage of the lever shown. **4**

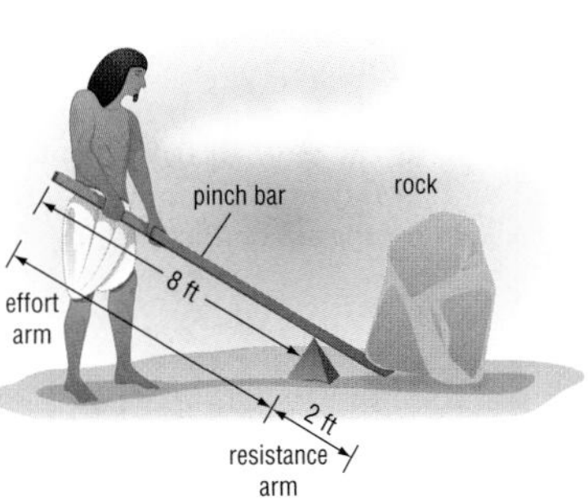

b. The force placed on the rock is the product of the mechanical advantage and the force applied to the end of the lever. If the Egyptian worker can apply a force of 180 pounds, what is the greatest weight he can lift with the lever? **720 lb**

c. To lift a 535-pound rock using a 7-foot lever with the fulcrum 2 feet from the rock, how much force will have to be used? **214 lb**

H.O.T. Problems
Use Higher-Order Thinking Skills

43. **FIND THE ERROR** Colleen and Sanson examined $\frac{12x + 36}{x^2 - x - 12}$ and found the excluded value(s). Is either of them correct? Explain.

Colleen

$\frac{12x + 36}{x^2 - x - 12} = \frac{12(x + 3)}{(x - 4)(x + 3)}$

The excluded values are 4 and -3.

Sanson

$\frac{12x + 36}{x^2 - x - 12} = \frac{12(x + 3)}{(x - 4)(x + 3)}$

$= \frac{12\cancel{(x + 3)}}{(x - 4)\cancel{(x + 3)}}$

$= \frac{12}{x - 4}$

The excluded value is 4.

44. **CHALLENGE** Compare and contrast the graphs of $y = x - 2$ and $y = \frac{x^2 + 5x - 14}{x + 7}$.

45. **REASONING** Explain why every polynomial is also a rational expression.

46. **OPEN ENDED** Write a rational expression with excluded values −2 and 2. Explain how you found the expression. **See margin.**

47. **REASONING** Is $\frac{2x^2 - 4x}{x - 2}$ in simplest form? Justify your answer. **See margin.**

48. **WRITING IN MATH** List the steps you would use to simplify $\frac{x^2 + x - 20}{x + 5}$. State the excluded value. **See margin.**

43. No; Colleen did not show the simplified expression and Sanson used the simplified expression to find the excluded values.

44. Sample answer: The graphs appear to be identical, but the second graph has an excluded value at $x = -7$, so there is a hole in the graph at $(-7, -9)$.

45. Every polynomial P can be written as $\frac{P}{1}$, where the numerator and denominator are polynomials; hence every polynomial is also a rational expression.

Additional Answers

47. No; the numerator and denominator have $x - 2$ as a common factor.

48. Sample answer: Factor the numerator as $(x + 5)(x - 4)$. Then divide the numerator and the denominator by the GCF, $x + 5$. The simplified expression is $x - 4$ and the excluded value is $x = -5$.

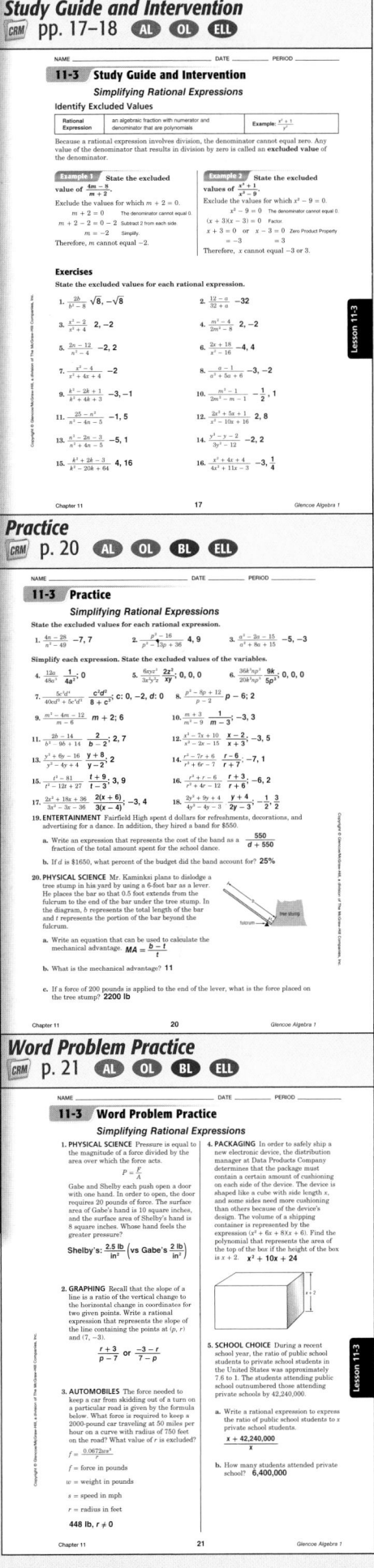

Study Guide and Intervention
CRM pp. 17–18 AL OL ELL

NAME ______ DATE ______ PERIOD ______

11-3 Study Guide and Intervention

Simplifying Rational Expressions

Identify Excluded Values

Rational Expression	an algebraic fraction with numerator and denominator that are polynomials	Example: $\frac{x^2 + 1}{y^2}$

Because a rational expression involves division, the denominator cannot equal zero. Any value of the denominator that results in division by zero is called an **excluded value** of the denominator.

Example 1 State the excluded value of $\frac{4m - 8}{m + 2}$.

Exclude the values for which $m + 2 = 0$.

$m + 2 = 0$ The denominator cannot equal 0.
$m + 2 - 2 = 0 - 2$ Subtract 2 from each side.
$m = -2$ Simplify.

Therefore, m cannot equal −2.

Example 2 State the excluded values of $\frac{x^2 + 1}{x^2 - 9}$.

Exclude the values for which $x^2 - 9 = 0$.

$x^2 - 9 = 0$ The denominator cannot equal 0.
$(x + 3)(x - 3) = 0$ Factor.
$x + 3 = 0$ or $x - 3 = 0$ Zero Product Property
$= -3$ $= 3$

Therefore, x cannot equal −3 or 3.

Exercises

State the excluded values for each rational expression.

1. $\frac{2b}{b^2 - 8}$ **$\sqrt{8}, -\sqrt{8}$**
2. $\frac{12 - a}{32 + a}$ **−32**
3. $\frac{x^2 - 2}{x^2 + 4}$ **2, −2**
4. $\frac{m^2 - 4}{2m^2 - 8}$ **2, −2**
5. $\frac{2n - 12}{n^2 - 4}$ **−2, 2**
6. $\frac{2x + 18}{x^2 - 16}$ **−4, 4**
7. $\frac{x^2 - 4}{x^2 + 4x + 4}$ **−2**
8. $\frac{a - 1}{a^2 + 5a + 6}$ **−3, −2**
9. $\frac{k^2 - 2k + 1}{k^2 + 4k + 3}$ **−3, −1**
10. $\frac{m^2 - 1}{2m^2 - m - 1}$ **$-\frac{1}{2}$, 1**
11. $\frac{25 - n^2}{n^2 - 4n - 5}$ **−1, 5**
12. $\frac{2x^2 + 5x + 1}{x^2 - 10x + 16}$ **2, 8**
13. $\frac{n^2 - 2n - 3}{n^2 + 4n - 5}$ **−5, 1**
14. $\frac{y^2 - y - 2}{3y^2 - 12}$ **−2, 2**
15. $\frac{k^2 + 2k - 3}{k^2 - 20k + 64}$ **4, 16**
16. $\frac{x^2 + 4x + 4}{4x^2 + 11x - 3}$ **−3, $\frac{1}{4}$**

Chapter 11 17 Glencoe Algebra 1

Lesson 11-3

Practice
CRM p. 20 AL OL BL ELL

NAME ______ DATE ______ PERIOD ______

11-3 Practice

Simplifying Rational Expressions

State the excluded values for each rational expression.

1. $\frac{4n - 28}{n^2 - 49}$ **−7, 7**
2. $\frac{p^2 - 16}{p^2 - 13p + 36}$ **4, 9**
3. $\frac{a^2 - 2a - 15}{a^2 + 8a + 15}$ **−5, −3**

Simplify each expression. State the excluded values of the variables.

4. $\frac{12a}{48a^3}$ **$\frac{1}{4a^2}$; 0**
5. $\frac{6xyz^3}{3x^2y^2z}$ **$\frac{2z^2}{xy}$; 0, 0, 0**
6. $\frac{36k^3np^2}{20k^2np^5}$ **$\frac{9k}{5p^3}$; 0, 0, 0**
7. $\frac{5c^3d^4}{40cd^2 + 5c^4d^2}$ **$\frac{c^2d^2}{8 + c^3}$; c: 0, −2, d: 0**
8. $\frac{p^2 - 8p + 12}{p - 2}$ **p − 6; 2**
9. $\frac{m^2 - 4m - 12}{m - 6}$ **m + 2; 6**
10. $\frac{m + 3}{m^2 - 9}$ **$\frac{1}{m - 3}$; −3, 3**
11. $\frac{2b - 14}{b^2 - 9b + 14}$ **$\frac{2}{b - 2}$; 2, 7**
12. $\frac{x^2 - 7x + 10}{x^2 - 2x - 15}$ **$\frac{x - 2}{x + 3}$; −3, 5**
13. $\frac{y^2 + 6y - 16}{y^2 - 4y + 4}$ **$\frac{y + 8}{y - 2}$; 2**
14. $\frac{r^2 - 7r + 6}{r^2 + 6r - 7}$ **$\frac{r - 6}{r + 7}$; −7, 1**
15. $\frac{t^2 - 81}{t^2 - 12t + 27}$ **$\frac{t + 9}{t - 3}$; 3, 9**
16. $\frac{r^2 + r - 6}{r^2 + 4r - 12}$ **$\frac{r + 3}{r + 6}$; −6, 2**
17. $\frac{2x^2 + 18x + 36}{3x^2 - 3x - 36}$ **$\frac{2(x + 6)}{3(x - 4)}$; −3, 4**
18. $\frac{2y^2 + 9y + 4}{4y^2 - 4y - 3}$ **$\frac{y + 4}{2y - 3}$; $-\frac{1}{2}, \frac{3}{2}$**

19. **ENTERTAINMENT** Fairfield High spent d dollars for refreshments, decorations, and advertising for a dance. In addition, they hired a band for $550.

a. Write an expression that represents the cost of the band as a fraction of the total amount spent for the school dance. **$\frac{550}{d + 550}$**

b. If d is $1650, what percent of the budget did the band account for? **25%**

20. **PHYSICAL SCIENCE** Mr. Kaminksi plans to dislodge a tree stump in his yard by using a 6-foot bar as a lever. He places the bar so that 0.5 foot extends from the fulcrum to the end of the bar under the tree stump. In the diagram, b represents the total length of the bar and t represents the portion of the bar beyond the fulcrum.

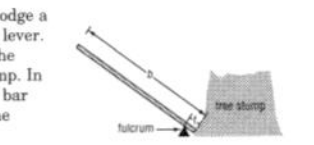

a. Write an equation that can be used to calculate the mechanical advantage. **$MA = \frac{b - t}{t}$**

b. What is the mechanical advantage? **11**

c. If a force of 200 pounds is applied to the end of the lever, what is the force placed on the tree stump? **2200 lb**

Chapter 11 20 Glencoe Algebra 1

Word Problem Practice
CRM p. 21 AL OL BL ELL

NAME ______ DATE ______ PERIOD ______

11-3 Word Problem Practice

Simplifying Rational Expressions

1. **PHYSICAL SCIENCE** Pressure is equal to the magnitude of a force divided by the area over which the force acts.

$P = \frac{F}{A}$

Gabe and Shelby each push open a door with one hand. In order to open, the door requires 20 pounds of force. The surface area of Gabe's hand is 10 square inches, and the surface area of Shelby's hand is 8 square inches. Whose hand feels the greater pressure?

Shelby's: $\frac{2.5 \text{ lb}}{\text{in}^2}$ (vs Gabe's $\frac{2 \text{ lb}}{\text{in}^2}$)

2. **GRAPHING** Recall that the slope of a line is a ratio of the vertical change to the horizontal change in coordinates for two given points. Write a rational expression that represents the slope of the line containing the points at (p, r) and $(7, -3)$.

$\frac{r + 3}{p - 7}$ or $\frac{-3 - r}{7 - p}$

3. **AUTOMOBILES** The force needed to keep a car from skidding out of a turn on a particular road is given by the formula below. What force is required to keep a 2000-pound car traveling at 50 miles per hour on a curve with radius of 750 feet on the road? What value of r is excluded?

$f = \frac{0.0672ws^2}{r}$

f = force in pounds
w = weight in pounds
s = speed in mph
r = radius in feet

448 lb, $r \neq 0$

4. **PACKAGING** In order to safely ship a new electronic device, the distribution manager at Data Products Company determines that the package must contain a certain amount of cushioning on each side of the device. The device is shaped like a cube with side length x, and some sides need more cushioning than others because of the device's design. The volume of a shipping container is represented by the expression $(x^2 + 6x + 8)(x + 6)$. Find the polynomial that represents the area of the top of the box if the height of the box is $x + 2$. **$x^2 + 10x + 24$**

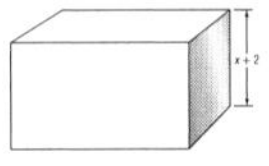

5. **SCHOOL CHOICE** During a recent school year, the ratio of public school students to private school students in the United States was approximately 7.6 to 1. The students attending public school outnumbered those attending private schools by 42,240,000.

a. Write a rational expression to express the ratio of public school students to x private school students. **$\frac{x + 42{,}240{,}000}{x}$**

b. How many students attended private school? **6,400,000**

Chapter 11 21 Glencoe Algebra 1

Lesson 11-3

Enrichment
CRM p. 22 OL BL

NAME ______ DATE ______ PERIOD ______

11-3 Enrichment

Shannon's Juggling Theorem

Mathematicians look at various mathematical ways to represent juggling. One way they have found to represent juggling is Shannon's Juggling Theorem. Shannon's Juggling Theorem uses the rational equation

$$\frac{f + d}{v + d} = \frac{b}{h}$$

where f is the flight time, or how long a ball is in the air, d is the dwell time, or how long a ball is in a hand, v is the vacant time, or how long a hand is empty, b is the number of balls, and h is the number of hands (either 1 or 2 for a real-life situation, possibly more for a computer simulation).

So, given the values for f, d, v, and h, it is possible to determine the number of balls being juggled. If the flight time is 9 seconds, the dwell time is 3 seconds, the vacant time is 1 second, and the number of hands is 2, how many balls are being juggled?

$\frac{f + d}{v + d} = \frac{b}{h}$ Original equation
$\frac{9 + 3}{1 + 3} = \frac{b}{2}$ Replace with the values given.
$\frac{12}{4} = \frac{b}{2}$ Simplify.
$24 = 4b$ Cross multiply.
6 Divide.

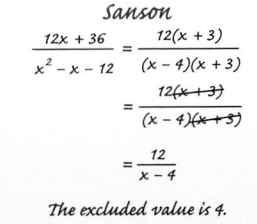

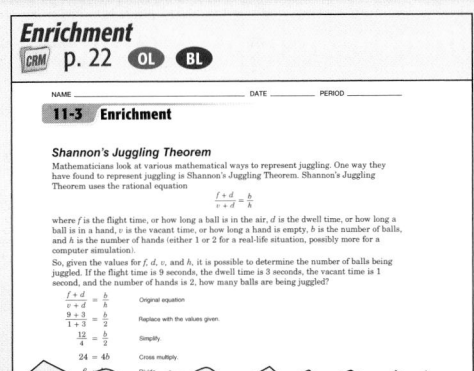

4 ASSESS

Crystal Ball Ask them to write how they think what they have learned today will connect with the next lesson on multiplying and dividing rational expressions.

PSAE PRACTICE 8.11.01, 6.11.10, 9.11.06, 8.11.02

49. Simplify $\frac{2x+4}{2}$. **C**

A $x+1$
B x
C $x+2$
D $\frac{x}{2}$

50. SHORT RESPONSE Shiro is buying a car for \$5800. He can pay the full amount in cash, or he can pay \$1000 down and \$230 a month for 24 months. How much more would he pay for the car on the second plan? **\$720**

51. GEOMETRY What is the name of the figure? **G**

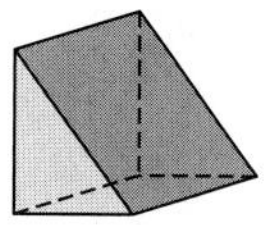

F triangular pyramid
G triangular prism
H rectangular prism
J triangulon

52. A rectangle has a length of 10 inches and a width of 5 inches. Another rectangle has the same area as the first rectangle but its width is 2 inches. Find the length of the second rectangle. **D**

A 30 in.
B 60 in.
C 20 in.
D 25 in.

Spiral Review

State the excluded value for each function. (Lesson 11-2)

53. $y = \frac{6}{x}$ **0**
54. $y = \frac{2}{x-5}$ **5**
55. $y = \frac{x-4}{x-3}$ **3**
56. $y = \frac{3x}{2x+6}$ **−3**

Solve. Assume that y varies inversely as x. (Lesson 11-1)

57. If $y = 10$ when $x = 4$, find x when $y = 2$. **20**
58. If $y = 12$ when $x = 3$, find x when $y = 6$. **6**
59. If $y = -5$ when $x = 3$, find x when $y = -3$. **5**
60. If $y = 21$ when $x = -6$, find x when $y = 7$. **−18**

61. CRAFTS Melinda is working on a quilt using the pattern shown. She has several triangular pieces of material with two sides that measure 6 inches. If these pieces are similar to the pattern shown, what is the length of the third side? (Lesson 10-7) **8.4 in.**

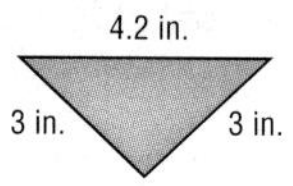

Find the distance between each pair of points whose coordinates are given. (Lesson 10-6)

62. (12, 3), (−8, 3) **20**
63. (0, 0), (5, 12) **13**
64. (6, 8), (3, 4) **5**
65. (−8, −4), (−3, −8) $\sqrt{41}$

Simplify. (Lesson 10-2)

66. $\sqrt{20}$ $2\sqrt{5}$
67. $\sqrt{18}$ $3\sqrt{2}$
68. $\sqrt{2} \cdot \sqrt{8}$ **4**
69. $2\sqrt{32}$ $8\sqrt{2}$
70. $\sqrt{5} \cdot \sqrt{6}$ $\sqrt{30}$
71. $\sqrt{40a^2}$ $2|a|\sqrt{10}$
72. $\sqrt{\frac{t}{8}}$ $\frac{\sqrt{2t}}{4}$
73. $\sqrt{\frac{2}{7}} \cdot \sqrt{\frac{7}{3}}$ $\frac{\sqrt{6}}{3}$

74. FINANCIAL LITERACY Determine the amount of an investment if \$250 is invested at an interest rate of 7.3% compounded quarterly for 40 years. (Lesson 9-7) **about \$4514.89**

Skills Review

Find the greatest common factor for each set of monomials. (Lesson 8-1)

75. $2x, 8x^2$ $2x$
76. $3y^2, 7y^3$ y^2
77. $7g, 10h$ **1**
78. $21c^2d^3, 14cd^2$ $7cd^2$
79. $9qt^2, 18q^2t^2, 27qt$ $9qt$
80. $10ab, 25a^2b^2, 30a^2b$ $5ab$

Differentiated Instruction BL

Extension Write the expression $\frac{7}{x-9} + 5$ on the board. Ask students to explain how adding 5 to the rational expression $\frac{7}{x-9}$ affects the excluded values in the expression. The excluded value is 9 whether or not 5 is added to $\frac{7}{x-9}$.

Graphing Technology Lab
Simplifying Rational Expressions

IL Math Online glencoe.com
- Other Calculator Keystrokes
- Graphing Technology Personal Tutor

IL Learning Standards **8.B.4a** Represent algebraic concepts with physical materials, words, diagrams, tables, graphs, equations and inequalities and use appropriate technology.

When simplifying rational expressions, you can use a graphing calculator to support your answer. If the graphs of the original expression and the simplified expression overlap, they are equivalent. You can also use the graphs to see excluded values.

ACTIVITY Simplify a Rational Expression

Simplify $\frac{x^2 - 16}{x^2 + 8x + 16}$.

Step 1 Factor the numerator and denominator.

- $\frac{x^2 - 16}{x^2 + 8x + 16} = \frac{(x - 4)(x + 4)}{(x + 4)(x + 4)}$
  $= \frac{(x - 4)}{(x + 4)}$

When $x = -4$, $x + 4 = 0$. Therefore, x cannot equal -4 because you cannot divide by zero.

Step 2 Graph the original expression.

- Set the calculator to Dot mode.
- Enter $\frac{x^2 - 16}{x^2 + 8x + 16}$ as Y1 and graph.

KEYSTROKES: MODE ▼ ▼ ▼ ▼ ▶ ENTER
Y= (X,T,θ,n x² − 16)
÷ (X,T,θ,n x² + 8
X,T,θ,n + 16) Zoom 6

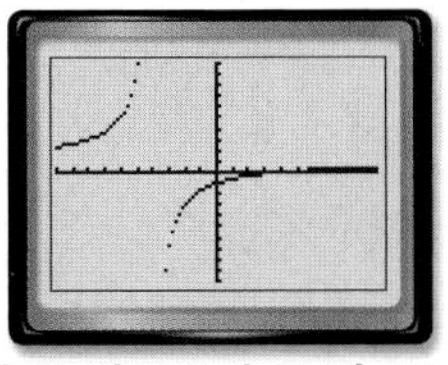

[−10, 10] scl: 1 by [−10, 10] scl: 1

Step 3 Graph the simplified expression.

- Enter $\frac{(x - 4)}{(x + 4)}$ as Y2 and graph.

KEYSTROKES: Y= ▼ (X,T,θ,n − 4)
÷ (X,T,θ,n + 4)
Graph

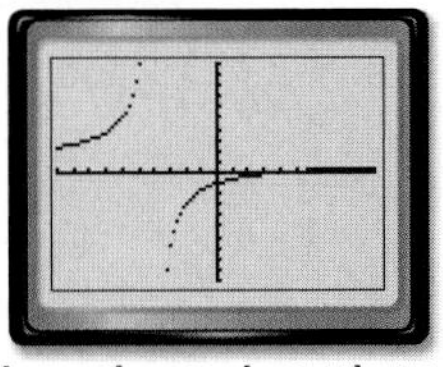

[−10, 10] scl: 1 by [−10, 10] scl: 1

Since the graphs overlap, the two expressions are equivalent.

Exercises

Simplify each expression. Then verify your answer graphically. Name the excluded values. 1–3. See Ch. 11 Answer Appendix for graphs.

1. $\frac{5x + 15}{x^2 + 10x + 21}$ $\frac{5}{x + 7}$; −3, −7
2. $\frac{x^2 - 8x + 12}{x^2 + 7x - 18}$ $\frac{x - 6}{x + 9}$; −9, 2
3. $\frac{2x^2 + 6x + 4}{3x^2 + 9x + 6}$ $\frac{2}{3}$; −1, −2
4. **a.** Simplify $\frac{3x - 8}{6x^2 - 16x}$. $\frac{1}{2x}$
   b. How can you use the TABLE function to verify that the original expression and the simplified expression are equivalent? Sample answer: Examine the values and verify that they are identical.
   c. How does the TABLE function show you that an x-value is an excluded value? It displays ERROR.

1 FOCUS

Objective Use a graphing calculator to simplify rational expressions, and verify solutions and excluded values.

Materials for Each Student

- TI-83/84 Plus or other graphing calculator

Teaching Tip

Be sure students understand that when they enter two functions that should produce identical graphs, it is impossible to tell from the screen whether there are two graphs or one. To make sure there are two graphs and that they overlap, have students press Trace. Tell students to use the up and down arrow keys to switch between the two graphs. Each time they press the keys, the equation in the upper left-hand corner of the screen should change but the values for x and y at the bottom of the screen should stay the same.

2 TEACH

Working in Cooperative Groups

Put students in groups of two or three, mixing abilities. Have groups complete the Activity and Exercises 1–3.

- Make sure students enter the equations exactly as shown in the keystrokes. If students fail to put the numerator and denominator in parentheses, the resulting graph may be incorrect.

Practice Have students complete Exercise 4.

3 ASSESS

Formative Assessment

Ask students when they would use a graphing calculator to confirm the simplification of a rational expression. Sample answer: when the simplification is very complicated

From Concrete to Abstract

Ask: Will the graphs of the original expression and the simplified expression always be the same? Graph $\frac{x^2 - 64}{x - 8}$ and its simplified version, $x + 8$. Explain how the graphs are different. When there are excluded values for the original rational expression and not for the simplified expression, the graphs might be slightly different; the first graph has a hole at $x = 8$ because it is an excluded value of the equation.

11-4 Lesson Notes

1 FOCUS

Vertical Alignment

Before Lesson 11-4
Multiply and divide polynomials.

Lesson 11-4
Multiply rational expressions.
Divide rational expressions.

After Lesson 11-4
Divide a polynomial by a monomial or a binomial.

2 TEACH

Scaffolding Questions

Have students read the *Why?* section of the lesson.

Ask:

- What is the simplification of the expression shown? 20,250 minutes
- In what way are the units in these expressions similar to variables? The common units in the numerator and denominator can be factored out.
- How do you know that you ended up with the correct units at the end of the simplification? The problem states that you want to know the number of minutes. The final unit left is minutes, which is the correct unit.

11-4 Multiplying and Dividing Rational Expressions

Then
You multiplied and divided polynomials.
(Lesson 7-7 and 7-2)

Now
- Multiply rational expressions.
- Divide rational expressions.

IL Learning Standards

7.A.4b Apply formulas in a wide variety of theoretical and practical real-world measurement applications involving perimeter, area, volume, angle, time, temperature, mass, speed, distance, density and monetary values.

IL Math Online

glencoe.com
- Extra Examples
- Personal Tutor
- Self-Check Quiz
- Homework Help

Why?

A recent survey showed 10- to 17-year olds talk on their cell phones an average of 3.75 hours per day during the summer. The expression below can be used to find the average number of minutes youth talk on their phones during summer, approximately 90 days.

$$90\,\cancel{\text{days}} \cdot \frac{3.75\,\cancel{\text{hours}}}{\cancel{\text{day}}} \cdot \frac{60\text{ minutes}}{1\,\cancel{\text{hour}}} = 20{,}250\text{ minutes}$$

Multiply Rational Expressions To multiply fractions, you multiply numerators and multiply denominators. Use this same method to multiply rational expressions.

Key Concept Multiplying Rational Expressions — For Your FOLDABLE

Words Let a, b, c, and d be polynomials with $b \neq 0$ and $d \neq 0$. Then, $\frac{a}{b} \cdot \frac{c}{d} = \frac{ac}{bd}$.

Example $\frac{x}{2x-3} \cdot \frac{4x^2}{5} = \frac{4x^3}{5(2x-3)}$

EXAMPLE 1 Multiply Expressions Involving Monomials

Find each product.

a. $\frac{r^2x}{9t^3} \cdot \frac{3t^4}{r}$

Divide by the common factors before multiplying.

$$\frac{r^2x}{9t^3} \cdot \frac{3t^4}{r} = \frac{\overset{r}{\cancel{r^2}}x}{\underset{3}{\cancel{9}}\underset{1}{\cancel{t^3}}} \cdot \frac{\overset{1}{\cancel{3}}\overset{t}{\cancel{t^4}}}{\underset{1}{\cancel{r}}}$$ **Divide by the common factors 3, *r*, and t^3.**

$$= \frac{rxt}{3}$$ **Simplify.**

b. $\frac{a+4}{a^2} \cdot \frac{a}{a^2+2a-8}$

$$\frac{a+4}{a^2} \cdot \frac{a}{a^2+2a-8} = \frac{a+4}{a^2} \cdot \frac{a}{(a+4)(a-2)}$$ **Factor the denominator.**

$$= \frac{\overset{1}{\cancel{a+4}}}{\underset{a}{\cancel{a^2}}} \cdot \frac{\overset{1}{\cancel{a}}}{\underset{1}{\cancel{(a+4)}}(a-2)}$$ **The GCF is $a(a+4)$.**

$$= \frac{1}{a(a-2)} \text{ or } \frac{1}{a^2-2a}$$ **Simplify.**

Check Your Progress

1A. $\frac{3x}{16x^2} \cdot \frac{8x^2}{3}$ $\frac{x}{2}$

1B. $\frac{x+3}{x} \cdot \frac{5}{x^2+7x+12}$ **1B.** $\frac{5}{x^2+4x}$

1C. $\frac{y^2-3y-4}{y+5} \cdot \frac{y+5}{y^2-4y}$ **1C.** $\frac{y+1}{y}$

Personal Tutor glencoe.com

Lesson 11-4 Resources

Resource	Approaching-Level	On-Level	Beyond-Level	English Learners
Teacher Edition		• Differentiated Instruction, p. 698	• Differentiated Instruction, pp. 694, 698	
Chapter Resource Masters	• Study Guide and Intervention, pp. 23–24 • Skills Practice, p. 25 • Practice, p. 26 • Word Problem Practice, p. 27	• Study Guide and Intervention, pp. 23-24 • Skills Practice, p. 25 • Practice, p. 26 • Word Problem Practice, p. 27 • Enrichment, p. 28 • Spreadsheet Activity, p. 29	• Practice, p. 26 • Word Problem Practice, p. 27 • Enrichment, p. 28	• Study Guide and Intervention, pp. 23–24 • Skills Practice, p. 25 • Practice, p. 26 • Word Problem Practice, p. 27
Transparencies	• 5-Minute Check Transparency 11-4	• 5-Minute Check Transparency 11-4	• 5-Minute Check Transparency 11-4	• 5-Minute Check Transparency 11-4
Other	• Study Notebook	• Study Notebook	• Study Notebook	• Study Notebook

StudyTip

Rational Expressions From this point on, assume that no denominator of a rational expression has a value of zero.

When you multiply fractions that involve units of measure, you can divide by the units in the same way that you divide by variables. Recall that this process is called *dimensional analysis*. You can use dimensional analysis to convert units of measure within a system and between systems.

Real-World EXAMPLE 2 Dimensional Analysis

SKI RACING Ann Proctor won the 2007 World Waterski Racing Championship race in her category when she finished the 88-kilometer course in 51.23 minutes. What was her average speed in miles per hour? (*Hint*: 1 km ≈ 0.62 mi)

$$\frac{88\text{ km}}{51.23\text{ min}} \cdot \frac{0.62\text{ mi}}{1\text{ km}} \cdot \frac{60\text{ min}}{1\text{ h}} = \frac{88\,\cancel{\text{km}}}{51.23\,\cancel{\text{min}}} \cdot \frac{0.62\text{ mi}}{1\,\cancel{\text{km}}} \cdot \frac{60\,\cancel{\text{min}}}{1\text{ h}}$$

$$= \frac{88 \cdot 0.62\text{ mi} \cdot 60}{51.23 \cdot 1 \cdot 1\text{ h}} \quad \text{Simplify.}$$

$$= \frac{3273.6\text{ mi}}{51.23\text{ h}} \quad \text{Multiply.}$$

$$\approx \frac{63.9\text{ mi}}{\text{h}} \quad \text{Divide the numerator and the denominator by 51.23.}$$

Her average speed was 63.9 miles per hour.

Check Your Progress

2. SKI RACING What was Ann Proctor's speed in feet per second? about 93.72 ft/s

Personal Tutor glencoe.com

Divide Rational Expressions To divide by a fraction, you multiply by the reciprocal. You can use this same method to divide by a rational expression.

Key Concept Dividing Rational Expressions

For Your FOLDABLE

Symbols Let a, b, c, and d be polynomials with $b \neq 0$, $c \neq 0$, and $d \neq 0$. Then, $\frac{a}{b} \div \frac{c}{d} = \frac{a}{b} \cdot \frac{d}{c} = \frac{ad}{bc}$.

Example $\frac{x-3}{x} \div \frac{2x^2}{5} = \frac{x-3}{x} \cdot \frac{5}{2x^2} = \frac{5(x-3)}{2x^3}$

EXAMPLE 3 Divide by a Rational Expression

Find $\frac{4}{15n^3} \div \frac{12}{25n}$.

$$\frac{4}{15n^3} \div \frac{12}{25n} = \frac{4}{15n^3} \cdot \frac{25n}{12} \quad \text{Multiply by } \frac{25n}{12}\text{, the reciprocal of } \frac{12}{25n}.$$

$$= \frac{\overset{1}{\cancel{4}}}{\underset{3n^2}{\cancel{15n^3}}} \cdot \frac{\overset{5}{\cancel{25n}}}{\underset{3}{\cancel{12}}} \quad \text{Divide by common factors 4, 5, and } n.$$

$$= \frac{5}{9n^2} \quad \text{Simplify.}$$

Check Your Progress

Find each quotient.

3A. $\frac{15y^2}{4x} \div \frac{5y}{8x^3}$ $6x^2y$

3B. $\frac{12a^2}{5b} \div \frac{25a}{6b^2}$ $\frac{72ab}{125}$

Personal Tutor glencoe.com

Multiply Rational Expressions

Example 1a shows how to multiply rational expressions involving monomials. **Example 1b** shows how to factor a quadratic expression before simplifying a product of rational expressions involving polynomials that are not monomials. **Example 2** shows how to use a process called *dimensional analysis* to multiply fractions in a real-world problem that involves units of measure.

Formative Assessment

Use the Check Your Progress exercises after each example to determine students' understanding of concepts.

Additional Examples

1 Find each product.

a. $\frac{7x^2y}{12z^3} \cdot \frac{14z}{49xy^4}$ $\frac{x}{6y^3z^2}$

b. $\frac{b+3}{4b-12} \cdot \frac{b^2-4b+3}{b^2-7b-30}$ $\frac{b-1}{4b-40}$

2 **SPACE** The velocity that a spacecraft must have in order to escape Earth's gravitational pull is called the *escape velocity*. The escape velocity for a spacecraft leaving Earth is about 40,320 kilometers per hour. What is this speed in meters per second? 11,200 m/s

Additional Examples also in Interactive Classroom PowerPoint® Presentations

IWB INTERACTIVE WHITEBOARD READY

Focus on Mathematical Content

Dimensional Analysis Dimensional analysis is the process of analyzing units to decide which conversion factors to use when converting between different units.

Watch Out!

Student Misconceptions The **Study Tip** states that, from this point forward, students can assume that no denominator of a rational expression has a value of zero. Ask students to discuss why this is an important assumption.

Divide Rational Expressions

Example 3 shows how to multiply by the reciprocal when dividing rational expressions. **Example 4** shows how to divide by rational expressions and polynomials. **Example 5** shows how to factor a quadratic expression before dividing a rational expression.

Additional Examples

3 Find $\frac{8}{20x^3} \div \frac{44}{25x^2}$. $\frac{5}{22x}$

4 Find each quotient.

a. $\frac{3x+9}{x^2} \div (x+3)$ $\frac{3}{x^2}$

b. $\frac{y-6}{2y+6} \div \frac{y+2}{y+3}$ $\frac{y-6}{2y+4}$

5 Find $\frac{x-5}{x^2-9x+18} \div \frac{x^2-25}{x-6}$. $\frac{1}{(x-3)(x+5)}$

TEACH with TECH

INTERACTIVE WHITEBOARD Use the board to help demonstrate canceling out common factors. Cross out the common factors as you simplify the expression, and drag the remaining factors to create the simplified expression.

ReadingMath

Rational Expressions In a rational expression, the fraction bar acts as a grouping symbol. In Example 5a, $\frac{4x+6}{x^2}$ is read *the quantity four x plus six divided by x squared.*

EXAMPLE 4 Divide by Rational Expressions and Polynomials

Find each quotient.

a. $\frac{2x+6}{x^2} \div (x+3)$

$\frac{2x+6}{x^2} \div (x+3) = \frac{2x+6}{x^2} \div \frac{x+3}{1}$ — Write the binomial as a fraction.

$= \frac{2x+6}{x^2} \cdot \frac{1}{x+3}$ — Multiply by the reciprocal of $x+3$.

$= \frac{2(x+3)}{x^2} \cdot \frac{1}{x+3}$ — Factor $4x+6$.

$= \frac{2(x+3)}{x^2} \cdot \frac{1}{x+3}$ or $\frac{2}{x^2}$ — Divide out the common factor and simplify.

b. $\frac{a-2}{4a+4} \div \frac{a+5}{a+1}$

$\frac{a-2}{4a+4} \div \frac{a+5}{a+1} = \frac{a-2}{4a+4} \cdot \frac{a+1}{a+5}$ — Multiply by the reciprocal.

$= \frac{a-2}{4(a+1)} \cdot \frac{a+1}{a+5}$ — Factor $4a+4$.

$= \frac{a-2}{4(a+5)}$ — The GCF is $a+1$ and simplify.

Check Your Progress

4A. $\frac{4d-8}{2d-6} \div \frac{2d-4}{d-4}$ $\frac{d-4}{d-3}$

4B. $\frac{b+4}{3b+2} \div \frac{3b+12}{b+1}$ $\frac{b+1}{3(3b+2)}$

Personal Tutor glencoe.com

Sometimes you must factor a quadratic expression before you can simplify the quotient of rational expressions.

StudyTip

Canceling Remember that only factors can be canceled, not individual terms.

EXAMPLE 5 Expression Involving Polynomials

Find $\frac{y-3}{y^2-10y+16} \div \frac{y^2-9}{y-8}$.

$\frac{y-3}{y^2-10y+16} \div \frac{y^2-9}{y-8}$

$= \frac{y-3}{y^2-10y+16} \cdot \frac{y-8}{y^2-9}$ — Multiply by the reciprocal, $\frac{y-8}{y^2-9}$.

$= \frac{y-3}{(y-2)(y-8)} \cdot \frac{y-8}{(y-3)(y+3)}$ — Factor $y^2-10y+16$ and y^2-9.

$= \frac{y-3}{(y-2)(y-8)} \cdot \frac{y-8}{(y-3)(y+3)}$ — The GCF is $(y-3)(y-8)$.

$= \frac{1}{(y-2)(y+3)}$ — Simplify.

Check Your Progress

Find each quotient.

5A. $\frac{p^2-4}{5p} \div \frac{p-2}{p+q}$ $\frac{(p+2)(p+q)}{5p}$

5B. $\frac{q^2+3q+2}{12} \div \frac{q+1}{q^2+4}$ $\frac{(q+2)(q^2+4)}{12}$

Personal Tutor glencoe.com

Differentiated Instruction BL

Logical Learners Challenge students to write one division and one multiplication problem consisting of two rational expressions that simplify to $\frac{x-1}{x-2}$.

Check Your Understanding

Example 1 p. 692

Find each product.

1. $\frac{2x^3}{7x} \cdot \frac{14}{x}$ **$4x$**
2. $\frac{3ab}{4c^4} \cdot \frac{16c^2}{9b}$ **$\frac{4a}{3c^2}$**
3. $\frac{t^2}{(t-5)(t+5)} \cdot \frac{t+5}{6t}$ **$\frac{t}{6(t-5)}$**
4. $\frac{8}{r+1} \cdot \frac{r^2-1}{2}$ **$4(r-1)$**

Example 2 p. 693

5. **SLOTHS** The slowest land mammal is the three-toed sloth. It travels 0.07 mile per hour on the ground. What is this speed in feet per minute? **6.16 ft/min**

6. **EXERCISE** One hour of moderate inline skating burns approximately 330 Calories. If Nelia plans to do inline skating for 3 hours a week, how many Calories will she burn in a year from the skating? **51,480 Calories**

Examples 3–5 pp. 693–694

Find each quotient.

7. $\frac{8}{3x^2} \div \frac{4}{x}$ **$\frac{2}{3x}$**
8. $\frac{c^5}{2} \div \frac{c^3}{6d^2}$ **$3c^2d^2$**
9. $\frac{b^2+6b+5}{6b+6} \div (b+5)$ **$\frac{1}{6}$**
10. $\frac{2x+8}{x+3} \div \frac{x+4}{x^2+6x+9}$ **$2(x+3)$**

Practice and Problem Solving

● = **Step-by-Step Solutions** begin on page R12. **Extra Practice** begins on page 815.

Example 1 p. 692

Find each product.

11. ● $\frac{10n^2}{4} \cdot \frac{2}{n}$ **$5n$**
12. $\frac{12c^3}{21b} \cdot \frac{14b^2}{6c}$ **$\frac{4bc^2}{3}$**
13. $\frac{x^5y}{2z^3} \cdot \frac{18z^4}{xy}$ **$9x^4z$**
14. $\frac{5c^3d}{c^4d} \cdot \frac{f^2d^3c}{10cf^4}$ **$\frac{d^3}{2cf^2}$**
15. $\frac{9}{t-2} \cdot \frac{(t+2)(t-2)}{3}$ **$3(t+2)$**
16. $\frac{(a+4)(a-5)}{a^2} \cdot \frac{6a}{a+4}$ **$\frac{6(a-5)}{a}$**
17. $\frac{(k+6)(k-1)}{k+2} \cdot \frac{(k+1)(k+2)}{(k+1)(k-1)}$ **$k+6$**
18. $\frac{(r-8)(r+3)}{r} \cdot \frac{2r}{(r+8)(r+3)}$ **$\frac{2(r-8)}{r+8}$**
19. $\frac{n^2+n-2}{n+2} \cdot \frac{4n}{n-1}$ **$4n$**
20. $\frac{y^2-1}{y^2-49} \cdot \frac{y-7}{y+1}$ **$\frac{y-1}{y+7}$**

Example 2 p. 693

21. **FINANCIAL LITERACY** A scarf bought in Italy cost 18 Euros. The exchange rate at the time was 1 U.S. dollar = 0.73 Euro.
    a. How much did the scarf cost in U.S. dollars? **about $24.66**
    b. If the exchange rate at the time was 1 Canadian dollar = 0.69 Euro, how much did the scarf cost in Canadian dollars? **about $26.09**

22. **ROLLER COASTERS** A roller coaster has 6 trains. Each train has 3 cars, and each car seats 4 people. Write and simplify an expression including units to find the total number of people that can ride the roller coaster at one time.
    6 trains $\cdot \frac{\text{3 cars}}{\text{1 train}} \cdot \frac{\text{4 people}}{\text{1 car}}$; 72 people

27. $\frac{b-2}{(b+5)(2b+3)}$
28. $\frac{5(k+3)}{k}$
29. $\frac{x}{2(x-4)}$
31. $\frac{(r+2)^2}{4}$

Examples 3–5 pp. 693–694

Find each quotient.

23. $\frac{x^5}{y} \div \frac{x}{y^2}$ **x^4y**
24. $\frac{3r^4}{k^2} \div \frac{18r^3}{k}$ **$\frac{r}{6k}$**
25. $\frac{21b^3}{4c^2} \div \frac{7}{6c^2}$ **$\frac{9b^3}{2}$**
26. $\frac{f^4g^2h}{x^2y} \div f^3g$ **$\frac{fgh}{x^2y}$**
27. $\frac{6b-12}{b+5} \div (12b+18)$
28. $\frac{k+3}{k+2} \div \frac{k}{5k+10}$
29. $\frac{5x^2}{x^2-5x+4} \div \frac{10x}{x-1}$
30. $\frac{n^2+7n+12}{16n^2} \div \frac{n+3}{2n}$ **$\frac{n+4}{8n}$**
31. $\frac{r+2}{r+1} \div \frac{4}{r^2+3r+2}$
32. $\frac{3a}{a^2+2a+1} \div \frac{a-1}{a+1}$ **$\frac{3a}{(a+1)(a-1)}$**

3 PRACTICE

Formative Assessment

Use Exercises 1–10 to check for understanding.

Use the chart at the bottom of this page to customize assignments for your students.

Differentiated Homework Options

Level	Assignment	Two-Day Option	
AL Basic	11–34, 53–54, 56–89	11–33 odd, 60–63	12–34 even, 53–54, 56–59, 64–89
OL Core	11–33 odd, 35–44, 45–49 odd, 50–54, 56–89	11–35, 60–63	35–54, 56–59, 64–89
BL Advanced	35–83, (optional: 84–89)		

Exercise Alert

Formulas For Exercises 44 and 52, students will need to know the formula for the volume of a rectangular prism.

Watch Out!

Find the Error For Exercise 53, students encounter two of the most common errors made when dividing and multiplying rational expressions. Suggest students write out each step to find the correct solution to the problem.

Tips for New Teachers

Sense-Making Discuss with students how they can verify that a dimensional analysis problem has been set up correctly. Also, encourage students to check the reasonableness of their answers when they solve a problem.

Additional Answers

52a.

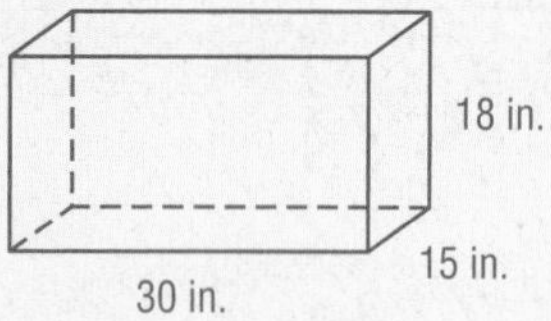

8100 in^3

56. Sample answer: You can use dimensional analysis in situations that involve units of measure when dividing rational expressions. For example, to change 30 miles/hour to feet/second, multiply $\frac{30 \text{ miles}}{1 \text{ hour}} \cdot \frac{5280 \text{ feet}}{1 \text{ mile}} \cdot \frac{1 \text{ hour}}{60 \text{ min}} \cdot \frac{1 \text{ min}}{60 \text{ s}}$

59. Sample answer: Write ratios comparing the number of days in one year and the number of hours in one day. Then multiply the ratios: $\frac{365 \text{ days}}{1 \text{ year}} \cdot \frac{24 \text{ hours}}{1 \text{ day}} =$ 8760 hours.

Real-World Link

Much of New Orleans sits 11 feet below sea level. Parts of the French Quarter have sunk as much as 2 feet in the past six decades.

Source: Imaginova

43. $\frac{1 \text{ cup}}{1 \text{ beat}} \cdot \frac{70 \text{ beats}}{1 \text{ minute}} \cdot \frac{1 \text{ gallon}}{16 \text{ cups}} \cdot \frac{60 \text{ minutes}}{1 \text{ hour}} = 262.5 \text{ gal/h}$

46. about \$4.28/day; the average cost of gasoline per day

47. about 71.6 mi/h; converting 32 meters per second to miles per hour

33. BEARS A grizzly bear runs 110 feet in 5 seconds. What is the average speed of the bear in miles per hour? **15 mi/h**

34. SEWING The fabric that Megan wants to buy for a costume she is making costs \$7.50 per yard. How many yards can she buy with \$24? **3.2 yd**

35. TRAVEL An airplane is making a 1250-mile trip. Its average speed is 540 miles per hour.

a. Write a division expression you can use to find the number of hours that the trip will take. Include the units. **1250 mi ÷ 540 mi/h**

b. Find the quotient. Round to the nearest tenth. **2.3 h**

36. VOLUNTEERING Tyree is passing out orange drink from a 3.5-gallon cooler. If each cup of orange drink is 4.25 ounces, about how many cups can he hand out? (*Hint*: There are 128 ounces in a gallon.) **about 105.4 cups**

37. LAND Louisiana loses about 30 square miles of land each year to coastal erosion, hurricanes, and other natural and human causes. Approximately how many square yards of land are lost per month? (*Hint*: Use 1 square mile = 3,097,600 square yards.) **7,744,000 yd²/mo**

38. GEOMETRY Write an expression to represent the length of the rectangle. $(x+6)(x-3)$

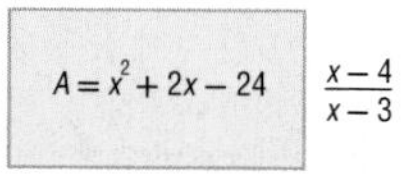

Convert each rate. Round to the nearest tenth.

39. 46 feet per second to miles per hour **about 31.4 mi/h**

40. 29.5 meters per second to kilometers per hour **106.2 km/h**

41. 28 milliliters per second to cups per minute. (*Hint*: 1 liter ≈ 0.908 quarts) **6.1 c/min**

42. 32.4 meters per second to miles per hour. (*Hint*: 1 mile ≈ 1.609 kilometers) **72.5 mi/h**

43. LIFE SCIENCE A human heart pumps about a cup of blood each time it beats. On average, a person's heart beats about 70 times a minute. Write and simplify an expression to find how many gallons of blood are pumped per hour.

44. GEOMETRY Refer to the prism at the right.

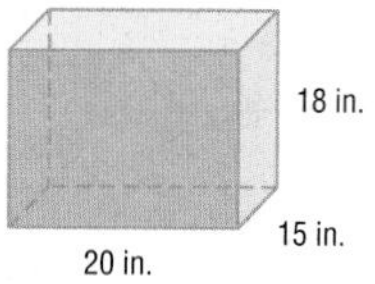

a. Find the volume in cubic inches. **5400 in³**

b. Use the ratio $\frac{1 \text{ foot}^3}{1728 \text{ inches}^3}$ to write a multiplication expression to convert the volume to cubic feet. Then convert the volume. $5400 \text{ in}^3 \cdot \frac{1 \text{ ft}^3}{1728 \text{ in}^3}$; 3.125 ft^3

Find each product. Describe what the final answer represents.

45. $\frac{\$9.80}{1 \text{ hour}} \cdot \frac{15 \text{ hours}}{1 \text{ week}} \cdot \frac{52 \text{ weeks}}{1 \text{ year}}$ **\$7644/yr; Sample answer: earnings per year**

46. $\frac{\$2.85}{1 \text{ gallon of gasoline}} \cdot \frac{15 \text{ gallons of gasoline}}{1 \text{ fill-up}} \cdot \frac{3 \text{ fill-ups}}{1 \text{ month}} \cdot \frac{1 \text{ month}}{30 \text{ days}}$

47. $\frac{32 \text{ meters}}{1 \text{ second}} \cdot \frac{60 \text{ seconds}}{1 \text{ minute}} \cdot \frac{60 \text{ minutes}}{1 \text{ hour}} \cdot \frac{1 \text{ kilometer}}{1000 \text{ meters}} \cdot \frac{1 \text{ mile}}{1.609 \text{ kilometers}}$

48. $\frac{\$32{,}000}{1 \text{ year}} \cdot \frac{1 \text{ year}}{52 \text{ weeks}} \cdot \frac{1 \text{ week}}{40 \text{ hours}}$ **about \$15.38; converting yearly salary to hourly wage**

49. SPACE The highest speed at which any spacecraft has ever escaped from Earth is 35,800 miles per hour by the *New Horizons* probe, which was launched in 2006. Convert this speed to feet per second. Round to the nearest tenth. **about 52,506.7 ft/s**

Real-World Link

The largest cylindrical aquarium ever built is located in a hotel lobby in Berlin. It is 25 meters high and contains 900,000 liters of seawater and 2500 tropical fish.

Source: South Travels

50. ELECTRICITY Simplify the expression below to find the cost of running a 3500-watt air conditioner for one week. **\$58.80**

$$3500 \text{ watts} \cdot \frac{1 \text{ kilowatt}}{1000 \text{ watts}} \cdot \frac{168 \text{ hours}}{1 \text{ week}} \cdot \frac{10 \text{ cents}}{1 \text{ kilowatt} \cdot \text{hours}} \cdot \frac{1 \text{ dollar}}{100 \text{ cents}}$$

51. AMUSEMENT PARKS In an amusement park ride, riders stand along the wall of a circular room with a radius of 3.1 meters. The room completes 27 rotations per minute.

a. Write an expression for the number of meters the room moves per second. (*Hint*: The circumference of a circle is $2\pi r$.) $\frac{27 \text{ rotations}}{1 \text{ min}} \cdot \frac{1 \text{ min}}{60 \text{ s}} \cdot \frac{2\pi(3.1) \text{ m}}{1 \text{ rotation}}$

b. Simplify the expression you wrote in Part **a** and describe what it means. **About 8.8 m/s; the room spins at a rate of 8.8 m/s.**

52. AQUARIUMS An aquarium is a rectangular prism 30 inches long, 15 inches wide, and 18 inches high.

C **a.** Sketch and label a diagram of the aquarium. Then find the volume of the tank in cubic inches. **See margin.**

b. Describe how to use the ratio $\frac{1 \text{ ft}^3}{1728 \text{ in}^3}$ to find the volume of the tank in cubic feet. Then find the volume. Round to the nearest tenth.

c. Water weighs 62 pounds per cubic foot. How much would the water in the tank weigh if the tank were filled? **about 291.4 lb**

52b. Sample answer: Multiply the volume in cubic inches by the ratio, ≈4.7.

H.O.T. Problems
Use Higher-Order Thinking Skills

53. FIND THE ERROR Mei and Tamika are finding $\frac{2x+6}{x+5} \div \frac{2}{x+5}$. Is either of them correct? Explain.

Neither; Tamika did not multiply by the reciprocal, and Mei incorrectly factored out the 2 in $2x + 6$.

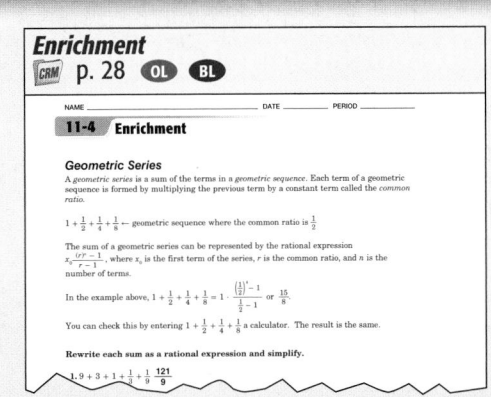

Mei

$\frac{2x+6}{x+5} \div \frac{2}{x+5}$

$= \frac{2x+6}{x+5} \cdot \frac{x+5}{2}$

$= x + 6$

Tamika

$\frac{2x+6}{x+5} \div \frac{2}{x+5}$

$= \frac{2(x+3)}{x+5} \cdot \frac{2}{x+5}$

$= \frac{4(x+3)}{(x+5)^2}$

54. REASONING Find the missing term. Justify your answer. **$\frac{5x^2}{7}$; $\frac{3}{2x} \cdot \frac{10x^3}{21} = \frac{5x^2}{7}$**

$$\frac{?}{\quad} \div \frac{10x^3}{21} = \frac{3}{2x}$$

55. CHALLENGE Find $\frac{x^2 - 3x - 10}{x^2 + 2x - 35} \cdot \frac{x^2 + 4x - 21}{x^2 + 9x + 14}$. Write in simplest form. **$\frac{x-3}{x+7}$**

56. WRITING IN MATH Give an example and describe how you could use dimensional analysis to solve a real-world problem involving rational expressions. **See margin.**

57. OPEN ENDED Give an example of a real-world situation that could be modeled by the quotient of two rational expressions. Provide an example of this quotient.

58. WRITE A QUESTION A classmate found that the product of two rational expressions is $\frac{9x - 3}{(x + 3)(3x + 1)}$. She wants to find the excluded values. Write a question to help her solve the problem.

59. WRITING IN MATH Describe how to use dimensional analysis to find the number of hours in one year. **See margin.**

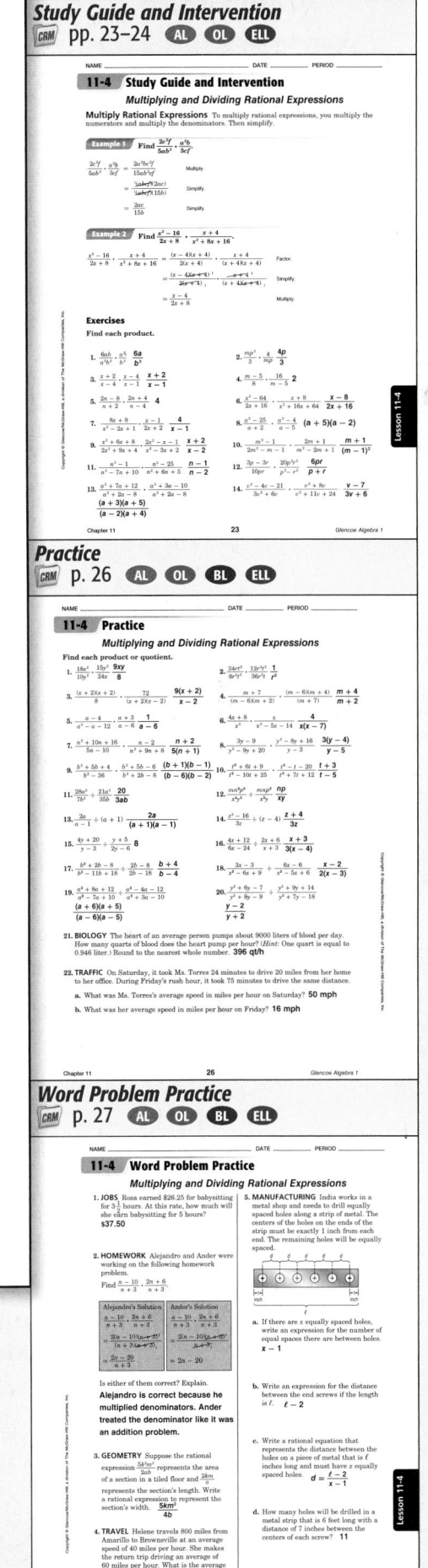

57. Sample answer: The height of a cylinder when you know an expression for the volume and radius; $\frac{V}{\pi r^2} = h$; $V = \pi(x^3 - 6x^2 + 9x)$, $r = (x - 3)$.

58. Sample answer: What values of x make the denominators that were multiplied equal to 0?

Study Guide and Intervention
CRM pp. 23–24 AL OL ELL

NAME ______ DATE ______ PERIOD ______

11-4 Study Guide and Intervention

Multiplying and Dividing Rational Expressions

Multiply Rational Expressions To multiply rational expressions, you multiply the numerators and multiply the denominators. Then simplify.

Example 1 Find $\frac{2c^2f}{5ab^2} \cdot \frac{a^2b}{3cf}$.

$\frac{2c^2f}{5ab^2} \cdot \frac{a^2b}{3cf} = \frac{2a^2bc^2f}{15ab^2cf}$ Multiply.

$= \frac{(abcf)(2ac)}{(abcf)(15b)}$ Simplify.

$= \frac{2ac}{15b}$ Simplify.

Example 2 Find $\frac{x^2 - 16}{2x + 8} \cdot \frac{x + 4}{x^2 + 8x + 16}$.

$\frac{x^2 - 16}{2x + 8} \cdot \frac{x + 4}{x^2 + 8x + 16} = \frac{(x-4)(x+4)}{2(x+4)} \cdot \frac{x+4}{(x+4)(x+4)}$ Factor.

$= \frac{(x-4)(x+4)}{2(x+4)} \cdot \frac{x+4}{(x+4)(x+4)}$ Simplify.

$= \frac{x-4}{2x+8}$ Multiply.

Exercises

Find each product.

1. $\frac{6ab}{a^2b^2} \cdot \frac{a^2}{b^2}$ **$\frac{6a}{b^3}$**
2. $\frac{mp^2}{3} \cdot \frac{4}{mp}$ **$\frac{4p}{3}$**
3. $\frac{x+2}{x-4} \cdot \frac{x-4}{x-1}$ **$\frac{x+2}{x-1}$**
4. $\frac{m-5}{8} \cdot \frac{16}{m-5}$ **2**
5. $\frac{2n-8}{n+2} \cdot \frac{2n+4}{n-4}$ **4**
6. $\frac{x^2-64}{2x+16} \cdot \frac{x+8}{x^2+16x+64}$ **$\frac{x-8}{2x+16}$**
7. $\frac{8x+8}{x^2-2x+1} \cdot \frac{x-1}{2x+2}$ **$\frac{4}{x-1}$**
8. $\frac{a^2-25}{a+2} \cdot \frac{a^2-4}{a-5}$ **$(a+5)(a-2)$**
9. $\frac{x^2+6x+8}{2x^2+9x+4} \cdot \frac{2x^2-x-1}{x^2-3x+2}$ **$\frac{x+2}{x-2}$**
10. $\frac{m^2-1}{2m^2-m-1} \cdot \frac{2m+1}{m^2-2m+1}$ **$\frac{m+1}{(m-1)^2}$**
11. $\frac{n^2-1}{n^2-7n+10} \cdot \frac{n^2-25}{n^2+6n+5}$ **$\frac{n-1}{n-2}$**
12. $\frac{3p-3r}{10pr} \cdot \frac{20p^2r^2}{p^2-r^2}$ **$\frac{6pr}{p+r}$**
13. $\frac{a^2+7a+12}{a^2+2a-8} \cdot \frac{a^2+3a-10}{a^2+2a-8}$ **$\frac{(a+3)(a+5)}{(a-2)(a+4)}$**
14. $\frac{v^2-4v-21}{3v^2+6v} \cdot \frac{v^2+8v}{v^2+11v+24}$ **$\frac{v-7}{3v+6}$**

Copyright © Glencoe/McGraw-Hill, a division of The McGraw-Hill Companies, Inc.

Chapter 11 23 Glencoe Algebra 1

Lesson 11-4

Practice
CRM p. 26 AL OL BL ELL

NAME ______ DATE ______ PERIOD ______

11-4 Practice

Multiplying and Dividing Rational Expressions

Find each product or quotient.

1. $\frac{18x^2}{10y^2} \cdot \frac{15y^3}{24x}$ **$\frac{9xy}{8}$**
2. $\frac{24rt^2}{8r^4t^3} \cdot \frac{12r^3t^2}{36r^2t}$ **$\frac{1}{r^2}$**
3. $\frac{(x+2)(x+2)}{8} \cdot \frac{72}{(x+2)(x-2)}$ **$\frac{9(x+2)}{x-2}$**
4. $\frac{m+7}{(m-6)(m+2)} \cdot \frac{(m-6)(m+4)}{(m+7)}$ **$\frac{m+4}{m+2}$**
5. $\frac{a-4}{a^2-a-12} \cdot \frac{a+3}{a-6}$ **$\frac{1}{a-6}$**
6. $\frac{4x+8}{x^2} \cdot \frac{x}{x^2-5x-14}$ **$\frac{4}{x(x-7)}$**
7. $\frac{n^2+10n+16}{5n-10} \cdot \frac{n-2}{n^2+9n+8}$ **$\frac{n+2}{5(n+1)}$**
8. $\frac{3y-9}{y^2-9y+20} \cdot \frac{y^2-8y+16}{y-3}$ **$\frac{3(y-4)}{y-5}$**
9. $\frac{b^2+5b+4}{b^2-36} \cdot \frac{b^2+5b-6}{b^2+2b-8}$ **$\frac{(b+1)(b-1)}{(b-6)(b-2)}$**
10. $\frac{t^2+6t+9}{t^2-10t+25} \cdot \frac{t^2-t-20}{t^2+7t+12}$ **$\frac{t+3}{t-5}$**
11. $\frac{28a^2}{7b^2} \div \frac{21a^3}{35b}$ **$\frac{20}{3ab}$**
12. $\frac{mn^2p^3}{x^4y^3} \div \frac{mnp^2}{x^3y}$ **$\frac{np}{xy}$**
13. $\frac{2a}{a-1} \div (a+1)$ **$\frac{2a}{(a+1)(a-1)}$**
14. $\frac{z^2-16}{3z} \div (z-4)$ **$\frac{z+4}{3z}$**
15. $\frac{4y+20}{y-3} \div \frac{y+5}{2y-6}$ **8**
16. $\frac{4x+12}{6x-24} \div \frac{2x+6}{x+3}$ **$\frac{x+3}{3(x-4)}$**
17. $\frac{b^2+2b-8}{b^2-11b+18} \div \frac{2b-8}{2b-18}$ **$\frac{b+4}{b-4}$**
18. $\frac{3x-3}{x^2-6x+9} \div \frac{6x-6}{x^2-5x+6}$ **$\frac{x-2}{2(x-3)}$**
19. $\frac{a^2+8a+12}{a^2-7a+10} \div \frac{a^2-4a-12}{a^2+3a-10}$ **$\frac{(a+6)(a+5)}{(a-6)(a-5)}$**
20. $\frac{y^2+6y-7}{y^2+8y-9} \div \frac{y^2+9y+14}{y^2+7y-18}$ **$\frac{y-2}{y+2}$**

21. **BIOLOGY** The heart of an average person pumps about 9000 liters of blood per day. How many quarts of blood does the heart pump per hour? (*Hint:* One quart is equal to 0.946 liter.) Round to the nearest whole number. **396 qt/h**

22. **TRAFFIC** On Saturday, it took Ms. Torres 24 minutes to drive 20 miles from her home to her office. During Friday's rush hour, it took 75 minutes to drive the same distance.

a. What was Ms. Torres's average speed in miles per hour on Saturday? **50 mph**

b. What was her average speed in miles per hour on Friday? **16 mph**

Copyright © Glencoe/McGraw-Hill, a division of The McGraw-Hill Companies, Inc.

Chapter 11 26 Glencoe Algebra 1

Word Problem Practice
CRM p. 27 AL OL BL ELL

NAME ______ DATE ______ PERIOD ______

11-4 Word Problem Practice

Multiplying and Dividing Rational Expressions

1. **JOBS** Rosa earned \$26.25 for babysitting for $3\frac{1}{2}$ hours. At this rate, how much will she earn babysitting for 5 hours? **\$37.50**

2. **HOMEWORK** Alejandro and Ander were working on the following homework problem.

Find $\frac{n-10}{n+3} \cdot \frac{2n+6}{n+3}$.

Alejandro's Solution	Ander's Solution
$\frac{n-10}{n+3} \cdot \frac{2n+6}{n+3}$	$\frac{n-10}{n+3} \cdot \frac{2n+6}{n+3}$
$= \frac{2(n-10)(n+3)}{(n+3)(n+3)}$	$= \frac{2(n-10)(n+3)}{n+3}$
$= \frac{2n-20}{n+3}$	$= 2n - 20$

Is either of them correct? Explain. **Alejandro is correct because he multiplied denominators. Ander treated the denominator like it was an addition problem.**

3. **GEOMETRY** Suppose the rational expression $\frac{5k^2m^3}{2ab}$ represents the area of a section in a tiled floor and $\frac{2km}{a}$ represents the section's length. Write a rational expression to represent the section's width. **$\frac{5km^2}{4b}$**

4. **TRAVEL** Helene travels 800 miles from Amarillo to Brownsville at an average speed of 40 miles per hour. She makes the return trip driving an average of 60 miles per hour. What is the average rate for the entire trip? (*Hint:* Recall that $t = d \div r$.) **48 mph**

5. **MANUFACTURING** India works in a metal shop and needs to drill equally spaced holes along a strip of metal. The centers of the holes on the ends of the strip must be exactly 1 inch from each end. The remaining holes will be equally spaced.

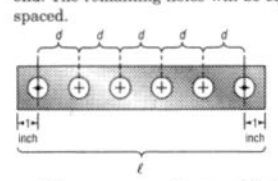

a. If there are x equally spaced holes, write an expression for the number of equal spaces there are between holes. **$x - 1$**

b. Write an expression for the distance between the end screws if the length is ℓ. **$\ell - 2$**

c. Write a rational equation that represents the distance between the holes on a piece of metal that is ℓ inches long and must have x equally spaced holes. **$d = \frac{\ell - 2}{x - 1}$**

d. How many holes will be drilled in a metal strip that is 6 feet long with a distance of 7 inches between the centers of each screw? **11**

Copyright © Glencoe/McGraw-Hill, a division of The McGraw-Hill Companies, Inc.

Chapter 11 27 Glencoe Algebra 1

Lesson 11-4

Enrichment
CRM p. 28 OL BL

NAME ______ DATE ______ PERIOD ______

11-4 Enrichment

Geometric Series

A *geometric series* is a sum of the terms in a *geometric sequence*. Each term of a geometric sequence is formed by multiplying the previous term by a constant term called the *common ratio.*

$1 + \frac{1}{2} + \frac{1}{4} + \frac{1}{8}$ ← geometric sequence where the common ratio is $\frac{1}{2}$

The sum of a geometric series can be represented by the rational expression $x_0\frac{(r)^n - 1}{r - 1}$, where x_0 is the first term of the series, r is the common ratio, and n is the number of terms.

In the example above, $1 + \frac{1}{2} + \frac{1}{4} + \frac{1}{8} = 1 \cdot \frac{\left(\frac{1}{2}\right)^4 - 1}{\frac{1}{2} - 1}$ or $\frac{15}{8}$.

You can check this by entering $1 + \frac{1}{2} + \frac{1}{4} + \frac{1}{8}$ a calculator. The result is the same.

Rewrite each sum as a rational expression and simplify.

1. $9 + 3 + 1 + \frac{1}{3} + \frac{1}{9}$ **$\frac{121}{9}$**

4 ASSESS

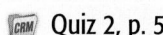

Yesterday's News Have students write how knowing how to factor a quadratic expression helped them with today's lesson.

Formative Assessment

Check for student understanding of concepts in Lessons 11-3 and 11-4.

CRM Quiz 2, p. 57

PSAE PRACTICE 8.11.17, 8.11.22, 10.11.05, 8.11.06

60. GEOMETRY The perimeter of a rectangle is 30 inches. Its area is 54 square inches. Find the length of the longest side. **B**

A 6 inches
B 9 inches
C 12 inches
D 30 inches

61. Find $\frac{c^2 - c - 6}{2c - 10} \div \frac{2c + 4}{3c - 15}$. **F**

F $\frac{3(c-3)}{4}$ H $\frac{4(c-3)}{3}$

G $\frac{c+5}{c-3}$ J $\frac{c-3}{c-5}$

62. EXTENDED RESPONSE The weekly salaries of six employees at a fast food restaurant are \$140, \$220, \$90, \$180, \$140, \$200.

a. What is the mean of the six salaries? **\$161.67**

b. What is the median of the six salaries? **\$160**

c. What is the mode of the six salaries? **\$140**

63. Tito has three times as many CDs as Dasan. Dasan has two thirds as many CDs as Brant. Brant has 27 CDs. How many CDs does Tito have? **A**

A 54 C 18
B 27 D 32

Spiral Review

Simplify each expression. State the excluded values of the variables. (Lesson 11-3)

64. $\frac{20x^2y}{25xy}$ $\frac{4}{5}x$; $x \neq 0, y \neq 0$

65. $\frac{14g^3h^2}{42gh^3}$ $\frac{g^2}{3h}$; $g \neq 0, h \neq 0$

66. $\frac{64qt}{16q^2t^3}$ $\frac{4}{qt^2}$; $q \neq 0, t \neq 0$

67. $\frac{y^2 + 10y + 16}{y + 2}$ $y + 8$; -2

68. $\frac{p^2 - 9}{p^2 - 5p + 6}$ $\frac{p+3}{p-2}$; 3, 2

69. $\frac{z^2 + z - 2}{z^2 - 3z + 2}$ $\frac{z+2}{z-2}$; 2, 1

Identify the asymptotes of each function. (Lesson 11-2)

70. $y = \frac{2}{x}$ $x = 0, y = 0$

71. $y = \frac{3}{x} + 5$ $x = 0, y = 5$

72. $y = \frac{1}{x-5} - 4$ $x = 5, y = -4$

73. $y = \frac{1}{x+3}$ $x = -3, y = 0$

74. $y = \frac{-1}{x+6} + 7$ $x = -6, y = 7$

75. $y = \frac{2}{x-8} - 3$ $x = 8, y = -3$

76. FORESTRY The number of board feet B that a log will yield can be estimated by using the formula $B = \frac{L}{16}(D^2 - 8D + 16)$, where D is the diameter in inches and L is the log length in feet. For logs that are 16 feet long, what diameter will yield approximately 256 board feet? (Lesson 8-6) **20 in.**

Find the degree of each polynomial. (Lesson 7-4)

77. 2 **0**

78. $-3a$ **1**

79. $5x^2 + 3x$ **2**

80. $d^4 - 6c^2$ **4**

81. $2x^3 - 4z + 8xz$ **3**

82. $3d^4 + 5d^3 - 4c^2 + 1$ **4**

83. DRIVING Tires should be kept within 2 pounds per square inch (psi) of the manufacturer's recommended tire pressure. If the recommendation for a tire is 30 psi, what is the range of acceptable pressures? (Lesson 5-5) $\{p \mid 28 \leq p \leq 32\}$

Skills Review

Factor each polynomial. (Lessons 8-3 and 8-4)

84. $x^2 - 18x - 40$ $(x + 2)(x - 20)$

85. $x^2 - 5x + 6$ $(x - 2)(x - 3)$

86. $x^2 - 2x - 24$ $(x + 4)(x - 6)$

87. $3x^2 + 7x - 20$ $(x + 4)(3x - 5)$

88. $2x^2 + x - 15$ $(x + 3)(2x - 5)$

89. $8x^2 - 4x - 40$ $4(x + 2)(2x - 5)$

Differentiated Instruction

OL BL

Extension Write $\frac{3}{x+4}$ on the board. Ask students to write rational expressions that are equivalent to the one on the board. Have students tell how the excluded values change from the original expression to the equivalent expressions. Sample answer: $\frac{3x - 12}{x^2 - 16}$; the excluded value in $\frac{3}{x+4}$ is $x = -4$; the excluded values in $\frac{3x - 12}{x^2 - 16}$ are $x = -4$ and $x = 4$.

Mid-Chapter Quiz

Lessons 11-1 through 11-4

IL Learning Standards 7.A.4b, 8.B.4a

1. Determine whether the table represents an inverse variation. Explain. (Lesson 11-1) Yes, each product is 16.

x	y
2	8
4	4
8	2
16	1

Assume that y varies inversely as x. Write an inverse variation equation that relates x and y. (Lesson 11-1)

2. $y = 5$ when $x = 10$ $y = \frac{50}{x}$

3. $y = -2$ when $x = 12$ $y = \frac{-24}{x}$

Solve. Assume that y varies inversely as x. (Lesson 11-1)

4. If $y = 6$ when $x = 3$, find x when $y = 5$. 3.6

5. If $y = 3$ when $x = 2$, find y when $x = 4$. 1.5

State the excluded value for each function. (Lesson 11-2)

6. $y = \frac{2}{x}$ 0

7. $y = \frac{1}{x - 6}$ 6

Identify the asymptotes of each function. (Lesson 11-2)

8. $y = \frac{3}{2x + 4}$ $x = -2$, $y = 0$

9. $y = \frac{2}{x - 4}$ $x = 4$, $y = 0$

10. **MULTIPLE CHOICE** Jorge has $x^2 + 5x + 6$ square yards of carpet. He wants to carpet rooms that have areas of $x^2 + 8x + 15$ square yards. Write and simplify an expression to show how many rooms he can carpet. (Lesson 11-3) B

A $\frac{x + 3}{x + 5}$

B $\frac{x + 2}{x + 5}$

C $\frac{x + 2}{x + 3}$

D $\frac{x + 6}{x + 5}$

Simplify each expression. State the excluded values of the variables. (Lesson 11-3)

11. $\frac{16x^2y^3}{8xy}$ $2xy^2$; $x \neq 0$, $y \neq 0$

12. $\frac{z - 5}{z^2 - 7z + 10}$ $\frac{1}{z - 2}$; 2, 5

13. $\frac{3x - 15}{x^2 - 25}$ $\frac{3}{x + 5}$; −5, 5

Find each product. (Lesson 11-4)

14. $\frac{(x + 5)(x - 3)}{x^3} \cdot \frac{5x}{x - 3}$ $\frac{5x + 25}{x^2}$

15. $\frac{a^2 + 2a + 1}{a + 1} \cdot \frac{a - 1}{a^2 - 1}$ 1

16. $\frac{m}{m^2 + 3m + 2} \cdot \frac{m + 2}{m^2}$ $\frac{1}{m^2 + m}$

17. **MULTIPLE CHOICE** Find the area of the rectangle. (Lesson 11-4) J

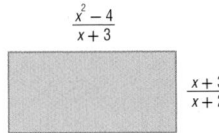

F $\frac{x + 2}{x - 2}$

G $\frac{x + 3}{x - 2}$

H 1

J $x - 2$

Find each quotient. (Lesson 11-4)

18. $\frac{x^4}{y^2} \div \frac{x}{y}$ $\frac{x^3}{y}$

19. $\frac{x + 3}{2x + 6} \div \frac{3x - 6}{4x - 8}$ $\frac{2}{3}$

20. $\frac{x^2 + 7x + 12}{x^2 - 25} \div \frac{x^2 - 9}{2x + 10}$ $\frac{2(x + 4)}{(x - 5)(x - 3)}$

21. **MOTOR VEHICLES** In 2005, the U.S. produced 4,411,300 motor vehicles. This was 10% of the total motor vehicle production for the whole world. How many motor vehicles were produced worldwide in 2005? 44,113,000 vehicles

Formative Assessment

Use the Mid-Chapter Quiz to assess students' progress in the first half of the chapter.

For problems answered incorrectly, have students review the lessons indicated in parentheses.

ExamView Assessment Suite Customize and create multiple versions of your Mid-Chapter Quiz and their answer keys.

FOLDABLES Follow-Up

Before students complete the Mid-Chapter Quiz, encourage them to review the information for Lessons 11-1 through 11-4 in their Foldables.

Intervention Planner

Tier 1 On Level	Tier 2 Strategic Intervention approaching grade level	Tier 3 Intensive Intervention 2 or more grades below level
If students miss about 25% of the exercises or less,	**If** students miss about 50% of the exercises,	**If** students miss about 75% of the exercises,
Then choose a resource: **SE** Lessons 11-1, 11-2, 11-3, and 11-4 **CRM** Skills Practice, pp. 7, 13,19, 25 **TE** Chapter Project, p. 666 IL Math Online Self-Check Quiz	**Then** choose a resource: **CRM** Study Guide and Intervention, Chapter 11, pp. 5, 11, 17, and 23 *Quick Review Math Handbook* IL Math Online Extra Examples, Personal Tutor, Homework Help	**Then** use *Math Triumphs, Alg. 1* IL Math Online Extra Examples, Personal Tutor, Homework Help, Review Vocabulary

11-5 Lesson Notes

1 FOCUS

Vertical Alignment

Before Lesson 11-5
Divide rational expressions.

Lesson 11-5
Divide a polynomial by a monomial.
Divide a polynomial by a binomial.

After Lesson 11-5
Simplify complex fractions involving polynomials.

2 TEACH

Scaffolding Questions

Have students read the *Why?* section of the lesson.

Ask:

- How might you read the expression given? the quantity v squared minus four squared, divided by two a
- How can the fraction be written so that the denominator divides each term in the numerator? $\frac{v^2}{2a} - \frac{4^2}{a}$
- Why does $\frac{4^2}{2a}$ not equal $\frac{2^2}{a}$? You have to follow the order of operations: $4^2 = 16$, then divide by $2a$ to get $\frac{8}{a}$.

11-5 Dividing Polynomials

Then
You divided rational expressions. (Lesson 11-5)

Now
- Divide a polynomial by a monomial.
- Divide a polynomial by a binomial.

IL Learning Standards

7.A.4b Apply formulas in a wide variety of theoretical and practical real-world measurement applications involving perimeter, area, volume, angle, time, temperature, mass, speed, distance, density and monetary values.
8.A.4b Represent mathematical patterns and describe their properties using variables and mathematical symbols.

IL Math Online

glencoe.com
- Extra Examples
- Personal Tutor
- Self-Check Quiz
- Homework Help
- Math in Motion

Why?

The equation below describes the distance d a horse travels when its initial velocity is 4 m/s, its final velocity is v m/s, and its acceleration is a m/s^2.

$$d = \frac{v^2 - 4^2}{2a}$$

There are different ways to simplify the expression.

Keep as one fraction.

$$\frac{v^2 - 4^2}{2a} = \frac{v^2 - 16}{2a}$$

Divide each term by $2a$.

$$\frac{v^2 - 4^2}{2a} = \frac{v^2}{2a} - \frac{4^2}{2a} = \frac{v^2}{2a} - \frac{8}{a}$$

Divide Polynomials by Monomials To divide a polynomial by a monomial, divide each term of the polynomial by the monomial.

EXAMPLE 1 Divide Polynomials by Monomials

Find each quotient.

a. $(2x^2 + 16x) \div 2x$

$(2x^2 + 16x) \div 2x = \frac{2x^2 + 16x}{2x}$ — **Write as a fraction.**

$= \frac{2x^2}{2x} + \frac{16x}{2x}$ — **Divide each term by $2x$.**

$= \frac{\overset{x}{\cancel{2x^2}}}{\underset{1}{\cancel{2x}}} + \frac{\overset{8}{\cancel{16x}}}{\underset{1}{\cancel{2x}}}$ — **Divide out common factors.**

$= x + 8$ — **Simplify.**

b. $(b^2 + 12b - 14) \div 3b$

$(b^2 + 12b - 14) \div 3b = \frac{b^2 + 12b - 14}{3b}$ — **Write as a fraction.**

$= \frac{b^2}{3b} + \frac{12b}{3b} - \frac{14}{3b}$ — **Divide each term by 3b.**

$= \frac{\overset{b}{\cancel{b^2}}}{\underset{3}{\cancel{3b}}} + \frac{\overset{4}{\cancel{12b}}}{\underset{1}{\cancel{3b}}} - \frac{14}{3b}$ — **Divide out common factors.**

$= \frac{b}{3} + 4 - \frac{14}{3b}$ — **Simplify.**

Check Your Progress

1A. $(3q^3 - 6q) \div 3q$ $q^2 - 2$

1B. $(4t^5 - 5t^2 - 12) \div 2t^2$ $2t^3 - \frac{5}{2} - \frac{6}{t^2}$

1C. $(4r^6 + 3r^4 - 2r^2) \div 2r$ $2r^5 + \frac{3}{2}r^3 - r$

1D. $(6w^3 - 3w) \div 4w^2$ $\frac{3}{2}w - \frac{3}{4w}$

Personal Tutor glencoe.com

Lesson 11-5 Resources

Resource	Approaching-Level	On-Level	Beyond-Level	English Learners
Teacher Edition	• Differentiated Instruction, p. 701	• Differentiated Instruction, pp. 701, 705	• Differentiated Instruction, pp. 701, 705	• Differentiated Instruction, p. 701
Chapter Resource Masters	• Study Guide and Intervention, pp. 30–31 • Skills Practice, p. 32 • Practice, p. 33 • Word Problem Practice, p. 34	• Study Guide and Intervention, pp. 30–31 • Skills Practice, p. 32 • Practice, p. 33 • Word Problem Practice, p. 34 • Enrichment, p. 35	• Practice, p. 33 • Word Problem Practice, p. 34 • Enrichment, p. 35	• Study Guide and Intervention, pp. 30–31 • Skills Practice, p. 32 • Practice, p. 33 • Word Problem Practice, p. 34
Transparencies	• 5-Minute Check Transparency 11-5	• 5-Minute Check Transparency 11-5	• 5-Minute Check Transparency 11-5	• 5-Minute Check Transparency 11-5
Other	• Study Notebook • Teaching Algebra with Manipulatives	• Study Notebook • Teaching Algebra with Manipulatives	• Study Notebook	• Study Notebook • Teaching Algebra with Manipulatives

Math *in Motion*, Animation glencoe.com

Divide Polynomials by Binomials You can also divide polynomials by binomials. When a polynomial can be factored and common factors can be divided out, write the division as a rational expression and simplify.

EXAMPLE 2 Divide a Polynomial by a Binomial

Find $(h^2 + 9h + 18) \div (h + 6)$.

$(h^2 + 9h + 18) \div (h + 6) = \frac{h^2 + 9h + 18}{h + 6}$ — **Write as a rational expression.**

$= \frac{(h + 3)(h + 6)}{h + 6}$ — **Factor the numerator.**

$= \frac{(h + 3)\cancel{(h + 6)}^{1}}{\cancel{h + 6}_{1}}$ — **Divide out common factors.**

$= h + 3$ — **Simplify.**

Check Your Progress

Find each quotient.

2A. $(b^2 - 2b - 15) \div (b + 3)$ $b - 5$

2B. $(x^2 + 11x + 24) \div (x + 8)$ $x + 3$

Personal Tutor glencoe.com

If the polynomial cannot be factored or if there are no common factors by which to divide, you must use long division.

EXAMPLE 3 Use Long Division

Find $(y^2 + 4y + 12) \div (y + 3)$ by using long division.

Step 1 Divide the first term of the dividend, y^2, by the first term of the divisor, y.

$$\begin{array}{r} y \\ y + 3\overline{)y^2 + 4y + 12} \\ \underline{(-)\ y^2 + 3y} \\ 1y + 12 \end{array}$$

$y^2 \div y = y$

Multiply y and $y + 3$

Subtract. Bring down the 12.

Step 2 Divide the first term of the partial dividend, $1y$, by the first term of the divisor, y.

$$\begin{array}{r} y + 1 \\ y + 3\overline{)y^2 + 4y + 12} \\ \underline{(-)\ y^2 + 3y} \\ 1y + 12 \\ \underline{(-)\ y + 3} \\ 9 \end{array}$$

Subtract. Bring down the 12.

Multiply 1 and $y + 3$.

Subtract.

So, $(y^2 + 4y + 12) \div (y + 3)$ is $y + 1$ with a remainder of 9. This answer can be written as $y + 1 + \frac{9}{y + 3}$.

Check Your Progress

3A. $(3x^2 + 9x - 15) \div (x + 5)$ $3x - 6 + \frac{15}{x + 5}$

3B. $(n^2 + 6n + 2) \div (n - 2)$ $n + 8 + \frac{18}{n - 2}$

Personal Tutor glencoe.com

Watch Out!

Polynomials When using long division, be sure the dividend is written in standard form. That is, the terms are written so that the exponents decrease from left to right.

$y^2 + 4y + 12$ yes

$4y + y^2 + 12$ no

Divide Polynomials by Monomials

Example 1 shows how to divide a polynomial by a monomial by dividing each term of the polynomial by the monomial.

Formative Assessment

Use the Check Your Progress exercises after each example to determine students' understanding of concepts.

Additional Example

1 Find each quotient.

a. $(4x^2 - 18x) \div 2x$ $2x - 9$

b. $(2y^2 - 3y - 9) \div 3y$ $\frac{2y}{3} - 1 - \frac{3}{y}$

Additional Examples also in Interactive Classroom PowerPoint® Presentations

IWB INTERACTIVE WHITEBOARD READY

Watch Out!

Preventing Errors As an alternative to dividing each term of the polynomial by the monomial, students can factor and then eliminate the GCF.

Remind students that only factors can be divided, not the terms.

Divide Polynomials by Binomials

Example 2 shows how to divide a polynomial by a binomial by factoring the dividend. **Example 3** shows how to use long division to divide a polynomial by a binomial when the polynomial cannot be factored. **Example 4** shows how to divide polynomials to solve a real-world problem. **Example 5** shows how to rename a polynomial with a missing term in order to divide the polynomial by a binomial.

Differentiated Instruction

AL OL BL ELL

If some students are able to read, comprehend, and explain the steps in the examples in this lesson easily,

Then pair those students with others who are having difficulty. Have the pairs work several example problems.

Additional Examples

2 Find $(2r^2 + 5r - 3) \div (r + 3)$. $2r - 1$

3 Find $(x^2 + 7x - 15) \div (x - 2)$ by using long division. $x + 9 + \frac{3}{x-2}$

4 **GEOMETRY** The area of a rectangle is represented by $3x + 90$. Its length is $(x - 3)$. Find $(3x + 90) \div (x - 3)$ to find the width of the rectangle. $3 + \frac{99}{x-3}$

5 Find $(x^3 - 34x + 45) \div (x - 5)$. The quotient is $x^2 + 5x - 9$.

Watch Out!

Preventing Errors Remind students to pay close attention to the signs in the binomials as they perform long division. For the binomial being subtracted, the sign of each term changes.

3 PRACTICE

Formative Assessment

Use Exercises 1–11 to check for understanding.

Use the chart at the bottom of the next page to customize assignments for your students.

TEACH with TECH

VIDEO RECORDING Record yourself as you work through examples showing how to divide polynomials. After class, post the videos to a video sharing Web site so students may use them for reference outside of class.

Real-World EXAMPLE 4 Divide Polynomials to Solve a Problem

PARTIES The expression $5x + 250$ represents the cost of renting a picnic shelter and food for x people. The total cost is divided evenly among all the people except for the two who bought decorations. Find $(5x + 250) \div (x - 2)$ to determine how much each person pays.

$$\begin{array}{r} 5 \\ x-2\overline{)5x+250} \\ (-)\ 5x - \ \ 10 \\ \hline 260 \end{array}$$

So, $5 + \frac{260}{x-2}$ represents the amount each person pays.

Check Your Progress

4. **GEOMETRY** The area of a rectangle is $(2x^2 + 10x - 1)$ square units, and the width is $(x + 1)$ units. What is the length? $2x + 8 + \frac{-9}{x+1}$ units

Personal Tutor glencoe.com

When a dividend is written in standard form and a power is missing, add a term of that power with a coefficient of zero.

EXAMPLE 5 Insert Missing Terms

Find $(c^3 + 5c - 6) \div (c - 1)$.

$$\begin{array}{r} c^2 + c + 6 \\ c-1\overline{)c^3 + 0c^2 + 5c - 6} \\ (-)\ c^3 - c^2 \qquad\qquad \\ \hline c^2 + 5c \qquad \\ (-)\ c^2 - \ c \qquad \\ \hline 6c - 6 \\ (-)\ 6c - 6 \\ \hline 0 \end{array}$$

Insert a c^2-term that has a coefficient of 0.
Multiply c^2 and $c - 1$.
Subtract. Bring down the $5c$.
Multiply c and $c - 1$.
Subtract. Bring down the -6.
Multiply 6 and $c - 1$.
Subtract.

So, $(c^3 + 5c - 6) \div (c - 1) = c^2 + c + 6$.

Check Your Progress Find each quotient.

5A. $(2r^3 + 2r^2 - 4) \div (r - 1)$ **5A.** $2r^2 + 4r + 4$

5B. $(x^4 + 2x^3 + 6x - 10) \div (x + 2)$ **5B.** $x^3 + 6 - \frac{22}{x+2}$

Personal Tutor glencoe.com

Check Your Understanding

Examples 1 and 2 pp. 700–701

Find each quotient.

1. $(8a^2 + 20a) \div 4a$ $2a + 5$

2. $(4z^3 + 1) \div 2z$ $2z^2 + \frac{1}{2z}$

3. $(12n^3 - 6n^2 + 15) \div 6n$ $2n^2 - n + \frac{5}{2n}$

4. $(t^2 + 5t + 4) \div (t + 4)$ $t + 1$

5. $(x^2 + 3x - 28) \div (x + 7)$ $x - 4$

6. $(x^2 + x - 20) \div (x - 4)$ $x + 5$

Example 4 p. 702

7. **CHEMISTRY** The formula $y = \frac{400 + 3x}{50 + x}$ describes a mixture when x liters of a 25% solution are added to a 90% solution. Find $(400 + 3x) \div (50 + x)$. $3 + \frac{250}{x+50}$

Examples 3 and 5 pp. 701–702

Find each quotient. Use long division.

8. $(n^2 + 3n + 10) \div (n - 1)$ $n + 4 + \frac{14}{n-1}$

9. $(4y^2 + 8y + 3) \div (y + 2)$ $4y + \frac{3}{y+2}$

10. $(4h^3 + 6h^2 - 3) \div (2h + 3)$ **10.** $2h^2 - \frac{3}{2h+3}$

11. $(9n^3 - 13n + 8) \div (3n - 1)$ **11.** $3n^2 + n - 4 + \frac{4}{3n-1}$

Focus on Mathematical Content

Long Division Long division can be used to divide a polynomial by a binomial whether or not the polynomial can be factored. If the polynomial is missing a term, use 0 for the coefficient of the missing term, then divide by the binomial. This is possible because a term with a zero coefficient has a value of zero, so it does not affect the quotient. It is simply a placeholder.

Practice and Problem Solving

= **Step-by-Step Solutions** begin on page R12. **Extra Practice** begins on page 815.

Examples 1 and 2 pp. 700–701

Find each quotient.

12. $(14x^2 + 7x) \div 7x$ $2x + 1$
13. $(a^3 + 4a^2 - 18a) \div a$ $a^2 + 4a - 18$
14. $(5q^3 + q) \div q$ $5q^2 + 1$
15. $(6n^2 - 12n + 3) \div 3n$ $2n - 4 + \frac{1}{n}$
16. $(8k^2 - 6) \div 2k$ $4k - \frac{3}{k}$
17. $(9m^2 + 5m) \div 6m$ $\frac{3}{2}m + \frac{5}{6}$
18. $(a^2 + a - 12) \div (a - 3)$ $a + 4$
19. $(x^2 - 6x - 16) \div (x + 2)$ $x - 8$
20. $(r^2 - 12r + 11) \div (r - 1)$ $r - 11$
21. $(k^2 - 5k - 24) \div (k - 8)$ $k + 3$
22. $(y^2 - 36) \div (y^2 + 6y)$ $\frac{y-6}{y}$
23. $(a^3 - 4a^2) \div (a - 4)$ a^2
24. $(c^3 - 27) \div (c - 3)$ $c^2 + 3c + 9$
25. $(4t^2 - 1) \div (2t + 1)$ $2t - 1$
26. $(6x^3 + 16x^2 - 60x + 39) \div (2x + 10)$
27. $(2h^3 + 8h^2 - 3h - 12) \div (h + 4)$ $2h^2 - 3$

Example 4 p. 702

28. **GEOMETRY** The area of a rectangle is $(x^3 - 4x^2)$ square units, and the width is $(x - 4)$ units. What is the length? x^2 units

29. **MANUFACTURING** The expression $-n^2 + 18n + 850$ represents the number of baseball caps produced by n workers. Find $(-n^2 + 18n + 850) \div n$ to write an expression for average number of caps produced per person. $-n + 18 + \frac{850}{n}$

Examples 3 and 5 pp. 701–702

Find each quotient. Use long division.

30. $(b^2 + 3b - 9) \div (b + 5)$
31. $(a^2 + 4a + 3) \div (a - 1)$
32. $(2y^2 - 3y + 1) \div (y - 2)$
33. $(4n^2 - 3n + 6) \div (n - 2)$
34. $(p^3 - 4p^2 + 9) \div (p - 1)$
35. $(t^3 - 2t - 4) \div (t + 4)$
36. $(6x^3 + 5x^2 + 9) \div (2x + 3)$
37. $(8c^3 + 6c - 5) \div (4c - 2)$

38. **GEOMETRY** B The volume of a prism with a triangular base is $10w^3 + 23w^2 + 5w - 2$. The height of the prism is $2w + 1$, and the height of the triangle is $5w - 1$. What is the measure of the base of the triangle? (*Hint*: $V = Bh$) $2w + 4$

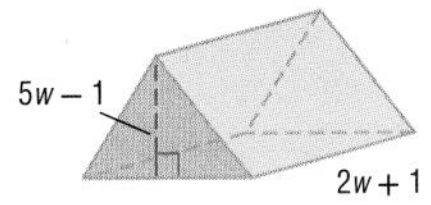

Use long division to find the expression that represents the missing length.

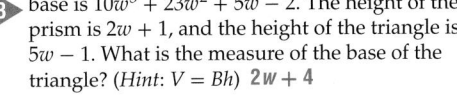

39. $x + 3$

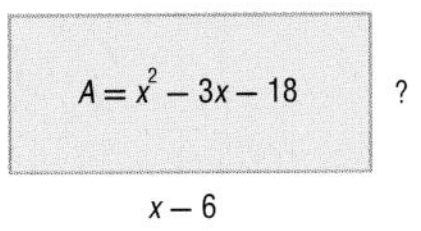

40. $2x + 4$

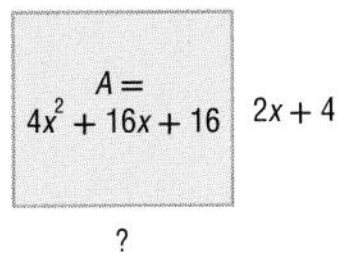

41. Determine the quotient when $x^3 + 11x + 14$ is divided by $x + 2$.

42. What is $14y^5 + 21y^4 - 6y^3 - 9y^2 + 32y + 48$ divided by $2y + 3$? $7y^4 - 3y^2 + 16$

43. **FUNCTIONS** Consider $f(x) = \frac{3x + 4}{x - 1}$.
   a. Rewrite the function as a quotient plus a remainder. Then graph the quotient, ignoring the remainder. See margin.
   b. Graph the original function using a graphing calculator. See margin.
   c. How are the graphs of the function and quotient related?
   d. What happens to the graph near the excluded value of x?

26. $3x^2 - 7x + 5 - \frac{11}{2x + 10}$

30. $b - 2 + \frac{1}{b + 5}$

31. $a + 5 + \frac{8}{a - 1}$

32. $2y + 1 + \frac{3}{y - 2}$

33. $4n + 5 + \frac{16}{n - 2}$

34. $p^2 - 3p - 3 + \frac{6}{p - 1}$

35. $t^2 - 4t + 14 - \frac{60}{t + 4}$

36. $3x^2 - 2x + 3$

37. $2c^2 + c + 2 - \frac{1}{4c - 2}$

41. $x^2 - 2x + 15 - \frac{16}{x + 2}$

43c. The graph of the quotient ignoring the remainder is an asymptote of the graph of the function.

43d. As x approaches 1 from the left, y approaches negative infinity. As x approaches 1 from the right, y approaches positive infinity.

Exercise Alert

Grid Paper For Exercise 43, students will need grid paper.

Tips for New Teachers

Reasoning Remind students that they can use multiplication to check their answers. For example, in Exercise 30 students could check their answer by multiplying $(b + 5)(b - 2) + 1$.

Additional Answers

43a. $f(x) = 3 + \frac{7}{x - 1}$

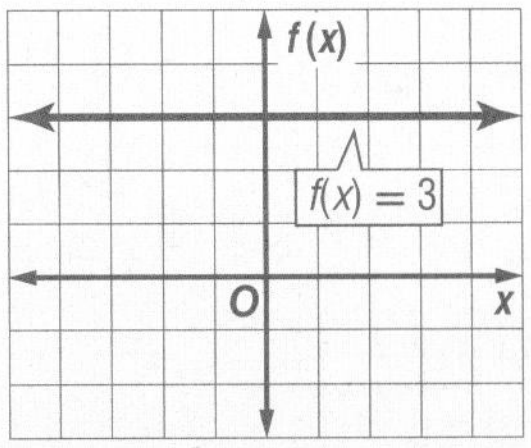

43b.

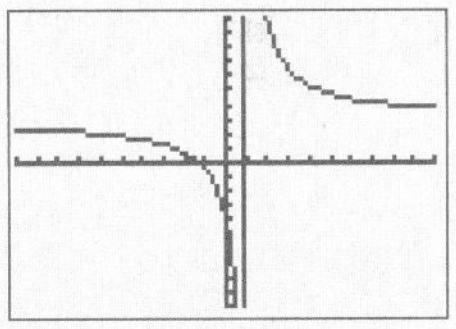

[–10, 10] scl:1 by [–10, 10] scl:1

Differentiated Homework Options

Level	Assignment	Two-Day Option	
AL Basic	12–37, 47, 49–79	13–37 odd, 51–54	12–36 even, 47, 49–50, 55–79
OL Core	13–37 odd, 38, 39, 41–47, 49–79	12–37, 51–54	38–47, 49–50, 55–79
BL Advanced	38–73, (optional: 74–79)		

44. ROAD TRIP The first Ski Club van has been on the road for 20 minutes, and the second van has been on the road for 35 minutes.

a. Write an expression for the amount of time that each van has spent on the road after an additional t minutes. **$t + 20$; $t + 35$**

b. Write a ratio for the first van's time on the road to the second van's time on the road and use long division to rewrite this ratio as an expression. Then find the ratio of the first van's time on the road to the second van's time on the road after 60 minutes, 200 minutes. **$\frac{t+20}{t+35}$; $1 - \frac{15}{t+35}$; about 0.84; about 0.94**

45. BOILING POINT The temperature at which water boils decreases by about 0.9°F for every 500 feet above sea level. The boiling point at sea level is 212°F.

a. Write an equation for the temperature T at which water boils x feet above sea level. **$T = 212 - \left(\frac{0.9}{500}\right)x$**

b. Mount Whitney, the tallest point in California, is 14,494 feet above sea level. At approximately what temperature does water boil on Mount Whitney? **185.9°F**

Real-World Link

The higher the altitude, the lower the temperature at which water boils. Tibet is at a high altitude. The temperature of boiling water in Tibet is lower than that of boiling water in the United States. Tibetans drink their tea while it is still boiling.

Source: *Did You Know?*

46. MULTIPLE REPRESENTATIONS In this problem, you will use picture models to help divide expressions.

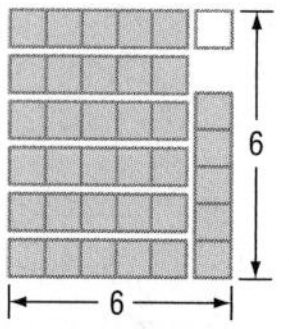

a. ANALYTICAL The first figure models $6^2 \div 7$. Notice that the square is divided into seven equal parts. What are the quotient and the remainder? What division problem does the second figure model? **$5\frac{1}{7}$; $7^2 \div 8$**

b. CONCRETE Draw figures for $3^2 \div 4$ and $2^2 \div 3$.

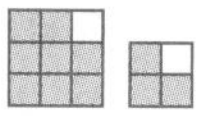

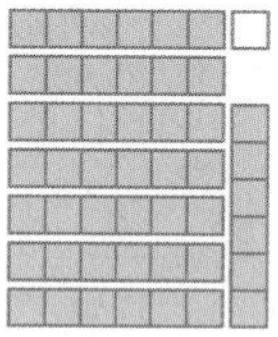

c. VERBAL Do you observe a pattern in the previous exercises? Express this pattern algebraically.

d. ANALYTICAL Use long division to find $x^2 \div (x + 1)$. Does this result match your expression from part **c**? **$x - 1 + \frac{1}{x+1}$; yes**

46c. $x^2 \div (x + 1) = x - 1 + \frac{1}{x+1}$

H.O.T. Problems Use Higher-Order Thinking Skills

47. FIND THE ERROR Alvin and Andrea are dividing $c^3 + 6c - 4$ by $c + 2$. Is either of them correct? Explain your reasoning. **Andrea; Alvin did not take into account the missing term.**

Alvin	Andrea
$c + 2\overline{)c^3 + 6c - 4}$ quotient $c^2 + 4c - 12$	$c + 2\overline{)c^3 + 0c^2 + 6c - 4}$ quotient $c^2 - 2c + 10$
$c^3 + 2c^2$	$c^3 + 2c^2$
$4c^2 - 4$	$-2c^2 + 6c$
$4c^2 + 8c$	$-2c^2 - 4c$
$-12c$	$10c - 4$
$-12c - 24$	$10c + 20$
24	-24

48. CHALLENGE The quotient of two polynomials is $4x^2 - x - 7 + \frac{11x + 15}{x^2 + x + 2}$. What are the polynomials? **Sample answer: $4x^4 + 3x^3 + 2x + 1$ and $x^2 + x + 2$**

49. OPEN ENDED Write a division problem involving polynomials that you would solve by using long division. Explain your answer.

50. WRITING IN MATH Describe the steps to find $(w^2 - 2w - 30) \div (w + 7)$.

49. Sample answer: $(a^2 + 4a - 22) \div (a - 3)$; The polynomial $a^2 + 4a - 22$ is prime, so the problem can be solved by using long division.

50. Sample answer: Divide the first term of the dividend, w^2, by the first term of the divisor, w. Write the answer, w, above the division bar and multiply w and $w + 7$. Subtract and bring down the -30 to get $-9w - 30$. Divide the first term of the partial dividend, $-9w$, by the first term of the divisor, w. Write the answer, -9, above the division bar and multiply -9 and $w + 7$. Subtract. The answer is $w - 9 + \frac{33}{w+7}$.

Study Guide and Intervention
CRM pp. 30–31 AL OL ELL

NAME ______ DATE ______ PERIOD ______

11-5 Study Guide and Intervention
Dividing Polynomials

Divide Polynomials by Monomials To divide a polynomial by a monomial, divide each term of the polynomial by the monomial.

Example 1 Find $(4r^2 - 12r) \div (2r)$.

$(4r^2 - 12r) \div 2r = \frac{4r^2 - 12r}{2r}$
$= \frac{4r^2}{2r} - \frac{12r}{2r}$ Divide each term.
$= \frac{\overset{2r}{4r^2}}{2r} - \frac{\overset{6}{12r}}{2r}$ Simplify.
$= 2r - 6$ Simplify.

Example 2 Find $(3x^2 - 8x + 4) \div (4x)$.

$(3x^2 - 8x + 4) \div 4x = \frac{3x^2 - 8x + 4}{4x}$
$= \frac{3x^2}{4x} - \frac{8x}{4x} + \frac{4}{4x}$
$= \frac{3x}{4} - 2 + \frac{1}{x}$

Exercises
Find each quotient.

1. $(x^3 + 2x^2 - x) \div x$ **$x^2 + 2x - 1$**
2. $(2x^3 + 12x^2 - 8x) \div (2x)$ **$x^2 + 6x - 4$**
3. $(x^2 + 3x - 4) \div x$ **$x + 3 - \frac{4}{x}$**
4. $(4m^2 + 6m - 8) \div (2m^2)$ **$2 + \frac{3}{m} - \frac{4}{m^2}$**
5. $(3x^3 + 15x^2 - 21x) \div (3x)$ **$x^2 + 5x - 7$**
6. $(8m^2p^2 + 4mp - 8p) \div p$ **$8m^2p + 4m - 8$**
7. $(8y^4 + 16y^2 - 4) \div (4y^2)$ **$2y^2 + 4 - \frac{1}{y^2}$**
8. $(16x^4y^2 + 24xy + 5) \div (xy)$ **$16x^3y + 24 + \frac{5}{xy}$**
9. $\frac{15x^3 - 25x + 30}{5}$ **$3x^2 - 5x + 6$**
10. $\frac{10a^2b + 12ab - 8b}{2a}$ **$5ab + 6b - \frac{4b}{a}$**
11. $\frac{6x^2 + 9x + 9}{3x}$ **$2x^2 + 3x + \frac{3}{x}$**
12. $\frac{m^2 - 12m + 42}{3m^2}$ **$\frac{1}{3} - \frac{4}{m} + \frac{14}{m^2}$**
13. $\frac{m^2p^2 - 5mp + 6}{m^2p^2}$ **$1 - \frac{5}{mp} + \frac{6}{m^2p^2}$**
14. $\frac{p^2 - 4pr + 6r^2}{pr}$ **$\frac{p}{r} - 4 + \frac{6r}{p}$**
15. $\frac{6a^2b^2 - 8ab + 12}{2a^2}$ **$3b^2 - \frac{4b}{a} + \frac{6}{a^2}$**
16. $\frac{2x^2y^3 - 4x^2y^2 - 8xy}{2xy}$ **$xy^2 - 2xy - 4$**
17. $\frac{9x^2y^2z - 2xyz + 12x}{xy}$ **$9xyz - 2z + \frac{12}{y}$**
18. $\frac{2a^3b^3 + 8a^2b^2 - 10ab + 12}{2a^2b^2}$ **$ab + 4 - \frac{5}{ab} + \frac{6}{a^2b^2}$**

Chapter 11 30 Glencoe Algebra 1

Practice
CRM p. 33 AL OL BL ELL

NAME ______ DATE ______ PERIOD ______

11-5 Practice
Dividing Polynomials

Find each quotient.

1. $(6q^2 - 18q - 9) \div 9q$ **$\frac{2q}{3} - 2 - \frac{1}{q}$**
2. $(y^2 + 6y + 2) \div 3y$ **$\frac{y}{3} + 2 + \frac{2}{3y}$**
3. $\frac{12a^2b - 3ab^2 + 42ab}{6a^2b}$ **$2 - \frac{b}{2a} + \frac{7}{a}$**
4. $\frac{2m^2p^2 + 56mp - 4m^3p^3}{8m^3p}$ **$\frac{p}{4} + \frac{7}{m^2} - \frac{p^2}{2m}$**
5. $(x^2 - 3x - 40) \div (x + 5)$ **$x - 8$**
6. $(3m^2 - 20m + 12) \div (m - 6)$ **$3m - 2$**
7. $(a^2 + 5a + 20) \div (a - 3)$ **$a + 8 + \frac{44}{a-3}$**
8. $(x^2 - 3x - 2) \div (x + 7)$ **$x - 10 + \frac{68}{x+7}$**
9. $(t^2 + 9t + 28) \div (t + 3)$ **$t + 6 + \frac{10}{t+3}$**
10. $(n^2 - 9n + 25) \div (n - 4)$ **$n - 5 + \frac{5}{n-4}$**
11. $\frac{6r^2 - 5r - 56}{3r + 8}$ **$2r - 7$**
12. $\frac{20w^2 + 39w + 18}{5w + 6}$ **$4w + 3$**
13. $(x^3 + 2x^2 - 16) \div (x - 2)$ **$x^2 + 4x + 8$**
14. $(t^3 - 11t - 6) \div (t + 3)$ **$t^2 - 3t - 2$**
15. $\frac{x^3 + 6x^2 + 3x + 1}{x - 2}$ **$x^2 + 8x + 19 + \frac{39}{x-2}$**
16. $\frac{6d^3 + d^2 - 2d + 17}{2d + 3}$ **$3d^2 - 4d + 5 + \frac{2}{2d+3}$**
17. $\frac{2k^3 + k^2 - 12k + 11}{2k - 3}$ **$k^2 + 2k - 3 + \frac{2}{2k+3}$**
18. $\frac{9y^3 - y - 1}{3y + 2}$ **$3y^2 - 2y + 1 - \frac{3}{3y+2}$**

19. **LANDSCAPING** Jocelyn is designing a bed for cactus specimens at a botanical garden. The total area can be modeled by the expression $2x^2 + 7x + 3$, where x is in feet.
a. Suppose in one design the length of the cactus bed is $4x$, and in another, the length is $2x + 1$. What are the widths of the two designs? **$\frac{x}{2} + \frac{7}{4} + \frac{3}{4x}$; $x + 3$**
b. If $x = 3$ feet, what will be the dimensions of the cactus bed in each of the designs? **12 ft by 3.5 ft; 7 ft by 6 ft**

20. **FURNITURE** Teri is upholstering the seats of four chairs and a bench. She needs $\frac{1}{4}$ square yard of fabric for each chair, and $\frac{1}{2}$ square yard for the bench. If the fabric at the store is 45 inches wide, how many yards of fabric will Teri need to cover the chairs and the bench if there is no waste? **$1\frac{1}{5}$ yd**

Chapter 11 33 Glencoe Algebra 1

Lesson 11-5

Word Problem Practice
CRM p. 34 AL OL BL ELL

NAME ______ DATE ______ PERIOD ______

11-5 Word Problem Practice
Dividing Polynomials

1. **TECHNOLOGY** The surface area (in square millimeters) of a rectangular computer microchip is represented by the expression $x^2 - 12x + 35$, where x is the number of circuits. If the width of the chip is $x - 5$ millimeters, write a polynomial that represents the length. **$x - 7$ mm**

2. **HOMEWORK** Your classmate Ava writes her answer to a homework problem on the chalkboard. She has simplified $\frac{6x^2 - 12x}{6}$ as $x^2 - 12x$. Is this correct? If not, what is the correct simplification? **This is not correct. She forgot to factor 6 from the $-12x$ term. The correct answer should be $\frac{6(x^2 - 2x)}{6} = x^2 - 2x$.**

3. **CIVIL ENGINEERING** Suppose 5400 tons of concrete costs $(500 + d)$ dollars. Write a formula that gives the cost C of t tons of concrete. **$\frac{500t + dt}{5400}$**

4. **SHIPPING** The Overseas Shipping Company loads cargo into a container to be shipped around the world. The volume of their shipping containers is determined by the following equation.
$x^3 + 21x^2 + 99x + 135$
The container's height is $x + 3$. Write an expression that represents the area of the base of the shipping container. **$x^2 + 18x + 45$**

5. **CIVIL ENGINEERING** Greenshield's Formula can be used to determine the amount of time a traffic light at an intersection should remain green.
$G = 2.1n + 3.7$
G = green time in seconds
n = average number of vehicles traveling in each lane per light cycle
Write a simplified expression to represent the average green light time per vehicle. **$2.1 + \frac{3.7}{n}$**

6. **SOLID GEOMETRY** The surface area of a right cylinder is given by the formula $S = 2\pi r^2 + 2\pi rh$.

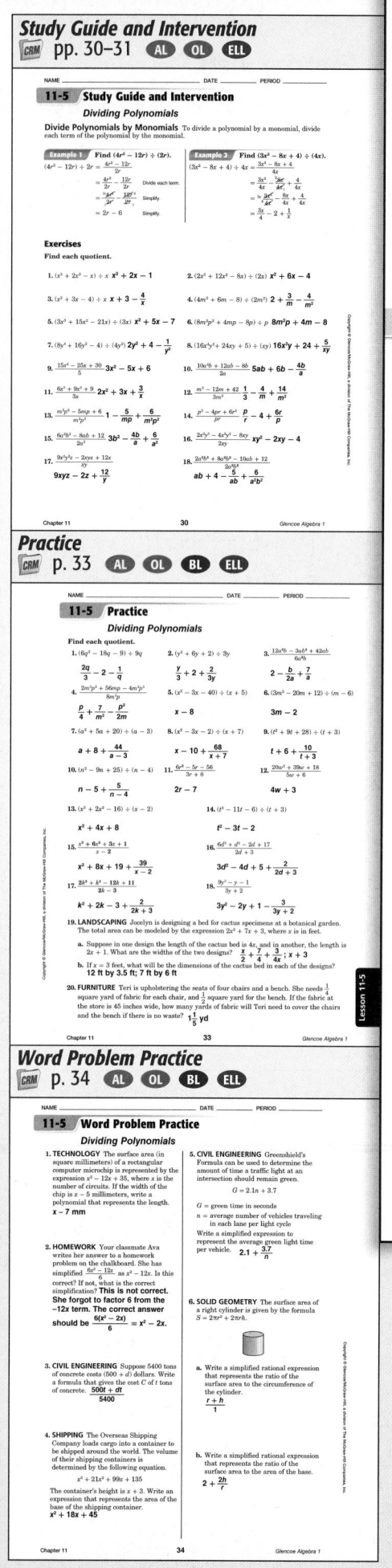

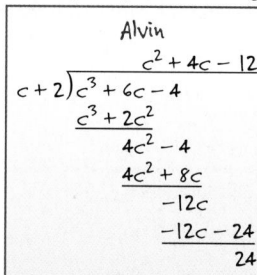

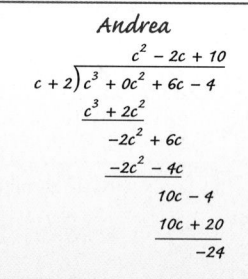

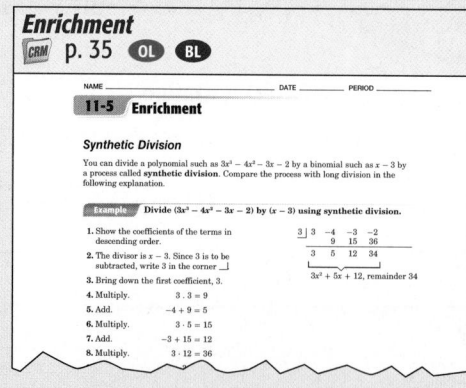

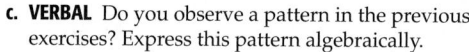

a. Write a simplified rational expression that represents the ratio of the surface area to the circumference of the cylinder. **$\frac{r + h}{1}$**
b. Write a simplified rational expression that represents the ratio of the surface area to the area of the base. **$2 + \frac{2h}{r}$**

Chapter 11 34 Glencoe Algebra 1

Enrichment
CRM p. 35 OL BL

NAME ______ DATE ______ PERIOD ______

11-5 Enrichment

Synthetic Division

You can divide a polynomial such as $3x^3 - 4x^2 - 3x - 2$ by a binomial such as $x - 3$ by a process called **synthetic division**. Compare the process with long division in the following explanation.

Example Divide $(3x^3 - 4x^2 - 3x - 2)$ by $(x - 3)$ using synthetic division.

1. Show the coefficients of the terms in descending order.
2. The divisor is $x - 3$. Since 3 is to be subtracted, write 3 in the corner ⌋.
3. Bring down the first coefficient, 3.
4. Multiply. $3 \cdot 3 = 9$
5. Add. $-4 + 9 = 5$
6. Multiply. $3 \cdot 5 = 15$
7. Add. $-3 + 15 = 12$
8. Multiply. $3 \cdot 12 = 36$

3	3	−4	−3	−2
		9	15	36
	3	5	12	34

$3x^2 + 5x + 12$, remainder 34

Multiple Representations In Exercise 46, students use verbal analysis and pictorial models to illustrate division of algebraic expressions.

PSAE PRACTICE 8.11.22, 7.11.03, 6.11.13

51. Simplify $\frac{21x^3 - 35x^2}{7x}$. A

A $3x^2 - 5x$ C $3x - 5$

B $4x^2 - 6x$ D $5x - 3$

52. EXTENDED RESPONSE The box shown is designed to hold rice.

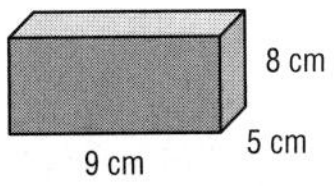

360 cm³

a. How much rice would fit in the box?

b. What is the area of the label on the box, if the label covers all surfaces? 314 cm²

53. Simplify $\frac{x^2 + 7x + 12}{x^2 + 5x + 6}$. G

F $x + 4$ H $x + 2$

G $\frac{x + 4}{x + 2}$ J $\frac{x + 2}{x + 4}$

54. Susana bought cards at 6 for $10. She decorated them and sold them at 4 for $10. She made $60 in profit. How many cards did she sell? D

A 53 C 60

B 25 D 72

Spiral Review

Find each product. (Lesson 11-4)

55. $\frac{3x^3}{8x} \cdot \frac{16}{x}$ $6x$

56. $\frac{3ad}{4c^4} \cdot \frac{8c^2}{6d}$ $\frac{a}{c^2}$

57. $\frac{t^2}{(t-4)(t+4)} \cdot \frac{t-4}{6t}$ $\frac{t}{6(t+4)}$

58. $\frac{10}{r-2} \cdot \frac{r^2-4}{2}$ $5(r+2)$

Find the zeros of each function. (Lesson 11-3)

59. $f(x) = \frac{x+2}{x^2 - 6x + 8}$ -2

60. $f(x) = \frac{x^2 - 3x - 4}{x^2 - x - 12}$ -1

61. $f(x) = \frac{x^2 + 6x + 9}{x^2 - 9}$ -3

62. SHADOWS A 25-foot flagpole casts a shadow that is 10 feet long and a nearby building casts a shadow that is 26 feet long. How tall is the building? (Lesson 10-7) 65 ft

Solve each equation. Check your solution. (Lesson 10-4)

63. $\sqrt{h} = 9$ 81

64. $\sqrt{x+3} = -5$ no solution

65. $3 + 5\sqrt{n} = 18$ 9

66. $\sqrt{x-5} = 2\sqrt{6}$ 29

Solve each equation by using the Quadratic Formula. Round to the nearest tenth if necessary. (Lesson 9-5)

67. $v^2 + 12v + 20 = 0$ $-10, -2$

68. $3t^2 - 7t - 20 = 0$ $-\frac{5}{3}, 4$

69. $5y^2 - y - 4 = 0$ $-0.8, 1$

70. $2x^2 + 98 = 28x$ 7

71. $2n^2 - 7n - 3 = 0$ $-0.4, 3.9$

72. $2w^2 = -(7w + 3)$ $-3, -0.5$

73. THEATER The drama club is building a backdrop using arches with a shape that can be represented by the function $f(x) = -x^2 + 2x + 8$, where x is the length of the arch in feet. The region under each arch is to be covered with fabric. (Lesson 9-2)

a. Graph the quadratic function and determine its x-intercepts. See margin.

b. What is the height of the arch? 9 ft

Skills Review

Find each sum. (Lesson 7-5)

74. $(3a^2 + 2a - 12) + (8a + 7 - 2a^2)$ $a^2 + 10a - 5$

75. $(2c^3 + 3cd - d^2) + (-5cd - 2c^3 + 2d^2)$ $-2cd + d^2$

Find the least common multiple for each set of numbers. (Concepts and Skills Bank Lesson 2)

76. 2, 4, 6 12

77. 3, 6, 8 24

78. 5, 12, 15 60

79. 14, 18, 24 504

Watch Out!

Find the Error For Exercise 47, remind students that, just as in division with whole numbers, an answer can be checked by multiplying the divisor by the quotient and then adding the remainder.

4 ASSESS

Name the Math On an index card, have students divide $x^2 + 9x - 2$ by $x + 1$. Beside each step, have students write one or two sentences explaining and justifying their methods.

Additional Answer

73a.

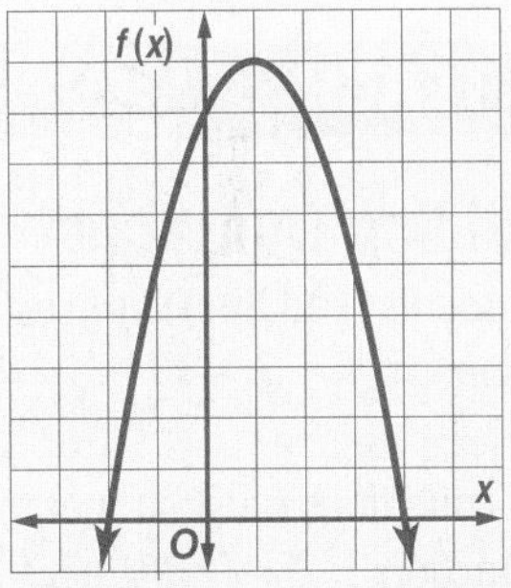

-2 and 4

Differentiated Instruction OL BL

Extension Ask half the class to find the value of $(2x^2 - 13x + 15) \div (2x - 3)$ for $x = 12$ by first substituting, then simplifying. Ask the other half of the class to divide first, then substitute. Have students discuss which of the two methods made it easier to evaluate the expression. For both methods, the resulting value is 7.

Lesson 11-5 Dividing Polynomials 705

11-6 Lesson Notes

1 FOCUS

Vertical Alignment

Before Lesson 11-6
Add and subtract polynomials.

Lesson 11-6
Add and subtract rational expressions with like denominators.
Add and subtract rational expressions with unlike denominators.

After Lesson 11-6
Solve rational equations.

2 TEACH

Scaffolding Questions

Have students read the *Why?* section of the lesson.

Ask:

- What conditions must be met to add fractions? They must have like denominators.
- Do you really need to change percents into fractions before adding them? Explain. No; percents are fractions of 100, so they can be added without converting them to fraction form.
- How do you simplify $\frac{38}{100}$? Divide the numerator and denominator by the common factor 2 to get $\frac{19}{50}$.

11-6 Adding and Subtracting Rational Expressions

Then
You added and subtracted polynomials. (Lesson 7-5)

Now
- Add and subtract rational expressions with like denominators.
- Add and subtract rational expressions with unlike denominators.

IL Learning Standards
8.A.4b Represent mathematical patterns and describe their properties using variables and mathematical symbols.

New Vocabulary
least common multiple (LCM)
least common denominator (LCD)

IL Math Online
glencoe.com
- Extra Examples
- Personal Tutor
- Self-Check Quiz
- Homework Help

Why?

A survey asked families how often they eat takeout. To determine the fraction of those surveyed who eat takeout more than once a week, you can add. Remember that percents can be written as fractions with denominators of 100.

2–3 times a week	plus	daily	equals	more than once a week.
$\frac{30}{100}$	+	$\frac{8}{100}$	=	$\frac{38}{100}$

Thus, $\frac{38}{100}$ or 38% eat takeout more than once a week.

How Many Times a Week Families Eat Takeout

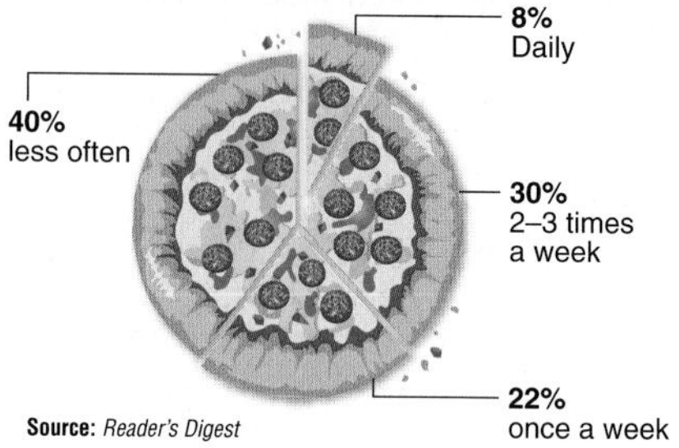

Source: *Reader's Digest*

Add and Subtract Rational Expressions with Like Denominators To add or subtract rational expressions that have the same denominator, add or subtract the numerators and write the sum or difference over the common denominator.

Key Concept For Your FOLDABLE

Add or Subtract Rational Expressions with Like Denominators

Let a, b, and c be polynomials with $c \neq 0$.

$$\frac{a}{c} + \frac{b}{c} = \frac{a+b}{c} \qquad \frac{a}{c} - \frac{b}{c} = \frac{a-b}{c}$$

EXAMPLE 1 Add Rational Expressions with Like Denominators

Find $\frac{5n}{n+3} + \frac{15}{n+3}$.

$\frac{5n}{n+3} + \frac{15}{n+3} = \frac{5n+15}{n+3}$ — The common denominator is $n + 3$.

$= \frac{5(n+3)}{n+3}$ — Factor the numerator.

$= \frac{5\cancel{(n+3)}^{1}}{\cancel{n+3}_{1}}$ — Divide by the common factor, $n + 3$.

$= \frac{5}{1}$ or 5 — Simplify.

Check Your Progress

Find each sum.

1A. $\frac{8c}{6} + \frac{5c}{6}$ $\frac{13c}{6}$

1B. $\frac{4t}{5xy} + \frac{7}{5xy}$ $\frac{4t+7}{5xy}$

1C. $\frac{3y}{3+y} + \frac{y^2}{3+y}$ y

Personal Tutor glencoe.com

Lesson 11-6 Resources

Resource	Approaching-Level	On-Level	Beyond-Level	English Learners
Teacher Edition	• Differentiated Instruction, p. 709	• Differentiated Instruction, pp. 709, 713	• Differentiated Instruction, p. 713	
Chapter Resource Masters	• Study Guide and Intervention, pp. 36–37 • Skills Practice, p. 38 • Practice, p. 39 • Word Problem Practice, p. 40	• Study Guide and Intervention, pp. 36–37 • Skills Practice, p. 38 • Practice, p. 39 • Word Problem Practice, p. 40 • Enrichment, p. 41	• Practice, p. 39 • Word Problem Practice, p. 40 • Enrichment, p. 41	• Study Guide and Intervention, pp. 36–37 • Skills Practice, p. 38 • Practice, p. 39 • Word Problem Practice, p. 40
Transparencies	• 5-Minute Check Transparency 11-6	• 5-Minute Check Transparency 11-6	• 5-Minute Check Transparency 11-6	• 5-Minute Check Transparency 11-6
Other	• Study Notebook	• Study Notebook	• Study Notebook	• Study Notebook

EXAMPLE 2 Subtract Rational Expressions with Like Denominators

Find $\frac{3m-5}{m+4} - \frac{4m+2}{m+4}$.

$\frac{3m-5}{m+4} - \frac{4m+2}{m+4} = \frac{(3m-5)-(4m+2)}{m+4}$ The common denominator is $m + 4$.

$= \frac{(3m-5)+[-(4m+2)]}{m+4}$ The additive inverse of $(4m + 2)$ is $-(4m + 2)$.

$= \frac{3m-5-4m-2}{m+4}$ Distributive Property

$= \frac{-m-7}{m+4}$ Simplify.

Watch Out!

Common Terms Remember that every term of the numerator and the denominator must be multiplied or divided by the same number for the fraction to be equivalent to the original.

Check Your Progress

Find each difference.

2A. $\frac{2h+4}{h+1} - \frac{5+h}{h+1}$ $\frac{h-1}{h+1}$

2B. $\frac{17h+4}{15h-5} - \frac{2h-6}{15h-5}$ $\frac{3h+2}{3h-1}$

Personal Tutor glencoe.com

You can sometimes use additive inverses to form like denominators.

EXAMPLE 3 Inverse Denominators

Find $\frac{3n}{n-4} + \frac{6n}{4-n}$.

$\frac{3n}{n-4} + \frac{6n}{4-n} = \frac{3n}{n-4} + \frac{6n}{-(n-4)}$ Rewrite $4 - n$ as $-(n - 4)$.

$= \frac{3n}{n-4} - \frac{6n}{n-4}$ Rewrite so the denominators are the same.

$= \frac{3n-6n}{n-4}$ or $-\frac{3n}{n-4}$ Subtract the numerators and simplify.

Check Your Progress

Find each sum or difference.

3A. $\frac{t^2}{t-3} + \frac{3}{3-t}$ $\frac{t^2-3}{t-3}$

3B. $\frac{2p}{p-1} - \frac{2p}{1-p}$ $\frac{4p}{p-1}$

Personal Tutor glencoe.com

Add and Subtract with Unlike Denominators The **least common multiple (LCM)** is the least number that is a multiple of two or more numbers or polynomials.

EXAMPLE 4 LCMs of Polynomials

Find the LCM of each pair of polynomials.

a. $6x$ and $4x^3$

Step 1 Find the prime factors of each expression.

$6x = 2 \cdot 3 \cdot x$ $\quad 4x^3 = 2 \cdot 2 \cdot x \cdot x \cdot x$

Step 2 Use each prime factor, 2, 3, and x, the greatest number of times it appears in either of the factorizations.

$6x = 2 \cdot 3 \cdot x$ $\quad 4x^3 = 2 \cdot 2 \cdot x \cdot x \cdot x$

LCM $= 2 \cdot 2 \cdot 3 \cdot x \cdot x \cdot x$ or $12x^3$

Add and Subtract Rational Expressions with Like Denominators

Example 1 shows how to add rational expressions with the same denominator. **Example 2** shows how to subtract rational expressions with like denominators by adding the additive inverse of the numerator of the expression being subtracted. **Example 3** shows how to add rational expressions with denominators that are additive inverses.

Formative Assessment

Use the Check Your Progress exercises after each example to determine students' understanding of concepts.

Additional Examples

1 Find $\frac{4b}{15} + \frac{16b}{15}$. $\frac{4b}{3}$

2 Find $\frac{7x+9}{x-3} - \frac{x-5}{x-3}$. $\frac{2(3x+7)}{x-3}$

3 Find $\frac{3x}{11-x} + \frac{-5x}{x-11}$. $\frac{8x}{11-x}$

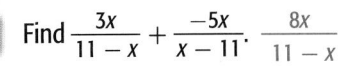

Additional Examples also in Interactive Classroom PowerPoint® Presentations

IWB INTERACTIVE WHITEBOARD READY

Add and Subtract Rational Expressions with Unlike Denominators

Example 4 shows how to find the least common multiple of two or more polynomials. **Example 5** shows how to add rational expressions with unlike denominators by using the least common multiple of the denominators to get equivalent expressions with a common denominator. **Example 6** shows how to add rational expressions to solve a real-world problem. **Example 7** shows how to subtract rational expressions with unlike denominators.

Focus on Mathematical Content

Adding Rational Expressions Whether the denominators of rational expressions are numbers, monomials, or binomials, the denominators must be the same in order to add two or more rational expressions. If the denominators are the same, the numerator of the sum is found by adding the numerators of the addends. The denominator of the sum is the same as for the addends. Sums should be simplified.

Lesson 11-6 Adding and Subtracting Rational Expressions 707

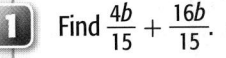

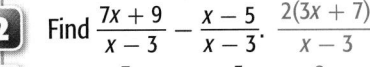

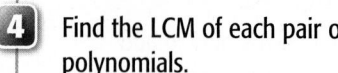

Additional Examples

4 Find the LCM of each pair of polynomials.

a. $12b^4c^5$ and $32bc^2$ $96b^4c^5$

b. $x^2 - 3x - 28$ and $x^2 - 8x + 7$ $(x + 4)(x - 7)(x - 1)$

5 Find $\frac{x + 7}{x^2 - 6x + 9} + \frac{x + 3}{x - 3}$ $\frac{(x + 2)(x - 1)}{(x - 3)^2}$

Focus on Mathematical Content

Subtracting Rational Expressions Whether the denominators of rational expressions are numbers, monomials, or binomials, the denominators must be the same in order to subtract the rational expressions. If the denominators are the same, add the inverse of the numerator of the rational expression to the numerator from which it is being subtracted, use the common denominator, and simplify.

TEACH with TECH

WIKI Have students demonstrate how to distinguish between equivalent expressions with a LCD from ones without a common denominator. Be sure they clearly explain how to find the LCD. Once all agree, post the results to your classroom Web site.

Review Vocabulary

Factored Form A monomial is in factored form when it is expressed as the product of prime numbers and variables, and no variable has an exponent greater than 1. (Lesson 8-1)

b. $n^2 + 5n + 4$ **and** $(n + 1)^2$

$n^2 + 5n + 4 = (n + 1)(n + 4)$ **Factor each expression.**

$(n + 1)^2 = (n + 1)(n + 1)$

$(n + 1)$ is a factor twice in the second expression. $(n + 4)$ is a factor once.

$\text{LCM} = (n + 1)(n + 1)(n + 4)$ or $(n + 1)^2(n + 4)$

Check Your Progress

4A. $8m^2t$ and $12m^2t^3$ $24m^2t^3$

4B. $x^2 - 2x - 8$ and $x^2 - 5x - 14$ **4B.** $(x + 2)(x - 4)(x - 7)$

Personal Tutor glencoe.com

To add or subtract fractions with unlike denominators, you need to rename the fractions using the least common multiple of the denominators, called the **least common denominator (LCD)**.

Key Concept

For Your FOLDABLE

Add or Subtract Rational Expressions with Unlike Denominators

Step 1 Find the LCD.

Step 2 Write each rational expression as an equivalent expression with the LCD as the denominator.

Step 3 Add or subtract the numerators and write the result over the common denominator.

Step 4 Simplify if possible.

StudyTip

Checking Answers You can check whether you have simplified a rational expression correctly by substituting values, but this does not guarantee that the expressions are always equal. If the results are different, check for an error.

EXAMPLE 5 Add Rational Expressions with Unlike Denominators

Find $\frac{3t + 2}{t^2 - 2t - 3} + \frac{t + 1}{t - 3}$.

Find the LCD. Since $t^2 - 2t - 3 = (t - 3)(t + 1)$, the LCD is $(t - 3)(t + 1)$.

$$\frac{3t + 2}{t^2 - 2t - 3} + \frac{t + 1}{t - 3} = \frac{3t + 2}{(t - 3)(t + 1)} + \frac{t + 1}{t - 3}$$ **Factor $t^2 - 2t - 3$.**

$$= \frac{3t + 2}{(t - 3)(t + 1)} + \frac{t + 1}{t - 3}\left(\frac{t + 1}{t + 1}\right)$$ **Write $\frac{t+1}{t-3}$ using the LCD.**

$$= \frac{3t + 2}{(t - 3)(t + 1)} + \frac{t^2 + 2t + 1}{(t - 3)(t + 1)}$$ **Simplify.**

$$= \frac{3t + 2 + t^2 + 2t + 1}{(t - 3)(t + 1)}$$ **Add the numerators.**

$$= \frac{t^2 + 5t + 3}{(t - 3)(t + 1)}$$ **Simplify.**

Check Your Progress Find each sum.

5A. $\frac{4d^2}{d} + \frac{d + 2}{d^2}$ $\frac{4d^3 + d + 2}{d^2}$

5B. $\frac{b + 3}{b} + \frac{b - 5}{b + 1}$ $\frac{2b^2 - b + 3}{b^2 + b}$

Personal Tutor glencoe.com

708 **Chapter 11** Rational Functions and Equations

Real-World Link

The distance a hang glider can travel is determined by its *glide ratio*, or the ratio of the forward distance traveled to the vertical distance dropped.

Source: HowStuffWorks

The formula time $= \frac{\text{distance}}{\text{rate}}$ is helpful in solving real-world applications.

Real-World EXAMPLE 6 Add Rational Expressions

HANG GLIDING For the first 5000 meters, a hang glider travels at a rate of x meters per minute. Then, due to a stronger wind, it travels 6000 meters at a speed that is 3 times as fast.

a. Write an expression to represent how much time the hang glider is flying.

Understand For the first 5000 meters, the hang glider's speed is x. For the last 6000 meters, the hang glider's speed is $3x$.

Plan Use the formula $d = r \times t$ or $t = \frac{d}{r}$ to represent the time t of each section of the hang glider's trip, with rate r and distance d.

Solve Time to fly 5000 meters: $\frac{d}{r} = \frac{5000}{x}$ — **$d = 5000, r = x$**

Time to fly 6000 meters: $\frac{d}{r} = \frac{6000}{3x}$ — **$d = 6000, r = 3x$**

Total flying time: $\frac{5000}{x} + \frac{6000}{3x}$

$\frac{5000}{x} + \frac{6000}{3x} = \frac{5000}{x}\left(\frac{3}{3}\right) + \frac{6000}{3x}$ — **The LCD is $3x$.**

$= \frac{15{,}000}{3x} + \frac{6000}{3x}$ — **Multiply.**

$= \frac{\cancel{21{,}000}^{7000}}{\cancel{3x}_{1}}$ or $\frac{7000}{x}$ — **Simplify.**

Check $\frac{5000}{x} + \frac{6000}{3x} = \frac{5000}{1} + \frac{6000}{3(1)}$ — **Let $x = 1$ in the original expression.**

$= 5000 + 2000$ or 7000 — **Simplify.**

$\frac{7000}{x} = \frac{7000}{1}$ or 7000 — **Let $x = 1$ in the answer expression. Simplify.**

Since the expressions have the same value for $x = 1$, the answer is reasonable. ✓

b. If the hang glider is flying at a rate of 600 meters per minute for the first 5000 meters, find the total amount of time that the hang glider is flying.

$\frac{7000}{x} = \frac{7000}{600}$ — **Substitute 600 for x in the expression.**

≈ 11.7 — **Simplify.**

So, the hang glider is flying for approximately 11.7 minutes.

c. If the hang glider flew for approximately 15 minutes, find the rate the hang glider flew for the first 5000 meters.

$\frac{7000}{x} = 15$ — **Set the expression equal to 15.**

$7000 = 15x$ — **Multiply each side by x.**

$446.7 \approx x$ — **Divide each side by 15 and simplify.**

The hang glider was flying at a rate of 466.7 meters per minute.

Check Your Progress $\frac{5}{r} + \frac{5}{1.2r}$; $\frac{11}{1.2r}$

6. TRAINS A train travels 5 miles from Lynbrook to Long Beach and then back. The train travels about 1.2 times as fast returning from Long Beach. If r is the train's speed from Lynbrook to Long Beach, write and simplify an expression for the total time of the round trip.

Personal Tutor glencoe.com

Additional Example

6 **BIKING** For the first 15 miles, a biker travels at x miles per hour. Then, due to a downhill slope, the biker travels 2 miles at a speed that is 2 times as fast.

a. Write an expression to represent how much time the biker is bicycling. $\frac{15}{x} + \frac{2}{2x}$ or $\frac{16}{x}$

b. If the biker is bicycling at a rate of 8 miles per hour for the first 15 miles, find the total amount of time the biker is bicycling. 2 hours

Tips for New Teachers

Additive Inverses Tell students to pay close attention to signs any time that they are dealing with additive inverses. It is easy to forget to change a sign when finding the additive inverse of an expression. Encourage students to use the Distributive Property to help them change the signs correctly.

Differentiated Instruction AL OL

If you think students should visualize the need to rename rational expressions using the LCD before they can actually add or subtract rational expressions,

Then have students highlight rational expressions, like those in Example 5, using a different color for each different denominator. Once the student rewrites the rational expressions with the same denominator, have him or her highlight them all with the same color.

Additional Example

7 Find $\frac{3}{x} - \frac{5x-2}{8x}$. $\frac{26-5x}{8x}$

3 PRACTICE

Formative Assessment

Use Exercises 1–14 to check for understanding.

Use the chart at the bottom of this page to customize assignments for your students.

To subtract rational expressions with unlike denominators, rename the expressions using the LCD. Then subtract the numerators.

EXAMPLE 7 Subtract Rational Expressions with Unlike Denominators

Find $\frac{5}{x} - \frac{2x+1}{4x}$.

$\frac{5}{x} - \frac{2x+1}{3x} = \frac{5}{x}\left(\frac{4}{4}\right) - \frac{2x+1}{4x}$ — Write $\frac{5}{x}$ using the LCD, $4x$.

$= \frac{20}{4x} - \frac{2x+1}{4x}$ — Simplify.

$= \frac{20-(2x+1)}{4x}$ — Subtract the numerators.

$= \frac{20-2x-1}{4x}$ or $\frac{19-2x}{4x}$ — Simplify.

StudyTip

Simplifying Answers When simplifying a rational expression, you can leave the denominator in factored form, or multiply the terms.

Check Your Progress

Find each difference.

7A. $\frac{6}{t+3} - \frac{7}{t}$ $\frac{-t-21}{t(t+3)}$

7B. $\frac{y}{y-3} - \frac{2}{y^2+y-12}$ $\frac{y^2+4y-2}{(y-3)(y+4)}$

Personal Tutor glencoe.com

Check Your Understanding

Examples 1–3 pp. 706–707

Find each sum or difference.

1. $\frac{3}{7n} + \frac{2}{7n}$ $\frac{5}{7n}$

2. $\frac{x+8}{2} + \frac{x}{2}$ $x+4$

3. $\frac{14r}{9-r} - \frac{2r}{r-9}$ **3.** $\frac{16r}{9-r}$

4. $\frac{7}{5t} - \frac{3+t}{5t}$ $\frac{4-t}{5t}$

Example 4 pp. 707–708

Find the LCM of each pair of polynomials.

5. $3t, 8t^2$ $24t^2$

6. $5m+15, 2m+6$ $10(m+3)$

7. $(x^2-8x+7), (x^2+x-2)$ $(x-7)(x-1)(x+2)$

Examples 5 and 7 pp. 708 and 710

Find each sum or difference.

8. $\frac{6}{n^4} + \frac{2}{n^2}$ $\frac{6+2n^2}{n^4}$

9. $\frac{3}{4x} + \frac{2}{5y}$ $\frac{15y+8x}{20xy}$

10. $\frac{4}{5n} - \frac{1}{10n^3}$ $\frac{8n^2-1}{10n^3}$

11. $\frac{8}{3c} - \frac{-5}{6d}$ $\frac{16d+5c}{6cd}$

12. $\frac{a}{a+4} + \frac{6}{a+2}$

13. $\frac{x}{x-3} - \frac{3}{x+2}$

Example 6 p. 709

14. EXERCISE Joseph walks 10 times around the track at a rate of x laps per hour. He runs 8 times around the track at a rate of $3x$ laps per hour. Write and simplify an expression for the total time it takes him to go around the track 18 times.

12. $\frac{a^2+8a+24}{(a+4)(a+2)}$ 13. $\frac{x^2-x+9}{x^2-x-6}$ 14. $\frac{10}{x} + \frac{8}{3x}$; $\frac{38}{3x}$

Practice and Problem Solving

● = Step-by-Step Solutions begin on page R12.
Extra Practice begins on page 815.

Examples 1–3 pp. 706–707

Find each sum or difference.

15 $\frac{a}{4} + \frac{3a}{4}$ a

16. $\frac{1}{6m} + \frac{5m}{6m}$ $\frac{1+5m}{6m}$

17. $\frac{5y}{6} - \frac{y}{6}$ $\frac{2y}{3}$

18. $\frac{11}{4r} - \frac{-1}{4r}$ $\frac{3}{r}$

19. $\frac{8b}{ab} + \frac{3a}{ab}$ $\frac{8b+3a}{ab}$

20. $\frac{t+2}{3} + \frac{t+5}{3}$ $\frac{2t+7}{3}$

21. $\frac{3c-7}{2c-1} + \frac{2c+1}{1-2c}$ $\frac{c-8}{2c-1}$

22. $\frac{15x}{33x-9} + \frac{3}{9-33x}$

23. $\frac{n+6}{10} - \frac{n+1}{10}$ $\frac{1}{2}$

24. $\frac{5x+2}{2x+5} - \frac{x-8}{2x+5}$ 2

25. $\frac{w+2}{8w} - \frac{2w-3}{8w}$

26. $\frac{3a+1}{a-1} - \frac{a+4}{a-1}$ $\frac{2a-3}{a-1}$

22. $\frac{5x-1}{11x-3}$

25. $\frac{-w+5}{8w}$

Differentiated Homework Options

Level	Assignment	Two-Day Option	
AL Basic	15–50, 72, 74–95	15–49 odd, 76–79	16–50 even, 72, 74–75, 80–95
OL Core	15–51 odd, 52, 53–69 odd, 70, 72, 74–95	15–50, 76–79	51–70, 72, 74–75, 80–95
BL Advanced	51–92, (optional: 93–95)		

Example 4 pp. 707–708

Find the LCM of each pair of polynomials. **29.** $(3r-1)(r+2)$

27. $x^3y,\ x^2y^2$ x^3y^2

28. $5ab,\ 10b$ $10ab$

29. $(3r-1),\ (r+2)$

30. $2n-10,\ 4n-20$ $4(n-5)$

31. $(x^2+9x+18),\ x+3$ $(x+6)(x+3)$

32. $(k^2-2k-8),\ (k+2)^2$ $(k-4)(k+2)^2$

Examples 5 and 7 pp. 708 and 710

Find each sum or difference.

33. $\frac{5}{4x}+\frac{1}{10x}$ $\frac{27}{20x}$

34. $\frac{6}{r}+\frac{2}{r^2}$ $\frac{6r+2}{r^2}$

35. $\frac{3}{2a}+\frac{1}{5b}$ $\frac{15b+2a}{10ab}$

36. $\frac{6g}{g+5}-\frac{g-2}{2g}$

37. $\frac{7}{4k+8}-\frac{k}{k+2}$ $\frac{7-4k}{4(k+2)}$

38. $\frac{5}{2d+2}-\frac{d}{d+5}$

39. $\frac{-2}{7r}+\frac{4}{t}$ $\frac{-2t+28r}{7rt}$

40. $\frac{n}{n-2}+\frac{n}{n+1}$

41. $\frac{d}{d+5}+\frac{7}{d-1}$

42. $\frac{4}{a}-\frac{1}{3a}$ $\frac{11}{3a}$

43. $\frac{6}{5t^2}-\frac{2}{3t}$ $\frac{18-10t}{15t^2}$

44. $\frac{7}{4r}-\frac{3}{t}$ $\frac{7t-12r}{4rt}$

45. $\frac{w-3}{w^2-w-20}+\frac{w}{w+4}$ $\frac{w^2-4w-3}{(w+4)(w-5)}$

46. $\frac{n}{2n+10}+\frac{1}{n^2-25}$ $\frac{n^2-5n+2}{2(n+5)(n-5)}$

47. $\frac{2x}{x^2+8x+15}-\frac{x+3}{x+5}$ $\frac{-x^2-4x-9}{(x+3)(x+5)}$

48. $\frac{r-3}{r^2+6r+9}-\frac{r-9}{r^2-9}$ $\frac{36}{(r-3)(r+3)^2}$

36. $\frac{11g^2-3g+10}{2g(g+5)}$

38. $\frac{-2d^2+3d+25}{(2d+2)(d+5)}$

40. $\frac{2n^2-n}{(n-2)(n+1)}$

41. $\frac{d^2+6d+35}{(d+5)(d-1)}$

Example 6 p. 709

49. TRAVEL Grace walks to her friend's house 2 miles away and then jogs back home. Her jogging speed is 2.5 times her walking speed w. $\frac{2}{w}+\frac{2}{2.5w}$; $\frac{7}{2.5w}$

a. Write and simplify an expression to represent the amount of time Grace spends going to and coming from her friend's house.

b. If Grace walks about 3.5 miles per hour, how many minutes did she spend going to and from her friend's house? **48 min**

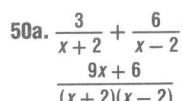

Real-World Link

In a recent year, there were nearly 12.8 million boats registered in the U.S.

Source: USCG Boating

50. BOATS A boat travels 3 miles downstream at a rate 2 miles per hour faster than the current, or $x+2$ miles per hour. It then travels 6 miles upstream at a rate 2 miles per hour slower than the current, or $x-2$ miles per hour.

a. Write and simplify an expression to represent the total time it takes the boat to travel 3 miles downstream and 6 miles upstream.

b. If the rate of the current x is 4 miles per hour, how long did it take the boat to travel the 9 miles? **3.5 hours**

51. SCHOOL Mr. Kim had 18 more geometry tests to grade than algebra tests. He graded 12 tests on Saturday and 20 tests on Sunday. Write an expression for the fraction of tests he graded if a represents the number of algebra tests. **See margin.**

52. PLAYS A total of 1248 people attended the school play. The same number x attended each of the two Sunday performances. There were twice as many people at the Saturday performance than at both Sunday performances. Write an expression to represent the fraction of people who attended on Saturday. $\frac{4x}{1248}=\frac{x}{312}$

50a. $\frac{3}{x+2}+\frac{6}{x-2}$; $\frac{9x+6}{(x+2)(x-2)}$

Find each sum or difference. **53–64. See margin.**

53. $\frac{x+5}{x^2-4}-\frac{3}{x^2-4}$

54. $\frac{18y}{9y+2}-\frac{-4}{-2-9y}$

55. $\frac{k^2-26}{k-5}-\frac{1}{5-k}$

56. $\frac{8}{c-1}+\frac{c}{1-c}$

57. $\frac{2}{x-1}+\frac{3}{x+1}-\frac{4x-2}{x^2-1}$

58. $\frac{x^2-x-12}{x^2-11x+30}-\frac{x-4}{18-x}$

59. $\frac{a^2-5a}{3a-18}-\frac{7a-36}{3a-18}$

60. $\frac{8n-3}{n^2+8n+12}-\frac{5n-9}{n^2+8n+12}$

61. $\frac{x^2-16}{x^3}+\frac{x^3+1}{x^4}$

62. $\frac{x}{7x-3}+\frac{x+2}{15x+30}$

63. $\frac{5x}{3x^2+19x-14}-\frac{1}{9x^2-12x+4}$

64. $\frac{2x+7}{x^2-y^2}+\frac{-5}{x^2-2xy+y^2}$

Tips for New Teachers

LCM or LCD Review with students that the least common multiple, LCM, is used to find a number or polynomial that is the least number that is a common multiple of two or more numbers or polynomials. The least common denominator, LCD, is the LCM of two or more denominators. We say that y^2x^2 is the LCM of y^2x and yx^2, while y^2x^2 is the LCD of $\frac{8}{y^2x}$ and $\frac{6}{yx^2}$.

Additional Answers

51. $\frac{32}{2a+18}$

53. $\frac{1}{x-2}$

54. $\frac{18y-4}{9y+2}$

55. $k+5$

56. $\frac{8-c}{c-1}$

57. $\frac{1}{x-1}$

58. $\frac{2x^3-34x^2+80x+96}{(x-5)(x-6)(x-18)}$

59. $\frac{a-6}{3}$

60. $\frac{3}{n+6}$

61. $\frac{2x^3-16x+1}{x^4}$

62. $\frac{22x^2+41x-6}{(7x-3)(15x+30)}$

63. $\frac{15x^2-11x-7}{9x^3+51x^2-80x+28}$

64. $\frac{2x^2+2x-2xy-12y}{(x-y)^2(x+y)}$

Lesson 11-6 Adding and Subtracting Rational Expressions 711

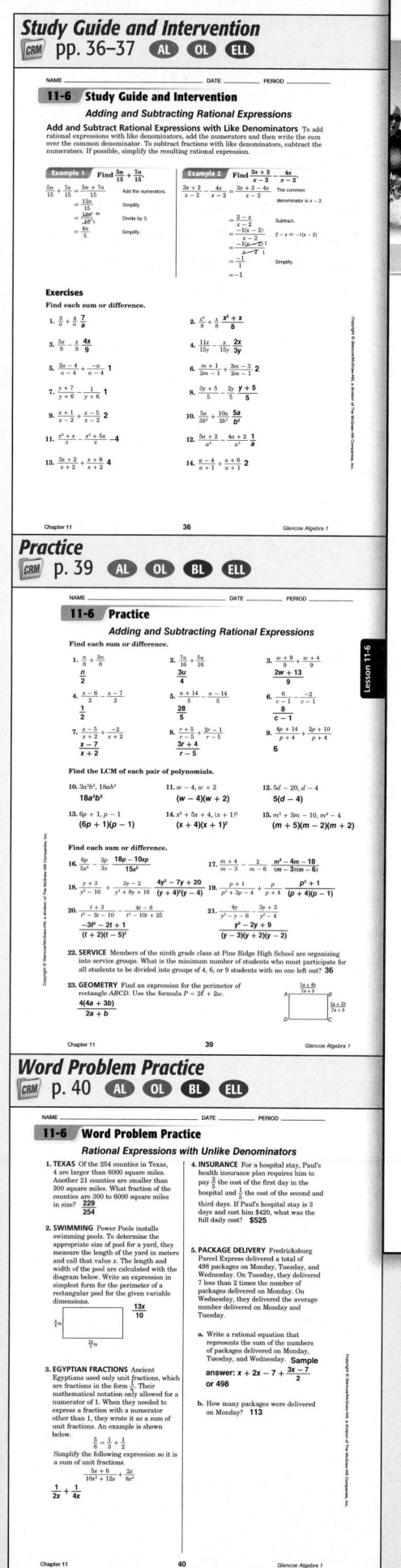

Study Guide and Intervention
CRM pp. 36–37 AL OL ELL

NAME ______ DATE ______ PERIOD ______

11-6 Study Guide and Intervention

Adding and Subtracting Rational Expressions

Add and Subtract Rational Expressions with Like Denominators To add rational expressions with like denominators, add the numerators and then write the sum over the common denominator. To subtract fractions with like denominators, subtract the numerators. If possible, simplify the resulting rational expression.

Example 1 Find $\frac{5n}{15} + \frac{7n}{15}$.

$\frac{5n}{15} + \frac{7n}{15} = \frac{5n + 7n}{15}$ Add the numerators.
$= \frac{12n}{15}$ Simplify.
$= \frac{\cancel{12n}^{4n}}{\cancel{15}_{5}}$ Divide by 3.
$= \frac{4n}{5}$ Simplify.

Example 2 Find $\frac{3x+2}{x-2} - \frac{4x}{x-2}$.

$\frac{3x+2}{x-2} - \frac{4x}{x-2} = \frac{3x+2-4x}{x-2}$ The common denominator is $x - 2$.
$= \frac{2-x}{x-2}$ Subtract.
$= \frac{-1(x-2)}{x-2}$ $2 - x = -1(x - 2)$
$= \frac{-1\cancel{(x-2)}^{1}}{\cancel{x-2}_{1}}$
$= \frac{-1}{1}$ Simplify.
$= -1$

Exercises

Find each sum or difference.

1. $\frac{3}{a} + \frac{4}{a}$ **$\frac{7}{a}$**
2. $\frac{x^2}{8} + \frac{x}{8}$ **$\frac{x^2 + x}{8}$**
3. $\frac{5x}{9} - \frac{x}{9}$ **$\frac{4x}{9}$**
4. $\frac{11x}{15y} - \frac{x}{15y}$ **$\frac{2x}{3y}$**
5. $\frac{2a-4}{a-4} + \frac{-a}{a-4}$ **1**
6. $\frac{m+1}{2m-1} + \frac{3m-3}{2m-1}$ **2**
7. $\frac{y+7}{y+6} - \frac{1}{y+6}$ **1**
8. $\frac{3y+5}{5} - \frac{2y}{5}$ **$\frac{y+5}{5}$**
9. $\frac{x+1}{x-2} + \frac{x-5}{x-2}$ **2**
10. $\frac{5a}{3b^2} + \frac{10a}{3b^2}$ **$\frac{5a}{b^2}$**
11. $\frac{x^2+x}{x} - \frac{x^2+5x}{x}$ **−4**
12. $\frac{5a+2}{a^2} - \frac{4a+2}{a^2}$ **$\frac{1}{a}$**
13. $\frac{3x+2}{x+2} + \frac{x+6}{x+2}$ **4**
14. $\frac{a-4}{a+1} + \frac{a+6}{a+1}$ **2**

Chapter 11 36 Glencoe Algebra 1

Practice
CRM p. 39 AL OL BL ELL

NAME ______ DATE ______ PERIOD ______

11-6 Practice

Adding and Subtracting Rational Expressions

Lesson 11-6

Find each sum or difference.

1. $\frac{n}{8} + \frac{3n}{8}$ **$\frac{n}{2}$**
2. $\frac{7u}{16} + \frac{5u}{16}$ **$\frac{3u}{4}$**
3. $\frac{w+9}{9} + \frac{w+4}{9}$ **$\frac{2w+13}{9}$**
4. $\frac{x-6}{2} - \frac{x-7}{2}$ **$\frac{1}{2}$**
5. $\frac{n+14}{5} - \frac{n-14}{5}$ **$\frac{28}{5}$**
6. $\frac{6}{c-1} - \frac{-2}{c-1}$ **$\frac{8}{c-1}$**
7. $\frac{x-5}{x+2} + \frac{-2}{x+2}$ **$\frac{x-7}{x+2}$**
8. $\frac{r+5}{r-5} + \frac{2r-1}{r-5}$ **$\frac{3r+4}{r-5}$**
9. $\frac{4p+14}{p+4} + \frac{2p+10}{p+4}$ **6**

Find the LCM of each pair of polynomials.

10. $3a^3b^2, 18ab^3$ **$18a^3b^3$**
11. $w - 4, w + 2$ **$(w - 4)(w + 2)$**
12. $5d - 20, d - 4$ **$5(d - 4)$**
13. $6p + 1, p - 1$ **$(6p + 1)(p - 1)$**
14. $x^2 + 5x + 4, (x + 1)^2$ **$(x + 4)(x + 1)^2$**
15. $m^2 + 3m - 10, m^2 - 4$ **$(m + 5)(m - 2)(m + 2)$**

Find each sum or difference.

16. $\frac{6p}{5x^2} - \frac{2p}{3x}$ **$\frac{18p - 10xp}{15x^2}$**
17. $\frac{m+4}{m-3} - \frac{2}{m-6}$ **$\frac{m^2 - 4m - 18}{(m-3)(m-6)}$**
18. $\frac{y+3}{y^2-16} + \frac{3y-2}{y^2+8y+16}$ **$\frac{4y^2 - 7y + 20}{(y+4)^2(y-4)}$**
19. $\frac{p+1}{p^2+3p-4} + \frac{p}{p+4}$ **$\frac{p^2+1}{(p+4)(p-1)}$**
20. $\frac{t+3}{t^2-3t-10} - \frac{4t-8}{t^2-10t+25}$ **$\frac{-3t^2 - 2t + 1}{(t+2)(t-5)^2}$**
21. $\frac{4y}{y^2-y-6} - \frac{3y+3}{y^2-4}$ **$\frac{y^2 - 2y + 9}{(y-3)(y+2)(y-2)}$**

22. **SERVICE** Members of the ninth grade class at Pine Ridge High School are organizing into service groups. What is the minimum number of students who must participate for all students to be divided into groups of 4, 6, or 9 students with no one left out? **36**

23. **GEOMETRY** Find an expression for the perimeter of rectangle *ABCD*. Use the formula $P = 2\ell + 2w$.
$\frac{4(4a + 3b)}{2a + b}$

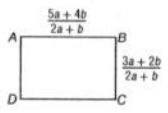

Chapter 11 39 Glencoe Algebra 1

Word Problem Practice
CRM p. 40 AL OL BL ELL

NAME ______ DATE ______ PERIOD ______

11-6 Word Problem Practice

Rational Expressions with Unlike Denominators

1. **TEXAS** Of the 254 counties in Texas, 4 are larger than 6000 square miles. Another 21 counties are smaller than 300 square miles. What fraction of the counties are 300 to 6000 square miles in size? **$\frac{229}{254}$**

2. **SWIMMING** Power Pools installs swimming pools. To determine the appropriate size of pool for a yard, they measure the length of the yard in meters and call that value x. The length and width of the pool are calculated with the diagram below. Write an expression in simplest form for the perimeter of a rectangular pool for the given variable dimensions. **$\frac{13x}{10}$**

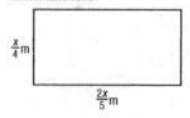

3. **EGYPTIAN FRACTIONS** Ancient Egyptians used only unit fractions, which are fractions in the form $\frac{1}{n}$. Their mathematical notation only allowed for a numerator of 1. When they needed to express a fraction with a numerator other than 1, they wrote it as a sum of unit fractions. An example is shown below.
$$\frac{5}{6} = \frac{1}{3} + \frac{1}{2}$$
Simplify the following expression so it is a sum of unit fractions.
$$\frac{5x+6}{10x^2+12x} + \frac{2x}{8x^2}$$
$\frac{1}{2x} + \frac{1}{4x}$

4. **INSURANCE** For a hospital stay, Paul's health insurance plan requires him to pay $\frac{2}{5}$ the cost of the first day in the hospital and $\frac{1}{5}$ the cost of the second and third days. If Paul's hospital stay is 3 days and cost him \$420, what was the full daily cost? **\$525**

5. **PACKAGE DELIVERY** Fredricksburg Parcel Express delivered a total of 498 packages on Monday, Tuesday, and Wednesday. On Tuesday, they delivered 7 less than 2 times the number of packages delivered on Monday. On Wednesday, they delivered the average number delivered on Monday and Tuesday.
   a. Write a rational equation that represents the sum of the numbers of packages delivered on Monday, Tuesday, and Wednesday. **Sample answer: $x + 2x - 7 + \frac{3x - 7}{2}$ or 498**
   b. How many packages were delivered on Monday? **113**

Chapter 11 40 Glencoe Algebra 1

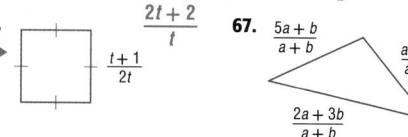

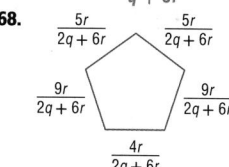

Real-World Link

A regular triathlon includes a 1.5-kilometer swim, a 40-kilometer bike ride, and a 10-kilometer run. The first Olympic triathlons were held in 2000 in Sydney, Australia.

Source: USA Triathlon

65. **TRIATHLONS** In a sprint triathlon, athletes swim 400 meters, bike 20 kilometers, and run 5 kilometers. An athlete bikes 12 times as fast as she swims and runs 5 times as fast as she swims.
   a. Simplify $\frac{400}{x} + \frac{20{,}000}{12x} + \frac{5000}{5x}$, an expression that represents the time it takes the athlete to complete the sprint triathlon. **$\frac{9200}{3x}$**
   b. If the athlete swims 40 meters per minute, find the total time it takes her to complete the triathlon. **about 76 min 40 seconds**

GEOMETRY Write an expression for the perimeter of each figure. **68. $\frac{16r}{q+3r}$**

66. **$\frac{2t+2}{t}$**

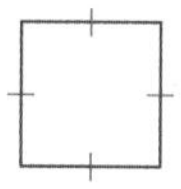

67. **8**

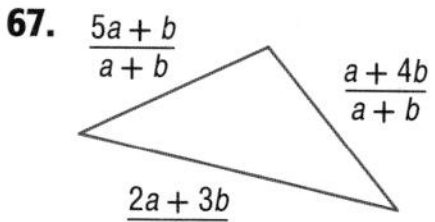

68.

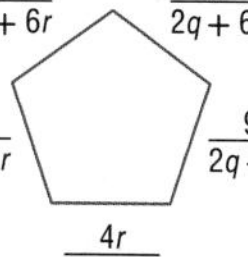

69. **BIKES** Marina rides her bike at an average rate of 10 miles per hour. On one day, she rides 9 miles and then rides around a large loop x miles long. On the second day, she rides 5 miles and then rides around the loop three times.
   a. Write an expression to represent the total time she spent riding her bike on those two days. (*Hint:* Use $t = \frac{d}{r}$, where t is time, d is distance, and r is rate.) Then simplify the expression. **$\frac{9+x}{10} + \frac{5+3x}{10}$; $\frac{7+2x}{5}$**
   b. If the loop is 2 miles long, how long did Marina ride on those two days? **2.2 hours**

70. **TRAVEL** The Showalter family drives 80 miles to a college football game. On the trip home, their average speed is about 3 miles per hour slower.
   a. Let x represent the average speed of the car on the way to the game. Write and simplify an expression to represent the total time it took driving to the game and then back home. **$\frac{80}{x} + \frac{80}{x-3}$; $\frac{160x - 240}{x(x-3)}$**
   b. If their average speed on the way to the game was 68 miles per hour, how long did it take the Showalter family to drive to the game and back? Round to the nearest tenth. **2.4 hours**

H.O.T. Problems
Use Higher-Order Thinking Skills

71. **CHALLENGE** Find $\left(\frac{4}{7y-2} + \frac{7y}{2-7y}\right)\left(\frac{y+5}{6} - \frac{y+3}{6}\right)$. **$\frac{4-7y}{21y-6}$**

72. **WRITING IN MATH** Describe in words the steps you use to find the LCM in an addition or subtraction of rational expressions with unlike denominators.

73. **CHALLENGE** Is the following statement *sometimes*, *always*, or *never* true? Explain. **See margin.**
$$\frac{a}{x} + \frac{b}{y} = \frac{ay + bx}{xy}$$

74. **OPEN ENDED** Describe a real-life situation that could be expressed by adding two rational expressions that are fractions. Explain what the denominator and numerator represent in both expressions.

75. **WRITING IN MATH** Describe how to add rational expressions with denominators that are additive inverses. **See margin.**

72. Sample answer: If possible, factor the polynomial in the denominator of each rational expression. The LCM of the denominators is the product of these factors each used the greatest number of times it appears in either of the factorizations. Write each rational expression using the LCM as a common denominator. Finally, add or subtract the rational expressions.

74. Sample answer: Survey data can be represented with rational expressions that are fractions; $\frac{a}{d} + \frac{3a-12}{d}$; the numerator is the number of people who gave a certain response to a survey and the denominator is the number of people who took the survey.

Enrichment
CRM p. 41 OL BL

NAME ______ DATE ______ PERIOD ______

11-6 Enrichment

Lesson 11-6

Sum and Difference of Any Two Like Powers

The sum of any two like powers can be written $a^n + b^n$, where n is a positive integer. The difference of like powers is $a^n - b^n$. Under what conditions are these expressions exactly divisible by $(a + b)$ or $(a - b)$? The answer depends on whether n is an odd or even number.

Use long division to find the following quotients. (*Hint:* Write $a^3 + b^3$ as $a^3 + 0a^2 + 0a + b^3$.) Is the numerator exactly divisible by the denominator? Write *yes* or *no*.

1. $\frac{a^3+b^3}{a+b}$ **yes**
2. $\frac{a^3+b^3}{a-b}$ **no**
3. $\frac{a^3-b^3}{a+b}$ **no**
4. $\frac{a^3-b^3}{a-b}$ **yes**
5. $\frac{a^4+b^4}{a+b}$ **no**
6. $\frac{a^4+b^4}{a-b}$ **no**
7. $\frac{a^4-b^4}{a+b}$ **yes**
8. $\frac{a^4-b^4}{a-b}$ **yes**
9. $\frac{a^5+b^5}{a+b}$ **yes**
10. $\frac{a^5+b^5}{a-b}$ **no**
11. $\frac{a^5-b^5}{a+b}$ **no**
12. $\frac{a^5-b^5}{a-b}$ **yes**

13. Use the words *odd* and *even* to complete the two statements.

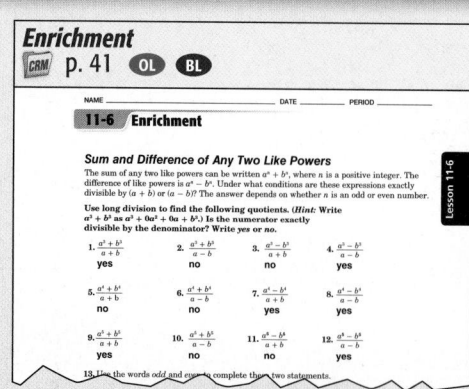

PSAE PRACTICE 8.11.18, 6.11.10, 10.11.04, 8.11.22

76. SHORT RESPONSE An object is launched upwards at 19.6 meters per second from a 58.8-meter-tall platform. The equation for the object's height h, in meters, at time t seconds after launch is $h(t) = -4.9t^2 + 19.6t + 58.8$. How long after the launch does the object strike the ground? **6 seconds**

77. Simplify $\frac{2}{5} + \frac{3}{25} + \frac{1}{10}$. **C**

A $\frac{2}{5}$ C $\frac{31}{50}$

B $\frac{3}{5}$ D $\frac{5}{31}$

78. STATISTICS Courtney has grades of 84, 65, and 76 on three math tests. What grade must she earn on the next test to have an average of exactly 80 for the four tests? **J**

F 84 H 98

G 80 J 95

79. Simplify $\frac{2}{x} + \frac{3}{x^2} + \frac{1}{2x}$. **C**

A $\frac{3x+2}{x^2}$ C $\frac{5x+6}{2x^2}$

B $\frac{6}{2x^2}$ D $\frac{6+x}{x^2}$

Spiral Review

Find each quotient. (Lesson 11-5) **82.** $2a^2 - 4a + 1$

80. $(6x^2 + 10x) \div 2x$ $3x + 5$ **81.** $(15y^3 + 14y) \div 3y$ $5y^2 + \frac{14}{3}$ **82.** $(10a^3 - 20a^2 + 5a) \div 5a$

Convert each rate. Round to the nearest tenth if necessary. (Lesson 11-4)

83. 23 feet per second to miles per hour **about 15.7 mi/h**

84. 118 milliliters per second to quarts per hour (*Hint*: 1 liter ≈ 1.06 quarts) **450.3 qt/h**

Find the length of the missing side. If necessary, round to the nearest hundredth. (Lesson 10-5)

85. 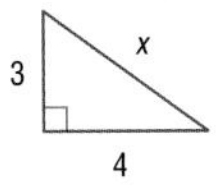

5

86. 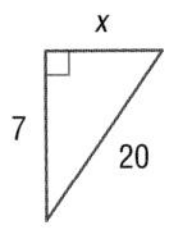

18.73

87. 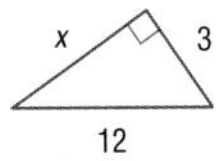

11.62

88. AMUSEMENT RIDE The height h in feet of a car above the exit ramp of a free-fall ride can be modeled by $h(t) = -16t^2 + s$. t is the time in seconds after the car drops, and s is the starting height of the car in feet. If the designer wants the ride to last 3 seconds, what should be the starting height in feet? (Lesson 8-6) **144 ft**

Express each number in scientific notation. (Lesson 7-3)

89. 12,300 1.23×10^4 **90.** 0.0000375 3.75×10^{-5} **91.** 1,255,000 1.255×10^6

92. FINANCIAL LITERACY Ruben has \$13 to order pizza. The pizza costs \$7.50 plus \$1.25 per topping. He plans to tip 15% of the total cost. Write and solve an inequality to find out how many toppings he can order. (Lesson 5-3)
$7.50 + 1.25t + 0.15(7.50 + 1.25t) \leq 13$; **3 or fewer toppings**

Skills Review

Find each quotient. (Lesson 11-4)

93. $\frac{12}{3x^2} \div \frac{6}{x}$ $\frac{2}{3x}$ **94.** $\frac{g^4}{2} \div \frac{g^3}{8d^2}$ $4gd^2$ **95.** $\frac{4y-8}{y+1} \div (y-2)$ $\frac{4}{y+1}$

4 ASSESS

Ticket Out the Door Ask students to choose two letters from A through F. On the board write the letters A through F. Under each letter write a different rational expression, three with the same denominator and three with denominators that are the additive inverse denominator of the first three. Ask students to first add the rational expressions that are under their two letters. Then have students subtract the rational expressions.

Formative Assessment

Check for student understanding of Lessons 11-5 and 11-6.

CRM Quiz 3, p. 58

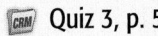

Additional Answers

73. always; $\frac{a}{x} + \frac{b}{y} = \frac{a}{x} \cdot \frac{y}{y} + \frac{b}{y} \cdot \frac{x}{x} = \frac{ay}{xy} + \frac{bx}{yx} = \frac{ay + bx}{xy}$

75. First, factor -1 out of one of the denominators so that it is like the other. Then rewrite the denominator without parentheses. Finally, add or subtract the numerators and write the result over the like denominator.

Differentiated Instruction OL BL

Extension Ask students to find $\frac{3x-4}{x^2-5x+4} + \frac{x+4}{x^2+3x-4}$. $\frac{4x-8}{(x-1)(x-4)}$

11-7 Lesson Notes

1 FOCUS

Vertical Alignment

Before Lesson 11-7
Simplify rational expressions.

Lesson 11-7
Simplify mixed expressions.
Simplify complex fractions.

After Lesson 11-7
Solve rational equations.

2 TEACH

Scaffolding Questions

Have students read the *Why?* section of the lesson.

Ask:

- What is the denominator of the complex fraction shown? $4\frac{2}{5}$
- What operation does the fraction bar represent? division
- How do you divide by a mixed number? Sample answer: Convert it to an improper fraction and multiply by the reciprocal.

11-7 Mixed Expressions and Complex Fractions

Then
You simplified rational expressions. (Lesson 11-3)

Now

- Simplify mixed expressions.
- Simplify complex fractions.

IL Learning Standards

7.A.4b Apply formulas in a wide variety of theoretical and practical real-world measurement applications involving perimeter, area, volume, angle, time, temperature, mass, speed, distance, density and monetary values.
7.B.4 Estimate and measure the magnitude and directions of physical quantities using rulers, protractors and other scientific instruments including timers, calculators and computers.

New Vocabulary
mixed expression
complex fraction

IL Math Online
glencoe.com

- Extra Examples
- Personal Tutor
- Self-Check Quiz
- Homework Help

Why?

A Top Fuel dragster can cover $\frac{1}{4}$ mile in $4\frac{2}{5}$ seconds. The average speed in miles per second can be described by the expression below. It is called a *complex fraction*.

$$\frac{\frac{1}{4}\text{ mile}}{4\frac{2}{5}\text{ seconds}}$$

Simplify Mixed Expressions An expression like $2 + \frac{4}{x+1}$ is called a **mixed expression** because it contains the sum of a monomial, 2, and a rational expression, $\frac{4}{x+1}$. You can use the LCD to change a mixed expression to a rational expression.

EXAMPLE 1 Change Mixed Expression to Rational Expressions

Write $2 + \frac{4}{x-1}$ as a rational expression.

$2 + \frac{4}{x-1} = \frac{2(x-1)}{x-1} + \frac{4}{x-1}$ — The LCD is $x - 1$.

$= \frac{2(x-1)+4}{x-1}$ — Add the numerators.

$= \frac{2x-2+4}{x-1}$ — Distributive Property

$= \frac{2x+2}{x-1}$ — Simplify.

Check Your Progress

Write each mixed expression as a rational expression.

1A. $2 + \frac{5}{x}$ $\frac{2x+5}{x}$

1B. $\frac{6y}{4y+8} + 5y$ $\frac{10y^2+23y}{2y+4}$

Personal Tutor glencoe.com

Simplify Complex Fractions A **complex fraction** has one or more fractions in the numerator or denominator. You can simplify by using division.

numerical complex fraction

$$\frac{\frac{2}{3}}{\frac{5}{8}} = \frac{2}{3} \div \frac{5}{8} = \frac{2}{3} \times \frac{8}{5} = \frac{16}{15}$$

algebraic complex fraction

$$\frac{\frac{a}{b}}{\frac{c}{d}} = \frac{a}{b} \div \frac{c}{d} = \frac{a}{b} \times \frac{d}{c} = \frac{ad}{bc}$$

To simplify a complex fraction, write it as a division expression. Then find the reciprocal of the second expression and multiply.

Lesson 11-7 Resources

Resource	Approaching-Level	On-Level	Beyond-Level	English Learners
Teacher Edition		• Differentiated Instruction, p. 716, 719	• Differentiated Instruction, pp. 716, 719	• Differentiated Instruction, p. 716
Chapter Resource Masters	• Study Guide and Intervention, pp. 42–43 • Skills Practice, p. 44 • Practice, p. 45 • Word Problem Practice, p. 46	• Study Guide and Intervention, pp. 43–43 • Skills Practice, p. 44 • Practice, p. 45 • Word Problem Practice, p. 46 • Enrichment, p. 47	• Practice, p. 45 • Word Problem Practice, p. 46 • Enrichment, p. 47	• Study Guide and Intervention, pp. 42–43 • Skills Practice, p. 44 • Practice, p. 45 • Word Problem Practice, p. 46
Transparencies	• 5-Minute Check Transparency 11-7	• 5-Minute Check Transparency 11-7	• 5-Minute Check Transparency 11-7	• 5-Minute Check Transparency 11-7
Other	• Study Notebook	• Study Notebook	• Study Notebook	• Study Notebook

714 Chapter 11 Rational Functions and Equations

Real-World EXAMPLE 2 Use Complex Fractions to Solve Problems

RACING Refer to the application at the beginning of the lesson. Find the average speed of the Top Fuel dragster in miles per minute.

$$\frac{\frac{1}{4}\text{ mile}}{4\frac{2}{5}\text{ seconds}} = \frac{\frac{1}{4}\text{ mile}}{4\frac{2}{5}\text{ }\cancel{\text{seconds}}} \times \frac{60\text{ }\cancel{\text{seconds}}}{1\text{ minute}}$$ **Convert seconds to minutes. Divide by common units.**

$$= \frac{\frac{1}{4} \times 60}{4\frac{2}{5}}$$ **Simplify.**

$$= \frac{\frac{60}{4}}{\frac{22}{5}}$$ **Express each term as an improper fraction.**

$$= \frac{\overset{15}{\cancel{60}} \times 5}{\underset{1}{\cancel{4}} \times 22}$$ **Use the rule $\frac{\frac{a}{b}}{\frac{c}{d}} = \frac{ad}{bc}$.**

$$= \frac{75}{22} \text{ or } 3\frac{9}{22}$$ **Simplify.**

So, the average speed of the Top Fuel dragster is $3\frac{9}{22}$ miles per minute.

Check Your Progress

2. RACING Refer to the information about the Jr. Dragster at the left. What is the average speed of the car in feet per second? $83\frac{43}{79}$ ft/s

Personal Tutor glencoe.com

Real-World Link

A Jr. Dragster is a half-scale verson of a Top Fuel dragster. This car, which can go $\frac{1}{8}$ mile in $7\frac{9}{10}$ seconds, is designed to be driven by kids ages 8–17 in the NHRA Jr. Drag Racing League.

Source: NHRA

To simplify complex fractions, you can either use the rule as in Example 2, or you can rewrite the fraction as a division expression, as shown below.

EXAMPLE 3 Complex Fractions Involving Monomials

Simplify $\frac{\frac{8t^2}{v}}{\frac{4t}{v^3}}$.

$$\frac{\frac{8t^2}{v}}{\frac{4t}{v^3}} = \frac{8t^2}{v} \div \frac{4t}{v^3}$$ **Write as a division expression.**

$$= \frac{8t^2}{v} \times \frac{v^3}{4t}$$ **To divide, multiply by the reciprocal.**

$$= \frac{\overset{2t}{\cancel{8t^2}}}{\underset{1}{\cancel{v}}} \times \frac{\overset{v^2}{\cancel{v^3}}}{\underset{1}{\cancel{4t}}} \text{ or } 2tv^2$$ **Divide by the common factors 4*t* and *v* and simplify.**

Check Your Progress

Simplify each expression.

3A. $\frac{\frac{g^3h}{b}}{\frac{gh^3}{b^2}}$ $\frac{g^2b}{h^2}$

3B. $\frac{\frac{-24m^3t^5}{p^2h}}{\frac{16pm^2}{t^4h}}$ $\frac{-3mt^9}{2p^3}$

Personal Tutor glencoe.com

Simplify Mixed Expressions

Example 1 shows how to change a mixed expression to a rational expression.

Formative Assessment

Use the Check Your Progress exercises after each example to determine students' understanding of concepts.

Additional Example

1 Write $3 + \frac{7}{x - 2}$ as a rational expression. $\frac{3x + 1}{x - 2}$

Additional Examples also in Interactive Classroom PowerPoint® Presentations

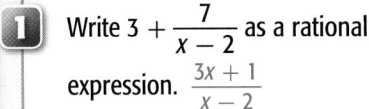

IWB INTERACTIVE WHITEBOARD READY

Simplify Complex Fractions

Example 2 shows how to use complex fractions to solve problems.
Example 3 shows how to simplify a complex fraction involving monomials.
Example 4 shows how to simplify a complex fraction involving polynomials.

Additional Examples

2 **RACING** Refer to the application at the beginning of the lesson. If the dragster can cover $\frac{1}{4}$ mile in $3\frac{1}{8}$ seconds, what is its average speed in miles per minute? $4\frac{4}{5}$ miles per minute

3 Simplify $\frac{\frac{a^5b}{c^2}}{\frac{ab^4}{c^4}}$. $\frac{a^4c^2}{b^3}$

TEACH with TECH

INTERACTIVE WHITEBOARD Display a complex fraction on the board. Rewrite this as a product of two fractions by dragging the fraction from the denominator and writing its reciprocal.

Watch Out!

Preventing Errors Point out that since one of the terms of a mixed expression is a monomial, the LCD will be the same as the denominator of the rational expression. Suggest that students still having difficulty write 3 as $\frac{3}{1}$ and then find the LCD.

Focus on Mathematical Content

Complex Fractions You can simplify an algebraic complex fraction in the same way that you simplify a numerical complex fraction. Multiply the numerator by the reciprocal of the denominator.

Additional Example

4 Simplify each expression.

a. $\dfrac{b + \frac{2}{b+3}}{b-4}$ $\dfrac{(b+2)(b+1)}{(b+3)(b-4)}$

b. $\dfrac{\frac{c^2 - 4c + 3}{c^2 + 9c + 14}}{\frac{c^2 - 9}{c + 2}}$ $\dfrac{c-1}{(c+7)(c+3)}$

Watch Out!

Preventing Errors When simplifying complex fractions, there are many steps in which errors can occur, even for those students who clearly understand the concept. Encourage students to write out each step of the simplifying process.

Complex fractions may also involve polynomials.

EXAMPLE 4 Complex Fractions Involving Polynomials

Simplify each expression.

a. $\dfrac{\frac{2}{y+3}}{\frac{5}{y^2-9}}$

$\dfrac{\frac{2}{y+3}}{\frac{5}{y^2-9}} = \dfrac{2}{y+3} \div \dfrac{5}{y^2-9}$ **Write as a division expression.**

$= \dfrac{2}{y+3} \times \dfrac{y^2-9}{5}$ **To divide, multiply by the reciprocal.**

$= \dfrac{2}{y+3} \times \dfrac{(y-3)(y+3)}{5}$ **Factor $y^2 - 9$.**

$= \dfrac{2}{\cancel{y+3}_{1}} \times \dfrac{(y-3)\cancel{(y+3)}^{1}}{5}$ **Divide by the GCF, $y + 3$.**

$= \dfrac{2(y-3)}{5}$ **Simplify.**

b. $\dfrac{\frac{n^2 + 7n - 18}{n^2 - 2n + 1}}{\frac{n^2 - 81}{n - 1}}$

$\dfrac{\frac{n^2 + 7n - 18}{n^2 - 2n + 1}}{\frac{n^2 - 81}{n - 1}} = \dfrac{n^2 + 7n - 18}{n^2 - 2n + 1} \div \dfrac{n^2 - 81}{n - 1}$ **Write as a division expression.**

$= \dfrac{n^2 + 7n - 18}{n^2 - 2n + 1} \times \dfrac{n - 1}{n^2 - 81}$ **Multiply by the reciprocal.**

$= \dfrac{(n-2)(n+9)}{(n-1)(n-1)} \times \dfrac{n-1}{(n-9)(n+9)}$ **Factor the polynomials.**

$= \dfrac{(n-2)\cancel{(n+9)}^{1}}{(n-1)\cancel{(n-1)}_{1}} \times \dfrac{\cancel{n-1}^{1}}{(n-9)\cancel{(n+9)}_{1}}$ **Divide out the common factors.**

$= \dfrac{n-2}{(n-1)(n-9)}$ **Simplify.**

StudyTip

Factoring When simplifying fractions involving polynomials, factor the numerator and the denominator of each expression if possible.

Check Your Progress

4A. $\dfrac{\frac{a+7}{4}}{\frac{a^2-49}{10}}$ $\dfrac{5}{2(a-7)}$

4B. $\dfrac{\frac{x+4}{x-1}}{\frac{x^2+6x+8}{2x-2}}$ $\dfrac{2}{x+2}$

4C. $\dfrac{\frac{c-d}{j+p}}{\frac{c^2-d^2}{j^2-p^2}}$ $\dfrac{j-p}{c+d}$

4D. $\dfrac{\frac{n^2+4n-21}{n^2-9n+18}}{\frac{n^2+3n-28}{n^2-10n+24}}$ 1

Personal Tutor glencoe.com

Differentiated Instruction OL BL ELL

Intrapersonal Learners Ask students to write their own Key Concepts for this lesson. Tell them to include simplifying mixed expressions as well as simplifying complex fractions. Have students share their Key Concepts with the class.

Check Your Understanding

Example 1 p. 714

Write each mixed expression as a rational expression.

1. $\frac{2}{n} + 4$ $\frac{2 + 4n}{n}$
2. $r + \frac{1}{3r}$ $\frac{3r^2 + 1}{3r}$
3. $6 + \frac{5}{t+1}$ $\frac{6t + 11}{t + 1}$
4. $\frac{x+7}{2x} - 5x$ $\frac{-10x^2 + x + 7}{2x}$

Example 2 p. 715

5. **ROWING** Rico rowed a canoe $2\frac{1}{2}$ miles in $\frac{1}{3}$ hour.
   a. Write an expression to represent his speed in miles per hour. $\frac{2\frac{1}{2}\text{ mi}}{\frac{1}{3}\text{ h}}$
   b. Simplify the expression to find his average speed. $\frac{15}{2}$ or $7\frac{1}{2}$ mi/h

Examples 3 and 4 pp. 715–716

Simplify each expression.

6. $\frac{2\frac{1}{3}}{1\frac{2}{5}}$ $\frac{5}{3}$ or $1\frac{2}{3}$
7. $\frac{\frac{4}{5}}{6\frac{2}{3}}$ $\frac{3}{25}$
8. $\frac{\frac{a^2}{b^3}}{\frac{b^5}{a}}$ $\frac{a^3}{b^8}$
9. $\frac{\frac{y^4}{x^2}}{\frac{xy^2}{2x^2}}$ $\frac{2y^2}{x}$
10. $\frac{\frac{6}{x-2}}{\frac{3}{x^2-x-2}}$ $2(x + 1)$
11. $\frac{\frac{r+s}{x^2-y^2}}{\frac{(r+s)^2}{x-y}}$ $\frac{1}{(x + y)(r + s)}$
12. $\frac{\frac{2+q}{q^2-4}}{\frac{q+4}{q^2-6q+8}}$ $\frac{q - 4}{q + 4}$
13. $\frac{\frac{p+3}{p^2+p-6}}{\frac{p^2+4p+3}{p^2+6p+9}}$ $\frac{p + 3}{p^2 - p - 2}$

Practice and Problem Solving

● = **Step-by-Step Solutions** begin on page R12.
Extra Practice begins on page 815.

Example 1 p. 714

Write each mixed expression as a rational expression.

14. $10 + \frac{6}{f}$ $\frac{10f + 6}{f}$
15. $p - \frac{7}{2p}$ $\frac{2p^2 - 7}{2p}$
16. $5a - \frac{2a}{b}$ $\frac{5ab - 2a}{b}$
17. $3h + \frac{1+h}{h}$ $\frac{3h^2 + h + 1}{h}$
18. $t + \frac{v+w}{v-w}$
19. $n^2 + \frac{n-1}{n+4}$
20. $(k + 2) + \frac{k-1}{k-2}$
21. $(d - 6) + \frac{d+1}{d-7}$
22. $\frac{h-3}{h+5} - (h + 2)$

18. $\frac{tv - tw + v + w}{v - w}$
19. $\frac{n^3 + 4n^2 + n - 1}{n + 4}$
20. $\frac{k^2 + k - 5}{k - 2}$
21. $\frac{d^2 - 12d + 43}{d - 7}$
22. $\frac{-h^2 - 6h - 13}{h + 5}$

Example 2 p. 715

23. **READING** Ebony reads $6\frac{3}{4}$ pages of a book in 9 minutes. What is her average reading rate in pages per minute? $\frac{3}{4}$ page/min
24. **HORSES** A thoroughbred can run $\frac{1}{2}$ mile in about $\frac{3}{4}$ minute. What is the horse's speed in miles per hour? 40 mi/h

Examples 3 and 4 pp. 715–716

Simplify each expression.

25. $\frac{2\frac{2}{9}}{3\frac{1}{3}}$ $\frac{2}{3}$
26. $\frac{5\frac{3}{5}}{2\frac{1}{7}}$ $2\frac{46}{75}$
27. $\frac{\frac{g^2}{h}}{\frac{g^5}{h^2}}$ $\frac{h}{g^3}$
28. $\frac{\frac{5n^4}{p^3}}{\frac{6n}{5p}}$ $\frac{25n^3}{6p^2}$
29. $\frac{\frac{2}{a}}{\frac{1}{a+6}}$ $\frac{2a + 12}{a}$
30. $\frac{\frac{t+5}{9}}{\frac{t^2-t-30}{12}}$
31. $\frac{\frac{j^2-16}{j^2+10j+16}}{\frac{15}{j+8}}$
32. $\frac{\frac{x-3}{x^2+3x+2}}{\frac{x^2-9}{x+1}}$

30. $\frac{4}{3(t - 6)}$
31. $\frac{(j - 4)(j + 4)}{15(j + 2)}$
32. $\frac{1}{(x + 2)(x + 3)}$

B

33. **COOKING** The Centralville High School Cooking Club has $12\frac{1}{2}$ pounds of flour with which to make tortillas. There are $3\frac{3}{4}$ cups of flour in a pound, and it takes about $\frac{1}{3}$ cup of flour per tortilla. How many tortillas can they make? about 140

3 PRACTICE

Formative Assessment

Use Exercises 1–13 to check for understanding.

Use the chart at the bottom of this page to customize assignments for your students.

Differentiated Homework Options

Level	Assignment	Two-Day Option	
AL Basic	14–32, 43–44, 46–80	15–31 odd, 48–51	14–32 even, 43–44, 46–47, 52–80
OL Core	15–31 odd, 33–36, 37–43 odd, 44, 46–80	14–32, 48–51	33–44, 46–47, 52–80
BL Advanced	33–74, (optional: 75–80)		

Lesson 11-7 Mixed Expressions and Complex Fractions **717**

Study Guide and Intervention
CRM pp. 42–43 AL OL ELL

NAME ______ DATE ______ PERIOD ______

11-7 Study Guide and Intervention

Mixed Expressions and Complex Fractions

Simplify Mixed Expressions Algebraic expressions such as $a + \frac{b}{c}$ and $5 + \frac{x+y}{x+3}$ are called **mixed expressions**. Changing mixed expressions to rational expressions is similar to changing mixed numbers to improper fractions.

Example 1 Simplify $5 + \frac{2}{n}$.

$5 + \frac{2}{n} = \frac{5 \cdot n}{n} + \frac{2}{n}$ LCD is n.

$= \frac{5n + 2}{n}$ Add the numerators.

Therefore, $5 + \frac{2}{n} = \frac{5n+2}{n}$.

Example 2 Simplify $2 + \frac{3}{n+3}$.

$2 + \frac{3}{n+3} = \frac{2(n+3)}{n+3} + \frac{3}{n+3}$

$= \frac{2n+6}{n+3} + \frac{3}{n+3}$

$= \frac{2n+6+3}{n+3}$

$= \frac{2n+9}{n+3}$

Therefore, $2 + \frac{3}{n+3} = \frac{2n+9}{n+3}$.

Exercises

Write each mixed expression as a rational expression.

1. $4 + \frac{6}{a}$ $\frac{4a+6}{a}$
2. $\frac{1}{9x} - 3$ $\frac{1-27x}{9x}$
3. $3x - \frac{1}{x^2}$ $\frac{3x^3-1}{x^2}$
4. $\frac{4}{x^2} - 2$ $\frac{4-2x^2}{x^2}$
5. $10 + \frac{60}{x+5}$ $\frac{10x+110}{x+5}$
6. $\frac{h}{h+4} + 2$ $\frac{3h+8}{h+4}$
7. $\frac{y}{y-2} + y^2$ $\frac{y^3-2y^2+y}{y-2}$
8. $4 - \frac{4}{2x+1}$ $\frac{8x}{2x+1}$
9. $1 + \frac{1}{x}$ $\frac{x+1}{x}$
10. $\frac{4}{m-2} - 2m$ $\frac{4-2m^2+4m}{m-2}$
11. $x^2 + \frac{x+2}{x-3}$ $\frac{x^3-3x^2+x+2}{x-3}$
12. $a - 3 + \frac{a-2}{a+3}$ $\frac{a^2+a-11}{a+3}$
13. $4m + \frac{3p}{2t}$ $\frac{8mt+3p}{2t}$
14. $2q^2 + \frac{q}{p+q}$ $\frac{q+2rq^2+2q^3}{r+q}$
15. $\frac{2}{y^2-1} - 4y^2$ $\frac{2-4y^4+4y^2}{y^2-1}$
16. $t^2 + \frac{p+t}{p-t}$ $\frac{pt^2-t^3+p+t}{p-t}$

Chapter 11 42 Glencoe Algebra 1

Practice
CRM p. 45 AL OL BL ELL

NAME ______ DATE ______ PERIOD ______

11-7 Practice

Mixed Expressions and Complex Fractions

Write each mixed expression as a rational expression.

1. $14 - \frac{9}{u}$ $\frac{14u-9}{u}$
2. $7d + \frac{4d}{c}$ $\frac{7dc+4d}{c}$
3. $3n + \frac{6-n}{n}$ $\frac{3n^2-n+6}{n}$
4. $5b - \frac{b+3}{2b}$ $\frac{10b^2-b-3}{2b}$
5. $3 + \frac{t+5}{t^2-1}$ $\frac{3t^2+t+2}{t^2-1}$
6. $2a + \frac{a-1}{a+1}$ $\frac{2a^2+3a-1}{a+1}$
7. $2p + \frac{p+1}{p-3}$ $\frac{2p^2-5p+1}{p-3}$
8. $4n^2 + \frac{n-1}{n^2-1}$ $\frac{4n^3+4n^2+1}{n+1}$
9. $(t+1) + \frac{4}{t+5}$ $\frac{t^2+6t+9}{t+5}$

Simplify each expression.

10. $\frac{3\frac{2}{5}}{2\frac{5}{6}}$ $\frac{6}{5}$
11. $\frac{\frac{m^2}{6p}}{\frac{3m}{p^2}}$ $\frac{mp}{18}$
12. $\frac{\frac{x^2-y^2}{x^2}}{\frac{x+y}{3x}}$ $\frac{3(x-y)}{x}$
13. $\frac{\frac{a-4}{a^2}}{\frac{a^2-16}{a}}$ $\frac{1}{a(a+4)}$
14. $\frac{\frac{q^2-7q+12}{q^2-16}}{q-3}$ $\frac{1}{q+4}$
15. $\frac{\frac{k^2+6k}{k^2+4k-5}}{\frac{k-8}{k^2-9k+8}}$ $\frac{k(k+6)}{k+5}$
16. $\frac{\frac{b^2+b-12}{b^2+3b-4}}{\frac{b-3}{b^2-b}}$ b
17. $\frac{g - \frac{10}{g+9}}{g - \frac{5}{g+4}}$ $\frac{(g+10)(g+4)}{(g+9)(g+5)}$
18. $\frac{y + \frac{6}{y-7}}{y - \frac{7}{y+6}}$ $\frac{(y-6)(y+6)}{(y-7)(y+7)}$

19. **TRAVEL** Ray and Jan are on a $12\frac{1}{2}$-hour drive from Springfield, Missouri, to Chicago, Illinois. They stop for a break every $3\frac{1}{4}$ hours.

a. Write an expression to model this situation. $\frac{12\frac{1}{2}}{3\frac{1}{4}}$

b. How many stops will Ray and Jan make before arriving in Chicago? **3**

20. **CARPENTRY** Tai needs several $2\frac{1}{4}$-inch wooden rods to reinforce the frame on a futon. She can cut the rods from a $24\frac{1}{2}$-inch dowel purchased from a hardware store. How many wooden rods can she cut from the dowel? **10**

Chapter 11 45 Glencoe Algebra 1

Word Problem Practice
CRM p. 46 AL OL BL ELL

NAME ______ DATE ______ PERIOD ______

11-7 Word Problem Practice

Mixed Expressions and Complex Fractions

1. **CYCLING** Natalie rode in a bicycle event for charity on Saturday. It took her $\frac{2}{3}$ of an hour to complete the 18-mile race. What was her average speed in miles per hour? **27 mph**

2. **QUILTING** Mrs. Tantora sews and sells Amish baby quilts. She bought $42\frac{3}{4}$ yards of backing fabric, and $2\frac{1}{4}$ yards are needed for each quilt she sews. How many quilts can she make with the backing fabric she bought? **19**

3. **TRAVEL** The Franz family traveled from Galveston to Waco for a family reunion. Driving their van, they averaged 30 miles per hour on the way to Waco and 45 miles per hour on the return trip home to Galveston. What is their average rate for the entire trip? (*Hint:* Remember that average rate equals total distance divided by total time and that time can be represented as a ratio of distance to rate.) **36 mph**

4. **PHYSICAL SCIENCE** The volume of a gas varies directly as the Kelvin temperature T and inversely as the pressure P, where k is the constant of variation.

$V = k\left(\frac{T}{P}\right)$

If $k = \frac{13}{157}$, find the volume in liters of helium gas at 273 degrees Kelvin and $\frac{13}{3}$ atmospheres of pressure. Round your answer to the nearest hundredth. **5.22 L**

5. **SAFETY** The Occupational Safety and Health Administration provides safety standards in the workplace to keep workers free from dangerous working conditions. OSHA recommends that for general construction there be 5 foot-candles of illumination in which to work. A foreman using a light meter finds that the illumination of a construction light on a surface 8 feet from the source is 11 foot-candles. The illumination produced by a light source varies inversely as the square of the distance from the source.

$I = \frac{k}{d^2}$ I is illumination (in foot-candles). d is the distance from the source (in feet). k is a constant.

a. Find the illumination of the same light at a distance of $15\frac{3}{4}$ feet. Round your answer to the nearest hundredth. **2.84 foot-candles**

b. Is there enough illumination at this distance to meet OSHA requirements for lighting? **no**

c. In order to comply with OSHA, what is the maximum allowable working distance from this light source? Round your decimal answer to nearest tenth. **11.9 ft**

Chapter 11 46 Glencoe Algebra 1

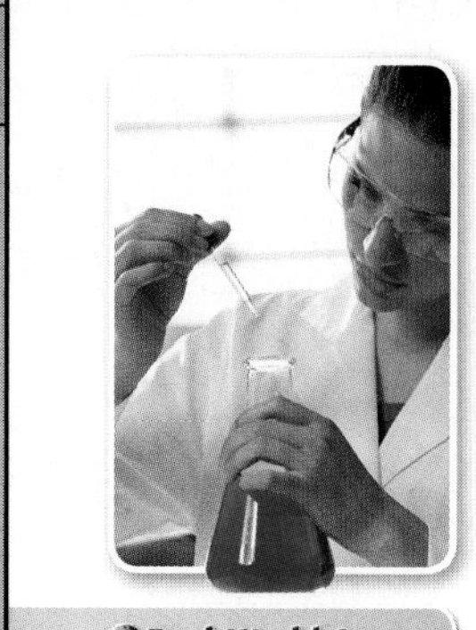

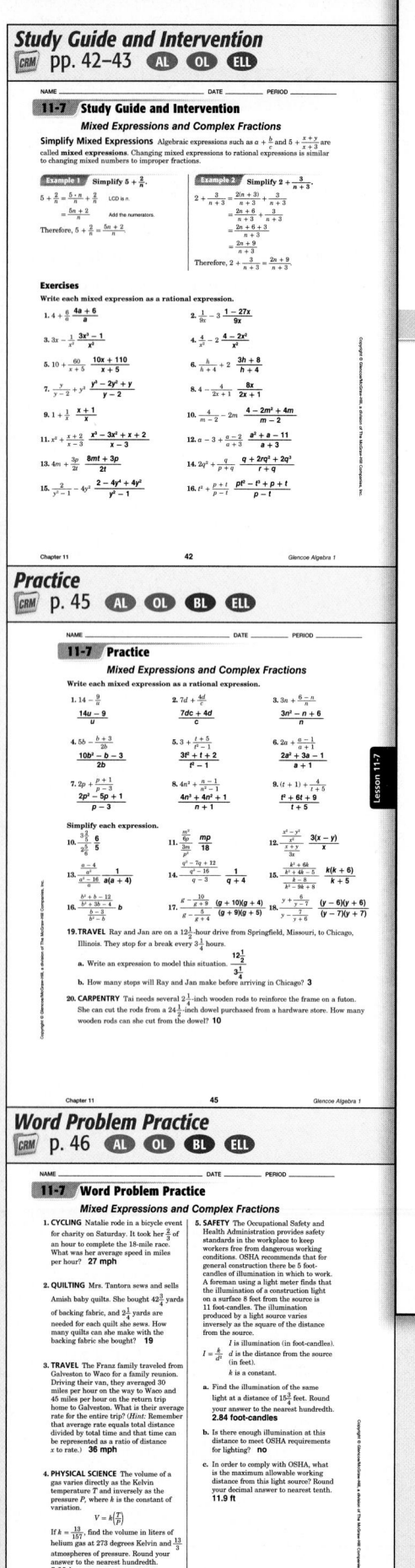

Real-World Career

Lab Technician
Lab technicians work with scientists, running experiments, conducting research projects, and running routine diagnostic samples. Lab technicians in any field need at least a two-year associate degree.

34. **SCOOTER** The speed v of an object spinning in a circle equals the circumference of the circle divided by the time T it takes the object to complete one revolution.

a. Use the variables v, r (the radius of the circle), and T to write a formula describing the speed of a spinning object. $v = \frac{2\pi r}{T}$

b. A scooter has tires with a radius of $3\frac{1}{2}$ inches. The tires make one revolution every $\frac{1}{10}$ second. Find the speed in miles per hour. Round to the nearest tenth. **12.5 mi/h**

35. **SCIENCE** The *density* of an object equals $\frac{m}{V}$, where m is the mass of the object and V is the volume. The densities of four metals are shown in the table. Identify the metal of each ball described below. (*Hint*: The volume of a sphere is $V = \frac{4}{3}\pi r^3$.)

Metal	Density (kg/m³)
copper	8900
gold	19,300
iron	7800
lead	11,300

a. A metal ball has a mass of 15.6 kilograms and a radius of 0.0748 meter. **copper**

b. A metal ball has a mass of 285.3 kilograms and a radius of 0.1819 meter. **lead**

36. **SIRENS** As an ambulance approaches, the siren sounds different than if it were sitting still. If the ambulance is moving toward you at v miles per hour and blowing the siren at a frequency of f, then you hear the siren as if it were blowing at a frequency h. This can be described by the equation $h = \frac{f}{1 - \frac{v}{s}}$, where s is the speed of sound, approximately 760 miles per hour.

a. Simplify the complex fraction in the formula. $\frac{fs}{s - v}$

b. Suppose a siren blows at 45 cycles per minute and is moving toward you at 65 miles per hour. Find the frequency of the siren as you hear it. **49.21 cycles/min**

C Simplify each expression.

37. $15 - \frac{17x+5}{5x+10}$ $\frac{58x+145}{5x+10}$

38. $\frac{\frac{b}{b+3} + 2}{b^2 - 2b - 8}$

39. $\frac{1 + \frac{2c^2 - 6c - 10}{c+7}}{2c+1}$ $\frac{c-3}{c+7}$

40. $\frac{y - \frac{12}{y-4}}{y - \frac{18}{y-3}}$

41. $\frac{\frac{x^2 - 4x - 32}{x+1}}{\frac{x^2 + 6x + 8}{x^2 - 1}}$

42. $\frac{\frac{r^2 - 9r}{r^2 + 7r + 10}}{\frac{r^2 + 5r}{r^2 + r - 2}}$

38. $\frac{3}{(b+3)(b-4)}$

40. $\frac{(y+2)(y-3)}{(y-4)(y+3)}$

41. $\frac{(x-8)(x-1)}{x+2}$

42. $\frac{(r-9)(r-1)}{(r+5)^2}$

H.O.T. Problems Use Higher-Order Thinking Skills

43. **REASONING** Describe the first step to simplify the expression below.

$$\frac{\left(\frac{y}{x} - \frac{x}{y}\right)}{\frac{x+y}{xy}}$$

43. Find the lowest common denominator for the fractions in the numerator and simplify to $\frac{y^2 - x^2}{xy}$.

44. **REASONING** Is $\frac{n}{1 - \frac{5}{p}} + \frac{n}{\frac{5}{p} - 1}$ *sometimes*, *always*, or *never* equal to 0? Explain.

44. Always; the expression can be simplified to $\frac{n}{1 - \frac{5}{p}} - \frac{n}{1 - \frac{5}{p}}$, $p \neq 0$.

45. **CHALLENGE** Simplify the rational expression below.

$$\frac{\frac{1}{t-1} + \frac{1}{t+1}}{\frac{1}{t} - \frac{1}{t^2}}$$ $\frac{2t^3}{(t-1)(t^2-1)}$

46. **OPEN ENDED** Write a complex fraction that, when simplified, results in $\frac{1}{x}$.

46. Sample answer: $\frac{\frac{x}{a}}{\frac{x^2}{a}}$

47. **WRITING IN MATH** Explain how complex fractions can be used to solve a problem involving distance, rate, and time. Give an example. **See Ch. 11 Answer Appendix.**

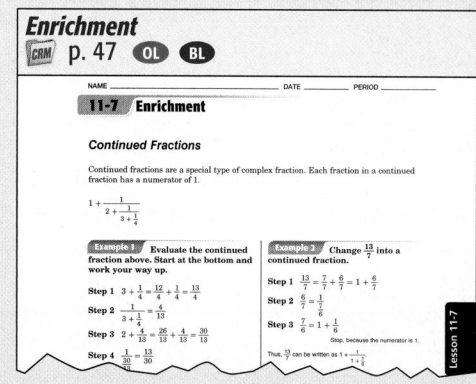

Enrichment
CRM p. 47 OL BL

NAME ______ DATE ______ PERIOD ______

11-7 Enrichment

Continued Fractions

Continued fractions are a special type of complex fraction. Each fraction in a continued fraction has a numerator of 1.

$1 + \frac{1}{2 + \frac{1}{3 + \frac{1}{4}}}$

Example 1 Evaluate the continued fraction above. Start at the bottom and work your way up.

Step 1 $3 + \frac{1}{4} = \frac{12}{4} + \frac{1}{4} = \frac{13}{4}$

Step 2 $\frac{1}{3 + \frac{1}{4}} = \frac{4}{13}$

Step 3 $2 + \frac{4}{13} = \frac{26}{13} + \frac{4}{13} = \frac{30}{13}$

Step 4 $\frac{1}{\frac{30}{13}} = \frac{13}{30}$

Example 2 Change $\frac{13}{7}$ into a continued fraction.

Step 1 $\frac{13}{7} = \frac{7}{7} + \frac{6}{7} = 1 + \frac{6}{7}$

Step 2 $\frac{6}{7} = \frac{1}{\frac{7}{6}}$

Step 3 $\frac{7}{6} = 1 + \frac{1}{6}$

Stop, because the numerator is 1.

Thus, $\frac{13}{7}$ can be written as $1 + \frac{1}{1 + \frac{1}{6}}$.

Exercise Alert

Formula For Exercise 34, students will need to know the formula for the circumference of a circle, $C = \pi d$ or $C = 2\pi r$.

PSAE PRACTICE 6.11.06, 6.11.13, 7.11.03, 8.11.22

48. A number is between 44 squared and 45 squared. 5 squared is one of its factors, and it is a multiple of 13. Find the number. **A**

A 1950
B 2000
C 2025
D 1975

49. SHORT RESPONSE Bernard is reading a 445-page book. He has already read 157 pages. If he reads 24 pages a day, how long will it take him to finish the book? **12 days**

50. GEOMETRY Angela wanted a round rug to fit her room that is 16 feet wide. The rug should just meet the edges. What is the area of the rug rounded to the nearest tenth? **J**

F 100.5 ft
G 804.2 ft^2
H 50.3 ft
J 201.1 ft^2

51. Simplify $7x + \frac{10}{2xy}$. **B**

A $\frac{7x + 10}{2xy}$
B $\frac{7x^2y + 5}{xy}$
C $\frac{17x}{2xy}$
D $\frac{7xy + 5}{x^2y}$

Spiral Review

Find each sum or difference. (Lesson 11-6)

52. $\frac{6}{7x} - \frac{5 + x}{7x}$ **$\frac{1 - x}{7x}$**
53. $\frac{4}{d - 1} + \frac{d}{1 - d}$ **$\frac{-d + 4}{d - 1}$**
54. $\frac{3q + 2}{2q + 1} + \frac{q - 5}{2q + 1}$ **$\frac{4q - 3}{2q + 1}$**
55. $\frac{2}{5m} - \frac{1}{15m^3}$ **$\frac{6m^2 - 1}{15m^3}$**
56. $\frac{10}{3g} - \frac{-3}{4h}$ **$\frac{9g + 40h}{12gh}$**
57. $\frac{b}{b + 3} + \frac{6}{b - 2}$ **$\frac{b^2 + 4b + 18}{(b + 3)(b - 2)}$**

Find each quotient. Use long division. (Lesson 11-5) **58–63. See margin.**

58. $(x^2 - 2x - 30) \div (x + 7)$
59. $(a^2 + 4a - 22) \div (a - 3)$
60. $(3q^2 + 20q + 11) \div (q + 6)$
61. $(3y^3 + 8y^2 + y - 7) \div (y + 2)$
62. $(6t^3 - 9t^2 + 6) \div (2t - 3)$
63. $(9h^3 + 5h - 8) \div (3h - 2)$

64. GEOMETRY Triangle ABC has vertices $A(7, -4)$, $B(-1, 2)$, and $C(5, -6)$. Determine whether the triangle has three, two, or no sides that are equal in length. (Lesson 10-6) **See margin.**

Graph each function. Determine the domain and range. (Lesson 10-1) **65–67. See margin.**

65. $y = 2\sqrt{x}$
66. $y = -3\sqrt{x}$
67. $y = \frac{1}{4}\sqrt{x}$

Factor each polynomial. If the polynomial cannot be factored, write *prime*. (Lesson 8-5)

68. $x^2 - 81$ **$(x - 9)(x + 9)$**
69. $a^2 - 121$ **$(a - 11)(a + 11)$**
70. $n^2 + 100$ **prime**
71. $-25 + 4y^2$ **$(2y - 5)(2y + 5)$**
72. $p^4 - 16$ **$(p - 2)(p + 2)(p^2 + 4)$**
73. $4t^4 - 4$ **$4(t - 1)(t + 1)(t^2 + 1)$**

74. PARKS A youth group traveling in two vans visited Mammoth Cave in Kentucky. The number of people in each van and the total cost of the cave are shown. Find the adult price and the student price of the tour. (Lesson 6-3) **adult: \$16; student: \$9**

Van	Number of Adults	Number of Students	Total Cost
A	2	5	\$77
B	2	7	\$95

Skills Review

Solve each equation. (Lesson 2-2 and 2-3)

75. $6x = 24$ **4**
76. $5y - 1 = 19$ **4**
77. $2t + 7 = 21$ **7**
78. $\frac{p}{3} = -4.2$ **−12.6**
79. $\frac{2m + 1}{4} = -5.5$ **−11.5**
80. $\frac{3}{4}g = \frac{1}{2}$ **$\frac{2}{3}$**

Differentiated Instruction OL BL

Extension Write $1 + \cfrac{1}{1 + \cfrac{1}{1 + \frac{1}{x}}}$ on the board. Ask students to write this mixed expression as a rational expression.

$\frac{3x + 2}{2x + 1}$

4 ASSESS

Name the Math Have students tell what mathematical procedures they used to simplify the expression in Exercise 31. Then have students substitute 2 for j in the original expression and in their simplified expressions. Students should see that when $j = 2$, the value of both expressions is $-\frac{1}{5}$.

Additional Answers

58. $x - 9 + \frac{33}{x + 7}$

59. $a + 7 - \frac{1}{a - 3}$

60. $3q + 2 - \frac{1}{q + 6}$

61. $3y^2 + 2y - 3 - \frac{1}{y + 2}$

62. $3t^2 + \frac{6}{2t - 3}$

63. $3h^2 + 2h + 3 - \frac{2}{3h - 2}$

64. two; $AB = BC = 10$

65.

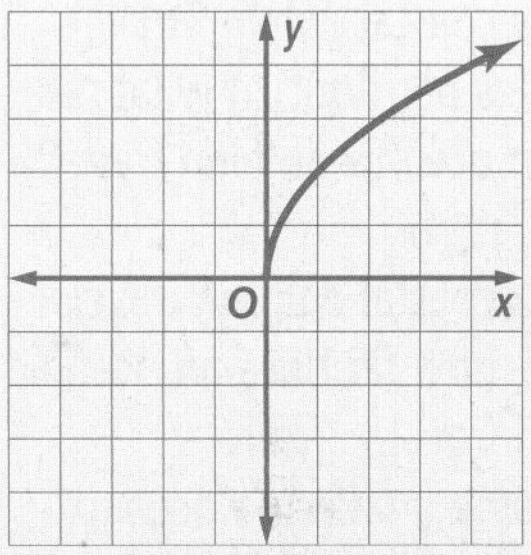

$D = \{x \mid x \geq 0\}$; $R = \{y \mid y \geq 0\}$

66.

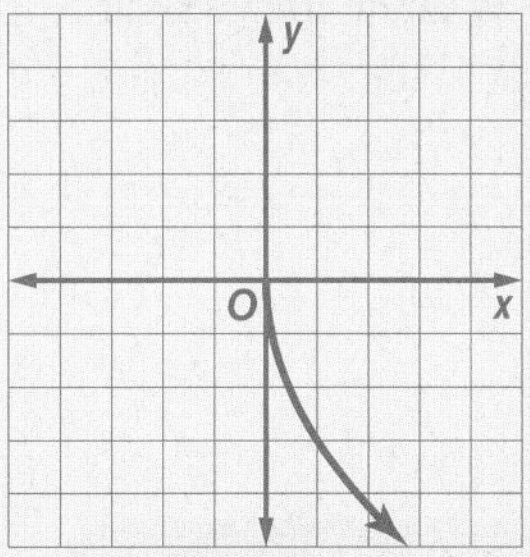

$D = \{x \mid x \geq 0\}$; $R = \{y \mid y \leq 0\}$

67.

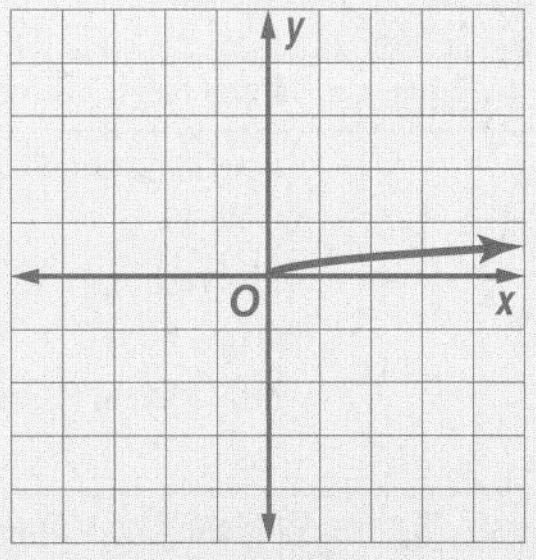

$D = \{x \mid x \geq 0\}$; $R = \{y \mid y \geq 0\}$

11-8 Lesson Notes

1 FOCUS

Vertical Alignment

Before Lesson 11-8
Solve proportions.

Lesson 11-8
Solve rational equations.
Use rational equations to solve problems.

After Lesson 11-8
Solve rational inequalities.

2 TEACH

Scaffolding Questions

Have students read the *Why?* section of the lesson.

Ask:

- When a coastal dolphin travels at x miles per hour, at what rate does an oceanic dolphin travel? $(x + 5)$ mi/h
- When a coastal dolphin travels 2 miles, how far does an oceanic dolphin travel? 3 miles
- In the time it takes an oceanic dolphin to swim 6 miles, what do you know about the coastal dolphin? It can swim 4 miles.

11-8 Rational Equations

Then
You solved proportions. (Lesson 2-6)

Now
- Solve rational equations.
- Use rational equations to solve problems.

IL Learning Standards
8.C.4b Apply algebraic properties and procedures with matrices, vectors, functions and sequences using data found in business, industry and consumer situations.

New Vocabulary
rational equation
extraneous solution
work problem
rate problem

IL Math Online
glencoe.com
- Extra Examples
- Personal Tutor
- Self-Check Quiz
- Homework Help

Why?

Oceanic species of dolphins can swim 5 miles per hour faster than coastal species of dolphins. An oceanic dolphin can swim 3 miles in the same time that it takes a coastal dolphin to swim 2 miles.

Dolphins

Species	Distance	Rate	Time
coastal	2 miles	x mph	t hours
oceanic	3 miles	$x + 5$ mph	t hours

Since time $= \frac{\text{distance}}{\text{rate}}$, the equation below represents this situation.

Time an oceanic dolphin swims 3 miles	equals	time a coastal dolphin swims 2 miles.
distance → 3 / rate → $x + 5$	$=$	2 ← distance / x ← rate

$$\frac{3}{x+5} = \frac{2}{x}$$

Solve Rational Equations A **rational equation** contains one or more rational expressions. When a rational equation is a proportion, you can use cross products to solve it.

Real-World EXAMPLE 1 Use Cross Products to Solve Equations

DOLPHINS Refer to the information above. Solve $\frac{3}{x+5} = \frac{2}{x}$ to find the speed of a coastal dolphin. Check the solution.

$\frac{3}{x+5} = \frac{2}{x}$ — **Original equation**

$3x = 2(x + 5)$ — **Find the cross products.**

$3x = 2x + 10$ — **Distributive Property**

$x = 10$ — **Subtract $2x$ from each side.**

So, a coastal dolphin can swim 10 miles per hour.

CHECK

$\frac{3}{x+5} = \frac{2}{x}$ — **Original equation**

$\frac{3}{10+5} \stackrel{?}{=} \frac{2}{10}$ — **Replace x with 10.**

$\frac{3}{15} \stackrel{?}{=} \frac{1}{5}$ — **Simplify.**

$\frac{1}{5} = \frac{1}{5}$ ✓ — **Simplify.**

Check Your Progress

Solve each equation. Check the solution.

1A. $\frac{7}{y-3} = \frac{3}{y+1}$ −4

1B. $\frac{13}{10} = \frac{2f+0.2}{7}$ 4.45

Personal Tutor glencoe.com

Lesson 11-8 Resources

Resource	Approaching-Level	On-Level	Beyond-Level	English Learners
Teacher Edition	• Differentiated Instruction, p. 723	• Differentiated Instruction, pp. 723, 726	• Differentiated Instruction, p. 726	• Differentiated Instruction, p. 723
Chapter Resource Masters	• Study Guide and Intervention, pp. 48–49 • Skills Practice, p. 50 • Practice, p. 51 • Word Problem Practice, p. 52	• Study Guide and Intervention, pp. 48–49 • Skills Practice, p. 50 • Practice, p. 51 • Word Problem Practice, p. 52 • Enrichment, p. 53 • Graphing Calculator, p. 54	• Practice, p. 51 • Word Problem Practice, p. 52 • Enrichment, p. 53	• Study Guide and Intervention, pp. 48–49 • Skills Practice, p. 50 • Practice, p. 51 • Word Problem Practice, p. 52
Transparencies	• 5-Minute Check Transparency 11-8	• 5-Minute Check Transparency 11-8	• 5-Minute Check Transparency 11-8	• 5-Minute Check Transparency 11-8
Other	• Study Notebook • Teaching Algebra with Manipulatives	• Study Notebook • Teaching Algebra with Manipulatives	• Study Notebook	• Study Notebook • Teaching Algebra with Manipulatives

Another method that can be used to solve any rational equation is to find the LCD of all the fractions in the equation. Then multiply each side of the equation by the LCD to eliminate the fractions.

EXAMPLE 2 **Use the LCD to Solve Rational Equations**

Solve $\frac{4}{y} + \frac{5y}{y+1} = 5$. Check the solution.

Step 1 Find the LCD.

The LCD of $\frac{4}{y}$ and $\frac{5y}{y+1}$ is $y(y + 1)$.

Step 2 Multiply each side of the equation by the LCD.

$\frac{4}{y} + \frac{5y}{y+1} = 5$	**Original equation**
$y(y+1)\left(\frac{4}{y} + \frac{5y}{y+1}\right) = y(y+1)(5)$	**Multiply each side by the LCD, $y(y + 1)$.**
$\left(\frac{\cancel{y}(y+1)}{1} \cdot \frac{4}{\cancel{y}}\right) + \left(\frac{y\cancel{(y+1)}}{1} \cdot \frac{5y}{\cancel{y+1}}\right) = y(y+1)(5)$	**Distributive Property**
$(y + 1)4 + y(5y) = y(y + 1)(5)$	**Simplify.**
$4y + 4 + 5y^2 = 5y^2 + 5y$	**Multiply.**
$4y + 4 + 5y^2 - 5y^2 = 5y^2 - 5y^2 + 5y$	**Subtract $5y^2$ from each side.**
$4y + 4 = 5y$	**Simplify.**
$4y - 4y + 4 = 5y - 4y$	**Subtract $4y$ from each side.**
$4 = y$	**Simplify.**

CHECK

$\frac{4}{y} + \frac{5y}{y+1} = 5$	**Original equation**
$\frac{4}{4} + \frac{5(4)}{4+1} \stackrel{?}{=} 5$	**Replace y with 4.**
$1 + 4 \stackrel{?}{=} 5$	**Simplify.**
$5 = 5$ ✓	**Simplify.**

Check Your Progress

Solve each equation. Check your solutions.

2A. $\frac{2b-5}{b-2} - 2 = \frac{3}{b+2}$ 1

2B. $1 + \frac{1}{c+2} = \frac{28}{c^2+2c}$ 4, −7

2C. $\frac{y+2}{y-2} - \frac{2}{y+2} = -\frac{7}{3}$ $-1, \frac{2}{5}$

2D. $\frac{n}{3n+6} - \frac{n}{5n+10} = \frac{2}{5}$ −3

Personal Tutor glencoe.com

Recall that any value of a variable that makes the denominator of a rational expression zero must be excluded from the domain.

In the same way, when a solution of a rational equation results in a zero in the denominator, that solution must be excluded. Such solutions are called **extraneous solutions**.

$\frac{4+x}{x-5} + \frac{1}{x} = \frac{2}{x+1}$ **5, 0, and −1 cannot be solutions.**

StudyTip

Solutions It is important to check the solutions of rational equations to be sure that they satisfy the original equation.

Vocabulary Link

extraneous
Everyday Use irrelevant or unimportant

extraneous solution
Math Use a result that is not a solution of the original equation

Solve Rational Equations

Example 1 shows how to use cross products to solve rational expressions when both sides of the equation are single fractions. **Example 2** shows how to solve rational equations by multiplying each side of the equation by the LCD to eliminate fractions. **Example 3** shows how to determine which solutions are extraneous solutions when both sides of a rational equation are multiplied by the LCD of the rational expressions that make up the equation.

Formative Assessment

Use the Check Your Progress exercises after each example to determine students' understanding of concepts.

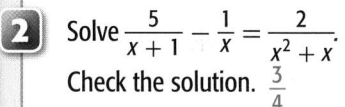

Additional Examples

1 **FRIENDS** Cabrini can run 3 miles an hour faster than Michael. Cabrini can run 5 miles in the same time it takes Michael to run 3 miles. Solve $\frac{5}{x+3} = \frac{3}{x}$ to find how fast Michael can run. Check the solution. $4\frac{1}{2}$ miles per hour

2 Solve $\frac{5}{x+1} - \frac{1}{x} = \frac{2}{x^2+x}$. Check the solution. $\frac{3}{4}$

Additional Examples also in Interactive Classroom PowerPoint® Presentations

IWB INTERACTIVE WHITEBOARD READY

TEACH with TECH

INTERACTIVE WHITEBOARD Display the graph of the radical function on the board. Solve the equation algebraically, and show students how this solution relates to the graph. Save your notes as a PDF and post on your class Web site.

Watch Out!

Preventing Errors Suggest students make a mental note of the values for the variable that make the denominator equal to zero.
Suggest that students check their solutions by substituting them back into the original equation.

Additional Example

3 Solve $\frac{3x}{x-1} + \frac{6x-9}{x-1} = 6$. State any extraneous solutions.
no solution; 1

Watch Out!

Student Misconceptions Emphasize that the equation must be solved in order to find the solution(s) and to determine whether the solutions are extraneous. The value of the variable that would make the denominator zero is not necessarily an extaneous solution of the rational equation.

Focus on Mathematical Content

Extraneous Roots It is always important to check a solution to an equation in the original equation, but it is especially important when each side of an equation has been multiplied by a variable. If your solution is an approximation, it is sometimes difficult to determine whether a discrepancy is due to rounding or if it is an incorrect solution.

Use Rational Equations to Solve Problems

Example 4 shows how to use rational equations to solve real-world work problems. **Example 5** shows how to use rational equations to solve real-world rate problems.

Additional Example

4 **TV INSTALLATION** On Saturdays, Lee helps her father install satellite TV systems. The jobs normally take Lee's father about $2\frac{1}{2}$ hours. But when Lee helps, the jobs only take them $1\frac{1}{2}$ hours. If Lee were installing a satellite system herself, how long would the job take?
$3\frac{3}{4}$ hours

EXAMPLE 3 Extraneous Solutions

Solve $\frac{2n}{n-5} + \frac{4n-30}{n-5} = 5$. State any extraneous solutions.

$\frac{2n}{n-5} + \frac{4n-30}{n-5} = 5$ — Original equation

$(n-5)\left(\frac{2n}{n-5} + \frac{4n-30}{n-5}\right) = (n-5)5$ — Multiply each side by the LCD, $n-5$.

$\left(\frac{\overset{1}{\cancel{n-5}}}{1} \cdot \frac{2n}{\underset{1}{\cancel{n-5}}}\right) + \left(\frac{\overset{1}{\cancel{n-5}}}{1} \cdot \frac{4n-30}{\underset{1}{\cancel{n-5}}}\right) = (n-5)5$ — Distributive Property

$2n + 4n - 30 = 5n - 25$ — Simplify.

$6n - 30 = 5n - 25$ — Add like terms.

$6n - 5n - 30 = 5n - 5n - 25$ — Subtract $5n$ from each side.

$n - 30 = -25$ — Simplify.

$n - 30 + 30 = -25 + 30$ — Add 30 to each side.

$n = 5$ — Simplify.

Since $n = 5$ results in a zero in the denominator of the original equation, it is an extraneous solution. So, the equation has no solution.

StudyTip

Solutions It is possible to get both a valid solution and an extraneous solution when solving a rational equation.

Check Your Progress

3. Solve $\frac{n^2-3n}{n^2-4} - \frac{10}{n^2-4} = 2$. State any extraneous solutions. −1; extraneous solution: −2

Personal Tutor glencoe.com

Use Rational Equations to Solve Problems You can use rational equations to solve **work problems**, or problems involving work rates.

Real-World EXAMPLE 4 Work Problem

JOBS At his part-time job at the zoo, Ping can clean the bird area in 2 hours. Natalie can clean the same area in 1 hour and 15 minutes. How long would it take them if they worked together?

Understand It takes Ping 2 hours to complete the job and Natalie $1\frac{1}{4}$ hours.

You need to find the rate that each person works and the total time t that it will take them if they work together.

Plan Find the fraction of the job that each person can do in an hour.

Ping's rate → $\frac{1 \text{ job}}{2 \text{ hours}} = \frac{1}{2}$ job per hour

Natalie's rate → $\frac{1 \text{ job}}{1\frac{1}{4} \text{ hours}}$ or $\frac{1 \text{ job}}{\frac{5}{4} \text{ hours}} = \frac{4}{5}$ job per hour

Since rate · time = fraction of job done, multiply each rate by the time t to represent the amount of the job done by each person.

722 Chapter 11 Rational Functions and Equations

StudyTip

Work Problems When solving work problems, remember that each term should represent the portion of a job completed in one unit of time.

Solve Fraction of job Ping completes plus fraction of job Natalie completes equals 1 job.

$$\frac{1}{2}t + \frac{4}{5}t = 1$$

$$10\left(\frac{1}{2}t + \frac{4}{5}t\right) = 10(1)$$ **Multiply each side by the LCD, 10.**

$$10\left(\frac{1}{2}t\right) + 10\left(\frac{4}{5}t\right) = 10$$ **Distributive Property**

$$5t + 8t = 10$$ **Simplify.**

$$t = \frac{10}{13}$$ **Add like terms and divide each side by 13.**

So, it would take them $\frac{10}{13}$ hour or about 46 minutes to complete the job if they work together.

Check In $\frac{10}{13}$ hour, Ping would complete $\frac{1}{2} \cdot \frac{10}{13}$ or $\frac{5}{13}$ of the job and Natalie would complete $\frac{4}{5} \cdot \frac{10}{13}$ or $\frac{8}{13}$ of the job. Together, they complete $\frac{5}{13} + \frac{8}{13}$ or 1 whole job. So, the answer is reasonable.✓

Check Your Progress

4. **RAKING** Jenna can rake the leaves in 2 hours. It takes her brother Benjamin 3 hours. How long would it take them if they worked together? $1\frac{1}{5}$ hour

Personal Tutor glencoe.com

Rational equations can also be used to solve **rate problems**.

Real-World EXAMPLE 5 Rate Problem

AIRPLANES An airplane takes off and flies an average of 480 miles per hour. Another plane leaves 15 minutes later and flies to the same city traveling 560 miles per hour. How long will it take the second plane to pass the first plane?

Record the information that you know in a table.

Plane	Distance	Rate	Time
1	d miles	480 mi/h	t hours
2	d miles	560 mi/h	$t - \frac{1}{4}$ hours

← Plane 2 took off 15 minutes, or $\frac{1}{4}$ hour, after Plane 1

Since both planes will have traveled the same distance when Plane 2 passes Plane 1, you can write the following equation.

Distance for Plane 1 = Distance for Plane 2

$$480 \cdot t = 560 \cdot \left(t - \frac{1}{4}\right)$$ **distance = rate • time**

$$480t = (560 \cdot t) - \left(560 \cdot \frac{1}{4}\right)$$ **Distributive Property**

$$480t = 560t - 140$$ **Simplify.**

$$-80t = -140$$ **Subtract 560t from each side.**

$$t = 1.75$$ **Divide each side by −80.**

So, the second plane passes the first plane after 1.75 hours.

Real-World Link

The longest nonstop commercial flight was 13,422 miles from Hong Kong Airport in China to London Heathrow in the United Kingdom. It took 22 hours and 42 minutes.

Source: *Guinness Book of World Records*

Check Your Progress

5. Lenora leaves the house walking at 3 miles per hour. After 10 minutes, her mother leaves the house riding a bicycle at 10 miles per hour. In how many minutes will Lenora's mother catch her? $14\frac{2}{7}$ min

Personal Tutor glencoe.com

Math *in Motion*, Animation glencoe.com

Additional Example

5 **BUS** A bus leaves a station and travels an average of 50 miles per hour towards a city. Another bus leaves the same station 20 minutes later and travels to the same city traveling 60 miles per hour. How long will it take the second bus to pass the first bus? 1 hour 40 minutes, or $1\frac{2}{3}$ hours

Differentiated Instruction

AL OL ELL

If you think students would benefit by acting out a concept in this lesson,

Then have students refer to Example 5. Ask students to design a rate problem that two students can act out, such as walking a certain distance. Have the two students start at different times. The student who starts later should take more steps per second than the other. Have another student record the time the one student passes the other. Then work out the problem to see if the calculations reflect the actual time.

3 PRACTICE

Formative Assessment

Use Exercises 1–8 to check for understanding.

Use the chart at the bottom of this page to customize assignments for your students.

Check Your Understanding

Examples 1–3 pp. 720–722

Solve each equation. State any extraneous solutions.

1. $\frac{2}{x+1} = \frac{4}{x}$ -2

2. $\frac{t+3}{5} = \frac{2t+3}{9}$ 12

3. $\frac{a+3}{a} - \frac{6}{5a} = \frac{1}{a}$ $-\frac{4}{5}$

4. $4 - \frac{p}{p-1} = \frac{2}{p-1}$ 2

5. $\frac{2t}{t+1} + \frac{4}{t-1} = 2$ -3

6. $\frac{x+3}{x^2-1} - \frac{2x}{x-1} = 1$

6. $-\frac{4}{3}$; extraneous: 1

Example 4 pp. 722–723

7. WEEDING Maurice can weed the garden in 45 minutes. Olinda can weed the garden in 50 minutes. How long would it take them to weed the garden if they work together? $\frac{15}{38}$ hour or about 0.4 hour

Example 5 p. 723

8. LANDSCAPING Hunter is filling a 3.5-gallon bucket to water plants at a faucet that flows at a rate of 1.75 gallons a minute. If he were to add a hose that flows at a rate of 1.45 gallons per minute, how many minutes would it take him to fill the bucket? Round to the nearest tenth. 1.1 min

Practice and Problem Solving

= **Step-by-Step Solutions** begin on page R12.
Extra Practice begins on page 815

Examples 1–3 pp. 720–722

Solve each equation. State any extraneous solutions.

9. $\frac{8}{n} = \frac{3}{n-5}$ 8

10. $\frac{6}{t+2} = \frac{4}{t}$ 4

11. $\frac{3g+2}{12} = \frac{g}{2}$ $\frac{2}{3}$

12. $\frac{5h}{4} + \frac{1}{2} = \frac{3h}{8}$ $-\frac{4}{7}$

13. $\frac{2}{3w} = \frac{2}{15} + \frac{12}{5w}$ -13

14. $\frac{c-4}{c+1} = \frac{c}{c-1}$ $\frac{2}{3}$

15. $\frac{x-1}{x+1} - \frac{2x}{x-1} = -1$ 0

16. $\frac{y+4}{y-2} + \frac{6}{y-2} = \frac{1}{y+3}$ $-4, -8$

17. $\frac{a}{a+3} + \frac{a^2}{a+3} = 2$ $-2, 3$

18. $\frac{12}{a+3} + \frac{6}{a^2-9} = \frac{8}{a+3}$ $\frac{3}{2}$

19. $\frac{3n}{n-1} + \frac{6n-9}{n-1} = 6$ no solution; extraneous: 1

20. $\frac{n^2-n-6}{n^2-n} - \frac{n-5}{n-1} = \frac{n-3}{n^2-n}$

20. no solution; extraneous: 1

Example 4 pp. 722–723

21. PAINTING It takes Noah 3 hours to paint one side of a fence. It takes Gilberto 5 hours. How long would it take them if they worked together? $\frac{15}{8}$ hours or $1\frac{7}{8}$ hours

22. DISHWASHING Ron works as a dishwasher and can wash 500 plates in two hours and 15 minutes. Chris can finish the 500 plates in 3 hours. About how long would it take them to finish all of the plates if they work together? $\frac{9}{7}$ hours or $1\frac{2}{7}$ hours

Example 5 p. 723

23. ICE A hotel has two ice machines in its kitchen. How many hours would it take both machines to make 60 pounds of ice? Round to the nearest tenth. 26.2 hours

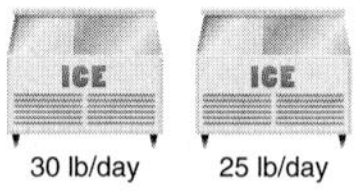

24. CYCLING Two cyclists travel in opposite directions around a 5.6-mile circular trail. They start at the same time. The first cyclist completes the trail in 22 minutes and the second in 28 minutes. At what time do they pass each other? 12.32 min

B GRAPHING CALCULATOR For each function, a) describe the shape of the graph, b) use factoring to simplify the function, and c) find the zeros of the function.

25. $f(x) = \frac{x^2 - x - 30}{x - 6}$

26. $f(x) = \frac{x^3 + x^2 - 2x}{x + 2}$

27. $f(x) = \frac{x^3 + 6x^2 + 12x}{x}$

25a. line
25b. $f(x) = \frac{(x+5)(x-6)}{x-6} = x + 5$
25c. -5
26a. parabola
26b. $f(x) = \frac{x(x+2)(x-1)}{x+2} = x(x-1)$
26c. 0, 1
27a. parabola
27b. $f(x) = x^2 + 6x + 12$
27c. no real zeros

28. PAINTING Morgan can paint a standard-sized house in about 5 days. For his latest job, Morgan hires two assistants. At what rate must these assistants work for Morgan to meet a deadline of two days? They must paint $\frac{3}{10}$ of the house each day for 2 days.

Differentiated Homework Options

Level	Assignment	Two-Day Option	
AL Basic	9–24, 37–63	9–23 odd, 41–44	10–24 even, 37–40, 45–63
OL Core	9–27 odd, 28–31, 33, 35, 37–63	9–24, 41–44	25–35, 37–40, 45–63
BL Advanced	25–60, (optional: 61–63)		

Real-World Link

Orange juice contains more than 10 times as much vitamin C as apple juice. Drinking an 8-ounce glass counts as one of the five recommended fruit and vegetable servings for the day.

Source: Ask Dr. Sears

29. AIRPLANES Headwinds push against a plane and reduce its total speed, while tailwinds push on a plane and increase its total speed. Let w equal the speed of the wind, r equal the speed set by the pilot, and s equal the total speed.

a. Write an equation for the total speed with a headwind and an equation for the total speed with a tailwind. **$s = r - w$; $s = r + w$**

b. Use the rate formula to write an equation for the distance traveled by a plane with a headwind and another equation for the distance traveled by a plane with a tailwind. Then solve each equation for time instead of distance.

30. MIXTURES A pitcher of fruit juice has 3 pints of pineapple juice and 2 pints of orange juice. Erin wants to add more orange juice so that the fruit juice mixture is 60% orange juice. Let x equal the pints of orange juice that she needs to add.

a. Copy and complete the table below.

Juice	Pints of Orange Juice	Total Pints of Juice	Percent of Orange Juice
original mixture	2	5	0.4
final mixture	2 + x	5 + x	0.6

b. Write and solve an equation to find the pints of orange juice to add. **$\frac{2 + x}{5 + x} = 0.6$; 2.5 pt**

31. DORMITORIES The number of hours h it takes to clean a dormitory varies inversely with the number of people cleaning it c and directly with the number of people living there p.

a. Write an equation showing how h, c, and p are related. (*Hint*: Include the constant k.) **$h = \frac{kp}{c}$**

b. It takes 8 hours for 5 people to clean the dormitory when there are 100 people there. How long will it take to clean the dormitory if there are 10 people cleaning and the number of people living in the dorm stays the same? **4 hours**

Solve each equation. State any extraneous solutions.

32. $\frac{4b + 2}{b^2 - 3b} + \frac{b + 2}{b} = \frac{b - 1}{b}$ **1**

33. $\frac{x^2 - x - 6}{x + 2} + \frac{x^3 + x^2}{x} = 3$ **$-1 \pm \sqrt{7}$; extraneous: 0, −2**

34. $\frac{y^2 + 5y - 6}{y^3 - 2y^2} = \frac{5}{y} - \frac{6}{y^3 - 2y^2}$ **$\frac{15}{4}$; extraneous: 0**

35. $\frac{x - \frac{6}{5}}{x} - \frac{x - 10\frac{1}{2}}{x - 5} = \frac{x + 21}{x^2 - 5x}$ **$\frac{50}{11}$**

H.O.T. Problems

Use **H**igher-**O**rder **T**hinking Skills

36. CHALLENGE Solve $\frac{2x}{x - 2} + \frac{x^2 + 3x}{(x + 1)(x - 2)} = \frac{2}{(x + 1)(x - 2)}$. **$-2, \frac{1}{3}$**

37. REASONING How is an excluded value of a rational expression related to an extraneous solution of a corresponding rational equation? Explain.

38. OPEN ENDED Write a problem about a real-world situation where work is being done. Write an equation that models the situation.

39. REASONING Find a counterexample for the following statement.

The solution of a rational equation can never be zero. **Sample answer: $\frac{x}{8} = 0$**

40. WRITING IN MATH Describe the steps for solving a rational equation that is not a proportion.

29b. $d = t(r - w)$, $d = t(r + w)$; $t = \frac{d}{r - w}$, $t = \frac{d}{r + w}$

37. The extraneous solution of a rational equation is an excluded value of one of the expressions in the equation.

38. Sample answer: Jordan can clean the kitchen in $\frac{2}{3}$ hour and his brother can clean it in 1 hour. The equation $\frac{3}{2}t + 1t = 1$ represents the time that it would take them to clean the kitchen if they do it together.

40. Sample answer: First, find the LCD of the fractions in the equation. Then multiply each side of the equation by the LCD. Simplify and use the order of operations to solve for the variable.

Study Guide and Intervention

CRM pp. 48–49 AL OL ELL

NAME ______ DATE ______ PERIOD ______

11-8 Study Guide and Intervention

Rational Equations

Solve Rational Equations **Rational equations** are equations that contain rational expressions. To solve equations containing rational expressions, multiply each side of the equation by the least common denominator.

Rational equations can be used to solve **work problems** and **rate problems**.

Example 1 Solve $\frac{x - 3}{3} + \frac{x}{2} = 4$.

$\frac{x - 3}{3} + \frac{x}{2} = 4$

$6\left(\frac{x - 3}{3} + \frac{x}{2}\right) = 6(4)$ — The LCD is 6.

$2(x - 3) + 3x = 24$ — Distributive Property

$2x - 6 + 3x = 24$ — Distributive Property

$5x = 30$ — Simplify.

$x = 6$ — Divide each side by 5.

The solution is 6.

Example 2 Solve $\frac{15}{x^2 - 1} = \frac{5}{2(x - 1)}$. State any extraneous solutions.

$\frac{15}{x^2 - 1} = \frac{5}{2(x - 1)}$ — Original equation

$30(x - 1) = 5(x^2 - 1)$ — Cross multiply.

$30x - 30 = 5x^2 - 5$ — Distributive Property

$0 = 5x^2 - 30x + 30 - 5$ — Add $-30x + 30$ to each side.

$0 = 5x^2 - 30x + 25$ — Simplify.

$0 = 5(x^2 - 6x + 5)$ — Factor.

$0 = 5(x - 1)(x - 5)$ — Factor.

$x = 1$ or $x = 5$ — Zero Product Property

The number 1 is an extraneous solution, since 1 is an excluded value for x. So, 5 is the solution of the equation.

Exercises

Solve each equation. State any extraneous solutions.

1. $\frac{x - 5}{5} + \frac{x}{4} = 8$ **20**
2. $\frac{3}{x} = \frac{6}{x + 1}$ **1**
3. $\frac{x - 1}{5} = \frac{2x - 2}{15}$ **1**
4. $\frac{8}{n - 1} = \frac{10}{n + 1}$ **9**
5. $t - \frac{4}{t + 3} = t + 3$ **$-4\frac{1}{3}$**
6. $\frac{m + 4}{m} + \frac{m}{3} = \frac{m}{3}$ **−4; 0 is extraneous**
7. $\frac{q + 4}{q - 1} + \frac{q}{q + 1} = 2$ **$-\frac{3}{2}$**
8. $\frac{5 - 2x}{2} - \frac{4x + 3}{6} = \frac{7x + 2}{6}$ **$\frac{10}{17}$**
9. $\frac{m + 1}{m - 1} - \frac{m}{1 - m} = 1$ **−2**
10. $\frac{x^2 - 9}{x - 3} + x^2 = 9$ **−3 or 2**
11. $\frac{2}{x^2 - 36} - \frac{1}{x - 6} = 0$ **−4; 6 is extraneous**
12. $\frac{4z}{z^2 + 4z + 3} = \frac{6}{z + 3} + \frac{4}{z + 1}$ **−3 is extraneous**
13. $\frac{4}{4 - p} - \frac{p^2}{p - 4} = 4$ **−6, 2**
14. $\frac{x^2 - 16}{x - 4} + x^2 = 16$ **−4, 3; 4 is extraneous**

Chapter 11 48 Glencoe Algebra 1

Practice

CRM p. 51 AL OL BL ELL

NAME ______ DATE ______ PERIOD ______

11-8 Practice

Rational Equations

Solve each equation. State any extraneous solutions.

1. $\frac{5}{n + 2} = \frac{7}{n + 6}$ **8**
2. $\frac{x}{x - 5} = \frac{x + 4}{x - 6}$ **4**
3. $\frac{k + 5}{k} = \frac{k - 1}{k + 9}$ **−3**
4. $\frac{2h}{h - 1} = \frac{2h + 1}{h + 2}$ **$-\frac{1}{5}$**
5. $\frac{4y}{3} + \frac{1}{2} = \frac{5y}{6}$ **−1**
6. $\frac{y - 2}{4} - \frac{y + 2}{5} = -1$ **−2**
7. $\frac{2q - 1}{6} - \frac{q}{3} = \frac{q + 4}{18}$ **−7**
8. $\frac{5}{p - 1} - \frac{3}{p + 2} = 0$ **$-\frac{13}{2}$**
9. $\frac{3t}{3t - 3} - \frac{1}{9t + 3} = 1$ **$-\frac{1}{2}$**
10. $\frac{4x}{2x + 1} - \frac{2x}{2x + 3} = 1$ **$\frac{3}{2}$**
11. $\frac{d - 3}{d} - \frac{d - 4}{d - 2} = \frac{1}{d}$ **4**
12. $\frac{3y - 2}{y - 2} + \frac{y^2}{2 - y} = -3$ **4; extraneous: 2**
13. $\frac{2}{m + 2} - \frac{m + 2}{m - 2} = \frac{7}{3}$ **$-1, \frac{2}{5}$**
14. $\frac{n + 2}{n} + \frac{n + 5}{n + 3} = -\frac{1}{n}$ **$-\frac{9}{5}, -1$**
15. $\frac{1}{z + 1} - \frac{6 - z}{6z} = 0$ **−3, 2**
16. $\frac{2p}{p - 2} + \frac{p + 2}{p^2 - 4} = 1$ **−3; extraneous: −2**
17. $\frac{x + 7}{x^2 - 9} - \frac{x}{x + 3} = 1$ **−2, 4**
18. $\frac{2n}{n - 4} - \frac{n + 6}{n^2 - 16} = 1$ **−5, −2**

19. **PUBLISHING** Tracey and Alan publish a 10-page independent newspaper once a month. At production, Alan usually spends 6 hours on the layout of the paper. When Tracey helps, layout takes 3 hours and 20 minutes.

a. Write an equation that could be used to determine how long it would take Tracey to do the layout by herself. **Sample answer: $\frac{1}{6}\left(\frac{10}{3}\right) + \frac{1}{t}\left(\frac{10}{3}\right) = 1$**

b. How long would it take Tracey to do the job alone? **7 h 30 min**

20. **TRAVEL** Emilio made arrangements to have Lynda pick him up from an auto repair shop after he dropped his car off. He called Lynda to tell her he would start walking and to look for him on the way. Emilio and Lynda live 10 miles from the auto shop. It takes Emilio $2\frac{1}{4}$ hours to walk the distance and Lynda 15 minutes to drive the distance.

a. If Emilio and Lynda leave at the same time, when should Lynda expect to spot Emilio on the road? **in $13\frac{1}{2}$ min**

b. How far will Emilio have walked when Lynda picks him up? **1 mi**

Chapter 11 51 Glencoe Algebra 1

Lesson 11-8

Word Problem Practice

CRM p. 52 AL OL BL ELL

NAME ______ DATE ______ PERIOD ______

11-8 Word Problem Practice

Rational Equations

1. **ELECTRICITY** The current in a simple electric circuit varies inversely as the resistance. If the current is 20 amps when the resistance is 5 ohms, find the current when the resistance is 8 ohms. **12.5 amps**

2. **MASONRY** Sam and Belai are masons who are working to build a stone wall that will be 120 feet long. Sam works from one end and is able to build one ten-foot section in 5 hours. Belai works from the other end and is able to finish a ten-foot section in 4 hours. How long will it take Sam and Belai to finish building the wall? **26 hours and 40 minutes**

3. **NUMBERS** The formula to find the sum of the first n whole numbers is sum $= \frac{n^2 + n}{2}$. In order to encourage students to show up early to a school dance, the dance committee decides to charge less for those who come to the dance early. Their plan is to charge the first student to arrive 1 penny. The second student through the door is charged 2 pennies; the third student through the door is charged 3 pennies, and so on. How much money, in total, would paid by the first 150 students? **11,325 pennies or $113.25**

4. **NAUTICAL** A ferry captain keeps track of the progress of his ship in the ship's log. One day, he records the following entry.

With the recent spring snow melt, the current is running strong today. The six-mile trip downstream to Whyte's landing was very quick. However, we only covered two miles in the same amount of time when we headed back upstream.

Write a rational equation using b for the speed of the boat and c for the speed of the stream and solve for b in terms of c. **$\frac{6}{b + c} = \frac{2}{b - c}$; $b = 2c$**

5. **HEALTH CARE** The total number of Americans waiting for kidney and heart transplants is approximately 66,500. The ratio of those awaiting a kidney transplant to those awaiting a heart transplant is about 20 to 1.

a. How many people are on each of the waiting lists? Round your answers to the nearest hundred. **kidney: 63,300; heart: 3200**

b. These two groups make up about $\frac{3}{4}$ of the transplant candidates for all organs. About how many organ transplant candidates are there altogether? Round your answer to the nearest thousand. **89,000**

Chapter 11 52 Glencoe Algebra 1

Enrichment

CRM p. 53 OL BL

NAME ______ DATE ______ PERIOD ______

11-8 Enrichment

Winning Distances

In 1999, Hicham El Guerrouj set a world record for the mile run with a time of 3:43.13 (3 min 43.13 s). In 1954, Roger Bannister ran the first mile under 4 minutes at 3:59.4. Had they run those times in the same race, how far in front of Bannister would El Guerrouj have been at the finish?

Use $\frac{d}{t} = r$. Since 3 min 43.13 s = 223.13 s, and 3 min 59.4 s = 239.4 s, El Guerrouj's rate was $\frac{5280 \text{ ft}}{223.13 \text{ s}}$ and Bannister's rate was $\frac{5280 \text{ ft}}{239.4 \text{ s}}$.

	r	t	d
El Guerrouj	$\frac{5280}{223.13}$	223.13	5280 feet
Bannister	$\frac{5280}{239.4}$	223.13	$\frac{5280}{239.4} \cdot 223.13$ or 4921.2 feet

Therefore, when El Guerrouj hit the tape, he would be 5280 − 4921.2, or 358.8 feet, ahead of Bannister. Let's see whether we can develop a formula for this type of problem.

Let D = the distance raced,
W = the winner's time,
and L = the loser's time

	r	t	d
Winner	$\frac{D}{W}$	w	$\frac{D}{W} \cdot W = D$

Lesson 11-8

Lesson 11-8 Rational Equations 725

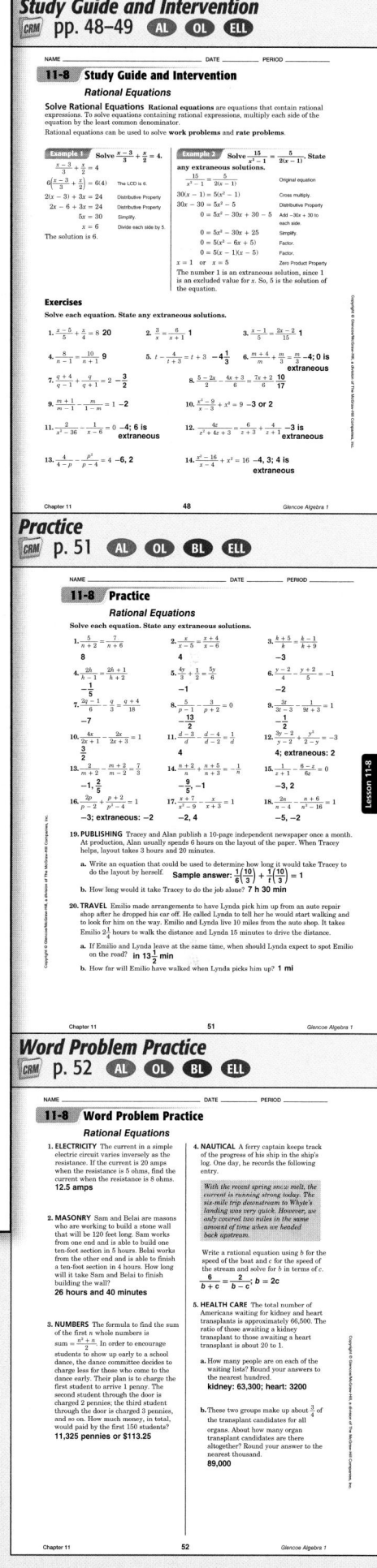

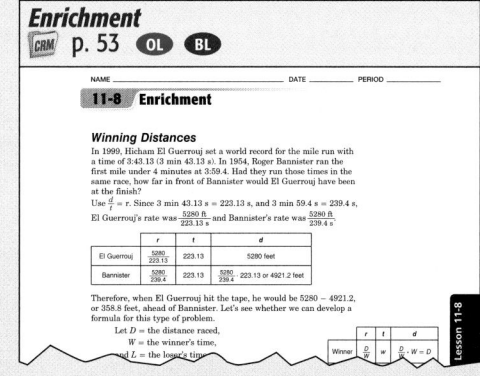

4 ASSESS

Yesterday's News Have students write how knowing how to simplify mixed expressions helped them with today's lesson.

Formative Assessment

Check for student understanding of Lessons 11-7 and 11-8.

CRM Quiz 4, p. 58

PSAE PRACTICE 6.11.17, 6.11.10, 8.11.02, 8.11.17

41. It takes Cheng 4 hours to build a fence. If he hires Odell to help him, they can do the job in 3 hours. If Odell built the same fence alone, how long would it take him? **D**

A $1\frac{5}{7}$ hours C 8 hours

B $3\frac{2}{3}$ hours D 12 hours

42. In the 1000-meter race, Zoe finished 200 meters ahead of Taryn and 400 meters ahead of Evan. When Taryn finished, how far was she ahead of Evan? **G**

F 400 m G 200 m H 150 m J 100 m

43. Twenty gallons of lemonade were poured into two containers of different sizes. Express the amount of lemonade poured into the smaller container in terms of g, the amount poured into the larger container. **D**

A $g + 20$ C $g - 20$

B $20 + g$ D $20 - g$

44. GRIDDED RESPONSE The gym has 2-kilogram and 5-kilogram disks for weight lifting. They have fourteen disks in all. The total weight of the 2-kilogram disks is the same as the total weight of the 5-kilogram disks. How many 2-kilogram disks are there? **10**

Spiral Review

Simplify each expression. (Lesson 11-7)

45. $\dfrac{\frac{c^2}{d}}{\frac{c^3}{d^2}}$ $\mathbf{\frac{d}{c}}$

46. $\dfrac{\frac{5g^3}{h^2}}{\frac{6g}{5h}}$ $\mathbf{\frac{25g^2}{6h}}$

47. $\dfrac{\frac{2}{b}}{\frac{4}{b-3}}$ $\mathbf{\frac{b-3}{2b}}$

48. $\dfrac{\frac{q-2}{9}}{\frac{q^2-6q+8}{12}}$ $\mathbf{\frac{4}{3(q-4)}}$

Find the LCM of each pair of polynomials. (Lesson 11-6)

49. $2h, 4h^2$ $\mathbf{4h^2}$

50. $5c^2, 12c^3$ $\mathbf{60c^3}$

51. $x - 4, x + 2$ $\mathbf{(x-4)(x+2)}$

52. $p - 7, 2(p - 14)$ $\mathbf{2(p-7)(p-14)}$

Look for a pattern in each table of values to determine which kind of model best describes the data. (Lesson 9-9)

53.

x	0	1	2	3	4
y	4	5	6	7	8

linear

54.

x	1	2	3	4	5
y	2	4	8	16	32

exponential

55.

x	−3	−2	−1	0	1
y	14	9	6	5	6

quadratic

56.

x	3	4	5	6	7
y	3	5	7	9	11

linear

57. GENETICS Brown genes B are dominant over blue genes b. A person with genes BB or Bb has brown eyes. Someone with genes bb has blue eyes. Mrs. Dunn has brown eyes with genes Bb, and Mr. Dunn has blue eyes. Write an expression for the possible eye coloring of their children. Then find the probability that a child would have blue eyes. (Lesson 7-8) $\mathbf{0.5Bb + 0.5b^2; \frac{1}{2}}$

Solve each inequality. Check your solution. (Lesson 5-2)

58. $\frac{b}{10} \leq 5$ $\mathbf{\{b \mid b \leq 50\}}$

59. $-7 > -\frac{r}{7}$ $\mathbf{\{r \mid r > 49\}}$

60. $\frac{5}{8}y \geq -15$ $\mathbf{\{y \mid y \geq -24\}}$

Skills Review

Determine the probability of each event if you randomly select a marble from a bag containing 9 red marbles, 6 blue marbles, and 5 yellow marbles. (Lesson 0-11)

61. P(blue) **0.3**

62. P(red) **0.45**

63. P(not yellow) **0.75**

Differentiated Instruction OL BL

Extension Solve $\frac{a}{x} = \frac{2}{3}$ for x in terms of a. $x = \frac{3a}{2}$

IL Math Online glencoe.com
- STUDY TO GO
- Vocabulary Review

Chapter Summary

Key Concepts

Inverse Variation (Lesson 11-1)

- You can use $\frac{x_1}{x_2} = \frac{y_2}{y_1}$ to solve problems involving inverse variation.

Rational Functions (Lesson 11-2)

- Excluded values are values of a variable that result in a denominator of zero.
- If vertical asymptotes occur, it will be at excluded values.

Rational Expressions (Lessons 11-3 and 11-4)

- Multiplying rational expressions is similar to multiplying rational numbers.
- Divide rational expressions by multiplying by the reciprocal of the divisor.

Dividing Polynomials (Lesson 11-5)

- To divide a polynomial by a monomial, divide each term of the polynomial by the monomial.

Adding and Subtracting Rational Expressions (Lesson 11-6)

- Rewrite rational expressions with unlike denominators using the least common denominator (LCD). Then add or subtract.

Complex Fractions (Lesson 11-7)

- Simplify complex fractions by writing them as division problems.

Solving Rational Equations (Lesson 11-8)

- Use cross products to solve rational equations with a single fraction on each side of the equals sign.

FOLDABLES® Study Organizer

Be sure the Key Concepts are noted in your Foldable.

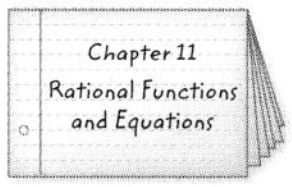

Key Vocabulary

asymptote (p. 679)
complex fraction (p. 714)
excluded value (p. 678)
extraneous solution (p. 721)
inverse variation (p. 670)
least common denominator (LCD) (p. 708)
least common multiple (LCM) (p. 707)
mixed expression (p. 714)
product rule (p. 671)
rate problems (p. 723)
rational equation (p. 720)
rational expression (p. 684)
rational function (p. 678)
work problems (p. 722)

Vocabulary Check

State whether each sentence is *true* or *false*. If *false*, replace the underlined word, phrase, expression, or number to make a true sentence.

1. The least common multiple for $x^2 - 25$ and $x - 5$ is $\underline{x - 5}$. **false; $x^2 - 25$**
2. If the product of two variables is a nonzero constant, the relationship is an <u>inverse variation</u>. **true**
3. If the line $x = a$ is a vertical <u>asymptote</u> of a rational function, then a is an excluded value. **true**
4. A rational expression is a fraction in which the numerator and denominator are <u>fractions</u>. **false; polynomials**
5. The excluded values for $\frac{x}{x^2 + 5x + 6}$ are $\underline{-2 \text{ and } -3}$. **true**
6. The equation $\frac{3x}{x - 2} = \frac{6}{x - 2}$ has an extraneous solution, $\underline{2}$. **true**
7. A <u>rational expression</u> has one or more fractions in the numerator and denominator. **false; complex fraction**
8. The expression $\frac{\frac{1}{2}}{\frac{3}{4}}$ can be simplified to $\frac{2}{3}$. **true**
9. A <u>direct variation</u> can be represented by an equation of the form $k = xy$, where k is a nonzero constant. **false; inverse variation**
10. The rational function $y = \frac{2}{x - 1} + 3$ has a horizontal asymptote at $\underline{y = 3}$. **true**

Formative Assessment

Key Vocabulary The page references after each word denote where that term was first introduced. If students have difficulty answering questions 1–10, remind them that they can use these page references to refresh their memories about the vocabulary.

Summative Assessment

CRM Vocabulary Test, p. 60

IL Math Online glencoe.com

Vocabulary PuzzleMaker improves students' mathematics vocabulary using four puzzle formats—crossword, scramble, word search using a word list, and word search using clues. Students can work online or from a printed worksheet.

FOLDABLES® Study Organizer

Dinah Zike's Foldables®

Have students look through the chapter to make sure they have included examples in their Foldables for each lesson of the chapter.

Suggest that students keep their Foldables handy while completing the Study Guide and Review pages. Point out that their Foldables can serve as a quick review when studying for the chapter test.

Lesson-by-Lesson Review

Intervention If the given examples are not sufficient to review the topics covered by the questions, remind students that the page references tell them where to review that topic in their textbook.

Two-Day Option Have students complete the Lesson-by-Lesson Review on pp. 728–730. Then you can use ExamView® Assessment Suite to customize another review worksheet that practices all the objectives of this chapter or only the objectives on which your students need more help.

Differentiated Instruction

Super DVD: Mindjogger Videoquizzes
Use this DVD as an alternative format of review for the test.

Additional Answer

19.

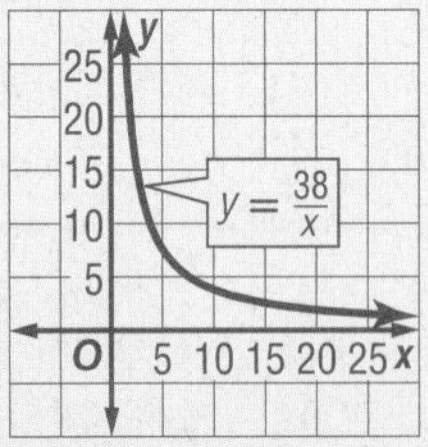

The vertical asymptote is at $x = 0$ and the horizontal asymptote is at $y = 0$.

Lesson-by-Lesson Review

11-1 Inverse Variation (pp. 669–676)

7.B.4

Solve. Assume that y varies inversely as x.

11. If $y = 4$ when $x = 1$, find x when $y = 12$ $\frac{1}{3}$

12. If $y = -1$ when $x = -3$, find y when $x = -9$ $-\frac{1}{3}$

13. If $y = 1.5$ when $x = 6$, find y when $x = -16$ $-\frac{9}{16}$

14. PHYSICS A 135-pound person sits 5 feet from the center of a seesaw. How far from the center should a 108-pound person sit to balance the seesaw? **6.25 ft or 6 ft 3 in.**

EXAMPLE 1

If y varies inversely as x and $y = 28$ when $x = 42$, find y when $x = 56$.

Let $x_1 = 42$, $x_2 = 56$, and $y_1 = 28$. Solve for y_2.

$\frac{x_1}{x_2} = \frac{y_2}{y_1}$ Proportion for inverse variation

$\frac{42}{56} = \frac{y_2}{28}$ Substitution

$1176 = 56y_2$ Cross multiply.

$21 = y_2$

Thus, $y = 21$ when $x = 56$.

11-2 Rational Functions (pp. 677–683)

8.C.4b

State the excluded value for each function.

15. $y = \frac{1}{x-3}$ **3**

16. $y = \frac{2}{2x-5}$ $\frac{5}{2}$

17. $y = \frac{3}{3x-6}$ **2**

18. $y = \frac{-1}{2x+8}$ **−4**

19. PIZZA PARTY Katelyn ordered pizza and soda for her study group for \$38. The cost per person y is given by $y = \frac{38}{x}$, where x is the number of people in the study group. Graph the function and describe the asymptotes. **See margin.**

EXAMPLE 2

State the excluded value for the function $y = \frac{1}{4x+16}$.

Set the denominator equal to zero.

$4x + 16 = 0$

$4x + 16 - 16 = 0 - 16$ Subtract 16 from each side.

$4x = -16$ Simplify.

$x = -4$ Divide each side by 4.

11-3 Simplifying Rational Expressions (pp. 684–691)

7.A.4b, 7.B.4

Simplify each expression.

20. $\frac{2xy^2}{16xyz}$ $\frac{y}{8z}$

21. $\frac{x+4}{x^2+12x+32}$ $\frac{1}{x+8}$

22. $\frac{x^2+10x+21}{x^3+x^2-42x}$ $\frac{x+3}{x(x-6)}$

23. $\frac{y^2-25}{y^2+3y-10}$ $\frac{y-5}{y-2}$

24. $\frac{3x^3}{3x^3+6x^2}$ $\frac{x}{x+2}$

25. $\frac{4y^2}{8y^4+16y^3}$ $\frac{1}{2y(y+2)}$

State the excluded values for each function.

26. $y = \frac{x}{x^2+9x+18}$ **−6, −3**

27. $y = \frac{10}{6x^2+7x-3}$ $-\frac{3}{2}, \frac{1}{3}$

EXAMPLE 3

Simplify $\frac{a^2-7a+12}{a^2-13a+36}$.

Factor and simplify.

$\frac{a^2-7a+12}{a^2-13a+36} = \frac{(a-3)(a-4)}{(a-9)(a-4)}$ Factor.

$= \frac{a-3}{a-9}$ Simplify.

MIXED PROBLEM SOLVING
For mixed problem-solving practice, see page 855.

11-4 Multiplying and Dividing Rational Expressions (pp. 692–698)

7.A.4b

Find each product or quotient.

28. $\frac{6x^2y^4}{12} \cdot \frac{3x^3y^2}{xy}$ $\frac{3x^4y^5}{2}$

29. $\frac{3x-6}{x^2-9} \cdot \frac{x+3}{x^2-2x}$ $\frac{3}{x^2-3x}$

30. $\frac{x^2}{x+4} \div \frac{3x}{x^2-16}$ $\frac{x(x-4)}{3}$

31. $\frac{3b-12}{b+4} \div (b^2-6b+8)$ $\frac{3}{(b+4)(b-2)}$

32. $\frac{2a^2+7a-15}{a+5} \div \frac{9a^2-4}{3a+2}$ $\frac{2a-3}{3a-2}$

33. **GEOMETRY** Find the area of the rectangle shown. Write the answer in simplest form. xy

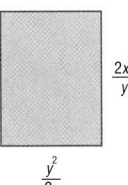

EXAMPLE 4

Find $\frac{7b^2}{9} \cdot \frac{6a^2}{b}$.

$\frac{7b^2}{9} \cdot \frac{6a^2}{b} = \frac{42a^2b^2}{9b}$ **Multiply.**

$= \frac{14a^2b}{3}$ **Simplify.**

EXAMPLE 5

Find $\frac{x^2-25}{x^2-9} \div \frac{x+5}{x-3}$.

$\frac{x^2-25}{x^2-9} \div \frac{x+5}{x-3} = \frac{(x+5)(x-5)}{(x+3)(x-3)} \div \frac{x+5}{x-3}$ **Factor.**

$= \frac{\overset{1}{\cancel{(x+5)}}(x-5)}{(x+3)\underset{1}{\cancel{(x-3)}}} \cdot \frac{\overset{1}{\cancel{x-3}}}{\underset{1}{\cancel{x+5}}}$ **Multiply by the reciprocal.**

$= \frac{x-5}{x+3}$ **Simplify.**

11-5 Dividing Polynomials (pp. 700–705)

7.A.4b

Find each quotient.

34. $(x^3-2x^2-22x+21) \div (x-3)$ $x^2+x-19-\frac{36}{x-3}$

35. $(x^3+7x^2+10x-6) \div (x+3)$ x^2+4x-2

36. $(5x^2y^2-10x^2y+5xy) \div 5xy$ $xy-2x+1$

37. $(48y^2+8y+7) \div (12y-1)$ $4y+1+\frac{8}{12y-1}$

38. **GEOMETRY** The area of a rectangle is $x^2+7x+13$. If the length is $(x+4)$, what is the width of the rectangle? $x+3+\frac{1}{x+4}$

EXAMPLE 6

Find $(4x^2+17x-1) \div (4x+1)$.

$$\begin{array}{r l}
 x + 4 & \\
4x+1\overline{)4x^2+17x-1} & \\
\underline{4x^2+x} & \textbf{Multiply } x \textbf{ and } 4x+1. \\
16x-1 & \textbf{Subtract, bring down } -1. \\
\underline{16x+4} & \textbf{Multiply 4 and } 4x+1. \\
-5 & \textbf{Subtract.}
\end{array}$$

The quotient is $x+4-\frac{5}{4x+1}$.

11-6 Adding and Subtracting Rational Expressions (pp. 706–713)

8.A.4b

Find each sum or difference.

39. $\frac{5a}{b} - \frac{2a}{b}$ $\frac{3a}{b}$

40. $\frac{-3}{2n-3} + \frac{2n}{2n-3}$ 1

41. $\frac{3}{y+1} - \frac{y}{y-3}$

42. $\frac{1}{x+1} + \frac{3}{x-2}$

43. **DESIGN** Miguel is decorating a room that is $\frac{2x}{x+4}$ feet long and $\frac{8}{x+4}$ feet wide. What is the perimeter of the room? 4 ft

EXAMPLE 7

Find $\frac{x^2}{x+1} + \frac{2x+1}{x+1}$.

$\frac{x^2}{x+1} + \frac{2x+1}{x+1} = \frac{x^2+2x+1}{x+1}$ **Add the numerators.**

$= \frac{(x+1)(x+1)}{x+1}$ **Factor.**

$= x+1$ **Simplify.**

41. $\frac{-y^2+2y-9}{(y+1)(y-3)}$

42. $\frac{4x+1}{(x+1)(x-2)}$

Chapter 11 Study Guide and Review 729

Problem Solving Review

For additional practice in problem solving for Chapter 11, see the Mixed Problem Solving Appendix, p. 855, in the Student Handbook section.

Anticipation Guide

Have students complete the Chapter 11 Anticipation Guide and discuss how their responses have changed now that they have completed Chapter 11.

CHAPTER 11 Study Guide and Review

11-7 Mixed Expressions and Complex Fractions (pp. 714–719)

7.A.4b, 7.B.4

Simplify each expression.

44. $\dfrac{\frac{a^2b^4}{c}}{\frac{a^3b}{c^2}}$ $\dfrac{b^3c}{a}$

45. $\dfrac{x-\frac{35}{x+2}}{x+\frac{42}{x+13}}$

46. $\dfrac{\frac{x^2-25}{x+2}}{\frac{x-5}{x^2-4}}$ $(x+5)(x-2)$

47. $\dfrac{y+9-\frac{6}{y+4}}{y+4+\frac{2}{y+1}}$

48. FABRICS Donna makes tablecloths to sell at craft fairs. A small one takes one-half yard of fabric, a medium one takes five-eighths yard, and a large one takes one and one-quarter yard.

a. How many yards of fabric does she need to make a tablecloth of each size? $2\frac{3}{8}$ yd

b. One bolt of fabric contains 30 yards of fabric. Can she use the entire bolt of fabric by making an equal number of each type of tablecloth? Explain.

EXAMPLE 8

Simplify $\dfrac{\frac{x+3}{6}}{\frac{x^2-2x-15}{x}}$.

Write as a division expression.

$$\frac{\frac{x+3}{6}}{\frac{x^2-2x-15}{x}} = \frac{x+3}{6} \div \frac{x^2-2x-15}{x}$$

$$= \frac{x+3}{6} \cdot \frac{x}{x^2-2x-15}$$

$$= \frac{x+3}{6} \cdot \frac{x}{(x+3)(x-5)}$$

$$= \frac{x}{6(x-5)}$$

45. $\dfrac{x^2+8x-65}{x^2+8x+12}$

47. $\dfrac{y^2+11y+10}{y^2+6y+8}$

48b. No; she needs $2\frac{3}{8}$ yards for one of each type. Since $30 \div 2\frac{3}{8}$ is not a whole number, she cannot use the entire bolt by making an equal number of each type.

11-8 Rational Equations (pp. 720–727)

8.C.4b

Solve each equation. State any extraneous solutions.

49. $\dfrac{5n}{6} + \dfrac{1}{n-2} = \dfrac{n+1}{3(n-2)}$ $\dfrac{2}{5}$, extraneous: 2

50. $\dfrac{4x}{3} + \dfrac{7}{2} = \dfrac{7x}{12} - 14$ $-\dfrac{70}{3}$

51. $\dfrac{11}{2x} + \dfrac{2}{4x} = \dfrac{1}{4}$ 24

52. $\dfrac{1}{x+4} - \dfrac{1}{x-1} = \dfrac{2}{x^2+3x-4}$ no solution

53. $\dfrac{1}{n-2} = \dfrac{n}{8}$ $-2, 4$

54. PAINTING Anne can paint a room in 6 hours. Oljay can paint a room in 4 hours. How long will it take them to paint the room working together? $\frac{12}{5}$ or $2\frac{2}{5}$ hours

EXAMPLE 9

Solve $\dfrac{3}{x^2+3x} + \dfrac{x+2}{x+3} = \dfrac{1}{x}$.

$$\frac{3}{x^2+3x} + \frac{x+2}{x+3} = \frac{1}{x}$$

$$x(x+3)\left(\frac{3}{x(x+3)}\right) + x(x+3)\left(\frac{x+2}{x+3}\right) = x(x+3)\left(\frac{1}{x}\right)$$

$$3 + x(x+2) = 1(x+3)$$

$$3 + x^2 + 2x = x + 3$$

$$x^2 + x = 0$$

$$x(x+1) = 0$$

$$x = 0 \text{ or } x = -1$$

The solution is −1, and there is an extraneous solution of 0.

IL Math Online glencoe.com
Chapter Test

Determine whether each table represents an inverse variation. Explain.

1.

x	y
2	10
4	12
8	14

No; the products are not the same.

2.

x	y
2	2
4	1
8	$\frac{1}{2}$

yes; $y = \frac{4}{x}$

Find each product or quotient.

3. $\frac{(x+6)(x-2)}{x^3} \cdot \frac{7x^2}{x-3}$ $\frac{7(x+6)(x-2)}{x(x-3)}$

4. $\frac{(x+3)}{y^2} \div \frac{x^2-9}{y}$ $\frac{1}{y(x-3)}$

Solve. Assume that y varies inversely as x.

5. If $y = 3$ when $x = 9$, find x when $y = 1$. 27

6. If $y = 2$ when $x = 0.5$, find y when $x = 3$. $\frac{1}{3}$

Simplify each expression. State the excluded values of the variables.

7. $\frac{z-6}{z^2-3z-18}$ $\frac{1}{z+3}$; $-3, 6$

8. $\frac{4x-28}{x^2-49}$ $\frac{4}{x+7}$; $-7, 7$

9. **MULTIPLE CHOICE** The area of a rectangle is $x^2 + 5x + 6$ square feet. If the width is $x + 2$, what is the length of the rectangle? B

A $x + 2$

B $x + 3$

C 1

D 3

Simplify each expression.

10. $\frac{2\frac{1}{3}}{3\frac{1}{2}}$ $\frac{2}{3}$

11. $\frac{\frac{x^2-25}{x-2}}{\frac{x-5}{x-2}}$ $x + 5$

12. $\frac{\frac{a-4}{a^2+6a+8}}{\frac{a^2-3a-4}{a^2-a-6}}$ 12. $\frac{a-3}{(a+1)(a+4)}$

13. $\frac{\frac{y^2+10y+24}{y^2-9}}{\frac{3y^2+17y-6}{2y^2-11y+15}}$ 13. $\frac{(y+4)(2y-5)}{(y+3)(3y-1)}$

Find each quotient.

14. $(2x^2 + 10x) \div 2x$ $x + 5$

15. $(4x^2 - 8x + 5) \div (2x + 1)$ $2x - 5 + \frac{10}{2x+1}$

16. $(3x^2 - 14x - 3) \div (x - 5)$ $3x + 1 + \frac{2}{x-5}$

Assume that y varies inversely as x. Write an inverse variation equation that relates x and y.

17. $y = 2$ when $x = 8$ $y = \frac{16}{x}$

18. $y = -3$ when $x = 1$ $y = -\frac{3}{x}$

Find each sum or difference.

19. $\frac{3}{x} + \frac{6}{x}$ $\frac{9}{x}$

20. $\frac{t-5}{t-6} + \frac{t+8}{t-6}$ $\frac{2t+3}{t-6}$

21. $\frac{1}{x-6} + \frac{3}{x-2}$ $\frac{4x-20}{(x-6)(x-2)}$

22. $\frac{5}{x^2-2x-24} + \frac{x}{x-6}$ $\frac{x^2+4x+5}{x^2-2x-24}$

State the excluded value or values for each function.

23. $y = \frac{6}{x-1}$ 1

24. $y = \frac{5}{x^2-5x-24}$ $-3, 8$

Identify the asymptotes of each function.

25. $y = \frac{2}{(x-4)(x+2)}$ $x = 4, x = -2, y = 0$

26. $y = \frac{4}{x^2+3x-28} + 2$ $x = 4, x = -7, y = 2$

27. **MULTIPLE CHOICE** Lee can shovel the driveway in 3 hours, and Susan can shovel the driveway in 2 hours. How long will it take them working together? H

F 6 hours

G 5 hours

H $\frac{6}{5}$ hour

J 4 hours

28. **PAINTING** Sydney can paint a 60-square foot wall in 40 minutes. Working with her friend Cleveland, the two of them can paint the wall in 25 minutes. How long would it take Cleveland to do the job himself? $\frac{10}{9}$ or $1\frac{1}{9}$ hours

CHAPTER 11 Practice Test

ExamView Assessment Suite Customize and create multiple versions of your chapter tests and their answer keys. All of the questions from the leveled chapter tests in the *Chapter 11 Resource Masters* are also available on ExamView Assessment Suite.

Intervention Planner

Tier 1 On Level	Tier 2 Strategic Intervention approaching grade level	Tier 3 Intensive Intervention 2 or more grades below level
If students miss about 25% of the exercises or less,	**If** students miss about 50% of the exercises,	**If** students miss about 75% of the exercises,
Then choose a resource:	**Then** choose a resource:	**Then** use *Math Triumphs, Alg. 1*
SE Lessons 11-1, 11-2, 11-3, 11-4, 11-5, 11-6, 11-7, and 11-8 **CRM** Skills Practice, pp. 7, 13, 19, 25, 32, 38, 44, and 50 **TE** Chapter Project, p. 666 IL Math Online Self-Check Quiz	**CRM** Study Guide and Intervention, Chapter 11, pp. 5, 11, 17, 23, 30, 36, 42, and 48 *Quick Review Math Handbook* IL Math Online Extra Examples, Personal Tutor, Homework Help	IL Math Online Extra Examples, Personal Tutor, Homework Help, Review Vocabulary

1 FOCUS

Objective Use the strategy of modeling with an equation to solve standardized test problems.

2 TEACH

Scaffolding Questions

Ask:

- What are the benefits of using an equation to model a situation? Sample answer: The equation can help you see the relationship between the parts of a complex problem.
- What do you look for when you are solving a problem that can be modeled by an equation? Sample answer: Unknown and known quantities and words to show how they are related

Model with an Equation

In order to successfully solve some standardized test questions, you will need to be able to write equations to model different situations. Use this lesson to practice solving these types of problems.

Strategies for Modeling with Equations

Step 1

Read the problem statement carefully.

Ask yourself:

- What am I being asked to solve?
- What information is given in the problem?
- What is the unknown quantity that I need to find?

Step 2

Translate the problem statement into an equation.

- Assign a variable to the unknown quantity.
- Write the word sentence as a mathematical number sentence.
- Look for keywords such as *is*, *is the same as*, *is equal to*, or *is identical to* that indicate where to place the equals sign.

Step 3

Solve the equation.

- Solve for the unknown in the equation.
- Check your answer to be sure it is reasonable and that it answers the question in the problem statement.

EXAMPLE

Read the problem. Identify what you need to know. Then use the information in the problem to solve.

It takes Craig 75 minutes to paint a small room. If Delsin can paint the same room in 60 minutes, how long would it take them to paint the room if they work together? Round to the nearest tenth.

A about 33.3 minutes
B about 38.4 minutes
C about 45.1 minutes
D about 50.3 minutes

Read the problem carefully. You know how long it takes Craig and Delsin to paint a room individually. Model the situation with an equation to find how long it would take them to paint the room if they work together.

Find the rate that each person works when painting individually.

Craig's rate: $\frac{1 \text{ job}}{75 \text{ minutes}} = \frac{1}{75}$ job per minute

Delsin's rate: $\frac{1 \text{ job}}{60 \text{ minutes}} = \frac{1}{60}$ job per minute

Let t represent the number of minutes it would take them to complete the job working together. Multiply each rate by the time t to represent the portion of the job done by each painter. Add these expressions and set them equal to 1 job. Then solve for t.

Portion that Craig completes	plus	portion that Delsin completes	equals	1 job.
$\frac{1}{75}t$	$+$	$\frac{1}{60}t$	$=$	1

Solve for t:

$\frac{1}{75}t + \frac{1}{60}t = 1$	**Original equation**
$300\left(\frac{1}{75}t + \frac{1}{60}t\right) = 1(300)$	**Multiply each side by the LCD, 300.**
$4t + 5t = 300$	**Simplify.**
$9t = 300$	**Combine like terms.**
$t \approx 33.3$	**Divide each side by 9.**

So, it would take Craig and Delsin about 33.3 minutes to paint the room working together. The correct answer is A.

Exercises

Read each problem. Identify what you need to know. Then use the information in the problem to solve.

1. Hana can finish a puzzle in 6 hours, while Eric can finish one in 5 hours. How long would it take them to finish a puzzle together? Round to the nearest tenth. D

   A about 1.8 hours
   B about 2.4 hours
   C about 2.5 hours
   D about 2.7 hours

2. Roberto wants to print 500 flyers for his landscaping business. His printer can complete the job in 35 minutes, and his brother's printer can print them in 45 minutes. How long would it take to print the flyers using both printers? Round to the nearest whole minute. H

   F about 15 minutes
   G about 18 minutes
   H about 20 minutes
   J about 23 minutes

Additional Example

STANDARDIZED TEST PRACTICE Cody and Alyssa work as lab assistants for a chemistry teacher. If Cody can prepare a lab for a class in 95 minutes and Alyssa can prepare a lab in 80 minutes, how long would it take them to prepare a lab together? Round to the nearest whole minute. A

A about 43 minutes
B about 46 minutes
C about 50 minutes
D about 61 minutes

3 ASSESS

Use Exercises 1 and 2 to assess students' understanding.

Diagnose Student Errors

Survey students' responses for each item. Class trends may indicate common errors and misconceptions.

1. A chose direct variation equation
   B chose direct variation equation
   C guess
   D correct
   E guess
2. F error in calculating denominator
   G error in addition or multiplication and/or dividing by common factor
   H error dividing by common factor in denominator
   J error in denominator
   K correct
3. A guess or calculation error
   B guess or calculation error
   C guess or calculation error
   D correct
   E guess
4. F guess
   G correct
   H guess
   J calculation error
   K guess
5. A guess
   B correct
   C guess
   D chose the number of bicycles instead of scooters
   E guess
6. F calculation error
   G correct
   H calculation error
   J calculation error
   K calculation error

Multiple Choice

Read each problem. Then fill in the correct answer on the answer document provided by your teacher or on a sheet of paper.

1. What is the inverse variation equation for the numbers shown in the table? **D**

x	y
−8	16
−4	32
2	−64
8	−16
16	−8

A $y = -2x$

B $y = 8x$

C $xy = 24$

D $xy = -128$

E $x = -2y$

2. Suppose a square has a side length given by the expression $\frac{x+5}{8x}$. What is the perimeter of the square? **K**

F $\frac{4x+20}{5x}$

G $\frac{2x+10}{x}$

H $\frac{x+5}{4x}$

J $\frac{4x+20}{4x}$

K $\frac{x+5}{2x}$

3. Find the distance between (3, −6) and (1, 4) on a coordinate grid. Round to the nearest tenth. **D**

A 8.1

B 8.5

C 9.6

D 10.2

E 14.0

Test-Taking Tip

Question 1 Sometimes you can eliminate answer choices as unreasonable because they are not in the proper form. Choices A, B, and E show direct variation equations, so they can be eliminated.

4. In 1985, the population of a country was about 3.66 million people. By 2005, this number had grown to about 4.04 million people. What was the annual rate of change in population from 1985 to 2005? **G**

F about 15,000 people per year

G about 19,000 people per year

H about 24,000 people per year

J about 38,000 people per year

K about 76,000 people per year

5. Ricky's Rentals rented 12 more bicycles than scooters last weekend for a total revenue of \$2,125. How many scooters were rented? **B**

Item	Rental Fee
Bicycle	\$20
Scooter	\$45

A 26

B 29

C 37

D 41

E 47

6. The table shows the relationship between calories and fat grams contained in orders of french fries from various restaurants.

Calories	Fat Grams
240	14
280	15
310	16
260	12
340	16
350	18
300	13

Assuming the data can best be described by a linear model, how many fat grams would be expected to be contained in a 315-calorie order of french fries? **G**

F 15 fat grams

G 16 fat grams

H 17 fat grams

J 18 fat grams

K 19 fat grams

Short Response/Gridded Response

Record your answers on the answer sheet provided by your teacher or on a sheet of paper.

7. Suppose the first term of a geometric sequence is 3 and the fourth term is 192.

a. What is the common ratio of the sequence? **4**

b. Write an equation that can be used to find the nth term of the sequence. $a_n = 3 \times 4^{n-1}$

c. What is the sixth term of the sequence? **3072**

8. GRIDDED RESPONSE Peggy is having a cement walkway installed around the perimeter of her swimming pool with the dimensions shown below. Write an expression for the total area of the pool and the walkway. Then evaluate the expression for $x = 3$ to find the area, in square feet, of the pool and walkway. **390**

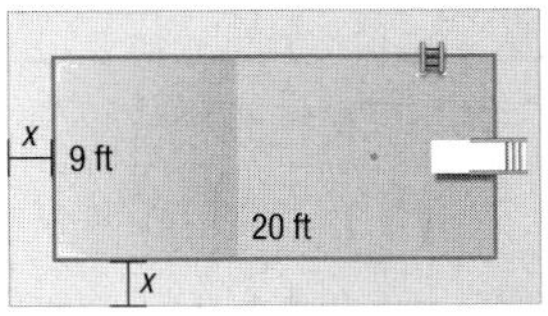
x
9 ft
20 ft
x

9. Use the equation $y = 2(4 + x)$ to answer each question.

x	y
1	10
2	12
3	14
4	16
5	18
6	20

a. Complete the following table for the different values of x.

b. Plot the points from the table on a coordinate grid. What do you notice about the points?

9b. Check students' graphs. Sample answer: The points lie in a straight line.

10. Jason received a $50 gift certificate for his birthday. He wants to buy a DVD and a poster from a media store. (Assume that sales tax is included in the prices.) Write and solve a linear inequality to show how much he would have left to spend after making these purchases. $x + 14.95 + 10.99 \leq 50;\ x \leq 24.06$

Weekend Blowout Sale
* All DVDs only $14.95
* All CDs only $11.25
* All posters only $10.99

11. Simplify the complex fraction. Show your work. $\frac{(5x + 10)}{(x - 6)}$

$$\frac{\frac{5}{x-3}}{\frac{x-6}{x^2 - x - 6}}$$

Extended Response

Record your answers on a sheet of paper. Show your work.

a. See margin.

12. Carl's father is building a tool chest that is shaped like a rectangular prism. He wants the tool chest to have a volume of 30 cubic feet. The height of the chest will be 1 foot shorter than the width. The length will be 3 feet longer than the height.

a. Sketch a model to represent the problem.

b. Write a polynomial that represents the volume of the tool chest. $w^3 + w^2 - 2w$

c. What are the dimensions of the tool chest? **2 feet high by 3 feet wide by 5 feet long**

Need Extra Help?												
If you missed Question...	1	2	3	4	5	6	7	8	9	10	11	12
Go to Lesson or Page...	11-1	11-6	10-6	3-3	6-2	4-5	9-8	7-7	1-4	2-3	11-7	8-6
IL Assessment Objectives	6.11.19	7.11.03	9.11.09	6.11.17	6.11.13	10.11.01	8.11.04	8.11.06	8.11.12	8.11.16	8.11.01	9.11.05

Formative Assessment

You can use these two pages to benchmark student progress.

CRM Standardized Test Practice, pp. 74–76

Answer Sheet Practice

Have students simulate taking a standardized test by recording their answers on a practice recording sheet.

CRM Student Recording Sheet, p. 55

Chapter Resource Master
CRM p. 55

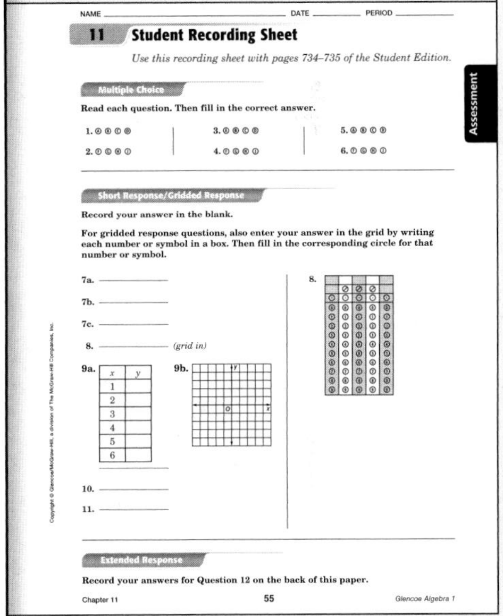
NAME ______ DATE ______ PERIOD ______

11 Student Recording Sheet

Use this recording sheet with pages 734–735 of the Student Edition.

Assessment

Multiple Choice

Read each question. Then fill in the correct answer.

1. Ⓐ Ⓑ Ⓒ Ⓓ   3. Ⓐ Ⓑ Ⓒ Ⓓ   5. Ⓐ Ⓑ Ⓒ Ⓓ
2. Ⓕ Ⓖ Ⓗ Ⓙ   4. Ⓕ Ⓖ Ⓗ Ⓙ   6. Ⓕ Ⓖ Ⓗ Ⓙ

Short Response/Gridded Response

Record your answer in the blank.

For gridded response questions, also enter your answer in the grid by writing each number or symbol in a box. Then fill in the corresponding circle for that number or symbol.

7a. ______
7b. ______
7c. ______
8. ______ (grid in)
9a.

x	y
1	
2	
3	
4	
5	
6	

9b.

10. ______
11. ______

Extended Response

Record your answers for Question 12 on the back of this paper.

Copyright © Glencoe/McGraw-Hill, a division of The McGraw-Hill Companies, Inc.

Chapter 11 55 Glencoe Algebra 1

ExamView Assessment Suite Create practice worksheets or tests that align to your state's standards, as well as TIMSS and NAEP tests.

Homework Option

Get Ready for Chapter 12 Assign students the exercises on p. 737 as homework to assess whether they possess the prerequisite skills needed for the next chapter.

Pages 674–675, Lesson 11-1

22. $xy = 40$

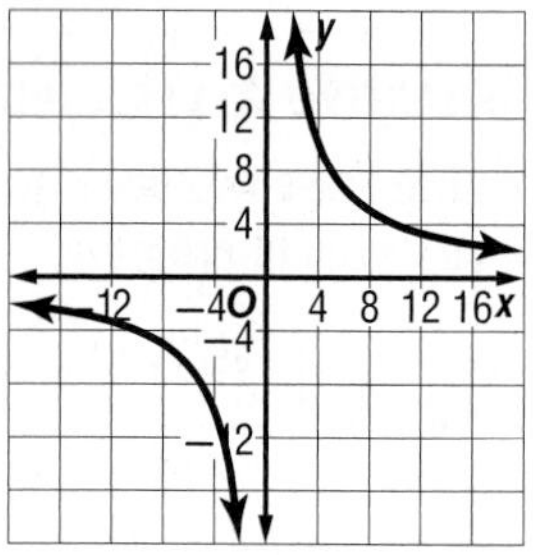

23. $xy = 72$

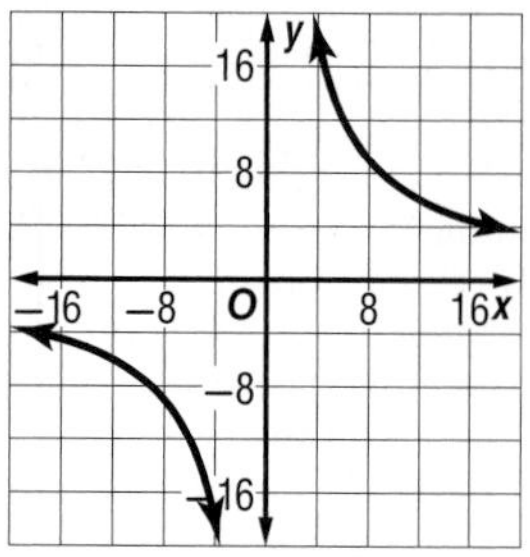

24. $xy = 18$

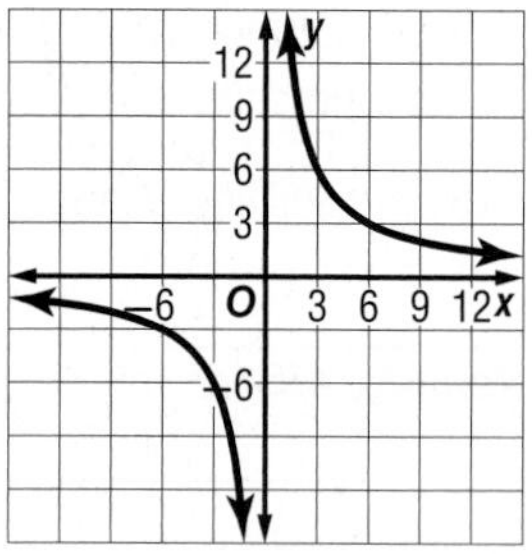

25. $xy = 12$

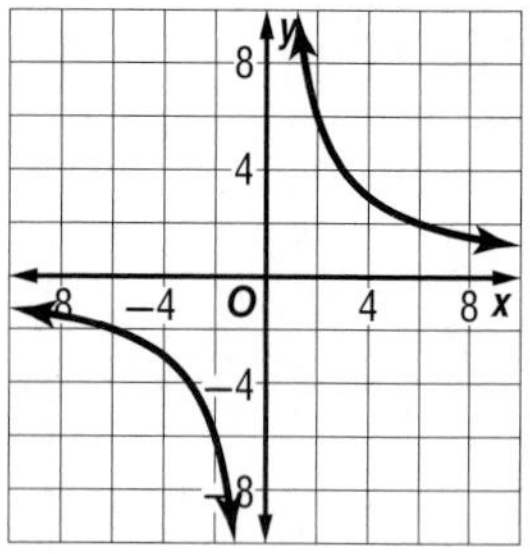

26. $xy = -64$

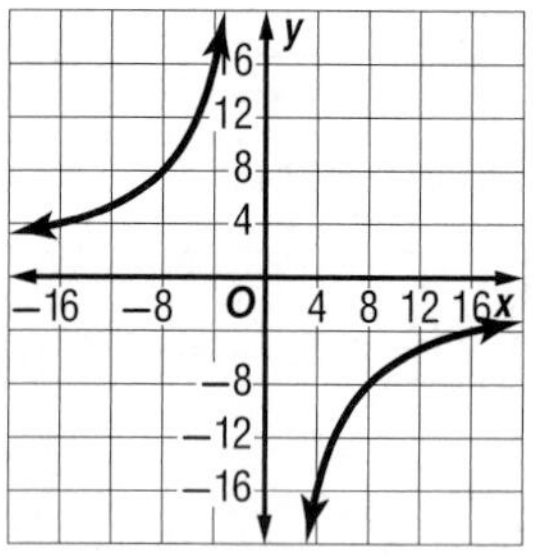

27. $xy = -108$

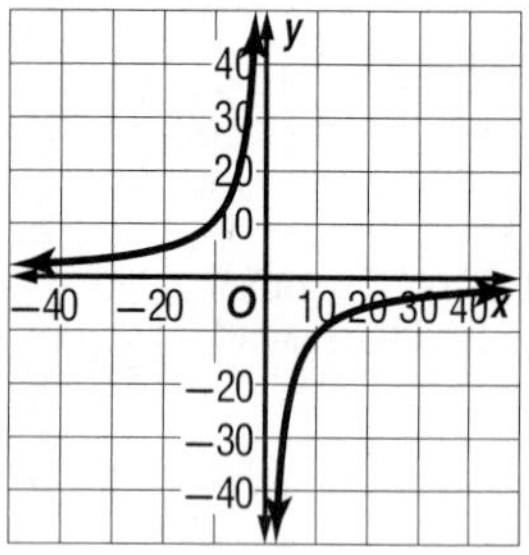

51c. $hw = 40$ or $w = \dfrac{40}{h}$

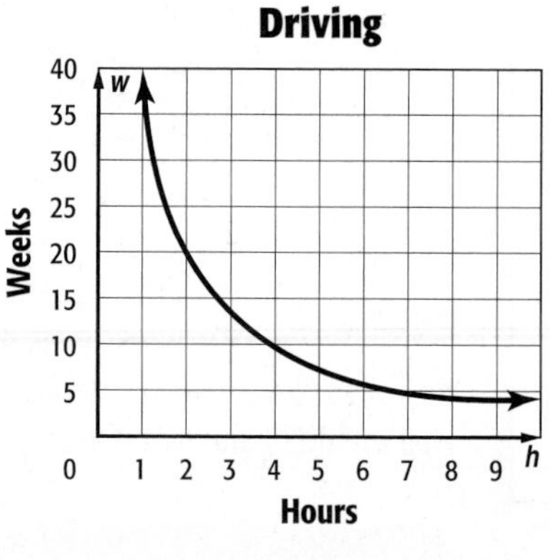

55. Sample answer: Newton's Law of Gravitational Force is an example of an inverse variation that models real-world situations. The gravitational force exerted on two objects is inversely proportional to the square of the distances between the two objects. The force exerted on the two objects, times the square of the distance between the two objects, is equal to the gravitational constant times the masses of the two objects.

56. Direct variation can be written as $y = kx$ where k is the constant of proportionality. The graph of a direct variation is a line through the origin with a slope of k. An inverse variation is written in the form $y = \frac{k}{x}$. The graph is a two-part curve (a hyperbola).

Page 679, Lesson 11-2, Check Your Progress

2.

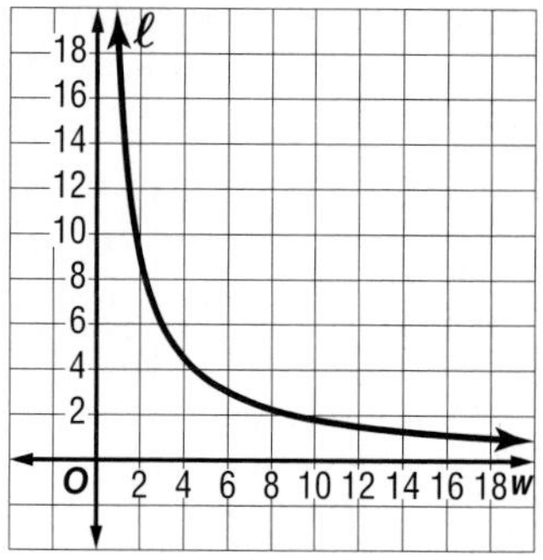

Pages 681–682, Lesson 11-2

6. $x = 0; y = 0$

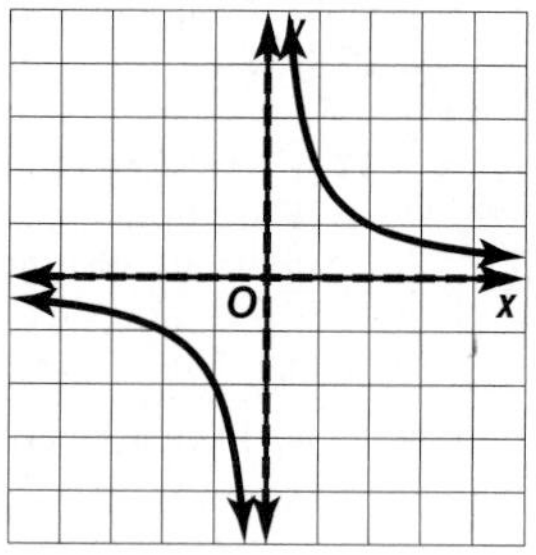

7. $x = 0; y = -1$

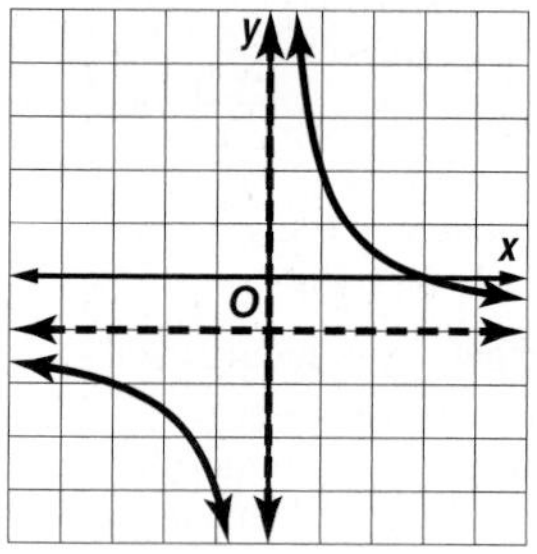

8. $x = 2; y = 0$

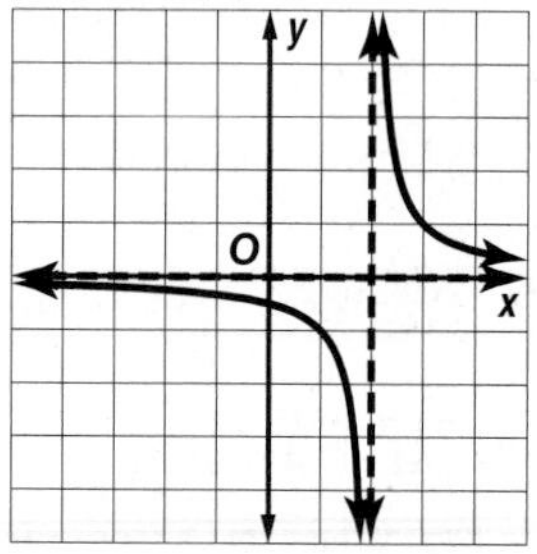

9. $x = -2; y = 0$

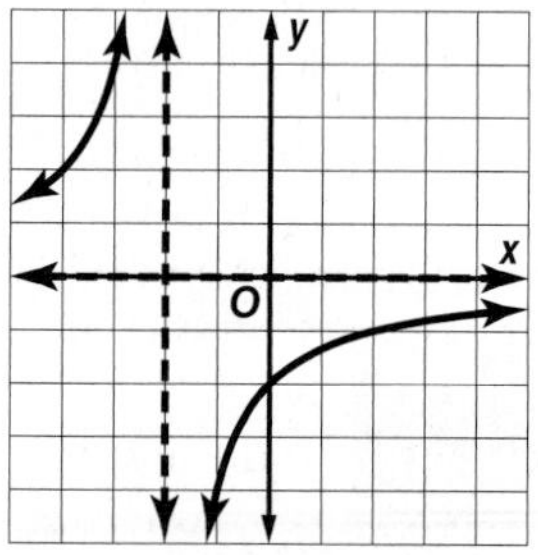

10. $x = 1; y = 2$

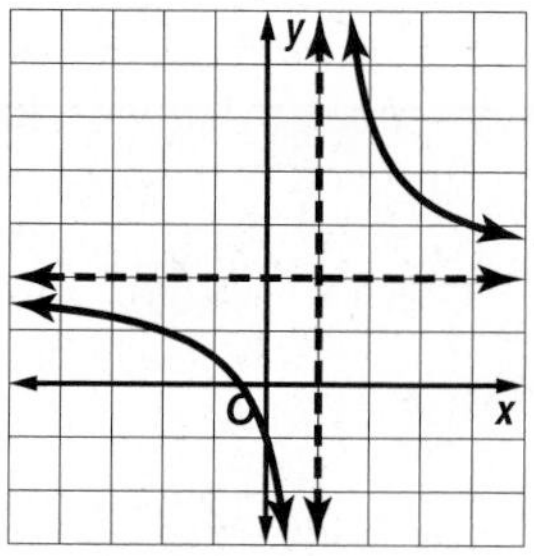

11. $x = -1; y = -5$

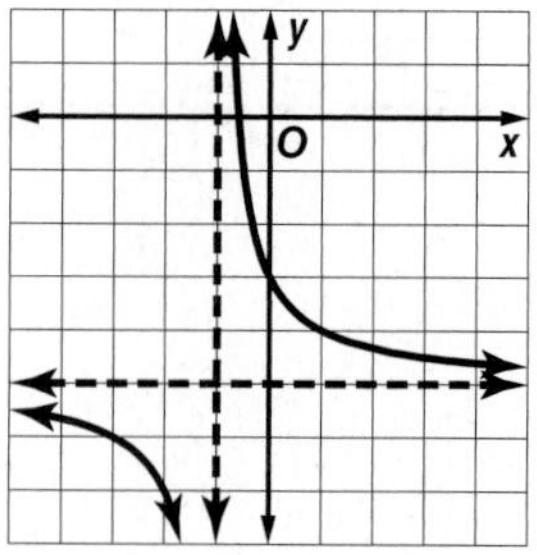

20a.

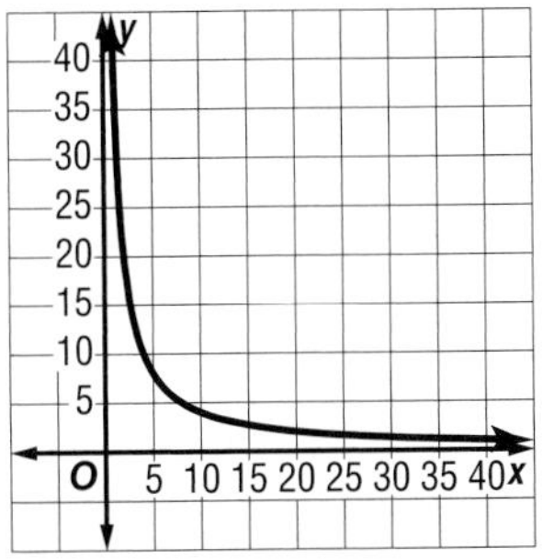

20b. 20b. asymptotes: x = 0 and y = 0

22. $x = 0; y = 0$

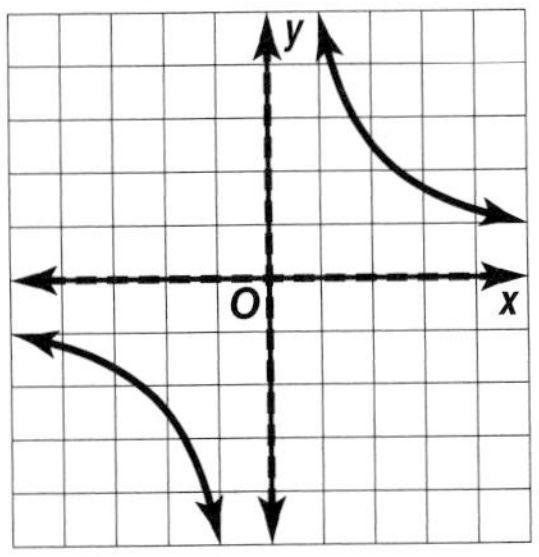

23. $x = 0; y = 0$

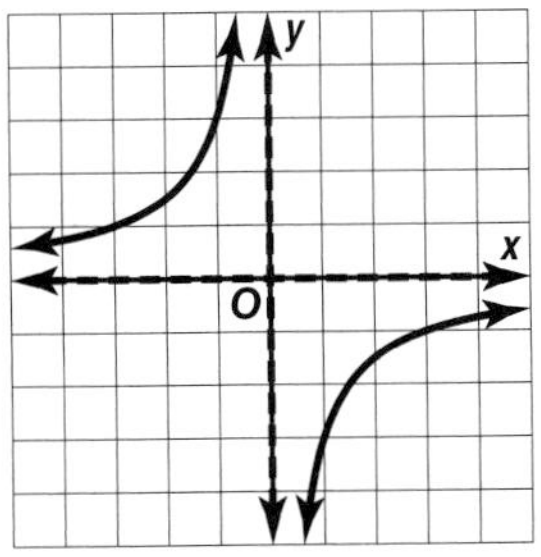

24. $x = 0; y = 3$

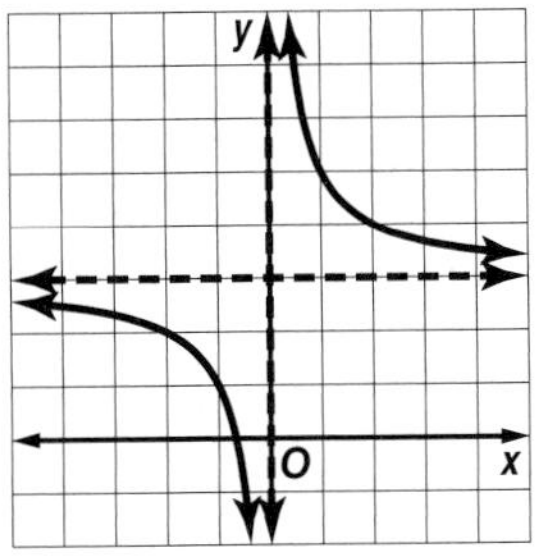

25. $x = 0; y = -2$

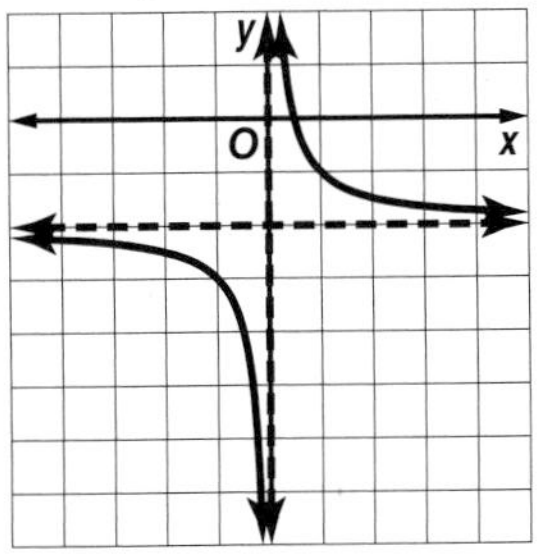

26. $x = -3; y = 0$

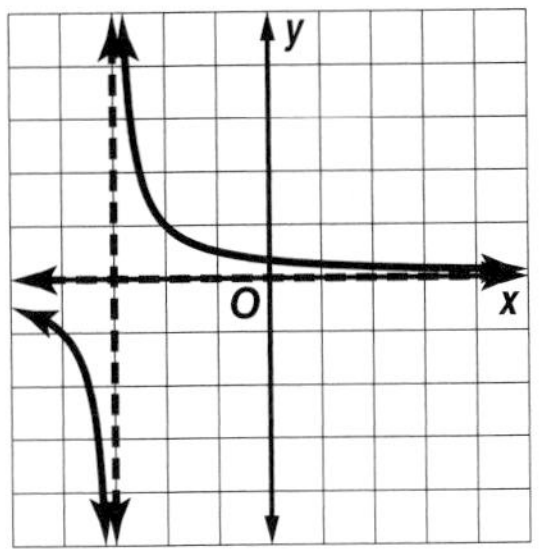

27. $x = 2; y = 0$

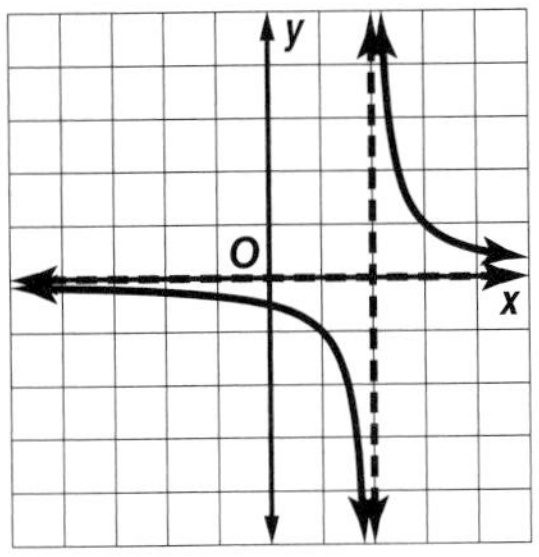

28. $x = -1; y = 0$

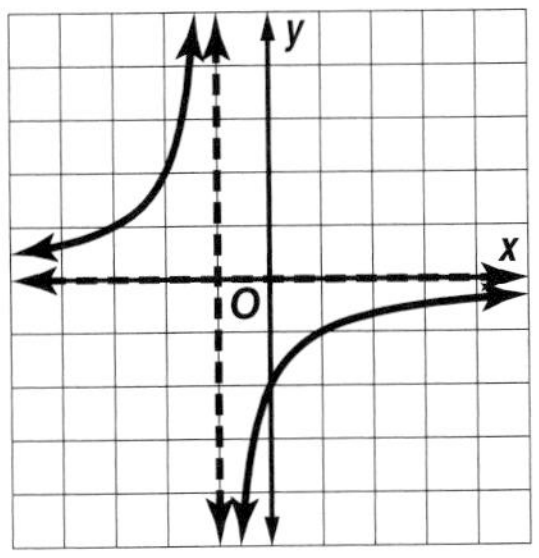

29. $x = 1; y = 0$

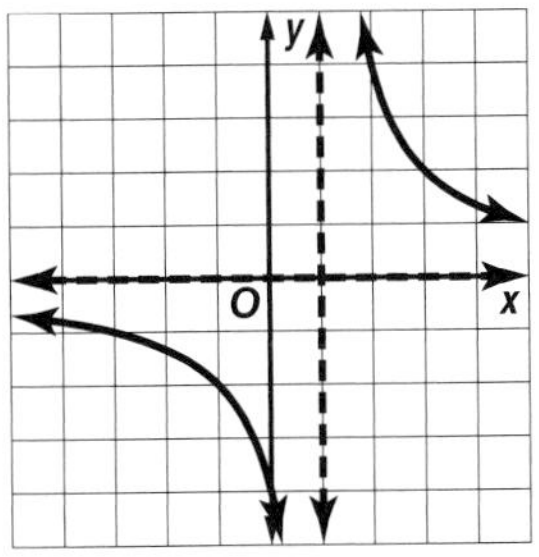

30. $x = 2; y = 1$

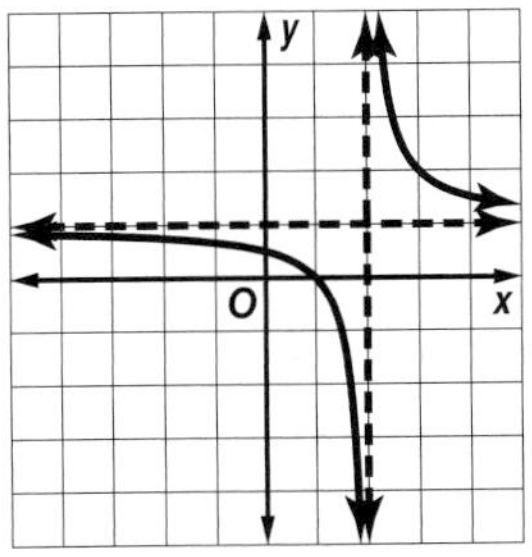

31. $x = 1; y = -2$

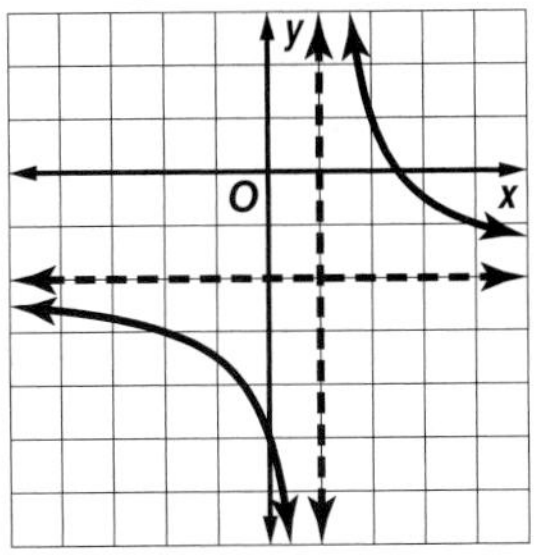

32. $x = -1; y = -4$

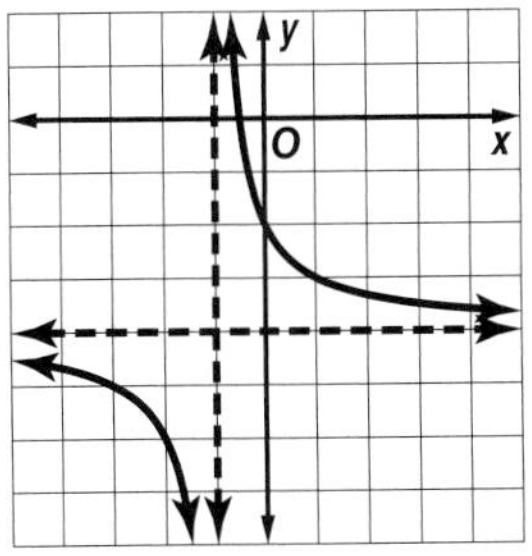

33. $x = -4; y = 3$

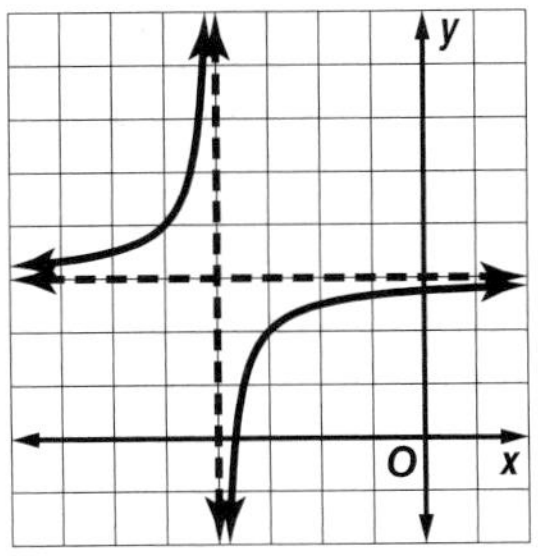

34a.

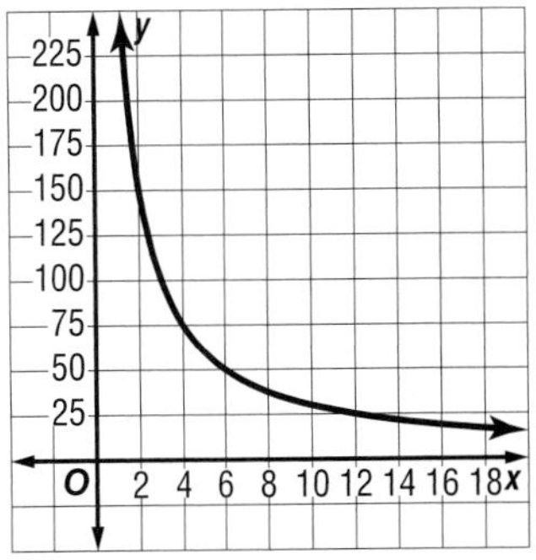

38.

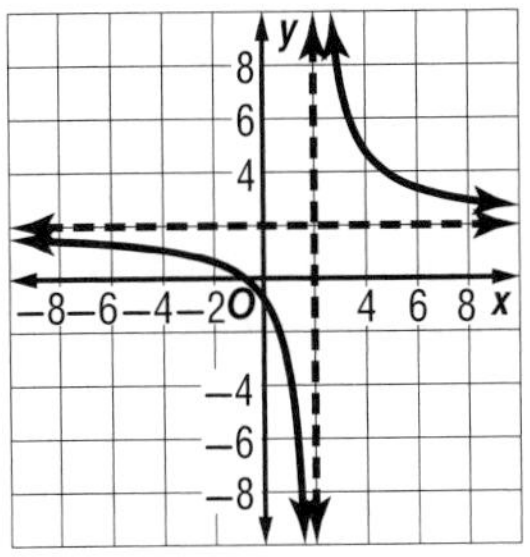

$x = 2; y = 2$

39.

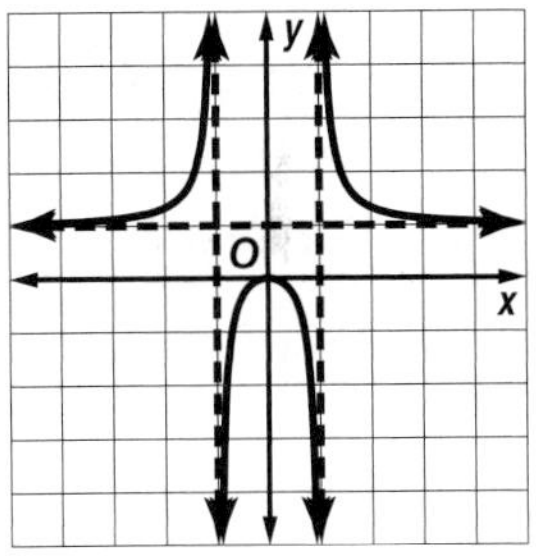

$x = -1, x = 1; y = 1$

40.

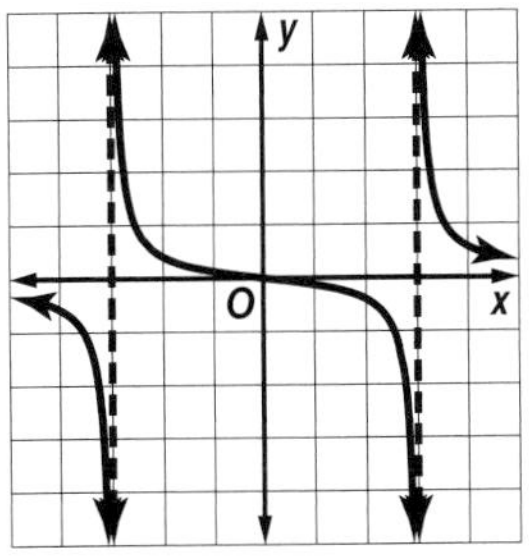

$x = 3, x = -3; y = 0$

44. Sample answer: $y = \frac{1}{x-3} + 1$; use the equation $y = \frac{a}{x-b} + c$. The vertical asymptote is $x = b$. So, $b = 3$. The horizontal asymptote is $y = c$. So, $c = 1$. Substituting the values for b and c and letting $a = 1$, the equation becomes $y = \frac{1}{x-3} + 1$.

47. The vertical asymptote of a rational function occurs for values of x that make the denominator zero.

Page 691, Extend 11-3

1.

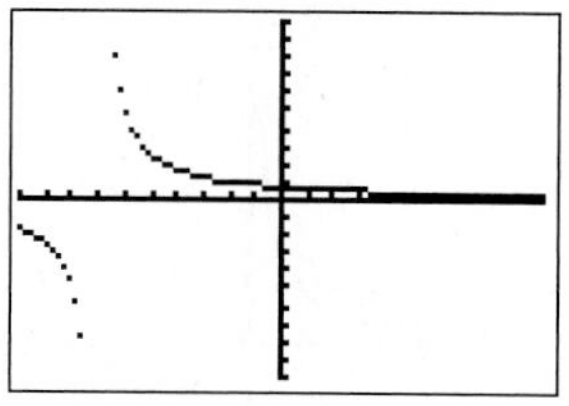

[−10, 10] scl: 1 by [−10,10] scl: 1

2.

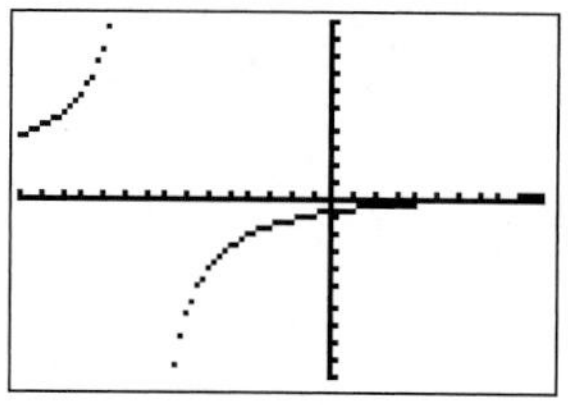

[−10, 10] scl: 1 by [−10,10] scl: 1

3.

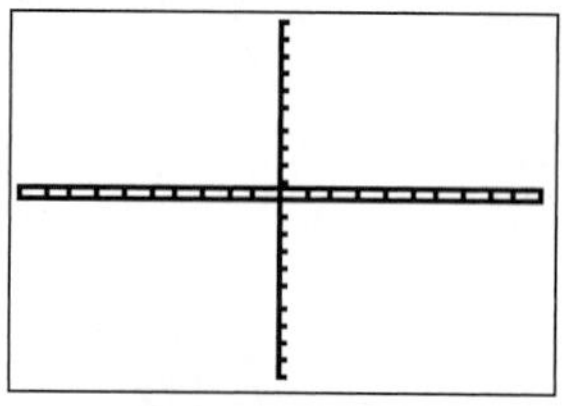

[−10, 10] scl: 1 by [−10,10] scl: 1

Page 718, Lesson 11-7

47. Sample answer: Time equals distance divided by rate or $\frac{d}{r}$. When the distance or the rate is given as a fraction or mixed number, the expression $\frac{d}{r}$ becomes a complex fraction. Example: Someone walks $\frac{3}{4}$ mile in $10\frac{1}{2}$ minutes; the time in miles per minute is $\frac{\frac{3}{4}}{10\frac{1}{2}}$, which simplifies to $\frac{1}{14}$ mi/min.

NOTES

CHAPTER 12

Chapter Planner

Diagnostic Assessment Quick Check, p. 737

	Explore 12-1 Pacing: 0.5 day	Lesson 12-1 Pacing: 1 day	Lesson 12-2 Pacing: 1 day	Lesson 12-3 Pacing: 1 day
Title	**Algebra Lab: Survey Questions**	**Designing a Survey**	**Analyzing Survey Results**	**Statistics and Parameters**
Objectives	• Investigate survey questions to determine whether they are biased or unbiased.	• Design surveys. • Identify various sampling techniques.	• Summarize survey results. • Evaluate survey results.	• Use statistics to analyze survey results. • Analyze data sets using statistics.
Key Vocabulary		sample, population, survey, observational study, experiment, biased sample, simple random sample, stratified random sample, systematic random sample	measure of central tendency quantitative data qualitative data	statistical inference, statistic parameter, univariate data, variance, standard deviation, measures of variation, mean, absolute deviation
ILS	10.B.4	10.B.4	10.A.4b, 10.B.4	8.A.4b
Multiple Representations		p. 744	p. 754	
Lesson Resources	**Additional Print Resources** • *Teaching Algebra with Manipulatives,* p.173 AL OL ELL	**Chapter 12 Resource Masters** • Study Guide and Intervention, pp. 5–6 AL OL ELL • Skills Practice, p. 7 AL OL ELL • Practice, p. 8 AL OL BL ELL • Word Problem Practice, p. 9 AL OL BL ELL • Enrichment, p. 10 OL BL **Transparencies** • 5-Minute Check Transparency 12-1 AL OL BL ELL **Additional Print Resources** • *Study Notebook* AL OL BL ELL	**Chapter 12 Resource Masters** • Study Guide and Intervention, pp. 11–12 AL OL ELL • Skills Practice, p. 13 AL OL ELL • Practice, p. 14 AL OL BL ELL • Word Problem Practice, p. 15 AL OL BL ELL • Enrichment, p. 16 OL BL • Quiz 1, p. 51 AL OL BL ELL **Transparencies** • 5-Minute Check Transparency 12-2 AL OL BL ELL **Additional Print Resources** • *Study Notebook* AL OL BL ELL	**Chapter 12 Resource Masters** • Study Guide and Intervention, pp. 17–18 AL OL ELL • Skills Practice, p. 19 AL OL ELL • Practice, p. 20 AL OL BL ELL • Word Problem Practice, p. 21 AL OL BL ELL • Enrichment, p. 22 OL BL **Transparencies** • 5-Minute Check Transparency 12-3 AL OL BL ELL **Additional Print Resources** • *Study Notebook* AL OL BL ELL
Technology for Every Lesson	**IL Math Online** glencoe.com • Extra Examples • Self-Check Quizzes • Personal Tutor • Homework Help	**CD/DVD Resources** IWB INTERACTIVE WHITEBOARD READY IWB StudentWorks Plus IWB Interactive Classroom IWB Diagnostic and Assessment Planner		• TeacherWorks Plus • eSolutions Manual Plus • ExamView Assessment Suite
Math in Motion	Animation			
Differentiated Instruction		pp. 742, 745	pp. 752, 755	pp. 758, 762

Formative Assessment Mid-Chapter Quiz, p. 763

KEY: AL Approaching Level OL On Level BL Beyond Level ELL English Learners

Suggested Pacing			
Time Periods	Instruction	Review & Assessment	Total
45-minute	8	2	10
90-minute	5	1	6

Statistics and Probability

Lesson 12-4 Pacing: 1 day	Lesson 12-5 Pacing: 1 day	Lesson 12-6 Pacing: 1 day	Extend 12-6 Pacing: 0.5 day	Lesson 12-7 Pacing: 1 day
Permutations and Combinations	**Probability of Compound Events**	**Probability Distributions**	**Graphing Technology Lab: The Normal Curve**	**Probability Simulations**
• Use permutations. • Use combinations.	• Find probabilities of independent and dependent events. • Find probabilities of mutually exclusive events.	• Find probabilities by using random variables. • Solve real-world problems using distributions.	• Use a graphing calculator to explore normal distribution curves.	• Design simulations to estimate probabilities. • Summarize data from simulations.
permutation sample space combination	compound event independent events dependent events mutually exclusive events	random variable probability distribution		theoretical probability experimental probability relative frequency simulation
Preparation for 10.C.5b	10.C.4a	10.C.4a, 10.C.4c	10.A.4b	10.C.4b
	p. 777	p. 783		
Chapter 12 Resource Masters • Study Guide and Intervention, pp. 23–24 AL OL ELL • Skills Practice, p. 25 AL OL ELL • Practice, p. 26 AL OL BL ELL • Word Problem Practice, p. 27 AL OL BL ELL • Enrichment, p. 28 OL BL • Quiz 2, p. 51 AL OL BL ELL **Transparencies** • 5-Minute Check Transparency 12-4 AL OL BL ELL **Additional Print Resources** • *Study Notebook* AL OL BL ELL	**Chapter 12 Resource Masters** • Study Guide and Intervention, pp. 29–30 AL OL ELL • Skills Practice, p. 31 AL OL ELL • Practice, p. 32 AL OL BL ELL • Word Problem Practice, p. 33 AL OL BL ELL • Enrichment, p. 34 OL BL • Graphing Calculator, p. 35 OL **Transparencies** • 5-Minute Check Transparency 12-5 AL OL BL ELL **Additional Print Resources** • *Study Notebook* AL OL BL ELL • *Teaching Algebra with Manipulatives,* p.174 AL OL ELL	**Chapter 12 Resource Masters** • Study Guide and Intervention, pp. 36–37 AL OL ELL • Skills Practice, p. 38 AL OL ELL • Practice, p. 39 AL OL BL ELL • Word Problem Practice, p. 40 AL OL BL ELL • Enrichment, p. 41 OL BL • Spreadsheet Activity, p. 42 OL • Quiz 3, p. 52 AL OL BL ELL **Transparencies** • 5-Minute Check Transparency 12-6 AL OL BL ELL **Additional Print Resources** • *Study Notebook* AL OL BL ELL	**Materials** • TI–83/84 Plus or other graphing calculator	**Chapter 12 Resource Masters** • Study Guide and Intervention, pp. 43–44 AL OL ELL • Skills Practice, p. 45 AL OL ELL • Practice, p. 46 AL OL BL ELL • Word Problem Practice, p. 47 AL OL BL ELL • Enrichment, p. 48 OL BL • Quiz 4, p. 52 AL OL BL ELL **Transparencies** • 5-Minute Check Transparency 12-7 AL OL BL ELL **Additional Print Resources** • *Study Notebook* AL OL BL ELL • *Teaching Algebra with Manipulatives,* p.175 AL OL ELL

IL Math Online glencoe.com
- Extra Examples
- Self-Check Quizzes
- Personal Tutor
- Homework Help

CD/DVD Resources IWB INTERACTIVE WHITEBOARD READY
- IWB StudentWorks Plus
- IWB Interactive Classroom
- IWB Diagnostic and Assessment Planner
- TeacherWorks Plus
- eSolutions Manual Plus
- ExamView Assessment Suite

	BrainPOP			
pp. 766, 770	pp. 773, 778	pp. 780, 784		pp. 789, 792

Summative Assessment
- Study Guide and Review, pp. 793–796
- Practice Test, p. 797

CHAPTER 12

Assessment and Intervention

SE = Student Edition, **TE** = Teacher Edition, **CRM** = Chapter Resource Masters

	Diagnosis	Prescription
Diagnostic Assessment	**Beginning Chapter 12**	
	Get Ready for Chapter 3 **SE**, p. 737	Response to Intervention **TE**, p. 737
	Beginning Every Lesson	
	Then, Now, Why? **SE** 5-Minute Check Transparencies	Chapter 0 **SE**, pp. P1–P45 Concepts and Skills Bank **SE,** pp. 857–867 *Quick Review Math Handbook*
Formative Assessment	**During/After Every Lesson**	
	Check Your Progress **SE**, every example Check Your Understanding **SE** H.O.T. Problems **SE** Spiral Review **SE** Additional Examples **TE** Watch Out! **TE** Step 0, Assess **TE** Chapter 12 Quizzes **CRM**, pp. 51–52 Self-Check Quizzes glencoe.com	**Tier 1 Intervention** Concepts and Skills Bank **SE**, pp. 857–867 Skills Practice **CRM**, Ch. 1–12 glencoe.com **Tier 2 Intervention** Differentiated Instruction TE Study Guide and Intervention Masters **CRM**, Ch. 1–12 *Quick Review Math Handbook* **Tier 3 Intervention** *Math Triumphs, Alg. 1,* Ch. 6
	Mid-Chapter	
	Mid-Chapter Quiz **SE**, p. 763 Mid-Chapter Test **CRM**, p. 53 ExamView Assessment Suite	**Tier 1 Intervention** Concepts and Skills Bank **SE**, pp. 857–867 Skills Practice **CRM**, Ch. 1–12 glencoe.com **Tier 2 Intervention** Study Guide and Intervention Masters **CRM,** Ch. 1–12 *Quick Review Math Handbook* **Tier 3 Intervention** *Math Triumphs, Alg. 1,* Ch. 6
	Before Chapter Test	
	Chapter Study Guide and Review **SE**, pp. 793–796 Practice Test **SE**, p. 797 Standardized Test Practice **SE**, pp. 798–801 Chapter Test glencoe.com Standardized Test Practice glencoe.com Vocabulary Review glencoe.com ExamView Assessment Suite	**Tier 1 Intervention** Concepts and Skills Bank **SE**, pp. 857–867 Skills Practice **CRM**, Ch. 1–12 glencoe.com **Tier 2 Intervention** Study Guide and Intervention Masters **CRM**, Ch. 1–12 *Quick Review Math Handbook* **Tier 3 Intervention** *Math Triumphs, Alg. 1,* Ch. 6
Summative Assessment	**After Chapter 12**	
	Multiple-Choice Tests, Forms 1, 2A, 2B **CRM**, pp. 55–60 Free-Response Tests, Forms 2C, 2D, 3 **CRM**, pp. 61–66 Vocabulary Test **CRM**, p. 54 Extended Response Test **CRM**, p. 67 Standardized Test Practice **CRM**, pp. 68–70 ExamView Assessment Suite	Study Guide and Intervention Masters **CRM**, Ch. 1–12 *Quick Review Math Handbook* glencoe.com

CHAPTER 12 Differentiated Instruction

Option 1 Reaching All Learners AL OL BL ELL

LOGICAL Have students write the digits 0–9 on index cards. Have them rearrange the cards in different ways to help them visualize how the permutation formula relates to the cards. Compare their results with the calculations in Example 5 on p. 767 (Lesson 12-4).

INTERPERSONAL Have students work in small groups. Tell them they will design a survey for the following situation: *You own a company that designs rides for amusement parks. You want to know which rides are liked best by the children who attend these types of parks.*

The survey should produce valid results and include the following:

- how they will conduct the survey,
- who will complete the survey,
- the size of the sample and why it is representative of the larger population,
- the type of sample(s) used for the survey, and
- the question(s) asked in the survey.

Have groups discuss how they might display the results and how they might use them as a business owner.

Option 2 Approaching Level AL

Review with students how to display a sample space with a tree diagram. Explain that the results show the possible outcomes and can help you find the probability of an event, but it is not a very useful method to use when the sample space is very large.

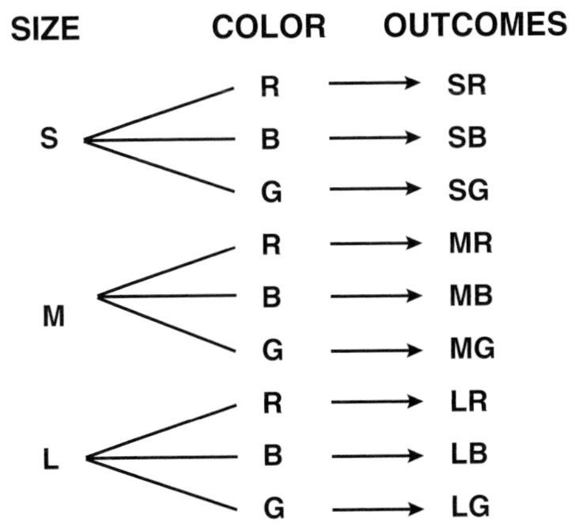

Option 3 English Learners ELL

Have students work in pairs or small groups to create a probability word scramble using the vocabulary words from this chapter. On one side of their paper, they should list the scrambled vocabulary words. On the other side they should list, in a different order, the definition of the words. Then have groups trade papers, unscramble the words, and connect each word with its definition.

Option 4 Beyond Level BL

Allow students to design their own experiments to find experimental probability, such as finding the probability of tossing a paper cup into a wastebasket, the probability of a student being able to read more than 10 words in 10 seconds, and so on.

Focus on Mathematical Content

Vertical Alignment

Before Chapter 12

Related Topics before Pre-Algebra

- find the probabilities of dependent and independent events
- use theoretical probabilities and experimental results to make predictions and decisions
- select and use different models to simulate an event
- evaluate methods of sampling to determine validity of an inference made from a set of data
- recognize misuses of graphical or numerical information and evaluate predictions and conclusions based on data analysis

Chapter 12

Related Topics from Algebra 1

- identify various sampling techniques and recognize a biased sample
- count outcomes using the Fundamental Counting Principle
- use combinations and permutations to determine probabilities
- find the probability of two independent events or dependent events, and find the probability of two mutually exclusive or inclusive events
- use random variables to compute probability, and use probability distributions to solve real-world problems
- use probability simulations to model real-world situations

After Chapter 12

Preparation for Algebra 2

This chapter reinforces skills needed in AP Statistics.

Lesson-by-Lesson Preview

12-1 Designing a Survey

A sample is a portion of a larger group called the population. A *random sample* is a sample that is chosen without preference. Three types of random samples are

- *simple random sample*–picks members from the population at random
- *stratified random sample*–first divides the population into groups, and then picks members at random
- *systematic random sample*–picks members by following a certain pattern

Samples can be biased or unbiased. Samples are biased if they favor one or more parts of a population.

12-2 Analyzing Survey Results

Once data from a survey have been collected, they need to be summarized in a way that allows them to be analyzed. The following measures of central tendency can be used.

- *mean*–the sum of the data divided by the number of items in the data set
- *median*–the middle number of the ordered data, or mean of the middle two numbers
- *mode*–the number(s) that occur most often

There are two types of data: quantitative data (has a number value) and qualitative data (cannot be given a number value, such as gender)

The reliability of a survey's report needs to be determined, and the way in which the results are displayed needs to be analyzed for any misleading methods. For example, the following circle graph is misleading because each section has not been accurately shaded for the percent given.

Should Suits be Worn in the Office?

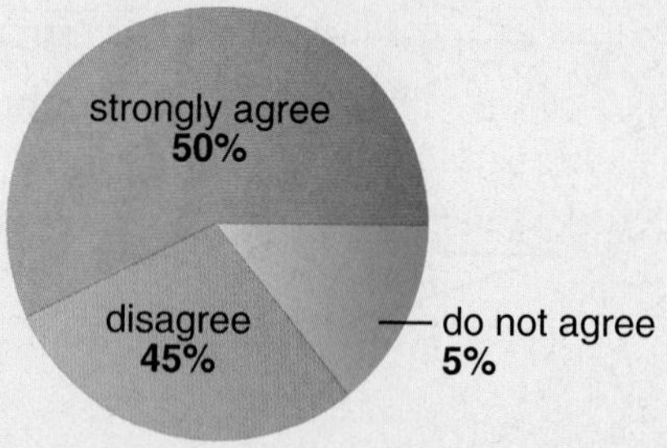

12-3 Statistics and Parameters

A *statistic* is a measure that describes characteristics of a sample, while a *parameter* is a measure that describes a characteristic of the population. A statistic can vary from sample to sample; a parameter will not change.

Data that involves only one variable is called *univariate data*. This type of data can be represented by the mean, median, and mode, as well as *measures of variation*. Measures of variation include the range, quartile, interquartile range, and the following:

- *mean absolute deviation*–the average of the absolute values of the differences between the mean and each value in the data set
- *standard deviation*–a calculated value that shows how the data deviates from the mean of the set of data. It is represented by the Greek symbol sigma, σ.
- *variance*–the square of the standard deviation.

12-4 Permutations and Combinations

A *permutation* is an arrangement or listing in which the order or placement of the arrangement is important.

- You can find the number of permutations by using the formula $\frac{n!}{(n-r)!}$, where n is the number of items to choose from, and r is the number of items to be chosen. The symbol for the number of permutations is ${}_nP_r$ or $P(n, r)$.

A *combination* is an arrangement or listing in which the order or placement is not important.

- The formula for finding the number of combinations is $\frac{n!}{(n-r)!r!}$, where n is the number of items to choose from and r is the number of items to be chosen. The symbol for the number of combinations is ${}_nC_r$ or $C(n, r)$.

12-5 Probability of Compound Events

A simple event is one event, while a compound event consists of two or more simple events.

- If two events occur separately and the outcome of one does not affect the outcome of the other, the events are *independent*. To find the probability of independent events, multiply the probability of the first event by the probability of the second event: $P(A) \cdot P(B)$.
- If the outcome of one event affects the outcome of another, the events are *dependent*. To find the probability of the two dependent events, multiply the probability of the first event by the probability of the second event after the first event occurs: $P(A) \cdot P(B \text{ following } A)$.
- *Mutually exclusive* events are events that cannot occur at the same time. Suppose event A and event B are mutually exclusive, then the probability that either A or B occurs is $P(A) + P(B)$.
- Events that are *not mutually exclusive* can occur at the same time. Suppose event A and event B are not mutually exclusive, then the probability that either A or B occurs is: $P(A) + P(B) - P(A \text{ and } B)$.

12-6 Probability Distributions

A *random variable* is a variable with a value that is the numerical outcome of a random event. A *probability distribution* shows all of the possible values of the random variable, X.

- The probabilities for each value of X add up to 1.
- Probability distributions can be shown in tables or graphs.

12-7 Probability Simulations

- Theoretical probability is determined mathematically and describes what should happen.
- Experimental probability describes what happens based on repeated experiments.

A simulation provides a way to find experimental probability by "acting out" an event that might be difficult to perform. It uses objects such as dice, coins, and spinners to simulate an event.

McGraw Hill Professional Development

Targeted professional development has been articulated throughout *Algebra 1*. More quality, customized professional development is available from McGraw-Hill Professional Development. Visit glencoe.com for details on each product.

- **Online Lessons** emphasize the strategies and techniques used to teach Algebra 1. Includes streaming video, interactive pages, and online tools.
- **Video Workshops** allow mentors, coaches, or leadership personnel to facilitate on-site workshops on educational strategies in mathematics and mathematical concepts.
- **MHPD Online** (www.mhpdonline.com) offers online professional development with video clips of instructional strategies, links, student activities, and news and issues in education.
- **Teaching Today** (teachingtoday.glencoe.com) gives secondary teachers practical strategies and materials that inspire excellence and innovation in teaching.

CHAPTER 12 Notes

Chapter Project

Food for a Food Bank

Students use what they have learned about surveys, statistics, and probability to work with cans of fruit.

- Say, "What is your favorite canned fruit? Bring a can of this fruit to class." Keep the cans from the first row (or another sample) of students separate from the others. List all the different types of fruit. Then tally the number and percent of each type from the sample students. Repeat for all the cans.
- Provide students with the data from the sample. Ask students to make a circle graph of this data. Have them identify the sample, population, data collection and sampling techniques, conclusion, sample statistics, and population parameters. Which measure of central tendency best describes the data? Why? What statistical inference can be made? How do the inferences compare to the data of all the cans?
- Ask students to determine how many ways one can of each type can be arranged.
- Place one can of each type on your desk. Tell students you want to choose *n* (name a number) of *t*, the total number of cans on your desk. Ask groups to determine how many ways the cans can be chosen.
- Place a different number of each type of fruit on your desk. Ask students to find the probability that a can of *r* (name the fruit) will be randomly chosen. Finally, donate the cans of fruit to a local food bank.

CHAPTER 12 Statistics and Probability

Then

In chapter 0, you calculated simple probability.

Now

In Chapter 12, you will:

- Design surveys and evaluate results.
- Use permutations and combinations.
- Find probabilities of compound events.
- Design and use simulations.

IL Learning Standards

10.B.4 Design and execute surveys or experiments, gather data to answer questions, and communicate results to an audience.

10.C.4a Solve problems of chance using the principles of probability including conditional settings.

Why?

RESTAURANTS A restaurant may ask their customers to complete a survey about their visit. The survey data can be analyzed using statistical methods. The restaurant staff can learn more about their customers and how to improve their experiences in the restaurant.

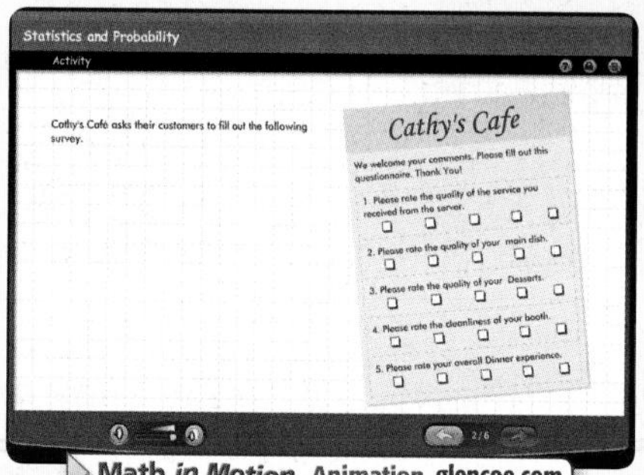

Math in Motion, Animation glencoe.com

Key Vocabulary Introduce the key vocabulary in the chapter using the routine below.

Define: A random sample is a sample that is chosen without any preference, representative of the entire population.

Example: Thirty students are in a class. Three of the thirty students are chosen at random to answer a survey.

Ask: If the three students were chosen for a certain reason, would this be a random sample? Explain why or why not. No; for it to be a random sample, the sample must be picked without preferences.

Get Ready for Chapter 12

Diagnose Readiness You have two options for checking Prerequisite Skills.

Text Option Take the Quick Check below. Refer to the Quick Review for help.

*Quick*Check

(Used in Lessons 12-4 and 12-5)

Determine the probability of each event if you randomly select a cube from a bag containing 6 red cubes, 4 yellow cubes, 3 blue cubes, and 1 green cube. (Lesson 0-11)

1. $P(\text{red})$ $\frac{3}{7}$
2. $P(\text{blue})$ $\frac{3}{14}$
3. $P(\text{not red})$ $\frac{4}{7}$
4. $P(\text{white})$ 0
5. Jim rolls a die with 6 sides. What is the probability of rolling a 5? (Lesson 0-11) $\frac{1}{6}$
6. Malika spins a spinner that is divided into 8 equal sections. Each section is a different color, including blue. What is the probability the spinner lands on the blue section? $\frac{1}{8}$

(Used in Lesson 12-4)

Find each product. (Lesson 0-5)

7. $\frac{5}{4} \cdot \frac{2}{3}$ $\frac{5}{6}$
8. $\frac{4}{19} \cdot \frac{7}{20}$ $\frac{7}{95}$
9. $\frac{4}{32} \cdot \frac{7}{32}$ $\frac{7}{256}$
10. $\frac{5}{12} \cdot \frac{6}{11}$ $\frac{5}{22}$
11. $\frac{56}{100} \cdot \frac{24}{100}$ $\frac{84}{625}$
12. $\frac{9}{34} \cdot \frac{17}{27}$ $\frac{1}{6}$

(Used in Lesson 12-5)

Write each fraction as a percent. Round to the nearest tenth. (Lesson 0-6)

13. $\frac{14}{17}$ 82.4%
14. $\frac{7}{8}$ 87.5%
15. $\frac{107}{125}$ 85.6%
16. $\frac{625}{1024}$ 61.0%
17. **SHOPPERS** At the mall, 700 of the 2000 people shopping were under the age of 21. What percent of the shoppers were under 21? 35%

*Quick*Review

EXAMPLE 1

Determine the probability of selecting a green cube if you randomly select a cube from a bag containing 6 red cubes, 4 yellow cubes, and 1 green cube.

There is 1 green cube and a total of 11 cubes in the bag.

$$\frac{1}{11} = \frac{\text{number of green cubes}}{\text{total number of cubes}}$$

The probability of selecting a green cube is $\frac{1}{11}$.

EXAMPLE 2

Find $\frac{4}{5} \cdot \frac{3}{4}$.

$\frac{4}{5} \cdot \frac{3}{4} = \frac{4 \cdot 3}{5 \cdot 4}$ Multiply the numerators and the denominators.

$= \frac{12}{20}$ Simplify.

$= \frac{3}{5}$ Rename in simplest form.

EXAMPLE 3

Write the fraction $\frac{33}{80}$ as a percent. Round to the nearest tenth.

$\frac{33}{80} \approx 0.413$ Simplify and round.

$0.413 \cdot 100 = 41.3$ Multiply the decimal by 100.

$\frac{33}{80}$ written as a percent is about 41.3%.

Online Option IL Math Online Take a self-check Chapter Readiness Quiz at glencoe.com.

Response to Intervention (RtI)

Use the *Quick Check* results and the Intervention Planner chart to help you determine your Response to Intervention. The If-Then statements in the chart below help you decide the appropriate tier of RtI and suggest intervention resources for each tier.

Intervention Planner

Tier 1 — On Level

If students miss about 25% of the exercises or less,

Then choose a resource:

SE Lessons 0-5, 0-6, and 0-11

IL Math Online Self-Check Quiz

Tier 2 — Strategic Intervention approaching grade level

If students miss about 50% of the exercises,

Then choose a resource:

Quick Review Math Handbook

IL Math Online Extra Examples, Personal Tutor, Homework Help

Tier 3 — Intensive Intervention 2 or more grades below level

If students miss about 75% of the exercises,

Then use *Math Triumphs, Alg. 1*, Ch. 6

IL Math Online Extra Examples, Personal Tutor, Homework Help, Review Vocabulary

FOLDABLES® Study Organizer

Dinah Zike's Foldables®

Focus Students write notes about probability and statistics for each lesson in this chapter.

Teach Have students make and label their Foldables as illustrated. For each lesson have students record definitions and examples on the appropriate sheets.

When to Use It Encourage students to add to their Foldables as they work through the chapter and to use them to review for the chapter test.

Differentiated Instruction

CRM Student-Built Glossary, pp. 1–2
Students should complete the chart by providing a definition of each term and an example as they progress through Chapter 12. This study tool can also be used to review for the chapter test.

Get Started on Chapter 12

You will learn several new concepts, skills, and vocabulary terms as you study Chapter 12. To get ready, identify important terms and organize your resources. You may wish to refer to **Chapter 0** to review prerequisite skills.

FOLDABLES® Study Organizer

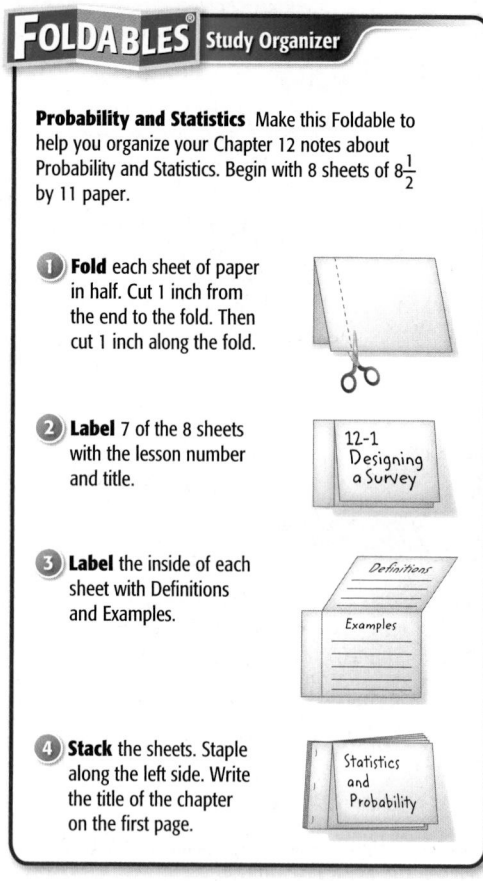

Probability and Statistics Make this Foldable to help you organize your Chapter 12 notes about Probability and Statistics. Begin with 8 sheets of $8\frac{1}{2}$ by 11 paper.

1. **Fold** each sheet of paper in half. Cut 1 inch from the end to the fold. Then cut 1 inch along the fold.

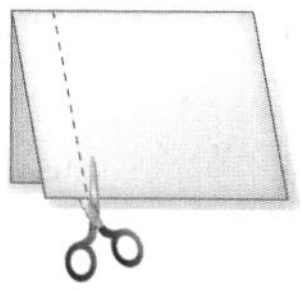

2. **Label** 7 of the 8 sheets with the lesson number and title.

3. **Label** the inside of each sheet with Definitions and Examples.

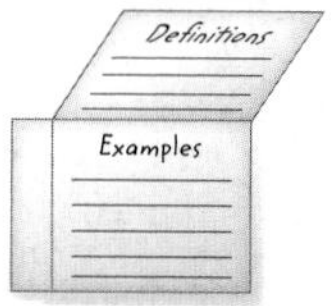

4. **Stack** the sheets. Staple along the left side. Write the title of the chapter on the first page.

IL Math Online glencoe.com

- Study the chapter online
- Explore **Math in Motion**
- Get extra help from your own **Personal Tutor**
- Use **Extra Examples** for additional help
- Take a **Self-Check Quiz**
- **Review Vocabulary** in fun ways

New Vocabulary

English		Español
population	p. 740	población
sample	p. 740	muestra
biased sample	p. 741	muestra sesgada
parameter	p. 756	parámetro
statistic	p. 756	estadística
standard deviation	p. 757	desviación estándar
univariate data	p. 757	data univariados
qualitative data	p. 758	datos cualitativos
quantitative data	p. 758	datos de cuantitativos
linear transformation	p. 760	transfomación lineal
factorial	p. 764	factorial
permutation	p. 764	permutación
combination	p. 765	combinación
compound event	p. 771	evento compuesto
independent events	p. 771	eventos independientes
complement	p. 772	complemento
dependent events	p. 772	eventos dependientes
mutually exclusive	p. 773	mutuamente exclusivos
random variable	p. 779	variable aleatoria
probability distribution	p. 780	distribución de probabilidad
simulation	p. 788	simulación

Review Vocabulary

probability • p. P33 • probilidad the ratio of favorable outcomes to the total possible outcomes

sample space • p. P33 • espacio muestral the list of all possible outcome

Multilingual eGlossary glencoe.com

EXPLORE 12-1 Algebra Lab

Survey Questions

IL Learning Standards **10.B.4 Design and execute surveys or experiments, gather data to answer relevant questions,** and communicate results and conclusions to an audience using traditional methods and contemporary technology.

For a survey to be valid, it should contain no bias or favoritism. Even though you may question people who are chosen randomly, questions may be worded to influence responses. These two different surveys on Internet sales tax had different results.

ACTIVITY

Analyze the difference between the two survey questions.

Question 1

Should there be sales tax on purchases made on the Internet?

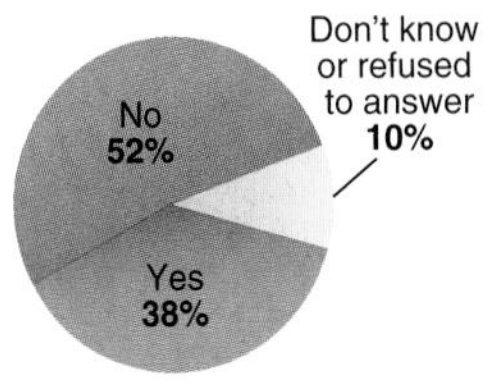

Question 2

Do you think people should or should not be required to pay the same sales tax for purchases made over the Internet as those made at a local store?

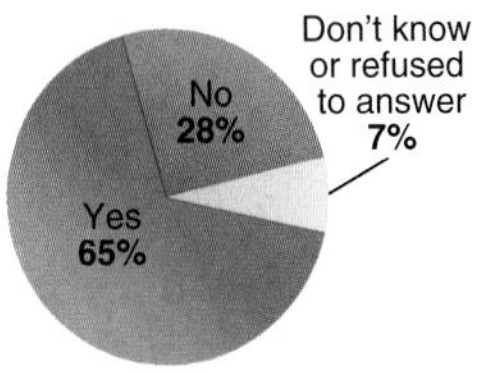

Notice that Question 2 includes more information. Pointing out that customers pay sales tax for items bought at a local store may give the people answering the survey a reason to say "yes."

Because they are random samples, the results of both of these surveys are accurate. However, the results could be used in a misleading way by someone with an interest in the issue. For example, an Internet retailer would prefer to state the results of Question 1.

Exercises

For Exercises 1 and 2, tell whether each question is likely to bias the results. Write *yes* or *no*. Explain your reasoning.

1. On a survey on environmental issues:
   a. "Due to diminishing resources, should a law be made to require recycling?"
   b. "Should the government require citizens to participate in recycling efforts?"
2. On a survey on education:
   a. "Should schools fund extracurricular sports programs?"
   b. "The budget of the River Valley School District is short of funds. Should taxes be raised in order for the district to fund extracurricular sports programs?"
3. You want to determine whether to serve hamburgers or pizza at a class party.
   a. Write a survey question that would likely produce biased results.
   b. Write a survey question that would likely produce unbiased results.

1a. Yes; the reference to diminishing resources will lead people to say yes.

1b. Yes; the mention of people being required to participate will lead them to say no.

2a. No; it gives no extra information that would lead people.

2b. Yes; it tells you that the school district is short of funds and will lead people to say no.

3a. Sample answer: I have a new grill to cook hamburgers on. Would you like to have hamburgers or pizza at the class party?

3b. Sample answer: Would you like to have hamburgers or pizza at the class party?

EXPLORE 12-1 Lesson Notes

1 FOCUS

Objective Investigate survey questions to determine whether they are biased or unbiased.

Teaching Tip

Prior to beginning the activity, ask students whether they have asked their parents for permission to attend an event and then tried to influence the way in which their parents answered. Have students share any methods they might have used to influence the answer.

2 TEACH

Working in Cooperative Groups

Have students of mixed abilities work in groups of two or three to complete the Activity and Exercises 1 and 2.

Ask:

- Why do you think more people answered *no* to Question 1 than to Question 2? Sample answer: People might not think about the taxes they pay for something sold in a store.
- Name a group of people who might like to use the results of Question 2. Explain. Sample answer: Local store owners; they might think that Internet retailers have an advantage because customers pay less for an item that is not taxed.

Practice Have students complete Exercise 3.

3 ASSESS

Formative Assessment

Use Exercise 2 to assess whether students recognize the difference between biased and unbiased questions.

From Concrete to Abstract

Use Exercise 3 to assess whether students can formulate biased and unbiased questions.

12-1 Lesson Notes

1 FOCUS

Vertical Alignment

Before Lesson 12-1
Organize data by using matrices.

Lesson 12-1
Design surveys.
Identify various sampling techniques.

After Lesson 12-1
Analyze data from surveys.

2 TEACH

Scaffolding Questions

Have students read the *Why?* section of the lesson.

Ask:

- What group does the sample of T-shirts represent? all of the T-shirts made on the day the sample is taken
- Suppose the manufacturer produces 200 T-shirts per day. If the first 50 T-shirts are sampled for defects, is this a random sample? No, all T-shirts should have an equal chance of being selected.
- How might the manufacturer select a random sample? Sample answer: Select every 10th T-shirt that is produced.

12-1 Designing a Survey

Then
You organized data by using matrices. (Lesson 6-7)

Now
- Design surveys.
- Identify various sampling techniques.

IL Learning Standards

10.B.4 Design and execute surveys or experiments, gather data to answer relevant questions, and communicate results and conclusions to an audience using traditional methods and contemporary technology.

New Vocabulary
sample
population
survey
observational study
experiment
biased sample
simple random sample
stratified random sample
systematic random sample

IL Math Online
glencoe.com
- Extra Examples
- Personal Tutor
- Self-Check Quiz
- Homework Help

Why?

When manufacturing T-shirts, many steps and items must be checked for quality. These include fabrication, care labels, tags, trims, print artwork, and embroidery. It would be costly for a company to have each T-shirt inspected. Instead, they inspect a certain number of T-shirts.

All of the T-shirts that are made are a population, and the T-shirts that are inspected are a sample of the population. The inspectors draw conclusions about the sample and apply those conclusions to the entire population.

Design a Survey A **sample** is some portion of a larger group, called the **population**. Since it is impractical to examine every item in a population, a sample is selected to represent the population. After the sample is analyzed, conclusions can be drawn about the entire population. The larger the sample size, or the more samples taken, the more closely it approximates the population.

To accurately draw a conclusion from data received from a sample, you will need to first decide on the best method of collecting the data.

Key Concept Data Collection Techniques — For Your FOLDABLE

Type	Definition/Use	Example
survey	• Data are from responses given by a sample of the population. • To make a general conclusion about the population.	To determine whether the student body is happy with the spring dance theme, the dance committee asks a random sample of 50 students for their opinion.
observational study	• Data are recorded after just observing the sample. • To compare reactions and draw a conclusion about responses of the population.	A toy company watches some children play and notes the toys they play with the most. They conclude that the population of two-year-olds prefers toys that sing to toys that do not make noise.
experiment	• Data are recorded after changing the sample. • To make general conclusions about what will happen during an event.	A quality control manager runs the assembly machines 10 times at a certain rate. Each time the product is defective. She concludes that it would happen every time the machine runs at that pace.

Lesson 12-1 Resources

Resource	Approaching-Level	On-Level	Beyond-Level	English Learners
Teacher Edition	• Differentiated Instruction, p. 742	• Differentiated Instruction, pp. 742, 745	• Differentiated Instruction, p. 745	
Chapter Resource Masters	• Study Guide and Intervention, pp. 5–6 • Skills Practice, p. 7 • Practice, p. 8 • Word Problem Practice, p. 9	• Study Guide and Intervention, pp. 5–6 • Skills Practice, p. 7 • Practice, p. 8 • Word Problem Practice, p. 9 • Enrichment, p. 10	• Practice, p. 8 • Word Problem Practice, p. 9 • Enrichment, p. 10	• Study Guide and Intervention, pp. 5–6 • Skills Practice, p. 7 • Practice, p. 8 • Word Problem Practice, p. 9
Transparencies	• 5-Minute Check Transparency 12-1	• 5-Minute Check Transparency 12-1	• 5-Minute Check Transparency 12-1	• 5-Minute Check Transparency 12-1
Other	• Study Notebook	• Study Notebook	• Study Notebook	• Study Notebook

StudyTip

Census A *census* is a survey in which every member of the population is questioned. So there is no sample.

EXAMPLE 1 Classify Data Collection Techniques

CHARITY A local charity is interested in finding out whether people are likely to give money to charity. They distributed 1000 questionnaires to people living in the neighborhood.

a. Identify the sample, and determine the population from which it was selected.

The sample is the 1000 people who received the questionnaires. The population is all the people in the neighborhood.

b. Classify the type of data collection used by this charity.

This is a survey. The data are from responses given by people in the sample.

Check Your Progress

Identify each sample, and suggest a population from which it was selected. Then classify the type of data collection used.

1A. RESEARCH A research facility analyzed two groups of rats to determine their reaction to sugar.

1B. RECYCLING The city council wants to start a recycling program. They send out a questionnaire to 1000 random citizens asking what they would recycle.

Personal Tutor glencoe.com

1A. sample: rats in the facility; population: all rats; experiment

1B. sample: 1000 random citizens; population: all of the citizens; survey

There are factors that affect the collection of data and the conclusions drawn. If a sample favors one group over another, then the data are invalid because it is a **biased sample**. A sample is *unbiased* if it is random. Members of a **random sample** have an equal probability of being chosen.

EXAMPLE 2 Identify if the Sample is Valid

Identify each sample as *biased* or *unbiased*. Explain your reasoning.

a. MUSIC Every fifth person coming into a grocery store is asked to name a favorite radio station.

Unbiased; the sample is a random selection of people.

b. MUSIC Every fifth person at the Country Music Showcase is asked to name their favorite radio station.

Biased; because they are at a country music show, people may be more likely to select a country music station.

Check Your Progress

2A. POLITICS A journalist visits a senior center and chooses 10 individuals randomly to poll about various political topics.

2B. SHOES A shoe company conducts an observation study that involves 10 girls and 2 boys to see which shoes are the most popular.

Personal Tutor glencoe.com

2A. Unbiased; every person at the senior center is just as likely to be chosen as any other.

2B. Biased; because there are more girls than boys, the survey will favor girls shoes over boys.

Design a Survey

Example 1 shows how to classify data collection techniques. **Example 2** shows how to identify biased or unbiased samples.

Formative Assessment

Use the Check Your Progress exercises after each example to determine students' understanding of concepts.

Additional Examples

1 **RETAIL** Each day, a department store chain selects one male and one female shopper randomly from each of its 57 stores and asks them survey questions about their shopping habits.

a. Identify the sample, and determine the population from which it was selected. Sample: 57 male and 57 female shoppers, population: shoppers in the chain's stores

b. Classify the type of data collection used by this department store. survey

2 Identify each sample as *biased* or *unbiased*. Explain your reasoning.

a. **STUDENT COUNCIL** The student council surveys the students in one classroom to decide the theme for the spring dance. Biased; it includes only the students in one classroom.

b. **SCHOOL** The Parent Association surveys the parents of every fifth student to decide whether to hold a fund-raiser. Unbiased; the parents are picked randomly, and all have a chance of being picked.

Additional Examples also in Interactive Classroom PowerPoint® Presentations

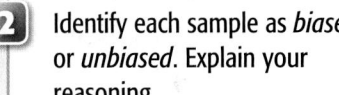

IWB INTERACTIVE WHITEBOARD READY

Focus on Mathematical Content

Samples and Populations By taking a sample of a population, you can estimate the characteristics of the population and make predictions based on the characteristics. A sample is a portion of a group, and the population is the group from which the sample is taken.

TEACH with TECH

STUDENT RESPONSE SYSTEM Give students a list of several data finding situations. Have students enter whether this situation is a survey, observational study, or experiment. The same can be done with different types of sampling. This will help you track student understanding of these new concepts.

Sampling Techniques

Example 3 shows how to classify a random sample.

Additional Example

3 **COMMUNITY** A neighborhood is divided into blocks. Then three residents are selected from each block for a survey on hours of operation for the community pool.

a. Identify the sample, and suggest a population from which it was selected. Sample: three residents from each block; population: the residents of the neighborhood

b. Classify the sample as *simple, stratified,* or *systematic*. Explain your reasoning. Stratified; the neighborhood is divided into categories before there is a random sample.

3A. Sample: every tenth cook; population: all of the cooks in the competition; stratified: the cooks were divided up first, then selected.

3B. Sample: the hamburger cooking in the 20-minute interval; population: all of the burgers cooked at the restaurant; systematic: the sample was selected at regular intervals.

3C. Sample: the plates with a sticker; population: all of the plates; simple; the sample is equally likely to be chosen as any other sample.

Sampling Techniques Sample data are often used to estimate a characteristic within an entire population, such as voting preferences. A random sample of a population is selected so that it is representative of the entire population without any preference. Three common types of random samples are listed below.

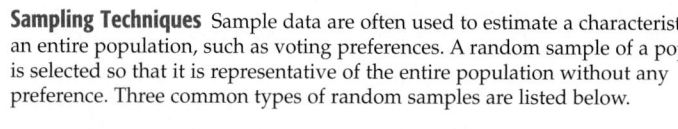

Key Concept — Random Samples (For Your FOLDABLE)

Type	Definition	Example
simple random sample	A sample that is equally likely to be chosen as any other sample from the population.	One hundred student ID numbers are randomly drawn from a hat, and those students are given a survey.
stratified random sample	The population is first divided in similar, nonoverlapping groups. A random sample is then selected from each group.	To reflect the diversity of the country, a candidate surveys citizens of various groups, based on their percent of the population.
systematic random sample	A sample in which the items in the sample are selected according to a specified time or item interval.	Every 10 minutes a toy is inspected. Or every 50th toy is inspected.

Real-World Link

Annually, in Pembroke Pines, Florida, the Jamaican Jerk Festival is held. A cooking competition is where each entrant must prepare any three dishes from the following categories: jerked pork, jerked chicken, jerked seafood, or other.

Source: Jamaican Jerk Festival

EXAMPLE 3 Classify a Random Sample

ZOOS Animals in a zoo are divided by continents. Then two animals were selected at random from each group to have their blood tested.

a. Identify the sample, and suggest a population from which it was selected.

The sample is the two animals selected from each continent. The population is the animals in the zoo.

b. Classify the sample as *simple*, *stratified*, or *systematic*. Explain your reasoning.

This is a stratified random sample. The animals are divided up into categories before there is a random selection.

Check Your Progress

Identify each sample, and suggest a population from which it was selected. Then classify the sample as *simple*, *stratified*, or *systematic*. Explain your reasoning.

3A. CONTESTS Refer to the information at the left. The cooks lined up randomly within their category, and every tenth cook in each category was selected to explain the rules.

3B. FOOD At a popular hamburger restaurant, the manager checks the quality of the burgers every 20 minutes, starting at a randomly selected time.

3C. SHOWER At a bridal shower, a sticker was placed on the bottom of three random plates. The guests who receive the starred plates will win a prize.

Personal Tutor glencoe.com

Differentiated Instruction (AL OL)

If students need further practice to understand the different types of random samples,

Then place students in small groups. Give each group a different number of colored beads to serve as a population. Have the groups model the different types of random samples with the beads. For example, for stratified random samples, students would first divide the beads into groups by color and then take random beads from each group. Have students describe how they would take a systematic random sample.

Check Your Understanding

Example 1 p. 741 **Identify each sample, and determine a population from which it was selected. Then classify the type of data collection used.**

1. sample: the 10 teens; population: all teens; observational study

1. **MUSIC** A record company wants to test five designs for an album cover. They randomly invite ten teens from a local high school to view the album covers.
2. **PARTIES** Federico is trying to decide on a theme and a color scheme for his party. He sends a survey in each invitation, asking guests for their opinions. See margin.

Example 2 p. 741 **Identify each sample as *biased* or *unbiased*. Explain your reasoning.**

3. Unbiased; each student is equally likely to be the tenth student.

3. **POLITICS** A group of students stands at the door of the school and asks every tenth student who they would vote for in the upcoming election and why.
4. **SHOPPING** Every fifteenth shopper at a clothing store is asked what they would want most for their birthday. See margin.

Example 3 p. 742 **Identify the sample, and suggest a population from which it was selected. Then classify the sample as *simple*, *stratified*, or *systematic*. Explain your reasoning.**

5. sample: the rookie cards; population: all of the cards; stratified, because the cards are divided before the sample is selected.

5. **SPORTS CARDS** Greg divides his rookie baseball cards by teams. Then he randomly selects cards and records the players' RBIs.
6. **TELEVISION** A nostalgia television network wants to conduct a cartoon marathon. To choose the episodes, they mail a questionnaire to people selected at random throughout the country. See margin.

Practice and Problem Solving

● = **Step-by-Step Solutions** begin on page R12.
Extra Practice begins on page 815.

Example 1 p. 741 **Identify each sample, and determine a population from which it was selected. Then classify the type of data collection used.**

7. sample: one hundred people; population: all people; experiment
8. sample: the people in the neighborhood with dogs; population: all of the people with dogs; survey

7. **FOOD** A frozen food company is considering creating frozen meals with tofu instead of meat. At a testing, they randomly give half of a group of 100 people the meals with meat and the other half the same meals with tofu and ask the people how they like the meals.
8. **PETS** The owners of dog care center want to know how many of each size crate they should order. They send flyers into the neighborhood to ask what size or breed of dog each person has.
9. **TRAVEL** A travel agency asks each of its customers for the past two years about their favorite and least favorite destinations. See margin.

Example 2 p. 741 **Identify each sample as *biased* or *unbiased*. Explain your reasoning.**

10. Biased; because they are at a fitness expo, the respondents are more likely to have a fitness magazine.

10. **MAGAZINES** A magazine publisher asks every tenth person at a fitness expo what magazines they have in their household.
11. **LIBRARY** The local library asks everyone who checks out a book if they also used the computers at the library. See margin.
12. **JEANS** A clothing chain gives its customers a card they can mail back that asks them questions about the customer's favorite brand of jeans. See margin.
13. **AMUSEMENT PARKS** An amusement park is deciding which rides to replace next year. As they leave the park, they ask teens what their least favorite ride is. See margin.

3 PRACTICE

Formative Assessment

Use Exercises 1–6 to check for understanding.

Use the chart at the bottom of this page to customize assignments for your students.

Additional Answers

2. sample: guests at the party; population: guests and guest of honor; survey
4. Biased; because they are in a clothing store, the respondents are more likely to say clothes.
6. Sample: the people that received the questionnaire; population: all the people who watch that station; simple: the selection is just a random choice of the population.
9. sample: the customers for the past two years; population: all past customers; survey
11. Biased; they only poll customers who check out books.
12. Unbiased; each customer is just as likely to be chosen.
13. Biased; because the park only asked teens, the respondents are more likely to select certain rides.

Differentiated Homework Options

Level	Assignment	Two-Day Option	
AL Basic	7–17, 22–40	7–17 odd, 25–28	8–16 even, 22–24, 29–40
OL Core	7–17 odd, 18–20, 22–40	7–17, 25–28	18–20, 22–24, 29–40
BL Advanced	18–39, (optional: 40)		

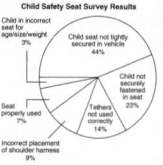

Example 3 p. 742

Identify the sample, and suggest a population from which it was selected. Then classify the sample as *simple*, *stratified*, or *systematic*. Explain your reasoning.

14. **TANNING** A tanning salon sorts its responses to a survey by the home states of the respondents. Then they are sorted to select teenagers.

15. **ART** Mitsu uses her blog about art to ask readers about their favorite medium and supply center. She then tabulates and publishes the results.

16. **CARS** The service manger at a car dealership inspects every fifth car to make sure cars are detailed after being serviced.

17. **MUSIC** A music store gives every fiftieth customer a free CD by a local artist. **See margin.**

14. sample: teenagers; population: all of the respondents; stratified: the responses were sorted before they were selected for the sample.

15. sample: the blog readers; population: all artists; simple: the sample is equally likely to be chosen.

16. sample: every fifth car serviced; population: all cars serviced; systematic: each selection was made at a regular interval.

18. **ELECTIONS** To estimate who the leading candidate is, the candidate's committee surveys a large group of people selected at random. The returns indicate that their candidate is leading 58% to 42%.
    a. Identify the sample. Suggest a population from which the sample was selected. **See margin.**
    b. State the method of data collection. **survey**
    c. Is the sample *biased* or *unbiased*? Explain. **See margin.**
    d. If unbiased, classify the random sample as *simple*, *stratified*, or *systematic*. **simple**

19. **SHOES** A shoe company surveys their customers about shoe design. This program keeps a count of styles and colors chosen by customers.
    a. Identify the sample. From what population was the sample selected? **See margin.**
    b. State the method of data collection. **observational study**
    c. Is the sample *biased* or *unbiased*? Explain. **See margin.**
    d. If unbiased, classify the sample as *simple*, *stratified*, or *systematic*. **systematic**

Real-World Link

The world's largest collection of Converse shoes is held by Joshua Mueller of Lakewood, Washington, consisting of 403 unique pairs.

Source: *The Guinness Book of World Records*

20. **MULTIPLE REPRESENTATIONS** Design and conduct your own survey. **See students' work.**
    a. **WRITING** Write a question you would like to answer through a survey. The question should be meaningful to you. Describe the method you will use to gather the data, and explain why you chose that method.
    b. **ANALYTICAL** Devise a method to conduct your survey using an unbiased sample. Explain why you chose your sample.
    c. **CONCRETE** Conduct your survey.
    d. **TABULAR** Record your results in a table.
    e. **GRAPHICAL** Use a graph (line, circle, histogram, etc…) or other visual or graphic method to present your results to the class.

H.O.T. Problems

Use Higher-Order Thinking Skills

21. **CHALLENGE** Consider the following survey proposal.
    Question: How do students feel about the new dress code?
    Method: Divide the student body by their four grade levels. Then, take a simple random sample from each of the four grades. Conduct the survey using this sample.
    Discuss the strengths and weaknesses of this survey. **21–23. See margin.**

22. **REASONING** Compare and contrast the three data collection techniques described in this lesson.

23. **OPEN ENDED** Describe a real-world example of an observational study.

24. **WRITING IN MATH** Explain why accurate surveys are important to companies, and how the companies use them. **See Ch. 12 Answer Appendix.**

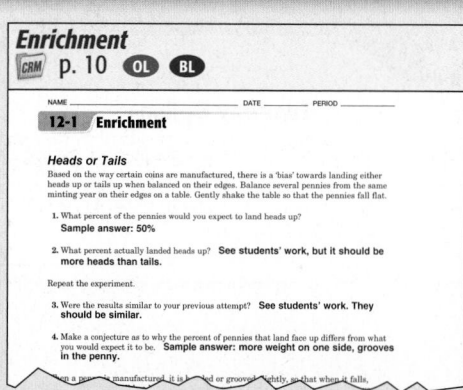

Multiple Representations In Exercise 20, students use writing, analysis, tabular information, and information organized in a graph when presenting the results of a survey.

Study Guide and Intervention
CRM pp. 5–6 AL OL ELL

NAME ________ DATE ________ PERIOD ________

12-1 Study Guide and Intervention

Designing a Survey

Design a Survey A **biased sample** is one in which one or more parts of the population is favored over the other. Random samples are unbiased because each unit is selected without favoritism.

Biased samples include **convenience samples** in which members of the population are included because they are the most convenient to choose. A **voluntary response** sample is another type of biased sample that includes only those members of the population who choose to participate in the sampling.

Example **SCHOOL The principal of a high school wanted to know if students in the school liked the attendance policy. He decided to survey the students in the third-hour study hall about whether they like the attendance policy. Fewer than one fourth of the students in the school have a study hall.**

a. Identify the sample and suggest a population from which it is chosen.
The sample includes only those students in the third-hour study hall. The population is the entire student body.

b. Classify the sample as *convenience* or *voluntary response*.
This sample is a convenience sample because it is convenient to sample students in a study hall during a certain period of the day.

Lesson 12-1

Exercises

Identify each sample, suggest a population from which it was selected. Then classify the sample as *convenience* or *voluntary response*.

1. **SCHOOL** The high school administration wanted to evaluate how homecoming week was conducted at the school. Each female member of the Student Council at the high school was asked if she liked homecoming activities. **female members of the Student Council; all students in the high school; convenience**

2. **MANUFACTURING** A clothing company wanted to check quality control of all its products. The plant manager decided to look at every fourth item inspected by Inspector X. There are 10 inspectors in the plant. **every fourth item inspected by Inspector X; entire product line of the company; convenience**

3. **SCHOOL** The counselors of a high school sent out a survey to senior students with questions about their plans for college. Some students did not plan to attend college. 40% of the seniors sent responses back. **40% of the seniors; all senior students; voluntary response**

4. **BUSINESS** A marketing group was asked to compile data on the effectiveness of advertisements for household products across the country. The group chose to conduct surveys at shopping malls. Every person walking by a survey taker in a shopping mall was asked if he/she would participate in a survey about household products. **persons shopping in a shopping mall; general population of the country; voluntary response**

Chapter 12 5 Glencoe Algebra 1

Practice
CRM p. 8 AL OL BL ELL

NAME ________ DATE ________ PERIOD ________

12-1 Practice

Designing a Survey

Identify each sample, suggest a population from which it was selected. Then classify the type of data collection used.

1. **GOVERNMENT** At a town council meeting, the chair asks 5 citizens attending for their opinions on whether to approve rezoning for a residential area. **5 citizens of a town; all citizens of a town; biased; convenience**

2. **BOTANY** To determine the extent of leaf blight in the maple trees at a nature preserve, a botanist divides the reserve into 10 sections, randomly selects a 200-foot by 200-foot square in the section, and then examines all the maple trees in the section. **the maple trees in a square area of each of 10 sections at a nature preserve; all the maple trees at the nature preserve; unbiased; stratified**

3. **FINANCES** To determine the popularity of online banking in the United States, a polling company sends a mail-in survey to 5000 adults to see if they bank online, and if they do, how many times they bank online each month. **5000 U.S. adults; all U.S. adults; biased; voluntary response**

Identify each sample as *biased* or *unbiased*. Explain your reasoning.

4. **SHOES** A shoe manufacturer wants to check the quality of its shoes. Every twenty minutes, 20 pairs of shoes are pulled off the assembly line for a quality inspection. **unbiased; the sample is systematically chosen**

5. **BUSINESS** To learn which benefits employees at a large company think are most important, the management has a computer select 50 employees at random. The employees are then interviewed by the Human Relations department. **unbiased; the sample is random**

For Question 6, identify the sample, and suggest a population from which it was selected. Then classify the sample as *simple*, *stratified*, or *systematic*. Explain your reasoning.

6. **BUSINESS** An insurance company checks every hundredth claim payment to ensure that claims have been processed correctly. **every hundredth claim payment at an insurance company; all claim payments at an insurance company; systematic; the sample was selected according to a specified interval**

7. **ENVIRONMENT** Suppose you want to know if a manufacturing plant is discharging contaminants into a local river. Describe an unbiased way in which you could check the river water for contaminants. **Sample answer: At a different time each day, take a 10-ounce sample of water from given locations just upstream and just downstream from where the plant discharges its wastes. Compare the samples for contaminants to see if any are entering the river from the discharge.**

8. **SCHOOL** Suppose you want to know the issues most important to teachers at your school. Describe an unbiased way in which you could conduct your survey. **Sample answer: Obtain a list of all teachers at the school. Assign each teacher a number, and then randomly select 10 numbers. Interview each of the teachers assigned one of the selected numbers.**

Chapter 12 8 Glencoe Algebra 1

Word Problem Practice
CRM p. 9 AL OL BL ELL

NAME ________ DATE ________ PERIOD ________

12-1 Word Problem Practice

Designing a Survey

For Exercises 1–4, identify the sample and the population from which it was selected, and state whether it is *biased* or *unbiased*. If unbiased, classify the sample as *simple*, *stratified*, or *systematic*. If biased, classify as *convenience* or *voluntary response*. Explain your reasoning.

1. **SCHOOL** Ms. Yeong chooses four students to pass out snacks each day. To choose the students, she writes the names of each of her 18 students on small pieces of paper, and places them in a cup. She mixes up the names and pulls out four to be the snack helpers. **sample: 4 helpers; population: the 18 students in the class; unbiased, simple random sample**

2. **ELECTIONS** In Summerville, residents vote for mayor at one of the eight precinct voting places near where they live. To acquire early election results for the evening news, a reporter stands outside one of the city's eight voting stations and asks as many people as possible for whom they voted. **sample: the voters the reporter interviews; population: all voters; biased, convenience sample**

3. **DISEASE** A European country's health department uses nets to trap birds near a local wildlife refuge. The bird is tested for the presence of the avian flu virus. **sample: birds captured; population: birds in the region; biased, convenience sample**

4. **SOIL** To check for the presence of harmful chemicals in the ground at a new construction site, geotechnical engineers divide the site into 12 rectangular areas and remove a pint of soil from each area for testing. **sample: 12 pt of soil; population: all of the soil on the site; unbiased, stratified random sample**

5. **CHILD SAFETY** The British Columbia Automobile Association performed a free child safety seat inspection for people that came in for the safety check. Only 7% of the 1000 seats inspected were properly used. The graph below shows the approximate percentages of results for the safety seat inspections.

Child Safety Seat Survey Results

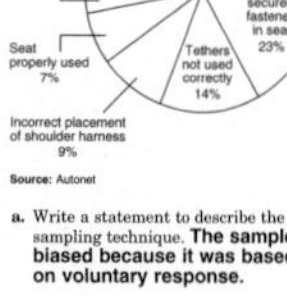

Source: Autonet

a. Write a statement to describe the sampling technique. **The sample is biased because it was based on voluntary response.**

b. Is it appropriate to say that 23% of children in child safety seats in British Columbia are not securely fastened in their seat? Explain. **No. This was not a random sample, so the data cannot be generalized to the population. We do not know how the seats are being used in vehicles that were not brought in.**

Lesson 12-1

Chapter 12 9 Glencoe Algebra 1

Enrichment
CRM p. 10 OL BL

NAME ________ DATE ________ PERIOD ________

12-1 Enrichment

Heads or Tails

Based on the way certain coins are manufactured, there is a 'bias' towards landing either heads up or tails up when balanced on their edges. Balance several pennies from the same minting year on their edges on a table. Gently shake the table so that the pennies fall flat.

1. What percent of the pennies would you expect to land heads up? **Sample answer: 50%**

2. What percent actually landed heads up? **See students' work, but it should be more heads than tails.**

Repeat the experiment.

3. Were the results similar to your previous attempt? **See students' work. They should be similar.**

4. Make a conjecture as to why the percent of pennies that land face up differs from what you would expect it to be. **Sample answer: more weight on one side, grooves in the penny.**

PSAE PRACTICE 8.11.17, 6.11.18, 7.11.03

25. GRIDDED RESPONSE The first stage of a rocket burns 28 seconds longer than the second stage. If the total burning time is 152 seconds, how many seconds is the first stage? **90**

26. Ms. Brinkman invested \$30,000; part at 5%, and part at 8%. The total interest on the investment was \$2100 after one year. How much did she invest at 8%? **C**

A \$10,000　　C \$20,000
B \$15,000　　D \$25,000

27. A pair of \$25 jeans is on sale for 15% off. What is the sale price? **F**

F \$21.25　　H \$23.25
G \$24.25　　J \$22.25

28. GEOMETRY A piece of wire 42 centimeters long is bent into the shape of a rectangle with a width that is twice its length. Find the dimensions of the rectangle. **B**

A 5 cm, 12 cm　　C 9 cm, 16 cm
B 7 cm, 14 cm　　D 11 cm, 18 cm

Spiral Review

Solve each equation. State any extraneous solutions. (Lesson 11-8)

29. $\frac{3}{c} = \frac{2}{c+2}$ **−6**

30. $\frac{4}{f} = \frac{2}{f-3}$ **6**

31. $\frac{j}{j+2} = \frac{j-6}{j-2}$ **−6**

32. $\frac{h-2}{h} = \frac{h-2}{h-5}$ **2**

33. $\frac{3m}{4} + \frac{1}{3} = \frac{3m+4}{6}$ **$\frac{4}{3}$**

34. $\frac{6}{5} + \frac{4p}{3} = \frac{8p}{5}$ **$\frac{9}{2}$**

35. $\frac{r-2}{r+2} - \frac{3r}{r-2} = -2$ **$-\frac{2}{5}$**

36. $\frac{t-3}{t+3} - \frac{2t}{t-3} = -1$ **0**

37. $\frac{4v}{2v+3} - \frac{2v}{2v-3} = 1$ **$\frac{1}{2}$**

38. SPORTS When air is pumped into a ball, the pressure required can be computed by using the formula $P = \frac{3412.94}{\frac{4\pi r^3}{3}}$, where P represents the pressure in pound per square inch (psi), and r is the radius of the ball in inches.

a. Simplify the complex fraction. $P = \frac{2559.7075}{\pi r^3}$

b. Suppose the air pressure inside the ball is 8 psi. Approximate the radius of the ball to the nearest hundredth. **4.67 inches**

39. ROLLER COASTERS Suppose a roller coaster climbs 208 feet higher than its starting point, moving horizontally 360 feet. When it comes down, it moves horizontally 44 feet. (Lesson 10-5)

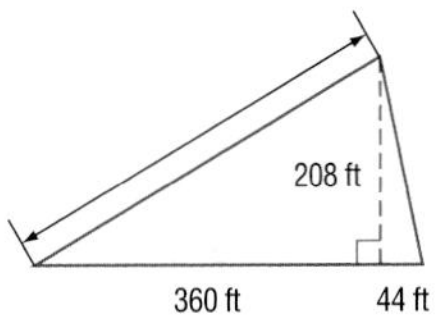

a. How far will it travel to get to the top of the ride? **≈415.8 ft**

b. How far will it travel on the downhill track? **≈212.6 ft**

Skills Review

40. PHYSICAL SCIENCE Mr. Blackwell's students recorded the height of an object above the ground after it was dropped from a height of 5 meters. (Lesson 1-7)

Time (s)	0	0.2	0.4	0.6	0.8	1
Height (cm)	500	480	422	324	186	10

Draw a graph showing the relationship between the height of the object and time. **See Ch. 12 Answer Appendix.**

Differentiated Instruction OL BL

Extension Pass out examples of opinion polls taken from news magazines and newspapers. Have students identify the sample and the population for the poll. Then have students describe how the people conducting the poll could make sure the sample was not biased.

4 ASSESS

Ticket Out the Door Write an example of each type of random sample and give one to each student. As students leave the room, ask them to identify the sample, suggest a population, and then classify the sample.

Additional Answers

17. Sample: every fiftieth customer; population: all of the customers; systematic: a customer was selected at a regular interval.

18a. the people that they surveyed; all voters

18c. Unbiased; each person is equally likely to be selected.

19a. the customers that order online; all customers

19c. Unbiased; each customer is equally likely to be chosen.

21. Sample answer: This method of selecting a sample is valid. Each student has an equally likely chance of being selected for the sample. A weakness may be that this would not reflect that one grade may feel more strongly about the dress code than another.

22. Sample answer: All three techniques give you information so that you can draw a conclusion about a population. A survey asks a series of questions. An observational study records reactions to a thing or situation. An experiment records the reaction or results of a created situation.

23. Sample answer: A video game company wants to know how their game compares with its competitors. So, they set up a room with the game and three games of their competitors and observe which games the people in the sample prefer.

12-2 Lesson Notes

1 FOCUS

Vertical Alignment

Before Lesson 12-2
Design surveys.

Lesson 12-2
Summarize survey results.
Evaluate survey results.

After Lesson 12-2
Use measures of variation to analyze data.

2 TEACH

Scaffolding Questions

Have students read the *Why?* section of the lesson.

Ask:

- What can you conclude from the overall mean? Sample answer: a mean rating of 2.2 out of 4 suggests a mediocre experience on the Web site.
- What can you tell about the number of people who responded to the survey? Sample answer: you cannot tell how many responded.
- Do you think the method of data collection results in a random sample? Explain. Sample answer: no; data collection appears to be voluntary, so it is not random.

12-2 Analyzing Survey Results

Then
You designed surveys. (Lesson 12-1)

Now
- Summarize survey results.
- Evaluate survey results.

IL Learning Standards

10.A.4b Analyze data using mean, median, mode, range, **variance and standard deviation of a data set, with and without the use of technology.**
10.B.4 Design and execute surveys or experiments, gather data to answer relevant questions, and **communicate results and conclusions to an audience using traditional methods and contemporary technology.** *Also addresses 7.A.4a.*

New Vocabulary
measures of central tendency
quantitative data
qualitative data

IL Math Online
glencoe.com
- Extra Examples
- Personal Tutor
- Self-Check Quiz
- Homework Help

Why?

Companies like to use surveys to get feedback on how they are doing in areas ranging from sales to their Web site.

A company recently received these results from a survey about their Web site.

What do these values mean? How were the data collected? Is the sample an accurate representation of their customers?

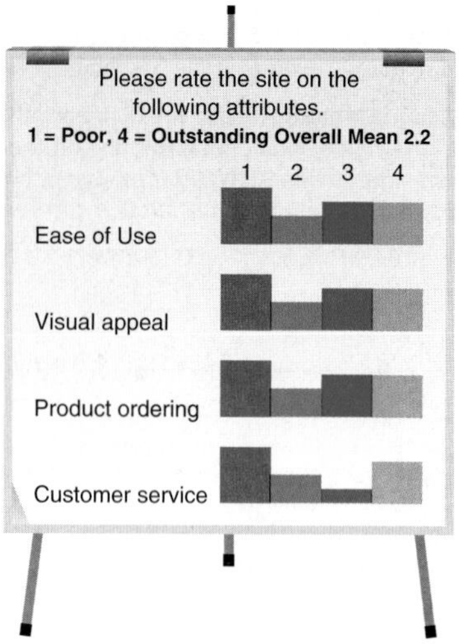

Summarize Survey Results Once data from a survey have been collected, they need to be summarized to be meaningful. We can summarize the data of a survey according to **measures of central tendency**.

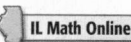

Concept Summary — **Measures of Central Tendency** — For Your FOLDABLE

Type	Description	When Best Used
mean	the sum of the data divided by the number of items in the data set	The data sets have no outliers.
median	the middle number of the ordered data, or the mean of the middle two numbers	The data set has outliers, but there are no big gaps in the middle of the data.
mode	the number or numbers that occur most often	The data set has many repeated numbers.

Some data cannot be analyzed using statistical methods. **Quantitative data** can be given and analyzed as numerical values. Some examples of these are test scores, hours that you have studied, or the weight of objects. **Qualitative data** cannot be given a numerical value. Some examples of these are gender, nationality, or television show preference.

It is also possible to have quantitative data and still not be able to find a measure of central tendency. This occurs when the data do not represent the same thing.

Lesson 12-2 Resources

Resource	Approaching-Level	On-Level	Beyond-Level	English Learners
Teacher Edition		• Differentiated Instruction, pp. 752, 755	• Differentiated Instruction, p. 755	
Chapter Resource Masters	• Study Guide and Intervention, pp. 11–12 • Skills Practice, p. 13 • Practice, p. 14 • Word Problem Practice, p. 15	• Study Guide and Intervention, pp. 11–12 • Skills Practice, p. 13 • Practice, p. 14 • Word Problem Practice, p. 15 • Enrichment, p. 16	• Practice, p. 14 • Word Problem Practice, p. 15 • Enrichment, p. 16	• Study Guide and Intervention, pp. 11–12 • Skills Practice, p. 13 • Practice, p. 14 • Word Problem Practice, p. 15
Transparencies	• 5-Minute Check Transparency 12–2	• 5-Minute Check Transparency 12–2	• 5-Minute Check Transparency 12–2	• 5-Minute Check Transparency 12–2
Other	• Study Notebook	• Study Notebook	• Study Notebook	• Study Notebook

EXAMPLE 1 Select a Method to Summarize

Which measure of central tendency best represents the data, if any? Justify your answer. Then find the measure.

Vegetable	Calories	Vegetable	Calories
asparagus	14	cauliflower	10
beans	30	celery	17
bell pepper	20	corn	66
broccoli	25	lettuce	9
cabbage	17	spinach	9
carrots	28	zucchini	17

a. NUTRITION The table shows the number of Calories per serving of each vegetable.

List the values from least to greatest: 9, 9, 10, 14, 17, 17, 17, 20, 25, 28, 30, 66.

There is one value that is much greater than the rest of the data, 66. Also, there does not appear to be big gap in the middle of the data. There are only two sets of identical numbers. So, the median would best represent the data.

{9, 9, 10, 14, 17, 17, 17, 20, 25, 28, 30, 66}

The median is 17 Calories.

b. CONCERTS An amphitheater conducted a survey in which they asked 1000 adults the last time they attended a concert.

Results	
Response	**Percentage**
at least 3 years ago	8
1–3 years ago	15
6 months to 1 year ago	45
less than 6 months ago	32

A measure of central tendency cannot be calculated for this set of data. Each percentage in the table represents something different.

For example, 15% of the respondents attended a concert 1 to 3 years ago, while 32% saw a concert less than 6 months ago. So, the median value of 23.5% has no meaning in this situation.

1A. Mode; the set of data has many repeating numbers; 86.

1B. Cannot be calculated; the data values represent different things.

Watch Out!

Percents Always make sure that a survey that gives data in percents tells the size of the sample.

Check Your Progress

1A. FINANCIAL LITERACY An electronics store records the number of customers it has during each hour of the day.

Number of Customers			
86	71	79	86
79	32	88	86
82	69	71	70
86	81	85	86

1B. BOOKS In a survey, students between the ages of thirteen and eighteen reported where they get their books. The responses were: teachers, 420; school library, 1320; public library, 1020; parents, 720; bookstore, 1020; Internet, 540; friends, 540; as a gift, 1020.

Personal Tutor glencoe.com

Evaluate Survey Results Once a survey has been conducted, data are summarized, a report of the findings and conclusions is made. However, bias can sometimes cause errors in the data, as well as how they are interpreted and reported.

You need to be able to judge the reliability of these survey reports. You can do this by making sure that the sample is random, large enough to be an accurate representation of the population, and that the source of the data is a reliable one.

Summarize Survey Results

Example 1 shows how to choose the best measure of central tendency, if there is one, to represent data.

Formative Assessment

Use the Check Your Progress exercises after each example to determine students' understanding of concepts.

Additional Example

1 Which measure of central tendency, if any, best represents the data? Justify your answer. Then find the measure.

a. CELL PHONES A company records the prices of cell phones it sells during a one-hour sale: $85, $50, $115, $80, $73, $55, $68, $110, $90, $55, $95, $60. Mean, there are no outliers and there is only one number that repeats twice; $78

b. BAND A high school band director conducted a survey in which she asked 500 adults the last time they attended a high school band performance.

Results Response	Percent
At least 10 years ago	30%
5–10 years ago	10%
1–5 years ago	25%
Within 1 year	35%

None; each percentage in the table represents something different.

Additional Examples also in Interactive Classroom PowerPoint® Presentations

IWB INTERACTIVE WHITEBOARD READY

Focus on Mathematical Content

Mean, Median, and Mode The mean and median of a data set can be the same or close when the values in the data set are evenly distributed from least to greatest value, but can be significantly different if there are outliers. There can be no mode, one mode, or more than one mode, the significance of which depends upon the number of times a value repeats and the number of values in the data set.

Evaluate Survey Results

Example 2 shows how to evaluate whether the results of a survey are biased or unbiased. **Example 3** shows how to identify whether a display of survey results is accurate or misleading.

Additional Example

2 **NEWSPAPERS** Given the following portion of a survey report, evaluate the validity of the information and conclusion.

Question: What is your major source of national news?

Sample: Random survey of 2000 households in a mid-sized community.

Conclusion: The local newspaper should expand its online presence in the community.

Results	
Choice	**Response**
Print newspaper	284
Online newspaper	575
Other online news	319
Television	822

Sample answer: The sample is random and appears to be representative, and the conclusion is supported by the data, so the survey and conclusion are valid.

TEACH with TECH

INTERACTIVE WHITEBOARD Write the data values on the board and drag them to rearrange them in order from least to greatest. Then, group and drag the lower half of the data to separate it from the upper half of the data. If there are an odd number of data values, do not move the middle value. Identify the middle number as the median.

Often newspaper, magazine, and television reports include the results of a survey. These surveys need to be judged for their validity before you make a decision based on them. Some questions that you may want to ask yourself are:

- What are the population and samples? Can I identify them easily? Are they biased?
- What is the source? Is the data source a reputable group? Could they be biased?
- Do the data actually support the conclusion?

Real-World Link

Generally, the larger the venue, the more you pay to get the best seats in the house. Arenas with 2000 to 4999 seats have a median price of $41.50 per seat.

Source: *USA TODAY*

EXAMPLE 2 Evaluate a Survey

YEARBOOKS Given the following portion of a survey report, evaluate the validity of the information and conclusion.

Question: **Should the school have an electronic yearbook this year?**

Sample: **Ballots were placed in random students' lockers.**

Conclusion: **The school should only offer an electronic yearbook this year.**

Results	
Choice	**Response**
electronic only	67%
traditional paper	22%
offer both	9%
no preference	2%

While the report states that students were chosen randomly, it does not say how many students were chosen. The results were given in percents. The 67% could mean about 34 out of 50. This may not be a large enough sample to represent a large school.

Check Your Progress

2. CONCERTS At a sold-out concert in a 5000-seat concert hall, every 10th attendee completed a survey.

Question: Did you feel that the price of the tickets was reasonable?

Conclusion: The prices for the tickets are reasonable and should remain the same.

Results	
Choice	**Response**
very reasonable	56
reasonable	185
somewhat reasonable	132
unreasonable	69
very unreasonable	58

2. The sample size is large enough, but the sample may be biased. The people questioned were already at a concert, so they were willing to pay the price of the tickets.

Personal Tutor glencoe.com

The way in which results are displayed can influence how you interpret those results. Here are some factors.

- If the scale of a line graph, bar graph, or histogram is large, any changes may appear to be small, when they actually could be quite significant. If the scale of a graph is small, small changes or differences can be made to appear quite large.

  Notice the scale in the graph at the right. This graph is misleading because it appears that gas prices are not increasing too much, when they are actually quite significant.

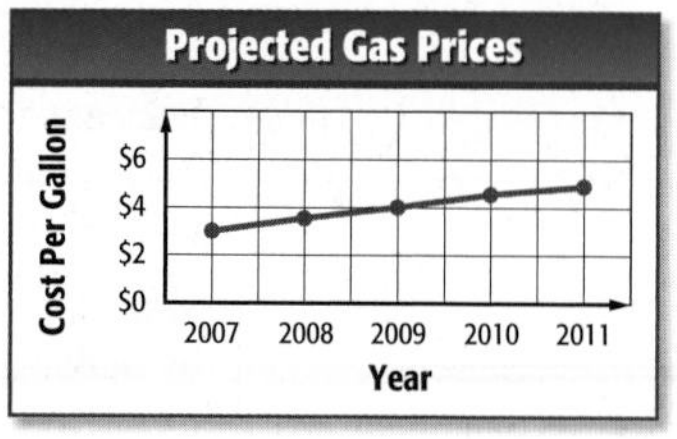

748 Chapter 12 Statistics and Probability

The following are features of a display that can influence the conclusion.

- The scales of graphs should be constant.
- Using percents rather than the actual numbers from a set of data can give a misleading result. However, if the numbers in the sample are large, percents best represent values.
- In a bar graph or histogram, all of the bars should have the same width. The heights of the bars represent the data values. Changing the width of a bar can exaggerate differences.
- If the colors on a circle graph, bar graph, or histogram are different shades of the same color, groups may visually blend together and influence how you interpret the results.

Real-World Link

Most public schools in the U.S. do not require uniforms, but have some kind of dress code. In 1994, a public school district in southern California made school uniforms mandatory that began a trend across the country.

Source: Schoolgirl Princess

EXAMPLE 3 Misleading Results

UNIFORMS A high school principal is considering whether to institute a school uniform policy. She sends out a survey to the students at her high school to get their opinions.

Question: How would you feel about having a school uniform policy?

Conclusion: It would not bother students if a uniform policy were instituted.

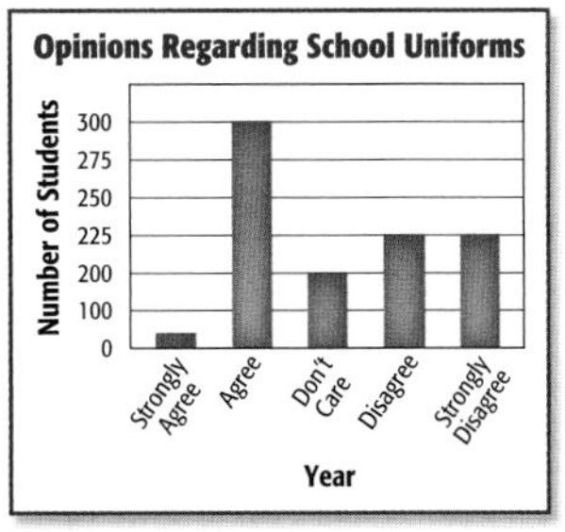

Determine whether the display gives an accurate picture of the survey results.

Upon first inspection, most of the students appear to agree with the uniforms. However, the scale in the graph is not constant. With a closer look, it appears that about 400 students either disagree or strongly disagree while a little more than 300 either agree or strongly agree.

In this case, the table is misleading, and the conclusion is invalid.

Check Your Progress

3. The city council wanted to see how local companies were donating resources to charities. The bar graph shows the results.

Question: How does your company contribute to local charities?

Conclusion: Donating money is the least popular contribution by local companies.

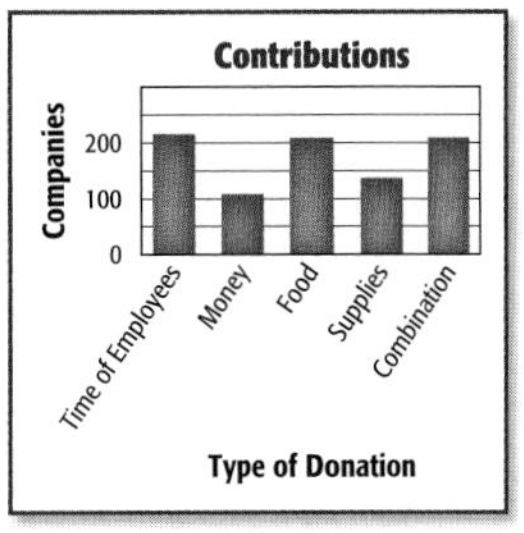

Determine whether the display gives an accurate picture of the survey results. Explain. **It is an accurate display, and the conclusion is valid.**

Personal Tutor glencoe.com

Additional Example

3 **ENVIRONMENT** The town council wants to find out which environmental issues they should approve for funding. They sent a survey to 1000 randomly selected registered voters in the city. The bar graph shows the results of the survey.

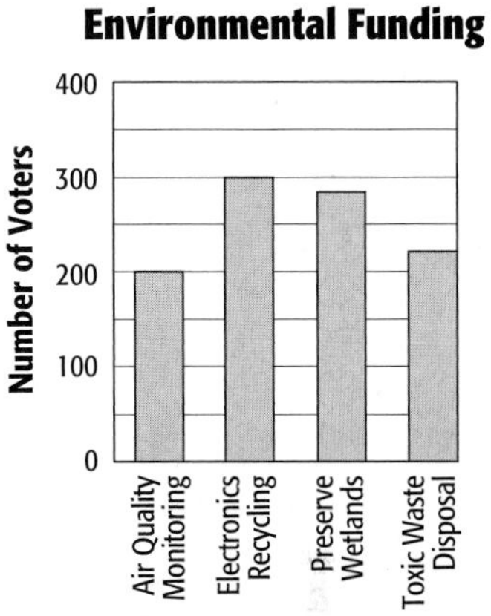

Question: Which environmental issue should be funded?

Conclusion: Air quality monitoring is the least popular environmental issue for the city to fund.

Determine whether the display gives an accurate picture of the survey results and supports the conclusion. The display seems accurate and supports the conclusion.

Lesson 12-2 Analyzing Survey Results 749

3 PRACTICE

Formative Assessment

Use Exercises 1–8 to check for understanding.

Use the chart at the bottom of the next page to customize assignments for your students.

Check Your Understanding

Example 1 p. 747

Which measure of central tendency best represents the data? Justify your answer. Then find the measure.

1. **RECYCLING** Archmont High School is recycling newspapers as a fundraiser to buy some benches for the courtyard. The newspapers are gathered into 5-inch bundles. Ms. Sato counted the bundles received each Friday for the first quarter of the school year: 15, 12, 14, 15, 18, 15, 13, 14, 13, 12.
Mode; there are repeating values in the data; 15.

2. **TRAVEL** An online travel agency wants to design tours for families with teens. So, they surveyed students about their favorite vacation destinations. The top five responses were: beach, 25%; theme parks, 22%; lakes, 21%; historical sites, 17%; mountains, 15%. **Cannot be calculated; the data values represent different things.**

Example 2 p. 748

Given each survey report, evaluate the validity of the information and conclusion.

3. **RADIO** A radio station is considering changing its format. It mails 1000 surveys to randomly selected houses within their listening area. They receive 750 responses.

Question: What type of radio station do you like?

Conclusion: The radio station should have a format of rap/hip-hop.

Results	
Choice	**Response**
talk/sports	26%
classic rock	32%
rap/hip-hop	39%
country	3%

3. Sample answer: Not valid; there is no mention of what kind of format the station currently has. People are more likely to respond if they already listen to that station or that format.

4. **SHOPPING** A shopping mall owner wants to know during what hours the most people prefer to shop. One day every 10th person who entered the mall was asked what times he or she preferred to shop.

Conclusion: The mall should remain open from 9:00 A.M. until 9:00 P.M.

Results	
Choice	**Response**
before 9:00 A.M.	26%
9:00 A.M.–12:00 noon	12%
12:00 noon–3:00 P.M.	26%
3:00 P.M.–6:00 P.M.	27%
6:00 P.M.–9:00 P.M.	9%

4. Sample answer: People are most likely to choose the time that they are currently at the mall as their favorite time to shop.

5. **VOLUNTEERING** Sample: 21,700 6th- to 12th-grade students surveyed by *USA Weekend*, Youthnoise.com, and a volunteer organization called Key Club.

Question: Are youth interested in volunteering?

Conclusion: Youth are interested in volunteering.

Sample answer: The Key Club is a volunteer organization, so the data are biased.

How many hours a year do you volunteer?	
Number of Hours	**Percent (%)**
fewer than 20 hours	30
20 to 39 hours	35
40 to 59 hours	13
60 to 80 hours	7
more than 80 hours	15

6. **SPORTS** Sample: *Scholastic Magazine* asked about 3585 kids with online subscriptions about their favorite sports.

Question: What are kids' favorite sports to compete in?

Results: baseball/softball, 271; football, 436; basketball, 570; soccer, 279; hockey, 197; track, 209; swimming, 319; gymnastics, 197; skating, 289; bowling, 202; other, 616

Conclusion: Basketball is kids' favorite sport in which to compete.

6. Sample answer: There is no evidence of bias, the source seems reputable, and the data supports the conclusion. The survey and conclusion seem valid.

Example 3
p. 749

Determine whether each display gives an accurate picture of the survey results. Explain.

7. The data in the graph support the conclusion. The display is accurate.

7. CONVERSATION A nationwide survey was conducted on the time students in grades six through twelve spend talking one-on-one with a family member. The responses were divided by regions and are displayed in the graph.

Conclusion: Students in the southeast talk with family members the most.

Conversation

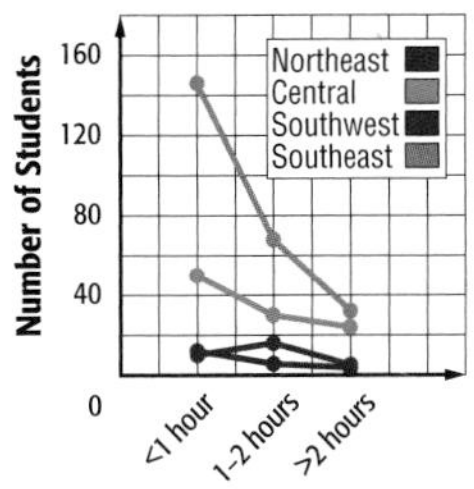

8. There is no conclusion for the data to support. So, we are unable to accurately judge the display.

8. TELEVISION A survey conducted by a media network asked adults how many hours of television they watched each week. The results are displayed in the graph.

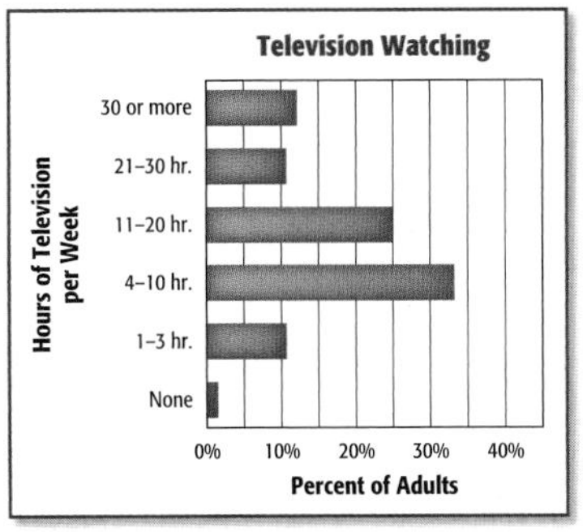

Practice and Problem Solving

= **Step-by-Step Solutions** begin on page R12.
Extra Practice begins on page 815.

Example 1
p. 747

Which measure of central tendency best represents the data? Justify your answer. Then find the measure.

10. Cannot be calculated; the data values represent different things.
11. Mean; the data are weighted and the weighted average needs to be calculated in order to determine the average customer response; 227.
12. Mode; there are repeated values in the data; $1.
13. Cannot be calculated; the data values represent different things.

9. FOOD A sub shop adds a new bread to its menu. To see if they should keep it, the manager counts how many orders of that bread type are taken each day: 10, 16, 14, 13, 17, 15, 18, 16, 19. **Mean; there are no outliers in the data; ≈ 15.33.**

10. MOVIES A video store wants to order additional movies. They conducted a survey to find their members' favorite type of movie. The responses were: comedy, 21%; drama, 19%; horror, 12%; science fiction, 17%; action and adventure, 18%; mystery and suspense, 13%.

11. MOTORCYCLES A motorcycle dealership conducted a telephone survey of its customers from the last five years about customer satisfaction. The results are listed in the table.

Response	Weight	Total
very satisfied	5	182
satisfied	4	252
okay	3	365
dissatisfied	2	169
very dissatisfied	1	54

12. CONTESTS A beverage company introduced a contest in which winning codes were printed on bottle caps. One code awarded the winner a $1 million prize, two codes awarded each winner a new car worth $20,000, and 50,000 codes awarded each winner a free beverage worth $1.

13. SUMMER ACTIVITIES In a survey, students were asked about their favorite summer activity. The responses are listed in the table.

Summer Activities			
swimming	650	camping	432
travel	885	reading	281
sports	1123	other	514

Watch Out!

Preventing Errors Remind students that it is easier to determine the measure that best represents data when the values are first ordered from least to greatest. Point out that outliers can be much less than or much greater than the other values.

Differentiated Homework Options

Level	Assignment	Two-Day Option	
AL Basic	9–24, 29, 31–51	9–23 odd, 33–36	10–24 even, 29, 31–32, 37–51
OL Core	9–23 odd, 25–29, 31–51	9–24, 33–36	25–29, 31–32, 37–51
BL Advanced	25–45, (optional: 46–51)		

Example 2 p. 748

Given each survey report, evaluate the validity of the information and conclusion.

14. Sample answer: The data are unbiased. The survey is valid.

14. SERVICES A salon wants to know which of its services gets used the most. It surveyed 1090 customers between January and March.

Question: For which service did you come in today?

Conclusion: The salon mostly does coloring and highlighting.

Results	
Choice	**Response**
haircut	294
styling	185
coloring/highlights	349
perm	153
combination of services	109

15. Sample answer: The data seem to be unbiased. The survey is valid.

15. FOOD The freshman class decided to have a picnic on National Sandwich Day. They took a survey of all freshmen to decide which sandwich to serve.

Question: Which sandwich would you eat on National Sandwich Day?

Conclusion: They should serve peanut butter and jelly sandwiches.

Results	
Choice	**Response**
grilled cheese	10.6%
reuben	17.4%
hamburger	18.2%
hot dog	16.3%
peanut butter and jelly	37.5%

16. Sample answer: valid

16. NEWSPAPERS To determine the popularity of the horoscope section, a newspaper sent at random a survey to 1000 of its subscribers.

Question: How often do you read your horoscope?

Results: every day, 9.9%; most days, 9.7%; not very often, 39.1%; never, 41.3%

Conclusion: The paper should eliminate the horoscope.

17. Sample answer: The sample is not mentioned.

17. MUSIC A music store wanted to know where people hear about new music.

Question: How do you hear about new music being released?

Results: radio, 27%; TV, 24%; magazines, 19%; friends, 25%; the Internet, 5%

Conclusion: People hear about new music from a variety of sources.

18. Sample answer: The data do not support the conclusion. The survey is invalid.

18. DRIVING *The Canton Repository* polled 750 people.

Question: Have you ever talked on a cell phone while driving a car?

Results: never, 20.7%; a few times, 48.7%; not anymore, 5.1%; always, 25.5%

Conclusion: The people of Canton are careless drivers.

19. Sample answer: The data seem unbiased, the source seems reputable, the data support the conclusion. The survey is valid.

19. ENTERTAINMENT A national survey of students in first through twelfth grades was published in *Scholastic Magazine.* They received 5564 total votes.

Question: What type of TV shows and movies do you watch most?

Results: action, 1329; cartoons, 1115; comedy, 1423; drama, 358; horror, 332; music video, 1007

Conclusion: Students prefer comedies to other types of shows.

20. Sample answer: The sample size is never mentioned.

20. BUSINESS A poll was conducted by Junior Achievement.

Question: Is starting a business challenging?

Results: very easy, 2.5%; easy, 8.9%; somewhat challenging, 43.4%; difficult but possible, 44.1%; almost impossible, 1.1%

Conclusion: Students are aware of the challenges in starting a business.

21. Sample answer: Because the source of the survey is Smart Girl, the sample is most likely to be girls and therefore, you are unable to make an unbiased conclusion about all teens.

21. READING A survey conducted by Smart Girl asked students why they read.

Results: just for fun, 25%; to learn new things, 24%; because they have to for school, 18%; because they get bored and have nothing else to do, 17%; their friends like to read and talk about books, 16%

Conclusion: Students read for a variety of reasons.

Differentiated Instruction

Visual/Spatial Learners Give small groups of students the following survey results on the average daily time students spend on homework: 0–29 minutes: 19; 30–59 minutes: 24; 60–89 minutes: 28; 90–110: 22; 120–149 minutes: 17. Have students prepare two histograms, one in which the left axis starts at 0 and one in which the left axis starts at 15. What kind of impression does the second histogram give? Differences are exaggerated.

22. The display accurately supports the conclusion.
23. Sample answer: The conclusion is too broad for the data presented.
24. The graph accurately supports the conclusion.
25. Sample answer: The Red Cross should continue to offer the babysitting class. While only 10% of its participants are in the class, the service is an important one.
26. The graph accurately supports the conclusion.

Example 3 p. 749 **Determine whether each display gives an accurate picture of the survey results.**

22. **MAGAZINES** The school library is ordering magazines. To make sure that they get ones that students will read, the librarian sends out a survey to 100 randomly chosen students from each grade.

Question: What type of magazine do you enjoy reading?

Conclusion: The library should order fashion, sports, music, and game magazines.

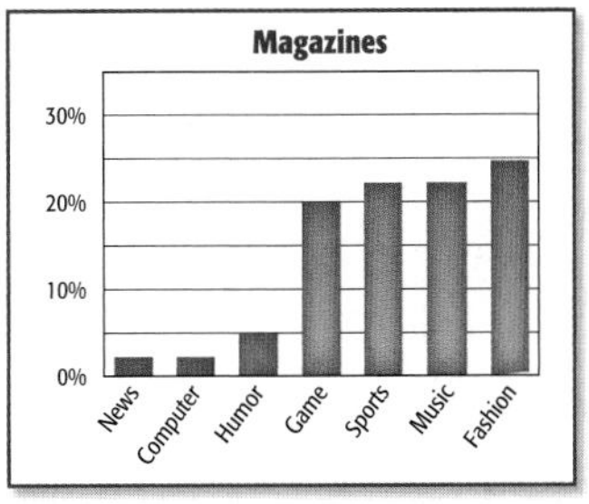

23. **ENVIRONMENT** A survey of 10,000 randomly chosen subscribers to an environmental magazine was conducted.

Question: What will be the biggest environmental challenge in the 21st century?

Conclusion: Finding places to put garbage is unimportant.

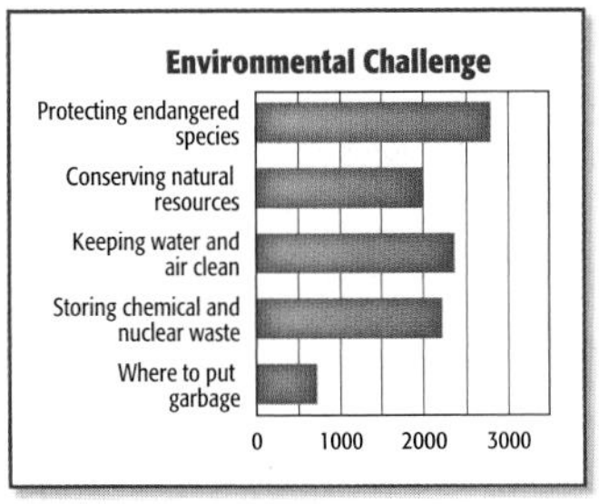

24. **ELECTIONS** A local elections board polled 498 high school seniors.

Question: Will elections ever be held online?

Conclusion: More seniors feel that elections will never be held online.

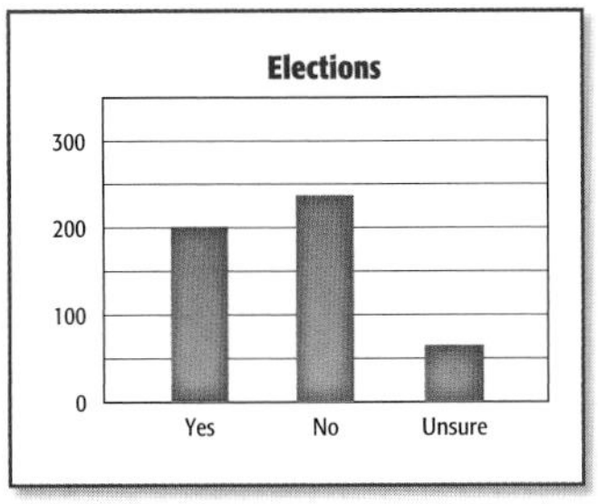

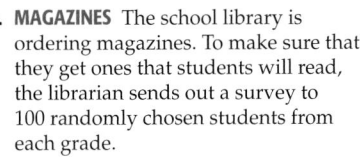

Real-World Link

First-time voters have become a focal point of political parties and interest groups. The number of new voters aged 18 to 24 has increased in recent years.

25. **SAFETY TRAINING** A chapter of the Red Cross offers classes designed for kids and teens in safety techniques. Of the participants, 74% take water safety class, 10% take babysitting classes, and 16% take first aid.

Question: Should the Red Cross continue babysitting classes? Write a valid conclusion using data to support your answer.

26. **BRACES** A journal for dentists conducted a nationwide survey of 5000 dentists. Does this graph accurately represent the data and conclusion? Justify your answer.

Question: What percent of patients do you refer to an orthodontist?

Conclusion: Many dentists refer more than half of their patients to orthodontists.

Percentage of Patients Referred

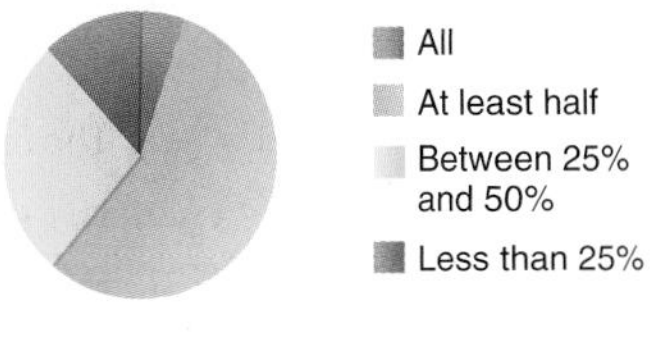

Study Guide and Intervention
CRM pp. 11–12 AL OL ELL

NAME ______ DATE ______ PERIOD ______

12-2 Study Guide and Intervention

Analyzing Survey Results

Summarize Survey Results To make survey data more useful, it can be summarized according to measures of central tendency: **mean**, **median**, and **mode**.

Type	Description	Most Useful When
mean	the sum of the data divided by the number of items in the data set	The data sets have no outliers.
median	the middle number of the ordered data, or the mean of the middle two numbers	The data sets have no outliers, but there are no big gaps in the middle of the data.
mode	the number or numbers that occur the most often	The data set has many repeated numbers.

Example **Which measure of central tendency best represents the data? Justify your answer. Then find the measure.**

a. **RESTAURANTS A restaurant records the number of people who order soup at lunch each day: {26, 25, 30, 32, 27, 28}.**

List the values from least to greatest: 25, 26, 27, 28, 30, 32. The data set does not have any outliers, and does not have any repeated numbers. The mean would best represent the data.

$$\frac{25 + 26 + 27 + 28 + 30 + 32}{6} = 28$$

The mean of the data is 28.

b. **SOCCER A soccer team keeps a record of the number of points it scores in each game: {2, 3, 2, 1, 4, 3, 1, 3, 3, 4}.**

List the values from least to greatest: 1, 1, 2, 2, 3, 3, 3, 3, 4, 4. The data set has four sets of repeated numbers. The mode best represents the data.
The mode is 3, the number that occurs the most often.

Exercises

Which measure of central tendency best represents the data? Justify your answer. Then find the measure.

1. **DEFECTS** A furniture manufacturer keeps records of how many units are defective each day: {7, 12, 9, 8, 10, 14, 8}. **mean, approximately 9.7**
2. **SCIENCE TESTS** Mr. Wharton records his students' scores on the last science test: {94, 88, 88, 94, 94, 84, 94, 88, 84, 94}. **mode, 94**
3. **PUPPIES** A veterinarian keeps records of the weights of puppies in ounces: {4.1, 3.8, 5.0, 4.6, 5.6, 4.7, 11.6}. **median, 4.7**
4. **COMMUTING** The local newspaper conducted a telephone survey of commuters to see how they get to work each day. The responses were: commuter rail, 22; bus, 17; subway, 18; walking, 15; car, 224. **median, 18**

Chapter 12 11 Glencoe Algebra 1

Lesson 12-2

Practice
CRM p. 14 AL OL BL ELL

NAME ______ DATE ______ PERIOD ______

12-2 Practice

Analyzing Survey Results

Which measure of central tendency best represents the data? Justify your answer. Then find the measure.

1. **CALCULATORS** The math department counts how many graphing calculators are in each classroom: {20, 19, 20, 20, 18, 19, 20, 18, 19}. **mode; 20**
2. **BUDGETING** The Brady family keeps track of its monthly electric bills: {$134, $122, $128, $127, $136, $120, $129}. **mean; $128**
3. **AUTOMATED TELLERS** A bank keeps track of how many customers use its ATM each hour: {39, 42, 44, 120, 54, 48, 43}. **median; 44**

Given the following portion of a survey report, evaluate the validity of the information and conclusion.

4. **HOMEWORK** Chris polled 16 of his friends during study hall.
Question: Do teachers at Edison High School assign too much homework?
Results: yes, 94%; no, 6%
Conclusion: Teachers at Edison High School should assign less homework.
The sample is not random, so the results may not be valid. Students have a vested interest in the results of the poll and may be biased.
5. **SMOKING** SurveyUSA polled 500 randomly selected adults in Kentucky.
Question: Do you want to see smoking banned from restaurants, bars, and most indoor public places in Kentucky?
Results: banned, 58%; allowed, 41%; not sure, 1%
Conclusion: The United States should ban smoking indoors.
The information appears valid. The conclusion may not be valid because the poll was taken only among people living in Kentucky.

Determine whether the display gives an accurate picture of the survey results.

6. **REDEVELOPMENT** A local news broadcast commissioned a poll of 600 randomly chosen Providence residents.
Question: Do you support or oppose the redevelopment of the waterfront?
Conclusion: Providence residents support redeveloping the waterfront.
The graph is potentially misleading because "strongly oppose" and "strongly support" are colored similarly. More residents oppose redeveloping the waterfront.

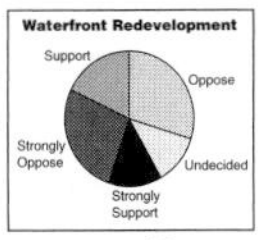

7. **PETS** Ernesto took a poll of randomly selected students at his high school and asked them how many pets they owned. He recorded the results and made the graph shown at the right. Write a valid conclusion using data to support your answer. **Answers will vary.**

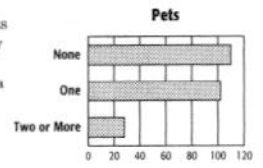

Chapter 12 14 Glencoe Algebra 1

Word Problem Practice
CRM p. 15 AL OL BL ELL

NAME ______ DATE ______ PERIOD ______

12-2 Word Problem Practice

Analyzing Survey Results

1. **PROPERTY TAXES** A landlord is keeping track of what he pays each month in property taxes so he can budget accordingly. For the first half of the year, the tax bills were $256, $256, $274, $256, $256, and $274. Which measure of central tendency best represents the data? Justify your answer. Then find the measure.
mode; because the data set has many repeated numbers; $256
2. **GAS PRICES** Quinnipiac University surveyed 1534 randomly chosen registered voters nationwide and asked them, "As a result of the recent rise in gas prices, have you cut back significantly on how much you drive?" Among those who make less than $30,000 a year, 67% said they had cut back on how much they drive while 30% said they had not. Based on this information, a newspaper made the conclusion that "Americans are cutting back on their driving because of high gas prices." Evaluate the validity of the information and conclusion.
The information may not be valid, because it does not state how many of those polled make less than $30,000—the sample size may be too small. The conclusion may not be valid either, because it there is no information given about Americans as a whole.
3. **BODYBUILDING** A bodybuilder keeps track of how many sets of each exercise he performs each day: {9, 8, 6, 5, 11, 7, 10}. Which measure of central tendency best represents the data? Justify your answer. Then find the measure.
mean; there are no outliers; 8
4. **TRANSPORTATION** The Ford Township School Board surveyed 86 randomly selected students to find out how students get to school each day.
Question: What mode of transportation did you use to get to school today?
Conclusion: Most students take the bus to school every day.

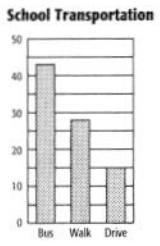

a. Evaluate the validity of the information.
The sample size may not be large enough to be a valid representation of the population.

b. Evaluate the validity of the conclusion.
The data indicate that more students either walk or drive each day than take the bus. Further, it is unclear if the students who took the bus that day are likely to take the bus every day.

c. Write a valid conclusion of your own using data to support your answer.
Answers may vary.

Chapter 12 15 Glencoe Algebra 1

Lesson 12-2

Enrichment
CRM p. 16 OL BL

NAME ______ DATE ______ PERIOD ______

12-2 Enrichment

Margin of Error

When conducting a survey, it is important to know how accurate your data are. You can learn more about the accuracy of a survey by calculating the **margin of error**, or the maximum statistical amount of the survey's uncertainty.

When calculating the margin of error, you must first define the **confidence level.** The confidence level tells how accurate the percentages given in the poll are, assuming the only error present is statistical error (i.e., no bias). Most polls use a confidence level of 95%, meaning that there is at least a 95% certainty that the "true" percentage will be within plus or minus the margin of error of the percentage given in the survey.

Margin of Error (90% confidence level) $\approx \frac{1.29}{\sqrt{n}}$

Margin of Error (95% confidence level) $\approx \frac{0.98}{\sqrt{n}}$

Margin of Error (99% confidence level) $\approx \frac{0.82}{\sqrt{n}}$

n = sample size

The calculations above assume the sample size n is significantly smaller than the population.

Example **ELECTIONS A poll of 300 randomly selected registered voters shows that the incumbent mayor of New Castle is leading her opponent by a 52% to 48% margin. Find the margin of error for the poll assuming a 95% confidence level.**

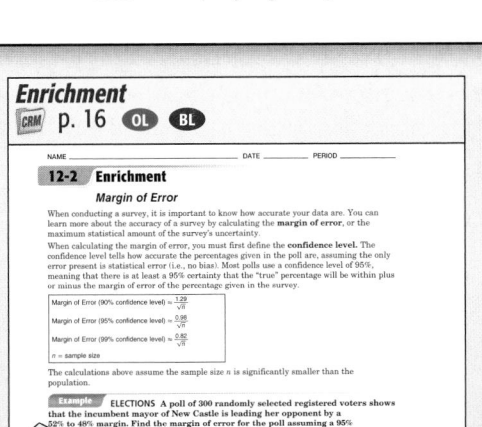

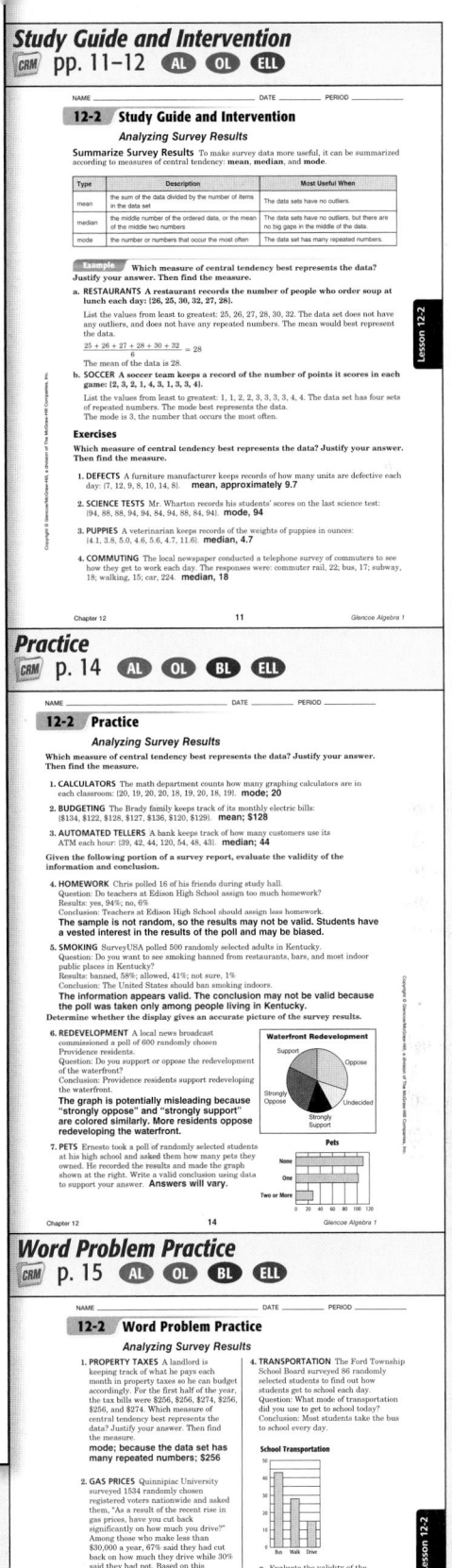

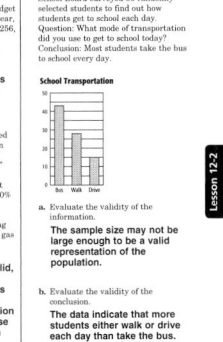

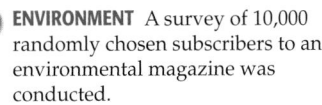

Multiple Representations In Exercise 28, students use a concrete model, a line plot, and statistical analysis to evaluate a statistical distribution.

Watch Out!

Find the Error For Exercise 29, suggest that students organize the data from least to greatest value and choose for themselves the measure they think best represents the data. Then have them compare their choice and reasoning to that of Pepita and Ben.

Real-World Link

Teenage girls are not that influenced by the behavior of celebrities. Of the 1700 teenage girls surveyed, only 5% thought that the excessive lifestyles of celebrities were cool. About 63% of the girls said that they were not influenced by celebrities.

Source: Yahoo News

27. CELEBRITIES A celebrity gossip magazine conducted a survey of their subscribers.

Question: Are you influenced by celebrities?

Conclusion: Their subscribers are not influenced by celebrities.

Does this graph accurately represent the data and conclusion? Justify your answer. **See margin.**

Influenced by Celebrities

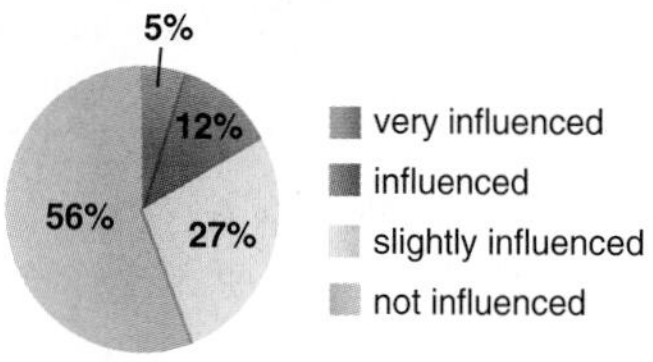

28. MULTIPLE REPRESENTATIONS In this problem, you will explore another way to analyze data.

a. CONCRETE Below is a distribution of coins in unequal stacks. Duplicate these stacks with coins. **See students' work; 8 moves.**

b. GRAPHICAL Make a line plot of the stacks. Above each of these columns, record how much each stack differs from the mean (the number of coins per stack). Find the absolute value of each of these values. **See margin; 3, 2, 2, 1, 0, 1, 1, 3, 3**

c. ANALYTICAL Move the coins one at a time to make the stacks equal. Avoid unnecessary moves. Count the moves. The number of moves tells us how much the original set of stacks differs from the set of equal stacks. **8 moves**

d. ANALYTICAL Find the mean of the absolute values. Describe what this value is and what it means in these circumstances.
1.78; The average difference of each each value from the mean of 5 is 1.78.

H.O.T. Problems

Use Higher-Order Thinking Skills

29. Ben; there were no large gaps, no repeated values, but there was an outlier of 32.

29. FIND THE ERROR Pepita and Ben are asked to decide which measure of central tendency to use given the data of test scores 84, 82, 80, 32, 87, 83, 85. Is either of them correct? Explain your reasoning.

Pepita	Ben
The mean is the best measure of central tendency because the data are clumped together, and there are no repeated values.	*The median is the best measure of central tendency because the data are clumped together, but there is an outlier, and there are no repeated values.*

30. CHALLENGE Find a set of numbers that satisfies each list of conditions.

a. The mean, median, and mode are all the same number. **Sample answer: 2, 2, 2**

b. The mean is greater than the median. **Sample answer: 4, 5, 9**

c. The mode is 10 and the median is greater then the mean. **Sample answer: 2, 10, 10, 12**

d. The mean is 6, the median is 5.5, and the mode is 9. **Sample answer: 3, 4, 5, 6, 9, 9**

31. OPEN ENDED Describe a survey you would like to conduct. Include the sample, population, method of questioning, and how you would display the results. **See margin.**

32. WRITING IN MATH Explain why a company may display survey results inaccurately. Give one example of how they might accomplish this. **See margin.**

Additional Answers

27. Yes; there are no similar colors and there is numerical data for each section.

28b.

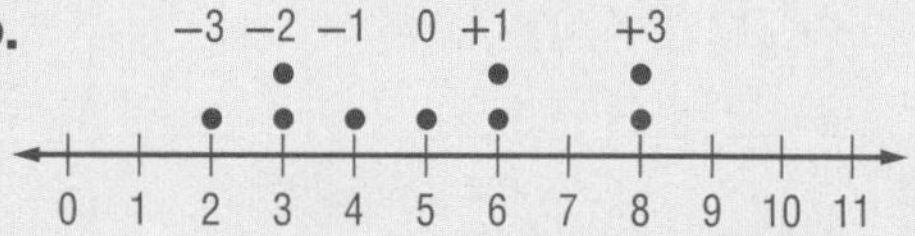

PSAE PRACTICE 8.11.17, 7.11.02, 7.11.03

33. At the county fair, 1000 tickets were sold. Adult tickets cost $8.50, children's tickets cost $4.50, and a total of $7300 was collected. How many children's tickets were sold? **D**

A 700 C 400
B 600 D 300

34. Edward has 20 dimes and nickels, which together total $1.40. How many nickels does he have? **F**

F 12 H 8
G 10 J 6

35. If 4.5 kilometers is about 2.8 miles, about how many miles is 6.1 kilometers? **C**

A 3.2 miles C 3.8 miles
B 3.6 miles D 4.0 miles

36. EXTENDED RESPONSE Three times the width of a certain rectangle exceeds twice its length by three inches, and four times its length is twelve more than its perimeter.

a. Translate the sentences into equations.
b. Find the dimensions of the rectangle.
c. What is the area of the rectangle? **315 in^2**

36a. $3w = 2\ell + 3$; $4\ell = 12 + P$
b. 21 in., 15 in.

Spiral Review

Identify each sample and suggest a population from which it is selected. State whether the sample is *biased* or *unbiased*. If unbiased, classify the sample as *simple, stratified,* or *systematic.* (Lesson 12-1)

37. SCHOOL Twenty names were drawn from a container containing identical pieces of paper with the names of every member of the senior class. These seniors were then asked who they would choose for senior class president. **20 seniors; senior class; unbiased; simple**

38. BOOKS To check the quality of the books being manufactured, an inspector checks every 50th book that comes off the line. **every 50th book; all books manufactured; unbiased; systematic**

39. COMPUTERS Mayfield High School participated in a survey to find out how teens feel about certain issues involving social networks. The responses are divided into group by each age and then tallied for each question. **Mayfield High School; everyone who participated in survey; stratified**

Find the zeros of each function. (Lesson 11-8)

40. $f(x) = \frac{x^2 - 8x + 15}{x^2 + 5x - 6}$ **3,5**

41. $f(x) = \frac{x^2 - x - 12}{x^2 - 6x + 8}$ **−3**

42. $f(x) = \frac{x^2 - x - 30}{x^2 - 3x - 18}$ **−5**

Find the values of the three trigonometric ratios for angle A. (Lesson 10-8) **43–45. See margin.**

43.

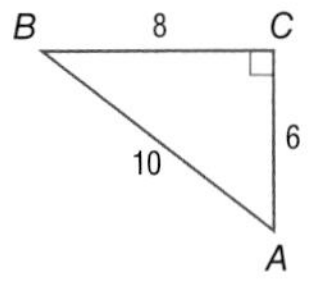

44.

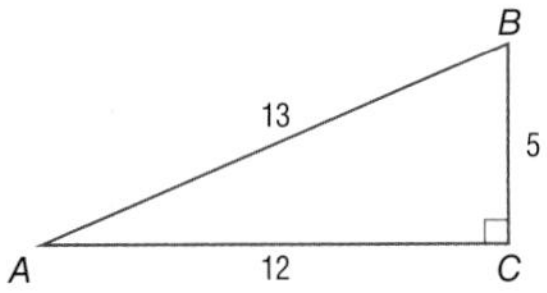

45.

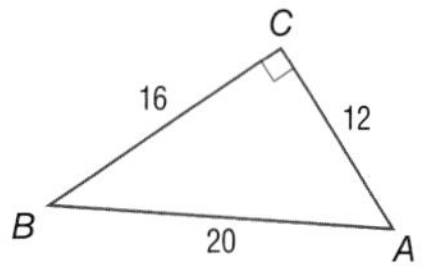

Skills Review

Find the mean, median, and mode to the nearest tenth for each set of data. (Lesson 0-12)

46. 100, 105, 100, 105, 100, 110 **103.3; 102.5; 100**

47. 12, 25, 14, 35, 42, 27, 31, 48 **29.3; 29; no mode**

48. 90, 85, 92, 99, 78, 82, 92, 90 **88.5; 90; 90 and 92**

49. 1, 5, 3, 7, 6, 2, 9, 2, 5, 1, 9, 1 **4.3; 4; 1**

50. 55, 65, 45, 35, 65, 25, 85 **53.6; 55; 65**

51. 25, 28, 21, 26, 25, 27, 29, 30 **26.4; 26.5; 25**

4 ASSESS

Name the Math Give students a set of data and have them explain how to identify the measure of central tendency that best represents the data. Then have them identify and find the measure.

Formative Assessment

Check for student understanding of concepts in Lessons 12-1 and 12-2.

CRM Quiz 1, p. 51

Additional Answers

31. Sample answer: I would like to conduct a survey about chewing gum in school. I would use a sample selected by randomly picking 50 names from each grade to represent the student body. I would give a series of questions that would evaluate the students' attitudes about the gum chewing policy. I would display the results in a series of bar graphs, one for each question.

32. A disreputable company may want to make their product seem more reliable than it really is. So, they create graphs and charts to show that their product is the most reliable and convince people to buy it. They might do this with a bar graph that has a very large scale and places the values from least to greatest.

43. $\sin A = \frac{4}{5}$; $\cos A = \frac{3}{5}$; $\tan A = \frac{4}{3}$

44. $\sin A = \frac{5}{13}$; $\cos A = \frac{12}{13}$; $\tan A = \frac{5}{12}$

45. $\sin A = \frac{4}{5}$; $\cos A = \frac{3}{5}$; $\tan A = \frac{4}{3}$

Differentiated Instruction OL BL

Extension Have the class discuss intentional and unintentional factors that might lead to misleading displays. Then have students analyze one of the exercises from Exercises 14–21 to determine possible factors that could lead to an intentionally and an unintentionally misleading display. Have students support their analysis with examples of the displays. Check students' work: Analysis should include both intentional and unintentional factors that could lead to a misleading display, and the displays should support their analysis.

Lesson 12-2 Analyzing Survey Results 755

12-3 Lesson Notes

1 FOCUS

Vertical Alignment

Before Lesson 12-3
Organize and summarize survey results.

Lesson 12-3
Compare sample statistics and population parameters.
Analyze data sets using statistics.

After Lesson 12-3
Model data using distribution curves.

2 TEACH

Scaffolding Questions

Have students read the *Why?* section of the lesson.

Ask:

- Will the mean ages of the students' samples of pennies vary? Explain. Sample answer: Yes; the samples are random, so each sample will have a different mix of ages of pennies.
- How is the mean of a sample of pennies different from the mean of all of the pennies? The mean of the samples will vary, but the mean of all of the pennies will not vary.

12-3 Statistics and Parameters

Then
You organized and summarized survey results. (Lesson 12-2)

Now
- Use statistics to analyze survey results.
- Analyze data sets using statistics.

IL Learning Standards
8.A.4b Represent mathematical patterns and describe their properties using variables and mathematical symbols.

New Vocabulary
statistical inference
statistic
parameter
univariate data
measures of variation
mean absolute deviation
standard deviation
variance

IL Math Online
glencoe.com
- Extra Examples
- Personal Tutor
- Self-Check Quiz
- Homework Help

Why?

At the start of every class period for one week, each of Mr. Day's algebra students randomly draws 9 pennies from a jar of 1000 pennies. Each student calculates the mean age of the random sample of pennies drawn and then returns the pennies to the jar.

How does the mean age for 9 pennies compare to the mean age of all 1000 pennies?

Statistics and Parameters In this situation, the statistics of a sample are used to draw conclusions about the entire population. This is called **statistical inference**.

In the scenario above, each student takes a random sample of pennies from the jar. The jar of 1000 pennies represents the population. A **statistic** is a measure that describes a characteristic of a sample. A **parameter** is a measure that describes a characteristic of a population. Parameters are usually estimated values based on the statistics of a carefully chosen random sample. A statistic can and usually will vary from sample to sample. A parameter will not change, for it represents the entire population.

EXAMPLE 1 Identify Statistics and Parameters

Identify the sample and the population for each situation. Then describe the sample statistic and the population parameter.

a. At a local university, a random sample of 40 scholarship applicants is selected. The mean grade-point average of the 40 applicants is calculated.

Sample: the group of 40 scholarship applicants
Population: all applicants
Sample statistic: mean grade-point average of the sample
Population parameter: mean grade-point average of all applicants

b. A stratified random sample of registered nurses is selected from all hospitals in a three-county area, and the median salary is calculated.

Sample: randomly selected registered nurses from hospitals in three-county area
Population: all nurses at the hospitals in the same region
Sample statistic: median salary of nurses in the sample
Population parameter: median salary of all nurses in sampled hospitals

Check Your Progress

1. **CEREAL** Starting with a randomly selected box of Co-Co-Chunks from the manufacturing line, every 50th box of cereal is removed and weighed. The mode weight of a day's sample is calculated. **See Ch. 12 Answer Appendix.**

Personal Tutor glencoe.com

Lesson 12-3 Resources

Resource	Approaching-Level	On-Level	Beyond-Level	English Learners
Teacher Edition		• Differentiated Instruction, pp. 758, 762	• Differentiated Instruction, pp. 758, 762	
Chapter Resource Masters	• Study Guide and Intervention, pp. 17–18 • Skills Practice, p. 19 • Practice, p. 20 • Word Problem Practice, p. 21	• Study Guide and Intervention, pp. 17–18 • Skills Practice, p. 19 • Practice, p. 20 • Word Problem Practice, p. 21 • Enrichment, p. 22	• Practice, p. 20 • Word Problem Practice, p. 21 • Enrichment, p. 22	• Study Guide and Intervention, pp. 17–18 • Skills Practice, p. 19 • Practice, p. 20 • Word Problem Practice, p. 21
Transparencies	• 5-Minute Check Transparency 12-3	• 5-Minute Check Transparency 12-3	• 5-Minute Check Transparency 12-3	• 5-Minute Check Transparency 12-3
Other	• Study Notebook	• Study Notebook	• Study Notebook	• Study Notebook

Review Vocabulary

bivariate data data that involve two variables (Lesson 4-5)

Statistical Analysis Data that involve only one variable are called **univariate data**. This kind of data can be represented by measures of central tendency, such as the mean, median, and mode. Univariate data can also be represented by **measures of variation**, such as range, quartiles, and interquartile range.

Concept Summary — **Measures of Variation** — For Your FOLDABLE

Type	Description	When Best Used
range	the difference between the greatest and least values	to describe which numbers are included in the data set
quartile	the values that divide the data set into four equal parts	to determine values in the upper or lower portions of a data set
interquartile range	the range of the middle half of a data set; the difference between the upper and lower quartiles	to determine what values lie in the middle half of the data set

The **mean absolute deviation** is the average of the absolute values of the differences between the mean and each value in the data set. Recall that absolute value is the distance from a number to zero on a number line.

Key Concept — **Mean Absolute Deviation** — For Your FOLDABLE

Step 1 Find the mean.

Step 2 Find the sum of the absolute values of the differences between each value in the set of data and the mean.

Step 3 Divide the sum by the number of values in the set of data.

Real-World Link

Recently, Japanese comics for girls, called "shojo," have become popular. These comics are available in three forms: comic books, graphic novels, and online comics.

Source: Disney Family

EXAMPLE 2 Use the Mean Absolute Deviation

MARKETING Each person that visited the Comic Book Shoppe's web site was asked to enter the number of times each month they buy a comic book. They received the following responses in one day: 2, 2, 3, 4, 14. Find the mean absolute deviation to the nearest tenth.

Step 1 The mean of this set of data is 5.

Step 2 Find the sum of the absolute values of the differences between each value and the mean.

$|2 - 5| + |2 - 5| + |3 - 5| + |4 - 5| + |14 - 5| = 3 + 3 + 2 + 1 + 9$ or 18

Step 3 Divide the sum by the number of values: $18 \div 5 = 3.6$.

Check Your Progress

2. DANCES The prom committee kept count of how many tickets it sold each day during lunch: 12, 32, 36, 41, 22, 47, 51, 33, 37, 49. Find the mean absolute deviation of these data. 9

Personal Tutor glencoe.com

Statistics and Parameters

Example 1 shows how to identify statistics in a sample and the parameters in a population.

Formative Assessment

Use the Check Your Progress exercises after each example to determine students' understanding of concepts.

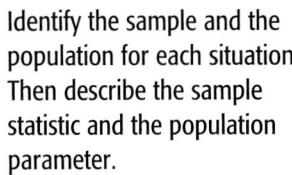

Additional Example

1 Identify the sample and the population for each situation. Then describe the sample statistic and the population parameter.

a. A movie rental business selects a random sample of 50 orders in one day. The median number of rentals per order is calculated. sample: 50 movie orders; population: all movie orders for the day of the sample; sample statistic: median number of rentals per order in the sample; population parameter: median number of rentals per order for all rentals the day of the sample

b. A stratified random sample of 2 trees of each species is selected from all trees at a nursery. The mean height of trees in the sample is calculated. sample: 2 trees of each species found at the nursery; population: all trees at the nursery; sample statistic: mean height of trees in the sample; population parameter: mean height of all trees at the nursery

Additional Examples also in Interactive Classroom PowerPoint® Presentations

IWB INTERACTIVE WHITEBOARD READY

Focus on Mathematical Content

Measures of Variation Measures of variation show the spread of the data. Range describes the spread of all values in the data. Quartiles and interquartile range describe the spread in the middle half of the data. Mean absolute deviation, variance, and standard deviation describe the spread around the mean. Two data sets can have the same range and mean, but the spread around the mean can be quite different.

Statistical Analysis

Example 2 shows how to find the mean absolute deviation in a data set. **Example 3** shows how to find the variance and the standard deviation in a data set. **Example 4** shows how to use a graphing calculator to find the standard deviation of a real-world data set.

Additional Examples

2 **PETS** A rescue agency records the number of pets adopted each month: 14, 18, 12, 17, 15, 20. Find the mean absolute deviation. ≈ 2.3

3 Find the mean, variance, and standard deviation of 5, 7, 8, 14, 16. 10, $\frac{90}{5}$ or 18, ≈ 4.2

TEACH with TECH

INTERACTIVE WHITEBOARD Use a spreadsheet or other software program to calculate various statistics from data collected from a survey. Keep this information displayed on the board as you teach students what it means and how to interpret it.

Additional Answers

1. sample: 1003 voters in Mercy County; population: all voters in Mercy County; sample statistic: the number of people in the sample who would vote for the incumbent candidate; population parameter: the number of people in the county who would vote for the incumbent candidate
2. sample: 1000 college students; population: all college students in the United States; sample statistic: mean of the money spent on books in a year by the sample; population parameter: mean of money spent on books by all college students in the United States

StudyTip

Symbols The mean of a sample and the mean of a population are calculated in the same way. $\bar{x}$ usually refers to the mean of a sample, but in this text, it will refer to the mean of a population.

The **standard deviation** is a calculated value that shows how the data deviates from the mean of the data. The standard deviation is represented by the lower-case Greek symbol sigma, σ. The **variance** of the data is the square of the standard deviation. Use the method below to calculate the variance and standard deviation.

Key Concept — Variance and Standard Deviation

For Your FOLDABLE

Step 1 Find the mean, $\bar{x}$.

Step 2 Find the square of the difference between each value in the set of data and the mean. Then sum the squares and divide by the number of values in the set of data. The result is the variance.

Step 3 Take the square root of the variance to find the standard deviation.

EXAMPLE 3 Find the Variance and Standard Deviation

Find the mean, variance, and standard deviation of 3, 6, 11, 12, and 13 to the nearest tenth.

Step 1 To find the mean, add the numbers and then divide by the number of values in the data set.

$$\bar{x} = \frac{3 + 6 + 11 + 12 + 13}{5} = \frac{45}{5} \text{ or } 9$$

Step 2 To find the variance, square the difference between each number and the mean. Then add the squares, and divide by the number of values.

$$\sigma^2 = \frac{(3-9)^2 + (6-9)^2 + (11-9)^2 + (12-9)^2 + (13-9)^2}{5}$$

$$= \frac{(-6)^2 + (-3)^2 + 2^2 + 3^2 + 4^2}{5}$$

$$= \frac{36 + 9 + 4 + 9 + 16}{5} \text{ or } \frac{74}{5}$$

Step 3 The standard deviation is the square root of the variance.

$\sigma^2 = \frac{74}{5}$ **Variance**

$\sqrt{\sigma^2} = \sqrt{\frac{74}{5}}$ **Take the square root of the variance.**

$\sigma \approx 3.8$ **Use a calculator.**

The mean is 9, the variance is $\frac{74}{5}$ or 14.8, and the standard deviation is about 3.8.

Check Your Progress

Find the mean, variance, and standard deviation of each set of data to the nearest tenth.

3A. 6, 10, 15, 11, 8 **10, 9.2, 3.0**

3B. 92, 84, 71, 83, 100 **86, 94, 9.7**

Personal Tutor glencoe.com

StudyTip

Categories of Data Quantitative data can also be called *measurement data.* Qualitative data is also known as *categorical data.*

The standard deviation illustrates the spread of a set of data. For example, when the mean is 75 and the standard deviation is 3, we know that almost all of the data values are very close to the mean. When the mean is 75 and the standard deviation is 15, then the data are more spread out and there may be an outlier.

Differentiated Instruction

OL BL

If students demonstrate understanding of how to use mean absolute deviation,

Then have students describe how they can use the mean absolute deviation to predict errors and to judge equality. For example, what does a greater or lesser value for the mean absolute deviation indicate when predicting the number of comics a certain group of people will purchase each month? Encourage students to use examples to explain their reasoning.

758 Chapter 12 Statistics and Probability

StudyTip

Symbols The standard deviation of a sample S and the standard deviation of a population σ are calculated in different ways. In this text, you will calculate the standard deviation of a population.

Real-World EXAMPLE 4 Statistical Analysis

NUTRITION Caleb kept track of the Calories he ate each day. Find the standard deviation of the data set.

Day	Sun	Mon	Tues	Wed	Thurs	Fri	Sat
Calories	1800	2000	2100	2250	1900	2500	2000

Use a graphing calculator to find the standard deviation. Clear all lists. Press STAT ENTER, and enter each data value into L1, pressing ENTER after each value. To view the statistics, press STAT ▶ 1 ENTER. So, the standard deviation is about 216.9.

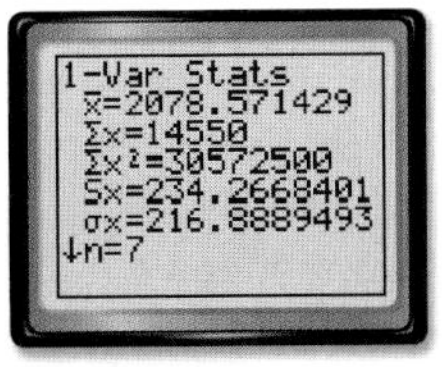

Check Your Progress

4. Caleb tracked his Calorie intake for another week: 1950, 2000, 2100, 2000, 1900, 2100, 2000. Find the standard deviation of his Calorie intake for this week. ≈67.8

Personal Tutor glencoe.com

Check Your Understanding

Example 1 p. 756 **Identify the sample and the population for each situation. Then describe the sample statistic and the population parameter.** 1–2. See margin.

1. **POLITICS** A random sample of 1003 Mercy County voters is asked if they would vote for the incumbent for governor. The percent responding *yes* is calculated.

2. **BOOKS** A random sample of 1000 U.S. college students is surveyed about how much they spend on books per year.

Example 2 p. 757 **Find the mean absolute deviation to the nearest tenth.**

3. **FINANCIAL LITERACY** Iye is waiting tables at the Pizza Pan Restaurant. He is keeping track of the tips that he receives each hour: \$20, \$31, \$24, \$22, \$35, \$12. 6

4. **PARTIES** Dalila kept an account of what each cousin gave toward their grandmother's birthday party: \$25, \$24, \$36, \$28, \$34, \$25, \$17. 4.9

Example 3 p. 758 **Find the mean, variance, and standard deviation of each set of data to the nearest tenth.**

5. 3, 4, 18, 21, 17 12.6, 57.0, 7.6

6. 12, 15, 18, 21 16.5, 11.3, 3.4

Example 4 p. 759

7. **ELECTRONICS** Ed surveyed his classmates to find out how many electronic gadgets each person has in their home. Find the standard deviation of the data set to the nearest tenth: 3, 10, 11, 10, 9, 11, 12, 8, 11, 8, 7, 12, 11, 11, 5. 2.5

Practice and Problem Solving

= Step-by-Step Solutions begin on page R12.
Extra Practice begins on page 815.

Example 1 p. 756 **Identify the sample and the population for each situation. Then describe the sample statistic and the population parameter.** 8–9. See margin.

8. A stratified random sample of high school students from each school in the county was polled about the time spent each week on extracurricular activities.

9. A stratified random sample of 2500 high school students across the country was asked how much money they spent each month.

Additional Example

4 **TEXT MESSAGES** Daisy kept track of the number of text messages she sent each month for 6 months. Find the standard deviation of the data set. ≈84.1

Month	Messages
January	985
February	1005
March	1100
April	950
May	1200
June	1010

3 ASSESS

Formative Assessment

Use Exercises 1–7 to check for understanding.

Use the chart at the bottom of this page to customize assignments for your students.

Additional Answers

8. sample: stratified random sample from schools in the county; population: all high school students in the county; sample statistic: time spent each week on extracurricular activities by the sample; population parameter: time spent each week on extracurricular activities by all students in the county

9. sample: stratified random sample of 2500 students nationwide; population: high school students in the country; sample statistic: how much money the 2500 students spent individually each month; population parameter: how much money all the students in the country spent individually each month

Differentiated Homework Options

Level	Assignment	Two-Day Option	
AL Basic	8–17, 22, 24–42	9–17 odd, 28–31	8–16 even, 22, 24–27, 31–42
OL Core	9–17 odd, 18–22, 24–42	8–17, 28–31	18–22, 24–27, 31–42
BL Advanced	18–36, (optional: 37–42)		

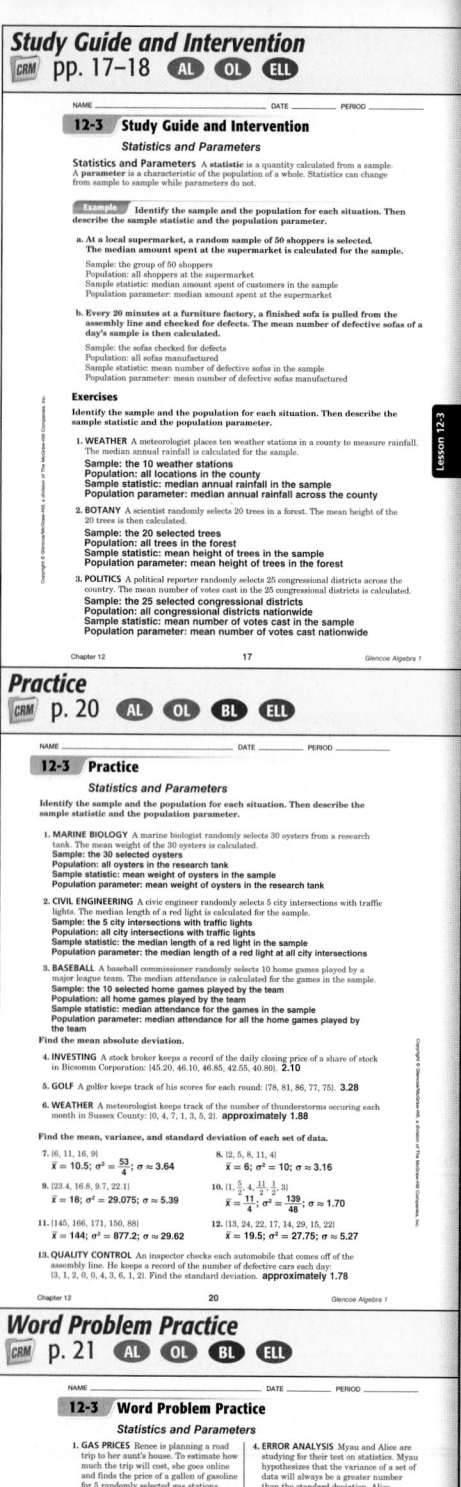

Example 2 p. 757

Find the mean absolute deviation to the nearest tenth.

10. DVDS Mr. Robinson asked his students to count the number of DVDs they owned. **14.3**

Number of DVDs					
26	39	5	82	12	14
0	3	15	19	41	6
2	0	11	1	19	29

11. SALES An amusement park manager wanted to keep track of how many bags of cotton candy were sold each hour: 16, 24, 15, 17, 22, 16, 18, 24, 17, 13, 25, 21. **3.5**

Example 3 p. 758

Find the mean, variance, and standard deviation of each set of data to the nearest tenth.

12. 3, 8, 7, 12 **7.5, 10.3, 3.2**

13. 76, 78, 83, 74, 75 **77.2, 10.2, 3.2**

14. 0.01, 0.03, 0.1, 0.5

15. 0.8, 0.01, 0.06, 0.02, 0.4, 0.8, 0.5

14. 0.2, 0.04, 0.2

15. 0.4, 0.1, 0.3

Example 4 p. 759

16. ONLINE AUCTIONS Scott makes keychains and sells them on an online auction site. He tracks the selling price of each keychain: \$3.25, \$4.50, \$5.00, \$5.75, \$2.25, \$8.50, \$6.00, \$3.50, \$4.50, \$5.00. Find the standard deviation to the nearest tenth. **1.6**

17. PART-TIME JOBS Ms. Johnson asks all of the girls on the tennis team how many hours each week they work at part-time jobs: 10, 12, 0, 6, 9, 15, 12, 10, 11, 20. Find the standard deviation to the nearest tenth. **5.0**

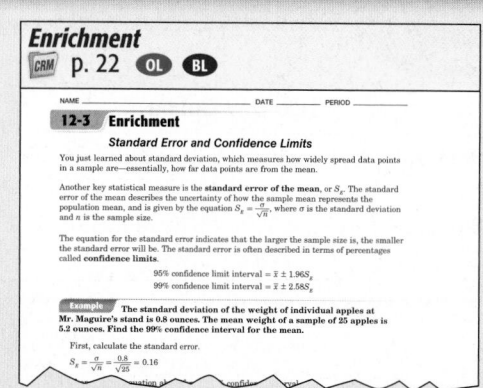

Real-World Link

One of the tallest players in the NBA was Yao Ming at 7 ft 5 in. One of the shortest NBA players was Earl Boykins at 5 ft 5 in.

Source: Inside Hoops

18. BASKETBALL The heights of players on an NBA team are shown.

B **a.** Find the mean and standard deviation. **79, ≈4.1**

Heights of Professional Basketball Players (in.)				
80	77	83	74	78
80	83	74	83	69
78	85	81	81	79

b. Suppose the 5′9″ player was traded for Earl Boykins. Find the mean and the standard deviation. Describe the effect this trade has on the calculations. **≈78.7, ≈4.8; The mean decreased and the standard deviation increased.**

c. Performing one or more operations on a data set transforms the data. If the operation can be written as a linear function, the transformation is a **linear transformation**. Convert each measure to centimeters then find the mean. Next, convert the mean to inches. How does this calculation compare to the mean found in part **a**? **The mean is 200.66 cm or 79 inches. This is the same as in part a.**

19. PENNIES Mr. Day has another jar of pennies on his desk. There are 30 pennies in this jar. Theo looks at 5 pennies from the jar and replaces them. Lydia looks at 10 pennies and replaces them, and Peter looks at 20 pennies and replaces them.

a. Identify the sample and the population for each situation. Then describe a statistic and a parameter. **See margin.**

Years of Pennies in Jar					
2001	1990	2000	1982	1991	1975
2007	1981	2005	2007	2003	2005
1997	1974	1992	1994	1991	1992
2000	1995	1999	2005	2006	2005
2004	2004	1998	2001	2002	2006

b. The years of Theo's pennies are 1974, 1975, 1981, 1999, 1992. Find the mean and mean absolute deviation. **≈1984, ≈9.0**

c. The years of Lydia's pennies are 2004, 1999, 2004, 2005, 1991, 2003, 2005, 2000, 2001, 1998. Find the mean and mean absolute deviation. **≈2001, ≈3.2**

d. The years of Peter's pennies are 2007, 2005, 1975, 2003, 2005, 1997, 1992, 1994, 1991, 1992, 2000, 1999, 2005, 1982, 2005, 2004, 1998, 2001, 2002, 2006. Find the mean and mean absolute deviation. **≈1998, ≈6.4**

e. Find the mean and mean absolute deviation for all of the pennies in the jar. Which sample was more similar to the full population? Explain. **See margin.**

Study Guide and Intervention

CRM pp. 17–18 AL OL ELL

NAME ______ DATE ______ PERIOD ______

12-3 Study Guide and Intervention

Statistics and Parameters

Statistics and Parameters A **statistic** is a quantity calculated from a sample. A **parameter** is a characteristic of the population of a whole. Statistics can change from sample to sample while parameters do not.

Example **Identify the sample and the population for each situation. Then describe the sample statistic and the population parameter.**

a. At a local supermarket, a random sample of 50 shoppers is selected. The median amount spent at the supermarket is calculated for the sample.

Sample: the group of 50 shoppers
Population: all shoppers at the supermarket
Sample statistic: median amount spent of customers in the sample
Population parameter: median amount spent at the supermarket

b. Every 20 minutes at a furniture factory, a finished sofa is pulled from the assembly line and checked for defects. The mean number of defective sofas of a day's sample is then calculated.

Sample: the sofas checked for defects
Population: all sofas manufactured
Sample statistic: mean number of defective sofas in the sample
Population parameter: mean number of defective sofas manufactured

Exercises

Identify the sample and the population for each situation. Then describe the sample statistic and the population parameter.

1. **WEATHER** A meteorologist places ten weather stations in a county to measure rainfall. The median annual rainfall is calculated for the sample.
Sample: the 10 weather stations
Population: all locations in the county
Sample statistic: median annual rainfall in the sample
Population parameter: median annual rainfall across the county

2. **BOTANY** A scientist randomly selects 20 trees in a forest. The mean height of the 20 trees is then calculated.
Sample: the 20 selected trees
Population: all trees in the forest
Sample statistic: mean height of trees in the sample
Population parameter: mean height of trees in the forest

3. **POLITICS** A political reporter randomly selects 25 congressional districts across the country. The mean number of votes cast in the 25 congressional districts is calculated.
Sample: the 25 selected congressional districts
Population: all congressional districts nationwide
Sample statistic: mean number of votes cast in the sample
Population parameter: mean number of votes cast nationwide

Lesson 12-3

Chapter 12 17 Glencoe Algebra 1

Practice

CRM p. 20 AL OL BL ELL

NAME ______ DATE ______ PERIOD ______

12-3 Practice

Statistics and Parameters

Identify the sample and the population for each situation. Then describe the sample statistic and the population parameter.

1. **MARINE BIOLOGY** A marine biologist randomly selects 30 oysters from a research tank. The mean weight of the 30 oysters is calculated.
Sample: the 30 selected oysters
Population: all oysters in the research tank
Sample statistic: mean weight of oysters in the sample
Population parameter: mean weight of oysters in the research tank

2. **CIVIL ENGINEERING** A civic engineer randomly selects 5 city intersections with traffic lights. The median length of a red light is calculated for the sample.
Sample: the 5 city intersections with traffic lights
Population: all city intersections with traffic lights
Sample statistic: the median length of a red light in the sample
Population parameter: the median length of a red light at all city intersections

3. **BASEBALL** A baseball commissioner randomly selects 10 home games played by a major league team. The median attendance is calculated for the games in the sample.
Sample: the 10 selected home games played by the team
Population: all home games played by the team
Sample statistic: median attendance for the games in the sample
Population parameter: median attendance for all the home games played by the team

Find the mean absolute deviation.

4. **INVESTING** A stock broker keeps a record of the daily closing price of a share of stock in Bicsomm Corporation: {45.20, 46.10, 46.85, 42.55, 40.80}. **2.10**

5. **GOLF** A golfer keeps track of his scores for each round: {78, 81, 86, 77, 75}. **3.28**

6. **WEATHER** A meteorologist keeps track of the number of thunderstorms occuring each month in Sussex County: {0, 4, 7, 1, 3, 5, 2}. **approximately 1.88**

Find the mean, variance, and standard deviation of each set of data.

7. {6, 11, 16, 9}
$\bar{x} = 10.5$; $\sigma^2 = \frac{53}{4}$; $\sigma \approx 3.64$

8. {2, 5, 8, 11, 4}
$\bar{x} = 6$; $\sigma^2 = 10$; $\sigma \approx 3.16$

9. {23.4, 16.8, 9.7, 22.1}
$\bar{x} = 18$; $\sigma^2 = 29.075$; $\sigma \approx 5.39$

10. $\{1, \frac{5}{2}, 4, \frac{11}{2}, \frac{1}{2}, 3\}$
$\bar{x} = \frac{11}{4}$; $\sigma^2 = \frac{139}{48}$; $\sigma \approx 1.70$

11. {145, 166, 171, 150, 88}
$\bar{x} = 144$; $\sigma^2 = 877.2$; $\sigma \approx 29.62$

12. {13, 24, 22, 17, 14, 29, 15, 22}
$\bar{x} = 19.5$; $\sigma^2 = 27.75$; $\sigma \approx 5.27$

13. **QUALITY CONTROL** An inspector checks each automobile that comes off of the assembly line. He keeps a record of the number of defective cars each day: {3, 1, 2, 0, 0, 4, 3, 6, 1, 2}. Find the standard deviation. **approximately 1.78**

Chapter 12 20 Glencoe Algebra 1

Word Problem Practice

CRM p. 21 AL OL BL ELL

NAME ______ DATE ______ PERIOD ______

12-3 Word Problem Practice

Statistics and Parameters

1. **GAS PRICES** Renee is planning a road trip to her aunt's house. To estimate how much the trip will cost, she goes online and finds the price of a gallon of gasoline for 5 randomly selected gas stations along the route. She then calculates the median price per gallon for the 5 selected gas stations.

a. Identify the sample and the population.
Sample: the 5 selected gas stations
Population: all gas stations along the route

b. Describe the sample statistic and the population parameter.
Sample statistic: median price per gallon of gasoline in the sample
Population parameter: median price per gallon of gasoline along the route

2. **SUMMER VACATION** Mr. Siipola's algebra class took a survey to find students' plans for the summer. The results are shown in the circle graph.

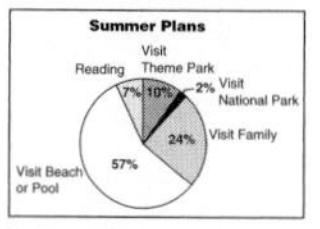

Find the mean absolute variation for the poll results. **16.4**

3. **HOCKEY** A hockey team keeps track of how many goals it scores each game: {2, 4, 0, 3, 7, 2}. Find the mean, variance, and standard deviation of the data.
$x = 3$, $\sigma^2 = \frac{14}{3}$, $\sigma \approx 2.16$

4. **ERROR ANALYSIS** Myau and Alice are studying for their test on statistics. Myau hypothesizes that the variance of a set of data will always be a greater number than the standard deviation. Alice believes that Myau is incorrect and that the standard variation can be a greater number than the variance. Who is correct? Explain.
Alice is correct. Sample answer: The standard deviation will be greater than the variance for closely related data. For example, the variance of the data set {5, 5, 5, 5, 6} is 0.232; the standard deviation is approximately 0.482.

5. **HEALTH CLUBS** To plan their future equipment purchases, the Northville Health Club randomly chooses 8 patrons and tracks how many minutes they spend on the treadmill: {30, 30, 45, 20, 60, 30, 30, 15}. The mean treadmill time is then calculated.

a. Identify the sample and the population. Then describe the sample statistic and the population parameter.
Sample: the 8 selected patrons
Population: all patrons using the treadmill
Sample statistic: mean time on the treadmill for the sample
Population parameter: mean time on the treadmill for all patrons who use it

b. Find the sample statistic specified in part a. **32.5 minutes**

c. Find the mean absolute deviation for the sample. **10**

d. Find the variance and standard deviation for the sample. $\sigma^2 = 175$; $\sigma \approx 13.23$

Lesson 12-3

Chapter 12 21 Glencoe Algebra 1

Enrichment

CRM p. 22 OL BL

NAME ______ DATE ______ PERIOD ______

12-3 Enrichment

Standard Error and Confidence Limits

You just learned about standard deviation, which measures how widely spread data points in a sample are—essentially, how far data points are from the mean.

Another key statistical measure is the **standard error of the mean**, or S_E. The standard error of the mean describes the uncertainty of how the sample mean represents the population mean, and is given by the equation $S_E = \frac{\sigma}{\sqrt{n}}$, where σ is the standard deviation and n is the sample size.

The equation for the standard error indicates that the larger the sample size is, the smaller the standard error will be. The standard error is often described in terms of percentages called **confidence limits**.

$$95\% \text{ confidence limit interval} = \bar{x} \pm 1.96S_E$$
$$99\% \text{ confidence limit interval} = \bar{x} \pm 2.58S_E$$

Example **The standard deviation of the weight of individual apples at Mr. Maguire's stand is 0.8 ounces. The mean weight of a sample of 25 apples is 5.2 ounces. Find the 99% confidence interval for the mean.**

First, calculate the standard error.

$S_E = \frac{\sigma}{\sqrt{n}} = \frac{0.8}{\sqrt{25}} = 0.16$

Real-World Link

A growing number of teens are completing marathons and 21-kilometer half-marathons at major races.

20. BABYSITTING Samantha wants to see if she is getting a fair wage for babysitting at \$8.50 per hour. She takes a survey of her friends to see what they charge per hour. The results are \$8, \$8.50, \$9, \$7.50, \$10, \$8.25, \$8.75. Find the mean absolute deviation of the data to the nearest tenth. **0.6**

21. RUNNING The results of a 5K race are published in a local paper. Over a thousand people participated, but only the times of the top 15 finishers are listed.

15th Annual 5K Road Race

Place	Time (min:s)	Place	Time (min:s)	Place	Time (min:s)
1	15:56	6	16:34	11	17:14
2	16:06	7	16:41	12	17:46
3	16:11	8	16:54	13	17:56
4	16:21	9	17:00	14	17:57
5	16:26	10	17:03	15	18:03

a. Find the mean and mean absolute deviation of the top 15 running times to the nearest tenth. (*Hint:* Convert each time to seconds.) **16.9 min, 33.3 seconds**

b. Identify the sample and population. **See margin.**

c. Analyze the sample. Classify the data as *qualitative* or *quantitative*. Can a statistical analysis of the sample be applied to the population? Explain. **See margin.**

H.O.T. Problems

Use **H**igher-**O**rder **T**hinking Skills

22. FIND THE ERROR Amy and Esteban are describing one way to increase the accuracy of a survey. Is either of them correct? Explain your reasoning.

Amy	Esteban
The survey should include as many people in the population as possible.	*The sample for the survey should be chosen randomly. Several random samples should be taken.*

23. CHALLENGE Find the mean and standard deviation of the population of data represented by the histogram. **8.75, 3.6**

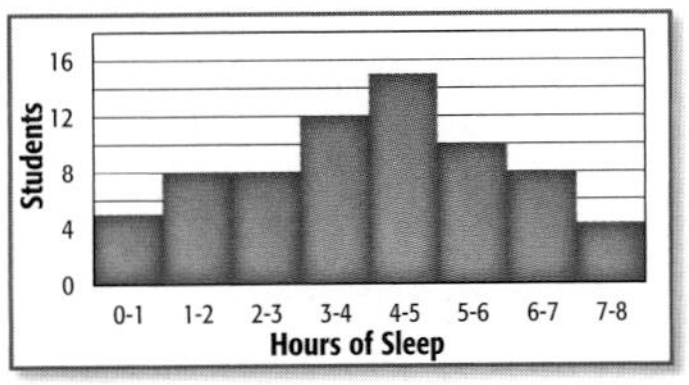

24. REASONING Determine whether the following statement is *sometimes, always,* or *never* true. Explain. *Two random samples taken from the same population will have the same mean and standard deviation.*

25. WRITING IN MATH Compare and contrast statistics and parameters. Include an example of each. **See margin.**

26. OPEN ENDED Describe a real-world situation in which it would be useful to use a sample mean to help estimate a population mean. Describe how you could collect a random sample from this population.

27. WRITING IN MATH Compare and contrast standard deviation and mean absolute deviation. **See margin.**

22. Both; both Amy's and Esteban's methods can result in an accurate survey.

24. False; if the samples are truly random, they would usually not contain identical elements. Therefore the mean and standard deviation would differ.

26. Sample answer: Poll of voters to determine if a particular presidential candidate is favored to win the election. Use a stratified random sample to call 100 people throughout the country.

Watch Out!

Find the Error Have the class discuss the factors that make a survey representative of the population. Then have students analyze the descriptions given by Amy and Esteban in Exercise 22. Encourage them to give specific reasons why they think the descriptions of the two students do or do not increase the accuracy of a survey.

Additional Answers

19a. Sample answer: The pennies chosen by Tyrone, Lydia, and Peter each represent a sample. The 30 pennies in the jar is the population. The sample statistic is the mean year of the pennies in the sample. The population parameter is the mean year of the pennies in the population.

19e. ≈1997, ≈7.4; Peter's sample was the most accurate. The mean year of his sample was 1 year off from the actual mean year. The samples that had more pennies were more accurate.

21b. The sample is the first 15 finishers of the race. The population is all of the people who ran the race.

21c. The data is quantitative. No, since the sample is the top 15 runners in the race, it is not random. So, it would not be accurate to apply the mean and standard deviation of the running times to the population.

25. A statistic is a characteristic that is computed on a sample of the population. A parameter is a characteristic of the entire population. Sample answer: To determine the average height of a student at your high school, you can measure the heights of a random sample of students at your school. The mean height of the sample is a statistic; the actual mean height of the students at your school is a parameter.

27. Both are calculated statistical values that show how each data value deviates from the mean of the data set. The mean absolute deviation is calculated by taking the mean of the absolute values of the differences between each number and the mean of the data set. To find the standard deviation, you square each difference and then take the square root of the mean of the squares.

4 ASSESS

Yesterday's News Have students write a sentence on how yesterday's lesson on summarizing and analyzing survey results helped with today's lesson on sample statistics and population parameters.

PSAE PRACTICE 6.11.18, 6.11.17, 10.11.05, 6.11.19

28. Melina bought a shirt that was marked 20% off for \$15.75. What was the original price? D

A \$16.69 C \$18.69
B \$17.69 D \$19.69

29. SHORT RESPONSE A group of students visited the Capitol building. Twenty students met with the local representative. This was 16% of the students. How many student ambassadors were there altogether? 125

30. The tallest 7 trees in a park have heights of 19, 24, 17, 26, 24, 20, and 18 meters. Find the median of their heights. G

F 17 H 21
G 20 J 24

31. It takes 3 hours for a boat to travel 27 miles upstream. The same boat travels 30 miles downstream in 2 hours. Find the speed of the boat. A

A 12 mph C 3 mph
B 14 mph D 5 mph

Spiral Review

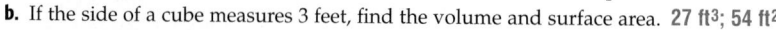

Tell which measure of central tendency best represents the data. Justify your answer. Then find the measure. (Lesson 12-2)

32. FOOD DRIVE A high school is offering an incentive to classes that bring in the canned goods. The pounds of food brought by the classes are represented by the data set 8, 12, 18, 25, 21, 5, 10, and 14. Median; there are not large gaps between numbers; 13.

33. TEST SCORES The results of the math test are 78, 81, 85, 86, 88, 85, 90, 91, 85, 95, and 98. Mode; one value is repeated; 85.

Identify each sample as *biased* or *unbiased*. Explain your reasoning. (Lesson 12-1)

34. SHOPPING Every tenth person walking into the mall is asked to name their favorite store. Unbiased; the sample is a random selection of people with no evidence of influence.

35. MUSIC Every fifth person at a rock concert is asked to name their favorite radio station. Biased; because they are at a rock concert, they are more likely to select a rock music station.

36. GEOMETRY If the side length of a cube is s, the volume is represented by s^3, and the surface area is represented by $6s^2$. (Lesson 7-1)

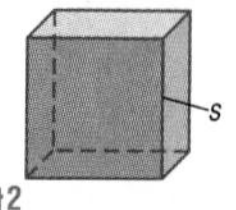

Yes; each is the product of variables and/or a real number.

a. Are the expressions for volume and surface area monomials? Explain.

b. If the side of a cube measures 3 feet, find the volume and surface area. 27 ft^3; 54 ft^2

c. Find a side length s such that the volume and surface area have the same measure. 6 units

d. The volume of a cylinder can be found by $V = \pi r^2 h$. Suppose you have two cylinders. Each dimension of the second is twice the measure of the first, so $V = \pi(2r)^2(2h)$. What is the ratio of the volume of the first cylinder to the second? 1:8

Skills Review

A bowl contains 3 red chips, 6 green chips, 5 yellow chips, and 8 orange chips. A chip is drawn randomly. Find each probability. (Lesson 0-11)

37. red $\frac{3}{22}$

38. orange $\frac{4}{11}$

39. yellow or green $\frac{1}{2}$

40. not orange $\frac{7}{11}$

41. not green $\frac{8}{11}$

42. red or orange $\frac{1}{2}$

Differentiated Instruction OL BL

Extension Have the class discuss intentional and unintentional factors that might lead to misleading displays. Then have students analyze one of the exercises from Exercises 16–18 to determine possible factors that could lead to an intentionally and an unintentionally misleading display. Have students support their analysis with examples of the displays. Check students' work: Analysis should include both intentional and unintentional factors that could lead to a misleading display, and the displays should support their analysis.

Mid-Chapter Quiz

Lessons 12-1 through 12-3

IL Learning Standards
10.A.4b, 10.B.4

Identify each sample, and suggest a population from which it was selected. Then classify the type of data collection used. (Lesson 12-1)
1–4. See Ch. 12 Answer Appendix.

1. **CEREAL** A cereal company invites 100 children and parents to test a new cereal.

2. **SCHOOL LUNCH** A school is creating a new lunch menu. They send out a questionnaire to all students with odd homeroom numbers to see what items should be on the new menu.

3. **MEDICINE** A research facility gave a new medicine to hamsters and determined that 1 out of every 50 hamsters that took the medicine lost its hair. They conclude that the same thing will happen to every 50 people who take the medicine.

4. **MASCOTS** The cheerleaders send out a flyer with pictures of options for the new mascot to all the girls in the school. The new mascot is chosen from the favorite from the survey.

Identify each sample as *biased* or *unbiased*. Explain your reasoning. (Lesson 12-1)
5–8. See Ch. 12 Answer Appendix.

5. **ART** Every fifth person leaving the art museum is asked to name their favorite piece.

6. **SHOPPING** Each person leaving the Earring Pagoda is asked to name their favorite store in the mall.

7. **FOOTBALL** Every 10th student leaving the student union at Ohio State is asked to name their favorite college football team.

8. **CLASSES** Every 5th person leaving the school is asked to name their favorite class.

9. **MULTIPLE CHOICE** Every 10 minutes, Kaleigh writes down whether the TV is showing a commercial or a program. Which of the following best describes the sample? (Lesson 12-1) **C**

A simple
B stratified
C systematic
D none of the above

Which measure of central tendency best represents the data? Justify your answer. Then find the measure. (Lesson 12-2)

Median; there is an outlier in the data; 2.5.

10. **PLAY AREA** Ian listed the ages of the children playing at the play area at the mall.
2, 3, 2, 2, 4, 2, 3, 2, 8, 3, 4, 2

Median; there is an outlier in the data; 23.

11. **RECYCLING** Marielle is in charge of recycling cans at her school. She counts the number of cans recycled each week.
22, 10, 23, 25, 24, 23, 25, 19

12. Does the following give an accurate picture of the survey results? (Lesson 12-2)

A survey of 500 students was conducted.
Question: What is the most important aspect of school?
Conclusion: Preparing for the future is not important at all. **No; the question is too broad.**

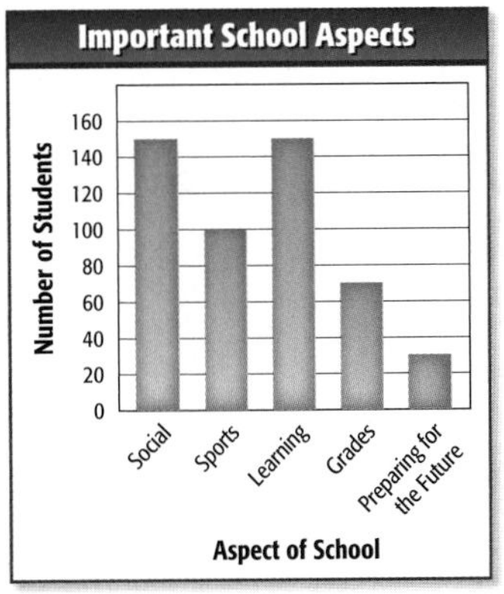

Find the mean, variance, and standard deviation to the nearest tenth for each set of data. (Lesson 12-3)

13. 2, 4, 5, 7, 7, 9
5.7, 5.2, 2.3

14. 13, 14, 18, 21
16.5, 10.3, 3.2

15. **MULTIPLE CHOICE** Several friends are chipping in to buy a gift for their teacher. Ignati is keeping track of how much each friend gives for the gift. Find the mean absolute deviation. (Lesson 12-3) **H**

$10, $5, $3, $6, $7, $8

F 2.22
G 6.5
H 1.833
J 2.4

CHAPTER 12 Mid-Chapter Quiz

Formative Assessment

Use the Mid-Chapter Quiz to assess students' progress in the first half of the chapter.

For problems answered incorrectly, have students review the lessons indicated in parentheses.

ExamView Assessment Suite Customize and create multiple versions of your Mid-Chapter Test and their answer keys.

FOLDABLES® Follow-Up

Before students complete the Mid-Chapter Quiz, encourage them to review the information for Lessons 12-1 through 12-3 in their Foldables.

Intervention Planner

Tier 1 On Level	Tier 2 Strategic Intervention approaching grade level	Tier 3 Intensive Intervention 2 or more grades below level
If students miss about 25% of the exercises or less,	**If** students miss about 50% of the exercises,	**If** students miss about 75% of the exercises,
Then choose a resource: **SE** Lessons 12-1, 12-2, and 12-3 **CRM** Skills Practice, pp. 7, 13, and 19 **TE** Chapter Project, p. 736 IL Math Online Self-Check Quiz	**Then** choose a resource: **CRM** Study Guide and Intervention, Chapter 12, pp. 5, 11 and 17 *Quick Review Math Handbook* IL Math Online Extra Examples, Personal Tutor, Homework Help	**Then** use *Math Triumphs, Alg. 1*, Ch. 6 IL Math Online Extra Examples, Personal Tutor, Homework Help, Review Vocabulary

12-4 Lesson Notes

1 FOCUS

Vertical Alignment

Before Lesson 12-4
Use the Fundamental Counting Principle.

Lesson 12-4
Use permutations.
Use combinations.

After Lesson 12-4
Find probability for compound events.

2 TEACH

Scaffolding Questions

Have students read the *Why?* section of the lesson.

Ask:

- Can a player be listed more than once in the team's lineup? no
- When the coach chooses a group of players to play in the game, is the order in which she chooses them important? no
- When the coach lists the players in the lineup, is the order in which she lists them important? yes

12-4 Permutations and Combinations

Then
You used the Fundamental Counting Principle. (Lesson 0-11)

Now
- Use permutations.
- Use combinations.

IL Learning Standards

Preparation for 10.C.5b Compute probabilities in counting situations involving permutations and combinations.

New Vocabulary
sample space
permutation
factorial
combination

IL Math Online
glencoe.com
- Extra Examples
- Personal Tutor
- Self-Check Quiz
- Homework Help

Why?

Angie's coach told her that she would bat sixth in the softball game. When a coach decides on the team's lineup, the order in which she fills in the names determines the order in which the players will bat.

Permutations The list of all of the people or objects in a group is called the **sample space**. When the objects are arranged so that order is important and every possible order of the objects is provided, the arrangement is called a **permutation**.

Suppose Angie's coach has 4 players in mind for the first 4 spots in the lineup. The Fundamental Counting Principle can be used to determine the number of permutations. A batter cannot bat first and second, so once that player is chosen, she is not available for the next choice.

number of permutations		choices for 1st batter		choices for 2nd batter		choices for 3rd batter		choices for 4th batter
P	$=$	4	$\cdot$	3	$\cdot$	2	$\cdot$	1
	$= 24$							

There are 24 different ways to arrange the first four batters.

Real-World EXAMPLE 1 Permutation

TRAVEL A travel agency is planning a vacation package in which travelers will visit 5 cities around Europe. How many ways can the agency arrange the 5 cities along the tour?

Number of ways to arrange the cities $= 5 \cdot 4 \cdot 3 \cdot 2 \cdot 1$
$= 120$

There are 120 ways to arrange the cities.

Check Your Progress

1. **MOVIES** Lloyd and five friends go to a movie. In how many different ways can they sit together in a row of 6 empty seats? 720

Personal Tutor glencoe.com

The expression used in Example 1 to calculate the number of permutations of the five cities, $5 \cdot 4 \cdot 3 \cdot 2 \cdot 1$, can be written as 5!, which is read *5 factorial*.

Key Concept Factorial

For Your FOLDABLE

Words The **factorial** of a positive integer n is the product of the positive integers less than or equal to n.

Symbols $n! = n \cdot (n - 1) \cdot (n - 2) \cdot \ldots \cdot 1$, where $n \geq 1$. Also, $0! = 1$.

Lesson 12-4 Resources

Resource	Approaching-Level	On-Level	Beyond-Level	English Learners
Teacher Edition	• Differentiated Instruction, p. 766	• Differentiated Instruction, pp. 766, 770	• Differentiated Instruction, p. 770	
Chapter Resource Masters	• Study Guide and Intervention, pp. 23–24 • Skills Practice, p. 25 • Practice, p. 26 • Word Problem Practice, p. 27	• Study Guide and Intervention, pp. 23–24 • Skills Practice, p. 25 • Practice, p. 26 • Word Problem Practice, p. 27 • Enrichment, p. 28	• Practice, p. 26 • Word Problem Practice, p. 27 • Enrichment, p. 28	• Study Guide and Intervention, pp. 23–24 • Skills Practice, p. 25 • Practice, p. 26 • Word Problem Practice, p. 27
Transparencies	• 5-Minute Check Transparency 12-4	• 5-Minute Check Transparency 12-4	• 5-Minute Check Transparency 12-4	• 5-Minute Check Transparency 12-4
Other	• Study Notebook	• Study Notebook	• Study Notebook	• Study Notebook

Suppose Angie's coach has 5 players in mind for the top 3 spots in the lineup. The Fundamental Counting Principle can be used to determine the number of permutations.

choices for 1st batter		choices for 2nd batter		choices for 3rd batter	
5	$\cdot$	4	$\cdot$	3	= 60 permutations

Notice that $5 \cdot 4 \cdot 3$ is the same as $\frac{5 \cdot 4 \cdot 3 \cdot 2 \cdot 1}{2 \cdot 1}$. This relationship is expressed in the following formula.

ReadingMath

Notation The number of permutations $P(n, r)$ of n objects taken r at a time can also be written as nPr.

Key Concept Permutation Formula — For Your FOLDABLE

Words The number of permutations of n objects taken r at a time is the quotient of $n!$ and $(n - r)!$.

Symbols $P(n, r) = \frac{n!}{(n - r)!}$

Real-World EXAMPLE 2 Use the Permutation Formula

LIBRARY The librarian is placing 6 of 10 magazines on a shelf in a showcase. How many ways can she arrange the magazines in the case?

$P(n, r) = \frac{n!}{(n - r)!}$ — Permutation Formula

$P(10, 6) = \frac{10!}{(10 - 6)!}$ — $n = 10$ and $r = 6$

$= \frac{10!}{4!}$ — Simplify.

$= \frac{10 \cdot 9 \cdot 8 \cdot 7 \cdot 6 \cdot 5 \cdot \cancel{4} \cdot \cancel{3} \cdot \cancel{2} \cdot \cancel{1}}{\cancel{4} \cdot \cancel{3} \cdot \cancel{2} \cdot \cancel{1}}$ — Divide by common factors.

$= 151{,}200$ — Simplify.

There are 151,200 ways for the librarian to arrange the magazines.

Check Your Progress

2. **FASHION** A designer has created 15 outfits and needs to select 10 for a fashion show. How many ways can the designer arrange the outfits for the show? 10,897,286,400

Personal Tutor glencoe.com

StudyTip

Permutations and Combinations If order matters in a group, the group is a *permutation*. If order does not matter in a group, the group is a *combination*.

Combinations A selection of objects in which order is not important is called a **combination**. To find all two-letter combinations of A, B, and C, you would list all of the arrangements of two letters, which are listed below.

AB   *BA*   *AC*   *CA*   *BC*   *CB*

Because order does not matter, AB and BA are the same, so there are 2! ways to write the same letters. Divide $P(n, r)$ by 2! to remove the groups with identical objects.

Permutations

Example 1 shows how to use the Fundamental Counting Principle to find the number of permutations.
Example 2 shows how to use the permutation formula to find the number of permutations.

Formative Assessment

Use the Check Your Progress exercises after each example to determine students' understanding of concepts.

Additional Examples

1. **CODES** Shaquille has a 4-digit pass code to access his e-mail account. The code is made up of the even digits 2, 4, 6, and 8. Each digit can be used only once. How many different pass codes could Shaquille have? 24

2. **CODES** A word processing program requires a user to enter a 5-digit registration code made up of the digits 1, 2, 3, 4, 5, 6, and 7. No digit can be used more than once. How many different registration codes are possible? 2520

Additional Examples also in Interactive Classroom PowerPoint® Presentations

IWB INTERACTIVE WHITEBOARD READY

TEACH with TECH

PORTABLE MEDIA PLAYER Have students look at their portable media player and find the number of songs on their favorite album. Then, have students calculate the number of 5-song playlists that could be created for that album, given that the order of the songs *does* matter. Discuss individual results with the class.

Focus on Mathematical Content

Permutations A permutation is an arrangement or listing in which order is important. For example, if the arrangement of DVDs on a shelf is alphabetical, then the order in which they are arranged is important and this situation is a permutation. The number of permutations is expressed as $P(n, r)$ or ${}_nP_r$, where n is the number of items to choose from and r is the number of items to be chosen. To find the number of permutations, use the formula ${}_nP_r = \frac{n!}{(n - r)!}$.

Combinations

Example 3 shows how to use combinations to solve a real-world problem. **Example 4** shows how to use the Combination Formula to solve a real-world problem. **Example 5** shows how to find a probability of an event using permutations and combinations.

Additional Examples

3 **SCHOOL** A group of 4 seniors, 5 juniors, and 7 sophomores have volunteered to be on a fundraising committee. Mr. Davidson needs to choose 12 students out of the group. How many ways can the 12 students be chosen? 1820

4 **MONEY** Sun has a bag full of coins. There are 10 pennies, 6 nickles, 4 dimes, and 2 quarters in the bag. How many ways can Sun pull 4 coins out of the bag? 7315

Tips for New Teachers

Reading The number of combinations of n objects taken r at a time can be written as $C(n, r)$ or ${}_nC_r$.

Focus on Mathematical Content

Combinations A combination is an arrangement or listing in which order is not important. For example, when choosing the decorations for a school party, the order in which the decorations are chosen does not matter, so this situation is a combination. The number of combinations are expressed as $C(n, r)$ or ${}_nC_r$, where n is the number of items to choose from and r is the number of items to be chosen. To find the number of combinations, use the formula $C(n, r) = \frac{n!}{(n-r)!r!}$.

Real-World Link

About 27% of teens make dinner for their families at least some of the time.

Source: *American Demographics*

Real-World EXAMPLE 3 Combination

FAMILY Horacio has 2 brothers and 2 sisters. Their parents assign chores to them each week. How many ways can two children be chosen to wash the dishes?

Since the order in which the children are chosen does not matter, we need to find the number of combinations of 5 children taken 2 at a time.

$C(n, r) = \frac{\text{number of permutations}}{\text{number of permutations with identical objects}}$

First find the number of permutations.

$P(5, 2) = \frac{5!}{3!}$ or 20 $\quad$ **$n = 5$ and $r = 2$**

Because we are choosing 2, there are $2! = 2$ permutations with identical objects.

$C(n, r) = \frac{20}{2}$ or 10

There are 10 possible ways to choose 2 children.

Check Your Progress

3. **TEST** Louis is given the option of answering any 10 out of the 12 questions on his history test. How many ways can he complete the test? **66**

Personal Tutor glencoe.com

We can now state a formula for combinations.

Key Concept Combination Formula

For Your FOLDABLE

Words The number of combinations of n objects taken r at a time is the quotient of $n!$ and $(n - r)!r!$.

Symbols $C(n, r) = \frac{n!}{(n-r)!r!}$

Real-World EXAMPLE 4 Use the Combination Formula

RETAIL Marques works part-time at a local department store. His manager asked him to choose for display 5 different styles of shirts from the wall of the store that has 8 shirts on it to put in a display. How many ways can Marques choose the shirts?

$C(n, r) = \frac{n!}{(n-r)!r!}$	**Combination Formula**
$= \frac{8!}{(8-5)!5!}$	**$n = 8$ and $r = 5$**
$= \frac{8!}{3!5!}$	**Simplify.**
$= \frac{8 \cdot 7 \cdot 6 \cdot \cancel{5} \cdot \cancel{4} \cdot \cancel{3} \cdot \cancel{2} \cdot \cancel{1}}{3 \cdot 2 \cdot 1 \cdot \cancel{5} \cdot \cancel{4} \cdot \cancel{3} \cdot \cancel{2} \cdot \cancel{1}}$	**Divide by common factors.**
$= \frac{336}{6}$ or 56	**There are 56 ways for Marques to select 5 shirts.**

StudyTip

Combination Formula The number of combinations is the quotient of the number of permutations of n objects taken r at a time and the number of permutations of r objects.

Check Your Progress

4. **SPRING DANCE** A group of four students is selecting corsages and boutonnières to wear to the spring dance. They can choose from 18 different flowers which consist of 4 roses, 6 carnations, and 8 tulips. In how many ways can 4 flowers be chosen to wear? **3060**

Personal Tutor glencoe.com

Differentiated Instruction

AL OL

Logical Learners After students learn how to calculate the number of combinations in Examples 3 and 4, discuss the difference between combinations and permutations. In Example 4, the order in which the shirts are chosen does not matter because only a group of shirts is being chosen. However, if Marques were deciding where in the display to place each shirt, then the order would matter.

766 Chapter 12 Statistics and Probability

Watch Out!

Combinations Not all everyday uses of the word *combination* are descriptions of mathematical combinations. Notice that in Example 5, the combination of a lock is described by a permutation.

We can use permutations or combinations to find the probability of an event.

Real-World EXAMPLE 5 Probability Using a Permutation

BICYCLES A combination lock requires a three-digit code made up of the digits 0 through 9. No number can be used more than once.

a. How many different arrangements are possible?

Since the order of the numbers in the code is important, this is a permutation of 10 digits taken 3 at a time.

$P(n, r) = \frac{n!}{(n - r)!}$ — Permutation Formula

$= \frac{10!}{(10 - 3)!}$ — $n = 10$ and $r = 3$

$= \frac{10!}{7!}$ — Simplify.

$= \frac{10 \cdot 9 \cdot 8 \cdot \cancel{7} \cdot \cancel{6} \cdot \cancel{5} \cdot \cancel{4} \cdot \cancel{3} \cdot \cancel{2} \cdot \cancel{1}}{\cancel{7} \cdot \cancel{6} \cdot \cancel{5} \cdot \cancel{4} \cdot \cancel{3} \cdot \cancel{2} \cdot \cancel{1}}$ — Divide by common factors.

$= 720$ — Simplify.

There are 720 possible codes.

b. What is the probability that all of the digits are odd?

Use the Fundamental Counting Principle to determine the number of ways for the three digits to be odd.

- There are five odd digits: 1, 3, 5, 7, and 9.
- The number of choices for the three digits, if they are odd, is $5 \cdot 4 \cdot 3$. So, the number of favorable outcomes is 60.

$P(\text{all digits odd}) = \frac{60}{720}$ ← number of favorable outcomes / ← number of possible outcomes

$= \frac{1}{12}$ — Simplify.

The probability that all of the digits are odd numbers is $\frac{1}{12}$ or about 8%.

Check Your Progress

SPANISH CLUB The Spanish club is electing a president, vice president, secretary, and treasurer. Rebekah and Lydia are among the nine students who are running.

5A. How many ways can the Spanish club choose their officers? 3024

5B. Assuming that the positions are chosen at random, what is the probability that either Rebekah or Lydia will be chosen as president or vice president?

5B. $\frac{5}{12}$ or about 41.7%

Personal Tutor glencoe.com

Check Your Understanding

Example 1 p. 764

1. CHARITY A youth charity group is holding a raffle and wants to display a picture of the 6 prizes on a flyer. How many ways can they arrange the prizes in a row? 720

Examples 2–4 pp. 765–766

Evaluate each expression.

2. $P(7, 2)$ 42 **3.** $P(9, 3)$ 504 **4.** $C(6, 4)$ 15 **5.** $C(5, 2)$ 10

6. RECYCLING Juana is setting recycling bins out for pick-up. She has one bin each for glass, plastic, paper and aluminum. How many ways can she arrange the bins in a row? 24

Additional Example

5 PARADE A group of 7 Army ROTC members, 5 Air Force ROTC members, 6 Navy ROTC members, and 4 Marine ROTC members have volunteered to participate in a flag-raising ceremony.

a. In how many ways can 12 ROTC members be chosen to march? 646,646

b. If the 12 ROTC members are chosen randomly, what is the probability that 3 ROTC members from each branch of the military will be selected? $\frac{28{,}000}{646{,}646}$

Tips for New Teachers

Pacing Because permutations and combinations are frequently confused, consider discussing many examples of each. For each example, show how to find the number of permutations or combinations.

3 PRACTICE

Formative Assessment

Use Exercises 1–8 to check for understanding.

Use the chart at the bottom of the next page to customize assignments for your students.

Watch Out!

Find the Error For Exercise 35, ask students if order is important in this problem. Then remind them that when the order is not important, the Combination Formula should be used.

Tips for New Teachers

Reasoning Remind students to check the reasonableness of their answers when finding permutations, combinations, and probabilities. For example, when finding a probability the answer must be a number between 0 and 1.

7. **FOOD** Linda is preparing to bake a cake. She gets the ingredients out and sets them on the counter top. Six of the 14 ingredients are spices. How many ways can she arrange the spices in a row on the countertop? **720**

Example 5 p. 767

8. **ICE CREAM** The Dairy Barn offers 5 varieties of chocolate ice cream, 4 varieties of candy-flavored ice cream, and 6 varieties of berry-flavored ice cream.
   a. In how many ways can a customer choose 3 different flavors of ice cream? **455**
   b. Does the selection involve a *permutation* or a *combination*? **combination**
   c. If the ice cream flavors are chosen randomly, what is the probability that a customer will select all chocolate? $\frac{2}{91}$ **or about 2.2%**

Practice and Problem Solving

● = **Step-by-Step Solutions** begins on page R12.
Extra Practice begins on page 815.

Example 1 p. 764

9. **PHOTOGRAPHY** The four captains of the football team are being arranged in a row for a newspaper photograph. How many ways can the photographer arrange the players for the photograph? **24**

10. **SCIENCE FAIR** There are 8 finalists in a science fair competition. How many ways can they stand in a row on the stage? **40,320**

11. **AMUSEMENT PARKS** Tino is entering an amusement park with 5 of his friends. At the gate they must go through a turnstile one by one. How many ways can Tino and his friends go in? **720**

12. **JOBS** At a fast food restaurant there are 4 employees that are capable of running the cash registers. How many ways can the manager arrange the employees at the four front counter registers? **24**

Examples 2–4 pp. 765–766

Evaluate each expression.

13. $P(6, 6)$ **720**
14. $P(5, 1)$ **5**
15. $P(4, 1)$ **4**
16. $P(7, 3)$ **210**
17. $C(7, 6)$ **7**
18. $C(5, 3)$ **10**
19. $C(5, 5)$ **1**
20. $C(3, 0)$ **1**

21. **DANCE** At the spring dance, Christy and 7 of her friends sit on one side of a table. How many ways can they fill the 10 empty seats? **1,814,400**

22. **JEWELRY** Jewel works at the jewelry store in the mall. Her manager asks her to place 3 of the 12 birthstone necklaces in the front display case. How many ways can she arrange the necklaces in the display case? **1320**

Example 5 p. 767

23. **MARBLES** Fifteen marbles out of 20 must be randomly selected. There are 7 red marbles, 8 purple marbles, and 5 green marbles from which to choose. What is the probability that 5 of each color are selected? $\frac{49}{646}$ **or about 7.59%**

24. **SCHOOL PLAY** Westerville High school is seeking volunteers to help decorate for the winter dance. In all, 4 freshmen, 5 sophomores, 6 juniors, and 8 seniors tried out for the 12 open spots.
   a. How many ways can the 12 spots be chosen? **1,352,078**
   b. If the students are chosen randomly, what is the probability that at least one senior will be chosen? $1 - \frac{455}{1,352,078}$ **or about 99.97%**

Differentiated Homework Options

Level	Assignment	Two-Day Option	
AL Basic	9–24, 35, 37–62	9–23 odd, 40–43	10–24 even, 35, 37–39, 44–62
OL Core	9–23 odd, 25–35, 37–62	9–24, 40–43	25–35, 37–39, 44–62
BL Advanced	25–56, (optional: 57–62)		

768 Chapter 12 Statistics and Probability

B Determine whether each situation involves a *permutation* or a *combination*.

25. choosing 3 different pizza toppings from a list of 12 **combination**
26. selecting 4 different ingredients out of 8 for a salad **combination**
27. choosing team captains for a football team **combination**
28. choosing the first-, second-, and third-place winner of an art competition **permutation**
29. selecting 5 books to read from a list of 8 **combination**
30. an arrangement of the letters in the word *probability* **permutation**

31. **GAMES** Tonisha is playing a game in which you make words to score points. There are 12 letters in the box, and she must choose 4. She cannot see the letters.
   a. Suppose the 12 letters are all different. In how many ways can she choose 4? **495**
   b. She chooses A, T, R, and E. How many different arrangements of three letters can she make? **24 arrangements**
   c. How many of the three-letter arrangements are words? List them. **9; ART, ATE, ARE, TAR, TEA, RAT, EAT, EAR, ERA**
32. **PAGEANTS** The Teen Miss USA pageant has 51 contestants. The judges choose Teen Miss USA and four runners-up.
   a. Does the selection involve a *permutation* or a *combination*? Explain. **permutation**
   b. In how many ways can the judges choose Teen Miss USA and four runners-up? **281,887,200**
33. **BASKETBALL** The coach had to select 5 out of 12 players on the team to start the game. How many different groups of players could be selected as starters? **792 groups**
34. **LOCKER** Christopher cannot remember the order of his locker combination. He only remembers that it contains the numbers 5, 16, and 31. What is the maximum number of attempts Christopher could make? **6 attempts**

35. Ming; since order is not important, combinations should have been used.
37. Determining class rank in a senior class; this is the only situation in which order matters.
38. Sometimes; the statement is true when $r = 1$ because order is irrelevant when choosing 1 item.

Real-World Link

A recent study found that schools with higher levels of student participation in the fine arts receive higher academic ratings and have lower dropout rates.

Source: The National Association for Music Education

H.O.T. Problems

Use Higher-Order Thinking Skills

35. **FIND THE ERROR** Sydney and Ming want to form a 4-person committee to be in charge of decorations for the dance. They are determining how many committees are possible if 10 people are available. Is either of them correct? C

Sydney	Ming
$P(10, 4) = \frac{10!}{(10-4)!}$ $= 5040$	$C(10, 4) = \frac{10!}{(10-4)!4!}$ $= 210$

36. **CHALLENGE** Seven identical mathematics books and 4 identical science books are to be stored on one shelf. In how many different ways can the books be arranged? **330**
37. **WHICH ONE DOESN'T BELONG?** Determine which situation does not belong. Explain.

choosing 5 players on a quiz team	choosing 10 colored marbles from a bag
choosing 4 horses from 6 to run race	ranking students in a senior class

38. **REASONING** Determine whether the statement $P(n, r) = C(n, r)$ is *sometimes*, *always*, or *never* true. Explain your reasoning.
39. **WRITING IN MATH** Write a situation in which order is not important when 3 of 8 objects are being selected. **Sample answer: choosing 3 clubs out of 8 to join**

Study Guide and Intervention
CRM pp. 23–24 AL OL ELL

NAME ______ DATE ______ PERIOD ______

12-4 Study Guide and Intervention
Permutations and Combinations

Permutations An arrangement or listing in which order or placement is important is called a **permutation.** For example, the arrangement AB of choices A and B is different from the arrangement BA of these same two choices.

Permutations	$P(n, r) = \frac{n!}{(n-r)!}$

Example 1 Find $P(6, 2)$.

$P(n, r) = \frac{n!}{(n-r)!}$ Definition of $p(n, r)$

$P(6, 2) = \frac{6!}{(6-2)!}$ $n = 6, r = 2$

$= \frac{6!}{4!}$ Simplify.

$= \frac{6 \cdot 5 \cdot 4 \cdot 3 \cdot 2 \cdot 1}{4 \cdot 3 \cdot 2 \cdot 1}$ Definition of factorial

$= 6 \cdot 5$ or 30 Simplify.

There are 30 permutations of 6 objects taken 2 at a time.

Example 2 **PASSWORDS A specific program requires the user to enter a 5-digit password. The digits cannot repeat and can be any five of the digits 1, 2, 3, 4, 7, 8, and 9.**

a. How many different passwords are possible?

$P(n, r) = \frac{n!}{(n-r)!}$

$P(7, 5) = \frac{7!}{(7-5)!}$

$= \frac{7 \cdot 6 \cdot 5 \cdot 4 \cdot 3 \cdot 2 \cdot 1}{2 \cdot 1}$

$= 7 \cdot 6 \cdot 5 \cdot 4 \cdot 3$ or 2520

There are 2520 ways to create a password.

b. What is the probability that the first two digits are odd numbers with the other digits any of the remaining numbers?

$P(\text{first two digits odd}) = \frac{\text{number of favorable outcomes}}{\text{number of possible outcomes}}$

Since there are 4 odd digits, the number of choices for the first digit is 4, and the number of choices for the second digit is 3. Then there are 5 choices left for the third digit, 4 for the fourth, and 3 for the fifth, so the number of favorable outcomes is $4 \cdot 3 \cdot 5 \cdot 4 \cdot 3$, or 720.

The probability is $\frac{720}{2520} \approx 28.6\%$.

Exercises

Evaluate each expression.

1. $P(7, 4)$ **840**
2. $P(12, 7)$ **3,991,680**
3. $[P(9, 9)][P(16, 2)]$ **87,091,200**
4. **CLUBS** A club with ten members wants to choose a president, vice-president, secretary, and treasurer. Six of the members are women, and four are men.
   a. How many different sets of officers are possible? **5040**
   b. What is the probability that all officers will be women. **7.1%**

Lesson 12-4

Chapter 12 23 Glencoe Algebra 1

Practice
CRM p. 26 AL OL BL ELL

NAME ______ DATE ______ PERIOD ______

12-4 Practice
Permutations and Combinations

Use the Fundamental Counting Principle to evaluate each of the following.

1. **ERRANDS** Wesley needs to stop at 6 stores on the way home from work. How many ways can Wesley arrange the 6 stops he needs to make? **720**
2. **VOTING** There are 8 people waiting in line to cast their votes. How many ways can the pepole line up to vote? **40,320**

Evaluate each expression.

3. $P(11, 3)$ **990**
4. $P(6, 3)$ **120**
5. $P(15, 3)$ **2730**
6. $C(10, 9)$ **10**
7. $C(12, 9)$ **220**
8. $C(7, 3)$ **35**
9. $C(7, 4)$ **35**
10. $C(12, 4)$ **495**
11. $P(13, 3)$ **1716**
12. $C(16, 12)$ **1820**
13. $C(17, 2)$ **136**
14. $C(16, 15)$ **16**
15. $P(20, 5)$ **1,860,480**
16. $P(11, 7)$ **1,663,200**
17. $P(13, 1)$ **13**
18. $C(19, 16)$ **969**
19. $P(15, 4)$ **32,760**
20. $C(14, 7)$ **3432**
21. **SPORTS** In how many orders can the top five finishers in a race finish? **120**
22. **JUDICIAL PROCEDURE** The court system in a community needs to assign 3 out of 8 judges to a docket of criminal cases. Five of the judges are male and three are female.
   a. Does the selection of judges involve a permutation or a combination? **combination**
   b. In how many ways could three judges be chosen? **56**
   c. If the judges are chosen randomly, what is the probability that all 3 judges are male? $\frac{5}{28}$**, or about 18%**

Chapter 12 26 Glencoe Algebra 1

Word Problem Practice
CRM p. 27 AL OL BL ELL

NAME ______ DATE ______ PERIOD ______

12-4 Word Problem Practice
Permutations and Combinations

1. **CHORES** In Ashley's family there are 4 children and their mother and father. If two of the six must help clear the table after dinner, how many ways can two people be paired? **15**
2. **PUBLIC SERVICE** A county computer randomly selects jurors from the lawyer-approved potential juror list. How many ways are there for 12 jurors to be chosen from a pool of 20? **125,970**

Potential Jurors	
Fred	Jennifer
Sally	Carla
Mike	Sam
Tom	Sylvia
Maria	Jamal
Ted	Greg
Carlos	Todd
Dorothy	Lauren
Irene	Maya
Trish	Luke

3. **SPORTS** Hans' basketball team decides to choose two captains each week so that many players get the chance to be captain. Each week, each of the 11 players writes his name on a slip of paper. The papers are then placed in a container and mixed. The last week's captains draw two slips of paper from the container; these two people are captains for the following week. How many different pairs of captains can be formed? **55**
4. **PUZZLES** A popular newspaper puzzle involves a series of letters that can be rearranged to form a word. Will is writing his own version of the game for a school project. He wants to scramble the following word for his puzzle.

   numbers

   How many ways are there to arrange the letters with the letter *b* as the first letter? **720**
5. **HORSE RACING** In the 133rd running of the Kentucky Derby in 2007, there were 22 contenders.
   a. How many different ways can the horses finish the race? **22!**
   b. How many different ways can horses place first, second, and third? **9240**
   c. If all 22 horses have an equal chance of winning and 3 of the horses are female, what is the probability that a female horse places first, second, and third? $\frac{6}{22!}$

Lesson 12-4

Chapter 12 27 Glencoe Algebra 1

Enrichment
CRM p. 28 OL BL

NAME ______ DATE ______ PERIOD ______

12-4 Enrichment

A Great Pizza Deal

A television commercial advertised a pizza deal in which customers could choose two pizzas each with up to five toppings chosen from a set of eleven toppings. On the commercial, a boy claims that there are 1024^2 or 1,048,576 ways for the customer to choose the two pizzas. Is this a valid claim?

Pizza Deal!!
For a limited time, you can choose 2 pizzas with up to 5 toppings for only
$7.99!!!!!!!

Topping	Yes	No
Pepperoni	☐	☐
Sausage	☐	☐
Tomato	☐	☐
Green olives	☐	☐
Black olives	☐	☐
Mushrooms	☐	☐
Extra Cheese	☐	☐
Peppers	☐	☐
Onions	☐	☐
Pineapple	☐	☐

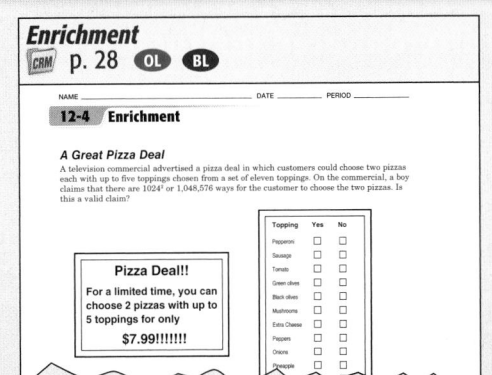

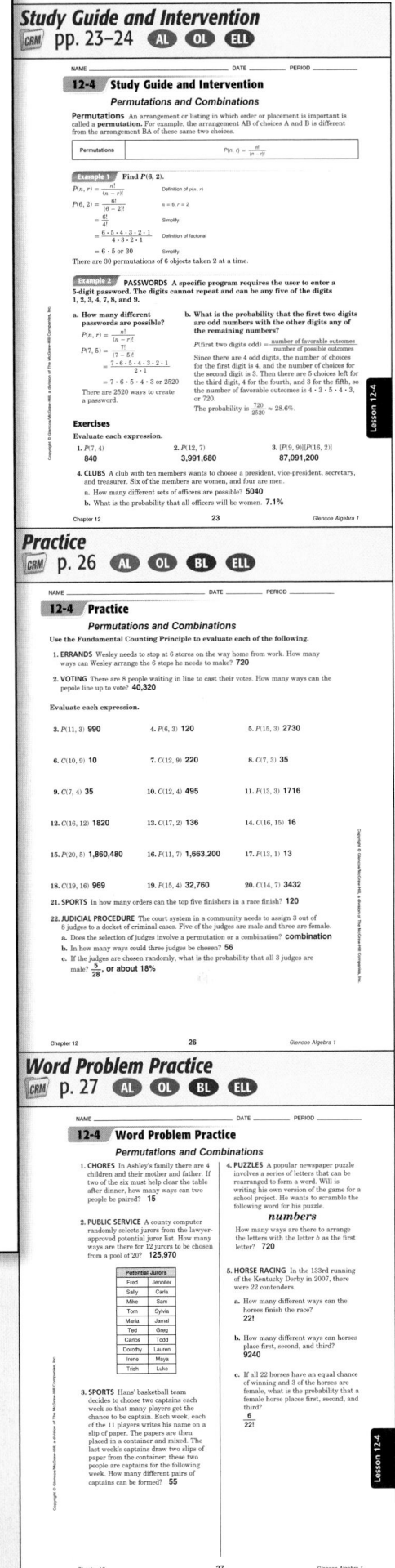

4 ASSESS

Crystal Ball Have students explain how today's concepts on permutation and combinations might help them with finding probabilities of compound events in the next lesson.

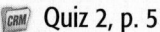

Formative Assessment

Check for student understanding of concepts in Lessons 12-3 and 12-4.

CRM Quiz 2, p. 51

PSAE PRACTICE 10.11.10, 6.11.17, 8.11.17, 10.11.07

40. A gardener wants to plant 3 different types of flowers along a path. If she is choosing from 8 different types of flowers, how many ways can the 3 flowers be planted? **C**

A 342 B 338 C 336 D 328

41. If Jack can tie 21 knots in 15 minutes, how many can he tie in 25 minutes if he continues at the same pace? **G**

F 18 G 35 H 36 J 37

42. Shante has 30 coins, quarters and dimes, that total $5.70. How many quarters does she have? **C**

A 12 C 18
B 15 D 20

43. SHORT RESPONSE There are 3 red candies in a bag of 20 candies. If you draw one without looking, what is the probability of drawing a red candy? $\frac{3}{20}$

Spiral Review

Find the mean, variance, and standard deviation of each set of data to the nearest tenth. (Lesson 12-3)

44. 76, 47, 59, 47, 72, 89 **65; 238.3; 15.4**

45. 20, 30, 10, 40, 20, 12, 50 **26; 187.4; 13.7**

46. 44, 34, 64, 74, 94, 104, 55 **67; 559.7; 23.7**

47. 1, 5, 9, 4, 2, 4, 8, 4, 2, 1 **4; 6.8; 2.6**

48. SURVEY A soda manufacturing company surveyed customers to find the number of cans of soda they drank in a week. They received the following responses: 14, 7, 3, 0, 10, 12, and 10. Which measure of central tendency best represents the data? Justify your answer. Then find the measure. (Lesson 12-2) **Mean; there are no outliers; 8.**

49. PET CARE Kendra takes care of pets while their owners are away. One week she has three dogs that all eat the same dog food at the rates shown. How many bags of food should Kendra buy for that week? (Lesson 11-6) **2 bags**

Max 12 days/bag Miles 15 days/bag Stormy 16 days/bag

Find each product. (Lesson 11-4)

50. $\frac{8}{x^2} \cdot \frac{x^4}{4x}$ $\mathbf{2x}$

51. $\frac{10r^3}{6n^3} \cdot \frac{42n^2}{35r^3}$ $\mathbf{\frac{2}{n}}$

52. $\frac{10y^3z^2}{6wx^3} \cdot \frac{12w^2x^2}{25y^2z^4}$ $\mathbf{\frac{4wy}{5xz^2}}$

53. $\frac{(n-1)(n+1)}{(n+1)} \cdot \frac{(n-4)}{(n-1)(n+4)}$ $\mathbf{\frac{n-4}{n+4}}$

54. $\frac{(x-8)}{(x+8)(x-3)} \cdot \frac{(x+4)(x-3)}{(x-8)}$ $\mathbf{\frac{x+4}{x+8}}$

55. $\frac{3a^2b}{2gh} \cdot \frac{24g^2h}{15ab^2}$ $\mathbf{\frac{12ag}{5b}}$

56. COOKING The formula $t = \frac{40(25 + 1.85a)}{50 - 1.85a}$ relates the time t in minutes that it takes to cook an average-size potato in an oven to the altitude a in thousands of feet. (Lesson 11-3)

a. What is the value of t for an altitude of 4500 feet? **4.5**

b. Calculate the time it takes to cook a potato at 3500 feet and at 7000 feet. How do your cooking times compare? **≈29 min; ≈41 min; The difference is about 12 minutes.**

Skills Review

Ten red tiles, 12 blue tiles, 8 green tiles, 4 yellow tiles, and 12 black tiles are placed in a bag and selected at random. Find each probability. (Lesson 0-11)

57. $P(\text{blue})$ $\frac{6}{23}$

58. $P(\text{red})$ $\frac{5}{23}$

59. $P(\text{black or yellow})$ $\frac{8}{23}$

60. $P(\text{green or red})$ $\frac{9}{23}$

61. $P(\text{not blue})$ $\frac{17}{23}$

62. $P(\text{not green})$ $\frac{19}{23}$

Differentiated Instruction OL BL

Extension Ask students whether they would expect the number of combinations of n items taken r at a time to be less or more than the number of permutations of n items taken r at a time. Have them explain their reasoning by using real-life examples. The number of combinations would be less than the number of permutations. Sample answer: If you listen to jazz recording A and jazz recording B in no particular order, this is a combination, and AB and BA are the same. If the order in which you listen to the recordings is important, then listening to the recordings in the order AB is different from listening to the recordings in the order BA. The number of combinations is therefore less than the number of permutations.

770 Chapter 12 Statistics and Probability

12-5 Probability of Compound Events

Then
You calculated simple probability. (Lesson 0-11)

Now
- Find probabilities of independent and dependent events.
- Find probabilities of mutually exclusive events.

IL Learning Standards

10.C.4a Solve problems of chance using the principles of probability including conditional settings.

IL Math Online

glencoe.com
- Extra Examples
- Personal Tutor
- Self-Check Quiz
- Homework Help
- Math in Motion

Why?

Evita is flying from Cleveland to Honolulu. The airline reports that the flight from Cleveland to Honolulu has a 40% on-time record. The airline also reported that they lose luggage 5% of the time. What is the probability that both the flight will be on time and Evita's luggage will arrive?

Independent and Dependent Events Recall that one event, like flying from Cleveland to Honolulu, is called a *simple event*. A **compound event** is made up of two or more simple events. So, the probability that the flight will be on time and the luggage arrives is an example of a compound event. The plane being on time may not affect whether luggage is lost. These two events are called **independent events** because the outcome of one event does not affect the outcome of the other.

Key Concept — Probability of Independent Events

For Your FOLDABLE

Words If two events, A and B, are independent, then the probability of both events occurring is the product of the probability of A and the probability of B.

Model

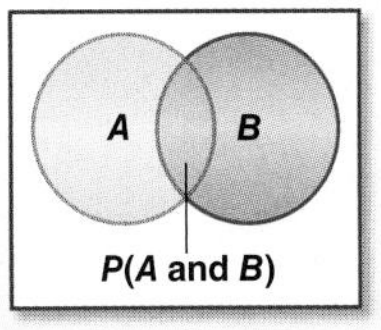

Symbols $P(A \text{ and } B) = P(A) \cdot P(B)$

Math in Motion, BrainPOP® glencoe.com

Real-World EXAMPLE 1 — Independent Events

MARBLES **A bag contains 6 black marbles, 9 blue marbles, 4 yellow marbles, and 2 green marbles. A marble is selected, replaced, and a second marble is selected. Find the probability of selecting a black marble, then a yellow marble.**

First marble: $P(\text{black}) = \frac{6}{21}$ ← number of black marbles / total number of marbles

Second marble: $P(\text{yellow}) = \frac{4}{21}$ ← number of yellow marbles / total number of marbles

$P(\text{black, yellow}) = P(\text{black}) \cdot P(\text{yellow})$ — Probability of independent events

$= \frac{6}{21} \cdot \frac{4}{21} \text{ or } \frac{24}{441}$ — Substitution

The probability is $\frac{24}{441}$ or about 5.4%.

Check Your Progress

Find each probability.

1A. $P(\text{blue, green})$ $\frac{18}{441}$ or about 4.1%

1B. $P(\text{not black, blue})$ $\frac{135}{441}$ or about 30.6%

Personal Tutor glencoe.com

12-5 Lesson Notes

1 FOCUS

Vertical Alignment

Before Lesson 12-5
Calculate simple probability.

Lesson 12-5
Find probabilities of independent and dependent events.
Find probabilities of mutually exclusive events.

After Lesson 12-5
Construct probability distributions.

2 TEACH

Scaffolding Questions

Have students read the *Why?* section of the lesson.

Ask:

- Suppose the flight is on time. Does this affect whether Evita's luggage is lost? no
- What does the word *independent* mean? free or unrelated
- Could the word *independent* be used to describe the relationship between "flight is on time" and "luggage is lost"? Yes, because a flight being on time does not affect whether luggage is lost; the events are independent of each other.

Lesson 12-5 Resources

Resource	Approaching-Level	On-Level	Beyond-Level	English Learners
Teacher Edition	• Differentiated Instruction, p. 773	• Differentiated Instruction, pp. 773, 778	• Differentiated Instruction, p. 778	
Chapter Resource Masters	• Study Guide and Intervention, pp. 29–30 • Skills Practice, p. 31 • Practice, p. 32 • Word Problem Practice, p. 33	• Study Guide and Intervention, pp. 29–30 • Skills Practice, p. 31 • Practice, p. 32 • Word Problem Practice, p. 33 • Enrichment, p. 34 • Graphing Calculator Activity, p. 35	• Practice, p. 32 • Word Problem Practice, p. 33 • Enrichment, p. 34	• Study Guide and Intervention, pp. 29–30 • Skills Practice, p. 31 • Practice, p. 32 • Word Problem Practice, p. 33
Transparencies	• 5-Minute Check Transparency 12-5	• 5-Minute Check Transparency 12-5	• 5-Minute Check Transparency 12-5	• 5-Minute Check Transparency 12-5
Other	• Study Notebook • Teaching Algebra with Manipulatives	• Study Notebook • Teaching Algebra with Manipulatives	• Study Notebook	• Study Notebook • Teaching Algebra with Manipulatives

Independent and Dependent Events

Example 1 shows how to find the probability of two independent events occurring. **Example 2** shows how to find the probability of dependent events occurring.

Formative Assessment

Use the Check Your Progress exercises after each example to determine students' understanding of concepts.

Additional Examples

1. **FLIGHTS** Rae is flying from Birmingham to Chicago on a flight with a 90% on-time record. On the same day, the chances of rain in Denver are predicted to be 50%. What is the probability that Rae's flight will be on time and that it will rain in Denver? 45%

2. **GAMES** At the school carnival, winners in the ring-toss game are randomly given a prize from a bag that contains 4 sunglasses, 6 hairbrushes, and 5 key chains. Three prizes are randomly chosen from the bag and not replaced. Find each probability.
   a. P(sunglasses, hairbrush, keychain) $\frac{4}{91}$
   b. P(hairbrush, hairbrush, not a hairbrush) $\frac{9}{91}$

Additional Examples also in Interactive Classroom PowerPoint® Presentations

IWB INTERACTIVE WHITEBOARD READY

When the outcome of one event affects the outcome of another event, they are **dependent events**. In Example 1, if the marble was not placed back in the bag, then drawing the two marbles would have been dependent events. The probability of drawing the second marble depends on what marble was drawn first.

Key Concept — Probability of Dependent Events (For Your FOLDABLE)

Words If two events, A and B, are dependent, then the probability of both events occurring is the product of the probability of A and the probability of B after A occurs.

Symbols $P(A \text{ and } B) = P(A) \cdot P(B \text{ following } A)$

Recall that the complement of a set is the set of all objects that do *not* belong to the given set. In a standard deck of cards, the complement of drawing a heart is drawing a diamond, club, or spade. So, the probability of drawing a heart is $\frac{13}{52}$, and the probability of not drawing a heart is $\frac{52-13}{52}$ or $\frac{39}{52}$.

The sum of the probabilities for any two complementary events is 1.

Real-World Link

A standard deck of cards consists of 52 cards. There are 4 suits: hearts, diamonds, clubs, and spades. There are 13 cards of each suit. An ace, 2, 3, 4, 5, 6, 7, 8, 9, 10, jack, queen, and king. The hearts and diamonds are red, and the clubs and spades are black.

Real-World EXAMPLE 2 Dependent Events

CARDS Cynthia randomly draws three cards from a standard deck one at a time without replacement. Find the probability that the cards are drawn in the given order.

a. P(diamond, spade, diamond)

First card: $P(\text{diamond}) = \frac{13}{52}$ or $\frac{1}{4}$ ← number of diamonds / total number of cards

Second card: $P(\text{spade}) = \frac{13}{51}$ ← number of spades / number of cards remaining

Third card: $P(\text{diamond}) = \frac{12}{50}$ or $\frac{6}{25}$ ← number of diamonds remaining / number of cards remaining

$P(\text{diamond, spade, diamond}) = P(\text{diamond}) \cdot P(\text{spade}) \cdot P(\text{diamond})$

$= \frac{1}{4} \cdot \frac{13}{51} \cdot \frac{6}{25}$ or $\frac{13}{850}$ Substitution

The probability is $\frac{13}{850}$ or about 1.5%.

b. P(four, four, not a jack)

After Cynthia draws the first two fours from the deck of 52 cards, there are 50 cards left. Since neither of these cards are jacks, there are still four jacks left in the deck. So, there are 52 − 2 − 4 or 46 cards that are not jacks.

$P(\text{four, four, not a jack}) = P(\text{four}) \cdot P(\text{four}) \cdot P(\text{not a jack})$

$= \frac{4}{52} \cdot \frac{3}{51} \cdot \frac{46}{50}$

$= \frac{552}{132{,}600}$ or $\frac{23}{5525}$

The probability is $\frac{23}{5525}$ or about 0.4%.

Problem-Solving Tip

Act It Out Acting out the situation can help you understand what the question is asking. Use a deck of cards to represent the situation described in the problem.

Check Your Progress Find each probability.

2A. P(two, five, not a five)   **2B.** P(heart, not a heart, heart)

2A. $\frac{752}{132{,}600}$ or about 0.6%
2B. $\frac{39}{850}$ or about 5%

Personal Tutor glencoe.com

TEACH with TECH

INTERACTIVE WHITEBOARD Use a Venn diagram to help students visualize a simple example using inclusive events. Let one circle represent condition A and let the other circle represent condition B. List each of the possible outcomes, and drag it into the appropriate part of the Venn diagram. Show students that you must subtract $P(A \text{ and } B)$ because it is the intersection of the two sets.

Mutually Exclusive Events Events that cannot occur at the same time are called **mutually exclusive events**. Suppose you wanted to find the probability of drawing a heart or a diamond. Since a card cannot be both a heart and a diamond, the events are mutually exclusive.

StudyTip

and* and *or While probabilities involving *and* deal with independent and dependent events, probabilities involving *or* deal with mutually exclusive and non-mutually exclusive events.

Key Concept: Mutually Exclusive Events

For Your FOLDABLE

Words If two events, A and B, are mutually exclusive, then the probability that either A or B occurs is the sum of their probabilities.

Symbols $P(A \text{ or } B) = P(A) + P(B)$

Model

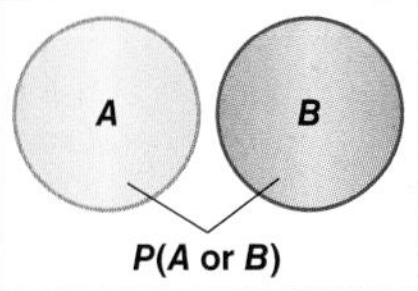

Real-World EXAMPLE 3 Mutually Exclusive Events

A die is being rolled. Find each probability.

a. $P(3 \text{ or } 5)$

Since a die cannot show both a 3 and a 5 at the same time, these events are mutually exclusive.

$P(\text{rolling a } 3) = \frac{1}{6}$ ← number of sides with a 3 / total number of sides

$P(\text{rolling a } 5) = \frac{1}{6}$ ← number of sides with a 5 / total number of sides

$P(3 \text{ or } 5) = P(\text{rolling a } 3) + P(\text{rolling a } 5)$ — **Probability of mutually exclusive events**

$= \frac{1}{6} + \frac{1}{6}$ — **Substitution**

$= \frac{2}{6} \text{ or } \frac{1}{3}$ — **Add.**

The probability of rolling a 3 or a 5 is $\frac{1}{3}$ or about 33%.

StudyTip

Alternative Method In Example 3a, you could have placed the number of possible outcomes over the total number of outcomes.

$\frac{1+1}{6} = \frac{2}{6} \text{ or } \frac{1}{3}$

b. $P(\text{at least } 4)$

Rolling at least a 4 means you can roll either a 4, 5, or a 6. So, you need to find the probability of rolling a 4, 5, or a 6.

$P(\text{rolling a } 4) = \frac{1}{6}$ ← number of sides with a 4 / total number of sides

$P(\text{rolling a } 5) = \frac{1}{6}$ ← number of sides with a 5 / total number of sides

$P(\text{rolling a } 6) = \frac{1}{6}$ ← number of sides with a 6 / total number of sides

$P(\text{at least } 4) = P(\text{rolling a } 4) + P(\text{rolling a } 5) + P(\text{rolling a } 6)$ — **Mutually exclusive events**

$= \frac{1}{6} + \frac{1}{6} + \frac{1}{6}$ — **Substitution**

$= \frac{3}{6} \text{ or } \frac{1}{2}$ — **Add.**

The probability of rolling at least a 4 is $\frac{1}{2}$ or about 50%.

Check Your Progress

3A. $P(\text{less than } 3)$ $\frac{1}{3}$ or about 33%

3B. $P(\text{even})$ $\frac{1}{2}$ or about 50%

Personal Tutor glencoe.com

Mutually Exclusive Events

Example 3 shows how to find the probability that either one or the other of two mutually exclusive events will occur. **Example 4** shows how to find the probability that either one or the other of two non-mutually exclusive events will occur.

Additional Example

3 A card is being drawn from a standard deck. Find each probability.

a. $P(7 \text{ or } 8)$ $\frac{2}{13}$

b. $P(\text{neither club nor heart})$ $\frac{1}{2}$

Focus on Mathematical Content

Mutually Exclusive Events Events that cannot occur at the same time are mutually exclusive. For example, if you randomly draw either a blue marble or a yellow marble from a bag of marbles, these events are mutually exclusive since you cannot draw a blue marble and a yellow marble at the same time. You find the probability of mutually exclusive events by finding the sum of the probabilities of each event. For example, if the probability of drawing a blue marble from the bag is $\frac{3}{8}$ and the probability of drawing a yellow marble is $\frac{1}{4}$, the probability of drawing either a blue marble or a yellow marble is $\frac{3}{8} + \frac{1}{4} = \frac{5}{8}$.

Differentiated Instruction

AL OL

Spatial/Visual Learners Bring a packet of raw sunflower seeds or other fast-sprouting seeds to class. Ensure that there are slightly more seeds than students. Explain that each student will take a seed and plant it either on school grounds or in a small plant pot. As students take a seed from the packet, lead them to understand that the number of seeds from which they can choose is a dependent event for all but the first student who chooses.

Additional Example

4 **GAMES** In the game of bingo, balls or tiles are numbered 1 through 75. These numbers correspond to columns on a bingo card, as shown in the table. A number is selected at random. What is the probability that it is a multiple of 5 or is in the N column? $\frac{9}{25}$

B	I	N	G	O
1–15	16–30	31–45	46–60	61–75

Tips for New Teachers

Sense-Making Point out to students that the Venn diagram of two mutually exclusive events does not have overlapping circles, while the Venn diagrams of two events that are not mutually exclusive will have overlapping circles. Ask students to explain why the diagrams are drawn that way.

ReadingMath

A or B Unlike everyday language, the expression *A* or *B* allows the possibility of both *A* and *B* occurring.

Suppose you want to find the probability of randomly drawing a 2 or a diamond from a standard deck of cards. Since it is possible to draw a card that is both a 2 and a diamond, these events are not mutually exclusive.

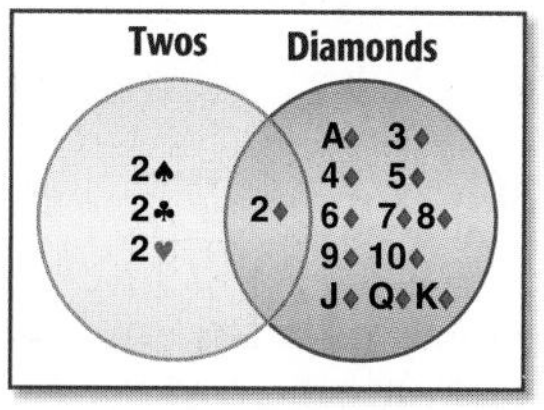

$P(2)$	$P(\text{diamond})$	$P(2, \text{diamond})$
$\frac{4}{52}$	$\frac{13}{52}$	$\frac{1}{52}$

In the first two fractions above, the probability of drawing the two of diamonds is counted twice, once for a two and once for a diamond. To find the correct probability, subtract P(2 of diamonds) from the sum of the first two probabilities.

$$P(2 \text{ or a diamond}) = P(2) + P(\text{diamond}) - P(2 \text{ of diamonds})$$
$$= \frac{4}{52} + \frac{13}{52} - \frac{1}{52}$$
$$= \frac{16}{52} \text{ or } \frac{4}{13}$$

The probability is $\frac{4}{13}$ or about 31%.

Watch Out!

Intersection of Events When determining the probability of events that are not mutually exclusive, you may count the intersection of the events twice since it occurs in both events. It only actually occurs once.

Key Concept — Events that are Not Mutually Exclusive

For Your FOLDABLE

Words If two events, *A* and *B*, are not mutually exclusive, then the probability that either *A* or *B* occurs is the sum of their probabilities decreased by the probability of both occurring.

Model

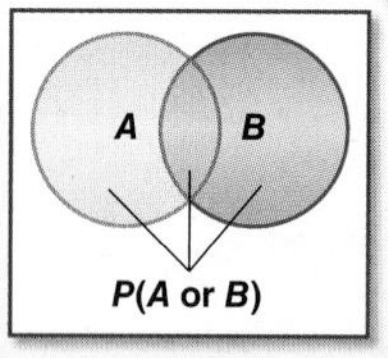

Symbols $P(A \text{ or } B) = P(A) + P(B) - P(A \text{ and } B)$

Real-World EXAMPLE 4 Events that are Not Mutually Exclusive

STUDENT ATHLETES Of 240 girls, 176 are on the Honor Roll, 48 play sports, and 36 are on the Honor Roll and play sports. What is the probability that a randomly selected student plays sports or is on the Honor Roll?

Since some students play sports and are on the Honor Roll, the events are not mutually exclusive.

$P(\text{sports}) = \frac{48}{240}$ $\quad P(\text{Honor Roll}) = \frac{176}{240}$ $\quad P(\text{sports and Honor Roll}) = \frac{36}{240}$

$$P(\text{sports or Honor Roll}) = P(\text{sports}) + P(\text{HR}) - P(\text{sports and HR})$$
$$= \frac{48}{240} + \frac{176}{240} - \frac{36}{240} \quad \textbf{Substitution}$$
$$= \frac{188}{240} \text{ or } \frac{47}{60} \quad \textbf{Simplify.}$$

The probability is $\frac{47}{60}$ or about 78%.

Check Your Progress

4. **PETS** Out of 5200 households surveyed, 2107 had a dog, 807 had a cat, and 303 had both a dog and a cat. What is the probability that a randomly selected household has a dog or a cat? $\frac{2611}{5200}$ or about 50%

Personal Tutor glencoe.com

Check Your Understanding

Examples 1 and 2
pp. 771–772

Determine whether the events are *independent* or *dependent*. Then find the probability.

1. **BABYSITTING** A toy bin contains 12 toys, 8 stuffed animals, and 3 board games. Marsha randomly chooses 2 items for the child she is babysitting. What is the probability that she chose 2 stuffed animals as the first two choices? dependent; $\frac{28}{253}$ or about 11%
2. **FRUIT** A basket contains 6 apples, 5 bananas, 4 oranges, and 5 peaches. Drew randomly chooses one piece of fruit, eats it, and chooses another. What is the probability that he chose a banana and then an apple? dependent; $\frac{3}{38}$ or about 8%
3. **MONEY** Nakos has 4 quarters, 3 dimes, and 2 nickels in his pocket. Nakos randomly picks two coins out of his pocket. What is the probability that he did not choose a dime either time, if he replaced the first coin before choosing a second coin? independent; $\frac{4}{9}$ or about 44%
4. **BOOKS** Joanna needs a book to prop up a table leg. She randomly selects a book, puts it back on the shelf, and selects another book. What is the probability that Joanna selected two math books? independent; $\frac{64}{289}$ or about 22%

Examples 3 and 4
pp. 773–774

A card is drawn from a standard deck of playing cards. Determine whether the events are *mutually exclusive* or *not* mutually exclusive. Then find the probability.

5. P(two or queen)
6. P(diamond or heart)
7. P(seven or club)
8. P(spade or ace)

5. mutually exclusive; $\frac{2}{13}$ or about 15%
6. mutually exclusive; $\frac{1}{2}$ or about 50%
7. not mutually exclusive; $\frac{4}{13}$ or about 31%
8. not mutually exclusive; $\frac{4}{13}$ or about 31%
9. independent; $\frac{1}{16}$ or about 6%
10. independent; $\frac{5}{6}$ or about 83%
12. independent; $\frac{1}{6}$ or about 17%

Practice and Problem Solving

● = **Step-by-Step Solutions** begin on page R12. **Extra Practice** begins on page 815.

Examples 1 and 2
pp. 771–772

Determine whether the events are *independent* or *dependent*. Then find the probability.

9. **COINS** If a coin is tossed 4 times, what is the probability of getting tails all 4 times?
10. **DICE** A die is rolled twice. What is the probability of rolling two different numbers?
11. **CANDY** A box of chocolates contains 10 milk chocolates, 8 dark chocolates, and 6 white chocolates. Sung randomly chooses a chocolate, eats it, and then randomly chooses another. What is the probability that Sung chose a milk chocolate and then a white chocolate? dependent; $\frac{5}{46}$ or about 11%
12. **DICE** A die is rolled twice. What is the probability of rolling the same numbers?
13. **PETS** Chuck and Rashid went to a pet store to buy dog food. They chose from 10 brands of dry food, 6 brands of canned food, and 3 brands of pet snacks. What is the probability that both chose dry food, if Chuck randomly chose first and liked the first brand he picked up? dependent; $\frac{5}{19}$ or about 26%
14. **CARS** A rental agency has 12 white sedans, 8 gray sedans, 6 red sedans, and 3 green sedans for rent. Mr. Escobar rents a sedan, returns it because the radio is broken, and gets another sedan. Assuming the returned sedan remains in circulation, what is the probability that Mr. Escobar was given a green sedan and then a gray sedan? independent; $\frac{24}{841}$ or about 3%

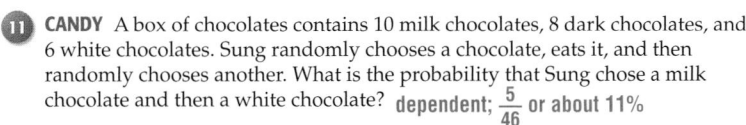

Real-World Link

About 65% of pet owners acquire their pets free or at low cost.

Source: National Council or Pet Population Study and Policy

3 PRACTICE

Formative Assessment

Use Exercises 1–8 to check for understanding.

Use the chart at the bottom of this page to customize assignments for your students.

Watch Out!

Preventing Errors Students are often confused about whether compound events are dependent, independent, mutually exclusive, or inclusive. You might want to preview Exercises 9–20 with the class before they begin the exercises. Ask students to identify the type of compound event in each exercise. If students consistently fail to identify the type of event, suggest that they review each of the examples in the lesson.

Differentiated Homework Options

Level	Assignment	Two-Day Option	
AL Basic	9–18, 34, 36–56	9–17 odd, 39–42	10–18 even, 34, 36–38, 43–56
OL Core	9–29 odd, 30–34, 36–56	9–18, 39–42	19–34, 36–38, 43–56
BL Advanced	19–50, (optional: 51–56)		

Examples 3 and 4
pp. 773–774

Determine whether the events are *mutually exclusive* or *not* mutually exclusive. Then find the probability.

Real-World Link

A bowling museum and hall of fame is located in St. Louis, Missouri. The museum spans 50,000 square feet and is 3 stories tall.

Source: International Bowling Museum and Hall of Fame

15. BOWLING Cindy's bowling records indicate that for any frame, the probability that she will bowl a strike is 30%, a spare 45%, and neither 25%. What is the probability that she will bowl either a spare or a strike for any given frame? **mutually exclusive; $\frac{3}{4}$ or 75%**

16. SPORTS CARDS Dario owns 145 baseball cards, 102 football cards, and 48 basketball cards. What is the probability that he randomly selects a baseball or a football card? **mutually exclusive; $\frac{247}{295}$ or about 84%**

17. SCHOLARSHIPS 3000 essays were received for a $5000 college scholarship. 2865 essays were the required length, 2577 of the applicants had the minimum required grade-point average, and 2486 had the required length and minimum grade-point average. What is the probability that an essay selected at random will have the required length or the required grade-point average?

18. KITTENS Ruby's cat had 8 kittens. The litter included 2 orange females, 3 mixed-color females, 1 orange male, and 2 mixed-color males. Ruby wants to keep one kitten. What is the probability that she randomly chooses a kitten that is female or orange? **not mutually exclusive; $\frac{3}{4}$ or about 75%**

B

CHIPS A restaurant serves red, blue, and yellow tortilla chips. The bowl of chips Gabriel receives has 10 red chips, 8 blue chips, and 12 yellow chips. After Gabriel chooses a chip, he eats it. Find each probability.

19. P(red, blue) **$\frac{8}{87}$ or about 9%**

20. P(blue, yellow) **$\frac{16}{145}$ or about 11%**

21. P(yellow, not blue) **$\frac{42}{145}$ or about 29%**

22. P(red, not yellow) **$\frac{17}{87}$ or about 20%**

23. SOCKS Damon has 14 white socks, 6 black socks, and 4 blue socks in his drawer. If he chooses two socks at random, what is the probability that the first two socks are white? **$\frac{91}{276}$ or about 33%**

Cards are being randomly drawn from a standard deck of cards. Once a card is drawn, it is not replaced. Find each probability.

24. P(heart or spade)

25. P(spade or club)

26. P(queen, then heart)

27. P(jack, then spade)

28. P(five, then red)

29. P(ace or black)

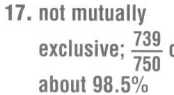

17. not mutually exclusive; $\frac{739}{750}$ or about 98.5%

24. $\frac{1}{2}$ or 50%

25. $\frac{1}{2}$ or 50%

26. $\frac{4}{221}$ or about 2%

27. $\frac{4}{221}$ or about 2%

28. $\frac{25}{663}$ or about 4%

29. $\frac{7}{13}$ or about 54%

C

30. CANDY A bag contains 10 red, 6 green, 7 yellow, and 5 orange jelly beans. What is the probability of randomly choosing a red jelly bean, replacing, randomly choosing another red jelly bean, replacing, and then randomly choosing an orange jelly bean? **$\frac{125}{5488}$ or about 2%**

31. SPORTS The extracurricular activities in which the senior class at Valley View High School participate are shown in the Venn diagram.

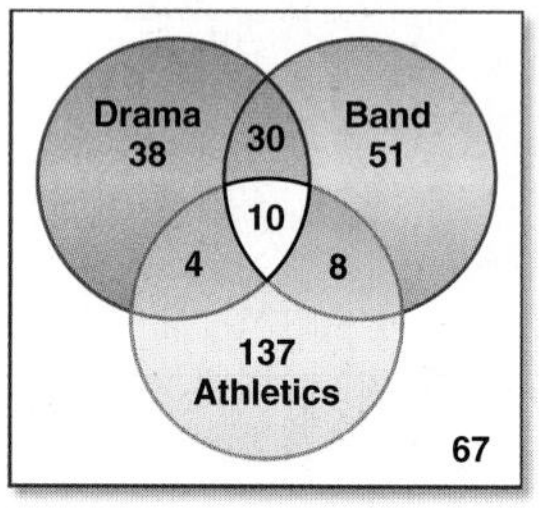

a. How many students are in the senior class? **345**

b. How many students participate in athletics? **159**

c. If a student is randomly chosen, what is the probability that the student participates in athletics or drama? **$\frac{227}{345}$ or about 66%**

d. If a student is randomly chosen, what is the probability that the student participates in only drama and band? **$\frac{2}{23}$ or about 9%**

Study Guide and Intervention
CRM pp. 29–30 AL OL ELL

NAME ______ DATE ______ PERIOD ______

12-5 Study Guide and Intervention
Probability of Compound Events

Independent and Dependent Events **Compound events** are made up of two or more simple events. The events can be **independent events** or they can be **dependent events**.

Probability of Independent Events	Outcome of first event does not affect outcome of second.	$P(A \text{ and } B) = P(A) \cdot P(B)$	Example: rolling a 6 on a die and then rolling a 5
Probability of Dependent Events	Outcome of first event does affect outcome of second.	$P(A \text{ and } B) = P(A) \cdot P(B \text{ following } A)$	Example: without replacing the first card, choosing an ace and then a king from a deck of cards

Example 1 **Find the probability that you will roll a six and then a five when you roll a die twice.**

By the definition of independent events, $P(A \text{ and } B) = P(A) \cdot P(B)$

First roll: $P(6) = \frac{1}{6}$

Second roll: $P(5) = \frac{1}{6}$

$P(6 \text{ and } 5) = P(6) \cdot P(5) = \frac{1}{6} \cdot \frac{1}{6} = \frac{1}{36}$

The probability that you will roll a six and then roll a five is $\frac{1}{36}$.

Example 2 **A bag contains 3 red marbles, 2 green marbles, and 4 blue marbles. Two marbles are drawn randomly from the bag and not replaced. Find the probability that both marbles are blue.**

By the definition of dependent events, $P(A \text{ and } B) = P(A) \cdot P(B \text{ following } A)$

First marble: $P(\text{blue}) = \frac{4}{9}$

Second marble: $P(\text{blue}) = \frac{3}{8}$

$P(\text{blue, blue}) = \frac{4}{9} \cdot \frac{3}{8} = \frac{12}{72} = \frac{1}{6}$

The probability of drawing two blue marbles is $\frac{1}{6}$.

Exercises

A bag contains 3 red, 4 blue, and 6 yellow marbles. One marble is selected at a time, and once a marble is selected, it is not replaced. Find each probability.

1. P(2 yellow) **$\frac{5}{26}$**
2. P(red, yellow) **$\frac{3}{26}$**
3. P(blue, red, yellow) **$\frac{6}{143}$**
4. George has two red socks and two white socks in a drawer. What is the probability of picking a red sock and a white sock in that order if the first sock is not replaced? **$\frac{1}{3}$**
5. Phyllis drops a penny in a pond, and then she drops a nickel in the pond. What is the probability that both coins land with tails showing? **$\frac{1}{4}$**
6. A die is rolled and a penny is dropped. Find the probability of rolling a two and showing a tail. **$\frac{1}{12}$**

Lesson 12-5

Practice
CRM p. 32 AL OL BL ELL

NAME ______ DATE ______ PERIOD ______

12-5 Practice
Probability of Compound Events

A bag contains 5 red, 3 brown, 6 yellow, and 2 blue marbles. Once a marble is selected, it is not replaced. Find each probability.

1. P(brown, then yellow, then red) **$\frac{3}{112}$**
2. P(red, then red, then blue) **$\frac{1}{84}$**
3. P(yellow, then yellow, then *not* blue) **$\frac{3}{28}$**
4. P(brown, then brown, then *not* yellow) **$\frac{1}{70}$**

A die is rolled and a card is drawn from a standard deck of 52 cards. Find each probability.

5. P(6 and king) **$\frac{1}{78}$**
6. P(odd number and black) **$\frac{1}{4}$**
7. P(less than 3 and heart) **$\frac{1}{12}$**
8. P(greater than 1 and black ace) **$\frac{5}{156}$**

A card is being drawn from a standard deck of playing cards. Determine whether the events are *mutually exclusive* or *not* mutually exclusive. Then find the probability.

9. P(spade or numbered card) **not; $\frac{10}{13}$**
10. P(ace or red queen) **mutually exclusive; $\frac{3}{26}$**
11. P(red or *not* face card) **not; $\frac{11}{13}$**
12. P(heart or *not* queen) **not; $\frac{49}{52}$**

Tiles numbered 1 through 25 are placed in a box. Tiles numbered 11 through 30 are placed in a second box. The first tile is randomly drawn from the first box. The second tile is randomly drawn from the second box. Find each probability.

13. P(both are greater than 15 and less than 20) **$\frac{4}{125}$**
14. The first tile is greater than 10 and the second tile is less than 25 or even. **$\frac{51}{100}$**
15. The first tile is a multiple of 3 or prime and the second tile is a multiple of 5. **$\frac{16}{125}$**
16. The first tile is less than 9 or odd and the second tile is a multiple of 4 or less than 21. **$\frac{51}{125}$**
17. **WEATHER** The forecast predicts a 40% chance of rain on Tuesday and a 60% chance on Wednesday. If these probabilities are independent, what is the chance that it will rain on both days? **24%**
18. **FOOD** Tomaso places favorite recipes in a bag for 4 pasta dishes, 5 casseroles, 3 types of chili, and 8 desserts.
    a. If Tomaso chooses one recipe at random, what is the probability that he selects a pasta dish or a casserole? **$\frac{9}{20}$**
    b. If Tomaso chooses one recipe at random, what is the probability that he does *not* select a dessert? **$\frac{3}{5}$**
    c. If Tomaso chooses two recipes at random without replacement, what is the probability that the first recipe he selects is a casserole and the second recipe he selects is a dessert? **$\frac{2}{19}$**

Word Problem Practice
CRM p. 33 AL OL BL ELL

NAME ______ DATE ______ PERIOD ______

12-5 Word Problem Practice
Probability of Compound Events

1. **BIRTHDAYS** On Juanita's birthday, her grandmother sends her a card. What is the probability that the man who delivered the mail has a birthday either the same day or one day before or after? Disregard February 29 as a possible birthday, and assume that all days are equally likely. **≈ 0.82%**

2. **SPORTS** The World Series is a "best of seven" game championship in which up to seven games are played, and one team has to win four games to win the Series. In the 2007 World Series, the Boston Red Sox swept the Colorado Rockies, meaning that they won the series by winning the first four games. If you assume that each team has an equal chance of winning each game, what is the probability of a World Series sweep? **0.0625 or 6.25%**

3. **BUSINESS** At Corrugated Packaging, Inc., a team of six employees is in charge of marketing and selling the company's products; three are women and three are men. The president of the company decides to send four team members to a national cardboard box conference. He wants to make sure he chooses names fairly, so he decides to put the names of his six sales employees in a hat and draw four names to see who will go to the conference. What is the probability that the team will consist of three women and one man? **0.2 or 20%**

4. **MAGIC** Iris performs a magic trick in which she holds a standard deck of cards and has each of three people randomly choose a card from the deck. Each person keeps his or her card as the next person draws. What is the probability that all three people will draw a heart? **0.0129 or 1.29%**

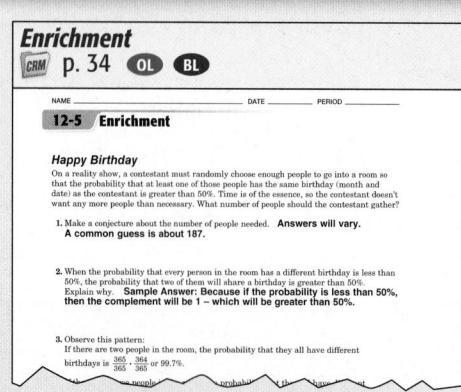

5. **STOCKS** Bruce has just purchased 100 shares of Out Clone, Inc. stock. The company is seeking FDA approval for a treatment that relieves the common cold. According to pharmaceutical experts, there is a 50% chance that FDA approval will be granted, and according to market insiders there is an 85% chance the value of the stock will double if FDA approval is granted.
    a. What is the probability that the FDA will approve the treatment and the value of Bruce's investment will double? **0.425 or 42.5%**
    b. What is the probability that the FDA will approve the treatment and the value of your stock will not double? **0.075 or 7.5%**
    c. Are these events dependent or independent? **Dependent; the probability that the stock price will double depends on the probability that the treatment will be approved.**

Lesson 12-5

Enrichment
CRM p. 34 OL BL

NAME ______ DATE ______ PERIOD ______

12-5 Enrichment

Happy Birthday

On a reality show, a contestant must randomly choose enough people to go into a room so that the probability that at least one of those people has the same birthday (month and date) as the contestant is greater than 50%. Time is of the essence, so the contestant doesn't want any more people than necessary. What number of people should the contestant gather?

1. Make a conjecture about the number of people needed. **Answers will vary. A common guess is about 187.**
2. When the probability that every person in the room has a different birthday is less than 50%, the probability that two of them will share a birthday is greater than 50%. Explain why. **Sample Answer: Because if the probability is less than 50%, then the complement will be 1 – which will be greater than 50%.**
3. Observe this pattern:
   If there are two people in the room, the probability that they all have different birthdays is $\frac{365}{365} \cdot \frac{364}{365}$ or 99.7%.

33b. Divide the overlap of the two circles by the $P(A)$ circle; $P(B/A) = \frac{P(A \text{ and } B)}{P(A)}$.

ReadingMath

Conditional Probability $P(B|A)$ is read the *probability* of *B, given A.*

33d. $P(\text{green}|\text{red}) = \frac{\frac{8}{33}}{\frac{2}{3}} = \frac{4}{11}$

33e. $P(B|A) = \frac{P(A \text{ and } B)}{P(A)}$

34. Aliyah; the individual probabilities should be added since we want the probability of blue *or* red, two mutually exclusive events.

36. $P(A)$, $P(B)$, $P(C)$, $P(A$ and $B)$, $P(A$ and $C)$, $P(B$ and $C)$, $P(A$ and B and $C)$; $P(A$ or B or $C) = P(A) + P(B) + P(C) - P(A$ and $B) - P(A$ and $C) - P(B$ and $C) + P(A$ and B and $C)$.

37. Sample answer: Choosing a CD to listen to, putting it back, and then choosing another CD to listen to would be an independent event since the CD was placed back before the second CD was chosen. Choosing a pair of jeans to wear would be a dependent event if I did not like the first pair chosen, and I did not put them back.

32. TILES Kirsten and José are playing a game. Kirsten places tiles numbered 1 to 50 in a bag. José selects a tile at random. If he selects a prime number or a number greater than 40, then he wins the game. What is the probability that José will win on his first turn? $\frac{11}{25}$ or 44%

33. MULTIPLE REPRESENTATIONS In this problem, you will explore conditional probability. **Conditional probability** is the probability that event B occurs given that event A has already occurred. It is calculated by dividing the probability of the occurrence of both events by the probability of the occurrence of the first event. The notation for conditional probability is $P(B \mid A)$.

a. **GRAPHICAL** Draw a Venn diagram to illustrate $P(A$ and $B)$. See margin.

b. **VERBAL** Write the formula for $P(B \mid A)$ given the Venn diagram.

c. **ANALYTICAL** A jar contains 12 marbles, of which 8 marbles are red and 4 marbles are green. If marbles are chosen without replacement, find $P(\text{red})$ and $P(\text{red, green})$. $P(\text{red}) = \frac{2}{3}$; $P(\text{red, green}) = \frac{8}{33}$

d. **ANALYTICAL** Using the probabilities from part **c** and the Venn diagram in part **a**, determine the probability of choosing a green marble on the second selection, given that the first marble selected was red.

e. **ANALYTICAL** Write a formula for finding a conditional probability.

f. **ANALYTICAL** Use the definition from part **e** to answer the following: At a basketball game, 80% of the fans cheered for the home team. In the same crowd, 20% of the fans were waving banners and cheering for the home team. What is the probability that a fan waved a banner given that the fan cheered for the home team? 25%

H.O.T. Problems Use Higher-Order Thinking Skills

34. FIND THE ERROR George and Aliyah are determining the probability of randomly choosing a blue or red marble from a bag of 8 blue marbles, 6 red marbles, 8 yellow marbles, and 4 white marbles. Is either of them correct? Explain.

George

$P(\text{blue or red}) = P(\text{blue}) \cdot P(\text{red})$
$= \frac{8}{26} \cdot \frac{6}{26}$
$= \frac{48}{676}$
about 7%

Aliyah

$P(\text{blue or red}) = P(\text{blue}) + P(\text{red})$
$= \frac{8}{26} + \frac{6}{26}$
$= \frac{14}{26}$
about 54%

35. CHALLENGE In some cases, if one bulb in a string of holiday lights fails to work, the whole string will not light. If each bulb in a set has a 99.5% chance of working, what is the maximum number of lights that can be strung together with at least a 90% chance that the whole string will light? 21

36. REASONING Suppose there are three events A, B, and C that are not mutually exclusive. List all of the probabilities you would need to consider in order to calculate $P(A$ or B or $C)$. Then write the formula you would use to calculate it.

37. OPEN ENDED Describe a situation in your life that involves dependent and independent events. Explain why the events are dependent or independent.

38. WRITING IN MATH Explain why the subtraction occurs when finding the probability of two events that are not mutually exclusive. See margin.

Multiple Representations In Exercise 33, students use formulas, Venn diagrams, and analysis to find a conditional probability.

Watch Out!

Find the Error For Exercise 34, point out to students that when two events are connected by the word *or*, the probability of the compound event is found by adding the individual event probabilities.

Additional Answers

33a.

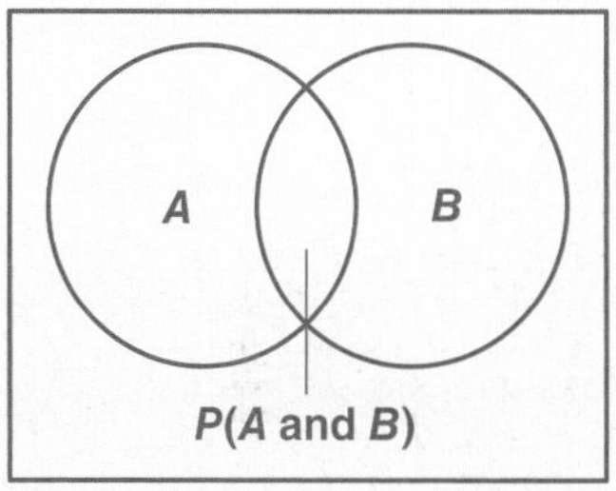

38. If two events are not mutually exclusive, they have item(s) in common. So the subtraction is needed to get rid of the items counted twice.

4 ASSESS

Ticket Out the Door Write probability examples on slips of paper, using each type of compound event. Give each student one of the examples. As students walk out the door, have them tell whether their events are independent, dependent, mutually exclusive, or inclusive, and have them give the probabilities of the events.

PSAE PRACTICE 10.11.10, 8.11.17, 7.11.03, 10.11.07

39. In how many ways can a committee of 4 be selected from a group of 12 people? **C**

A 48
B 483
C 495
D 11,880

40. A total of 925 tickets were sold for $5925. If adult tickets cost $7.50 and children's tickets cost $3.00, how many adult tickets were sold? **F**

F 700 H 325
G 600 J 225

41. SHORT RESPONSE A circular swimming pool with a diameter of 28 feet has a deck of uniform width built around it. If the area of the deck is 60π square feet, find its width. **2 ft**

42. The probability of heads landing up when you flip a coin is $\frac{1}{2}$. What is the probability of getting tails if you flip it again? **C**

A $\frac{1}{4}$ C $\frac{1}{2}$
B $\frac{1}{3}$ D $\frac{3}{4}$

Spiral Review

43. SHOPPING The Millers have twelve grandchildren, 5 boys and 7 girls. For their anniversary, the grandchildren decided to pool their money and have three of them shop for the entire group. (Lesson 12-4)

a. Does this situation represent a *combination* or *permutation*? **combination**

b. How many ways are there to choose the three? **220**

c. What is the probability that all three will be girls? $\frac{210}{1320}$ **or 16%**

44. ECOLOGY A group of 1000 randomly selected teens were asked if they believed there was global warming. The results are shown in the table. Find the mean absolute deviation to the nearest tenth. (Lesson 12-3) **100.8**

Teen Ecology Survey Results

Response	Number
Yes, strongly agree	312
Yes, mildly agree	340
No, I don't think so	109
No, absolutely not	116
Not sure	123

Solve each equation. State any extraneous solutions. (Lesson 11-8)

45. $\frac{4}{a} = \frac{3}{a-2}$ **8**

46. $\frac{3}{x} = \frac{1}{x-2}$ **3**

47. $\frac{x}{x+1} = \frac{x-6}{x-1}$ $-\frac{3}{2}$

48. $\frac{2n}{3} + \frac{1}{2} = \frac{2n-3}{6}$ **−3**

49. COOKING Hannah was making candy using a two-quart pan. As she stirred the mixture, she noticed that the pan was about $\frac{2}{3}$ full. If each piece of candy has a volume of about $\frac{3}{4}$ ounce, approximately how many pieces of candy will Hannah make? (*Hint:* There are 32 ounces in a quart.) (Lesson 11-3) **about 57 pieces**

50. GEOMETRY A rectangle has a width of $3\sqrt{5}$ centimeters and a length of $4\sqrt{10}$ centimeters. Find the area of the rectangle. Write as a simplified radical expression. (Lesson 10-2) $60\sqrt{2}$ **cm²**

Skills Review

Solve each equation. Check your solution. (Lesson 10-4)

51. $\sqrt{-3a} = 6$ **−12**

52. $\sqrt{a} = 100$ **10,000**

53. $\sqrt{-k} = 4$ **−16**

54. $5\sqrt{2} = \sqrt{x}$ **50**

55. $3\sqrt{7} = \sqrt{-y}$ **−63**

56. $3\sqrt{4a} - 2 = 10$ **4**

Differentiated Instruction OL BL

Extension Have students write an example of how they could use probability calculations in their daily lives. The example should include both a description of how the probability calculation could be used and a sample calculation with sample data.

12-6 Probability Distributions

Why?

A gaming software company with five online games on the market is interested in how many games their customers play. They surveyed 1000 randomly chosen customers. The results of the survey are shown.

Number of Computer Games	Number of Customers
1	130
2	110
3	150
4	500
5	110

Then
You found probabilities with permutations and combinations. (Lesson 12-4)

Now
- Find probabilities by using random variables.
- Solve real-world problems using distributions.

IL Learning Standards
10.C.4a Solve problems of chance using the principles of probability including conditional settings.
10.C.4c Propose and interpret discrete probability distributions, with and without the use of technology.

New Vocabulary
random variable
discrete random variable
probability distribution
probability graph

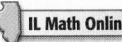

IL Math Online
glencoe.com
- Extra Examples
- Personal Tutor
- Self-Check Quiz
- Homework Help

Random Variables and Probability A variable with a value that is the numerical outcome of a random event is called a **random variable**. A random variable with a finite number of possibilities is a **discrete random variable**. We can let the random variable G represent the number of different games. So, G can equal 1, 2, 3, 4, or 5.

EXAMPLE 1 Random Variables

A graduation supply company offers 5 items that can be purchased for graduation: a diploma frame, graduation picture, cap and gown, senior key ring, and class pin. The school takes a poll of the seniors to see how many of these items each senior is buying. The results are shown.

Number of Items Being Purchased	Number of Seniors
0	12
1	122
2	134
3	115
4	145
5	97

a. Find the probability that a randomly chosen senior is buying exactly 3 items.

Let X represent the number of items being purchased. There is only one outcome in which 3 items are being purchased, and there are 625 seniors.

$P(X = 3) = \frac{\text{3 items being purchased}}{\text{seniors surveyed}}$ ***P(X = n)* is the probability of *X* occurring *n* times.**

$= \frac{115}{625}$ or $\frac{23}{125}$

The probability is $\frac{23}{125}$ or 18.4%

b. Find the probability that a randomly chosen senior buys at least 4 items.

There 145 + 97 or 242 seniors who are purchasing at least 4 items.

$P(X \geq 4) = \frac{242}{625}$

The probability is $\frac{242}{625}$ or about 38.7%.

Check Your Progress

GRADES After an algebra test, there are 7 students with As, 9 with Bs, 11 with Cs, 3 with Ds, and 2 with Fs.

1A. Find the probability that a randomly chosen student has a C. $\frac{11}{32}$ or about 34.4%

1B. Find the probability that a randomly chosen student has at least a B. $\frac{1}{2}$ or 50%

Personal Tutor glencoe.com

12-6 Lesson Notes

1 FOCUS

Vertical Alignment

Before Lesson 12-6
Find probabilities with permutations and combinations.

Lesson 12-6
Find probabilities by using random variables.
Solve real-world problems using distributions.

After Lesson 12-6
Conduct probability simulations.

2 TEACH

Scaffolding Questions

Have students read the *Why?* section of the lesson.

Ask:
- Could a particular customer appear in more than one row of the table? no
- What percent of the customers played only 1 game? 13%
- What is the total of the percents of customers represented by all the rows of the table? 100%

Random Variables and Probability

Example 1 shows how to use random variables to find probabilities.

Lesson 12-6 Resources

Resource	Approaching-Level	On-Level	Beyond-Level	English Learners
Teacher Edition	• Differentiated Instruction, p. 780	• Differentiated Instruction, pp. 780, 784	• Differentiated Instruction, p. 784	
Chapter Resource Masters	• Study Guide and Intervention, pp. 36–37 • Skills Practice, p. 38 • Practice, p. 39 • Word Problem Practice, p. 40	• Study Guide and Intervention, pp. 36–37 • Skills Practice, p. 38 • Practice, p. 39 • Word Problem Practice, p. 40 • Enrichment, p. 41 • Spreadsheet Activity, p. 42	• Practice, p. 39 • Word Problem Practice, p. 40 • Enrichment, p. 41	• Study Guide and Intervention, pp. 36–37 • Skills Practice, p. 38 • Practice, p. 39 • Word Problem Practice, p. 40
Transparencies	• 5-Minute Check Transparency 12-6	• 5-Minute Check Transparency 12-6	• 5-Minute Check Transparency 12-6	• 5-Minute Check Transparency 12-6
Other	• Study Notebook	• Study Notebook	• Study Notebook	• Study Notebook

Formative Assessment

Use the Check Your Progress exercises after each example to determine students' understanding of concepts.

Additional Example

1 **PETS** The owner of a pet store asked customers how many pets they owned. The results of this survey are shown in the table.

Number of Pets	0	1	2	3	4
Number of Customers	3	37	33	18	9

a. Find the probability that a randomly chosen customer has 2 pets. $\frac{33}{100}$ or 33%

b. Find the probability that a randomly chosen customer has at least 3 pets. $\frac{27}{100}$ or 27%

Additional Examples also in Interactive Classroom PowerPoint® Presentations

IWB INTERACTIVE WHITEBOARD READY

TEACH with TECH

INTERACTIVE WHITEBOARD Choose two students to work through an example in front of the class. Have one student explain how to calculate a frequency distribution, and have the other student explain how to create a graph.

StudyTip

Discrete and Continuous Data Data is discrete if the observations can be counted; for example, the number of kittens in a litter. Data is continuous if the data can take on any value within an interval. For example, the height of each person in a sample is continuous data.

Probability Distributions A **probability distribution** is the probability of every possible value of the random variable. A **probability graph** is a bar graph that displays a probability distribution.

Key Concept — Properties of Probability Distributions

For Your FOLDABLE

- The probability of each value of X is greater than or equal to 0 and is less than or equal to 1.
- The sum of the probabilities of all values of X is 1.

EXAMPLE 2 Probability Distribution

PIZZA The table shows the probability distribution of the number of times a customer orders pizza each month.

Pizzas Ordered Per Month	
X = Number of Pizzas	Probability
0	0.10
1	0.12
2	0.44
3	0.24
4+	0.10

a. Show that the distribution is valid.

- For each value of X, the probability is greater than or equal to 0 and less than or equal to 1.
- The sum of the probabilities, $0.10 + 0.12 + 0.44 + 0.24 + 0.10$, is 1.

b. What is the probability that a customer orders pizza fewer than three times per month?

The probability of a compound event is the sum of the probabilities of each individual event. The probability of a customer ordering fewer than 3 times per month is the sum of the probability of ordering 2 times per month plus the probability of ordering one time per month.

$P(X < 3) = P(X = 2) + P(X = 1) + P(X = 0)$ — **Sum of individual probabilities**

$= 0.44 + 0.12 + 0.10$ — **$P(X = 2) = 0.44$, $P(X = 1) = 0.12$, and $P(X = 0) = 0.10$**

$= 0.66$ — **Add.**

c. Make a probability graph of the data.

Use the data from the probability distribution table to draw a bar graph. Remember to label each axis and give the graph a title.

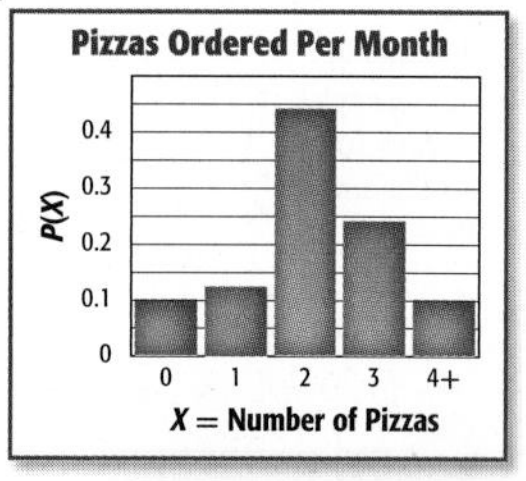

Real-World Link

In October of 2007, Joseph Jones, then a high school senior, ate 83 slices of pepperoni pizza within 10 minutes at an eating competition.

Source: About Pizza

Check Your Progress

The table shows the probability distribution of adults who play golf by age range.

Golfers By Age	
A = Ages	Probability
18–24	0.13
25–34	0.18
35–44	0.21
45–54	0.19
55–64	0.12
65+	0.17

2A. Show that the distribution is valid.

2B. What is the probability that an adult golfer is 35 years old or older? **0.69 = 69%**

2C. Make a probability graph of the data. **See Ch. 12 Answer Appendix.**

2A. Each value is greater than 0 and less than 1; $0.13 + 0.18 + 0.21 + 0.19 + 0.12 + 0.17 = 1$.

Personal Tutor glencoe.com

Focus on Mathematical Content

Discrete vs. Continuous All the random variables discussed in this lesson are discrete, which means that only certain values are possible for the variable. For a continuous random variable, all real numbers interval are possible values for the variable.

Differentiated Instruction

AL OL

Visual/Spatial Learners Give small groups of students the following probability distribution. The number of hours a student spends on homework in an average week, X is: 0, 1, 2, 3, 4, 5+. The probability $P(x)$ is: 0.05, 0.05, 0.10, 0.15, 0.45, 0.20. Have students prepare a probability graph of the data. Use the graph to determine the probability that a student studies 4 hours or more in an average week. 0.65 or 65%

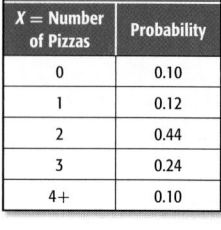

Check Your Understanding

Example 1 p. 779

1a. $\frac{47}{1000}$ or 4.7%
1b. $\frac{2871}{5000}$ or about 57.4%
2a. All of the values are between 0 and 1; $0.15 + 0.19 + 0.26 + 0.22 + 0.18 = 1$.
2b. $0.6 = 60\%$

1. GPS A car dealership surveys 10,000 of its customers who have a GPS system to ask how often they have used the system within the past year. The results are shown.

a. Find the probability that a randomly chosen customer will have used the GPS system more than 20 times.

b. Find the probability that a randomly chosen customer will have used the GPS system no more than 10 times.

Customers Using the GPS System	
Uses	**Customers**
0	1382
1–5	2350
6–10	2010
11–15	1863
16–20	1925
21+	470

Example 2 p. 780

2. JEANS A fashion boutique ordered jeans with different numbers of stripes down the outside seams. The table shows the probability distribution of the number of each type of jean sold in a particular week.

a. Show that the distribution is valid.

b. What is the probability that a randomly chosen pair of jeans has fewer than 3 stripes?

c. Make a probability graph of the data. **See Ch. 12 Answer Appendix.**

Types of Jeans Sold	
X = Number of Stripes	**Probability**
0	0.15
1	0.19
2	0.26
3	0.22
4	0.18

Example 1 p. 779

3a. $\frac{1}{5}$ or 20%
3b. $\frac{68}{165}$ or about 41.2%

3. HOME THEATER An electronics store sells the components and speakers for home theaters. The store surveyed its customers to see how many of the 10 components they bought. The results are shown.

a. Find the probability that a randomly chosen customer bought 5 or 6 components.

b. Find the probability that a randomly chosen customer bought fewer than 5 components.

Home Theater Components Purchased	
Components	**Customers**
0–2	26
3–4	42
5–6	33
7–8	24
9–10	40

Practice and Problem Solving

● = **Step-by-Step Solutions** begin on page R12.
Extra Practice begins on page 815.

Example 1 p. 779

4a. $\frac{9}{23}$ or about 39.1%
4b. $\frac{58}{115}$ or about 50.4%
5a. $\frac{26}{75}$ or about 34.7%
5b. $\frac{47}{150}$ or about 31.3%

4. FOOD DRIVE Ms. Valdez's biology class held a food drive. The class kept track of the types of food donated.

a. Find the probability that a randomly chosen product will be soup.

b. Find the probability that a randomly chosen product will be a boxed dinner or pasta.

Food Drive Donations Count	
Product	**Packages**
boxed dinner	36
pasta	22
juice	12
soup	45

5. SCHOOL SPIRIT The student council wants to organize a spirit club to cheer at school sporting events. They surveyed the student body and asked students how many sporting events they typically attend each year.

Number of Sporting Events	0–5	6–10	11–15	16–20	21+
Number of Students	96	112	204	108	80

a. Find the probability a randomly chosen student attended at most 10 events.

b. Find the probability a randomly chosen student attended at least 16 events.

Probability Distributions

Example 2 shows how to determine whether a probability distribution for a real-world situation is valid, and how to use a probability table and histogram to represent the probability distribution.

Additional Example

2 POPULATION The table shows the probability distribution of students in each grade at Sunnybrook High School.

X = Grade	$P(X)$
9	0.29
10	0.26
11	0.25
12	0.2

a. Show that the distribution is valid. For each value of X, the probability is greater than or equal to 0 and less than or equal to 1. Also, $0.29 + 0.26 + 0.25 + 0.2 = 1$, so the sum of the probabilities is 1.

b. If a student is chosen at random, what is the probability that he or she is in grade 11 or 12? $P(X = 11) + P(X = 12) = 0.45$

c. Make a probability graph of the data.

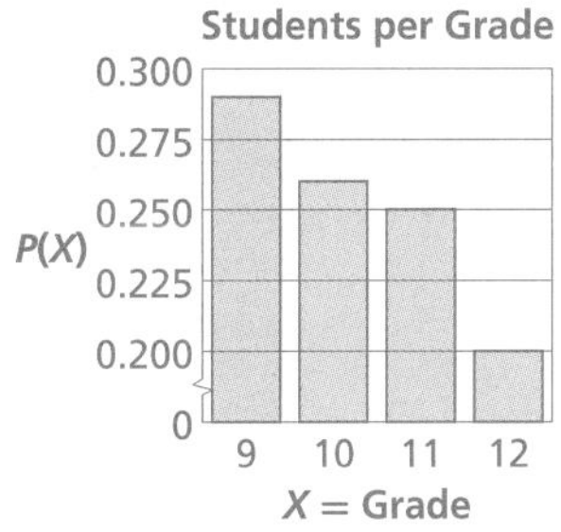

Differentiated Homework Options

Level	Assignment	Two-Day Option	
AL Basic	4–10, 15–37	5–9 odd, 19–22	4–10 even, 15–18, 23–37
OL Core	5–9 odd, 10–13, 16–37	4–10, 19–22	11–13, 16–18, 23–37
BL Advanced	11–34, (optional: 35–37)		

3 PRACTICE

Formative Assessment

Use Exercises 1–3 to check for understanding.

Use the chart at the bottom of this page to customize assignments for your students.

Exercise Alert

Dice For Exercise 13, each student will need a six-sided die.

Multiple Representations In Exercise 13, students use a die and a table of experimental results to show the difference between experimental and theoretical probability.

Additional Answers

8a. All of the values are between 0 and 1; $0.35 + 0.31 + 0.02 + 0.11 + 0.19 + 0.02 = 1$.

8c.

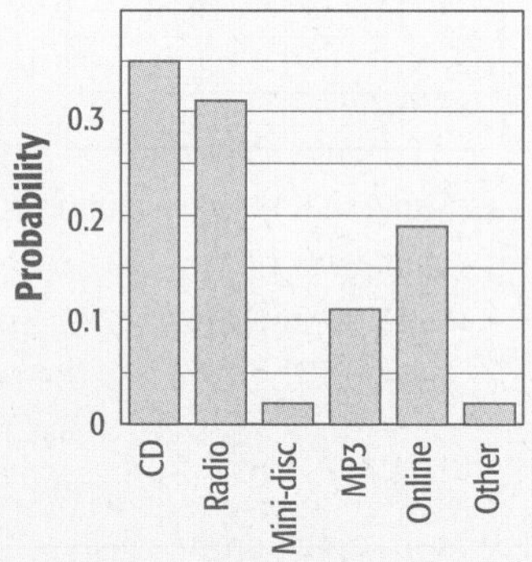

9c.

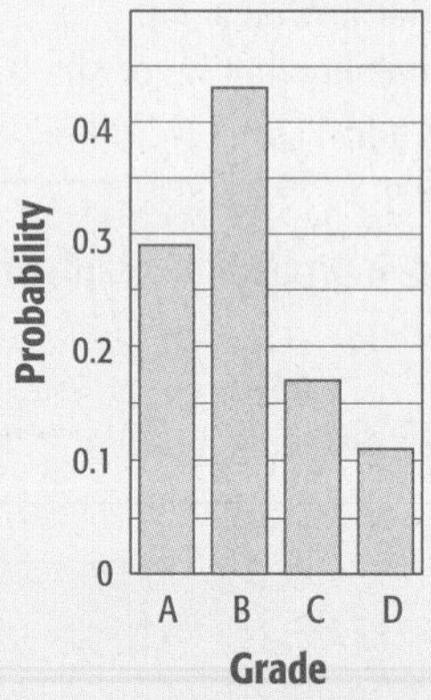

11c.

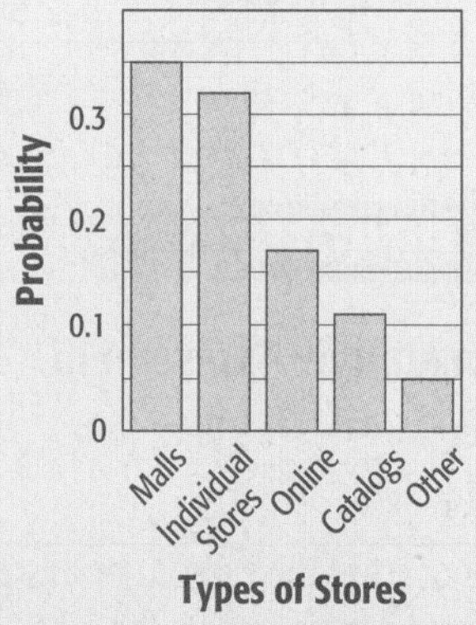

Real-World Career

Executive chefs plan the menu and oversee kitchen operations in a restaurant. They are required to have years of training and experience.

6. RESTAURANTS Kwan Chinese Restaurant has a delivery service. Mr. Kwan is keeping track of how many deliveries they have each week for a year. The results are shown.

a. Find the probability that there will be more than 20 deliveries in a randomly chosen week.

b. Find the probability that there will be fewer than 21 deliveries in a randomly chosen week.

Kwan Chinese Restaurant Deliveries

Deliveries Per Week	Weeks
0–5	0
6–10	9
11–20	18
21–25	12
26+	13

7. PARTY Chrystal owns a company that plans parties for children. Throughout the year she has kept a count of each party theme she has used. The table shows the results of her tally.

Theme of Party	animal	circus	superhero	sports	music	other
Number of Parties	42	15	9	45	32	35

a. Find the probability that a randomly chosen theme will be animal or sports.

b. Find the probability that a randomly chosen theme will not be animal or sports.

Example 2 p. 780

6a. $\frac{25}{52}$ or about 48.1%

6b. $\frac{27}{52}$ or about 51.9%

7a. $\frac{87}{178}$ or about 48.9%

7b. $\frac{91}{178}$ or about 51.1%

9a. All of the values are between 0 and 1; $0.29 + 0.43 + 0.17 + 0.11 + 0 = 1$.

10a. All of the values are between 0 and 1; $0.17 + 0.10 + 0.04 + 0.12 + 0.18 + 0.15 + 0.24 = 1$.

8. MUSIC A Web site conducted a survey on the format of music teens listened to. The table shows the probability distribution of the results.

a. Show that the distribution is valid. **See margin.**

b. What is the probability that the type of format randomly chosen will be an MP3 or online? **0.3 = 30%**

c. Make a probability graph of the data. **See margin.**

Formats for Music

Format	Probability
CDs	0.35
radio	0.31
mini-disc	0.02
MP3	0.11
online	0.19
other	0.02

9. GRADES Mr. Rockwell's Algebra class took a chapter test last week. The table shows the probability distribution of the results.

a. Show that the distribution is valid.

b. What is the probability that a student chosen at random will have no higher than a B? **0.71 = 71%**

c. Make a probability graph of the data. **See margin.**

Algebra Test Grades

Grade	Probability
A	0.29
B	0.43
C	0.17
D	0.11
F	0

10. SKATE PARKS The park department asked the counties that had skate parks what equipment was allowed to be used in their park. The table shows the probability distribution of the results.

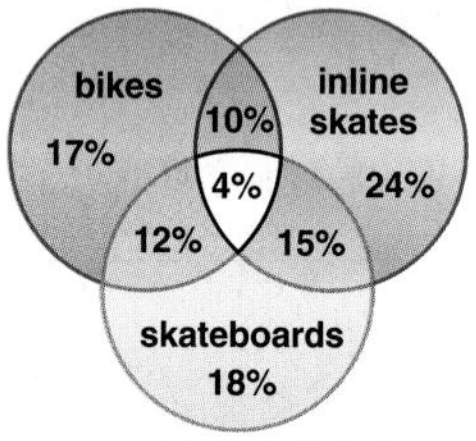

a. Show that the distribution is valid.

b. What is the probability that a park chosen at random allows bikes or skateboards? **0.76 = 76%**

c. Make a probability graph of the data. **See Ch. 12 Answer Appendix.**

13d. $0.15 = \frac{3}{20} = 15\%$; $0.4 = \frac{2}{5} = 40\%$; $0.75 = \frac{3}{4} = 75\%$; The first set of probabilities were predictions based on everything being equal. The second set were based on what actually happened.

14. Sample answer: The problem with this probability distribution is that shooting foul shots is not a random event. Events involving athletic ability should not be considered when making probability distributions.

Real-World Link

Dice games have been in existence at least since 6000 BC. Found objects such as sea shells, pebbles, and nut shells were used before cubical dice became commonplace.

Source: NTL World

11. MARKETING A retail marketing group conducted a survey on teen shopping habits and asked where the teens did most of their holiday shopping. The table shows the probability distribution of the results

Types of Stores	malls	individual stores	online	catalogs	other
Probability	0.35	0.32	0.17	0.11	0.05

a. Show that the distribution is valid. **All of the values are between 0 and 1; $0.35 + 0.32 + 0.17 + 0.11 + 0.05 = 1$.**

b. What is the probability that a shopper chosen at random will shop online or in a catalog? **$0.28 = 28\%$**

c. Make a probability graph of the data. **See margin.**

12. SPORTS CARDS Joshua mixed up all of his sports cards and placed them in a bag. Then he told his sister Drea that she could keep whatever card she randomly drew out of the bag.

Joshua's Sports Cards

Sport	Number Sold
baseball	53
football	27
basketball	39
hockey	21

a. What is the probability that a randomly chosen card is hockey or football?

b. Make a probability distribution table for the data. Round to the nearest hundredth.

c. Is the distribution valid? Why or why not?

d. Make a probability graph of the data. **See Ch. 12 Answer Appendix.**

12a. $\frac{12}{35}$ or about 34.3%

12b.

Sports	Probability
baseball	0.38
football	0.19
basketball	0.28
hockey	0.15

12c. Yes; all the values are between 0 and 1, and $0.38 + 0.19 + 0.28 + 0.15 = 1$.

13. MULTIPLE REPRESENTATIONS In this problem, you will explore the differences between a prediction and what actually happens.

a. **VERBAL** What is the probability of rolling a 2 on a die? What is the probability of rolling a 1 or a 6? What is the probability of rolling an odd number?

b. **ANALYTICAL** Roll the die 20 times. Record the value of the die after each roll.

c. **ANALYTICAL** Determine the probability distribution for X = value of the die.

d. **VERBAL** From your probability distribution, what is the probability of rolling a 2? What is the probability of rolling a 1 or a 6? What is the probability of rolling an odd number? Explain why the numbers may not be the same. **See margin.**

13a. $\frac{1}{6}, \frac{1}{3}, \frac{1}{2}$

13b. Sample answer: 1: 6; 2: 3; 3: 7; 4: 0; 5: 2; 6: 2

13c. Sample answer:

1	0.3
2	0.15
3	0.35
4	0
5	0.1
6	0.1

H.O.T. Problems

Use Higher-Order Thinking Skills

14. CHALLENGE What is wrong with the probability distribution shown? Explain your reasoning. **See margin.**

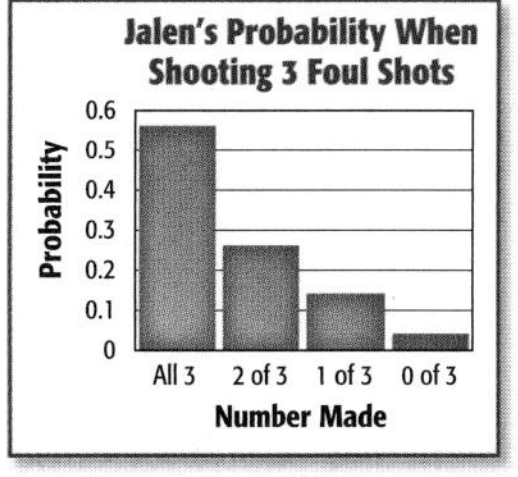

15. REASONING Suppose two dice are rolled twelve times. Which sum is most likely to occur? Make a table to show the probability distribution. Then make a probability graph to confirm your answer. **15–17. See Ch. 12 Answer Appendix.**

16. REASONING Explain why the sum of the probabilities in a probability distribution should always be 1. Include an example.

17. OPEN ENDED Write a real-world problem in which you could find a probability distribution. Create a probability graph for your data.

18. WRITING IN MATH Write a real-world story in which you are the owner of a business. Explain how you could use a probability distribution to help you make a business decision. **See margin.**

Additional Answer

18. Sample answer: I own a cosmetics store. As part of my inventory, I keep track of each type of cosmetic that I sell. A probability distribution would help me to decide how much of each type of item to keep in stock.

Study Guide and Intervention

CRM pp. 36–37 AL OL ELL

NAME ______ DATE ______ PERIOD ______

12-6 Study Guide and Intervention

Probability Distributions

Random Variables and Probability A **random variable** X is a variable whose value is the numerical outcome of a random event.

Example **A teacher asked her students how many siblings they have. The results are shown in the table at the right.**

Number of Siblings	Number of Students
0	1
1	15
2	8
3	2
4	1

a. Find the probability that a randomly selected student has 2 siblings.

The random variable X can equal 0, 1, 2, 3, or 4. In the table, the value $X = 2$ is paired with 8 outcomes, and there are 27 students surveyed.

$$P(X = 2) = \frac{2 \text{ siblings}}{27 \text{ students surveyed}} = \frac{8}{27}$$

The probability that a randomly selected student has 2 siblings is $\frac{8}{27}$, or 29.6%.

b. Find the probability that a randomly selected student has at least three siblings.

$$P(X \geq 3) = \frac{2 + 1}{27}$$

The probability that a randomly selected student has at least 3 siblings is $\frac{1}{9}$, or 11.1%.

Exercises

For Exercises 1–3, use the grade distribution shown at the right. A grade of A = 5, B = 4, C = 3, D = 2, F = 1.

X = Grade	5	4	3	2	1
Number of studets	6	9	5	4	1

1. Find the probability that a randomly selected student in this class received a grade of C. **$\frac{1}{5}$**

2. Find the probability that a randomly selected student in this class received a grade lower than a C. **$\frac{1}{5}$**

3. What is the probability that a randomly selected student in this class passes the course, that is, gets at least a D? **$\frac{24}{25}$**

4. The table shows the results of tossing 3 coins 50 times. What is the probability of getting 2 or 3 heads? **48%**

X = Number of Heads	0	1	2	3
Number of Times	6	20	19	5

Chapter 12 36 *Glencoe Algebra 1*

Practice

CRM p. 39 AL OL BL ELL

NAME ______ DATE ______ PERIOD ______

12-6 Practice

Probability Distributions

For Exercises 1–3, the spinner shown is spun two times.

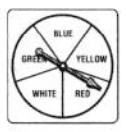

1. Write the sample space with all possible outcomes.
BB, BW, BR, BY, BG, WB, WW, WR, WY, WG, RB, RW, RR, RY, RG, YB, YW, YR, YY, YG, GB, GW, GR, GY, GG

2. Find the probability distribution X, where X represents the number of times the spinner lands on blue for $X = 0$, $X = 1$, and $X = 2$.
$P(X = 0) = 0.64$, $P(X = 1) = 0.32$, $P(X = 2) = 0.04$

3. Make a probability graph of the data.

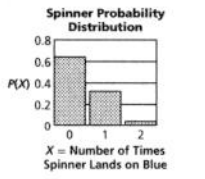

4. **TELECOMMUNICATIONS** Use the table that shows the probability distribution of the number of telephones per student's household at Wilson High.

X = Number of Telephones	1	2	3	4	5+
Probability	0.01	0.16	0.34	0.39	0.10

a. Show that the distribution is valid.
$0.01 + 0.16 + 0.34 + 0.39 + 0.10 = 1$

b. If a student is chosen at random, what is the probability that there are more than 3 telephones at the student's home? **0.49**

c. Make a probability graph of the data.

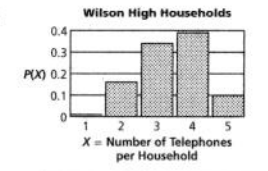

5. **LANDSCAPING** Use the table that shows the probability distribution of the number of shrubs (rounded to the nearest 50) ordered by corporate clients of a landscaping company over the past five years.

X = Number of Shrubs	50	100	150	200	250
Probability	0.11	0.24	0.45	0.16	0.04

a. Define a random variable and list its values. **Let x = the number of shrubs ordered; $x = 50, 100, 150, 200, 250$**

b. Show that the distribution is valid. **$0.11 + 0.24 + 0.45 + 0.16 + 0.04 = 1$**

c. What is the probability that a client's (rounded) order was at least 150 shrubs? **0.65**

Chapter 12 39 *Glencoe Algebra 1*

Lesson 12-6

Word Problem Practice

CRM p. 40 AL OL BL ELL

NAME ______ DATE ______ PERIOD ______

12-6 Word Problem Practice

Probability Distributions

1. **GAMES** A spinner for an adventure game decides how a player will move. Write the sample space with all possible outcomes if the spinner is spun twice.

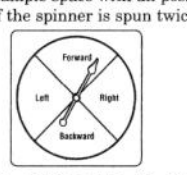

FF, FB, FL, FR, BF, BB, BL, BR, LF, LB, LL, LR, RF, RB, RL, RR

2. **JOBS** The probability distribution table shows the results of a newspaper survey that asked babysitters how much they make per hour.

Hourly Pay	\$3	\$4	\$5	\$6	\$7+
Probability	0.1	0.2	0.5	0.15	0.05

What is the probability that a babysitter chosen at random from the survey makes more than \$5 per hour? **$0.20 = 20\%$**

3. **TIME** James looks at his 12-hour digital clock when he wakes up in the middle of the night. Make a probability graph for all of the possible outcomes if you let X equal the first digit of the time. For instance, if it is 3:41, the first digit is a 3.

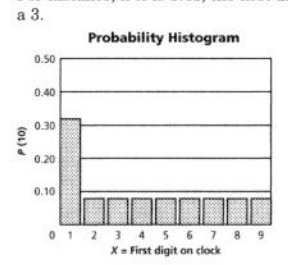

4. **DARTS** Suppose two darts are thrown at a traditional dart board and land near the center, but not on a bullseye. What is the probability that the sum of their scores is less than or equal to 5?
$10 \div 400 = 0.025 = 2.5\%$

5. **TENNIS** All season Oliver's tennis coach has kept track of where each of his serves has landed during practice. The results are shown in the probability distribution table. A serve in region 2 is "in", while a serve in any other region is a fault. A serve in region 1 represents hitting the net.

Region	1	2	3	4	5
Probability	0.19	0.52	0.15	0.09	0.05

a. What is the probability that any one of Oliver's serves does not hit the net and is a fault? **0.29 or 29%**

b. Make a probability graph that represents the data in the table.

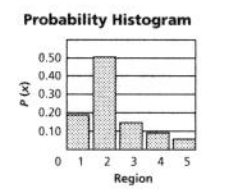

Chapter 12 40 *Glencoe Algebra 1*

Enrichment

CRM p. 41 OL BL

NAME ______ DATE ______ PERIOD ______

12-6 Enrichment

Lesson 12-6

Binomial Distribution

A binomial distribution is a particular type of probability distribution. To determine a probability a binomial distribution uses the binomial coefficients and the formula $nCk \cdot p^k(1 - p)^{n-k}$ where n is the number of selections, k is the desired outcome, and p is the probability of the desired outcome.

So, if we have a bag that contains 4 red balls and 8 black balls, we can use this formula to determine the probability of drawing exactly 2 red balls out of 5 draws if we return the ball after each draw.

Use the formula to determine the probability: $C(5, 2) \cdot \left(\frac{4}{12}\right)^2\left(1 - \frac{4}{12}\right)^3 = \frac{80}{243}$

So, the probability of choosing exactly 2 red balls out of 5 draws is $\frac{80}{243}$.

Exercises

1. Determine the probability of drawing exactly 3 black balls.
$\frac{80}{243}$

2. Compare the probability found in problem 1 to the probability found in the example. Explain why they compare the way they do

4 ASSESS

Crystal Ball Have students write how they think today's lesson on probability distributions will connect with the next lesson on probability simulations.

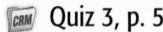

Formative Assessment

Check for student understanding of concepts in Lessons 12-5 and 12-6.

CRM Quiz 3, p. 52

PSAE PRACTICE 8.11.17, 10.11.07, 7.11.03

19. A bucket contains 10 balls numbered 1, 1, 2, 3, 4, 4, 4, 5, 6, and 6. A ball is randomly chosen from the bucket. What is the probability of drawing a ball with a number greater than 6? **D**

A $\frac{1}{5}$ C 1

B $\frac{3}{10}$ D 0

20. SHORT RESPONSE Mr. Bahn has $20,000 to invest. He invests part at 6% and the rest at 7%. He earns $1280 in interest within a year. How much did he invest at 7%? **$8000**

21. Suppose there are 10 tickets in a box for a drawing numbered as follows: 1, 2, 2, 3, 4, 4, 6, 6, 9, and 9. A single ticket is randomly chosen from the box. What is the probability of drawing a ticket with a number less than 10? **J**

F 0 G $\frac{1}{5}$ H $\frac{3}{10}$ J 1

22. GEOMETRY The height of a triangle is 5 inches less than the length of its base. If the area of the triangle is 52 square inches, find the base and the height. **C**

A 15 in., 9 in. C 13 in., 8 in.

B 11 in., 7 in. D 17 in., 11 in.

Spiral Review

23. PET TOYS A pet store has a bin of clearance items that contains 6 balls, 5 tug toys, 8 rawhide chews, and 4 chew toys, all in equal-sized boxes. If Johnda reaches in the box and pulls out two items, what is the probability that she will pull out a tug toy each time? (Lesson 12-5) $\frac{10}{253}$ **or about 4%**

A die is rolled and a spinner is spun like the one shown. Find the probability. (Lesson 12-4)

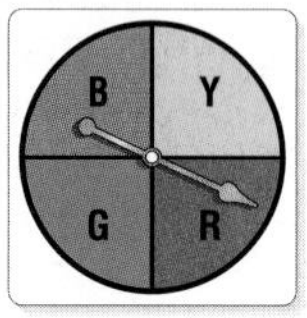

24. $P(3 \text{ and } Y)$ $\frac{1}{24}$

25. $P(\text{even and } G)$ $\frac{1}{8}$

26. $P(\text{prime number and } R \text{ or } B)$ $\frac{1}{4}$

27. $P(4 \text{ and not } Y)$ $\frac{1}{8}$

28. GAMES For a certain game, each player rolls four dice at the same time. (Lesson 12-3) **Combination; order is not important in this case.**

a. Do the outcomes of rolling the four dice represent permutations or combinations? Explain.

b. How many outcomes are possible? **1296**

c. What is the probability that four dice show the same number on a single roll? $\frac{1}{216}$

Find each sum. (Lesson 11-6)

29. $\frac{4}{a^2} + \frac{6}{a}$ $\frac{6a+4}{a^2}$

30. $\frac{3}{b^3} + \frac{7}{b^2}$ $\frac{7b+3}{b^3}$

31. $\frac{4}{d+6} + \frac{5}{d-5}$ $\frac{9d+10}{(d+6)(d+5)}$

32. $\frac{f}{f+5} + \frac{4}{f-4}$ $\frac{f^2+20}{(f+5)(f-4)}$

33. $\frac{8h}{h+6} + \frac{h}{h-3}$ $\frac{9h(h-2)}{(h+6)(h-3)}$

34. $\frac{7k}{k-3} + \frac{k}{k+2}$ $\frac{8k^2+11k}{(k-3)(k+2)}$

Skills Review

35. Write an expression to represent the probability of tossing a coin n times and getting n heads. Express as a power of 2. (Lesson 7-2) $\frac{1}{2^n}$

36. Write an expression to represent the probability of rolling a die n times and getting 3 n times. Express as a power of 6. (Lesson 7-2) $\frac{1}{6^n}$

37. Write an expression to represent the probability of rolling a die n times and getting a prime number n times. Express as a power. (Lesson 7-2) $\frac{1}{2^n}$

Differentiated Instruction

Extension On the board, draw curves that represent a normal and a skewed distribution of data, including curves skewed to the left and right. Then have students consider which curve the histogram in Exercise 9 most closely resembles. Ask students to support their reasoning with as many details as possible. Accept all reasonable answers. Sample answer: Skewed distribution to the right; most of the data are to the right of the mean, which indicates that the data are distributed to the right.

EXTEND 12-6

Graphing Technology Lab: The Normal Curve

IL Math Online glencoe.com
- Other Calculator Keystrokes
- Graphing Technology Personal Tutor

IL Learning Standards — **10.A.4b** Analyze data using mean, median, mode, range, variance and standard deviation of a data set, with and without the use of technology.

When there are a large number of values in a data set, the frequency distribution tends to cluster around the mean of the set in a distribution (or shape) called a **normal distribution**. The graph of a normal distribution is called a **normal curve**. Since the shape of the graph resembles a bell, the graph is also called a *bell curve*.

Data sets that have a normal distribution include reaction times of drivers that are the same age, achievement test scores, and the heights of people that are the same age.

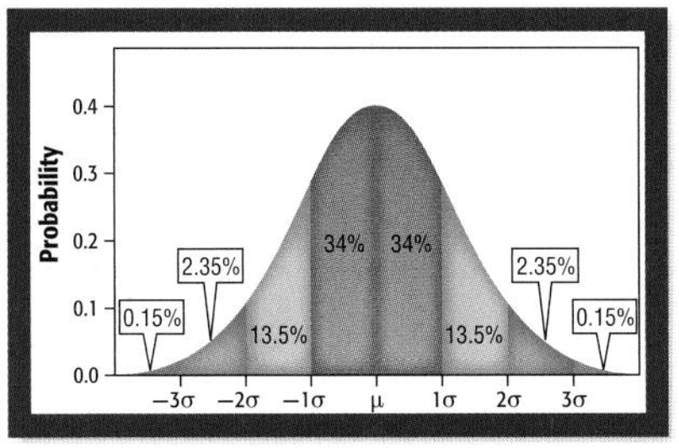

You can use a graphing calculator to graph and analyze a normal distribution if the mean and standard deviation of the data are known.

ACTIVITY 1 Graph a Normal Distribution

HEIGHT The mean height of 15-year-old boys in the city where Isaac lives is 67 inches, with a standard deviation of 2.8 inches. Use a normal distribution to represent these data.

Step 1 Set the viewing window.

- Xmin = 67 [−] 3 [×] 2.8 or 58.6
- Xmax = 67 [+] 3 [×] 2.8 or 75.4
- Xscl = 2.8
- Ymin = 0
- Ymax = 1 [÷] (2 [×] 2.8)
- Yscale = 1

Step 2 By entering the mean and standard deviation into the calculator, we can graph the corresponding normal curve. Enter the values using the following keystrokes.

KEYSTROKES: [Y=] [2nd] [DISTR] [ENTER] [X,T,θ,n] [,] 67 [,] 2.8 [)] [Graph]

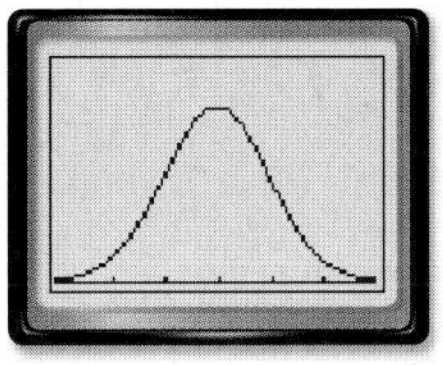

[58.6, 75.4] scl: 2.8 by [0, 0.17857142] scl: 1

(continued on the next page)

EXTEND 12-6

Lesson Notes

1 FOCUS

Objective Use a graphing calculator to explore normal distribution curves.

Materials for Each Student

- TI-83/84 Plus or other graphing calculator

Teaching Tip

Before starting students on the activity, discuss normal distributions using the graphic on the page. Some other examples of normally distributed random variables are lengths of newborn babies, blood pressure, lengths of objects made by machines, and useful lives of some manufactured items.

2 TEACH

Working in Cooperative Groups

Have students work in pairs, mixing abilities to work through Activities 1 and 2.

- For a continuous normally distributed variable, the height of the curve represents only a probability density.
- The total area under the curve is equal to 1.
- The probability that a variable takes on a value within a given interval is equal to the area under the curve between the endpoints of the curve interval.
- The probability that the height (to the nearest inch) of a particular 15-year old is 67 inches is equal to the area under the normal curve from 66.5 inches to 67.5 inches.

EXTEND
12-6 Lesson Notes

Practice Have students complete Exercise 1–6.

3 ASSESS

Formative Assessment

Use Exercise 2 to assess whether students can use the **normalpdf** command to find normal probabilities.

From Concrete to Abstract

Exercise 4 asks students to find an open ended probability using a different normal distribution.

The probability of a range of values is the area under the curve.

ACTIVITY 2 Analyze a Normal Distribution

Use the graph to answer questions about the data. What is the probability that Isaac will be at least 67 inches tall when he is 15?

The sum of all the y-values up to $x = 67$ would give us the probability that Isaac will be less than or equal to 67 inches. This is also the area under the curve. We will shade the area under the curve from negative infinity to 67 inches and find the area of the shaded portion of the graph.

Step 1 ShadeNorm Function

KEYSTROKES: [2nd] [DISTR] [▶] [ENTER]

Step 2 Shade the graph.

Next enter the lowest value, highest value, mean, and standard deviation.

On the TI-84 Plus, 1×10^{-99} represents negative infinity.

KEYSTROKES: 1 [2nd] [EE] [(–)] 99 [,] 67 [,] 67 [,] 2.8 [)] [ENTER]

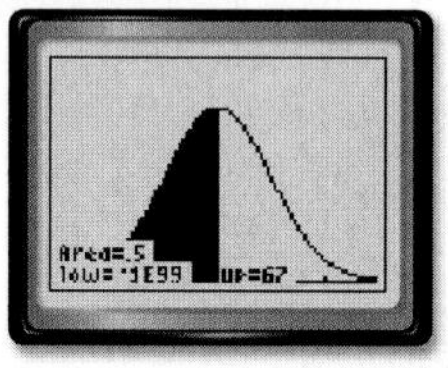

[58.6, 75.4] scl: 2.8 by [0, 0.17857142] scl: 1

The area is given as 0.5. The probability that Isaac will be 67 inches tall is 0.5 or 50%. Since the mean value is 67, we expect the probability to be 50%.

Exercises

1. What is the probability that Isaac will be at least 6 feet tall when he is 15? **about 4%**
2. What is the probability that Isaac will be between 65 and 68 inches? **about 40%**
3. If the mean height of 15-year-old girls in the same city is 64 inches with a standard deviation of 2.1, what is the probability that Isaac's sister, Maria, will be at least 64 inches tall when she is 15? **50%**
4. What is the probability that Maria will be no taller than 5 feet when she is 15 years old? **about 3%**

5. Both curves have a bell shape. This curve has a longer tail at the right.

6. On this curve, an outlier is plotted at the right, where the y-values are smaller.

Extension

Refer to the curve at the right.

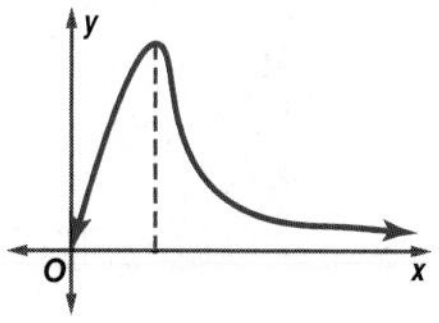

5. Compare this curve to the normal curve in Activity 1.
6. Describe where an outlier of the data set would be graphed on this curve.

12-7 Probability Simulations

Why?

Alex has been practicing his penalty kicks. He expects to be able to make at least 63% of his penalty kicks. To test this, he takes 50 penalty kicks, of which he makes 33.

Experimental Probability and Expected Value

Experimental probability is determined using data from tests or experiments. Alex's experimental probability is 63%. Therefore, he *expects* to make 63% of his future kicks.

Experimental probability should not be confused with theoretical probability. **Theoretical probability** is the likeliness of an event happening. For example, when tossing a coin, the theoretical probability of it landing on heads is always 0.5, while an experiment tossing many coins may produce a different *experimental* probability.

Experimental probability is the ratio of the number of times an outcome occurs to the total number of events or trials. The ratio is also known as the **relative frequency.**

$$\text{experiment probability} = \frac{\text{frequency of an outcome}}{\text{total number of trials}}$$

It is often useful to perform an **empirical study**. In this study, an experiment is performed repeatedly, data are collected and combined, the results are analyzed, and an expected value can be calculated. The **expected value** is the average value that is expected for the outcome of one trial.

Then
You used probability distributions. (Lesson 12-6)

Now
- Design simulations to estimate probabilities.
- Summarize data from simulations.

IL Learning Standards
10.C.4b Design and conduct simulations, with and without the use of technology.

New Vocabulary
experimental probability
theoretical probability
relative frequency
empirical study
expected value
simulation

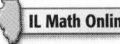

IL Math Online
glencoe.com
- Extra Examples
- Personal Tutor
- Self-Check Quiz
- Homework Help

Real-World EXAMPLE 1 Experimental Probability

a. SOCCER What is the experimental probability that Alex successfully makes his goal kicks?

$$\text{experimental probability} = \frac{33}{50} \quad \begin{array}{l}\leftarrow \text{frequency of successes}\\ \leftarrow \text{total number of goal kicks}\end{array}$$

The experimental probability of the test is $\frac{33}{50}$ or 66%.

b. SOCCER Alex takes 50 kicks two more times. He makes 29 of the first 50 kicks and 34 of the second 50. What is the experimental probability of all three tests?

$$\text{experimental probability} = \frac{96}{150} \text{ or } \frac{16}{25}$$

The experimental probability of the three tests was $\frac{16}{25}$ or 64%.

Check Your Progress

1. **GAMES** Hakeem rolls a die 20 times. A 4 appears 5 times. What is the experimental probability of rolling a 4? $\frac{1}{4}$ or 25%

Personal Tutor glencoe.com

12-7 Lesson Notes

1 FOCUS

Vertical Alignment

Before Lesson 12-7
Use probability distributions.

Lesson 12-7
Design simulations to estimate probabilities.
Summarize data from simulations.

2 TEACH

Scaffolding Questions

Have students read the *Why?* section of the lesson.

Ask:
- If Alexander thinks he can make at least 66% of his goal kicks, how many out of 50 kicks should he expect to make? at least 33
- How did Alexander's actual performance compare with his prediction? He made 66% of his kicks, which agrees with his expectation.

Theoretical and Experimental Probability

Example 1 shows how to find the experimental probability of data using an empirical study.

Lesson 12-7 Resources

Resource	Approaching-Level	On-Level	Beyond-Level	English Learners
Teacher Edition	• Differentiated Instruction, p. 789	• Differentiated Instruction, p. 789	• Differentiated Instruction, p. 792	
Chapter Resource Masters	• Study Guide and Intervention, pp. 43–44 • Skills Practice, p. 45 • Practice, p. 46 • Word Problem Practice, p. 47	• Study Guide and Intervention, pp. 43–44 • Skills Practice, p. 45 • Practice, p. 46 • Word Problem Practice, p. 47 • Enrichment, p. 48	• Practice, p. 46 • Word Problem Practice, p. 47 • Enrichment, p. 48	• Study Guide and Intervention, pp. 43–44 • Skills Practice, p. 45 • Practice, p. 46 • Word Problem Practice, p. 47
Transparencies	• 5-Minute Check Transparency 12-7	• 5-Minute Check Transparency 12-7	• 5-Minute Check Transparency 12-7	• 5-Minute Check Transparency 12-7
Other	• Study Notebook • Teaching Algebra with Manipulatives	• Study Notebook • Teaching Algebra with Manipulatives	• Study Notebook	• Study Notebook • Teaching Algebra with Manipulatives

Formative Assessment

Use the Check Your Progress exercises after each example to determine students' understanding of concepts.

Additional Example

1 **MEDICAL RESEARCH** Researchers at a pharmaceutical company expect a new drug to work successfully in 70% of patients. To test the drug's effectiveness, the company performs three clinical studies of 100 volunteers who use the drug for six months. The results of the studies are shown in the table.

Study of New Medicine

Result	Study 1	Study 2	Study 3
Expected Success Rate	70%	70%	70%
Condition Improved	61%	74%	67%
No Improvement	39%	25%	33%
Condition Worsened	0%	1%	0%

a. What is the experimental probability that the drug was successful for Study 1? 61%

b. What is the experimental probability that the drug would cause a patient to show no improvement for all three studies? $\frac{97}{300}$ or about 32%

Additional Examples also in Interactive Classroom PowerPoint® Presentations

IWB INTERACTIVE WHITEBOARD READY

Performing Simulations

Example 2 shows how to simulate a situation. **Example 3** shows how to conduct a simulation of a situation and then determine and compare the theoretical and experimental probability of the situation.

Performing Simulations A **simulation** allows you to find an experimental probability by using objects to act out an event that would be difficult or impractical to perform. You can conduct simulations using one or more objects such as dice, coins, marbles, or spinners. The theoretical probability of objects you choose should be identical to the experimental probability.

Real-World Link

Trivia quizzes and quiz shows have a great history in the U.S. Here are some dates in trivia quiz history.

1935: First radio quiz show

1950: First real TV quiz show "Truth or Consequences"

1955: First big money TV quiz show "The $64,000 Question"

Source: Trivia Wisdom

Real-World EXAMPLE 2 Simulation

In a trivia game, a player answers one of three questions on a card, two of which are multiple choice.

a. What could be used to simulate getting a multiple-choice question? Explain.

You could use a die, where rolling 1 through 4 represents a multiple-choice question and rolling 5 or 6 does not.

b. Describe a way to conduct the simulation if 3 out of 5 are multiple-choice.

A spinner with five equally sized spaces, three of which are colored red, could be used. If the spinner lands on red, then the question is multiple choice.

Check Your Progress

2. Of the 48 games remaining on Bobbie's favorite basketball team's schedule, 24 will not be televised.

A. What could be used to simulate whether the next game will be televised?

B. Describe a simulation if 36 of the 48 games will not be televised.

Personal Tutor glencoe.com

2A. Sample answer: You could use a coin, where heads means it is televised and tails means it is not.

2B. Sample answer: Flip 2 coins. If both coins are tails, the game will be televised. Otherwise, it will not be televised.

Real-World EXAMPLE 3 Experimental Probability and Expected Value

QUALITY CONTROL **Eloy inspects automobile frames as they come through the assembly line. From previous observations, he expects to find a weld defect in one out of ten of the frames each day.**

a. What objects can be used to model the possible outcomes of the automobile inspection? Explain.

Use a simulation that has 10 objects, where 1 out of the 10 objects represents a defect. One possible simulation would be to place 10 marbles in a bag. Let 1 red marble represent the defects and 9 yellow marbles represent the good automobiles. One marble at a time can be drawn out of the bag, the results recorded, and the marble replaced in the bag. Repeat this 9 more times representing 10 automobiles.

b. What is the expected value that there is one automobile frame found with defects in a certain day?

On average, 1 out of 10 automobiles has a defect. So, the expected value is $\frac{1}{10}$ or 10%.

c. Run the simulation using Eloy's expectation of defects. What is the experimental probability of having a defect for every ten frames?

After 50 simulations, or 500 drawings, 57 had a defect, so the experimental probability of getting a defect is $\frac{57}{500}$ or 11.4%.

Defects	Frequency	Total
0	12	0
1	24	24
2	10	20
3	3	9
4	1	4
		57

Focus on Mathematical Content

Theoretical and Experimental Probability Theoretical probability describes what should occur given the number of events or trials and the sample space. Experimental probability describes the actual results of repeated trials or events. Experimental probability is the ratio of the number of times an outcome occurred to the total number of events or trials. As the number of trials increases, experimental probability more closely approximates theoretical probability.

ReadingMath

Law of Large Numbers The *Law of Large Numbers* states that as the number of trial increases, the experimental probability gets closer to the theoretical probability.

d. How does the experimental probability compare to the expected value?

The expected value is 10%, and the experimental probability is 15%. They are relatively close. As the number of trials increased it would get closer to the expected value.

Check Your Progress

3. **TELEVISION** Anthony's favorite show is going to be replayed by a cable channel. They are going to play one episode each day in a random order. Anthony missed 3 of the 22 episodes.

 A. What objects can be used to model the possible outcomes of one of the shows that he missed being aired on the first day? See Ch. 12 Answer Appendix.

 B. What is the expected value that it will be a show he missed? $\frac{3}{22}$ or about 14%

 C. The results of a simulation Anthony performed are shown. What is the experimental probability that it will be a show he missed? $\frac{5}{50}$ or 10%

 D. How does the experimental probability compare to the expected value? See Ch. 12 Answer Appendix.

Show	Frequency
missed	5
watched	45

Personal Tutor glencoe.com

Check Your Understanding

Example 1 p. 787

1. **GAMES** Games at the fair require the majority of players to lose in order for game owners to make a profit. New games are tested to make sure they have sufficient difficulty. The results of three test groups are listed in the table. The owners want a maximum of 33% of players to win. There were 50 participants in each test group.

 a. What is the experimental probability that the participant was a winner in the second group? $\frac{3}{10}$ or 30%

Result	Group 1	Group 2	Group 3
Winners	13	15	19
Losers	37	35	31

 b. What is the experimental probability of winning for all three groups?

1b. $\frac{47}{150}$ or about 31%

2. **BATTING AVERAGE** In a computer baseball game, a baseball player has a batting average of 300. That is, he gets a hit 300 out of 1000, or 30%, of the times he is at bat. What could be used to simulate the player taking a turn at bat? See Ch. 12 Answer Appendix.

Example 2 p. 788

3. **TEST** On a true-false test, Marlene answered 16 out of the 20 questions correctly by guessing randomly.

 a. What could be used to simulate her correctly answering a question? Explain.

 b. Describe a way to simulate the next 20 questions. See Ch. 12 Answer Appendix.

 See Ch. 12 Answer Appendix.

Example 3 p. 788

4. **LOTTERIES** In a certain state, lottery numbers are five-digit numbers. Each digit can be 1, 2, 3, 4, 5, or 6. Once a week, a winning number is chosen randomly.

 a. How many five-digit numbers are possible? Explain how you calculated the number of possible outcomes. See Ch. 12 Answer Appendix.

 b. Perform a simulation for winning the lottery. Describe the objects you used. See Ch. 12 Answer Appendix.

 c. According to your experiment, if you buy one ticket, what is the experimental probability of winning? See students' work.

 d. How does your experimental probability compare to the theoretical probability of winning? See Ch. 12 Answer Appendix.

Differentiated Instruction

AL OL

If students need more practice with probability simulations,

Then give each student or pair of students a single die. Have them toss the die 100 times and then create a probability distribution table to record the number of times each number comes up. Then have them calculate the experimental probability for each number and compare the results to the theoretical probabilities.

Additional Examples

2 Miguel makes 50% of the basketball free throws he attempts.

a. What could be used to simulate Miguel's free-throw attempts? Explain. a coin, with heads representing a made free throw

b. Describe a way to simulate the next 20 free-throw attempts. Toss the coin to simulate one attempt. Record the result, and repeat 19 more times.

3 **DOGS** Ekta raises purebred dogs. One of her dogs had a litter of four puppies.

a. What objects can be used to simulate the possible outcomes of the genders of the puppies? One possible simulation would be to toss four coins, one for each puppy, with heads representing female and tails representing male.

b. Find the theoretical probability that there are two female and two male puppies. $\frac{3}{8}$

c. The results of a simulation Ekta performed are shown in the table. What is the experimental probability that there are exactly three male puppies? $\frac{12}{50}$ or 24%

Outcomes	Frequency
4 female, 0 male	3
3 female, 1 male	13
2 female, 2 male	18
1 female, 3 male	12
0 female, 4 male	4

d. How does the experimental probability compare to the theoretical probability of a litter with three males? The experimental probability, 24%, is very close to the theoretical probability, 25%.

3 PRACTICE

Formative Assessment

Use Exercises 1–4 to check for understanding.

Use the chart at the bottom of this page to customize assignments for your students.

Exercise Alerts

Dice For Exercises 4, 9, and 13 each student will need a six-sided die.

Coins For Exercise 11, each student will need four coins.

Additional Answers

6. Sample answer: a spinner divided into 4 sections where $\frac{1}{4}$ represents country, $\frac{1}{3}$ represents pop, $\frac{1}{8}$ represents rap, and $\frac{7}{24}$ represents rock
7. Sample answer: a bag of 4 marbles with a different color for each marble that represents each choice for the question

8a. Sample answer: Use 16 marbles, 1 red marble representing the defect and 15 white marbles representing the good pair of jeans, placed in a bag. Draw a marble, record the result, and replace it.

10a. Sample answer: A spinner with 4 sections divided equally; each section could represent a prize.

12a. Sample answer: Since there are 5 prizes, a die can be rolled and the number 6 ignored. Each number on the die can represent a prize. If a 6 is rolled, reroll.

12c. See students' work. Use a random number generator on a graphing calculator. The results of any simulation will vary. Over time, the results of many simulations will approach the theoretical probability.

Practice and Problem Solving

● = **Step-by-Step Solutions** begin on page R12.
Extra Practice begins on page 815.

Example 1 p. 787

5. **CARDS** Javier is drawing a card from a standard deck of cards, recording the suit, and then replacing the card in the deck. The table below shows his results.

Suit	clubs	diamonds	hearts	spades
Frequency	7	4	5	9

a. Find the experimental probability of drawing a heart. **$\frac{1}{5}$ or 20%**

b. Find the experimental probability of drawing a black card. **$\frac{16}{25}$ or 64%**

c. Javier repeated his test. The results are shown below. Find the experimental probability of drawing a spade for both tests. **$\frac{3}{10}$ or 30%**

Suit	clubs	diamonds	hearts	spades
Frequency	5	8	6	6

Example 2 p. 788

6. **CDs** There are 6 country CDs, 8 pop CDs, 3 rap CDs, and 7 rock CDs in a storage case. What could be used for a simulation to determine the probability of randomly selecting any one type of CD? **See margin.**

7. **TESTS** What could be used to simulate guessing on a multiple-choice test with 4 possible answers for each question? **See margin.**

Example 3 p. 788

8. **JEANS** Julie examines the stitching on pairs of jeans that are produced at a manufacturing plant. She expects to find defects in 1 out of every 16 pairs.

a. What can be used to model the possible outcome of a pair of jeans having defects? Explain. **See margin.**

b. What is the expected value that a random pair of jeans has a defect? **$\frac{1}{16}$ or 6.25%**

c. The results of simulations using Julie's expectations are shown. What is the experimental probability that a random pair of jeans will have a defect? **3.8 %**

d. How does the experimental probability compare to the expected value? **The experimental probability is a little less than the expected value.**

Defects	Frequency
0	71
1	9
2	11
3	6
4	3

Real-World Link

Women between the ages of 16 and 24 have an average of 8 pairs of jeans.

Source: Cotton Incorporated

B

9. **DIE ROLL** Roll a die 25 times and record your results. Find each probability based on your results.

a. What is the probability of rolling a 2? **See students' work.**

b. What is the probability of rolling a prime number? **See students' work.**

c. What is the probability of rolling an even number or 3? **See students' work.**

d. Compare your results to the theoretical probabilities. **See students' work.**

10. **PRIZES** For its tenth anniversary, a video store randomly gives each customer a prize from the following choices: a free movie rental, a free video game rental, a free bag of popcorn, or a free pre-viewed movie. The chance of winning each prize is equal.

a. What could be used to perform a simulation of this situation? Explain. **See margin.**

b. How could you use this simulation to model the next 50 free items?

10b. Sample answer: Spin the spinner, record the result, and repeat 49 more times.

Differentiated Homework Options

Level	Assignment	Two-Day Option	
AL Basic	5–8, 15, 17–39	5, 7, 20–23	6, 8, 15, 17–19 , 24–39
OL Core	5, 7, 9–15, 17–39	5–8, 20–23	9–15, 17–19, 24–39
BL Advanced	9–39		

Math History Link

Ada Byron Lovelace (1815–1852)
Lovelace is known for generating a sequence of numbers using an early model of a computer. She is credited with being the first computer programmer. In 1980, the U.S. Department of Defense named a programming language after her.

11. COIN TOSS Toss 4 coins, one at a time, 20 times, and record the number of heads and tails. Find each probability based on your results. **a–c. See students' work.**

a. *P*(any three coins will show tails)

b. *P*(any two coins will show heads)

c. *P*(the first coin will show heads and the fourth coin will show tails)

12. PRIZES For a promotion, the concession stands at a football stadium are giving away free items. Every time a customer buys something, a wheel is spun to choose the customer's prize. Each prize is equally likely.

a. Other than a spinner, what object could be used to simulate this situation? Explain. **See margin.**

b. Perform the simulation until you have received at least one of each item. **See students' work.**

c. In your simulation, how many items must be bought to win every prize? Choose another representation to solve the problem. How do the solutions compare? **See margin.**

13. GRAPHING CALCULATOR With every purchase at a fast-food restaurant, you receive a scratchoff game card with two circles. You choose one circle to scratch. One reveals a prize, and the other reveals "Sorry. Try Again." The chance that the prize on a card is cash is 5%, a sandwich is 20%, a drink is 50%, and fries is 25%. Determine how many game cards you must scratch to win the cash.

a. Generate a list of 100 random 0s and 1s in L1 of the calculator. 0 means you did not win a prize, and 1 means you won a prize. **a–d. See Ch. 12 Answer Appendix.**

b. Generate a list of 100 random integers from 1 to 20 in L2. Let each 1 represent the cash prize.

c. In L3, multiply the values in L1 and L2 together. What value represents that you won the cash prize? Explain.

d. From your simulation, how many game cards had to be scratched to win the cash?

14. ROLLING A DIE Multiply each number on a die by the probability of rolling that number. Add these values. **See margin.**

a. What is the expected value of one roll of a die? **3.5**

b. Find the expected value of the sum of the numbers on two dice. **7**

H.O.T. Problems

Use **H**igher-**O**rder **T**hinking Skills **15, 17–19. See Ch. 12 Answer Appendix.**

15. REASONING The experimental probability of heads when a coin is tossed 15 times is *sometimes*, *never*, or *always* equal to the theoretical probability. Explain.

16. CHALLENGE Lenora tested her tennis ball machine by running 5 simulations. The experimental probability of the machine being accurate is 7% higher than the results of the 5th simulation. Determine the results of the 5th simulation. **80%**

Simulation	Accuracy
1	95%
2	85%
3	90%
4	85%

17. REASONING Find a counterexample to the following statement. Explain.

It is possible for an experimental probability to be 0 if the theoretical probability is 1.

18. OPEN ENDED Describe a situation at your school that could be represented by a simulation. What could you use to simulate the situation?

19. WRITING IN MATH Compare and contrast experimental and theoretical probability.

Additional Answer

$$14a.\ 1\left(\frac{1}{6}\right) + 2\left(\frac{1}{6}\right) + 3\left(\frac{1}{6}\right) + 4\left(\frac{1}{6}\right) + 5\left(\frac{1}{6}\right) + 6\left(\frac{1}{6}\right) = \frac{21}{6} \text{ or } 3.5$$

Enrichment

CRM p. 48 OL BL

NAME ______ DATE ______ PERIOD ______

12-7 Enrichment

Game Shows

On a popular game show of the 1970s contestants were presented with three doors. Behind one of the doors was a prize. Behind the other two doors were gag prizes. A contestant was asked to select a door. Instead of showing the contestant what was behind the selected door; the host would reveal a gag prize behind one of the doors that was not chosen. After the gag prize was revealed, the contestant was given the choice to switch doors or stay with the door originally chosen. In this simulation, you will determine whether it is better to stay, switch, or if it does not matter.

1. Make a conjecture as to whether it is better to stay, switch, or does not matter once a gag prize is shown. **See students' work.**

2. Find another person to do this simulation with. Use three colored cards to represent the three doors. Two of the cards should be the same color and the third should be a different color. One person should act as the "host" and the other as the "contestant." The "contestant" wins if the uniquely colored card is chosen. The host shuffles the ca... places them ... in front

	Won	Lost
Stay		
Switch		

Study Guide and Intervention

CRM pp. 43–44 AL OL ELL

NAME ______ DATE ______ PERIOD ______

12-7 Study Guide and Intervention

Probability Simulations

Theoretical and Experimental Probability The probability used to describe events mathematically is called **theoretical probability**. For example, the mathematical probability of rolling a 4 with a number cube is $\frac{1}{6}$, or $P(4) = \frac{1}{6}$. **Experimental probability** is the ratio of the number of times an outcome occurs in an experiment to the total number of events or trials, known as the **relative frequency**.

Experimental Probability	$\frac{\text{frequency of an outcome}}{\text{total number of trials}}$

Example 1 **Matt recorded that it rained 8 times in November and snowed 3 times. The other days, it was sunny. There are 30 days in November. Suppose Matt uses these results to predict November's weather next year. What is the probability that a day in November will be sunny?**

$$\text{Experimental Probability} = \frac{\text{frequency of outcome}}{\text{total number of trials}} = \frac{(30 - 8 - 3)}{30} = \frac{19}{30} = 63.3\%$$

The probability that it will be sunny on a day in November is 63.3%.

Example 2 **A football team noticed that 9 of the last 20 coin tosses to choose which team would receive the ball first resulted in tails. What is the experimental probability of the coin landing on tails? What is the theoretical probability?**

$$\text{Experimental Probability} = \frac{\text{frequency of outcome}}{\text{total number of trials}} = \frac{\text{number of tails}}{\text{total number of tossess}} = \frac{9}{20} = 45\%$$

In this case, the experimental probability that a coin toss will be tails is 45%. If the coin is fair, the mathematical probability is 50%.

Exercises

1. **DIE ROLL** A math class decided to test whether a die is fair, that is, whether the experimental probability equals the theoretical probability. The results for 100 rolls are shown at the right.

1: 6	2: 15
3: 4	4: 13
5: 15	6: 47

a. What is the theoretical probability of rolling a 6? **16.7%**

b. What is the experimental probability of rolling a 6? **47%**

c. Is the die fair? Explain your reasoning. **Probably not; theoretical probability ≠ experimental probability.**

Lesson 12-7

Chapter 12 43 *Glencoe Algebra 1*

Practice

CRM p. 46 AL OL BL ELL

NAME ______ DATE ______ PERIOD ______

12-7 Practice

Probability Simulations

1. **MARBLES** Place 5 red, 4 yellow, and 7 green marbles in a box. Randomly draw two marbles from the box, record each color, and then return the marbles to the box. Repeat this procedure 50 times.

a. Based on your results, what is the experimental probability of selecting two yellow marbles? **Answers will vary. The theoretical probability is 0.05.**

b. Based on your results, what is the experimental probability of selecting a green marble and a yellow marble? **Answers will vary. The theoretical probability is about 0.233.**

c. Compare your results to the theoretical probabilities. **The theoretical probability in Exercise 1 is 0.05, and in Exercise 2 is about 0.233.**

2. **OPTOMETRY** Color blindness occurs in 4% of the male population. What could you use to simulate this situation? **Sample answer: a deck of playing cards in which 1 card is red and 24 are black**

3. **SCHOOL CURRICULUM** Laurel Woods High randomly selected students for a survey to determine the most important school issues among the student body. The school wants to develop a curriculum that addresses these issues. The survey results are shown in the table.

School Issues	
Issue	Number Ranking Issue Most Important
Grades	37
School Standards	17
Popularity	84
Dating	76
Violence	68
Drugs, including tobacco	29

a. Find the experimental probability distribution of the importance of each issue. **P(Grades) ≈ 0.119, P(School Standards) ≈ 0.055, P(Popularity) ≈ 0.270, P(Dating) ≈ 0.244, P(Violence) ≈ 0.219, P(Drugs) ≈ 0.093**

b. Based on the survey, what is the experimental probability that a student chosen at random thinks the most important issue is grades or school standards? **about 0.174**

c. The enrollment in the 9th and 10th grades at Laurel Woods High is 168. If their opinions are reflective of those of the school as a whole, how many of them would you expect to have chosen popularity as the most important issue? **about 45**

d. Suppose the school develops a curriculum incorporating the top three issues. What is the probability that a student selected at random will think the curriculum addresses the most important issue at school? **about 0.733**

Chapter 12 46 *Glencoe Algebra 1*

Word Problem Practice

CRM p. 47 AL OL BL ELL

NAME ______ DATE ______ PERIOD ______

12-7 Word Problem Practice

Probability Simulations

1. **GAMES** Suppose you spin the spinner below 20 times. You get 6 red, 4 blue, 5 yellow, and 5 green. What is the theoretical probability of spinning red? What is the experimental probability of spinning red? **25%; 30%**

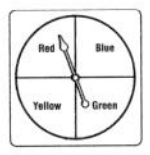

2. **EARTHQUAKES** Geologists conclude that there is a 62% probability of a magnitude 6.7 or greater quake striking the San Francisco Bay region before 2032. Does this represent *empirical probability, theoretical probability,* or *experimental probability?* **empirical**

3. **TOYS** There is a toy on the market that is sold as a mother dog with her puppies. Each mother dog comes with 2, 3, or 4 puppies. The number of puppies in the package remains a surprise until the toy is purchased and opened. Suppose the toy company has stated that one half of the toy packages contain 2 puppies, one third of the packages contain 3 puppies, and one sixth of the packages contain 4 puppies. Describe what could be used to perform a simulation for determining the probability of randomly receiving a certain number of puppies. **Sample answer: A number cube could be used to simulate the random event of receiving 2, 3, or 4 puppies. Let #1-3 represent receiving 2 puppies; let #4 and 5 represent receiving 3 puppies; let #6 represent receiving 4 puppies.**

4. **AUTOMOBILES** A consumer group surveyed its members and found that many of them had flats or blowouts with a certain brand of tire. Out of a total of 20,224 tires purchased, 984 developed problems within the first 1000 miles. Lea has just had one of these tires installed on her car. What is the probability that her tire will have a flat or blowout in the first 1000 miles? **about 4.9%**

5. **POLYGRAPH TESTING** A former FBI detective has developed a voice stress analysis device to determine whether or not a person is telling the truth. He claims that the device is accurate 95% of the time. Additionally, a traditional polygraph machine has a reported accuracy rate of 80%.

a. Suppose four criminal suspects are given the voice stress analysis. According to the reported empirical probability, what is the probability that the device can correctly analyze the accuracy of all four suspects' statements? Round your answer to the nearest tenth of a percent. **81.5%**

b. If a randomly chosen person is given both the voice stress analysis and the traditional polygraph to validate his or her statements, what is the probability that both devices are able to correctly determine the accuracy of the person's statements? **76%**

Lesson 12-7

Chapter 12 47 *Glencoe Algebra 1*

4 ASSESS

Yesterday's News Have students describe how yesterday's lesson on probability distributions helped them with today's lesson on probability simulations.

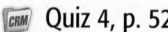

Formative Assessment

Check for student understanding of concepts in Lessons 12-6 and 12-7.

CRM Quiz 4, p. 52

TEACH with TECH

INTERACTIVE WHITEBOARD Use the student response system as a way to collect random data. For example, you could simulate rolling a number cube by giving students 6 letters to choose from as answer choices. Have each student choose one letter at random. Or, use either the Interactive Classroom software or the whiteboard software to roll simulated dice. Discuss the results of the simulation with the class.

PSAE PRACTICE 7.11.03, 10.11.10, 8.11.02

20. GEOMETRY Suppose a covered water tank in the shape of a right circular cylinder is thirty feet long and eight feet in diameter. What is the surface area of the cylinder? **A**

A 272π ft^2 C 286π ft^2
B 153π ft^2 D 248π ft^2

21. SHORT RESPONSE How many different ways can the letters P, Q, R, S be arranged? **24**

22. In how many ways can the letters in the word STATISTICS be arranged? **F**

F 50,400 H 15,400
G 20,800 J 3480

23. Two consecutive numbers have a sum of 91. What are the numbers? **C**

A 41, 50 C 45, 46
B 44, 47 D 49, 42

Spiral Review

24. The table shows a class's grade distribution, where $A = 4.0$, $B = 3.0$, $C = 2.0$, $D = 1.0$, and $F = 0$. (Lesson 12-6)

G = Grade	0	1.0	2.0	3.0	4.0
Probability	0.05	0.05	0.30	0.35	0.25

a. Is the probability distribution valid? Explain. **Yes; the probabilities add up to 1.**

b. What is the probability that a student passes the course? **95%**

c. What is the probability that a student chosen at random from the class receives a grade of C or better? **90%**

Review problems are color coded by lesson. Each student draws and then returns a colored ball from a bucket to see which lesson to review. There are 5 red, 10 yellow, 5 blue, and 2 green balls. Find each probability described. (Lesson 12-4)

25. P(yellow) **26.** P(red) **27.** P(red, blue) **28.** P(yellow, green)

25. $\frac{10}{22}$ **or about 45.5%**
26. $\frac{5}{32}$ **or about 22.7%**
27. $\frac{25}{484}$ **or about 5.2%**
28. $\frac{20}{484}$ **or about 4.1%**

29. PARTIES Student Council is planning a party for the school volunteers. There are five 66-ounce unopened bottles of soda left from a recent dance. When poured over ice, $5\frac{1}{2}$ ounces of soda fills a cup. How many servings of soda do they have? (Lesson 11-7) **60**

Write an inverse variation equation that relates x and y. Assume that y varies inversely as x. Then solve. (Lesson 11-1)

30. If $y = 8.5$ when $x = -1$, find x when $y = -1$. $xy = -8.5$; **8.5**

31. If $y = 8$ when $x = 1.55$, find x when $y = -0.62$. $xy = 12.4$; **−20**

32. If $y = 6.4$ when $x = 4.4$, find x when $y = 3.2$. $xy = 28.16$; **8.8**

33. TOPOGRAPHY To determine the mileage between landmarks, the U.S. military superimposes a coordinate grid over a map of the region. The units on this grid are approximately equal to 50,000 feet. So, a distance of 3 units on the grid equals an actual distance of 3(50,000) or 150,000 feet. Suppose the locations of two landmarks are at (132, 428) and (254, 105). Find the actual distance between these landmarks to the nearest mile. (Lesson 10-6) **3270 mi**

Write each fraction as a percent rounded to the nearest whole number. (Lesson 0-6)

34. $\frac{26}{58}$ **45%** **35.** $\frac{55}{125}$ **44%** **36.** $\frac{14}{128}$ **11%** **37.** $\frac{82}{110}$ **75%** **38.** $\frac{76}{124}$ **61%** **39.** $\frac{23}{86}$ **27%**

Differentiated Instruction BL

Extension Have students work in groups of three or four to design an experiment that has eight possible outcomes. Have them brainstorm ways to simulate the outcome and then select a method and build the simulator. Students should create a probability distribution table and compare the theoretical and experimental probabilities of the situation. Have students present their results to the class.

IL Math Online glencoe.com
- STUDY TO GO
- Vocabulary Review

Chapter Summary

Key Concepts

Designing a Survey and Analyzing Results
(Lessons 12-1 and 12-2)

- The three methods for collecting data are surveys, observational studies, and experiments.
- A sample is biased if one group is favored over another.
- Data can be organized by mean, median, mode, range, quartile and interquartile range.

Statistics (Lesson 12-3)

- A parameter is a characteristic of a whole population.
- The mean absolute value is the average of the absolute values of differences between the mean and each value and the data set.

Permutations and Combinations (Lesson 12-4)

- In a permutation, the order of objects is important, $P(n,r) = \frac{n!}{(n-r)!}$
- In a combination, the order of objects is not important, $C(n,r) = \frac{n!}{(n-r)!r!}$

Probability Distributions and Simulations
(Lessons 12-6 and 12-7)

- For each value of X, $0 \leq P(X) \leq 1$. The sum of the probabilities for all values of X is 1.
- Theoretical probability describes expected outcomes, while experimental probability describes tested outcomes.
- Simulations are used to perform experiments that would be difficult or impossible to perform in real life.

FOLDABLES® Study Organizer

Be sure the Key Concepts are noted in your Foldable.

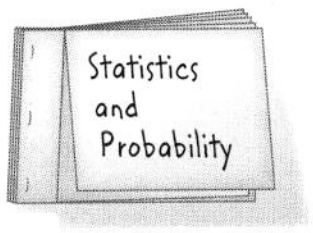

Key Vocabulary

biased sample (p. 741)
combination (p. 765)
complement (p. 772)
compound event (p. 771)
conditional probability (p. 777)
dependent events (p. 772)
discrete random variable (p. 779)
empirical study (p. 787)
experiment (p. 740)
experimental probability (p.787)
factorial (p. 764)
independent events (p. 771)
mean absolute deviation (p. 757)
mutually exclusive (p. 773)
parameter (p. 756)
permutation (p. 764)
population (p. 740)
probability distribution (p. 780)
qualitative data (p. 758)
quantitative data (p. 758)
random variable (p. 779)
relative frequency (p. 787)
sample (p. 740)
simple random sample (p. 742)
simulation (p. 788)
standard deviation (p. 758)
statistic (p. 756)
statistical inference (p. 756)
stratified random sample (p. 742)
survey (p. 740)
systemic random sample (p. 742)
theoretical probability (p. 787)
univariate data (p. 757)
variance (p. 758)

Vocabulary Check

Choose the word or term that best completes each sentence.

1. The arrangement in which order is important is called a (combination, permutation). **permutation**
2. Rolling one die and then another are (dependent, independent) events. **independent**
3. The sum of probabilities of complements equals (0, 1). **1**
4. Randomly drawing a marble from a jar and then drawing another marble are dependent events if the marbles (are, are not) replaced. **are not**
5. Events that cannot occur at the same time are (mutually exclusive, inclusive). **mutually exclusive**

CHAPTER 12 Study Guide and Review

Formative Assessment

Key Vocabulary The page reference after each word denotes where that term was first introduced. If students have difficulty answering questions 1–5, remind them that they can use these page references to refresh their memories about the vocabulary terms.

Summative Assessment

CRM Vocabulary Test, p. 54

IL Math Online glencoe.com

Vocabulary PuzzleMaker improves students' mathematics vocabulary using four puzzle formats–crossword, scramble, word search using a word list, and word search using clues. Students can work online or from a printed worksheet.

FOLDABLES® Study Organizer

Dinah Zike's Foldables®

Have students look through the chapter to make sure they have included examples in their Foldables for each lesson of the chapter.

Suggest that students keep their Foldables handy while completing the Study Guide and Review pages. Point out that their Foldables can serve as a quick review when studying for the chapter test.

Lesson-by-Lesson Review

Intervention If the given examples are not sufficient to review the topics covered by the questions, remind students that the page references tell them where to review that topic in their textbooks.

Two-Day Option Have students complete the Lesson-by-Lesson Review on pp. 794–796. Then you can use ExamView® Assessment Suite to customize another review worksheet that practices all the objectives of this chapter or only the objectives on which your students need more help.

Differentiated Instruction

Super DVD: MindJogger Videoquizzes Use this DVD as an alternative format of review for the test.

Additional Answer

6. The sample is all girls in the school. The population is all students in the school. It is a survey.

Lesson-by-Lesson Review

12-1 Designing a Survey (pp. 739–745)

10.B.4

6. **SCHOOL DANCE** The homecoming dance committee is trying to decide on a theme. They send out a questionnaire to all of the girls in the school. Identify the sample and suggest a population from which it was selected. Then, classify the type of data collection used. **See margin.**

7. **GOVERNMENT** To determine whether voters support a new trade agreement, 5 people from the list of registered voters in each state and in the District of Columbia are selected at random. Is the sample *biased* or *unbiased*? **unbiased**

8. **CANDY BARS** To ensure that all of the chocolate bars are the appropriate weight, every 50th bar on the conveyor belt in the candy factory is removed and weighed. Is the sample *simple*, *stratified*, or *systematic*? **systematic**

EXAMPLE 1

For the situation, identify the sample and suggest a population from which it was selected. Then, classify the type of data collection used.

An artist is trying to choose a cover for a children's book. She sends out a flyer with the two covers to all of the students at one school. She asks them to check their favorite cover.

The sample is all of the students at the one school.
The population is all children who read books.
The type of data collection is a survey.

EXAMPLE 2

People listening to a country music radio station are asked to name their favorite type of music. Identify the sample as *biased* or *unbiased*.

The sample is biased because people listening to a country music station are more likely to vote for country music as their favorite.

12-2 Analyzing Survey Results (pp. 746–755)

10.A.4b, 10.B.4

Tell which measure of center best represents the data. Then find the measure of center.

9. **CLASSROOM** Sophia keeps track of the ages of the students in her class. She wants to best represent the ages of her classmates: 13, 14, 13, 13, 14, 13, 13, 15, 14, 13, 14, 14, 10. **median; 13**

10. **PETS** Jason conducts a survey about the number of pets his friends have. He wants to best represent the number of pets: 0, 2, 1, 2, 4, 0, 2, 3, 1, 2, 1, 2, 3, 2, 4, 3, 10. **mode; 2**

11. **LUNCH PRICES** The cafeteria wants to show the best representation of how much students spend on lunch: 2, 3, 4, 3, 2, 4, 1, 3, 4, 2, 3, 3, 4, 3. **median; 3**

EXAMPLE 3

FINANCIAL LITERACY A company wants to show the best representation of an employee's salary. The salaries of the employees in the company are $25,000, $30,000, $28,000, $29,000, $30,000, and $65,000. Tell which measure of center best represents the data. Then find the measure of center.

List the values from least to greatest: $25,000, $28,000, $29,000, $30,000, $30,000, $65,000.

There is one value that is much greater than the rest of the data, $65,000. Also, there does not appear to be a big gap in the middle of the data. The median would best represent the data.

The median is $29,500.

MIXED PROBLEM SOLVING
For mixed problem-solving practice, see page 845.

12-3 Statistics and Parameters (pp. 756–762)

8.A.4b

Find the mean absolute deviation to the nearest tenth.

12. **SHOVELING SIDEWALKS** Ben is shoveling sidewalks to raise money over break. He is keeping track of how many he shovels each day: 2, 4, 3, 5, 3. **0.9**

13. **CANDY BARS** Luci is keeping track of the number of candy bars each member of the drill team sold. **13.3**

20, 25, 30, 50, 40, 60, 20, 10, 42

Find the mean, variance, and standard deviation to the nearest tenth for each set of data.

14. 1, 1, 3, 4, 6 **3, 3.6, 1.9**

15. 10, 11, 11, 10, 12, 13, 14, 10 **11.4; 2; 1.4**

16. 3, 5, 6, 2, 1, 5 **3.7, 3.2, 1.8**

17. 10, 11, 10, 11, 12 **10.8, 0.6, 0.8**

18. 15, 16, 16, 15, 16, 17, 18 **16.1, 1.0, 1.0**

19. **FOOD** A fast food company polled a random sample of its customers to find how many times a month they eat out: 10, 3, 12, 15, 7, 8, 4, 12, 9, 14, 12. Find the mean absolute deviation of the data set to the nearest tenth. **3.1**

EXAMPLE 4

GIFTS Joshua is collecting money from his family for his grandmother. He keeps track of how much was donated: 10, 5, 20, 15, 10. Find the mean absolute deviation.

First, find the mean of the data.

$$\frac{10 + 5 + 20 + 15 + 10}{5} = \frac{60}{5} = 12$$

Next, find the absolute value of the difference between the mean and each value.

$|10 - 12| = 2; |5 - 12| = 7; |20 - 12| = 8;$
$|15 - 12| = 3; |10 - 12| = 2$

Now, find the mean of the differences.

$$\frac{2 + 7 + 8 + 3 + 2}{5} = \frac{22}{5} = 4.4$$

The mean absolute deviation is 4.4.

EXAMPLE 5

Find the mean, variance, and standard deviation for 2, 4, 3, 5, and 6.

mean: $\frac{2 + 4 + 3 + 5 + 6}{5} = \frac{20}{5} = 4$

$$\sigma^2 = \frac{(2 - 4)^2 + (4 - 4)^2 + (3 - 4)^2 + (5 - 4)^2 + (6 - 4)^2}{5}$$

$$\sigma^2 = \frac{4 + 0 + 1 + 1 + 4}{5} \text{ or } 2$$

$$\sigma = \sqrt{2} \text{ or about } 1.4$$

12-4 Probability with Permutations and Combinations (pp. 764–770)

Preparation for 10.C.5b

Evaluate each expression.

20. $C(10, 3)$ **120**

21. $C(9, 5)$ **126**

22. $P(6, 3)$ **120**

23. $P(5, 4)$ **120**

24. **PHOTOS** The Spanish teacher at South High School wants to arrange 7 students who traveled to Mexico for a yearbook photo.

a. Is this a permutation or combination? **permutation**

b. How many ways can the students be arranged? **5040**

EXAMPLE 6

Find $C(8, 3)$.

$$C(8, 3) = \frac{8!}{(8 - 3)!3!} = \frac{8!}{5!3!} = \frac{8 \cdot 7 \cdot 6 \cdot 5 \cdot 4 \cdot 3 \cdot 2 \cdot 1}{5 \cdot 4 \cdot 3 \cdot 2 \cdot 1 \cdot 3 \cdot 2 \cdot 1}$$

$$= \frac{8 \cdot 7 \cdot 6}{6} = 56$$

EXAMPLE 7

Find $P(4, 2)$.

$$P(4, 2) = \frac{4!}{(4 - 2)!} = \frac{4 \cdot 3 \cdot 2 \cdot 1}{2 \cdot 1} = 4 \cdot 3 = 12$$

Chapter 12 Study Guide and Review 795

Problem Solving Review

For additional practice in problem solving for Chapter 12, see the Mixed Problem Solving Appendix, p. 856, in the Student Handbook section.

Additional Answer

31. For each X, the probability is greater than or equal to 0 and less than or equal to 1, and $0.18 + 0.36 + 0.34 + 0.08 + 0.04 = 1$, so the sum of the probabilities is 1.

CHAPTER 12 Study Guide and Review

12-5 Probability of Compound Events (pp. 771–778)

10.C.4a

A box contains 8 red chips, 6 blue chips, and 12 white chips. Three chips are randomly drawn from the box and are not replaced.

25. P(red, white, blue) 26. P(red, red, red) $\frac{7}{325}$

27. P(red, white, white) 28. P(blue, blue) $\frac{3}{65}$

One card is randomly drawn from a standard deck of 52 cards. Find each probability.

29. P(heart or red) $\frac{1}{2}$

30. P(10 or spade) $\frac{4}{13}$

25. $\frac{12}{325}$ 27. $\frac{22}{325}$

EXAMPLE 8

A bag of colored paper clips contains 30 red clips, 22 blue clips, and 22 green clips. Find each probability if three clips are drawn randomly from the bag and are not replaced. Find P(blue, red, green).

First clip: $P(\text{blue}) = \frac{22}{74}$ Second clip: $P(\text{red}) = \frac{30}{73}$

Third clip: $P(\text{green}) = \frac{22}{72}$

$P(\text{blue, red, green}) = \frac{22}{74} \cdot \frac{30}{73} \cdot \frac{22}{72} = \frac{605}{16{,}206}$

12-6 Probability Distributions (pp. 779–786)

10.C.4a, 10.C.4c

A local cable provider asked its subscribers how many television sets they had in their homes. The results of their survey are shown in the probability distribution.

X = Number of Televisions	Probability
1	0.18
2	0.36
3	0.34
4	0.08
5+	0.04

31. Show that the distribution is valid. **See margin.**

32. If a household is selected at random, what is the probability that it has fewer than 4 televisions? **0.88**

EXAMPLE 9

The table shows the probability distribution for the number of activities in which students at Midpark High School participate.

X = Number of Activities	Probability
0	0.04
1	0.12
2	0.37
3	0.30
4+	0.17

What is the probability that a randomly chosen student participates in 1 to 3 activities?

$P(1 \leq X \leq 3) = P(X = 1) + P(X = 2) + P(X = 3)$

$= 0.12 + 0.37 + 0.30$

$= 0.79$ or 79%

12-7 Probability Simulations (pp. 787–792)

10.C.4b

The results of a simulation of coin flipping are shown.

Outcome	Frequency
heads	25
tails	75

33. What is the experimental probability of heads? **0.25** **34. 0.75** **35. 0.50**

34. What is the experimental probability of tails?

35. What is the theoretical probability of heads?

36. How can guessing randomly on a true-false question be simulated? **flipping a coin**

EXAMPLE 10

On a multiple-choice test with four choices, Maya answered 18 out of 20 correctly by guessing randomly. Describe a way to simulate this method.

A spinner with 4 equal sections could be spun 20 times with the results of each spin being recorded.

IL Math Online glencoe.com
Chapter Test

Identify each sample, and suggest a population from which it was selected. Then classify the type of data collection used. 1–2. See margin.

1. **TOYS** A toy company invites 50 children in to test a new toy and records the reactions.

2. **FLOWERS** A nursery is sending out questionnaires to determine which flowers people like best. They send the questionnaires out to all people over 50 on their mailing list.

3. **MULTIPLE CHOICE** On a multiple-choice test with four choices, Zack answered 12 out of 20 questions correctly. What could be used to simulate his correctly answering a question? C

A tossing a coin

B rolling a six-sided number cube

C spinning a spinner with four equal sections

D rolling a three-sided number cube

Evaluate each expression.

4. $P(7, 5)$ 2520

5. $C(10, 4)$ 210

6. $C(7, 2)$ 21

7. $P(6, 3)$ 120

Which measure of central tendency best represents the data? Justify your answer. Then find the measure.

8. **VOTING** The polling place kept a list of all the ages of the people who voted: 21, 25, 32, 41, 32, 20, 65, 33, 30, 72. Median; there are outliers in the data; 32.

9. **SHOPPING** A department store kept track of the number of items shoppers purchased on a given day: 3, 5, 4, 3, 4, 5, 5, 3, 2, 3, 2, 10. Median; there are outliers in the data; 3.5.

Find the mean, variance, and standard deviation to the nearest tenth for each set of data.

10. 4, 5, 5, 6, 6, 8, 9, 10 6.6, 4.0, 2.0

11. 22, 25, 27, 30 26, 8.5, 2.9

12. 10, 10, 12, 14 11.5, 2.8, 1.7

13. **SALES** Nate is keeping track of how much people spent at the school bookstore in one day. Find the mean absolute deviation for the data to the nearest tenth: 1, 1, 2, 3, 4, 5, 12. 2.6

Identify each sample as *biased* or *unbiased*. Explain your reasoning.

14. **NEWSPAPERS** A survey is sent to all people who subscribe to *The Dispatch* to determine what newspaper people prefer to read. See margin.

15. **SHOPPING** Each person leaving the Maxtowne Mall is asked to name their favorite clothing store in the mall. See margin.

16. **PIZZA** How many ways can 3 different toppings be chosen from a list of 10 toppings? 120

17. What is the theoretical probability of tossing heads when a coin is tossed? $\frac{1}{2}$

18. A die is rolled twice. What is the probability of getting a 2 then a 3? $\frac{1}{36}$

19. **EDUCATION** Kristin surveys 200 people in her school to determine how many nights a week students do homework. The results are shown.

Number of Nights	Number of Students
0	10
1	30
2	50
3	90
4	10
5 or more	10

a. Find the probability that a randomly chosen student will have studied more than 4 nights. 5%

b. Find the probability that a randomly chosen student will have studied no more that 3 nights. 90%

20. **MULTIPLE CHOICE** The second graders are divided into boys and girls. Then 2 girls and 2 boys are chosen at random to represent the class at the Pride Assembly. Which of the following best describes the sample? G

F simple

G stratified

H systematic

J none of the above

CHAPTER 12 Practice Test

ExamView Assessment Suite Customize and create multiple versions of your chapter tests and their answer keys. All of the questions from the leveled chapter test in the *Chapter 12 Resource Masters* are also available on ExamView Assessment Suite.

Additional Answers

1. The sample is the 50 children; the population is all children; observational study
2. The sample is all people over 50 who are on the mailing list; the population is all customers on the mailing list; survey

14. Biased; since the survey is done from subscribers to a particular newspaper, the repondents are more likely to choose *The Dispatch.*

15. Unbiased; all people leaving the mall were asked.

Intervention Planner

Tier 1 On Level

If students miss about 25% of the exercises or less,

Then choose a resource:

SE Lessons 12-1, 12-2, 12-3, 12-4, 12-5, 12-6, and 12-7

CRM Skills Practice, pp. 7, 13, 19, 25, 31, 38, and 45

TE Chapter Project, p. 736

IL Math Online Self-Check Quiz

Tier 2 Strategic Intervention approaching grade level

If students miss about 50% of the exercises,

Then choose a resource:

CRM Study Guide and Intervention, Chapter 12, pp. 5, 11, 17, 23, 29, 36, and 43

IL Math Online Extra Examples, Personal Tutor, Homework Help

Tier 3 Intensive Intervention 2 or more grades below level

If students miss about 75% of the exercises,

Then use *Math Triumphs, Alg. 1,* Ch. 6

IL Math Online Extra Examples, Personal Tutor, Homework Help, Review Vocabulary

1 FOCUS

Objective Use the strategy of organizing data to solve standardized test problems.

2 TEACH

Scaffolding Questions

Ask:

- What are some ways in which you can organize data? Sample answers: lists, tables, graphs, Venn diagrams, tree diagrams
- Is it possible to organize data in more than one way? Explain. Answers will vary.
- What factors do you consider when you are thinking of ways in which you can organize data? Sample answers: the type of graph that would best represent the data; the type of method I am most familiar with or most comfortable using; the type of organizing that works best with the data

CHAPTER 12 Preparing for Standardized Tests

Organize Data

Sometimes you may be given a set of data that you need to analyze in order to solve problems on a standardized test. Use this lesson to practice organizing data to help you solve problems.

Strategies for Organizing Data

Step 1

When you are given a problem statement containing data, consider:

- **making a list** of the data.
- **using a table** to organize the data.
- **using a data display** (such as a bar graph, Venn diagram, circle graph, line graph, or box-and-whisker plot) to organize the data.

Step 2

Organize the data.

- Create your table, list, or data display.
- If possible, fill in any missing values that can be found by intermediate computations.

Step 3

Analyze the data to solve the problem.

- Reread the problem statement to determine what you are being asked to solve.
- Use the properties of algebra to work with the organized data and solve the problem.
- If time permits, go back and check your answer.

EXAMPLE

Read the problem. Identify what you need to know. Then use the information in the problem to solve. Show your work.

Of the 24 students in a music class, 10 play the flute, 14 play the piano, and 13 play the guitar. Two students play the flute only, 5 the piano only, and 7 the guitar only. One student plays the flute and the guitar but not the piano. Two students play the piano and guitar but not the flute. Three students play all the instruments. If a student is selected at random, what is the probability that he or she plays the piano and flute, but not the guitar?

Scoring Rubric	
Criteria	**Score**
Full Credit: The answer is correct and a full explanation is provided that shows each step.	2
Partial Credit: • The answer is correct, but the explanation is incomplete. • The answer is incorrect, but the explanation is correct.	1
No Credit: Either an answer is not provided or the answer does not make sense.	0

Read the problem carefully. The data is difficult to analyze as it is presented. Use a Venn diagram to organize the data and solve the problem.

Example of a 2-point response:

Use a Venn diagram to organize the data. Fill in all of the information given in the problem statement. There are 14 students who play the piano, so 14 − 5 − 2 − 3 or 4 students play the piano and the flute, but not the guitar. Find the probability.

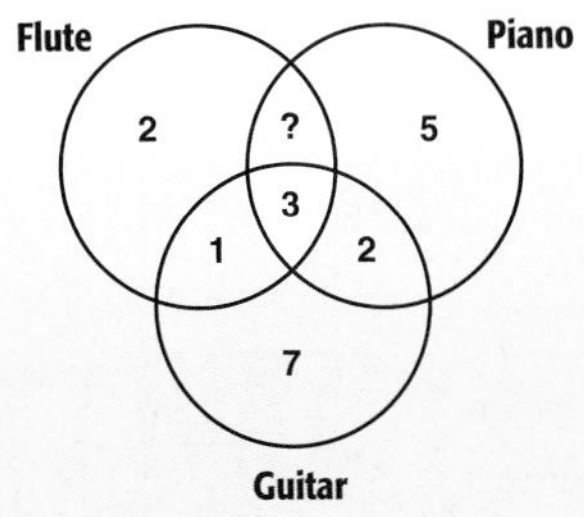

$P(\text{piano and flute}) = \frac{4}{24}$ or $\frac{1}{6}$

So, the probability that a randomly selected student plays the piano and flute but not the guitar is $\frac{1}{6}$.

Exercises

Read the problem. Identify what you need to know. Then use the information in the problem to solve. Show your work.

1. There are 40 students, 9 camp counselors, and 5 teachers at Camp Kern. Each person is assigned to one activity this afternoon. There are 9 students going hiking and 17 students going horseback riding. Of the camp counselors, 2 will supervise the hike and 3 will help with the canoe trip. There are 2 teachers helping with the canoe trip and 2 going horseback riding. Suppose a person is selected at random during the afternoon activities. What is the probability that the one selected is a student on the canoe trip or a camp counselor on a horse? Express your answer as a fraction. $\frac{143}{180}$

2. The table shows the number of coins in a piggy bank.

Coin	Number
Penny	16
Nickel	18
Dime	20
Quarter	10

   a. Find the probability that a randomly selected coin will be a dime. $\frac{5}{16}$

   b. Find the probability that a randomly selected coin will be either a nickel or a quarter. $\frac{7}{16}$

3. It takes Craig 40 minutes to mow his family's lawn. His brother Jacob can do the same job in 50 minutes. How long would it take them to mow the lawn together? Round your answer to the nearest tenth of a minute. 22.2

Additional Example

SHORT RESPONSE Of the 32 students in a class, 22 own dogs, 17 own cats, and 8 own birds. Nine students own dogs only, 7 own cats only, and 2 own birds only. One student owns a dog, a cat, and a bird. Eight students own a cat and a dog, but not a bird. One student owns a cat and a bird, but not a dog. If a student is selected at random, what is the probability that the student owns a dog and a bird, but not a cat?

Sample 2-point response

Use a Venn diagram to organize the data. Then fill in the information given in the problem.

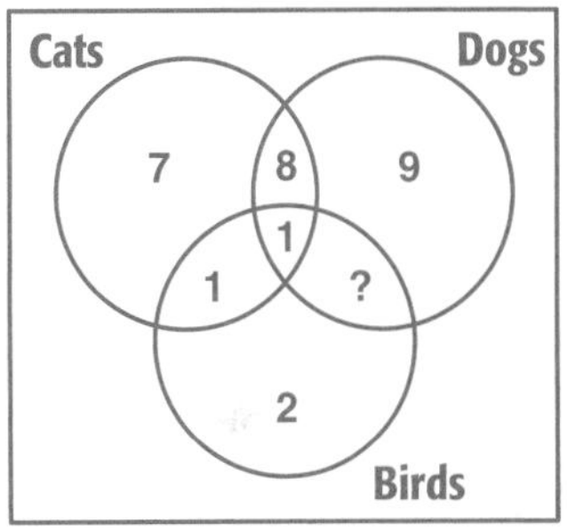

There are 22 students who own dogs, so 22 − 9 − 8 − 1 = 4 students who own a dog and a bird, but not a cat.

Find the probability: $P(\text{only dog and bird}) = \frac{4}{32}$ or $\frac{1}{8}$.

So, the probability of randomly selecting a student who owns a dog and a bird, but not a cat is 0.125 or 12.5%.

3 ASSESS

Use Exercises 1–3 to assess students' understanding.

Diagnose Student Errors

Survey students' responses for each item. Class trends may indicate common errors and misconceptions.

1. A correct
B guess
C factored incorrectly
D factored numerator instead of denominator
E guess

2. F chose measure not affected by outliers
G chose measure not affected by outliers
H chose measure not affected by outliers
J chose measure not affected by outliers
K correct

3. A chose a factor
B chose a factor
C chose a factor
D correct
E chose a factor

4. F misunderstood concept of combinations
G misunderstood concept of combinations
H correct
J calculation error
K calculation error

5. A chose feature that describes graph
B chose feature that describes graph
C correct
D chose feature that describes graph
E chose feature that describes graph

6. F interpreted y-intercept incorrectly instead of slope
G interpreted y-intercept instead of slope
H correct
J interpreted slope incorrectly
K interpreted slope incorrectly

PSAE Practice

Cumulative, Chapters 1 through 12

Multiple Choice

Read each question. Then fill in the correct answer on the answer document provided by your teacher or on a sheet of paper.

1. What are the excluded values of the variable in the expression $\frac{x^2 - x - 12}{x^2 - x - 2}$? **A**

A $-1, 2$
B $-2, 2$
C $-2, 1$
D $-3, 4$
E $3, -4$

2. The table shows the number of Calories in twelve snacks. Which measure of central tendency is *most* affected by the outlier 342 Calories? **K**

Number of Calories in Snacks					
122	87	149	121	179	105
64	138	342	72	99	114

F quartile
G median
H mode
J range
K mean

3. Which of the following is *not* a factor of $x^4 - 6x^2 - 27$? **D**

A $x^2 + 3$
B $x + 3$
C $x - 3$
D $x^2 - 3$
E $x^2 - 9$

4. Eduardo wants to choose 3 of his 20 CDs at random to take on a road trip. How many ways can he do this if the order is *not* important? **H**

F 60
G 84
H 1140
J 1482
K 6840

5. Which of the following does *not* accurately describe the graph $y = -2x^2 + 4$? **C**

A The parabola is symmetric about the y-axis.
B The parabola opens downward.
C The parabola has the origin as its vertex.
D The parabola crosses the x-axis twice.
E The parabola crosses the y-axis at 4.

6. Suppose the position of a hiker is given by the function $p(t) = -2.5t + 2{,}037$, where t is the number of minutes. Which of the following is the best interpretation of the slope of the function? **H**

F The hiker's initial position was 2,037 feet below sea level.
G The hiker's initial position was 2,037 feet above sea level.
H The hiker is descending at a rate of 2.5 meters per minute.
J The hiker is ascending at a rate of 2.5 meters per minute
K The hiker will reach the peak after 25 hours.

7. Jorge has made 39 out of 52 free throw attempts this season. What is the experimental probability that he makes a free throw? **C**

A 54%
B 68%
C 75%
D 79%
E 91%

8. Which equation passes through the points $(-1, -3)$ and $(-2, 3)$. **F**

F $y = -6x - 9$
G $y = -\frac{1}{4}x + 3$
H $y = 4x - 5$
J $y = \frac{2}{3}x + 1$
K $y = \frac{3}{2}x - \frac{1}{3}$

9. At a museum, each child admission costs \$5.75 and each adult costs \$8.25. How much does it cost a family that consists of 2 adults and 4 children? **B**

A \$34.50
B \$39.50
C \$44.50
D \$47.44
E \$49.50

Test-Taking Tip

Question 4 Since order is not important, you are looking for the number of combinations of CDs that can be chosen.

7. A guess or used wrong numbers to calculate
B guess or used wrong numbers to calculate
C correct
D guess or used wrong numbers to calculate
E guess

8. F correct
G misunderstood calculation of slope and y-intercept
H misunderstood calculation of slope and y-intercept
J misunderstood calculation of slope and y-intercept
K misunderstood calculation of slope and y-intercept

9. A guess or calculation error
B correct
C switched costs for children and adults
D multiplied costs
E guess or calculation error

Short Response/Gridded Response

Record your answers on the answer sheet provided by your teacher or on a sheet of paper.

10. GRIDDED RESPONSE Suppose Colleen spins the spinner below 80 times and records the results in a frequency table. How many times should she expect to spin a vowel? **32**

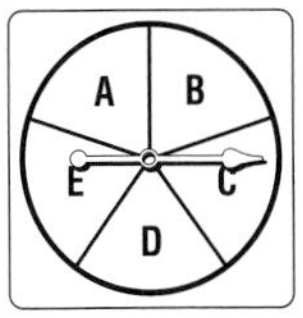

11. What is the value of sin B? Express your answer as a fraction. $\frac{5}{13}$

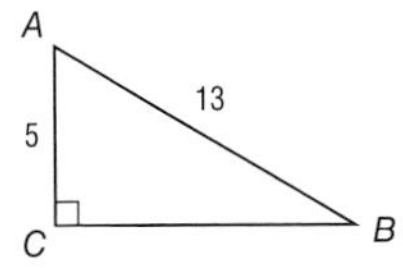

12. Graph $f(x) \geq |x - 2|$ on a coordinate grid. **See margin.**

13. GRIDDED RESPONSE Find the standard deviation of the set of data below to the nearest tenth. **3.4**

14	11	9	6
10	16	15	13
9	12	19	10

14. Larissa has 5 peanut butter cookies, 7 chocolate chip cookies, 4 sugar cookies, and 9 oatmeal raisin cookies in a jar. If she picks two cookies at random without replacing them, what is the probability that she will choose a peanut butter cookie then a sugar cookie? Express your answer as a fraction. $\frac{1}{30}$

15. Write an expression that describes the area in square units of a triangle with a height of $4c^3d^2$ and a base of $3cd^4$. $6c^4d^6$

16. Casey made 84 field goals during the basketball season for a total of 183 points. Each field goal was worth either 2 or 3 points. How many 2-point and 3-point field goals did Casey make during the season?

17. GRIDDED RESPONSE The booster club pays $180 to rent a concession stand at a football game. They purchase cans of soda for $0.25 and sell them at the game for $1.15. How many cans of soda must they sell to break even? **200**

16. 15 3-point field goals and 69 2-point field goals

Extended Response

Record your answers on a sheet of paper. Show your work.

18. To predict whether or not an issue on a ballot will pass or fail, a committee randomly calls 250 houses with area codes that are inside the voting district and asks the opinions of registered voters. Based on these efforts, the committee determines that 71% (±2.5%) of the voting population supports the issue. The committee concludes that the issue will pass. **a–e. See margin.**

a. Identify the sample.

b. Describe the population.

c. What method of data collection did the committee use: survey, experiment, or observational survey? Explain.

d. Is the sample *biased* or *unbiased*. Explain.

e. If unbiased, classify the sample as *simple*, *stratified*, or *systematic*. Explain.

Need Extra Help?

If you missed Question...	1	2	3	4	5	6	7	8	9	10	11	12	13	14	15	16	17	18
Go to Lesson or Page...	11-2	12-2	8-5	12-4	9-3	9-3	12-7	4-2	1-3	12-7	10-8	5-6	12-3	12-5	7-1	6-5	2-4	12-1
IL Assessment Objectives	6.11.06	10.11.05	8.11.01	10.11.10	8.11.08	8.11.05	10.11.07	8.11.07	6.11.13	10.11.07	9.11.19	8.11.08	6.11.08	10.11.07	7.11.03	8.11.17	6.11.13	10.11.01

Formative Assessment

You can use these two pages to benchmark student progress.

CRM Standardized Test Practice, pp. 68–70

Answer Sheet Practice

Have students simulate taking a standardized test by recording their answers on a practice recording sheet.

CRM Student Recording Sheet, p. 49

Chapter Resource Master
CRM p. 49

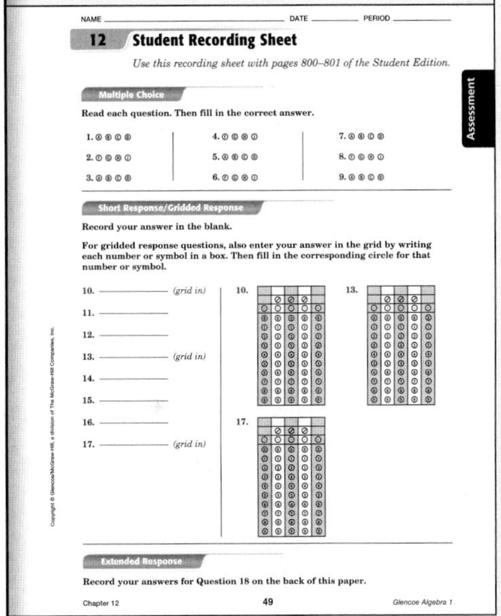
NAME DATE PERIOD

12 Student Recording Sheet

Use this recording sheet with pages 800–801 of the Student Edition.

Multiple Choice

Read each question. Then fill in the correct answer.

Short Response/Gridded Response

Record your answer in the blank.

For gridded response questions, also enter your answer in the grid by writing each number or symbol in a box. Then fill in the corresponding circle for that number or symbol.

Extended Response

Record your answers for Question 18 on the back of this paper.

Chapter 12 49 Glencoe Algebra 1

ExamView Assessment Suite Create practice worksheets or tests that align to your state's standards, as well as TIMSS and NAEP tests.

12.

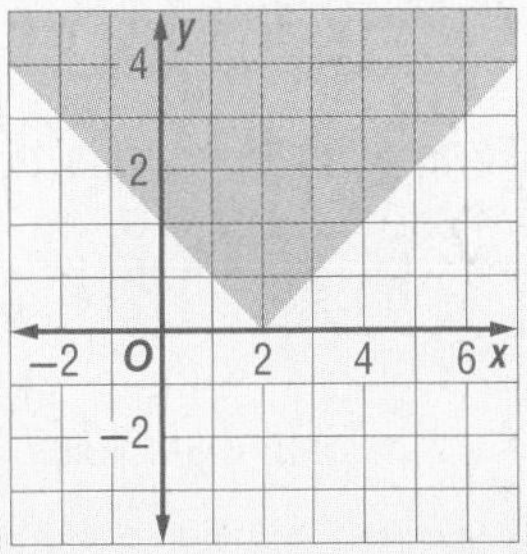

18a. Sample answer: registered voters in the voting district

b. Sample answer: all registered voters in the voting district

c. survey; Sample answer: no observations were made and no experiments were ran

d. Sample answer: unbiased because each voter is equally likely to be called.

e. simple; Sample answer: each voter in the voting district is equally likely to be called.

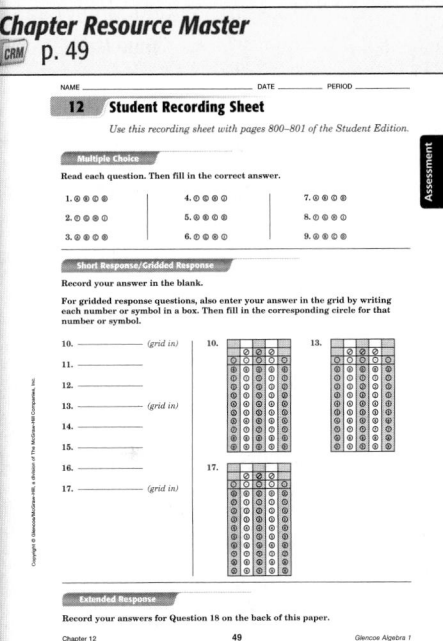

Pages 744–745, Lesson 12-1

24. Sample answer: They need accurate surveys to make decisions about how to market and sell products that will earn the company the most profit. They also make decisions about marketing and advertising and how to reach their target audience. And they make decisions about the types of products they will develop or continue to sell.

40.

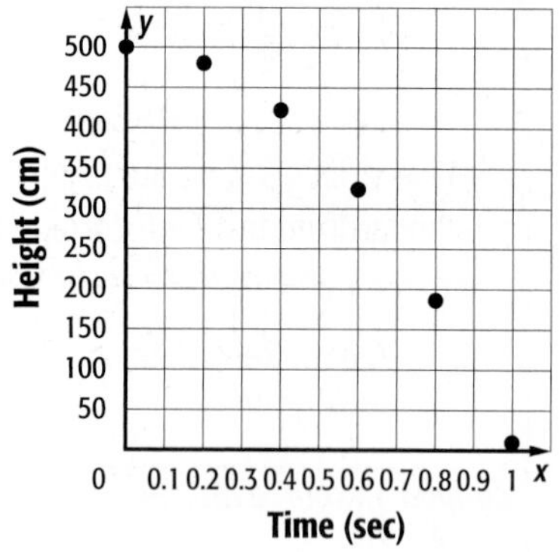

Page 756, Lesson 12-3 (Check Your Progress)

1. Sample: boxes that are removed and weighed; population: all boxes made in the factory; sample statistic: mode weight of the weighed boxes; population parameter: mode weight of all boxes.

Page 763, Mid-Chapter Quiz

1. The sample is the 100 children and parents; the population is all parents and children; observational study
2. The sample is all students with odd homeroom numbers; the population is all students in the school; survey
3. The sample is the 50 hamsters; the population is all people who will take the medicine; experiment
4. The sample is the all the girls in the school; the population is all the students in the school; survey
5. Unbiased; each museum visitor has an equal chance of being the fifth person leaving the museum.
6. Biased; since the respondents are leaving a particular store in the mall, their responses may be biased.
7. Biased; since the respondents are students at Ohio State, they are more likely to choose their own football team.
8. Unbiased; each student is equally likely to be the fifth student.

Page 780, Lesson 12-6 (Check Your Progress)

2C. **Golfers' Ages**

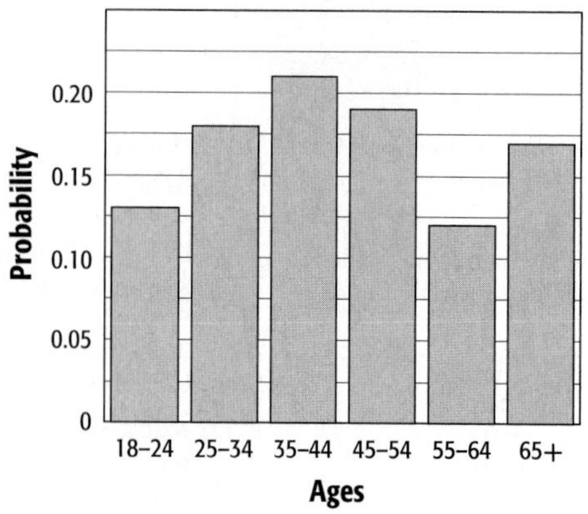

Pages 781–783, Lesson 12-6

2c. **Striped Jeans**

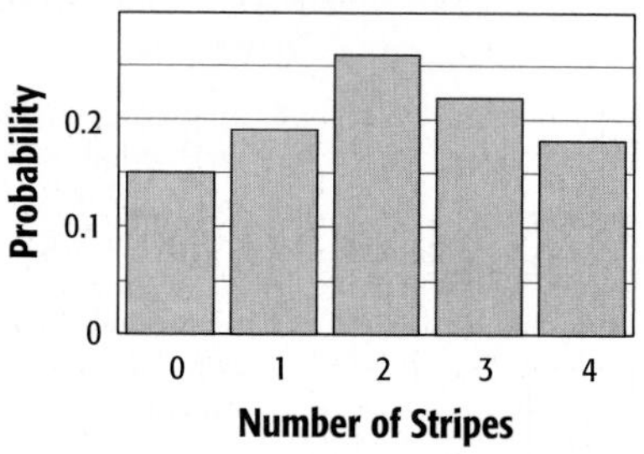

10c. **Equipment Allowed**

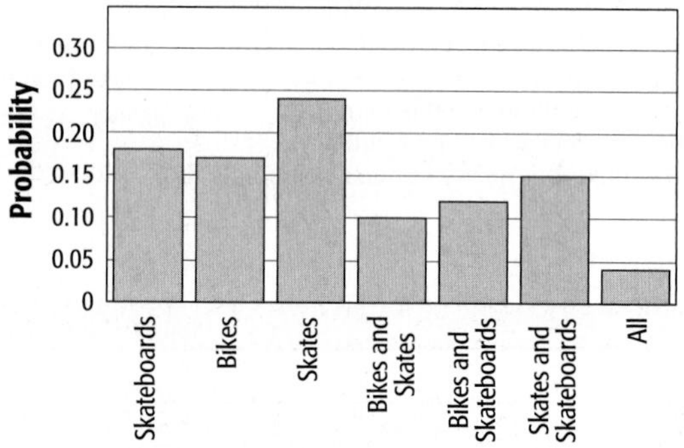

12d. **Sports Cards Sold**

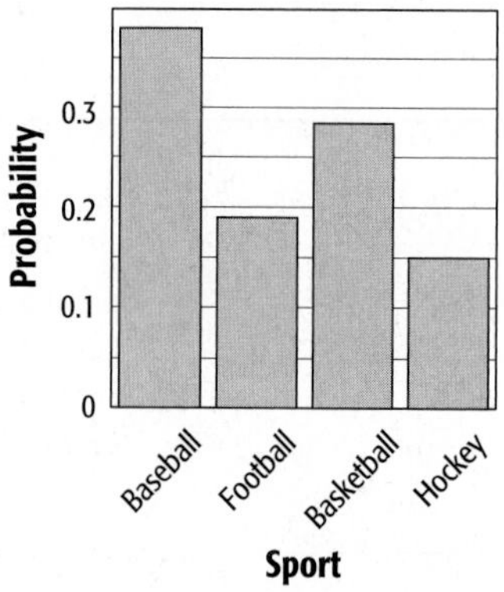

15. The sum 7 is most likely to happen.

X = Sum of Dice	2	3	4	5	6	7	8	9	10	11	12
Probability	$\frac{1}{36}$	$\frac{1}{18}$	$\frac{1}{12}$	$\frac{1}{9}$	$\frac{5}{36}$	$\frac{1}{6}$	$\frac{5}{36}$	$\frac{1}{9}$	$\frac{1}{12}$	$\frac{1}{18}$	$\frac{1}{36}$

Sum of Number Showing on the Dice

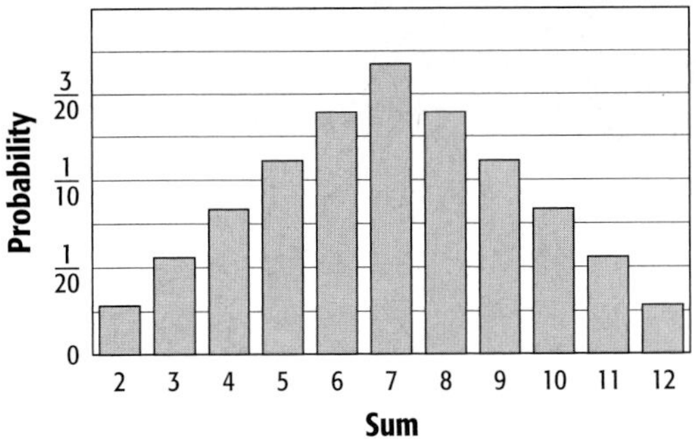

16. Since the probability is found by dividing the number of desired outcomes by the number of possible outcomes, the sum of the probability of each outcome is 1. For example, if a jar contains 2 red marbles, 1 green marble, and 3 blue marbles the probability of drawing a red marble is $\frac{2}{2+1+3}$ or $\frac{1}{3}$, the probability of drawing a green marble is $\frac{1}{2+1+3}$ or $\frac{1}{6}$, and the probability of drawing a blue marble is $\frac{3}{2+1+3}$ or $\frac{1}{2}$. The sum of the probabilities in the distribution is 1.

17. Sample answer: There are 870 students in a school: 179 freshmen, 215 sophomores, 211 juniors, and 265 seniors. Find the probability distribution for each class. What is the probability that a randomly chosen student is a sophomore?

Student Body

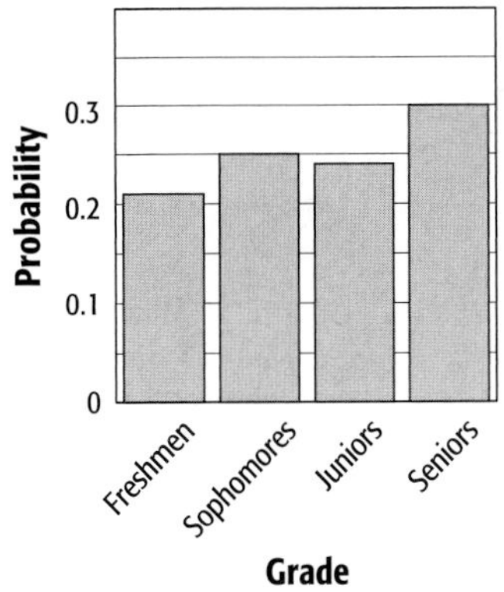

Page 789, Lesson 12-7 (Check Your Progress)

3A. Sample answer: You could use a random number generator, using integer values 1–22, with 1–3 representing a show he missed and 4–22 representing a show he watched.

3D. The experimental probability, 10%, is close to the theoretical probability, 14%.

Pages 789–791, Lesson 12-7

2. Sample answer: A spinner with 3 red sections of 10 equal sections; a spin on a red section simulates a hit.

3a. Sample answer: flipping a coin in which heads represents true and tails represents false

3b. Flip the coin, record the results, and flip the coin 19 more times.

4a. 7776 numbers; Find 6 • 6 • 6 • 6 • 6 since there are 6 possibilities for each digit.

4b. Sample answer: Roll five dice and record the results each time. Each roll represents one person picking a winning number.

4d. See students' work. The theoretical probability is $\frac{1}{7776}$ or about 0.00013.

13a. Sample answer:

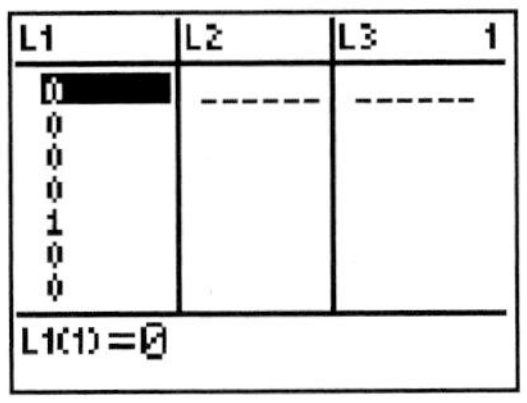

13b. Sample answer:

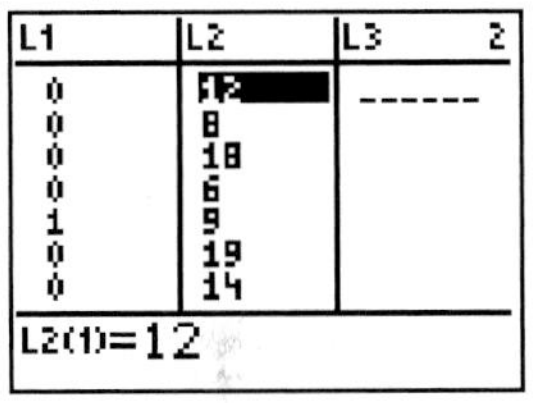

13c. A value of 1 in the third list means you won the cash prize because a 1 in the first list represents you won a prize and a 1 in the second list represents the cash prize.

13d. Sample answer:

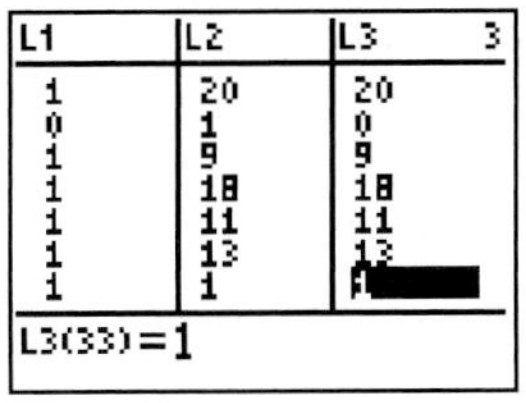

33 cards would have to be scratched in order to win the cash prize.

15. Never; the theoretical probability of getting heads from a coin toss is one half, or 7.5 times of 15 tosses. However, in an experiment you can never achieve 7.5 tails, only whole numbers.

17. The theoretical probability of tossing a coin and showing heads or tails is 1, since it will always show one or the other. So when tossing a coin in an experiment, showing heads or tails will always happen, making the experimental probability always greater than 0.

18. Sample answer: Simulating the number of field goals a kicker on the football team will make on his next attempts. A spinner could be used where a section represents the field goal was made and a section represents the field goal was missed.

19. Theoretical probabilities are based on expected or calculated results, but experimental probabilities are based on trial results. The probabilities become closer and closer as more trials are done in the experiments.

Student Handbook

Built-In Workbooks

Reference

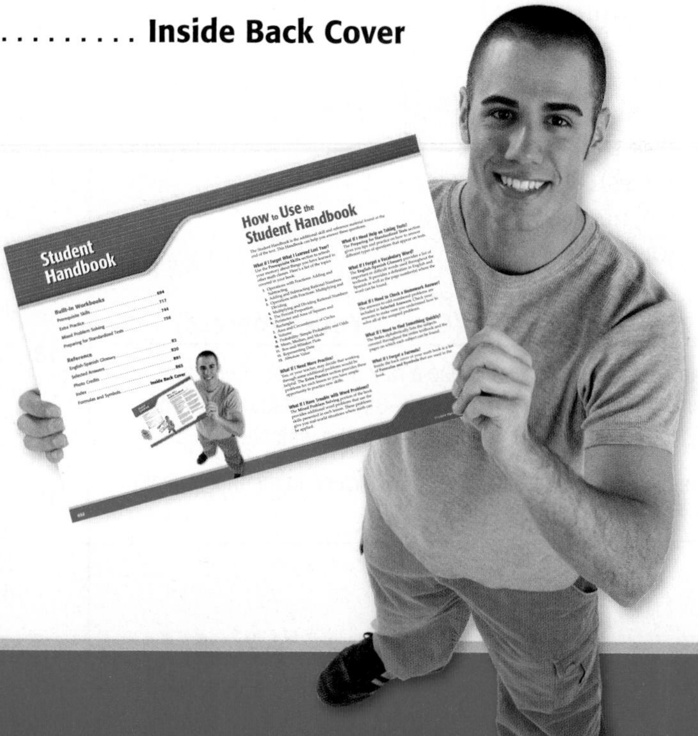

How to Use the Student Handbook

The Student Handbook is the additional skill and reference material found at the end of the text. This Handbook can help you answer these questions.

What If I Need Problem-Solving Practice?

You have probably used several different problem-solving strategies in previous math courses. The **Problem-Solving Handbook** section provides example and problems for refreshing your skills at using various strategies.

What If I Need More Practice?

You, or your teacher, may decide that working through some additional problems would be helpful. The **Extra Practice** section provides these problems for each lesson so you have ample opportunity to practice new skills.

What If I Have Trouble with Word Problems?

The **Mixed Problem Solving** portion of the book provides additional word problems that use the skills presented in each lesson. These problems give you real-world situations where math can be applied.

What if I Forget What I Learned Last Year?

Use the **Concepts and Skills Bank** section to refresh your memory about things you have learned in other math classes. Here's a list of the topics covered in your book.

1. Converting Units of Measure
2. Factors and Multiples
3. Prime Factorization
4. Measuring Angles
5. Venn Diagrams
6. Misleading Graphs

What If I Need to Check a Homework Answer?

The answers to odd-numbered problems are included in **Selected Answers and Solutions**. Check your answers to make sure you understand how to solve all of the assigned problems.

What If I Forget a Vocabulary Word?

The **English-Spanish Glossary** provides a list of important or difficult words used throughout the textbook. It provides a definition in English and Spanish as well as the page number(s) where the word can be found.

What If I Need to Find Something Quickly?

The **Index** alphabetically lists the subjects covered throughout the entire textbook and the pages on which each subject can be found.

What if I Forget a Formula?

Inside the back cover of your math book is a list of **Formulas and Symbols** that are used in the book.

Problem-Solving Handbook

Problem-Solving Strategy: Look for a Pattern

There are many problem-solving strategies in mathematics. One of the most common is to **look for a pattern**. To use this strategy, analyze the first few numbers or figures in a pattern and identify a rule that relates the first number or figure in the pattern to the second, and then to the third, and so on. Then use the rule to extend the pattern and find a solution.

EXAMPLE

Refer to the graph. Describe the pattern in the coordinates and predict the next point in the pattern in the positive direction.

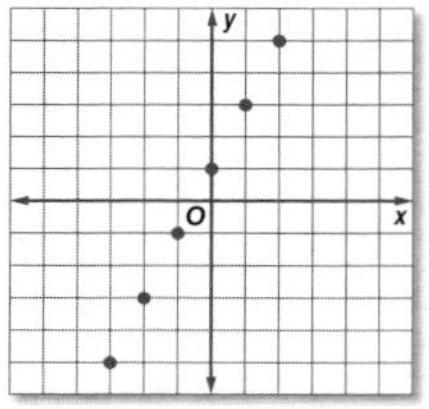

Step 1 List the coordinates of the points shown on the graph.

(−3, −5), (−2, −3), (−1, −1), (0, 1), (1, 3), and (2, 5)

Step 2 Identify the pattern in the x-coordinates and the y-coordinates.

As the x-coordinates increase by 1, the y-coordinates increase by 2 each time. So in the positive direction, the next point is (2 + 1, 5 + 2) or (3, 7).

Practice

Solve each problem by looking for a pattern.

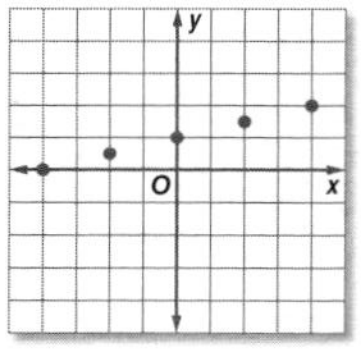

1. The graph of a function passes through the points shown.
   a. Describe the pattern in the coordinates, and predict the next point in the pattern in the positive direction.
   b. Predict the next point in the pattern in the negative direction. $\left(-6, -\frac{1}{2}\right)$

1a. The x-coordinates increase by 2 as the y-coordinates increase by $\frac{1}{2}$. The next point on the graph would be $\left(6, 2\frac{1}{2}\right)$.

2. List the first five common multiples of 3, 4, and 6. Write an expression to describe all common multiples of 3, 4, and 6. **12, 24, 36, 48, 60; 12x**
3. What is the perimeter of the twelfth figure? **28**

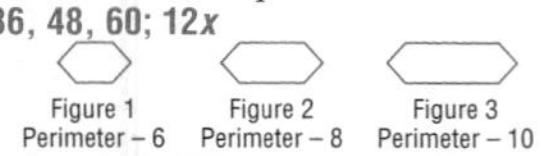

4. The football parent booster group sold hot chocolate at the game on Friday night. The table shows the total amount of money raised based on the number of cups of hot chocolate sold. Use this data table to determine how much money would be raised selling 75 cups of hot chocolate. **$56.25**

Number of Cups Sold	Amount of Money Raised ($)
15	11.25
30	22.50
45	33.75
60	45.00
75	?

Problem-Solving Strategy: Create a Table

One strategy for solving problems is to **create a table**. A table allows you to organize information in an understandable way.

Real-World EXAMPLE

A fruit machine accepts dollars, and each piece of fruit costs 65 cents. If the machine gives only nickels, dimes, and quarters, what combinations of those coins are possible as change for a dollar?

The machine will give back $1.00 − $0.65 or 35 cents in change in a combination of nickels, dimes, and quarters.

Make a table showing different combinations of nickels, dimes, and quarters that total 35 cents. Organize the table by starting with the combinations that include the most quarters.

Quarters	Dimes	Nickels
1	1	0
1	0	2
0	3	1
0	2	3
0	1	5
0	0	7

The total for each combination of the coins is 35 cents. There are 6 combinations possible.

Practice

1–8. See Student Handbook Answer Appendix for tables.

Solve each problem by creating a table.

1. How many ways can you make change for a half-dollar using only nickels, dimes, and quarters? **10**
2. A penny, a nickel, a dime, and a quarter are in a purse. How many amounts of money are possible if you grab two coins at random? **6**
3. How many ways can you receive change for a quarter if at least one coin is a dime? **6**
4. Johanna had a bag of four marbles. One marble is blue. Two marbles are green. One marble is orange. How many different ways are there to draw the marbles out of the bag one at a time? **10**
5. At Midas High School, students are selling popcorn at a football game. Each small bag of popcorn is $1.25. Each large bag of popcorn is $2.25. Create a table to show the purchase price of up to five bags of each size of popcorn.
6. Make a table to show the ordered pairs that satisfy the equation $f(x) = 3x^3 - 4$. Use the domain of integers between 3 and 10.
7. The equation of a line is $y = \frac{1}{2}x - 2$. Create a table to show five ordered pairs with x-coordinates belonging to the set $\{-2, -1, 0, 1, 2\}$.
8. Aria asked her friends whether they used wrapping paper, gift bags, recycled paper, or no wrapping to wrap birthday presents. Create a table to show how many students preferred each method of the 24 students she asked. Then predict how many would choose each method if 120 students were asked.

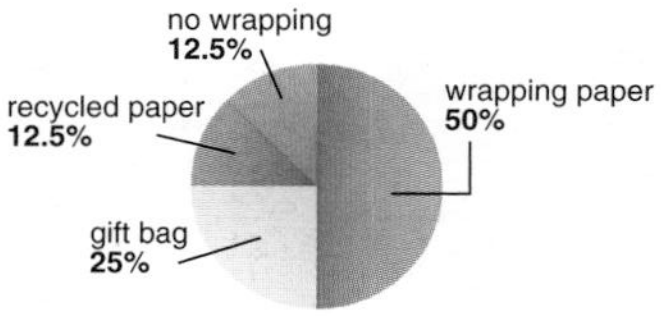

Problem-Solving Strategy: Make a Chart

Data presented in a problem can be organized by **making a chart**. This problem-solving strategy allows you to see patterns and relationships among data.

Real-World EXAMPLE

It takes an average driver 1.5 seconds to begin braking after they see an obstruction. The driver can safely decelerate a car or light truck with good tires on a dry street surface at the rate of about 15 feet per second (fps). The distance vehicle will travel while braking can be found by multiplying the initial velocity by the deceleration time and dividing by 2. Find the stopping distance for a car traveling at 45, 55, 65 and 75 miles per hour.

Step 1 Make a chart that includes the given information and the information to be found. Before setting up your chart, think about how speed, distance, and time are related.

Since the distance is listed in feet, find the rate of speed it takes to stop in feet per second. To convert from miles per hour to feet per second, multiply by a conversion factor of $\frac{3600 \text{ s}}{5280 \text{ ft}}$. Then find the deceleration time by dividing the initial velocity by 15 fps.

Initial Velocity (mph)	Initial Velocity (fps)	Deceleration Time (s)	Distance Traveled before Braking (ft)	Distance Traveled while Braking (ft)	Total Stopping Distance (ft)
45	66	4.4			
55	80.7	5.38			
65	95.3	6.35			
75	110	7.33			

Step 2 To find the distance traveled before braking, multiply the initial velocity by the reaction time, 1.5 seconds. Then find the distance traveled while braking. Add to find the total stopping distance.

Initial Velocity (mph)	Initial Velocity (fps)	Deceleration Time (s)	Distance Traveled before Braking (ft)	Distance Traveled while Braking (ft)	Total Stopping Distance (ft)
45	66	4.4	99	145.2	244.2
55	80.7	5.38	121.05	217.08	338.13
65	95.3	6.35	142.95	302.58	445.53
75	110	7.33	165	403.15	568.15

Practice

1–4. See Student Handbook Answer Appendix for Charts.

Solve each problem by making a chart.

1. As the length of a square doubles, the area increases by a scale factor. Using the squares in the diagram, make a chart of each length and each area. Then find the scale factor. 4

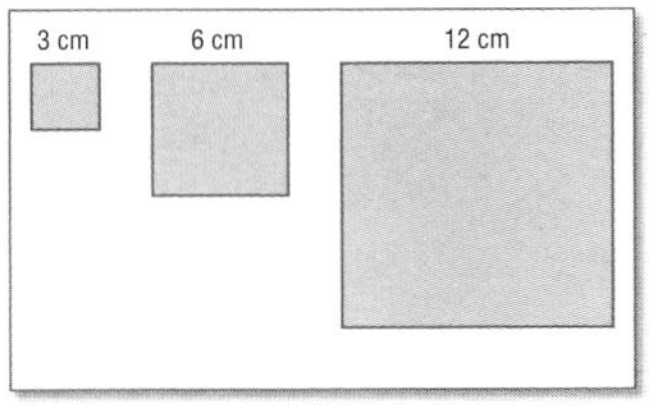

2. Given the functions $f(x) = 2x + 3$ and $g(x) = -x - 3$, use a table to find $f(x) - g(x)$ for all positive integers less than or equal to 6.

3. The chart shows at which point drivers determine when they are going to fill the gas tank. Make a chart to show how many people of 200 surveyed would be expected to have each response.

Source: *Bruskin/Goldring for Exxon*

4. The following table shows the official state reptile in each state. Make a tally chart that shows how many states have turtles (tortoise, terrapin), snakes, alligators, lizards, toads, or none. Find the ratio of states with alligators to states with no official state reptile. $\frac{3}{26}$

AL	red-bellied turtle	LA	American alligator	OH	black racer (snake)
AK	none	ME	none	OK	collared lizard
AZ	ridge-nosed rattlesnake	MD	diamondback terrapin	OR	none
AR	none	MA	garter snake	PA	none
CA	desert tortoise	MI	painted turtle	RI	none
CO	none	MN	Blanding's turtle	SC	loggerhead turtle
CT	none	MS	American alligator	SD	none
DE	none	MO	three-toed turtle	TN	eastern box turtle
FL	American alligator	MT	none	TX	Texas horned lizard
GA	gopher tortoise	NE	none	UT	none
HI	none	NV	desert tortoise	VT	none
ID	none	NH	none	VA	none
IL	painted turtle	NJ	none	WA	none
IN	none	NM	whiptail lizard	WV	none
IA	none	NY	snapping turtle	WI	none
KS	ornate box turtle	NC	eastern box turtle	WY	horned toad
KY	none	ND	none		

Problem-Solving Strategy: Guess-and-Check

To solve some problems, you can make a reasonable guess and then check it in the problem. You can then use the results to improve your guess until you find the solution. This strategy is called **guess-and-check**.

EXAMPLE

The product of two even consecutive integers is close to 1000.

Make a guess. Let's try 24 and 26. → $24 \times 26 = 624$ ← This product is too low.

Adjust the guess upward.
Try 30 and 32. → $30 \times 32 = 960$ ← This product is still too low.

Adjust the guess upward again.
Try 34 and 36. → $34 \times 36 = 1224$ ← This product is too high.

Try between 30 and 34.
Try 32 and 34. → $32 \times 34 = 1088$ ← This is the correct product.

The integers are 32 and 34.

Practice

Solve each problem by using the guess-and-check strategy.

1. The product of two consecutive odd integers is 783. What are the integers? **27, 29**
2. Brianne is three times as old as Camila. Four years from now she will be just two times as old as Camila. How old are Brianne and Camila now? **12, 4**
3. Rafael is burning a CD for Selma. The CD will hold 35 minutes of music. Which songs should he select from the list to record the maximum time on the CD without going over?

Song	A	B	C	D	E	F	G	H	I	J
Time	5 min 4 s	9 min 10 s	4 min 12 s	3 min 9 s	3 min 44 s	4 min 30 s	5 min 0 s	7 min 21 s	4 min 33 s	5 min 58 s

4. Each hand in the human body has 27 bones. There are 6 more bones in the fingers than in the wrist. There are 3 fewer bones in the palm than in the wrist. How many bones are in each part of the hand? **f: 4, w: 8, p: 5**
5. The Science Club sold candy bars and soft pretzels to raise money for an animal shelter. They raised a total of \$62.75. They made 25¢ profit on each candy bar and 30¢ profit on each pretzel sold. How many of each did they sell?
6. The product of two consecutive even integers is 4224. Find the integers. **64 and 66**
7. Odell has the same number of quarters, dimes, and nickels. In all he has \$4 in change. How many of each coin does he have? **10**
8. Anita sold tickets to the school musical. She had 2 types of bills worth \$75 for the tickets she sold. If all the money that the club collected was in \$5 bills, \$10 bills, and \$20 bills, how many of each bill did Anita have?
9. Two angles of a triangle are shown. Find the third angle if the three angles have a sum of 180°. **110°**

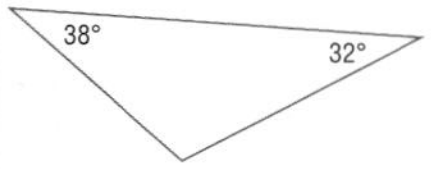

3. Songs A, D, E, F, G, H, and J run for a total of 34 minutes 46 seconds.
5. Sample answer: 125 candy bars and 105 pretzels
8. Sample answer: 3 \$5-bills, 2 \$10-bills, and 7 \$20-bills

Problem-Solving Strategy: Work Backward

On most problems, a set of conditions or facts is given and an end result must be found. However some problems start with the result and ask for something that happened earlier. The strategy of **working backward** can be used to solve problems like this. To use this strategy, start with the end result and *undo* each step.

Real-World EXAMPLE

Kendrick spent half of the money he had this morning on lunch. After lunch, he loaned his friend a dollar. Now he has \$1.50. How much money did Kendrick start with?

Start with end result, \$1.50, and work backward to find the amount Kendrick started with.

Kendrick now has \$1.50. → \$1.50
Undo the \$1 he loaned to his friend. → + 1.00 ← Add \$1.00 to undo giving his friend \$1.00.
\$2.50
Undo the half he spent for lunch. → × 2 ← Multiply by 2 to undo spending half the original amount.
\$5.00

The amount Kendrick started with was \$5.00.

CHECK Kendrick started with \$5.00. If he spent half of that, or \$2.50, on lunch and loaned his friend \$1.00, he would have \$1.50 left. This matches the amount stated in the problem, so the solution is correct.

Practice

Solve each problem by working backward.

1. A certain number is multiplied by 3, and then 5 is added to the result. The final answer is 4. What is the number? **12**
2. A certain bacteria doubles its population twice each day. After 3 full days, there are 1600 bacteria in a culture. How many bacteria were there at the beginning of the first day? **25 bacteria**
3. To catch a 7:30 A.M. bus, Don needs 30 minutes to get dressed, 30 minutes for breakfast, and 5 minutes to walk to the bus stop. What time should he wake up? **6:15 A.M.**
4. Find the length of the side of the quadrilateral if the perimeter is 83 meters. **18 m**

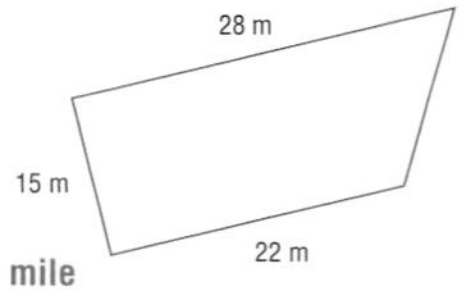

5. Troy lives $1\frac{1}{8}$ miles from his school. If he has walked $\frac{1}{4}$ mile to meet a friend and then they walked another $\frac{1}{2}$ mile to meet another friend, how far do they still need to walk to get to school? **$\frac{3}{8}$ mile**
6. If a lizard in its cage weighs 23 pounds, find the weight of the lizard if the cage weighs 19 pounds and the sand weighs 2 pounds. **2 lb**
7. Mattie spent \$125.50 on three items at the mall. She bought one pair of socks for \$1.20, one pair of shoes for \$48.95. How much money did she spend on the jacket she purchased? **\$75.35**

Problem-Solving Strategy: Solve a Simpler Problem

One of the strategies you can use to solve a problem is to **solve a simpler problem**. To use this strategy, first solve a simpler or more familiar case of the problem. Then use the same concept and relationships to solve the original problem.

EXAMPLE

Find the sum of the number 1 through 500.

Consider a simpler problem. Find the sum of the numbers 1 through 10. Notice that you can group the addends into partial sums as shown below.

$1 + 2 + 3 + 4 + 5 + 6 + 7 + 8 + 9 + 10 = 55$

11
11
11
11
11

The number of sums is 5, or half the number of addends.

Each partial sum is 11, the sum of the first and last numbers.

The sum is 5×11 or 55.

Use the same concepts to find the sum of the numbers 1 through 500.

$1 + 2 + 3 + \ldots + 499 + 500 = 250 \times 501$
$= 125{,}250$

Multiply half the number of addends, 250, by the sum of the first and last numbers, 501.

Practice

Solve each problem by solving a simpler problem.

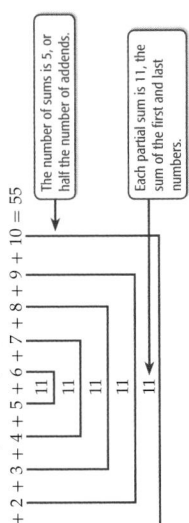

1. Find the number of squares of any size in the game board shown at the right. 205 squares
2. Find the sum of the numbers through 1000. 500,500
3. How many links are needed to join 30 pieces of chain into one long chain? 29 links
4. Three people can pick six baskets of apples in one hour. How many baskets of apples can 2 people pick in one-half hour? 2 baskets
5. A shirt shop has 112 orders for T-shirt designs. Three designers can make 2 shirts in 2 hours. How many designers are needed to complete the orders in 8 hours? 42 designers
6. Find the area of the figure at the right. 24 cm^2
7. To add $\frac{3}{8}$ and $\frac{7}{12}$, how could you solve a simpler problem that leads to the answer?
8. If one fourth of the 136 freshmen at Bayridge High School packed their lunches, explain how to use a simpler problem to find the number of students.
9. Explain how to find the greatest common factor of 35 and 49 using a simpler problem.

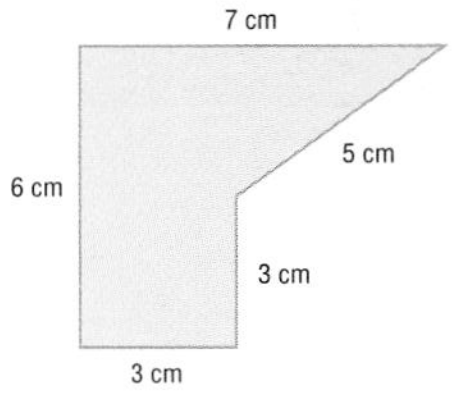

7. Find the least common multiple between 8 and 12 by finding the prime factors of each.
8. Find one fourth of 100 or 25 and add that to one fourth of 36 or 9. $25 + 9 = 34$.
9. Find the factors of 35: 1, 5, 7, and 35. Then find the factors of 49: 1, 7, and 49. The greatest factor that they have in common is 7.

Problem-Solving Strategy: Draw a Diagram

Another strategy for solving problems is to **draw a diagram**. There will be times when a sketch or diagram will give you a better picture of how to tackle a mathematics problem. Adding details like units, labels, and numbers to the drawing or sketch can help you make decisions on how to solve the problem.

Real-World EXAMPLE

Imani is trying to determine the number of 9-inch tiles needed to cover her patio. The rectangular patio measures 8-feet by 10-feet. What is the minimum number of 9-inch tiles Imani should purchase?

First, draw a diagram of the situation. Express the measurement of the patio in inches.

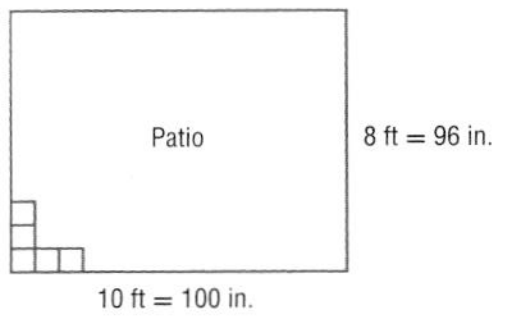

If each tile is 9 inches square, the minimum number of tiles for the width of the patio is $96 \div 9 \approx 10.7$ or 11 tiles.

The minimum number of tiles for the length of the patio is $120 \div 9 \approx 13.3$ or 14 tiles.

So the minimum number of tiles Imani needs to cover the patio is 11×14 or 154 tiles.

Practice

Solve each problem by drawing a diagram.

1. The area of a rectangular flower bed is 24 square feet. If the sides are whole number dimensions, how many combinations of lengths and widths are possible for the flower bed? List them. 8; (1, 24), (2, 12), (3, 8), (4, 6), (6, 4), (8, 3), (12, 2), (24, 1)
2. Kevin was hired to paint a mural on a wall that measures 5 feet by 20 feet. Starting from the center of the wall, he will paint a square that measures 3 feet. The dimensions of the next square will be 0.5 times greater than and centered on the previous square. How many squares can Kevin paint on the wall? 4
3. It takes 42 minutes to cut a 2-inch by 4-inch piece of wood into 7 equally sized pieces. How long will it take to cut a similar 2-inch by 4-inch piece into 4 equally sized pieces? 21 min
4. Find the number of line segments that can be drawn between any two vertices of an octagon. 28
5. How many different teams of 3 players can be chosen from 8 players? 56
6. A right triangle has measures of 11, 60, and 61 millimeters. Find the area of the triangle. 330 mm^2
7. Nitarren is trying to decide how many 9 inch diameter pies will fit on her dessert table that measures 4 feet by 2 feet. How many pies could Nitarren fit on the table? 10 pies

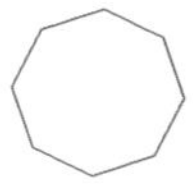

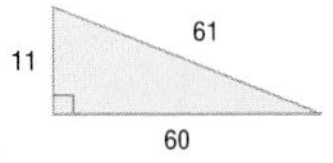

Problem Solving Handbook

Problem-Solving Strategy: Use Estimation

When you need to make a decision on the basis of inexact information, a common strategy is to **use estimation**. Often estimation is used when an exact answer is not required or when mental math is used rather than a calculator or paper and pencil. You should use estimation to determine if your answer is reasonable.

Real-World EXAMPLE

In a recent year, 51 million international visitors came to the United States. Given the information in the table, estimate what percentage of the visitors were from Japan.

Source: Travel Industry Association

Step 1 Determine about how many international visitors came to the United States.

51 million or 51,000,000 would be an easier number to work with if it was rounded to only one digit in the ten millions place, so round 51,000,000 to 50,000,000.

Step 2 Determine from the chart the number of visitors who were from Japan.

According to the chart, 5,000,000 visitors to the United States were from Japan.

Step 3 To determine the percentage, divide.

$$\frac{\text{number of visitors from Japan}}{\text{total number of visitors}} = \frac{5{,}000{,}000}{50{,}000{,}000}$$

$$= 0.1 \text{ or } 10\%$$

About 10% of the visitors to the United States in 2000 were from Japan.

Practice

Solve each problem by using estimation.

1. Use the table at the right to find the total area of the Great Lakes. **about 94,000 mi²**
2. The length of Fun Center's go-kart track is 843 feet. If Nadia circled the track 9 times, about how many feet did she travel? **about 7560 ft**
3. The Student Council is making pizzas to sell at the football game on Friday. Each pizza requires $2\frac{1}{4}$ cups of cheese. If Student Council members make 25 pizzas, how many cups of cheese will they need? **about 55 c**
4. In Florida, National Parks, State Parks, and State Forests have acreage shown in the table. If the total land and water area is 65,754.59 square miles, about what percentage of the total area is parks and forests? Use 1 square mile = 640 acres. **about 10%**

Great Lakes	
Great Lake	Area (mi²)
Lake Superior	31,698
Lake Huron	23,011
Lake Michigan	22,316
Lake Erie	9922
Lake Ontario	7320

Type of Park	Area (in acres)
National Parks	2,571,164.45
State Parks	890,000
State Forests	723,000

Source: RAND Florida

Problem-Solving Strategy: Eliminate Unnecessary Information

A useful problem-solving strategy is to learn how to **eliminate unnecessary information**. If there is a diagram, it is important to determine if all or some of the information is necessary to find a solution.

Real-World EXAMPLE

Twila is making a quilt that shows a house repeating on each block of the quilt. Which information is unnecessary to find the area of the white door of the house?

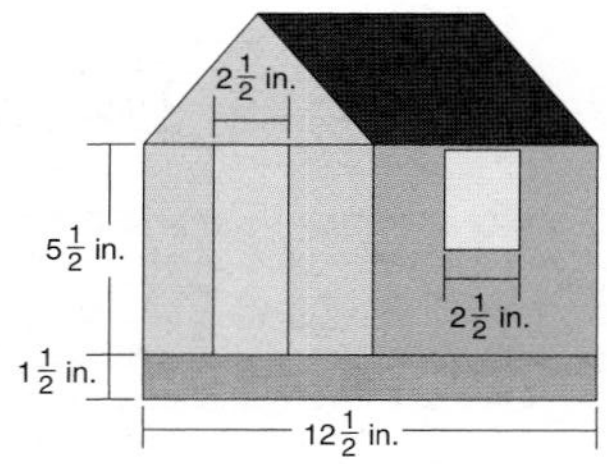

The dimensions needed to find the area of the door are the length and width of the door. So, the dimensions of $2\frac{1}{2}$ inches by $5\frac{1}{2}$ inches are needed. The other dimensions, such as the width of the window or the size of the square, are unnecessary.

Practice

Solve each problem by eliminating unnecessary information.

1. Which information is not necessary to find the temperature difference between the record lows in Alaska and Maine?

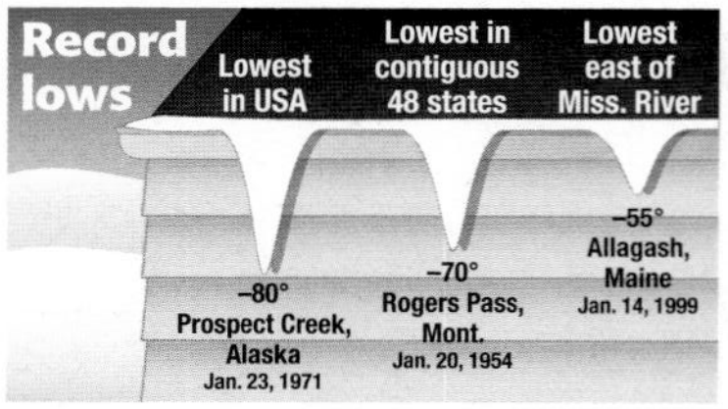

Source: National Oceanic and Atmospheric Administration

2. The Gemini North telescope was placed in Mauna Kea, Hawaii, in the year 2000. The Gemini South telescope was placed in Cerro Pachon, Chili, in the year 2001. Each of the twin telescopes are 8.1 meters in diameter. What information is not necessary to find the circumference of the base of the telescopes?
3. Which information is not necessary to find the difference in height between the tallest building and the 4th tallest building?

Rank	Building, city	Year	Stories	Height	
				m	ft
1.	Taipei 101, Taipei, Taiwan	2004	101	508	1,667
2.	Petronas Tower 1, Kuala Lumpur, Malaysia	1998	88	452	1,483
3.	Petronas Tower 2, Kuala Lumpur, Malaysia	1998	88	452	1,483
4.	Sears Tower, Chicago	1974	110	442	1,451
5.	Jin Mao Building, Shanghai	1999	88	421	1,381

Source: Council on Tall Building and Urban Habitat

1. the low temperature in Montana, the dates of each record low
2. the years and locations of the telescopes
3. the height of the Petronas Towers 1 and 2 and the height of the Jin Mao Building

Problem-Solving Strategy: Write an Equation

A natural outcome of recognizing mathematical patterns and organizing data is to **write an equation**. Look at a set of data or read a word problem to determine which values are constants and which values vary. Figure out the dependent and independent variables in order to write an equation to reflect the given situation.

Real-World EXAMPLE

For every $10 gift card sold, the theater department at Wallace High School earns $1.25. Write an equation to represent the amount raised based on the number of cards sold.

Step 1 Make a table of data to represent the number of cards sold and the amount of money raised.

Number of Cards	Amount of Money ($)
1	1.25
2	2.50
3	3.75
4	5.00

Step 2 Find the value that varies.The value that varies is the number of cards sold and the amount raised based on the number of cards sold.

Step 3 Find the value that is constant for each card sold. The value that is constant for each card sold is the amount of money raised per card, $1.25. This is the slope of the line.

Step 4 Write the equation that shows how the total amount changes based on the number of cards sold.

The equation is $y = 1.25x$.

Practice

Solve each problem by writing an equation.

1. Write an equation that can be used to find the number of Korean War Veterans. $\frac{13.3}{100} = \frac{x}{23,425,051}$

Type of Veterans	Total Number of Veterans 23,425,051
Gulf War veterans	18.7%
Vietnam-era veterans	33.5%
Korean War veterans	13.3%
World War II veterans	13.9%

Source: U.S. Census Bureau

2. The land area of Alaska is 571,951 square miles. Montana's land area is 145,552 square miles. Write an equation to find how much larger Alaska's land area is compared to Montana. $x + 145,552 = 571,951$ or $x = 571,951 - 145,552$
3. Increasingly, Internet users are using broadband Internet in their homes. Write an equation for the slope of this data in the five years shown. $m = \frac{66 - 6}{2005 - 2000}$

Broadband at Home	
Survey date	Users (in millions)
June 2000	6
May 2005	66

Source: Pew Internet Project

4. Iceland spent approximately 8.8% of its gross domestic product (GDP) on public health expenditures in 2006, the highest percentage of all countries. If Iceland had a GDP of $11,380,000,000 in 2006, write an equation to show how much money was spent on public health expenditures. $\frac{8.8}{100} = \frac{x}{11,380,000,000}$

Extra Practice

Lesson 1-1 Variables and Expressions (pp. 5–9)

Write an algebraic expression for each verbal expression.

1. the sum of b and 21 $b + 21$
2. the product of x and 7 $7x$
3. the sum of 4 and 6 times a number z $4 + 6z$
4. the sum of 8 and −2 times n $8 + (-2n)$
5. one-half the cube of a number x $\frac{1}{2}x^3$
6. four-fifths the square of m $\frac{4}{5}m^2$

Write a verbal expression for each algebraic expression. Sample answers given.

7. $2n$ 2 times n
8. 10^7 ten to the seventh power
9. m^5 m to the fifth power
10. xy the product of x and y
11. $5n^2 - 6$ five times n squared minus 6
12. $9a^3 + 1$ nine times a cubed plus 1
13. $17 - 4m^5$ seventeen minus 4 times m to the fifth power
14. $\frac{12z^2}{5}$ 12 times z squared divided by 5
15. $3x^2 - 2x$ 3 times x squared minus 2 times x

Lesson 1-2 Order of Operations (pp. 10–15)

Evaluate each expression.

1. $3 + 8 \div 2 - 5$ 2
2. $4 + 7 \cdot 2 + 8$ 26
3. $5(9 + 3) - 3 \cdot 4$ 48
4. $9 - 3^2$ 0
5. $(8 - 1) \cdot 3$ 21
6. $4(5 - 3)^2$ 16
7. $3(12 + 3) - 5 \cdot 9$ 0
8. $5^3 + 6^3 - 5^2$ 316
9. $16 \div 2 \cdot 5 \cdot 3 \div 6$ 20
10. $7(5^3 + 3^2)$ 938
11. $\frac{9 \cdot 4 + 2 \cdot 6}{6 \cdot 4}$ 2
12. $25 - \frac{1}{3}(18 + 9)$ 16
13. 2^4 16
14. 10^2 100
15. 7^3 343
16. 20^3 8000
17. 3^6 729
18. 4^5 1024
19. 10^6 1,000,000
20. 3^5 243
21. 15^3 3375

Evaluate each expression if $a = 2$, $b = 5$, $x = 4$, and $n = 10$.

22. $8a + b$ 21
23. $48 + ab$ 58
24. $a(6 - 3n)$ −48
25. $bx + an$ 40
26. $x^2 - 4n$ −24
27. $3b + 16a - 9n$ −43
28. $n^2 + 3(a + 4)$ 118
29. $(2x)^2 + an - 5b$ 59
30. $[a + 8(b - 2)]^2 \div 4$ 169
31. $(3b^2)^3 + 2x$ 421,883
32. $b^2 + 3n^3 - 4(x - 8)^2$ 2961
33. $[x + 2n(3a + 4)] - a^4$ 188

Lesson 1-3 Properties of Numbers (pp. 16–22)

Evaluate each expression using the properties of numbers. Name the property used in each step. 1–3. See Student Handbook Answer Appendix.

1. $\frac{2}{3}[15 \div (12 - 2)]$
2. $\frac{7}{4}\left[4 \cdot \left(\frac{1}{8} \cdot 8\right)\right]$
3. $[(18 \div 3) \cdot 0] \cdot 10$

Use the properties of numbers to evaluate each expression.

4. $23 + 8 + 37 + 12$ 80
5. $19 + 46 + 81 + 54$ 200
6. $10.25 + 2.5 + 3.75$ 16.5
7. $22.5 + 17.6 + 44.5$ 84.6
8. $2\frac{1}{3} + 6 + 3\frac{2}{3} + 4$ 16
9. $5\frac{6}{7} + 15 + 4\frac{1}{7} + 25$ 50
10. $6 \cdot 8 \cdot 5 \cdot 3$ 720
11. $18 \cdot 5 \cdot 2 \cdot 5$ 900
12. $0.25 \cdot 7 \cdot 8$ 14
13. $90 \cdot 12 \cdot 0.5$ 540
14. $5\frac{1}{3} \cdot 4 \cdot 6$ 128
15. $4\frac{5}{6} \cdot 10 \cdot 12$ 580

Lesson 1-4 The Distributive Property (pp. 23–29)

Use the Distributive Property to rewrite each expression. Then evaluate.

1. $5(2 + 9)$ **55**
2. $8(10 + 20)$ **240**
3. $6(y + 4)$ **$6y + 24$**
4. $9(3n + 5)$ **$27n + 45$**
5. $32\left(x - \frac{1}{8}\right)$ **$32x - 4$**
6. $c(7 - d)$ **$7c - cd$**

Simplify each expression. If not possible, write *simplified*.

7. $13a + 5a$ **$18a$**
8. $21x - 10x$ **$11x$**
9. $8(3x + 7)$ **$24x + 56$**
10. $4m - 4n$ **simplified**
11. $3(5am - 4)$ **$15am - 12$**
12. $15x^2 + 7x^2$ **$22x^2$**
13. $9y^2 + 13y^2 + 3$ **$22y^2 + 3$**
14. $11a^2 - 11a^2 + 12a^2$ **$12a^2$**
15. $6a + 7a + 12b + 8b$ **$13a + 20b$**
16. $5a + 6b + 7a$ **$12a + 6b$**
17. $8x + 4y + 9x$ **$17x + 4y$**
18. $3a + 5b + 2c + 8b$ **$3a + 13b + 2c$**

Lesson 1-5 Equations (pp. 31–37)

Find the solution of each equation if the replacement sets are $x = \{0, 2, 4, 6, 8\}$ and $y = \{1, 3, 5, 7, 9\}$.

1. $x - 4 = 4$ **8**
2. $25 - y = 18$ **7**
3. $3x + 1 = 25$ **8**
4. $5y - 4 = 11$ **3**
5. $14 = \frac{96}{x} + 2$ **8**
6. $0 = \frac{y}{3} - 3$ **9**

Solve each equation.

7. $x = \frac{27 + 9}{2}$ **18**
8. $\frac{18 - 7}{13 - 2} = y$ **1**
9. $n = \frac{6(5) + 3}{2(4) + 3}$ **3**
10. $\frac{5(4) - 6}{2^2 + 3} = z$ **2**
11. $\frac{7^2 + 9(2 + 1)}{2(10) - 1} = t$ **4**
12. $a = \frac{3^3 + 5^2}{2(3 - 1)}$ **13**

Lesson 1-6 Relations (pp. 38–44)

Describe what is happening in each graph.

1. The graph shows the average monthly high temperatures for a city over a one-year period.

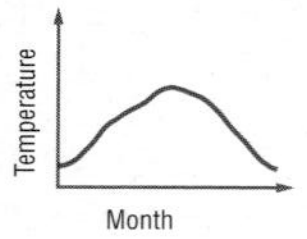

Sample answer: The temperatures increase from January through the summer and then begin to decrease again.

2. The graph shows the speed of a roller coaster car during a two-minute ride. **Sample answer: The roller coaster goes down a small hill, coasts at about the same speed, increases in speed on the way down the hill, decreases again on the way up the hill, increases down another hill, and then slows down for the end of the ride.**

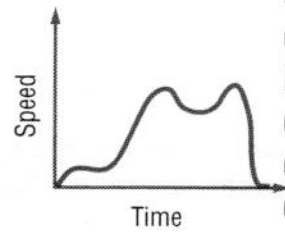

Express the relation shown in each table, mapping, or graph as a set of ordered pairs. Then describe the domain and range.

3.

x	y
1	3
2	4
3	5
4	6
5	7

{(1, 3), (2, 4), (3, 5), (4, 6), (5, 7)}; D = {1, 2, 3, 4, 5}; R = {3, 4, 5, 6, 7}

4.

x	y
−4	1
−2	3
0	1
2	3
4	1

{(−4, 1), (−2, 3), (0, 1), (2, 3), (4, 1)}; D = {−4, −2, 0, 2, 4}; R = {1, 3}

5.

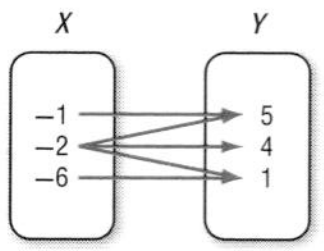

{(−1, 5), (−2, 5), (−2, 4), (−2, 1), (−6, 1)}; D = {−1, −2, −6}; R = {5, 4, 1}

Lesson 1-7 Functions (pp. 45–52)

Determine whether each relation is a function. Explain.

1.

x	y
1	3
2	5
1	−7
2	9

No; the relation is not one-to-one.

2.

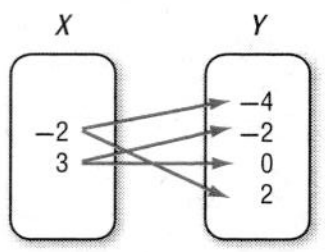

No; the relation is not one-to-one.

3.

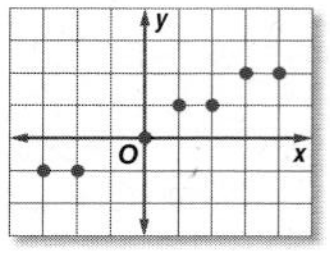

Yes; the relation is one-to-one.

4. $x^2 + y = 11$ **Yes; the relation is one-to-one.**
5. $y = 2$ **Yes; the relation is one-to-one.**
6. $\{(-2, 4), (1, 3), (5, 2), (1, 4)\}$ **No; the relation is not one-to-one.**

If $f(x) = 2x + 5$ and $g(x) = 3x^2 - 1$, find each value.

7. $f(-4)$ **−3**
8. $g(2)$ **11**
9. $f(3) - 5$ **6**
10. $g(a + 1)$ **$3a^2 + 6a + 2$**

Lesson 1-8 Logical Reasoning and Counterexamples (pp. 54–59)

Identify the hypothesis and conclusion of each statement.

1. If an animal is a dog, then it barks. **hypothesis: an animal is a dog; conclusion: it barks**
2. If a figure is a pentagon, then it has five sides. **hypothesis: a figure is a pentagon; conclusion: it has five sides**
3. If $3x - 1 = 8$, then $x = 3$. **hypothesis: $3x - 1 = 8$; conclusion: $x = 3$**
4. If 0.5 is the reciprocal of 2, then $0.5 \cdot 2 = 1$. **hypothesis: 0.5 is the reciprocal of 2; conclusion: $0.5 \cdot 2 = 1$**

Identify the hypotheses and conclusion of each statement. Then write the statement in if-then form. **5–8. See Student Handbook Answer Appendix.**

5. A square has four congruent sides.
6. $6a + 10 = 34$ when $a = 4$.
7. The video store is open every night.
8. The band will not practice on Thursday.

Find a counterexample for each conditional statement.

9. If the season is spring, then it does not snow. **It can snow in May in some locations.**
10. If you live in Portland, then you live in Oregon. **You may live in Portland, Maine.**
11. If $2y + 4 = 10$, then $y < 3$. **If $y = 3$, then $2y + 4 = 10$, is true, but $y < 3$ is false.**
12. If $a^2 > 0$, then $a > 0$. **Sample answer: $a = -1$**

Lesson 2-1 Writing Equations (pp. 75–80)

Translate each sentence into a formula.

1. A number z times 2 minus 6 is the same as m divided by 3. **$2z - 6 = m \div 3$**
2. The cube of a decreased by the square of b is equal to c. **$a^3 - b^2 = c$**
3. Twenty-nine decreased by the product of x and y is the same as z. **$29 - xy = z$**
4. The perimeter P of an isosceles triangle is the sum of twice the length of leg a and the length of the base b. **$P = 2a + b$**
5. Thirty increased by the quotient of r and t is equal to v. **$30 + (r \div t) = v$**
6. The area A of a rhombus is half the product of lengths of the diagonals a and b. **$A = 0.5ab$**

Translate each equation into a sentence. **7–12. See Student Handbook Answer Appendix for sample answers.**

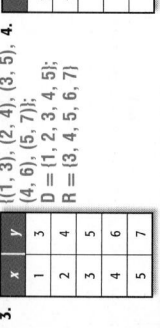

7. $0.5x + 3 = -10$
8. $\frac{n}{-6} = 2n + 1$
9. $18 - 5h = 13h$
10. $n^2 = 16$
11. $2x^2 + 3 = 21$
12. $\frac{m}{n} + 4 = 12$

Lesson 2-2 Solving One-Step Equations (pp. 81–89)

Solve each equation. Check your solution.

1. $-2 + g = 7$ **9**
2. $9 + s = -5$ **−14**
3. $-4 + y = -9$ **−5**
4. $m + 6 = 2$ **−4**
5. $t + (-4) = 10$ **14**
6. $v - 7 = -4$ **3**
7. $a - (-6) = -5$ **−11**
8. $-2 - x = -8$ **6**
9. $d + (-44) = -61$ **−17**
10. $b - (-26) = 41$ **15**
11. $p - 47 = 22$ **69**
12. $-63 - f = -82$ **19**
13. $7p = 35$ **5**
14. $-3x = -24$ **8**
15. $2y = -3$ **−1.5**
16. $62y = -2356$ **−38**
17. $\frac{a}{-6} = -2$ **12**
18. $\frac{c}{-59} = -7$ **413**
19. $\frac{7}{10} - a = \frac{1}{2}$ **$\frac{1}{5}$**
20. $f - \left(-\frac{1}{8}\right) = \frac{3}{10}$ **$\frac{7}{40}$**
21. $-4\frac{5}{12} = t - \left(-10\frac{1}{36}\right)$ **$-14\frac{4}{9}$**
22. $x + \frac{3}{8} = \frac{1}{4}$ **$-\frac{1}{8}$**
23. $1\frac{7}{16} + s = \frac{9}{8}$ **$-\frac{5}{16}$**
24. $17\frac{8}{9} = d + \left(-2\frac{5}{6}\right)$ **$20\frac{13}{18}$**
25. $-\frac{5}{9}r = 7\frac{1}{2}$ **$-13\frac{1}{2}$**
26. $2\frac{1}{6}j = 5\frac{1}{5}$ **$2\frac{2}{5}$**
27. $3 = 1\frac{7}{11}q$ **$1\frac{5}{6}$**

Lesson 2-3 Solving Multi-Step Equations (pp. 90–96)

Solve each equation. Check your solution.

1. $2x - 5 = 3$ **4**
2. $4t + 5 = 37$ **8**
3. $7a + 6 = -36$ **−6**
4. $47 = -8g + 7$ **−5**
5. $-3c - 9 = -24$ **5**
6. $5k - 7 = -52$ **−9**
7. $5s + 4s = -72$ **−8**
8. $3x - 7 = 2$ **3**
9. $8 + 3x = 5$ **−1**
10. $-3y + 7.569 = 24.069$ **−5.5**
11. $7 - 9.1f = 137.585$ **−14.35**
12. $6.5 = 2.4m - 4.9$ **4.75**
13. $\frac{n}{5} + 6 = -2$ **−40**
14. $\frac{d}{4} - 8 = -5$ **12**
15. $-\frac{4}{13}y - 7 = 6$ **$-42\frac{1}{4}$**
16. $\frac{p + 3}{10} = 4$ **37**
17. $\frac{h - 7}{6} = 1$ **13**
18. $\frac{5f + 1}{8} = -3$ **−5**
19. $\frac{4n - 8}{-2} = 12$ **−4**
20. $\frac{-3t - 4}{2} = 8$ **$-6\frac{2}{3}$**
21. $4.8a - 3 + 1.2a = 9$ **2**

Lesson 2-4 Solving Equations with the Variable on Each Side (pp. 97–102)

Solve each equation. Check your solution.

1. $5x + 1 = 3x - 3$ **−2**
2. $6 - 8n = 5n + 19$ **−1**
3. $-3z + 5 = 2z + 5$ **0**
4. $\frac{2}{3}h + 5 = -4 - \frac{1}{3}h$ **−9**
5. $\frac{1}{2}a - 4 = 3 - \frac{1}{4}a$ **$9\frac{1}{3}$**
6. $6(y - 5) = 18 - 2y$ **6**
7. $-28 + p = 7(p - 10)$ **7**
8. $\frac{1}{3}(b - 9) = b + 9$ **−18**
9. $-4x + 6 = 0.5(x + 30)$ **−2**
10. $4(2y - 1) = -8(0.5 - y)$ **all numbers**
11. $1.9s + 6 = 3.1 - s$ **−1**
12. $2.85y - 7 = 12.85y - 2$ **−0.5**
13. $2.9m + 1.7 = 3.5 + 2.3m$ **3**
14. $3(x + 1) - 5 = 3x - 2$ **all numbers**
15. $\frac{x}{2} - \frac{1}{3} = \frac{x}{3} - \frac{1}{2}$ **−1**
16. $\frac{6v - 9}{3} = v$ **3**
17. $\frac{3t + 1}{4} = \frac{3}{4}t - 5$ **no solution**
18. $0.4(x - 12) = 1.2(x - 4)$ **0**
19. $3y - \frac{4}{5} = \frac{1}{3}y$ **$\frac{3}{10}$**
20. $\frac{3}{4}x - 4 = 7 + \frac{1}{2}x$ **44**
21. $-0.2(1 - x) = 2(4 + 0.1x)$ **no solution**
22. $3.2(y + 1) = 2(1.4y - 3)$ **−23**

Lesson 2-5 Solving Equations Involving Absolute Value (pp. 103–109)

Solve each open sentence.

1. $|c - 5| = 4$ **{9, 1}**
2. $|e + 3| = 7$ **{−10, 4}**
3. $|4 - g| = 6$ **{−2, 10}**
4. $|10 - k| = 8$ **{2, 18}**
5. $|2j + 4| = 12$ **{−8, 4}**
6. $|2r - 6| = 10$ **{−2, 8}**
7. $|6 - 3w| = 8$ **$\{-\frac{2}{3}, \frac{14}{3}\}$**
8. $|7 + 2x| = 14$ **$\{-\frac{21}{2}, \frac{3}{2}\}$**
9. $|4z + 6| = 12$ **$\left\{-\frac{9}{2}, \frac{3}{2}\right\}$**

Evaluate each expression when $a = 7$, $b = 5$, and $c = -2$.

10. $|a - b|$ **2**
11. $|b - a|$ **2**
12. $|2a + c|$ **12**
13. $-|c| + |b|$ **3**
14. $-|b| + |a + c|$ **0**
15. $|4b - c|$ **22**

Lesson 2-6 Ratios and Proportions (pp. 111–118)

Solve each proportion. If necessary, round to the nearest hundredth.

1. $\frac{4}{5} = \frac{x}{20}$ **16**
2. $\frac{b}{63} = \frac{3}{7}$ **27**
3. $\frac{y}{5} = \frac{3}{4}$ **3.75**
4. $\frac{7}{4} = \frac{3}{a}$ **$\frac{12}{7}$**
5. $\frac{t - 5}{4} = \frac{3}{2}$ **11**
6. $\frac{x}{9} = \frac{0.24}{3}$ **0.72**
7. $\frac{n}{3} = \frac{n + 4}{7}$ **3**
8. $\frac{12q}{-7} = \frac{30}{14}$ **$-\frac{5}{4}$**
9. $\frac{1}{y - 3} = \frac{3}{y - 5}$ **2**
10. $\frac{x}{8.71} = \frac{4}{17.42}$ **2**
11. $\frac{a - 3}{8} = \frac{3}{4}$ **9**
12. $\frac{6p - 2}{7} = \frac{5p + 7}{8}$ **5**
13. $\frac{2}{9} = \frac{k + 3}{2}$ **$-\frac{23}{9}$ or $-2.\overline{5}$**
14. $\frac{5m - 3}{4} = \frac{5m + 3}{6}$ **3**
15. $\frac{w - 5}{4} = \frac{w + 3}{3}$ **−27**
16. $\frac{96.8}{t} = \frac{12.1}{7}$ **56**
17. $\frac{r - 1}{r + 1} = \frac{3}{5}$ **4**
18. $\frac{4n + 5}{5} = \frac{2n + 7}{7}$ **0**

Determine whether each pair of ratios are equivalent ratios. Write *yes* or *no*.

19. $\frac{3}{4}, \frac{7}{8}$ **no**
20. $\frac{3.8}{2}, \frac{4.1}{4}$ **no**
21. $\frac{8}{9}, \frac{17.6}{19.8}$ **yes**
22. $\frac{5}{6}, \frac{20}{24}$ **yes**
23. $\frac{5}{4}, \frac{30.5}{24.4}$ **yes**
24. $\frac{1}{3}, \frac{3}{1}$ **no**

Lesson 2-7 Percent of Change (pp. 119–125)

State whether each percent of change is a percent of *increase* or a percent of *decrease*. Then find each percent of change. Round to the nearest whole percent.

1. original: $100; new: $67 **decrease, 33%**
2. original: 62 acres; new: 98 acres **increase, 58%**
3. original: 322 people; new: 289 people **decrease, 10%**
4. original: 78 pennies; new: 36 pennies **decrease, 54%**
5. original: $212; new: $230 **increase, 8%**
6. original: 35 mph; new: 65 mph **increase, 86%**

Find the final price of each item.

7. television: $299; discount: 20% **$239.20**
8. book: $15.95; sales tax: 7% **$17.07**
9. software: $36.90; sales tax: 6.25% **$39.21**
10. boots: $49.99; discount: 15%; sales tax: 3.5% **$43.98**
11. jacket: $65; discount: 30%; sales tax: 4% **$47.32**
12. backpack: $28.95; discount: 10%; sales tax: 5% **$27.36**

Lesson 2-8 Literal Equations and Dimensional Analysis (pp. 126–131)

Solve each equation or formula for x.

1. $x + r = q$ $q - r$
2. $ax + 4 = 7$ $\frac{3}{a}$
3. $2bx - b = -5$ $\frac{-5 + b}{2b}$
4. $\frac{x - c}{c + a} = a$ $a^2 + ac + c$
5. $\frac{x + y}{c} = d$ $cd - y$
6. $\frac{ax + 1}{2} = b$ $\frac{2b - 1}{a}$
7. $d(x - 3) = 5$ $\frac{3d + 5}{d}$
8. $nx - a = bx + d$ $\frac{a + d}{n - b}$
9. $3x - r = r(-3 + x)$ $\frac{-2r}{3 - r}$
10. $y = \frac{5}{9}(x - 32)$ $\frac{9}{5}y + 32$
11. $A = \frac{1}{2}h(x + y)$ $\frac{2A}{h} - y$
12. $A = 2\pi r^2 + 2\pi rx$ $\frac{A}{2\pi r} - r$

Solve each equation or formula for the variable indicated.

13. $S = 2b(a + c) + 2ac$, for b 13. $b = \frac{S - 2ac}{2(a + c)}$
14. $g(h + 8) = -j$, for h $h = -\frac{j}{g} - 8$
15. $\frac{11n + p}{t} = 8$, for p $p = 8t - 11n$
16. $\frac{u - 10v}{7} = w$, for u $u = 7w + 10v$
17. $\frac{9x - y}{z - 10} = 12$, for x 17. $x = \frac{12(z - 10) + y}{9}$
18. $\frac{2k - 3}{m + p} = 5$, for k $K = \frac{5(m + p) + 3}{2}$
19. $14h + j = 2h$, for h $h = -\frac{j}{12}$
20. $-18k + m = 22k$, for k $k = \frac{m}{40}$
21. $39k + 3j = -6m$, for j $j = -2m - 13k$

Lesson 2-9 Weighted Averages (pp. 132–138)

1. **ADVERTISING** An advertisement for grape drink claims that the drink contains 10% grape juice. How much pure grape juice would have to be added to 5 quarts of the drink to obtain a mixture containing 40% grape juice? 2.5 qt
2. **GRADES** In Ms. Pham's social studies class, a test is worth four times as much as homework. If a student has an average of 85% on tests and 95% on homework, what is the student's average? 87%
3. **ENTERTAINMENT** At the Golden Oldies Theater, tickets for adults cost \$5.50 and tickets for children cost \$3.50. How many of each kind of ticket were purchased if 21 tickets were bought for \$83.50? 5 adults, 16 children
4. **FOOD** Wes is mixing peanuts and chocolate pieces. Peanuts sell for \$4.50 a pound and the chocolate sells for \$6.50 a pound. How many pounds of chocolate mixes with 5 pounds of peanuts to obtain a mixture that sells for \$5.25 a pound? 3 lb
5. **TRAVEL** Missoula and Bozeman are 210 miles apart. Sheila leaves Missoula for Bozeman and averages 55 miles per hour. At the same time, Casey leaves Bozeman and averages 65 miles per hour as he drives to Missoula. When will they meet? How far will they be from Bozeman? 1.75 h; 113.75 mi

Lesson 3-1 Graphing Linear Equations (pp. 153–160)

Determine whether each equation is a linear equation. Write *yes* or *no*. If *yes*, write the equation in standard form.

1. $3x = 2y$ yes; $3x - 2y = 0$
2. $2x - 3 = y^2$ no
3. $4x = 2y + 8$ yes; $4x - 2y = 8$
4. $5x - 7y = 2x - 7$ yes; $3x - 7y = -7$
5. $2x + 5x = 7y + 2$ yes; $7x - 7y = 2$
6. $\frac{1}{x} + \frac{5}{y} = -4$ no

Graph each equation by using the x- and y-intercepts or by making a table. 7–18. See Student Handbook Answer Appendix.

7. $3x + y = 4$
8. $y = 3x + 1$
9. $3x - 2y = 12$
10. $2x - y = 6$
11. $2x - 3y = 8$
12. $y = -2$
13. $y = 5x - 7$
14. $x = 4$
15. $x + \frac{1}{3}y = 2$
16. $5x - 2y = 8$
17. $4.5x + 2.5y = 9$
18. $\frac{1}{2}x + 3y = 12$

Lesson 3-2 Solving Linear Equations by Graphing (pp. 161–168)

Solve each equation. 7. $y = 12$; no solution

1. $-x + 6 = 0$ $x = 6$
2. $8x + 2 = 0$ $x = -\frac{1}{4}$
3. $4x + 3 = -2 + 4x$ $y = -5$; no solution
4. $-2x + 5 = 5$ $x = 0$
5. $3 = 4x - 1$ $x = 1$
6. $\frac{1}{2}x + 5 = -1$ $x = -12$
7. $6x - 4 = 8 + 6x$
8. $\frac{1}{2} = 3x - 4$ $x = \frac{3}{2}$ or $1\frac{1}{2}$
9. $7 = -x - 4$ $x = -11$

Lesson 3-3 Rate of Change and Slope (pp. 170–178)

Find the slope of the line that passes through each pair of points.

1. 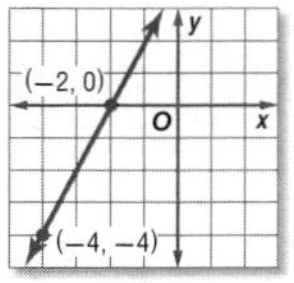

2

2. 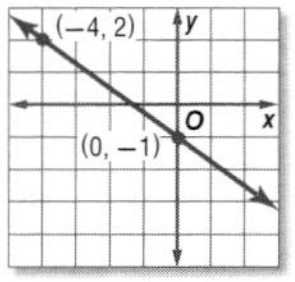

$-\frac{3}{4}$

3. $(-2, 2), (3, -3)$ -1
4. $(-2, -8), (1, 4)$ 4
5. $(3, 4), (4, 6)$ 2
6. $(-5, 4), (-1, 11)$ $\frac{7}{4}$
7. $(18, -4), (6, -10)$ $\frac{1}{2}$
8. $(-4, -6), (-4, -8)$ undefined
9. $(0, 0), (-1, 3)$ -3
10. $(-8, 1), (2, 1)$ 0

Find the value of r so the line that passes through each pair of points has the given slope.

11. $(-1, r), (1, -4), m = -5$ 6
12. $(r, -2), (-7, -1), m = -\frac{1}{4}$ -3

Lesson 3-4 Direct Variation (pp. 180–186)

Name the constant of variation for each equation. Then find the slope of the line that passes through each pair of points.

1. 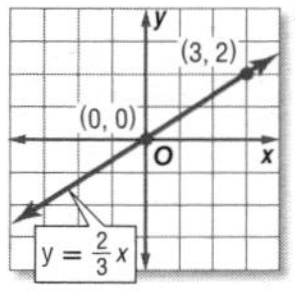

$\frac{2}{3}$; $\frac{2}{3}$

2. 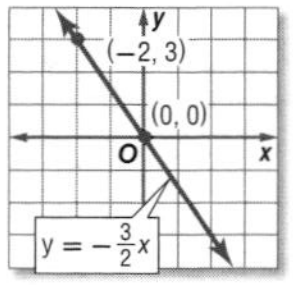

$-\frac{3}{2}$; $-\frac{3}{2}$

3. 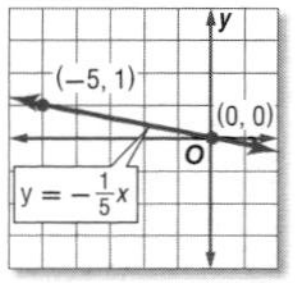

$-\frac{1}{5}$; $-\frac{1}{5}$

Graph each equation. 4–6. See Student Handbook Answer Appendix.

4. $y = 5x$
5. $y = -6x$
6. $y = -\frac{4}{3}x$

Suppose y varies directly as x. Write a direct variation equation that relates x and y. Then solve.

7. If $y = 45$ when $x = 9$, find y when $x = 7$. $y = 5x$; 35
8. If $y = -7$ when $x = -1$, find x when $y = -84$. $y = 7x$; -12

Lesson 3-5 Arithmetic Sequences as Linear Functions (pp. 187–194)

Determine whether each sequence is an arithmetic sequence. Write *yes* or *no*. Explain.

1. $-2, -1, 0, 1, \ldots$ yes; 1
2. $3, 5, 8, 12, \ldots$ no
3. $2, 4, 8, 16, \ldots$ no
4. $-21, -16, -11, -6, \ldots$ yes; 5
5. $0, 0.25, 0.5, 0.75, \ldots$ yes; 0.25
6. $\frac{1}{3}, \frac{1}{9}, \frac{1}{27}, \frac{1}{81}, \ldots$ no

Find the next three terms of each arithmetic sequence.

7. $3, 13, 23, 33, \ldots$ 43, 53, 63
8. $-4, -6, -8, -10, \ldots$ −12, −14, −16
9. $-2, -1.4, -0.8, -0.2, \ldots$ 0.4, 1.0, 1.6
10. $5, 13, 21, 29, \ldots$ 37, 45, 53
11. $\frac{3}{4}, \frac{7}{8}, 1, \frac{9}{8}, \ldots$ $\frac{5}{4}, \frac{11}{8}, \frac{3}{2}$
12. $-\frac{1}{3}, -\frac{5}{6}, -\frac{4}{3}, -\frac{11}{6}, \ldots$ $-\frac{7}{3}, -\frac{17}{6}, -\frac{10}{3}$

Write an equation for the *n*th term of the arithmetic sequence. Then graph the first five terms in the sequence. 13–16. See Student Handbook Answer Appendix.

13. $-3, 1, 5, 9, \ldots$
14. $25, 40, 55, 70, \ldots$
15. $-9, -3, 3, 9, \ldots$
16. $-3.5, -2, -0.5, \ldots$

Lesson 3-6 Proportional and Nonproportional Relationships (pp. 195–200)

Write an equation in function notation for each relation.

1. 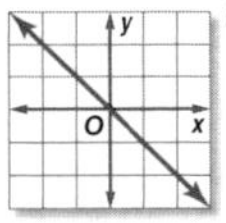 $f(x) = -x$
2. 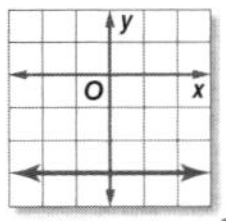 $f(x) = -3$
3. 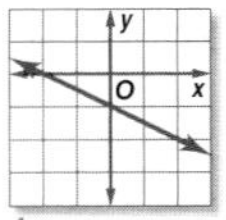 $f(x) = -\frac{1}{2}x - 1$
4. 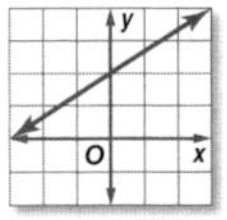 $f(x) = \frac{2}{3}x + 2$

The table shows the number of cups of flour used to make batches of brownies.

Batches of brownies	1	2	3	4
Cups of flour	4	8	12	16

5a. Write an equation for the data given. $y = 4x$

5b. Graph the equation. See Student Handbook Answer Appendix.

5c. Find the number of cups of flour needed for 6 batches of brownies. 24 cups

Lesson 4-1 Graphing Equations in Slope-Intercept Form (pp. 214–221)

Write an equation, in slope-intercept form, of the line with the given slope and *y*-intercept.

1. *m*: 5, *y*-intercept: −15 $y = 5x - 15$
2. *m*: −6, *y*-intercept: 3 $y = -6x + 3$
3. *m*: 0.3, *y*-intercept: −2.6 $y = 0.3x - 2.6$
4. *m*: $-\frac{4}{3}$, *y*-intercept: $\frac{5}{3}$ $y = \frac{4}{3}x + \frac{5}{3}$
5. *m*: $-\frac{2}{5}$, *y*-intercept: 2 $y = -\frac{2}{5}x + 2$
6. *m*: $\frac{7}{4}$, *y*-intercept: −2 $y = \frac{7}{4}x - 2$

Write an equation in slope-intercept form for each graph shown.

7. 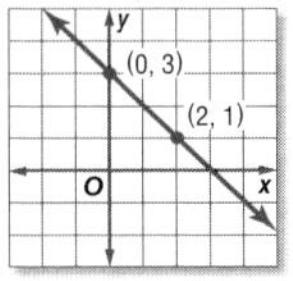

$y = -x + 3$

8. 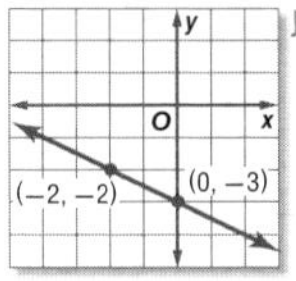

$y = -\frac{1}{2}x - 3$

9. 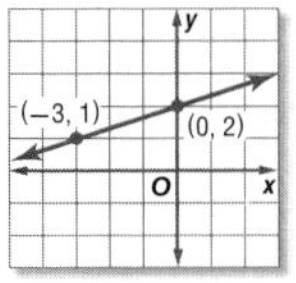

$y = \frac{1}{3}x + 2$

Graph each equation. 10–12. See Student Handbook Answer Appendix.

10. $y = 5x - 1$
11. $y = -2x + 3$
12. $3x - y = 6$

Lesson 4-2 Writing Equations in Slope-Intercept Form (pp. 224–230)

Write an equation of the line that passes through the given point and has the given slope.

1. $(0, 0); m = -2$ $y = -2x$
2. $(-3, 2); m = 4$ $y = 4x + 14$
3. $(0, 5); m = -1$ $y = -x + 5$
4. $(-2, 3); m = -\frac{1}{4}$ $y = -\frac{1}{4}x + \frac{5}{2}$
5. $(1, -5); m = \frac{2}{3}$ $y = \frac{2}{3}x - \frac{17}{3}$
6. $\left(\frac{1}{2}, \frac{1}{4}\right); m = 8$ $y = 8x - \frac{15}{4}$

Write an equation of the line that passes through each pair of points.

7. $(-1, 7), (8, -2)$ $y = -x + 6$
8. $(4, 0), (0, 5)$ $y = -\frac{5}{4}x + 5$
9. $(8, -1), (7, -1)$ $y = -1$
10. $(-2, 3), (1, 3)$ $y = 3$
11. $(0, 0), (-4, 3)$ $y = -\frac{3}{4}x$
12. $\left(-\frac{1}{2}, \frac{1}{2}\right), \left(\frac{1}{4}, \frac{3}{4}\right)$ $y = \frac{1}{3}x + \frac{2}{3}$

Lesson 4-3 Writing Equations in Point-Slope Form (pp. 231–236)

Write an equation in point-slope form for the line that passes through each point with the given slope. Then graph the equation.

1. $(5, -2), m = 3$ $y + 2 = 3(x - 5)$
2. $(0, 6), m = -2$ $y - 6 = -2x$
3. $(-3, 1), m = 0$ $y - 1 = 0$
4. $(-2, -4), m = \frac{3}{4}$ $y + 4 = \frac{3}{4}(x + 2)$

Write each equation in standard form.

5. $y + 3 = 2(x - 4)$ $2x - y = 11$
6. $y + 3 = -\frac{1}{2}(x + 6)$ $x + 2y = -12$
7. $y - 4 = -\frac{2}{3}(x - 5)$ $2x + 3y = 22$
8. $y + 2 = \frac{4}{3}(x - 6)$ $4x - 3y = 30$
9. $y - 1 = 1.5(x + 3)$ $3x - 2y = -11$
10. $y + 6 = -3.8(x - 2)$ $19x + 5y = 8$

Write each equation in slope-intercept form.

11. $y - 1 = -2(x + 5)$ $y = -2x - 9$
12. $y + 3 = 4(x - 1)$ $y = 4x - 7$
13. $y - 6 = -4(x - 2)$ $y = -4x + 14$
14. $y + 1 = \frac{4}{5}(x + 5)$ $y = \frac{4}{5}x + 3$
15. $y - 2 = -\frac{3}{4}(x - 2)$ $y = -\frac{3}{4}x + \frac{7}{2}$
16. $y + \frac{1}{4} = \frac{2}{3}\left(x + \frac{1}{2}\right)$ $y = \frac{2}{3}x + \frac{1}{12}$

Lesson 4-4 Parallel and Perpendicular Lines (pp. 237–243)

Write the slope-intercept form of an equation for the line that passes through the given point and is parallel to the graph of each equation. Then write an equation in slope-intercept form for the line that passes through the given point and is perpendicular to the graph of each equation.

1. $(1, 6), y = 4x - 2$ $y = 4x + 2$; $y = -\frac{1}{4}x + \frac{25}{4}$
2. $(4, 6), y = 2x - 7$ $y = 2x - 2$; $y = -\frac{1}{2}x + 8$
3. $(-3, 0), y = \frac{2}{3}x + 1$ $y = \frac{2}{3}x + 2$; $y = -\frac{3}{2}x - \frac{9}{2}$
4. $(5, -2), y = -3x - 7$ $y = -3x + 13$; $y = \frac{1}{3}x - \frac{11}{3}$
5. $(0, 4), 3x + 8y = 4$ $y = -\frac{3}{8}x + 4$; $y = \frac{8}{3}x + 4$
6. $(2, 3), x - 5y = 7$ $y = \frac{1}{5}x + \frac{13}{5}$; $y = -5x + 13$

Determine whether the graphs of each pair of equations are *parallel*, *perpendicular*, or *neither*.

7. $y = -2x + 11$
   $y + 2x = 23$ parallel
8. $3y = 2x + 14$
   $2x - 3y = 2$ parallel
9. $y = -5x$
   $y = 5x - 18$ neither

Lesson 4-5 Scatter Plots and Lines of Fit (pp. 245–252)

Determine whether each graph shows a **positive correlation**, *a* **negative correlation**, *or* **no correlation**. *If there is a correlation, describe its meaning in the situation.*

1. 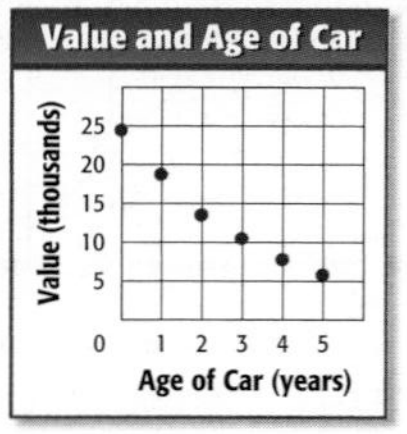

Negative; the value of a car decreases as it goes.

2. 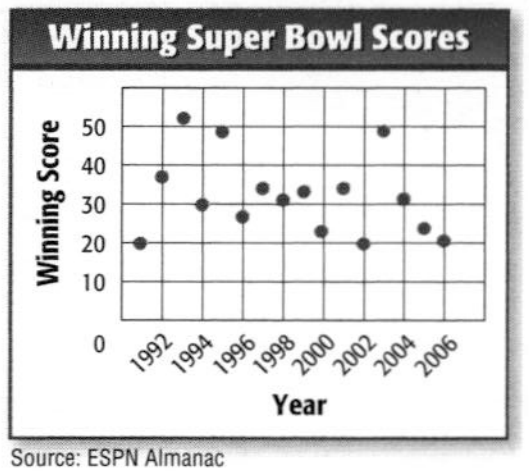

Source: ESPN Almanac

no correlation

Lesson 4-6 Regression and Median-Fit Lines (pp. 253–260)

1. **COMPUTERS** The media center is keeping track of student computer use to determine if they need to purchase more computers. There are 6 computers in the center. The results of the 10-day tracking period are recorded in the table. Write an equation for the regression line for the data. Then find the correlation coefficient. $y = 0.127x + 58.6$; $r = 0.024$

Student Computer Use

Day	1	2	3	4	5	6	7	8	9	10
Number of Students	48	62	75	70	32	52	70	63	81	40

2. **STOCKS** For a class project, the students were asked to keep track of a stock price for a company of local interest. They were to record the closing price of the stock at the end of each Friday for 8 weeks. Marcus was out of town one week and missed the price for week 4. Find the equation for the data, and approximate the price for week 4. $y = 0.917x + 27.2$; about 30.9

Weekly Closing Stock Price for Barney's International

Week	1	2	3	5	6	7	8
Closing Price	29	27	29	33	34	33	34

Lesson 4-7 Special Functions (pp. 261–269)

Graph each function. 1–7. See Student Handbook Answer Appendix.

1. $f(x) = -3[\![x]\!]$
2. $g(x) = [\![4x]\!]$
3. $h(x) = 2[\![x]\!] - 3$
4. $f(x) = |x + 2|$
5. $g(x) = |3x - 1|$
6. $f(x) = \begin{cases} -2x \text{ if } x < 3 \\ x + 1 \text{ if } x \geq 3 \end{cases}$
7. **PARKING** Short-term parking at the airport is \$2 for the first half-hour and \$1 for each half-hour after that. Draw a graph that represents this information.

Short-Term Parking Fees

Hours	Fees
$0 < h \leq \frac{1}{2}$	\$2
$\frac{1}{2} < h \leq 1$	\$3
$1 < h \leq 1\frac{1}{2}$	\$4

Lesson 5-1 Solving Inequalities by Addition and Subtraction (pp. 283–288)

1–16. See Student Handbook Answer Appendix.

Solve each inequality. Check your solution, and then graph it on a number line.

1. $c + 9 \leq 3$
2. $d - (-3) < 13$
3. $z - 4 > 20$
4. $h - (-7) > -2$
5. $-11 > d - 4$
6. $2x > x - 3$
7. $2x - 3 \geq x$
8. $16 + w < -20$
9. $14p > 5 + 13p$
10. $-7 < 16 - z$
11. $1.1v - 1 > 2.1v - 3$
12. $\frac{1}{2}t + \frac{1}{4} \geq \frac{3}{2}t - \frac{2}{3}$
13. $9x < 8x - 2$
14. $-2 + 9n \leq 10n$
15. $a - 2.3 \geq -7.8$
16. $5z - 6 > 4z$

Define a variable, write an inequality, and solve each problem. Check your solution.

17. The sum of a number and negative six is greater than 9. Sample answer if n = the number: $n + (-6) > 9$; $\{n \mid n > 15\}$
18. Negative five times a number is less than the sum of negative six times the number and 12. Sample answer if n = the number: $-5n < -6n + 12$; $\{n \mid n < 12\}$

Lesson 5-2 Solving Inequalities by Multiplication and Division (pp. 290–295)

Solve each inequality. Check your solution.

1. $7b \geq -49$ $\{b \mid b \geq -7\}$
2. $-5j < -60$ $\{j \mid j > 12\}$
3. $\frac{w}{3} > -12$ $\{w \mid w > -36\}$
4. $\frac{p}{5} < 8$ $\{p \mid p < 40\}$
5. $-8f < 48$ $\{f \mid f > -6\}$
6. $-0.25t \geq -10$ $\{t \mid t \leq 40\}$
7. $\frac{g}{-8} < 4$ $\{g \mid g > -32\}$
8. $-4.3x < -2.58$ $\{x \mid x > 0.6\}$
9. $4c \geq -6$ $\{c \mid c \geq -1.5\}$
10. $6 \leq 0.8n$ $\{n \mid n \geq 7.5\}$
11. $\frac{2}{3}m \geq -22$ $\{m \mid m \geq -33\}$
12. $-25 > -0.05a$ $\{a \mid a > 500\}$
13. $-15a < -28$ $\{a \mid a > \frac{28}{15}\}$
14. $-\frac{7}{9}x < 42$ $\{x \mid x > -54\}$
15. $0.375y \leq 32$ $\{y \mid y \leq \frac{256}{3}\}$
16. $-7y \geq 91$ $\{y \mid y \leq -13\}$

Define a variable, write an inequality, and solve each problem. Then check your solution. 17–19. Let n = the number.

17. Negative one times a number is greater than −7. $-n > -7$; $\{n \mid n < 7\}$
18. Three fifths of a number is at least negative 10. $\frac{3}{5}n \geq -10$; $\{n \mid n \geq -\frac{50}{3}\}$
19. Seventy-five percent of a number is at most 100. $0.75n \leq 100$; $\{n \mid n \leq 133.\overline{3}\}$

Lesson 5-3 Solving Multi-Step Inequalities (pp. 296–301)

Solve each inequality. Check your solution.

1. $3y - 4 > -37$ $\{y \mid y > -11\}$
2. $7s - 12 < 13$ $\{s \mid s < \frac{25}{7}\}$
3. $-5q + 9 > 24$ $\{q \mid q < -3\}$
4. $-6v - 3 \geq -33$ $\{v \mid v \leq 5\}$
5. $-2k + 12 < 30$ $\{k \mid k > -9\}$
6. $-2x + 1 < 16 - x$ $\{x \mid x > -15\}$
7. $15t - 4 > 11t - 16$ $\{t \mid t > -3\}$
8. $13 - y \leq 29 + 2y$ $\{y \mid y \geq -\frac{16}{3}\}$
9. $5q + 7 \leq 3(q + 1)$ $\{q \mid q \leq -2\}$
10. $2(w + 4) \geq 7(w - 1)$ $\{w \mid w \leq 3\}$
11. $-4t - 5 > 2t + 13$ $\{t \mid t < -3\}$
12. $\left\{\frac{2t + 5}{3}\right\} < -9$ $\{t \mid t < -16\}$
13. $\frac{z}{4} + 7 \geq -5$ $\{z \mid z \geq -48\}$
14. $13r - 11 > 7r + 37$ $\{r \mid r > 8\}$
15. $8c - (c - 5) > c + 17$ $\{c \mid c > 2\}$
16. $-5(k + 4) \geq 3(k - 4)$ $\{k \mid k \leq -1\}$
17. $9m + 7 < 2(4m - 1)$ $\{m \mid m < -9\}$
18. $3(3y + 1) < 13y - 8$ $\{y \mid y > \frac{11}{4}\}$
19. $5x \leq 10(3x + 4)$ $\{x \mid x \geq -\frac{8}{5}\}$
20. $3\left(a + \frac{2}{3}\right) \geq a - 1$ $\{a \mid a \geq -\frac{3}{2}\}$

Lesson 5-4 Solving Compound Inequalities (pp. 304–309)

Solve each compound inequality. Then graph the solution set. **1–16. See Student Handbook Answer Appendix.**

1. $2 + x < -5$ *or* $2 + x > 5$
2. $-4 + t > -5$ *or* $-4 + t < 7$
3. $3 \le 2g + 7$ *and* $2g + 7 \le 15$
4. $2v - 2 \le 3v$ *and* $4v - 1 \ge 3v$
5. $3b - 4 \le 7b + 12$ *and* $8b - 7 \le 25$
6. $-9 < 2z + 7 < 10$
7. $5m - 8 \ge 10 - m$ *or* $5m + 11 < -9$
8. $12c - 4 \le 5c + 10$ *or* $-4c - 1 \le c + 24$
9. $2h - 2 \le 3h \le 4h - 1$
10. $3p + 6 < 8 - p$ *and* $5p + 8 \ge p + 6$
11. $2r + 8 > 16 - 2r$ *and* $7r + 21 < r - 9$
12. $-4j + 3 < j + 22$ *and* $j - 3 < 2j - 15$
13. $2(q - 4) \le 3(q + 2)$ *or* $q - 8 \le 4 - q$
14. $\frac{1}{2}w + 5 \ge w + 2 \ge \frac{1}{2}w + 9$
15. $n - (6 - n) > 10$ *or* $-3n - 1 > 20$
16. $-(2x + 5) \le x + 5 \le 2x - 9$
17. **WIND SPEED** The Fujita Scale (F-scale) is the official classification system for tornado damage. One factor used to classify a tornado is wind speed. Use the information in the table to write an inequality for the range of wind speeds of an F3 tornado. **$158 \le w \le 206$**

F-Scale	Wind Speed
F0	40–72 mph
F1	73–112 mph
F2	113–157 mph
F3	158–206 mph
F4	207–260 mph
F5	261–318 mph

Lesson 5-5 Inequalities Involving Absolute Value (pp. 310–314)

Solve each inequality. Then graph the solution set. **1–12. See Student Handbook Answer Appendix.**

1. $|x + 4| < 10$
2. $|y - 3| \ge 3$
3. $|2x + 5| > 2$
4. $\left|\frac{2x - 3}{5}\right| \ge 4$
5. $\left|\frac{3m - 2}{2}\right| \ge 7$
6. $\left|\frac{2n + 8}{3}\right| < 2$
7. $|5v + 2| < 4$
8. $|w - 8| \ge 14$
9. $|3x + 2| > 8$
10. $\left|\frac{4m + 5}{3}\right| \ge 5$
11. $\left|\frac{y + 4}{5}\right| < 4$
12. $\left|\frac{3h - 5}{2}\right| > 5$

Lesson 5-6 Graphing Inequalities in Two Variables (pp. 315–320)

Determine which ordered pairs are part of the solution set for each inequality.

1. $x + y \ge 0$, {(0, 0), (1, −3), (2, 2), (3, −3)} **{(0, 0), (2, 2), (3, −3)}**
2. $2x + y \le 8$, {(0, 0), (−1, −1), (3, −2), (8, 0)} **{(0, 0), (−1, −1), (3, −2)}**

Graph each inequality. **3–8. See Student Handbook Answer Appendix.**

3. $y \le -2$
4. $x < 4$
5. $x + y < -2$
6. $3y - 2x \le 2$
7. $y > 4x - 1$
8. $3x + y > 1$
9. **DELIVERIES** A delivery truck with a 4000-pound weight limit is transporting televisions that weigh 77 pounds each and microwaves that weigh 55 pounds each.
   a. Define variables and write an inequality for this situation. **Sample answer: Let t = the weight of a television and let m = the weight of a microwave; $77t + 55m \le 4000$.**
   b. Will the truck be able to deliver 35 televisions and 25 microwaves at once? Explain. **No, the weight will be greater than 4000 pounds.**

Lesson 6-1 Graphing Systems of Equations (pp. 333–339)

Graph each system of equations. Then determine whether the system has no solution, one solution, or infinitely many solutions. If the system has one solution, name it. **1–12. See Student Handbook Answer Appendix for graphs.**

1. $y = 3x$; $4x + 2y = 30$ **(3, 9)**
2. $x = -2y$; $x + y = 1$ **(2, −1)**
3. $y = x + 4$; $3x + 2y = 18$ **(2, 6)**
4. $x + y = 6$; $x - y = 2$ **(4, 2)**
5. $x + y = 6$; $3x + 3y = 3$ **no solution**
6. $y = -3x$; $4x + y = 2$ **(2, −6)**
7. $2x + y = 8$; $x - y = 4$ **(4, 0)**
8. $\frac{1}{5}x - y = \frac{12}{5}$; $3x - 5y = 6$ **(−3, −3)**
9. $x + 2y = 0$; $y + 3 = -x$ **(−6, 3)**
10. $x + 2y = -9$; $x - y = 6$ **(1, −5)**
11. $x + \frac{1}{2}y = 3$; $y = 3x - 4$ **(2, 2)**
12. $\frac{2}{3}x + \frac{1}{2}y = 2$; $4x + 3y = 12$ **infinitely many**

Lesson 6-2 Substitution (pp. 342–347)

Use substitution to solve each system of equations. If the system does not have exactly one solution, state whether it has no solutions or infinitely many solutions.

1. $y = x$; $5x = 12y$ **(0, 0)**
2. $y = 7 - x$; $2x - y = 8$ **(5, 2)**
3. $x = 5 - y$; $3y = 3x + 1$ **$\left(\frac{7}{3}, \frac{8}{3}\right)$**
4. $3x + y = 6$; $y + 2 = x$ **(2, 0)**
5. $x - 3y = 3$; $2x + 9y = 11$ **$\left(4, \frac{1}{3}\right)$**
6. $3x = -18 + 2y$; $x + 3y = 4$ **$\left(-\frac{46}{11}, \frac{30}{11}\right)$**
7. $x + 2y = 10$; $-x + y = 2$ **(2, 4)**
8. $2x = 3 - y$; $2y = 12 - x$ **(−2, 7)**
9. $6y - x = -36$; $y = -3x$ **$\left(\frac{36}{19}, -\frac{108}{19}\right)$**
10. $\frac{3}{4}x + \frac{1}{3}y = 1$; $x - y = 10$ **(4, −6)**
11. $x + 6y = 1$; $3x - 10y = 31$ **(7, −1)**
12. $3x - 2y = 12$; $\frac{3}{2}x - y = 3$ **no solution**
13. $2x + 3y = 5$; $4x - 9y = 9$ **$\left(\frac{12}{5}, \frac{1}{15}\right)$**
14. $x = 4 - 8y$; $3x + 24y = 12$ **infinitely many**
15. $3x - 2y = -3$; $25x + 10y = 215$ **(5, 9)**

Lesson 6-3 Elimination Using Addition and Subtraction (pp. 348–354)

Use elimination to solve each system of equations.

1. $x + y = 7$; $x - y = 9$ **(8, −1)**
2. $2x - y = 32$; $2x + y = 60$ **(23, 14)**
3. $-y + x = 6$; $y + x = 5$ **$\left(\frac{11}{2}, -\frac{1}{2}\right)$**
4. $s + 2t = 6$; $3s - 2t = 2$ **(2, 2)**
5. $x = y - 7$; $2x - 5y = -2$ **(−11, −4)**
6. $3x + 5y = -16$; $3x - 2y = -2$ **(−2, −2)**
7. $x - y = 3$; $x + y = 3$ **(3, 0)**
8. $x + y = 8$; $2x - y = 6$ **$\left(\frac{14}{3}, \frac{10}{3}\right)$**
9. $2s - 3t = -4$; $s = 7 - 3t$ **(1, 2)**
10. $-6x + 16y = -8$; $6x - 42 = 16y$ **no solution**
11. $3x + 0.2y = 7$; $3x = 0.4y + 4$ **(2, 5)**
12. $9x + 2y = 26$; $1.5x - 2y = 13$ **$\left(\frac{26}{7}, -\frac{26}{7}\right)$**
13. $x = y$; $x + y = 7$ **(3.5, 3.5)**
14. $4x - \frac{1}{3}y = 8$; $5x + \frac{1}{3}y = 6$ **$\left(\frac{14}{9}, -\frac{16}{3}\right)$**
15. $2x - y = 3$; $\frac{2}{3}x - y = -1$ **(3, 3)**

Lesson 6-4 Elimination Using Multiplication (pp. 355–360)

Use elimination to solve each system of equations.

1. $-3x + 2y = 10$, $-2x - y = -5$ **(0, 5)**
2. $2x + 5y = 13$, $4x - 3y = -13$ **(−1, 3)**
3. $5x + 3y = 4$, $-4x + 5y = -18$ **(2, −2)**
4. $\frac{1}{3}x - y = -1$, $\frac{1}{5}x - \frac{2}{5}y = -1$ **(−9, −2)**
5. $3x - 5y = 8$, $4x - 7y = 10$ **(6, 2)**
6. $x - 0.5y = 1$, $0.4x + y = -2$ **(0, −2)**
7. $x + 8y = 3$, $4x - 2y = 7$ $\left(\frac{31}{17}, \frac{5}{34}\right)$
8. $4x - y = 4$, $x + 2y = 3$ $\left(\frac{11}{9}, \frac{8}{9}\right)$
9. $3y - 8x = 9$, $y - x = 2$ $\left(-\frac{3}{5}, \frac{7}{5}\right)$
10. $x + 4y = 30$, $2x - y = -6$ $\left(\frac{2}{3}, \frac{22}{3}\right)$
11. $3x - 2y = 0$, $4x + 4y = 5$ $\left(\frac{1}{2}, \frac{3}{4}\right)$
12. $9x - 3y = 5$, $x + y = 1$ $\left(\frac{2}{3}, \frac{1}{3}\right)$
13. $2x - 7y = 9$, $-3x + 4y = 6$ **(−6, −3)**
14. $2x - 6y = -16$, $5x + 7y = -18$ **(−5, 1)**
15. $6x - 3y = -9$, $-8x + 2y = 4$ $\left(\frac{1}{2}, 4\right)$

Lesson 6-5 Applying Systems of Linear Equations (pp. 362–368)

Determine the best method to solve each system of equations. Then solve the system.

1. $y = 2x + 1$, $y = -3x + 1$ **graphing; (0, 1)**
2. $y = 5x - 8$, $y = 3x$ **substitution; (4, 12)**
3. $x + 2y = -6$, $x = y + 3$ **substitution; (0, −3)**
4. $2x - 3y = 5$, $y = -6x$ **substitution; (0.25, 1.5)**
5. $x = -1$, $y = 8$ **graphing; (−1, 8)**
6. $4x + y = 5$, $-4x - 2y = 9$ **elimination (+); (4.75, −14)**
7. $-7x + 3y = -4$, $2x + 3y = 5$ **elimination (−); (1, 1)**
8. $4x - y = 11$, $x + 2y = 5$ **elimination (×); (3, 1)**
9. $2y - x = -7$, $x + 3y = 5$ **elimination (+);** $\left(\frac{31}{5}, -\frac{2}{5}\right)$
10. $-13x + 8y = -6$, $3x - 4y = 2$ **elimination (×);** $\left(\frac{2}{7}, -\frac{2}{7}\right)$
11. $-x + 7y = 9$, $-4x + 6y = -8$ **elimination (×); (5, 2)**
12. $2x + 5y = 7$, $5x - 2y = 13$ **elimination (×);** $\left(\frac{79}{29}, \frac{9}{29}\right)$
13. $12x - 3y = 7$, $x = 2 + 13y$ **substitution;** $\left(\frac{5}{9}, -\frac{1}{9}\right)$
14. $6x = 5$, $9y - 2x = 7$ **elimination (×);** $\left(\frac{5}{6}, \frac{26}{27}\right)$
15. $17x + 8y = -4$, $-8y - 2x = 9$ **elimination (+);** $\left(\frac{1}{3}, -\frac{29}{24}\right)$

Lesson 6-6 Organizing Data Using Matrices (pp. 369–375)

Perform the indicated matrix operations. If the matrix does not exist, write *impossible*.

1. $\begin{bmatrix} 3 & 5 \\ -7 & 2 \end{bmatrix} + \begin{bmatrix} -2 & 6 \\ 8 & -1 \end{bmatrix}$ $\begin{bmatrix} 1 & 11 \\ 1 & 1 \end{bmatrix}$
2. $[0 \quad -1 \quad 3] + \begin{bmatrix} 5 \\ -2 \\ -3 \end{bmatrix}$ **impossible**
3. $\begin{bmatrix} 45 & 36 & 18 \\ 63 & 29 & 5 \end{bmatrix} - \begin{bmatrix} 45 & -2 & 36 \\ 18 & 9 & 10 \end{bmatrix}$ $\begin{bmatrix} 0 & 38 & -18 \\ 45 & 20 & -5 \end{bmatrix}$
4. $4[-8 \quad 2 \quad 9] - 3[2 \quad -7 \quad 6]$ $[-38 \quad 29 \quad 18]$
5. $5\begin{bmatrix} 6 & -2 \\ 5 & 4 \end{bmatrix} - 2\begin{bmatrix} 6 & -2 \\ 5 & 4 \end{bmatrix} + 4\begin{bmatrix} 7 & -6 \\ -4 & 2 \end{bmatrix}$ $\begin{bmatrix} 46 & -30 \\ -1 & 20 \end{bmatrix}$
6. $1.3\begin{bmatrix} 3.7 \\ -5.4 \end{bmatrix} + 4.1\begin{bmatrix} 6.4 \\ -3.7 \end{bmatrix} - 6.2\begin{bmatrix} -0.8 \\ 7.4 \end{bmatrix}$ $\begin{bmatrix} 36.01 \\ -68.07 \end{bmatrix}$

Use matrices A, B, C, D, and E to find the following.

$A = \begin{bmatrix} 1 & 0 \\ 0 & 1 \end{bmatrix}, B = \begin{bmatrix} -1 & 0 \\ 0 & -1 \end{bmatrix}, C = \begin{bmatrix} 2 & -2 \\ -3 & 3 \end{bmatrix}, D = \begin{bmatrix} -2 & 2 \\ 3 & -3 \end{bmatrix}, E = \begin{bmatrix} 5 & -3 \\ -2 & 4 \end{bmatrix}$

7. $A + B$ $\begin{bmatrix} 0 & 0 \\ 0 & 0 \end{bmatrix}$
8. $C + D$ $\begin{bmatrix} 0 & 0 \\ 0 & 0 \end{bmatrix}$
9. $A - B$ $\begin{bmatrix} 2 & 0 \\ 0 & 2 \end{bmatrix}$
10. $4B$ $\begin{bmatrix} -4 & 0 \\ 0 & -4 \end{bmatrix}$
11. $D - C$ $\begin{bmatrix} -4 & 4 \\ 6 & -6 \end{bmatrix}$
12. $E + 2A$ $\begin{bmatrix} 7 & -3 \\ -2 & 6 \end{bmatrix}$
13. $D - 2B$ $\begin{bmatrix} 0 & 2 \\ 3 & -1 \end{bmatrix}$
14. $2A + 3E - D$ $\begin{bmatrix} 19 & -11 \\ -9 & 17 \end{bmatrix}$

Lesson 6-7 Using Matrices to Solve Systems of Equations (pp. 376–381)

Write an augmented matrix equation for each system of equations.

1. $5a + 3b = 6$, $2a - b = 9$ $\left[\begin{array}{cc|c} 5 & 3 & 6 \\ 2 & -1 & 9 \end{array}\right]$
2. $3x + 4y = -8$, $2x - 3y = 6$ $\left[\begin{array}{cc|c} 3 & 4 & -8 \\ 2 & -3 & 6 \end{array}\right]$
3. $m + 3p = 1$, $4m - p = -22$ $\left[\begin{array}{cc|c} 1 & 3 & 1 \\ 4 & -1 & -22 \end{array}\right]$
4. $4c - 3d = -1$, $5c - 2d = 39$ $\left[\begin{array}{cc|c} 4 & -3 & -1 \\ 5 & -2 & 39 \end{array}\right]$
5. $x + 2y - z = 6$, $-2x + 3y + z = 1$, $x + y + 3z = 8$ $\left[\begin{array}{ccc|c} 1 & 2 & -1 & 6 \\ -2 & 3 & 1 & 1 \\ 1 & 1 & 3 & 8 \end{array}\right]$
6. $2a - 3b - c = 4$, $4a + b + c = 15$, $a - b - c = -2$ $\left[\begin{array}{ccc|c} 2 & -3 & -1 & 4 \\ 4 & 1 & 1 & 15 \\ 1 & -1 & -1 & -2 \end{array}\right]$

Solve each matrix equation or system of equations.

7. $\left[\begin{array}{cc|c} 3 & 4 & 33 \\ 2 & -5 & -1 \end{array}\right]$ **(7, 3)**
8. $\left[\begin{array}{cc|c} -1 & 1 & 0 \\ 7 & -6 & 3 \end{array}\right]$ **(3, 3)**
9. $\left[\begin{array}{cc|c} 1 & 0 & -29 \\ 0 & 1 & 52 \end{array}\right]$ **(−29, 52)**
10. $5x - y = 7$, $8x + 2y = 4$ **(1, −2)**
11. $3m + t = 4$, $2m + 2t = 3$ $\left(\frac{5}{4}, \frac{1}{4}\right)$
12. $6c + 5d = 7$, $3c - 10d = -4$ $\left(\frac{2}{3}, \frac{3}{5}\right)$
13. $3a - 5b = 1$, $a + 3b = 5$ **(2, 1)**
14. $2r - 7t = 24$, $-r + 8t = -21$ **(5, −2)**
15. $x + y = -3$, $3x - 10y = 43$ **(1, −4)**
16. $2m - 3p = 3$, $-4m + 9p = -8$ $\left(\frac{1}{2}, -\frac{2}{3}\right)$
17. $x + y = 1$, $2x - 2y = -12$ **(−2.5, 3.5)**

Lesson 6-8 Systems of Inequalities (pp. 382–387)

Solve each system of inequalities. **1–12. See Student Handbook Answer Appendix.**

1. $x \le 5$, $y \ge -3$
2. $y < 3$, $y - x \ge -1$
3. $x + y < 5$, $x < 2$
4. $y + x < 2$, $y \ge x$
5. $x + y \le 2$, $y - x \le 4$
6. $y \le x + 4$, $y - x \ge 1$
7. $y < \frac{1}{3}x + 5$, $y > 2x + 1$
8. $y + x \ge 1$, $y - x \ge -1$
9. $|x| > 2$, $|y| \le 5$
10. $x \le 2$, $y \le 3$, $y \ge -\frac{2}{3}x + 3$
11. $y \le x$, $y \le -x + 4$, $y \ge -1$
12. $y \le -1$, $3x - 2y \ge 6$

Lesson 7-1 Multiplying Monomials (pp. 401–407)

Determine whether each expression is a monomial. Write *yes* or *no*. Explain your reasoning. **1–4. See Student Handbook Answer Appendix for explanations.**

1. $n^2 - 3$ **no**
2. 5^3 **yes**
3. $9a^2b^3$ **yes**
4. $15 - x^2y$ **no**

Simplify each expression.

5. $a^5(a)(a^7)$ a^{13}
6. $(r^3t^4)(r^4t^4)$ r^7t^8
7. $(x^3y^4)(xy^3)$ x^4y^7
8. $(bc^3)(b^4c^3)$ b^5c^6
9. $(-3mp^2)(5m^3p^2)$ $-15m^4p^4$
10. $[(3^3)^2]^2$ **531,441**
11. $(3n3t^2)(-4n^3t^2)$ $-12n^6t^4$
12. $x^3(x^4y^3)$ x^7y^3
13. $(1.1g^2h^4)^3$ $1.331g^6h^{12}$
14. $-\frac{3}{4}a(a^2b^3c^4)$ $-\frac{3}{4}a^3b^3c^4$
15. $\left(\frac{1}{2}w^3\right)^2(6w^4)^2$ $9w^{14}$
16. $[(-2^3)^3]^2$ **262,144**

GEOMETRY Express the volume of each solid as a monomial.

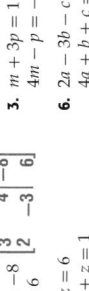

17.
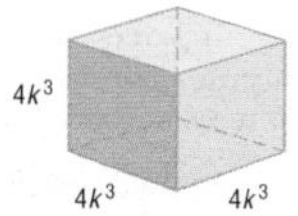

$64k^9$ **units³**

18.
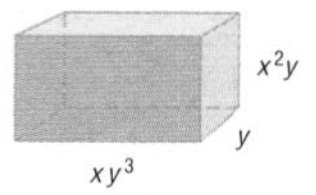

x^3y^5 **units³**

19.
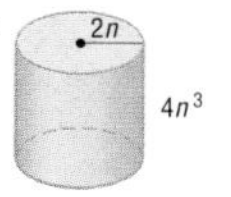

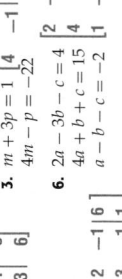

$16\pi n^5$ **units³**

Lesson 7-2 Dividing Monomials (pp. 408–415)

Simplify. Assume that no denominator is equal to zero.

1. $\frac{6^{10}}{6^7}$ 6^3 or 216
2. $\frac{b^6c^5}{b^3c^2}$ b^3c^3
3. $\frac{(-a)^4b^8}{a^4b^7}$ b
4. $\frac{(-x)^3y^3}{x^3y^6}$ $-\frac{1}{y^3}$
5. $\frac{12ab^5}{4a^4b^3}$ $\frac{3b^2}{a^3}$
6. $\frac{24x^5}{-8x^2}$ $-3x^3$
7. $\frac{-9h^2k^4}{18h^5j^3k^4}$ $-\frac{1}{2h^3j^3}$
8. $\left(\frac{2a^2b^4}{3a^3b}\right)^2$ $\frac{4b^6}{9a^2}$
9. $a^5b^0a^{-7}$ $\frac{1}{a^2}$
10. $\frac{(-u^{-3}v^3)^2}{(u^3v)^{-3}}$ u^3v^9
11. $\left(\frac{a^3}{b^2}\right)^{-3}$ $\frac{b^6}{a^9}$
12. $\left(\frac{2x}{y^{-3}}\right)^{-2}$ $\frac{1}{4x^2y^6}$
13. $\frac{(-r)s^5}{r^{-3}s^{-4}}$ $-r^4s^9$
14. $\frac{28a^{-4}b^0}{14a^3b^{-1}}$ $\frac{2b}{a^7}$
15. $\frac{(j^2k^3m)^4}{(jk^4)^{-1}}$ $j^9k^{16}m^4$
16. $\left(\frac{-2x^4y}{4y^2}\right)^0$ 1
17. $\left(\frac{-18x^0a^{-3}}{-6x^{-2}a^{-3}}\right)$ $3x^2$
18. $\left(\frac{2a^3b^{-2}}{2^{-1}a^{-5}b^3}\right)^{-1}$ $\frac{b^5}{4a^8}$
19. $\left(\frac{5n^{-1}m^2}{2nm^{-2}}\right)^0$ 1
20. $\frac{(3ab^2c)^{-3}}{(2a^2bc^2)^2}$ $\frac{1}{108a^7b^8c^7}$

Lesson 7-3 Scientific Notation (pp. 416–422)

Express each number in scientific notation.

1. 1,400,322 1.400322×10^6
2. 134,490,000 1.3449×10^8
3. 0.00009 9×10^{-5}
4. 0.004500 4.5×10^{-3}
5. 12,000,000 1.2×10^7
6. 0.0000233 2.33×10^{-5}

Express each number in standard form.

7. 2.23×10^{-2} 0.0223
8. 5.4×10^3 5400
9. 3.334×10^{-9} 0.000000003334
10. 4.7×10^{-6} 0.0000047
11. 5.22×10^4 52,200
12. 7.256×10^{-1} 0.7256

Evaluate. Express the results in both scientific notation and standard form.

13. $(2.3 \times 10^{-2})(2.55 \times 10^3)$ 58.65; 5.865×10^1
14. $(5.23 \times 10^{-7})(8.2 \times 10^5)$ 0.42886; 4.2886×10^{-1}
15. $\frac{3.344 \times 10^6}{4.2 \times 10^{-3}}$ 796,190,476.2; 7.961904762×10^8
16. $\frac{2.644 \times 10^{-5}}{3.2 \times 10^{-2}}$ 0.00082625; 8.2625×10^4

Lesson 7-4 Polynomials (pp. 424–429)

State whether each expression is a polynomial. If so, identify it as a *monomial*, a *binomial*, or a *trinomial*.

1. $5x^2y + 3xy - 7$ yes; trinomial
2. 0 yes; monomial
3. $\frac{5}{k} - k^2y$ no
4. $3a^2x - 5a$ yes; binomial

Find the degree of each polynomial.

5. $a + 5c$ 1
6. $14abcd - 6d^3$ 4
7. $\frac{a^3}{4}$ 3
8. 10 0
9. $-4h^5$ 5
10. $\frac{x^2}{3} - \frac{x}{2} + \frac{1}{5}$ 2
11. -6 0
12. $a^2b^3 - a^3b^2$ 5

Arrange the terms of each polynomial so that the powers of *x* are in ascending order.

13. $2x^2 - 3x + 4x^3 - x^5$ $-3x + 2x^2 + 4x^3 - x^5$
14. $x^3 - x^2 + x - 1$ $-1 + x - x^2 + x^3$
15. $2a + 3ax^2 - 4ax$ $2a - 4ax + 3ax^2$
16. $-5bx^3 - 2bx + 4x^2 - b^3$ $-b^3 - 2bx + 4x^2 - 5bx^3$
17. $x^8 + 2x^2 - x^6 + 1$ $1 + 2x^2 - x^6 + x^8$
18. $cdx^2 - c^2d^2x + d^3$ $d^3 - c^2d^2x + cdx^2$

Arrange the terms of each polynomial so that the powers of *x* are in descending order.

19. $5x^2 - 3x^3 + 7 + 2x$ $-3x^3 + 5x^2 + 2x + 7$
20. $-6x + x^5 + 4x^3 - 20$ $x^5 + 4x^3 - 6x - 20$
21. $5b + b^3x^2 + \frac{2}{3}bx$ $b^3x^2 + \frac{2}{3}bx + 5b$
22. $21p^2x + 3px^3 + p^4$ $3px^3 + 21p^2x + p^4$
23. $3ax^2 - 6a^2x^3 + 7a^3 - 8x$ $-6a^2x^3 + 3ax^2 - 8x + 7a^3$
24. $\frac{1}{3}s^2x^3 + 4x^4 - \frac{2}{5}s^4x^2$ $4x^4 + \frac{1}{3}s^2x^3 - \frac{2}{5}s^4x^2$

Lesson 7-5 Adding and Subtracting Polynomials (pp. 433–438)

Find each sum or difference.

1. $(3a^2 + 5) + (4a^2 - 1)$ $7a^2 + 4$
2. $(5x - 3) + (-2x + 1)$ $3x - 2$
3. $(6z + 2) - (9z + 3)$ $-3z - 1$
4. $(-4n + 7) - (-7n - 8)$ $3n + 15$
5. $(-7t^2 + 4ts - 6s^2) + (-5t^2 - 12ts + 3s^2)$ $-12t^2 - 8ts - 3s^2$
6. $(6a^2 - 7ab - 4b^2) - (2a^2 + 5ab + 6b^2)$ $4a^2 - 12ab - 10b^2$
7. $(4a^2 - 10b^2 + 7c^2) + (-5a^2 + 2c^2 + 2b)$ $-a^2 - 10b^2 + 9c^2 + 2b$
8. $(z^2 + 6z - 8) - (4z^2 - 7z - 5)$ $-3z^2 + 13z - 3$
9. $(4d + 3e - 8f) - (-3d + 10e - 5f + 6)$ $7d - 7e - 3f - 6$
10. $(7g + 8h - 9) + (-g - 3h - 6k)$ $6g + 5h - 9 - 6k$
11. $(9x^2 - 11xy - 3y^2) - (x^2 - 16xy + 12y^2)$ $8x^2 + 5xy - 15y^2$
12. $(-3m + 9mn - 5n) + (14m - 5mn - 2n)$ $11m + 4mn - 7n$
13. $(6 - 7y + 3y^2) + (3 - 5y - 2y^2) + (-12 - 8y + y^2)$ $2y^2 - 20y - 3$
14. $(-7c^2 - 2c - 5) + (9c - 6) + (16c^2 + 3) + (-9c^2 - 7c + 7)$ -1

Lesson 7-6 Multiplying a Polynomial by a Monomial (pp. 439–444)

Find each product.

1. $-3(8x + 5)$ $-24x - 15$
2. $3b(5b + 8)$ $15b^2 + 24b$
3. $1.1a(2a + 7)$ $2.2a^2 + 7.7a$
4. $\frac{1}{2}x(8x - 6)$ $4x^2 - 3x$
5. $7xy(5x^2 - y^2)$ $35x^3y - 7xy^3$
6. $5y(y^2 - 3y + 6)$ $5y^3 - 15y^2 + 30y$
7. $-ab(3b^2 + 4ab - 6a^2)$ $-3ab^3 - 4a^2b^2 + 6a^3b$
8. $4m^2(9m^2n + mn - 5n^2)$ $36m^4n + 4m^3n - 20m^2n^2$
9. $4st^2(-4s^2t^3 + 7s^5 - 3st^3)$ $-16s^3t^5 + 28s^6t^2 - 12s^2t^5$

Simplify each expression.

10. $-3a(2a - 12) + 5a$ $-6a^2 + 41a$
11. $6(12b^2 - 2b) + 7(-2 - 3b)$ $72b^2 - 33b - 14$
12. $x(x - 6) + x(x - 2) + 2x$ $2x^2 - 6x$
13. $11(n - 3) + 2(n^2 + 22n)$ $2n^2 + 55n - 33$
14. $-2x(x + 3) + 3(x + 3)$ $-2x^2 - 3x + 9$
15. $4m(n - 1) - 5n(n + 1)$ $4mn - 4m - 5n^2 - 5n$

Solve each equation.

16. $-6(11 - 2x) = 7(-2 - 2x)$ 2
17. $11(n - 3) + 5 = 2n + 44$ 8
18. $a(a - 6) + 2a = 3 + a(a - 2)$ -1.5
19. $q(2q + 3) + 20 = 2q(q - 3)$ $-\frac{20}{9}$
20. $w(w + 12) = w(w + 14) + 12$ -6
21. $x(x - 3) + 4x - 3 = 8x + x(3 + x)$ $-\frac{3}{10}$
22. $-3(x + 5) + x(x - 1) = x(x + 2) - 3$ -2
23. $n(n - 5) + n(n + 2) = 2n(n - 1) + 1.5$ -1.5

Lesson 7-7 Multiplying Polynomials (pp. 447–452)

Find each product.

1. $(d + 2)(d + 5)$ $d^2 + 7d + 10$
2. $(z + 7)(z - 4)$ $z^2 + 3z - 28$
3. $(m - 8)(m - 5)$ $m^2 - 13m + 40$
4. $(a + 2)(a - 19)$ $a^2 - 17a - 38$
5. $(c + 15)(c - 3)$ $c^2 + 12c - 45$
6. $(x + y)(x - 2y)$ $x^2 - xy - 2y^2$
7. $(2x - 5)(x + 6)$ $2x^2 + 7x - 30$
8. $(7a - 4)(2a - 5)$ $14a^2 - 43a + 20$
9. $(4x + y)(2x - 3y)$ $8x^2 - 10xy - 3y^2$
10. $(7v + 3)(v + 4)$ $7v^2 + 31v + 12$
11. $(7s - 8)(3s - 2)$ $21s^2 - 38s + 16$
12. $(4g + 3h)(2g - 5h)$ $8g^2 - 14gh - 15h^2$
13. $(4a + 3)(2a - 1)$ $8a^2 + 2a - 3$
14. $(7y - 1)(2y - 3)$ $14y^2 - 23y + 3$
15. $(2x + 3y)(4x + 2y)$ $8x^2 + 16xy + 6y^2$
16. $(12r - 4s)(5r + 8s)$ $60r^2 + 76rs - 32s^2$
17. $(-a + 1)(-3a - 2)$ $3a^2 - a - 2$
18. $(2n - 4)(-3n - 2)$ $-6n^2 + 8n + 8$
19. $(x - 2)(x^2 + 2x + 4)$ $x^3 - 8$
20. $(3x + 5)(2x^2 - 5x + 11)$ $6x^3 - 5x^2 + 8x + 55$
21. $(4s + 5)(3s^2 + 8s - 9)$ $12s^3 + 47s^2 + 4s - 45$
22. $(5x - 2)(-5x^2 + 2x + 7)$ $-25x^3 + 20x^2 + 31x - 14$
23. $(-n + 2)(-2n^2 + n - 1)$ $2n^3 - 5n^2 + 3n - 2$
24. $(x^2 - 7x + 4)(2x^2 - 3x - 6)$ $2x^4 - 17x^3 + 23x^2 + 30x - 24$
25. $(x^2 + x + 1)(x^2 - x - 1)$ $x^4 - x^2 - 2x - 1$
26. $(a^2 + 2a + 5)(a^2 - 3a - 7)$ $a^4 - a^3 - 8a^2 - 29a - 35$
27. $(5x^4 - 2x^2 + 1)(x^2 - 5x + 3)$ $5x^6 - 25x^5 + 13x^4 + 10x^3 - 5x^2 - 5x + 3$

Lesson 7-8 Special Products (pp. 453–458)

Find each product. **4.** $100x^2 - 121y^2$ **18.** $a^3 - 3a^2 + 3a - 1$ **19.** $2x^3 + 5x^2 - 8x - 20$ **20.** $16x^3 - 64x^2 - x + 4$ **21.** $x^4 - 41x^2 + 400$

1. $(t + 7)^2$ $t^2 + 14t + 49$
2. $(w - 12)(w + 12)$ $w^2 - 144$
3. $(q - 4h)^2$ $q^2 - 8qh + 16h^2$
4. $(10x + 11y)(10x - 11y)$
5. $(4p + 3)^2$ $16p^2 + 24p + 9$
6. $(2b - 4d)(2b + 4d)$ $4b^2 - 16d^2$
7. $(a + 2b)^2$ $a^2 + 4ab + 4b^2$
8. $(3x + y)^2$ $9x^2 + 6xy + y^2$
9. $(6m + 2n)^2$ $36m^2 + 24mn + 4n^2$
10. $(3m - 7d)^2$ $9m^2 - 42md + 49d^2$
11. $(5b - 6)(5b + 6)$ $25b^2 - 36$
12. $(1 + x)^2$ $1 + 2x + x^2$
13. $(5x - 9y)^2$ $25x^2 - 90xy + 81y^2$
14. $(8a - 2b)(8a + 2b)$ $64a^2 - 4b^2$
15. $\left(\frac{1}{4}x + 4\right)^2$ $\frac{1}{16}x^2 + 2x + 16$
16. $\left(\frac{1}{2}x - 10\right)\left(\frac{1}{2}x + 10\right)$ $\frac{1}{4}x^2 - 100$
17. $\left(\frac{1}{3}n - m\right)\left(\frac{1}{3}n + m\right)$ $\frac{1}{9}n^2 - m^2$
18. $(a - 1)(a - 1)(a - 1)$
19. $(x + 2)(x - 2)(2x + 5)$
20. $(4x - 1)(4x + 1)(x - 4)$
21. $(x - 5)(x + 5)(x + 4)(x - 4)$
22. $(a + 1)(a + 1)(a - 1)(a - 1)$ $a^4 - 2a^2 + 1$
23. $(n - 1)(n + 1)(n - 1)$ $n^3 - n^2 - n + 1$
24. $(2c + 3)(2c + 3)(2c - 3)(2c - 3)$ $16c^4 - 72c^2 + 81$
25. $(4d + 5g)(4d + 5g)(4d - 5g)(4d - 5g)$ $256d^4 - 800g^2d^2 + 625g^4$

Lesson 8-1 Monomials and Factoring (pp. 471–474)

Factor each monomial completely. **2.** $-1 \cdot 2 \cdot 2 \cdot 2 \cdot 2 \cdot 2 \cdot 2 \cdot a \cdot a \cdot a \cdot b$

1. $240mn$ $2 \cdot 2 \cdot 2 \cdot 2 \cdot 3 \cdot 5 \cdot m \cdot n$
2. $-64a^3b$
3. $-26xy^2$ $-1 \cdot 2 \cdot 13 \cdot x \cdot y \cdot y$
4. $-231xy^2z$ $-1 \cdot 3 \cdot 7 \cdot 11 \cdot x \cdot y \cdot y \cdot z$
5. $44rs^2t^3$ $2 \cdot 2 \cdot 11 \cdot r \cdot s \cdot s \cdot t \cdot t \cdot t$
6. $-756m^2n^2$ $-1 \cdot 2 \cdot 2 \cdot 3 \cdot 3 \cdot 3 \cdot 7 \cdot m \cdot m \cdot n \cdot n$

Find the GCF of each set of monomials.

7. 16, 60 **4**
8. 15, 50 **5**
9. 45, 80 **5**
10. 29, 58 **29**
11. 55, 305 **5**
12. 126, 252 **126**
13. 128, 245 **1**
14. $7y^2, 14y^2$ $7y^2$
15. $4xy, -6x$ $2x$
16. $35t^2, 7t$ $7t$
17. $16pq^2, 12p^2q, 4pq$ $4pq$
18. 5, 15, 10 **5**
19. $12mn, 10mn, 15mn$ mn
20. $14xy, 12y, 20x$ **2**
21. $26jk^4, 16jk^3, 8j^2$ $2j$

Lesson 8-2 Using the Distributive Property (pp. 476–482)

Use the Distributive Property to factor each polynomial. **8.** $2mn(m^2n - 8n + 4)$ **9.** $(2x + b)(a + 3c)$ **10.** $(2m + r)(3x - 2)$ **11.** $(3x - 4)(a - 2b)$ **12.** $(a + 1)(a - 2b)$

1. $10a^2 + 40a$ $10a(a + 4)$
2. $15wx - 35wx^2$ $5wx(3 - 7x)$
3. $27a^2b + 9b^3$ $9b(3a^2 + b^2)$
4. $11x + 44x^2y$ $11x(1 + 4xy)$
5. $16y^2 + 8y$ $8y(2y + 1)$
6. $14mn^2 + 2mn$ $2mn(7n + 1)$
7. $25a^2b^2 + 30ab^3$ $5ab^2(5a + 6b)$
8. $2m^3n^2 - 16mn^2 + 8mn$
9. $2ax + 6xc + ba + 3bc$
10. $6mx - 4m + 3rx - 2r$
11. $3ax - 6bx + 8b - 4a$
12. $a^2 - 2ab + a - 2b$
13. $8ac - 2ad + 4bc - bd$ $(2a + b)(4c - d)$
14. $2e^2g + 2fg + 4e^2h + 4fh$ $2(e^2 + f)(g + 2h)$
15. $x^2 - xy - xy + y^2$ $(x - y)(x - y)$

Solve each equation. Check your solutions.

16. $a(a - 9) = 0$ $\{0, 9\}$
17. $d(d + 11) = 0$ $\{-11, 0\}$
18. $z(z - 2.5) = 0$ $\{0, 2.5\}$
19. $(2y + 6)(y - 1) = 0$ $\{-3, 1\}$
20. $(4n - 7)(3n + 2) = 0$ $\left\{-\frac{2}{3}, \frac{7}{4}\right\}$
21. $(a - 1)(a + 1) = 0$ $\{-1, 1\}$
22. $10x^2 - 20x = 0$ $\{0, 2\}$
23. $8b^2 - 12b = 0$ $\{0, 1.5\}$
24. $14d^2 + 49d = 0$ $\{0, -3.5\}$
25. $15a^2 = 60a$ $\{0, 4\}$
26. $33x^2 = -22x$ $\left\{-\frac{2}{3}, 0\right\}$
27. $32x^2 = 16x$ $\left\{0, \frac{1}{2}\right\}$

Lesson 8-3 Quadratic Equations: $x^2 + bx + c = 0$ (pp. 485–491)

Factor each trinomial.

1. $x^2 - 9x + 14$ $(x - 7)(x - 2)$
2. $a^2 - 9a - 36$ $(a - 12)(a + 3)$
3. $x^2 + 2x - 15$ $(x + 5)(x - 3)$
4. $n^2 - 8n + 15$ $(n - 5)(n - 3)$
5. $b^2 + 22b + 21$ $(b + 21)(b + 1)$
6. $c^2 + 2c - 3$ $(c + 3)(c - 1)$
7. $x^2 - 5x - 24$ $(x - 8)(x + 3)$
8. $n^2 - 8n + 7$ $(n - 7)(n - 1)$
9. $m^2 - 10m - 39$ $(m - 13)(m + 3)$
10. $z^2 + 15z + 36$ $(z + 12)(z + 3)$
11. $s^2 - 13st - 30t^2$ $(s - 15t)(s + 2t)$
12. $y^2 + 2y - 35$ $(y + 7)(y - 5)$
13. $r^2 + 3r - 40$ $(r + 8)(r - 5)$
14. $x^2 + 5x - 6$ $(x + 6)(x - 1)$
15. $x^2 - 4xy - 5y^2$ $(x - 5y)(x + y)$
16. $r^2 + 16r + 63$ $(r + 9)(r + 7)$
17. $v^2 + 24v - 52$ $(v + 26)(v - 2)$
18. $k^2 - 27kj - 90j^2$ $(k - 30j)(k + 3j)$

Solve each equation. Check your solutions.

19. $a^2 + 3a - 4 = 0$ $\{-4, 1\}$
20. $x^2 - 8x - 20 = 0$ $\{-2, 10\}$
21. $b^2 + 11b + 24 = 0$ $\{-8, -3\}$
22. $y^2 + y - 42 = 0$ $\{-7, 6\}$
23. $k^2 + 2k - 24 = 0$ $\{-6, 4\}$
24. $r^2 - 13r - 48 = 0$ $\{-3, 16\}$
25. $n^2 - 9n = -18$ $\{3, 6\}$
26. $2z + z^2 = 35$ $\{-7, 5\}$
27. $-20x + 19 = -x^2$ $\{1, 19\}$
28. $10 + a^2 = -7a$ $\{-5, -2\}$
29. $z^2 - 57 = 16z$ $\{-3, 19\}$
30. $x^2 = -14x - 33$ $\{-11, -3\}$

Lesson 8-4 Quadratic Equations: $ax^2 + bx + c = 0$ (pp. 493–498)

Factor each trinomial, if possible. If the trinomial cannot be factored using integers, write *prime*.

1. $4a^2 + 4a - 63$ $(2a - 7)(2a + 9)$
2. $3x^2 - 7x - 6$ $(3x + 2)(x - 3)$
3. $4r^2 - 25r + 6$ $(4r - 1)(r - 6)$
4. $2z^2 - 11z + 15$ $(2z - 5)(z - 3)$
5. $3a^2 - 2a - 21$ $(3a + 7)(a - 3)$
6. $4y^2 + 11y + 6$ $(4y + 3)(y + 2)$
7. $6n^2 + 7n - 3$ $(2n + 3)(3n - 1)$
8. $5x^2 - 17x + 14$ $(5x - 7)(x - 2)$
9. $2n^2 - 11n + 13$ **prime**
10. $5a^2 - 3a + 15$ **prime**
11. $18v^2 + 24v + 12$ $6(3v^2 + 4v + 2)$
12. $4k^2 + 2k - 12$ $2(2k - 3)(k + 2)$
13. $10x^2 - 20xy + 10y^2$ $10(x - y)(x - y)$
14. $12c^2 - 11cd - 5d^2$ $(3c + d)(4c - 5d)$
15. $30n^2 - mn - m^2$ $(5n - m)(6n + m)$

Solve each equation. Check your solutions.

16. $8t^2 + 32t + 24 = 0$ $\{-3, -1\}$
17. $6y^2 + 72y + 192 = 0$ $\{-8, -4\}$
18. $5x^2 + 3x - 2 = 0$ $\left\{-1, \frac{2}{5}\right\}$
19. $9x^2 + 18x - 27 = 0$ $\{-3, 1\}$
20. $4x^2 - 4x - 4 = 4$ $\{-1, 2\}$
21. $12n^2 - 16n - 3 = 0$ $\left\{\frac{1}{6}, \frac{3}{2}\right\}$
22. $12x^2 - x - 35 = 0$ $\left\{-\frac{5}{3}, \frac{7}{4}\right\}$
23. $18x^2 + 36x - 14 = 0$ $\left\{-\frac{7}{3}, \frac{1}{3}\right\}$
24. $15a^2 + a - 2 = 0$ $\left\{-\frac{2}{5}, \frac{1}{3}\right\}$
25. $14b^2 + 7b - 42 = 0$ $\left\{-2, \frac{3}{2}\right\}$
26. $13r^2 + 21r - 10 = 0$ $\left\{-2, \frac{5}{13}\right\}$
27. $35y^2 - 60y - 20 = 0$ $\left\{-\frac{2}{7}, 2\right\}$

Lesson 8-5 Quadratic Equations: Differences of Squares (pp. 499–504)

Factor each polynomial, if possible. If the polynomial cannot be factored, write prime. **1–15. See Student Handbook Answer Appendix.**

1. $x^2 - 9$
2. $a^2 - 64$
3. $4x^2 - 9y^2$
4. $1 - 9z^2$
5. $16a^2 - 9b^2$
6. $8x^2 - 12y^2$
7. $a^2 - 4b^2$
8. $75r^2 - 48$
9. $x^2 - 36y^2$
10. $3a^2 - 16$
11. $9x^2 - 100y^2$
12. $49 - a^2b^2$
13. $5a^2 - 48$
14. $169 - 16t^2$
15. $8r^2 - 4$
16. $-45m^2 + 5$ $-5(3m - 1)(3m + 1)$

Solve each equation by factoring. Check your solutions.

17. $4x^2 = 16$ $\{\pm 2\}$
18. $2x^2 = 50$ $\{\pm 5\}$
19. $9n^2 - 4 = 0$ $\left\{\pm\frac{2}{3}\right\}$
20. $a^2 - \frac{25}{36} = 0$ $\left\{\pm\frac{5}{6}\right\}$
21. $\frac{16}{9} - b^2 = 0$ $\left\{\pm\frac{4}{3}\right\}$
22. $18 - \frac{1}{2}x^2 = 0$ $\{\pm 6\}$
23. $20 - 5g^2 = 0$ $\{\pm 2\}$
24. $16 - \frac{1}{4}p^2 = 0$ $\{\pm 8\}$
25. $\frac{1}{4}c^2 - \frac{4}{9} = 0$ $\left\{\pm\frac{4}{3}\right\}$
26. $2q^3 - 2q = 0$ $\{-1, 0, 1\}$
27. $3r^3 = 48r$ $\{-4, 0, 4\}$
28. $100d - 4d^3 = 0$ $\{-5, 0, 5\}$

Lesson 8-6 Quadratic Equations: Perfect Squares (pp. 505–512)

Determine whether each trinomial is a perfect square trinomial. Write *yes* or *no*. If so, factor it.

1. $x^2 + 12x + 36$ yes; $(x + 6)^2$
2. $n^2 - 13n + 36$ no
3. $a^2 + 4a + 4$ yes; $(a + 2)^2$
4. $x^2 - 10x - 100$ no
5. $2n^2 + 17n + 21$ no
6. $4a^2 - 20a + 25$ yes; $(2a - 5)^2$

Factor each polynomial, if possible. If the polynomial cannot be factored, write *prime*.

7. $3x^2 - 75$ $3(x - 5)(x + 5)$
8. $4p^2 + 12pr + 9r^2$ $(2p + 3r)^2$
9. $6a^2 + 72$ $6(a^2 + 12)$
10. $s^2 + 30s + 225$ $(s + 15)^2$
11. $24x^2 + 24x + 9$ $3(8x^2 + 8x + 3)$
12. $1 - 10z + 25z^2$ $(1 - 5z)^2$
13. $28 - 63b^2$ $7(2 - 3b)(2 + 3b)$
14. $4c^2 + 2c - 7$ prime

Solve each equation. Check your solutions.

15. $x^2 + 22x + 121 = 0$ $\{-11\}$
16. $343d^2 = 7$ $\pm\frac{1}{7}$
17. $(a - 7)^2 = 5$ $7 \pm \sqrt{5}$
18. $c^2 + 10c + 36 = 11$ $\{-5\}$
19. $16s^2 + 81 = 72s$ $\left\{\frac{9}{4}\right\}$
20. $9p^2 - 42p + 20 = -29$ $\left\{\frac{7}{3}\right\}$

Lesson 9-1 Graphing Quadratic Functions (pp. 525–536)

Use a table of values to graph each function. State the domain and range. 1–3. See Student Handbook Answer Appendix.

1. $y = x^2 + 6x + 8$
2. $y = -x^2 + 3x$
3. $y = -x^2$

4–12. See Student Handbook Answer Appendix.

Find the vertex, the equation of the axis of symmetry, and the y-intercept.

4. $y = -x^2 + 2x - 3$
5. $y = 3x^2 + 24x + 80$
6. $y = x^2 - 4x - 4$
7. $y = 5x^2 - 20x + 37$
8. $y = 3x^2 + 6x + 3$
9. $y = 2x^2 + 12x$
10. $y = x^2 - 6x + 5$
11. $y = x^2 + 6x + 9$
12. $y = -x^2 + 16x - 15$

Consider each equation. 13–18. See Student Handbook Answer Appendix.

a. Determine whether the function has *maximum* or *minimum* value.
b. State the maximum or minimum value.
c. What are the domain and range of the function.

13. $y = 4x^2 - 1$
14. $y = -2x^2 - 2x + 4$
15. $y = 6x^2 - 12x - 4$
16. $y = -x^2 - 1$
17. $y = -x^2 + x + 1$
18. $y = -5x^2 - 3x + 2$

Lesson 9-2 Solving Quadratic Equations by Graphing (pp. 537–543)

Solve each equation by graphing. 1–6. See Student Handbook Answer Appendix for graphs.

1. $a^2 - 25 = 0$ $-5, 5$
2. $n^2 - 8n = 0$ $0, 8$
3. $d^2 + 36 = 0$ $\emptyset$
4. $b^2 - 18b + 81 = 0$ 9
5. $x^2 + 3x + 27 = 0$ $\emptyset$
6. $-y^2 - 3y + 10 = 0$ $-5, 2$

Solve each equation by graphing. If integral roots cannot be found, estimate the roots to the nearest tenth. 7–15. See Student Handbook Answer Appendix for graphs.

7. $x^2 + 2x - 3 = 0$ $-3, 1$
8. $-x^2 + 6x - 5 = 0$ $1, 5$
9. $-a^2 - 2a + 3 = 0$ $-3, 1$
10. $2r^2 - 8r + 5 = 0$ $0.8, 3.2$
11. $-3x^2 + 6x - 9 = 0$ $\emptyset$
12. $c^2 + c = 0$ $-1, 0$
13. $3t^2 + 2 = 0$ $\emptyset$
14. $-b^2 + 5b + 2 = 0$ $-0.4, 5.4$
15. $3x^2 + 7x = 1$ $-2.5, 0.1$

Lesson 9-3 Transformations of Quadratic Functions (pp. 544–551)

Describe how the graph of each function is related to the graph of $f(x) = x^2$.

1. $g(x) = x^2 - 5$ translated down
2. $h(x) = \frac{1}{2}x^2$ Compressed vertically
3. $h(x) = -x^2 + 5$ reflected across the x-axis, translated up
4. $g(x) = x^2 + 9$ translated up
5. $g(x) = -3x^2$ reflected across the x-axis, stretched vertically
6. $h(x) = -x^2 - 6$ reflected across the x-axis, translated down
7. $g(x) = \frac{3}{4}x^2 + 4$ compressed vertically, translated up
8. $h(x) = 1.2x^2 - 7.5$ stretched vertically, translated down
9. $g(x) = -7 - \frac{4}{3}x^2$ reflected across the x-axis, stretched vertically, translated down

List the functions in order from the most compressed to the least compressed graph.

10. $g(x) = -2.3x^2, h(x) = \frac{2}{3}x^2$ $h(x), g(x)$
11. $g(x) = 5x^2, h(x) = \frac{1}{2}x^2$ $h(x), g(x)$
12. $g(x) = -x^2, h(x) = \frac{5}{3}x^2, f(x) = -2.5x^2$ $g(x), h(x), f(x)$
13. $g(x) = -6x^2, h(x) = 2x^2, f(x) = 0.4x^2$ $f(x), h(x), g(x)$

Lesson 9-4 Solving Quadratic Equations by Completing the Square (pp. 552–557)

Solve each equation by taking the square root of each side. Round to the nearest tenth if necessary.

1. $x^2 - 4x + 4 = 9$ $-1, 5$
2. $t^2 - 6t + 9 = 16$ $-1, 7$
3. $b^2 + 10b + 25 = 11$ $-8.3, -1.7$
4. $a^2 - 22a + 121 = 3$ $9.3, 12.7$
5. $x^2 + 2x + 1 = 81$ $-10, 8$
6. $t^2 - 36t + 324 = 85$ $8.8, 27.2$

Find the value of c that makes each trinomial a perfect square.

7. $a^2 + 20a + c$ 100
8. $x^2 + 10x + c$ 25
9. $t^2 + 12t + c$ 36
10. $y^2 - 9y + c$ $\frac{81}{4}$
11. $p^2 - 14p + c$ 49
12. $b^2 + 13b + c$ $\frac{169}{4}$

Solve each equation by completing the square. Round to the nearest tenth if necessary.

13. $a^2 - 8a - 84 = 0$ $-6, 14$
14. $c^2 + 6 = -5c$ $-3, -2$
15. $p^2 - 8p + 5 = 0$ $0.7, 7.3$
16. $2y^2 + 7y - 4 = 0$ $-4, \frac{1}{2}$
17. $t^2 + 3t = 40$ $5, -8$
18. $x^2 + 8x - 9 = 0$ $-9, 1$
19. $y^2 + 5y - 84 = 0$ $-12, 7$
20. $t^2 + 12t + 32 = 0$ $-4, -8$
21. $2x - 3x^2 = -8$ $2, -1.3$
22. $2y^2 - y - 9 = 0$ $-1.9, 2.4$
23. $2z^2 - 5z - 4 = 0$ $-0.6, 3.1$
24. $8t^2 - 12t - 1 = 0$ $-0.1, 1.6$

Lesson 9-5 Solving Quadratic Equations by Using the Quadratic Formula (pp. 558–565)

Solve each equation by using the Quadratic Formula. Round to the nearest tenth if necessary.

1. $x^2 - 8x - 4 = 0$ $-0.5, 8.5$
2. $x^2 + 7x - 8 = 0$ $-8, 1$
3. $x^2 - 5x + 6 = 0$ $2, 3$
4. $y^2 - 7y - 8 = 0$ $-1, 8$
5. $m^2 - 2m = 35$ $-5, 7$
6. $4n^2 - 20n = 0$ $0, 5$
7. $m^2 + 4m + 2 = 0$ $-0.6, -3.4$
8. $2t^2 - t - 15 = 0$ $-2.5, 3$
9. $5t^2 = 125$ $-5, 5$
10. $t^2 + 16 = 0$ $\emptyset$
11. $-4x^2 + 8x = -3$ $-0.3, 2.3$
12. $3k^2 + 2 = -8k$ $-2.4, -0.3$
13. $8t^2 + 10t + 3 = 0$ $-0.8, -0.5$
14. $3x^2 - \frac{5}{4}x - \frac{1}{2} = 0$ $0.7, -0.3$
15. $-5b^2 + 3b - 1 = 0$ $\emptyset$
16. $n^2 - 3n + 1 = 0$ $2.6, 0.4$
17. $2z^2 + 5z - 1 = 0$ $0.2, -2.7$
18. $3h^2 = 27$ $3, -3$

State the value of the discriminant for each equation. Then determine the number of real solutions of the equation.

19. $3f^2 + 2f = 6$ 76; 2 real roots
20. $2x^2 = 0.7x + 0.3$ 2.89; 2 real roots
21. $3w^2 - 2w + 8 = 0$ −92; no real roots
22. $4r^2 - 12r + 9 = 0$ 0; 1 real root
23. $x^2 - 5x = -9$ −11; no real roots
24. $25t^2 + 30t = -9$ 0; 1 real root

Lesson 9-6 Exponential Functions (pp. 567–572)

Graph each function. State the y-intercept, and state the domain and range. Then use the graph to determine the approximate value of the given expression. Use a calculator to confirm the value. 1–3. See Student Handbook Answer Appendix for graphs.

1. $y = 7^x$; $7^{1.5}$ 1; 18.5
2. $\left(\frac{1}{3}\right)^x$; $\left(\frac{1}{3}\right)^{5.6}$ 1; 0.002
3. $y = \left(\frac{3}{5}\right)^x$; $\left(\frac{3}{5}\right)^{-4.2}$ 1; 8.5

Graph each function. State the y-intercept. 4–15. See Student Handbook Answer Appendix for graphs.

4. $y = 3^x + 1$ 2
5. $y = 2^x - 5$ −4
6. $y = 2^{x+3}$ 8
7. $y = 3^{x+1}$ 3
8. $y = \left(\frac{2}{3}\right)^x$ 1
9. $y = 5\left(\frac{2}{5}\right)^x$ 5
10. $y = 5(3^x)$ 5
11. $y = 4(5)^x$ 4
12. $y = 2(5)^x + 1$ 3
13. $y = \left(\frac{1}{2}\right)^{x+1}$ $\frac{1}{2}$
14. $y = \left(\frac{1}{8}\right)^x$ 1
15. $y = \left(\frac{3}{4}\right)^x - 2$ −1

Determine whether the data in each table display exponential behavior. Explain why or why not.

16.

x	−1	0	1	2
y	−5	−1	3	7

No; the domain values are at regular intervals and the range values have a common difference of 4.

17.

x	1	2	3	4
y	25	125	625	3125

Yes; the domain values are at regular intervals and the range values have a common factor of 5.

Lesson 9-7 Growth and Decay (pp. 573–579)

1. **FARMING** Mr. Rogers purchased a combine for \$175,000 for his farming operation. It is expected to depreciate at a rate of 18% per year. What will be the value of the combine in 3 years? \$96,489.40
2. **REAL ESTATE** The Jacksons bought a house for \$65,000 in 1992. Houses in the neighborhood have appreciated at the rate of 4.5% a year. How much is the house worth in 2003? \$105,485.45
3. **POPULATION** In 1950, the population of a city was 50,000. Since then, the population has increased by 2.25% per year. If it continues to grow at this rate, what will the population be in 2005? about 170,000
4. **BEARS** In a particular state, the population of black bears has been decreasing at the rate of 0.75% per year. In 1990, it was estimated that there were 400 black bears in the state. If the population continues to decline at the same rate, what will the population be in 2010? 344 bears
5. **INVESTMENTS** Determine the amount of an investment if \$500 is invested at an interest rate of 5.75% compounded monthly for 25 years. about \$2097.86

Lesson 9-8 Geometric Sequences as Exponential Functions (pp. 580–585)

1. **MONEY** Marco deposited \$8500 in a 4-year certificate of deposit earning 7.25% compounded monthly. Write an equation for the amount of money Marco will have at the end of the four years. Then find the amount. $M = 8500\left(1 + \frac{0.0725}{12}\right)^{12(4)}$; \$11,349.73
2. **TRANSPORTATION** Elise is buying a new car for \$21,500. The rate of depreciation on this type of car is 8% per year. Write an equation for the value of the car in 5 years. Then find the value of the car in 5 years. $V = 21{,}500(1 - 0.08)^5$; \$14,170.25; \$11,349.73
3. **POPULATION** In 2000, the town of Belgrade had a population of 3422. For each of the next 8 years, the population increased by 4.9% per year. Find the projected population of Belgrade in 2008. 5017

Lesson 9-9 Analyzing Functions with Successive Differences (pp. 586–591)

Graph each set or ordered pairs. Determine whether the ordered pairs represent a *linear* function, a *quadratic* function, or an *exponential* function. 1–8. See Student Handbook Answer Appendix.

1. (−2, 1), (−1, −2), (0, −3), (1, −2), (2, 1)
2. (−4, −5), (−2, −4), (0, −3), (2, −2), (4, 0)
3. (−3, 1), (−2, 2), (−1, 4), (0, 8), (1, 16)

Determine which model best describes the data. Then write an equation for the function that models the data.

4.

x	−2	−1	0	1	2
y	1	0.25	0	0.25	1

5.

x	−1	0	1	2	3
y	$\frac{2}{3}$	2	6	18	54

6.

x	−6	−5	−4	−3	−2
y	2	2.5	3	3.5	4

7. **COMPUTER GAME** Kylie started a game of computer "Tag, You're It". She tagged two friends and so there are three players after round 1. Each of them tagged three friends, and so on. The table shows the number of players after the first few rounds. Determine which function best models the number of players and then write a function that models the data.

Round	1	2	3	4	5
Players	3	9	27	81	243

8. **ROCKET** The table shows the height of a rocket that is launched from ground level after a period of 4 consecutive seconds. Determine which model best represents the height of the rocket with respect to time. Then write a function that models the data.

Times(s)	0	1	2	3	4
Height (ft)	0	1.2	4.8	10.8	19.2

Lesson 10-1 Square Root Functions (pp. 605–610)

1–12. See Student Handbook Answer Appendix.

Graph each function. Determine the domain and range of the function.

1. $y = \sqrt{x - 4}$
2. $y = \sqrt{x + 3} - 1$
3. $y = \frac{1}{3}\sqrt{x + 2}$
4. $y = \sqrt{2x + 5}$
5. $y = -\sqrt{4x}$
6. $y = 2\sqrt{x}$
7. $y = -3\sqrt{x}$
8. $y = \sqrt{x} + 5$
9. $y = \sqrt{2x} - 1$
10. $y = 5\sqrt{x} + 1$
11. $y = \sqrt{x + 1} - 2$
12. $y = 6 - \sqrt{x + 3}$

Lesson 10-2 Simplifying Radical Expressions (pp. 612–617)

Simplify. 18. $10|my|\sqrt{2y}$

1. $\sqrt{50}$ $5\sqrt{2}$
2. $\sqrt{200}$ $10\sqrt{2}$
3. $\sqrt{162}$ $9\sqrt{2}$
4. $\sqrt{700}$ $10\sqrt{7}$
5. $\frac{\sqrt{3}}{\sqrt{5}}$ $\frac{\sqrt{15}}{5}$
6. $\frac{\sqrt{72}}{\sqrt{6}}$ $2\sqrt{3}$
7. $\sqrt{\frac{8}{7}}$ $\frac{2\sqrt{14}}{7}$
8. $\sqrt{\frac{7}{32}}$ $\frac{\sqrt{14}}{8}$
9. $\sqrt{\frac{5}{8}} \cdot \sqrt{\frac{2}{6}}$ $\frac{\sqrt{30}}{12}$
10. $\sqrt{\frac{2}{3}} \cdot \sqrt{\frac{3}{2}}$ 1
11. $\sqrt{\frac{2x}{30}}$ $\frac{\sqrt{15x}}{15}$
12. $\sqrt{\frac{50}{z^2}}$ $\frac{5\sqrt{2}}{|z|}$
13. $\sqrt{10} \cdot \sqrt{20}$ $10\sqrt{2}$
14. $\sqrt{7} \cdot \sqrt{3}$ $\sqrt{21}$
15. $6\sqrt{2} \cdot \sqrt{3}$ $6\sqrt{6}$
16. $5\sqrt{6} \cdot 2\sqrt{3}$ $30\sqrt{2}$
17. $\sqrt{4x^4y^3}$ $2x^2|y|\sqrt{y}$
18. $\sqrt{200m^2y^3}$
19. $\sqrt{12tx^3}$ $2|x|\sqrt{3xt}$
20. $\sqrt{175a^4b^6}$ $5a^2|b^3|\sqrt{7}$
21. $\sqrt{\frac{54}{g^2}}$ $\frac{3\sqrt{6}}{|g|}$
22. $\sqrt{99x^3y^7}$ $3|xy^3|\sqrt{11xy}$
23. $\sqrt{\frac{32c^5}{9d^2}}$ $\frac{4c^2\sqrt{2c}}{3|d|}$
24. $\sqrt{\frac{27p^4}{3p^2}}$ $3|p|$

Lesson 10-3 Operations with Radical Expressions (pp. 619–623)

Simplify.

1. $3\sqrt{11} + 6\sqrt{11} - 2\sqrt{11}$ $7\sqrt{11}$
2. $6\sqrt{13} + 7\sqrt{13}$ $13\sqrt{13}$
3. $2\sqrt{12} + 5\sqrt{3}$ $9\sqrt{3}$
4. $9\sqrt{7} - 4\sqrt{2} + 3\sqrt{2}$ $9\sqrt{7} - \sqrt{2}$
5. $3\sqrt{5} - 5\sqrt{3}$ in simplest form
6. $4\sqrt{8} - 3\sqrt{5}$ $8\sqrt{2} - 3\sqrt{5}$
7. $2\sqrt{27} - 4\sqrt{12}$ $-2\sqrt{3}$
8. $8\sqrt{32} + 4\sqrt{50}$ $52\sqrt{2}$
9. $\sqrt{45} + 6\sqrt{20}$ $15\sqrt{5}$
10. $2\sqrt{63} - 6\sqrt{28} + 8\sqrt{45}$ $-6\sqrt{7} + 24\sqrt{5}$
11. $14\sqrt{3t} + 8$ $22\sqrt{3t}$
12. $7\sqrt{6x} - 12\sqrt{6x}$ $-5\sqrt{6x}$
13. $5\sqrt{7} - 3\sqrt{28}$ $-\sqrt{7}$
14. $7\sqrt{8} - \sqrt{18}$ $11\sqrt{2}$
15. $7\sqrt{98} + 5\sqrt{32} - 2\sqrt{75}$ $69\sqrt{2} - 10\sqrt{3}$
16. $4\sqrt{6} + 3\sqrt{2} - 2\sqrt{5}$ in simplest form
17. $-3\sqrt{20} + 2\sqrt{45} - \sqrt{7}$ $-\sqrt{7}$
18. $4\sqrt{75} + 6\sqrt{27}$ $38\sqrt{3}$
19. $10\sqrt{\frac{1}{5}} - \sqrt{45} - 12\sqrt{\frac{5}{9}}$ $-5\sqrt{5}$
20. $\sqrt{15} - \sqrt{\frac{3}{5}}$ $\frac{4\sqrt{15}}{5}$
21. $3\sqrt{\frac{1}{3}} - 9\sqrt{\frac{1}{12}} + \sqrt{243}$ $\frac{17\sqrt{3}}{2}$

Find each product.

22. $\sqrt{3}(\sqrt{5} + 2)$ $\sqrt{15} + 2\sqrt{3}$
23. $\sqrt{2}(\sqrt{2} + 3\sqrt{5})$ $2 + 3\sqrt{10}$
24. $(\sqrt{2} + 5)^2$ $27 + 10\sqrt{2}$
25. $(3 - \sqrt{7})(3 + \sqrt{7})$ 2
26. $(\sqrt{2} + \sqrt{3})(\sqrt{3} + \sqrt{2})$ $2\sqrt{6} + 5$
27. $(4\sqrt{7} + \sqrt{2})(\sqrt{3} - 3\sqrt{5})$ $4\sqrt{21} - 12\sqrt{35} + \sqrt{6} - 3\sqrt{10}$

Lesson 10-4 Radical Equations (pp. 624–628)

Solve each equation. Check your solution.

1. $\sqrt{5x} = 5$ 5
2. $4\sqrt{7} = \sqrt{-m}$ -112
3. $\sqrt{t} - 5 = 0$ 25
4. $\sqrt{3b} + 2 = 0$ no solution
5. $\sqrt{x} - 3 = 6$ 81
6. $5 - \sqrt{3x} = 1$ $\frac{16}{3}$
7. $2 + 3\sqrt{y} = 13$ $\frac{121}{9}$
8. $\sqrt{3g} = 6$ 12
9. $\sqrt{a} - 2 = 0$ 4
10. $\sqrt{2j} - 4 = 8$ 72
11. $5 + \sqrt{x} = 9$ 16
12. $\sqrt{5y + 4} = 7$ 9
13. $7 + \sqrt{5c} = 9$ $\frac{4}{5}$
14. $2\sqrt{5t} = 10$ 5
15. $\sqrt{44} = 2\sqrt{p}$ 11
16. $4\sqrt{x - 5} = 15$ $\frac{305}{16}$
17. $4 - \sqrt{x - 3} = 9$ no solution
18. $\sqrt{10x^2 - 5} = 3x$ $\sqrt{5}$
19. $\sqrt{2a^2 - 144} = a$ 12
20. $\sqrt{3y + 1} = y - 3$ 8
21. $\sqrt{2x^2 - 12} = x$ $2\sqrt{3}$
22. $\sqrt{b^2 + 16} + 2b = 5b$ $\frac{1 + \sqrt{325}}{24}$
23. $\sqrt{m + 2} + m = 4$ 7
24. $\sqrt{3 - 2c} + 3 = 2c$ 1

Lesson 10-5 The Pythagorean Theorem (pp. 630–635)

If c is the measure of the hypotenuse of a right triangle, find each missing measure. If necessary, round to the nearest hundredth.

1. $b = 20, c = 29, a = ?$ 21
2. $a = 7, b = 24, c = ?$ 25
3. $a = 2, b = 6, c = ?$ 6.32
4. $b = 10, c = \sqrt{200}, a = ?$ 10
5. $a = 3, c = 3\sqrt{2}, b = ?$ 3
6. $a = 6, c = 14, b = ?$ 12.65
7. $a = \sqrt{11}, c = \sqrt{47}, b = ?$ 6
8. $a = \sqrt{13}, b = 6, c = ?$ 7
9. $a = \sqrt{6}, b = 3, c = ?$ 3.87
10. $b = \sqrt{75}, c = 10, a = ?$ 5
11. $b = 9, c = \sqrt{130}, a = ?$ 7
12. $a = 9, c = 15, b = ?$ 12

Determine whether each set of measures can be sides of a right triangle. Then determine whether they form a Pythagorean Triple.

13. (14, 48, 50) yes, yes
14. (20, 30, 40) no
15. (21, 72, 75) yes, yes
16. $(5, 12, \sqrt{119})$ yes, no
17. (15, 39, 36) yes, yes
18. $(10, 12, \sqrt{22})$ no
19. (2, 3, 4) no
20. $(\sqrt{7}, 8, \sqrt{71})$ yes, no

4. $6\sqrt{2}$ or 8.49 5. $\sqrt{29}$ or 5.39 7. $2\sqrt{13}$ or 7.21

Lesson 10-6 The Distance and Midpoint Formulas (pp. 636–641)

Find the distance between each pair of points with the given coordinates.

1. (4, 2), (−2, 10) 10
2. (−5, 1), (7, 6) 13
3. (4, −2), (1, 2) 5
4. (−2, 4), (4, −2)
5. (3, 1), (−2, −1)
6. (−2, 4), (7, −8) 15
7. (−5, 0), (−9, 6)
8. (5, −1), (5, 13) 14
9. $(3\sqrt{2}, 7), (5\sqrt{2}, 9)$ $2\sqrt{3}$ or 3.46
10. (6, 3), (10, 0) 5
11. (3, 6), (5, −5) $5\sqrt{5}$ or 11.18
12. (−4, 2), (5, 4) $\sqrt{85}$ or 9.22

Find the possible values of a if the points with the given coordinates are the indicated distance apart.

13. $(0, 0), (a, 3); d = 5$ -4 or 4
14. $(2, -1), (-6, a); d = 10$ -7 or 5
15. $(1, 0), (a, 6); d = \sqrt{61}$ -4 or 6

Lesson 10-7 Similar Triangles (pp. 642–647)

Determine whether each pair of triangles is similar. Justify your answer.

1. 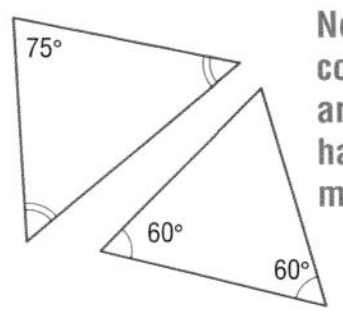

No; corresponding angles do not have equal measures.

2. 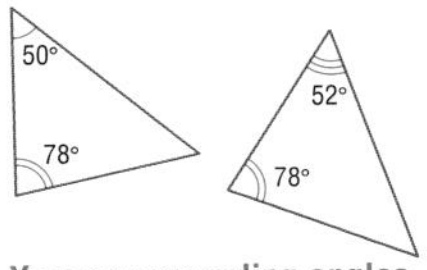

Yes; corresponding angles have equal measures.

3. 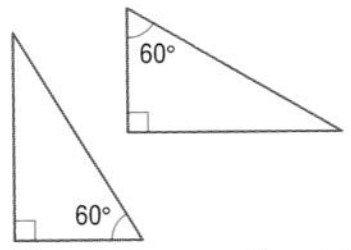

Yes; corresponding angles have equal measures.

For each set of measures given, find the measures of the missing sides if $\triangle ABC \sim \triangle DEF$.

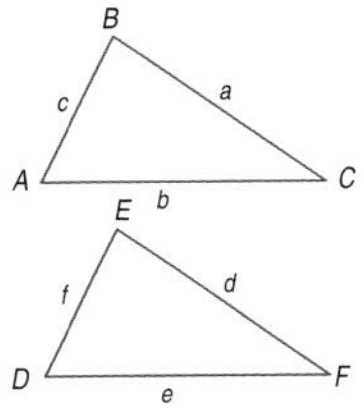

4. $a = 5, d = 10, b = 8, c = 7$ $e = 16, f = 14$
5. $a = 2, b = 3, c = 4, d = 3$ $e = 4.5, f = 6$
6. $a = 6, d = 4.5, e = 7, f = 7.5$ $b = 9\frac{1}{3}, c = 10$
7. $a = 15, c = 20, b = 18, f = 10$ $d = 7.5, e = 9$
8. $f = 17.5, d = 8.5, e = 11, a = 1.7$ $b = 2.2, c = 3.5$

Lesson 10-8 Trigonometric Ratios (pp. 649–655)

Find the values of the three trigonometric ratios for angle X.

1. 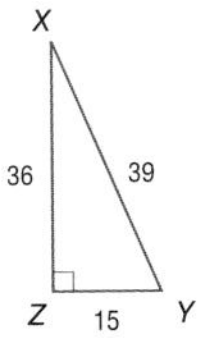

$\cos X = \frac{36}{39}$ or $\frac{12}{13}$, $\sin X = \frac{15}{39}$ or $\frac{5}{13}$, $\tan X = \frac{15}{36}$ or $\frac{5}{12}$

2. 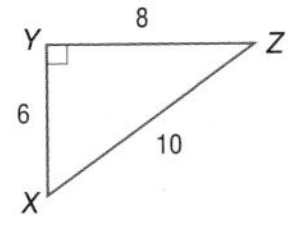

$\sin X = \frac{8}{10}$ or $\frac{4}{5}$, $\cos X = \frac{6}{10}$ or $\frac{3}{5}$, $\tan X = \frac{8}{6}$ or $\frac{4}{3}$

Use a calculator to find the values of each trigonometric ratio to the nearest ten-thousandth.

3. tan 42° 0.9004
4. sin 19° 0.3256
5. cos 78° 0.2079

Lesson 11-1 Inverse Variation (pp. 669–676)

Assume that y varies inversely as x. Write an inverse variation equation that relates x and y. Then graph the equation. **1–6. See Student Handbook Answer Appendix.**

1. $y = 10$ when $x = 7.5$
2. $y = -5$ when $x = 3$
3. $y = -6$ when $x = -2$
4. $y = 1$ when $x = -0.5$
5. $y = -2.5$ when $x = 3$
6. $y = -2$ when $x = -1$

Solve. Assume that y varies inversely as x.

7. If $y = 54$ when $x = 4$, find x when $y = 27$. **8**
8. If $y = 18$ when $x = 6$, find x when $y = 12$. **9**
9. If $y = 12$ when $x = 24$, find x when $y = 9$. **32**
10. If $y = 8$ when $x = -8$, find y when $x = -16$. **4**
11. If $y = 3$ when $x = -8$, find y when $x = 4$. **12**
12. If $y = 27$ when $x = \frac{1}{3}$, find y when $x = \frac{3}{4}$. **12**
13. If $y = -3$ when $x = -8$, find y when $x = 2$. **12**
14. If $y = -3$ when $x = -3$, find x when $y = 4$. **2.25**
15. If $y = -7.5$ when $x = 2.5$, find y when $x = -2.5$. **7.5**
16. If $y = -0.4$ when $x = -3.2$, find x when $y = -0.2$. **−6.4**

Lesson 11-2 Rational Functions (pp. 677–683)

Identify the asymptotes of each rational function.

1. $f(x) = \frac{1}{x+4}$ **$x = -4; y = 0$**
2. $f(x) = \frac{x-2}{x+3}$ **$x = -3; y = 1$**
3. $f(x) = \frac{x}{x+2}$ **$x = -2; y = 1$**
4. $f(x) = \frac{1}{x-5}$ **$x = 5; y = 0$**
5. $f(x) = \frac{3x}{x+1}$ **$x = -1; y = 3$**
6. $f(x) = \frac{x}{x-6}$ **$x = 6; y = 1$**

State the excluded value for each function.

7. $f(x) = \frac{x+2}{x+3}$ **$x = -3$**
8. $y = \frac{5}{x}$ **$x = 0$**
9. $y = \frac{x}{x-5}$ **$x = 5$**
10. $y = \frac{2}{3x-3}$ **$x = 1$**
11. $y = \frac{x}{2x+1}$ **$x = \frac{-1}{2}$**
12. $y = \frac{3}{x+2}$ **$x = -2$**

Lesson 11-3 Simplifying Rational Expressions (pp. 684–691)

State the excluded values for each rational expression.

1. $\frac{x}{x+1}$ **−1**
2. $\frac{m}{n}$ **$n \neq 0$**
3. $\frac{c-2}{c^2-4}$ **−2, 2**
4. $\frac{b^2-5b+6}{b^2-8b+15}$ **3, 5**

Simplify each expression. State the excluded values of the variables.

5. $\frac{13a}{39a^2}$ **$\frac{1}{3a}$; $a \neq 0$**
6. $\frac{38x^2}{42xy}$ **$\frac{19x}{21y}$; $x, y \neq 0$**
7. $\frac{p+5}{2(p+5)}$ **$\frac{1}{2}$; $-p \neq -5$**
8. $\frac{a+b}{a^2-b^2}$ **$\frac{1}{a-b}$; $a \neq \pm b$**
9. $\frac{y+4}{y^2-16}$ **$\frac{1}{y-4}$; $y \neq -4, 4$**
10. $\frac{c^2-4}{c^2+4c+4}$ **$\frac{c-2}{c+2}$; $c \neq -2$**
11. $\frac{a^2-a}{a-1}$ **a; $a \neq 1$**
12. $\frac{x^2+4}{x^4-16}$ **$\frac{1}{x^2-4}$; $x \neq \pm 2$**
13. $\frac{r^3-r^2}{r-1}$ **r^2; $r \neq 1$**
14. $\frac{4t^2-8}{4t-4}$ **$\frac{t^2-2}{t-1}$; $t \neq 1$**
15. $\frac{6y^3-12y^2}{12y^2-18}$ **$\frac{y^2(y-2)}{2y^2-3}$; $y \neq \pm\frac{\sqrt{6}}{2}$**
16. $\frac{5x^2+10x+5}{3x^2+6x+3}$ **$\frac{5}{3}$; $x \neq -1$**

Lesson 11-4 Multiplying and Dividing Rational Expressions (pp. 692–698)

Find each product.

1. $\frac{a^2b}{b^2c} \cdot \frac{c}{d}$ **$\frac{a^2}{bd}$**
2. $\frac{6a^2n}{8n^2} \cdot \frac{12n}{9a}$ **a**
3. $\frac{2a^2d}{3bc} \cdot \frac{9b^2c}{16ad^2}$ **$\frac{3ab}{8d}$**
4. $\frac{10n^3}{6x^3} \cdot \frac{12n^2x^4}{25n^2x^2}$ **$\frac{4n^3}{5x}$**
5. $\frac{6m^3c}{10a^2} \cdot \frac{4a^2m}{9c^3}$ **$\frac{4m^4}{15c^2}$**
6. $\frac{5n-5}{3} \cdot \frac{9}{n-1}$ **15**
7. $\frac{(a-5)(a+1)}{(a+1)(a+7)} \cdot \frac{(a+7)(a-6)}{(a+8)(a-5)}$ **$\frac{a-6}{a+8}$**
8. $\frac{x-1}{(x+2)(x-3)} \cdot \frac{x+2}{(x-3)(x-1)}$ **$\frac{1}{(x-3)^2}$**
9. $\frac{a^2}{a-b} \cdot \frac{3a-3b}{a}$ **$3a$**
10. $\frac{2a+4b}{5} \cdot \frac{25}{6a+8b}$ **$\frac{5a+10b}{3a+4b}$**

Find each quotient.

11. $\frac{5m^2p}{12a^2} \div \frac{30m^4}{18ap}$ **$\frac{p^2}{4am^2}$**
12. $\frac{25g^7h}{28t^3} \div \frac{5g^5h^2}{42s^2t^3}$ **$\frac{15g^2s^2}{2h}$**
13. $\frac{6a+4b}{36} \div \frac{3a+2b}{45}$ **$\frac{5}{2}$**
14. $\frac{x^2y}{18z} \div \frac{2yz}{3x^2}$ **$\frac{x^4}{12z^2}$**
15. $\frac{p^2}{14tr^3} \div \frac{2r^2p}{7t}$ **$\frac{p}{4r^5}$**
16. $\frac{5d-f}{5d+f} \div (25d^2-f^2)$ **$\frac{1}{(5d+f)^2}$**
17. $\frac{t^2-2t-15}{t-5} \div \frac{t+3}{t+5}$ **$t+5$**
18. $\frac{5x+10}{x+2} \div (x+2)$ **$\frac{5}{x+2}$**
19. $\frac{3d}{2d^2-3d} \div \frac{9}{2d-3}$ **$\frac{1}{3}$**

Lesson 11-5 Dividing Polynomials (pp. 700–705)

Find each quotient.

1. $(2x^2-11x-20) \div (2x+3)$ **$x-7+\frac{1}{2x+3}$**
2. $(a^2+10a+21) \div (a+3)$ **$a+7$**
3. $(m^2+4m-5) \div (m+5)$ **$m-1$**
4. $(x^2-2x-35) \div (x-7)$ **$x+5$**
5. $(c^2+6c-27) \div (c+9)$ **$c-3$**
6. $(y^2-6y-25) \div (y+7)$ **$y-13+\frac{66}{(y+7)}$**
7. $(3t^2-14t-24) \div (3t+4)$ **$t-6$**
8. $(2r^2-3r-35) \div (2r+7)$ **$r-5$**
9. $\frac{12n^2+36n+15}{6n+3}$ **$2n+5$**
10. $\frac{10x^2+29x+21}{5x+7}$ **$2x+3$**
11. $\frac{4t^3+17t^2-1}{4t+1}$ **t^2+4t-1**
12. $\frac{2a^3+9a^2+5a-12}{a+3}$ **$2a^2+3a-4$**
13. $\frac{27c^2-24c+8}{9c-2}$ **$3c-2+\frac{4}{9c-2}$**
14. $\frac{4b^3+7b^2-2b+4}{b+2}$ **$4b^2-b+\frac{4}{b+2}$**

Lesson 11-6 Adding and Subtracting Rational Expressions (pp. 706–713)

Find each sum.

1. $\frac{4}{z}+\frac{3}{z}$ **$\frac{7}{z}$**
2. $\frac{a}{12}+\frac{2a}{12}$ **$\frac{a}{4}$**
3. $\frac{5}{2t}+\frac{-7}{2t}$ **$\frac{-1}{t}$**
4. $\frac{y}{2}+\frac{y}{2}$ **y**
5. $\frac{k}{3}+\frac{2k}{7}$ **$\frac{13k}{21}$**
6. $\frac{5}{2a}+\frac{-3}{6a}$ **$\frac{2}{a}$**
7. $\frac{6}{5x}+\frac{7}{10x^2}$ **$\frac{12x+7}{10x^2}$**
8. $\frac{4a}{2a+6}+\frac{3}{a+3}$ **$\frac{2a+3}{a+3}$**
9. $\frac{3t+2}{3t-2}+\frac{t+2}{t^2-4}$ **9. $\frac{3t^3+5t^2-8t-12}{3t^3+2t^2-12t-8}$**
10. $\frac{-3}{a-5}+\frac{-6}{a^2-5a}$ **$\frac{-3a-6}{a^2-5a}$**

Find each difference.

11. $\frac{5x}{24}-\frac{3x}{24}$ **$\frac{x}{12}$**
12. $\frac{7p}{3}-\frac{8p}{3}$ **$\frac{-p}{3}$**
13. $\frac{8k}{5m}-\frac{3k}{5m}$ **$\frac{k}{m}$**
14. $\frac{8}{m-2}-\frac{6}{m-2}$ **$\frac{2}{m-2}$**
15. $\frac{y}{b+6}-\frac{2y}{b+6}$ **$\frac{-y}{b+6}$**
16. $\frac{a+2}{6}-\frac{a+3}{6}$ **$-\frac{1}{6}$**
17. $\frac{3z}{7w^2}-\frac{2z}{w}$ **$\frac{3z-14wz}{7w^2}$**
18. $\frac{p}{t^2}-\frac{r}{3t}$ **$\frac{3p-rt}{3t^2}$**
19. $\frac{a}{a^2-4}-\frac{4}{a+2}$ **$\frac{-3a+8}{a^2-4}$**
20. $\frac{m}{m-p}-\frac{5}{m}$ **$\frac{m^2-5m+5p}{m^2-mp}$**
21. $\frac{y+5}{y-5}-\frac{2y}{y^2-25}$ **$\frac{y^2+8y+25}{y^2-25}$**

Find the LCM for each pair of polynomials.

22. $27a^2bc, 36ab^2c^2$ **$108a^2b^2c^2$**
23. $3m-1, 6m-2$ **$6m-2$**
24. x^2+2x+1, x^2-2x-3 **$(x+1)^2(x-3)$**

Lesson 11-7 Mixed Expressions and Complex Fractions (pp. 714–719)

Write each mixed expression as a rational expression.

1. $4 + \frac{2}{x}$ $\frac{4x+2}{x}$
2. $8 + \frac{5}{3t}$ $\frac{24t+5}{3t}$
3. $3b + \frac{b+1}{2b}$ $\frac{6b^2+b+1}{2b}$
4. $3z + \frac{z+2}{z}$ $3z^2 + \frac{z+2}{z}$
5. $\frac{2}{a-2} + a^2$ $\frac{a^3-2a^2+2}{a-2}$
6. $3r^2 + \frac{4}{2r+1}$ $\frac{6r^3+3r^2+4}{2r+1}$

Simplify each expression.

7. $\frac{3\frac{1}{2}}{4\frac{3}{4}}$ $\frac{14}{19}$
8. $\frac{\frac{x^2}{y}}{\frac{y}{x^3}}$ $\frac{x^5}{y^2}$
9. $\frac{\frac{t^4}{u}}{\frac{t^3}{u^2}}$ tu
10. $\frac{\frac{x-3}{x+1}}{\frac{x^2}{y^2}}$ $\frac{y^2(x-3)}{x^2(x+1)}$
11. $\frac{\frac{y}{3}+\frac{5}{6}}{2+\frac{5}{y}}$ $\frac{y}{6}$
12. $\frac{\frac{1}{x}+\frac{1}{y}}{\frac{1}{y}-\frac{1}{x}}$ $\frac{x+y}{x-y}$
13. $\frac{\frac{t-2}{t^2-4}}{t^2+5t+6}$ $t+3$
14. $\frac{a+\frac{2}{a+1}}{a-\frac{3}{a-2}}$ 14. $\frac{(a-2)(a^2+a+2)}{(a+1)(a^2-2a-3)}$

Lesson 11-8 Rational Equations (pp. 720–727)

Solve each equation. State any extraneous solutions.

1. $\frac{k}{6} + \frac{2k}{3} = -\frac{5}{2}$ -3
2. $\frac{2x}{7} + \frac{27}{10} = \frac{4x}{5}$ 5.25
3. $\frac{18}{b} = \frac{3}{b+3}$ 5
4. $\frac{3}{5x} + \frac{7}{2x} = 1$ $\frac{41}{10}$
5. $\frac{2a-3}{6} = \frac{2a}{3} + \frac{1}{2}$ -3
6. $\frac{3x+2}{x} + \frac{x+3}{x} = 5$ 5
7. $\frac{2b-3}{7} - \frac{b}{2} = \frac{b+3}{14}$ $-\frac{9}{4}$
8. $\frac{2y}{y-4} - \frac{3}{5} = 3$ 9
9. $\frac{2t}{t+3} + \frac{3}{t} = 2$ 3
10. $\frac{5x}{x+1} + \frac{1}{x} = 5$ $\frac{1}{4}$
11. $\frac{r-2}{r+2} - \frac{2r}{r+9} = 6$ $-6, -3$
12. $\frac{m}{m+1} + \frac{5}{m-1} = 1$ $-\frac{3}{2}$
13. $\frac{2x}{x-3} - \frac{4x}{3-x} = 12$ 6
14. $\frac{14}{b-6} = \frac{1}{2} + \frac{6}{b-8}$ $10, 20$
15. $\frac{a}{4a+15} - 3 = -2$ -5
16. $\frac{5x}{3x+10} + \frac{2x}{x+5} = 2$ $-4, 5$
17. $\frac{2a-3}{a-3} - 2 = \frac{12}{a+2}$ $\frac{14}{3}$
18. $\frac{z+3}{z-1} + \frac{z+1}{z-3} = 2$ 2

Lesson 12-1 Designing a Survey (pp. 739–745)

Identify each sample, suggest a population from which it was selected, and state whether it is *unbiased* (random) or *biased*. If unbiased, classify the sample as *simple*, *stratified*, or *systematic*. If biased, classify as *convenience* or *voluntary response*.

1. The sheriff has heard that many dogs in the county do not have licenses. He checks the licenses of the first ten dogs he encounters. **10 dogs from a county; all dogs in the county; biased; convenience**
2. Every fifth car is selected from the assembly line. The cars are also identified by the day of the week during which they were produced. **2. a group of automobiles manufactured at a particular plant; all automobiles manufactured at the plant; unbiased; stratified random sample**
3. A table is set up outside of a large department store. All people entering the store are given a survey about their preference of brand for blue jeans. As people leave the store, they can return the survey. **3. a group of people shopping at a department store; all people shopping at the department store; biased; voluntary response**
4. A community is considering building a new swimming pool. Every twentieth person on a list of residents is contacted for their opinion. **a group of community residents; all residents of the community; unbiased; systematic random sample**
5. A group of custom chopper builders are interested in finding the type of art work people prefer on their bikes. They line up a group of each of their choppers at a show to see which designs people appear to prefer. **sample: the people at the show; population: all people; observational study**

Lesson 12-2 Analyzing Survey Results (pp. 746–755)

Tell which measure of center best represents the data. Justify your answer. Then find the measure of center.

1. **COMPUTER USAGE** To determine if they need to add more computers for internet access at the Grandview Library, the staff kept track of the number of patrons who used the computers each evening between 5PM and 8PM during a two-week period. {32, 12, 45, 38, 26, 29, 31, 22, 40, 20, 24, 27} **Mean; there are no outliers; 28**
2. **CHOCOLATE MILK** The preschool cafeteria staff wanted to decide if they should continue to order chocolate milk for the children. For two weeks they kept a count of the number of half-pints of chocolate milk requested by the children. {21, 17, 17, 21, 18, 18, 21, 18, 19, 20} **Mode; repeated values; 18**

Given the following portion of a survey report, evaluate the validity of the information and conclusion.

3. **ONLINE SURVEYS** An online survey was conducted by an advertising firm to determine how many potential customers they might reach. The firm sent out 10,000 surveys and received 2,300 online responses. **Question:** How many hours per week, outside of work time, do you spend on your computer? **Results:** 0–2, 4%; 3–6, 20%; 7–12, 32%; 13–20, 20%; 21–30, 12%; more than 30, 12%. **Conclusion:** One-third of all adults spend between 7 and 12 hours each week on their home computers. **3. Sample answer: There is bias because they are using an online survey to ask a question about online time. The conclusion only applies to people who are already online users.**

Lesson 12-3 Statistics and Parameters (pp. 756–762)

Identify the sample and the population for each situation. Then describe the sample statistic and the population parameter. **1–2. See Student Handbook Answer Appendix.**

1. As part of their quality control program, the Venice Pizza Parlor called 125 of its delivery customers to see if they were satisfied with the delivery service. The percentage of those responding YES is calculated.
2. A random stratified sample of 1,200 high school band members from across the country is surveyed about how many hours they spend practicing each week during football season.

Find the mean, variance, and standard deviation of each set of data.

3. {7, 10, 22, 15, 11} **mean = 13; variance = 26.8; $\sigma \approx 5.2$**
4. {11, 16, 20, 17} **4. mean = 16; variance = 10.5; $\sigma \approx 3.2$**
5. {45, 40, 54, 67, 44} **5. mean = 50; variance = 93.2; $\sigma \approx 9.7$**

Lesson 12-4 Permutations and Combinations (pp. 764–770)

Determine whether each situation involves a permutation or combination. Explain your reasoning. **1–4. See Student Handbook Answer Appendix for explanations.**

1. three topping flavors for a sundae from ten topping choices **combination**
2. selection and placement of four runners on a relay team from 8 runners **permutation**
3. five rides to ride at an amusement park with twelve rides **combination**
4. first, second, and third place winners for a 10K race **permutation**

Evaluate each expression.

5. $P(5, 2)$ **20**
6. $P(7, 7)$ **5040**
7. $C(10, 2)$ **45**
8. $C(6, 5)$ **6**

Lesson 12-5 Probability of Compound Events (pp. 771–778)

1. **SIBLINGS** Perry took a survey of his classmates to see how many siblings each had. The results are in the table.
   a. Find the probability that a randomly chosen classmate will have 4 siblings. $\frac{3}{24} = 12.5\%$
   b. Find the probability that a randomly chosen classmate will have less than 3 siblings. $\frac{15}{24} = 62.5\%$

Classmates' Siblings	
Number of Siblings	Number of Classmates
0	3
1	8
2	4
3	5
4	3
5	1

2. **CARS** A customer visiting a new car lot was looking for a convertible. The Buyers Co. lot had 8 black, 6 white, 4 silver, 5 red and 7 green convertibles to consider.
   a. Find the probability that a randomly chosen car will be silver. $\frac{4}{30} = 13.3\%$
   b. Find the probability that a randomly chosen car will be red or black. $\frac{13}{30} = 43.3\%$

Lesson 12-6 Probability Distributions (pp. 779–786)

Toss 4 coins, one at a time, 50 times and record your results.

1. Based on your results, what is the probability that any two coins show tails? **Sample answer: 0.36**
2. Based on your results, what is the probability that the first and fourth coins show heads? **Sample answer: 0.06**
3. What is the theoretical probability that all four coins show heads? $\frac{1}{16}$

Use the table that shows the results of a survey about household occupancy.

Number in Household	Number of Households
1	172
2	293
3	482
4	256
5 or more	148

4. Find the experimental probability distribution for the number of households of each size. **$P(1) \approx 12.7\%$; $P(2) \approx 21.7\%$; $P(3) \approx 35.7\%$; $P(4) \approx 18.9\%$; $P(5 \text{ or more}) \approx 11.0\%$**
5. Based on the survey, what is the probability that a person chosen at random lives in a household with five or more people? **about 0.11 or 11%**
6. Based on the survey, what is the probability that a person chosen at random lives in a household with 1 or 2 people? **about 0.34 or 34%**

Lesson 12-7 Probability Simulations (pp. 787–792)

Determine whether the events are independent or dependent. Then find the probability.

1. A bag of colored candies contains 12 red, 5 brown, 7 orange, 6 blue, 4 green and 6 purple candies. Alex reaches in the bag and pulls out one piece of candy and then a second piece without replacement. What is the probability that the first two choices are blue? **dependent; $\frac{1}{52}$, or about 1.9%**
2. Gretchen and her friends are having a sleepover and movie marathon. They have rented four movies: a comedy, a horror movie, a mystery and a romance. What is the probability that they will watch a mystery and then a romance? **dependent; $\frac{1}{12}$, or about 8.3%**
3. For a special game, the sides on a number cube are colored red for the odd numbers, 1, 3, and 5, and green for the even numbers, 2, 4 and 6. What is the probability on two rolls of the cube of getting a green side, followed by a 4? **independent; $\frac{1}{12}$, or about 8.3%**

Mixed Problem Solving

Chapter 1 Expressions, Equations, and Functions (pp. 2–71)

1. **GEOMETRY** The area of a rectangle is the product of the length ℓ and the width w. (Lesson 1-1)
   a. Write an expression for the area of a rectangle. **$A = \ell w$**
   b. Write an expression in terms of ℓ for the area of a rectangle that is twice as wide as it is long. **$A = 2\ell^2$**

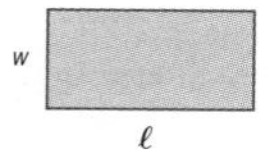

2. **SIGNS** A restaurant has a cylindrical shaped sign made to look like a bucket of their fried chicken. The volume of a cylinder can be found by the product of the radius squared, the height of the cylinder and π.
   a. Write an expression for the volume of a cylinder. **$V = r^2(h)(\pi)$**
   b. Evaluate the volume of the sign if the radius is 3 feet and the height is 6 feet. **$3^2(6)(\pi)$, 54π cu. ft.**
   c. For a bill board on the freeway, the dimensions of the sign were changed to a 9 foot diameter and a height of 9 feet. Find the volume of the bucket on the billboard. (Lesson 1-2) **182π cu. ft.**
3. **TRAVEL** Ticket prices for an amusement park are shown in the table below. There are two adults and three children in the Careen family. The children's ages are 11, 8, and 4. (Lesson 1-3)
   a. Write an expression for the cost c of the day at the amusement park for the family. **$c = (2 + 1)(71) + 2(60)$**
   b. Find the cost of the day at the amusement park. **$333**
   c. What is the cost per day of the vacation if the family stayed three days? **$317**
   d. What is the cost per day of the vacation if the family stayed seven days? **$145.86**

Length of Vacation	1-Day	3-Day	7-Day
Guests (Ages 10+)	$71	$203	$219
Guests (Ages 3–9)	$60	$171	$182

4. **FOOD** The cafeteria has the following menu.

Menu	
Items	Cost ($)
pizza	2.75
sandwich	1.50
fries	0.75
drink	1.25

Charlie gets lunch for himself and two friends. Charlie wants pizza and a drink. His friends each have a sandwich, fries, and a drink. (Lesson 1-4)
   a. Write and evaluate an expression to find the total cost. **2.75 + 1.25 + 2(1.50 + 0.75 + 1.25)**
   b. How much would it cost if Charlie bought the same thing as his friends? **$10.50**
5. **DISTANCE** In a given amount of time, Jena drove twice as far as Rita. Altogether they drove 120 miles. Find the number of miles driven by Jena. (Lesson 1-5) **80 mi**
6. **GRAPH** Describe what is happening in the graph. The graph represents Nikki's trip to the store. (Lesson 1-6) **Nikki went to the store, then came back home.**

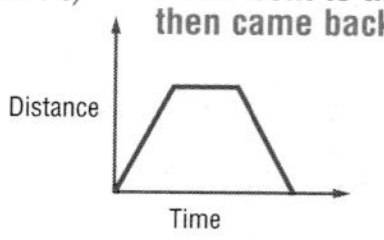

7. Is the following relation a function? Explain. (Lesson 1-7) **Yes; for each input there is exactly one output.**

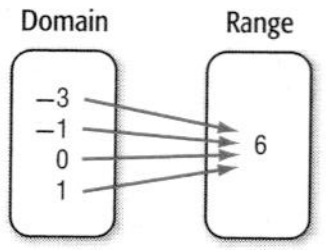

8. Find a counterexample for the following statement. *If you read music, you sing in a choir.* (Lesson 1-7) **A person could read music and be in the band.**
9. Identify the hypothesis and conclusion of the following statement. Then write the statement in if-then form. *Mei and Janel will go to the mall after school.* (Lesson 1-7) **See Student Handbook Answer Appendix.**

Chapter 2 Linear Equations (pp. 72–149)

1. **BABY-SITTING** As a part-time job, Andrea babysits. She charges \$4 per hour and \$5 for gas money. Write an equation that could be used to find how much she will make if she babysits for 4 hours. (Lesson 2-1)
   $T = 4(4) + 5$, where T is total earnings.

2. **WORLD RECORD** At 107 inches, Robert Pershing Wadlow was the tallest man to ever live. If the average 15-year-old male is 68 inches tall, write and solve an equation to find the number of inches taller Mr. Wadlow was than the average 15-year-old male. (Lesson 2-1) **$68 + x = 107$; 39 in.**

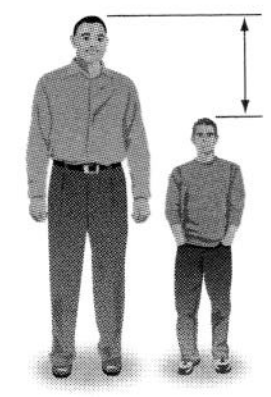

3. Three fifths of Marcus's classmates have brown eyes. There are 18 students who have brown eyes. Determine how many students are in the class. (Lesson 2-2) **$\frac{3}{5}x = 18$; 30 students**

4. **LOCKER NUMBERS** Andy, Kayla, and Samantha have 3 lockers in a row. The lockers are numbered consecutively and the sum of the locker numbers is 756. Write and solve an equation to find all three locker numbers. (Lesson 2-3) **$y + (n + 1) + (n + 2) = 756$; 251; 252; 253**

5. **BEAD WORK** Sarah said, "I counted my beads, and I have three more than 4 times a certain mystery number." Jasmine had the same amount of beads as Sarah, but said she had 9 less than 5 times the mystery number. They challenged their art teacher to discover the mystery number. (Lesson 2-4)
   a. What equation could the art teacher use to find the number? **$4x + 3 = 5x - 9$**
   b. What is the mystery number? **12**
   c. How many beads does each girl have? **51 beads**

6. **DRIVING** A car has an average fuel economy of 23 miles per gallon. The car gets 4 miles per gallon fewer in city driving and 4 miles per gallon more in highway driving. Write and solve an absolute value equation to find the fuel economy of the car in city and highway driving. (Lesson 2-5) **$|f - 23| = 4$; 19 mpg, 27 mpg**

7. **LAWN CARE** José's mom tells him she will pay him \$20 if he mows the lawn in an hour, plus or minus 15 minutes. If it takes José 73 minutes to mow the lawn, will his mom pay him? Explain your reasoning. (Lesson 2-5)
   See Student Handbook Answer Appendix.

8. **ARCHITECTURE** Isaac drew the following floor plan of his room. Write and solve a proportion to find the actual length of his room if the actual width is 12 meters. (Lesson 2-6) **$\frac{4}{12} = \frac{5}{x}$; 15 m**

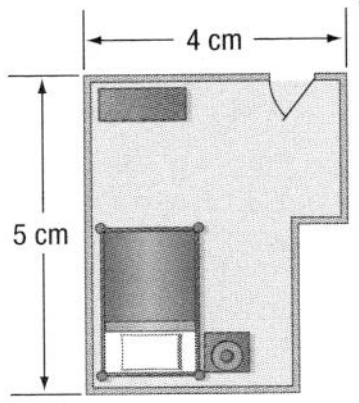

9. **CARS** Daniel's father purchased a vintage car when it was new. He paid \$3334. Last year, he sold it for \$28,250. (Lesson 2-7)
   a. Determine the percent of change to the nearest percent. **747%**
   b. Is this a percent of *increase* or *decrease*? Explain. **See Student Handbook Answer Appendix.**

10. **WEATHER** Emily went to Canada for vacation. Listening to the weather report, she heard that the high for the day was going to be 23°C. She remembered that the formula for changing Fahrenheit to Celsius was $C = \frac{5}{9}(F - 32)$. (Lesson 2-8)
    a. Solve the formula for F. **$F = \frac{9}{5}C + 32$**
    b. Use the new formula to find that day's high temperature in degrees Fahrenheit. **73.4°F**
    c. If the low temperature for the day was 16°C, find the day's low in °F. **60.8°F**

11. **TRANSPORTATION** Hector rode his bike to Matthew's house. It took him 10 minutes to ride the 3-mile trip. When it was time to leave, he saw that his tire had gone flat and he would need to walk home. It took him 45 minutes to walk home. What was his average speed for the round trip? Express your answer in miles per hour rounded to the nearest tenth. (Lesson 2-9) **6.5 mph**

Chapter 3 Linear Functions (pp. 150–209)

1. **MOVIES** Tickets for the movies cost \$5 for students and \$8 for adults. The equation $5x + 8y = 80$ represents the number of students x and adults y who can attend a movie for \$80. (Lesson 3-1)
   a. Use the x- and y-intercepts to graph the equation. **See Student Handbook Answer Appendix.**
   b. Describe what these values mean in the context of this situation. **See Student Handbook Answer Appendix.**

2. **FUNDRAISING** Shawn's class is selling candy to raise money for a class trip. They paid \$55 for the candy, and they are selling each candy bar for \$1.75. The function $y = 1.75x - 55$ represents their profit y for selling x candy bars. (Lesson 3-2)
   a. Find the zero of the function. **≈ 31.43**
   b. Describe what the zero means in the context of this situation. **The students must sell at least 32 candy bars to make a profit.**
   c. Graph the function. **See Student Handbook Answer Appendix.**

3. **PHOTOS** The average cost of using an online photo finisher decreased from \$0.50 per print to \$0.27 per print between 2002 and 2005. Find the average rate of change in the cost. Explain what the rate of change means. (Lesson 3-3) **See Student Handbook Answer Appendix.**

4. **WAGES** The weekly salary Enrique earns w varies directly as the hours h that he works. (Lesson 3-4)
   a. Write this situation as an equation. **$w = hk$**
   b. Graph the equation if Enrique makes \$11.50 an hour. **See Student Handbook Answer Appendix.**
   c. How many hours does Enrique have to work to earn \$690? **60 hours**

5. **MONEY** The table represents Tiffany's income. (Lesson 3-5)

Hours Worked	Income (\$)
1	20.50
2	29.00
3	37.50
4	46.00

   a. Write an equation for this sequence. **$a(n) = 12 + 8.5n$**
   b. Use the equation to find Tiffany's income if she works 20 hours. **\$182**

6. **SAVINGS** Payat has \$680 in a savings account. He makes a deposit after he receives each paycheck. After one month he has \$758 in the account. The next month the balance is \$836. The balance after the third month is \$914. (Lesson 3-5)
   a. Write a function to represent the arithmetic sequence. **$s(n) = 78n + 680$**
   b. Graph the function. **See Student Handbook Answer Appendix.**
   c. How much will Payat have in his savings account at the end of six months? **\$1148**

7. **SALES** Percy sells cell phones in the mall. In addition to his salary, he receives a bonus for each cell phone that he sells. The table shows the number of phones he sells and the amount of his bonus. (Lesson 3-6)

Number of Phones	Bonus Pay (\$)
1	65
2	130
3	195
4	260
5	325

   a. Graph the data. **See Student Handbook Answer Appendix.**
   b. Write an equation to describe this relationship. **$b = 65c$**
   c. Determine the amount of his bonus if Percy sells 10 phones. **\$650**

8. **STRAWBERRIES** The table below shows the cost of picking your own strawberries at a local farm. (Lesson 3-6)

Number of Pounds	Total Cost (\$)
1	1.25
2	2.50
3	3.75
4	5.00

   a. Graph the data. **See Student Handbook Answer Appendix.**
   b. Write an equation in function notation to describe this relationship. **$f(x) = 1.25x$**
   c. How much would 6 pounds of strawberries cost if you picked them yourself? **\$7.50**
   d. How much would 9.5 pounds of strawberries cost if you picked them yourself? **\$11.88**

Mixed Problem Solving

Chapter 4 Linear Functions and Relations (pp. 210–279)

1. **FINANCES** Brandon is saving money to purchase a new video game system. He has $94 and plans to save $7 each week for the next several weeks. (Lesson 4-1)
   a. Write an equation for the total amount S that he has saved after w weeks. $S = 7w + 94$
   b. Graph the equation.
   c. Find out how much Brandon will have saved after 8 weeks. $150
   b. See Student Handbook Answer Appendix.
2. **PHOTOGRAPHY** An online photo processing company produces printed and bound photo albums. The standard price for an album includes up to 20 pages. There is a fee for every two additional pages. To make a 30-page book, you pay $29.94. To make a 42-page book, you pay $41.88. (Lesson 4-2) a. $1.99
   a. What is the cost for each additional 2 pages?
   b. What is the cost of a 20-page book? $19.99
3. **FITNESS** The graph shows the cost of a membership to the local gym. Write an equation in point-slope form to find the total price y for any number of months x. (Lesson 4-3)

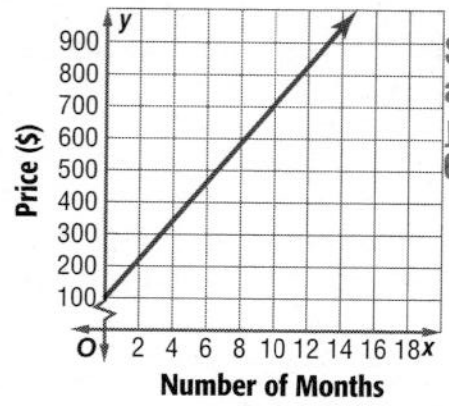

Sample answer: $y - 700 = 60(x - 10)$

4. **MAPS** The map below shows Interstate Highways 80 and 70 through a portion of Wyoming and Colorado. (Lesson 4-4)

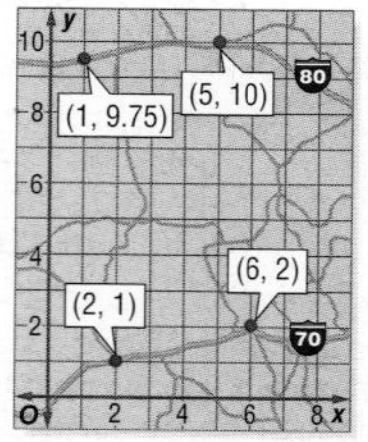

a. The slope of I-80 is $\frac{1}{16}$. The slope of I-70 is $\frac{1}{4}$.

   a. Find the slope of the lines that approximate the path of each highway.
   b. Are the highways parallel? no

5. **PLANETS** The table shows the distance between selected planets and the Sun and the diameters of the planets. Draw a scatter plot and determine what relationship exists, if any, in the data. (Lesson 4-5) See Student Handbook Answer Appendix for scatter plot; no relationship.

Planet	Distance from Sun (10^6 mi)	Diameter (mi)
Mercury	36.0	3032
Venus	67.2	7521
Earth	93.0	7926
Mars	141.6	2159

6. **ATTENDANCE** Rodeo Houston is an event that features rodeo events, a Bar-B-Que competition, concerts by top performers, art auction and contributes scholarships to youth organizations. The attendance for the rodeo championships are listed in the table below.

Year	2002	2004	2006	2008
Attendance	68,266	70,668	72,867	71,165

   a. Find an equation for the median-fit line. $y = 483.17x + 67{,}983.67$
   b. According to the equation, how many attended the rodeo's championship in 2009? 72,332

7. **PARKING** Mika was visiting the state library. The fees for parking are shown in the table. (Lesson 4-7)

Time	Cost
15 minutes or less	free
first hour	$0.50
each addtional hour or partial hour	additional $1.00
maximum daily rate	$5.00

   a. Draw a graph that shows the parking fee y for the time spent parked x. See Student Handbook Answer Appendix.
   b. If Mika visited the state library for three and a half hours, how much did she pay for parking? $3.50

Chapter 5 Linear Inequalities (pp. 280–329)

1. **SHOPPING** Jeff is buying a new car but owes $3000 on his old one. Jeff can spend no more than $18,000 to pay off his old car and buy a new one. (Lesson 5-1) $c + 3000 \leq 18{,}000$
   a. Write an inequality to show how much Jeff can spend on his new car.
   b. Solve the inequality. $c \leq 15{,}000$
2. **TOMATOES** There are more than 10,000 varieties of tomatoes. One seed company produces seed packages for 200 varieties of tomatoes. For how many varieties do they not provide seeds? (Lesson 5-1) See Student Handbook Answer Appendix.
3. **SURVEYS** Of the students at Davidson High School, fewer than 92 students said they like strawberry ice cream. This is about one sixth of those surveyed. (Lesson 5-2)
   a. Write an inequality to represent this situation. $\frac{1}{6}n < 92$
   b. How many students were surveyed? no more than 552
4. **ARCHITECTURE** The dimensions of Lisle's room are shown below. If the area of the room is at least 96 square feet, what is the least width the room could have? (Lesson 5-2)

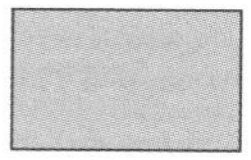

   a. Define a variable. width = w
   b. Write an inequality. $12w \geq 96$
   c. Solve the problem. $w \geq 8$
5. **SAVINGS** Ramone is raking yards for $22 per yard to earn money for a car. So far he has $2150 saved. The car that Ramone wants to buy costs at least $8290. (Lesson 5-3) $2150 + 22y \geq 8290$
   a. Write an inequality to show how many more yards Ramone still needs to rake to earn enough money to buy the car.
   b. Solve the inequality. 279 yd
6. **CHARITY** Avery High School holds a walk-a-thon each fall to raise money for charity. This year they want to raise at least $375. Each student earns $0.75 for every half mile walked. How many miles will the students need to walk? (Lesson 5-3) at least 250 mi
7. **SALES** A school buys 500 T-shirts. In addition to the price per shirt, there is a $45 set-up fee. The school can afford to spend no more than $2295. (Lesson 5-3) $500x + 45 \leq 2295$
   a. Write an inequality to show the relationship.
   b. What must the price be for the school to afford the shirts? less than $4.50
8. **FISH TANK** The temperature in a fish tank must be at least 77°F and at most 83°F. (Lesson 5-4)
   a. Write a compound inequality that describes acceptable temperatures for a fish tank.
   b. Graph the inequality. a–b. See Student Handbook Answer Appendix.
9. **MOVIES** A recent survey showed that 73% of young adults had seen a movie recently. The margin of sampling error was within 5 percentage points. Find the range of young adults who saw a movie recently. (Lesson 5-5) $\{m \mid 68 \leq m \leq 78\}$
10. **SNOW** When the temperature in the clouds is 7°F plus or minus 3°F, star-shaped crystals of snow form. At 14°F plus or minus 4°F, plate-shaped crystals are formed. (Lesson 5-5)
    a. Find the range of temperature that produces star-shaped crystals. $\{s \mid 4 \leq s \leq 10\}$
    b. Find the range of temperature that produces plate-shaped crystals. $\{s \mid 10 \leq s \leq 18\}$
11. **JOBS** It takes a librarian 1 minute to renew a library card and 3 minutes to make a new card. Together, she can spend no more than 30 minutes renewing and making cards. Write an inequality to represent this situation, if x is the number of cards she renews and y is the number of new cards she makes. (Lesson 5-6) $x + 3y \leq 30$
12. **MOVING** A moving company charges $95 an hour and $0.08 per mile. If Brianna has only $500 for moving expenses, can she afford to hire this moving company if it will take 5 hours and the houses are 75 miles apart? (Lesson 5-6) yes
13. **DELIVERIES** A delivery truck is transporting the items shown. (Lesson 5-6)

See Student Handbook Answer Appendix.

Item	Weight (lb)
television	48
computer	21

If the delivery truck has a 2500-pound weight limit, will the truck be able to deliver 30 televisions and 45 computers? Explain.

Chapter 6 Systems of Linear Equations and Inequalities (pp. 330–397)

1. **FUNDRAISERS** The French Club is selling heart-shaped lollipops to raise money for a trip to Quebec. They paid $20 for the candy mold, and the ingredients for each lollipop cost $0.50. They plan to sell the lollipops for $1.00. (Lesson 6-1)
   a. Write an equation for the cost of supplies y for the number of lollipops sold x, and an equation for the income y for the number of lollipops sold x. **$y = 0.50x + 20$, $y = x$**
   b. Graph each equation. **See Student Handbook Answer Appendix.**
   c. How many lollipops do they need to sell before they begin to make a profit? **40 lollipops**

2. **COMPUTER REPAIR** An in-home computer repair provider charges $40 per hour for installations and $60 per hour for troubleshooting and repair. Last week the busiest employee worked 40 hours and brought in $2100. How many hours did the employee spend doing each type of service? (Lesson 6-2) **15 hours installation, 25 hours troubleshooting and repair**

3. **TOURS** The Snider family and the Rollins family are traveling together on a trip to visit a candy factory. The number of people in each family and the total cost are shown in the table below. Find the adult admission price and the children's admission price. (Lesson 6-3) **adults $14; children $10**

Family	Number of Adults	Number of Children	Total Cost
Snider	2	3	$58
Rollins	2	1	$38

4. **GEOGRAPHY** In 2004, the state capital with the smallest population was Montpelier, Vermont. The state capital with the largest population was Phoenix, Arizona. The difference between the two populations was 1,410,006. The population of Phoenix was 3,881 more than 176 times as large as the population of Montpelier. Find the population of each city. (Lesson 6-4) **Montpelier, 8035; Phoenix, 1,418,041**

5. **CANOEING** A canoe travels 10 miles upstream in 2.5 hours. The return trip takes the canoe 2 hours. Find the rate of the boat in still water and the rate of the current. (Lesson 6-4) **canoe: 4.5 mph, current: 0.5 mph**

6. **FAIR** At a county fair, the cost for 4 slices of pizza and 2 orders of French fries is $21.00. The cost of 2 slices of pizza and 3 orders of French fries is $16.50. To find out how much a single slice of pizza and an order of French fries costs, determine the best method to solve the system of equations. Then solve the system. (Lesson 6-5) **$3.75; $3**

7. **OFFICE SUPPLIES** At a sale, Ricardo bought 24 reams of paper and 4 inkjet cartridges for $320. Britney bought 2 reams of paper and 1 inkjet cartridge for $50. The reams of paper were all the same price and the inkjet cartridges were all the same price. A system of equations can be used to represent this situation. Determine the best method to solve the system of equations. Then solve the system. (Lesson 6-5) **See Student Handbook Answer Appendix.**

8. **ELEVATIONS** The highest and lowest elevations for several states are shown in the table below. (Lesson 6-6)

State	Highest Elevation (ft)	Lowest Elevation (ft)
Alaska	20,320	0
California	14,494	−282
Colorado	14,433	3,315
Hawaii	13,796	0
Louisiana	535	−8
Wyoming	13,804	3,099

   a. Write a matrix to organize the given data. **See Student Handbook Answer Appendix.**
   b. What are the dimensions of the matrix? **6×2**
   c. Which state has the highest elevation? the lowest elevation? **Alaska; California**

9. **KENNEDY SPACE CENTER** Admission to the Kennedy Space Center for 2 adults and 3 children costs $160. Admission for 5 adults and 2 children is $246. (Lesson 6-7)
   a. Write a system of linear equations to model the situation. Let a represent adult admission, and let c represent child admission. **See Student Handbook Answer Appendix.**
   b. Write the augmented matrix. **See Student Handbook Answer Appendix.**
   c. What is the price for adult and child admissions? **adult admission $38; child admission $28**

Chapter 7 Polynomials (pp. 398–467)

1. **POOLS** Find the area of the swimming pool below. (Lesson 7-1) **$20x^2y$**

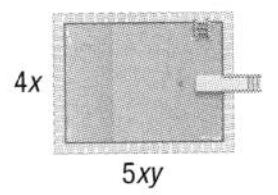

2. **GARDENING** Felipe is planting a flower garden that is shaped like a trapezoid. Use the formula $A = \frac{1}{2}h(b_1 + b_2)$ to find the area of Felipe's garden. (Lesson 7-1) **$15a^2$**

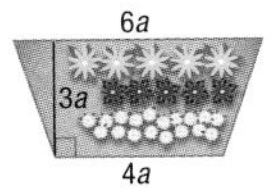

3. **GEOMETRY** The area of a rectangle is $36m^4n^6$ square meters. The length of the rectangle is $6m^3n^3$ meters. What is the width of the rectangle? (Lesson 7-2) **$6mn^3$ m**

4. **ASTRONOMY** The order of magnitude of the mass of Earth is about 10^{24}. The order of magnitude of the mass of the Moon is about 10^{22}. How many orders of magnitude as big is the Earth as the Moon? (Lesson 7-2) **2**

5. **MAMMALS** A blue whale has been caught that was 4.2×10^5 pounds. The smallest mammal is a bumblebee bat, which is about 0.0044 pound. (Lesson 7-3)
   a. Write the whale's weight in standard form. **420,000**
   b. Write the bat's weight in scientific notation. **4.4×10^{-3}**
   c. How many orders of magnitude as big is a blue whale as a bumblebee bat? **8**

6. **GARDENS** Megan had a square garden. She expanded this garden by 3 feet in one direction and 5 feet in the other. (Lesson 7-4)
   a. Write a polynomial to describe the area of the new garden if the old garden was x feet wide. **$(x + 5)(x + 3) = x^2 + 8x + 15$**
   b. If the original width was 12 feet, find the area of the new garden. **255 ft²**
   c. Find the area of the new garden if the original width was 16. **399 ft²**

7. **GEOMETRY** Write a polynomial that represents the area of the figure. (Lesson 7-5) **$xz + \frac{1}{2}yz$**

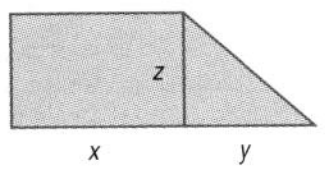

8. **GEOMETRY** Find the perimeter and area of the rectangle shown below. (Lesson 7-5) **$10x^2 + 12x + 2$; $20x^3 + 23x^2 - 2x - 6$**

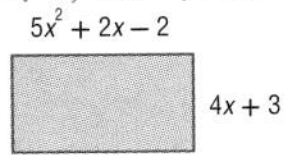

9. **SHOPPING** Nicole bought x shirts for $15.00 each, y pairs of pants for $25.72 each, and z belts for $12.53 each. Sales tax on these items was 7%. Write an expression to find the total cost of Nicole's purchases. (Lesson 7-6) **$16.05x + $27.52y + $13.41z**

10. **MANUFACTURING** A company is designing a box for dry pasta in the shape of a rectangular prism. The length is 2 inches more than twice the width, and the height is 3 inches more than the length. Write an expression for the volume of the box. (Lesson 7-7) **$4w^3 + 14w^2 + 10w$**

11. **GEOMETRY** Write an expression for the area of the trapezoid shown. (Lesson 7-11) **$\frac{5}{2}x^2 + \frac{17}{2}x + 3$**

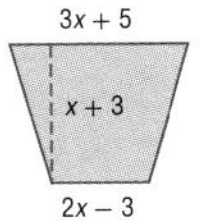

12. **CARPENTRY** Miguel's room is x feet on each side. He adds book shelves that are 2 feet deep to two adjacent walls. (Lesson 7-8)
   a. Show how the new area of the floor space can be modeled by the square of a binomial. **$(x - 2)^2$**
   b. Find the square of this binomial. **$x^2 - 4x + 4$**

13. **TOYS** A flying disk shaped like a circle has a radius of $x - 4$ centimeters. (Lesson 7-8)
   a. Write an expression representing the area of the flying disk. **$\pi(x - 4)^2$**
   b. If x is 15, what is the area of the flying disk? **380.1 cm²**

Chapter 8 Factoring and Quadratic Equations (pp. 468–521)

1. **CANDY** Sada was packing candy into gift bags. She has 42 chocolate truffles, 96 pieces of taffy, and 108 jelly beans. Sada wants to package the same number of candies in each bag, and each bag should have every type of candy. (Lesson 8-1)
   a. If she puts the greatest possible number of candies in each bag, how many bags can she make? **6 bags**
   b. How many pieces of each type of candy will be in each bag?
   7 chocolate truffles, 16 pieces of taffy, 18 jelly beans
2. **VOLUNTEERING** Catalina's class collected soap, washcloths, and toothbrushes to give to several homeless shelters in the area. The number of each item collected is shown in the table below. (Lesson 8-1)

Item	Number
soap	84
washcloth	24
toothbrush	72

   a. If she puts the greatest possible number of items in each box, how many boxes can she make? **12 boxes**
   b. How many of each item will be in each box? **7 soaps, 2 washcloths, 6 toothbrushes**
3. **SOCCER** Jorge is kicking a soccer ball straight up into the air. The height of the ball is described by the equation $h = -16r^2 + 20t$, where h is the height of the ball and t is the time in seconds. How long will it take the ball to hit the ground? (Leson 8-2) **1.25 seconds**
4. **PHOTOGRAPHY** Kelsey has a 4-inch by 6-inch photograph she wants to frame with a mat. The area of the picture and mat is twice as large as the area of the picture itself. If she wants the mat to be the same width on all sides, what are the outside dimensions of the mat? (Lesson 8-3) **6 in. by 8 in.**

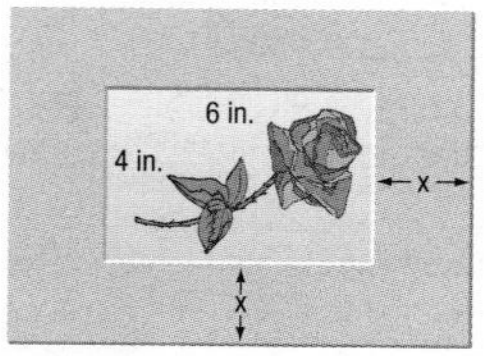

5. **BALLET** A ballet dancer is practicing a leap from the stage to an upper deck. If her initial velocity as she leaps is 18 feet per second, how long is she in the air before she lands on the upper deck, 5 feet above the lower deck? (Lesson 8-4) $\frac{5}{8}$ **second**

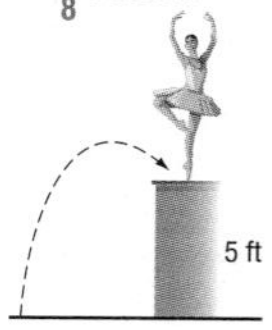

6. **GRAPHICS** A computer cartoonist uses the equations $y = x^2 - 4$ and $y = 4 - x^2$ as the basis for his drawing of a fish. The graphs of the two equations intersect at the roots of the equations. Find the roots. (Lesson 8-5) ± 2

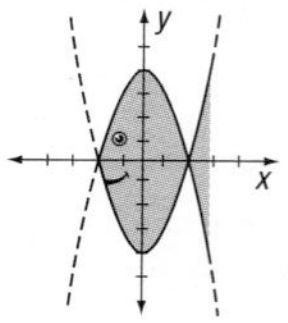

7. **STORAGE** Chase is building a box for the shelves in his father's garage. In order to fit the shelves as neatly as possible, the box needs to be 1 inch taller and 5 inches longer than it is wide. (Lesson 8-6)
   a. Let w represent the width of the box. Write an expression for each remaining dimensions in terms of w. $h = w + 1$, $\ell = w + 5$
   b. If the volume of the box is 2112 cubic feet, what are the dimensions of the box? **11 in. by 12 in. by 16 in.**

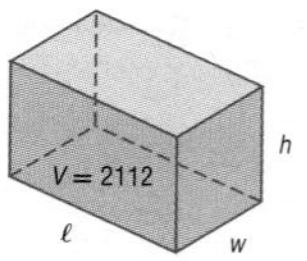

8. **RECREATION** Danille and Pete make a slingshot to shoot water balloons. If a water balloon shoots up with an initial velocity of 64 feet per second, how long is it until it hits the ground? (Lesson 8-6) **4 seconds**

Chapter 9 Quadratic and Exponential Functions (pp. 522–601)

1. **PHYSICAL SCIENCE** A model rocket is launched with a velocity of 64 feet per second. The equation $h = -16t^2 + 64t$ gives the height of the rocket t seconds after it is launched. (Lesson 9-1)
   a. Graph the function. **See Student Handbook Answer Appendix.**
   b. What is the maximum height that the rocket reaches? **64 ft**
   c. How many seconds is the rocket in the air? **4 seconds**
2. **FIREWORKS** Some fireworks are fired vertically into the air from the ground at an initial velocity of 80 feet per second. The equation $h(t) = -16t^2 + 80t$ models the height h, in feet, of the fireworks after t seconds. Find the highest point reached by the projectile just as it explodes. (Lesson 9-1) **100 ft**
3. **BASEBALL** The International Space Agency has landed a robotic explorer on a planet. The robot launches a baseball directly upward at 147 ft/s. The equation for the path of the baseball is $h = -49t^2 + 147t$, where h is the height of the baseball in feet and t is time in seconds. Assuming no wind, how long will it take for the ball to land on the surface? (Lesson 9-2) **3 seconds**
4. **DESIGN** For a design competition, Maggie dropped a device from the bleachers. The equation of the device's height in feet h after t second is $h = -16t^2 + 20$. Compare the graph of this function with its parent graph. (Lesson 9-3) **See Student Handbook Answer Appendix.**
5. **PHYSICS** An object is launched at 17.2 m/s from a 25-meter tall platform. The equation for the object's height h at time t seconds after launch is $h(t) = -4.9t^2 + 17.2t + 25$, where h is in meters. (Lesson 9-4)
   a. Graph this equation. **See Student Handbook Answer Appendix.**
   b. When does the object strike the ground? **4.62 seconds**
6. **GEOMETRY** The area of a square can be tripled by increasing its length by 6 centimeters and increasing its width by 3 centimeters.

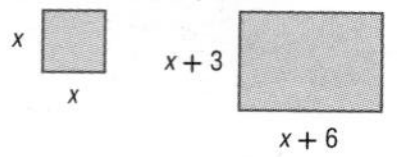

   What is the length of the side of the square? (Lesson 9-4) **6 cm**
7. **FENCE** Jackie and Ken are building a fence around a rectangular field. They want to enclose an area of 75 square feet. The width should be 3 feet longer than the length of the field. What are the dimensions of the field? Round to the nearest tenth, if necessary. (Lesson 9-5) **7.3 ft, 10.3 ft**
8. **VOLLEYBALL** A volleyball is thrown straight up. The equation that describes its motion is $h(t) = -16t^2 + 48t + 4$, where h represents the height in feet and t represents time in seconds. How long will it take for the ball to hit the ground? Round to the nearest hundredth, if necessary. (Lesson 9-5) **approximately 3.44 seconds**
9. **BIOLOGY** The function $f(t) = 50(1.07)^t$ models the growth of a fly population, where $f(t)$ is the number of flies and t is time in days. After three weeks, approximately how many flies are in this population? (Lesson 9-6) **207**
10. **INVESTMENT** Nicholas invested $2000 with a 5.75% interest rate compounded monthly. How much money will Nicholas have after 5 years? (Lesson 9-7) **$2664.35**
11. **RESTAURANTS** The total restaurant sales in the United States increased at an annual rate of about 5.2% between 1996 and 2004. In 1996, total sales were $310 billion. (Lesson 9-7)
    a. Write an equation for the average sales per year t years after 1996. $y = 310(1.052)^t$
    b. Predict the total restaurant sales in 2012. **about $698 billion**
12. **TENNIS** Each year a local country club sponsors a tennis tournament. Play starts with 256 participants. During each round, half of the players are eliminated. How many players remain after 6 rounds? (Lesson 9-8) **4**
13. **CAR CLUB** The table shows the number of car club members for four consecutive years after it began. (Lesson 9-9)

Time (years)	0	1	2	3	4
Members	10	20	40	80	160

    a. Determine which model best represents the data. **exponential**
    b. Write a function that models the data. $y = (10)2^x$
    c. Predict the number of car club members after 6 years. **640**

Chapter 10 Radical Functions and Geometry (pp. 602–665)

1. **PENDULUMS** The period of a pendulum is the time in seconds it takes to swing from one side to the other and back. If the length of the pendulum ℓ is given in meters, the period T is given by $T = 2\pi\sqrt{\frac{\ell}{g}}$, where g is the gravitational constant, 9.8 meters per second squared. The Foucault Pendulum at the Pantheon in Paris, France, has a length of 67 meters. Find the period of the Foucault Pendulum. (Lesson 10-1) **16.4 seconds**

2. **KINETIC ENERGY** The speed v of a ball in meters per second can be determined by the equation $v = \sqrt{\frac{2k}{m}}$, where k is the kinetic energy in Joules and m is the mass of the ball in kilograms. (Lesson 10-2)
   a. Simplify the formula if the mass of the ball is 2 kilograms. $v = \sqrt{k}$
   b. If the ball is traveling 10 meters per second, what is the kinetic energy of the ball in Joules? **100 joules**

3. **WALLPAPER** Ruby is designing a wallpaper border using a pattern of two triangles. If the measurements given are in inches, find the exact length of the segment shown. Then find the length to the nearest quarter inch. (Lesson 10-3) $9\sqrt{3} + 9\sqrt{2}$ **in.**; $28\frac{1}{4}$ **in.**

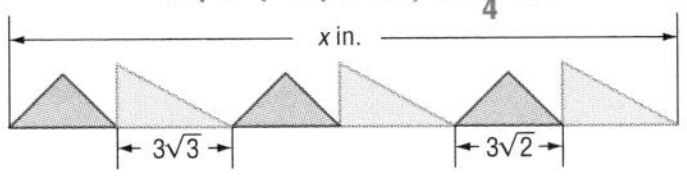

4. **SOUND** The speed of sound V in meters per second near Earth's surface is given by $V = 20\sqrt{t + 273}$, where t is the surface temperature in degrees Celsius. (Lesson 10-3)
   a. What is the speed of sound near Earth's surface at $-1°C$ and at $6°C$ in simplest form? $80\sqrt{17}$ **m/sec**; $60\sqrt{30}$ **m/sec**
   b. Approximately how much faster is the speed of sound at 6°C than at −1°C? **4.23 m/sec**

5. **SKYDIVING** The approximate time t in seconds that it takes an object to fall a distance of d feet is given by $t = \sqrt{\frac{d}{16}}$. Suppose a parachutist falls 13 seconds before the parachute opens. How far does the parachutist fall during this time period? (Lesson 10-4) **2704 ft**

6. **DELIVERY** Ben and Amado are delivering a freezer. The bank in front of the house is the same height as the back of the truck. They set up their ramp as shown. What is the length of the slanted part of the ramp to the nearest foot? (Lesson 10-5) **7 ft**

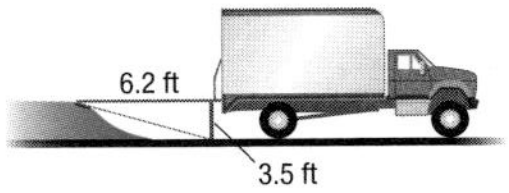

7. **LADDER** An 18-foot ladder is leaning against a building. For stability, the base of the ladder must be 3 feet away from the wall. How far up the wall does the ladder reach? (Lesson 10-5) **17.7 ft**

8. **SNOWMOBILES** Tai went snowmobiling with friends. His starting and ending points are shown on the graph. Use the Distance Formula to find how far he has to ride if he can ride straight home. (Lesson 10-6) $\sqrt{41}$ **or 6.4 mi**

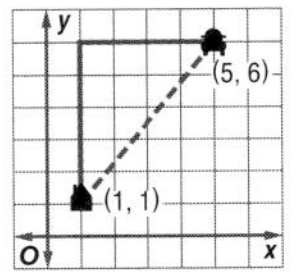

9. **FLAGS** Sarah needs to determine the height of the flag pole in her yard. On a sunny afternoon, Sarah's shadow is 2 feet 6 inches long. She is 5 feet 3 inches tall. The shadow of the flag pole is 6 feet long. How tall is the flag pole to the nearest tenth of a foot? (Lesson 10-7) **12.6 ft**

10. **SCHOOL** For a class project, Hailey needs to measure the height of her school. Hailey places a mirror 75 feet from the base of the school and backs 10 feet away from the mirror. If Hailey is 5 feet tall, how tall is the school? (Lesson 10-7) **37.5 ft**

11. **LIGHTHOUSE** How tall is the lighthouse? (Lesson 10-8) **128.6 ft**

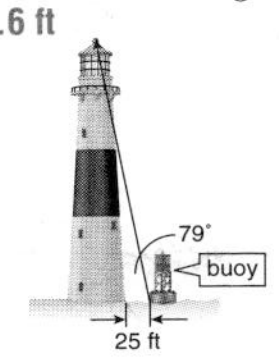

Chapter 11 Rational Functions and Equations (pp. 666–735)

1. **GEOMETRY** The length of a rectangle with a constant area is inversely proportional to its width. A rectangle has a length of 10 inches and a width of 6 inches. Another rectangle, has the same area as the first rectangle, but its width is 3 inches. Find the length of the second rectangle. (Lesson 11-1) **20 in.**

2. **PHYSICS** Given a constant force, the acceleration of an object varies inversely with its mass. A shot putter uses a constant force to put a mass of 8 pounds with an acceleration of 10 feet per second squared. If the shot putter uses the same force on a 16-pound mass, what would be the acceleration? (Lesson 11-1) **5 ft/s²**

3. **PHYSICS** A rectangle has an area of 36 square feet. The function $\ell = \frac{36}{w}$ shows the relationship between the length and width of the rectangle. Graph the function. (Lesson 11-2) **See Student Handbook Answer Appendix.**

4. **RUNNING** A runner runs 12 miles each morning. Her average speed y is given by $y = \frac{12}{x}$, where x is the time it takes her to run 12 miles. (Lesson 11-2)
   a. Graph the function. **See Student Handbook Answer Appendix.**
   b. Describe the asymptotes. $x = 0$ **and** $y = 0$

5. **PAINTING** The area of each wall in Isabel's room can be expressed as $2x^2 + 5x + 3$ square feet. A gallon of paint will cover an area that can be expressed as $x^2 - 3x - 4$ square feet. Write an expression that gives the number of gallons of paint that Isabel will need to buy to paint her room. (Lesson 11-3) $\frac{2x + 3}{x - 4}$

6. **TORTOISE** A giant tortoise can travel 0.17 mile per hour. What is this speed in feet per minute? (Lesson 11-4) **14.96 ft/min**

7. **EXCHANGE RATE** A pair of shoes bought in France cost 125 euros. The exchange rate at the time was 1 U. S. dollar = 0.68 euro. How much did the shoes cost in U. S. dollars? (Lesson 11-4) **$183.82**

8. **GAS** A motorcycle travels 225 kilometers with 5 liters of gas. How many liters of gas are needed to travel 135 kilometers? (Lesson 11-4) **3 L**

9. **HOUSING** The total cost per month for a dorm is $2250 split equally among 15 students. If 10 more students join the dorm and each pays the same rate as each of the original 15 students, what will be the monthly expenditure? (Lesson 11-4) **$3750**

10. **GEOMETRY** The area of a rectangle is $3x^2 - 6x - 24$ square units. What is the length? (Lesson 11-5) $3x + 6$

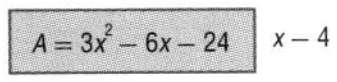

11. **GARDENING** Trey planted a triangular garden. Write an expression for the perimeter of the triangle. (Lesson 11-6) $\frac{11a + 7}{a + 1}$

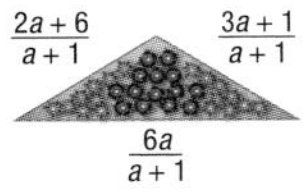

12. **TRACK** Trina walked 7 times around the track at a rate of t laps per hour. She ran around the track 10 times at a rate of $4t$ laps per hour. Write and simplify an expression for the total time it took her to go around the track 17 times. (Lesson 11-6) $\frac{7}{t} + \frac{10}{4t} = \frac{38}{4t}$ **or** $\frac{19}{2t}$

13. **PLAY** A total of 1374 people attended three plays. Let p be the number of people who attended the third play. There were twice as many people at the second play than the third and three times as many people at the first play than the third. Write an expression to represent the fraction of people who attended the first and second plays. (Lesson 11-6) $\frac{5p}{1374}$

14. **READING** Garcia reads $11\frac{1}{2}$ pages of a book in 8 minutes. What is his average reading rate in pages per minute? (Lesson 11-7) $1\frac{7}{16}$ **pg/min**

15. **RACING** A drag racer drove $\frac{1}{4}$ mile in about $11\frac{3}{4}$ seconds. What is the speed in miles per hour? (Lesson 11-7) $76\frac{28}{47}$ **mph**

16. **CAR REPAIR** Jack and Ivan are working on Ivan's car. Jack can complete the job in 6 hours, but Ivan will take 8 hours. They work together for two hours and Jack has to go. How long will it take Ivan to finish his car? (Lesson 11-8) $3\frac{1}{3}$ **hours**

Chapter 12 Probability and Statistics (pp. 736–801)

1. **CANDY** Alicia asked every fourth student that came in the classroom to choose their favorite from three types of candy. (Lesson 12-1)

   a. Identify the sample, and suggest a population from which it was selected. **See Student Handbook Answer Appendix.**

   b. Classify the type of data collection used. **survey**

   c. Identify the sample as *biased* or *unbiased*. Explain your reasoning. **See Student Handbook Answer Appendix.**

   d. Classify the sample as *simple*, *stratified*, or *systematic*. Explain your reasoning. **See Student Handbook Answer Appendix.**

2. **HOUSING** A listing was made of the rents paid for apartments in a particular neighborhood: {\$450, \$590, \$650, \$520, \$480, \$800, \$720, \$1600, \$600}. Which measure of central tendency best represents the data? Justify your selection, and then find the measure. (Lesson 12-2) **See Student Handbook Answer Appendix.**

3. **CLUBS** Given the following portion of a survey report, evaluate the validity of the information and conclusion. (Lesson 12-2)

   Question: Should the media club meet before or after school?

   Sample: Students were randomly given an invitation to vote while waiting in the school commons for school to start.

   Results: 68% before school, 24% after school, 8% no preference

   Conclusion: The media club should meet before school.

   See Student Handbook Answer Appendix.

4. **GRADES** Lynette took 5 tests in life science this grading period. Find the mean, variance, and standard deviation of the grades she earned: {76, 88, 82, 91, 78}. (Lesson 12-3) **82, 32.8, 5.7**

5. **FOOTBALL** The following table shows information about the number of carries a running back had over a number of years. Find the mean absolute deviation of the number of carries. (Lesson 12-3) **26.4**

Year	Number of Carries	Yards per Carry	Yards	Touchdowns
2002	40	3.7	148	0
2003	90	4.2	378	2
2004	105	4	420	3
2005	115	3.3	379.5	7
2006	140	4.3	602	9

6. **BAND** In a high school band, six girls and four boys play trumpets. Before auditions at the beginning of the year, the new band director randomly assigns chairs to the students. (Lesson 12-4)

   a. How many ways can the band director assign first chair, second chair, and third chair? **720 ways**

   b. What is the probability that the first three chairs will be assigned to boys? $\frac{1}{30}$ **or 3.3%**

7. **CARDS** If you have drawn and kept the 8 of spades and the 7 of hearts from a standard deck of cards, what is the chance you will draw another 7 or a spade next? (Lesson 12-5) $\frac{7}{25}$

8. **COOKING** Nate has a shelf with 3 cans of green beans, 2 cans of corn, and 5 cans of peas and a shelf of 1 package each of egg noodles, rice and ziti. In the freezer, he has 2 pounds of chicken and 3 pounds of beef. If he randomly grabs one item from each area to put in a casserole, what is the probability that he makes a chicken-corn-ziti casserole? (Lesson 12-5) $\frac{2}{75}$ **or 2.7%**

9. **COATS** The table shows the probability distribution of the number of each type of coat that was sold in a particular week at a sports store. (Lesson 12-6)

Types of Coats Sold

X = Number of Zippered Pockets	Probability
0	0.03
1	0.08
2	0.08
3	0.10
4	0.30
5	0.41

   a. Show that the distribution is valid. **See Student Handbook Answer Appendix.**

   b. What is the probability that a randomly chosen coat has fewer than 4 pockets? **0.29**

   c. Make probability graph of the data. **See Student Handbook Answer Appendix.**

10. **BASKETBALL** Liam plays basketball. Last year, he made 80% of his attempted free throws. What objects can be used to model the possible outcomes of his next free throw? Explain. (Lesson 12-7) **See Student Handbook Answer Appendix.**

❶ Converting Units of Measure

ILS 7.C.4c Convert within and between measurement systems and monetary systems using technology where appropriate.

There are three types of measurement: length, capacity, and mass. There are two measuring systems that we use: customary and metric.

The general rule when converting between units of measurement is:

- to convert from larger units to smaller units, multiply;
- to convert from smaller units to larger units, divide.

The diagram below shows the relationship between metric units of length

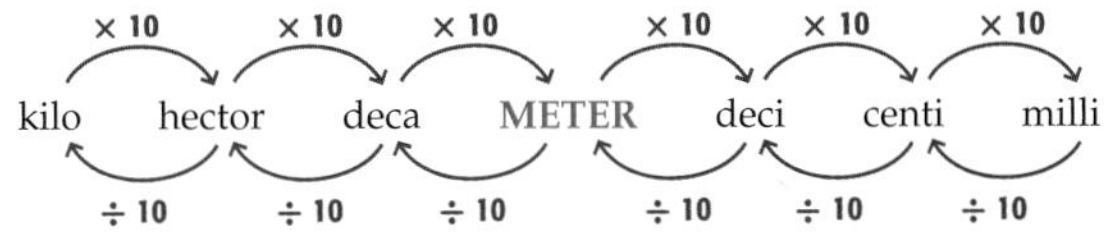

Units of Length	
Customary	**Metric**
1 foot (ft) = 12 inches (in.) 1 yard (yd) = 3 feet 1 mile(mi) = 1760 yards or 5280 feet	1 kilometer (km) = 1000 meters (m) 1 meter (m) = 100 centimeters (cm) 1 centimeter (cm) = 10 millimeters (mm)

Comparing Metric and Customary Units of Length	
Conversion Factors	**Examples**
1 millimeter (mm) ≈ 0.04 inch (in.)	height of a comma
1 centimeter (cm) ≈ 0.4 inch (in.)	half the width of a penny
1 meter (m) ≈ 1.1 yards or 3.3 feet (ft)	width of a doorway
1 kilometer (km) ≈ 0.6 mile (mi)	length of a city block

EXAMPLE 1 Units of Length

Complete each sentence.

1A. 5 m = _?_ cm

5(100) = 500 — **To convert from meters to centimeters, multiply by 100.**

5 m = 500 cm

1B. 63 m = _?_ km

63 ÷ 1000 = 0.063 — **To convert from meters to kilometers, divide by 1000.**

63 m = 0.063 km

Units of Capacity	
Customary	**Metric**
1 cup (c) = 8 fluid ounces (fl oz) 1 pint (pt) = 2 cups (c) 1 quart (qt) = 2 pints (pt) 1 gallon (gal) = 4 quarts	1 liter (L) = 1000 milliliters (mL)

Comparing Metric and Customary Units of Capacity	
Conversion Factors	**Examples**
1 milliliter (mL) ≈ 0.03 fluid ounce (fl oz)	drop of water
1 liter (L) ≈ 1 quart (qt)	bottle of ketchup

1 Lesson CSB Notes

1 FOCUS

Vertical Alignment

Lesson CSB-1
Convert units of measurement between and within customary and metric systems.

After Lesson CSB-1
Convert compound units between and within customary and metric systems.

2 TEACH

Example 1 shows how to convert length units. **Example 2** shows how to convert units of capacity. **Example 3** shows how to convert units of mass.

Additional Example

Complete each sentence.

1A. 10 yd = _?_ ft 30

1B. 13.2 ft ≈ _?_ m 4

Additional Examples

Complete each sentence.

2A. 6.5 L = ? mL 6500

2B. 12 pt = ? qt 6

2C. 5 mL ≈ ? fl oz 0.15

Complete each sentence.

3A. 7.48 lb ≈ ? kg 3.4

3B. 4.5 g = ? mg 4500

3C. 36 oz = ? lb 2.25

Tips for New Teachers

It may help some students if they construct arrow diagrams, similar to the ones provided for metric units, for customary units.

3 ASSESS

Formative Assessment

Use Exercises 1–15 to assess whether students understand how to use the given conversion factors to convert one unit to another.

Name the Math Ask students to describe the operations required to change a smaller unit to a larger one and vice-versa.

EXAMPLE 2 Units of Capacity

Complete each sentence.

2A. 8 gal = ? quarts

8(4) = 32 **Larger → smaller, multiply.**

8 gal = 32 qt

2B. 24 fl oz = ? c

24 ÷ 8 = 3 **Smaller → larger, divide.**

24 fl oz = 3 c

2C. 16 pt = ? gal

16 ÷ 2 = 8 qt **Convert from pt to qt.**

8 ÷ 4 = 2 gal **Convert from qt to gal**

16 pt = 2 gal

Customary Units of Weight	Metric Units of Weight
1 pound (lb) = 16 ounces (oz) 1 ton (T) = 2000 pounds (lb)	1 kilogram (kg) = 1000 grams (g) 1 gram (g) = 1000 milligrams (mg)

Comparing Metric and Customary Units of Mass	
Conversion Factors	**Examples**
1 gram (g) = 0.04 ounce (oz)	one raisin
1 kilogram (kg) = 2.2 pounds (lb)	a pineapple

EXAMPLE 3 Units of Mass

Complete each sentence.

3A. 6.8 kg = ? lb

6.8(2.2) = 14.96 **Larger → smaller, multiply.**

6.8 kg = 14.96 lb

3B. 1.6 oz = ? g

1.6 ÷ 0.04 = 40 **Smaller → larger, divide.**

1.6 oz = 40 g

3C. 1T = ? kg

1(2000) = 2000 lb **Convert from T to lb.**

2000 ÷ 2.2 ≈ 909.1 kg **Convert from lb to kg.**

1T ≈ 909 kg

Exercises

Complete each sentence.

1. 5 km = ? m **5000**
2. 3.5 cm = ? mm **35**
3. 6L = ? mL **6000**
4. 37 c = ? pt **18.5**
5. 0.2 mi = ? ft **1056**
6. 400 yd = ? ft **1200**
7. 18 cm = ? in. **7.2**
8. 0.75 L = ? qt **0.75**
9. 93.5 lb = ? kg **42.5**
10. 210 mm = ? cm **21**
11. 65 g = ? kg **0.065**
12. 20 mL = ? L **0.02**
13. 52.9 kg = ? lb **116.38**
14. 800 fl oz = ? mL **26,666.67**
15. 9.05 yd = ? m **8.23**

Concepts and Skills Bank

② Factors and Multiples

Two or more numbers that are multiplied to form a **product** are called **factors**.

For example, because 6(7) = 42, 6 and 7 are factors of 42.

Factor Rules		
This number is a factor of...	**Example**	**Reason**
2 if the ones digit is divisible by 2.	164	4 is divisible by 2.
3 if the sum of the digits is divisible by 3.	123	$1 + 2 + 3 = 6$, and 6 is divisible by 3.
5 if the ones digit is 0 or 5.	120	The ones digit is a 0.
6 if the number is divisible by 2 and 3.	48	48 is divisible by 2 and 3.
9 if the sum of the digits is divisible by 9.	189	$1 + 8 + 9 = 18$, and 18 is divisible by 9.
10 if the ones digit is 0.	1250	The ones digit is 0.

EXAMPLE 1

Determine whether 138 has a factor of 2, 3, 5, 6, 9, or 10.

Number	Factor?	Reason
2	yes	8 is divisible by 2.
3	yes	$1 + 3 + 8 = 12$, and 12 is divisible by 3.
5	no	The ones digit is not 0 or 5.
6	yes	138 has a factor of 2 and 3.
9	no	$1 + 3 + 8 = 12$, and 12 is not divisible by 9.
10	no	The ones digit is not 0.

So, 138 has factors of 2, 3, and 6.

You can also use the factor rules to find all of the factors of a number. Use division to find the other factor in each factor pair.

EXAMPLE 2

List all of the factors of 72.

Number	Factor?	Factor Pairs
1	yes	$1 \cdot 72$
2	yes	$2 \cdot 36$
3	yes	$3 \cdot 24$
4	yes	$4 \cdot 18$
5	no	...
6	yes	$6 \cdot 12$
7	no	...
8	yes	$8 \cdot 9$
9	yes	$9 \cdot 8$

You can stop finding factors when the numbers start repeating.

So, the factors of 72 are 1, 2, 3, 4, 6, 8, 9, 12, 18, 24, 36, and 72.

A multiple is the product of a specific number and any whole number. So, 64 is a multiple of 4 because 4(16) = 64.

Concepts and Skills Bank

2 Lesson CSB Notes

1 FOCUS

Vertical Alignment

Lesson CSB-2
Determine factors and multiples of numbers.

After Lesson CSB-2
Determine whether a number is prime or composite.
Find the prime factorization of a number.

2 TEACH

Example 1 shows how to determine whether a given number is a factor of another. **Example 2** shows how to find all the factors of a given number. **Example 3** shows how to determine whether a given number is a multiple of another.

Additional Examples

1. Determine whether 80 has a factor of 2, 3, 5, 6, 9, or 10. Yes: 2, 5, 10 No: 3, 6, 9
2. List all the factors of 56. 1, 2, 4, 7, 8, 14, 28, 56

Concepts and Skills Bank

Additional Example

3 Determine if 216 is a multiple of 8. yes

Tips for New Teachers

Point out to students that if one number is a factor of a second number, then the second number is a multiple of the first.

3 ASSESS

Formative Assessment

Use Exercises 1–5 to assess whether students understand how to find factors and multiples of given numbers.

Crystal Ball Ask students how they think today's study of factors will help them with prime factorization in Lesson 3.

Additional Answers

19. 1, 2, 4, 7, 14, 28

20. 1, 3, 5, 15, 25, 75

21. 1, 2, 7, 14

22. 1, 3, 19, 57

23. 1, 3, 9, 27, 81

24. 1, 2, 4, 13, 26, 52

25. 1, 2, 3, 6, 7, 14, 21, 42

26. 1, 3, 7, 9, 21, 63

27. 1, 2, 3, 4, 5, 6, 10, 12, 15, 20, 30, 60

28. 1, 2, 3, 5, 6, 9, 10, 15, 18, 30, 45, 90

29. 1, 2, 3, 6, 19, 38, 57, 114

30. 1, 2, 4, 31, 62, 124

31. 1, 2, 3, 6, 17, 34, 51, 102

32. 1, 3, 5, 9, 15, 27, 45, 135

33. 1, 5, 73, 365

34. 1, 3, 5, 9, 15, 25, 45, 75, 225

Concepts and Skills Bank

EXAMPLE 3

Determine whether 375 is a multiple of 15.

We can use the factor rules to help determine multiples. Since 15 = 3(5), check 3 and 5.

Number	Factor of 375?	Factor Pairs	Is 375 a Multiple?
3	yes	3 • 125	Yes, 375 is a multiple of 3.
5	yes	5 • 75	Yes, 375 is a multiple of 5.
15	yes	15 • 25	Yes, 375 is a multiple of 15.

Since 375 ÷ 15 = 25 with no remainder, 375 is a multiple of 15.

Exercises

Determine whether each number has a factor of 2, 3, 5, 6, 9, or 10.

1. 39 3
2. 46 2,
3. 35 5
4. 18 2, 3, 6, 9
5. 44 2
6. 23 none
7. 22 2
8. 66 2, 3, 6
9. 212 2
10. 250 2, 5, 10
11. 118 2
12. 378 2, 3, 6, 9
13. 995 5
14. 510 2, 3, 5, 6, 10
15. 5010 2, 3, 5, 6, 10
16. 1052 2
17. 32,460 2, 3, 5, 6, 10
18. 3039 3

List all of the factors of each number. 19–34. See margin.

19. 28
20. 75
21. 14
22. 57
23. 81
24. 52
25. 42
26. 63
27. 60
28. 90
29. 114
30. 124
31. 102
32. 135
33. 365
34. 225

Determine whether the first number is a multiple of the second.

35. 49, 3 no
36. 64, 9 no
37. 63, 3 yes
38. 60, 6 yes
39. 135, 5 yes
40. 102, 4 no
41. 121, 11 yes
42. 905, 12 no
43. 364, 9 no
44. 536, 3 no
45. 657, 7 no
46. 234, 6 yes
47. 282, 31 no
48. 3612, 12 yes
49. 3585, 65 no

50. MUSIC Seventy-two members of the marching band will march in the Homecoming Parade. They will need to march in rows with the same number of students in each row.

a. Can the band be arranged in rows of 7? Explain. No; 7 is not a factor of 72.

b. How many different ways could the marching band members be arranged? Describe the arrangements. See margin.

51. CALENDARS Years that are multiples of 4, called *leap years*, are 366 days long. Use the rule given below to determine whether 2010, 2015, 2016, 2022, and 2032 are leap years. See margin.

If the last two digits form a number divisible by 4, then the number is divisible by 4.

50b. 12 ways; 1 row of 72, 2 rows of 36, 3 rows of 24, 4 rows of 18, 6 rows of 12, 8 rows of 9, 9 rows of 8, 12 rows of 6, 18 rows of 4, 24 rows of 3, 36 rows of 2, 72 rows of 1

51. 2010 no, 2015 no, 2016 yes, 2022 no, 2032 yes

③ Prime Factorization

A **prime number** is a whole number greater than 1, for which the only factors are 1 and itself. A whole number greater than 1 that has more than two factors is a **composite number**. The numbers 0 and 1 are *neither* prime *nor* composite. Notice that 0 has an endless number of factors and 1 has only one factor, itself.

EXAMPLE 1 Identify Numbers as Prime or Composite

Determine whether each number is *prime* or *composite*.

a. 27

The numbers 1, 3, and 9 divide into 27 evenly. So, 27 is a composite number.

b. 41

The only numbers that divide evenly into 41 are 1 and 41. So, 41 is a prime number.

A whole number expressed as the product of prime factors is called the **prime factorization**. The prime factors can be written in any order usually from the least prime factor to the greatest prime factor. Disregarding order, there is only one way to write the prime factorization of a whole number.

EXAMPLE 2 Prime Factorization of a Whole Number

Write the prime factorization of 120.

Method 1 Find the least prime factors.

$120 = 2 \cdot 60$	The least prime factor of 120 is 2.
$= 2 \cdot 2 \cdot 30$	The least prime factor of 60 is 2.
$= 2 \cdot 2 \cdot 2 \cdot 15$	The least prime factor of 30 is 2.
$= 2 \cdot 2 \cdot 2 \cdot 3 \cdot 5$	The least prime factor of 15 is 3.

Method 2 Use a factor tree.

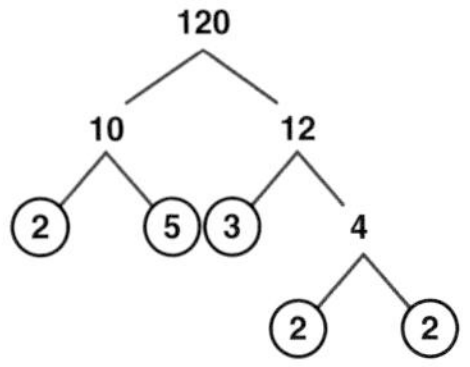

Choose any two factors of 120 to begin.
Keep finding factors until each branch ends in a prime factor.

The prime factorization is complete because 2, 3, and 5 are prime numbers. Thus, the prime factorization of 120 is $2 \cdot 2 \cdot 2 \cdot 3 \cdot 5$ or $2^3 \cdot 3 \cdot 5$.

Exercises

Determine whether each number is *prime* or *composite*.

1. 48 composite
2. 29 prime
3. 63 composite
4. 75 composite
5. 71 prime
6. 43 prime

Write the prime factorization of each number. Use exponents for repeated factors.

7. 20 $2^2 \cdot 5$
8. 28 $2^2 \cdot 7$
9. 64 2^6
10. 120 $2^3 \cdot 3 \cdot 5$
11. 140 $2^2 \cdot 5 \cdot 7$
12. 85 $5 \cdot 17$
13. 144 $2^4 \cdot 3^2$
14. 221 $13 \cdot 17$
15. 84 $2^2 \cdot 3 \cdot 7$
16. 275 $5^2 \cdot 11$
17. 210 $2 \cdot 3 \cdot 5 \cdot 7$
18. 441 $3^2 \cdot 7^2$
19. 351 $3^3 \cdot 13$
20. 900 $2^2 \cdot 3^2 \cdot 5^2$
21. 1350 $2 \cdot 3^3 \cdot 5^2$

3 Lesson CSB Notes

1 FOCUS

Vertical Alignment

Lesson CSB-3
Determine the prime factorization of a number.

After Lesson CSB-3
Determine the prime factorization of an algebraic expression.

2 TEACH

Example 1 shows how to determine whether a number is prime or composite. **Example 2** shows how to find the prime factorization of a number.

Additional Examples

1 Determine whether each number is prime or composite.

a. 37 prime

b. 51 composite

2 Write the prime factorization of 90. $2 \cdot 3 \cdot 3 \cdot 5$ or $2 \cdot 3^2 \cdot 5$

Tips for New Teachers

Remind students that 1 is not included in a prime factorization because 1 is not a prime number.

3 ASSESS

Formative Assessment

Use Exercises 1–21 to assess whether students understand how to find the prime factorization of a number.

Name the Math Ask students to explain the difference between a prime number and a composite number.

4 Lesson CSB Notes

1 FOCUS

Vertical Alignment

Lesson CSB-4
Use a protractor to measure the size of an angle.
Use a protractor to draw an angle with a given size.
Classify angles by their sizes.

After Lesson CSB-4
Draw triangles and measure their angles.
Classify triangles.

2 TEACH

Example 1 shows how to use a protractor to measure an angle. **Example 2** shows how to use a protractor to draw an angle with a given measure.

Additional Examples

1 Use a protractor to measure ∠*DEF*.

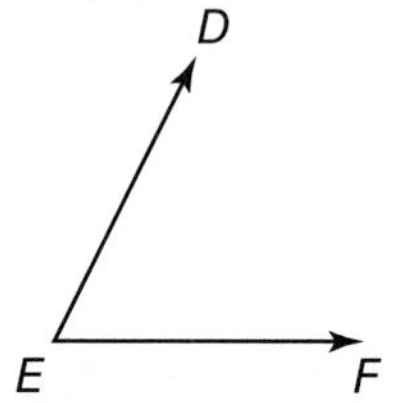

63°

2 Draw ∠*P* with a measure of 140°.

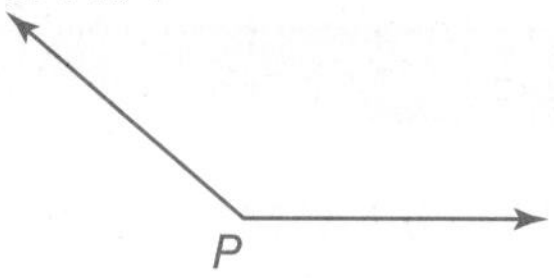

4 Measuring Angles

The most common measure of angles is the **degree** (°). You can use a **protractor** to measure angles in degrees.

EXAMPLE 1

Use a protractor to measure ∠*ABC*.

Step 1 Place the center point of the protractor's base on vertex *B*. Align the straight side with the side $\overline{AB}$ so that the marker for 0° is on the side.

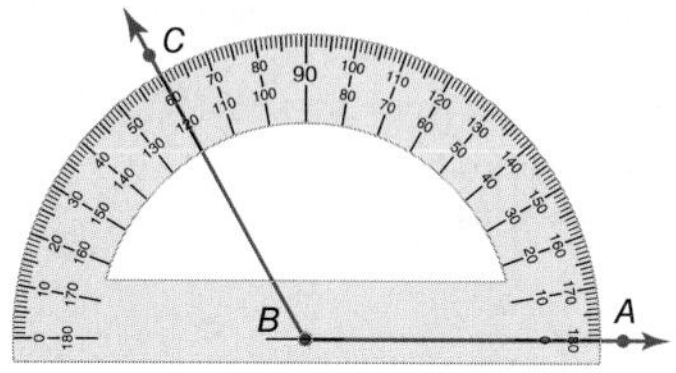

Step 2 Use the scale that begins with 0° at $\overline{AB}$. Read where the other side of the angle, $\overline{BC}$, crosses this scale.

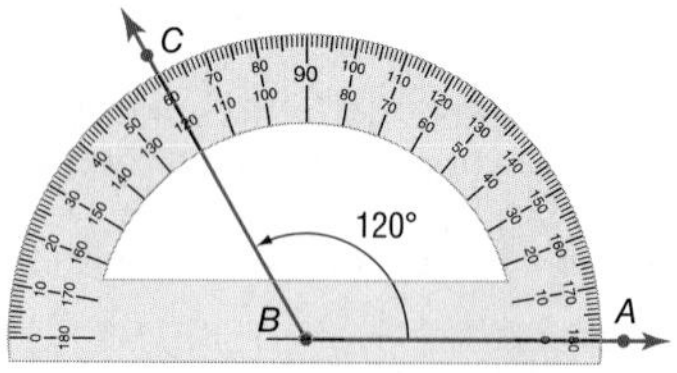

The measure of ∠*ABC* is 120°. Use the symbols *m*∠*ABC* = 120°.

If the sides of the angle are too small to reach the scale on the protractor, you can extend the sides until they are long enough.

Notice that there are measurements going in two directions on the protractor. One is on the outside of the other. You may use either scale for measuring, but you must use the one where one of your sides lines up with 0° to get the correct measurement.

Acute angles have measures less than 90°.
Right angles have measures equal to 90°.
Obtuse angles have measures between 90° and 180°.
Straight angles have measures equal to 180°.

So we can classify ∠*ABC* as an obtuse angle.

A protractor can also be used to draw an angle of a certain measure.

EXAMPLE 2

Draw ∠*D* with a measure of 85°.

Step 1 Draw a ray with an endpoint *D*. Make sure that the ray is long enough so that it crosses the edge of the protractor.

Step 2 Place the center point of the protractor on *D*. Align the mark labeled 0 with the ray you drew.

Step 3 Use the scale that begins with 0. Locate the mark labeled 85. Then draw the other side of the angle.

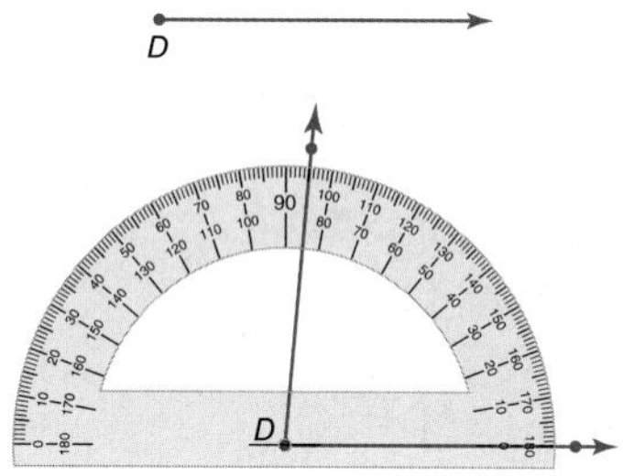

We can classify this angle as an acute angle.

Additional Answers

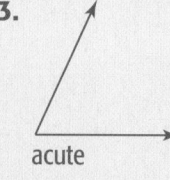

21.

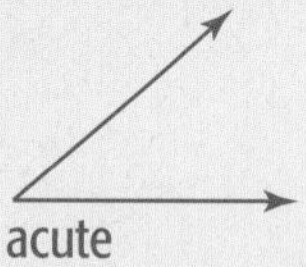

acute

22.

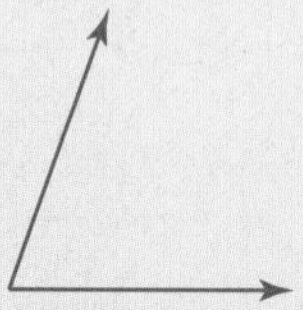

acute

23.

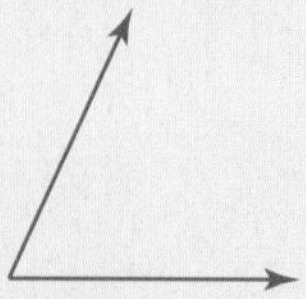

acute

24.

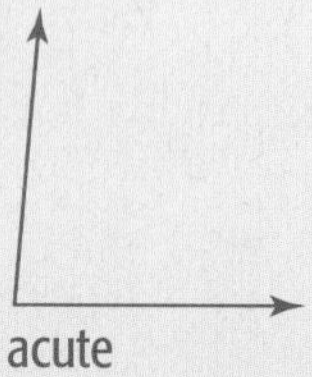

acute

Exercises

Use the protractor to find the measure of each angle. Then classify each angle as *acute, right, obtuse,* or *straight*.

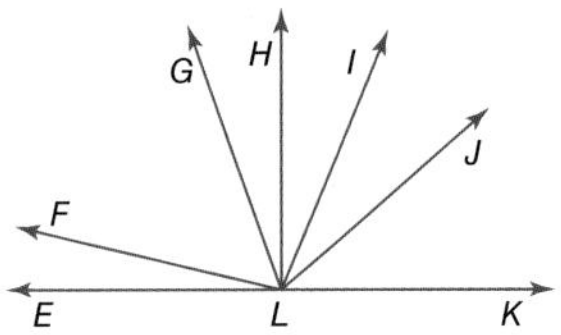

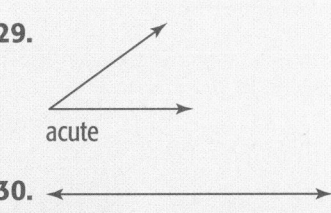

1. ∠*JLK* 40°; acute
2. ∠*ELF* 13°; acute
3. ∠*ELK* 180°; straight
4. ∠*GLJ* 70°; acute
5. ∠*FLI* 100°; obtuse
6. ∠*JLF* 128°; obtuse
7. ∠*GLF* 57°; acute
8. ∠*ILG* 45°; acute
9. ∠*ILK* 67°; acute
10. ∠*GLK* 110°; obtuse

11. Does ∠*FLI* have the same measure as ∠*ELH*? Explain. No; $m\angle FLI = 100°$ and $m\angle ELH = 90°$.
12. Which angle, if any, has the same measure as ∠*ELH*? Explain. $m\angle KLH$ is also 90°.

Use a protractor to measure each angle. Then classify each angle as *acute, right, obtuse,* or *straight*.

13. 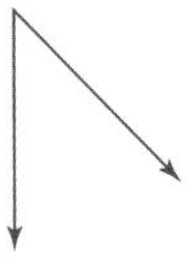
45°; acute

14. 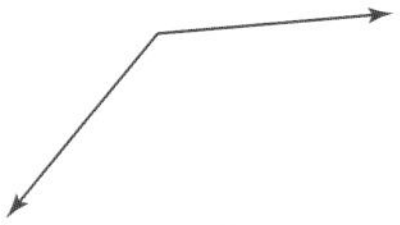
135°; obtuse

15. 
15°; acute

16. 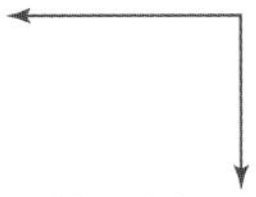
90°; right

17. 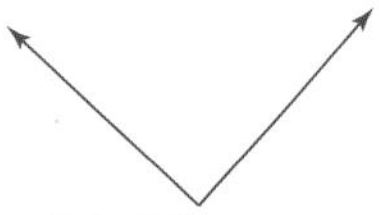
90°; right

18. 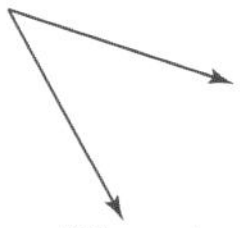
43°; acute

19. 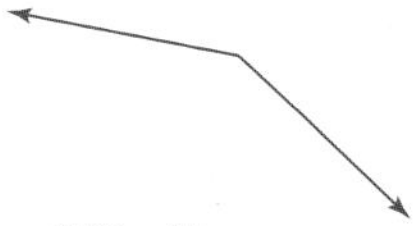
152°; obtuse

20. 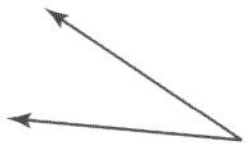
31°; acute

21–32. See margin.

Use a protractor to draw an angle with each measurement. Then classify each angle.

21. 40°	**22.** 70°	**23.** 65°
24. 85°	**25.** 95°	**26.** 110°
27. 155°	**28.** 140°	**29.** 35°
30. 180°	**31.** 20°	**32.** 165°

Tips for New Teachers

Using Protractors Protractors frequently have two scales, one for angles opening to the left and one for angles opening to the right. Remind students to make sure and identify any acute angle as being between 0° and 90°, and any obtuse angle as being between 90° and 180°.

3 ASSESS

Formative Assessment

Use Exercises 1–32 to assess whether students understand how to measure, draw, and classify angles.

Ticket Out the Door Have students draw and label an acute angle, an obtuse angle, and a right angle on a piece of paper.

Additional Answers

25. 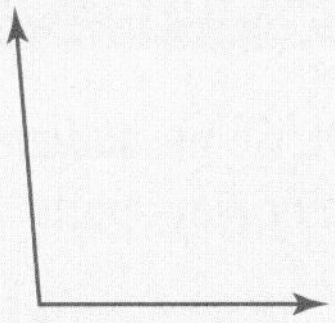
obtuse

26. 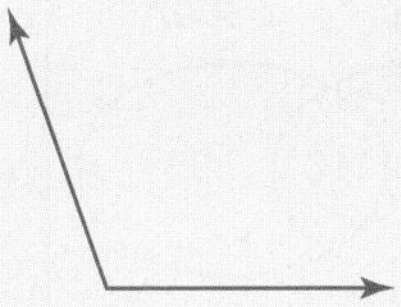
obtuse

27. 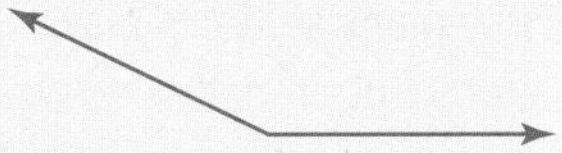
obtuse

28. 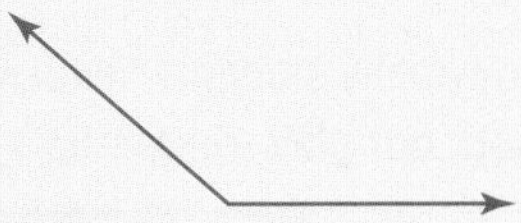
obtuse

29. 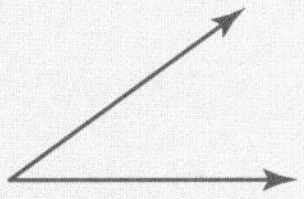
acute

30.
straight

31. 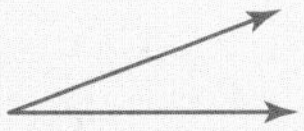
acute

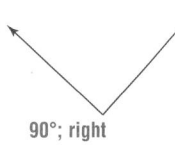

32. 
obtuse

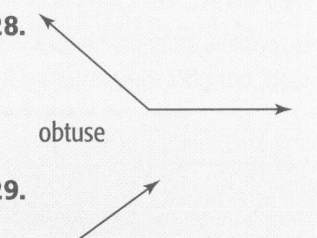

5 Lesson CSB Notes

1 FOCUS

Vertical Alignment

Lesson CSB-5
Use Venn diagrams to identify common factors.

After Lesson CSB-5
Draw Venn diagrams to show relationships among sets of numbers.

2 TEACH

Example 1 shows how to interpret a two-circle Venn diagram. **Example 2** shows how to interpret a three-circle Venn diagram.

Additional Example

1 **AFTER SCHOOL** Some students work part-time or play sports after school.

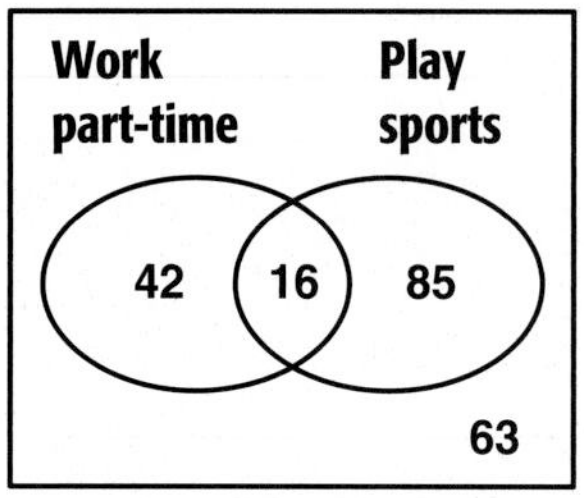

a. How many students play sports but do not work? 85

b. How many students work and play sports? 16

c. How many students neither work nor play sports? 63

5 Venn Diagrams

A Venn diagram shows the relationships among sets of numbers or objects by using overlapping circles in a rectangle.

The Venn diagram at the right shows the factors of 12 and 20. The common factors are in both circles.

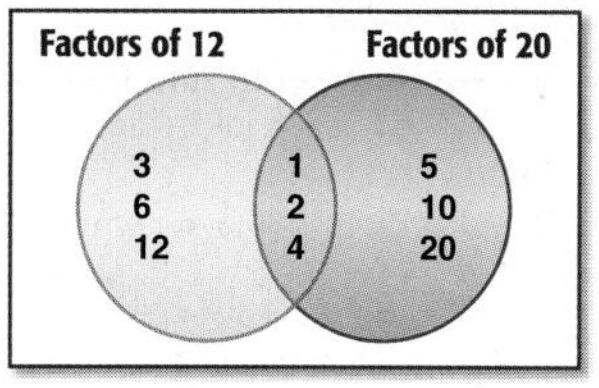

EXAMPLE 1

COLLEGE Members of a senior class were polled and asked what type of federal financial aid they are receiving for college.

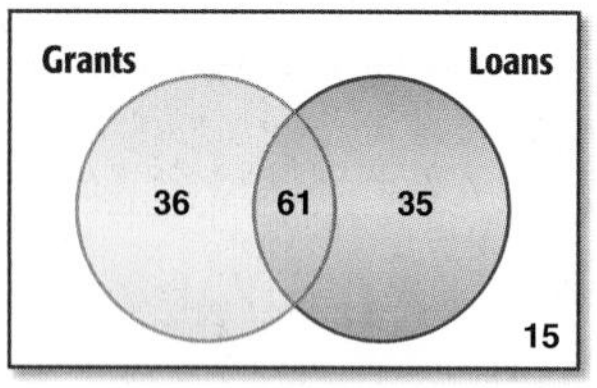

a. How many students are only receiving grants?

The number only in the grant circle is 36. So, 36 seniors are receiving only grants.

b. How many students are receiving both loans and grants?

The value in both circles is 61. So, 61 seniors are receiving both loans and grants.

c. How many students are not receiving any grants or loans?

The value outside of the circles is 15. So, 15 seniors are not receiving any grants or loans.

EXAMPLE 2

Refer to the Venn diagram at the right.

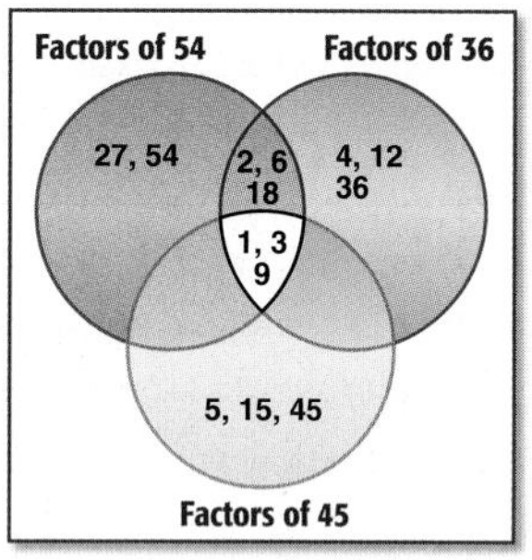

a. What are the factors in all three circles?

The factors in all three circles are 1, 3, and 9.

b. What is the greatest common factor of all three numbers?

The greatest common factor of all three numbers is 9.

c. What factors are shared only by 54 and 36?

The factors 2, 6, 18 are shared only by 54 and 36.

d. What is the greatest common factor of 54 and 36?

The greatest common factor between 54 and 36 is 18.

e. What factors are shared only by 54 and 45?

There are no factors shared by only 54 and 45. The factors that they have in common are shared by all three numbers.

f. What is the greatest common factor of 54 and 45?

The greatest common factor between 54 and 45 is 9.

Concepts and Skills Bank

864 Concepts and Skills Bank

Exercises

Refer to the Venn diagram at the right.

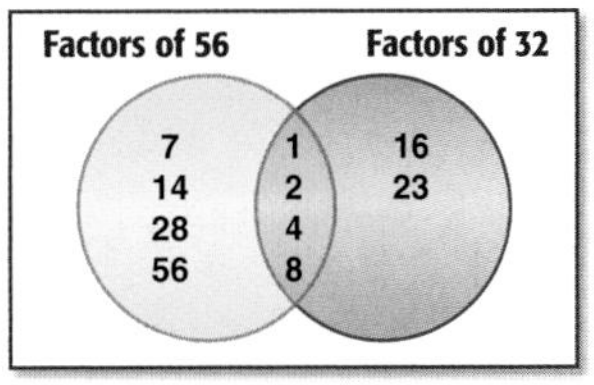

1. Which factors are in both circles? 1, 2, 4 and 8
2. What is the greatest common factor of 56 and 32? The greatest common factor is 8.

Refer to the Venn diagram at the right.

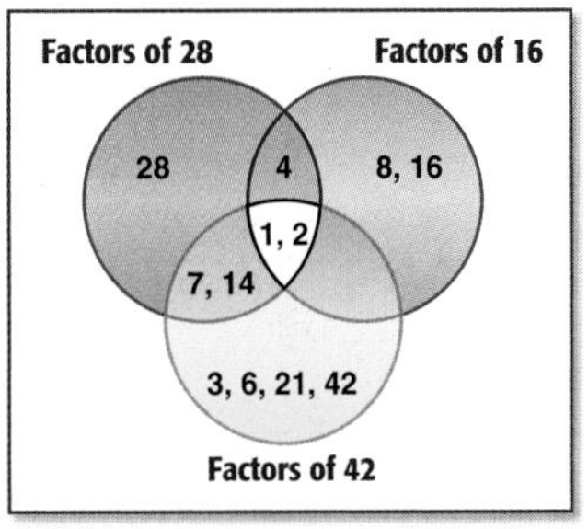

3. What are the factors in all three circles? 1 and 2
4. What is the greatest common factor of all three numbers? 2
5. What factors are shared only by 28 and 42? 7 and 14
6. What is the greatest common factor of 28 and 42? 14
7. What factors are shared only by 16 and 42? none
8. What is the greatest common factor of 16 and 42? 2

TRANSPORTATION Twenty people who have traveled across the country in the last year were asked if they used land or air transportation. The results are shown in the Venn diagram.

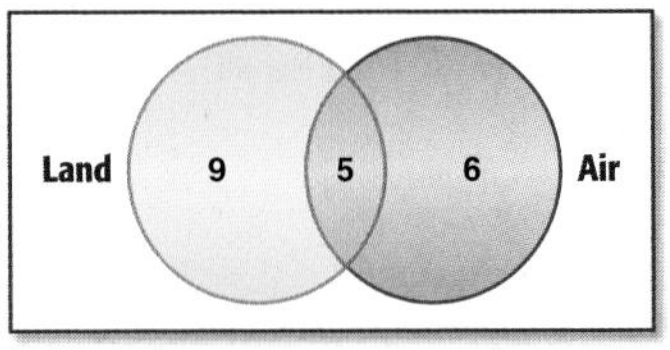

9. How many people traveled across the country by land? 14
10. Explain what the 5 in the diagram represents. the number of people who traveled cross country by both land and air in the last year

SPORTS Ten students were asked which sports they played in the past month. Use the Venn diagram shown at the right to answer the following questions.

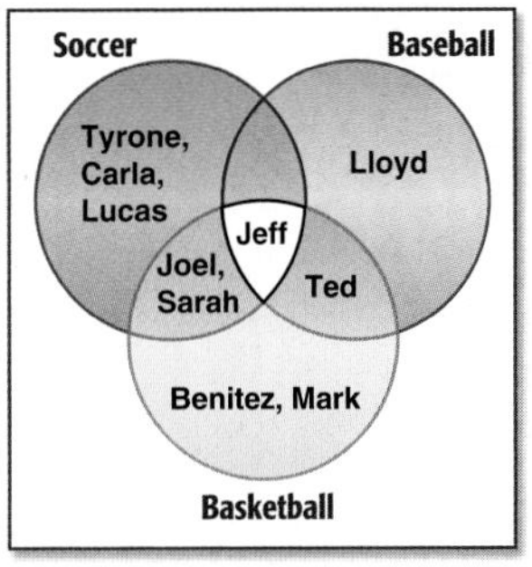

11. Which student(s) have played basketball in the last month? Benitez, Mark, Joel, Sarah, Jeff, and Ted
12. Who played only basketball and baseball? Ted
13. Which student(s) have played only soccer in the last month? Tyrone, Carla, Lucas
14. Who played only soccer and baseball? none
15. Which student(s) have played all three sports? Jeff
16. Who played at least two of the three sports? Joel, Sarah, Ted, and Jeff
17. What sports did Ted participate in the past month? baseball and basketball

MEDIA A hundred teens were polled and asked which of three news sources they use daily. The results are shown in the Venn Diagram at the right. 20. and 22. See margin.

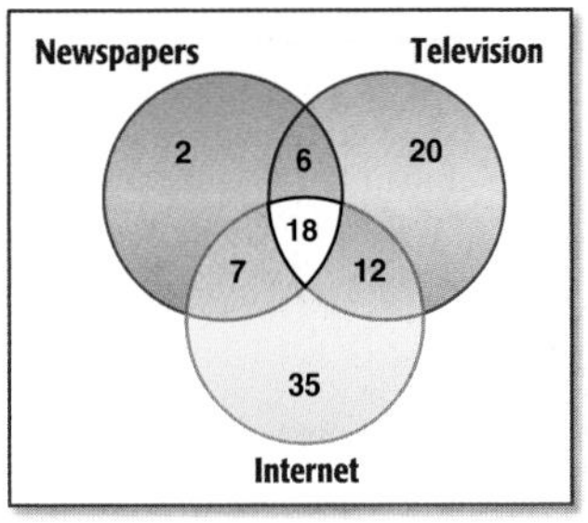

18. How many teens use only television as a daily news source? 20
19. How many teens use television as a daily news source? 56
20. Which news source(s) was used by exactly 6 teens?
21. How many teens use only the Internet as a daily news source? 35
22. Which new source(s) was used by exactly 7 teens?
23. How many teens use all three as daily news sources? 18

Additional Answers

20. newspapers and television

22. the Internet and newspapers

Additional Example

2 Refer to the Venn diagram shown below.

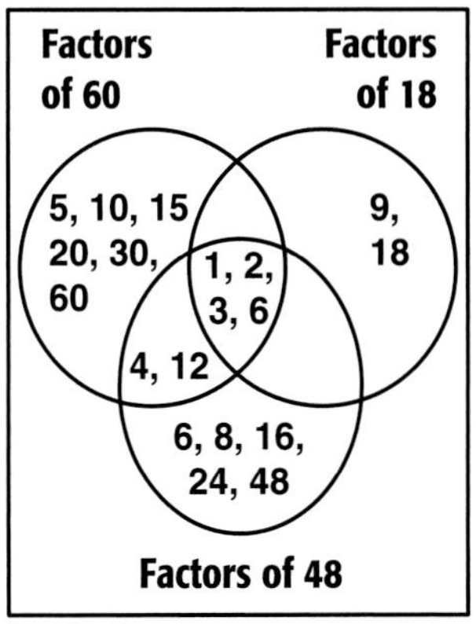

a. What are the factors in all three circles? 1, 2, 3, 6

b. What is the greatest common factor of all three numbers? 6

c. What factors are shared only by 60 and 48? 4, 12

d. What is the greatest common factor of 60 and 48? 12

e. What factors are shared only by 60 and 18? none

f. What is the greatest common factor of 60 and 18? 6

Tips for New Teachers

Using Venn Diagrams Remind students that common factors appear where circles overlap. Factors contained in only one circle are not common to any of the other numbers.

3 ASSESS

Formative Assessment

Use Exercises 1–23 to assess whether students understand how to use Venn diagrams to identify common factors in pairs or triples of numbers.

Yesterday's News Ask students to explain how their work with factors in Lesson 2 helped them with this lesson.

6 Lesson CSB Notes

1 FOCUS

Vertical Alignment

Lesson CSB-6
Recognize misleading uses of graphical displays of data.

After Lesson CSB-6
Construct accurate graphical displays of data.

2 TEACH

Example 1 shows how to identify misleading scaling on a bar graph.

Additional Example

1 The graphs show the annual home sales in a town. Which graph appears to show the greatest increase in home sales? The bottom graph

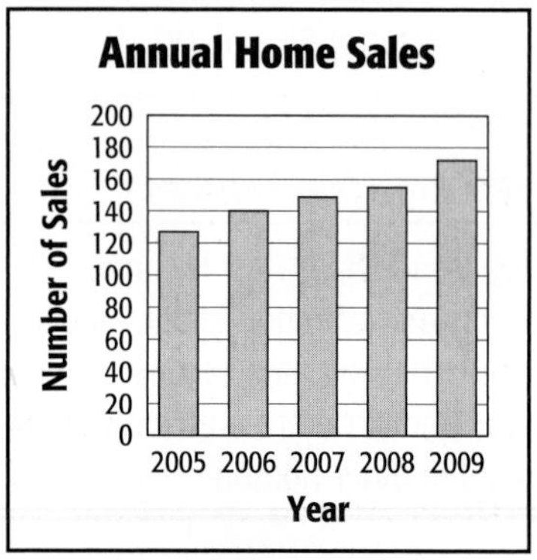

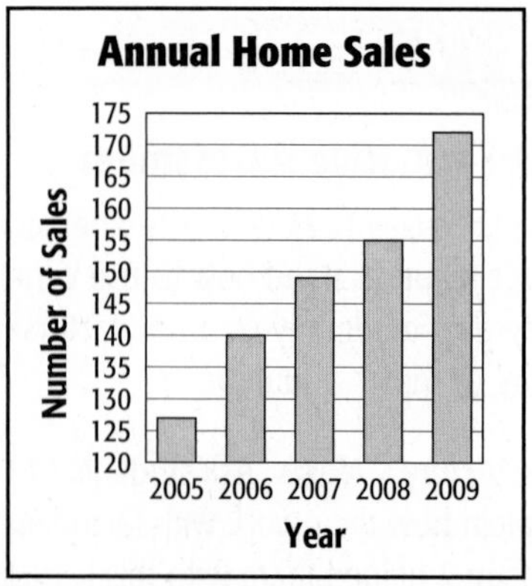

Concepts and Skills Bank

6 Misleading Graphs

The graphs below show the monthly sales of a local magazine.

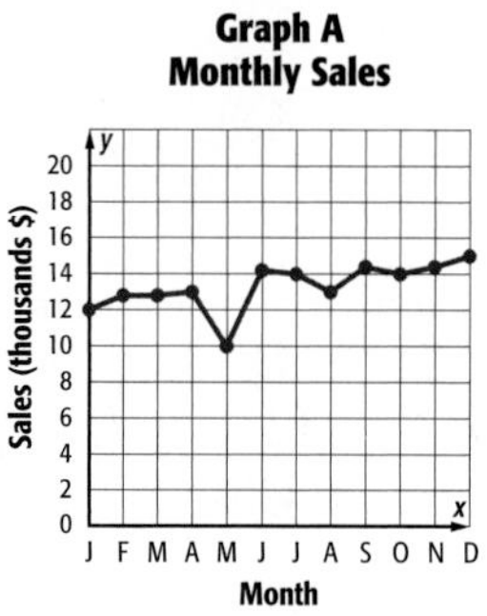

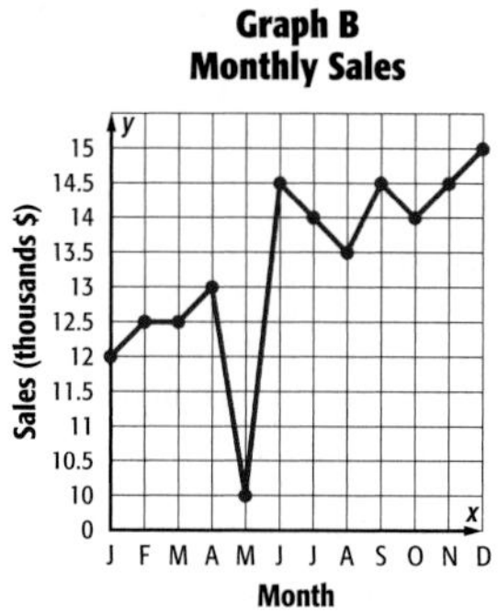

The graphs show the same information. However, while the first graph shows fairly steady sales, the second graph shows dramatic increases and decreases in sales. The graphs have the same horizontal axis, but notice that the scales are very different on the vertical axis. By changing the scale on a graph, the visual impression can be changed so that it is misleading.

EXAMPLE 1

The graphs show the number of visitors at a lodge in the Smoky Mountains each year. Which graph appears to show the greatest increase in the number of visitors?

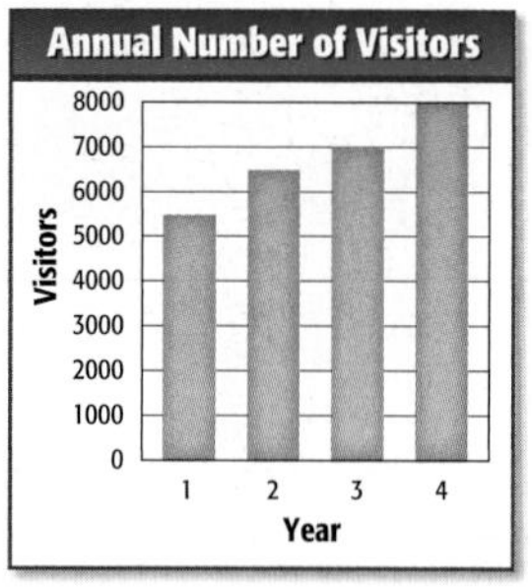

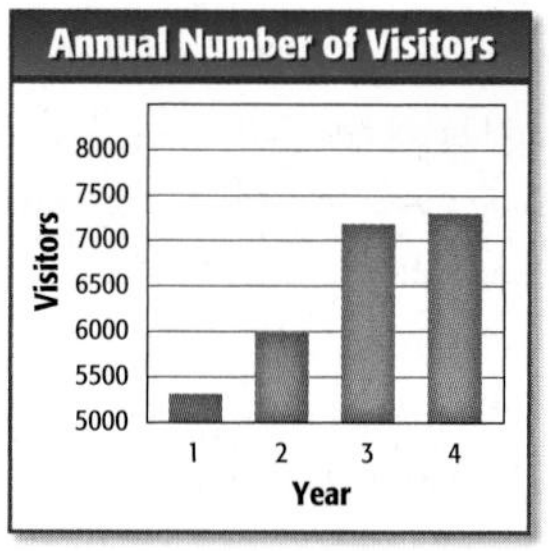

The graph on the right appears to show the greatest growth. The increments are 500 on the vertical axis, rather than 1000 like the first graph. The vertical axis of the graph on the left begins at 0, while the vertical axis of the graph on the right begins at 5000.

More Hints:

- Be sure that both axes have a scale that remains the same throughout the graph.
- Make sure that graphs with pictures, use the same picture throughout the graph.

Concepts and Skills Bank

Exercises

1. **TRAFFIC** The graphs display the number of cars that went through a tollbooth during the previous hour. Which graph appears to show the greatest increase in the number of vehicles? Explain.

1. The first graph; all of the numbers appear higher on the graph. The vertical scale is different, and the vertical axis in the second graph begins at 100 not 0.

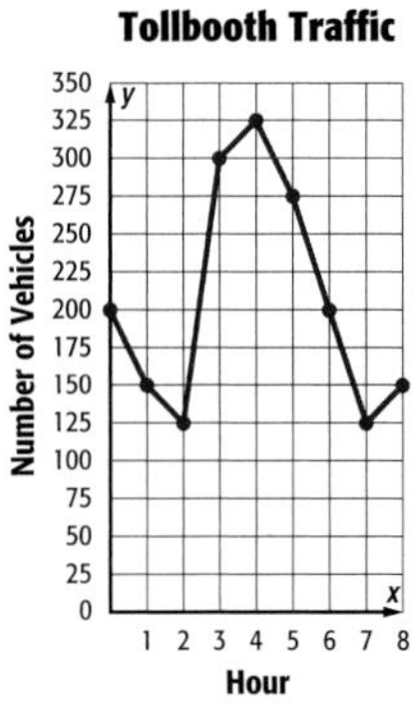

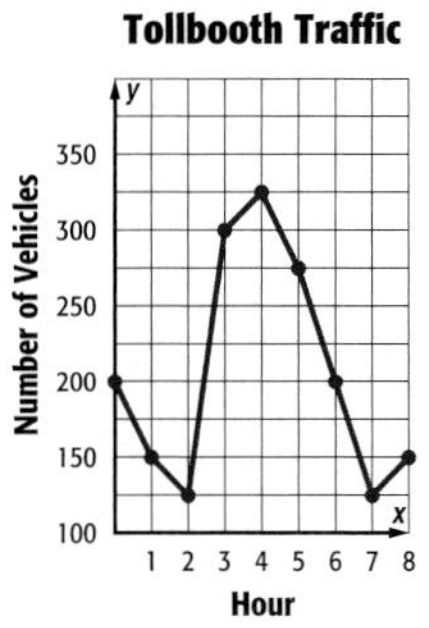

2. Which graph appears to have higher gas prices? Explain.

The second graph; the scale on the vertical axis has a smaller range which emphasizes differences.

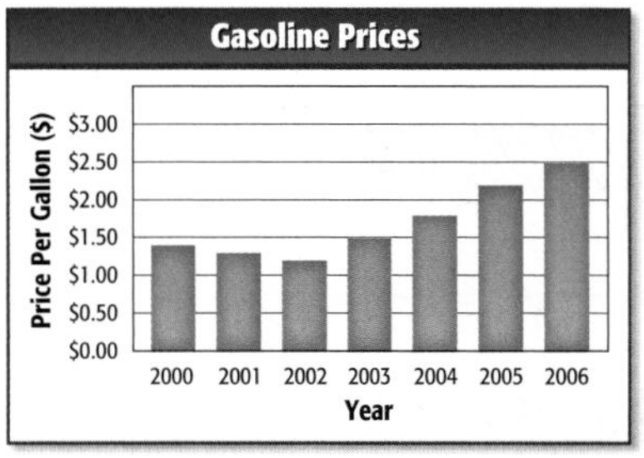

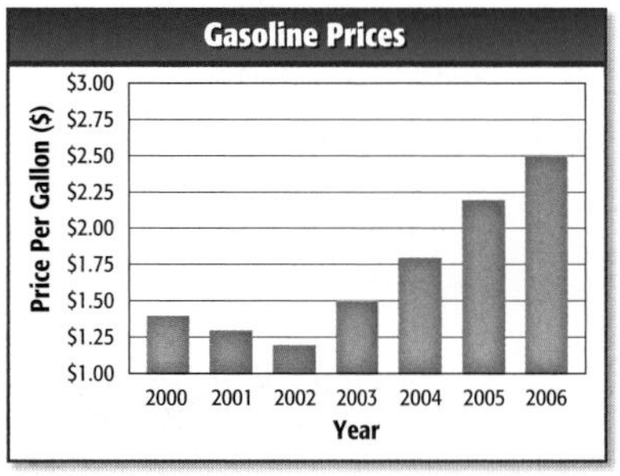

3. **BUSINESS** According to the information in the graph below, there were no visitors to the ski resort in 1999. Determine if this statement is accurate. Justify your response.

No; sample answer: The scale on the vertical axis does not start at 0, so we can only determine that the number of visitors was less than 2000.

Tips for New Teachers

Point out that vertical scales on graphs of count data should start at 0 to avoid being deceptive. Both scales should increase uniformly.

3 ASSESS

Formative Assessment

Use Exercises 1–3 to assess whether students understand how the choice of scale can influence the way graphical data are interpreted.

Ticket Out the Door Ask each student to sketch a graph that is in some way misleading.

Concepts and Skills Bank

Page 805, Problem-Solving Strategy: Create a Table

1.

quarters	dimes	nickels
2	0	0
1	2	1
1	1	3
1	0	5
0	5	0
0	4	2
0	3	4
0	2	6
0	1	8
0	0	10

2.

quarters	dimes	nickels	pennies	total (cents)
1	1	0	0	35
1	0	1	0	30
1	0	0	1	26
0	1	1	0	15
0	1	0	1	11
0	0	1	1	6

3.

dimes	nickels	pennies
2	1	0
2	0	5
1	3	0
1	2	5
1	1	10
1	0	15

4.

1st	2nd	3rd	4th
B	G	G	0
B	0	G	G
B	G	0	G
G	B	G	0
G	G	B	0
G	B	0	G
G	G	0	B
G	0	B	G
G	0	G	B
0	B	G	G
0	G	B	G
0	G	G	B

5.

Number of Bags	Small Popcorn ($)	Large Popcorn ($)
1	1.25	2.25
2	2.50	4.50
3	3.75	6.75
4	5.00	9.00
5	6.25	11.25

6.

x	$f(x) = 3x^3 - 4$	$f(x)$
4	$3(4^3) - 4$	188
5	$3(5^3) - 4$	371
6	$3(6^3) - 4$	644
7	$3(7^3) - 4$	1025
8	$3(8^3) - 4$	1532
9	$3(9^3) - 4$	2183

7.

x	$y = \frac{1}{2}x - 2$	y	(x, y)
−2	$\frac{1}{2}(-2) - 2$	−3	(−2, −3)
−1	$\frac{1}{2}(-1) - 2$	$-2\frac{1}{2}$	$\left(-1, -2\frac{1}{2}\right)$
0	$\frac{1}{2}(0) - 2$	−2	(0, −2)
1	$\frac{1}{2}(1) - 2$	$-1\frac{1}{2}$	$\left(1, -1\frac{1}{2}\right)$
2	$\frac{1}{2}(2) - 2$	−1	(2, −1)

8.

Method of Wrapping	24 students surveyed	120 students surveyed
Recycled paper	3	15
Gift bags	6	30
Wrapping paper	12	60
No wrapping	3	15

Page 807, Problem-Solving Strategy: Make a Chart

1.

Length of Square (cm)	Area of Square (cm^2)
3	9
6	36
12	144

2.

Integer Value	$f(x) = 2x + 3$	$g(x) = -x - 3$	$f(x) - g(x)$
1	5	−4	9
2	7	−5	12
3	9	−6	15
4	11	−7	18
5	13	−8	21
6	15	−9	24

3.

Response	Percentage	Number of People
Half a tank	34%	68
Quarter of a tank	50%	100
Less than a quarter of a tank	14%	28
Empty	2%	4

4.

Type of Reptile	Tally of States	Number of States
turtle, tortoise, terapin	𝍸 𝍸 IIII	14
snake	III	3
alligator	III	3
lizard	III	3
toad	I	1
none	𝍸 𝍸 𝍸 𝍸 𝍸 I	26

Page 815, Extra Practice, Lesson 1-3

1. $\frac{2}{3}[15 \div (10)]$ Substitution

$= \frac{2}{3}\left(\frac{3}{2}\right)$ Substitution

$= 1$ Multiplicative Inverse

2. $\frac{7}{4}[4 \cdot 1]$ Multiplicative Inverse

$= \frac{7}{4}(4)$ Multiplicative Identity

$= 7$ Substitution

3. $[(6) \cdot 0] \cdot 10$ Substitution

$= (0) \cdot 10$ Multiplicative Prop. of 0

$= 0$ Multiplicative Prop. of 0

Page 817, Extra Practice, Lesson 1-8

5. Hypothesis: a figure is a square; Conclusion: it has four congruent sides; If a figure is a square, the it has four congruent sides.

6. Hypothesis: $a = 4$; Conclusion: $6a + 10 = 34$; if $a = 4$, then $6a + 10 = 34$.

7. Hypothesis: it is night; Conclusion: the video store is open; If it is night, then the video store is open.

8. Hypothesis: It is Thursday; Conclusion: the band will not practice; If it is Thursday, then the band will not practice.

Page 817, Extra Practice, Lesson 2-1

7. Sample answer: The sum of five tenths times x and three is equal to negative ten.

8. Sample answer: The quotient of n and negative six is the same as the sum of two times n and one.

9. Sample answer: Eighteen decreased by five times h is the same as thirteen times h.

10. Sample answer: The square of n is equal to sixteen.

11. Sample answer: The sum of 3 and twice x squared is equal to twenty-one.

12. Sample answer: The sum of 4 and the quotient of m and n is equal to twelve.

Page 820, Extra Practice, Lesson 3-1

7.

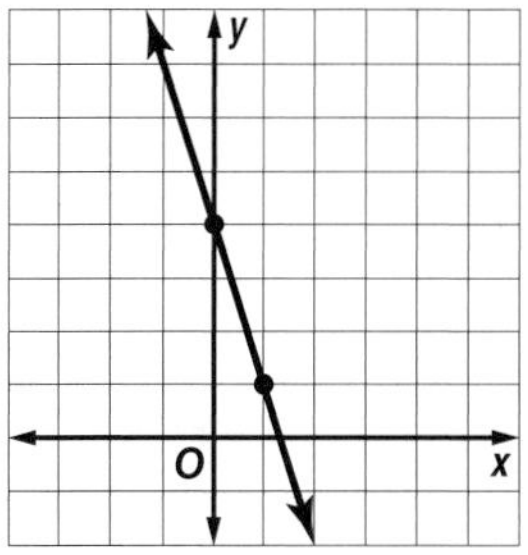

8.

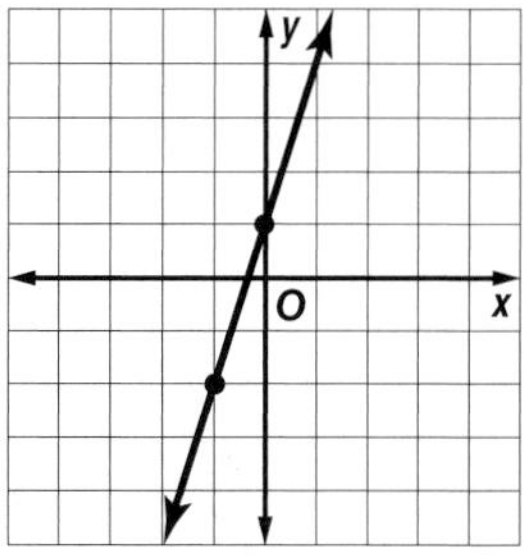

9.

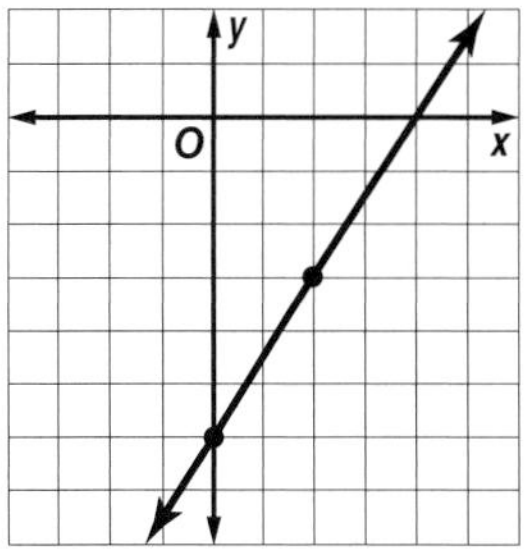

10.

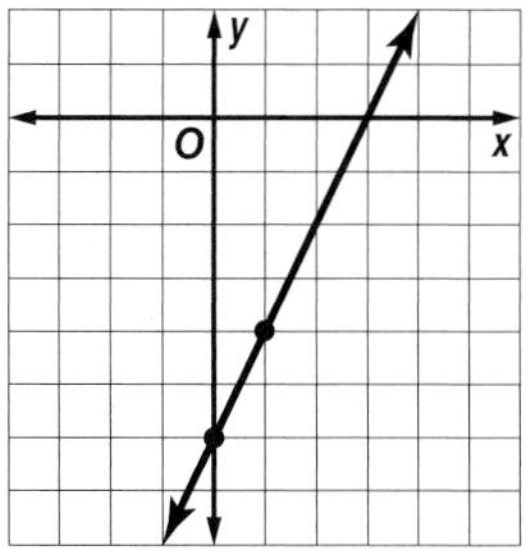

11.

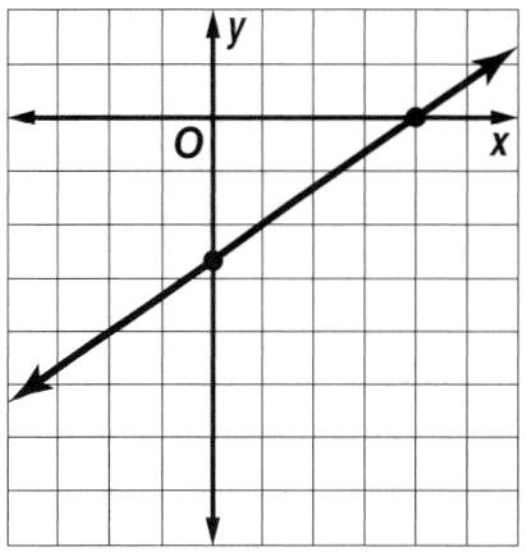

12.

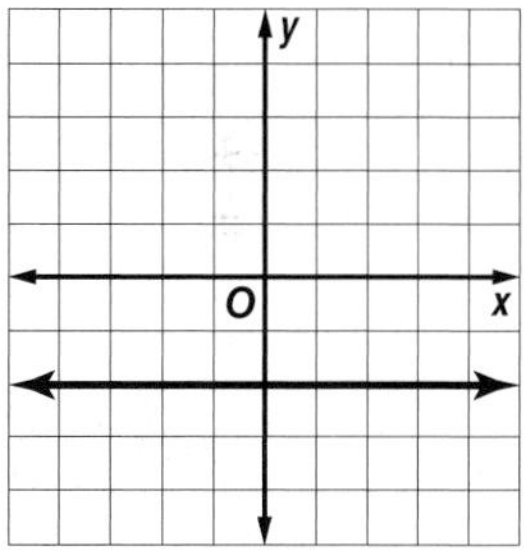

13.

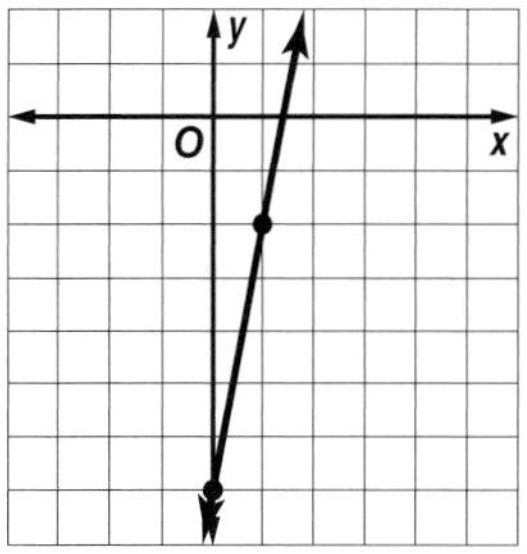

14.

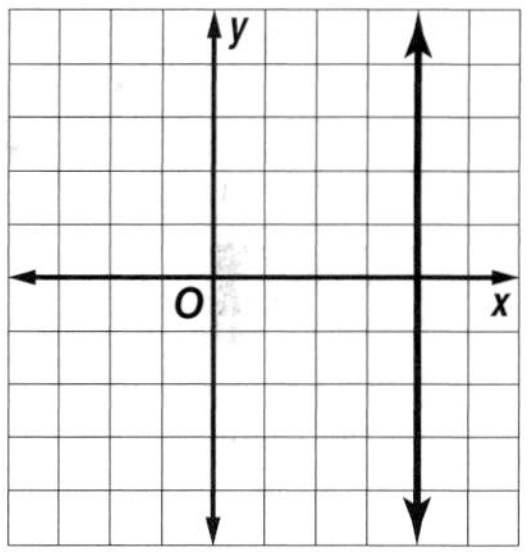

15.

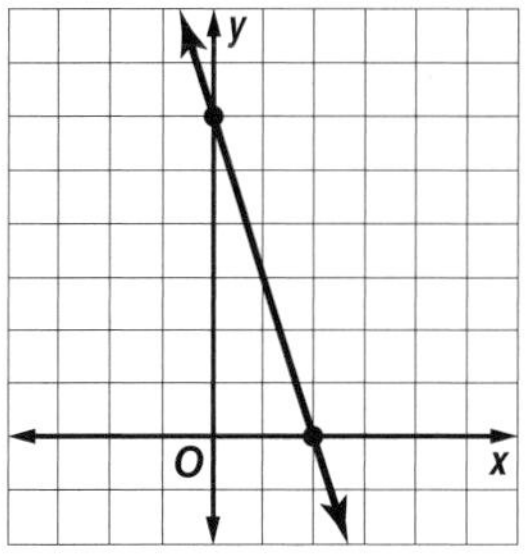

16.

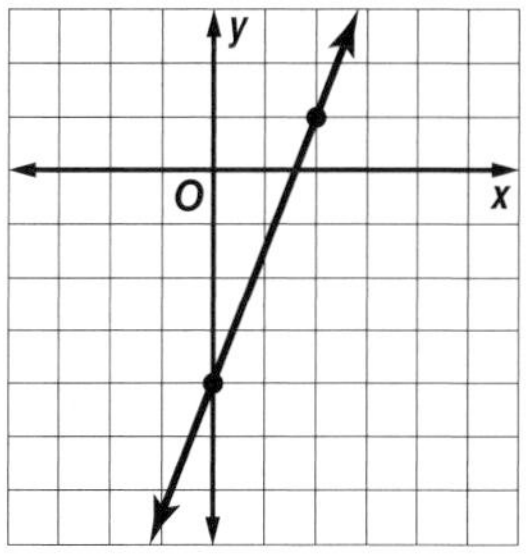

17.

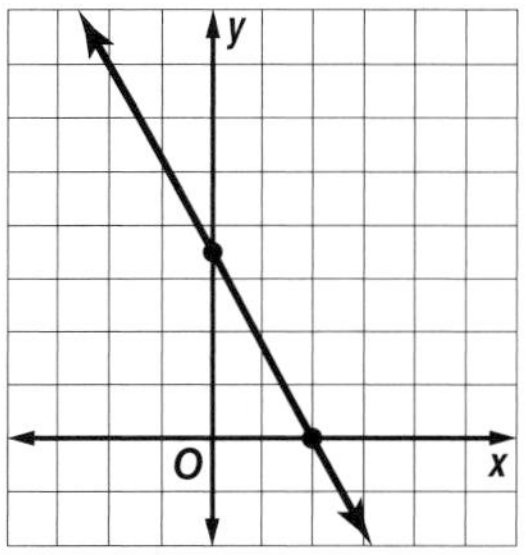

18.

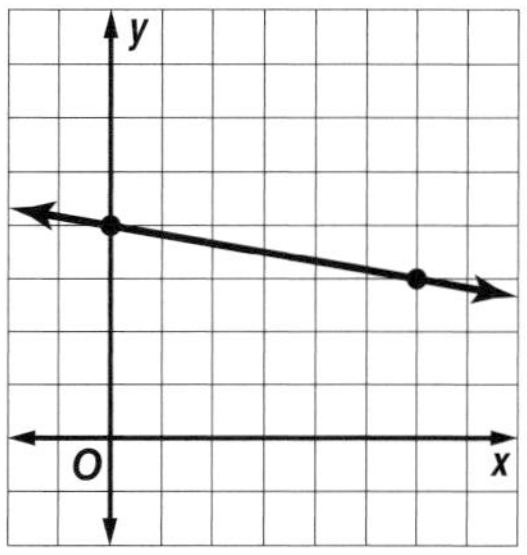

Page 821, Extra Practice, Lesson 3-4

4.

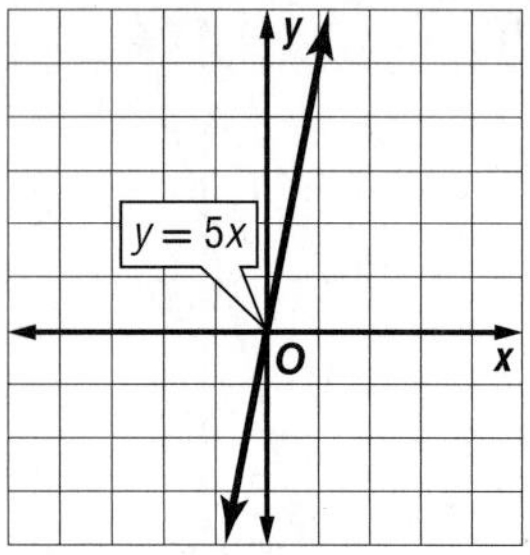

5.

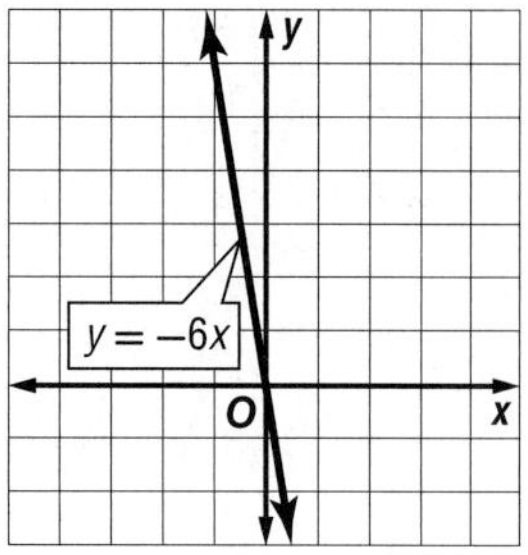

6.

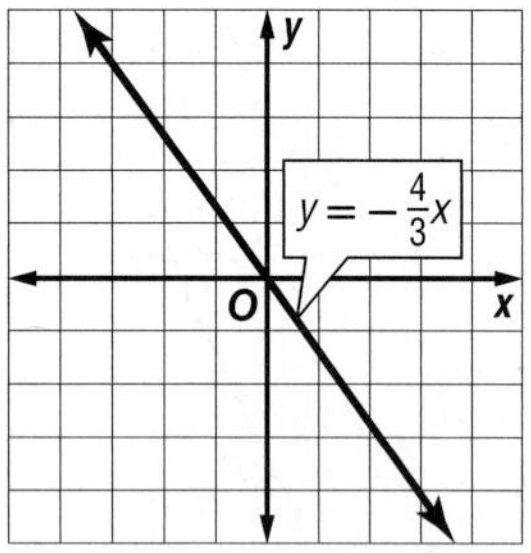

Page 822, Extra Practice, Lesson 3-5

13. $a_n = -7 + 4n$

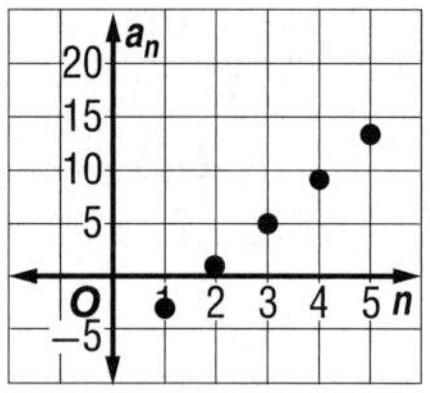

14. $a_n = 10 + 15n$

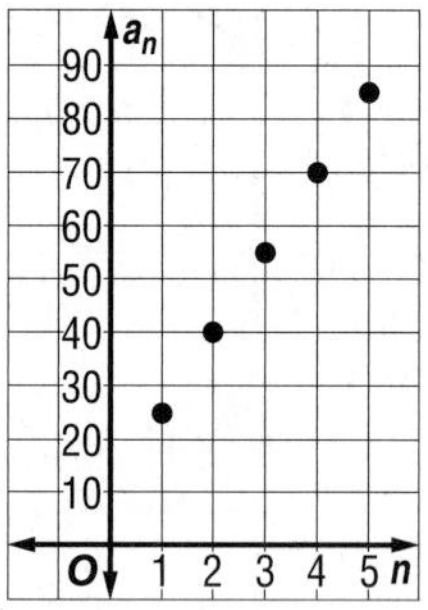

15. $a_n = -15 + 6n$

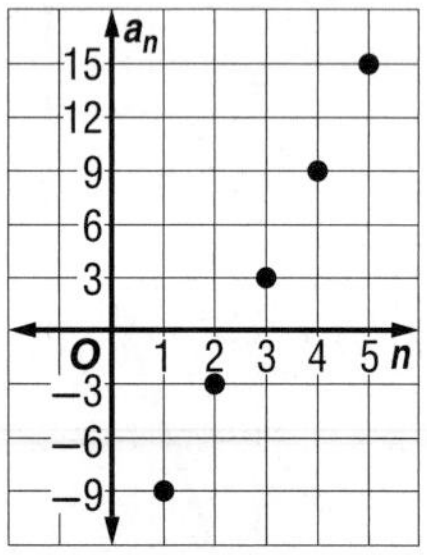

16. $a_n = -5 + 1.5n$

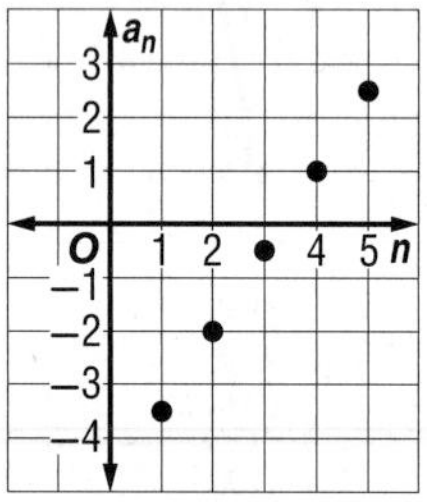

Page 822, Extra Practice, Lesson 3-6

5b.

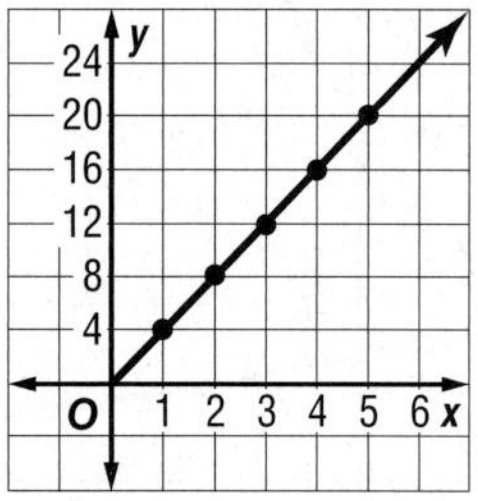

Page 822, Extra Practice, Lesson 4-1

10.

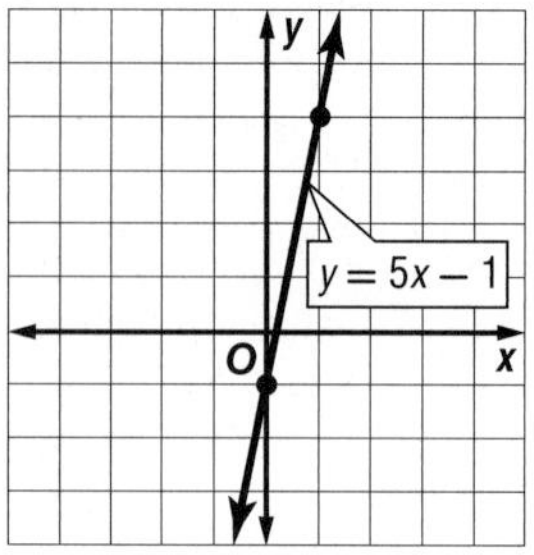

11.

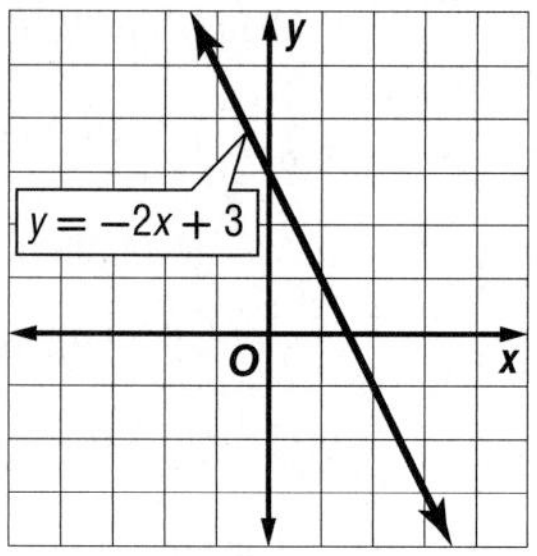

12.

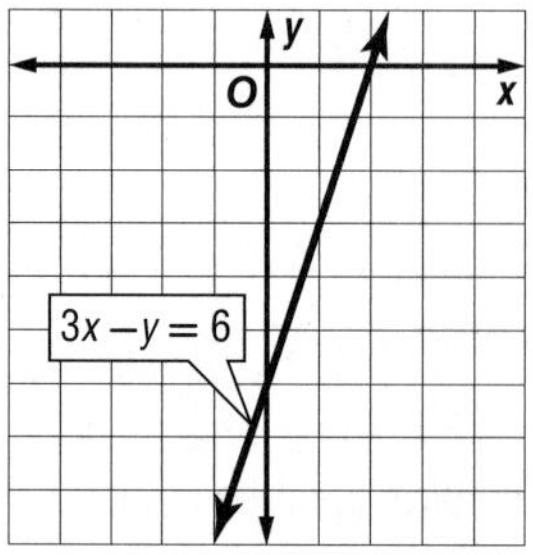

Page 823, Extra Practice, Lesson 4-2

1.

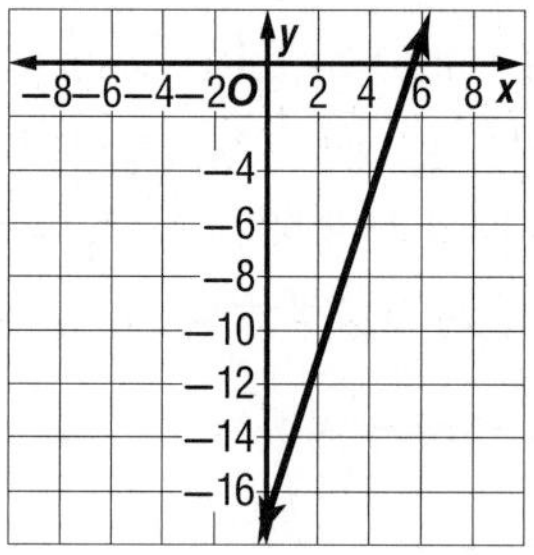

2.

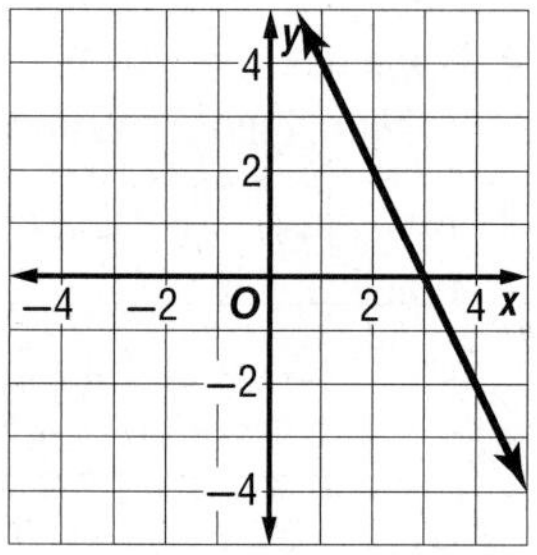

3.

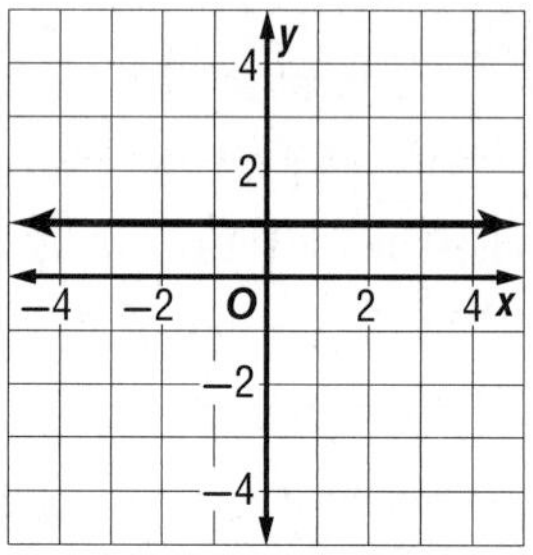

4.

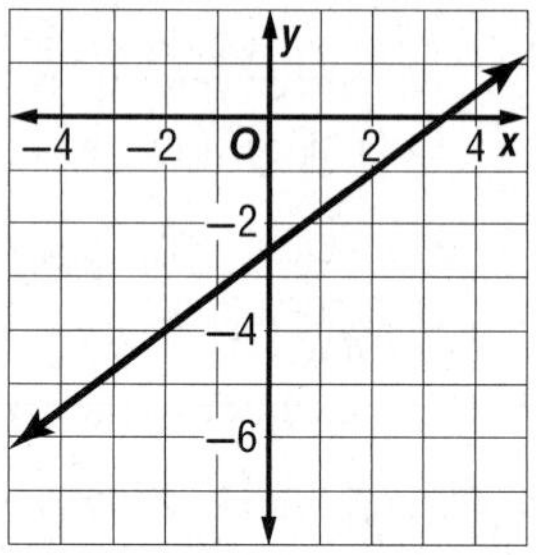

Page 824, Extra Practice, Lesson 4-7

1.

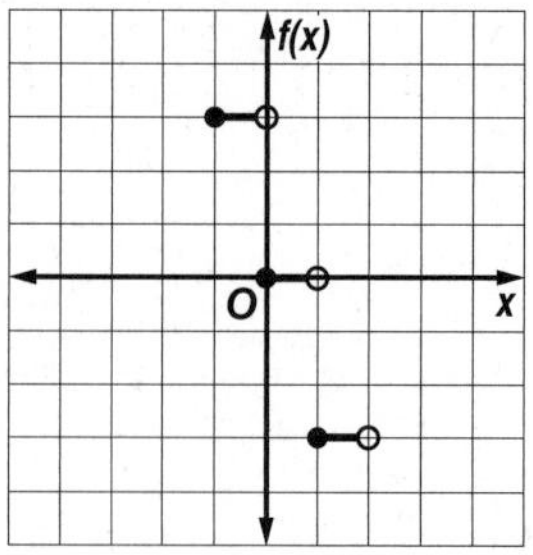

2.

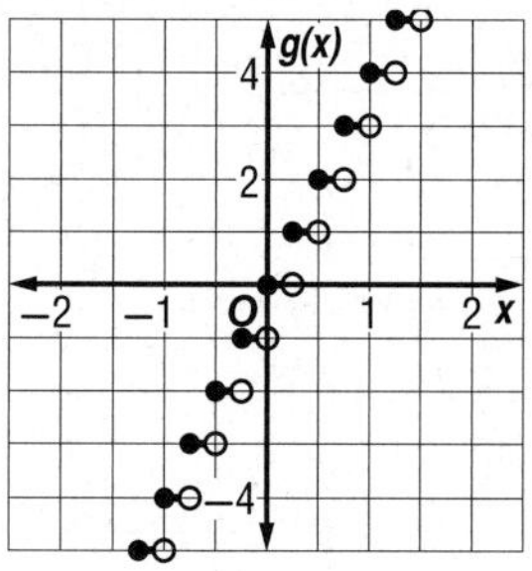

3.

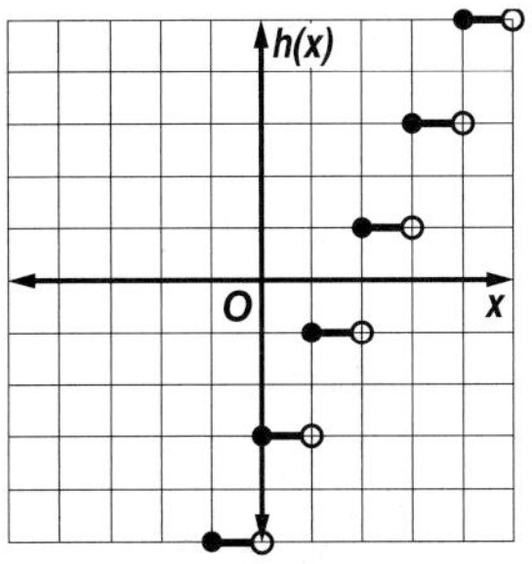

4.

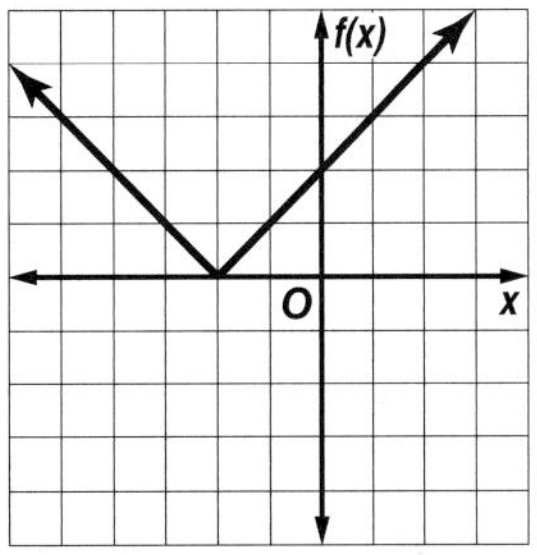

5.

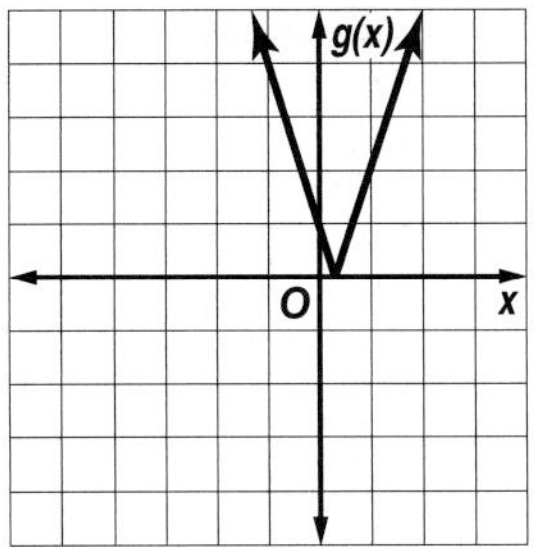

6.

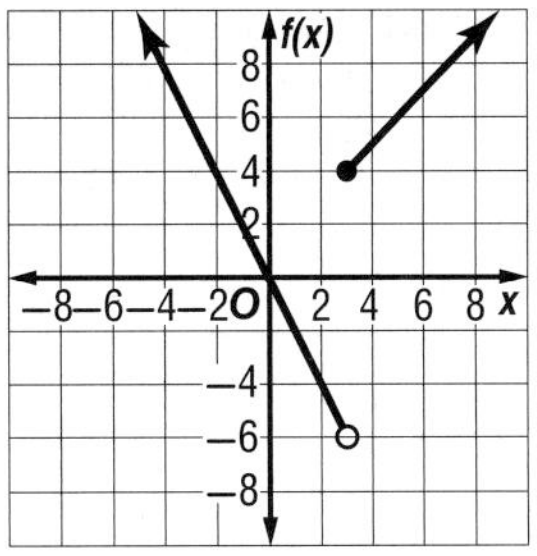

7.

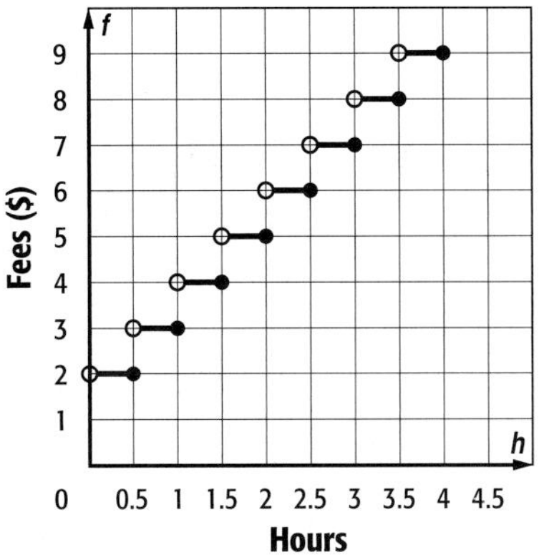

Page 825, Extra Practice, Lesson 5-1

1. $\{c \mid c \le -6\}$

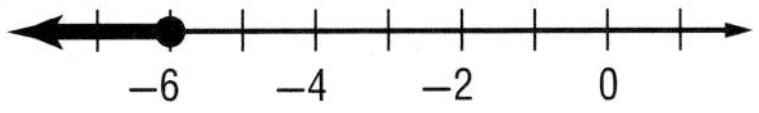

2. $\{d \mid d < 10\}$

3. $\{z \mid z > 24\}$

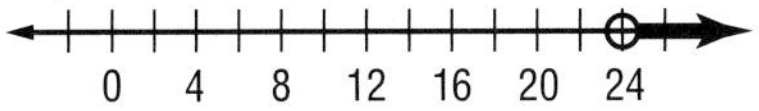

4. $\{h \mid h > -9\}$

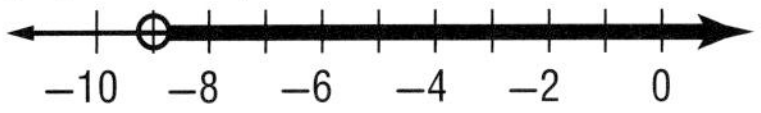

5. $\{d \mid d < -7\}$

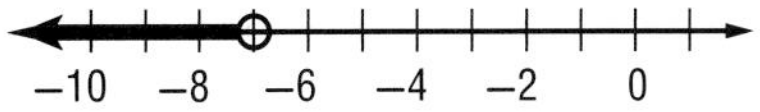

6. $\{x \mid x > -3\}$

7. $\{x \mid x \ge 3\}$

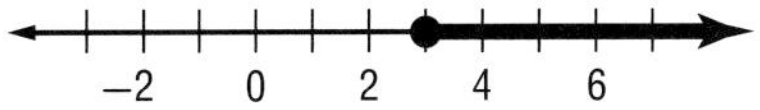

8. $\{w \mid w < -36\}$

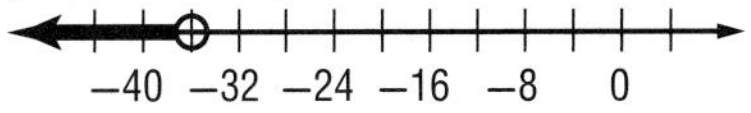

9. $\{p \mid p > 5\}$

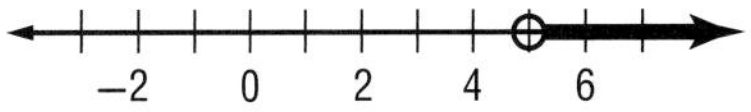

10. $\{z \mid z < 23\}$

11. $\{v \mid v < 2\}$

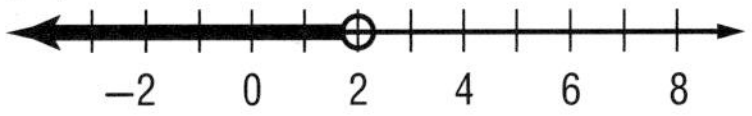

12. $\left\{t \,\middle|\, t \le \frac{11}{12}\right\}$

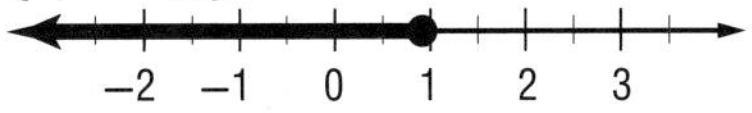

13. $\{x \mid x < -2\}$

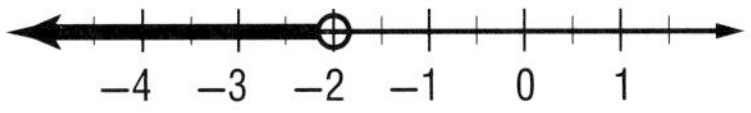

14. $\{n \mid n \ge -2\}$

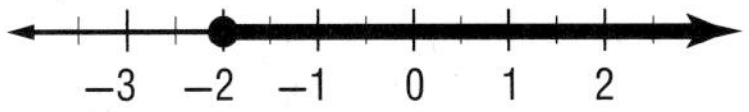

15. $\{a \mid a \ge -5.5\}$

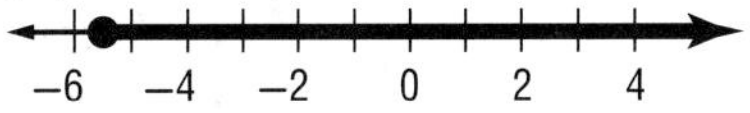

16. $\{z \mid z > 6\}$

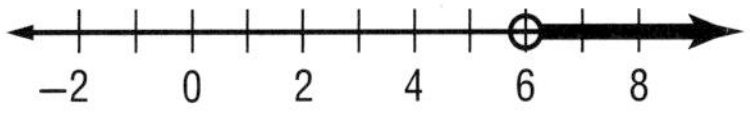

Page 826, Extra Practice, Lesson 5-4

1. $\{x \mid x > -7 \text{ or } x > 3\}$

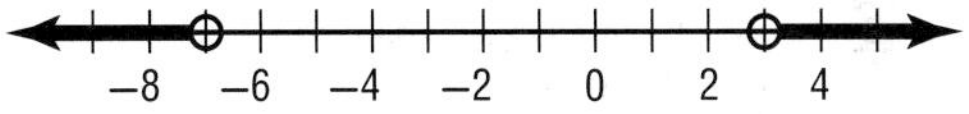

2. $\{t \mid t \text{ is a real number.}\}$

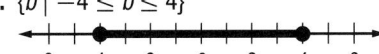

3. $\{g \mid -2 \le g \le 4\}$

4. $\{v \mid v \ge 1\}$

5. $\{b \mid -4 \le b \le 4\}$

6. $\{z \mid -8 < z < 1.5\}$

7. $\{m \mid m < -4 \text{ or } m \ge 3\}$

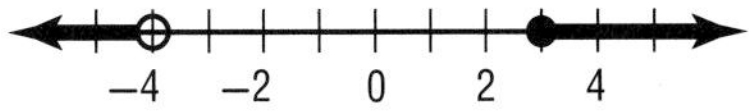

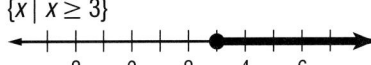

8. $\{c \mid c \text{ is a real number.}\}$

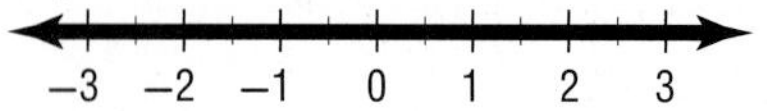

9. $\{h \mid h \geq 1\}$

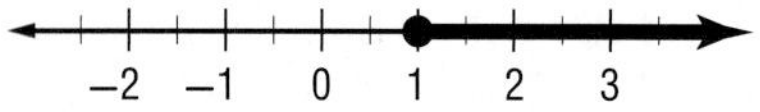

10. $\left\{p \,\middle|\, -\frac{1}{2} \leq p < \frac{1}{2}\right\}$

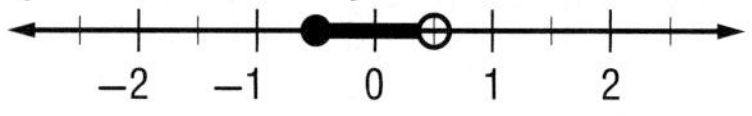

11. $\varnothing$

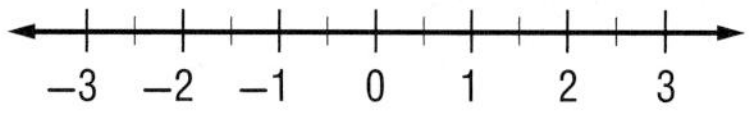

12. $\{j \mid j > 12\}$

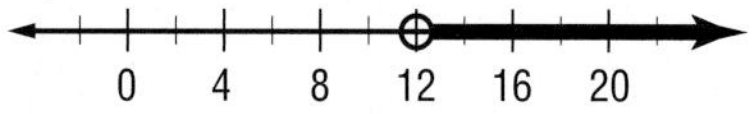

13. $\{q \mid q \text{ is a real number}\}$

14. $\varnothing$

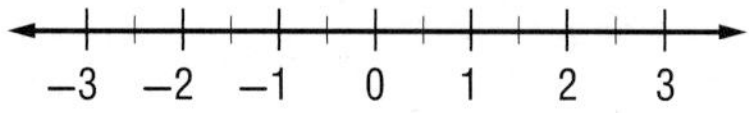

15. $\{n \mid n < -7 \text{ or } n > 8\}$

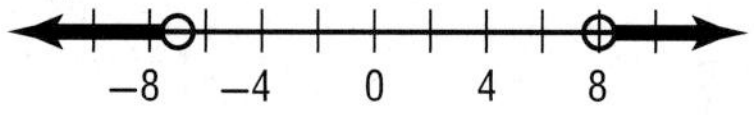

16. $\{x \mid x \geq 14\}$

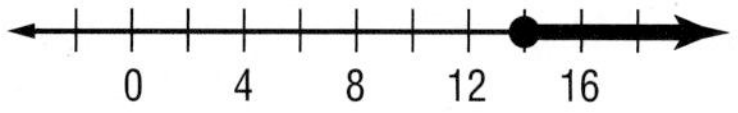

Page 826, Extra Practice, Lesson 5-5

1. $\{x \mid -14 < x < 6\}$

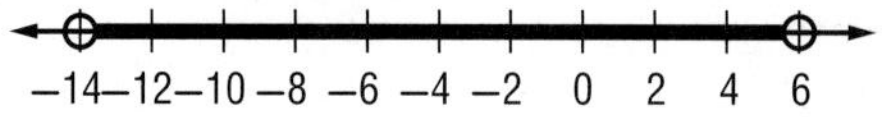

2. $\{y \mid y \leq 0 \text{ or } y \geq 6\}$

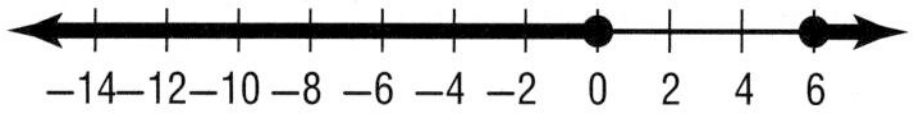

3. $\left\{x \,\middle|\, x < -\frac{7}{2} \text{ or } x > -\frac{3}{2}\right\}$

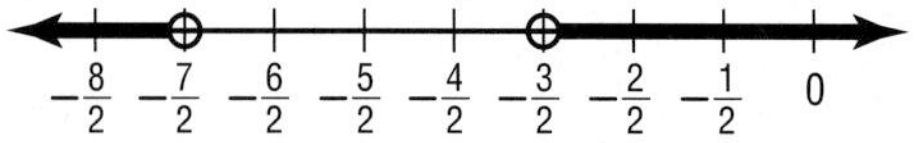

4. $\left\{x \,\middle|\, x \leq -\frac{17}{2} \text{ or } x \geq -\frac{23}{2}\right\}$

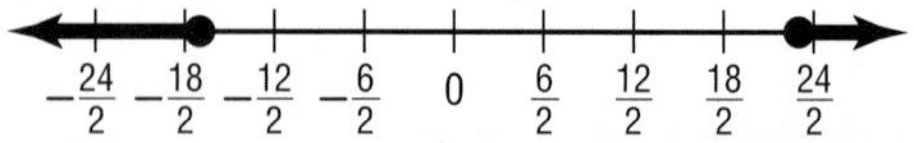

5. $\left\{m \,\middle|\, m \leq -4 \text{ or } m \geq \frac{16}{3}\right\}$

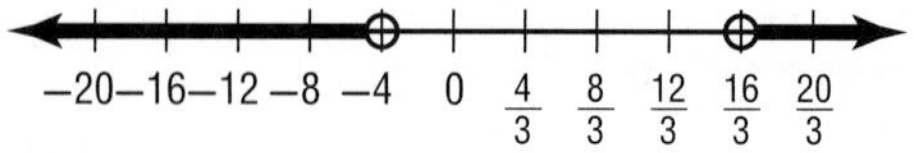

6. $\{n \mid -7 < n < -1\}$

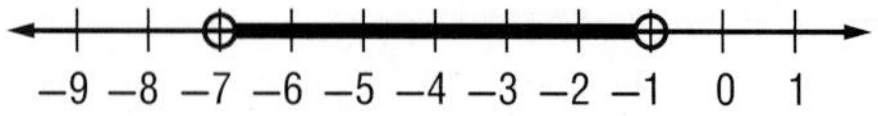

7. $\left\{v \,\middle|\, -\frac{6}{5} < v < \frac{2}{5}\right\}$

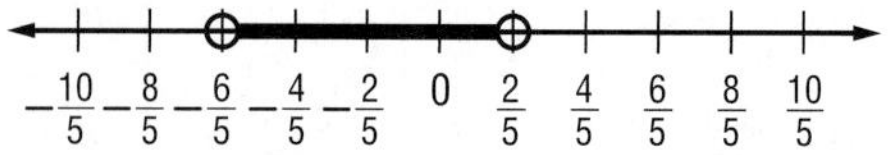

8. $\{w \mid w \leq -6 \text{ or } w \geq 22\}$

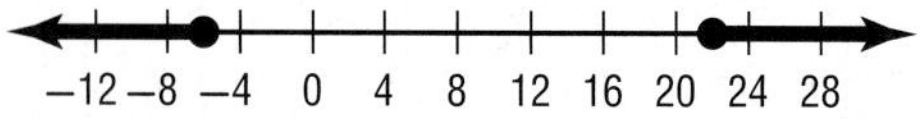

9. $\left\{x \,\middle|\, x < -\frac{10}{3} \text{ or } x > 2\right\}$

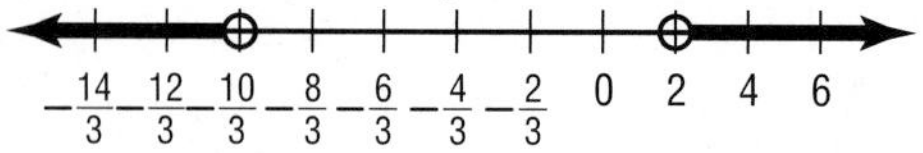

10. $\left\{m \,\middle|\, m \leq -5 \text{ or } m \geq \frac{5}{2}\right\}$

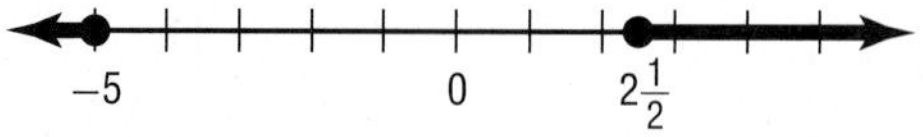

11. $\{y \mid -24 < y < 16\}$

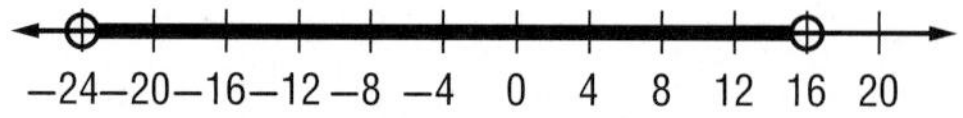

12. $\left\{h \,\middle|\, h < -\frac{5}{3} \text{ or } h > 5\right\}$

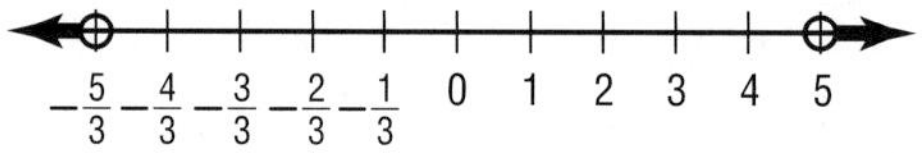

Page 826, Extra Practice, Lesson 5-6

3.

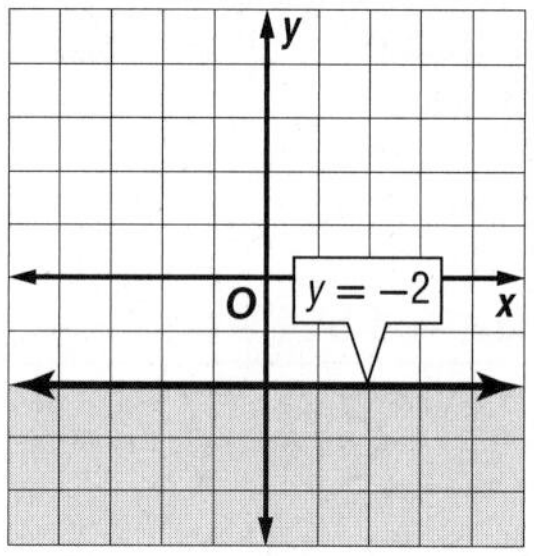

4.

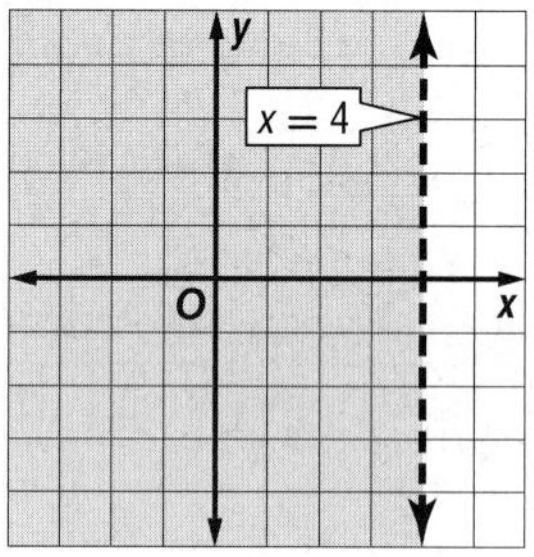

5.

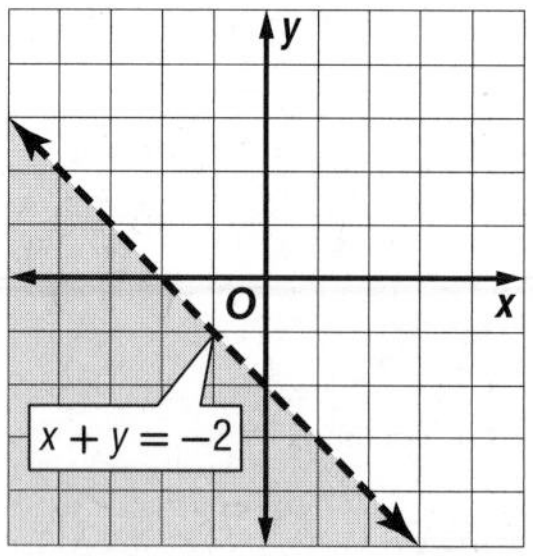

6.

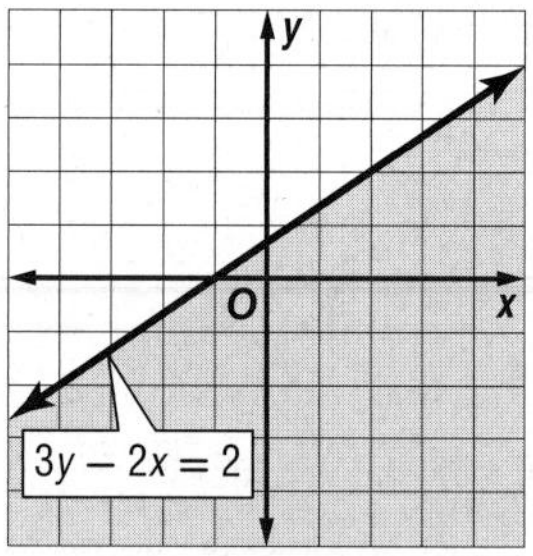

7.

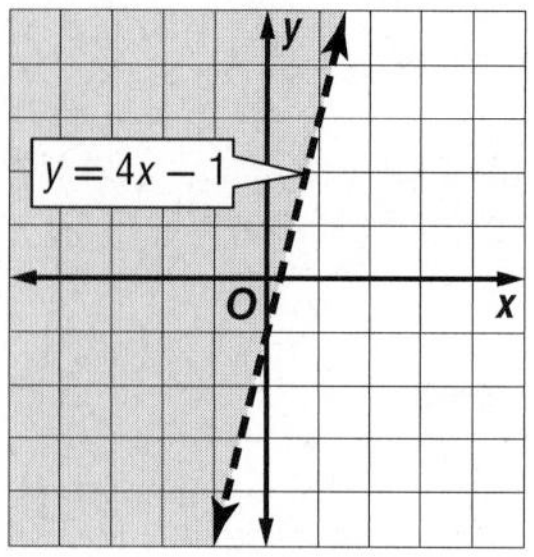

8.

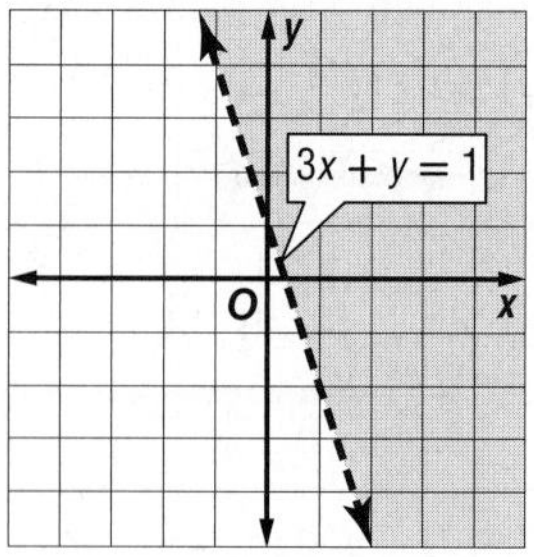

Page 827, Extra Practice, Lesson 6-1

1.
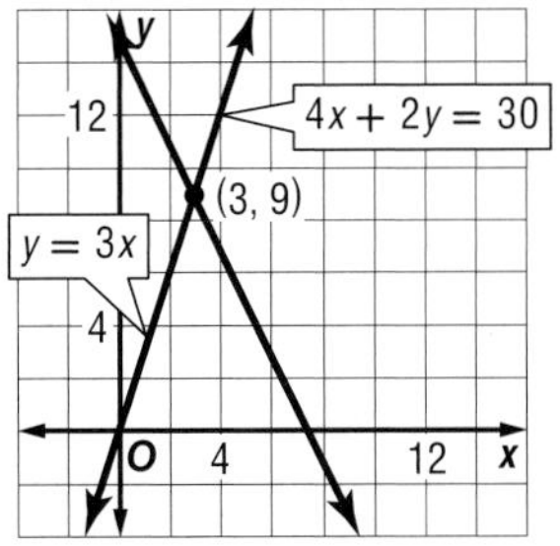

2.
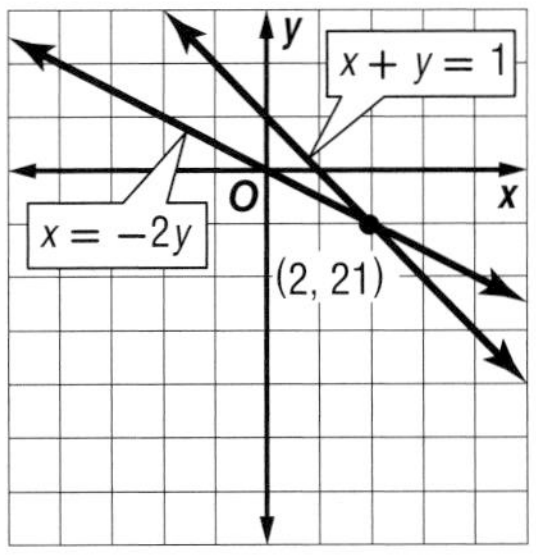

3.
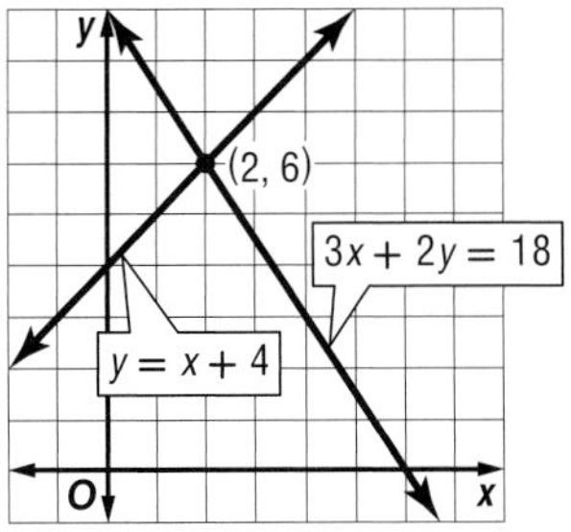

4.
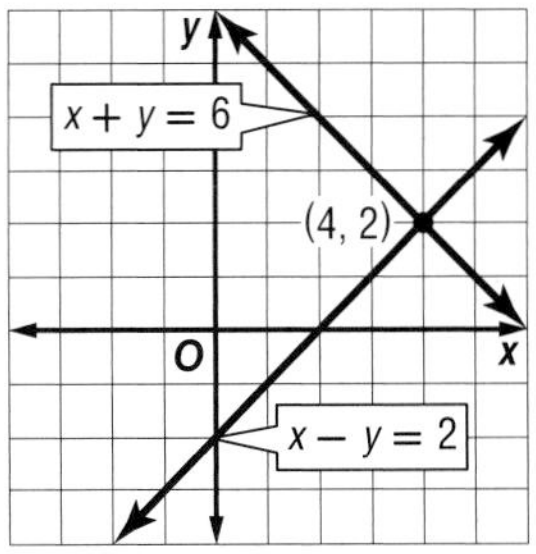

5.
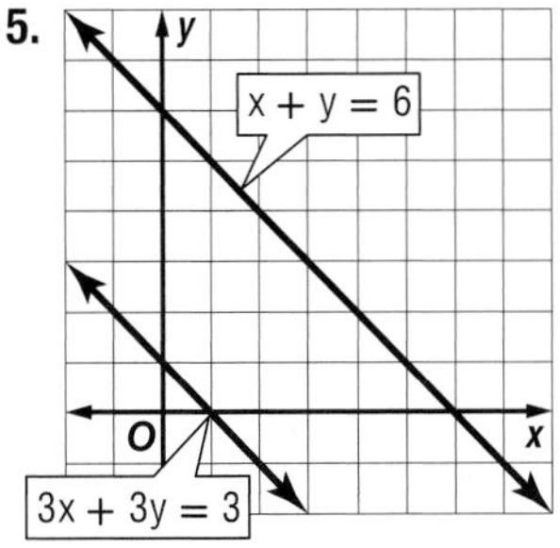

6.
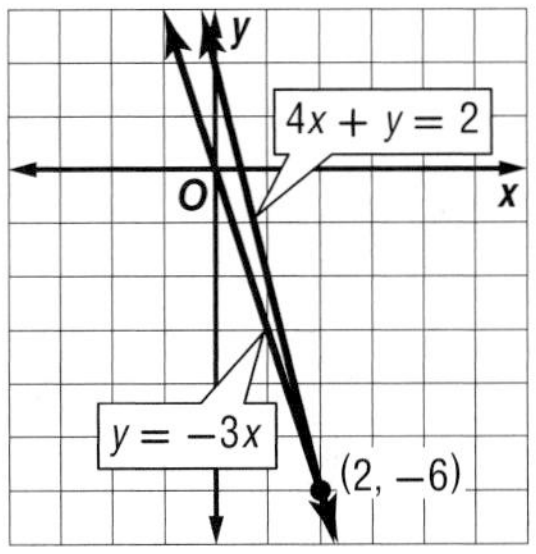

7.
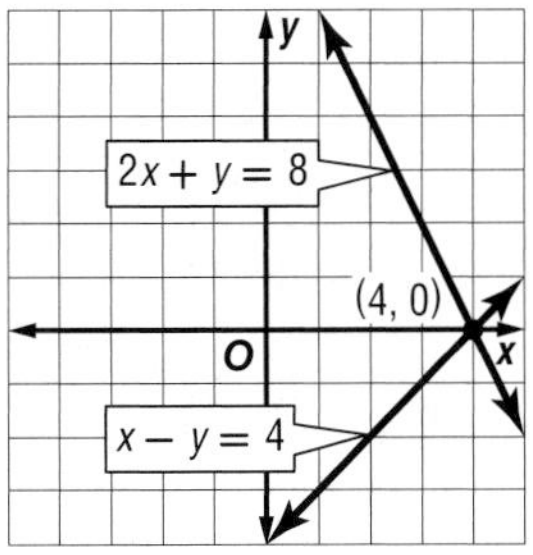

8.
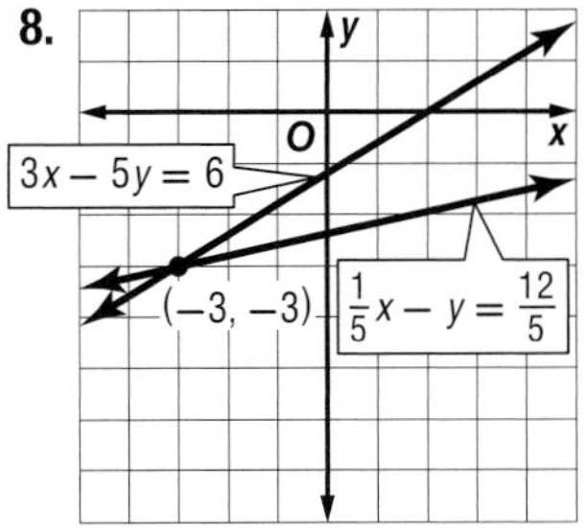

9.
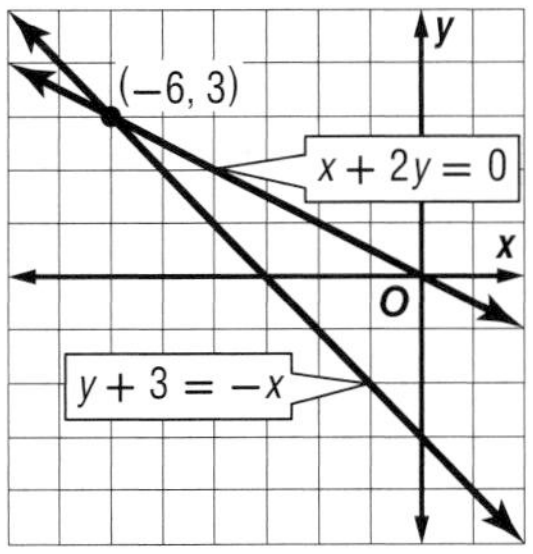

10.
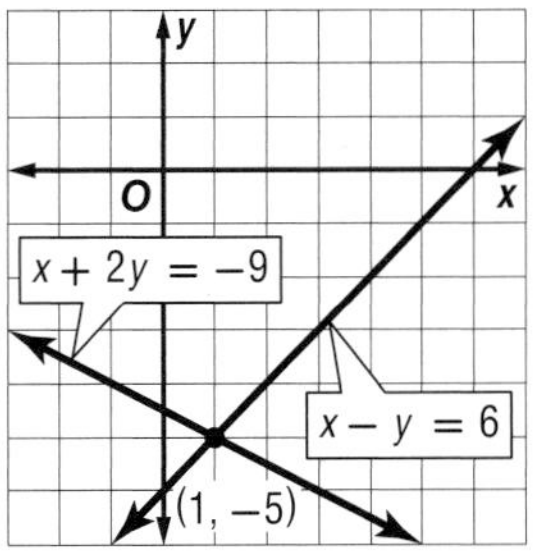

11.
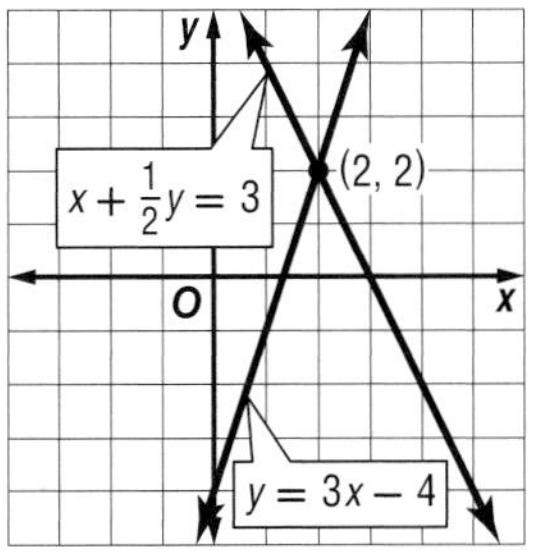

12.
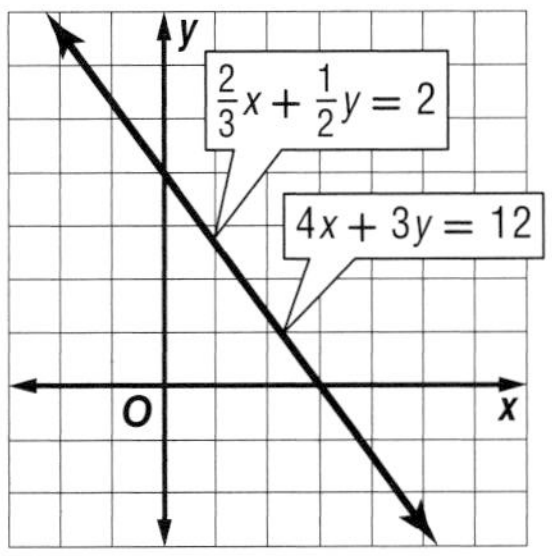

Page 829, Extra Practice, Lesson 6-8

1.
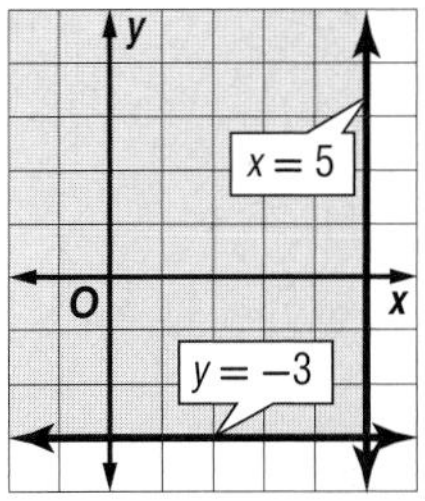

2.
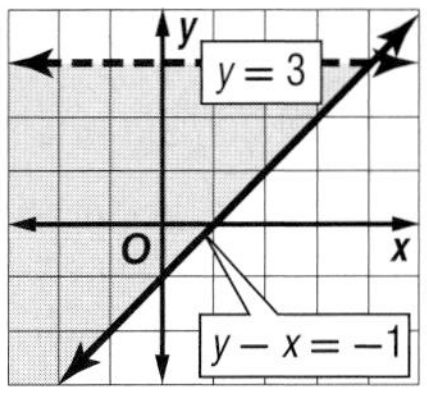

3.
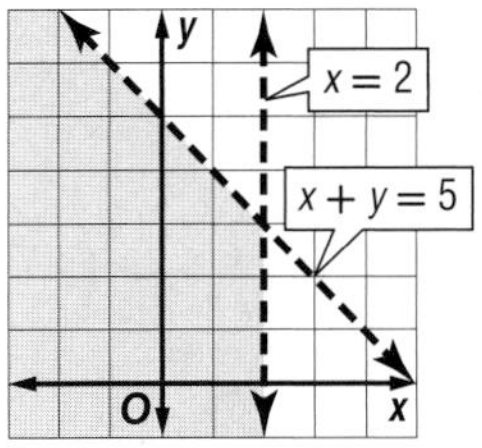

4.
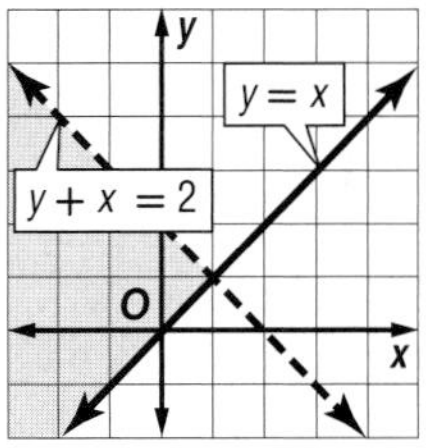

5.
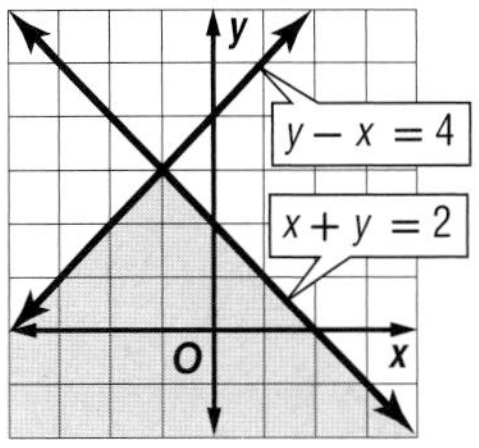

6.
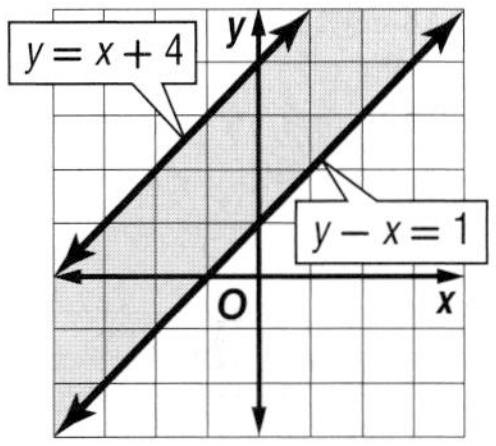

7.
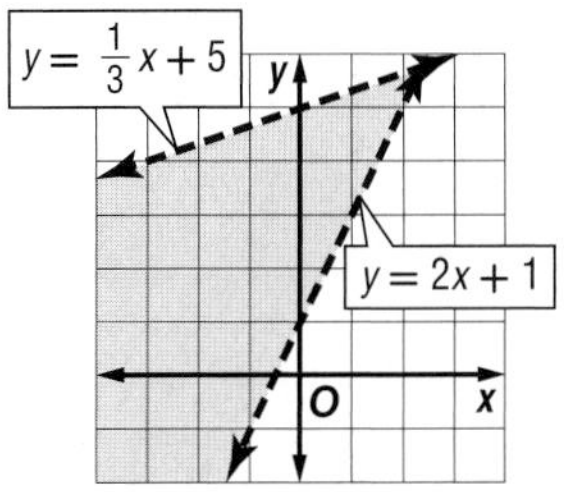

8.
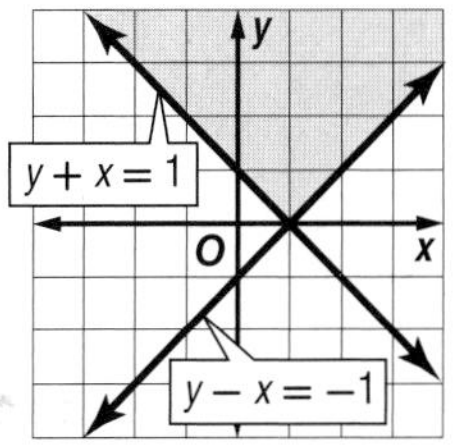

9.
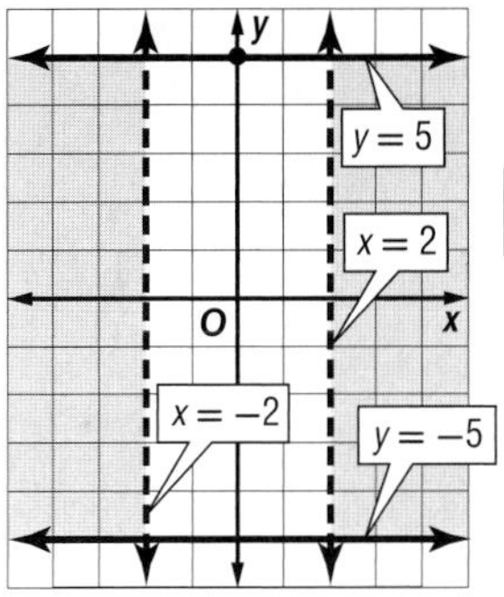

10.
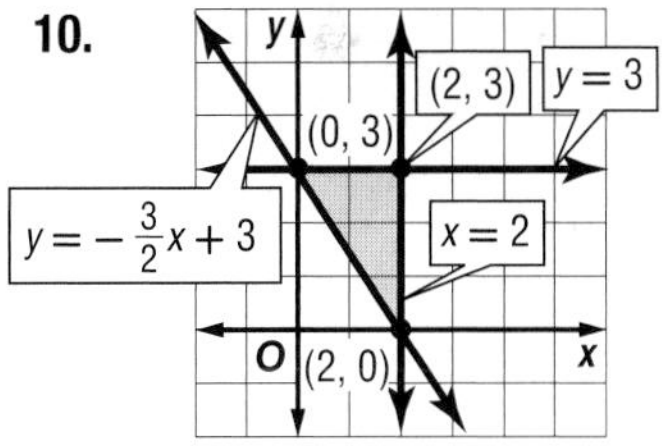

11.
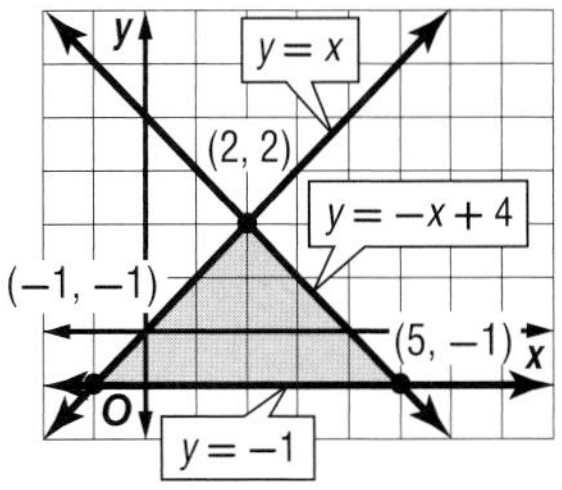

12.
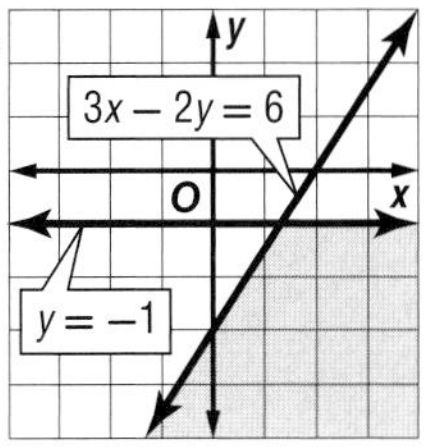

Page 829, Extra Practice, Lesson 7-1

1. It shows subtraction, not multiplication of variables.
2. It is a real number and therefore a monomial.
3. It is a product of a number and two variables.
4. It shows subtraction, not multiplication of variables.

Page 833, Extra Practice, Lesson 8-5

1. $(x-3)(x+3)$
2. $(a-8)(a+8)$
3. $(2x-3y)(2x+3y)$
4. $(1-3z)(1+3z)$
5. $(4a-3b)(4a+3b)$
6. $4(2x^2-3y^2)$
7. $(a-2b)(a+2b)$
8. $3(5r-4)(5r+4)$
9. $(x-6y)(x+6y)$
10. prime
11. $(3x-10y)(3x+10y)$
12. $(7-ab)(7+ab)$
13. prime
14. $(13-4t)(13+4t)$
15. $4(2r^2-1)$

Page 834, Extra Practice, Lesson 9-1

1. D = {all real numbers}, R = $\{y \mid y \geq -1\}$

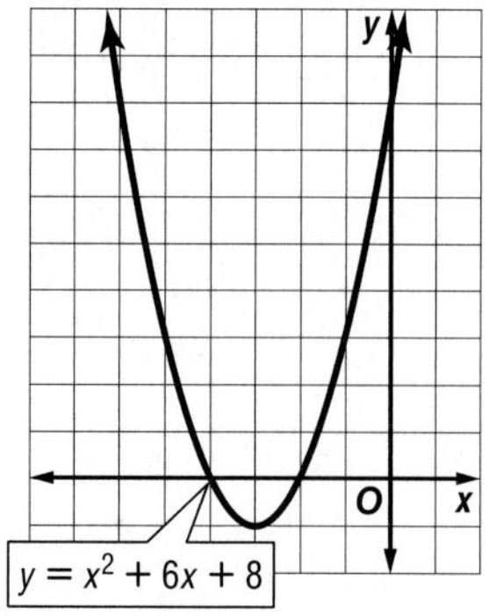

2. D = {all real numbers}, R = $\left\{y \mid y \leq 2\frac{1}{4}\right\}$

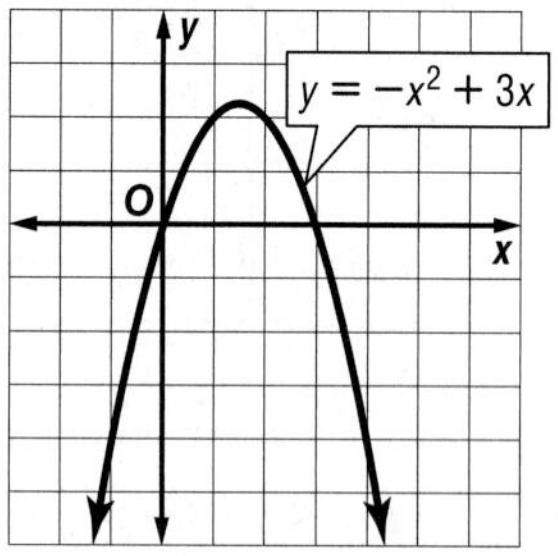

3. D = {all real numbers}, R = $\{y \mid y \leq 0\}$

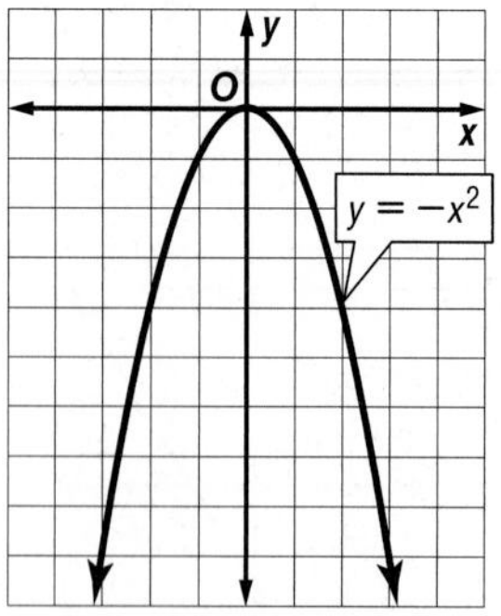

4. $(1, -2)$; $x = 1$; $(0, -3)$

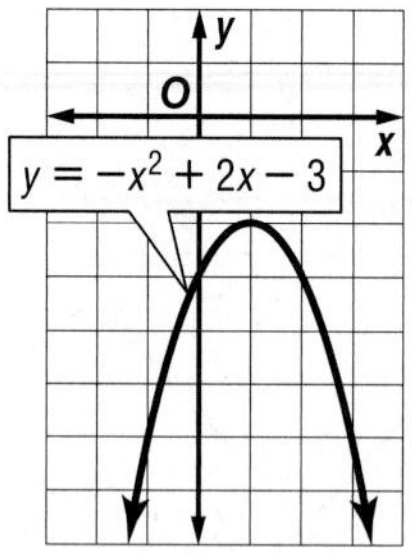

5. $(-4, 32)$; $x = -4$; $(0, 80)$

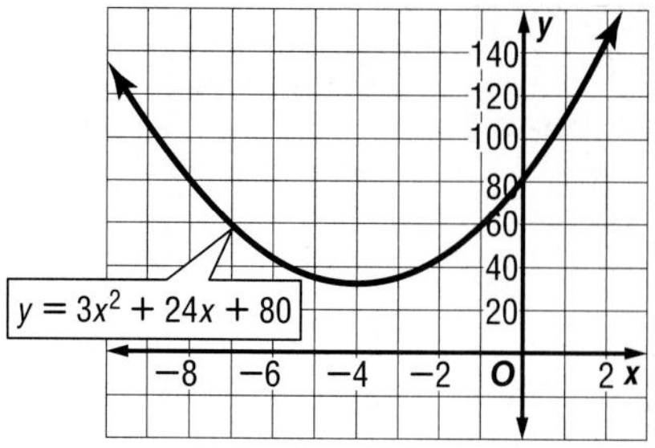

6. $(2, -8)$; $x = 2$; $(0, -4)$

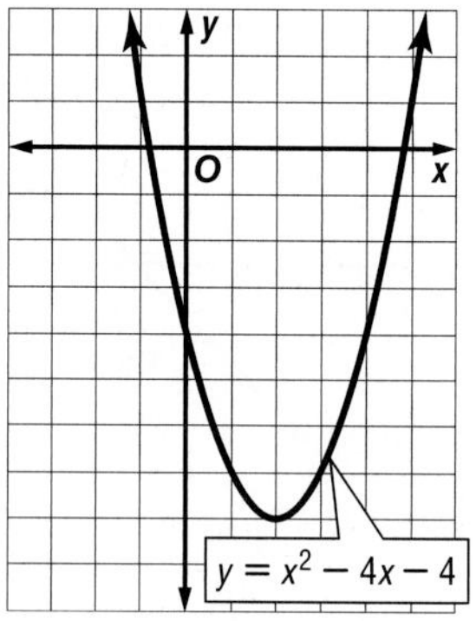

7. $(2, 17)$; $x = 2$; $(0, 37)$

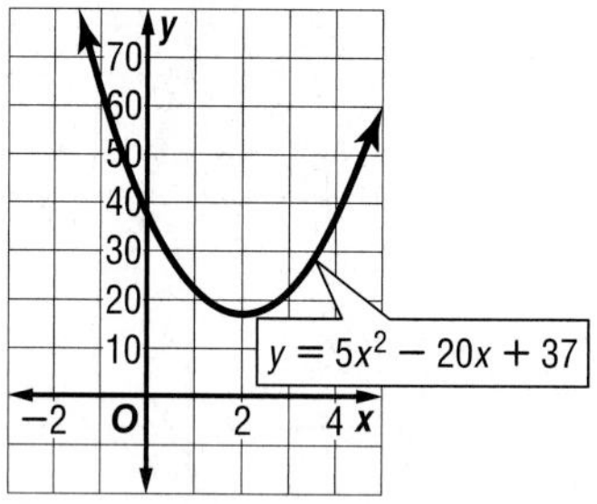

8. $(-1, 0)$; $x = -1$; $(0, 3)$

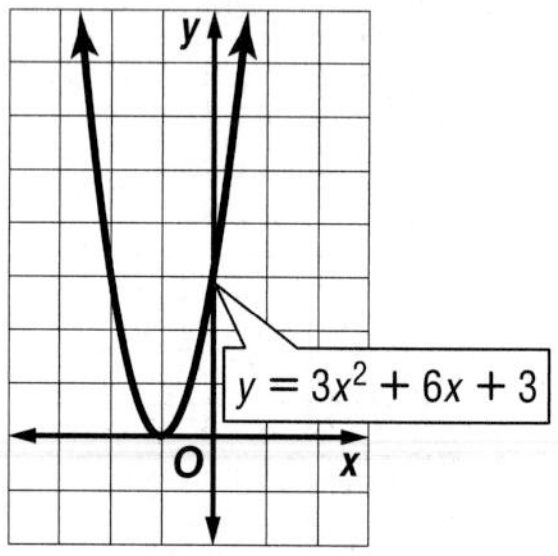

9. $(-3, -18)$; $x = -3$; $(0, 0)$

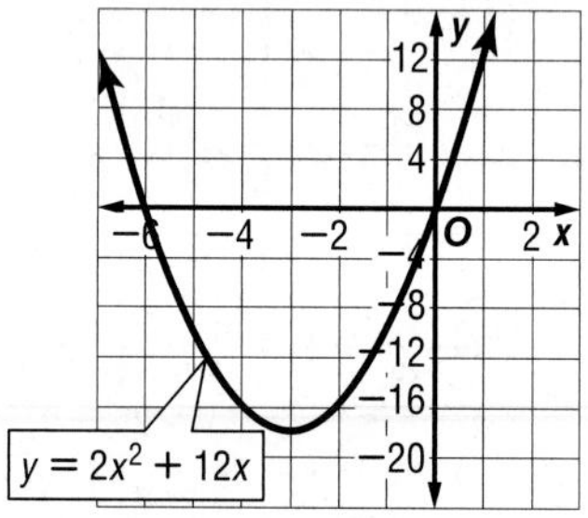

10. $(3, -4)$; $x = 3$; $(0, 5)$

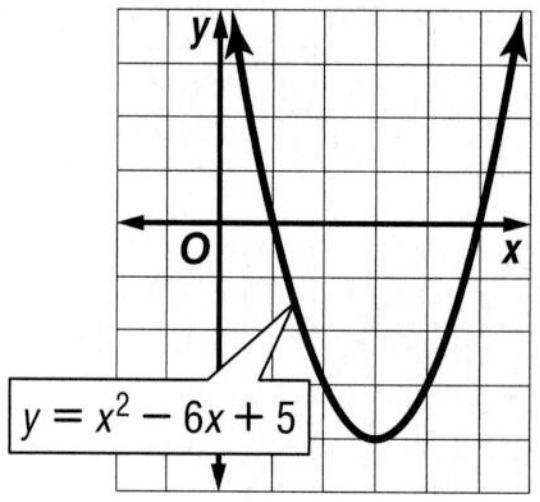

11. $(-3, 0)$; $x = -3$; $(0, 9)$

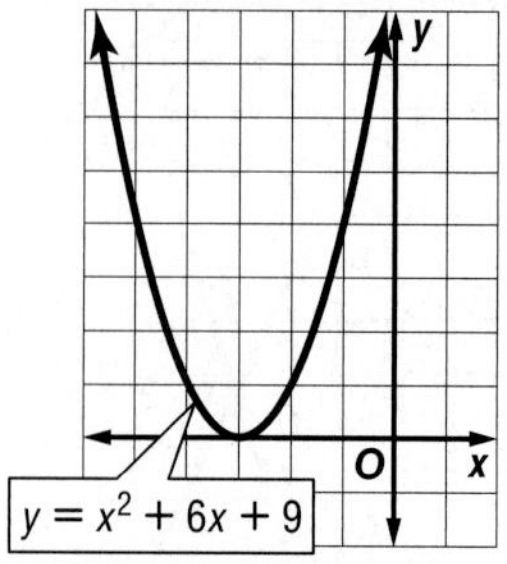

12. (8, 49); $x = 8$; (0, −15)

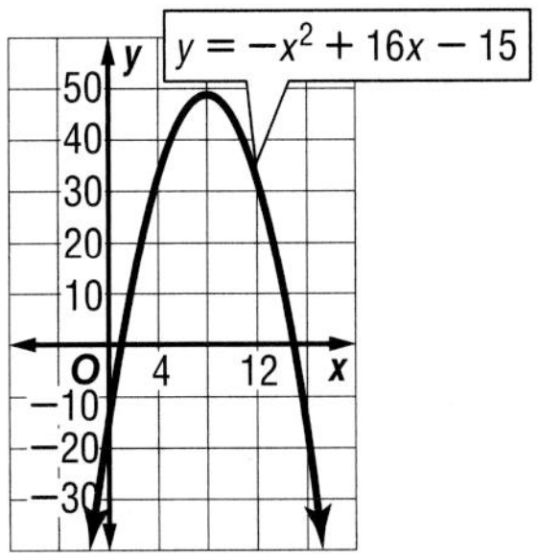

13. minimum; (0, −1);
D = {all real numbers},
R = $\{y \mid y \geq -1\}$

14. maximum; $\left(-\frac{1}{2}, 4\frac{1}{2}\right)$;
D = {all real numbers},
R = $\left\{y \mid y \leq 4\frac{1}{2}\right\}$

15. minimum; (1, −10);
D = {all real numbers},
R = $\{y \mid y \geq -10\}$

16. maximum; (0, −1);
D = {all real numbers},
R = $\{y \mid y \leq -1\}$

17. maximum; $\left(\frac{1}{2}, 1\frac{1}{4}\right)$;
D = {all real numbers},
R = $\left\{y \mid y \leq 1\frac{1}{4}\right\}$

18. maximum; (−0.3, 2.45); D = {all real numbers},
R = $\{y \mid y \leq 2.45\}$

Page 834, Extra Practice, Lesson 9-2

1.

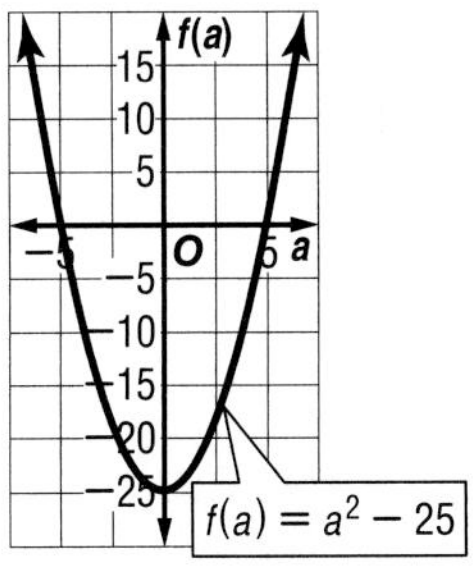

2.

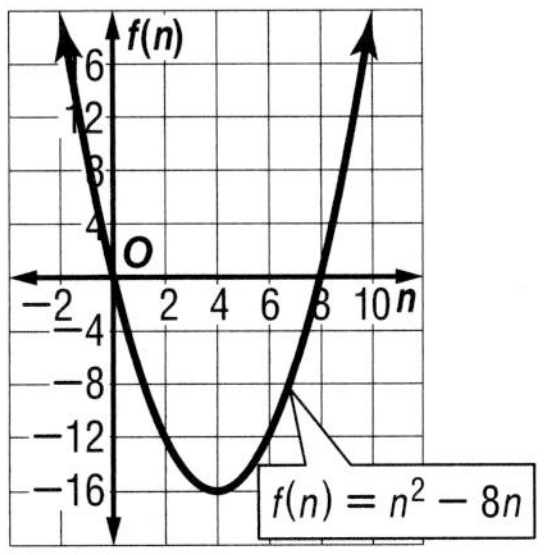

3.

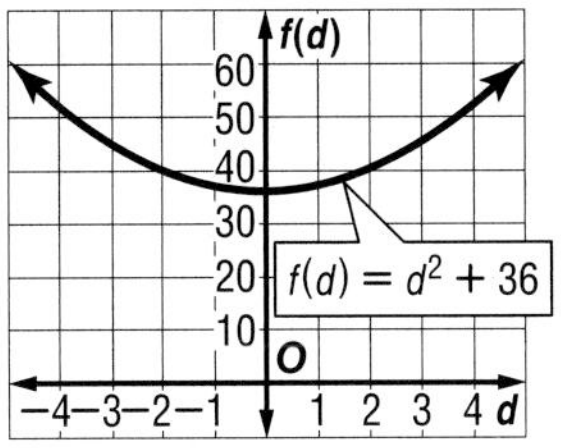

4.

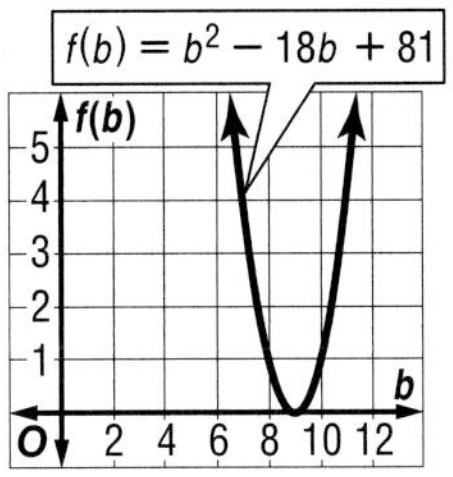

5.

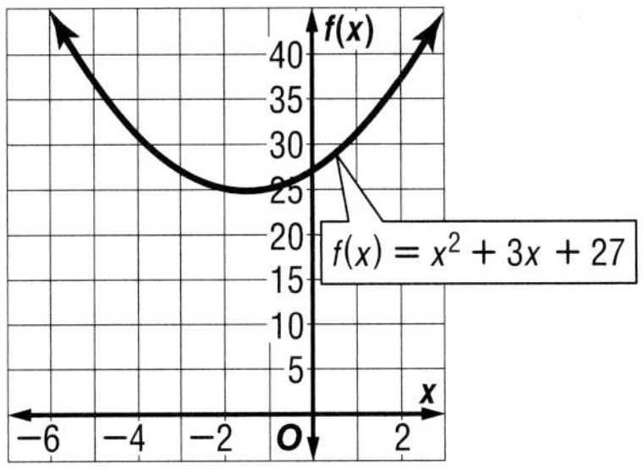

6.

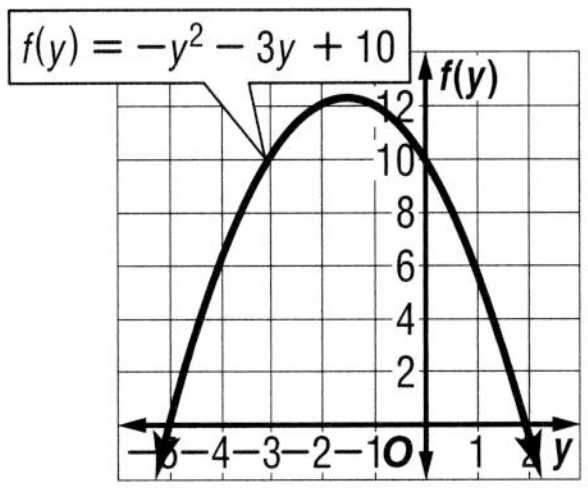

7.

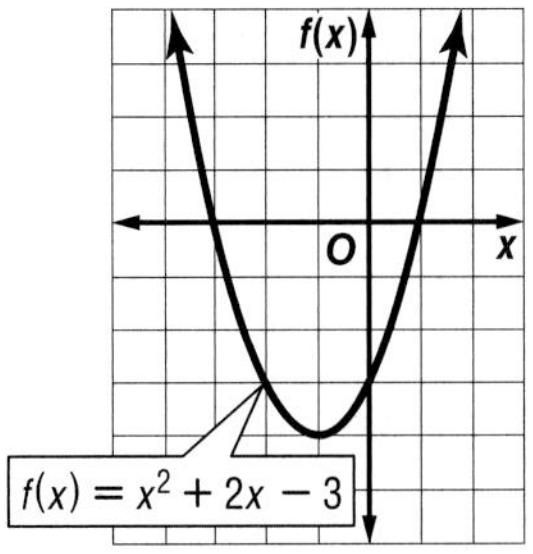

8.

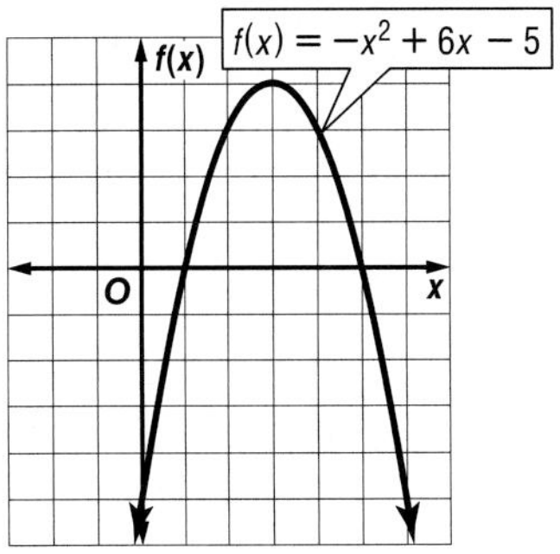

9.

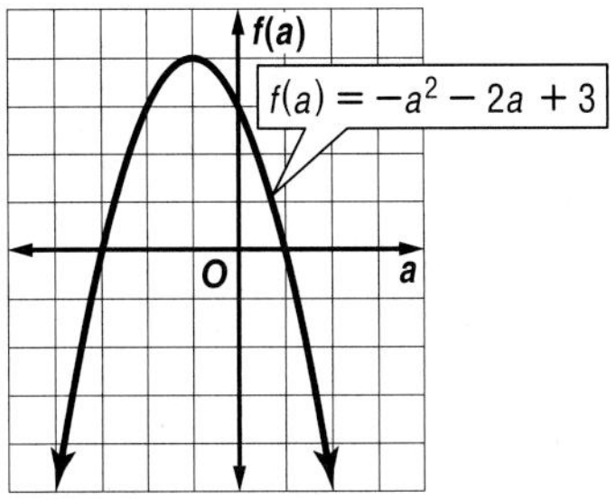

10.

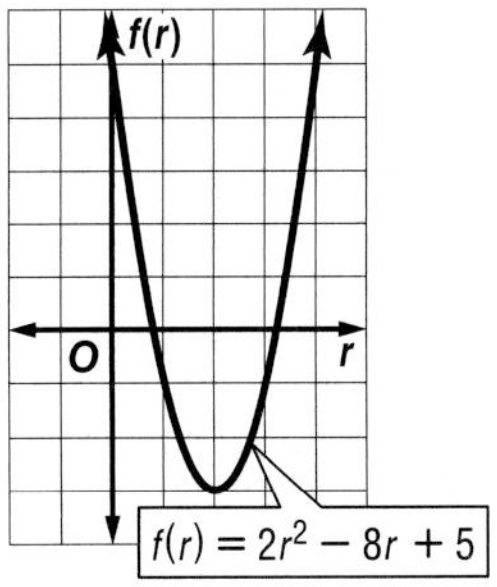

11.

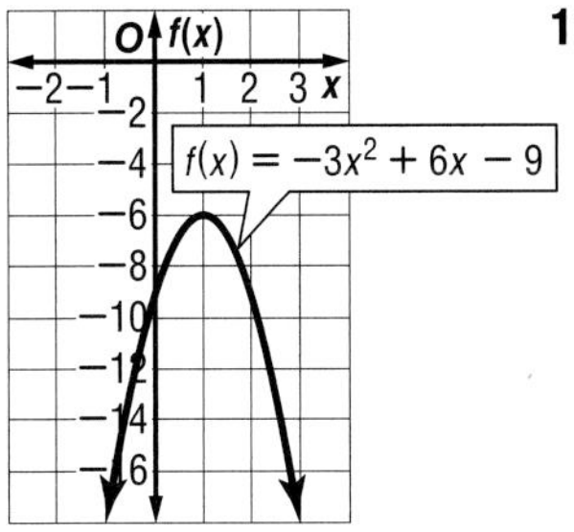

12.

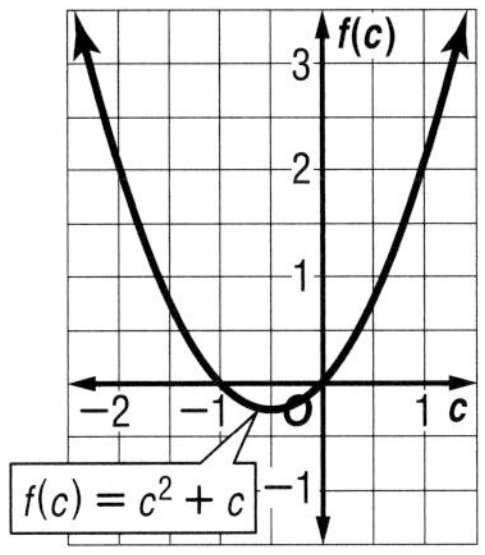

13.

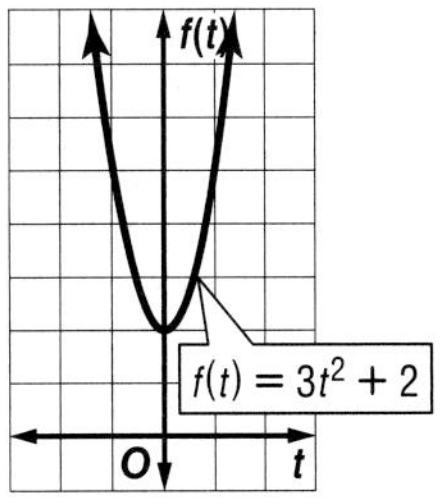

14.

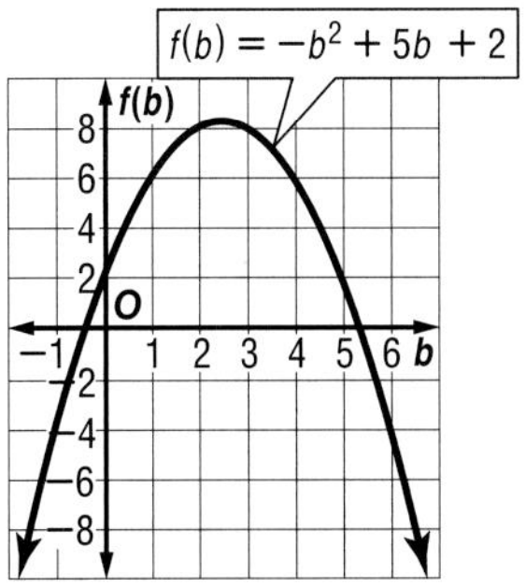

15. 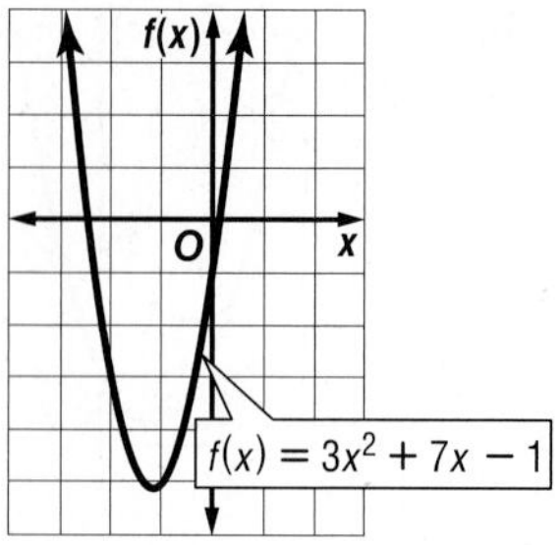

Page 836, Extra Practice, Lesson 9-6

1. 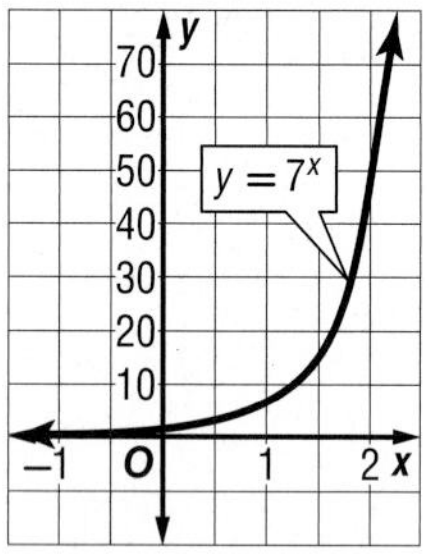

D = {all real numbers},
R = {y | y > 0}

2. 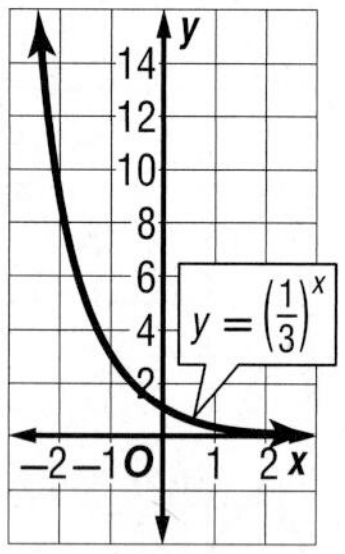

D = {all real numbers},
R = {y | y > 0}

3. 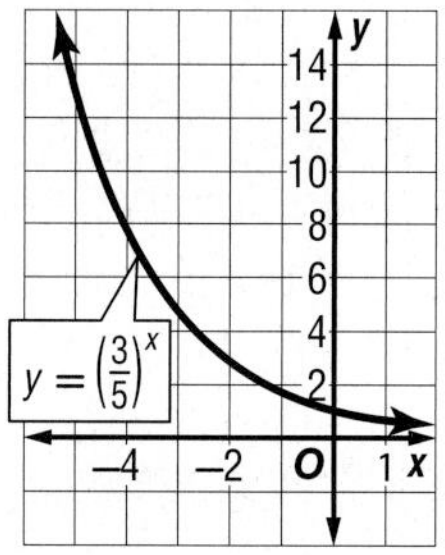

D = {all real numbers},
R = {y | y > 0}

4. 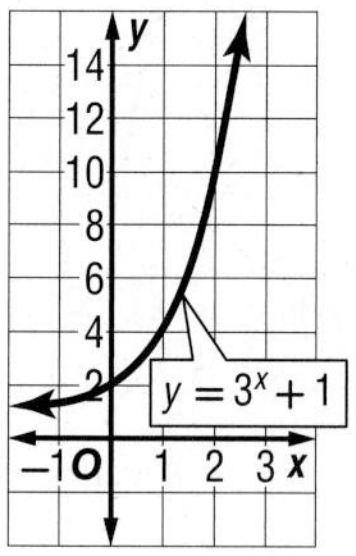

5. 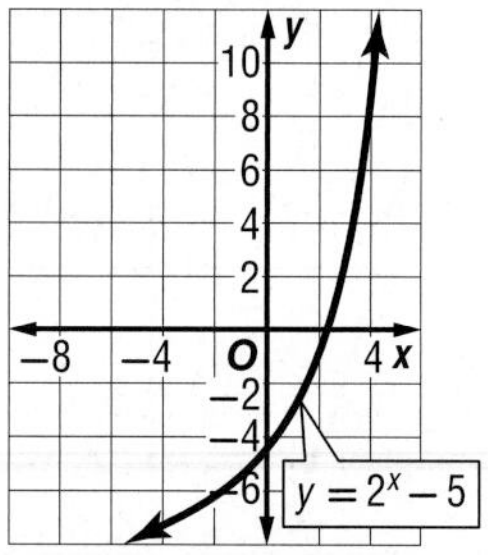

6. 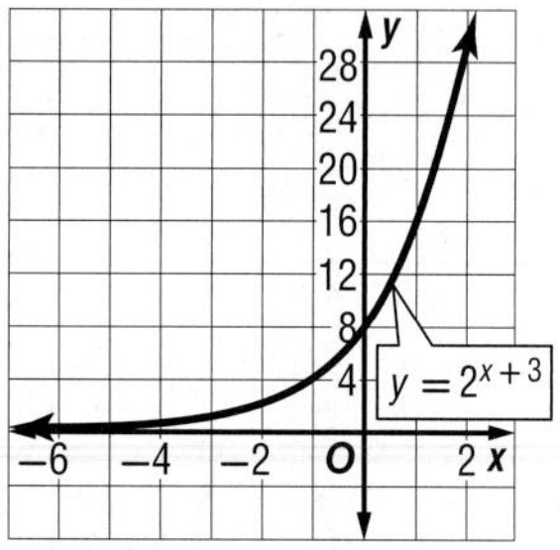

7. 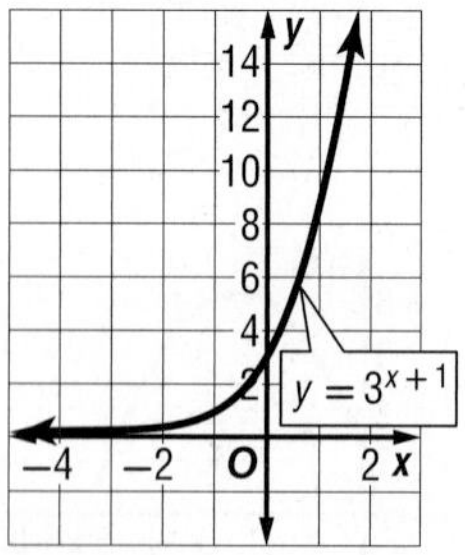

8. 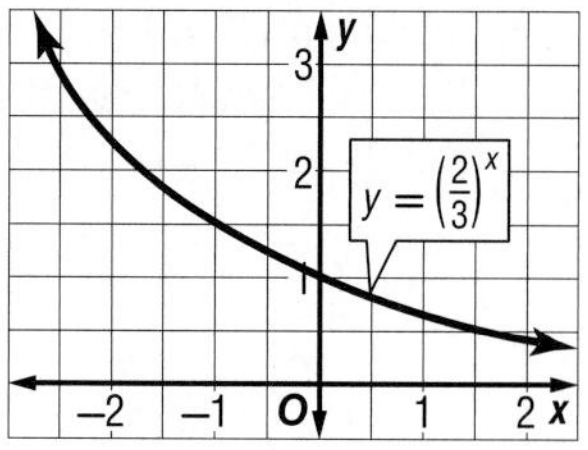

9. 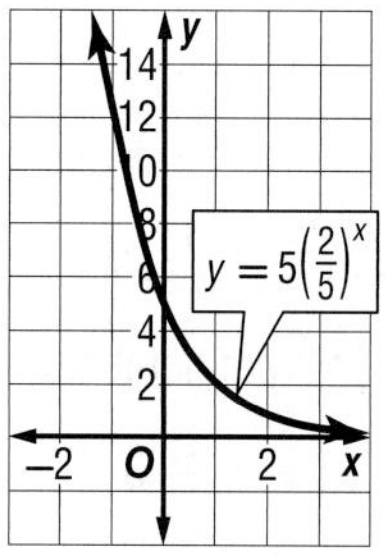

10. 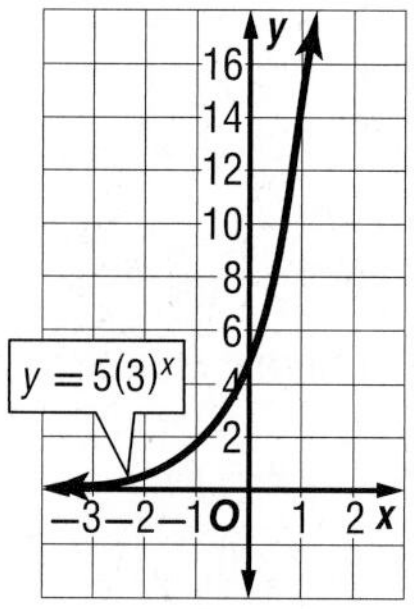

11. 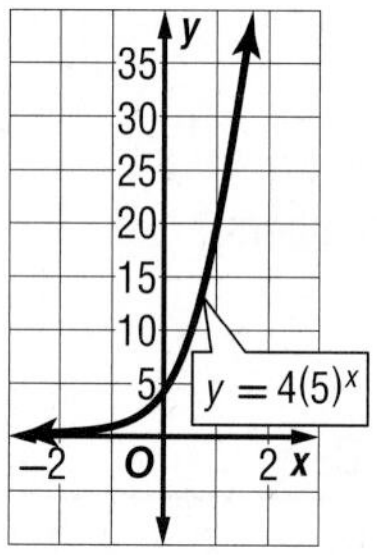

12. 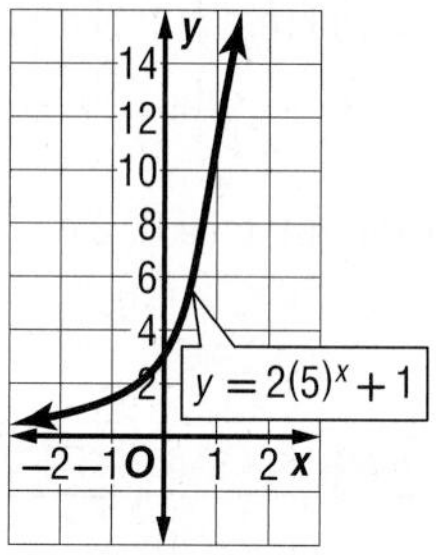

13. 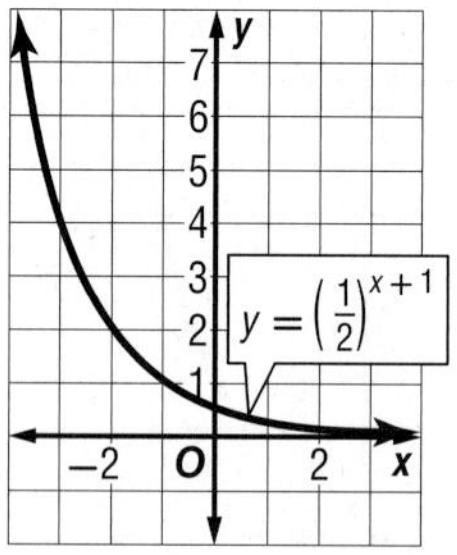

14. 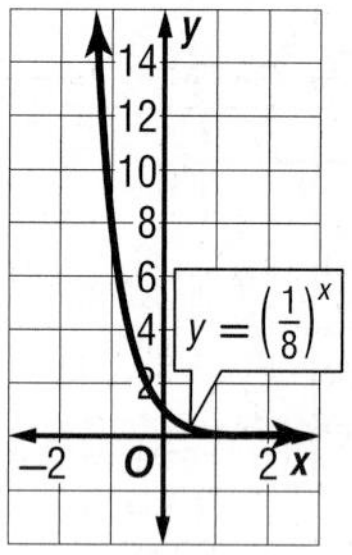

15. 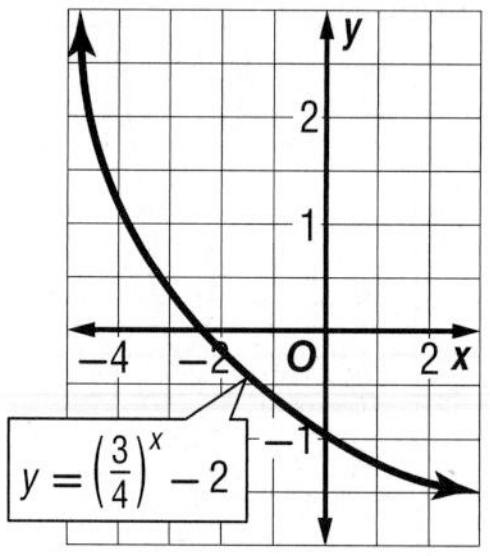

Page 837, Extra Practice, Lesson 9-9

1. quadratic;

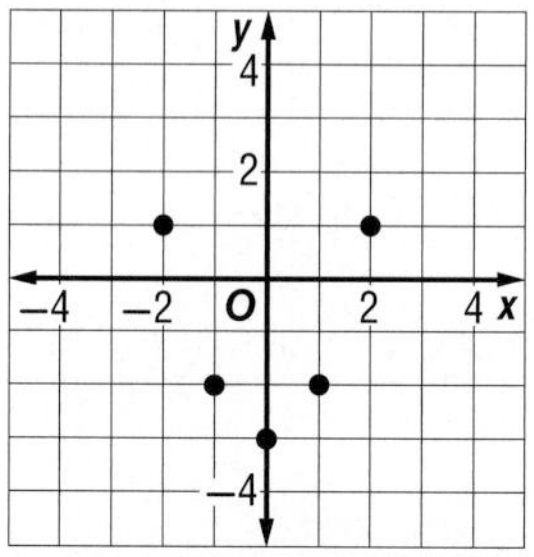

2. linear;

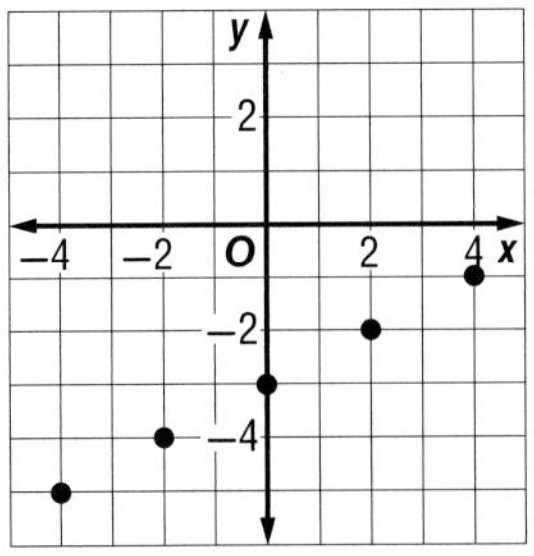

3. exponential;

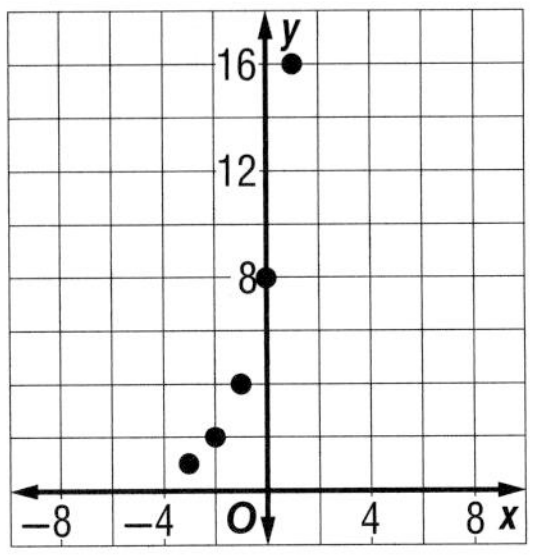

4. quadratic; $y = 0.25x^2$

5. exponential; $y = 2 \cdot 3^x$

6. linear; $y = \frac{1}{2}x + 5$

7. exponential; $y = 3^x$

8. quadratic; $y = 1.2x^2$

Page 837, Extra Practice, Lesson 10-1

1. $D = \{x \mid x \geq 4\}$; $R = \{y \mid y \geq 0\}$

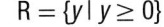

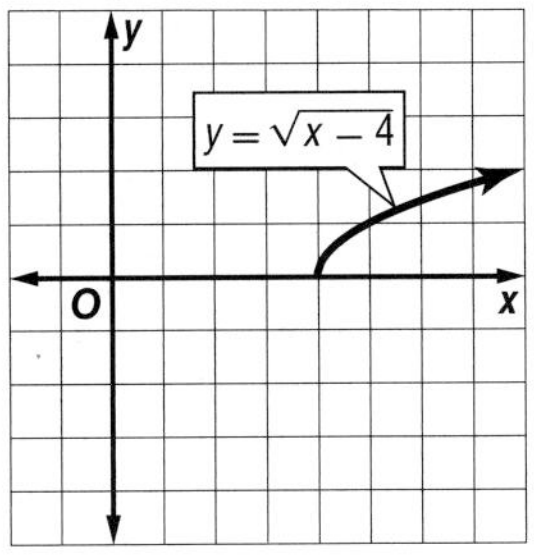

2. $D = \{x \mid x \geq -3\}$; $R = \{y \mid y \geq -1\}$

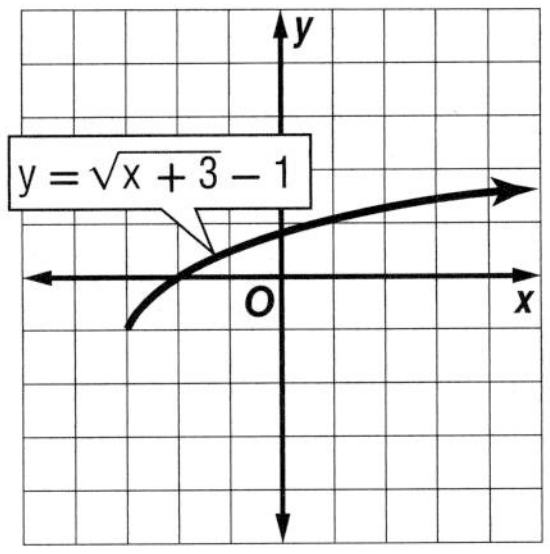

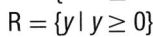

3. $D = \{x \mid x \geq -2\}$; $R = \{y \mid y \geq 0\}$

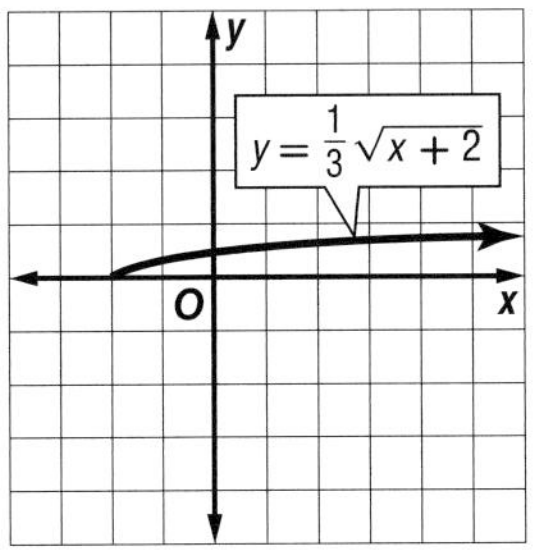

4. $D = \{x \mid x \geq -2.5\}$; $R = \{y \mid y \geq 0\}$

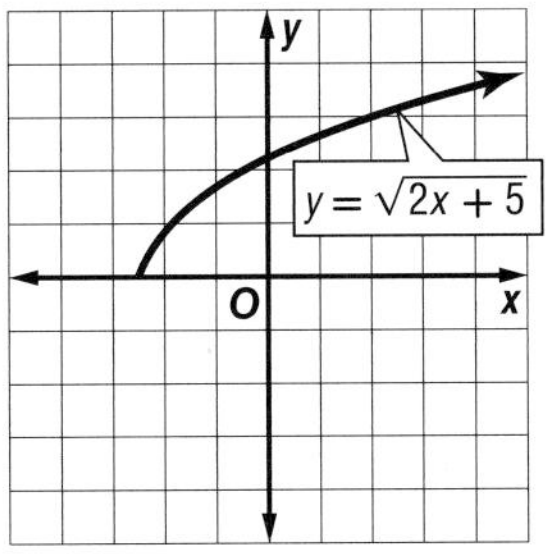

5. $D = \{x \mid x \geq 0\}$; $R = \{y \mid y \leq 0\}$

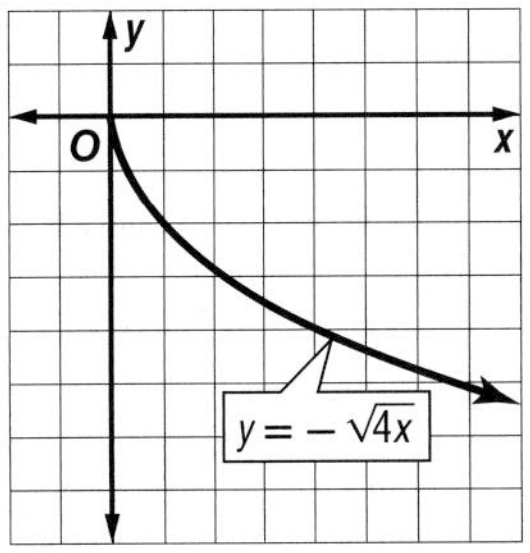

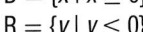

6. $D = \{x \mid x \geq 0\}$; $R = \{y \mid y \geq 0\}$

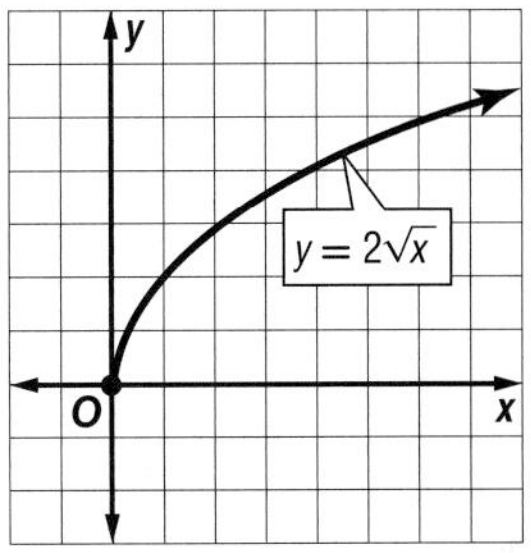

7. $D = \{x \mid x \geq 0\}$; $R = \{y \mid y \leq 0\}$

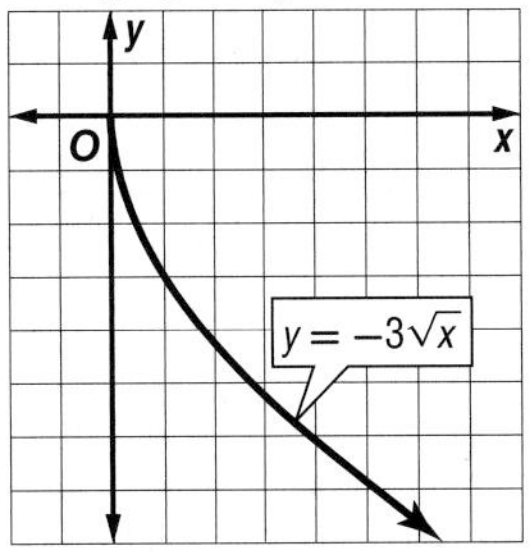

8. $D = \{x \mid x \geq 0\}$; $R = \{y \mid y \geq 5\}$

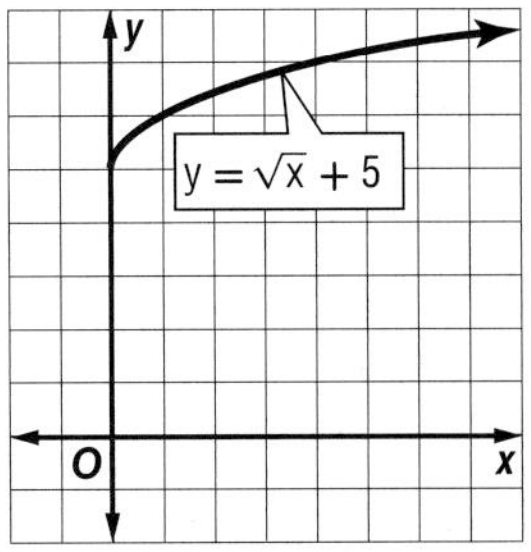

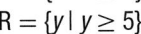

9. $D = \{x \mid x \geq 0\}$; $R = \{y \mid y \geq -1\}$

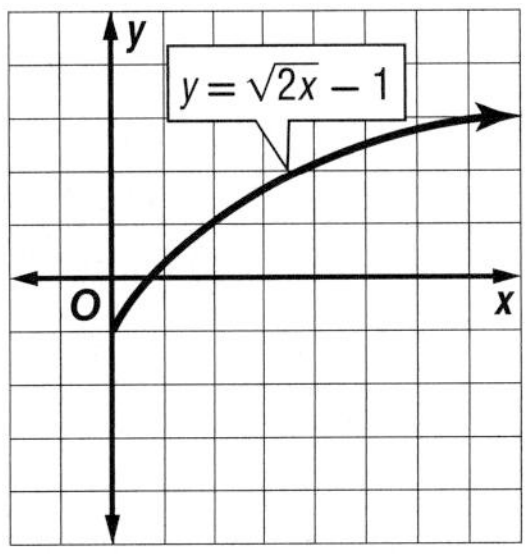

10. $D = \{x \mid x \geq 0\}$; $R = \{y \mid y \geq 1\}$

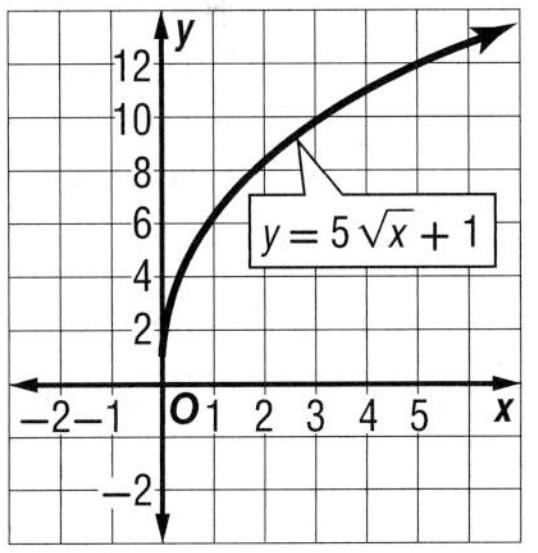

11. $D = \{x \mid x \geq -1\}$; $R = \{y \mid y \geq -2\}$

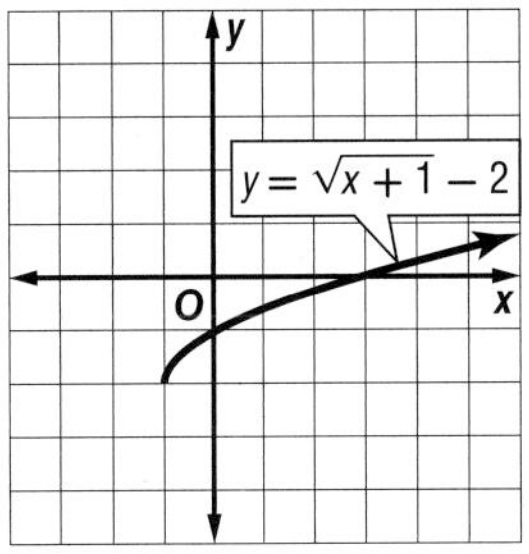

12. $D = \{x \mid x \geq -3\}$; $R = \{y \mid y \leq 6\}$

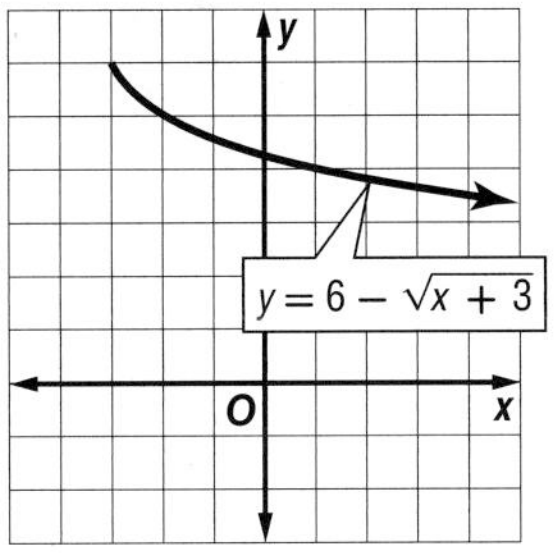

Page 840, Extra Practice, Lesson 11-1

1. $y = \frac{75}{x}$

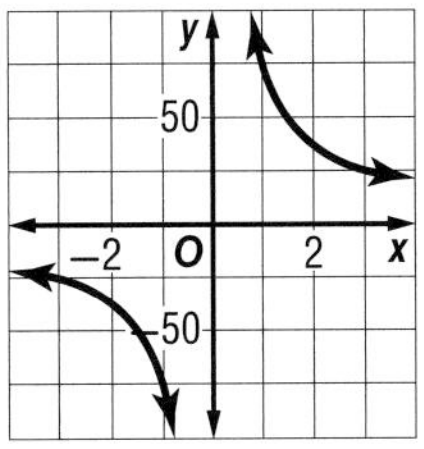

2. $y = \frac{-15}{x}$

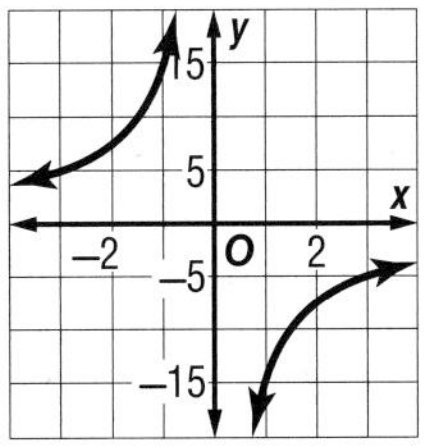

3. $y = \frac{12}{x}$

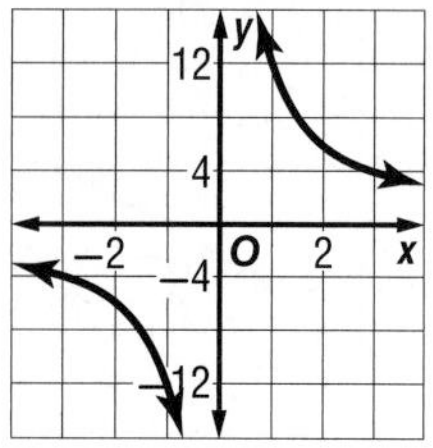

4. $y = \frac{-0.5}{x}$

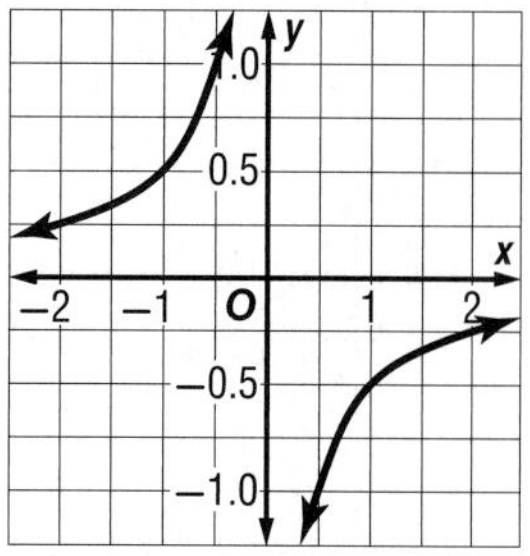

5. $y = \frac{-7.5}{x}$

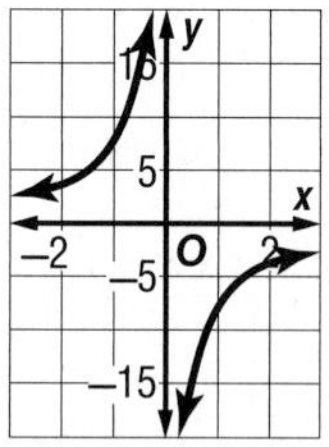

6. $y = \frac{2}{x}$

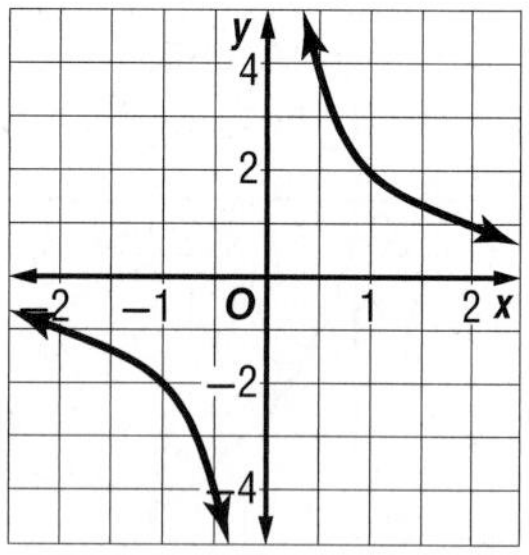

Page 843, Extra Practice, Lesson 12-3

1. The sample consists of 125 delivery customers. The population is all the delivery customers for that time period. The sample statistic is the number of people in the sample who were satisfied with their delivery and responded YES. The population parameter is the number of customers who used the delivery service and were satisfied.

2. The sample is 1200 high school band members. The population is all the high school band members across the country. The sample statistic is the mean of the number of hours they spent practicing each week during football season. The population parameter is the mean number of practice hours spent by all the high school band players in the United States.

Page 843, Extra Practice, Lesson 12-4

1. Order is not important.
2. Order of runners can make a difference.
3. Order is not important.
4. Order of winning is important.

Page 845, Mixed Problem Solving, Chapter 1

9. H: it is after school; C: Mei and Janel will go to the mall; If it is after school, then Mei and Janel will go to the mall.

Page 846, Mixed Problem Solving, Chapter 2

7. Yes; he took 1 hour and 13 minutes, which was within the time constraint set by his mother.

9b. Sample answer: increase because the car was sold for a greater amount than the purchase price.

Page 847, Mixed Problem Solving, Chapter 3

1a. **Movies**

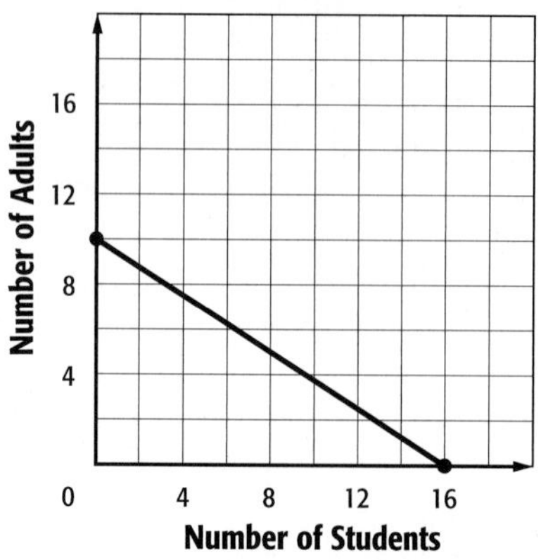

1b. If there are no students, then there are 10 adults. If there are no adults, then there are 16 students.

2c. **Fundraising**

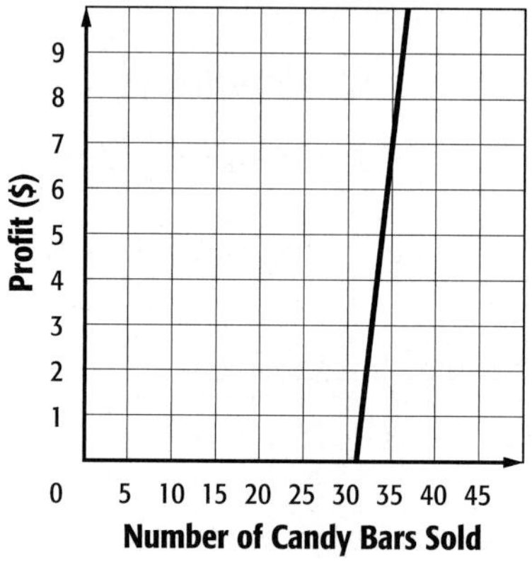

3. 0.08; an average decrease in cost of $0.08 per year.

4b. **Salary**

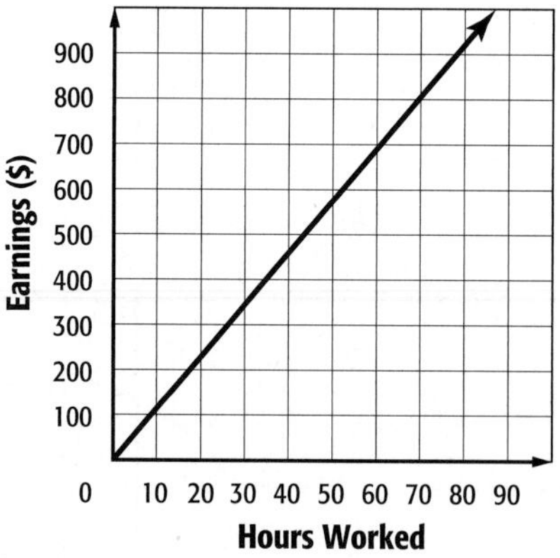

6b. **Savings Account**

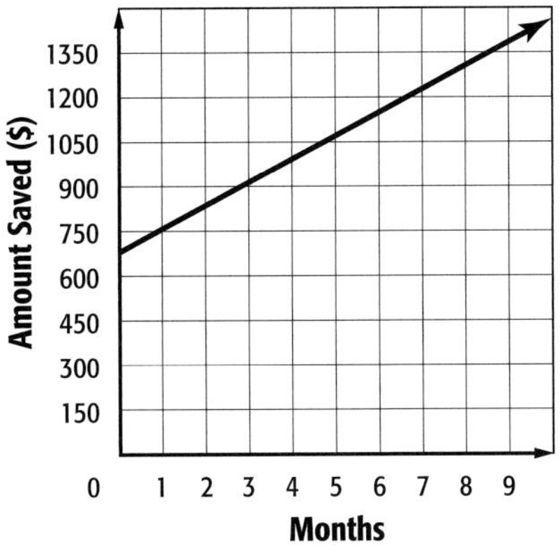

7a. **Bonus**

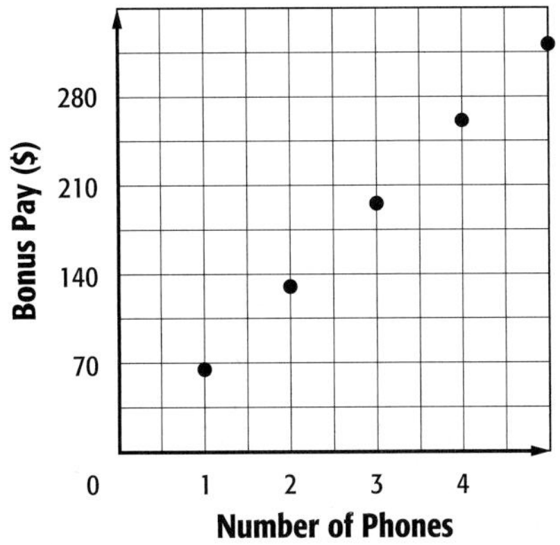

8a. **Strawberries**

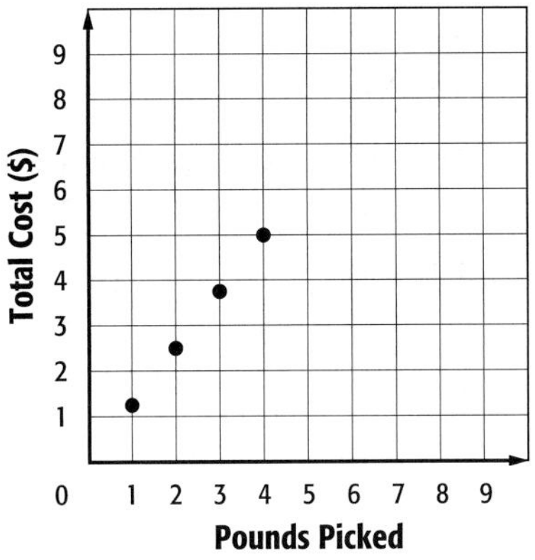

Page 848, Mixed Problem Solving, Chapter 4

1b. **Saving Money**

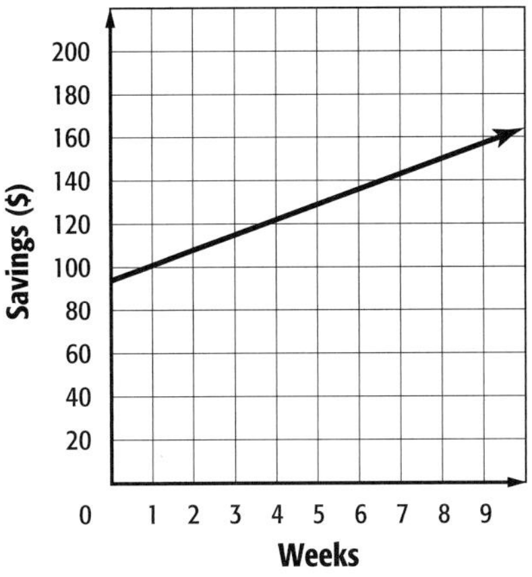

5.

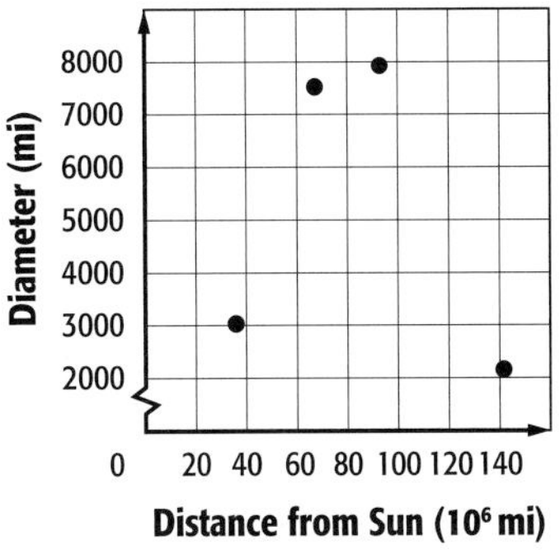

7a. **Parking**

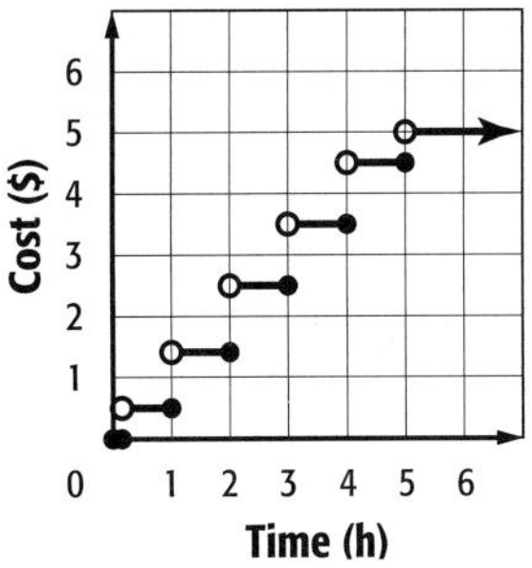

Page 849, Mixed Problem Solving, Chapter 5

2. Sample answer: Let $t =$ the number of tomato varieties for which they do not produce seeds, $t + 200 > 10{,}000$; $\{t \mid t > 9800\}$.

8a. $\{t \mid 77 \le t \le 83\}$

8b.

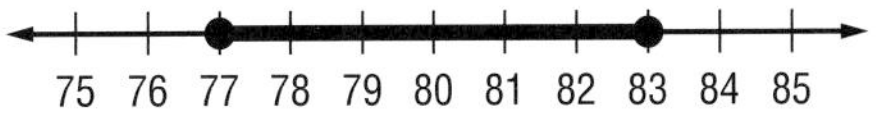

13. Yes, the total weight of the items is 2385 pounds which is under the truck's weight limit.

Page 850, Mixed Problem Solving, Chapter 6

1b.

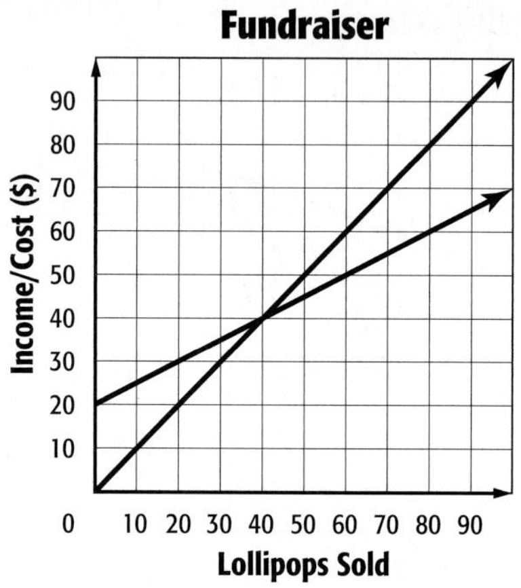

7. $24p + 4c = 320$, $2p + c = 50$; substitution; paper \$7.50 per ream, inkjet cartridges \$35 each.

8a. $\begin{bmatrix} 20{,}320 & 0 \\ 14{,}494 & -282 \\ 14{,}433 & 3315 \\ 13{,}796 & 0 \\ 535 & -8 \\ 13{,}804 & 3099 \end{bmatrix}$

9a. $2a + 3c = 160$, $5a + 2c = 246$

9b. $\left[\begin{array}{cc|c} 2 & 3 & 160 \\ 5 & 2 & 246 \end{array}\right]$

Page 853, Mixed Problem Solving, Chapter 9

1a.

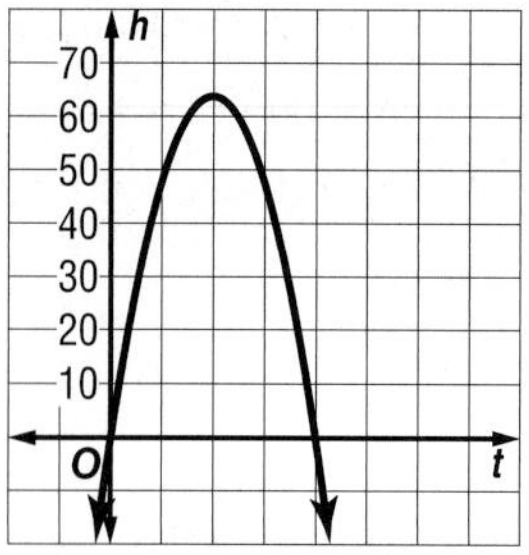

4. The graph of the parent function $h = t^2$ is reflected across the x-axis, stretched vertically, and translated up 20 units.

5a.

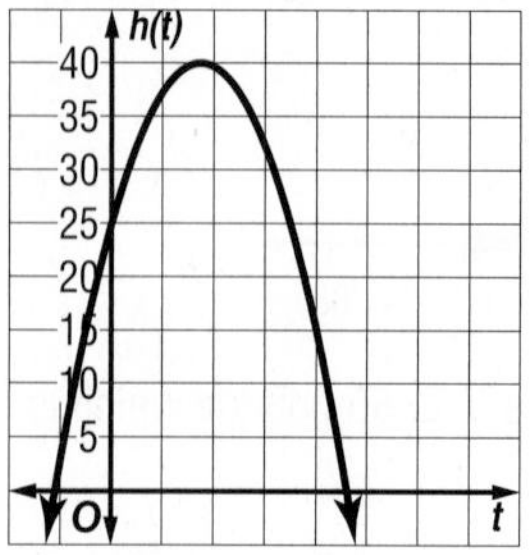

Page 855, Mixed Problem Solving, Chapter 11

3.

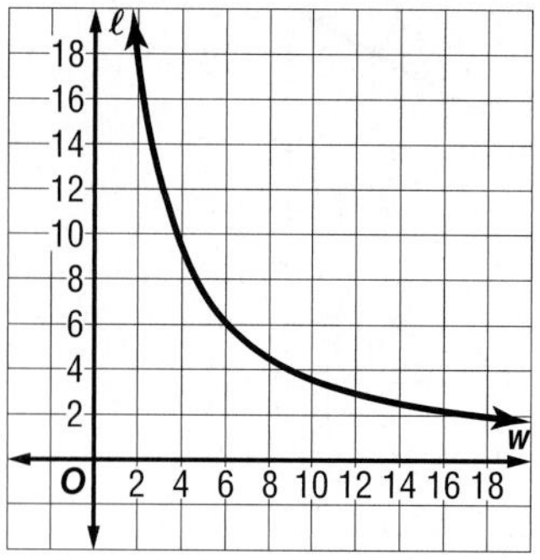

4a.

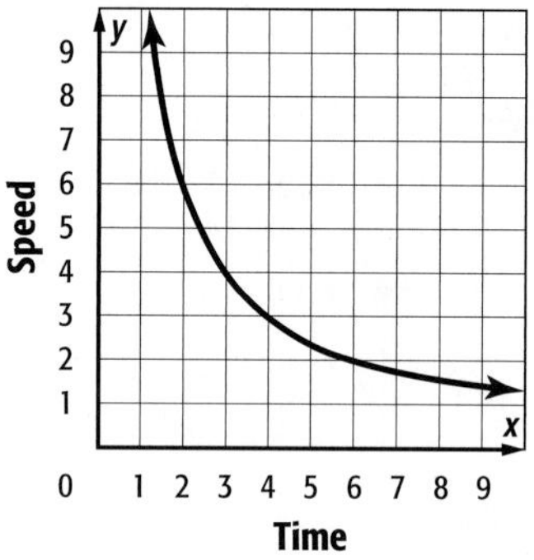

Page 856, Chapter 12 Statistics and Probability

1a. sample: every fourth student to walk in the classroom; population: every student that comes into the classroom

1c. Unbiased; there is no reason that every fourth student would be inclined to choose one candy over another.

1d. Simple; the selection is just a random choice of the population.

2. Median; there is an outlier with no gaps in the middle of the data; \$600.

3. While the report states that the students were chosen randomly, it does not say how many students were chosen. The number of students invited to vote may not be large enough to be a valid sample of the student body. Furthermore, the data was collected from a sample of students that were early for school. Students who were likely to vote for after school were not yet present. The results were given in percentages; again there is no mention of how many students were asked to ensure a large enough sample. The 24% could mean 1 out of 4.

9a. $0.03 + 0.08 + 0.08 + 0.10 + 0.30 + 0.41 = 1$

9c.

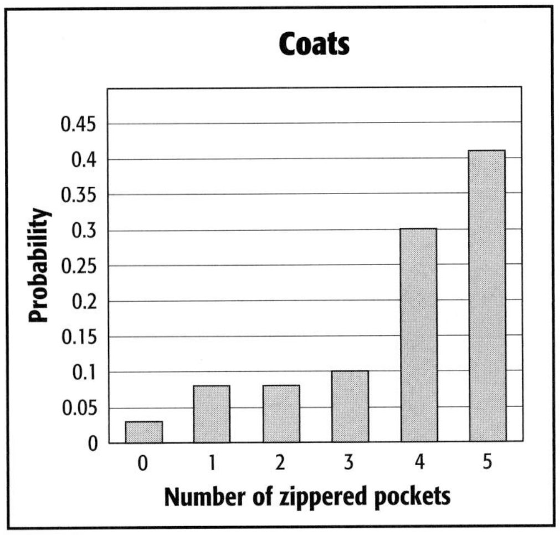

10. Sample answer: A bag with 8 white marbles to stand for successful throws and 2 red marbles to stand for misses; the probability of success is $\frac{8}{10}$ or 80% and the probability of a miss is $\frac{2}{10}$ or 20%.

Student Handbook Answer Appendix

Key Concepts

Chapter 1

Expressions, Equations, and Functions

Translating Verbal to Algebraic Expressions (p. 6)
- **Addition** more than, sum, plus, increased by, added to
- **Subtraction** less than, subtracted from, difference, decreased by, minus
- **Multiplication** product of, multiplied by, times, of
- **Division** quotient of, divided by

Order of Operations (p. 10)
- **Step 1** Evaluate expressions inside grouping symbols.
- **Step 2** Evaluate all powers.
- **Step 3** Multiply and/or divide from left to right.
- **Step 4** Add and/or subtract from left to right.

Reflexive Property (p. 16)
Any quantity is equal to itself.

Symmetric Property (p. 16)
If one quantity equals a second quantity, then the second quantity equals the first.

Transitive Property (p. 16)
If one quantity equals a second quantity and the second quantity equals a third quantity, then the first quantity equals the third quantity.

Substitution Property (p. 16)
A quantity may be substituted for its equal in any expression.

Additive Identity (p. 16)
For any number a, the sum of a and 0 is a.

Additive Inverse (p. 16)
A number and its opposite are additive inverses of each other. The sum of a number and its additive inverse is 0.

Multiplicative Identity (p. 17)
For any number a, the product of a and 1 is a.

Multiplicative Property of Zero (p. 17)
For any number a, the product of a and 0 is 0.

Multiplicative Inverse (p. 17)
For every number $\frac{a}{b}$, where $a, b \neq 0$, there is exactly one number $\frac{b}{a}$ such that the product of $\frac{a}{b}$ and $\frac{b}{a}$ is 1.

Commutative Property (p. 18)
The order in which you add or multiply numbers does not change their sum or product.

Key Concepts

Associative Property (p. 18)
The way you group three or more numbers when adding or multiplying does not change their sum or product.

Distributive Property (p. 23)
For any numbers a, b, and c, $a(b + c) = ab + ac$ and $(b + c)a = ba + ca$ and $a(b - c) = ab - ac$ and $(b - c)a = ba - ca$.

Function (p. 45)
A function is a relation in which each element of the domain is paired with *exactly* one element of the range.

Chapter 2 Linear Equations

Addition Property of Equality (p. 83)
If an equation is true and the same number is added to each side of the equation, the resulting equivalent equation is also true.

Subtraction Property of Equality (p. 84)
If an equation is true and the same number is subtracted from each side of the equation, the resulting equivalent equation is also true.

Multiplication Property of Equality (p. 84)
If an equation is true and each side is multiplied by the same nonzero number, the resulting equation is equivalent.

Division Property of Equality (p. 84)
If an equation is true and each side is divided by the same number, the resulting equation is true.

Steps for Solving Equations (p. 99)
Step 1 Simplify the expressions on each side. Use the Distributive Property as needed.
Step 2 Use the Addition and/or Subtraction Properties of Equality to get the variables on one side and the numbers without variables on the other side. Simplify.
Step 3 Use the Multiplication or Division Property of Equality to solve.

Absolute Value Equations (p. 104)
When solving equations that involve absolute values, there are two cases to consider.
Case 1 The expression inside the absolute value symbol is positive.
Case 2 The expression inside the absolute value symbol is negative.

Means-Extremes Property of Proportion (p. 112)
In a proportion, the product of the extremes is equal to the product of the means.

Chapter 3 Linear Functions

Standard Form of a Linear Equation (p. 153)
The standard form of a linear equation is $Ax + By = C$, where $A \geq 0$, A and B are not both zero, and A, B, and C are integers with a greatest common factor of 1.

Linear Function (p. 161)
A linear function is a function with a graph of a line.

Rate of Change (p. 170)
If x is the independent variable and y is the dependent variable, then

rate of change $= \dfrac{\text{change in } y}{\text{change in } x}$.

Slope (p. 173)
The slope of a line is the ratio of the rise to the run.

Arithmetic Sequence (p. 187)
An arithmetic sequence is a numerical pattern that increases or decreases at a constant rate called the *common difference.*

***n*th Term of an Arithmetic Sequence** (p. 188)
The nth term of an arithmetic sequence with first term a_1 and common difference d is given by $a_n = a_1 + (n - 1)d$, where n is a positive integer.

Proportional Relationship (p. 195)
A relationship is proportional if its equation is of the form $y = kx$, $k \neq 0$. The graph passes through (0, 0).

Chapter 4 Linear Functions and Equations

Slope-Intercept Form (p. 214)
The slope-intercept form of a linear equation is $y = mx + b$, where m is the slope and b is the y-intercept.

Point-Slope Form (p. 231)
The linear equation $y - y_1 = m(x - x_1)$ is written in point-slope form, where (x_1, y_1) is a given point on a non-vertical line and m is the slope of the line.

Writing Equations (p. 232)

Given the Slope and One Point	Given Two Points
Step 1 Substitute the values of m, x, and y into the slope-intercept form and solve for b. Or, use the point-slope form. Substitute the value of m and let x and y be (x_1, y_1). **Step 2** Write the slope-intercept form using the values of m and b.	**Step 1** Find the slope. **Step 2** Choose one of the two points to use. **Step 3** Follow the steps for writing an equation given the slope and one point.

Parallel and Perpendicular Lines (p. 240)

Parallel Lines	Perpendicular Lines
Two nonvertical lines are parallel if they have the same slope.	Two nonvertical lines are perpendicular if the product of their slopes is −1.

Key Concepts

Using a Linear Function to Model Data (p. 246)

Step 1 Make a scatter plot. Determine whether any relationship exists in the data.

Step 2 Draw a line that seems to pass close to most of the data points.

Step 3 Use two points on the line of fit to write an equation for the line.

Step 4 Use the line of fit to make predictions.

Greatest Integer Function (p. 261)
The greatest integer function can be described by an equation of the form $f(x) = [\![x]\!]$.

Absolute Value Function (p. 262)

$$f(x) = |x|, \text{ defined as } f(x) = \begin{cases} x \text{ if } x > 0 \\ 0 \text{ if } x = 0 \\ -x \text{ if } x < 0 \end{cases}$$

Chapter 5 — Linear Inequalities

Addition Property of Inequalities (p. 283)
If any number is added to each side of a true inequality, the resulting inequality is also true.

Subtraction Property of Inequalities (p. 284)
If any number is subtracted from each side of a true inequality, the resulting inequality is also true.

Multiplication Property of Inequalities (p. 290)
If a true inequality is multiplied by a positive number, the resulting inequality is also true. If a true inequality multiplied by a negative number, the direction of the inequality sign is changed to make the resulting inequality also true.

Division Property of Inequalities (p. 292)
If a true inequality is divided by a positive number, the resulting inequality is also true. If a true inequality is divided by a negative number, the direction of the inequality sign is changed to make the resulting inequality also true.

Graphing Linear Inequalities (p. 315)

Step 1 Graph the boundary. Use a solid line when the inequality contains $\leq$ or $\geq$. Use a dashed line when the inequality contains $<$ or $>$.

Step 2 Use a test points to determine which half-plane should be shaded.

Step 3 Shade the half-plane that contains the solution.

Chapter 6 — Systems of Linear Equations and Inequalities

Solving by Substitution (p. 342)

Step 1 When necessary, solve at least one equation for one variable.

Step 2 Substitute the resulting expression from Step 1 into the other equation to replace the variable. Then solve the equation.

Step 3 Substitute the value from Step 2 into either equation, and solve for the other variable. Write the solution as an ordered pair.

Solving by Elimination Using Addition (p. 348)

Step 1 Write the system so like terms with the same or opposite coefficients are aligned.

Step 2 Add or subtract the equations eliminating one variable. Then solve the equation.

Step 3 Substitute the value from Step 2 into one of the equations and solve for the other variable. Write the solution as an ordered pair.

Solving by Elimination Using Multiplication (p. 355)

Step 1 Multiply at least one equation by a constant to result in two equations that contain opposite terms.

Step 2 Add or subtract the equations eliminating one variable. Then solve the equation.

Step 3 Substitute the value from Step 2 into one of the equations and solve for the other variable. Write the solution as an ordered pair.

Elementary Row Operations (p. 377)
The following operations can be performed on an augmented matrix.
- Interchange any two rows.
- Multiply all entries in a row by a nonzero constant.
- Replace one row with the sum of that row and a multiple of another row.

Chapter 7 — Polynomials

Product of Powers (p. 402)
To multiply two powers that have the same base, add their exponents.

Power of a Power (p. 402)
To find the power of a power, multiply the exponents.

Power of a Product (p. 403)
To find the power of a product, find the power of each factor and multiply.

Simplify Expressions (p. 404)
To simplify a monomial expression, write an equivalent expression in which:
- each base appears exactly once,
- there are no powers of powers, and
- all fractions are in simplest form.

Quotient of Powers (p. 408)
To divide two powers with the same base, subtract the exponents.

Power of a Quotient (p. 409)
To find the power of a quotient, find the power of the numerator and the power of the denominator.

Zero Exponent Property (p. 410)
Any nonzero number raised to the zero power is equal to 1.

Negative Exponent Property (p. 410)
For any nonzero number a and any integer n, a^{-n} is the reciprocal of a^n. Also, the reciprocal of $a^{-n} = a^n$.

Standard Form to Scientific Notation (p. 416)

Step 1 Move the decimal point until it is to the right of the first nonzero digit. The result is a real number a.

Step 2 Note the number of places n and the direction that you moved the decimal point.

Step 3 If the decimal point is moved left, write the number as $a \times 10^n$. If the decimal point is moved right, write the number as $a \times 10^{-n}$.

Step 4 Remove the extra zeros.

Scientific Notation to Standard Form (p. 417)

Step 1 In $a \times 10^n$, note whether $n > 0$ or $n < 0$.

Step 2 If $n > 0$, move the decimal point n places right. If $n < 0$, move the decimal point $-n$ places left.

Step 3 Insert zeros, decimal point, and commas as needed to indicate place value

FOIL Method (p. 448)

To multiply two binomials, find the sum of the products of F the *First* terms, O the *Outer* terms, I the *Inner* terms, L and the *Last* terms.

Square of a Sum (p. 453)

The square of $a + b$ is the square of a plus twice the product of a and b plus the square of b.

Square of a Difference (p. 454)

The square of $a - b$ is the square of a minus twice the product of a and b plus the square of b.

Product of a Sum and a Difference (p. 455)

The product of $a + b$ and $a - b$ is the square of a minus the square of b.

Chapter 8 Factoring and Quadratic Equations

Factoring by Grouping (p. 477)

A polynomial can be factored by grouping only if all of the following conditions exist.

- There are four or more terms.
- Terms have common factors that can be grouped together.
- There are two common factors that are identical or additive inverses of each other.

Zero Product Property (p. 478)

If the product of two factors is 0, then at least one of the factors must be 0.

Factoring $x^2 + bx + c$ (p. 485)

To factor trinomials in the form $x^2 + bx + c$, find two integers, m and p, with a sum of b and a product of c. Then write $x^2 + bx + c$ as $(x + m)(x + p)$.

Factoring $ax^2 + bx + c$ (p. 493)

To factor trinomials in the form $ax^2 + bx + c$, find two integers, m and p, with a sum of b and a product of ac. Then write $ax^2 + bx + c$ as $ax^2 + mx + px + c$, then factor by grouping.

Difference of Squares (p. 499)

$a^2 - b^2 = (a + b)(a - b)$ or $(a - b)(a + b)$

Factoring Perfect Square Trinomials (p. 505)

$a^2 + 2ab + b^2 = (a + b)(a + b) = (a + b)^2$

$a^2 - 2ab + b^2 = (a - b)(a - b) = (a - b)^2$

Square Root Property (p. 508)

To solve a quadratic equation in the form $x^2 = n$, take the square root of each side.

Chapter 9 Quadratic and Exponential Functions

Quadratic Functions (p. 525)

A quadratic function can be described by an equation of the form $f(x) = ax^2 + bx + c$.

Maximum and Minimum Values (p. 528)

The graph of $f(x) = ax^2 + bx + c$, where $a \neq 0$:

- opens up and has a minimum value when $a > 0$, and
- opens down and has a maximum value when $a < 0$.
- The range of a quadratic function is all real numbers greater than or equal to the minimum, or all real numbers less than or equal to the maximum.

Graph Quadratic Functions (p. 529)

Step 1 Find the equation of the axis of symmetry.

Step 2 Find the vertex, and determine whether it is a maximum or minimum.

Step 3 Find the y-intercept.

Step 4 Use symmetry to find additional points on the graph, if necessary.

Step 5 Connect the point with a smooth curve.

Vertical Translations (p. 544)

The graph of $f(x) = x^2 + c$ is the graph of $f(x) = x^2$ translated vertically.
If $c > 0$, the graph of $f(x) = x^2$ is translated $|c|$ units up.
If $c < 0$, the graph of $f(x) = x^2$ is translated $|c|$ units down.

Dilations (p. 545)

The graph of $f(x) = ax^2$ is the graph of $f(x) = x^2$stretche or compress vertically.
If $|a| > 1$, the graph of $f(x) = x^2$ is stretched vertically.
If $0 < |a| < 1$, the graph of $f(x) = x^2$ is compressed vertically.

Reflections (p. 545)

The graph of the function $-f(x)$ is the reflection of the graph of $f(x) = x^2$ across the x-axis.
The graph of the function $f(-x)$ is the reflection of the graph of $f(x) = x^2$ across the y-axis.

Completing the Square (p. 552)

To complete the square for any quadratic expression of the form $x^2 + bx$, follow the steps below

Step 1 Find one half of b, the coefficient of x.

Step 2 Square the result in Step 1.

Step 3 Add the result of Step 2 to $x^2 + bx$.

The Quadratic Formula (p. 558)
The solutions of a quadratic equation $ax^2 + bx + c = 0$, where $a \neq 0$ are given by the Quadratic Formula.

$$x = \frac{-b \pm \sqrt{b^2 - 4ac}}{2a}$$

Exponential Function (p. 567)
An exponential function is a function that can be described by an equation of the form $y = ab^x$, where $a \neq 0$, $b > 0$, and $b \neq 1$.

General Equation for Exponential Growth (p. 573)
$y = a(1 + r)^t$

General Equation for Compound Interest (p. 574)
$A = P\left(1 + \frac{r}{n}\right)^{nt}$

General Equation for Exponential Decay (p. 574)
$y = a(1 - r)^t$

***n*th term of a Geometric Sequence** (p. 580)
The *n*th term a_n of a geometric sequence with first term a_1 and common ratio r is given by the following formula, where n is any positive integer.

$$a_n = a_1 r^{n-1}$$

Chapter 10
Radical Functions and Geometry

Square Root Function (p. 605)
A square root function can be described by an equation that contains the square root of a variable.

Graphing of Square Root Functions of the Form $y = a\sqrt{x + h} + c$ (p. 606)
Step 1 Draw the graph of $y = a\sqrt{x}$. The graph starts at the origin and passes through the point at $(1, a)$. If $a > 0$, the graph is in quadrant I. If $a < 0$, the graph is reflected across the *x*-axis and is in quadrant IV.

Step 2 Translate the graph $|c|$ units up if $c > 0$ and down if $c < 0$.

Step 3 Translate the graph $|h|$ units left if $h > 0$ and right if $h < 0$.

Product Property of Square Roots (p. 612)
For any nonnegative real numbers a and b, the square root of ab is equal to the square root of a times the square root of b.

Quotient Property of Square Roots (p. 613)
For any real numbers a and b, where $a \geq 0$ and $b > 0$, the square root of $\frac{a}{b}$ is equal to the square root of a divided by the square root of b.

Power Property of Equality (p. 624)
If you square both sides of an equation, the resulting equation is still true.

The Pythagorean Theorem (p. 630)
If a triangle is a right triangle, then the square of the length of the hypotenuse is equal to the sum of the squares of the lengths of the legs.

Converse of the Pythagorean Theorem (p. 631)
If a triangle has side lengths a, b, and c such that $c^2 = a^2 + b^2$, then the triangle is a right triangle. If $c^2 \neq a^2 + b^2$, then the triangle is not a right triangle.

The Distance Formula (p. 636)
The distance d between any two points with coordinates (x_1, y_1) and (x_2, y_2) is given by $d = \sqrt{(x_2 - x_1)^2 + (y_2 - y_1)^2}$.

The Midpoint Formula (p. 638)
The midpoint M of a line segment with endpoints at (x_1, y_1) and (x_2, y_2) is given by $M = \left(\frac{x_1 + x_2}{2}, \frac{y_1 + y_2}{2}\right)$.

Similar Triangles (p. 642)
If two triangles are similar, then the measures of their corresponding angles are equal, and the measures of their corresponding sides are proportional.

Trigonometric Ratios (p. 649)

$$\text{sine of } \angle A = \frac{\text{leg opposite } \angle A}{\text{hypotenuse}}$$

$$\text{cosine of } \angle A = \frac{\text{leg adjacent to } \angle A}{\text{hypotenuse}}$$

$$\text{tangent of } \angle A = \frac{\text{leg opposite } \angle A}{\text{leg adjacent to } \angle A}$$

Inverse Trigonometric Functions (p. 651)
If $\angle A$ is an acute angle and the sine of A is x, then the inverse sine of x is the measure of $\angle A$.
If $\angle A$ is an acute angle and the cosine of A is x, then the inverse cosine of x is the measure of $\angle A$.
If $\angle A$ is an acute angle and the tangent of A is x, then the inverse tangent of x is the measure of $\angle A$.

Chapter 11
Rational Functions and Equations

Inverse Variation (p. 670)
y varies inversely as x if there is some nonzero constant k such that $y = \frac{k}{x}$ or $xy = k$, where $x \neq 0$ and $y \neq 0$.

Product Rule for Inverse Variations (p. 671)
If (x_1, y_1) and (x_2, y_2) are solutions of an inverse variation, then the products x_1y_1 and x_2y_2 are equal.

Rational Function (p. 678)
A rational function can be described by an equation of the form $y = \frac{p}{q}$, where p and q are polynomials and $q \neq 0$.

Asymptotes (p. 679)
A rational function in the form $y = \frac{a}{x - b} + c$ has a vertical asymptote at the x-value that makes the denominator equal zero, $x = b$. It has a horizontal asymptote at $y = c$.

Simplifying Rational Expressions (p. 685)
Let a, b, and c be polynomials with $a \neq 0$ and $c \neq 0$.

$$\frac{ba}{ca} = \frac{b \cdot a}{c \cdot a} = \frac{b}{c}$$

Multiplying Rational Expressions (p. 692)
Let a, b, c, and d be polynomials with $b \neq 0$ and $d \neq 0$.

$$\frac{a}{b} \cdot \frac{c}{d} = \frac{ac}{bd}$$

Dividing Rational Expressions (p. 693)
Let a, b, c, and d be polynomials with $b \neq 0$, $c \neq 0$, and $d \neq 0$.

$$\frac{a}{b} \div \frac{c}{d} = \frac{a}{b} \cdot \frac{d}{c} = \frac{ad}{bc}$$

Add or Subtract Rational Expressions (p. 708)
Use the following steps to add or subtract rational expressions with unlike denominators.

Step 1 Find the LCD.

Step 2 Write each rational expression as an equivalent expression with the LCD as the denominator.

Step 3 Add or subtract the numerators and write the result over the common denominator.

Step 4 Simplify if necessary.

Chapter 12
Statistics and Probability

Data Collection Techniques (p. 740)
survery Data are from responses given by sample of the population.
observational study Data are recorded after just observing the sample.
experiment Data are recorded after changing the sample.

Random Samples (p. 742)
simple random sample A sample that is equally likely to be chosen as any other sample from the population.
stratified random sample The population is first divided in similar, nonoverlapping groups. A sample is then selected from each group.
systematic random sample Items in the sample are selected according to a specified time or item interval.

Measures of Central Tendency (p. 746)
mean the sum of the data divided by the number of items in the data set
median the middle number of the ordered data, or the mean of the middle two numbers
mode the number or numbers that occur most often

Measures of Variation (p. 757)
range the difference between the greatest and least values
quartile the values that divide the data set into four equal parts
interquartile range the range of the middle half of a data set; the difference between the upper and lower quartiles

Mean Absolute Deviation (p. 757)
Step 1 Find the mean.

Step 2 Find the sum of the absolute values of the differences between each value in the set of data and the mean.

Step 3 Divide the sum by the number of values in the set of data.

Variance and Standard Deviation (p. 758)
Step 1 Find the mean, $\bar{x}$.

Step 2 Find the square of the difference between each value in the set of data and the mean. Then divide by the number of values in the set of data. The result is the variance.

Step 3 Take the square root of the variance.

Factorial (p. 764)
The factorial of a positive integer n is the product of the positive integers less than or equal to n.

Permutation Formula (p. 765)
The number of permutations of n objects taken r at a time is the quotient of $n!$ and $(n - r)!$.

Combination Formula (p. 766)
The number of combinations of n objects taken r at a time is the quotient of $n!$ and $(n - r)!r!$.

Probability of Independent Events (p. 771)
If two events, A and B, are independent, then the probability of both events occurring is the product of the probability of A and the probability of B.

Probability of Dependent Events (p. 772)
If two events, A and B, are dependent, then the probability of both events occurring is the product of the probability of A and the probability of B after A occurs.

Mutually Exclusive Events (p. 773)
If two events, A and B, are mutually exclusive, then the probability that either A or B occurs is the sum of their probabilities.

Events that are Not Mutually Exclusive (p. 774)
If two events, A and B, are not mutually exclusive, then the probability that either A or B occurs is the sum of their probabilities decreased by the probability of both occurring.

Properties of Probability Distributions (p. 780)
1. The probability of each value of X is greater than or equal to 0 and is less than or equal to 1.
2. The sum of the probabilities of all values of X is 1.

For Homework Help, go to Hotmath.com
Complete, step-by-step solutions of most odd-numbered exercises are provided free of charge.

Chapter 0 Preparing for Algebra

Pages P5–P6 *Lesson 0-1*

1. estimate; about 700 mi **3.** estimate; about 7 times **5.** exact; $98.75

Pages P7–P10 *Lesson 0-2*

1. integers, rationals **3.** irrationals **5.** irrationals **7.** rationals **9.** rationals **11.** irrationals

13. 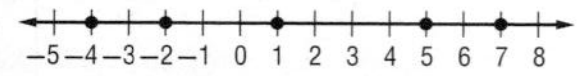

15. 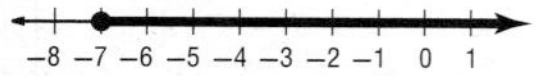

17. 

19. $\frac{5}{9}$ **21.** $\frac{13}{99}$ **23.** −5 **25.** $\pm\frac{4}{7}$ **27.** 7 **29.** −2.5 **31.** $\frac{5}{18}$ **33.** 5 **35.** 12

Pages P11–P12 *Lesson 0-3*

1. 5 **3.** −27 **5.** −22 **7.** −32 **9.** 22 **11.** 5 **13.** 8 **15.** −9 **17.** −115 **19.** 17° **21.** $150 **23.** $125

Pages P13–P16 *Lesson 0-4*

1. < **3.** < **5.** = **7.** 3.06, $3\frac{1}{6}$, $3\frac{3}{4}$, 3.8 **9.** −0.5, $-\frac{1}{9}$, $\frac{1}{10}$, 0.11 **11.** $\frac{3}{5}$ **13.** $\frac{1}{16}$ **15.** 1 **17.** $2\frac{2}{3}$ **19.** $\frac{1}{9}$ **21.** $\frac{1}{6}$ **23.** $\frac{17}{30}$ **25.** $\frac{1}{4}$ **27.** −36.9 **29.** −19.33 **31.** 153.8 **33.** 93.3 **35.** $-\frac{5}{6}$ **37.** $\frac{9}{20}$ **39.** $\frac{2}{3}$ **41.** $\frac{3}{10}$

Pages P17–P19 *Lesson 0-5*

1. 0.85 **3.** −7.05 **5.** 60 **7.** −4.8 **9.** −1.52 **11.** $\frac{6}{35}$ **13.** $\frac{2}{33}$ **15.** $\frac{21}{4}$ or $5\frac{1}{4}$ **17.** $-\frac{1}{2}$ **19.** $-\frac{1}{8}$ **21.** $\frac{10}{11}$ **23.** $\frac{5}{2}$ or $2\frac{1}{2}$ **25.** $\frac{7}{6}$ or $1\frac{1}{6}$ **27.** $-\frac{23}{14}$ or $-1\frac{9}{14}$ **29.** $-\frac{3}{16}$ **31.** 2 **33.** 3 **35.** $-\frac{3}{10}$ **37.** $\frac{9}{2}$ or $4\frac{1}{2}$ **39.** $\frac{11}{20}$ **41.** $\frac{5}{18}$ **43.** 3 slices **45.** 34 uniforms **47.** 6 ribbons

Pages P20–P22 *Lesson 0-6*

1. $\frac{1}{20}$ **3.** $\frac{11}{100}$ **5.** $\frac{39}{50}$ **7.** $\frac{3}{500}$ **9.** $\frac{14}{1}$ **11.** 40% **13.** 160 **15.** 9.5 **17.** 48 **19.** 0.25% **21.** 24.5 **23.** 150% **25.** 90% **27.** 5% **29a.** 20 g **29b.** 2350 mg **29c.** 44% **31.** 6 animals

Pages P23–P25 *Lesson 0-7*

1. 20 m **3.** 90 in. **5.** 32 in. **7.** 29 ft **9.** 25.0 in. **11.** 31.4 in. **13.** 23.2 m **15.** 848.2 in. **17.** 13.4 cm **19.** 10.3 ft

Pages P26–P28 *Lesson 0-8*

1. 6 cm² **3.** 120 m² **5.** 81 ft² **7.** 9 ft² **9.** 14.1 in² **11.** 12.6 ft² **13.** 50.3 cm² **15.** 201.1 in² **17.** 1620 ft² **19.** 19.6 mi² **21.** 22.1 cm² **23.** 4.0 cm²

Pages P29–P30 *Lesson 0-9*

1. 30 cm³ **3.** 48 yd³ **5.** 1404 ft³ **7.** 20 m³ **9.** 27 m³ **11.** 2070 in³ **13.** 1 ft **15.** 4 cm **17.** 2770.9 in³ **19a.** 128 ft³ **19b.** 80 ft³ **19c.** 5 ft 4 in.

Pages P31–P32 *Lesson 0-10*

1. 68 in² **3.** 220 mm² **5.** 37 ft² **7.** 48 m² **9.** 216 in² **11.** 480.7 in² **13.** 24 m² **15.** 77 ft² **17.** 40.8 in²

Pages P33–P36 *Lesson 0-11*

1. $\frac{4}{15}$ **3.** $\frac{1}{2}$ **5.** $\frac{5}{6}$ **7.** $\frac{1}{2}$ **9.** $\frac{2}{3}$ **11.** 20 **13.** 12 codes **15.** $\frac{11}{24}$ **17.** 1:5 **19.** 13:11 **21.** 16 orders

Pages P37–P39 *Lesson 0-12*

1. 5; 5; 5 **3.** 54; 53; 53 **5.** 9; 4; no mode **7.** 6; 6; no mode **9.** 28; 19; 7; 26 **11.** 16; 10; 5; 17 **13.** 6; 7; 5; 9 **15.** mean: $2.50; median: $2.25; mode: $2.00 **17.** 89 **19.** about 92.7 **21.** 118.5 min

Pages P40–P43 *Lesson 0-13*

1. 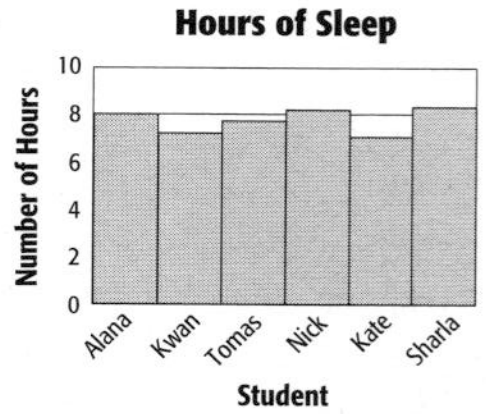

3. 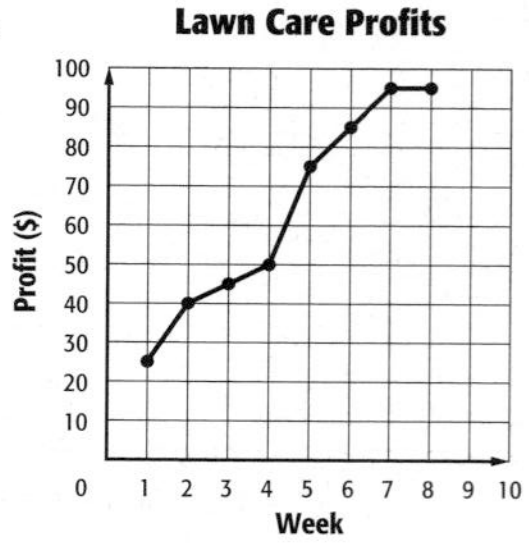

5.

Stem	Leaf
1	8 8
2	1 3 6 6 6 8
3	0 1 1 2 3 4
4	7

Key: 1|8 = 18

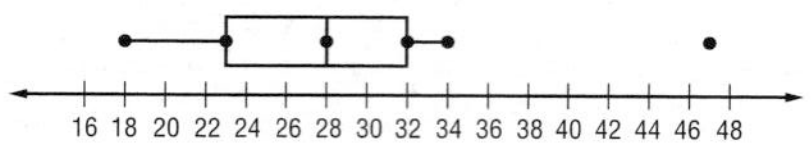

Removing 47 leaves Q_1 the same, changes Q_2 to 27 and Q_3 to 31.

7. 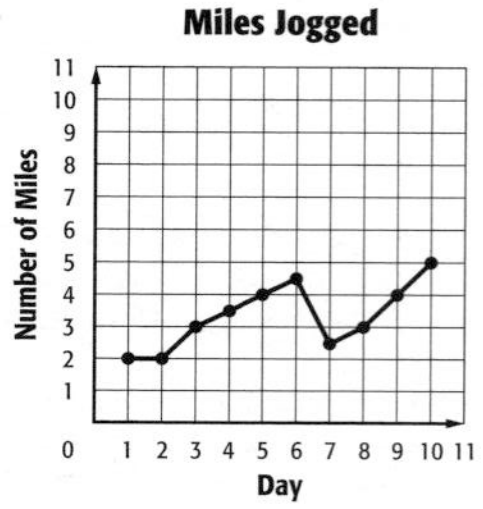

Chapter 1 Expressions, Equations, and Functions

Page 3 *Get Ready*

1. $\frac{2}{3}$ **3.** 3 **5.** *simplest form* **7.** 19 **9.** $\frac{8}{11}$ **11.** 8.2 cm **13.** 20 m **15.** 34.02 **17.** 1.9 **19.** 0.56

Pages 5–9 *Lesson 1-1*

1. Sample answer: the product of 2 and m **3.** Sample answer: a squared minus 18 times b **5.** $6 - t$ **7.** $1 - \frac{r}{7}$ **9.** $n^3 + 5$ **11.** Sample answer: four times a number q **13.** Sample answer: 15 plus r **15.** Sample answer: 3 times x squared **17** Sample answer: 6 more than the product of 2 and a **19.** $7 + x$ **21.** $5n$ **23.** $\frac{f}{10}$ **25.** $3n + 16$ **27.** $k^2 - 11$ **29.** $\pi r^2 h$ **31.** Sample answer: twenty-five plus six times a number squared **33.** Sample answer: three times a number raised to the fifth power divided by two

35 a. Words: $\frac{3}{4}$ of the number of dreams
Expression: $\frac{3}{4} \cdot d$
The expression is $\frac{3}{4}d$.
b. $\frac{3}{4}(28) = 21$ dreams

37a.

10^2	•	10^1	=	10 • 10 • 10	=	10^3
10^2	•	10^2	=	10 • 10 • 10 • 10	=	10^4
10^2	•	10^3	=	10 • 10 • 10 • 10 • 10	=	10^5
10^2	•	10^4	=	10 • 10 • 10 • 10 • 10• 10	=	10^6

37b. $10^2 \cdot 10^x = 10^{(2+x)}$ **37c.** The exponent of the product of two powers is the sum of the exponents of the powers with the same bases. **39.** Sample answer: x is the number of minutes it takes to walk between my house and school. $2x + 15$ represents the amount of time in minutes I spend walking each day since I walk to and from school and I take my dog on a 15 minute walk. **41.** 6 **43.** D **45.** $\frac{31}{36}$

47. 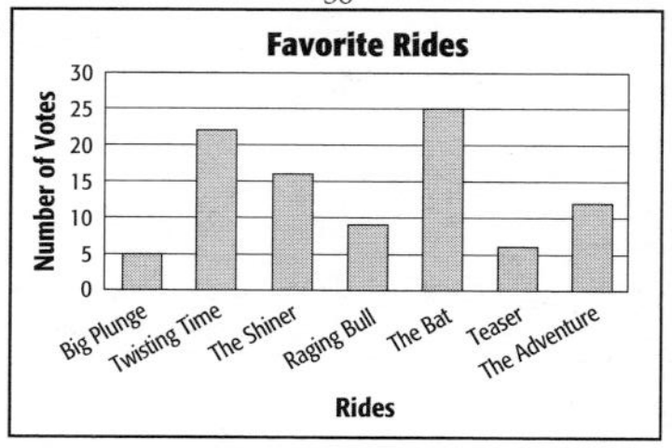

49. mean = 5.6; median = 6.5; mode = 7 **51.** mean = 15.25; median = 15.5; mode = 24 **53.** $\frac{21}{55}$ **55.** $\frac{20}{9}$ **57.** 1.46 **59.** 24.61 **61.** 21.16

Pages 10–15 *Lesson 1-2*

1. 81 **3.** 243
5 $5 \cdot 5 - 1 \cdot 3 = 25 - 3$
$= 22$
7. 28 **9.** 12 **11.** 20 **13.** 20 + 3 × 4.95; $34.85 **15.** 49 **17.** 64 **19.** 14 **21.** 36 **23.** 14 **25.** 142 **27.** 36 **29.** 3 **31.** 1
33 $(2t + 3g) \div 4 = (2(11) + 3(2)) \div 4$
$= (22 + 6) \div 4$
$= (28) \div 4$
$= 7$
35. 149 **37.** 3344 − 148 = 3196 **39.** 16 **41.** 729 **43.** 177 **45.** 324 **47.** 29 **49.** 4080 **51.** $\frac{97}{31}$ **53.** 0 **55.** 28(7) + 12(9.75) + 30(7) + 15(9.75); $669.25

57 a. 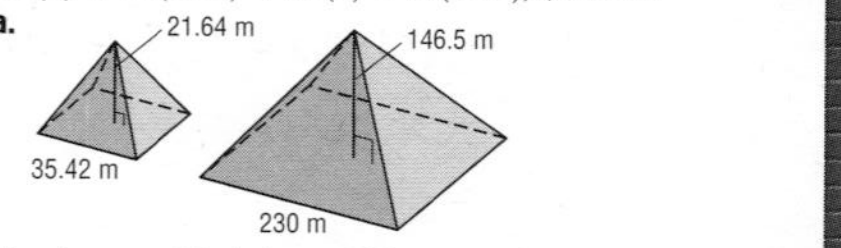

b. Words: one third times 230 squared times 146.5 m minus one third times 35.42 squared times 21.64 m

c. Expression: $\frac{1}{3}(230)^2(146.5) - \frac{1}{3}(35.42)^2(21.64)$
$\approx 2583283.33 - 9049.68$
$\approx 2574233.656\ m^3$

59. Curtis; Tara subtracted 10 − 9 before multiplying 4 by 10. **61.** 5 + 4 − 3 − 2 − 1 **63.** Sample answer: Area of a trapezoid: $\frac{1}{2}h(b_1 + b_2)$;

according to the order of operations, you have to add the lengths of the bases together first and then multiply by the height and by $\frac{1}{2}$. **65.** A
67. $\frac{5}{16}$; $\frac{1}{4}$; Experimental probability is what happens in the trials. In this case the experimental probability is the probability that the customers have actually received popcorn. Theoretical probability is what should happen theoretically.
69. 14 minus 9 times c **71.** the difference of 4 and v divided by w **73.** 9π units^2 **75.** $12b$ units^2
77. 2.57 **79.** 13.192 **81.** $\frac{2}{3}$

Pages 16–22 Lesson 1-3

1. $(1 \div 5)5 \cdot 14$
$= \frac{1}{5} \cdot 5 \cdot 14$ Substitution
$= (1) \cdot 14$ Multiplicative Inverse
$= 14$ Multiplicative Identity

3. $5(14 - 5) + 6(3 + 7) = 5(9) + 6(10)$ Substitution
$= 45 + 60$ Substitution
$= 105$ Substitution

5. $23 + 42 + 37$
$= 23 + 37 + 42$ Commutative (+)
$= (23 + 37) + 42$ Associative (+)
$= 60 + 42$ Substitution
$= 102$ Substitution

7. $3 \cdot 7 \cdot 10 \cdot 2$
$= 3 \cdot 2 \cdot 7 \cdot 10$ Commutative (×)
$= (3 \cdot 2) \cdot (7 \cdot 10)$ Associative (×)
$= 6 \cdot 70$ Substitution
$= 420$ Substitution

9 $3(22 - 3 \cdot 7) = 3(22 - 21)$ Substitution
$= 3(1)$ Substitution
$= 3$ Multiplicative Identity

11. $\frac{3}{4}[4 \div (7 - 4)]$
$= \frac{3}{4}[4 \div 3]$ Substitution
$= \frac{3}{4} \times \frac{4}{3}$ Substitution
$= 1$ Multiplicative Inverse

13. $2(3 \cdot 2 - 5) + 3 \cdot \frac{1}{3}$
$= 2(6 - 5) + 3 \cdot \frac{1}{3}$ Substitution
$= 2(1) + 3 \cdot \frac{1}{3}$ Substitution
$= 2 + 3 \cdot \frac{1}{3}$ Multiplicative Identity
$= 2 + 1$ Multiplicative Inverse
$= 3$ Substitution

15. $2 \cdot \frac{22}{7} \cdot 14^2 + 2 \cdot \frac{22}{7} \cdot 14 \cdot 7$
$= 2 \cdot \frac{22}{7} \cdot 196 + 2 \cdot \frac{22}{7} \cdot 14 \cdot 7$ Substitution
$= \frac{44}{7} \cdot 196 + \frac{44}{7} \cdot 14 \cdot 7$ Substitution
$= 1232 + 616$ Substitution
$= 1848$ Substitution
The surface area is about 1848 in^2.

17. $25 + 14 + 15 + 36$
$= 25 + 15 + 14 + 36$ Commutative(+)
$= (25 + 15) + (14 + 36)$ Associative(+)
$= 40 + 50$ Substitution
$= 90$ Substitution

19. $3\frac{2}{3} + 4 + 5\frac{1}{3} = 3\frac{2}{3} + 5\frac{1}{3} + 4$ Commutative (+)
$= \left(3\frac{2}{3} + 5\frac{1}{3}\right) + 4$ Associative (+)
$= 9 + 4$ Substitution
$= 13$ Substitution

21. $4.3 + 2.4 + 3.6 + 9.7$
$= 4.3 + 9.7 + 2.4 + 3.6$ Commutative (+)
$= (4.3 + 9.7) + (2.4 + 3.6)$ Associative (+)
$= 14 + 6$ Substitution
$= 20$ Substitution

23. $12 \cdot 2 \cdot 6 \cdot 5 = 12 \cdot 6 \cdot 2 \cdot 5$ Commutative (×)
$= (12 \cdot 6) \cdot (2 \cdot 5)$ Associative (×)
$= 72 \cdot 10$ Substitution
$= 720$ Substitution

25. $0.2 \cdot 4.6 \cdot 5 = (0.2 \cdot 4.6) \cdot 5$ Associative (×)
$= 0.92 \cdot 5$ Substitution
$= 4.6$ Substitution

27. $1\frac{5}{6} \cdot 24 \cdot 3\frac{1}{11} = 1\frac{5}{6}\left(24 \cdot 3\frac{1}{11}\right)$ Associative (×)
$= 1\frac{5}{6} \cdot \frac{816}{11}$ Substitution
$= 136$ Substitution

29a. Sample answer: $2(10.95) + 3(7.5) + 2(5) + 5(18.99)$; $2(10.95 + 5) + 3(7.5) + 5(18.99)$
29b. $149.35

31 $4(-1) + 9(4) - 2(6) = -4 + 36 - 12$
$= 32 - 12$
$= 20$

33. −18 **35.** 192 **37.** Additive Identity; $35 + 0 = 35$ **39.** 0; Additive Identity **41.** 7; Reflexive Property **43.** 3; Multiplicative Identity **45.** 2; Commutative Property **47.** 3; Multiplicative Inverse **49a.** $4 + 5x + 4 + 5x + 3y$ **b.** 49 units
51. 88 units
53 **a.**

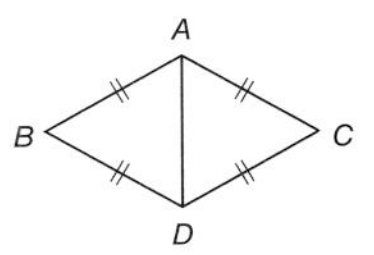

b. $\overline{AD} \cong \overline{AD}$ by the Reflexive Property. The Transitive Property shows that if $\overline{AB} \cong \overline{AC}$ and $\overline{AC} \cong \overline{DC}$, then $\overline{AB} \cong \overline{DC}$ and if $\overline{AB} \cong \overline{BD}$ and $\overline{AB} \cong \overline{AC}$, then $\overline{BD} \cong \overline{AC}$.
c. Since the sides are all congruent, each side has a length x. So, $P = x + x + x + x$.
55. Sample answer: You cannot divide by 0.
57. Sometimes; when a number is subtracted from itself then it holds but otherwise it does not.
59. $(2j)k = 2(jk)$; The other three sentences illustrate the Commutative Property of Addition or Multiplication. This equation represents the Associative Property of Multiplication. **61.** D
63. C **65.** 14 **67.** 6 **69.** 26 ft; 40 ft^2
71. about 64.7 % **73.** $\frac{23}{2}$ **75.** $\frac{6}{35}$ **77.** $\frac{6}{11}$ **79.** 6

Pages 23–29 Lesson 1-4

1. $25(12 + 15)$; \$675 **3.** $\left(6 + \frac{1}{9}\right)9$; 55 **5.** $g(5) + (-9)(5)$; $5g - 45$ **7.** simplified
9. $4(2x + 6)$
$= 4(2x) + 4(6)$ Distributive Property
$= 8x + 24$ Multiply.

11 $4(5 + 3 + 4) = 4(8 + 4)$
$= 4(12)$
$= 48$ activities

13. $6(4) + 6(5)$; 54 **15.** $6(6) - 6(1)$; 30 **17.** $14(8) - 14(5)$; 42 **19.** $4(7) - 4(2)$; 20 **21.** $7(500 - 3)$; 3479
23. $36\left(3 + \frac{1}{4}\right)$; 117 **25.** $2(x) + 2(4)$; $2x + 8$
27. $4(8) + (-3m)(8)$; $32 - 24m$ **29.** $18r$ **31.** $2m + 7$
33. $34 - 68n$ **35.** $13m + 5p$ **37.** $4fg + 17g$
39. $7(a^2 + b) - 4(a^2 + b)$
$= 7a^2 + 7b - 4a^2 - 4b$ Substitution
$= 7a^2 - 4a^2 + 7b - 4b$ Commutative (+)
$= (7 - 4)a^2 + (7 - 4)b$ Distributive Prop.
$= 3a^2 + 3b$ Substitution

41 A hexagon has six sides so an expression for the perimeter is $6(3x + 5)$.
$6(3x + 5) = 6(3x) + 6(5)$
$= 18x + 30$ units

43. $14m + 11g$ **45.** $12k^3 + 12k$ **47.** $19x + 8$
49. $9 - 54b$ **51.** $12c - 6cd^2 + 6d$ **53.** $7y^3 + y^4$
55a. $2(x + 3)$
55b.

Area	Factored form
$2x + 6$	$2(x + 3)$
$3x + 3$	$3(x + 1)$
$3x - 12$	$3(x - 4)$
$5x + 10$	$5(x + 2)$

55c. Divide each term of the expression by the same number. Then write the expression as a product. **57.** It should be considered a property of both. Both operations are used in $a(b + c) = ab + ac$. **59.** You can use the Distributive Property to calculate quickly by expressing any number as a sum or difference of a more convenient number. Answers should include the following: Both methods result in the correct answer. In one method you multiply then add, and in the other you add then multiply. **61.** G **63.** about $\frac{1}{3}$ or 33%
65. $0.24 \cdot 8 \cdot 7.05 = (0.24 \cdot 8) \cdot 7.05$ Associative (×)
$= 1.92 \cdot 7.05$ Substitution
$= 13.536$ Substitution

67. $\frac{4[6(30) + 3(20)]}{60}$; 16 hours **69.** 21:48
71. 384 in^2 **73.** 15 **75.** 60 **77.** 192

Pages 31–37 Lesson 1-5

1. 13 **3.** 12 **5.** B **7.** 3 **9.** all real numbers
11. {12} **13.** {5} **15.** {16} **17.** {3} **19.** 14 **21.** 2
23. 2 **25.** 5 **27.** no solution **29.** all real numbers

31 $(2^4 - 3 \cdot 5)q + 13 = (2 \cdot 9 - 4^2)q + \left(\frac{3 \cdot 4}{12} - 1\right)$
$(16 - 15)q + 13 = (18 - 16)q + (1 - 1)$
$1q + 13 = 2q + 0$
$1q + 13 = 2q$
$13 = 2q - 1q$
$13 = 1q$
$q = 13$

33. 41 students
35 Words: the number of calories equals 2836 plus 3091
Expression: $C = 2836 + 3091$ Solve: $C = 5927$
37.

x	$3x - 2$	y
−2	$3(-2) - 2$	−8
−1	$3(-1) - 2$	−5
0	$3(0) - 2$	−2
1	$3(1) - 2$	1
2	$3(2) - 2$	4

39. 20 **41.** 66 **43.** 5 **45.** $c = 15$ **47a.** $5 = \frac{1000}{r}$; 20
47b.

Intial Pressure p_1 (mm Hg)	Final Pressure p_2 (mm Hg)	Resistance r (mm Hg/L/min)	Blood Flow Rate F (L/min)
100	0	20	5
100	0	30	≈ 3.33
165	5	40	4
90	30	10	12

49. solution **51.** not a solution **53.** solution
55. solution
57.

x	$3x + 5$	y
−2	$3(-2) + 5$	−1
−1	$3(-1) + 5$	2
0	$3(0) + 5$	5
1	$3(1) + 5$	8
2	$3(2) + 5$	11

59.

x	$\frac{1}{2}x + 2$	y
−2	$\frac{1}{2}(-2) + 2$	1
−1	$\frac{1}{2}(-1) + 2$	1.5
0	$\frac{1}{2}(0) + 2$	2
1	$\frac{1}{2}(1) + 2$	2.5
2	$\frac{1}{2}(2) + 2$	3

61a.

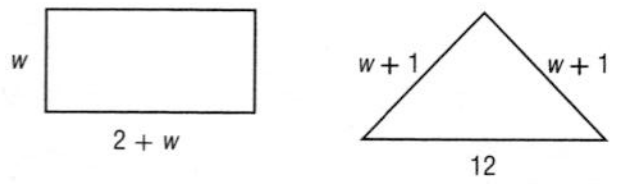

61b. perimeter of rectangle = $2(2 + w) + 2w$ or $4 + 4w$; perimeter of triangle = $2(w + 1) + 12 = 2w + 14$.

61c. $4 + 4w = 2w + 14$; $w = 5$ in.

63b.

Layers	1	2	3	4	5	6	7
Cubes	4	8	12	16	20	24	28

c. From the table, we can tell that each layer adds 4 more cubes. Notice $8 - 4 = 4$; $12 - 8 = 4$; $16 - 12 = 4$; $20 - 16 = 4$; $24 - 20 = 4$; $28 - 24 = 4$

d. The number of cubes is 4 times the number of layers, or $c = 4L$.

65. Sample answer: $3x + 12 = 3(x + 4)$ **67.** Tom; Li-Cheng added 6 + 4 instead of dividing 6 by 8. She did not follow the order of operations. **69.** Sample answer: $3x - 2 = -23$ **71.** C **73.** G **75.** 30 (500 + 750) **77.** $p = \frac{1}{12}$; Multiplicative Inverse **79.** 1040 in^3 **81.** $\frac{3}{20}$ **83.** estimate; 10 gal **85.** 6.74 **87.** 1.65 **89.** $\frac{29}{28}$

Pages 38–44 Lesson 1-6

1.

x	y
4	3
−2	2
5	−6

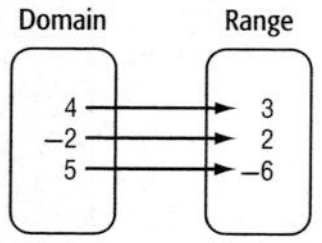

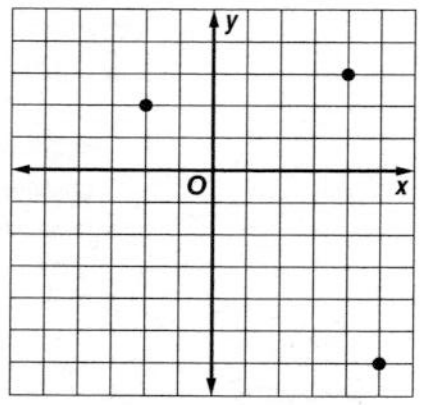

$D = \{-2, 4, 5\}$; $R = \{-6, 2, 3\}$

3. I: the temperature of the compound; D: the pressure of the compound **5.** I: number of concert tickers, D: cost of tickets **7.** The track team starts by running or walking, and then stops for a short period of time, then continues at the same pace. Finally, they run or walk at a slower pace.

9.

x	y
0	0
−3	2
6	4
−1	1

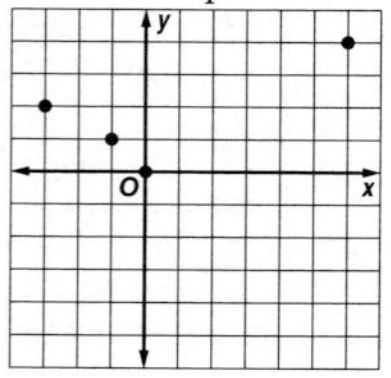

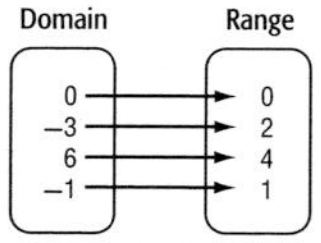

$D = \{0, -3, 6, -1\}$;
$R = \{0, 2, 4, 1\}$

11.

x	y
6	1
4	−3
3	2
−1	−3

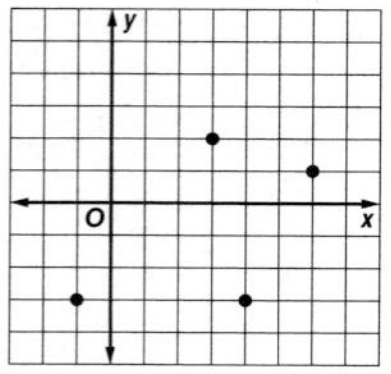

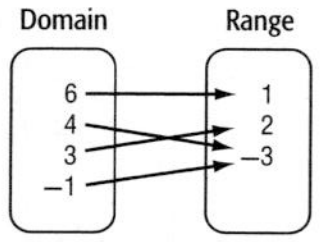

$D = \{6, 4, 3, -1\}$;
$R = \{1, -3, 2\}$

13.

x	y
6	7
3	−2
8	8
−6	2
2	−6

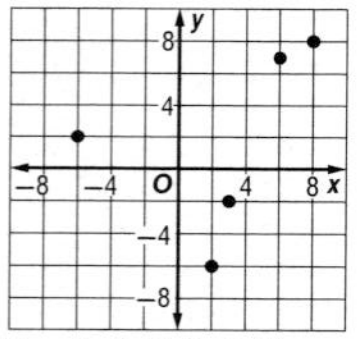

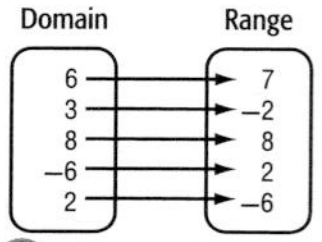

$D = \{-6, 2, 3, 6, 8\}$;
$R = \{-6, -2, 2, 7, 8\}$

15. The number of students who attend is the independent variable because it does not depend on the amount of food there will be. The amount of food is the dependent variable because it depends on the number of students who attend.

17. The bungee jumper starts at the maximum height, and then jumps. After the initial jump, the jumper bounces up and down until coming to a rest.

19. Use the graph to determine what is happening to the value of the baseball card. The values are continually increasing.

21. (1, 5); The dog walker earns $5 for walking 1 dog. **23.** I: number of dogs walked; D: amount earned **25.** (5, 6); In the year 2005, sales were about $6 million. **27.** {(1, 2.50), (2, 5.50), (5, 10.00), (8, 18.75)}; D = {1, 2, 5, 8}; R = {2.50, 5.50, 10.00, 18.75} **29.** {(4, −1), (8, 9), (−2, −6), (7, −3)} **31.** {(4, −2), (−1, 3), (−2,−1), (1, 4)}

33. Sample answer:

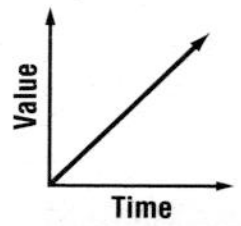

35. Sample answer:

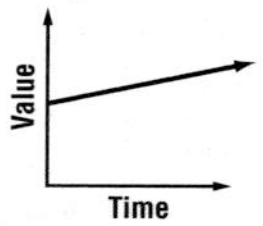

37a.

b	$w = 2\left(\frac{b}{3}\right)$	w
100	$w = 2\left(\frac{100}{3}\right)$	66.7
105	$w = 2\left(\frac{105}{3}\right)$	70
110	$w = 2\left(\frac{110}{3}\right)$	73.3
115	$w = 2\left(\frac{115}{3}\right)$	76.7
120	$w = 2\left(\frac{120}{3}\right)$	80
125	$w = 2\left(\frac{125}{3}\right)$	83.3
130	$w = 2\left(\frac{130}{3}\right)$	86.7

b. The independent variable is the body weight b. The dependent variable is the water weight w.

c. The domain is the set of b values. D = {100, 105, 110, 115, 120, 125, 130}. The range is the set of all w values. R = {66.7, 70, 73.3, 76.7, 80, 83.3, 86.7}

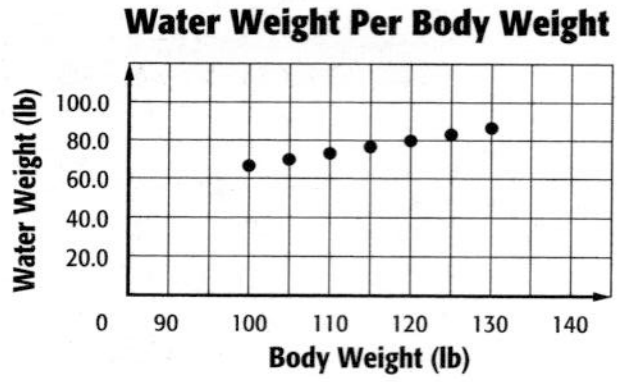

d. Graph the following ordered pairs: (66.7, 100), (70, 105), (73.3, 110), (76.7, 115), (80, 120), (83.3, 125), (86.7, 130).

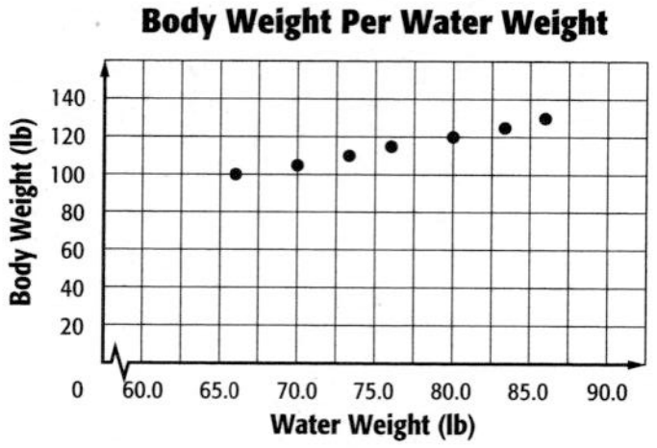

This graph shows what a person's body weight would be based on their water weight.

41. Reversing the coordinates gives (1, 0), (3, 1), (5, 2), and (7, 3).

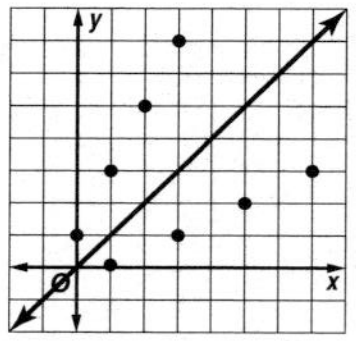

Each point in the original relation is the same distance from the line as the corresponding points of the reverse relation. The graphs are symmetric about the line $y = x$.

43. B **45.** (−1, −3) **47.** {2} **49.** {3} **51.** $\frac{1}{8}$ **53.** 50.27 cm **55.** 64 **57.** 6.25 **59.** 49

Pages 45–52 Lesson 1-7

1. Yes; for each input there is exactly one output. **3.** No; the domain value 2 is paired with both 2 and −4. **5.** no; when $x = 0$, $y = 1$ and $y = 6$ **7.** yes; its graph passes the vertical line test

9a. {(0, 48,560), (1, 48,710), (2, 48,948), (3, 49,091)}

9b.

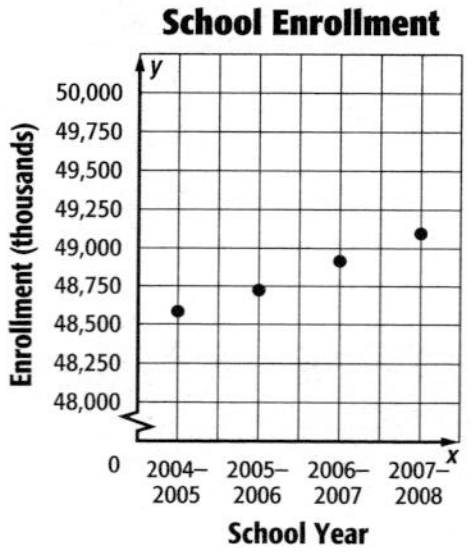

11. $f(-3) = 6(-3) + 7$
$= -18 + 7$
$= -11$

13. $6r - 5$ **15.** $a^2 + 5$ **17.** $6q + 13$ **19.** $b^2 - 7$ **21.** no **23.** yes **25.** yes **27.** yes **29.** yes **31.** yes **33.** −1 **35.** 14 **37.** −4 **39.** $-8y - 3$ **41.** $-2c + 7$ **43.** $-10d - 15$

45a. Create a table using the rule given.

t	0.8t + 72	f(t)
0	0.8(0) + 72	72
10	0.8(10) + 72	80
20	0.8(20) + 72	88
30	0.8(30) + 72	96
40	0.8(40) + 72	104
50	0.8(50) + 72	112

Plot the ordered pairs on a coordinate plane.

For Homework Help, go to Hotmath.com

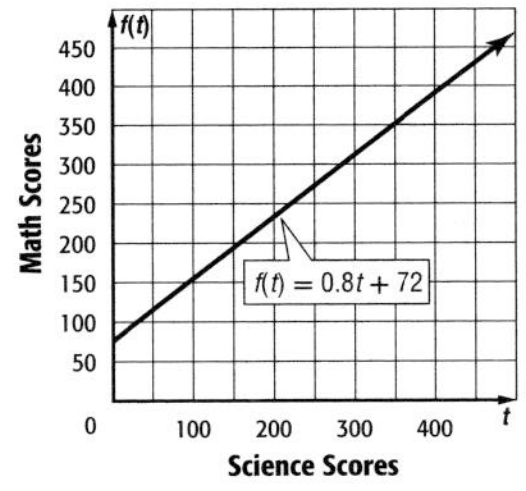

b. $308 = 0.8t + 72$
$236 = 0.8t$
$295 = t$

c. The domain is the set of science scores, the range is the set of math scores.

47 The graph represents a function because each x-value is paired with only one y-value.
49. Sample answer: {(−2, 3), (0, 3), (2, 5)}

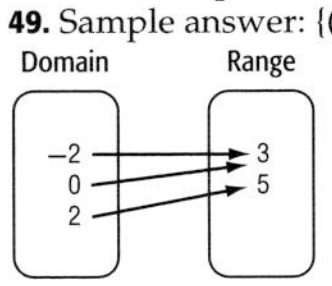

51. $f(g + 3.5) = -4.3g - 17.05$ **53.** Sample answer: $f(x) = 3x + 2$ **55.** Sample answer: Functions can be used in traffic safety studies to determine the relationship between the speed of a car and the distance it takes to stop. This can help plan intersections and speed limits. This function can also help law enforcement officials to understand the cause of an accident. **57.** J **59.** her first game **61.** $\frac{13}{2}$ **63.** $4(1.99) + 10(0.25) + 4(1.85) = C$, where C is the cost of the items Tom needs. $C = 17.86$, so the cost is \$17.86, which is not less than \$10. **65.** sample answer: two thirds times x **67.** 38.016 cm^3 **69.** 288,000 mm^3 **71.** −1 **73.** 40 **75.** 65

Pages 54–59 Lesson 1-8

1. H: the game is on Saturday; C: Eduardo will play **3.** H: $52 - 4x = 28$; C: $x = 6$ **5.** H: two lines are perpendicular; C: they form right angles; If two lines are perpendicular, then they form right angles.
7 No valid conclusion. The last number could be a 5 instead of a 0.
9. No valid conclusion; the last digit is a 5.
11. A one-page paper is assigned. **13.** $y = -1$
15 Hypothesis: You are in a grocery store. Conclusion: you will buy food.
17. H: x equals y, and y equals z; C: x equals z
19. H: you play basketball; C: you are tall
21. H: it is after class; C: Joe will go to the mall; If it is after class, then Joe will go to the mall. **23.** H: $m < 12$; C: $5m - 8 < 52$; If $m < 12$, then $5m - 8 < 52$. **25.** H: two numbers are even; C: their sum is an even number; If two numbers are even, then their sum is an even number. **27.** H: you are a science teacher; C: you like to conduct experiments; If you are a science teacher, then you like to conduct experiments. **29.** No valid conclusion; the statement does not say that Belinda will not receive an A in the course if she scores lower than a 90% on the exam. **31.** Belinda did not score higher than 90% on the exam. **33.** You attend the banquet, but do not eat because you are feeling ill. **35.** $6 \div 3 = 2$ **37.** $(-1)^2 = 1$ **39.** The number is 2, an even number.

43 a.

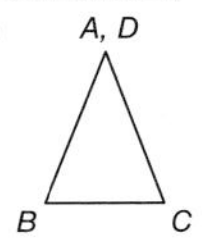

b.

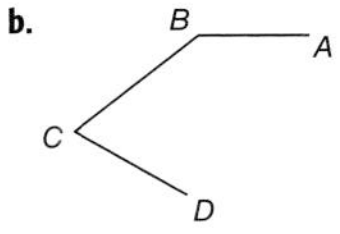

45. No; sample answer: Let $b = 4$ and $c = 5$; then $2 + (4 \times 5) \neq (2 + 4)(2 + 5)$. **47.** Sample answer: If you go swimming, then you get wet; H: you go swimming; C: you get wet. **49.** Sample answer: If you live in Ohio, then you live in Columbus. You do not have to live in Columbus, you could live in Canton. **51.** A **53.** G **55.** yes **57.** yes **59.** $\frac{1}{5}$ **61.** 38 cm **63.** 81 **65.** 150.0625 **67.** 625

Pages 62–66 Chapter 1 Study Guide and Review

1. true **3.** false; not in simplest form **5.** true **7.** false; multiplicative identity **9.** The product of 3 and x squared. **11.** $x + 9$ **13.** $4x - 5$ **15.** 216 **17.** $2.50 + 3.25g$ **19.** 18 **21.** 2 **23.** 3 **25.** 5 **27.** 2.75(3) + 4.25(2); \$16.75

29. $[5 \div (8 - 6)]$
$= [5 \div 2]\frac{2}{5}$ Substitution
$= \frac{5}{2} \cdot \frac{2}{5}$ Substitution
$= 1$ Multiplicative Inverse

31. $2 \cdot \frac{1}{2} + 4(4 \cdot 2 - 7)$
$= 2 \cdot \frac{1}{2} + 4(8 - 7)$ Substitution
$= 2 \cdot \frac{1}{2} + 4(1)$ Substitution
$= 1 + 4(1)$ Multiplicative Inverse
$= 1 + 4$ Multiplicative Identity
$= 5$ Substitution

33. $7\frac{2}{5} + 5 + 2\frac{3}{5}$
$= 7\frac{2}{5} + 2\frac{3}{5} + 5$ Commutative (+)
$= (7\frac{2}{5} + 2\frac{3}{5}) + 5$ Associative (+)
$= 10 + 5$ Substitution
$= 15$ Substitution

35. $5.3 + 2.8 + 3.7 + 6.2$
$= 5.3 + 3.7 + 2.8 + 6.2$ Commutative (+)
$= (5.3 + 3.7) + (2.8 + 6.2)$ Associative (+)
$= 9 + 9$ Substitution
$= 18$ Substitution

37. $(2 + 3)6$
$= (2)6 + (3)6$
$= 12 + 18$
$= 30$

39. $8(6 - 2)$
$= 8(6) - 8(2)$
$= 48 - 16$
$= 32$

41. $-2(5 - 3)$
$= -2(5) - -2(3)$
$= -10 + 6$
$= -4$

43. $3(x + 2)$
$= 3(x) + 3(2)$
$= 3x + 6$

45. $6(d - 3)$
$= 6(d) - 6(3)$
$= 6d - 18$

47. $(9y - 6)(-3)$
$= (9y)(-3) - (6)(-3)$
$= -27y + 18$

49. $4(3 + 5 + 4)$; 48 **51.** 7 **53.** 9 **55.** 5 **57.** 9

59.

x	y
1	3
2	4
3	5
4	6

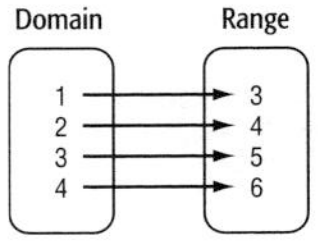

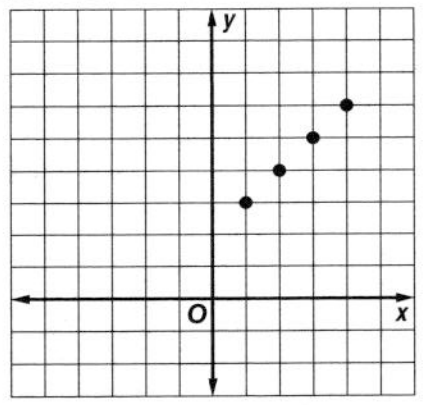

D = {1, 2, 3, 4}; R = {3, 4, 5, 6}

61.

x	y
−2	4
−1	3
0	2
−1	2

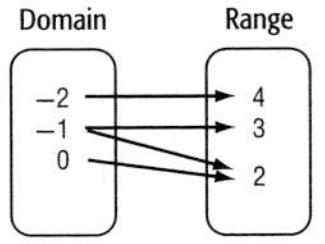

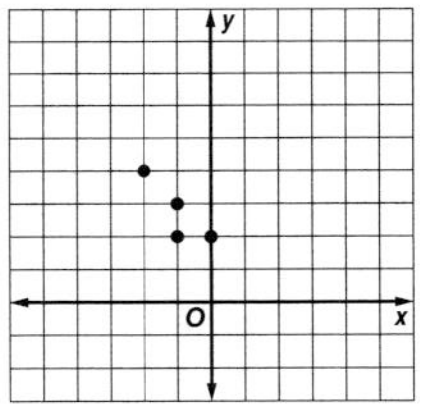

D = {−2, −1, 0}; R = {2, 3, 4}

63. {(−2, −2), (0, −3), (2, −2), (2, 0), (4, −1)}
65. function **67.** function **69.** −2 **71.** 4
73. $2m + 8$
75.

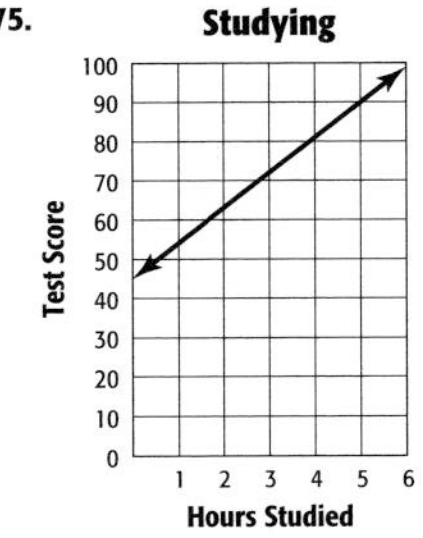

77. Hypothesis: $2x + 7 > 31$; Conclusion: $x > 12$
79. $x = 16$

Chapter 2 Linear Equations

Page 73 Get Ready

1. $3n - 4$ **3.** $2b - 11$ **5.** 2 **7.** 11 **9.** 11 **11.** \$28.40 **13.** 20% **15.** 21%

Pages 75–80 Lesson 2-1

1. $15 - 3r = 6$
3 Words: A number squared plus 12 is the same as the quotient of p and 4.
Equation: $n^2 = p \div 4$
The equation is $n^2 = p \div 4$.

5. $8 + 3k = 5k - 3$ **7.** $\frac{25}{t} + 6 = 2t + 1$ **9.** $1900 + 30w = 2500$; 20 **11.** $P = 5s$ **13.** $4\pi r^2 = S$ **15.** Sample answer: The product of seven and m minus q is equal to 23. **17.** Sample answer: Three times the sum of g and eight is the same as 4 times h minus 10. **19.** Sample answer: A team of gymnasts competed in a regional meet. Each member of the team won 3 medals. There were a total of 45 medals won by the team. How many team members were there? **21.** $f - 5g = 25 - f$ **23.** $4(14 + c) = a^2$ **25.** $3 \cdot 10 = 12f$; $2\frac{1}{2}$ flats

27 Words: C is five ninths times the difference of F and 32.
Equation: $C = \frac{5}{9} \cdot (F - 32)$
The equation is $C = \frac{5}{9}(F - 32)$.

29. $I = prt$ **31.** Sample answer: Four times m is equal to fifty-two. **33.** Sample answer: Fifteen less than the square of r equals the sum of t and nineteen. **35.** Sample answer: One third minus four fifths of z is four thirds of y cubed. **37.** Sample answer: Ashley has a credit card that charges 12% interest on the principal balance. If Ashley's payment was $224, what was the principal balance on the credit card? **39.** Sample answer: Fred was teaching his friends a new card game. Each player gets 5 cards, and 7 cards are placed in the center of the table. Since there are 52 cards in a deck, find how many players can play the game. **41.** C **43.** D

45 Words: the number of tent stakes + packets of drink mix + bottles of water = 17
$d = 3t$
$w = t + 2$
$t + d + w = 17$
$t + 3t + (t + 2) = 17$
$5t + 2 = 17$
$5t + 2 - 2 = 17 - 2$
$5t = 15$
$t = 3$
She brought 3 tent stakes.

47. Sample answer: My favorite television show has 30 new episodes each year. So far eight have aired. How many new episodes are left?
49. $\ell = \frac{P - 2w}{2}$ **51.** C **53.** 180 m **55.** I could have been born in Florida, moved to Kentucky, and still live in Kentucky. **57.** 10 is divisible by 2, but not by 4. **59a.** independent: number of sides; dependent: interior angle sum **59b.** Domain: all integers greater than or equal to 3; Range: all positive integer multiples of 180 **59c.** Discrete; sample answer: There cannot be a polygon with 3.5 sides, so the function cannot be continuous. **59d.** 1440 **61.** 1,000,000 **63.** 125

Pages 83–89 Lesson 2-2

1. 28 **3.** $\frac{5}{6}$ **5.** 9 **7.** −4.1 **9.** $-3\frac{1}{4}$ **11.** 16
13. $\frac{10}{9}$ or $1\frac{1}{9}$ **15.** $-\frac{4}{7}$ **17.** $22.75 **19.** 116 **21.** 22
23. −11

25
$-16 - (-t) = -45$
$-16 + 16 - (-t) = -45 + 16$
$t = -29$
Check: $-16 + (-29) = -45$
$-45 = -45$ Yes

27. −32 **29.** −7 **31.** $1\frac{1}{8}$ **33.** $1\frac{2}{7}$ **35.** −708 **37.** 33
39. −2 **41.** $-1\frac{1}{9}$ **43.** $24.9 = 8.1 + t$; 16.8 hours

45. −77 **47.** $\frac{16}{3}$ **49.** −10 **51.** $-\frac{10}{7}$ or $-1\frac{3}{7}$
53. 18 **55.** 225 **57.** $\frac{2}{3} = -8n$; $n = -\frac{1}{12}$
59. $\frac{4}{5} = \frac{10}{16}n$; $n = \frac{32}{25}$

61 Words: Four and four fifths times a number is one and one fifth.
Equation: $4\frac{4}{5} \cdot n = 1\frac{1}{5}$
The equation is $4\frac{4}{5}n = 1\frac{1}{5}$.
Solve:
$4\frac{4}{5}n = 1\frac{1}{5}$
$\frac{24}{5}n = \frac{6}{5}$
$5\left(\frac{24}{5}n\right) = 5\left(\frac{6}{5}\right)$
$24n = 6$
$n = \frac{6}{24}$
$n = \frac{1}{4}$

63. $555 = 139 + p$; 416 **65.** $180 = t + 154$; 26 s
67. $1.6 - m = 0.8$; $0.8 million

69 Words: 45 million fewer than 57 million is the number who have blogs.
Equation: 57 − 45
Solve: 57 − 45 = 12 million

71a. $350 + m = 1000$; $650 **71b.** $350 + 225 + m = 1000$; $425 **71c.** $6t = 1000$; 167 **73.** Sample answer: $12 + n = 25$; subtract 12 from each side or add −12 to each side.
75a. Sometimes; $0 + 0 = 0$ but $2 + 2 \neq 2$.
75b. Always; this is the Addition Identity Property. **77.** Sample answer: If we multiply each side of the first equation by 3 the result is the second equation. So, they have the same solution although they have different variables. **79.** C
81. F **83.** $2r + 3k = 13$ **85.** $m^2 - p^3 = 16$
87. Sample answer: If it is Monday, then the trash is picked up. **89.** Sample answer: If $x^2 - 3x = 40$, then $x = 8$. **91.** $12(5 + 18 + 12)$; 420 hours

Pages 91–96 Lesson 2-3

1
$3m + 4 = -11$
$3m + 4 - 4 = -11 - 4$
$3m = -15$
$m = -5$
Check: $3m + 4 = -11$
$3(-5) + 4 = -11$
$-15 + 4 = -11$
$-11 = -11$ Yes

3. −55 **5.** 61 **7.** $12 - 2n = -34$; 23
9. $n + (n + 2) + (n + 4) = 75$; 23, 25, 27 **11.** −5
13. −5 **15.** 70 **17.** 27 **19.** 16 **21.** −61

23 Equation: $49.99 + 0.15m = 100$
$49.99 - 49.99 + 0.15m = 100 - 49.99$
$0.15m = 50.01$
$m \approx 333$

So, he can use the phone for 650 + 333 or 983 minutes.
25. $17 = 6x - 13$; $n = 5$ **27.** $n + (n + 2) + (n + 4) = 141$; 45, 47, 49 **29.** $n + (n + 1) + (n + 2) + (n + 3) = -142$; −37, −36, −35, −34 **31.** $-7\frac{3}{5}$ **33.** −72
35. 108 **37.** $\frac{4}{5}$ **39.** $\frac{33}{14}$ **41.** $7\frac{1}{4}$ yr or 7 yr 3 mo

43
$3.7q + 26.2 = 111.67$
$3.7q + 26.2 - 26.2 = 111.67 - 26.2$
$3.7q = 85.47$
$q = 23.1$

45. 31.6 **47.** −3.5 **49.** 5
51a. $5x + 275 = x(6 + 15 + 9)$; 11 visits
51b.

Visits	Cost for Members	Cost for Nonmembers
3	290	90
6	305	180
9	320	270
12	335	360
15	350	450

51c.

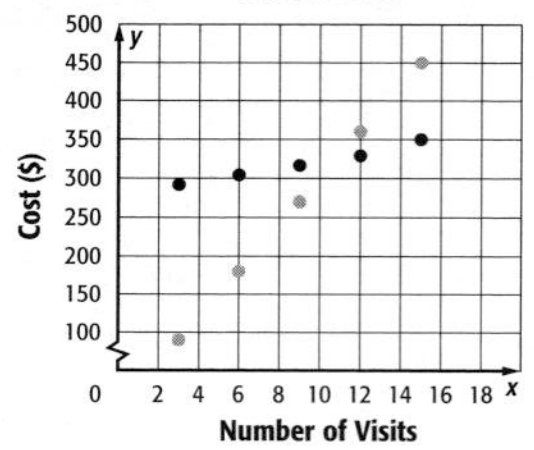

Both functions are linear. If a person is going to visit the park fewer than 11 times, it will be cheaper to be a nonmember. **53.** Sample answer: A pair of designer jeans costs $60. This is $40 more than twice the cost of a T-shirt. How much is the T-shirt? The T-shirt costs $10. **55.** 15 sides
57. Sample answer: In order to solve the equation $4k + 20 = 236$, you would first subtract 20 from each side and then divide each side by 4. **59.** 84
61. B **63.** 1,379 **65.** Three times a number h is increased by 7 to equal 20. **67.** Three multiplied by a number p is the same as the difference of 8 times p and r. **69.** The product of $\frac{1}{2}$ and v is equal to the product of $\frac{2}{3}$ and v plus 4. **71.** 0; Additive Identity **73.** 4; Additive Inverse **75.** 53 **77.** 1000

Pages 97–102 Lesson 2-4

1. 4 **3.** −7 **5.** no solution **7.** all numbers
9. A **11.** 4

13
$6 + 3t = 8t - 14$
$6 + 3t - 3t = 8t - 3t - 14$
$6 = 5t - 14$
$6 + 14 = 5t - 14 + 14$
$20 = 5t$
$4 = t$
Check: $6 + 3t = 8t - 14$
$6 + 3(4) = 8(4) - 14$
$6 + 12 = 32 - 14$
$18 = 18$ Yes

15. $2\frac{2}{5}$ **17.** 6 **19.** −5 **21.** 1 **23.** −4, −2
25. no solution **27.** all numbers **29.** −25 **31.** 15
33. 3 **35.** −2 **37.** −2, 0

39 Equation: $1500 + 0.80x = 1.59x$
Solve: $1500 + 0.80x = 1.59x$
$1500 + 0.80x - 0.80x = 1.59x - 0.80x$
$1500 = 0.79x$
$1899 \approx x$

41a. Sample answer: $y = 2x + 4$

x	−2	−1	0	1	2
y	0	2	4	6	8

$y = -x - 2$

x	−2	−1	0	1	2
y	0	−1	−2	−3	−4

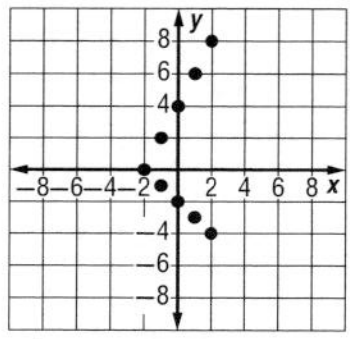

41b. −2 **41c.** Sample answer: The solution in part b is the x-coordinate for the point of intersection on the graph. **43.** Sample answer: $2x + 1 = \frac{3}{2}x - 2$; First I chose $\frac{3}{2}$ as the fractional coefficient. Then I chose 2 for the coefficient for the variable on the other side of the equation. After substituting −6 in for x on both sides, 1 must be added to the left and 2 must be subtracted from the right to balance the equation. **45a.** Incorrect; the 2 must be distributed over both g and 5; 6. **45b.** correct **45c.** Incorrect; to eliminate $-6z$ on the right side of the equal sign, $6z$ must be added to each side of the equation; 1.
47. Sample answer: If the equation has variables on both sides of the equation, you must add or subtract so that the variable only appears on one side of the equation. After that step, solving the equation uses the same steps. **49.** J **51.** A
53. $-2\frac{2}{3}$ **55.** −15 **57.** −15 **59.** $34 **61.** 2; Multiplicative Identity **63.** $\frac{2}{3}$; Additive Identity
65. 7; Substitution **67.** $5(m + k) = 7k$ **69.** 5

71. −24 **73.** 11

Pages 103–109 Lesson 2-5

1. 15 **3.** −4

5. {4, −2}; 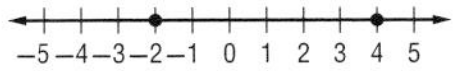

7. {−6, −2} 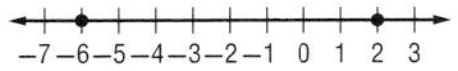

9. ∅ 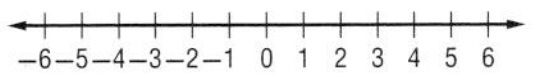

11 Find the point that is the same distance from −2 and 4. This is the midpoint between −2 and 4, which is 1.The distance from −2 to 1 is 3 units. The distance from 4 to 1 is 3 units. So, an equation is $|x - 1| = 3$

13 $|2x + z| + 2y = |2(2.1) + (-4.2)| + 2(3)$
$= |4.2 + (-4.2)| + 6$
$= |0| + 6$
$= 0 + 6$
$= 6$

15. −7.4 **17.** 8.4 **19.** −9.6 **21.** 0.4

23. {−11, −9}; 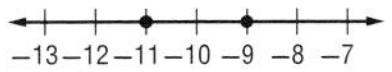

25. {7, −3}; 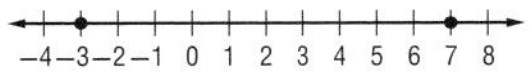

27. ∅ 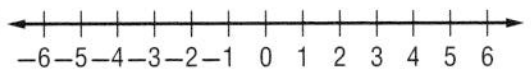

29. {0, 6} 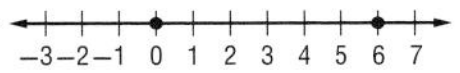

31. 11% to 19% **33.** $|x| = 4$ **35.** $|x - 1| = 4$

37. {−24, 16}

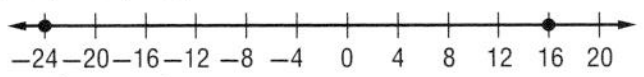

39. $\left\{3, -\frac{9}{5}\right\}$ 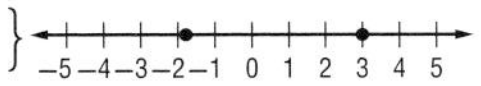

41. no solution 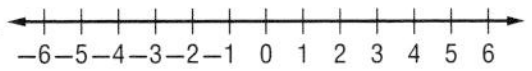

43a. $|x - 52| = 2$; {50, 54} **43b.** $|x - 53| = 1$; {52, 53} **43c.** 203 and 214 seconds **45a.** 47 to 53 mph **45b.** The slower the speed that the speedometer is calibrated at the more accurate the setting.

47. $|x| = 1\frac{1}{2}$ **49.** $\left|x - \frac{1}{4}\right| = \frac{1}{4}$ **51.** $\left|x + \frac{1}{3}\right| = 1$

53 **a.** Words: The number of people is 20,000, plus or minus 1,000.
Variable: Let h be the number of people who can clearly hear voices.
Equation: $|h - 20{,}000| = 1{,}000$

b. Solve the equation found in part **a.**
$|h - 20{,}000| = 1{,}000$
$h - 20{,}000 = 1{,}000$ or $h - 20{,}000 = -1{,}000$
$h - 20{,}000 + 20{,}000 = 1{,}000 + 20{,}000$ or
$h - 20{,}000 + 20{,}000 = -1{,}000 + 20{,}000$
$h = 21{,}000$ or $h = 19{,}000$

c. To find the range, find $21{,}000 - 19{,}000 = 2{,}000$

55 **a.** Let p = the number of points awarded for each question; $|p| = 10$

b. Sample answer:

Number of questions correct	points
0	0
1	10
2	20
3	30
4	40
5	50

c. Sample answer: In science class, absolute values can be used for tolerance ranges of pollution on plants.

57. Sometimes; when $x = -1$, the value is 0.
59. Sometimes; when c is a negative value whose absolute value is greater than x, the inequality is true. **61.** An absolute value represents a distance from zero on a number line. A distance can never be a negative number. **63.** Wesley; the absolute value of a number cannot be a negative number.

65. D **67.** A **69.** $\frac{1}{2}n + 16 = \frac{2}{3}n - 4$; 120 **71.** 10 in

73. $\frac{2}{5}n = -24$; −60 **75.** $12 = \frac{1}{5}n$; 60

Pages 111–117 Lesson 2-6

1. no

3 $\frac{1.4}{2.1}$ is written in simplified form. $\frac{2.8}{4.4} = \frac{1.4}{2.2}$.
Since the fractions are not equal, the ratios are not equivalent.

5. 5 **7.** about 253.3 min or 4 hours 13.3 min

9. yes **11.** no **13.** yes **15.** 40 **17.** 29.25 **19.** 9.8

21. 1.32 **23.** 0.84

25 $\frac{t}{0.3} = \frac{1.7}{0.9}$
$0.9t = 1.7(0.3)$
$0.9t = 0.51$
$t \approx 0.57$

27. 6 **29.** 11 **31.** about \$262.59 **33.** 150 mi **35.** 18

37. 0.8 **39.** 11 **41.** 130 students

43 **a.** Write each ratio.

for 2000, $\frac{\text{indoor theaters}}{\text{total theaters}} = \frac{35{,}567}{36{,}250}$

for 2001, $\frac{\text{indoor theaters}}{\text{total theaters}} = \frac{34{,}490}{35{,}173}$

for 2002, $\frac{\text{indoor theaters}}{\text{total theaters}} = \frac{35{,}170}{35{,}836}$

for 2003, $\frac{\text{indoor theaters}}{\text{total theaters}} = \frac{35{,}361}{35{,}995}$

for 2004, $\frac{\text{indoor theaters}}{\text{total theaters}} = \frac{36{,}012}{36{,}653}$

for 2005, $\frac{\text{indoor theaters}}{\text{total theaters}} = \frac{37{,}092}{37{,}740}$

for 2006, $\frac{\text{indoor theaters}}{\text{total theaters}} = \frac{37{,}776}{38{,}425}$

b. None of the ratios form a proportion.

45a.

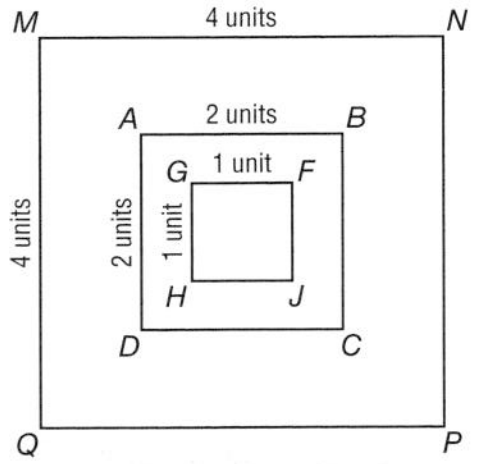

45b.

ABCD		MNPQ		GFHJ	
Side length	2	Side length	4	Side length	1
Perimeter	8	Perimeter	16	Perimeter	4

45c. If the length of a side is increased by a factor, the perimeter is also increased by that factor. If the length of the sides are decreased by a factor, the perimeter is also decreased by the same factor.
47. Ratios and rates each compare two numbers by using division. However, rates compare two measurements that involve different units of measure. **49.** Neither; Tim inverted the woman-to-man comparison when he wrote the second ratio. Aisha wrote a proportion that is equivalent to Tim's incorrect proportion. **51.** C **53.** G **55.** ∅
57. {10, −7} **59.** 30 years **61.** −7 **63.** −48 **65.** 13
67. 5.5 **69.** 3.5

Pages 119–124 Lesson 2-7

1 It is an increase.
$125 - 78 = 47$
$47 \div 78 \approx 0.60.$
The percent of increase is about 60%.

3. inc.; 33% **5.** 146 mi **7.** \$38.42 **9.** \$53.07
11. \$17.21 **13.** \$22.10

15 It is a decrease.
$16 - 10 = 6$
$6 \div 16 \approx 0.38.$
The percent of decrease is about 38%.

17. dec.; 77% **19.** inc.; 127% **21.** inc.; 90%
23. \$12,400 **25.** \$47.48 **27.** \$27.31 **29.** \$10.66
31. \$76.49 **33.** \$16.42 **35.** \$11.99 **37.** \$48.04
39. about 13.5% increase **41a.** First girl's dress - \$15; Second girl's dress = \$25.50 **41b.** The second girl. by \$0.50

43 Find the percent of increase or decrease for each grocery item. Ground beef had the biggest increase with a 41.1% increase.

45. Sample answer: A CD is on sale for \$9.99. If tax is 6.5%, what will the CD cost? **47.** Xavier; Maddie divided by the new amount instead of the original amount. **49.** Sample answer: To determine whether a percent of change is a percent of increase or decrease, compare the new amount with the old amount. If the new amount is greater, the change is an increase. If the new amount is less, the change is a decrease. To find the percent of change, subtract the original from the new amount. Then write a proportion, comparing the change to the original amount. The answer should be written as a percent. **51.** \$72 **53.** C **55.** 12
57. 4 **59.** 5.6 **61.** 3 **63.** −6 **65.** −7 **67.** If two lines are perpendicular, then they meet to form four right angles. If two lines meet to form four right angles, then they are perpendicular.
69. Sample answer: Six more than twice a number f equals nineteen. **71.** Sample answer: The product of three and a number a when added to 5 is equal to the difference of 27 and two times a.
73. Sample answer: The fourth power of a number d increased by sixty-four is three times that number d to the third power plus seventy-seven.

Pages 126–131 Lesson 2-8

1 $5a + c = -8a$
$5a - 5a + c = -8a - 5a$
$c = -13a$
$-\frac{c}{13} = a$

3. $k = -7n - m$ **5a.** $h = \frac{V}{\pi r^2}$ **5b.** 8 in.
7. about 0.43875 ft

9 $x = b - cd$
$x - b = -cd$
$\frac{x - b}{-d} = c$

11. $m = \frac{-n + p}{10}$ **13.** $v = \frac{9}{5}(z - w)$ **15.** $f = \frac{6g - 10}{d}$

17a. $v_f = at + v_i$ **17b.** 10 ft/s² **19.** 49.8 L

21. $t = \frac{w - 11v}{31}$ **23.** $c = \frac{-13 + f}{10 - d}$ **25.** 1.0 mm/s

27. 3.9 km/s **29.** $t - 7 = r + 6$; $t = r + 13$

31. $\frac{9}{10}g = 7 + \frac{2}{3}k$; $k = \frac{3}{2}\left[\frac{9}{10}g - 7\right]$

33 $S = 2w(\ell + h) + 2lh$
$214 = 2(6)(7 + h) + 2(7)h$
$214 = 12(7 + h) + 14h$
$214 = 84 + 12h + 14h$
$130 = 26h$
$5 = h$
So, 5 inches.

35. about 396 in³ **37.** Sandrea; she performed each step correctly; Fernando omitted the negative sign from $-5b$. **39a.** $x = \frac{y - 1}{yn - 1}$ **39b.** $y = -\frac{1}{3}x$ **41.** D
43. 15 **45.** \$101.76 **47.** \$46.33 **49.** \$56.95
51. 1.67 **53.** 5.14 **55.** 50(7.50) + 90(5.00); \$825
57. −0.5 **59.** −1.5 **61.** 2

Pages 132–138 Lesson 2-9

1

	Weight	Price	Total Price
Soup	10	0.15	0.15(10)
Salad	x	0.20	$0.20x$
Total			3.30

$0.15(10) + 0.20x = 3.30$
$1.50 + 0.20x = 3.30$
$0.20x = 1.80$
$x = 9$
She bought 9 oz of salad.
3. 10 mph **5.** 2 hours
7 a.

	Amount	Percent	Total
Metallic Balloons	b	\$2.00	$2.00b$
Bunches of helium Balloons	$b - 36$	\$3.50	$3.50(b - 36)$

b. $2.00b + 3.50(b - 36) = 281$
c. $2.00b + 3.50(b - 36) = 281$
$2b + 3.5b - 126 = 281$
$5.5b - 126 = 281 + 126$
$5.5b = 407$
$b = 74$
There were 74 dozen metallic balloons sold.
d. $b - 36 = 74 - 36$
$= 38$
There were 38 dozen bunches of balloons sold.
9. about 16.67 gal **11.** about 22.2 mph **13.** $1\frac{1}{7}$hours or 1 h 8 min 34 s **15.** 10 gal **17.** 10.89 mph
19 a. $D = rt$
$= 65(6)$
$= 390$ He could drive 390 miles.
b. $D = rt$
$\frac{D}{r} = t$
$\frac{625}{65} = t$
$9.62 \approx t$ It will take about 9.62 hours.
21. 33 mi **23.** Sample answer: For a 50% solution being added to a 100% solution to produce a 75% resulting solution, the quantity of each must be the same. **25.** Sample answer: How many grams of salt must be added to 36 grams of a 15% salt solution to obtain a 50% salt solution? **27.** B
29. C **31.** $\frac{-5 + b}{2b}$ **33.** $\frac{A}{2\pi r} - r$ **35.** Sample answer: The quotient of n and -6 is the same as the sum of two times n and one. **37.** Sample answer: The sum of three and twice x squared is equal to twenty-one. **39.** (4, 25); Sample answer: If four cars are washed, \$25 is earned. **41.** \$583.50
43. -2 **45.** -7 **47.** 24

Pages 139–144 Study Guide and Review

1. false, variable **3.** true **5.** false, ratio **7.** false, decrease **9.** $5x + 3 = 15$ **11.** $\frac{1}{2}m^3 = 4m - 9$
13. h squared minus five times h plus six is equal to zero. **15.** width: 8 ft, length: 19 ft **17.** -5 **19.** 2.1
21. 6 **23.** 14 **25.** 6 **27.** -11 **29.** 17 **31.** 2
33. 38.1 **35.** 19, 21, 23 **37.** 3 **39.** -2 **41.** 2
43. -8 **45.** 21 **47.** 28 **49.** -144 **51.** $\{-5, 17\}$

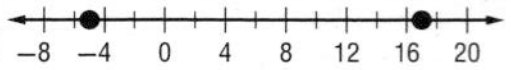

53. $\{-27, 63\}$

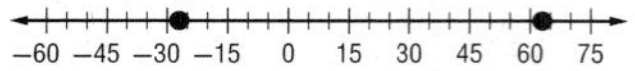

55. yes **57.** 20 **59.** 12 **61.** increase, 25%
63. decrease, 17% **65.** \$52.19 **67.** \$55.20
69. \$33.75 **71.** $y = \frac{9 - 3x}{2}$ **73.** $m = \frac{15 - 9n}{-5}$
75. $y = \frac{5}{2}(m - n)$ **77.** $h = \frac{2A}{a + b}$ **79.** 52 mph

Chapter 3 Linear Functions

Page 151 Get Ready

1.

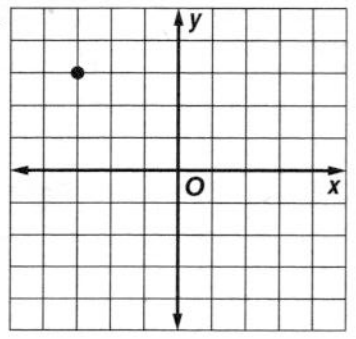

3.

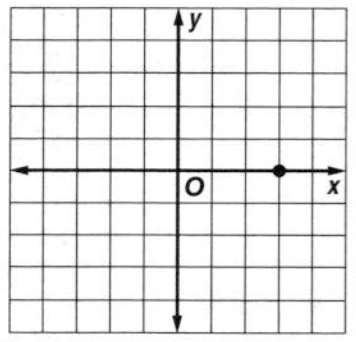

5.

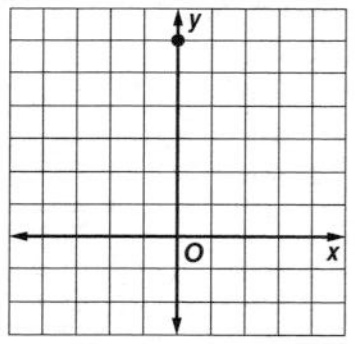

7. $(3, -1)$ **9.** $(3, 2)$ **11.** $(5, 0)$ **13.** $y = -3x + 1$
15. $y = \frac{5}{2}x - 6$ **17.** $y = -10x + 6$ **19.** $\frac{1}{4}$ **21.** 0
23. about \$13.5 million

Pages 153–160 Lesson 3-1

1. yes; $x - y = -5$ **3.** yes; $y = 1$ **5.** 25, -4; The x-intercept 25 means that after 25 minutes, the temperature is 0°F. The y-intercept -4 means that at time 0, the temperature is -4°F.

7.

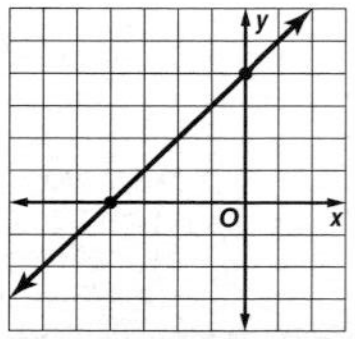

9.

x	$x + 2y = 4$	y	(x, y)
-4	$(-4) + 2y = 4$	4	$(-4, 4)$
-2	$(-2) + 2y = 4$	3	$(-2, 3)$
0	$(0) + 2y = 4$	2	$(0, 2)$
2	$(2) + 2y = 4$	1	$(2, 1)$
4	$(4) + 2y = 4$	0	$(4, 0)$

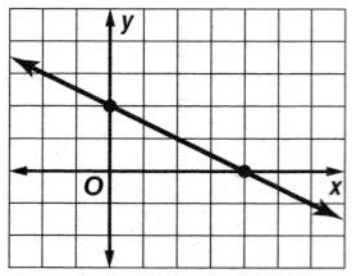

11.

x	$y = 3$	y	(x, y)
-2	$y = 3$	3	$(-2, 3)$
-1	$y = 3$	3	$(-1, 3)$
0	$y = 3$	3	$(0, 3)$
1	$y = 3$	3	$(1, 3)$
2	$y = 3$	3	$(2, 3)$

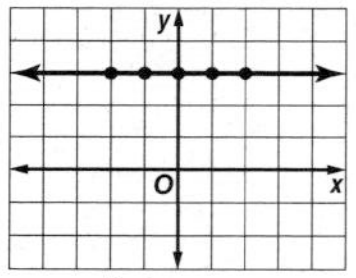

13 $5x + y^2 = 25$
Since the y term is squared, this equation cannot be written in the form $AX + BY = c$, so it is not a linear equation.
15. no **17.** yes; $4x + y = 0$ **19.** 3, 4 **21.** 6, 20; The x-intercept represents the number of seconds that it takes the Eagle to land. The y-intercept represents the initial height of the Eagle.
23.

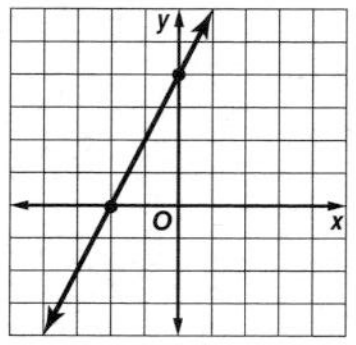

25.

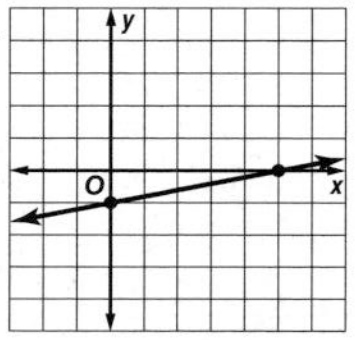

27.

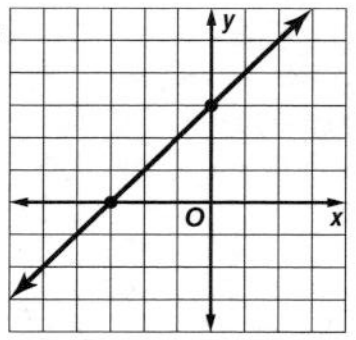

29.

x	y
-2	0
-2	1
-2	2

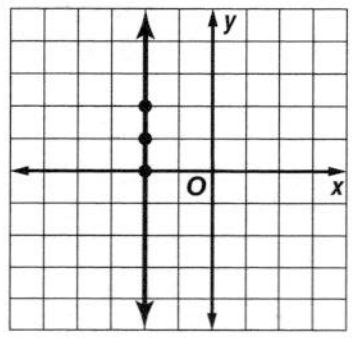

31.

x	y
-1	8
0	0
1	-8

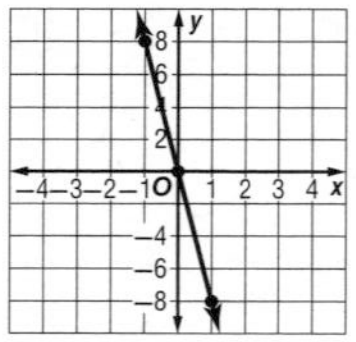

33.

x	y
0	8
1	7
2	6

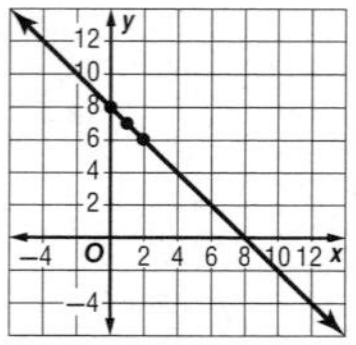

35 a. The domain is all real numbers so there are infinitely many solutions. Select values from the domain and make a table.

v	$p = 0.15v$	p	(v, p)
0	$p = 0.15(0)$	0	(0, 0)
2	$p = 0.15(2)$	0.3	(2, 0.3)
4	$p = 0.15(4)$	0.6	(4, 0.6)
6	$p = 0.15(6)$	0.9	(6, 0.9)
8	$p = 0.15(8)$	1.2	(8, 1.2)
10	$p = 0.15(10)$	1.5	(10, 1.5)

b. Create ordered pairs and graph them.

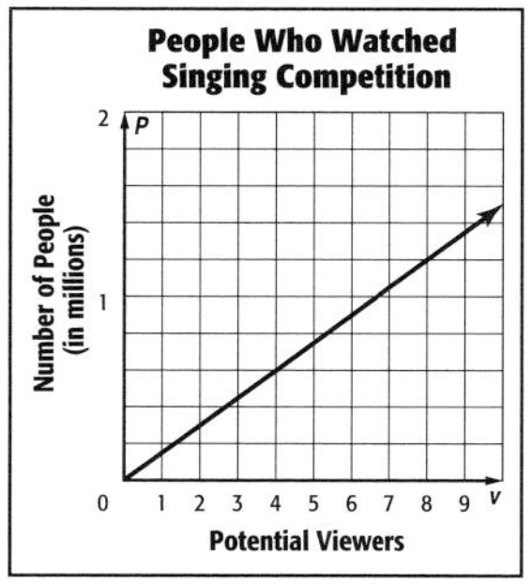

c. Using the graph, when there are 14 million potential viewers, there will about 2.1 million people who watch.
d. A negative does not make sense because you cannot have a negative number of viewers.

37. yes; $3x - 4y = 60$ **39.** yes; $3a = 2$
41. yes; $9m - 8n = -60$
43.

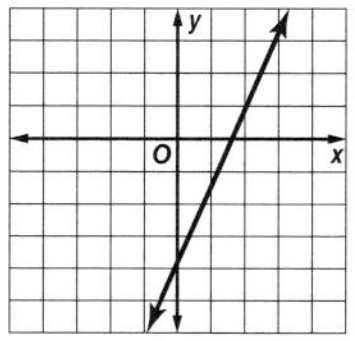

45.

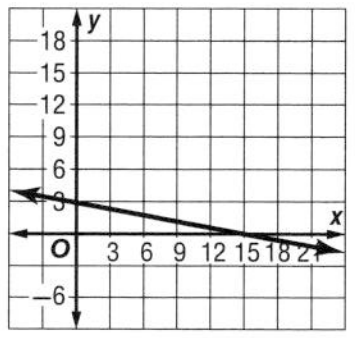

47.

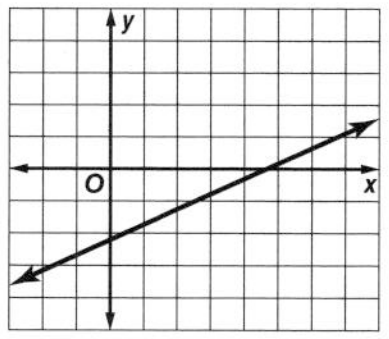

49. No; Sample answer: The rental car would cost \$176. Mrs. Johnson only has \$160 to spend.
51 $5x + 3y = 15$
To find the x-intercept, let $y = 0$.
$5x + 3y = 15$
$5x + 3(0) = 15$
$5x = 15$
$x = 3$
The x-intercept is 3. This means the graph intersects the x-axis at (3, 0).
To find the y-intercept, let $x = 0$.
$5x + 3y = 15$
$5(0) + 3y = 15$
$3y = 15$
$y = 5$
The y-intercept is 5. This means the graph crosses the y-axis at (0, 5).

53. $2\frac{1}{2}$; $-1\frac{2}{3}$ **55.** 12; −3
57a.

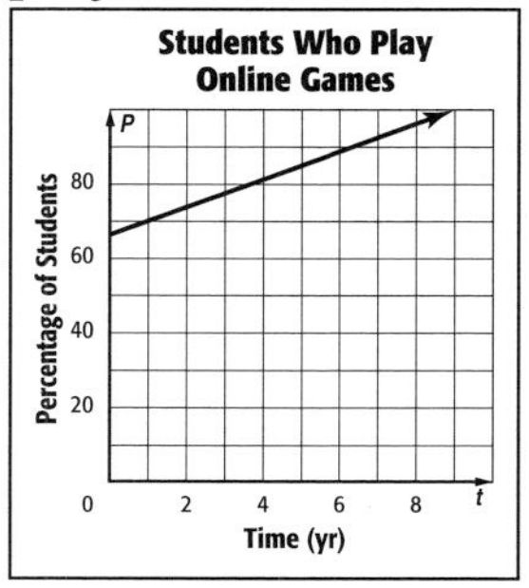

57b. 96%
59.

Perimeter of a Square	
Side Length	Perimeter
1	4
2	8
3	12
4	16

Sample answer: Yes; we used the formula $P = 4s$, which is linear.

Area of a Square	
Side Length	Area
1	1
2	4
3	9
4	16

Sample answer: No; we used the formula $A = s^2$, which is not linear.

Volume of a Cube	
Side Length	Volume
1	1
2	8
3	27
4	64

Sample answer: No; we used the formula $V = s^3$, which is not linear.

61. Sample answer: $y = 8$; horizontal line
63. Sample answer: $x - y = 0$; line through (0, 0)

65. D **67.** \$30 **69.** 270 rolls of solid wrap, 210 rolls of print wrap **71.** $g = \frac{5+m}{2+h}$ **73.** $z = \frac{c-b}{2}$
75. $-\frac{23}{14}$ **77.** −56

Pages 161–166 Lesson 3-2

1. 3 **3.** $\frac{1}{2}$ **5.** no solution **7.** no solution
9. Tyrone must deliver 40 newspapers for the papers in his bag to weigh 0 pounds. **11.** −3
13. no solution **15.** $-\frac{10}{7}$ or $-1\frac{3}{7}$
17 $5x - 5 = 5x + 2$
$5x - 5 + 5 = 5x + 2 + 5$
$5x = 5x + 7$
$5x - 5x = 5x - 5x + 7$
$0 = 7$
There are no solutions.
19. no solution **21.** no solution **23.** 100; She can download a total of 100 songs before the gift card is completely used. **25.** −8 **27.** $\frac{10}{3}$ or $3\frac{1}{3}$
29. $-\frac{34}{13}$ or $-2\frac{8}{13}$ **31.** $\frac{17}{25}$ **33.** $\frac{15}{8}$ or $1\frac{7}{8}$ **35.** 3
37. 4:00 P.M. **39.** −3 **41.** −2 **43.** $\frac{9}{8}$ or $1\frac{1}{8}$
45 **a.** Sample answers given:

Number of Songs Downloaded	Total Cost (\$)	Total Cost / Number Songs Downloaded
2	4	$\frac{4}{2} = 2$
4	8	$\frac{8}{4} = 2$
6	12	$\frac{12}{6} = 2$
8	16	$\frac{16}{8} = 2$
10	20	$\frac{20}{10} = 2$

b. As the number of songs downloaded increases by 2, the cost increases by 4.
c. The value of the total cost divided by the number of songs downloaded represents the cost per song. It costs \$2 per song.
47. 3 **49.** Sample answer: $3 + 4x = 0$; $y = 3 + 4x$ or $f(x) = 3 + 4x$ **51.** A **53.** B **55.** −5, 10 **57.** 7, −2
59. H: a number is divisible by 10; C: it is divisible by 5; If a number is divisible by 10, then it is divisible by 5. **61.** $\frac{5}{2}$ **63.** $-\frac{1}{2}$ **65.** $\frac{2}{3}$ **67.** 11

Pages 170–178 Lesson 3-3

1. $\frac{4}{3}$ **3a.** 2.005; There was an average increase in ticket price of \$2.005 per year. **3b.** Sample answer: 1998–2000; A steeper segment means a greater rate of change. **3c.** Sample answer: 1998–2000; Ticket prices show a sharp increase. **5.** No; the y-values do not decrease by a constant amount. **7.** −1
9. $\frac{7}{9}$ **11.** 0 **13.** −8
15 rate of change $= \frac{\text{change in } y}{\text{change in } x}$
$= \frac{9-15}{2-1}$
$= \frac{-6}{1}$
$= -6$
17. $\frac{1}{2}$ **19a.** Sample answer: $P = -1811.67t + 19548.30$ **19b.** The car value depreciates by \$1811.67 each year. **19c.** \$6866.61 **21.** No; the y-values do not increase at a constant rate.
23. Yes; both the x-values and the y-values increase at a constant rate.
25 $m = \frac{y_2 - y_1}{x_2 - x_1}$
$= \frac{1-(-2)}{1-8}$
$= \frac{1+2}{1-8}$
$= -\frac{3}{7}$
27. undefined **29.** $\frac{5}{17}$ **31.** 0 **33.** undefined
35. $\frac{10}{3}$ **37.** $\frac{3}{4}$ **39.** 6 **41.** Sample answer: about 0.5
43. $\frac{15}{4}$ **45.** $-\frac{2}{3}$
47 **a.** Plot the ordered pairs on a coordinate plane. Connect the points with a line.

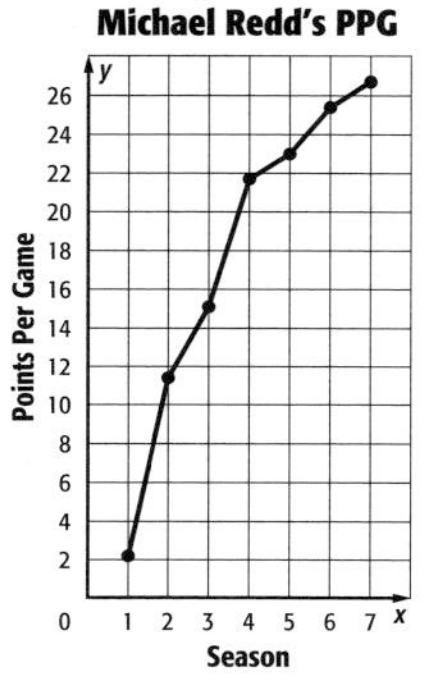

b. The steepest line is between 2000–2001 and 2001–2002, so that is when the PPG increased the most.
c. The rate of change was much more dramatic or steeper in the first four years, whereas it leveled off in the last few years.
49. The rate of change is $2\frac{1}{4}$ inches of growth per week. **51.** Sample answer: Slope can be used to describe a rate of change. Rate of change is a ratio that describes how much one quantity changes with respect to a change in another quantity. The slope of a line is also a ratio and it is the ratio of the change in the y-coordinates to the change in the x-coordinates. **53.** A **55.** \$4 **57.** −6 **59.** 4

For Homework Help, go to Hotmath.com

61. −1, 2 **63.** 12 **65.** $\frac{5}{16}$ **67.** 5

Pages 180–186 Lesson 3-4

1. $-\frac{4}{5}$; $-\frac{4}{5}$

3.

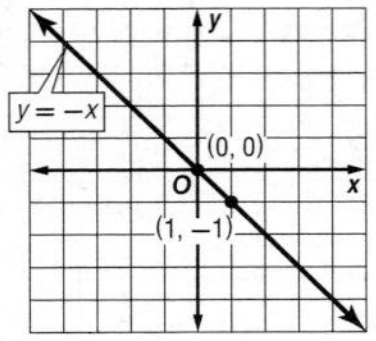

5.

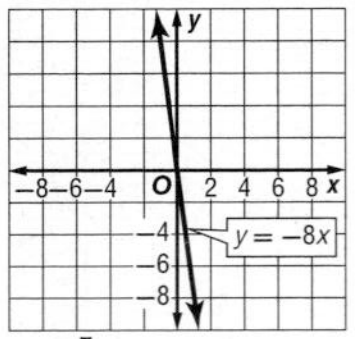

7. $y = \frac{5}{4}x$; 40

9a. $y = \frac{12}{5}x$;

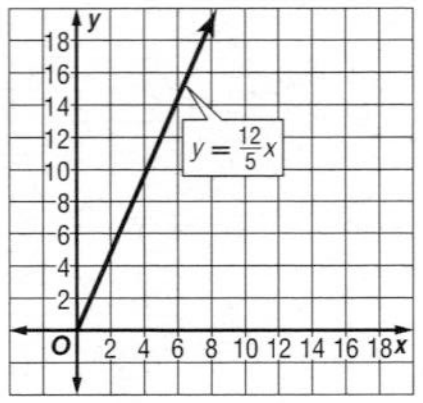

9b. 40

11 The constant of variation is −5.

$m = \frac{5-0}{-1-0}$

$= \frac{5}{-1}$

$= -5$

13. $-\frac{1}{5}$; $-\frac{1}{5}$ **15.** −12; −12

17.

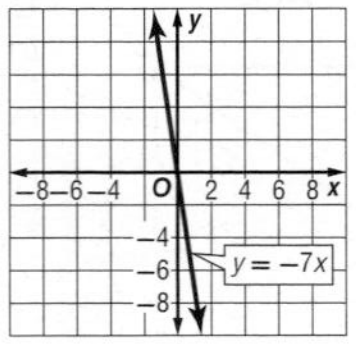

19.

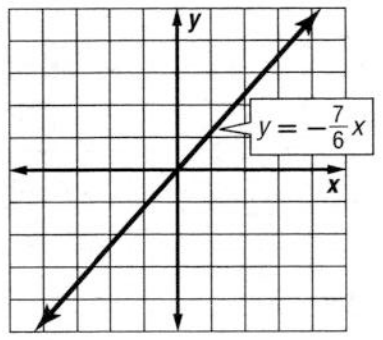

21.

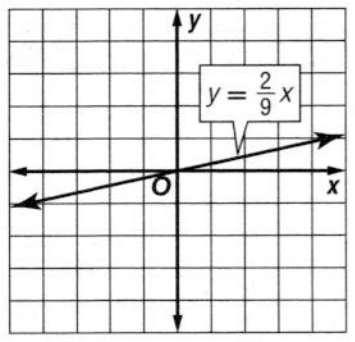

23.

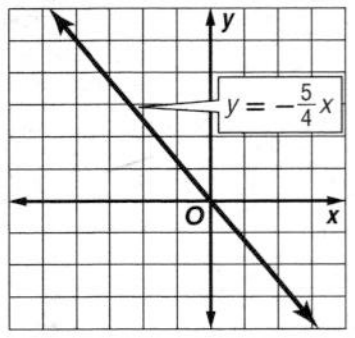

25 $y = kx$

$22 = k(8)$

$\frac{11}{4} = k$

Therefore, the direct variation equation is

$y = \frac{11}{4}x$.

$y = \frac{11}{4}x$

$y = \frac{11}{4}(-16)$

$y = 11(-4)$

$y = -44$

Therefore, $y = -44$ when $x = -16$.

27. $y = 14x$; $1\frac{1}{7}$ **29a.** $y = 1800x$ **29b.** 7 yr 6 mo

31. $y = 20x$; $\frac{5}{4}$ **33.** $y = -3.75x$; −30

35. dark green **37.** lime green

39 Since the songs are $0.99 each, the equation is $T = 0.99s$. The graph of the equation runs through the origin with a slope of 0.99.

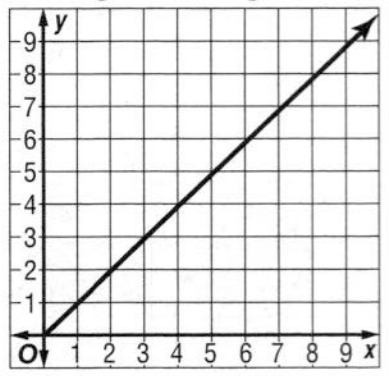

41a.

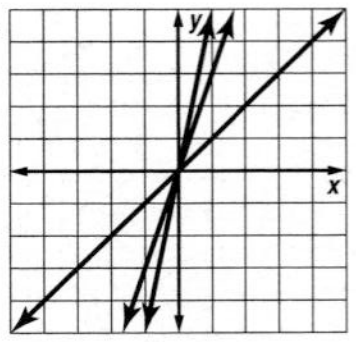

41b. Sample answer: The constant of variation, slope, and rate of change of a graph all have the same value. **41c.** Sample answer: Find the absolute value of k in each equation. The one with the great value of $|k|$ has the steeper graph.

43. $C = 9.95n$ **45.** $z = \frac{1}{9}x$; It is the only equation that is a direct variation. **47.** Sample answer: $y = 0.50x$ represents the cost of x apples.

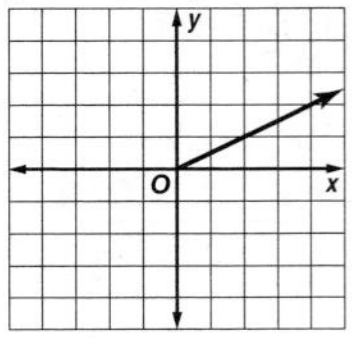

The rate of change, 0.50, is the cost per apple.

49. Neither; the slope is constant, but it is k.

51. A **53.** D **55.** 5.8; There was an average increase of 5.8 channels per year.

57.

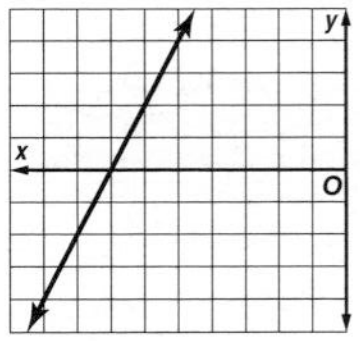

−7

59.

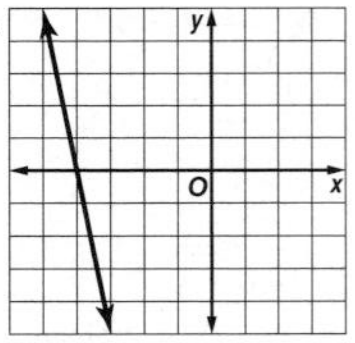

−4

61.

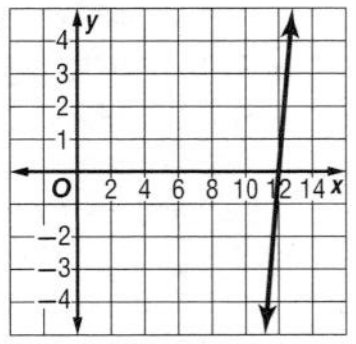

12

63. 12 **65.** −2 **67.** −28 **69.** −12 **71.** −6 **73.** −12

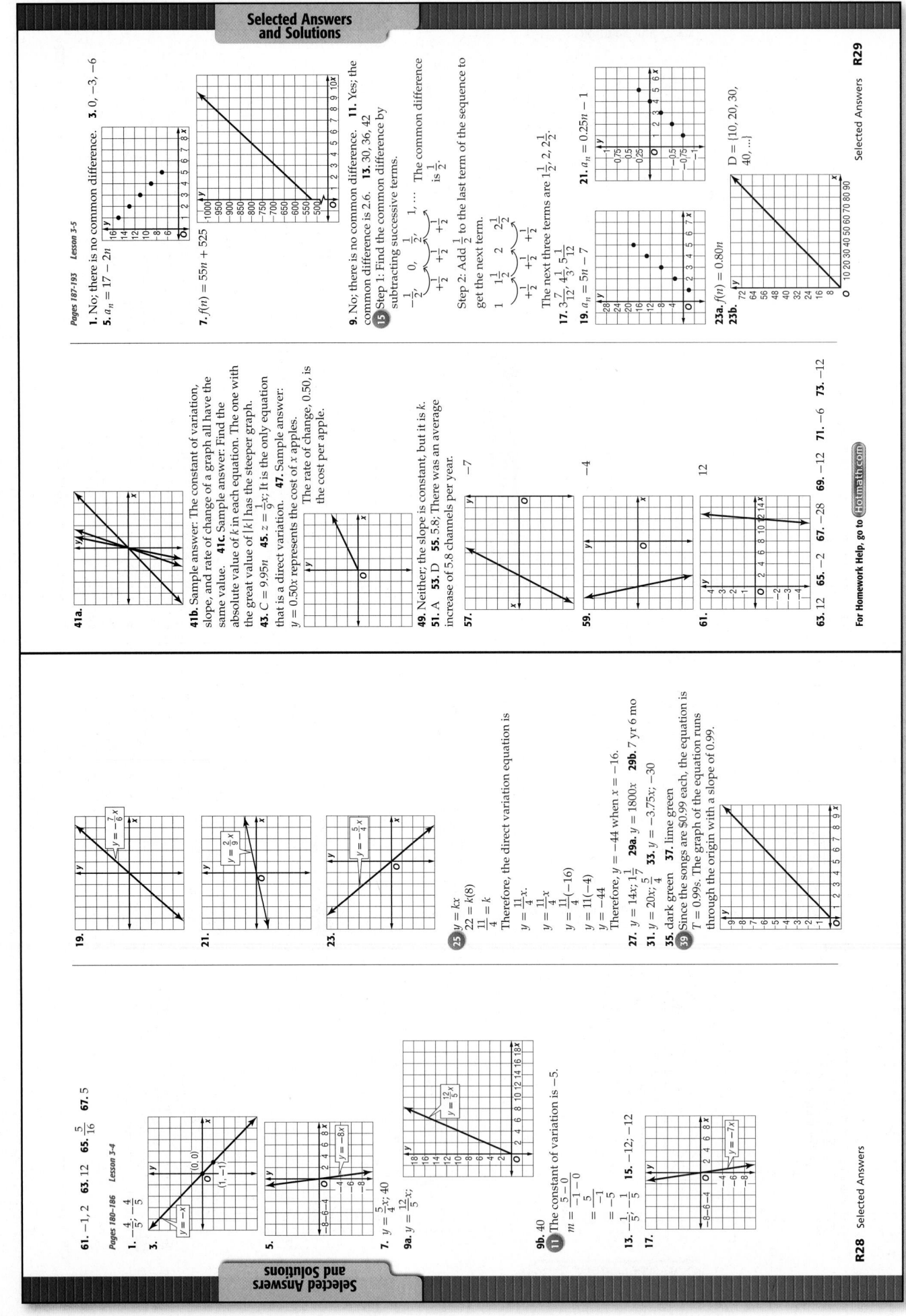

Pages 187–193 Lesson 3-5

1. No; there is no common difference. **3.** 0, −3, −6

5. $a_n = 17 - 2n$

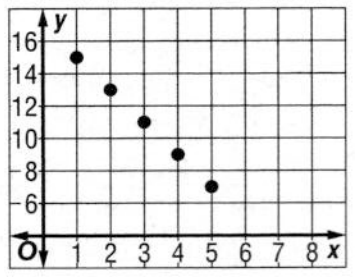

7. $f(n) = 55n + 525$

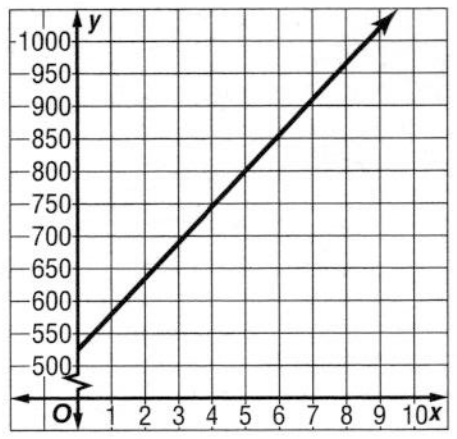

9. No; there is no common difference. **11.** Yes; the common difference is 2.6. **13.** 30, 36, 42

15 Step 1: Find the common difference by subtracting successive terms.

$-\frac{1}{2}$, 0, $\frac{1}{2}$, 1, … (each step $+\frac{1}{2}$) The common difference is $\frac{1}{2}$.

Step 2: Add $\frac{1}{2}$ to the last term of the sequence to get the next term.

1, $1\frac{1}{2}$, 2, $2\frac{1}{2}$ (each step $+\frac{1}{2}$)

The next three terms are $1\frac{1}{2}$, 2, $2\frac{1}{2}$.

17. $3\frac{7}{12}$, $4\frac{1}{3}$, $5\frac{1}{12}$

19. $a_n = 5n - 7$

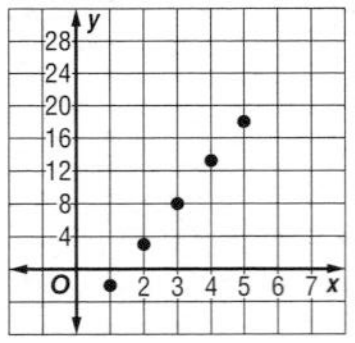

21. $a_n = 0.25n - 1$

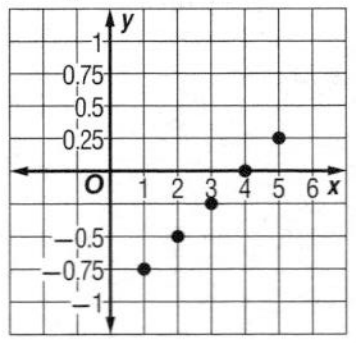

23a. $f(n) = 0.80n$

23b.

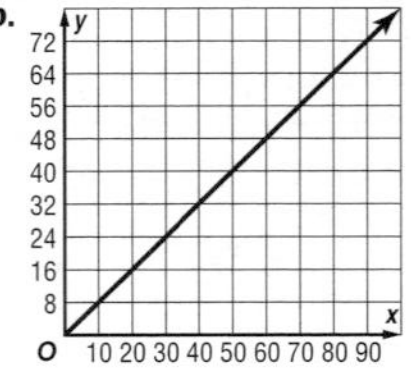

D = {10, 20, 30, 40, …}

25 The ordered pairs are (10, 7.50), (15, 8.75), (20, 10), (25, 11.25). So, the rate of change is $\frac{8.75 - 7.50}{15 - 10} = \frac{1.25}{5} = 0.25$.
The cost is $0.25 per word.
$f(n) = 0.25n + b$
$7.50 = 0.25(10) + b$
$7.50 = 2.50 + b$
$5 = b$
So, the equation is $f(n) = 0.25n + 5$.
27. 77 **29.** 25,646 **31a.** Sample answer: the first two terms are both 1. Starting with the third term, the two previous terms are added together to get the next term; 5, 8, 13, 21, 34. **31b.** $a_n = a_{n-2} + a_{n-1}$ **31c.** 610 **31d.** There is no common difference. **33.** −1 **35a.** Yes; there is a common difference.; x; $5x + 1, 6x + 1, 7x + 1$.
35b. No; there is no common difference.
37. 8 yr **39.** H **41.** 3, 3 **43.** $-\frac{3}{7}$ **45.** 3 **47.** 2
49. Sample answer: $453{,}000 - d = 369{,}000$; 84,000
51–55.

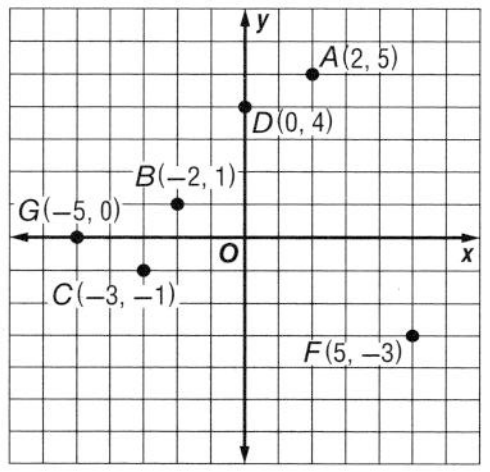

Pages 195–200 Lesson 3-6

1a.

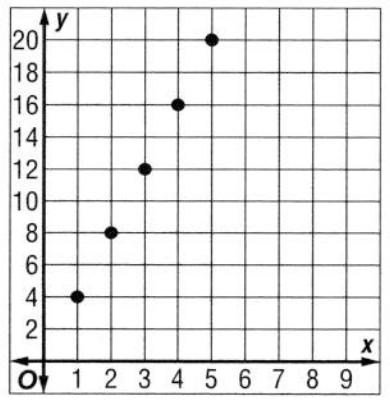

1b. $y = 4x$ **1c.** The perimeter is 4 times the length of the side.
3. $f(x) = -x + 3$

5 Select points from the graph and place them in a table.

x	0	1	2	3
y	0	2	4	6

The difference between the x-values is 1, while the difference between the y-values is 2. This suggests that $y = 2x$.
This works for each ordered pair, so the equation is $f(x) = 2x$.
7. $f(x) = 3x - 2$ **9.** $f(n) = 3n - 3$; Nonproportional; the function does not describe a direct variation.

11. $y = 2.25x + 2.50$
13 **a.** Sample answer:

Number of T-shirts ordered	5	10	15	20	25
Cost ($)	13	23	33	43	53

b. In functional notation, the equation is $C(t) = 2t + 3$.
c. The equation goes through (0, 3) and has a slope of 2.
d. The relationship is nonproportional because $\frac{13}{5} \neq \frac{23}{10} \neq \frac{33}{15} \neq \frac{43}{20} \neq \frac{53}{25}$.

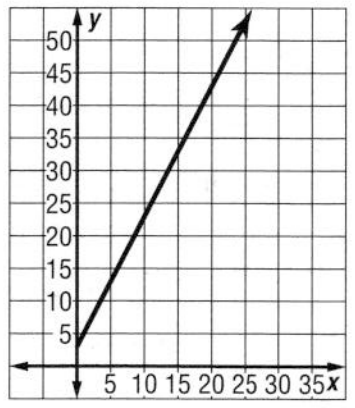

15. Sample answer: 4, 7, 10, 13; add a common difference of 3;
$a_n = 3n + 1$. **17.** $f(n) = 3n + 2$ is the related function for the arithmetic sequence 5, 8, 11, 14, …, but it is not proportional. The line through (1, 5) and (2, 8) does not pass through (0, 0). **19.** D
21. H **23.** 43, 53, 63 **25.** $\frac{5}{4}, \frac{11}{8}, \frac{3}{2}$ **27.** $y = 7x$; −12 **29a.** $V = \frac{1}{3}\pi r^2 h$ **29b.** about 3142 cm^3
31. $y = 3x - 5$
33.

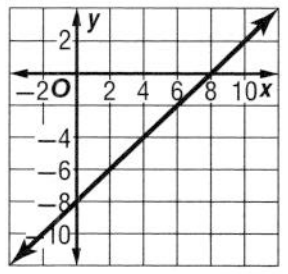

35.

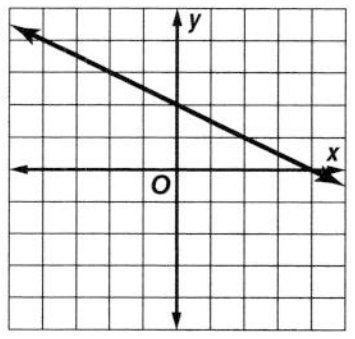

Pages 201–204 Study Guide and Review

1. true **3.** false; common difference **5.** true
7. false; The slope of $y = 5$ is 0. **9.** true
11. −8, 6
13.

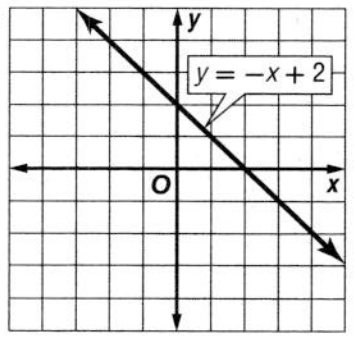

15.

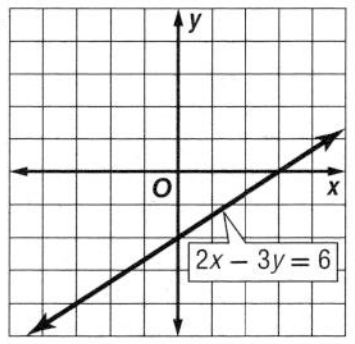

17a.

t	0	1	2	3	4	5
d	0	1.6	3.2	4.8	6.4	8

Speed of Sound

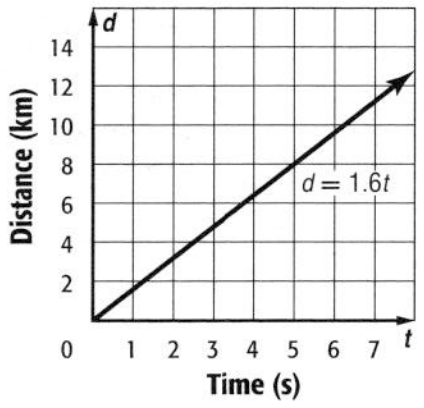

17b. about 11 km **19.** 6 **21.** $-\frac{1}{2}$
23. −7

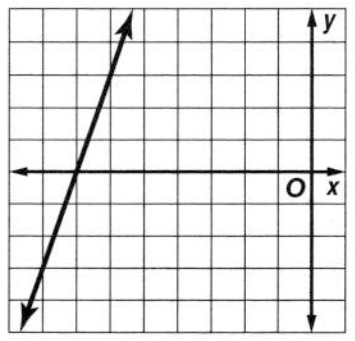

25. 9

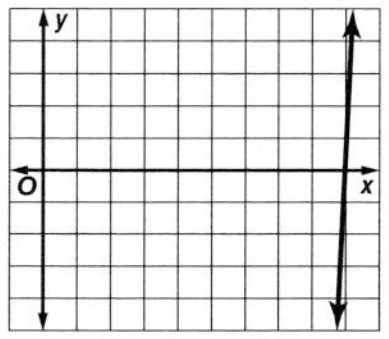

27. 3 **29.** $-\frac{1}{2}$ **31.** −0.046; an average decrease in cost of $0.046 per year
33.

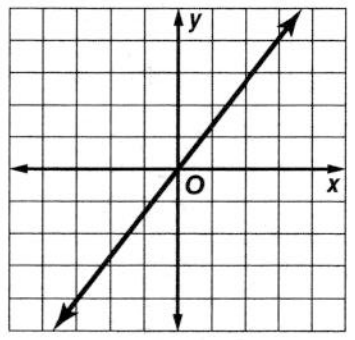

35. $y = 7.5x$; $y = 60$ **37.** $y = -x$; $y = -7$ **39.** 26, 31, 36 **41.** $a_n = 5n + 1$ **43.** $a_n = 4820n$; 15 s

For Homework Help, go to Hotmath.com

45a.

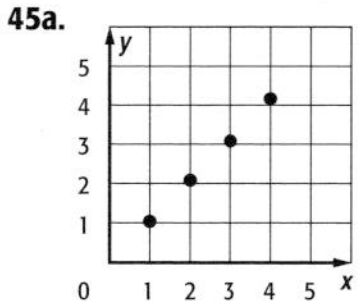

45b. $f(x) = 1.25x$ **45c.** $7.50

Chapter 4 Linear Functions and Relations

Page 211 Get Ready

1. 13 **3.** 14 **5.** $282.50 **7.** $x = 3 + 2y$
9. $x = \frac{3}{4}y + 3$ **11.** (4, 2) **13.** (2, −4) **15.** (−3, −3)

Pages 214–221 Lesson 4-1

1 $y = mx + b$
$y = 2x + 4$
To graph, plot the y-intercept (0, 4). Then use the slope of 2 to move up 2 and right 1 from the y-intercept to find the next point. Connect the points with a straight line.

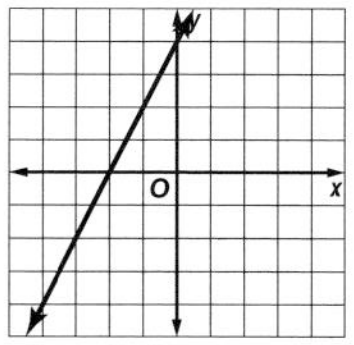

3. $y = \frac{3}{4}x - 1$

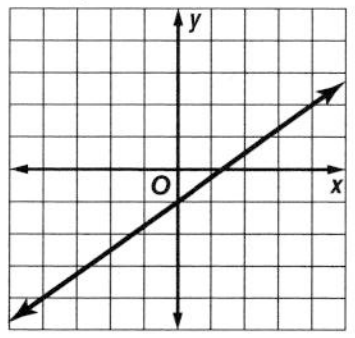

5.

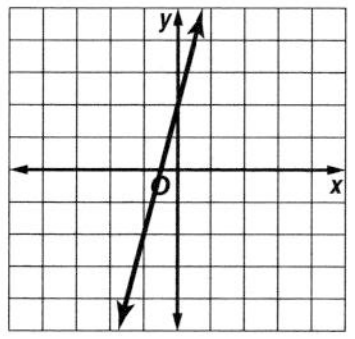

7.

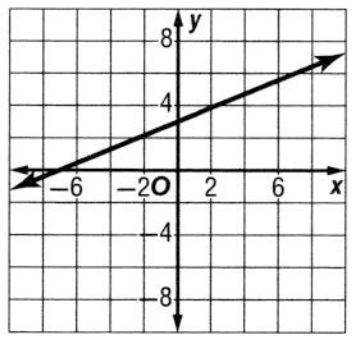

9.

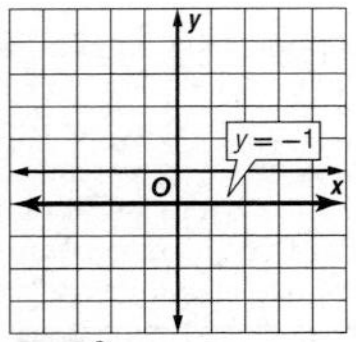

11. $y = \frac{2}{3}x + 2$ **13.** not possible **15a.** $S = 10w + 75$

15b.

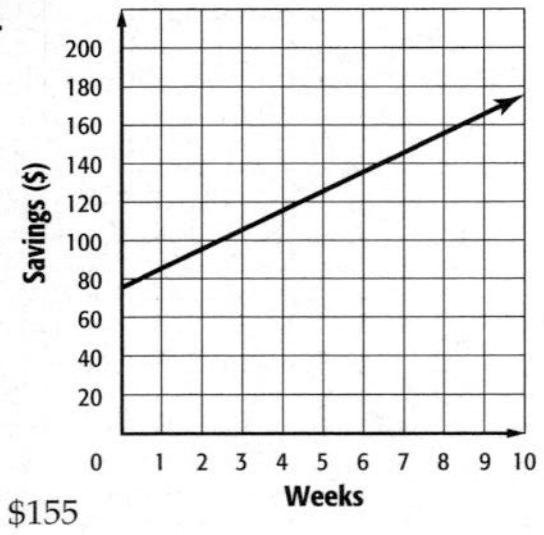

15c. $155

17 $y = mx + b$
$y = 5x + 8$
To graph, plot the y-intercept (0, 8). Then use the slope of 5 to move up 5 and right 1 from the y-intercept to find the next point. Connect the points with a straight line.

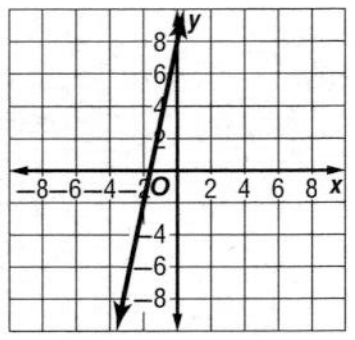

19. $y = -4x + 6$

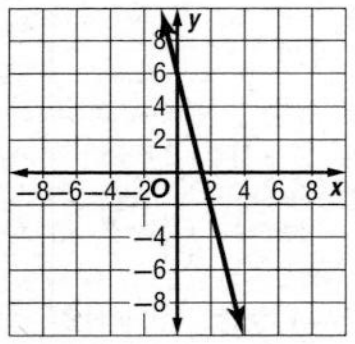

21. $y = 3x - 4$

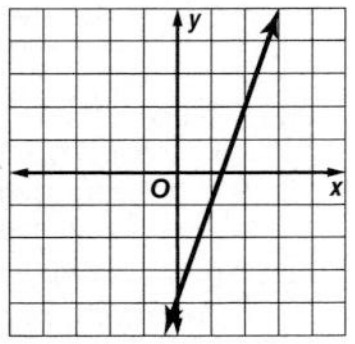

23.

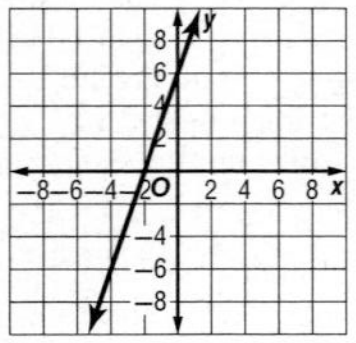

25.

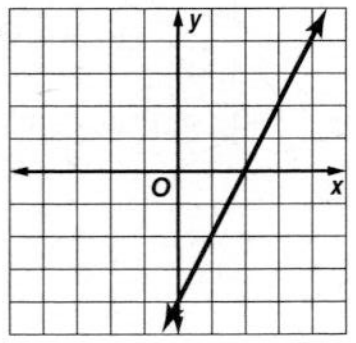

27.

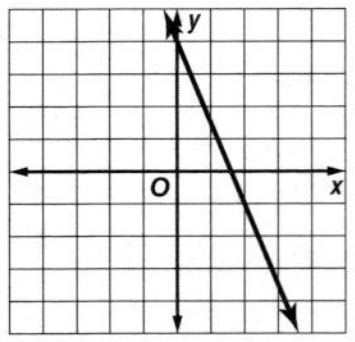

29.

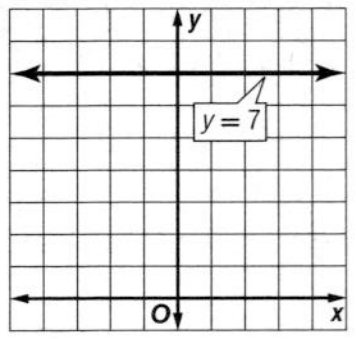

31.

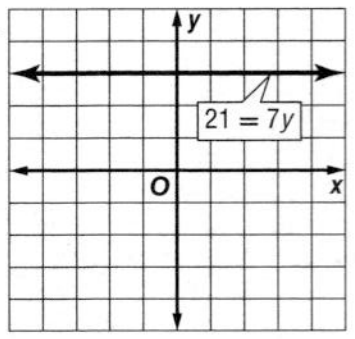

33. $y = -\frac{3}{5}x + 4$ **35.** $y = \frac{1}{2}x - 3$

37 **a.** Words: the population is 1267 plus 123 per year.
Equation: $P = 1267 + 123t$
b. Graph the equation by plotting the y-intercept of (0, 1267). Then use the slope of 123 to move up 123 up and 1 right.

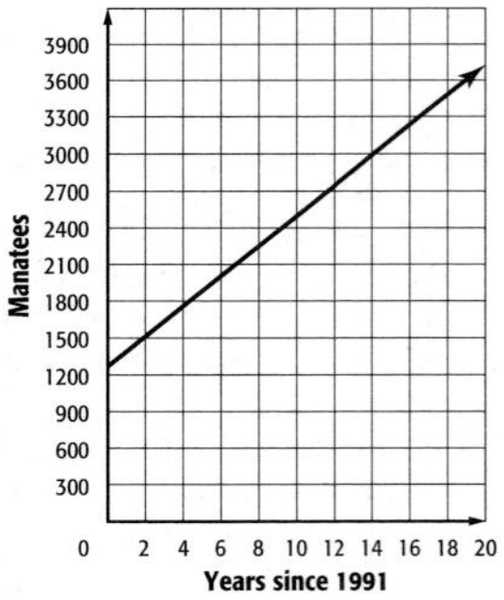

c. $P = 1267 + 123t$
$P = 1267 + 123(15)$
$P = 1267 + 1845$
$P = 3112$ manatees

39. $y = \frac{2}{3}x - 5$ **41.** $y = -\frac{3}{7}x + 2$ **43.** $y = 5$

45.

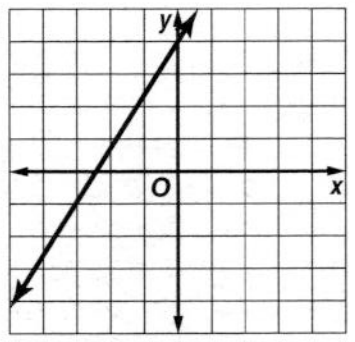

47.

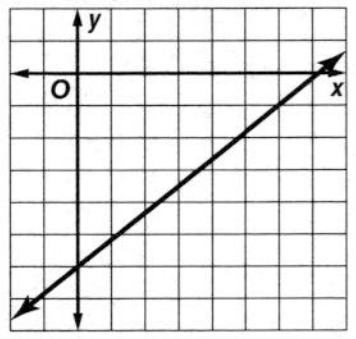

49.

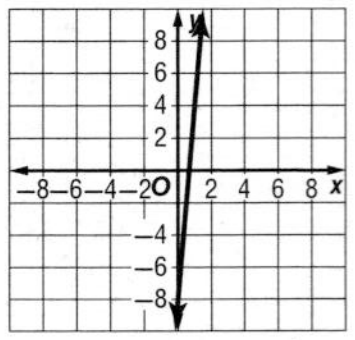

51a. $T = 157c + 218$ **b.** $5242 **53.** $y = 0.5x + 7.5$ **55.** $y = -1.5x - 0.25$ **57.** $y = 3x$ **59a.** $C = 45m + 145$ **59b.** The cost per month to maintain the membership. **59c.** The start up fee **59d.** $1225 **61a.** $C = 3.25 + 0.5256t$

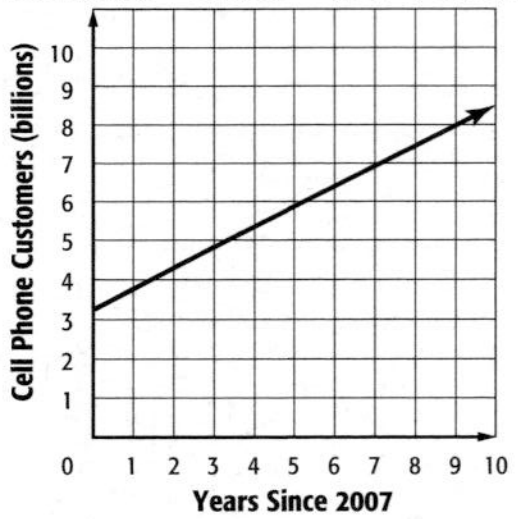

61b. 5.3524 billion **61c.** 2019 **63.** No; because a vertical line has no slope, it cannot be written in slope-intercept form. **65.** Sample answer: We would first have to rewrite the equation in slope-intercept form. The rate of change is also the slope, so, the coefficient for the x-variable is the rate of change. Assume that the coefficient of y is not 0. **67.** B **69.** C **71.** $a_n = 4_n - 1$; nonproportional, does not contain (0, 0) **73.** $a_n = 3_n + 10$; nonproportional, does not contain (0, 0) **75a.** $25,500 **75b.** $142,500 **77.** $y = -4x$; – 5 **79.** $y = 0.8x$; – 7.5 **81.** $-\frac{2}{5}$ **83.** 0

Pages 224–230 Lesson 4-2

1. $y = 3x - 12$ **3.** $y = -x + 6$ **5.** $y = -3x + 9$ **7.** $y = 5x + 8$ **9a.** $C = 35p + 75$ **9b.** $600

11 $y = mx + b$
$4 = -1(-1) + b$
$4 = 1 + b$
$3 = b$
So, the equation is $y = -x + 3$.

13. $y = 8x - 55$ **15.** $y = 2x + 2$ **17.** $y = -x + 3$ **19.** $y = 7x - 16$ **21.** $y = 2x$ **23a.** $y = 9.575x + 337.1$ **23b.** 452 million **25.** $y = \frac{1}{2}x$ **27.** $y = -\frac{3}{4}x + 8\frac{1}{2}$ **29.** $y = \frac{2}{7}x - 2\frac{4}{7}$ **31a.** $G = 6.4t + 49.7$

31b.

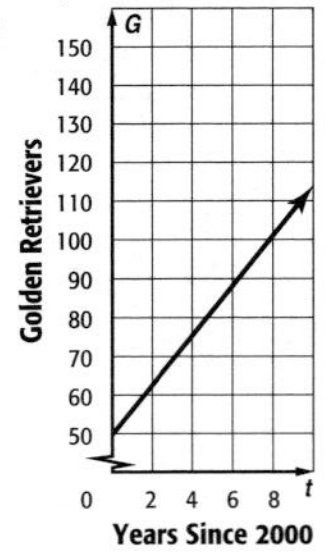

31c. 126,500 **33a.** $2.75 **33b.** $35.40

35 First, find the slope.

$$m = \frac{y_2 - y_1}{x_2 - x_1} = \frac{5 - (-3)}{2 - 5} = \frac{5 + 3}{2 - 5} = \frac{8}{-3} = -\frac{8}{3}$$

Next, use the slope-intercept formula.

$$y = mx + b$$
$$5 = -\frac{8}{3}(2) + b$$
$$5 = -\frac{16}{3} + b$$
$$\frac{31}{3} = b$$
$$10\frac{1}{3} = b$$

So, the equation is $y = -2\frac{2}{3}x + 10\frac{1}{3}$.

37. $y = -x - \frac{7}{12}$ **39.** Yes; substituting 6 and −2 for x and y, respectively, results in an equation that is true. **41.** B; x represents the number of raffle tickets sold, y represents the total amount of money in the treasury. **43a.** 605.2 **43b.** 2032; In that year the waste would be 0 tons. After that, the waste would be a negative amount, which is impossible.

45 **a.** $C = 52t + b$
$275 = 52(5) + b$
$275 = 260 + b$

For Homework Help, go to Hotmath.com

$15 = b$

So, the equation is $C = 52t + 15$.

b.

Number of tickets	3	4	6	7
Cost ($)	171	223	327	379

c. Graph the equation by graphing the y-intercept (0, 15) and use the slope of 52 to find the next point.

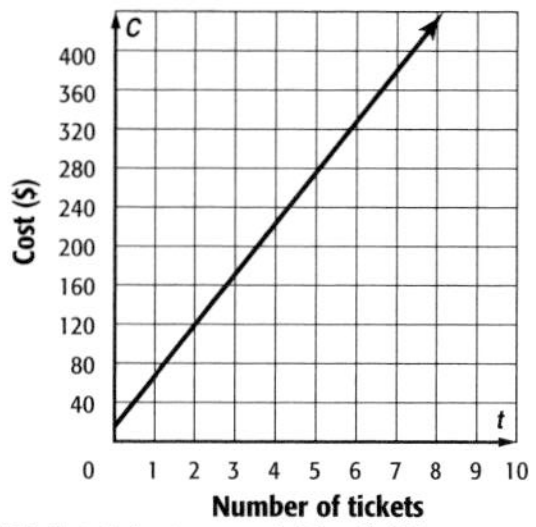

Eight tickets would be $431.

47. Jacinta; Teresa switched the x- and y-coordinates on the point that she entered in step 3.

49a. $y = -\frac{A}{B}x + \frac{C}{B}$ **49b.** slope $= -\frac{A}{B}$

49c. y-intercept $= \frac{C}{B}$ **49d.** no, $B \neq 0$ **51.** Sample answer: If the problem is about something that could suddenly change, such as weather or prices, the graph could suddenly spike up. You need a constant rate of change to produce a linear graph.

53. D **55.** B

57.

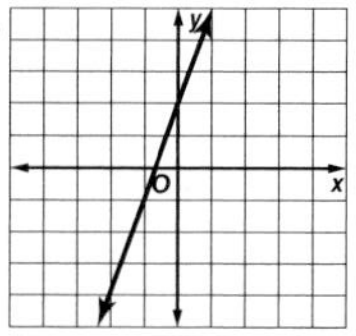

59.

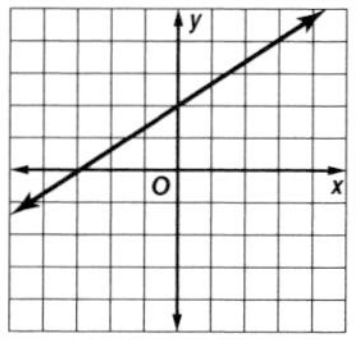

61.

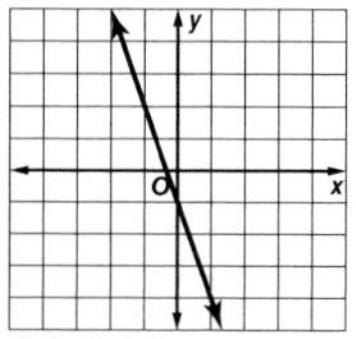

63. $f(x) = -2x$

65a.

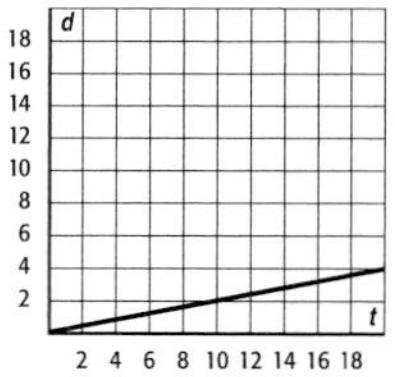

65b. about 14 seconds

67. −22 **69.** −207 **71.** 1.5 **73.** 7 **75.** −1 **77.** 1

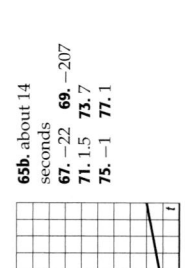

Pages 231–236 Lesson 4-3

1 $y - y^2 = m(x - x^2)$

$(y - 5) = -6(x - (-2))$

$(y - 5) = -6(x + 2)$

Plot the point $(-2, 5)$ and use the slope of -6 to find the next point.

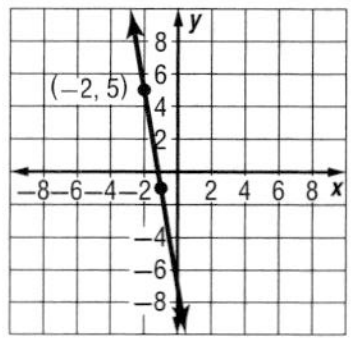

3. $y - 3 = -\frac{1}{2}(x - 4)$

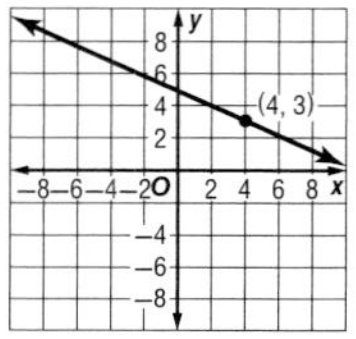

5. $5x + y = -22$ **7.** $y = 4x + 34$ **9.** $y = x + 13$

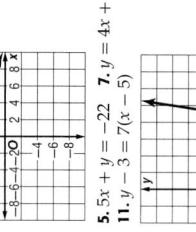

11. $y - 3 = 7(x - 5)$

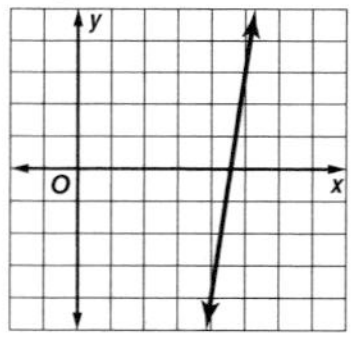

13. $y + 3 = -1(x + 6)$

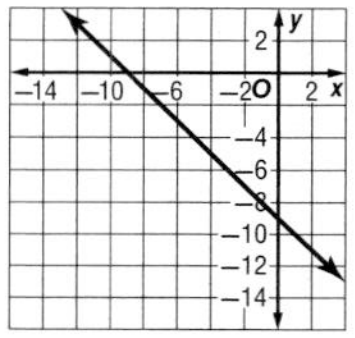

15. $y - 11 = \frac{4}{3}(x + 2)$

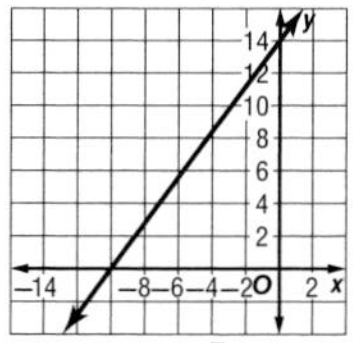

17. $y + 9 = -\frac{7}{5}(x + 2)$ **19.** $2x - y = 6$

21. $6x + y = -45$ **23.** $9x - 10y = 43$

25. $x + 6y = -7$ **27.** $y = -2x + 20$

29. $y = -6x - 47$ **31.** $y = \frac{1}{6}x - \frac{8}{3}$ **33.** $y = -\frac{2}{3}x - 5$

35 The slope is −5 and the point is (6, 4). So, the equation is $y - 4 = -5(x - 6)$. Replace x with 2 to determine how many were rented the second week.

$y - 4 = -5(2 - 6)$

$y - 4 = -5(-4)$

$y - 4 = 20$

$y = 24$

So, 24 copies were rented.

37. $11x + 12y = 58$ **39.** $14x - 10y = 91$

41. $y + 1 = \frac{3}{2}(x + 4)$

43

$y + \frac{3}{5} = x - \frac{2}{5}$

$y + \frac{3}{5} - \frac{3}{5} = x - \frac{2}{5} - \frac{3}{5}$

$y = x - \frac{5}{5}$

$y = x - 1$

45. $y = \frac{5}{6}x$ **47.** $y - 4 = \frac{4}{7}(x + 9)$; $y = \frac{4}{7}x + \frac{64}{7}$; $4x - 7y = -64$ **49.** $y + 4 = 3(x + 1)$; The slope-intercept form is not $y = 3x + 2$. **51.** Sample answer: Jocari spent $14 to go to an amusement park and ride ponies. The price she paid included admission. The 5 pony rides cost $2 each; $y - 14 = 2(x - 5)$, $y = 2x + 4$. **53.** Sample answer: $y - g = \frac{j - g}{h - f}(x - f)$

55. B **57.** J **59.** $y = x - 2$ **61.** $y = -2x + 1$

63. $y = -2$ **65.** $y = -2x + 6$ **67.** $y = \frac{1}{2}x + 3$

69. $y = 3$ **71.** Yes; there are only 364 seats.

73. $a = \frac{v - r}{t}$ **75.** $b = \frac{-t + 5}{4}$

Pages 237–243 Lesson 4-4

1. $y = \frac{1}{2}x + 2\frac{1}{2}$ **3.** Slope of $\overline{AC} = \frac{1 - 7}{-2 - 5}$ or $\frac{6}{7}$; slope of $\overline{BD} = \frac{-3 - 4}{3 - (-3)}$ or $-\frac{7}{6}$; the paths are perpendicular.

5 Graph each line on a coordinate plane. $y = -2x$ and $4y = 2x + 4$ are perpendicular to $2y = x$; $2y = x$ and $4y = 2x + 4$ are parallel.

7. $y = 2x + 7$ **9.** $y = \frac{3}{2}x$ **11.** $y = x - 5$

13. $y = -5x + 2$ **15.** $y = -\frac{3}{4}x + 1\frac{1}{2}$ **17.** Yes; the line containing $\overline{AD}$ and the line containing $\overline{BC}$ have the same slope, $\frac{1}{3}$. Therefore one pair of sides is parallel. The slope of $\overline{AB}$ is undefined and the slope of $\overline{CD}$ is $-\frac{5}{3}$. **19.** Yes; the slopes are −6 and $\frac{1}{6}$. **21.** $2x - 8y = -24$ and $4x + y = -2$ are perpendicular; $2x - 8y = -24$ and $x - 4y = 4$ are parallel.

23 The slope of the given line is −2. So, the slope of a line perpendicular is $\frac{1}{2}$.

$y = mx + b$

$-2 = \frac{1}{2}(-3) + b$

$-2 = -\frac{3}{2} + b$

$-\frac{1}{2} = b$

The equation is $y = \frac{1}{2}x - \frac{1}{2}$.

25. $y = -3x - 7$ **27.** $y = -\frac{1}{5}x + 8\frac{3}{5}$ **29.** $y = 2x + 16$ **31.** $y = -\frac{1}{5}x - \frac{3}{25}$ **33.** neither

35. perpendicular **37.** neither **39.** $y = 7x$

41 Find the slopes.

$m = \frac{-1 - 6}{4 - 2}$

$= \frac{-7}{2}$

$= -\frac{7}{2}$

$m = \frac{12 - 10}{14 - 7}$

$= \frac{2}{7}$

Since the slopes are opposite reciprocals, the objects are perpendicular.

43a.

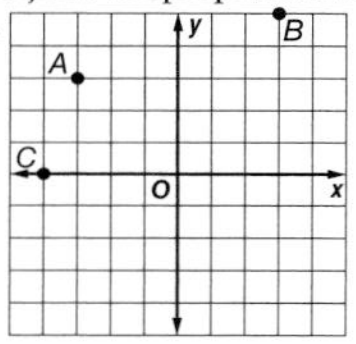

43b. Sample answer: (2, 2); $\overline{AB}$ and $\overline{CD}$ both have slope $\frac{1}{3}$, and $\overline{AC}$ and $\overline{BD}$ both have slope 3.

43c. Two; sample answer: Move C to (−2, 0) and move D to (4, 2). Moving C changes the slpoe of $\overline{AC}$ to −3. This is the opposite reciprocal of the slope $\overline{AC}$, $\frac{1}{3}$. Moving D also changes the slope of $\overline{BD}$ so $\overline{BD}$ is perpendicular to $\overline{AB}$ and $\overline{CD}$ and it is parallel to $\overline{AC}$. **45.** Always; horizontal lines and vertical lines intersect at right angles. **47.** Carmen is correct; she correctly determined the slope of the perpendicular line. **49.** A **51.** B **53.** $-4x + y = 5$

For Homework Help, go to Hotmath.com

55. $5x + y = -8$ **57.** $-5x + 6y = -14$
59a. $C = 10h + 15$ **59b.** \$95 **61.** $y = -5x - 21$
63. $y = 2x - 1$ **65.** $y = -5x - 6$ **67.** simplified
69a. $25(5) + 10(8.5) + 35(5) + 12(8.5)$ **69b.** \$487
71.
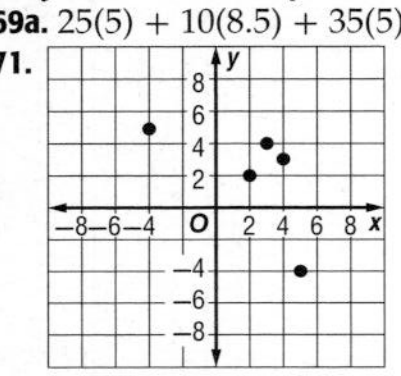
D = {3, 4, 2, 5, −4}; R = {4, 3, 2, −4, 5}

73.
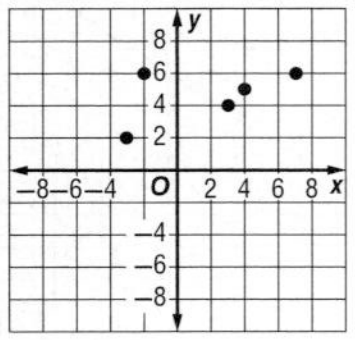
D = {7, 3, 4, −2, −3}; R = {6, 4, 5, 6, 2}

Pages 245–251 Lesson 4-5

1. Positive; the longer you practice free throws, the more free throws you will make.
3a. **Median Age of Females When First Married**
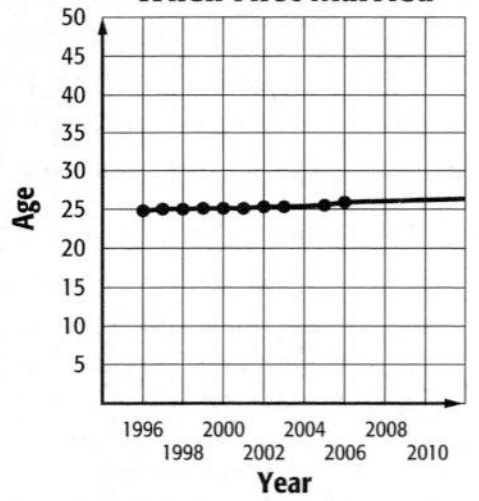

Positive; independent variable is year and dependent variable is median age of females when they were first married. **3b.** See above graph. **3c.** Sample answer: Using (1996, 24.8) and (2006, 25.9) and rounding, $y = 0.11x - 194.8$ **3d.** Sample answer: 27.0 **3e.** Yes, according to the equation, the median age would be 31.4, which is likely.

5 As the height increases, the percentage decreases. The graph shows a slight negative correlation. This correlation means that the taller a player is, the lower their percentage of 3-point shots made is.

7 There is not pattern to the graph, so there is no correlation between the speed of a vehicle and the miles per gallon.

9a. $y = -1783x + 78{,}349$ **9b.** 56,953 **9c.** No; the average attendance will fluctuate with other variables such as how good the team is that year.

11 a. The independent variable is the duration of the eruptions and the dependent variable is the interval of the eruptions. This is because the duration of the eruptions is not affected by the interval.

"Old Faithful"
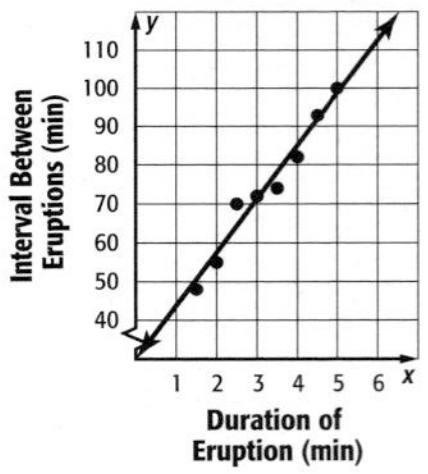

The interval increases as the duration increases, so there is a positive correlation between the independent and dependent variables.

b. Use (2, 55) and (4, 82)

$$m = \frac{y_2 - y_1}{x_2 - x_1} = \frac{82 - 55}{4 - 2} = \frac{27}{2} = 13.5$$

So, the slope is 13.5.
$y = 13.5x + b$
$55 = 13.5(2) + b$
$55 = 27 + b$
$28 = b$
$y = 13.5x + 28$
$y = 13.5(7.5) + 28$
$y = 101.25 + 28$
$y = 129.25$ min

c. Sample answer: The duration of an eruption is not dependent on the previous interval. Only the interval can be predicted by the length of the eruption.

13. Sample answer: The salary of an individual and the years of experience that they have; this would be a positive correlation because the more experience an individual has, the higher the salary would probably be. **15.** Neither; line g has the same number of points above the line and below the line. Line f is close to 2 of the points, but for the rest of the data there are 3 points above and 3 points below the line. **17.** Sample answer: You can visualize a line to determine whether the data has a positive or negative correlation. The following graph shows the ages and heights of people. To predict a person's age given his or her height, write a linear equation for the line of fit. Then substitute the person's height and solve for the corresponding age. You can use the pattern in the scatter plot to make decisions.

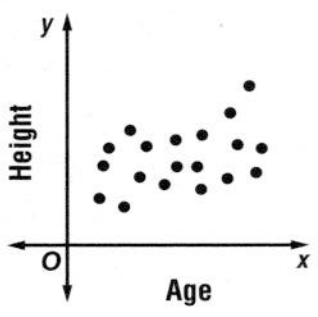

19. F **21.** 22 days
23. neither
25. perpendicular
27. $2x + y = 1$ **29.** $-x + 2y = -12$ **31.** $2x + 5y = 26$

33.
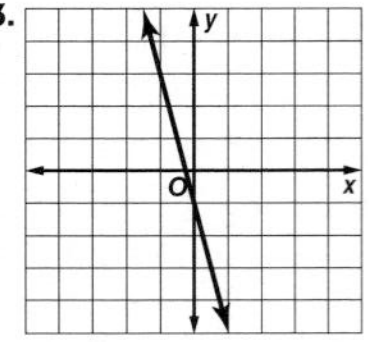

35. $\frac{4}{7}$ **37.** $\frac{3}{5}$

39. 16 **41.** 1.5 h
43.
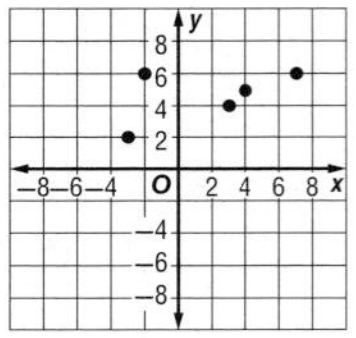
D = {7, 3, 4, −2, −3}; R = {6, 4, 5, 2}

Pages 253–260 Lesson 4-6

1. $y = 1.18x + 11$; 0.7181
3a. $y = -271.88x + 554.48$ **3b.** \$78.69

Rental Properties
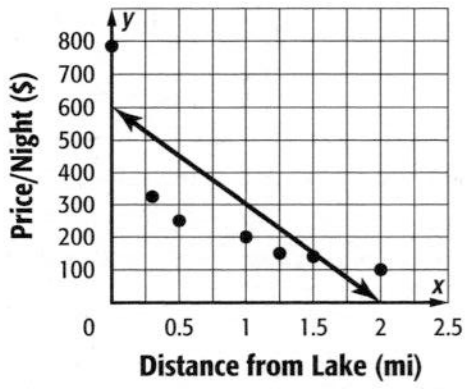

5 Step 1: Enter the data by pressing STAT and selecting the Edit option. Let the year 2000 be represented by 0. Enter the years since 2000 into List 1 (L1). These will represent the x-values. Enter the number of auditions into List 2 (L2). These will represent the y-values.
Step 2: Perform the regression by pressing STAT and selecting the CALC option. Scroll down to LinReg($ax + b$) and press ENTER.
The equation is $y = 3.54x + 19.68$.
The correlation coefficient is 0.9007.

7 a. Enter the data using 0 for 1975. Use med-med to find $y = 609.08x + 1680.8$.
b. $2003 - 1975 = 28$. Substitute 28 into the equation in **a** to get 18,734.32. There were about 18,735 entrants in 2003.

9a. $y = 0.095x - 94.58$
9b.
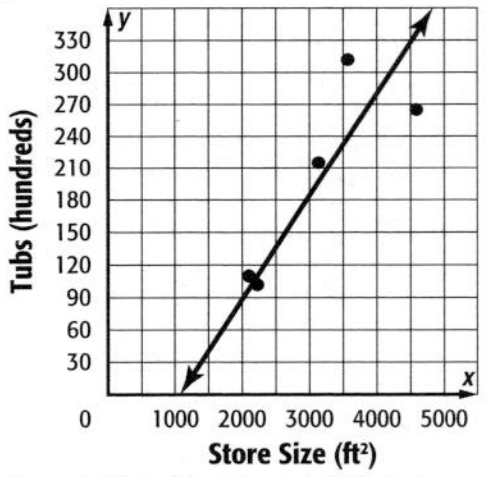

9c. about 48 tubs; about 380 tubs
11a. $y = 9.8x + 28.79$ **11b.** \$146.39 **11c.** Sample answer: No; the number is not within a reasonable range of the other pairs of jeans.

13 Step 1: Enter the data by pressing STAT and selecting the Edit option. Let the year 1998 be represented by 0. Enter the years since 1998 into List 1 (L1). These will represent the x-values. Enter the amount raised into List 2 (L2). These will represent the y-values.
Step 2: Perform the regression by pressing STAT and selecting the CALC option. Scroll down to LinReg($ax + b$) and press ENTER.
The equation is $y = 420.17x + 1682.22$.
The correlation coefficient is 0.9464.

15a. $y = 87{,}390.5x + 4{,}018{,}431$ **15b.** about 5,591,460 **17a.** $y = 361.38x + 4840.6$
17b.
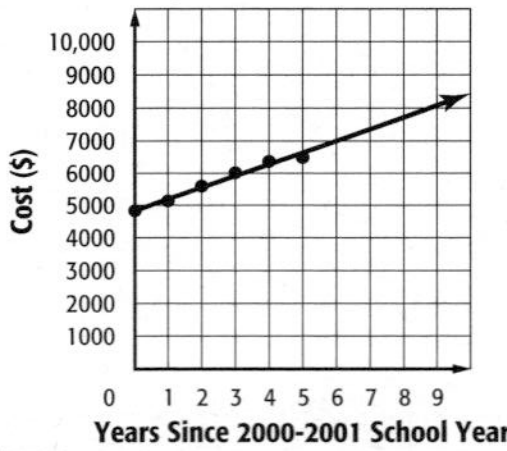

17c. \$12,068.28
19.
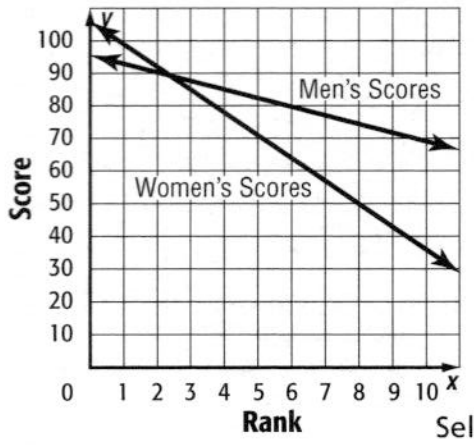

Sample answer: Men: $y = -2.92x + 95.92$; women: $y = -7x + 106$; women's scores have a steeper slope than men's.

23. C **25.** H **27a.** negative correlation **27b.** \$3600 **27c.** No; according to the line of fit, the cost would be \$0. **29.** $3x - y = 1$ **31.** $2x + y = 8$ **33.** $2x - 3y = -21$ **35.** $\frac{4}{7}$ **37.** $\frac{3}{5}$ **39.** 3 **41.** $a^2 - a + 1$

43.

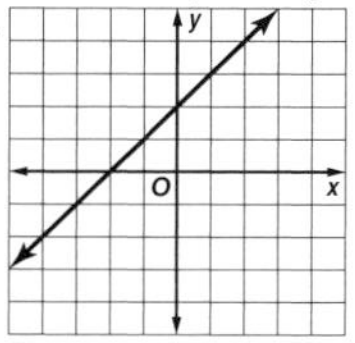

45.

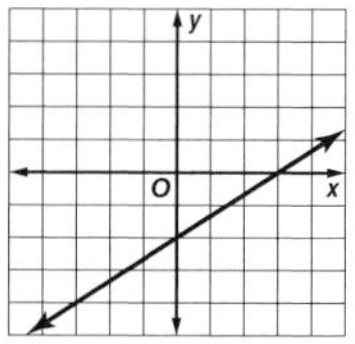

Pages 261–268 Lesson 4-7

1.

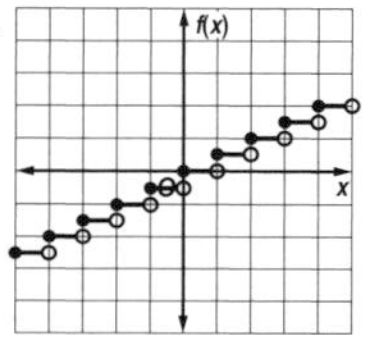

D = all real numbers, R = all integer multiples of 0.5

3.

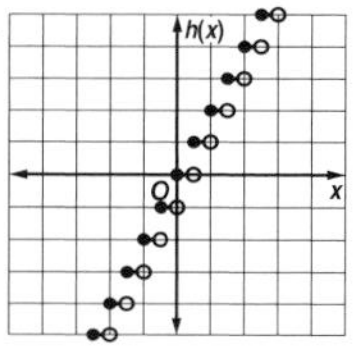

D = all real numbers, R = all integers

5.

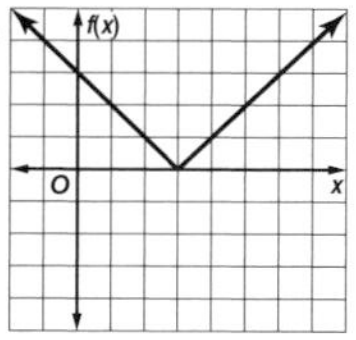

D = all real numbers, R = $f(x) \geq 0$

7.

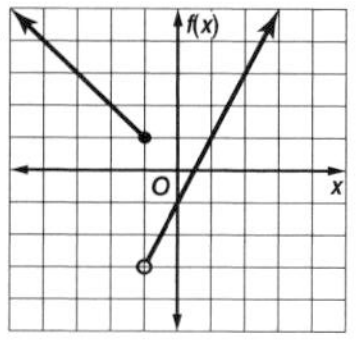

D = all real numbers, R = $f(x) > -3$

9 $f(x) = 3[\![x]\!]$

Create a table.

x	$3[\![x]\!]$	$f(x)$
0	$3[\![0]\!]$	0
0.25	$3[\![0.25]\!]$	0
0.5	$3[\![0.5]\!]$	0
1	$3[\![1]\!]$	3
1.25	$3[\![1.25]\!]$	3
1.5	$3[\![1.5]\!]$	3
2	$3[\![2]\!]$	6
2.25	$3[\![2.25]\!]$	6
2.5	$3[\![2.5]\!]$	6
3	$3[\![3]\!]$	9

Graph on a coordinate grid.

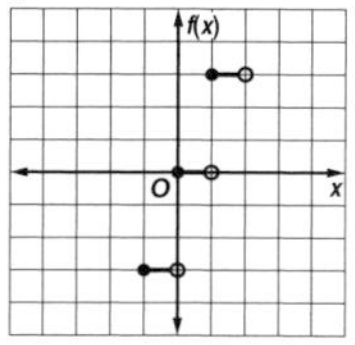

D = all real numbers, R = all integer multiples of 3

11.

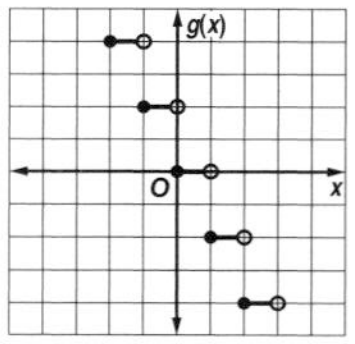

D = all real numbers, R = all even integers

13.

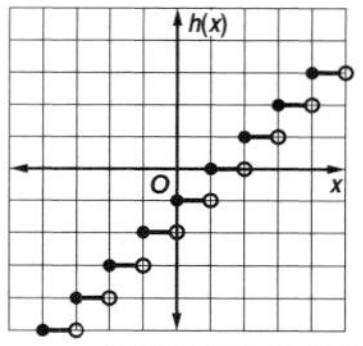

D = all real numbers, R = all integers

15a.

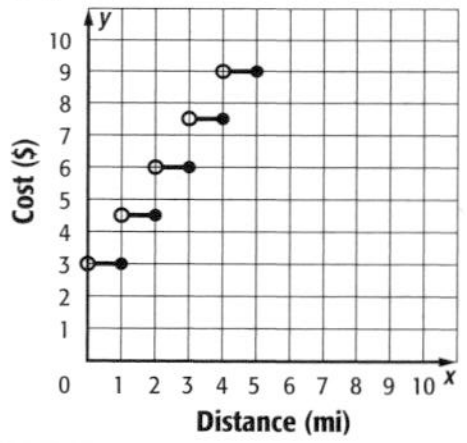

15b. \$16.50

17.

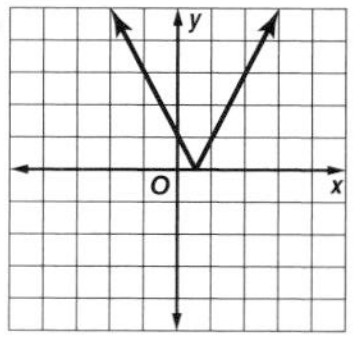

D = all real numbers, R = $y \geq 0$

19.

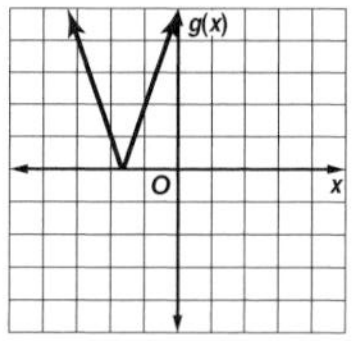

D = all real numbers, R = $g(x) \geq 0$

21.

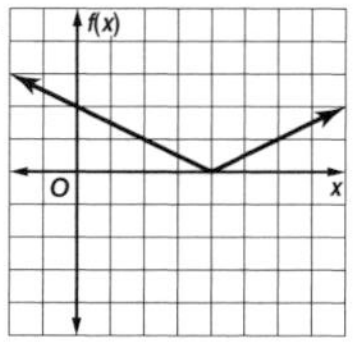

D = all real numbers, R = $f(x) \geq 0$

23.

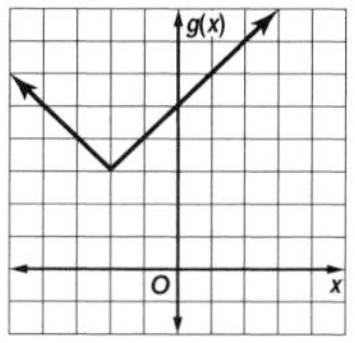

D = all real numbers, R = $g(x) \geq 3$

25.

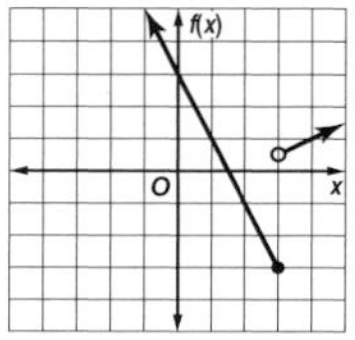

D = all real numbers, R = all real numbers

27.

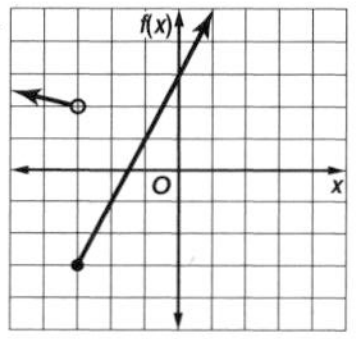

D = all real numbers, R = $f(x) \geq -3$

29.

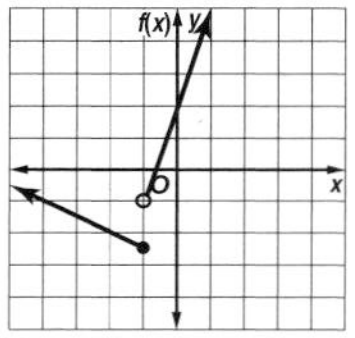

D = all real numbers, R = $f(x) \geq -2.5$

31 The graph extends infinitely to the left and to the right, so the domain is all real numbers. The range is all real numbers greater than or equal to 4 because the line increases from both sides of (6, 4).

33. D = all real numbers; R = all integers

35. D = all real numbers; R = $y > -4$

37.

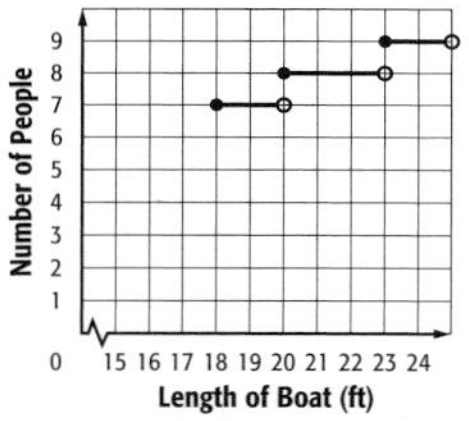

39. D **41.** B

43 a.

Number of Orders	Total Price
$1 \leq x \leq 10$	$10 + (10 + 4 + 2)x = 10 + 16x$
$11 \leq x < 20$	$(10 + 16x)(0.95) = 9.5 + 15.20x$
$x \geq 20$	$(10 + 16x)(0.90) = 9 + 14.40x$

b. $y = \begin{cases} 10 + 16x \text{ if } 1 \leq x \leq 10 \\ 9.50 + 15.20x \text{ if } 11 \leq x \leq 20 \\ 9 + 14.40x \text{ if } x \geq 20 \end{cases}$

c.

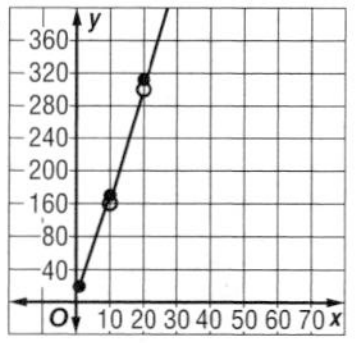

45a.

x	−5	−4	−3	−2	−1	0	1	2	3	4	5
$f(x)$	13	11	9	7	5	3	5	7	9	11	13

45b.

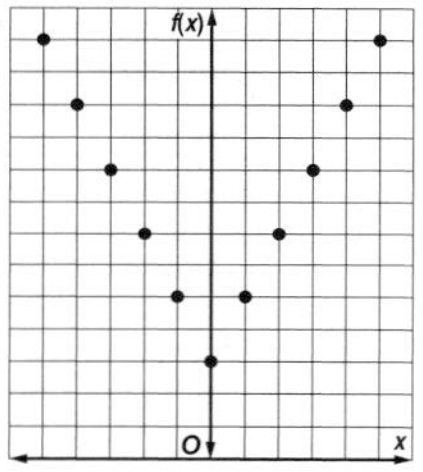

45c.

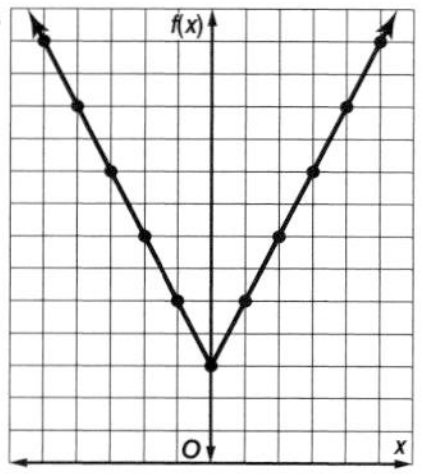

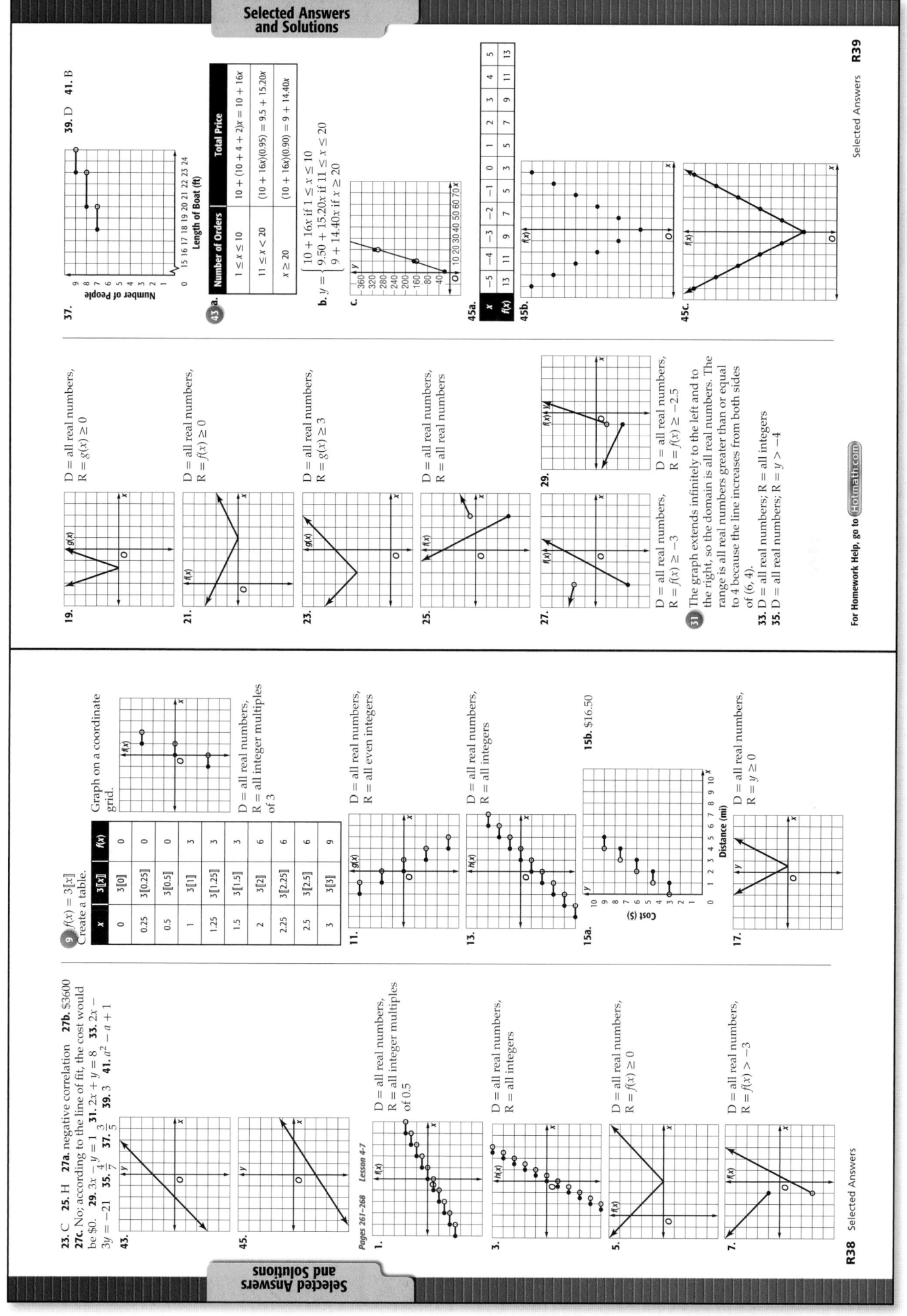

45d. The graph is shifted 1.5 units to the right and 3 units up.

47. 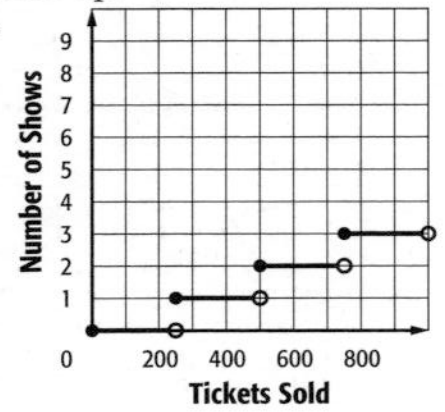

49 $g(x) = \frac{1}{3}|x| + 4$

Set up a table.

x	$\frac{1}{3}\lvert x\rvert + 4$	$g(x)$
−6	$\frac{1}{3}\lvert -6\rvert + 4$	6
−3	$\frac{1}{3}\lvert -3\rvert + 4$	5
0	$\frac{1}{3}\lvert 0\rvert + 4$	4
3	$\frac{1}{3}\lvert 3\rvert + 4$	5
6	$\frac{1}{3}\lvert 6\rvert + 4$	6

Plot on a coordinate grid.

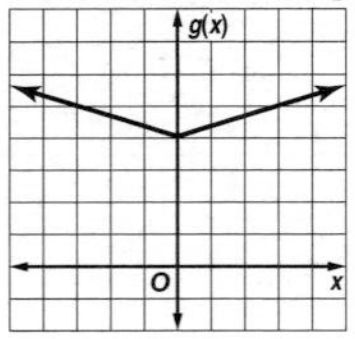

51. 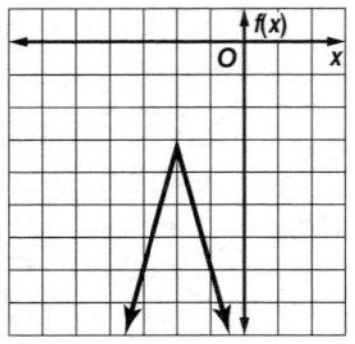

53. 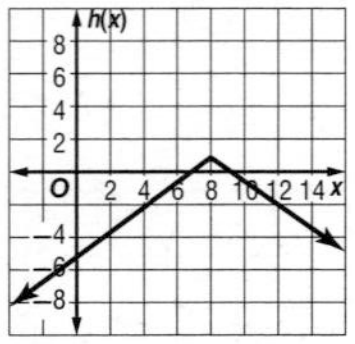

55. No; the pieces of the graph overlap vertically, so the graph fails the vertical line test.

57. $f(x) = \begin{cases} \frac{1}{2}x - 3 & \text{if } x > 6 \\ -\frac{1}{2}x - 1 & \text{if } x \le 6 \end{cases}$

59. Sample answer: The cost of exceeding the allotted minutes on your cell phone plan is billed per minute. So, if you are 2.5 minutes over, you are charged for 3 minutes of overage. The graph of this is called a step function because you can't trace the graph without picking up your pencil. There is a range of x-values that have the same y-value on the graph. **61.** C **63.** B **65.** $y = 2.3x + 1.5$ **67.** $y = 10.7x + 10.1$ **69.** Positive; it means the more you study, the better your test score. **71.** −4.4 **73.** 1.2 **75.** −3 **77.** 21 **79.** $-\frac{1}{3}$

Pages 270–274 Study Guide and Review

1. T **3.** F; scatter plot **5.** T **7.** T **9.** F, greatest integer function

11. 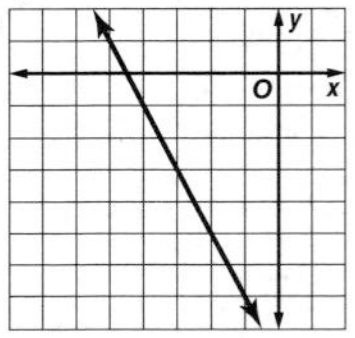 $y = -2x - 9$

13. 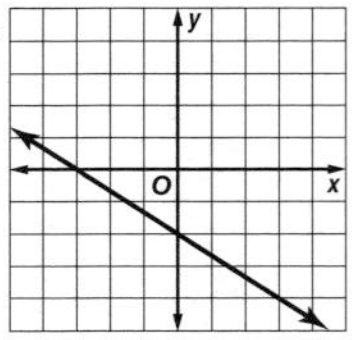 $y = -\frac{5}{8}x - 2$

15. 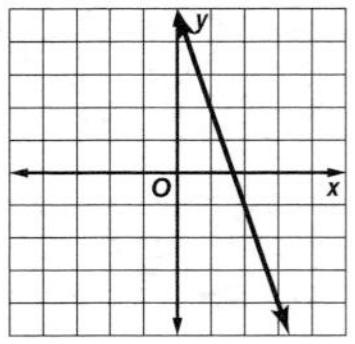

17. 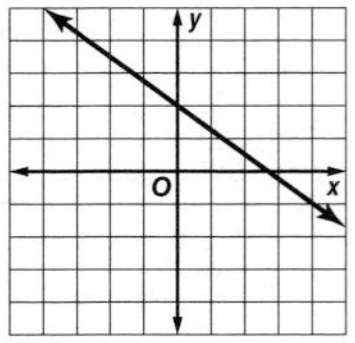

19. $y = 3x - 1$ **21.** $y = \frac{2}{5}x + \frac{1}{5}$ **23.** $y = x - 3$ **25.** $y = \frac{1}{2}x + \frac{7}{2}$ **27.** $y = 60x + 450$ **29.** $y - 1 = -3(x + 2)$ **31.** $5x - y = 7$ **33.** $x - 2y = 11$

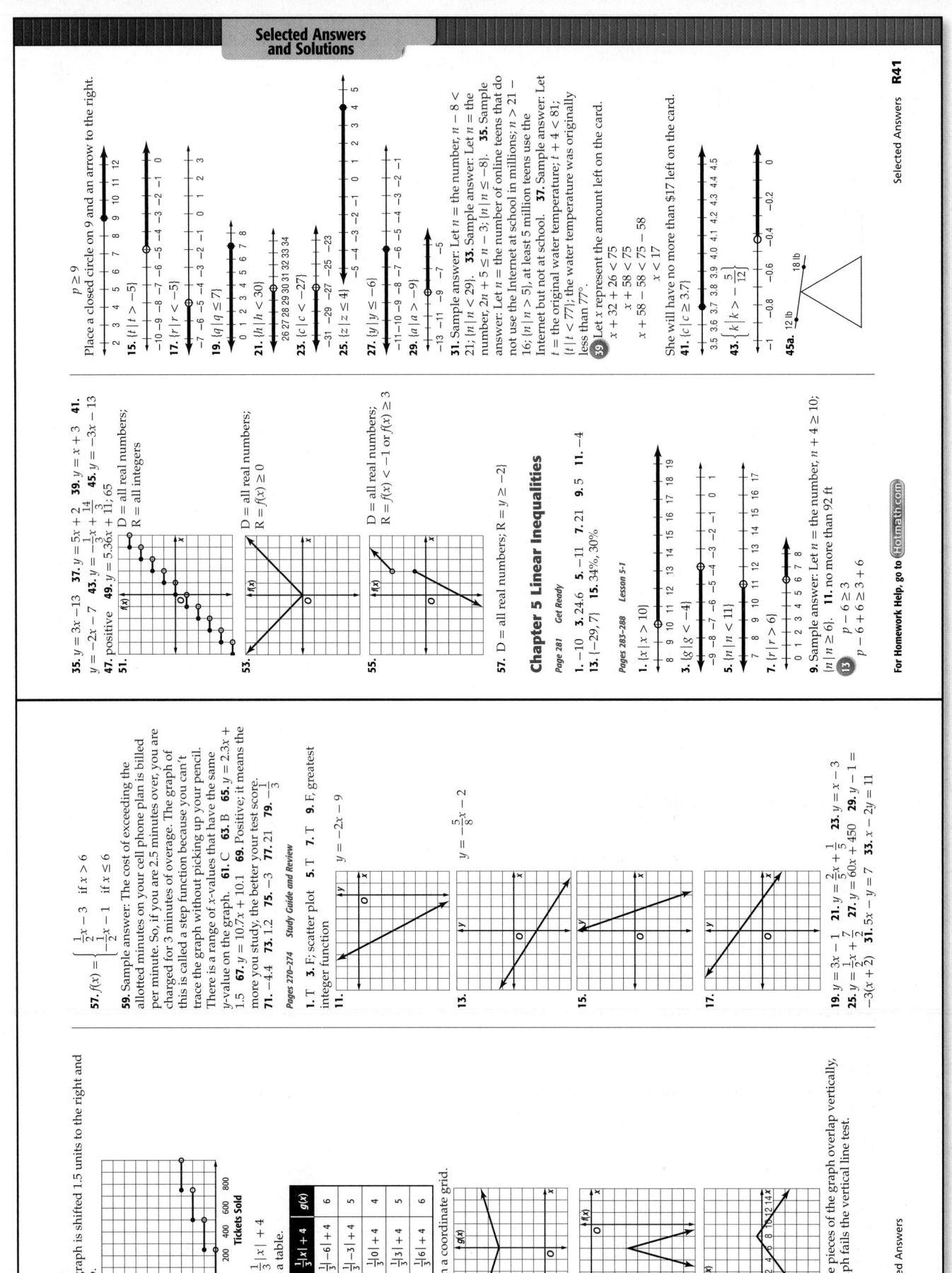

35. $y = 3x - 13$ **37.** $y = 5x + 2$ **39.** $y = x + 3$ **41.** $y = -2x - 7$ **43.** $y = -\frac{1}{3}x + \frac{14}{3}$ **45.** $y = -3x - 13$ **47.** positive **49.** $y = 5.36x + 11$; 65

51. 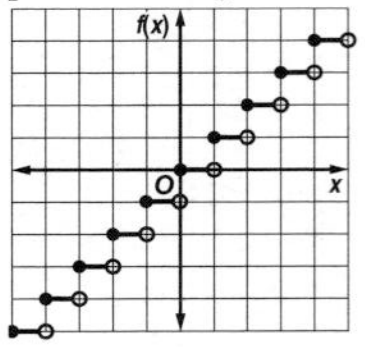 D = all real numbers; R = all integers

53. 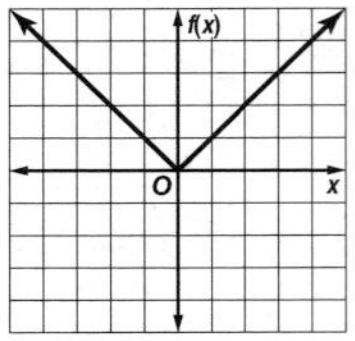 D = all real numbers; R = $f(x) \ge 0$

55. 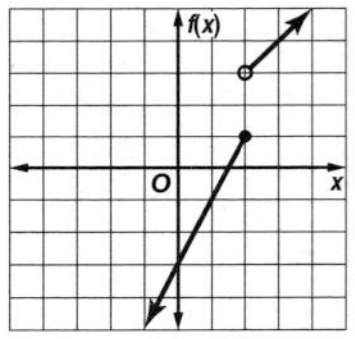 D = all real numbers; R = $f(x) < -1$ or $f(x) \ge 3$

57. D = all real numbers; R = $y \ge -2\}$

Chapter 5 Linear Inequalities

Page 281 Get Ready

1. −10 **3.** 24.6 **5.** −11 **7.** 21 **9.** 5 **11.** −4 **13.** {−29, 7} **15.** 34%, 30%

Pages 283–288 Lesson 5-1

1. $\{x \mid x > 10\}$

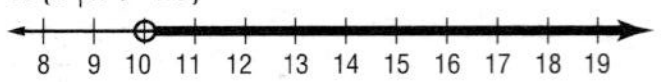

3. $\{g \mid g < -4\}$

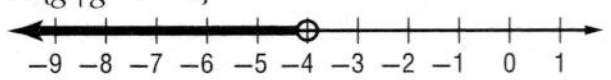

5. $\{n \mid n < 11\}$

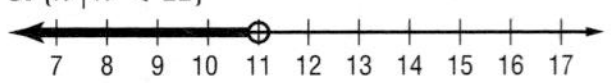

7. $\{r \mid r > 6\}$

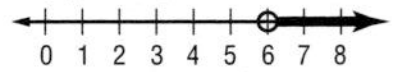

9. Sample answer: Let n = the number, $n + 4 \ge 10$; $\{n \mid n \ge 6\}$. **11.** no more than 92 ft

13
$p - 6 \ge 3$
$p - 6 + 6 \ge 3 + 6$
$p \ge 9$

Place a closed circle on 9 and an arrow to the right.

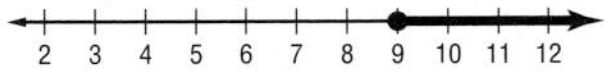

15. $\{t \mid t > -5\}$

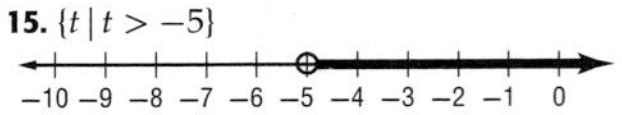

17. $\{r \mid r < -5\}$

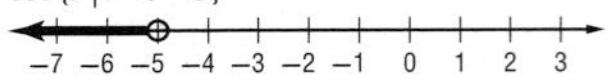

19. $\{q \mid q \le 7\}$

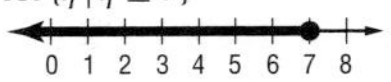

21. $\{h \mid h < 30\}$

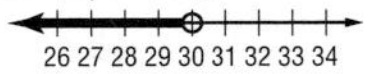

23. $\{c \mid c < -27\}$

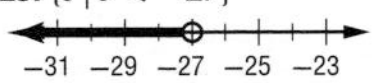

25. $\{z \mid z \le 4\}$ 

27. $\{y \mid y \le -6\}$

29. $\{a \mid a > -9\}$

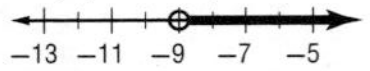

31. Sample answer: Let n = the number, $n - 8 < 21$; $\{n \mid n < 29\}$. **33.** Sample answer: Let n = the number, $2n + 5 \le n - 3$; $\{n \mid n \le -8\}$. **35.** Sample answer: Let n = the number of online teens that do not use the Internet at school in millions; $n > 21 - 16$; $\{n \mid n > 5\}$, at least 5 million teens use the Internet but not at school. **37.** Sample answer: Let t = the original water temperature; $t + 4 < 81$; $\{t \mid t < 77\}$; the water temperature was originally less than 77°.

39 Let x represent the amount left on the card.
$x + 32 + 26 < 75$
$x + 58 < 75$
$x + 58 - 58 < 75 - 58$
$x < 17$

She will have no more than $17 left on the card.

41. $\{c \mid c \ge 3.7\}$

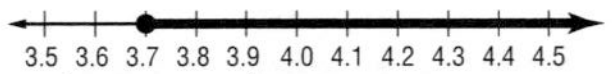

43. $\left\{k \,\middle|\, k > -\frac{5}{12}\right\}$

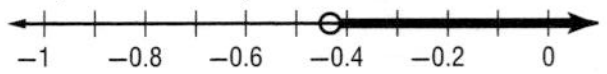

45a. 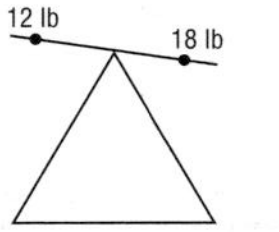

45c.

	12	<	18
2	24	<	36
3	36	<	54
4	48	<	72
$\frac{1}{2}$	6	<	9
$\frac{1}{3}$	4	<	6
$\frac{1}{4}$	3	<	$4\frac{1}{2}$

45d. If a true inequality is multiplied by a positive number, the resulting inequality is also true. If a true inequality is divided by a positive number, the resulting inequality is also true. **47.** 10 **49.** 3 **51.** 26 **53.** $c < a < d < b$ **55.** Solving linear inequalities is similar to solving linear equations. You must isolate the variable on one side of the inequality. To graph, if the problem is a less than or a greater than inequality, an open circle is used. Otherwise a dot is used. If the variable is on the left hand side of the inequality, and the inequality sign is less than (or less than or equal to), the graph extends to the left; otherwise it extends to the right. **57.** C **59.** B

61.

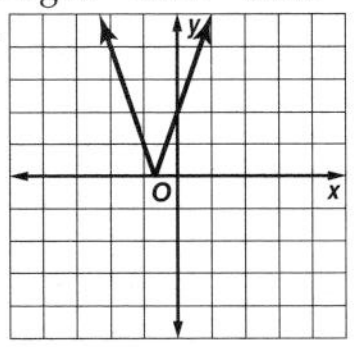

63.

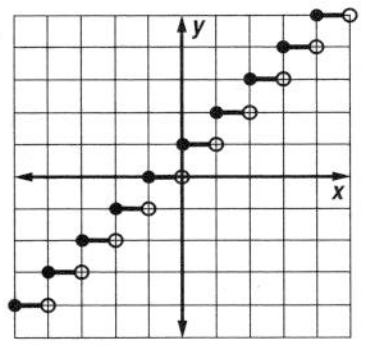

65. $y = -x - 2$ **67.** $y = -2x - 1$ **69.** blue **71.** 25 **73.** $y = 7x$; \$210 **75.** −30 **77.** $\frac{1}{10}$ **79.** 16 **81.** $-\frac{1}{9}$

Pages 290–295 Lesson 5-2

1. Let d = the number of DVDs sold; $15d > 5500$; $d > 366.67$; the band sold at least 367 DVDs. **3.** $r \geq 8$ **5.** $h < -10$ **7.** $v > -12$ **9.** $z \geq -8$ **11.** Let p = the number of pay periods for which Rodrigo will need to save; $25p \geq 560$; $p \geq 22.4$; Rodrigo will need to save for 23 weeks.

13 $\frac{1}{2}a < 20$

$2\left(\frac{1}{2}a\right) < 2(20)$

$a < 40$

Check by substituting values less than 40.

15. $d \geq 68$ **17.** $f < 432$ **19.** $j \leq -16$ **21.** $p \leq 16$ **23.** $y > -16$ **25.** $v < 12$ **27.** $b \leq -\frac{3}{4}$ **29.** $f < -\frac{5}{7}$ **31.** no more than 4 **33.** no more than 32 people **35.** b **37.** d

39 $\frac{2}{3}x < 42$

$3\left(\frac{2}{3}x\right) < 3(42)$

$2x < 126$

$x < 63$

fewer than 63 employees

41a.

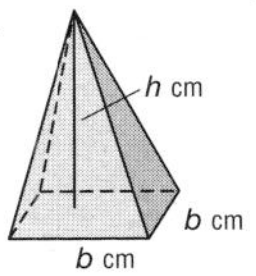

41b. $h = \frac{216}{b^2}$

41c.

b	1	3	6	9	12
h	216	24	6	$\frac{8}{3}$	$\frac{3}{2}$

41d. $b < h$ when $0 < b < 6$; $b > h$ when $h < 6$.

43. $\frac{-96c}{-96} > \frac{12c}{-96}$; $c > -\frac{d}{8}$; $-96c \cdot -\frac{1}{96} > 12d \cdot -\frac{1}{96}$ $c > -\frac{d}{8}$

45. Sometimes; the statement is true when $a > 0$ and $b < 0$. **47.** Sample answer: The inequality symbol changes directions when multiplying or dividing by a negative number so that the inequality remains true. For example, dividing $-2x > 4$ by −2 results in $x < -2$. **49.** 10 in. **51.** C

53. $\left\{y \mid y \geq -\frac{11}{26}\right\}$

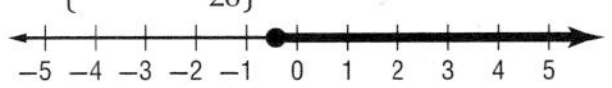

55. D = {all real numbers}; R = $\{y \mid y \geq 0\}$
57. D = {all real numbers}; R = $\{y \mid y \leq 1\}$

59. 2 hours **61.** {1, 7} **63.** 2 **65.** $\frac{33}{8}$ **67.** 3

Pages 296–301 Lesson 5-3

1. $4n + 60 \leq 800$; $n \leq 185$; at most 185 lb per person

3 $6h - 10 \geq 32$

$6h - 10 + 10 \geq 32 + 10$

$6h \geq 42$

$h \geq 7$

$\{h \mid h \geq 7\}$

5. $\{x \mid x < -12\}$ **7.** Sample answer: Let n = the number; $4n - 6 > 8 + 2n$; $\{n \mid n > 7\}$. **9.** $\{v \mid v \geq 0\}$ **11.** ∅

13 $21 > 15 + 2a$

$21 - 15 > 2a$

$6 > 2a$

$3 > a$ $\{a \mid a < 3\}$

15. $\{w \mid w > 56\}$ **17.** $\{w \mid w < -3\}$ **19.** $\left\{p \mid p > -\frac{24}{5}\right\}$

21. $\{h \mid h < -15\}$ **23.** Sample answer: Let n = the number; $\frac{2}{3}n + 6 \geq 22$; $\{n \mid n \geq 24\}$. **25.** Sample answer: Let n = the number; $8n - 27 \leq -n + 18$; $\{n \mid n \leq 5\}$. **27.** Sample answer: Let n = the number; $3(n + 7) > 5n - 13$; $\{n \mid n < 17\}$

29. $\left\{n \mid n > -\frac{1}{3}\right\}$ **31.** ∅ **33.** $\{t \mid t \geq -1\}$ **35.** Sample answer: Let s = the amount of sales made, $35{,}000 + 0.08s > 65{,}000$; $\{s \mid s > 375{,}000\}$; the sales must be more than \$375,000.

37.

$6(m - 3) > 5(2m + 4)$	Original inequality
$6m - 18 > 10m + 20$	Distributive Property
$6m - 18 - 6m > 10m + 20 - 6m$	Subtract 6*m* from each side.
$-18 > 4m + 20$	Simplify.
$-18 - 20 > 4m + 20 - 20$	Subtract 20 from each side.
$-38 > 4m$	Simplify.
$\frac{-38}{4} > \frac{4m}{4}$	Divide each side by 4.
$-9.5 > m$	Simplify.
$\{m \mid m < -9.5\}$	

39a. $5t + 565 \geq 1500$; $t \geq 187$

39b.

41 **a.** Words: temperature can be greater than 104

$t > 104$

b. $F > 104$

$\frac{9}{5}C + 32 > 104$

$\frac{9}{5}C > 72$

$5\left(\frac{9}{5}C > 72\right)$

$9C > 360$

$C > 40$

43. 1, 3, 5, 7; 3, 5, 7, 9; 5, 7, 9, 11; 7, 9, 11, 13

45. $\left\{x \mid x \geq \frac{1}{2}\right\}$ **47.** $\{m \mid m \geq 18\}$ **49.** $\{x \mid x \leq 8\}$

51. $\{x \mid x > -6\}$ **53.** $\{x \mid x \geq 1.5\}$ **55.** Add $3p$ and 2 to each side. The inequality becomes $9 \geq 3p$. Then divide each side by 3 to get $3 \geq p$. **57.** Sample answer: $2x + 4 > 2$ and $3x + 1 > -2$ both have the graph of $x > -1$. **59.** Sample answer: The solution set for an inequality that results in a false statement is the empty set, as in $12 < -15$. The solution set for an inequality in which any value of x results in a true statement is all real numbers, as in $12 \leq 12$. **61.** G **63.** D **65.** $\{b \mid b > -4\}$

67. $\{h \mid h < 14\}$

69. $\{m \mid m \geq 1\}$

71. 4

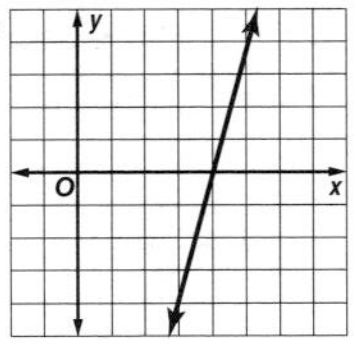

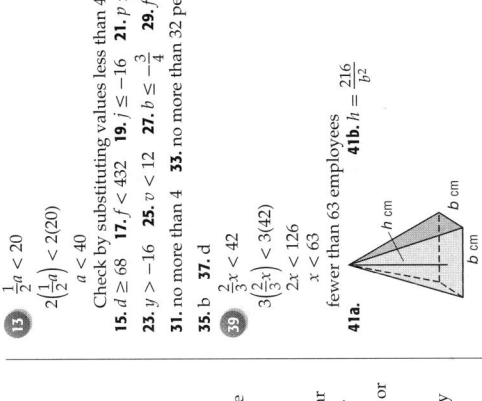

73. 118.0 million
75. 8 **77.** 12(29.95 + 4) or 12(29.95) + 12(4); \$407.40

79.

81.

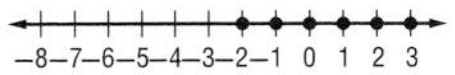

83.

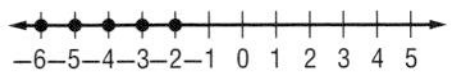

Pages 304–309 Lesson 5-4

1. $\{p \mid 12 \leq p \leq 16\}$

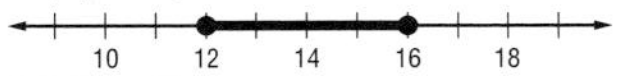

3. $\{a \mid a > 5\}$

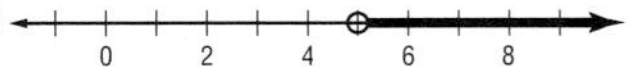

5. 11 psi ≤ x ≤ 56 psi

7 $n + 2 \leq -5$ and $n + 6 \geq -6$

$n + 2 - 2 \leq -5 - 2$ and $n + 6 - 6 \geq -6 - 6$

$n \leq -7$ $n \geq -12$

The solution set is $\{n \mid -12 \leq n \leq -7\}$.

9. $\{t \mid t \geq 1$ or $t < -1\}$

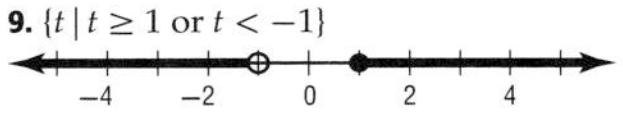

11. $\{c \mid -1 \leq c < 2\}$

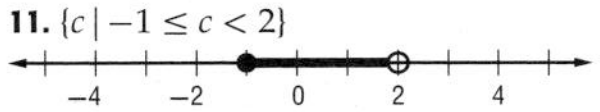

13. $\{m \mid m$ is a real number.$\}$

15. $\{y \mid y < -3\}$

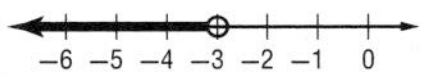

17. Sample answer: Let x = the smaller of two consecutive odd numbers, then $8 \leq 2x + 2 \leq 24$; $3 \leq x \leq 11$; 3, 5; 5, 7; 7, 9; 9, 11; 11, 13

19 The graph shows $x > -3$ and $x \leq 2$, so the inequality is $-3 < x \leq 2$.

21. $x < -4$ or $x > -3$ **23.** $x \leq -3$ or $x > 0$

25. $\left\{a \mid -3 < a \leq \frac{1}{2}\right\}$

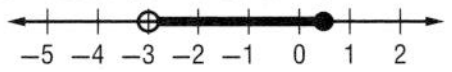

27. $\{n \mid n < -3 \text{ or } n > -3\}$ 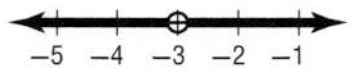

29. Sample answer: Let n = the number; $5 \le n - 8 \le 14$; $\{n \mid 13 \le n \le 22\}$. **31.** $-5n > 35$ or $-5n < 10$; $\{n \mid n < -7 \text{ or } n > -2\}$ **33.** $t < 75$ or $t > 90$
35. Sample answer: Let t = the temperature; $23 \le t \le 33$.
37a. Category 3 has wind speeds between 111 and 130: $111 \le x \le 130$
Category 4 has wind speeds between 131 and 155: $131 \le x \le 155$
b. The union is all values between 111 and 155: $111 \le x \le 155$.
The intersection is all values they have in common, which is none. The intersection is the empty set, $\varnothing$.
39. Neither; Chloe did not add 5 to 3, and Jonas did not add 5 to 7. **41.** Sample answer: $x \le 2$ or $x \ge 4$ **43.** Sample answer: The speed at which a roller coaster runs while staying on the track could represent a compound inequality that is an intersection. **45.** H **47.** B **49.** at least 22 subscriptions **51.** 5.6 **53.** 3.94 **55.** 3.28 **57.** Ian will buy a DVD box set. **59.** The DVD box set cost $70 or more.

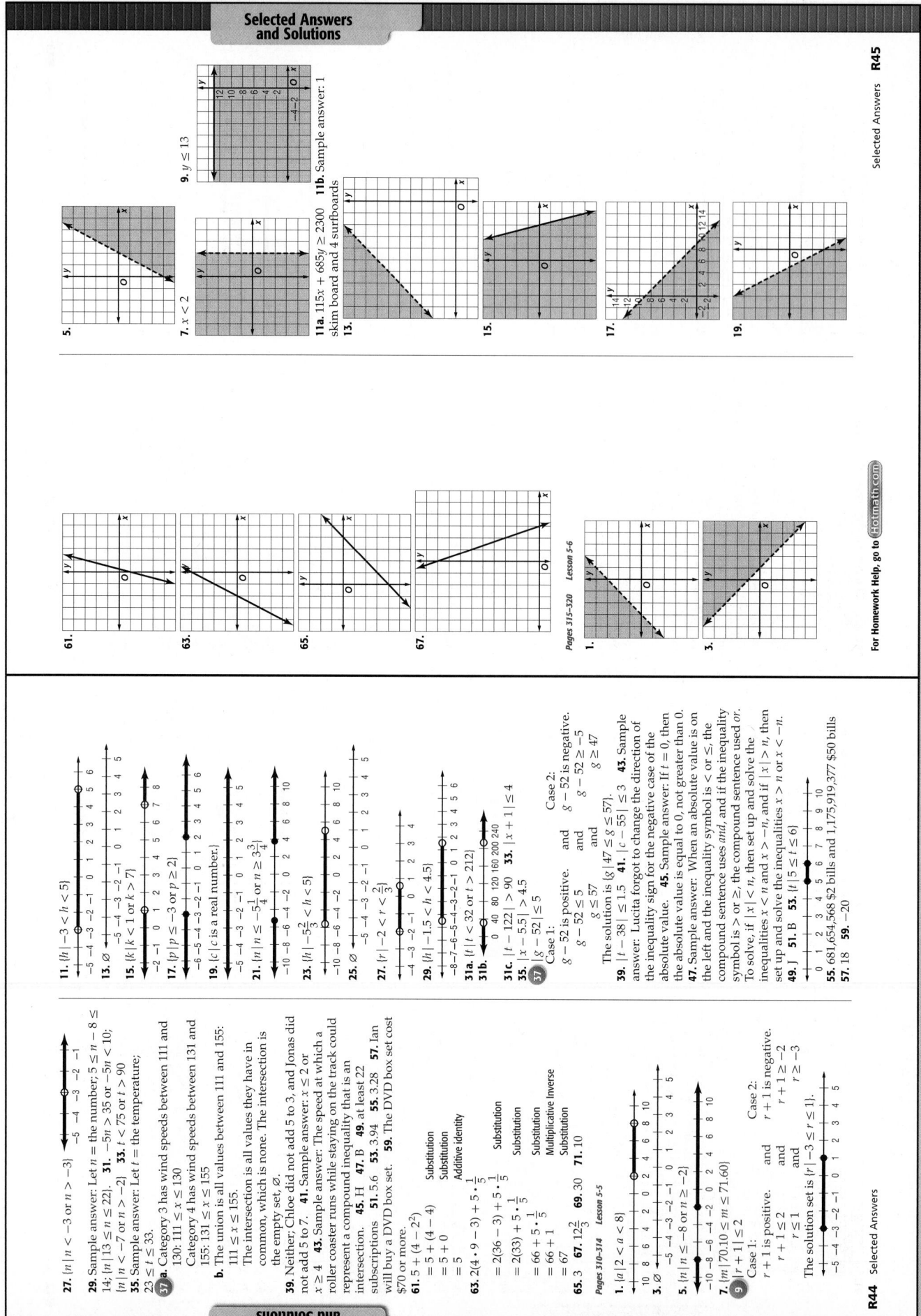

61. $5 + (4 - 2^2)$
$= 5 + (4 - 4)$ Substitution
$= 5 + 0$ Substitution
$= 5$ Additive identity

63. $2(4 \cdot 9 - 3) + 5 \cdot \frac{1}{5}$
$= 2(36 - 3) + 5 \cdot \frac{1}{5}$ Substitution
$= 2(33) + 5 \cdot \frac{1}{5}$ Substitution
$= 66 + 5 \cdot \frac{1}{5}$ Substitution
$= 66 + 1$ Multiplicative Inverse
$= 67$ Substitution

65. 3 **67.** $12\frac{2}{3}$ **69.** 30 **71.** 10

Pages 310–314 Lesson 5-5

1. $\{a \mid 2 < a < 8\}$
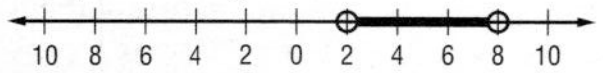
3. $\varnothing$ 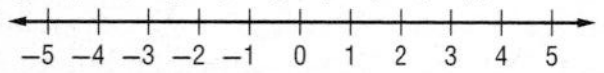
5. $\{n \mid n \le -8 \text{ or } n \ge -2\}$
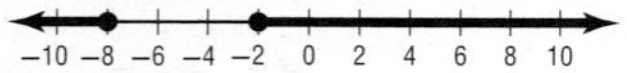
7. $\{m \mid 70.10 \le m \le 71.60\}$
9. $|r + 1| \le 2$

Case 1:		Case 2:
$r + 1$ is positive.	and	$r + 1$ is negative.
$r + 1 \le 2$	and	$r + 1 \ge -2$
$r \le 1$	and	$r \ge -3$

The solution set is $\{r \mid -3 \le r \le 1\}$.
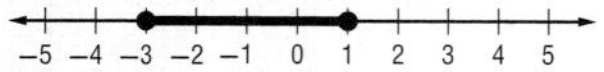

11. $\{h \mid -3 < h < 5\}$
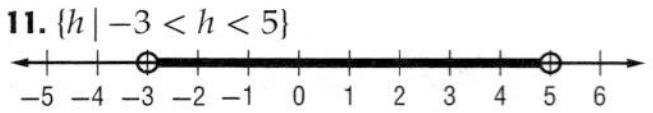
13. $\varnothing$ 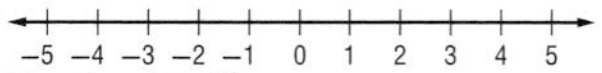
15. $\{k \mid k < 1 \text{ or } k > 7\}$
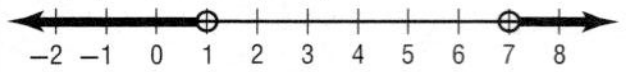
17. $\{p \mid p \le -3 \text{ or } p \ge 2\}$
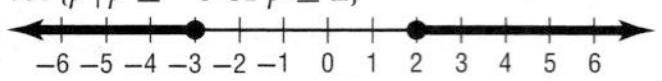
19. $\{c \mid c$ is a real number.$\}$
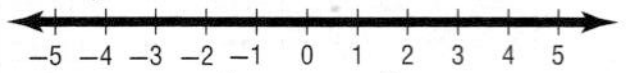
21. $\{n \mid n \le -5\frac{1}{4} \text{ or } n \ge 3\frac{3}{4}\}$
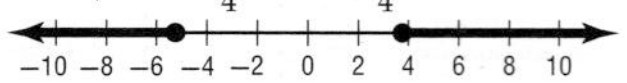
23. $\{h \mid -5\frac{2}{3} < h < 5\}$
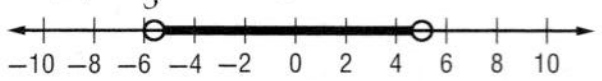
25. $\varnothing$ 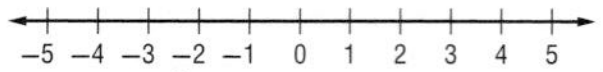
27. $\{r \mid -2 < r < \frac{2}{3}\}$

29. $\{h \mid -1.5 < h < 4.5\}$
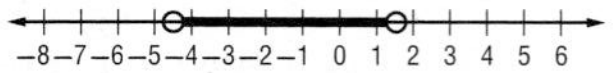
31a. $\{t \mid t < 32 \text{ or } t > 212\}$
31b. 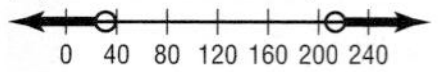
31c. $|t - 122| > 90$ **33.** $|x + 1| \le 4$
35. $|x - 5.5| > 4.5$
37 $|g - 52| \le 5$

Case 1:		Case 2:
$g - 52$ is positive.	and	$g - 52$ is negative.
$g - 52 \le 5$	and	$g - 52 \ge -5$
$g \le 57$	and	$g \ge 47$

The solution is $\{g \mid 47 \le g \le 57\}$.
39. $|t - 38| \le 1.5$ **41.** $|c - 55| \le 3$ **43.** Sample answer: Lucita forgot to change the direction of the inequality sign for the negative case of the absolute value. **45.** Sample answer: If $t = 0$, then the absolute value is equal to 0, not greater than 0.
47. Sample answer: When an absolute value is on the left and the inequality symbol is $<$ or $\le$, the compound sentence uses *and*, and if the inequality symbol is $>$ or $\ge$, the compound sentence used *or*. To solve, if $|x| < n$, then set up and solve the inequalities $x < n$ and $x > -n$, and if $|x| > n$, then set up and solve the inequalities $x > n$ or $x < -n$.
49. J **51.** B **53.** $\{t \mid 5 \le t \le 6\}$
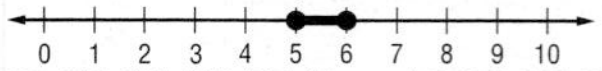
55. 681,654,568 $2 bills and 1,175,919,377 $50 bills
57. 18 **59.** -20

61. 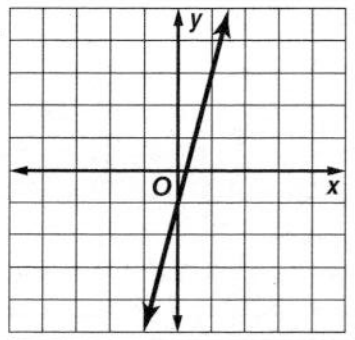
63. 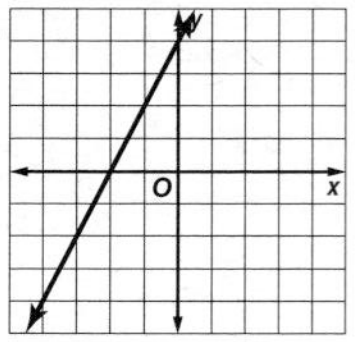
65. 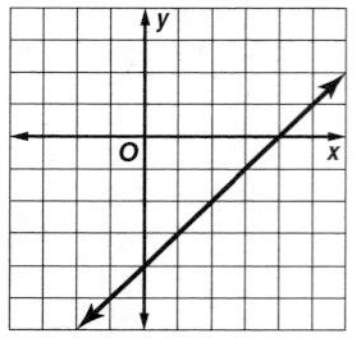
67. 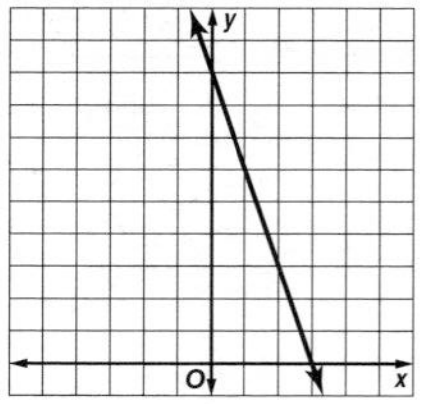

Pages 315–320 Lesson 5-6

1. 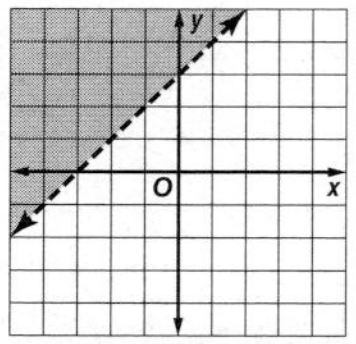
3. 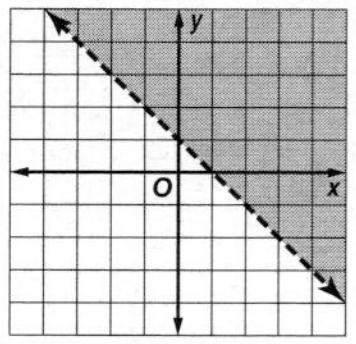
5. 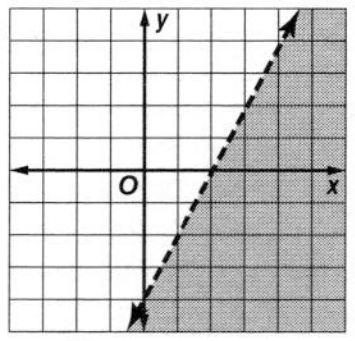
7. $x < 2$
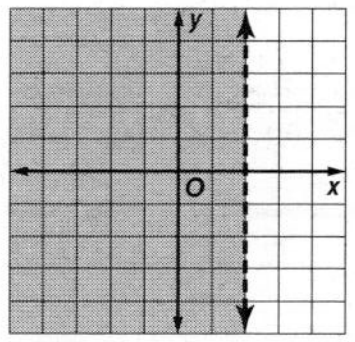
9. $y \le 13$
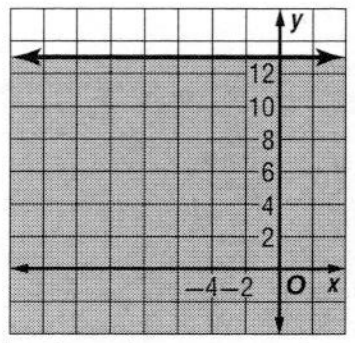
11a. $115x + 685y \ge 2300$ **11b.** Sample answer: 1 skim board and 4 surfboards
13. 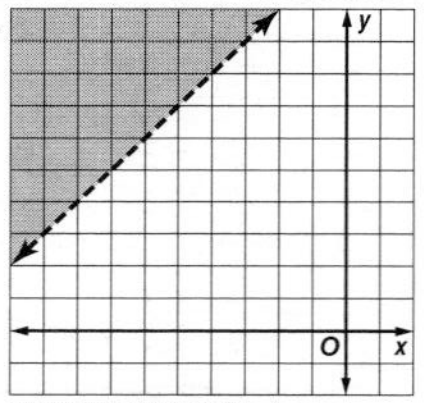
15. 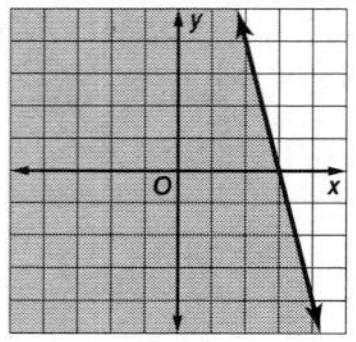
17. 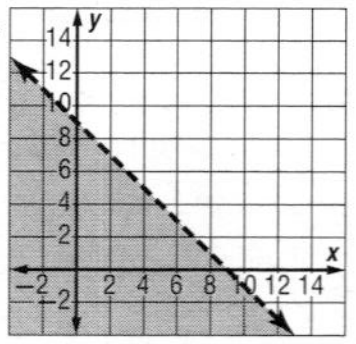
19. 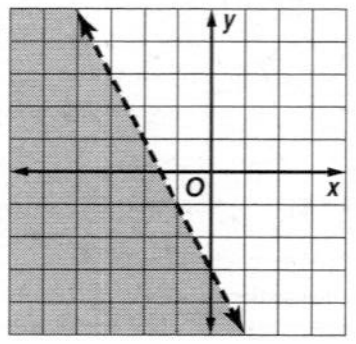

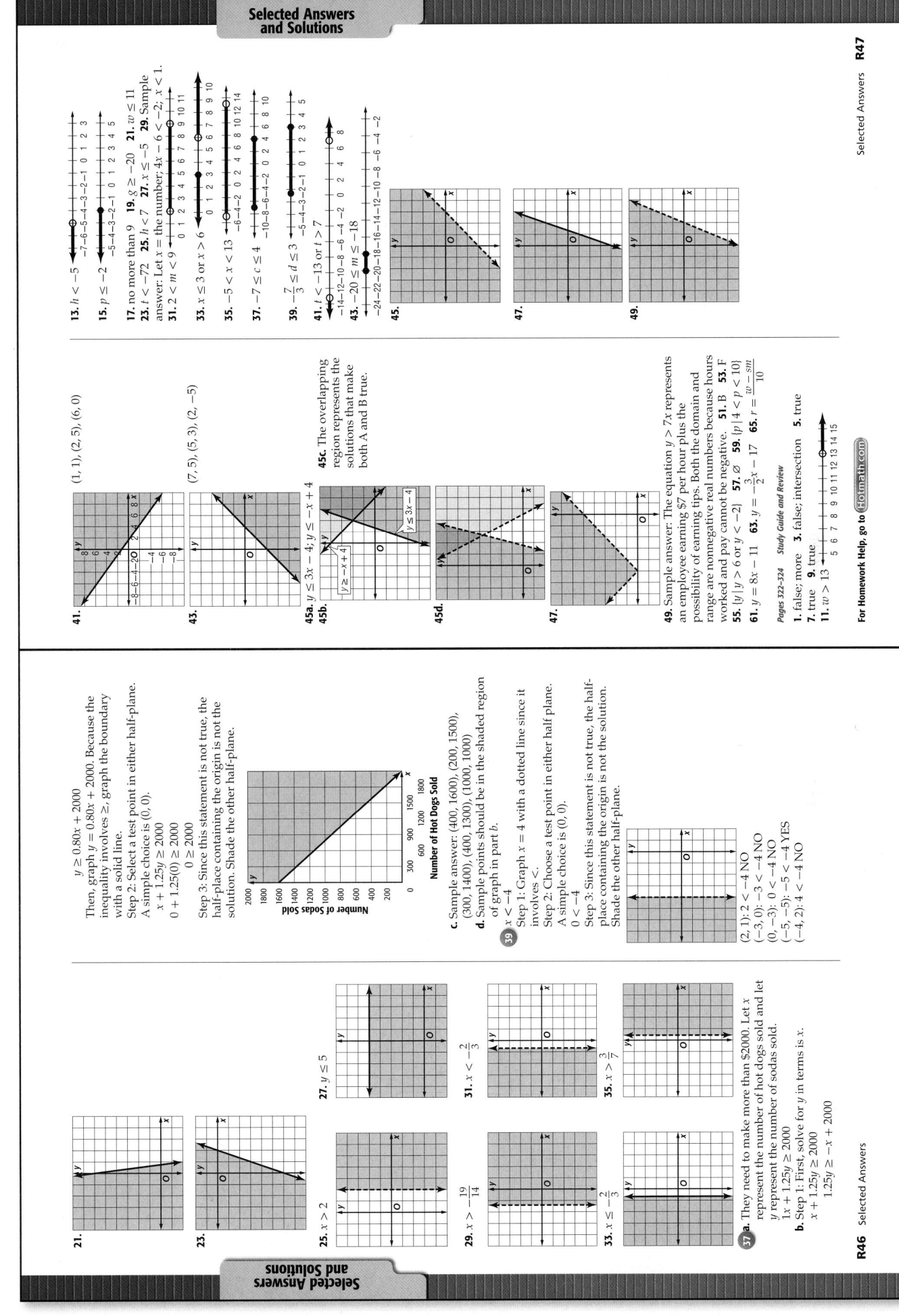

21. 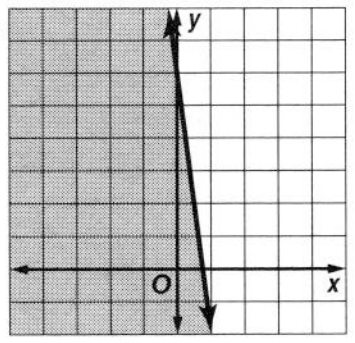

23. 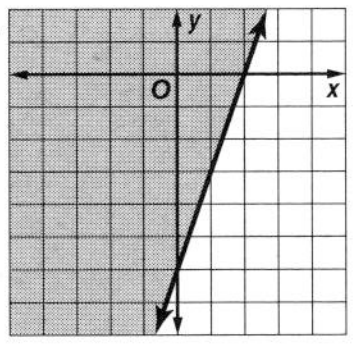

25. $x > 2$ 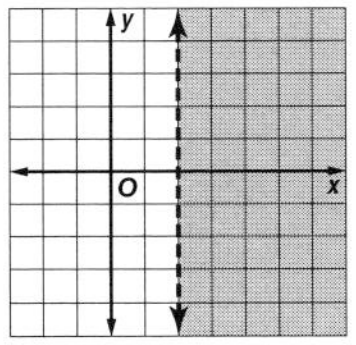

27. $y \leq 5$ 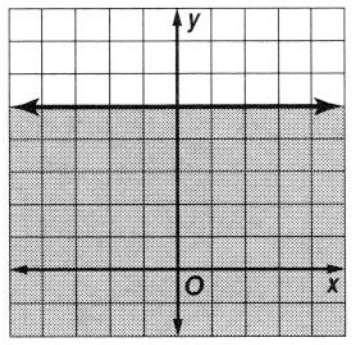

29. $x > -\frac{19}{14}$ 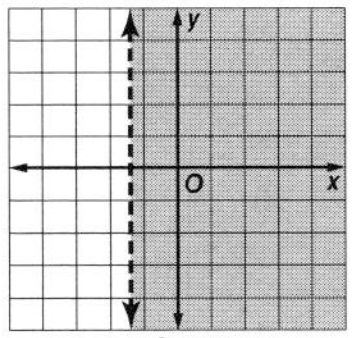

31. $x < -\frac{2}{3}$ 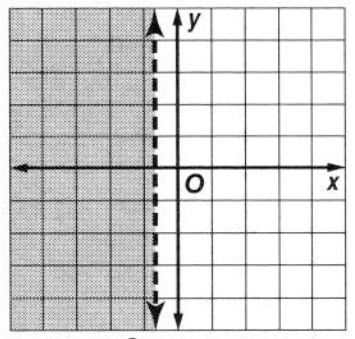

33. $x \leq -\frac{2}{3}$ 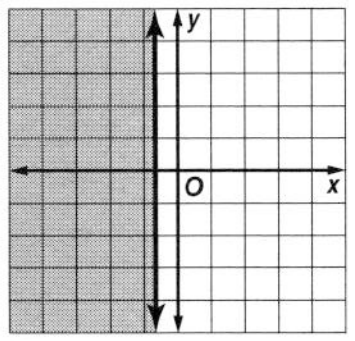

35. $x > \frac{3}{7}$ 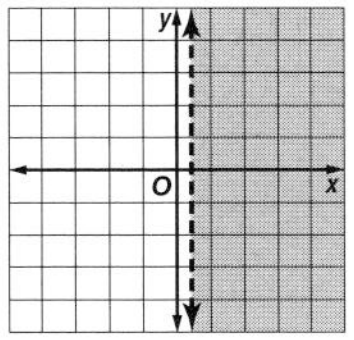

37a. They need to make more than \$2000. Let x represent the number of hot dogs sold and let y represent the number of sodas sold.
$1x + 1.25y \geq 2000$

b. Step 1: First, solve for y in terms is x.
$x + 1.25y \geq 2000$
$1.25y \geq -x + 2000$
$y \geq 0.80x + 2000$
Then, graph $y = 0.80x + 2000$. Because the inequality involves $\geq$, graph the boundary with a solid line.
Step 2: Select a test point in either half-plane. A simple choice is (0, 0).
$x + 1.25y \geq 2000$
$0 + 1.25(0) \geq 2000$
$0 \geq 2000$
Step 3: Since this statement is not true, the half-place containing the origin is not the solution. Shade the other half-plane.

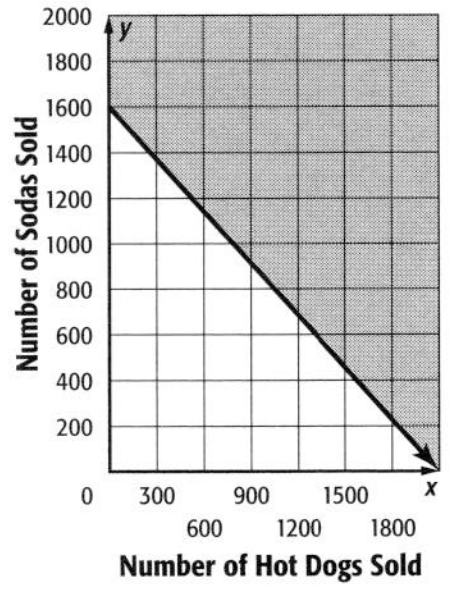

c. Sample answer: (400, 1600), (200, 1500), (300, 1400), (400, 1300), (1000, 1000)

d. Sample points should be in the shaded region of graph in part *b*.

39. $x < -4$
Step 1: Graph $x = 4$ with a dotted line since it involves $<$.
Step 2: Choose a test point in either half plane. A simple choice is (0, 0).
$0 < -4$
Step 3: Since this statement is not true, the half-place containing the origin is not the solution. Shade the other half-plane.

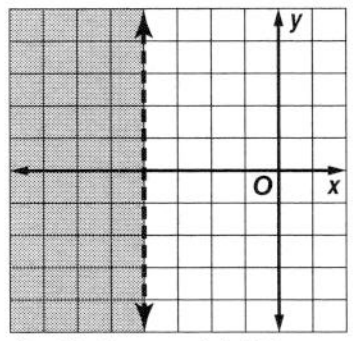

(2, 1): $2 < -4$ NO
(−3, 0): $-3 < -4$ NO
(0, −3): $0 < -4$ NO
(−5, −5): $-5 < -4$ YES
(−4, 2): $4 < -4$ NO

41. 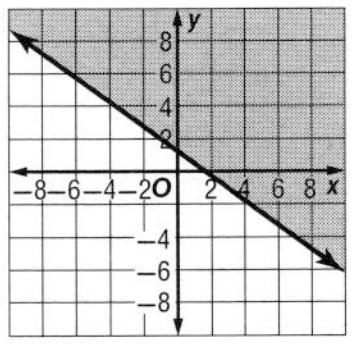 (1, 1), (2, 5), (6, 0)

43. 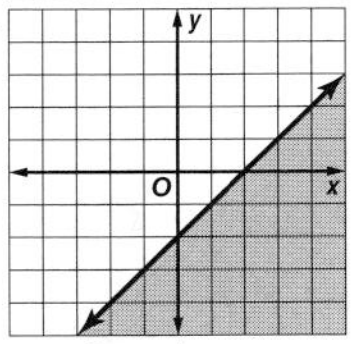 (7, 5), (5, 3), (2, −5)

45a. $y \leq 3x - 4$; $y \leq -x + 4$

45b. 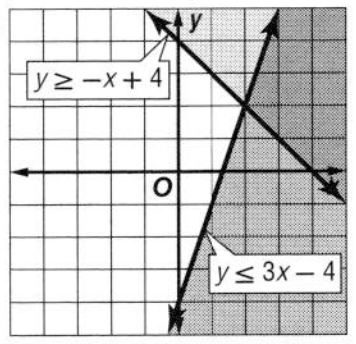

45c. The overlapping region represents the solutions that make both A and B true.

45d. 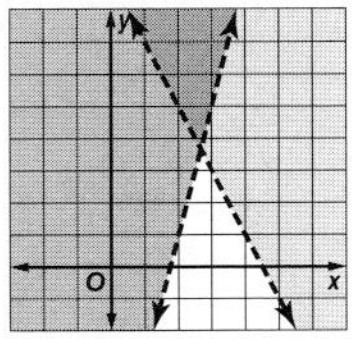

47. 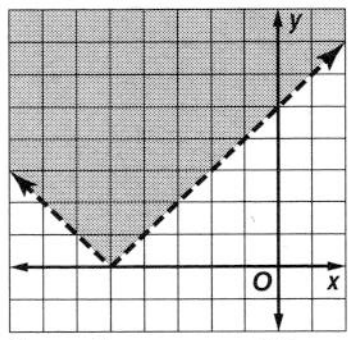

49. Sample answer: The equation $y > 7x$ represents an employee earning \$7 per hour plus the possibility of earning tips. Both the domain and range are nonnegative real numbers because hours worked and pay cannot be negative. **51.** B **53.** F **55.** $\{y \mid y > 6 \text{ or } y < -2\}$ **57.** ∅ **59.** $\{p \mid 4 < p < 10\}$ **61.** $y = 8x - 11$ **63.** $y = -\frac{3}{2}x - 17$ **65.** $r = \frac{w - sm}{10}$

Pages 322–324 Study Guide and Review

1. false; more **3.** false; intersection **5.** true **7.** true **9.** true
11. $w > 13$ 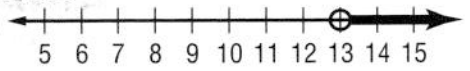

13. $h < -5$ 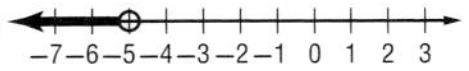

15. $p \leq -2$ 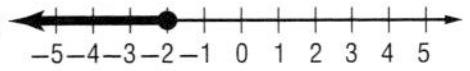

17. no more than 9 **19.** $g \geq -20$ **21.** $w \leq 11$ **23.** $t < -72$ **25.** $h < 7$ **27.** $x \leq -5$ **29.** Sample answer: Let x = the number; $4x - 6 < -2$; $x < 1$.

31. $2 < m < 9$ 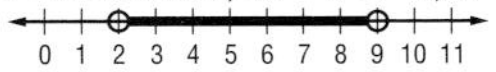

33. $x \leq 3$ or $x > 6$ 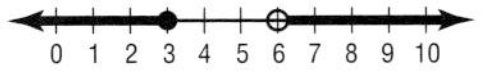

35. $-5 < x < 13$ 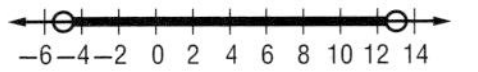

37. $-7 \leq c \leq 4$ 

39. $-\frac{7}{3} \leq d \leq 3$ 

41. $t < -13$ or $t > 7$ 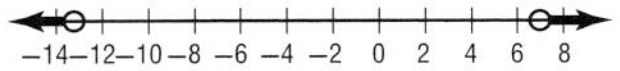

43. $-20 \leq m \leq -18$ 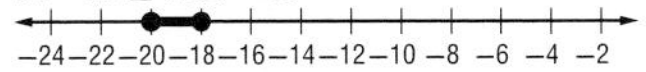

45. 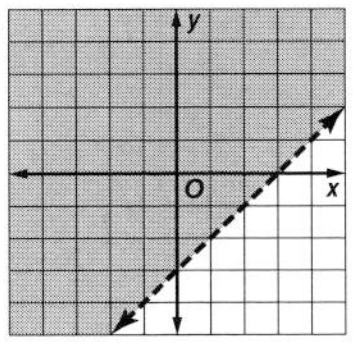

47. 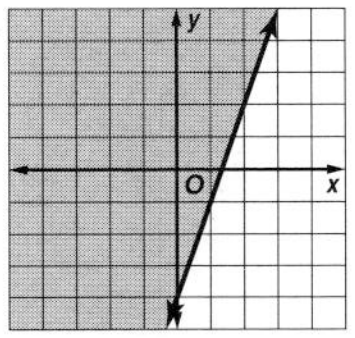

49. 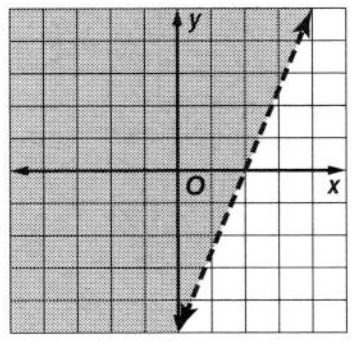

51. (1, 2), (3, −2)

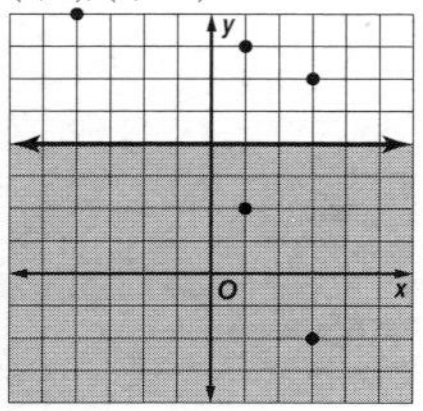

53. 2x + 3y ≤ 24

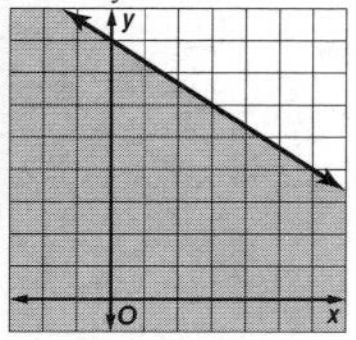

Chapter 6 Systems of Linear Equations and Inequalities

Page 331 Get Ready

1. (4, 0) **3.** (−2, −3) **5.** (−1, −1) **7.** $x = 6 - 2y$
9. $m = 2n + 6$ **11.** $l = \frac{P - 2w}{2}$ **13.** $b = \frac{2A}{h}$

Pages 333–339 Lesson 6-1

1. consistent and independent **3.** inconsistent
5. consistent and independent
7. 1 solution, (−4, 0)

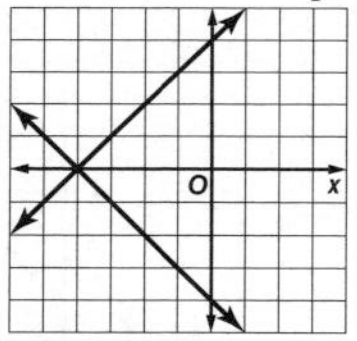

9a. Alberto: $y = 20x + 35$; Ashanti: $y = 10x + 85$
9b.

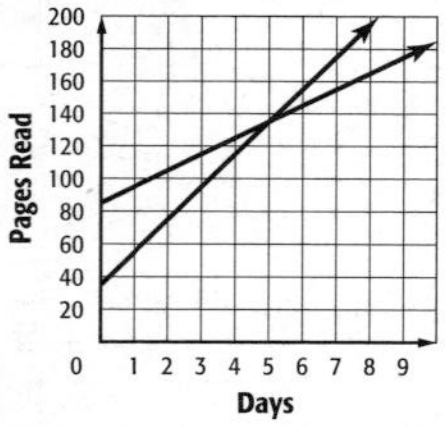

9c. (5, 135); Alberto will have read more after 5 days.

11. consistent and independent
13 Since these two graphs intersect at one point, there is exactly one solution. Therefore, the system is consistent and independent.

15. consistent and independent
17. 1 solution; $\left(-\frac{5}{6}, -1\frac{1}{3}\right)$

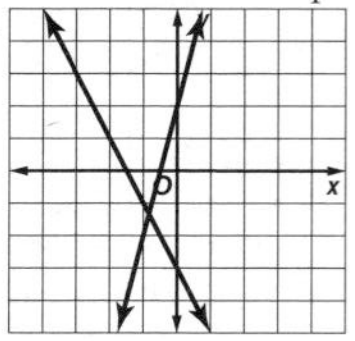

19. infinitely many

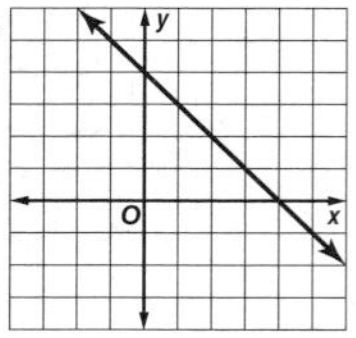

21. 1 solution; (5, −1)

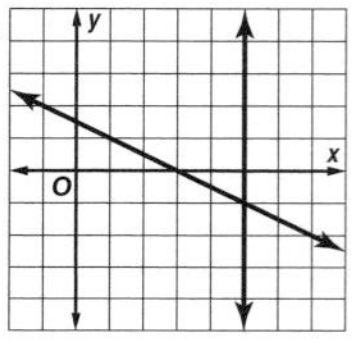

23. no solution

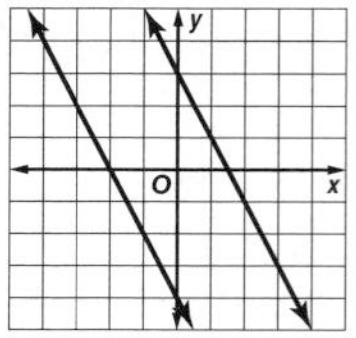

25a. Akira: $y = 30x + 22$; Jen: $y = 20x + 53$
25b.

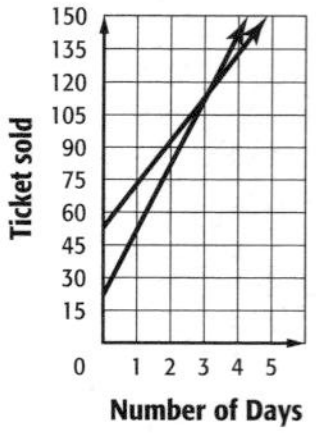

25c. (3.1, 115); After about 3 days Akira will have sold more tickets.

27 Graph the two equations on the same coordinate plane. The graphs appear to intersect at (−4, −2). Check by substituting into the equations.

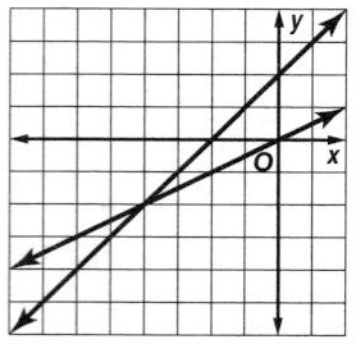

$y = \frac{1}{2}x$
$-2 = \frac{1}{2}(-4)$
$-2 = -2$ Yes
$y = x + 2$
$-2 = -4 + 2$
$-2 = -2$ Yes
So, the solution is (−4, −2).

29. 1 solution, (7, −3)

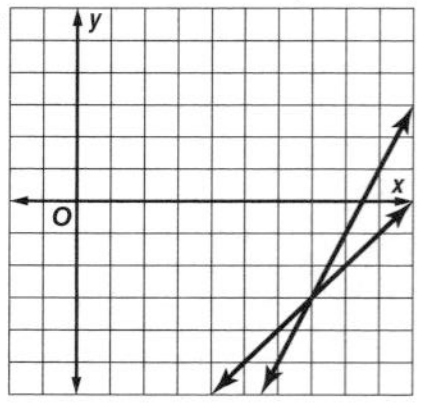

31. 1 solution, (5, 3)

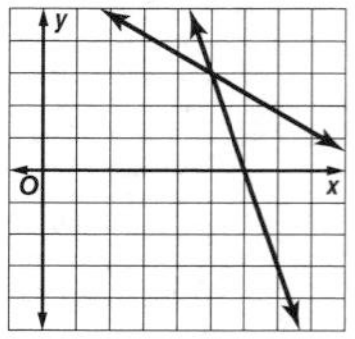

33. infinitely many

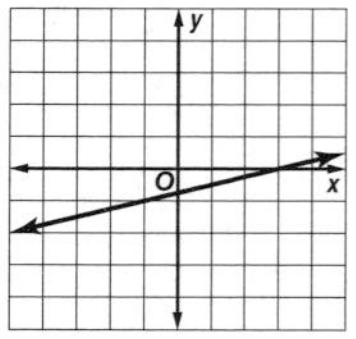

35. no solution

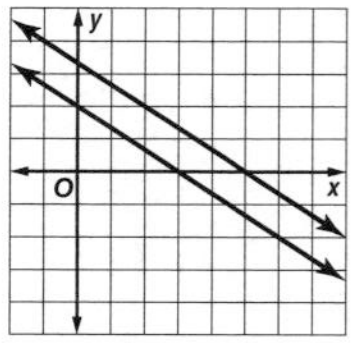

37. no solution

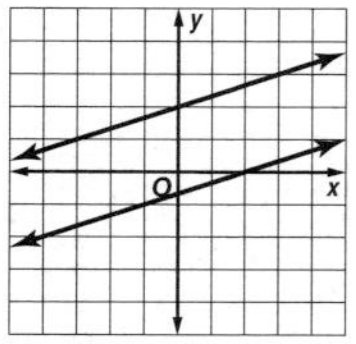

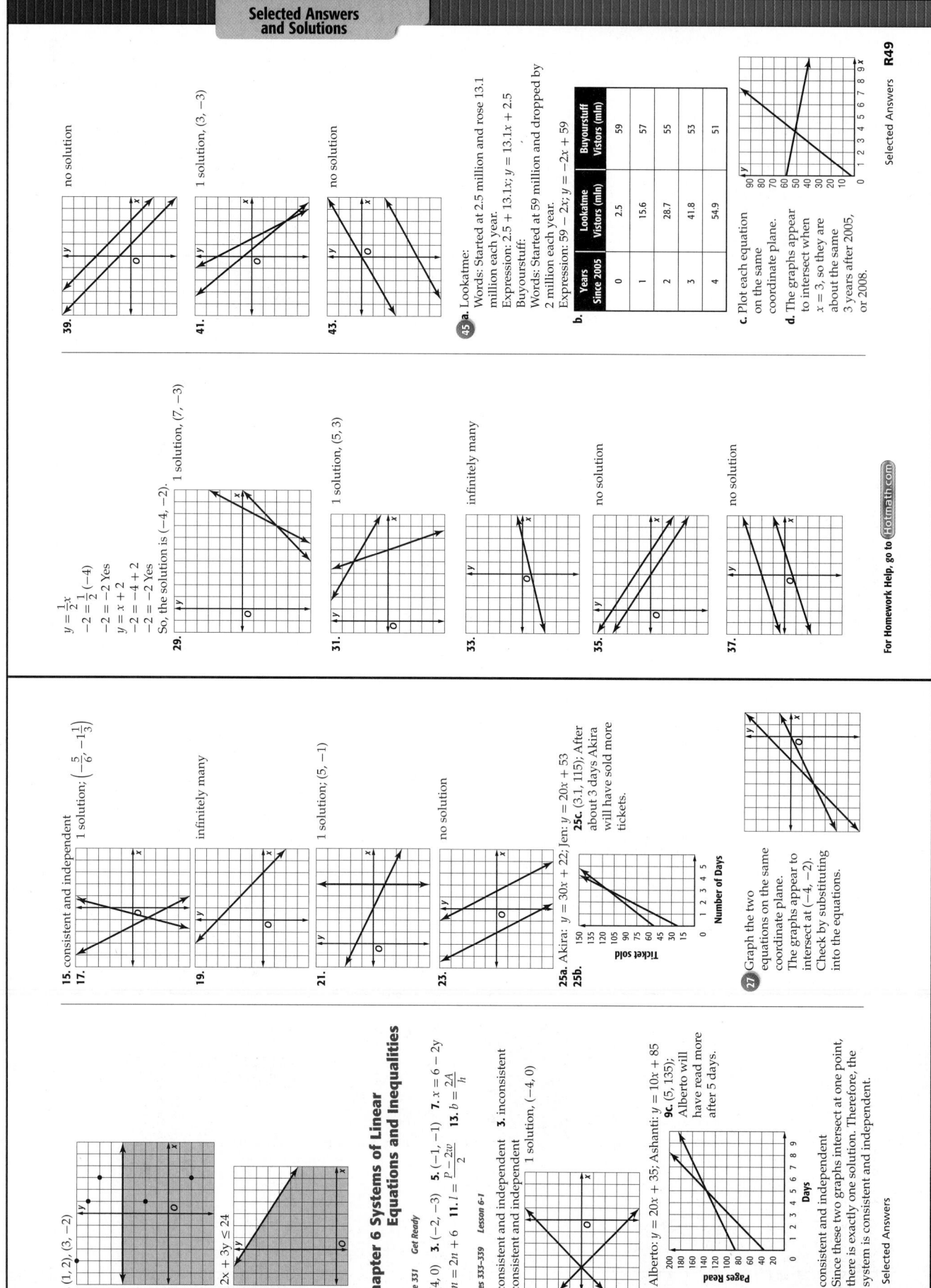

39. no solution

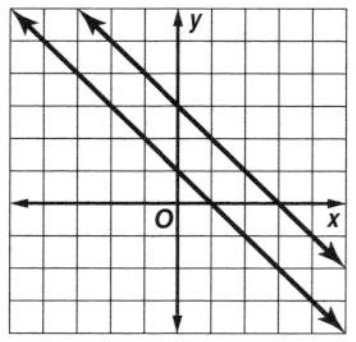

41. 1 solution, (3, −3)

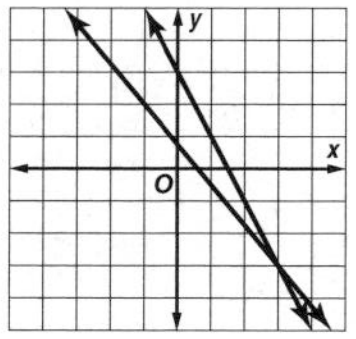

43. no solution

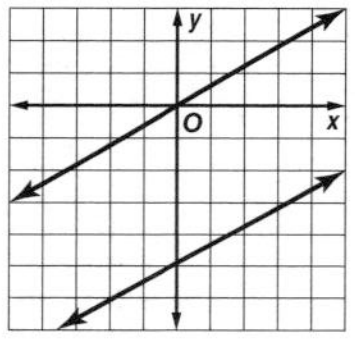

45 a. Lookatme:
Words: Started at 2.5 million and rose 13.1 million each year.
Expression: $2.5 + 13.1x$; $y = 13.1x + 2.5$
Buyourstuff:
Words: Started at 59 million and dropped by 2 million each year.
Expression: $59 - 2x$; $y = -2x + 59$

b.

Years Since 2005	Lookatme Vistors (mln)	Buyourstuff Vistors (mln)
0	2.5	59
1	15.6	57
2	28.7	55
3	41.8	53
4	54.9	51

c. Plot each equation on the same coordinate plane.

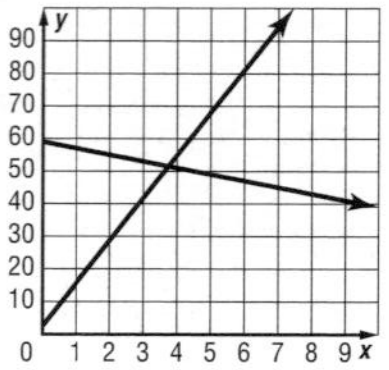

d. The graphs appear to intersect when $x = 3$, so they are about the same 3 years after 2005, or 2008.

e. The domain, or input values will be all values greater than 0 since negative values do not make sense for years. So, D = $\{x \mid x \geq 0\}$
The range, or output values will be all values greater than 0 since negative values do not make sense for the number of visitors. So, R = $\{y \mid y \geq 0\}$.

47. Francisca; if the item is less than \$100, then \$10 off is better. If the item is more than \$100, then the 10% is better. **49.** If the equations are linear and have more than one common solution, they must be consistent and dependent, which means that they have an infinite number of solutions in common. **51.** Sample answers: $y = 5x + 3$; $y = -5x - 3$; $2y = 10x - 6$ **53.** 14,745,600,000 bacteria **55.** H

57.
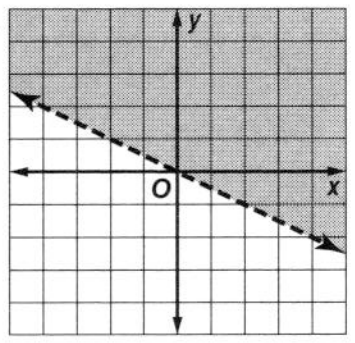

59.
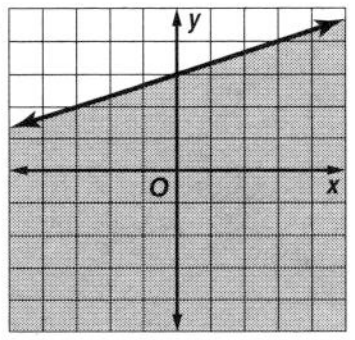

61.
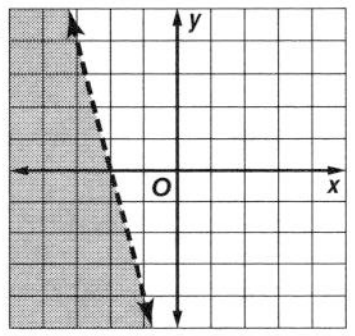

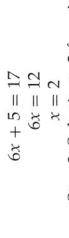

63. 1475 to 1525 books **65.** $y = -3x - 8$
67. $y = \frac{1}{2}x - 3$ **69.** 22 **71.** 92 **73.** −16 **75.** 7

Pages 342–347 Lesson 6-2

1. (5, 10) **3.** (2, 0) **5.** infinitely many
7a. $x = m\angle X$, $y = m\angle Y$; $x + y = 180$, $x = 24 + y$
7b. $x = 102°$, $y = 78°$
9 Step 1: One equation is already solved for y.
$y = 4x + 5$
$2x + y = 17$
Step 2: Substitute $4x + 5$ for y in the second equation.
$2x + y = 17$
$2x + 4x + 5 = 17$
$6x + 5 = 17$
$6x = 12$
$x = 2$
Step 3: Substitute 2 for x in either equation to find y.
$y = 4x + 5$
$y = 4(2) + 5$
$y = 8 + 5$
$y = 13$
The solution is (2, 13).

11. (−3, −11) **13.** (−1, 0) **15.** infinitely many
17. (2, 3) **19.** no solution **21.** (2, 0) **23a.** Let x = number of years since 2000, and let y = the number of nurses; supply, $y = -8000x + 1{,}890{,}000$; demand, $y = 82{,}000x + 2{,}000{,}000$ **23b.** during 1998

25 a. Men: 1:51:39 = 60 + 51 = 111, then round up because the number of seconds is greater than 30. So 1:51:39 rounds to 112.
1:49:31 = 60 + 49 = 109, then round up because the number of seconds is greater than 30. So, 1:49:31 rounds to 110.
Women: 1:54:33 = 60 + 54 = 114, then round up because the number of seconds is greater than 30. So, 1:54:31 rounds to 115.
1:58:03 = 60 + 58 = 118, then round down because the number of seconds is less than 30. So, 1:58:03 rounds to 118.

b. The y-intercept is (0, 112). Find the rate of change.

$$m = \frac{112 - 110}{0 - 5} = \frac{2}{-5} = -0.4$$

So, the equation is $y = -0.4x + 112$.
The y-intercept is (0, 115). Find the rate of change.

$$m = \frac{118 - 115}{5 - 0} = \frac{3}{5} = 0.6$$

So, the equation is $y = 0.6x + 115$.

c. never; If you graph the two equations, the graphs do not cross in the positive values of x. Negative values will not make sense in terms of the word problem.

27. Neither; Guillermo substituted incorrectly for b. Cara solved correctly for b, but misinterpreted the pounds of apples bought. **29.** Sample answer: The solutions found by each of these methods should be the same. However, it may be necessary to estimate using a graph. So, when a precise solution is needed, you should use substitution. **31.** An equation containing a variable with a coefficient of 1 can easily be solved for the variable. That expression can then be substituted into the second equation for the variable.

33. $\frac{5}{6}$ **35.** C

37.
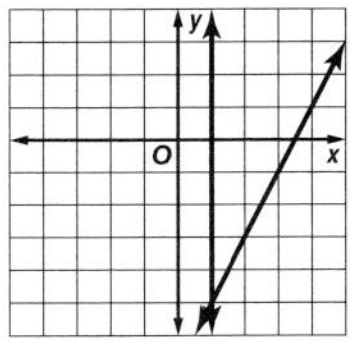
one solution; (1,–5)

39.
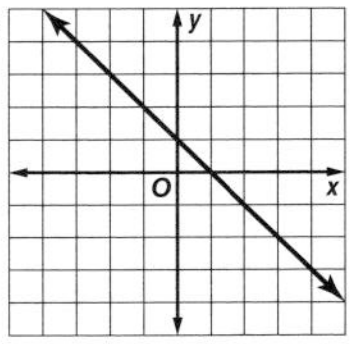
infinitely many solutions

41. $v \geq -2$ **43.** $q \leq -40$ **45.** $t \geq 3$
47. $55b + 15$ **49.** $11h^2 + 12h$

Pages 348–354 Lesson 6-3

1. (2, 3)
3 Step 1: The like terms are already aligned.
$7f + 3g = -6$
$7f - 2g = -31$
Step 2: Subtract the equations.

$$\begin{array}{rl} 7f + 3g = & -6 \\ (-)\ 7f - 2g = & -31 \\ \hline 5g = & 25 \\ g = & 5 \end{array}$$

Step 3: Substitute 5 for g in either equation to find f.
$7f + 3(5) = -6$
$7f + 15 = -6$
$7f = -21$
$f = -3$
The solution is (−3, 5).

5. 6, 18 **7.** (−3, 4) **9.** (−3, 1) **11.** (4, −2)
13. (8, −7) **15.** (4, 7) **17.** (4, 1.5) **19.** 5, 17

21

Three times a number	minus	another number	is	−3.
$3x$	−	y	=	−3
The first number	plus	the second number	is	11.
x	+	y	=	11

Steps 1 and 2: Write the equations vertically and add.

$$\begin{array}{rl} 3x - y = & -3 \\ x + y = & 11 \\ \hline 4x \quad = & 8 \\ x \quad = & 2 \end{array}$$

Step 3: Substitute 2 for x in either equation to find y.
$x + y = 11$
$2 + y = 11$
$y = 9$
The numbers are 2 and 9.

23. adult, \$5.95; children, \$3.95 **25.** (2, −1)
27. $\left(-\frac{5}{6}, 3\right)$ **29.** $\left(2\frac{7}{9}, 13\frac{1}{3}\right)$ **31a.** $x + y = 66$; $x = 30 + y$ **31b.** (48, 18) **31c.** There are 48 teams that are not from the U.S. and 18 teams that are from the U.S.

31d.
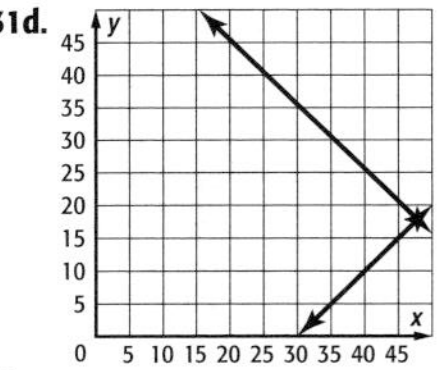

33 a. One way to get 15 points is to use 4 pennies and 3 paper clips.
$4(3) + 3 = 12 + 3$
$= 15$

b. The total number of objects is 9.
$p + c = 9$
Pennies are worth 3 points each and paper clips are worth 1 point each for a total of 15 points.
$3p + c = 15$
Solve:

$$\begin{array}{rl} p + c = & 9 \\ (-)\ 3p + c = & 15 \\ \hline -2p \quad = & -6 \\ p = & 3 \end{array}$$

Substitute 3 for p in either equation to find c,
$p + c = 9$
$3 + c = 9$
$c = 6$
So, $p = 3$ and $c = 6$.

c.

p	$c = 9 - p$	$3p + c$
0	9	$3(0) + 9 = 9$
1	8	$3(1) + 8 = 11$
2	7	$3(2) + 7 = 13$
3	6	$3(3) + 6 = 15$
4	5	$3(4) + 5 = 17$
5	4	$3(5) + 4 = 19$

For Homework Help, go to Hotmath.com

d. Yes, since the pennies are 3 points each, 3 of them makes 9 points. Add the 6 points from 6 paper clips and you get 15 points.

35. The result of the statement is false, so there is no solution. **37.** Sample answer: $-x + y = 5$; I used the solution to create another equation with the coefficient of the x-term being the opposite of its corresponding coefficient. **39.** Sample answer: It would be most beneficial when one variable has either the same or opposite coefficients in each of the equations. **41.** A **43.** B **45.** (15, 5) **47.** (3, 11) **49.** (−2, 2) **51.** Yes; each pair of opposite sides have the same or an undefined slope, so they are parallel. **53.** −5 **55.** −20 **57.** $11w^2 - 9w$ **59.** $-2y - 35$

Pages 355–360 Lesson 6-4

1. (3, 2)

3 Eliminate y:

$(4x + 2y = -14)(-3)$ $\quad$ $-12x - 6y = 42$

$(5x + 3y = -17)(2)$ $\quad$ $10x + 6y = -34$

$-2x = 8$

$x = -4$

Now, substitute −4 for x in either equation to find the value of y.

$4x + 2y = -14$

$4(-4) + 2y = -14$

$-16 + 2y = -14$

$2y = 2$

$y = 1$

The solution is (−4, 1).

5. 6 mph **7.** (−1, 3) **9.** (−3, 4) **11.** (−2, 3) **13.** (3, 5) **15.** (1, −5) **17.** (0, 1)

19 Seven times a number plus three times another number equals −1.

$7x + 3y = -1$

The sum of the two numbers is −3.

$x + y = -3$

$7x + 3y = -1$ $\quad$ $7x + 3y = -1$

$(x + y = -3)(-3)$ $\quad$ $-3x - 3y = 9$

$4x = 8$

$x = 2$

Now, substitute 2 for x in either equation to find y.

$x + y = -3$

$2 + y = -3$

$y = -5$ The two numbers are 2 and −5.

21. (2.5, 3.25) **23.** $\left(3, \frac{1}{2}\right)$ **25a.** $120n + 180s = 1500$ **25b.** $90n + 120s = 1050$ **25c.** (5, 5); To be cost-effective, the robots must save the time of 5 nurses and 5 support staff.

27 a. Let x be the cost of a batting token and y be the cost of the miniature golf games.

For the first group, the equation is $16x + 3y = 30$.

For the second group, the equation is $22x + 5y = 43$.

b. Solve.

$(16x + 3y = 30)(5)$ $\quad$ $80x + 15y = 150$

$(22x + 5y = 43)(-3)$ $\quad$ $-66x - 15y = -129$

$14x = 21$

$x = 1.5$

Now, substitute 1.5 for x in either equation to find y.

$16x + 3y = 30$

$16(1.5) + 3y = 30$

$24 + 3y = 30$

$3y = 6$

$y = 2$

A batting token costs $1.50 and a game of miniature golf costs $2.

29. One of the equations will be a multiple of the other. **31.** Sample answer: $2x + 3y = 6$, $4x + 9y = 5$ **33.** Sample answer: A variable that has a nonzero coefficient in each equation may be eliminated using multiplication. Calculations may be easier if a variable requiring only one equation to be multiplied or a variable with a smaller coefficient is eliminated. **35.** G **37.** D

39. (−1, −1) **41.** (9, 3) **43.** (0, 6)

45. $m \leq 13$ and $m \geq -3$

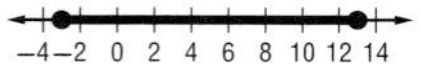

47. $w > 1$ or $w < -10$

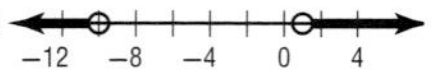

49. $A = \frac{1}{2}bh$ **51.** $V = \ell wh$ **53.** $A = \pi r^2$

Pages 362–367 Lesson 6-5

1. elim (×); (2, −5) **3.** elim (+); $(-\frac{1}{3}, 1)$

5a. $4t + 3j = 181$; $t + 2j = 94$ **5b.** Substitution **5c.** Each T-shirt cost $16 and each pair of jeans cost $39. **7.** subst.; (2, −2) **9.** elim. (−); $\left(1, -\frac{1}{2}\right)$

11 $-5x + 4y = 7$

$-5x - 3y = -14$

Since there are no coefficients of 1, elimination is the best method.

$(-5x + 4y = 7)(-1)$ $\quad$ $5x - 4y = -7$

$-5x - 3y = -14$ $\quad$ $-5x - 3y = -14$

$-7y = -21$

$y = 3$

Now substitute 3 for y in either equation to find x,

$-5x + 4y = 7$

$-5x + 4(3) = 7$

$-5x + 12 = 7$

$-5x = -5$

$x = 1$

The solution is (1, 3).

13. $m + t = 40$ and $m = 3t - 4$; 29 movies, 11 television shows **15.** 880 books; If they sell this number, then their income and expenses both equal $35,200.

17 a. Let x be the cost per pound of the aluminum cans and y be the cost per pound of the newspapers.

For Mara, the equation is $9x + 26y = 3.77$.

For Ling, the equation is $9x + 114y = 4.65$.

b. Elimination is the best method for solving these equations.

$(9x + 26y = 3.77)(-1)$ $\quad$ $-9x - 26y = -3.77$

$9x + 114y = 4.65$ $\quad$ $9x + 114y = 4.65$

$88y = 0.88$

$y = 0.01$

Now substitute 0.01 for y in either equation to find x.

$9x + 26y = 3.77$

$9x + 26(0.01) = 3.77$

$9x + 0.26 = 3.77$

$9x = 3.51$

$x = 0.39$

The aluminum cans are $0.39 per pound. This solution is reasonable.

19a. $1.15 **19b.** $9.15 **21.** Sample answer: $x + y = 12$ and $3x + 2y = 29$, where x represents the cost of a student ticket for the basketball game and y represents the cost of an adult ticket; substitution could be used to solve the system; (5, 7) means the cost of a student ticket is $5 and the cost of an adult ticket is $7.

23. Graphing: (2, 5)

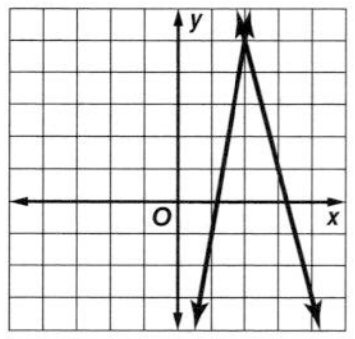

elimination by addition:

$4x + y = 13$

$6x - y = 7$

$10x = 20$

$x = 2$

$4(2) + y = 13$

$y = 5$

substitution:

$y = -4x + 13$

$6x - (-4x + 13) = 7$

$6x + 4x - 13 = 7$

$10x = 20$

$x = 2$

$4(2) + y = 13$

$y = 5$

25. The third system; this system is the only one that is not a system of linear equations. **27.** A **29.** 10 ft **31.** (0, 3) **33.** (2, 1)

35.

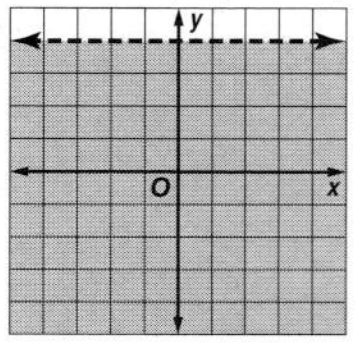

37.

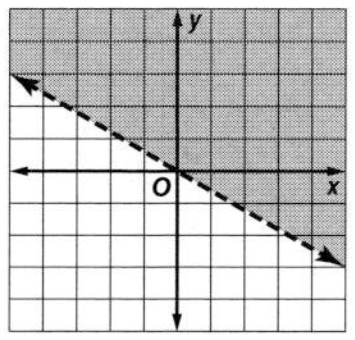

39. −12.31 **41.** 6.6 **43.** −93.19

Pages 369–375 Lesson 6-6

1. 2 × 4; second row and first column **3.** 1 × 4; first row and third column

5a.

	Weekday	Weekend
Single	69	89
Double	79	109
Suite	99	139

5b. 3 × 2 **5c.** suite on a weekend; single on a weekday

7. $\begin{bmatrix} 12 & 1 & 14 \\ -9 & 19 & 9 \\ -8 & -7 & -3 \end{bmatrix}$ **9.** impossible **11.** 5 × 2; second row and first column

13 The matrix has 4 rows and 6 columns, so the dimensions are 4 × 6. 7 is located in the third column and fourth row.

15. 6 × 4; second row and fourth column

17 a. Enter the data into a matrix.

	Land area	People
Ohio	40,948	277.3
Florida	53,926	296.4
New York	47,213	401.9
North Carolina	48,710	165.2

b. The matrix has 4 rows and 2 columns, so the dimensions are 4 × 2.

c. New York has the most people per square mile, 401.9.

North Carolina has the least people per square mile, 165.2.

19. $\begin{bmatrix} -6 & 1 & 0 \\ 7 & -8 & 15 \end{bmatrix}$ **21.** $\begin{bmatrix} 10 & -5 & 0 \\ 5 & -15 & 25 \\ 35 & 50 & -55 \\ 40 & -45 & -20 \end{bmatrix}$

23. $[-3 \quad 12 \quad -11 \quad -10]$

25a. On Saturday at the store on Elm St., $245 in glazed donuts were sold.

25b. $\begin{bmatrix} 95 & 205 & 70 & 51 \\ 105 & 245 & 79 & 49 \end{bmatrix}$; $\begin{bmatrix} 167 & 295 & 99 & 79 \\ 159 & 289 & 107 & 88 \end{bmatrix}$

25c. $\begin{bmatrix} 262 & 500 & 169 & 130 \\ 264 & 534 & 186 & 137 \end{bmatrix}$

Main Street: Chocolate 262, Glazed 500, Powered 169, Lemon filled 130

Elm Street: Chocolate 264, Glazed 534, Powdered 186, Lemon filled 137

25d. glazed **27.** $[-16 \quad 25 \quad 9]$ **29.** impossible

31

$$\begin{bmatrix} -5 & 2 \\ 12 & -11 \\ 9 & 0 \\ -1 & 7 \\ 6 & 5 \\ -4 & 2 \end{bmatrix} + 4\begin{bmatrix} 10 & 4 \\ -1 & -3 \\ 5 & -8 \\ -9 & 0 \\ 1 & 4 \\ -3 & 2 \end{bmatrix} = \begin{bmatrix} -5 & 2 \\ 12 & -11 \\ 9 & 0 \\ -1 & 7 \\ 6 & 5 \\ -4 & 2 \end{bmatrix} + \begin{bmatrix} 40 & 16 \\ -4 & -12 \\ 20 & -32 \\ -36 & 0 \\ 4 & 16 \\ -12 & 8 \end{bmatrix}$$

$$= \begin{bmatrix} -5+40 & 2+16 \\ 12+(-4) & -11+(-12) \\ 9+20 & 0+(-32) \\ -1+(-36) & 7+0 \\ 6+4 & 5+16 \\ -4+(-12) & 2+8 \end{bmatrix}$$

$$= \begin{bmatrix} 35 & 18 \\ 8 & -23 \\ 29 & -32 \\ -37 & 7 \\ 10 & 21 \\ -16 & 10 \end{bmatrix}$$

33. Sample answer: $\begin{bmatrix} 6 & 1 & 9 \\ 1 & 3 & 2 \end{bmatrix}$ and $\begin{bmatrix} 1 & 3 & 2 \\ 4 & 2 & 2 \end{bmatrix}$

35. Sample answer: $\begin{bmatrix} 4 & 5 \\ 5 & 1 \end{bmatrix}$ **37.** Sample answer:

The number of miles hiked on a 3-day hiking trip. On the first day, 5 miles were hiked. On the second day, 8 miles were hiked. On the third day, 10 miles were hiked.

	Miles
Day 1	5
Day 2	8
Day 3	10

39. C **41.** G **43.** $x + y = 500$, $0.25x + 0.5y = 170$; 320 gal of 25%; 180 gal of 50% **45.** $(2, -7)$ **47.** $1.5a - 0.3a \geq 75$; $a \geq 62.5$; at least 63 apples **49.** 42, 48, 54 **51.** $25(28 + 18) = \$1150$ **53.** -3 **55.** -153 **57.** 23

Pages 376–381 Lesson 6-7

1. $\left[\begin{array}{cc|c} -1 & 3 & -10 \\ 5 & -2 & 7 \end{array}\right]$ **3.** $\left[\begin{array}{cc|c} 1 & 2 & -1 \\ 2 & -2 & -9 \end{array}\right]$

5 Place the coefficients of the equations and the constants into a matrix.

$$\left[\begin{array}{cc|c} 3 & 4 & -5 \\ 2 & -1 & 6 \end{array}\right]$$

7. $(-1, -2)$ **9.** $(-1, 6)$ **11a.** $3n + 4b = 22.25$ $3n + 10b = 29.75$ **11b.** $\left[\begin{array}{cc|c} 3 & 4 & 22.25 \\ 3 & 10 & 29.75 \end{array}\right]$

11c. new: \$5.75; used: \$1.25

13. $\left[\begin{array}{cc|c} -4 & -3 & -8 \\ 1 & 1 & -12 \end{array}\right]$ **15.** $\left[\begin{array}{cc|c} -6 & 1 & -15 \\ 1 & -2 & 13 \end{array}\right]$

17. $\left[\begin{array}{cc|c} 1 & -1 & 7 \\ 9 & -5 & 23 \end{array}\right]$ **19.** $(-5, 4)$ **21.** $(-2, -4)$

23. $(3, -7)$ **25.** $(-4, -8)$ **27.** $(3, -4)$ **29.** $\left(\frac{3}{2}, \frac{1}{3}\right)$

31. $x = 16, y = -2$ **33.** $3x + 2y = 7$, $-x - 4y = 5$

35 Place the coefficients of the matrix into equations.
$-x + 9y = 12$
$2x + 3y = -7$

37 First, write the equations.
$x + y = 16$
$22x + 40y = 460$
Now, write the augmented matrix for the equations.

$$\left[\begin{array}{cc|c} 1 & 1 & 16 \\ 22 & 40 & 460 \end{array}\right]$$

Step 1: To make the first element in row 2 zero, multiply row 1 by -22 and add to row 2.

$$\left[\begin{array}{cc|c} 1 & 1 & 16 \\ 0 & 18 & 108 \end{array}\right]$$

Step 2: To make the second element in row 2 one, divide row 2 by 18.

$$\left[\begin{array}{cc|c} 1 & 1 & 16 \\ 0 & 1 & 6 \end{array}\right]$$

Step 3: To make the second element in row 1 zero, multiply row 2 by -1 and add to row 2.

$$\left[\begin{array}{cc|c} 1 & 0 & 10 \\ 0 & 1 & 6 \end{array}\right]$$

The solution is $x = 10$ and $y = 6$. So there are 10 boxes of notebooks and 6 boxes of mugs.

39. 5 movies and 3 games **41.** infinitely many **43.** no solution **45.** infinitely many **47.** Sample answer: The graphs of these two lines are parallel, so the system has no solution. **49.** $(0, 2)$ **51.** Sample answer: An augmented matrix consists of the coefficients and constant terms of a system. Row operations are used until the coefficient portion of the matrix is the identity matrix. The x-coordinate is the top number in the constant portion of the matrix, and the y-coordinate is the bottom number in the constant portion of the matrix. **53.** A **55.** B

57. $\begin{bmatrix} 11 & -18 \\ -3 & 18 \\ -12 & -4 \end{bmatrix}$ **59.** impossible

61. $\{p \mid 28 \leq p \leq 32\}$ **63.** $y = 2x - 5$

65. $y = \frac{2}{3}x + 1$ **67.** $y = -\frac{1}{2}x + \frac{3}{2}$ **69.** $-9 + 24x$ **71.** $-24m + 12$ **73.** $48c + 36b$

Pages 382–386 Lesson 6-8

1.

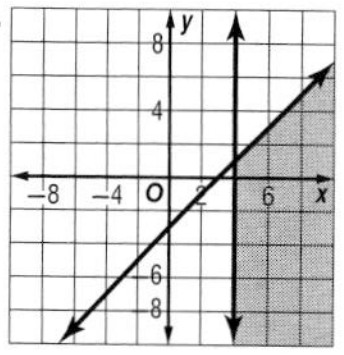

3.

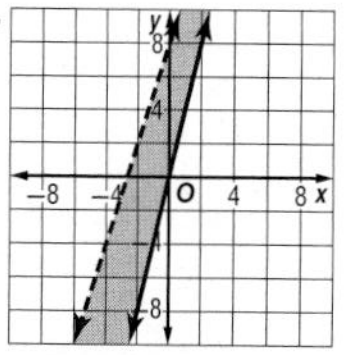

5.

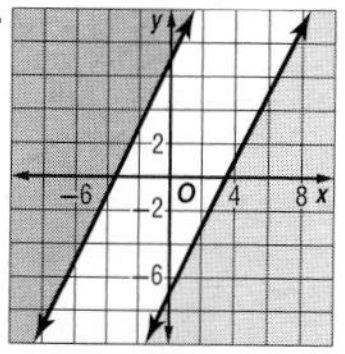

no solution

7.

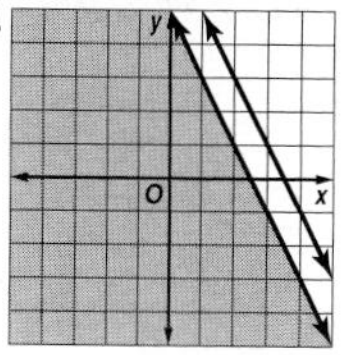

9a. Let h = the height of the driver in inches and w = the weight of the driver in pounds; $h < 79$ and $w < 295$.

Driving Requirements

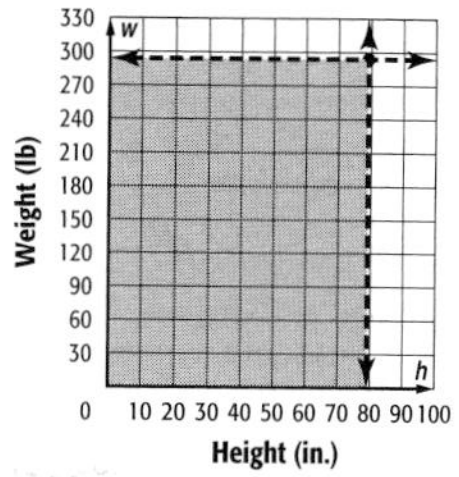

9b. Sample answer: 72 in. and 220 lb **9c.** Yes, the point falls in the overlapping region.

11 Graph both inequalities on the same coordinate plane.
$y \geq 0$ has a solid line.
$y \leq x - 5$ has a solid line.
The solution is the intersection of the shading.

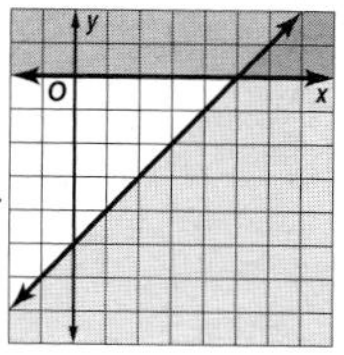

13.

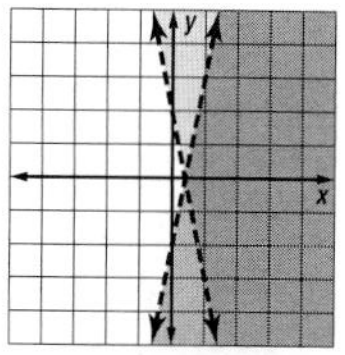

15.

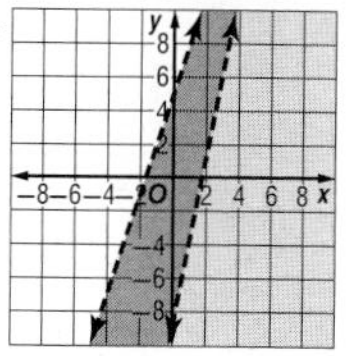

17.

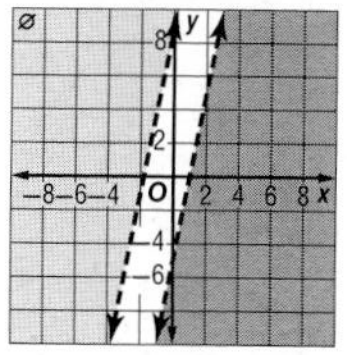

no solution

19.

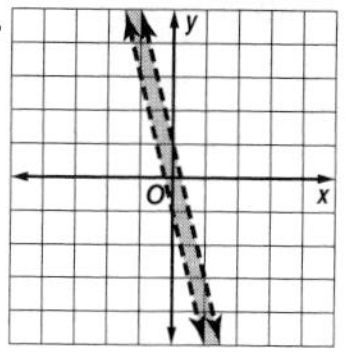

21.

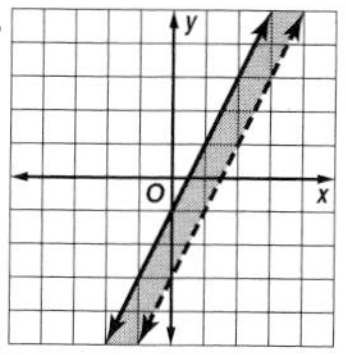

23.
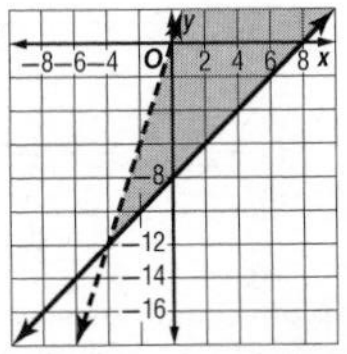

25a. Let f = square footage and let p = price; $1000 \leq f \leq 17{,}000$ and $10{,}000 \leq p \leq 150{,}000$

Ice Rink Resurfacers

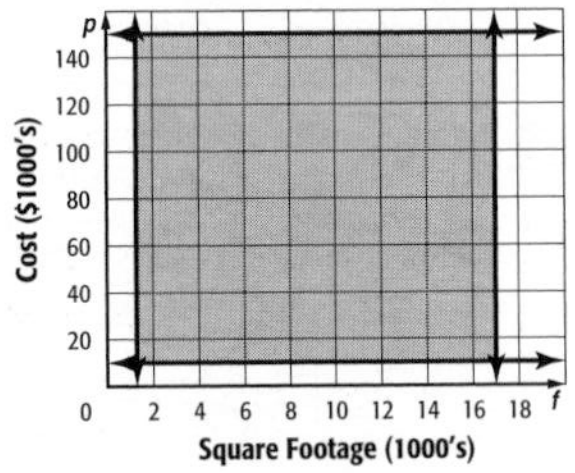

25b. Sample answer: an ice resurfacer for a rink of 5000 ft^2 and a price of $20,000 **25c.** Yes; the point satisfies each inequality.

27.
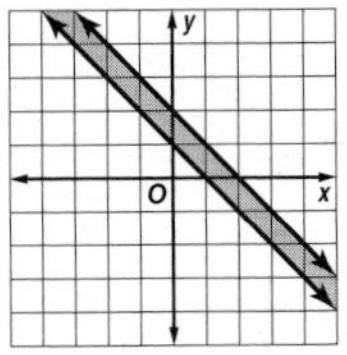

29.
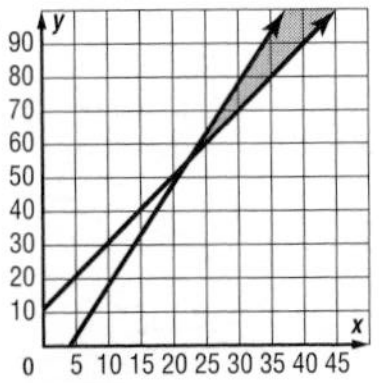

31.
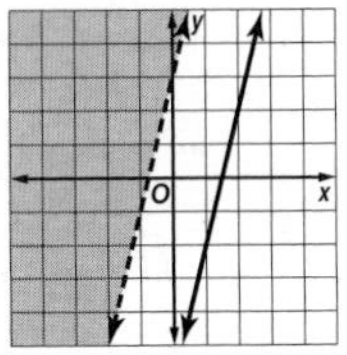

33.
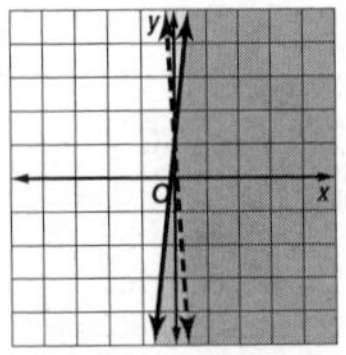

35.
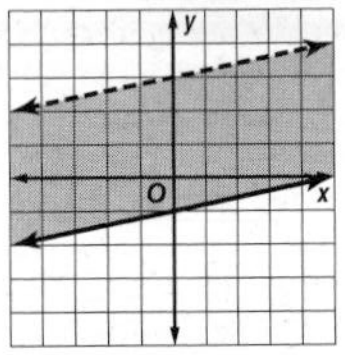

37a. Let x be the number of hours she works for a photographer and y be the number of hours she works coaching.
$x + y \leq 20$
$15x + 10y \geq 90$

b. Graph both inequalities on the same grid. $x + y \leq 20$ and $15x + 10y \geq 90$ have solid lines.
The solution is the intersection of the shading.

Earnings

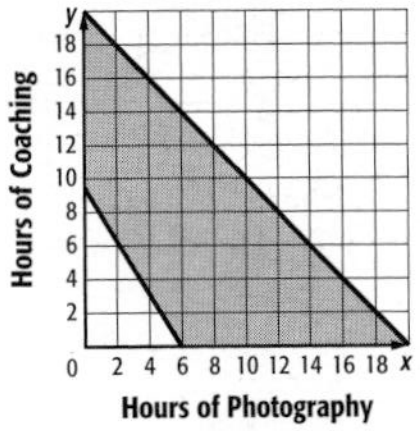

c. Two ordered pairs that are in the shaded area are (6, 10) and (8, 10). This means she could work for the photographer for 6 hours and coach for 10 or work for the photographer for 8 hours and coach for 10.

d. (2, 2) is not a solution because it does not fall in the shaded region. She would not earn enough money.

39. Sometimes; sample answer: $y > 3, y < -3$ will have no solution, but $y > -3, y < 3$ will have solutions. **41.** Sample answer: $3x - y < -4$

43. Sample answer: The yellow region represents the beats per minute below the target heart rate. The blue region represents the beats per minute above the target heart rate. The green region represents the beats per minute within the target heart rate. Shading in different colors clearly shows the overlapping solution set of the system of inequalities. **45.** D **47.** A **49.** (−3, −3)

51. (−2, 8) **53.** (6, 7) **55.** $\begin{bmatrix} 1 & -4 & 5 \\ 3 & -6 & 0 \\ 1 & -5 & 1 \end{bmatrix}$

57. $\begin{bmatrix} 7 & 14 & 7 \\ -3 & 4 & -6 \\ 3 & -1 & 13 \end{bmatrix}$ **59.** $\begin{bmatrix} -6 & -18 & -2 \\ 6 & -10 & 6 \\ -2 & -4 & -12 \end{bmatrix}$

61.
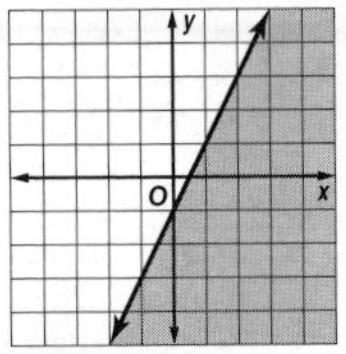

63.
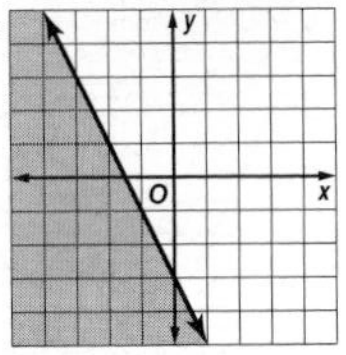

65. 16

Pages 388–392 Study Guide and Review

1. true **3.** false; dependent **5.** true **7.** false; element **9.** true

11.
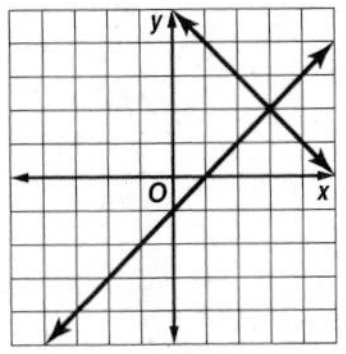
one; (3, 2)

13.
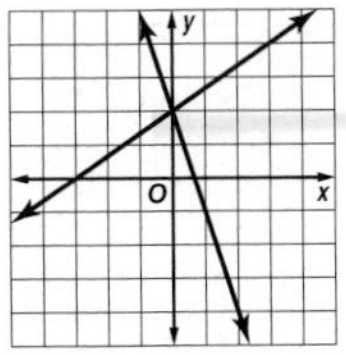
one; (0, 2)

15.
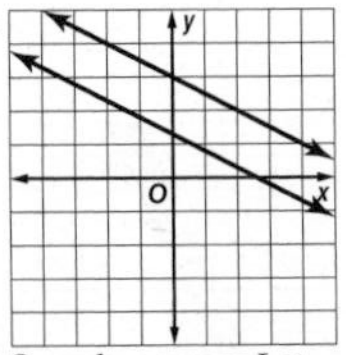
no solution

17. Sample answer: Let x be one number and y the other number; $x + y = 14$; $x - y = 4$; (9, 5) **19.** (2, −10) **21.** (2, −6) **23.** (−3, 4) **25.** (9, 4) **27.** (4, −2) **29.** $\left(\frac{1}{2}, 6\right)$ **31.** (−3, 5) **33.** Sample answer: Let f be the first type of card and let c be the second type of card; $f + c = 24$, $f + 3c = 50$; 11, $1 cards and 13, $3 cards. **35.** (5, 7) **37.** (2, 5) **39.** (6, −1) **41.** (1, −2) **43.** (2, −6) **45.** (24, −4) **47.** (−2, 1) **49.** (2, 5) **51.** Sample answer: Let d represent the dimes and let q represent the quarters; $d + q = 25$, $0.10d + 0.25q = 4$; 15 dimes, 10 quarters **53.** $\begin{bmatrix} -1 & -4 & 7 \\ -14 & 0 & -10 \end{bmatrix}$ **55.** 176 votes

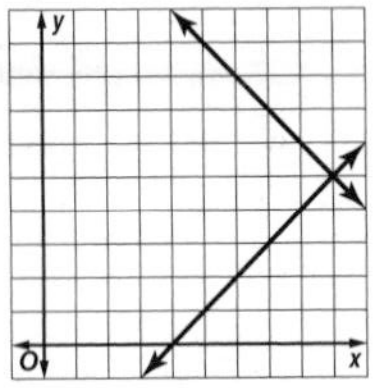

57. (3, −2) **59.** (−4, −2) **61.** (3, −2) **63.** (3, −7) **65.** (9, 1)

67.
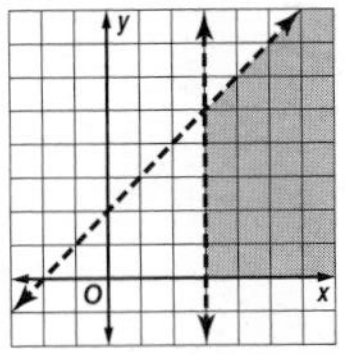

69.
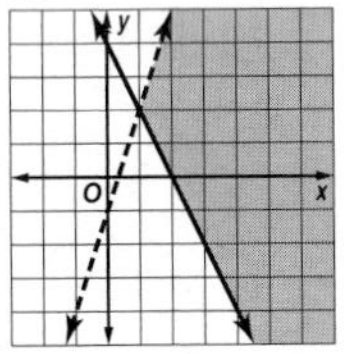

71.

Jobs

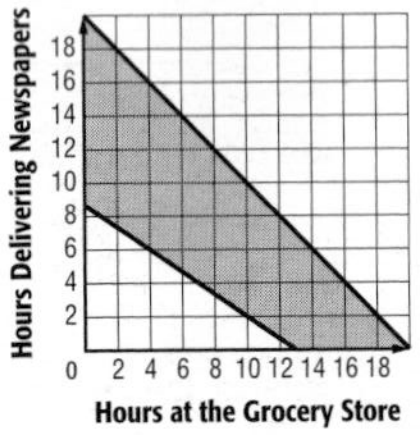

Chapter 7 Nonlinear Expressions, Equations, and Functions

Page 399 *Get Ready*

1. 4^5 **3.** 6^2 **5.** b^6 **7.** $\left(\frac{1}{3}\right)^8$ or $\frac{1}{3^8}$ **9.** 8 **11.** 27
13. $\frac{4}{9}$ **15.** $\frac{1}{32}$ **17.** 105 cm^3

Pages 404–407 *Lesson 7-1*

1. Yes; constants are monomials. **3.** No; there is a variable in the denominator. **5.** Yes; this is a product of a number and variables. **7.** k^4

9 $2q^2(9q^4) = (2 \cdot 9)(q^2 \cdot q^4)$
$= 18q^{2+4}$
$= 18q^6$

11. 3^8 or 6561 **13.** $16a^8b^{18}c^2$ **15.** $81p^{20}t^{24}$ **17.** $800x^8y^{12}z^4$ **19.** $-18g^7h^3j^{10}$ **21.** Yes; constants are monomials. **23.** No; there is addition and more than one term. **25.** Yes; this can be written as the product of a number and a variable.

27 $(q^2)(2q^4) = 2(q^2 \cdot q^4)$
$= 2q^{2+4}$
$= 2q^6$

29. $9w^8x^{12}$ **31.** $7b^{14}c^8d^6$ **33.** $j^{20}k^{28}$ **35.** 28 *or* 256 **37.** $4096r^{12}t^6$ **39.** $20c^5d^5$ **41.** $16a^{21}$ **43.** $512g^{27}h^{18}$ **45.** $294p^{27}r^{19}$ **47.** $30a^5b^7c^6$ **49.** $0.25x^6$ **51.** $-\frac{27}{64}c^3$ **53.** $-9x^3y^9$ **55.** $2,985,984r^{28}w^{32}$ **57a.** $0.12c$ **57b.** \$280 **59.** $15x^7$

61 **a.** $V = \pi r^2 h$
$= \pi(2p^3)^2(4p^3)$
$= \pi(22)(p^3)^2(4p^3)$
$= \pi(4)(p^6)(4p^3)$
$= \pi(4 \cdot 4)(p^6 \cdot p^3)$
$= \pi(16)(p^{6+3})$
$= 16\pi p^9$

b.

radius	height	Volume
$4p$	p^7	$16\pi p^9$
$4p^2$	p^5	$16\pi p^9$
$2p^3$	$4p^3$	$16\pi p^9$
$2p^4$	$4p$	$16\pi p^9$
$2p$	$4p^7$	$16\pi p^9$

c. If the height of the container is doubled, the volume of the container is doubled. So, the volume is $32\pi p^9$

63a.

Power	3^4	3^3	3^3	3^1	3^0	3^{-1}	3^{-3}	3^{-3}	3^{-4}
Value	81	27	9	3	1	$\frac{1}{3}$	$\frac{1}{9}$	$\frac{1}{27}$	$\frac{1}{81}$

63b. 1 and $\frac{1}{5}$ **63c.** $\frac{1}{a^n}$ **63d.** Any nonzero number raised to the zero power is 1.

65a.

Equation	Related Expression	Power of x	Linear or Nonlinear
$y = x$	x	1	linear
$y = x^2$	x^2	2	nonlinear
$y = x^3$	x^3	3	nonlinear

65b.

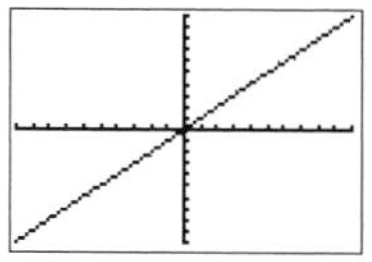

[−10, 10] scl: 1 by [−10, 10] scl: 1

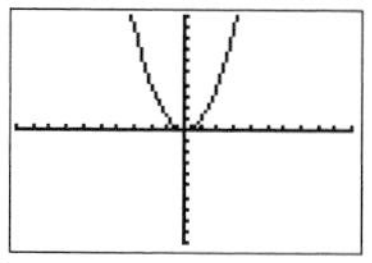

[−10, 10] scl: 1 by [−10, 10] scl: 1

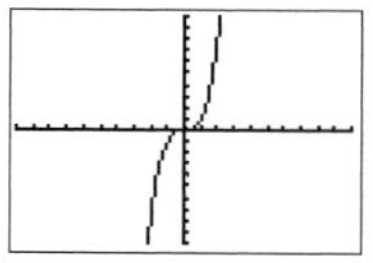

[−10, 10] scl: 1 by [−10, 10] scl: 1

65c. See chart for 65a. **65d.** If the power of x is 1, the equation or its related expression is linear. Otherwise, it is nonlinear. **67.** Sample answer: The area of a circle or $A = \pi r^2$, where r is the radius, can be used to find the area of any circle. The area of a rectangle or $A = w \times \ell$, where w is the width and ℓ is the length, can be used to find the area of any rectangle. **69.** F **71.** The x-intercept does not change.

73.

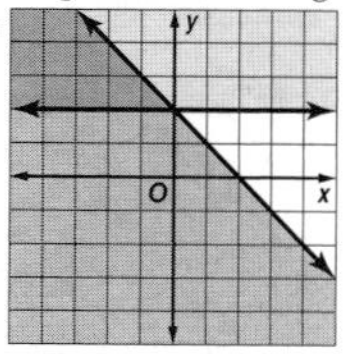

75.

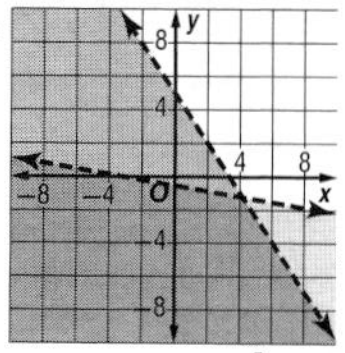

77. impossible **79.** $\begin{bmatrix} -2 & -5 & -16 \\ 11 & -1 & 9 \\ 18 & -3 & 12 \end{bmatrix}$ **81.** 8
83. −7.05 **85.** 13

Pages 412–415 *Lesson 7-2*

1. t^3u^3

3 $\frac{m^6r^5p^3}{m^5r^2p^3} = \left(\frac{m^6}{m^5}\right)\left(\frac{r^5}{r^2}\right)\left(\frac{p^3}{p^3}\right)$
$= m^{6-5}r^{5-2}p^{3-3}$
$= m^1r^3p^0$
$= mr^3$

5. ghm **7.** xyz **9.** $\frac{4a^6b^{10}}{9}$ **11.** $\frac{32c^{15}d^{25}}{3125g^{10}}$ **13.** 1

15. $\frac{g^2h^4}{f^3}$ **17.** $\frac{a^5c^{13}}{3b^9}$ **19.** m^2p **21.** $\frac{r^4p^2}{4m^3t^4}$ **23.** $\frac{9x^2y^8}{25z^4}$

25. $\frac{p^6t^{21}}{1000}$ **27.** a^2b^7c

29 $\left(\frac{2r^3t^6}{5u^9}\right)^4 = \frac{2^4(r^3)^4(t^6)^4}{5^4(u^9)^4}$
$= \frac{16r^{12}t^{24}}{625u^{36}}$

31. 1 **33.** $\frac{p^4r^2}{t^3}$ **35.** $\frac{-f}{4}$ **37.** k^2mp^2 **39.** $\frac{3t^7}{u^6v^2}$ **41.** $\frac{r^3}{t^2x^{10}}$ **43.** 10^6; 10^8; about 10^2 or 100 times as many users as hosts **45.** $-\frac{w^9}{3}$ **47.** $1600k^{13}$ **49.** $\frac{5q}{r^6t^3}$ **51.** $\frac{4g^{12}}{h^4}$ **53.** $\frac{4x^8y^4}{z^6}$ **55.** $\frac{16z^2}{y^8}$ **57.** 100

59 **a.** the probability is $\frac{1}{6}$ multiplied d times, or $\left(\frac{1}{6}\right)^d$.

b. $\left(\frac{1}{6}\right)^d = (6^{-1})^d$
$= 6^{-d}$

61. Sometimes; sample answer: The equation is true when $x = 0$, $y = 2$, and $z = 3$, but it is false when $x = 1$, $y = 2$, and $z = 3$.

63. $\frac{1}{x^n} = \frac{x^0}{x^n} = x^{0-n} = x^{-n}$ **65.** The Quotient of Powers Property is used when dividing two powers with the same base. The exponents are subtracted. The Power of a Quotient Property is used to find the power of a quotient. You find the power of the numerator and the power of the denominator. **67.** J **69.** B

71.

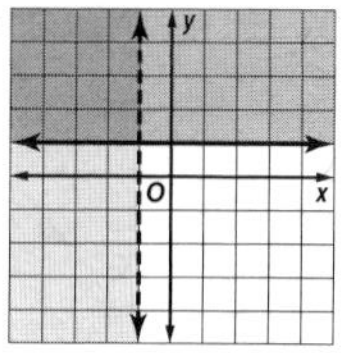

73.

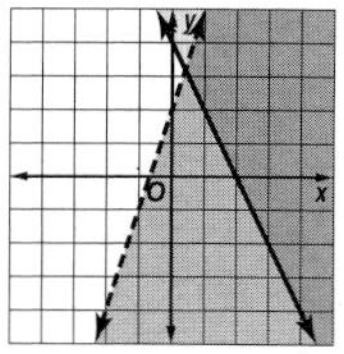

75. $h > 5$ **77.** $u \leq 35$ **79.** $n \geq -2$ **81.** 87 **83.** 121 **85.** 10,000 **87.** 125 **89.** 4096

Pages 419–422 *Lesson 7-3*

1. 1.85×10^8 **3.** 5.64×10^{-4} **5.** 1.3×10^{10} **7.** 19,800,000 **9.** 0.00000003405 **11.** 1.74×10^{15}; 1,740,000,000,000,000 **13.** 4.7138×10^{-2}; 0.047138 **15.** 4.5×10^3; 4,500 **17.** 8.5×10^{-13}; 0.00000000000085 **19a.** 0.01, 0.000001 **19b.** 1×10^{-2}, 1×10^{-6} **19c.** 0.00000000001; 1×10^{-11}

21 58,600,000
Step 1: 58,600,000 ⟶ 5.8600000
Step 2: The decimal point moved 7 places to the left, so $n = 7$.
Step 3: 58,600,000 = 5.8600000 × 10^7
Step 4: 5.86×10^7

23. 1.3×10^{-6} **25.** 7.09×10^{-10} **27.** 5.5×10^9 **29.** 94,000,000 **31.** 0.0005 **33.** 0.00000622 **35.** 11,000,000 **37.** 8×10^7; 80,000,000

39 $(6.5 \times 10^7)(7.2 \times 10^{-2}) = (6.5 \times 7.2)(10^7 \times 10^{-2})$
$= 46.8 \times 10^5$
$= (4.68 \times 10^1) \times 10^5$
$= 4.68 \times 10^6$
$= 4,680,000$

41. 2.2×10^7; 22,000,000 **43.** 1.7889×10^{-6}; 0.0000017889 **45.** 6.89×10^5; 689,000 **47.** 4.7008×10^3; 4700.8 **49.** 5×10^{-6}; 0.000005 **51.** 2.448×10^{-10}; 0.0000000002448 **53.** 2.205×10^{-5}; 0.00002205 **55.** 2.325×10^5; 232,500 **57.** 6.1×10^{-8}; 0.000000061 **59.** 1.935×10^2; 193.5 **61.** 9×10^{-4}; 0.0009 **63.** 3×10^5

65.

Time	Kilometers Traveled
1 day	2.592×10^{10}
1 week	1.8144×10^{11}
1 month	7.776×10^{11}
1 year	9.4608×10^{12}

67 $(6.623 \times 10^9) \div (1.483 \times 10^8) = (6.623 \div 1.483) \times (10^9 \div 10^8)$
$\approx 4.47 \times 10^1$
There are about 44.7 persons per square kilometer.

69a. corn: 9.29×10^7, 92,900,000; soybeans: 6.41×10^7, 64,100,000; cotton: 1.11×10^7, 11,100,000

69b. about 1.4493×100; 1.4493 **69c.** about 8.3694×10^0; 8.3694 **71.** Pete is correct; Syreeta moved the decimal point in the wrong direction. **73.** Always; if the numbers are $a \times 10^m$ and $b \times 10^n$ in scientific notation, then $1 \le a < 10$ and $1 \le b < 10$. So $1 \le ab < 100$. **75.** Sample answer: Divide the numbers to the left of the × symbols. Then divide the powers of 10. If necessary, rewrite the results in scientific notation. To convert that to standard form, check to see if the exponent is positive or negative. If positive, move the decimal point to the right, and if negative, to the left. The number of places to move the decimal point is the absolute value of the exponent. Fill in with zeros as needed.

77. H **79.** B **81.** 6^2 or 36 **83.** $\frac{81a^{16}b^{16}}{4096c^8}$ **85.** $\frac{n^6p^3}{8}$
87. $y = 3x - 1$ **89.** $y = -2x - 12$
91. $y = \frac{2}{3}x + 7$ **93.** $13u$
95. simplified **97.** $65 + 52a$

Pages 426–429 Lesson 7-4

1. yes; trinomial **3.** yes; monomial **5.** yes; binomial **7.** 0 **9.** 1
11 Step 1: Find the degree of each term.
$12 \to 0$
$-7q^2t \to 2 + 1 = 3$
$8r \to 1$
Step 2: The degree of the polynomial is the highest degree in the polynomial, 3
13. 4 **15.** $2x^5 + 3x - 12$; 2 **17.** $-5z^4 - 2z^2 + 4z$; -5 **19a.** 3300 students **19b.** 6000 students
21. yes; monomial **23.** No; the exponent is a variable. **25.** yes; binomial **27.** 1 **29.** 3 **31.** 7
33. $7y^3 + 8y$; 7
35 Step 1: Find the degree of each term.
$-4d^4 \to 4$
$1 \to 0$
$-d^2 \to 2$
Step 2: Write the terms in descending order:
$-4d^4 - d^2 + 1$
The leading coefficient is -4
37. $-r^3 + r + 2$; -1 **39.** $-b^6 - 9b^2 + 10b$; -1
41. quadratic trinomial **43.** quartic binomial
45. quintic polynomial **47a.** $\frac{1}{3}\pi r^2h$ **47b.** about 9.42 in³ **47c.** about 6.7 in. **49.** $6x^2$
51 **a.** Sample answer:

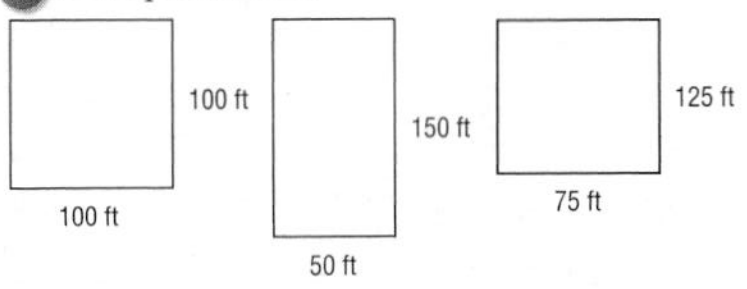

b.

Rectangle	Length	Width	Area
1	100 ft	100 ft	10,000 ft²
2	50 ft	150 ft	7500 ft²
3	75 ft	125 ft	9375 ft²
4	x ft	(200 – x) ft	x(200 – x) ft²

c.

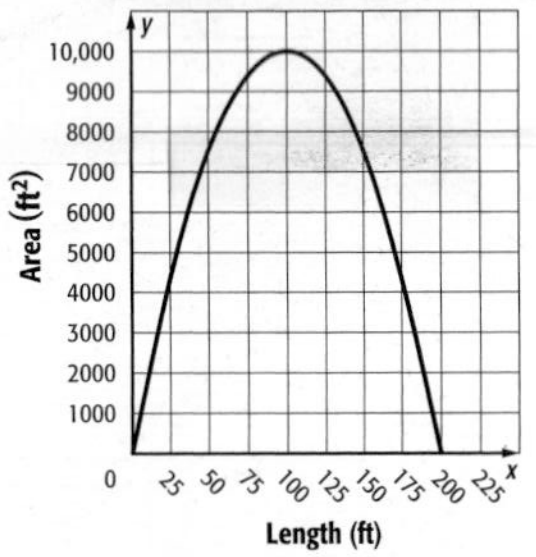

The highest point of the graph is (100, 10,000), so largest area possible is 10,000 ft².
d. The length and the width of the rectangle must be 100 feet each to have the largest area.
53. $2x + 1$, where x is an integer **55.** Sample answer: $x^3 - x^2 + 1$ **57.** D **59.** 500 **61.** 0.0000006
63. 810,000 **65.** 0.000000132 **67.** $\frac{1}{a^4}$ **69.** 1
71. $\frac{p^8}{k^4m^2}$ **73.** 6 two-seat, 11 four-seat
75. $12t^2 - 3t$ **77.** simplified **79.** $\frac{5u}{2} + u^2$

Pages 435–438 Lesson 7-5

1. $4x^3 + 5$ **3.** $-a^2 + 6a - 3$ **5.** $-8z^3 - 3z^2 - 2z + 13$
7 $(2c^2 + 6c + 4) + (5c^2 - 7)$
$= [2c^2 + 5c^2] + 6c + [4 + (-7)]$
$= 7c^2 + 6c + (-3)$
$= 7c^2 + 6c - 3$
9a. $D = 6n + 14$ **9b.** 116,000 students
9c. 301,000 student
11 $(2x + 3x^2) - (7 - 8x^2)$
$= (2x + 3x^2) + (-7 + 8x^2)$
$= [3x^2 + 8x^2] + 2x + (-7)$
$= 11x^2 + 2x - 7$
13. $2z^2 + z - 11$ **15.** $-2b^2 + 2a + 9$ **17.** $7x^2 - 2xy - 7y$ **19.** $3x^2 - rxt - 8r^2x - 6rx^2$ **21.** $-cd^2 + 6cd - 10$
23. $9x + 4y - 17z$ **25.** $2c^2 - c + 8$ **27.** $12x + 1\frac{1}{4}$
29. $4x$ **31.** $6x + 16y$ **33a.** $182 - 6x$ **33b.** 39, 97, 44
35 **a.** Words: $15 plus $0.15 per mile
Expression: 15 + 0.15m
The expression is $15 + 0.15m$.
b. $15 + 0.15m = 15 + 0.15(145)$
$= 15 + 21.75$
$= 36.75$
The cost is $36.75.
c. $4(15 + 0.15m) = 4[15 + 0.15(105)]$
$= 4(15 + 15.75)$
$= 4(30.75)$
$= 123$
The cost is $123.
d. $7(15 + 0.15m) = 7[15 + 0.15(220)]$
$= 7(15 + 33)$
$= 7(48)$
$= 336$
The cost is $336.
37. Sample answer: $3x^3 - 8x + 9$, $x^3 - x + 1$
39. Sample answer: $(2x - 3) - (4x - 3) = -2x$ but $(4x - 3) - (2x - 3) = 2x$ **41.** Sample answer: To add polynomials in a horizontal format, you combine like terms. For the vertical format, you write the polynomials in standard form, align like terms in columns, and combine like terms. To subtract polynomials in a horizontal format you find the additive inverse of the polynomial you are subtracting, and then combine like terms. For the vertical format you write the polynomials in standard form, align like terms in columns, and subtract by adding the additive inverse. **43.** $8x + 12$ units **45.** C **47.** 1 **49.** 5 **51.** 3 **53.** 5
55. $80,000 **57.** no **59.** no **61.** yes; 0.5 **63.** $-2n^8$
65. $-40u^5z^9$ **67.** 64 **69.** $288x^8y^{10}z^6$

Pages 441–444 Lesson 7-6

1. $-15w^3 + 10w^2 - 20w$ **3.** $32k^2m^4 + 8k^3m^3 + 20k^2m^2$
5 $2ab(7a^4b^2 + a^5b - 2a) = 2ab(7a^4b^2) + 2ab(a^5b) + 2ab(-2a)$
$= 14a^5b^3 + 2a^6b^2 + (-4a^2b)$
$= 14a^5b^3 + 2a^6b^2 - 4a^2b$
7. $4t^3 + 15t^2 - 8t + 4$ **9.** $-5d^4c^2 + 8d^2c^2 - 4d^3c + dc^4$ **11.** 20 **13.** $-\frac{20}{9}$ **15.** 20 **17.** 1 **19.** $f^3 + 2f^2 + 25f$ **21.** $10j^5 - 30j^4 + 4j^3 + 4j^2$ **23.** $8t^5u^3 - 40t^4u^5 + 8t^3u$ **25.** $-8a^3 + 20a^2 + 4a - 12$ **27.** $-9g^3 + 21g^2 + 12$ **29.** $8n^4p^2 + 12n^2p^2 + 20n^2 - 8np^3 + 12p^2$
31 $7(t^2 + 5t - 9) + t = t(7t - 2) + 13$
$7t^2 + 35t - 63 + t = 7t^2 - 2t + 13$
$7t^2 + 36t - 63 = 7t^2 - 2t + 13$
$36t - 63 = -2t + 13$
$38t = 76$
$t = 2$
33. $\frac{43}{6}$ **35.** $\frac{30}{43}$ **37.** $20np^4 + 6n^3p^3 - 8np^2$
39. $-q^3w^3 - 35q^2w^4 + 8q^2w^2 - 27qw$ **41a.** 53.50 − 0.25h **41b.** $50.50
43 **a.** $A = \ell w$
$= (1.5x + 24)x$
$= 1.5x^2 + 24x$
b. $x(x - 9) = x^2 - 9x$
c. $2(2.5x) = 2(2.5)(36)$
$= 180$ ft
$2(x + 6) = 2(36 + 6)$
$= 2(42)$
$= 84$ ft
Perimeter = 180 + 84 or 264 ft
Number of stepping stones = 264 ÷ 3 or 88 stones
45. Ted; Pearl used the Distributive Property incorrectly. **47.** $8x^2y^{-2} + 24x^{-10}y^8 - 16x^{-3}$
49. Sample answer: $3n$, $4n + 1$; $12n^2 + 3n$ **51.** B
53. A **55.** $-3x^2 + 1$ **57.** $-9a^2 + 4a + 7$ **59.** $6ab + 2a + 4b$ **61.** 1 **63.** 2 **65.** 5 **67.** $y - 3{,}600{,}000 = 300{,}000(x - 1990)$; 9,600,000 people **69.** $f(x) = -0.5x$ **71.** $6y^3$ **73.** $15z^7 - 6z^4$ **75.** $-8p^5 + 10p^{10}$

Pages 450–452 Lesson 7-7

1. $x^2 + 7x + 10$ **3.** $b^2 - 4b - 21$ **5.** $16h^2 - 26h + 3$ **7.** $4x^2 + 72x + 320$ **9.** $16y^4 + 28y^3 - 4y^2 - 21y - 6$ **11.** $10n^4 + 11n^3 - 52n^2 - 12n + 48$
13. $2g^2 + 15g - 50$
15 $(4x + 1)(6x + 3) = 4x(6x) + 4x(3) + 1(6x) + 1(3)$
$= 24x^2 + 12x + 6x + 3$
$= 24x^2 + 18x + 3$
17. $24d^2 - 62d + 35$ **19.** $49n^2 - 84n + 36$
21. $25r^2 - 49$ **23.** $33z^2 + 7yz - 10y^2$ **25.** $2y^3 - 17y^2 + 37y - 22$ **27.** $m^4 + 2m^3 - 34m^2 + 43m - 12$
29. $6b^5 - 3b^4 - 35b^3 - 10b^2 + 43b + 63$ **31.** $2m^3 + 5m^2 - 4$ **33.** $4\pi x^2 + 12\pi x + 9\pi - 3x^2 - 5x - 2$
35 **a.** $A = \ell w$
$= (3y + 4)(6y - 5)$
$= 3y(6y) + 3y(-5) + 4(6y) + 4(-5)$
$= 18y^2 - 15y + 24y - 20$
$= 18y^2 + 9y - 20$
b. $3y + 4 = 31$
$3y = 27$
$y = 9$
So, the width is $6y - 5 = 6(9) - 5$
$= 54 - 5$
$= 49$
$A = \ell w$
$= (31)(49)$
$= 1519$ ft²
37. $a^2 - 4ab + 4b^2$ **39.** $x^2 - 10xy + 25y^2$
41. $125g^3 + 150g^2h + 60gh^2 + 8h^3$ **43a.** $x > 4$; If $x = 4$, the width of the rectangular sandbox would be zero and if $x < 4$ the width of the rectangular sandbox would be negative. **43b.** square **43c.** 4 ft²
45. Always; you can group two adjacent terms of a trinomial, treat the trinomial as the sum of two quantities, and apply the FOIL method. For example, $(2x + 3)(x^2 + 5x + 7) = (2x + 3)[x^2 + (5x + 7)] = 2x(x^2) + 2x(5x + 7) + 3(x^2) + 3(5x + 7)$. Then use the Distributive Property and simplify. **47.** Sample answer: $x - 1$, $x^2 - x - 1$. $(x - 1)(x^2 - x - 1) = x^3 - 2x^2 + 1$ **49.** The Distributive Property can be used with a vertical or horizontal format by

For Homework Help, go to Hotmath.com

distributing, multiplying, and combining like terms. The FOIL method is used with a horizontal format. You multiply the first, outer, inner, and last terms of the binomials and then combine like terms. A rectangular method can also be used by writing the terms of the polynomials along the top and left side of a rectangle and then multiplying the terms and combining like terms.

51. F **53.** $\frac{3}{2}$ **55.** $4a^2 + 5$ **57.** $3n^3 - 6n^2 + 10$
59. $4b + c + 2$ **61.** $-7m^3 - 3m^2 - m + 17$
63. $-56t^{12}$ **65.** $50y^6 - 27y^9$

Pages 455–457 Lesson 7-8

1. $x^2 + 10x + 25$
3 $(2x + 7y)^2 = (2x)^2 + 2(2x)(7y) + (7y)^2$
$= 4x^2 + 28xy + 49y^2$
5. $g^2 - 8gh + 16h^2$ **7a.** $0.5Dy + 0.5y^2$ **7b.** 50%
9. $x^2 - 25$ **11.** $81t^2 - 36$ **13.** $b^2 - 12b + 36$
15. $x^2 + 12x + 36$ **17.** $81 - 36y + 4y^2$ **19.** $25t^2 - 20t + 4$ **21a.** $(T + t)^2 = T^2 + 2Tt + t^2$
21b. TT: 25%; Tt: 50%; tt: 25%
23 $(b + 7)(b - 7) = b^2 - (7)^2$
$= b^2 - 49$
25. $16 - x^2$ **27.** $9a^4 - 49b^2$ **29.** $64 - 160a + 100a^2$ **31.** $9t^2 - 144$ **33.** $9q^2 - 30qr + 25r^2$
35. $g^2 + 10gh + 25h^2$ **37.** $9a^8 - b^2$ **39.** $64a^4 - 81b^6$
41. $\frac{4}{25}y^2 - \frac{16}{5}y + 16$ **43.** $4m^3 + 16m^2 - 9m - 36$
45. $2x^2 + 2x + 5$ **47.** $6x + 3$ **49.** $c^3 + 3c^2d + 3cd^2 + d^3$ **51.** $f^3 + f^2g - fg^2 - g^3$
53. $n^3 - n^2p - np^2 + p^3$
55 a. $A = 3.14(r + 9)^2$
$= 3.14(r^2 + 18r + 81)$
$\approx (3.14r^2 + 56.52r + 254.34)\text{ft}^2$
b. $38^2 - (3.14r^2 + 56.52r + 254.34)$
$= 1444 - 3.14r^2 - 56.52r - 254.34$
$\approx (1189.66 - 3.14r^2 - 56.52r)\text{ft}^2$

57. Sample answer: $(2c + d)(2c - d)$; The product of these binomials is a difference of two squares and does not have a middle term. The other three do.
59. 81 **61.** Sample answer: To find the square of a sum, apply the FOIL method or apply the pattern. The square of the sum of two quantities is the first quantity squared plus two times the product of the two quantities plus the second quantity squared. The square of the difference of two quantities is the first quantity squared minus two times the product of the two quantities plus the second quantity squared. The product of the sum and difference of two quantities is the square of the first quantity minus the square of the second quantity. **63.** D **65.** C **67.** $2c^2 + 5c - 3$
69. $8h^2 - 34h + 21$ **71.** $40m^2 + 47m + 12$
73. $3c^2 - 2c$ **75.** $-13d^2 - 18d$ **77.** $19p^2 - 18p$
79. (2, 0) **81.** $t < 18$ or $t > 22$ **83.** $y = \frac{1}{5}x + 6$
85. 15 lb **87.** $2^3 \cdot 3 \cdot 5$ **89.** $3 \cdot 5 \cdot 11$

Pages 459–462 Chapter 7 Study Guide and Review

1. binomial **3.** trinomial **5.** power of a power
7. scientific notation **9.** polynomial **11.** x^9
13. $20a^6b^6$ **15.** $64r^{18}t^6$ **17.** $8x^{15}$ **19.** $45\pi x^4$
21. $\left(\frac{27x^3y^9}{8z^3}\right)$ **23.** $\frac{c^6}{a^3}$ **25.** x^6 **27.** $\frac{6}{yx^3}$ **29.** 2.3×10^6
31. about 9.1×10^{-2} **33.** $-x^4 + 1$ **35.** $3x^5 + x^3 - 2x^2 + 6x - 2$ **37.** $-2x^3 - 3$ **39.** $-x^2 - x + 6$
41. $4x^2 + 4x + 8$ **43.** 1 **45.** 2 **47.** $x^2 + 4x - 21$
49. $6r^2 + rt - 35t^2$ **51.** $10x^2 + 7x - 12$
53. $9x^2 - 12x + 4$ **55.** $4x^2 - 9$ **57.** $9m^2 - 4$

Chapter 8 Factoring and Quadratic Equations

Page 469 Chapter 8 Get Ready

1. $a(a) + a(5)$; $a^2 + 5a$ **3.** $n(n) + n(-3n^2) + n(2)$; $n^2 - 3n^3 + 2n$ **5.** $5(9 + 3 + 6)$; \$90 **7.** $x^2 + 3x - 4$
9. $3x^2 + 11x - 20$ **11.** $54a^2 - 12ab - 2b^2$ **13.** $9 - 6a + a^2$ **15.** $9x^2 - 12xy + 4y^2$ **17.** $x^2 - 36\text{ in}^2$

Pages 472–474 Lesson 8-1

1. $2 \cdot 2 \cdot 3 \cdot g \cdot g \cdot h \cdot h \cdot h \cdot h$ **3.** $-1 \cdot 17 \cdot x \cdot x \cdot x \cdot y \cdot y \cdot z$ **5.** $24cd$ **7.** xy^3 **9.** 1 in.
11 $-35a^3c^2 = -1 \cdot 35a^3c^2$
$= -1 \cdot 5 \cdot 7 \cdot a \cdot a \cdot a \cdot c \cdot c$
13. $3 \cdot 3 \cdot 3 \cdot 3 \cdot n \cdot n \cdot n \cdot n \cdot n \cdot p$ **15.** $11 \cdot 11 \cdot a \cdot b \cdot c \cdot c \cdot c$ **17.** $2z$ **19.** $4r$ **21.** $5t$ **23.** height 1 in., base 56 in.; height 2 in., base 28 in.; height 4 in., base 14 in.; height 28 in., base 2 in.; height 14 in., base 4 in.; height 7 in., base 8 in.; height 56 in., base 1 in.; height 8 in., base 7 in.
25 $80 = 5 \cdot 16, 8 \cdot 10, 10 \cdot 8, 16 \cdot 5, 20 \cdot 4$
So, the DVDs can be arranged as 5 DVDs on 16 shelves, 8 DVDs on 10 shelves, 10 DVDs on 8 shelves, 16 DVDs on 5 shelves, 20 DVDs on 4 shelves.
27. 11, 13; 17, 19; 29, 31; 41, 43; 59, 61 **29.** 22 and 33 **31.** False; sample answer: The monomials $99x^5y^{11}z^{30}$ and $101abc$ have a GCF of 1. **33.** Sample answer: $6y^3$, $12y^4$, $18y^5$; 6 is the greatest numerical factor that all three monomials have in common, and y^3 is the highest power of y that they all have in common. **35.** A **37.** B **39.** $a^2 - 8a + 16$
41. $z^2 - 10z + 25$ **43.** $y^2 + 4y + 4$ **45.** $2m^2 + 5m - 12$ **47.** $t^2 + 11t + 18$ **49.** $p^2 + 6pq + 9q^2$
51. (2, 7) **53.** (−4, 3) **55.** $8x - 14$ **57.** $-6h^2 + h$
59. $5(y - 2)$

Pages 479–482 Lesson 8-2

1. $3(7b - 5a)$ **3.** $gh(10gh + 9h - g)$
5 $np + 2n + 8p + 16 = (np + 2n) + (8p + 16)$
$= n(p + 2) + 8(p + 2)$
$= (n + 8)(p + 2)$
7. $(b + 5)(3c - 2)$ **9.** 0, −10 **11.** 0, $\frac{3}{4}$

13a. 0, 2.08125 **13b.** 17.3 ft, 2.6 ft **15.** $8(2t - 5y)$
17. $2k(k + 2)$ **19.** $2ab(2ab + a - 5b)$
21 $fg - 5g + 4f - 20 = (fg - 5g) + (4f - 20)$
$= g(f - 5) + 4(f - 5)$
$= (g + 4)(f - 5)$
23. $(h + 5)(j - 2)$ **25.** $(9q - 10)(5p - 3)$
27. $(3d - 5)(t - 7)$ **29.** $(3t - 5)(7h - 1)$
31. $(r - 5)(5b + 2)$ **33.** $gf(5f + g + 15)$
35. $3cd(9d - 6cd + 1)$ **37.** $2(8u - 15)(3t + 2)$
39. 0, 3 **41.** $-\frac{1}{2}$, −2 **43.** 0, −3 **45a.** ab
45b. $(a + 6)(b + 6)$ **45c.** $6(a + b + 6)$
47a.

x	y
0	0
1	9
2	12
3	9
4	0

47b.
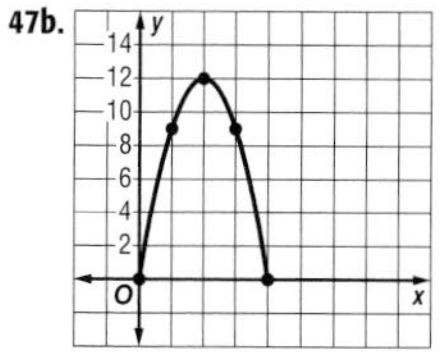

47c. 12 ft
49 $h = 64t - 16t^2$
$0 = 64t - 16t^2$
$0 = 16t(4 - t)$
$16t = 0$ or $4 - t = 0$
$t = 0$ or $4 = t$
So, the arrow hits the ground after 4 seconds.
51a. 3 and −2
51b.

x^2	$+3x$
$-2x$	-6

51c.

	x	$+3$
x	x^2	$+3x$
-2	$-2x$	-6

$(x + 3)(x - 2)$

51d. Sample answer: Place x^2 in the top left-hand corner and place −40 in the lower right-hand corner. Then determine which two factors have a product of −40 and a sum of −3. Then place these factors in the box. Then find the factor of each row and column. The factors will be listed on the very top and far left of the box. **53.** If $a = 0$ and $b = 0$, then all real numbers are solutions. If $a \neq 0$, then the solutions are $-\frac{b}{a}$ and $\frac{b}{a}$. **55.** Sample answer: $a = 0$ or $a = b$ for any real values of a and b. **57.** D
59. 350 **61.** 5 **63.** $8x$ **65.** $8c^2d$ **67.** $0.5Bb + 0.5b^2$; $\frac{1}{2}$
69. p^7r^5 **71.** $81x^2y^{14}$ **73.** 16,777,216 **75.** $\{y \mid y > -11\}$ **77.** $\{k \mid k > -9\}$ **79.** $\{z \mid z \geq -48\}$

81. $a^2 + 7a + 10$ **83.** $z^2 - 9z + 8$ **85.** $x^2 - 13x + 42$

Pages 489–491 Lesson 8-3

1. $(x + 2)(x + 12)$ **3.** $(n + 7)(n - 3)$ **5.** −3, 7
7. 6, 9 **9.** −8, 9 **11.** 8 in. by 12 in. **13.** $(y - 9)(y - 8)$ **15.** $(n - 7)(n + 5)$ **17.** $(x - 2)(x - 20)$
19. $(m + 6)(m - 7)$
21 $y^2 + y = 20$
$y^2 + y - 20 = 0$
$(y + 5)(y - 4) = 0$
$y + 5 = 0$ or $y - 4 = 0$
$y = -5$ $y = 4$
23. −2, −9 **25.** 2, 16 **27.** −4, −14 **29.** 4, 12
31. $(x - 6)$ ft **33.** $(q + 2r)(q + 9r)$ **35.** $(x - y)(x - 5y)$
37 a. Sample answer: Let w represent the width of the swimming pool. So, the length of the pool is $w + 20$.
$A = \ell w$
$= (w + 20)w$
$525 = (w + 20)w$
b. $525 = (w + 20)w$
$525 = w^2 + 20w$
$0 = w^2 + 20w - 525$
$0 = (w + 35)(w - 15)$
$w + 35 = 0$ or $w - 15 = 0$
$w = -35$ $w = 15$
c. The solution of 15 means that the width is 15 feet and the length is 35 feet. The solution −35 does not make sense because length cannot be negative.
39. $4x - 26$ **41.** Charles; Jerome's answer once multiplied is $x^2 - 6x - 16$. The middle term should be positive. **43.** −15, −9, 9, 15 **45.** 4, 6
47. $x^2 + 19x - 20$; $(x - 1)(x + 20)$ **49.** Sample answer: Find factors m and n such that $m + n = b$ and $mn = c$. If b and c are positive, then m and n are positive. If b is negative and c is positive, then m and n are negative. When c is negative, m and n have different signs and the factor with the greater absolute value has the same sign as b.
51. 204 **53.** A **55.** $11x(1 + 4xy)$
57. $(2x + b)(a + 3c)$ **59.** $(x - y)(x - y)$
61. $\begin{bmatrix} 12 & -9 & 12 \\ 1 & -3 & -10 \end{bmatrix}$ **63.** impossible **65.** about 6 ft
67. $(3x - 4)(a - 2b)$

Pages 496–498 Lesson 8-4

1. $(3x + 2)(x + 5)$ **3.** prime **5.** $-\frac{3}{2}$, −3 **7.** $\frac{4}{3}$, 2
9a. 6 ft **9b.** 6 seconds
11 $2x^2 + 19x + 24$

factors of 48	sum of 19
3, 16	19

$2x^2 + 3x + 16x + 24 = (2x^2 + 3x) + (16x + 24)$

$= x(2x + 3) + 8(2x + 3)$
$= (x + 8)(2x + 3)$

13. $2(2x + 5)(x + 7)$ **15.** $(4x - 5)(x - 2)$ **17.** prime **19.** prime **21.** prime **23.** $\frac{3}{2}, -6$ **25.** $\frac{2}{3}, 8$ **27.** $-\frac{1}{3}, 2$ **29a.** $10 = -16t^2 + 20t + 6$ **29b.** 1 sec **29c.** Less; sample answer: It starts closer to the ground so the shot will not have as far to fall.

31 Words: 6 times the square of a number plus 11 times the number equals 2

Equation: $6 \cdot x^2 + 11 \cdot x = 2$
$6x^2 + 11x = 2$
$6x^2 + 11x - 2 = 0$

factors of −12	sum of 11
−1, 12	11

$6x^2 + 11x - 2 = 0$
$6x^2 - 1x + 12x - 2 = 0$
$(6x^2 - 1x) + (12x - 2) = 0$
$x(6x - 1) + 2(6x - 1) = 0$
$(x + 2)(6x - 1) = 0$
$x + 2 = 0$ or $6x - 1 = 0$
$x = -2$ $\quad 6x = 1$
$x = \frac{1}{6}$

The numbers are −2 and $\frac{1}{6}$.

33. $-(x + 2)(4x + 7)$ **35.** $-(2x - 7)(3x - 5)$ **37.** $-(3x - 4)(4x + 5)$ **39a.** a^2 and b^2 **39b.** $a^2 - b^2$ **39c.** width: $a - b$, length: $a + b$ **39d.** $(a - b)(a + b)$ **39e.** $(a - b)(a + b)$; the figure with area $a^2 - b^2$ and the rectangle with area $(a - b)(a + b)$ have the same area, so $a^2 - b^2 = (a - b)(a + b)$. **41.** $(12x + 20y)$ in.; The area of the square equals $(3x + 5y)(3x + 5y)$ in^2, so the length of one side is $(3x + 5y)$ in. The perimeter is $4(3x + 5y)$ or $(12x + 20y)$ in. **43.** Sample answer: $10x^2 + x - 3 = 0$; The polynomial factors into $(2x - 1)(5x + 3) = 0$, so the solutions are $\frac{1}{2}$ and $-\frac{3}{5}$. **45.** 6 **47.** J **49.** $(x - 2)(x - 7)$ **51.** $(x + 3)(x - 8)$ **53.** $(r + 8)(r - 5)$ **55.** {0, 9} **57.** {0, 2} **59.** {0, 4}

61. Green Paint

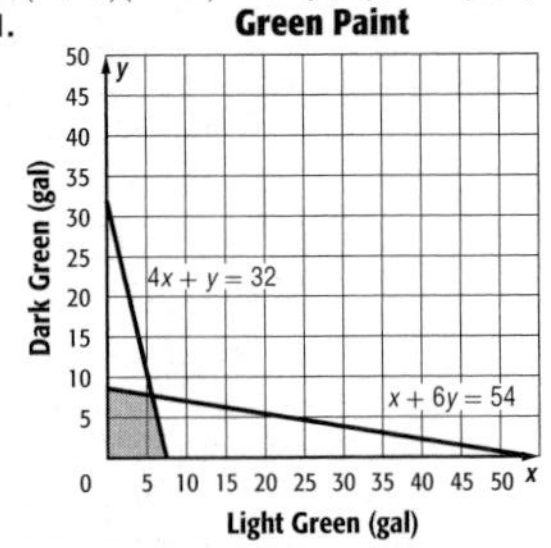

Sample answers: 2 light, 8 dark; 6 light, 8 dark; 7 light, 4 dark

63. $\{d \mid d \le 5 \text{ or } d > 7\}$

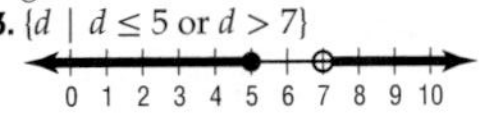

65. ∅

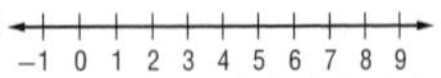

67. $\{y \mid 3 < y < 6\}$

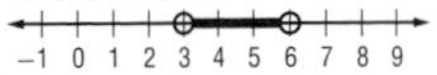

69. 4 **71.** 8 **73.** 11

Pages 501–504 Lesson 8-5

1. $(x + 3)(x - 3)$ **3.** $9(m + 4)(m - 4)$ **5.** $(u^2 + 9)(u + 3)(u - 3)$

7 $20r^4 - 45n^4 = 5(4r^4 - 9n^4)$
$= 5\left((2r^2)^2 - (3n^2)^2\right)$
$= 5(2r^2 + 3n^2)(2r^2 - 3n^2)$

9. $(c + 1)(c - 1)(2c + 3)$ **11.** $(t + 4)(t - 4)(3t + 2)$ **13.** 36 mph **15.** $(q + 11)(q - 11)$ **17.** $6(n^2 + 1)(n + 1)(n - 1)$ **19.** $(r + 3t)(r - 3t)$ **21.** $h(h + 10)(h - 10)$ **23.** $(x + 9)(x - 9)(2x - 1)$ **25.** $7(h^2 + p^2)(h + p)(h - p)$ **27.** $6k^2(h^2 + 3k)(h^2 - 3k)$ **29.** $(f + 8)(f - 8)(f + 2)$ **31.** $10q(q + 11)(q - 11)$ **33.** $p^3r(r + 1)(r - 1)(r^2 + 1)$ **35.** $(r + 10)(r - 10)(r - 5)$ **37.** $(a + 7)(a - 7)$ **39.** $3(m^4 + 81)$ **41.** $2(a + 4)(a - 4)(6a + 1)$ **43.** $3(m + 5)(m - 5)(5m + 4)$ **45a.** $-0.5x(x - 9)$ **45b.** 9 ft **45c.** 10.125 ft

47 a. $S = -25m^2 + 125m$
$0 = -25m^2 + 125m$
$0 = -25m(m - 5)$
$0 = -25m$ or $0 = m - 5$
$0 = m$ $\quad 5 = m$
So, they will stop selling in month 5.

b. The peak will occur halfway between 0 and 5, or 2.5.

c. The peak amount is $S = -25(2.5)^2 + 125(2.5)$
$= -156.25 + 312.5$
$= 156.25$
The peak is 156,250 copies.

49 $100 = 25x^2$
$0 = 25x^2 - 100$
$0 = 25(x^2 - 4)$
$0 = 25(x + 2)(x - 2)$
$x + 2 = 0$ or $x - 2 = 0$
$x = -2$ $\quad x = 2$

51. $\frac{3}{8}, -\frac{3}{8}$ **53.** −45, 45 **55.** $\frac{3}{16}, -\frac{3}{16}$ **57.** Lorenzo; sample answer: Checking Elizabeth's answer gives us $16x^2 - 25y^2$. The exponent on x in the final product should be 4. **59.** $(x^4 - 3)(x^4 + 3) \cdot (x^8 + 9)$ **61.** false; $a^2 + b^2$ **63.** When the difference of squares pattern is multiplied together using the FOIL method, the outer and inner terms are opposites of each other. When these terms are added together, the sum is zero. **65.** G **67a.** Car A, because it is traveling at 65 mph, and Car B is traveling at 60 mph. **67b.** $5t - 10$ **67c.** 2.5 mi **69.** prime **71.** {3, 6} **73.** {6, 16}

75. $\{t \mid t \ge 4\}$

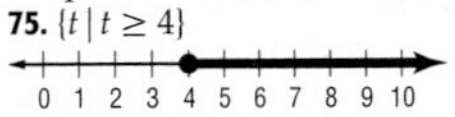

77. $\{k \mid k > 4\}$

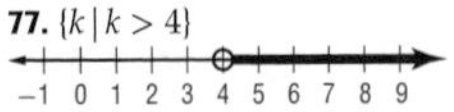

79. $\{m \mid m \ge 3\}$

81. the seventh week **83.** $x^2 - 4x + 4$ **85.** $4x^2 - 20x + 25$ **87.** $16x^2 + 40x + 25$

Pages 509–512 Lesson 8-6

1. yes; $(5x + 6)^2$ **3.** $(x - 4)(2x + 7)$ **5.** $4(x^2 + 16)$ **7.** ±3 **9.** $\frac{3}{8}$ **11.** 0.6 second **13.** yes; $(4x - 7)^2$

15 Since the last term is not a perfect square, the trinomial is not a perfect square trinomial

17. prime **19.** $8(y - 5z)(y + 5z)$ **21.** $2m(2m - 7)(3m + 5)$ **23.** $3(2x - 7)^2$ **25.** $3p(2p + 1)(2p - 1)$ **27.** $2t(t + 6)(2t - 7)$ **29.** $2a(a - b)(b + 1)(b - 1)$ **31.** $3k(k - 4)(k - 4)$ **33.** prime

35 $(y - 4)^2 = 7$
$y - 4 = \pm\sqrt{7}$
$y = 4 \pm \sqrt{7}$

37. $\frac{3}{4}$ **39.** 6 **41.** $\frac{1}{3}$ **43.** $8 \pm \sqrt{6}$ **45.** 20 ft **47.** $|4x + 5|$ **49a.** $w^3 + 14w^2 + 48w$ **49b.** 4 in. wide by 10 in. long by 12 in. high

51 a. 42 in. = 3.5 ft., width = w, length = $w + 5$, height = 3.5
Area of the surface = $\ell \cdot w$ or $(w + 5)(w)$
$V = \ell \cdot w \cdot h$
$1750 = (w + 5)(w)(3.5)$
$500 = (w + 5)(w)$
Area of the surface is 500 ft^2

b. $500 = (w + 5)(w)$
$= w^2 + 5w$
$0 = w^2 + 5w - 500$
$= (w + 25)(w - 20)$
$0 = w + 25$ or $0 = w - 20$
$-25 = w$ $\quad 20 = w$
The dimensions are 20 ft by 25 ft by 42 in.

c. Because the volume is doubled, we can double any one of the dimensions. 40 ft by 25 ft by 42 in., 20 ft by 50 ft by 42 in., or 20 ft by 25 ft by 84 in.

d. Because 2 of the dimensions are doubled the volume is increased by a factor of 4.
The ratio is 1:4

53. Adriano; sample answer: Debbie did not factor the expression completely. **55.** Sample answer: $x^2 - 3x + \frac{9}{4} = 0; \left\{\frac{3}{2}\right\}$ **57.** First look for a GCF in all the terms and factor the GCF out of all the terms. Then, if the polynomial has two terms, check if the terms are the differences of squares and factor if so. If the polynomial has three terms, check if the polynomial is a perfect square polynomial and factor if so. If the polynomial has four or more terms, factor by grouping. If the polynomial does not have a GCF and cannot be factored, the polynomial is a prime polynomial. **59.** Sample answer: $x^4 - 1$; 1, −1 **61.** B **63.** H **65.** $(x - 4)(x + 4)$ **67.** $(1 - 10p)(1 + 10p)$ **69.** $(5n - 1)(5n + 1)$ **71.** {−2, 4} **73.** {−2, 1} **75.** {2, 3} **77.** 10^1 or 10 **79.** $\frac{1}{10{,}000}$ **81.** $-\frac{2}{3}$ **83.** $\frac{3}{8}$ **85.** undefined

Pages 513–516 Chapter 8 Study Guide and Review

1. false; sample answer: $x^2 + 5x + 7$ **3.** true **5.** true **7.** true **9.** false; difference of squares **11.** $2 \cdot 2 \cdot 7 \cdot x \cdot x \cdot x$ **13.** $2 \cdot 2 \cdot 17 \cdot c \cdot d \cdot d \cdot d$ **15.** 11 **17.** $6ab$ **19.** 12 by 12 **21.** $7xy(2x - 3 + 5y)$ **23.** $(a + b)(a - 4c)$ **25.** $(3a + 5b)(8m - 3n)$ **27.** 0, 2 **29.** $0, \frac{5}{2}$ **31.** $(x - 5)(x - 3)$ **33.** $(x - 6)(x + 1)$ **35.** −10, 5 **37.** −8, −4 **39.** −10, −1 **41.** $2(2x - 1)(3x + 7)$ **43.** $3(x - 5)(x + 3)$ **45.** $\frac{3}{4}, -\frac{4}{5}$ **47.** $2, \frac{1}{4}$ **49.** $3x + 7$ **51.** $(8 + 5x)(8 - 5x)$ **53.** $3(x + 1)(x - 1)$ **55.** $\frac{5}{3}, -\frac{5}{3}$ **57.** −5, 5 **59.** $(x + 6)^2$ **61.** $(3y - 2)^2$ **63.** $(x^2 + 1)(x + 1)(x - 1)$ **65.** 16, −6 **67.** −4, 4 **69.** 2.5 ft

Chapter 9 Quadratic and Exponential Functions

Page 523 Chapter 9 Get Ready

1.

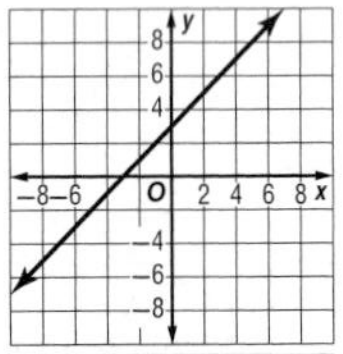

3.

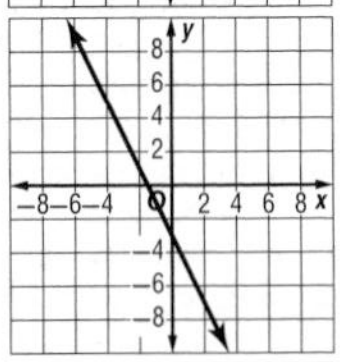

5.

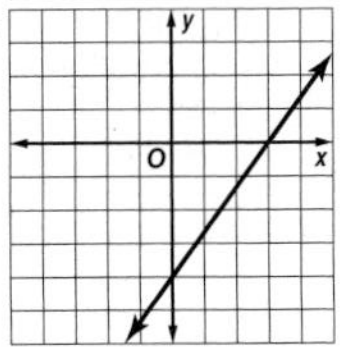

For Homework Help, go to Hotmath.com

7.

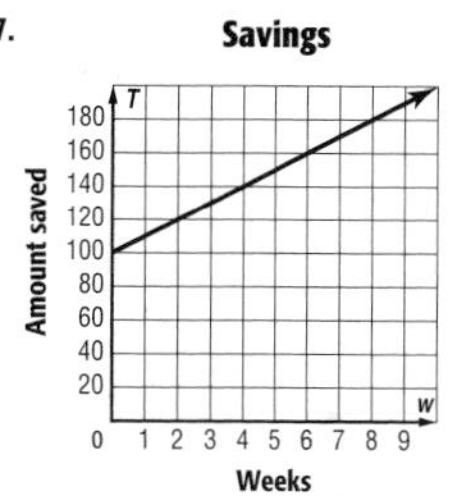

9. no **11.** yes; $(x + 10)^2$ **13.** yes; $(k - 8)^2$ **15.** no **17.** 34, 42, 50 **19.** 11, 13, 15

Pages 531–535 Lesson 9-1

1.

x	y
−3	0
−2	−6
−1	−8
0	−6
1	0
2	10

D = {all real numbers}; R = $\{y \mid y \geq -8\}$

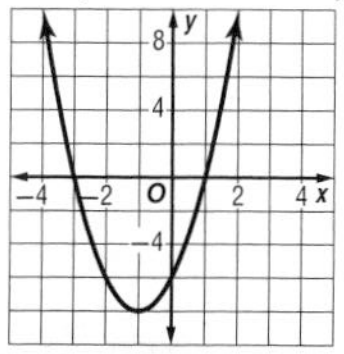

3.

x	y
−1	4
0	−3
1	−8
2	−11
3	−12
4	−11
5	−8
6	−3
7	4

D = {all real numbers}; R = $\{y \mid y \geq -12\}$

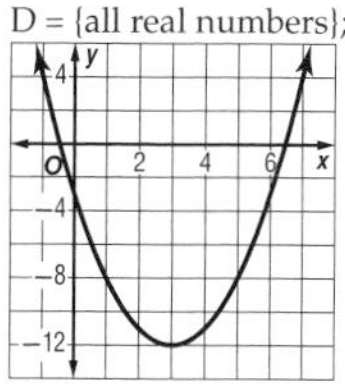

5. vertex (−1, 5), axis of symmetry $x = -1$, y-intercept 3 **7.** vertex (−2, −12), axis of symmetry $x = -2$, y-intercept −4 **9.** vertex (1, 2), axis of symmetry $x = 1$, y-intercept −1 **11.** vertex (2, 1), axis of symmetry $x = 2$, y-intercept 5

13 a. Since the a value is −1, the graph opens downward and has a maximum.

b. In this equation $a = -1$, $b = 4$, and $c = -3$.

$$x = \frac{-b}{2a} = \frac{-4}{2(-1)} = 2$$

To find the vertex, use the value you found for the x-coordinate of the vertex. To find the y-coordinate, substitute the value for x in the original equation.

$$\begin{aligned} y &= -x^2 + 4x - 3 \\ &= -(2)^2 + 4(2) - 3 \\ &= -4 + 8 - 3 \\ &= 1 \end{aligned}$$

The maximum is at (2, 1).

c. The domain of the function is D = $\{x \mid x$ is all real numbers$\}$. The range is R = $\{y \mid y \leq 1\}$.

15a. maximum **15b.** 6 **15c.** D = {all real numbers}; R = $\{y \mid y \leq 6\}$

17.

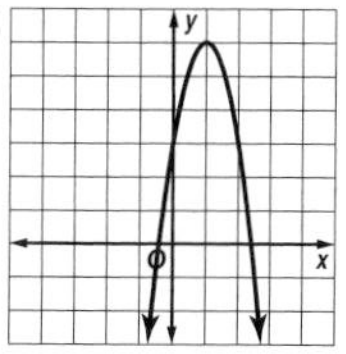

19.

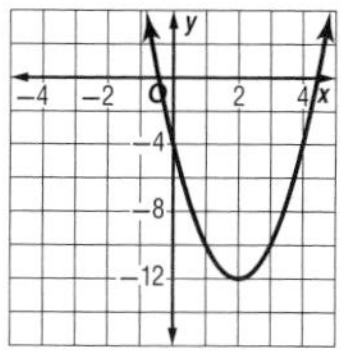

21a.

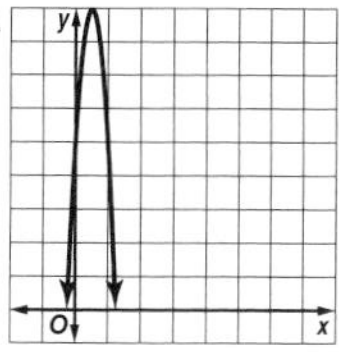

21b. 5 ft **21c.** 9 ft

23.

x	y
−3	13
−2	7
−1	5
0	7
1	13

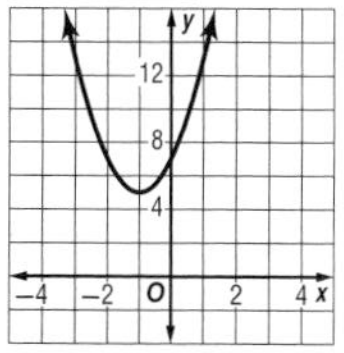

D = {all real numbers}; R = $\{y \mid y \geq 5\}$

25.

x	y
0	5
−1	−4
−2	−7
−3	−4
−4	5

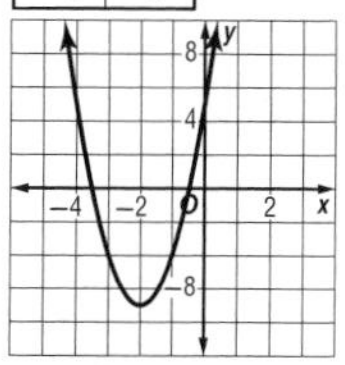

D = {all real numbers}; R = $\{y \mid y \geq -7\}$

27.

x	y
3	2
2	−1
1	−2
0	−1
−1	2

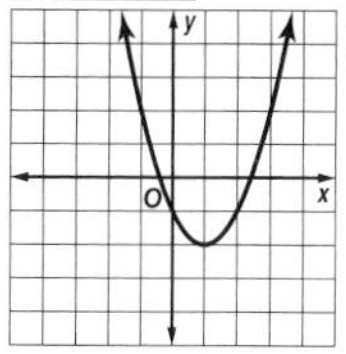

D = {all real numbers}; R = $\{y \mid y \geq -2\}$

29. vertex (0, 1), axis of symmetry $x = 0$, y-intercept 1 **31.** vertex (1, 1), axis of symmetry $x = 1$, y-intercept 4 **33.** vertex (0, 0), axis of symmetry $x = 0$, y-intercept 0

35 In this equation $a = 2$, $b = 12$, and $c = 10$.

$$x = \frac{-b}{2a} = \frac{-12}{2(2)}$$

The equation for the axis of symmetry is $x = -3$.

To find the vertex, use the value you found for the axis of symmetry as the x-coordinate of the vertex. To find the y-coordinate, substitute the value for x in the original equation.

$$\begin{aligned} y &= 2x^2 + 12x + 10 \\ &= 2(-3)^2 + 12(-3) + 10 \\ &= -8 \end{aligned}$$

The vertex is at (−3, −8).

The y-intercept occurs at $(0, c)$. So, in this case, the y-intercept occurs is 10.

37. vertex (−3, 4), axis of symmetry $x = -3$, y-intercept −5 **39.** vertex (2, −14), axis of symmetry $x = 2$, y-intercept 14 **41.** vertex (1, −15), axis of symmetry $x = 1$, y-intercept −18 **43a.** maximum **43b.** 9 **43c.** D = {all real numbers}, R = $\{y \mid y \leq 9\}$ **45a.** minimum **45b.** −48 **45c.** D = {all real numbers}, R = $\{y \mid y \geq -48\}$ **47a.** maximum **47b.** 33 **47c.** D = {all real numbers}, R = $\{y \mid y \leq 33\}$ **49a.** maximum **49b.** 4 **49c.** D = {all real numbers}, R = $\{y \mid y \leq 4\}$ **51a.** maximum **51b.** 3 **51c.** D = {all real numbers}, R = $\{y \mid y \leq 3\}$

53.

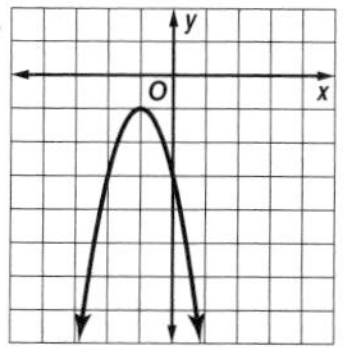

55.

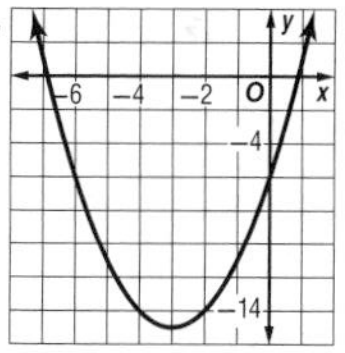

57.

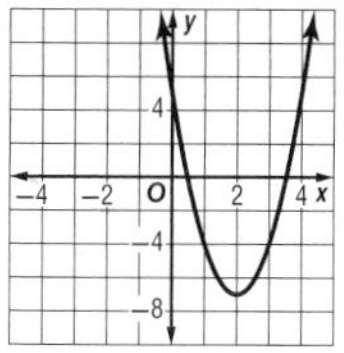

59.

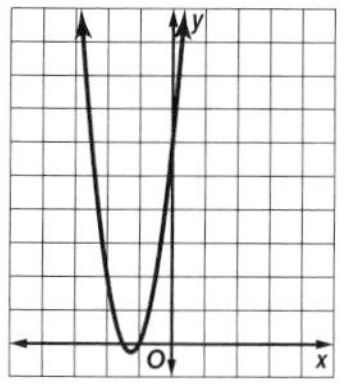

(−1.25, −0.25)

For Homework Help, go to Hotmath.com

61. 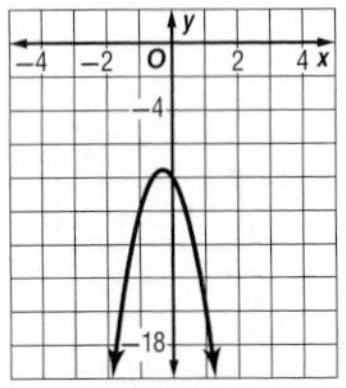 (−0.3, −7.55)

63a. 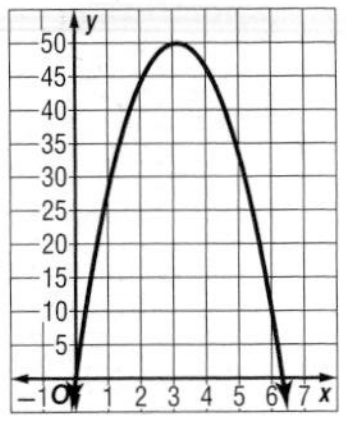

63b. 0 m **63c.** ≈ 50.0 m **63d.** ≈6.4 seconds
63e. D = {x | 0 ≤ x ≤ 6.4}; R = {y | 0 ≤ y ≤ 50.0}

65 a. $h = -16t^2 + 90t$
$= -16(1)^2 + 90(1)$
$= 74$ ft

b. $126 = -16t^2 - 90t$
$0 = -16t^2 - 90t - 126$
$0 = (t - 3)(-16t + 42)$
$t = 3$ and $t = 2.625$

c. $h = -16t^2 + 90t$
$0 = -16t^2 + 90t$
$0 = -16t(t - 5)$
$t = 0$ and $t = 5.625$

These represent the time that the ball leaves the ground initially and the time it returns to the ground.

67 a.

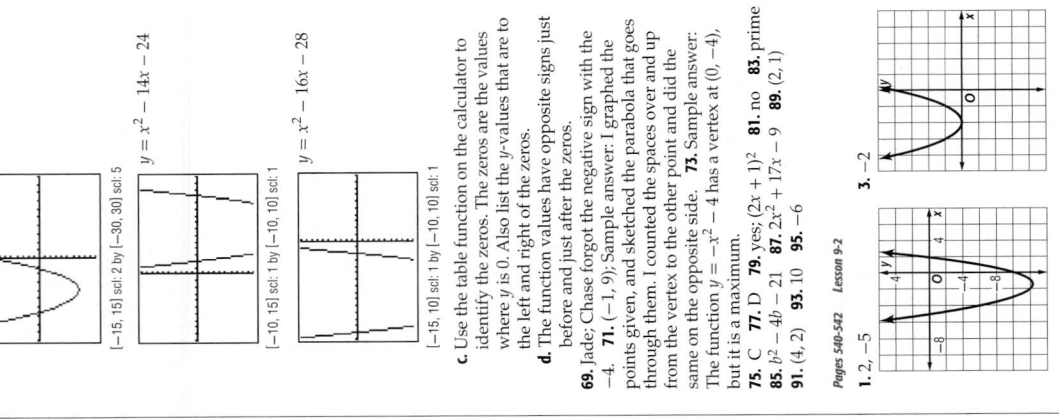

Equation	Related Function	Zeros	y-Values
$x^2 - x = 12$	$y = x^2 - x - 12$	−3, 4	−3: 8, −6; 4: −6, 8
$x^2 + 8x = 9$	$y = x^2 + 8x - 9$	−9, 1	−9: 11, −9; 1: −9, 11
$x^2 = 14x - 24$	$y = x^2 - 14x + 24$	2, 12	2: 11, −9; 12: −9, 11
$x^2 + 16x = -28$	$y = x^2 + 16x + 28$	−14, −2	−14: 13, −11; −2: −11, 3

b. Use a graphing calculator to graph.

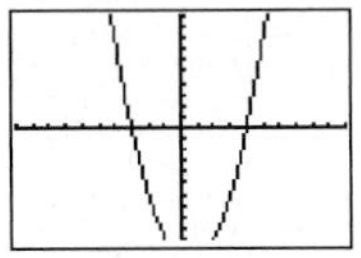
$y = x^2 - x - 12$

[−10, 10] scl: 1 by [−10, 10] scl: 1

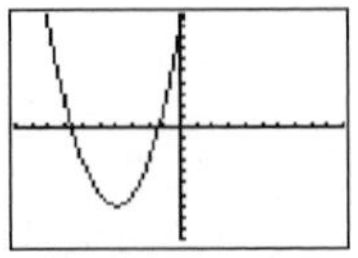
$y = x^2 - 8x - 9$

[−15, 15] scl: 2 by [−30, 30] scl: 5

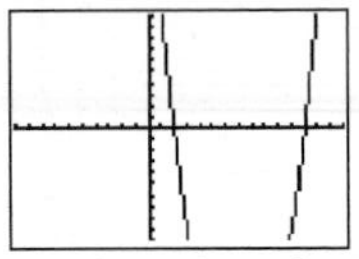
$y = x^2 - 14x - 24$

[−10, 15] scl: 1 by [−10, 10] scl: 1

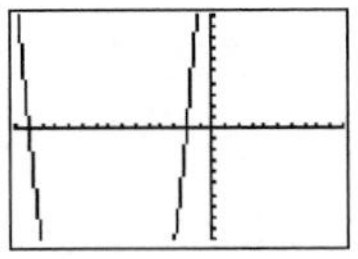
$y = x^2 - 16x - 28$

[−15, 10] scl: 1 by [−10, 10] scl: 1

c. Use the table function on the calculator to identify the zeros. The zeros are the values where y is 0. Also list the y-values that are to the left and right of the zeros.

d. The function values have opposite signs just before and just after the zeros.

69. Jade; Chase forgot the negative sign with the −4. **71.** (−1, 9); Sample answer: I graphed the points given, and sketched the parabola that goes through them. I counted the spaces over and up from the vertex to the other point and did the same on the opposite side. **73.** Sample answer: The function $y = -x^2 - 4$ has a vertex at (0, −4), but it is a maximum.

75. C **77.** D **79.** yes; $(2x + 1)^2$ **81.** no **83.** prime **85.** $b^2 - 4b - 21$ **87.** $2x^2 + 17x - 9$ **89.** (2, 1) **91.** (4, 2) **93.** 10 **95.** −6

Pages 540–542 Lesson 9-2

1. 2, −5

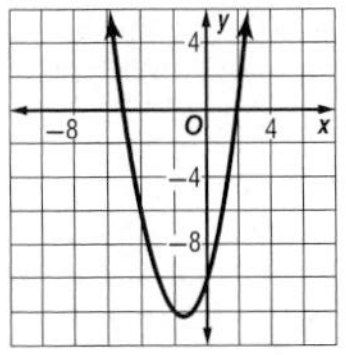

3. −2

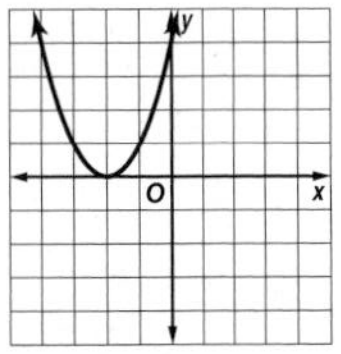

5. −5.2, 0.2

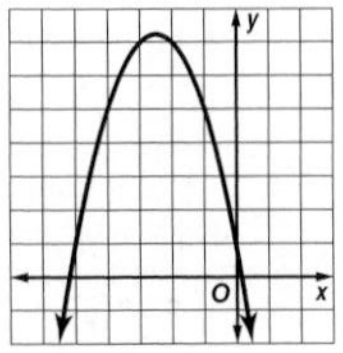

7. 5, −5

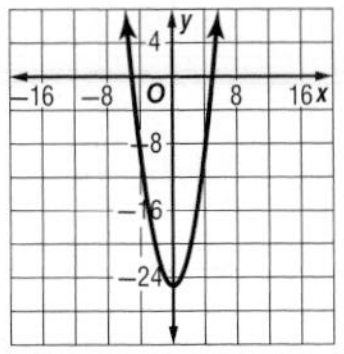

9. about 8.4 seconds

11 Step 1: Graph the related function of $f(x) = x^2 + 2x - 24 = 0$

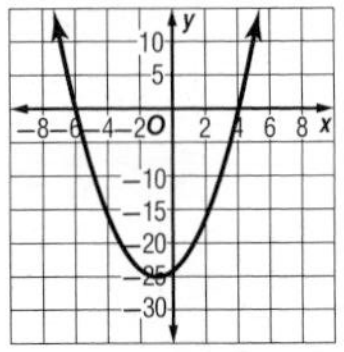

Step 2: The x-intercepts appear to be at −6 and 4, so the solutions are −6 and 4.

13. ∅

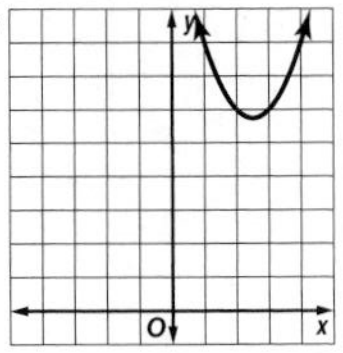

15. 1

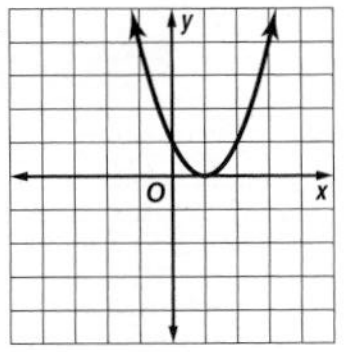

17. ∅

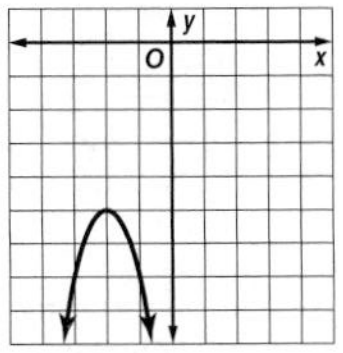

19. −6

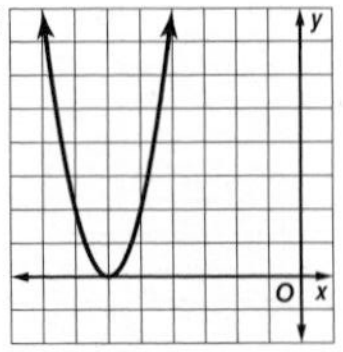

21. 8, −10

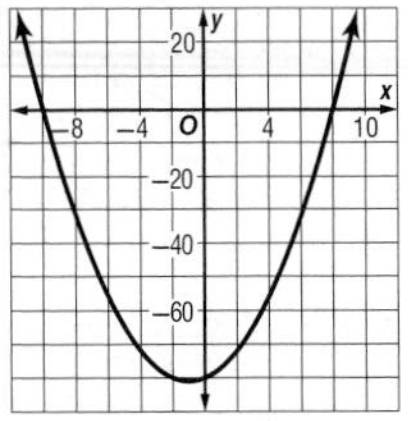

23. 6.9, −2.9

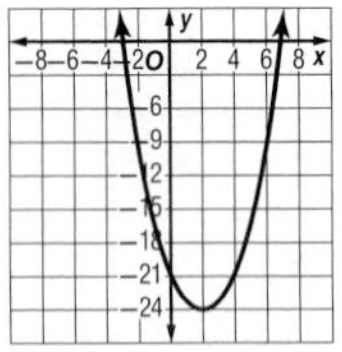

25. 3.3, 1.2

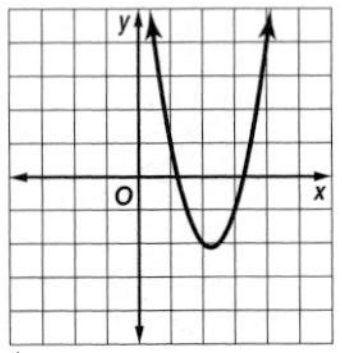

27. 3.1, −8.1

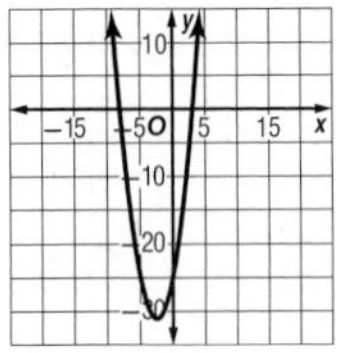

29. about 11.6 seconds **31.** 0; no real roots **33.** 2; −4, −8 **35.** −3, 4

37 a. $h = -16t^2 + 30t + 10$
$0 = -16t^2 + 30t + 10$
Graph the equation and find the x-intercepts.

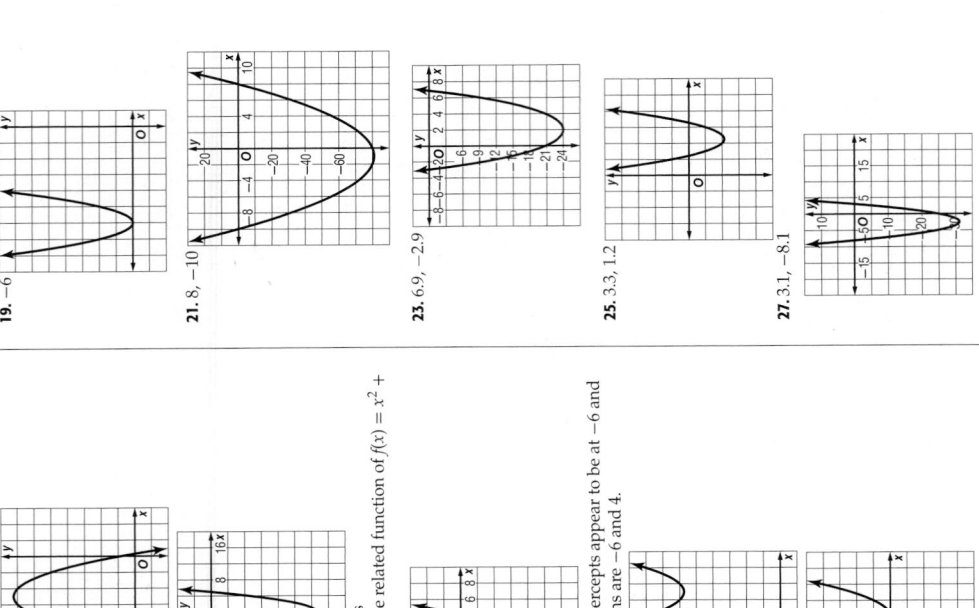

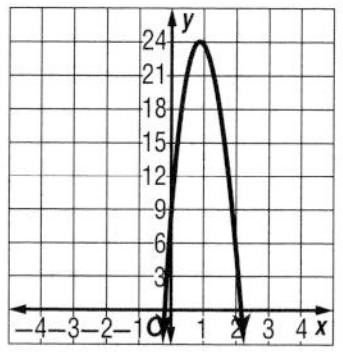

The positive x-intercept appears to be at 2.2, so she is in the air 2.2 seconds.

b. From the graph, she appears to hit a height of 15 feet at 0.2 seconds and 1.7 seconds.

c. $x = \frac{-b}{2a}$

$= \frac{-30}{2(-16)}$

$h = (-16)(0.9375)^2 + 30(0.9375) + 10$

≈ 24 feet

Her maximum height is about 24 feet, so she gets the bonus points.

39. −2, 1, 4 **41.** Iku; sample answer: The zeros of a quadratic function are the x-intercepts of the graph. Since the graph does not cross the x-axis, there are no x-intercepts and no real zeros.
43. Sometimes; for (1, 3), the y-value is greater than 2, but for (1, −1), it is less than 2. **45.** 1.5 and −1.5; Sample answer: Make a table of values for x from −2.0 to 2.0. Use increments of 0.1. **47.** A

49. about 21.4 mi

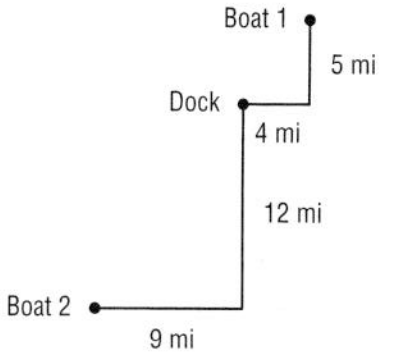

51. $x = 0$; (0, 0); min

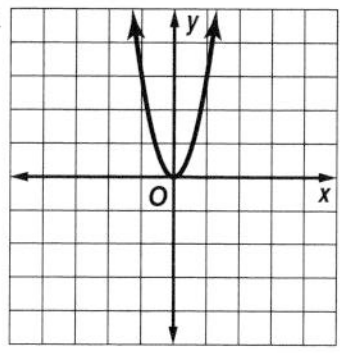

53. $x = 2$; (2, −3); max

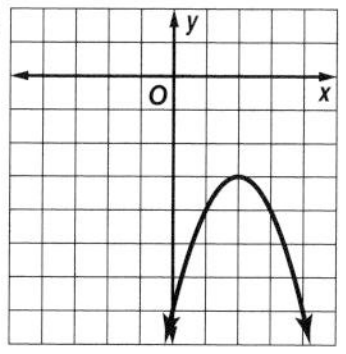

55. $x = -\frac{1}{3}$; $\left(-\frac{1}{3}, \frac{2}{3}\right)$; min

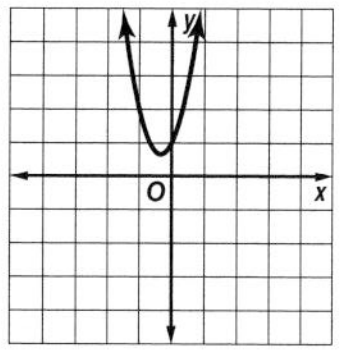

57. −4, 4 **59.** $-\frac{3}{2}, \frac{5}{2}$ **61.** $-3 \pm \sqrt{5}$ **63.** $7n^2 + 1$
65. $-3b^4 + 2b^3 - 9b^2 + 13$ **67.** $x + y = 180$; $x = y + 24$; 102°, 78° **69.** $y - 6 = -7(x + 3)$

71.

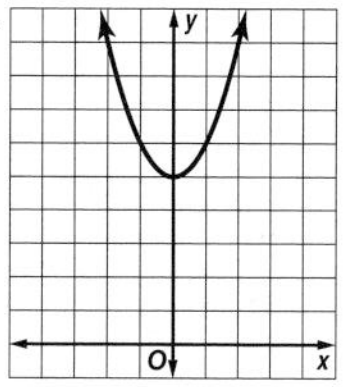

73.

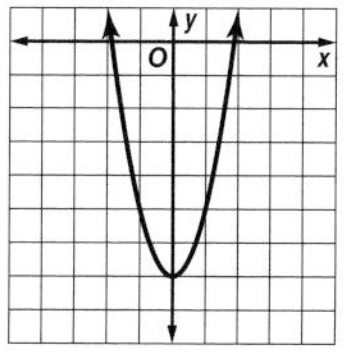

75.

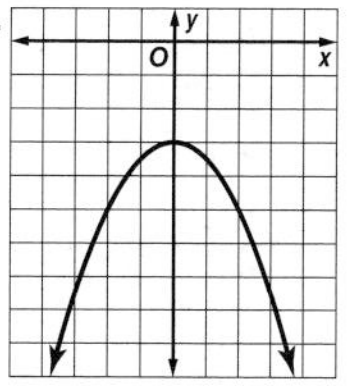

Pages 547-549 Lesson 9-3

1. translated down **3.** reflected across the x-axis, translated up **5.** reflected across the x-axis, stretched vertically **7.** C
9 The function can be written as $f(x) = ax^2 + c$ where $a = -1$ and $c = -7$. Since $-7 < 0$ and $-1 < 0$ the graph of $y = -x^2 - 7$ translates the graph of $y = x^2$ down 7 units and reflects it across the x-axis. **11.** compressed vertically, translated up **13.** stretched vertically, translated up
15. stretched vertically, translated up
17. stretched vertically, translated down **19.** A
21. F **23.** E **25.** $g(x)$, $h(x)$ **27.** $h(x)$, $g(x)$, $f(x)$
29 **a.** The two equations are $h = -16t^2 + 20{,}000$ and $h = -16t^2 + 30{,}000$
b. The rock from the 20,000-inch cliff will hit the ground first because it started lower and fell at the same rate as the other one.
31. Translate the graph of $f(x)$ down.
33. Compress vertically the graph of $f(x)$.
35a. Sometimes; this only occurs if $c = 0$. For any other value, the graph will be translated up or down. **35b.** Always; the negative sign only reflects the graph over the x-axis. Both graphs are dilated by a factor of a. **35c.** Never; the coefficient of x^2-term would have to be negative for the graph to open downward. **37.** Sample answer: Not all reflections over the y-axis produce the same graph. If the vertex of the original graph is not on the y-axis, the graph will not have the y-axis as its axis of symmetry and its reflection across the y-axis will be a different parabola. **39.** Sample answer: For $y = ax^2$, the parent graph is stretched vertically if $a > 1$ or compressed vertically if $0 < a < 1$. The y-values in the table will all be multiplied by a factor of a. For $y = x^2 + c$, the parent graph is translated up if c is positive and moved down if c is negative. The y-values in the table will all have the constant c added to them or subtracted from them. For $y = ax^2 + c$, the graph will either be stretched vertically or compressed vertically based upon the value of a and then will be translated up or down depending on the value of c. The y-values in the table will be multiplied by a factor of a and the constant c added to them.
41. D **43.** B **45.** 4, 6

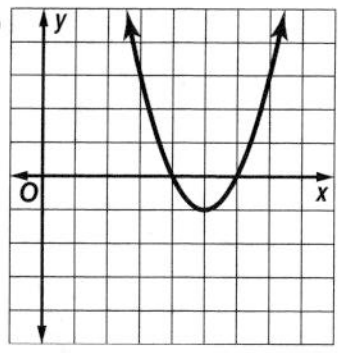

47. $-1, \frac{3}{2}$

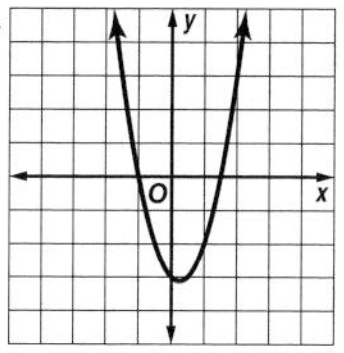

49. $-\frac{5}{3}, \frac{3}{4}$

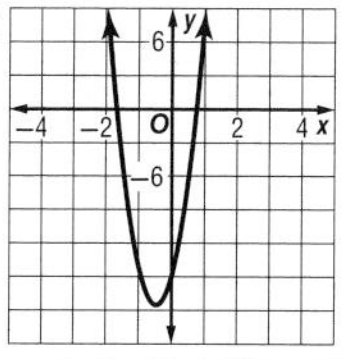

51. (2, 2); $x = 2$; 6 **53.** $1.50t + 1.25mt$

55. $\{f \mid f > -8\}$ **57.** $(4x - 3)^2$ **59.** $(5x - 6)^2$
61. $(6x - 7)^2$

Pages 554-557 Lesson 9-4

1 Step 1: Find $\frac{1}{2}$ of $-18 = -9$
Step 2: Square the result in step 1: $(-9)^2 = 81$
Step 3: Add the result of step 2 to $x^2 - 18x$: $x^2 - 18x + 81$
Thus, $c = 81$.
3. $\frac{81}{4}$ **5.** −5.2, 1.2 **7.** −2.4, 0.1 **9.** 8 ft by 18 ft
11. 144 **13.** $\frac{289}{4}$ **15.** $\frac{169}{4}$ **17.** $\frac{225}{4}$
19 $x^2 + 6x - 16 = 0$

$x^2 + 6x = 16$

$x^2 + 6x + 9 = 16 + 9$

$(x + 3)^2 = 25$

$x + 3 = \pm 5$

$x = -3 \pm 5$

The solutions are 2 and −8.
21. −1, 9 **23.** −0.2, 11.2 **25.** ∅ **27.** −2.6, 1.1
29. −1.1, 6.1 **31.** on the 30th and 40th days after purchase **33.** 5.3 **35.** −21 and −23 **37.** −1, 2
39. 0.2, 0.9 **41.** −8.2, 0.2
43 **a.** The object on Earth will reach the ground first because it is falling at a faster rate.
b. Mars: $0 = -1.855t^2 + 120$

$-120 = -1.855t^2$

$64.69 \approx t^2$

$\pm 8.0 \approx t$

So, $t \approx 8.0$ seconds

Earth: $0 = -4.9t^2 + 120$

$-120 = -4.9t^2$

$24.49 = t^2$

$\pm 4.9 \approx t$

So, $t = 4.9$ seconds.

c. Sample answer: Yes, the acceleration due to gravity is much greater on Earth than on Mars, so the time to reach the ground should be much less.
45. −30 and 30
47a–b.

Trinomial	$b^2 - 4ac$	Number of Roots
$x^2 - 8x + 16$	0	1
$2x^2 - 11x + 3$	97	2
$3x^2 + 6x + 9$	−72	0
$x^2 - 2x + 7$	−24	0
$x^2 + 10x + 25$	0	1
$x^2 + 3x - 12$	57	2

47c. If $b^2 - 4ac$ is negative, the equation has no solutions. If $b^2 - 4ac$ is zero, the equation has one solution. If $b^2 - 4ac$ is positive, the equation has 2 solutions. **47d.** 0 because $b^2 - 4ac$ is negative. The equation has no real solutions because taking the square root of a negative number does not produce a real number. **49.** None; sample answer: If you add $\left(\frac{b}{2}\right)^2$ to each side of the equation and each

For Homework Help, go to Hotmath.com

side of the inequality, you get $x^2 + bx + \left(\frac{b}{2}\right)^2 = c + \left(\frac{b}{2}\right)^2$ and $c + \left(\frac{b}{2}\right)^2 < 0$. Since the left side of the last equation is a perfect square, it cannot equal the negative number $c + \left(\frac{b}{2}\right)^2$. So, there are no real solutions. **51.** Sample answer: $x^2 - 8x + 16 = 0$ **53.** B **55.** 32 **57.** translated down **59.** expanded vertically, translated up **61.** expanded vertically, translated up **63.** $40 = -16t^2 + 250$; about 3.6 s **65.** 16 **67.** 1 **69.** $\frac{1}{m^3b^3}$ **71.** $\{z \mid -8 < z < -2\}$ **73.** $\{y \mid y \geq 5.5 \text{ or } y \leq -2.5\}$ **75.** $\{c \mid -2.2 \leq c \leq 3\}$ **77.** ± 10 **79.** ± 7.8 **81.** not a real number

Pages 562–564 Lesson 9-5

1. −3, 5 **3.** 6.4, 1.6 **5.** 0.6, 2.5 **7.** $-6, \frac{1}{2}$ **9.** $\pm\frac{5}{3}$ **11.** −3; no real solutions **13.** 0; one real solution **15.** The discriminant is −890.24, so the equation has no solutions. Thus, Eva will not reach a height of 20 feet.

17 $x^2 + 16 = 0$

For this equation, $a = 1$, $b = 0$, and $c = 16$

$$x = \frac{-b \pm \sqrt{b^2 - 4ac}}{2a}$$
$$= \frac{0 \pm \sqrt{(0)^2 - 4(1)(16)}}{2(1)}$$
$$= \frac{\sqrt{-64}}{2}$$

So, there is no real solution. The solution can be written ∅.

19. 2.2, −0.6 **21.** $-3, -\frac{6}{5}$ **23.** 0.5, −2 **25.** 0.5, −1.2 **27.** 3 **29.** −1.2, 5.2 **31.** −2, 5 **33.** −6.2, −0.8 **35.** −0.07; no real solution **37.** 12.64; two real solutions **39.** 0; one real solution **41a.** in 1993 and 2023 **41b.** Sample answer: No; the parabola has a maximum at about 66, meaning only 66% of the population would ever have high-speed Internet. **43.** 0 **45.** 1 **47.** −1.4, 2.1

49 a. $(20 - 2x)(25 - 7x) = 375$

b. $500 - 50x - 140x + 14x^2 = 375$

$14x^2 - 190x + 125 = 0$

$$x = \frac{-b \pm \sqrt{b^2 - 4ac}}{2a}$$
$$= \frac{190 \pm \sqrt{(190)^2 - 4(14)(125)}}{2(14)}$$
$$= \frac{190 \pm \sqrt{29100}}{28}$$
$$\approx 0.7 \text{ and } 12.9$$

c. The margins should be 0.7 in. on the sides and 4(0.7) or 2.8 in. on the top and 3(0.7) or 2.1 in. on the bottom.

51. $k < \frac{9}{40}$ **53.** none **55.** two **57.** Sample answer: positive discriminant: $f(x) = x^2 - 4$, negative discriminant: $f(x) = x^2 + 4$, zero discriminant: $f(x) = x^2 - 8x + 16$ **59.** D **61.** G **63.** $\frac{4}{3}, \frac{3}{2}$ **65.** $\frac{5}{2}$

67. Translate down 6. **69.** Positive; as time goes on, more people use electronic tax returns.

71. $12x + 3y \leq 60$

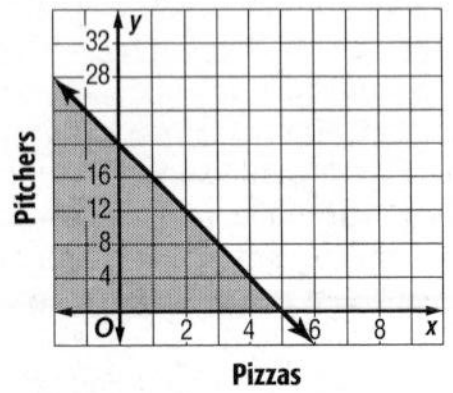

73. 4 **75.** 0 **77.** −75

Pages 570–572 Lesson 9-6

1.
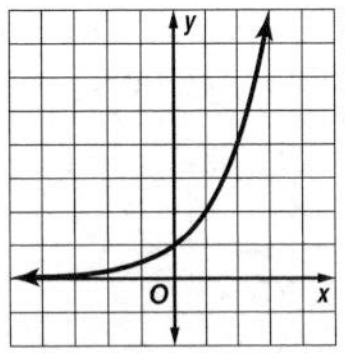
1; D = {all real numbers}; R = $\{y \mid y > 0\}$; $2^{1.5} \approx 2.8$

3.
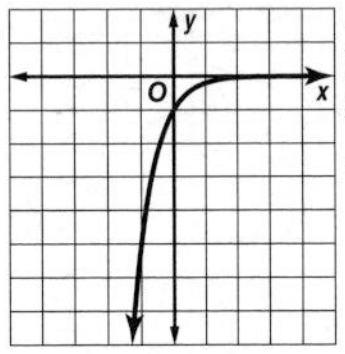
−1; D = {all real numbers}; R = $\{y \mid y < 0\}$; $-\left(\frac{1}{5}\right)^{-0.5} \approx -2.2$

5.
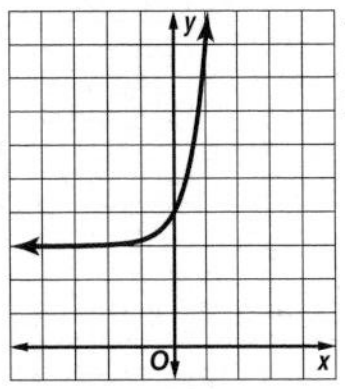
4; D = {all real numbers}; R = $\{y \mid y > 3\}$

7a. D = $\{d \mid d \geq 0\}$, the number of days is greater than or equal to 0; R = $\{y \mid y \geq 100\}$, the number of fruit flies is greater than or equal to 100. **7b.** about 198 fruit flies **9.** Yes; the domain values are at regular intervals, and the range values have a common factor of 4.

11.
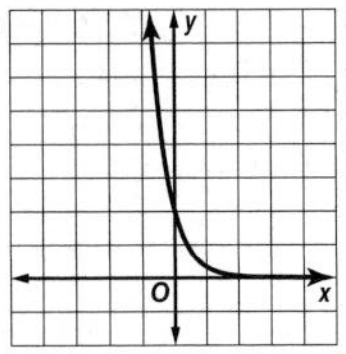
2; D = {all real numbers}; R = $\{y \mid y > 0\}$; $\left(\frac{1}{6}\right)^{1.5} \approx 0.1$

13.
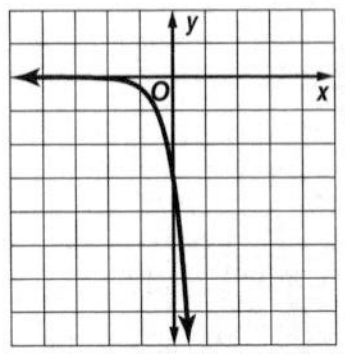
−3; D = {all real numbers}; R = $\{y \mid y < 0\}$; $-3(9)^{-0.5} \approx -1$

15.
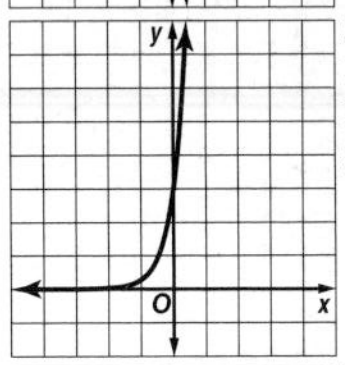
3; D = {all real numbers}; R = $\{y \mid y > 0\}$; $3(11)^{-0.2} \approx 1.9$

17.
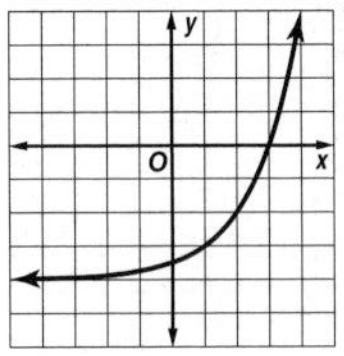
The y-intercept is −3.5; D = {all real numbers}; R = $\{y \mid y > -4\}$

19.
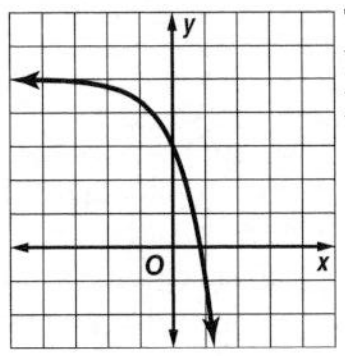
The y-intercept is 3; D = {all real numbers}; R = $\{y \mid y < 5\}$

21 No; the domain values are at regular intervals of 4.

$2 \times (-2) = 4$
$-4 \times (-2) = 8$
$8 \times (-2) = -16$
$-16 \times (-2) = 32$

The range values differ by the common factor of −2. The range values do not have a positive common factor.

23. Yes; the domain values are at regular intervals, and the range values have a common factor of 2.

25 $P = 1.5^x$
$= 1.5^4$
≈ 5.06 or 506%

This enlargement is about 506% bigger than the original.

27. exponential **29.** linear **31.** quadratic **33.** about 198 students **35.** a vertical stretch by a factor of 3 **37.** a translation down 3 units **39.** a vertical stretch by a factor of 5 and a reflection over the x-axis. **41.** $f(x) = 3(2)^x$ **43.** Sample answer: The number of teams competing in a basketball tournament can be represented by $y = 2^x$, where the number of teams competing is y and the number of rounds is x.

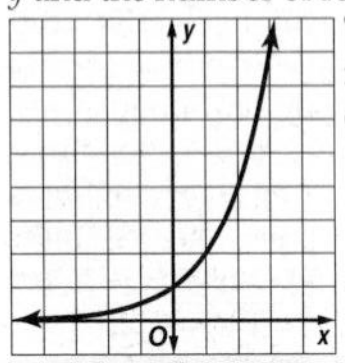
The y-intercept of the graph is 1. The graph increases quickly for $x > 0$.

45. Sample answer: First, look for a pattern by making sure that the domain values are at regular intervals and the range values differ by a common factor. **47.** B **49.** A **51.** −5, 0.5 **53.** ±5 **55.** 3.1, 10.9 **57.** 2.52×10^2, 252 **59.** 32 km²/min² **61.** (−5, 20) **63.** 9, 11, 13 **65.** 16.5, 19, 21.5 **67.** $\frac{7}{2}, \frac{17}{4}, 5$

Pages 575–577 Lesson 9-7

1. about \$37,734.73 **3a.** $y = 2200(0.98)^t$ **3b.** about 1624 **5.** about 92,095,349

7 $A = P\left(1 + \frac{r}{n}\right)^{nt}$
$= 6600\left(1 + \frac{0.045}{12}\right)^{12(4)}$
$= 6600(1.00375)^{48}$
≈ 7898.97 or about \$7898.97

9. Sample answer: No; she will have about \$199.94 in the account in 4 years.

11 $y = a(1 + r)^t$
$= 1{,}211{,}537(1 + 0.0106)^{20}$
$= 1{,}211{,}537(1.0106)^{20}$
$\approx 1{,}495{,}969$

13a. $I = 221{,}000(1.086)^t$ **13b.** about \$645,922 **15a.** \$316.82 **15b.** \$19,009.20 **17.** about 9.2 yr **19.** A population is 200 and increasing at a rate of 5% annually. **21.** C **23.** D

25.
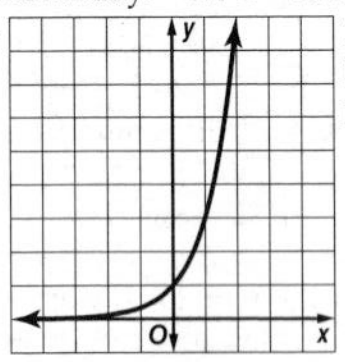
1; D = {all real numbers}, R = $\{y \mid y > 0\}$

27.
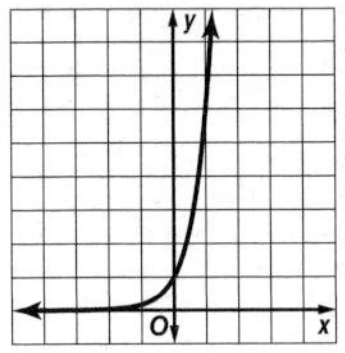
1; D = {all real numbers}, R = $\{y \mid y > 0\}$ **29.** −0.8, 2.1 **31.** −2 **33.** −2.1, 3.6 **35.** parallel **37.** neither **39.** \$14.77 **41.** \$37.45

For Homework Help, go to Hotmath.com

43.

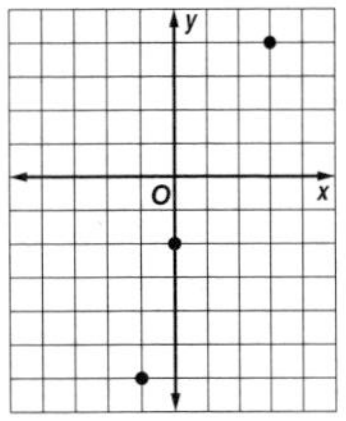

Pages 583–585 Lesson 9-8

1. Geometric; the common ratio is $\frac{1}{5}$.
3. Arithmetic; the common difference is 3.
5. 160, 320, 640 **7.** $-\frac{1}{16}, -\frac{1}{64}, -\frac{1}{256}$ **9.** $a_n = -6 \cdot (4)^{n-1}$; -1536 **11.** $a_n = 72 \cdot \left(\frac{2}{3}\right)^{n-1}$; $\frac{4096}{2187}$

13. **Experiment**

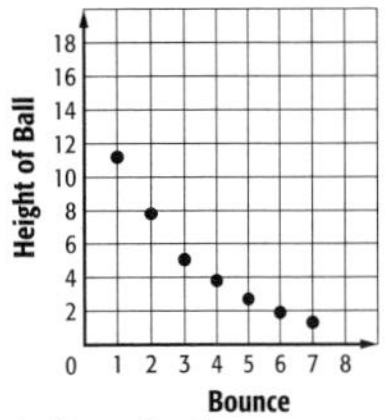

15. Arithmetic; the common difference is 10.
17. Geometric; the common ratio is $\frac{1}{2}$.
19. Neither; there is no common ratio or difference.
21 Step 1: Find the common ratio.

$36 \times \frac{1}{3} = 12$

$12 \times \frac{1}{3} = 4$

The common ratio is $\frac{1}{3}$.

Step 2: Multiply each term by the common ratio to find the next three terms.

$4\left(\frac{1}{3}\right) = \frac{4}{3}$

$\left(\frac{4}{3}\right)\left(\frac{1}{3}\right) = \frac{4}{9}$

$\left(\frac{4}{9}\right)\left(\frac{1}{3}\right) = \frac{4}{27}$

So, the next three terms are $\frac{4}{3}, \frac{4}{9}$, and $\frac{4}{27}$.

23. $\frac{25}{4}, \frac{25}{16}, \frac{25}{64}$ **25.** $2, \frac{1}{4}, \frac{1}{32}$ **27.** 134,217,728
29. −1,572,864 **31.** 19,683

33a. $1 \times 2 = 2$
$2 \times 2 = 4$
The common ratio is 2, so the second option forms a geometric sequence.

b. first option: She will receive $30(9) = \$270$
second option: In the 9th week, she will get $a_n = a_1r^{n-1}$.
$a_n = 1(2)^{9-1}$
$= 1(2)^8$
$= 256$
In the 8th week, she will get $a_n = a_1r^{n-1}$.
$a_n = 1(2)^{8-1}$
$= 1(2)^7$
$= 128$
Over the nine weeks she will earn: 1 + 2 + 4 + 8 + 16 + 32 + 64 + 128 + 256 or $511.
She should choose the second option.

35. 9; $\frac{1}{3}$

37a.

Richter Number (x)	Increase in Magnitude (y)	Rate of Change (slope)
1	1	–
2	10	9
3	100	90
4	1,000	900
5	10,000	9000

37b.

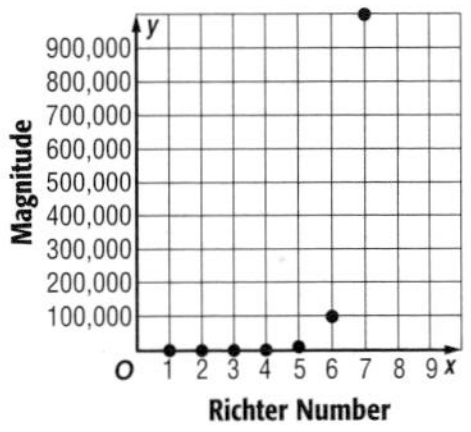

37c. The graph appears to be exponential. The rate of change between any two points does not match any others. **37d.** $1 \cdot (10)^{x-1} = y$ **39.** Neither Haro calculated the exponent incorrectly; Matthew did not enclose the common ratio in parentheses.
41. $1, \frac{3}{4}, \frac{9}{16}, \ldots$ **43.** B **45.** 15 dimes and 20 quarters **47.** 162, 486, 1458 **49.** $\frac{1}{16}, -\frac{1}{32}, \frac{1}{64}$ **51.** 0.1296, 0.07776, 0.046656

53.

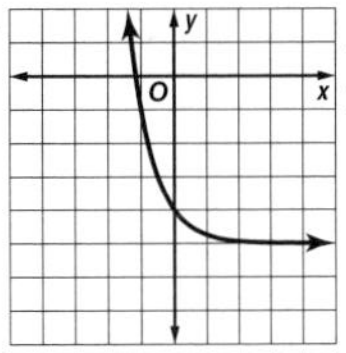

−4;
D = {all real numbers};
R = $\{y \mid y > -5\}$

55.

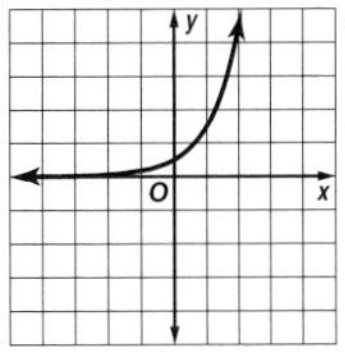

$\frac{1}{2}$;
D = {all real numbers};
R = $\{y \mid y > 0\}$

57. at least $3747 **59.** $y = -3x - \frac{2}{3}$ **61.** $y = \frac{1}{2}x - 9$
63. $y = -6x - 7$ **65.** 7412.01 **67.** 371.50
69. 96,150.24

Pages 589–591 Lesson 9-9

1.

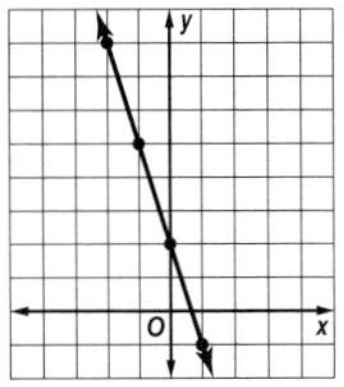

linear

3.

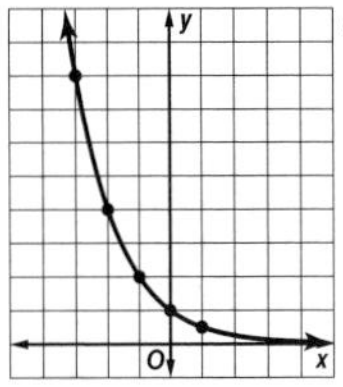

exponential

5. quadratic **7.** exponential **9.** exponential; $y = 3 \times 3^x$ **11.** linear; $y = \frac{1}{2}x + \frac{5}{2}$ **13.** linear: $y = 0.5x + 3$

15.

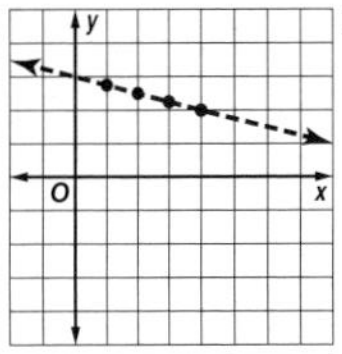

linear

17.

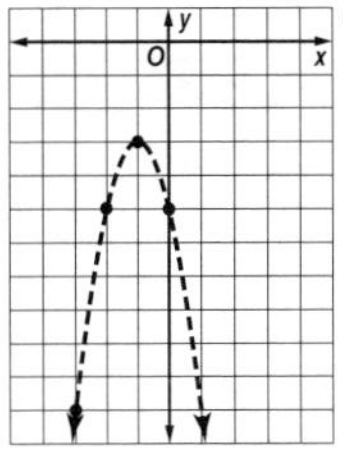

quadratic

19.

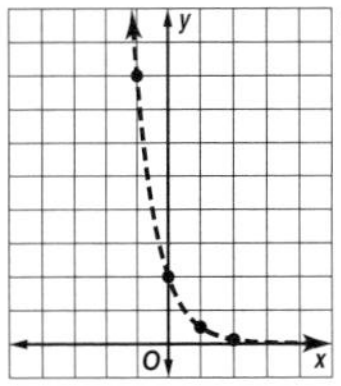

exponential

21 Look for a pattern in the y-values. Start with comparing first differences.

10, 2.5, 0, 2.5, 10
first differences: −7.5, −2.5, 2.5, 7.5

The first differences are not all equal. So, the table of values does not represent a linear function. Find the second differences and compare.

−7.5, −2.5, 2.5, 7.5
second differences: +5, +5, +5

The second differences are all equal, so the table of values represents a quadratic function.
Write an equation for the function that models the data.
The equation has the form $y = ax^2$. Find the value of a by choosing one of the ordered pairs from the table of values. Let's use (2, 10).
$y = ax^2$
$10 = a(2)^2$
$10 = 4a$
$\frac{5}{2} = a$
$2.5 = a$
An equation that models the data is $y = 2.5x^2$.

23. exponential; $y = 0.2 \cdot 5^x$
25. linear; $y = -5x - 0.25$
27a. Graph the ordered pairs on a coordinate plane.

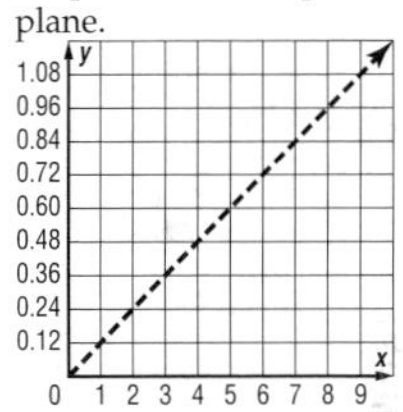

The graph appears to be linear.

b. Look at the first differences of the y-values.
0.12, 0.24, 0.36, 0.48, 0.60, 0.72
first differences: +0.12, +0.12, +0.12, +0.12, +0.12
The common difference is 0.12.
The equation is $y = 0.12x$.

c. $y = 0.12x$
$= 0.12(10)$
$= \$1.20$

29a.

Time (hour)	0	1	2	3	4
Amount of Bacteria	12	36	108	324	972

29b. exponential **29c.** $b = 12 \times 3^t$ **29d.** 78,732
31. Sample answer: $y = 2x^2 - 5$ **33.** $y = 4x + 1$
35. The data can be graphed to determine which function best models the data. Also, differences and ratios of the y-values can be used. If the first differences are constant, the data are modeled by a linear function. If the second differences are constant, but the first difference are not, the data

For Homework Help, go to Hotmath.com

can be modeled by a quadratic function. If the ratios are constant, then the data can be modeled by an exponential function.
37. A **39.** B **41.** $a_n = 1(2)^{n-1}$; 64 **43.** $a_n = 4(-3)^{n-1}$; 2916 **45.** $a_n = 22(2)^{n-1}$; 1408
47. $x^2 - 8x + 16$ **49.** $16x^2 - 56x + 49$
51. $25x^2 - 36y^2$ **53.** $C = 10h + 15$; \$95
55. yes; $2x + y = 6$ **57.** yes; $y = -5$ **59.** no
61.

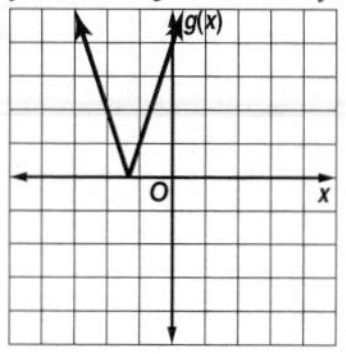

Pages 592–596 Chapter 9 Study Guide and Review

1. true **3.** false; parabola **5.** false; two **7.** true **9.** true **11a.** minimum **11b.** 0 **11c.** D = all real numbers; R = $y \mid y \geq 0\}$ **13a.** minimum **13b.** −4 **13c.** D = all real numbers; R = $\{y \mid y \geq -4\}$ **15a.** maximum **15b.** 16 **15c.** D = all real numbers; R = $\{h \mid h \leq 16\}$ **17.** 3 **19.** −4.6, 0.6 **21.** −0.8, 3 **23.** shifted up 8 units **25.** vertical stretch **27.** vertical compression **29.** $y = 2x^2 - 3$ **31.** 1, −7 **33.** 10, −2 **35.** −0.7, 7.7 **37.** −8, 6 **39.** −0.7, 0.5 **41.** −5, 1.5 **43.** −2.5, 1.5 **45.** y-intercept 1; D = {all real numbers}; R = $\{y \mid y > 0\}$

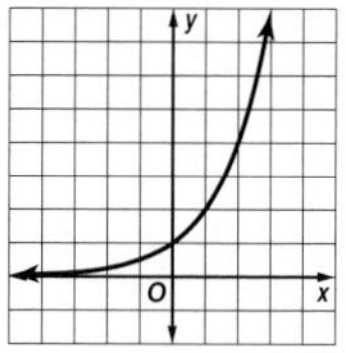

47. y-intercept 3; D = {all real numbers}; R = $\{y \mid y > 0\}$

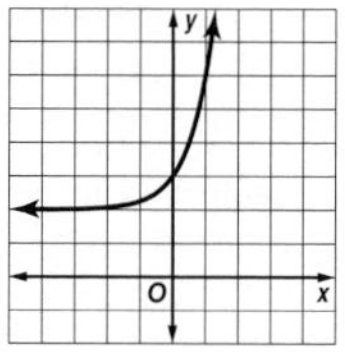

49. about 568 **51a.** $1200(1 - 0.03)^5$ **51b.** \$1030.48
53. 81, 243, 729 **55.** $a_n = -1(-1)^{n-1}$
57. $a_n = 256\left(\frac{1}{2}\right)^{n-1}$ **59.** quadratic; $y = 3x^2$
61. quadratic; $y = -x^2$ **63.** linear; $y = 1.50x + 1$

Chapter 10 Advanced Functions and Equations

Page 603 Chapter 10 Get Ready

1. 9.06 **3.** 3.87 **5.** 10 ft **7.** $13x - 3y$ **9.** $3m + 3n + 10$ **11.** 0, 2 **13.** 2, 5 **15.** 10 **17.** yes

Pages 608–610 Lesson 10-1

1.

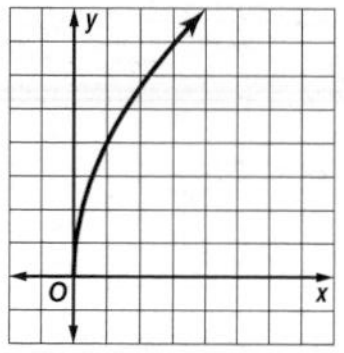

vertical stretch of $y = \sqrt{x}$; D = $\{x \mid x \geq 0\}$, R = $\{y \mid y \geq 0\}$

3.

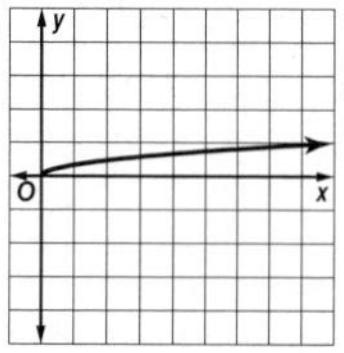

vertical compression of $y = \sqrt{x}$; D = $\{x \mid x \geq 0\}$, R = $\{y \mid y \geq 0\}$

5.

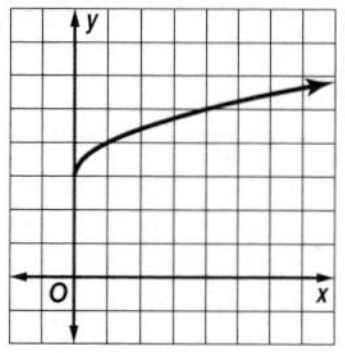

translated up 3; D = $\{x \mid x \geq 0\}$, R = $\{y \mid y \geq 3\}$

7.

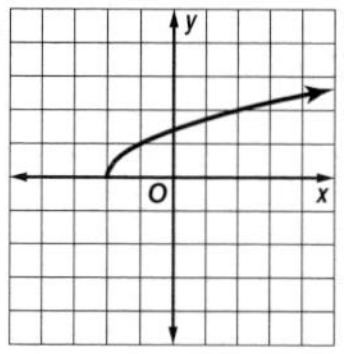

translated left 2; D = $\{x \mid x \geq -2\}$, R = $\{y \mid y \geq 0\}$

9.

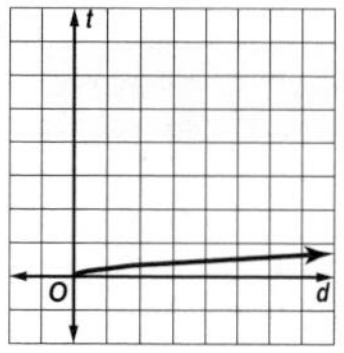

D = $\{d \mid d \geq 0\}$, R = $\{t \mid t \geq 0\}$

11.

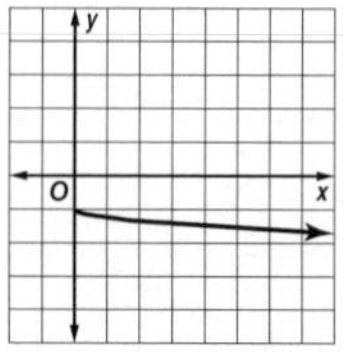

vertical compression of $\sqrt{x}$, reflected across the x-axis and translated down 1; D = $\{x \mid x \geq 0\}$, R = $\{y \mid y \leq -1\}$

13.

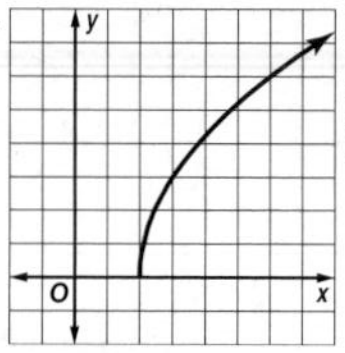

translated right 2 and vertical stretch of $\sqrt{x}$; D = $\{x \mid x \geq 2\}$, R = $\{y \mid y \geq 0\}$

15 Step 1: Make a table. Choose nonnegative values for x.

x	y
0	0
0.5	≈0.35
1	0.5
2	0.71
3	0.87
4	1

Step 2: Plot the points and draw a smooth curve.

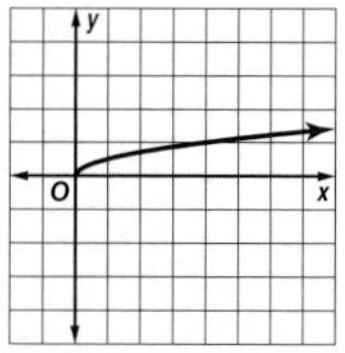

The graph is a vertical compression of $\sqrt{x}$. The domain is $\{x \mid x \geq 0\}$. The range is $\{y \mid y \geq 0\}$.

17.

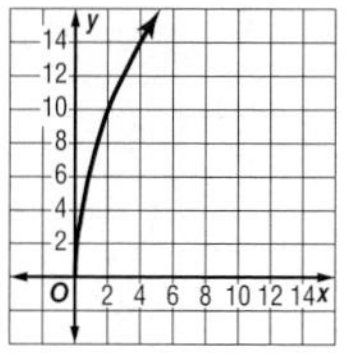

vertical stretch of $\sqrt{x}$; D = $\{x \mid x \geq 0\}$, R = $\{y \mid y \geq 0\}$

19.

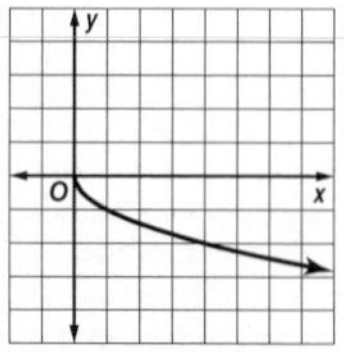

reflected across the x-axis; D = $\{x \mid x \geq 0\}$, R = $\{y \mid y \leq 0\}$

21.

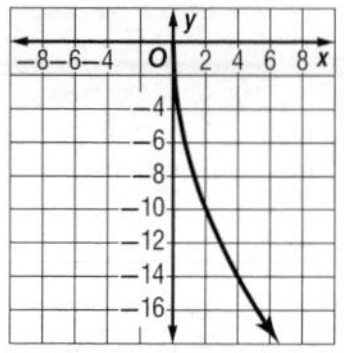

vertical stretch of $\sqrt{x}$ and reflected across the x-axis; D = $\{x \mid x \geq 0\}$, R = $\{y \mid y \leq 0\}$

23.

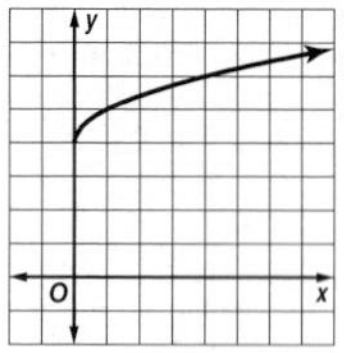

translated up 4; D = $\{x \mid x \geq 0\}$, R = $\{y \mid y \geq 4\}$

25.

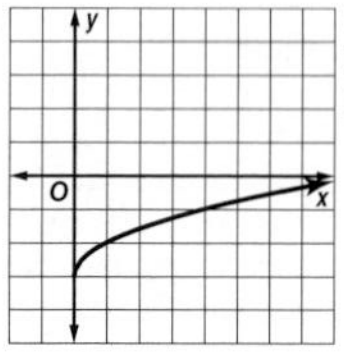

translated down 3; D = $\{x \mid x \geq 0\}$, R = $\{y \mid y \geq -3\}$

27.

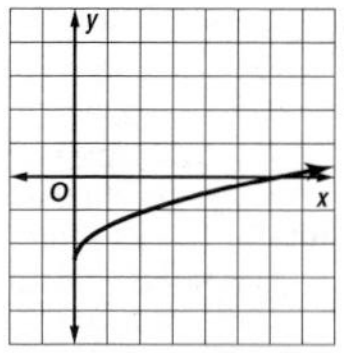

translated down 2.5; D = $\{x \mid x \geq 0\}$, R = $\{y \mid y \geq -2.5\}$

29.

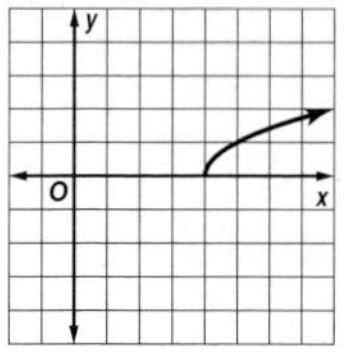

translated right 4; D = $\{x \mid x \geq 4\}$, R = $\{y \mid y \geq 0\}$

31. 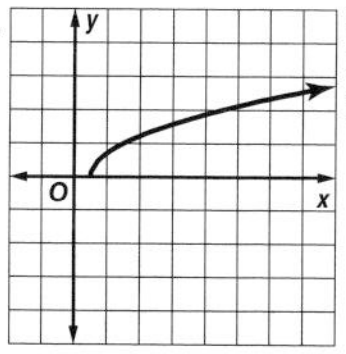
translated right 0.5;
D = {$x \mid x \geq 0.5$},
R = {$y \mid y \geq 0$}

33. 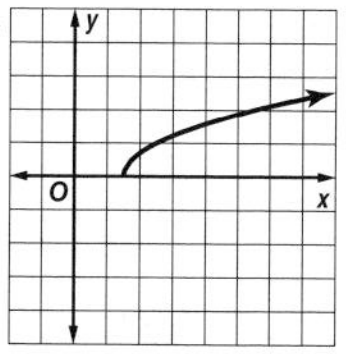
translated right 1.5;
D = {$x \mid x \geq 1.5$},
R = {$y \mid y \geq 0$}

35. 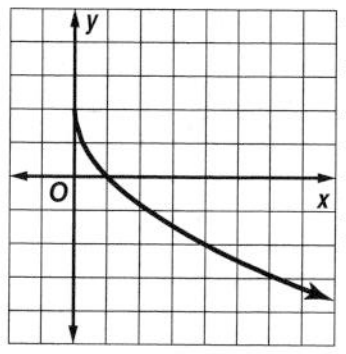
vertical stretch of $y = \sqrt{x}$, reflected across the x-axis, and translated up 2;
D = {$x \mid x \geq 0$},
R = {$y \mid y \leq 2$}

37. 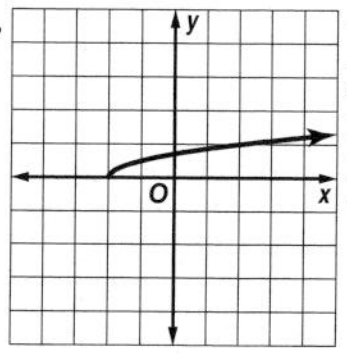
vertical compression of $y = \sqrt{x}$ and translated left 2;
D = {$x \mid x \geq -2$},
R = {$y \mid y \geq 0$}

39. 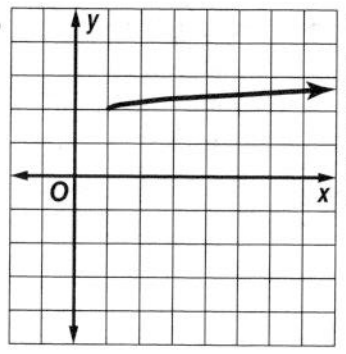
vertical compression of $y = \sqrt{x}$ and translated up 2 and right 1;
D = {$x \mid x \geq 1$},
R = {$y \mid y \geq 2$}

41. 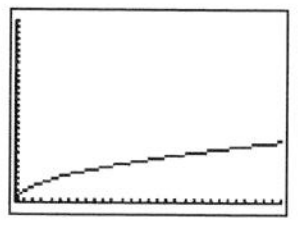
[0, 28] scl: 1 by [0, 28] scl: 1

43 a. Use a graphing calculator to graph the equation.

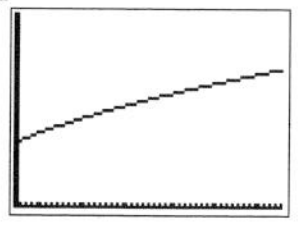
[0, 1000] scl: 20 by [0, 1000] scl: 0.1

b. $c = 331.5\sqrt{1 + \frac{t}{273.15}}$
$= 331.5\sqrt{1 + \frac{55}{273.15}}$
$= 331.5\sqrt{1.201}$
≈ 363.3 m/s

c. When $t = 65°C$:
$c = 331.5\sqrt{1 + \frac{t}{273.15}}$
$= 331.5\sqrt{1 + \frac{65}{273.15}}$
$= 331.5\sqrt{1.238}$
≈ 368.8 m/s

So, an increase of 10°C increases the speed by about 5.5 m/s.

45. False; sample answer: The domain of $y = \sqrt{x + 3}$ includes −1, −2, and −3.

47. $y = \sqrt{x - 4}$

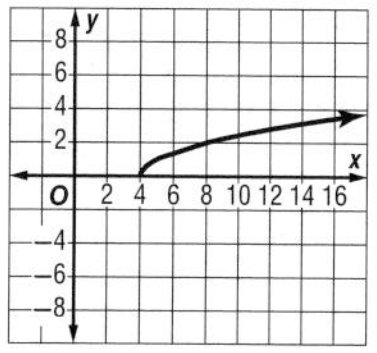

49. $y = \sqrt{x} + 3$; it is a translation of $y = \sqrt{x}$; the other equations represent vertical stretches or compressions. **51.** The value of a is negative. For the function to have negative y-values, the value of a must be negative.
53. A **55.** D

57. 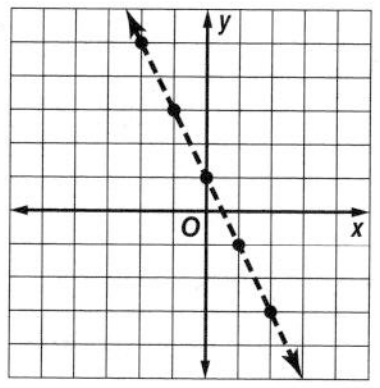
linear

59. 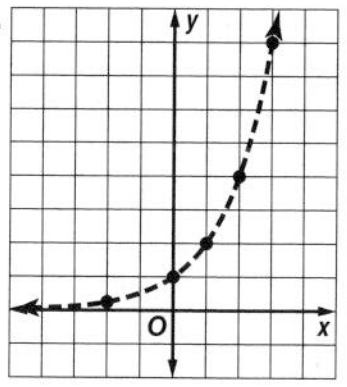
exponential

61. 1280; 5120; 20,480 **63.** 2, 4, 8 **65.** Positive; as the number of grams of fat increases, the amount of Calories increases. **67.** $-3 \cdot 11 \cdot a \cdot a \cdot b$
69. $-2 \cdot 3 \cdot 3 \cdot 3 \cdot 7 \cdot n \cdot q \cdot q \cdot r \cdot r$ **71.** $-2 \cdot 2 \cdot 2 \cdot 2 \cdot 2 \cdot 5 \cdot x \cdot x \cdot y \cdot y \cdot y \cdot y$

Pages 615–617 Lesson 10-2

1. $2\sqrt{6}$ **3.** 10 **5.** $3\sqrt{6}$ **7.** $2x^2|y^3|\sqrt{15y}$
9. $3b^2|c|\sqrt{11ab}$ **11.** $\frac{9 - 3\sqrt{5}}{4}$ **13.** $\frac{2 + 2\sqrt{10}}{-9}$
15. $\frac{24 + 4\sqrt{7}}{29}$ **17.** $2\sqrt{13}$ **19.** $6\sqrt{2}$ **21.** $9\sqrt{3}$
23. $5\sqrt{2}$ **25.** $12\sqrt{14}$ **27.** $15|t|$ **29.** $2|a||b|\sqrt{7b}$
31. $21|m|\sqrt{7mp}$ **33.** $2|a^3||b|\sqrt{5b}$

35 a. $v = \sqrt{64h}$
$= \sqrt{8 \cdot 8h}$
$= \sqrt{8^2} \cdot \sqrt{h}$
$= 8\sqrt{h}$
b. $v = 8\sqrt{h}$
$= 8\sqrt{134}$
≈ 92.6 ft/s

37 $\sqrt{\frac{32}{t^4}} = \frac{\sqrt{32}}{\sqrt{t^4}}$
$= \frac{\sqrt{16 \cdot 2}}{t^2}$
$= \frac{\sqrt{16} \cdot \sqrt{2}}{t^2}$
$= \frac{4\sqrt{2}}{t^2}$

39. $\frac{2|c|\sqrt{51ac}}{9|a|}$ **41.** $\frac{3\sqrt{15}}{20}$ **43.** $\frac{35 - 7\sqrt{3}}{22}$
45. $\frac{6\sqrt{3} + 9\sqrt{2}}{2}$ **47.** $\frac{5\sqrt{6} - 5\sqrt{3}}{3}$ **49a.** $I = \frac{\sqrt{PR}}{R}$
49b. 3.9 amps

51.

Distance	3	6	9	12	15
Height	6	24	4	96	150

53. $\pm\frac{\sqrt{3}}{3}$ **55.** Sample answer: $1 + \sqrt{2}$ and $1 - \sqrt{2}$; $(1 + \sqrt{2})(1 - \sqrt{2}) = 1 - 4 = -3$ **57.** No radicals can appear in the denominator of a fraction. So, rationalize the denominator to get rid of the radicand in the denominator. Then check if any of the radicands have perfect square factors other than 1. If so, simplify. **59.** H **61.** 507.50

63. 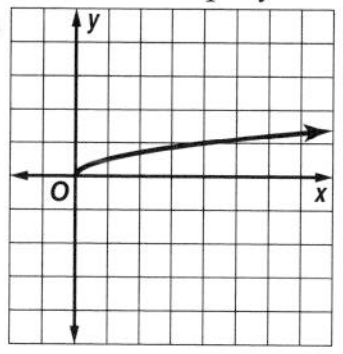
vertical compression of $y = \sqrt{x}$;
D = {$x \mid x \geq 0$},
R = {$y \mid y \geq 0$}

65. 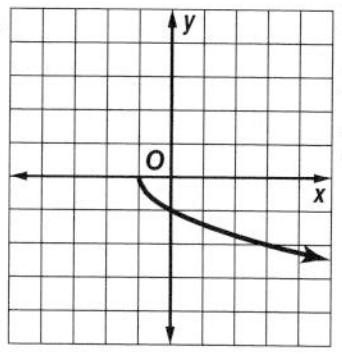
reflected across the x-axis and translated left 1;
D = {$x \mid x \geq -1$},
R = {$y \mid y \leq 0$}

67. 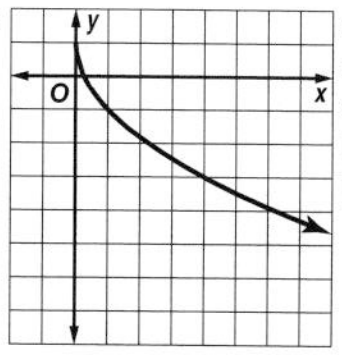
stretched vertically, reflected across the x-axis, and translated up 1
D = {$x \mid x \geq 0$},
R = {$y \mid y \leq 1$}

69. quadratic **71.** about 2,050,422 **73.** ∅
75. −2.9, 2.4 **77.** −0.5, 0.6 **79.** $(2 - 3a)(2 + 3a)$
81. $2(4x^2 + y^2)(2x - y)(2x + y)$ **83.** $(x + 3)(x - 3)(x - 3)$ **85.** $2^3 \cdot 3$ **87.** $2^2 \cdot 3^2 \cdot 5$ **89.** $2^2 \cdot 3 \cdot 5$

Pages 621–623 Lesson 10-3

1 $3\sqrt{5} + 6\sqrt{5} = (3 + 6)\sqrt{5}$
$= 9\sqrt{5}$

3. $-5\sqrt{7}$ **5.** $8\sqrt{5}$ **7.** $5\sqrt{2} + 2\sqrt{3}$ **9.** $72\sqrt{3}$
11. $\sqrt{21} + 3\sqrt{6}$ **13.** $14.5 + 3\sqrt{15}$ **15.** $11\sqrt{6}$
17. $3\sqrt{2}$ **19.** $5\sqrt{10}$ **21.** $60 + 32\sqrt{10}$ **23.** $3\sqrt{5} + 6 - \sqrt{30} - 2\sqrt{6}$ **25.** $5\sqrt{5} + 5\sqrt{2}$ **27.** $\frac{-4\sqrt{5}}{5}$
29. $\sqrt{2}$ **31.** $14 - 6\sqrt{5}$

33 a. $v_0 = \sqrt{v^2 - 64h}$
$= \sqrt{(120)^2 - 64(225)}$
$= \sqrt{0}$
$= 0$ ft/s

b. Sample answer: In the formula, we are taking the square root of the difference, not the square root of each term.

35. $\sqrt{170}$; about 13 amps **37.** $(a\sqrt{b} + c\sqrt{f}) \cdot (a\sqrt{b} - c\sqrt{f}) = a^2\sqrt{b^2} - ac\sqrt{bf} + ac\sqrt{bf} - c^2\sqrt{f^2} = a^2b - c^2f$; Sample answer: This pattern is the difference of squares. **39.** Sample answer: You can use the FOIL method. You multiply the first terms within the parentheses. Then you multiply the outer terms within the parentheses. Then you would multiply the inner terms within the parentheses. And, then you would multiply the last terms within each parentheses. Combine any like terms and simplify any radicals. Sample answer: $(\sqrt{2} + \sqrt{3})(\sqrt{5} + \sqrt{7}) = \sqrt{10} + \sqrt{14} + \sqrt{15} + \sqrt{21}$ **41.** C **43.** C **45.** $2\sqrt{6}$
47. $5|a|b^2\sqrt{2ab}$ **49.** $3|c|d^2f^2\sqrt{7cf}$

For Homework Help, go to Hotmath.com

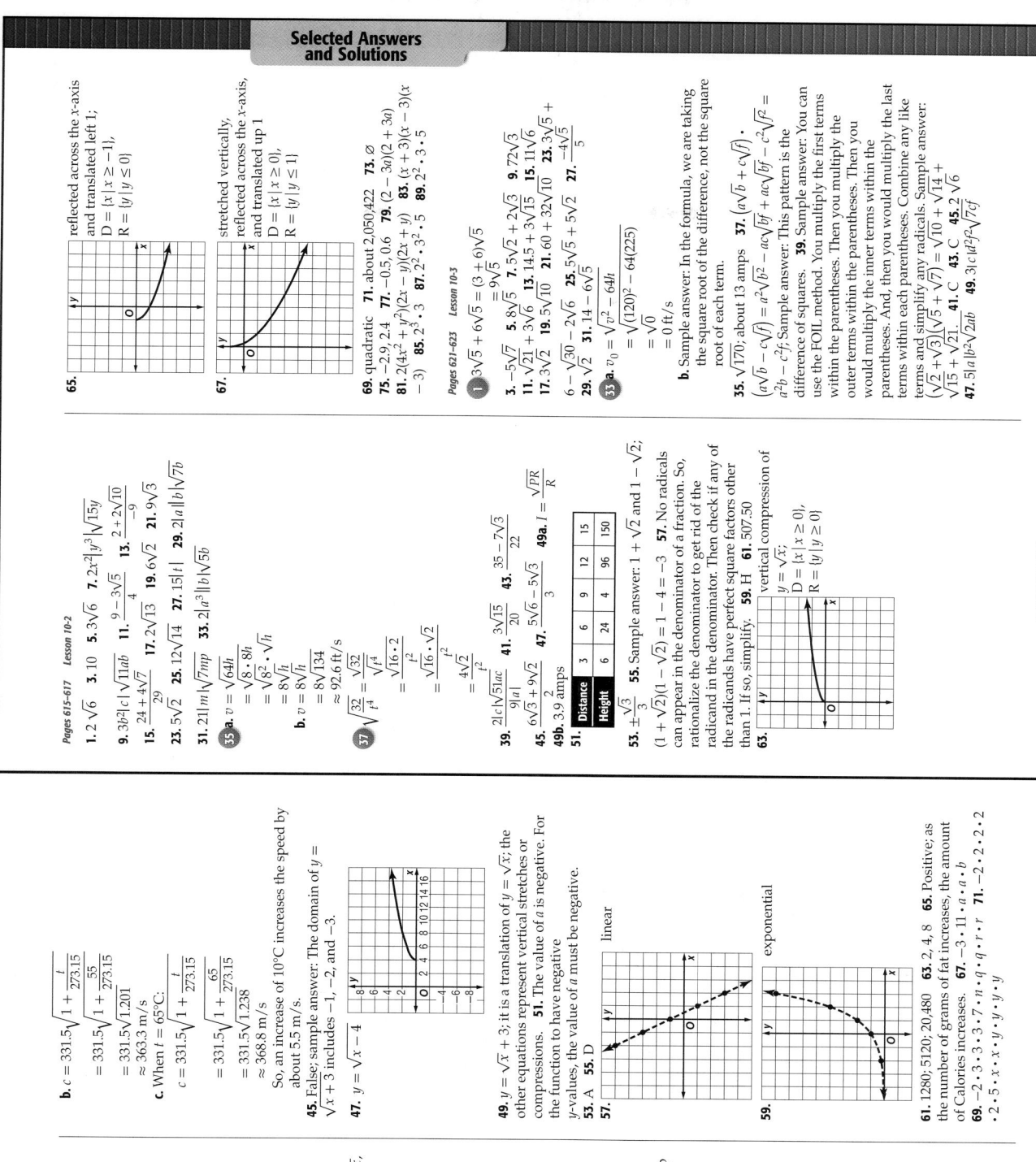

51. 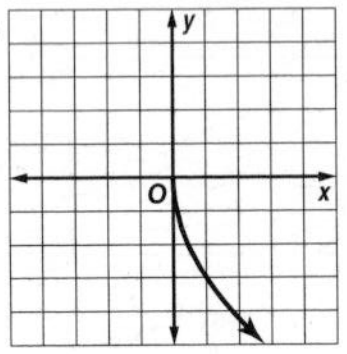
stretched vertically and reflected across the x-axis
D = $\{x \mid x \geq 0\}$,
R = $\{y \mid y \leq 0\}$

53. 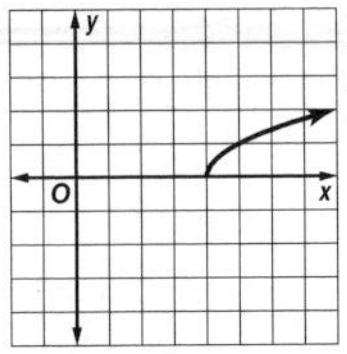
translated right 4;
D = $\{x \mid x \geq 4\}$,
R = $\{y \mid y \geq 0\}$

55. 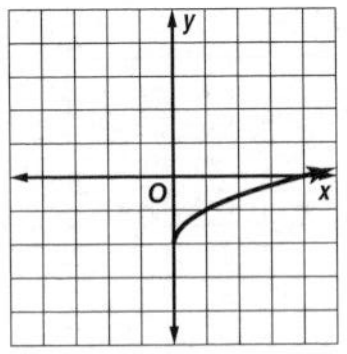
translated down 2;
D = $\{x \mid x \geq 0\}$,
R = $\{y \mid y \geq -2\}$

57. $(x + 3)(x + 9)$ **59.** $(p - 8)(p - 9)$ **61.** $(y - 7)(y + 6)$ **63.** -0.5 **65.** 18.7 **67.** 24

Pages 626–628 Lesson 10-4

1. $r = \frac{\sqrt{\pi x}}{2\pi}$ **3.** 2 **5.** 10 **7.** 6

9
$\sqrt{a} + 11 = 21$
$\sqrt{a} = 10$
$(\sqrt{a})^2 = (10)^2$
$a = 100$

11. 39 **13.** 17 **15.** 3 **17.** 6 **19.** 7 **21a.** 52 ft **21b.** Increases; sample answer: If the length is longer, the quotient and square root will be a greater number than before. **23.** no solution **25.** 235.2 **27.** 3

29 a.
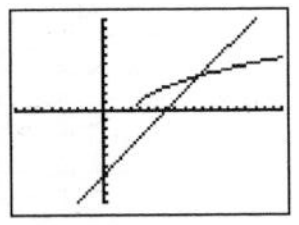
[−10, 20] scl: 1 by [−10, 10] scl: 1

c.
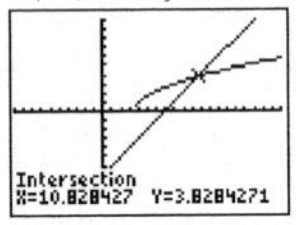

[−10, 20] scl: 1 by [−10, 10] scl: 1

d.
$\sqrt{2x - 7} = x - 7$
$(\sqrt{2x - 7})^2 = (x - 7)^2$
$2x - 7 = x^2 - 14x + 49$
$0 = x^2 - 16x + 56$
$x = \frac{-b \pm \sqrt{b^2 - 4ac}}{2a}$
$= \frac{16 \pm \sqrt{(16)^2 - 4(1)(56)}}{2(1)}$
$= \frac{16 \pm \sqrt{32}}{2}$
≈ 10.83 and 5.17

When checking, 5.17 does not work, so the answer is about 10.83 which is the same as we got using the calculator.

31. Jada; Fina had the wrong sign for $2b$ in the fourth step. **33.** Sample answer: In the first equation, you have to isolate the radical first by subtracting 1 from each side. Then square each side to find the value of x. In the second equation, the radical is already isolated, so square each side to start. Then subtract 1 from each side to solve for x. **35.** Sometimes; the equation is true for $x \geq 2$, but false for $x < 2$. **37.** Sample answer: Add or subtract any expressions that are not in the radicand from each side. Multiply or divide any values that are not in the radicand to each side. Square each side of the equation. Solve for the variable as you did previously. **39.** C **41.** D

43. $4\sqrt{3}$ **45.** $42\sqrt{2}$ **47.** $\frac{c^2\sqrt{5cd}}{2|d^3|}$ **49.** about 1.3 s and 4.7 s **51.** $(2p + 3)(3p - 2)$ **53.** prime **55.** $(2a + 3)(a - 6)$ **57.** Yes; $4x^3$ is the product of a number and three variables. **59.** No; $4n + 5p$ shows addition, not multiplication alone of numbers and variables. **61.** Yes; $\frac{1}{5}abc^{14}$ is the product of a number, $\frac{1}{5}$, and several variables.

63. 1,000,000 **65.** $64v^2$ **67.** $1000y^6$

Pages 632–635 Lesson 10-5

1. 5 **3.** 18.03 **5a.** about 127 ft **5b.** about 127 ft **5c.** about 132 ft **7.** yes **9.** no

11
$a^2 + b^2 = c^2$
$(2)^2 + b^2 = 12^2$
$4 + b^2 = 144$
$b^2 = 140$
$b \approx 11.83$

13. 29.66 **15.** 5.29 **17.** 7.21

19
$a^2 + b^2 = c^2$
$(20)^2 + (26)^2 = c^2$
$400 + 676 = c^2$
$1076 = c^2$
$2.8 \approx c$

The diagonal of the TV stand is about 32.8 inches which is larger than 27 inches, so the TV will fit.

21. no; no **23.** no; no **25.** no, no **27.** yes; yes **29a.** about 20.20 **29b.** 111.1 units^2 **31.** a 30-ft ladder **33.** 8.06 **35.** about 4.24 m **37.** $5\sqrt{3}$ in. or about 8.66 in. **39.** about 6.7 ft **41.** about 42.5 in.

43
$a^2 + b^2 = c^2$
$(8)^2 + x^2 = (x + 2)^2$
$64 + x^2 = x^2 + 4x + 4$
$64 = 4x + 4$
$60 = 4x$
$15 = x$

So, $b = 15$ and $c = 15 + 2$, or 17

45. $a = 65$; $b = 72$ **47.** $a = 9$; $b = 40$; $c = 41$ **49.** about 3.29 cm; about 7.29 cm **51.** $8\sqrt{2}$ **53.** Sample answer:

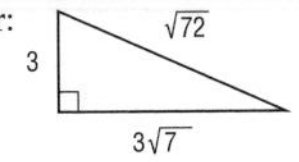

55. C **57.** $88 **59.** 256 **61.** 10 **63.** 3 **65.** $7\sqrt{3}$ **67.** $10\sqrt{7}$ **69.** $12\sqrt{5} - 5\sqrt{3}$ **71.** about $37.27 million; about $41.74 million; about $46.75 million **73.** compressed vertically **75.** translated up 10 **77.** reflected across the x-axis, translated down $\frac{4}{3}$ **79.** $b^2 + 10b + 16$ **81.** $y^2 - 4y - 32$ **83.** $2w^2 + 9w - 35$ **85.** 20 **87.** 8

Pages 638–641 Lesson 10-6

1. $2\sqrt{34}$

3
$d = \sqrt{(x_2 - x_1)^2 + (y_2 - y_1)^2}$
$= \sqrt{(6 - 3)^2 + (-2 - 0)^2}$
$= \sqrt{(3)^2 + (-2)^2}$
$= \sqrt{9 + 4}$
$= \sqrt{13}$

5a. $2\sqrt{29}$ or about 10.77 ft **5b.** $\sqrt{5}$ or about 2.24 ft **7.** −4 or 4 **9.** −18 or 6 **11.** (4, 0) **13.** $\left(-\frac{1}{2}, 0\right)$ **15.** (1, 6) **17.** $\left(-\frac{19}{2}, 14\right)$ **19.** 3 **21.** $\sqrt{34}$ **23.** $\sqrt{106}$ **25.** $\sqrt{365}$ **27.** $\sqrt{29}$ **29.** $8\sqrt{2}$ **31.** −9 **33.** 2 or 4 **35.** 3 or 7 **37.** $\left(\frac{7}{2}, \frac{5}{2}\right)$ **39.** (−2, 7)

41
$M = \left(\frac{x_1 + x_2}{2}, \frac{y_1 + y_2}{2}\right)$
$= \left(\frac{-5 + 3}{2}, \frac{5 + (-3)}{2}\right)$
$= \left(\frac{-2}{2}, \frac{2}{2}\right)$
$= (-1, 1)$

43. $\frac{10}{3}$ or $3\frac{1}{3}$ **45.** $2\sqrt{14}$ **47.** $\sqrt{68} + \sqrt{26} + \sqrt{104} + \sqrt{82}$; 32.6 units

49 a.
$d = \sqrt{(x_2 - x_1)^2 + (y_2 - y_1)^2}$
$= \sqrt{(10)^2 + (8)^2}$
$= \sqrt{100 + 64}$
$= \sqrt{164}$
≈ 12.80 miles

b.
$d = \sqrt{(x_2 - x_1)^2 + (y_2 - y_1)^2}$
$= \sqrt{(6)^2 + (12)^2}$
$= \sqrt{36 + 144}$
$= \sqrt{180}$
≈ 13.42 miles

c.
$d = \sqrt{(x_2 - x_1)^2 + (y_2 - y_1)^2}$
$= \sqrt{(16)^2 + (4)^2}$
$= \sqrt{256 + 16}$
$= \sqrt{272}$
$= 4\sqrt{17}$
≈ 16.49 miles

51. (3.375, −0.25) **53.** $\left(\frac{11}{30}, \frac{23}{20}\right)$ **55.** Sample answer: The Distance Formula requires values to be squared. Once the coordinates and a are substituted into the formula and simplified, the result is a quadratic equation that can result in two possible values for a once solved.

57. Sample answer:
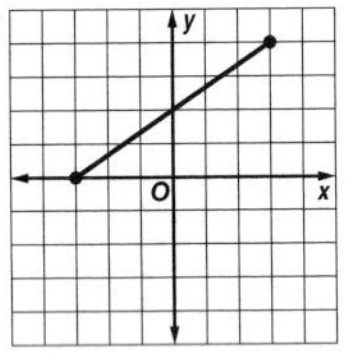

59. 15 mi **61.** H **63.** 65 **65.** 10.72 **67.** 8.19 **69.** 0.06 **71.** 18 **73.** 8.17 **75.** 1.32

Pages 644–647 Lesson 10-7

1. Yes; the angle measures are equal.

3
$\frac{a}{x} = \frac{b}{y} = \frac{c}{z}$
$\frac{4}{6} = \frac{6}{y} = \frac{8}{z}$
$\frac{4}{6} = \frac{6}{y}$
$4y = 6(6)$
$4y = 36$
$y = 9$
$\frac{4}{6} = \frac{8}{z}$
$4z = 6(8)$
$4z = 48$
$z = 12$

5. $c = 6$; $y = 25$ **7.** 17 ft **9.** No; the sides are not proportional. **11.** No; the angle measures are not equal. **13.** Yes; the angle measures are equal. **15.** $m = 3$; $k = 8$ **17.** $k = 4.2$; $r = 0.28$ **19.** $h = \sqrt{5}$; $r = 2$ **21.** 20 in. from S

23
$\frac{1}{10} = \frac{x}{151}$
$1(151) = 10x$
$151 = 10x$
$15.1 = x$
$15\frac{1}{10}$ in. $= x$

25 a. first pair: 3 to 6 or 1 to 2
second pair: 4 to 12 or 1 to 3
third pair: 6 to 24 or 1 to 4

b.

Similar Triangles		Ratios	Perimeter	Ratio of perimeters
Pair 1	smaller triangle	1:2	$2 + 3 + 4 = 9$	1:2
	larger triangle		$4 + 6 + 8 = 18$	
Pair 2	smaller triangle	1:3	$3 + 4 + 5 = 12$	1:3
	larger triangle		$9 + 12 + 15 = 36$	
Pair 3	smaller triangle	1:4	$4 + 6 + 8 = 18$	1:4
	larger triangle		$16 + 24 + 32 = 72$	

c. The perimeters are in the same proportion as the side measures of the two similar triangles.
d. It would be the same or 1:6.
27. $\triangle XYZ \sim \triangle XZW$, $\triangle XYZ \sim \triangle ZYW$, $\triangle XZW \sim \triangle ZYW$; the triangles are similar to each other because the angle measures are equal. **29.** $\triangle PQR$ has a base that is twice the base and twice the height of $\triangle ABC$. The triangles are similar because their corresponding angles are congruent. The area of $\triangle PQR$ is four times the area of $\triangle ABC$.

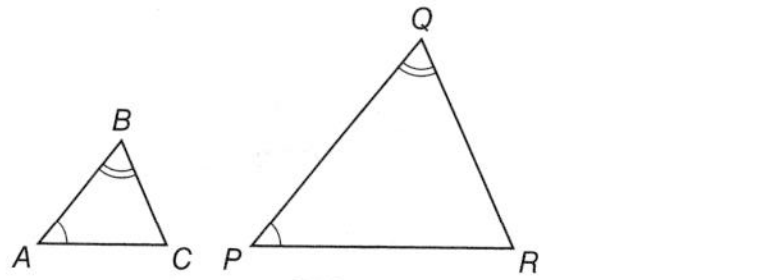

31. D **33.** A **35.** $\sqrt{37}$ **37.** 2 **39.** $5\sqrt{2}$ **41.** yes **43.** yes **45.** no **47.** about 2017 **49.** $4(a - 3b)(a + 3b)$ **51.** $2(5g + 2)^2$ **53.** $2(5n + 1)(2n + 3)$ **55.** $-\frac{1}{3}$ **57.** 2.25 **59.** 8

Pages 652–655 Lesson 10-8

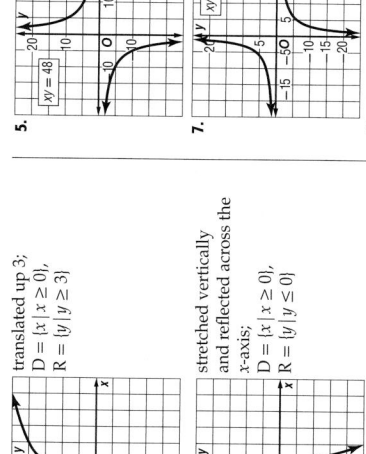

1. $\sin A = \frac{24}{25}$; $\cos A = \frac{7}{25}$; $\tan A = \frac{24}{7}$

3 $\sin A = \frac{\text{opposite}}{\text{hypotenuse}} = \frac{5}{13}$

$\cos A = \frac{\text{adjacent}}{\text{hypotenuse}} = \frac{12}{13}$

$\tan A = \frac{\text{opposite}}{\text{adjacent}} = \frac{5}{12}$

5. 0.6018 **7.** 0.2493 **9.** $m\angle X \approx 51°$; $XY \approx 4.4$; $YZ \approx 5.4$ **11.** $m\angle Q \approx 60°$; $RQ \approx 2.9$; $PQ \approx 5.8$ **13.** about 11,326.2 ft **15.** 66° **17.** 33° **19.** $\sin B = \frac{5}{13}$; $\cos B = \frac{12}{13}$; $\tan B = \frac{5}{12}$ **21.** 0.0349 **23.** 0.7193 **25.** 0.9563 **27.** 0.5

29 Step 1: Find the measure of $\angle Y$.
$180° - (90° + 47°) = 43°$
Step 2: Find $\overline{XY}$ or z. Since you are given the measure of the side opposite $\angle X$, and are finding the measure of the hypotenuse, use the sine ratio.

$\sin 47° = \frac{16}{z}$

$z\sin 47° = 16$

$z = \frac{16}{\sin 47°}$

$z \approx 21.9$

Step 3: Find $\overline{XZ}$ or y. Since you are given the measure of the side opposite $\angle X$, and are finding the measure of the side adjacent to $\angle X$, use the tangent ratio.

$\tan 47° = \frac{16}{y}$

$y\tan 47° = 16$

$y = \frac{16}{\tan 47°}$

$y \approx 14.9$

31. $\angle R = 76°$; $QR = 7.2$; $\overline{PR} = 1.7$ **33.** $\angle Y = 39°$; $\overline{WU} = 11.3$; $\overline{UY} = 18.0$ **35.** about 53 ft **37.** 62° **39.** 31° **41.** 50°

43 $\tan 8° = \frac{5000}{x}$

$x\tan 8° = 5000$

$x = \frac{5000}{\tan 8°}$

$x \approx 35{,}577$ ft

45. $\sin A = \frac{\sqrt{7}}{4}$; $\tan A = \frac{\sqrt{7}}{3}$ **47.** $\cos A = \frac{\sqrt{15}}{4}$; $\tan A = \frac{\sqrt{15}}{15}$ **49.** about 0.5 mi **51.** $a = 5$; $c = 5$ **53.** Sample answer: Find the measure of $\angle A$ in the following triangle; $m\angle A \approx 56°$.

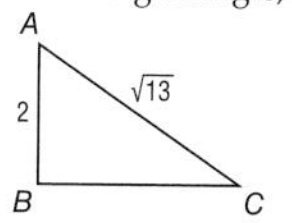

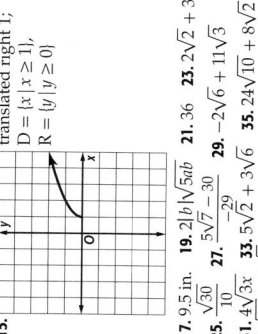

55. Use the angle given and the measure of the known side to set up one of the trigonometric ratios. The sine ratio uses the opposite side and hypotenuse of the triangle. The cosine ratio uses the adjacent side and hypotenuse of the triangle. The tangent ratio uses the opposite and adjacent sides of the triangle. Set up the ratio and solve for the unknown measure. **57.** F **59a.** increase **59b.** Sample answer: The sum of their squares is 16^2 or 256. **59c.** about 15.7 ft **61.** $a = 27$; $c = 12$ **63.** $a = 5$; $f = 8$ **65.** (7, 3) **67.** The amount of sales must be more than $260,000. **69.** 8 **71.** 4.62

Pages 656–660 Chapter 10 Study Guide and Review

1. false; Sample answer: 3, 4, and 5 **3.** true **5.** false; longest **7.** false; $\{x \mid x \geq 0\}$ **9.** true

11.

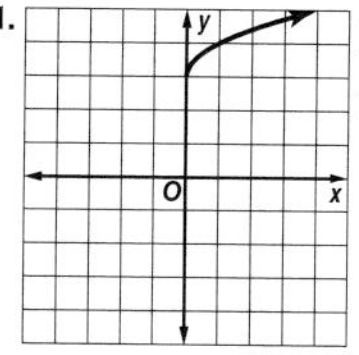

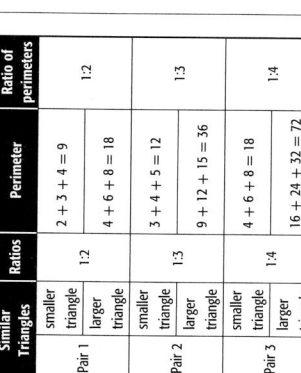

translated up 3;
$D = \{x \mid x \geq 0\}$,
$R = \{y \mid y \geq 3\}$

13.

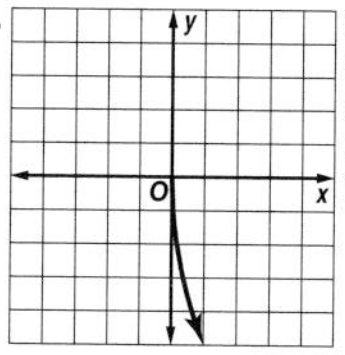

stretched vertically and reflected across the x-axis;
$D = \{x \mid x \geq 0\}$,
$R = \{y \mid y \leq 0\}$

15.

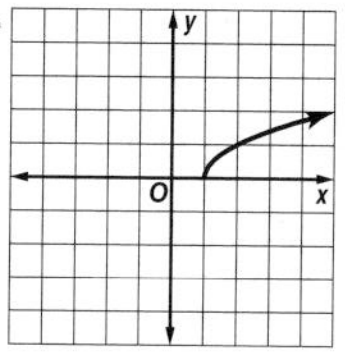

translated right 1;
$D = \{x \mid x \geq 1\}$,
$R = \{y \mid y \geq 0\}$

17. 9.5 in. **19.** $2|b|\sqrt{5ab}$ **21.** 36 **23.** $2\sqrt{2} + 3$ **25.** $\frac{\sqrt{30}}{10}$ **27.** $\frac{5\sqrt{7} - 30}{-29}$ **29.** $-2\sqrt{6} + 11\sqrt{3}$ **31.** $4\sqrt{3x}$ **33.** $5\sqrt{2} + 3\sqrt{6}$ **35.** $24\sqrt{10} + 8\sqrt{2} + 6\sqrt{15} + 2\sqrt{3}$ **37.** no solution **39.** 32 **41.** 12 **43.** 1600 ft **45.** yes **47.** no **49.** yes **51.** no **53.** 5; $\left(-\frac{1}{2}, 4\right)$ **55.** 9.2; $\left(-3, -\frac{7}{2}\right)$ **57.** 18 or −8 **59.** about 4.1 ft **61.** $e = 6, f = 7.5$ **63.** $d = 10$, $e = 14$ **65.** $\cos A = \frac{5}{13}$, $\sin A = \frac{12}{13}$, $\tan A = \frac{12}{5}$ **67.** 6 ft

Chapter 11 Rational Functions and Equations

Page 667 Chapter 11 Get Ready

1. $\frac{8}{3}$ **3.** $\frac{21}{2}$ **5.** $\frac{10}{3}$ or $3\frac{1}{3}$ inches **7.** $5cd$ **9.** $4xy$ **11.** $2x(x - 2)^2$ **13.** $3x(2y + 5)$ **15.** $(x + 3)$, $(x + 2)$

Pages 673–676 Lesson 11-1

1. Direct; the data in the table can be represented by the equation $y = 2x$. **3.** Inverse; $xy = 4$.

5.

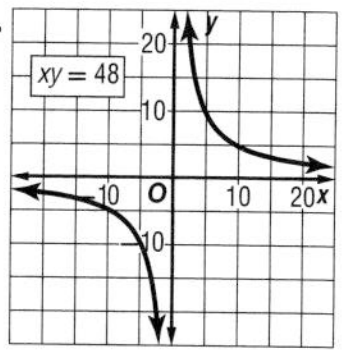

7.

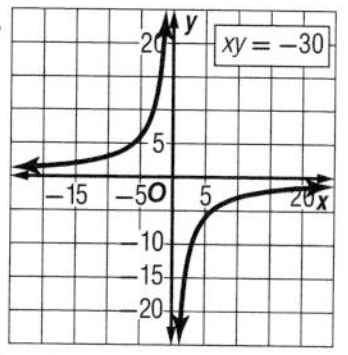

9 $x_1y_1 = x_2y_2$
$(4)(8) = x_2(2)$
$32 = 2x_2$
$16 = x_2$

11. −7.5

13a.

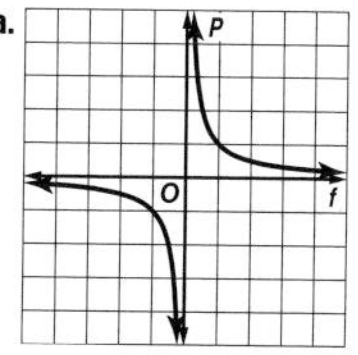

13b. 5 to −2.5 diopters **15.** Direct; $y = -3x$ **17.** Inverse; $xy = -40$ **19.** Inverse; $xy = \frac{1}{4}$ **21.** Direct; $y = 9x$

23.

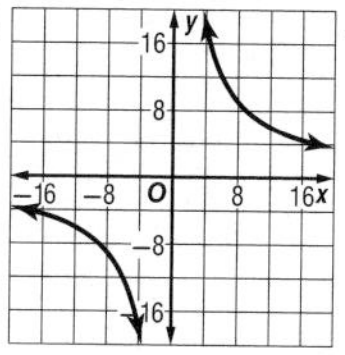

$xy = 72$

25.

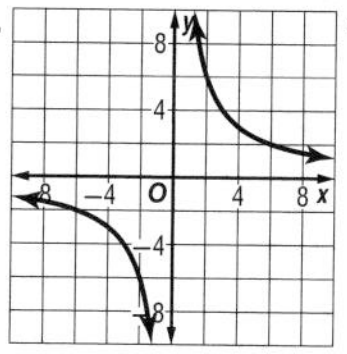

$xy = 12$

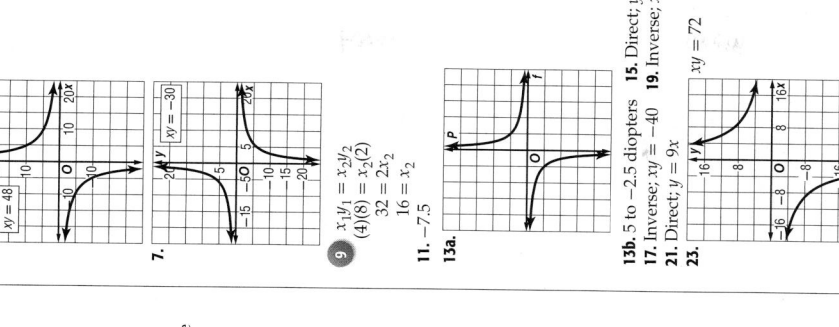

27. 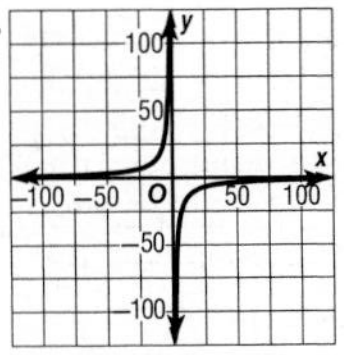 $xy = -108$

29. 15 **31.** −3 **33.** 9.6

35 $x_1y_1 = x_2y_2$
$(420)(523) = (707)y_2$
$219{,}660 = 707y_2$
$311 \approx y_2$
approximately 311 cycles per second

37. Direct; the number of lemonades times the cost per lemonade equals the total cost. So the ratio $\frac{\text{total cost}}{\text{number of lemonades}}$ is a constant $1.50.

39. Inverse; the number of friends times the number of tokens per person equals the constant 30. **41.** Inverse; $xy = 21$ **43.** Direct; $y = \frac{1}{2}x$

45 $x_1y_1 = x_2y_2$
$(9.2)(6) = x_2(3)$
$55.2 = 3x_2$
$18.4 = x_2$

47. 2.5 **49.** $4

51a.

Hours per Week h	Number of Weeks w
1	40
2	20
4	10
5	8
8	5
10	4

51b. The number of weeks decreases.

51c. $hw = 40$ or $w = \frac{40}{h}$

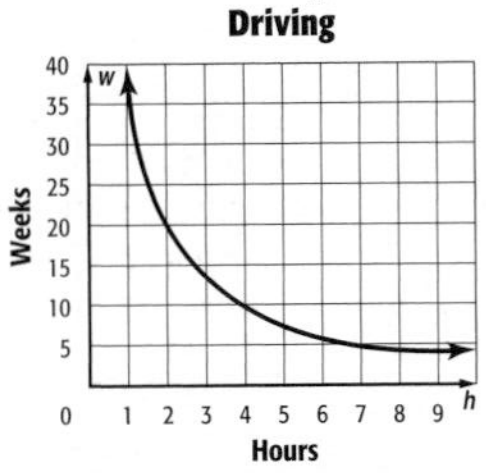

53. direct variation **55.** Sample answer: Newton's Law of Gravitational Force is an example of an inverse variation that models real-world situations. The gravitational force exerted on two objects is inversely proportional to the square of the distances between the two objects. The force exerted on the two objects, times the square of the distance between the two objects, is equal to the gravitational constant times the masses of the two objects. **57.** B **59.** C **61.** $\sin A = 0.7241$, $\cos A = 0.6897$, $\tan A = 1.05$ **63.** $\sin A = 0.8182$, $\cos A = 0.5750$, $\tan A = 1.4230$ **65.** $\frac{9}{10}$ **67.** 1 **69.** no solution **71.** 7^2 or 49 **73.** $\frac{q^4}{2p^5}$ **75.** $\frac{4a^4b^2}{c^6}$ **77.** $\frac{1}{mn}$

Pages 681–683 Lesson 11-2

1. $x = 0$ **3.** $x = 1$

5. 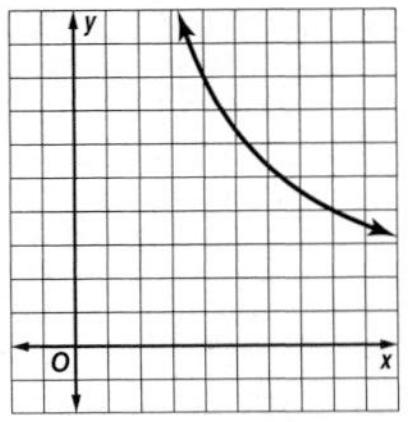

7. $x = 0; y = -1$ 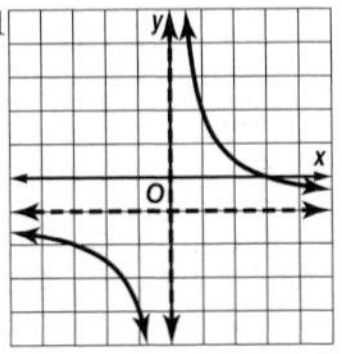

9. $x = -2; y = 0$ 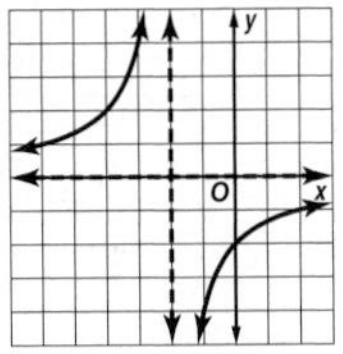

11. $x = -1; y = -5$ 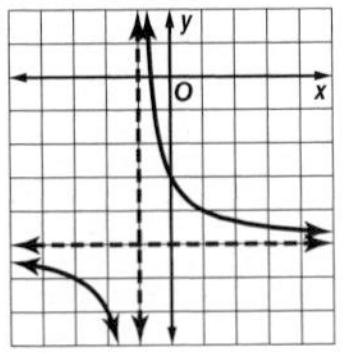

13. $x = 8$ **15.** $x = -6$ **17.** $x = -5$ **19.** $x = -7$

21. 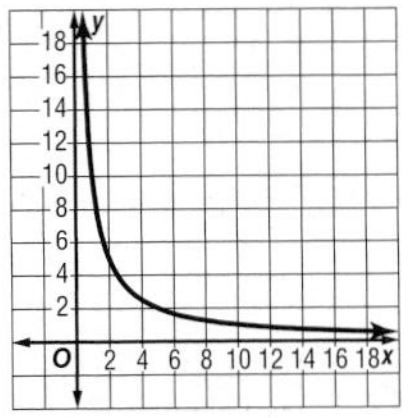

23 Step 1: Identify and graph the asymptotes using dashed lines.
vertical asymptote: $x = 0$
horizontal asymptote: $y = 0$
Step 2: Make a table of values and plot the points. Then connect them.

x	−2	−1	1	2
y	$\frac{3}{2}$	3	3	$\frac{3}{2}$

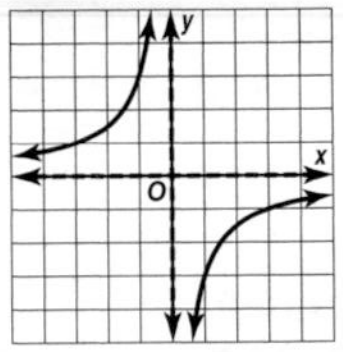

25. $x = 0; y = -2$ 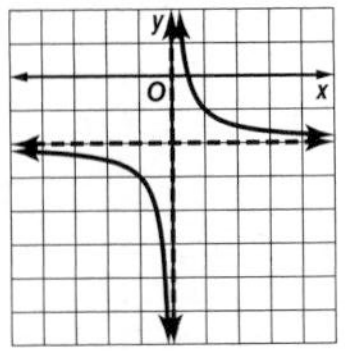

27. $x = 2; y = 0$ 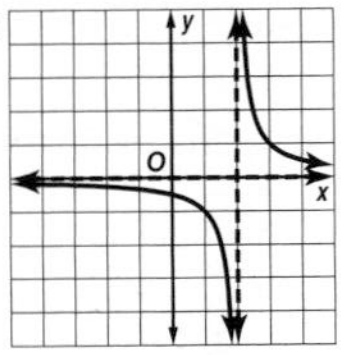

29. $x = 1; y = 0$ 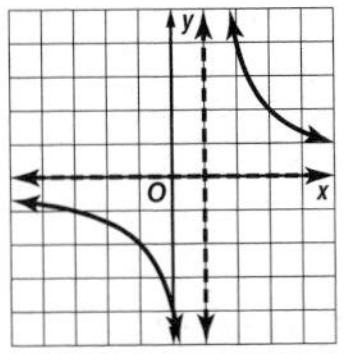

31. $x = 1; y = -2$ 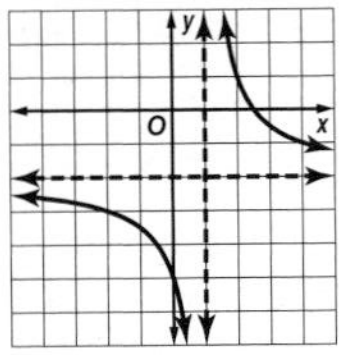

33. $x = -4; y = 3$ 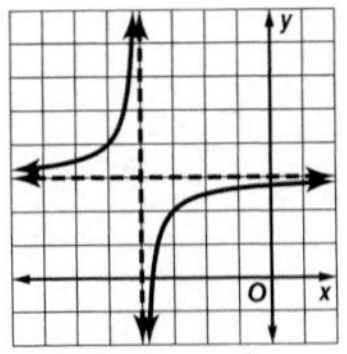

35a. $x = 3$ and $y = 2$ **35b.** $y = \frac{1}{x-3} + 2$

37a. Sample answer: The total cost of the trip equals the cost of a ticket plus the cost of the star-naming package divided by the number of people. **37b.** $y = \frac{95}{p} + 8.50$

37c. 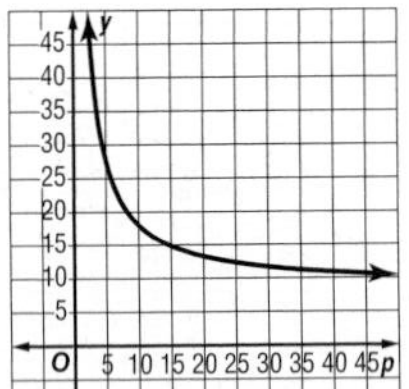

37d. Sample answer: 15 people

39. 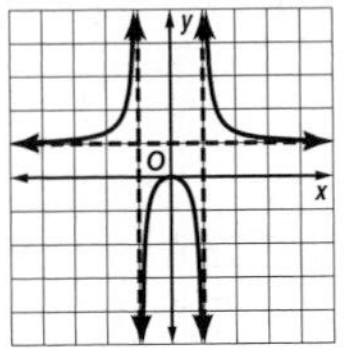 $x = -1, x = 1; y = 1$

41 a. The domain will be positive values since negative values do not make sense for the base of a trapezoid.
The range must also be positive values since negative values do not make sense for the height.
D = {all positive real numbers}
R = {all positive real numbers}

b. Step 1: Identify and graph the asymptotes using dashed lines.
vertical asymptote: $b_1 = -8$
horizontal asymptote: $h = 0$
Step 2: Make a table of values and plot the points. Then connect them.

b_1	2	4	6	8
h	12.8	10.7	9.1	8

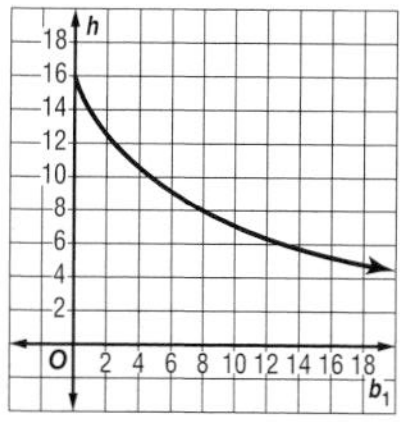

c. When $b_1 = 10$, h will be about 7 units.
43. The graph of $y = \frac{1}{x+5} - 2$ is the graph of $y = \frac{1}{x}$ translated 5 units to the left and 2 units down.
45. False; sample answer: The graph of $y = \frac{1}{x}$ has no x- or y-intercepts. **47.** The vertical asymptote of a rational function occurs for values of x that make the denominator zero. **49.** 45 seconds
51. D **53.** 78° **55.** 40° **57.** 60° **59.** 61.85
61. 10.54 **63.** 9.22 **65.** $\sqrt{465}$ or about 21.56 mi
67. $(w + 16)(w - 3)$ **69.** $(3 + a)(24 + a)$
71. $(d - 2)(d - 5)$ **73.** $(n + 9)(n - 6)$
75. $(4b - 3)(6b + 1)$ **77.** $2(x - 3)(3x + 2)$

Pages 687–690 Lesson 11-3

1. 4, −4 **3.** 16.9 units of force

5 $\frac{(-3r)(10r^4)}{6r^5} = \frac{-30r^5}{6r^5}$
$= -5r^0$
$= -5$

The excluded value is when $6r^5 = 20$, or when $r = 0$.

7. $x + 7$; −4 **9.** $-\frac{3}{9+y}$; −9, 9 **11.** 3 **13.** 1, −1
15. 3, −8 **17.** $\frac{2\pi(5t)}{\pi(5t)^2} = \frac{2}{5t}$; 0 **19.** $\frac{16}{n^2}$; $n \neq 0, p \neq 0$
21. $-2c$; 0 **23.** $\frac{a}{a-6}$; 6, −3 **25.** $x - 4$; −8
27. $\frac{2p}{p+7}$; 7, −7 **29.** $\frac{-(8+c)}{c+1}$; 8, −1

31 $f(x) = \frac{x^2 + 3x - 4}{x^2 + 9x + 20}$
$= \frac{(x+4)(x-1)}{(x+4)(x+5)}$
$= \frac{x-1}{x+5}$

When $x = 1$, $f(x) = 0$, so 1 is the zero of $f(x)$.

33. 2, 4 **35.** 0, 6 **37a.** $\frac{250\pi}{t}$ **37b.** about 157 ft/min
39. $\frac{4x^4 - 5y^2}{y^3}$; $x, y \neq 0$

41 **a.** Surface area: $2(2x^2) + 2(x^2) + 2(2x^2)$
$= 4x^2 + 2x^2 + 4x^2$
$= 10x^2$

Volume: $2x(x)(x) = 2x^3$

So, the ratio is $\frac{10x^2}{2x^3} = \frac{5}{x}$.

The excluded value is when $2x^3 = 0$, or when $x = 0$.

b. Surface area: $2\pi a^2 + 2\pi ab$
Volume: $\pi a^2 b$
So, the ratio is $\frac{2\pi a^2 + 2\pi ab}{\pi a^2 b} = \frac{2\pi a^2}{\pi a^2 b} + \frac{2\pi ab}{\pi a^2 b}$
$= \frac{2a + 2b}{ab}$

The excluded value is when $\pi a^2 b = 0$, or when $a = 0$ or $b = 0$.

43. No; Colleen did not show the simplified expression, and Sanson used the simplified expression to find the excluded value. **45.** Every polynomial P can be written as $\frac{P}{1}$, where the numerator and denominator are polynomials; hence every polynomial is also a rational expression. **47.** No; the numerator and denominator have $x - 2$ as a common factor.
49. C **51.** G **53.** 0 **55.** 3 **57.** 20 **59.** 5
61. 8.4 in. **63.** 13 **65.** $\sqrt{41}$ **67.** $3\sqrt{2}$ **69.** $8\sqrt{2}$
71. $2|a|\sqrt{10}$ **73.** $\frac{\sqrt{6}}{3}$ **75.** $2x$ **77.** 1 **79.** $9qt$

Pages 695–698 Lesson 11-4

1. $4x$ **3.** $\frac{t}{6(t-5)}$ **5.** 6.16 ft/min **7.** $\frac{2}{3x}$ **9.** $\frac{1}{6}$

11 $\frac{10n^2}{4} \cdot \frac{2}{n} = \frac{5n}{1} \cdot \frac{1}{1}$
$= 5n$

13. $9x^4z$ **15.** $3(t + 2)$ **17.** $k + 6$ **19.** $4n$
21a. about \$24.66 **21b.** about \$26.09 **23.** x^4y
25. $\frac{9b^3}{2}$ **27.** $\frac{b-2}{(b+5)(2b+3)}$ **29.** $\frac{x}{2(x-4)}$
31. $\frac{(r+2)^2}{4}$ **33.** 15 mi/h **35a.** 1250 mi ÷ 540 mi/h
35b. 2.3 h **37.** 7,744,000 yd²/mo **39.** about 31.4 mi/h **41.** 6.1 c/min **43.** $\frac{1 \text{ cup}}{1 \text{ beat}} \cdot \frac{70 \text{ beats}}{1 \text{ minute}} \cdot \frac{1 \text{ gallon}}{16 \text{ cups}} \cdot \frac{60 \text{ minutes}}{1 \text{ hour}} = 262.5$ gal/h

45 $\frac{\$9.80}{1 \text{ hour}} \cdot \frac{15 \text{ hours}}{\text{week}} \cdot \frac{52 \text{ weeks}}{\text{year}} = \frac{\$7644}{\text{year}}$

This answer represents earning per year.

47. about 71.6 mi/h; converting 32 meters per second to miles per hour **49.** about 52,506.7 ft/s

51 **a.** $\frac{27 \text{ rotations}}{1 \text{ minute}} \cdot \frac{1 \text{ minute}}{60 \text{ seconds}} \cdot \frac{2\pi(3.1) \text{ meters}}{\text{rotation}}$

b. $\frac{27 \text{ rotations}}{1 \text{ minute}} \cdot \frac{1 \text{ minute}}{60 \text{ seconds}} \cdot \frac{2\pi(3.1) \text{ meters}}{\text{rotation}}$
$\approx \frac{8.8 \text{ meters}}{\text{second}}$

This means that the room moves about 8.8 meters per second.

53. Neither; Tamika did not multiply by the reciprocal, and Mei incorrectly factored out the 2 in $2x + 6$. **55.** $\frac{x-3}{x+7}$ **57.** Sample answer: The height of a cylinder when you know an expression for the volume and radius; $\frac{V}{\pi r^2} = h$; $V = \pi(x^3 - 6x^2 + 9x)$, $r = (x - 3)$. **59.** Sample answer: Write ratios comparing the number of days in one year and the number of hours in one day. Then multiply the ratios: $\frac{365 \text{ days}}{1 \text{ year}} \cdot \frac{24 \text{ hours}}{1 \text{ day}}$; 8760 hours.

61. F **63.** A **65.** $\frac{g^2}{3h}$; $g \neq 0, h \neq 0$ **67.** $y + 8$; −2
69. $\frac{z+2}{z-2}$; 2, 1 **71.** $x = 0, y = 5$ **73.** $x = -3, y = 0$
75. $x = 8, y = -3$ **77.** 0 **79.** 2 **81.** 3 **83.** $\{p \mid 28 \leq p \leq 32\}$ **85.** $(x - 2)(x - 3)$ **87.** $(x + 4)(3x - 5)$
89. $4(x + 2)(2x - 5)$

Pages 702–705 Lesson 11-5

1 $(8a^2 + 20a) \div 4a = \frac{8a^2}{4a} + \frac{20a}{4a}$
$= 2a + 5$

3. $2n^2 - n + \frac{5}{2n}$ **5.** $x - 4$ **7.** $3 + \frac{250}{x+50}$
9. $4y + \frac{3}{y+2}$ **11.** $3n^2 + n - 4 + \frac{4}{3n-1}$ **13.** $a^2 + 4a - 18$ **15.** $2n - 4 + \frac{1}{n}$ **17.** $\frac{3}{2}m + \frac{5}{6}$ **19.** $x - 8$

21 $(k^2 - 5k - 24) \div (k - 8) = \frac{(k^2 - 5k - 24)}{(k-8)}$
$= \frac{(k-8)(k+3)}{k-8}$
$= k + 3$

23. a^2 **25.** $2t - 1$ **27.** $2h^2 - 3$ **29.** $-n + 18 + \frac{850}{n}$
31. $a + 5 + \frac{8}{a-1}$ **33.** $4n + 5 + \frac{16}{n-2}$ **35.** $t^2 - 4t + 14 - \frac{60}{t+4}$ **37.** $2c^2 + c + 2 - \frac{1}{4c-2}$ **39.** $x + 3$
41. $x^2 - 2x + 15 - \frac{16}{x+2}$

43a.

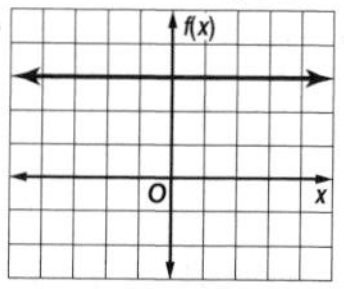

$f(x) = 3 + \frac{7}{x-1}$

43b.

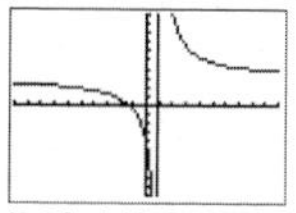

[−10, 10] scl: 1 by [−10, 10] scl:1

43c. The graph of the quotient ignoring the remainder is an asymptote of the graph of the function. **43d.** As x approaches 1 from the left, y approaches negative infinity. As x approaches 1 from the right, y approaches positive infinity.

45 **a.** Words: 212° decreases by 0.9 for every 500 feet above sea level.

Equation: $T = 212 - \left(\frac{0.9}{500}\right)x$

b. $212 - \left(\frac{0.9}{500}\right)x = 212 - \left(\frac{0.9}{500}\right)(14{,}494)$
$= 212 - 26.1$
$= 185.9°$ F

47. Andrea; Alvin did not take into account the missing term. **49.** Sample answer: $(a^2 + 4a - 22) \div (a - 3)$; The polynomial $a^2 + 4a - 22$ is prime, so the problem can be solved by using long division.

51. A **53.** G **55.** $6x$ **57.** $\frac{t}{6(t+4)}$ **59.** −2 **61.** −3
63. 81 **65.** 9 **67.** −10, −2 **69.** −0.8, 1 **71.** −0.4, 3.9 **73a.**

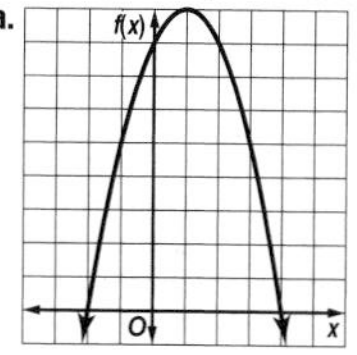

−2 and 4

73b. 9 ft **75.** $-2cd + d^2$ **77.** 24 **79.** 504

Pages 710–713 Lesson 11-6

1. $\frac{5}{7n}$ **3.** $\frac{16r}{9-r}$ **5.** $24t^2$ **7.** $(x - 7)(x - 1)(x + 2)$
9. $\frac{15y + 8x}{20xy}$ **11.** $\frac{16d + 5c}{6cd}$ **13.** $\frac{x^2 - x + 9}{x^2 - x - 6}$

15 $\frac{a}{4} + \frac{3a}{4} = \frac{a + 3a}{4}$
$= \frac{4a}{a}$
$= a$

17. $\frac{2y}{3}$ **19.** $\frac{8b + 3a}{ab}$ **21.** $\frac{c-8}{2c-1}$ **23.** $\frac{1}{2}$ **25.** $\frac{-w+5}{8w}$
27. x^3y^2 **29.** $(3r - 1)(r + 2)$ **31.** $(x + 6)(x + 3)$
33. $\frac{27}{20x}$ **35.** $\frac{15b + 2a}{10ab}$ **37.** $\frac{7 - 4k}{4(k+2)}$ **39.** $\frac{-2t + 28r}{7rt}$
41. $\frac{d^2 + 6d + 35}{(d+5)(d-1)}$ **43.** $\frac{18 - 10t}{15t^2}$ **45.** $\frac{w^2 - 4w - 3}{(w+4)(w-5)}$
47. $\frac{-x^2 - 4x - 9}{(x+3)(x+5)}$ **49a.** $\frac{2}{w} + \frac{2}{2.5w}$; $\frac{7}{2.5w}$ **49b.** 48 min
51. $\frac{32}{2a+18}$

53 $\frac{x+5}{x^2-4} - \frac{3}{x^2-4} = \frac{x+5-3}{x^2-4}$
$= \frac{x+2}{(x+2)(x-2)}$
$= \frac{1}{x-2}$

55. $k + 5$ **57.** $\frac{1}{x-1}$ **59.** $\frac{a-6}{3}$ **61.** $\frac{2x^3 - 16x + 1}{x^4}$
63. $\frac{15x^2 - 11x - 7}{9x^3 + 51x^2 - 80x + 28}$ **65a.** $\frac{9200}{3x}$ **65b.** about 76 min 40 seconds **67.** 8

69 **a.** $t = D/r$
Day 1: $t = \frac{9 + x}{10}$
Day 2: $t = \frac{5 + 3x}{10}$
So, the total for the 2 days was
$\frac{9+x}{10} + \frac{5+3x}{10} = \frac{9 + x + 5 + 3x}{10}$
$= \frac{14 + 4x}{10}$
$= \frac{7 + 2x}{5}$

b. $\frac{7+2x}{5} = \frac{7 + 2(2)}{5}$
$= \frac{7+4}{5}$
$= \frac{11}{5}$ or 2.2 Marina rode her bike 2.2 hours on those 2 days.

For Homework Help, go to Hotmath.com

71. $\frac{4-7y}{21y-6}$ **73.** always; $\frac{a}{x}+\frac{b}{y}=\frac{a}{x}\cdot\frac{y}{y}+\frac{b}{y}\cdot\frac{x}{x}=\frac{ay}{xy}+\frac{bx}{yx}=\frac{ay+bx}{xy}$, $x, y \neq 0$ **75.** First, factor −1 out of one of the denominators so that it is like the other. Then rewrite the denominator without parentheses. Finally, add or subtract the numerators and write the result over the like denominator. **77.** C **79.** C **81.** $5y^2+\frac{14}{3}$ **83.** about 15.7 mi/h **85.** 5 **87.** 11.62 **89.** 1.23×10^4 **91.** 1.255×10^6 **93.** $\frac{2}{3x}$ **95.** $\frac{4}{y+1}$

Pages 171–719 Lesson 11-7

1. $\frac{2+4n}{n}$ **3.** $\frac{6t+11}{t+1}$ **5a.** $\frac{2\frac{1}{2}\text{ mi}}{\frac{1}{3}\text{h}}$ **5b.** $\frac{15}{2}$ or $7\frac{1}{2}$ mi/h **7.** $\frac{3}{25}$ **9.** $\frac{2y^2}{x}$ **11.** $\frac{1}{(x+y)(r+s)}$ **13.** $\frac{p+3}{p^2-p-2}$

15 $\frac{p-7}{2p}=\frac{p(2p)}{2p}-\frac{7}{2p}$
$=\frac{2p^2}{2p}-\frac{7}{2p}$
$=\frac{2p^2-7}{2p}$

17. $\frac{3h^2+h+1}{h}$ **19.** $\frac{n^3+4n^2+n-1}{n+4}$ **21.** $\frac{d^2-12d+43}{d-7}$ **23.** $\frac{3}{4}$ page/min **25.** $\frac{2}{3}$ **27.** $\frac{h}{g^3}$ **29.** $\frac{2a+12}{a}$ **31.** $\frac{(j-4)(j+4)}{15(j+2)}$ **33.** about 140

35 $D=\frac{m}{V}$; $V=\frac{4}{3}\pi r^3$
$D=\frac{m}{\frac{4}{3}\pi r^3}$
$D=\frac{3m}{4\pi r^3}$

a. $D=\frac{3(15.6)}{4\pi(0.0748)^3}\approx 8898.794862$ or 8900
The metal is copper.

b. $D=\frac{3(285.3)}{4\pi(0.1819)^3}\approx 11{,}316.57654$ or 11,300
The metal is lead.

37. $\frac{58x+145}{5x+10}$ **39.** $\frac{c-3}{c+7}$ **41.** $\frac{(x-8)(x-1)}{x+2}$

43. Find the lowest common denominator for the fractions in the numerator and simplify to $\frac{y^2-x^2}{xy}$.

45. $\frac{2t^3}{(t-1)(t^2-1)}$ **47.** Sample answer: Time equals distance divided by rate or $\frac{d}{r}$. When the distance or the rate is given as a fraction or mixed number, the expression $\frac{d}{r}$ becomes a complex fraction. Example: Someone walks $\frac{3}{4}$ mile in $10\frac{1}{2}$ minutes; the time in miles per minute is $\frac{\frac{3}{4}}{10\frac{1}{2}}$, which simplifies to $\frac{1}{14}$ mi/min. **49.** 12 days **51.** B **53.** $\frac{-d+4}{d-1}$ **55.** $\frac{6m^2-1}{15m^3}$ **57.** $\frac{b^2+4b+18}{(b+3)(b-2)}$ **59.** $a+7-\frac{1}{a-3}$ **61.** $3y^2+2y-3-\frac{1}{y+2}$

63. $3h^2+2h+3-\frac{2}{3h-2}$

65.

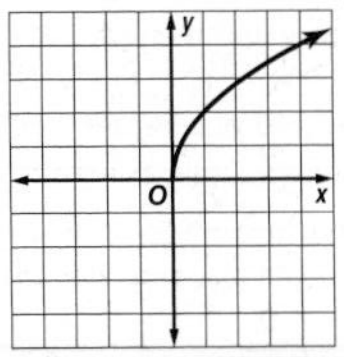

D = {x | x ≥ 0}; R = {y | y ≥ 0}

67.

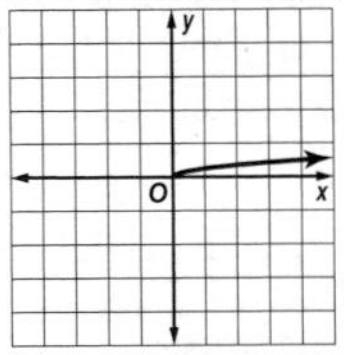

D = {x | x ≥ 0}; R = {y | y ≥ 0}

69. $(a-11)(a+11)$ **71.** $(2y-5)(2y+5)$ **73.** $4(t-1)(t+1)(t^2+1)$ **75.** 4 **77.** 7 **79.** −11.5

Pages 724–726 Lesson 11-8

1. −2 **3.** $-\frac{4}{5}$ **5.** −3 **7.** $\frac{15}{38}$ hour or about 0.4 hour

9 $\frac{8}{n}=\frac{3}{n-5}$
$8(n-5)=3n$
$8n-40=3n$
$-40=-5n$
$8=n$

11. $\frac{2}{3}$ **13.** −13 **15.** 0 **17.** −2, 3 **19.** no solution; extraneous: 1 **21.** $\frac{15}{8}$ hours or $1\frac{7}{8}$ hours **23.** 26.2 hours **25a.** line **25b.** $f(x)=\frac{(x+5)(x-6)}{x-6}=x+5$ **25c.** −5 **27a.** parabola **27b.** $f(x)=x^2+6x+12$ **27c.** no real zeros **29a.** $s=r-w$; $s=r+w$ **29b.** $d=t(r-w)$, $d=t(r+w)$; $t=\frac{d}{r-w}$, $t=\frac{d}{r+w}$

31 **a.** $h=\frac{kp}{c}$
b. $8=\frac{k(100)}{5}$
$8=20k$
$\frac{2}{5}=k$
$h=\frac{\frac{2}{5}p}{c}$
$=\frac{\frac{2}{5}(100)}{10}$
= 4 hours

33. $-1\pm\sqrt{7}$; extraneous: −2 and 0 **35.** $\frac{50}{11}$ **37.** The extraneous solution of a rational equation is the excluded value of one of the expressions in the equation. **39.** Sample answer: $\frac{x}{8}=0$ **41.** D **43.** D **45.** $\frac{d}{c}$ **47.** $\frac{b-3}{2b}$ **49.** $4h^2$ **51.** $(x-4)(x+2)$ **53.** linear **55.** quadratic **57.** $0.5Bb+0.5b^2$; $\frac{1}{2}$

59. {r | r > 49} **61.** 0.3 **63.** 0.75

Pages 727–731 Chapter 11 Study Guide and Review

1. false; x^2-25 **3.** true **5.** true **7.** false; complex fraction **9.** false; inverse variation **11.** $\frac{1}{3}$ **13.** $-\frac{9}{16}$ **15.** 3 **17.** 2

19.

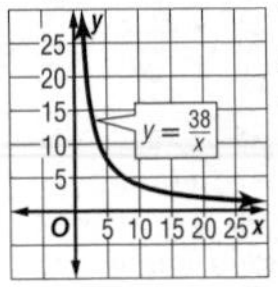

The vertical asymptote is at $x = 0$ and the horizontal asymptote is at $y = 0$.

21. $\frac{1}{x+8}$ **23.** $\frac{y-5}{y-2}$ **25.** $\frac{1}{2y(y+2)}$ **27.** $-\frac{3}{2}, \frac{1}{3}$ **29.** $\frac{3}{x^2-3x}$ **31.** $\frac{3}{(b+4)(b-2)}$ **33.** xy **35.** x^2+4x-2 **37.** $4y+1+\frac{8}{12y-1}$ **39.** $\frac{3a}{b}$ **41.** $\frac{-y^2+2y-9}{(y+1)(y-3)}$ **43.** 4 ft **45.** $\frac{x^2+8x-65}{x^2+8x+12}$ **47.** $\frac{y^2+11y+10}{y^2+6y+8}$ **49.** $\frac{2}{5}$, extraneous: 2 **51.** 24 **53.** −2, 4

Chapter 12 Probability and Statistics

Page 737 Chapter 12 Get Ready

1. $\frac{3}{7}$ **3.** $\frac{4}{7}$ **5.** $\frac{1}{6}$ **7.** $\frac{5}{6}$ **9.** $\frac{7}{256}$ **11.** $\frac{84}{625}$ **13.** 82.4% **15.** 85.6% **17.** 35%

Pages 743–745 Lesson 12-1

1. Sample: the 10 teens; population: all teens; observational study **3.** Unbiased; each student is equally likely to be the tenth student. **5.** Sample: the rookie cards; population: all of the cards; stratified, because the cards are divided before the sample is selected.

7 Sample answer: The sample is the 100 people the test. The population is all people. The type of data collection is an experiment because they give the people the food and ask what they think.

9. Sample: the customers for the past two years; population: all past customers; survey **11.** Biased; they only poll customers who check out books. **13.** Biased; because the park only asked teens, the respondents are more likely to select certain rides.

15 Sample answer: The sample is the blog readers. The population is all artists. This sample is simple because the sample is equally likely to be chosen.

17. Sample: every fiftieth customer; population: all of the customers; systematic: a customer was selected at a regular interval. **19a.** the people that they surveyed; all customers **19b.** observational study **19c.** Unbiased; each person is equally likely to be chosen. **19d.** systematic **21.** Sample answer: This method of selecting a sample is valid. Each student has an equally likely chance of being selected for the sample. A weakness may be that this would not reflect that one grade may feel more strongly about the dress code than another. **23.** Sample answer: A video game company wants to know how their game compares with its competitors. So, they set up a room with the game and three games of their competitors and observe which game the people in the sample prefer. **25.** 90 **27.** F **29.** −6 **31.** −6 **33.** $\frac{4}{3}$ **35.** $-\frac{2}{5}$ **37.** $\frac{1}{2}$ **39a.** ≈ 415.8 ft **39b.** ≈ 212.6 ft

Pages 750–755 Lesson 12-2

1. Mode; there are repeating values in the data; 15.

3 Sample answer: Not valid; there is no mention of what kind of format the station currently has. People are more likely to respond if they already listen to that station or that format.

5. Sample answer: The Key Club is volunteer organization, so the data may be biased.
7. The data in the graph support the conclusion. The display is accurate.

9 List the values from least to greatest: 10, 13, 14, 15, 16, 16, 17, 18, 19.
There is no one value that is much greater or less than the rest of the data. Also, there does not appear to be a big gap in the middle of the data. So, the mean would best represent the data. The mean is approximately 15.33.

11. Mean; the data are weighted and the weighted average needs to be calculated in ordered to determine customer response. **13.** Cannot be calculated; the data values represent different things. **15.** Sample answer: The data seem to be unbiased. The survey is valid.

17 This is not valid because the sample is not mentioned and there is no way to determine the sample size.

19. Sample answer: The data seem unbiased, the source seems reputable, the data support the conclusion. The survey is valid. **21.** Sample answer: Because the source of the survey is Smart Girl, the sample is most likely to be girls and therefore, you are unable to make an unbiased conclusion about all teens.

23 Sample answer: The conclusion is too broad for the data presented.

25. Sample answer: The Red Cross should continue to offer the babysitting class. While only 10% of its participants are in the class, that is still one of the higher percents, and the service is an important one. **27.** Yes; there are no similar colors and there is numerical data for each section. **29.** Ben; there were no large gaps, no repeated values, but there was an outlier of 32. **31.** Sample answer: I would like to conduct a survey about chewing gum in school. I would use a sample selected by randomly picking 50 names from each grade to represent the student body. I would give a series of questions that would evaluate the students' attitudes about the gum chewing policy. I would display the results in a series of bar graphs, one for each question. **33.** D **35.** C **37.** 20 seniors; senior class; unbiased; simple **39.** Mayfield High School; everyone who participated in survey; stratified **41.** −3 **43.** $\sin A = \frac{4}{5}$; $\cos A = \frac{3}{5}$; $\tan A = \frac{4}{3}$

45. $\sin A = \frac{4}{5}$; $\cos A = \frac{3}{5}$; $\tan A = \frac{4}{3}$

47. 29.3; 29; no mode **49.** 4.3; 4; 1 **51.** 26.4; 26.5; 25

Pages 759–762 Lesson 12-3

1. sample: 1003 voters in Mercy County; population: all voters in Mercy County; sample statistic: the number of people in the sample who would vote for the incumbent candidate; population parameter: the number of people in the county who would vote for the incumbent candidate **3.** 6 **5.** 12.6, 57.0, 7.6 **7.** 2.5

9 Sample: stratified random sample from schools in the county
Population: all high shool students in the county
Sample Statistic: time spent each week on extracurricular activites by the sample
Population Parameter: time spent each week on extracurricular activites by all students in the county

11. 3.5

13 Step 1: To find the mean, add the numbers and then divide by how many numbers are in the data set.

$x = \frac{76 + 78 + 83 + 74 + 75}{5}$

$= \frac{386}{5}$

$= 77.2$

Step 2: To find the variance, square the difference between each number and the mean. Then divide by the number of values.

$\sigma^2 = [(76 - 77.2)^2 + (78 - 77.2)^2 + (83 - 77.2)^2 + (74 - 77.2)^2 + (75 - 77.2)^2] \div 5$

$= \frac{50.8}{5}$

≈ 10.2

Step 3: The standard deviation is the square root of the variance.

$\sigma^2 = 10.2$

$\sqrt{\sigma^2} = \sqrt{10.2}$

$\sigma \approx 3.2$

15. 0.4, 0.1, 0.3 **17.** 5.0 **19.a.** Sample answer: The pennies chosen by Tyrone, Lydia, and Peter each represent a sample. The 30 pennies in the jar is the population. The sample statistic is the mean year of the pennies in the sample. The population parameter is the mean year of the pennies in the population. **19b.** ≈ 1984, ≈ 9.0

19c. ≈ 2001, ≈ 3.2 **19d.** ≈ 1998, ≈ 6.4

19e. ≈ 1997, ≈ 7.4; Peter's sample was the most accurate. The mean year of his sample was 1 year off from the actual mean year. The samples that had more pennies were more accurate.

21 **a.** Step 1: To find the mean, add the numbers and then divide by how many numbers are in the data set.

$x = 956 + 966 + 971 + 981 + 986 + 991 + 1001 + 1014 + 1020 + 1023 + 1034 + 1066 + 1076 + 1077 + 1083/15$

$= \frac{15245}{15}$

$= 1016.3$ seconds or 16.9 minutes

Step 2: To find the mean absolute deviation, first find the sum of the absolute values of the differences between each value in the set of data and the mean.

$|956 - 1016.5| + |966 - 1016.5| + |971 - 1016.5| + |981 - 1016.5| + |986 - 1016.5| + |994 - 1016.5| + |1001 - 1016.5| + |1014 - 1016.5| + |1020 - 1016.5| + |1023 - 1016.5| + |1034 - 1016.5| + |1066 - 1016.5| + |1076 - 1016.5| + |1077 - 1016.5| + |1083 - 1016.5| = 499.5$

Step 3: Then divide the sum by the number of values in the data set.

$\frac{499.5}{15} \approx 33.3$ seconds

b. The sample is the top 15 runners. The population is all the people who ran.

c. The data is quantitative. No, since the sample is the top 15 runners in the race, it is not random. So, it would not be accurate to apply the mean and standard deviation of the running times to the population.

23. 8.75, 3.6 **25.** A statistic is a characteristic that is computed on a sample of the population. A parameter is a characteristic of the entire population. Sample answer: To determine the average height of a student at your high school, you can measure the heights of a random sample of students at your school. The mean height of the sample is a statistic; the actual mean height of the students at your school is a parameter.

27. Both are calculated statistical values that show how each data value deviates from the mean of the data set. The mean absolute deviation is calculated by taking the mean of the absolute values of the differences between each number and the mean of the data set. To find the standard deviation, you square each difference and then take the square root of the mean of the squares. **29.** 125 **31.** A

33. Mode; one value is repeated; 85. **35.** Biased; because they are at a rock concert, they are more likely to select a rock music station. **37.** $\frac{3}{22}$

39. $\frac{1}{2}$ **41.** $\frac{8}{11}$

Pages 767–770 Lesson 12-4

1. 720

3 $P(n, r) = \frac{n!}{(n - r)!}$

$P(9, 3) = \frac{9!}{(9 - 3)!}$

$= \frac{9!}{6!}$

$= \frac{9 \cdot 8 \cdot 7 \cdot 6 \cdot 5 \cdot 4 \cdot 3 \cdot 2 \cdot 1}{6 \cdot 5 \cdot 4 \cdot 3 \cdot 2 \cdot 1}$

$= 504$

5. 10 **7.** 720

9 The number of ways is $4 \cdot 3 \cdot 2 \cdot 1 = 24$ ways

11. 720 **13.** 720 **15.** 4 **17.** 7 **19.** 1 **21.** 1,814,400

23. $\frac{49}{646}$ or about 7.59%

25 This is a combination because the order of the toppings put on the pizza does not matter.

27. combination **29.** combination **31a.** 495

31b. 24 arrangements **31c.** 9; ART, ATE, ARE, TAR, TEA, RAT, EAT, EAR, ERA **33.** 792 groups **35.** Ming; since order is not important, combinations should have been used.

37. Determining class rank in a senior class; this is the only situation in which order matters.

39. Sample answer: choosing 3 clubs out of 8 to join **41.** G **43.** $\frac{3}{20}$ **45.** 26; 187.4, 13.7

47. 4, 6.8, 2.6 **49.** 2 bags **51** $\frac{2}{n}$ **53.** $\frac{n - 4}{n + 4}$

55. $\frac{12ag}{5b}$ **57.** $\frac{6}{23}$ **59.** $\frac{8}{23}$ **61.** $\frac{17}{23}$

Pages 775–778 Lesson 12-5

1. dependent; $\frac{28}{253}$ or about 11% **3.** independent; $\frac{4}{9}$ or about 44% **5.** mutually exclusive; $\frac{2}{13}$ or about 15% **7.** not mutually exclusive; $\frac{4}{13}$ or about 31%

9. independent; $\frac{1}{16}$ or about 6%

11 These events are dependent because the chocolate is not being replaced.

First, milk chocolate: $P = \frac{10}{24}$

Second, white chocolate: $P = \frac{6}{23}$

$P(\text{milk, then white}) = \left(\frac{10}{24}\right)\left(\frac{6}{23}\right)$

$= \frac{60}{552}$

$= \frac{5}{46}$ or about 11%

13. dependent; $\frac{5}{19}$ or about 26% **15.** mutually exclusive; $\frac{3}{4}$ or 75% **17.** not mutually exclusive; $\frac{739}{750}$ or about 98.5% **19.** $\frac{8}{87}$ or about 9%

21. $\frac{42}{145}$ or about 29%

23 choose white sock: $P = \frac{14}{24}$

choose white sock: $P = \frac{13}{23}$

$P(\text{milk, then white}) = \left(\frac{14}{24}\right)\left(\frac{13}{23}\right)$

$= \frac{182}{552}$

$= \frac{91}{276}$ or about 33%

25. $\frac{1}{2}$ or 50% **27.** $\frac{4}{221}$ or about 19% **29.** $\frac{7}{13}$ or about 54% **31a.** 345 **31b.** 159 **31c.** $\frac{227}{345}$ or about 66% **31d.** $\frac{2}{23}$ or about 9%

33 **a.**

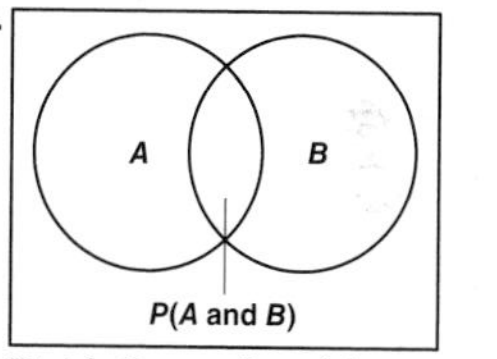

b. Divide the overlap of the two circles by the $P(A)$ circle; $P(B/A) = \frac{P(A \text{ and } B)}{P(A)}$.

c. $P(\text{red}) = \frac{8}{12} = \frac{2}{3}$

$P(\text{red, green}) = \left(\frac{2}{3}\right)\left(\frac{4}{11}\right)$

$= \frac{8}{33}$

d. $P(\text{green/red}) = \frac{\frac{8}{33}}{\frac{2}{3}}$

$= \frac{8}{33} \cdot \frac{3}{2}$

$= \frac{4}{11}$

e. $P(B \mid A) = \frac{P(A \text{ and } B)}{P(A)}$

f. $P(B \mid A) = \frac{P(A \text{ and } B)}{P(A)}$

$= \frac{0.20}{0.80}$

$= 0.25$ or 25%

35. 21 **37.** Sample answer: Choosing a CD to listen to, putting it back, and then choosing another CD to listen to would be an independent event since the CD was placed back before the second CD was chosen. Choosing a pair of jeans to wear would be a dependent event if I did not like the first pair chosen, and I did not put them back.

39. C **41.** 2 ft **43a.** combination **43b.** 220

43c. $\frac{210}{1320}$ or 16% **45.** 8 **47.** $-\frac{3}{2}$ **49.** about 57 pieces **51.** −12 **53.** −16 **55.** −63

Pages 781–784 Lesson 12-6

1a. $\frac{47}{1000} = 0.047 = 4.7\%$ **1b.** $\frac{2871}{5000} = 0.5742 = 57.4\%$ **3a.** $\frac{1}{5} = 0.2 = 20\%$ **3b.** $\frac{68}{165} \approx 0.4121 \approx 41.2\%$

5a. $P = \frac{96}{100} + \frac{112}{600}$
$= \frac{208}{600}$
$= \frac{26}{75}$ or about 34.7%

b. $P = \frac{108}{600} + \frac{80}{600}$
$= \frac{188}{600}$
$= \frac{47}{150}$ or about 31.3%

7a. $\frac{87}{178} \approx 0.4888 \approx 48.9\%$ **7b.** $\frac{91}{178} \approx 0.5112 \approx 51.1\%$

9a. All of the values in data are between 0 and 1. $0.29 + 0.43 + 0.17 + 0.11 + 0 = 1$ so the distribution is valid.
b. $P = 0.43 + 0.17 + 0.11 + 0$
$= 0.71$ or 71%
c. Use the data from the probability distribution table to draw a graph. Remember to label each axis and give the graph a title.

Algebra Test Grades

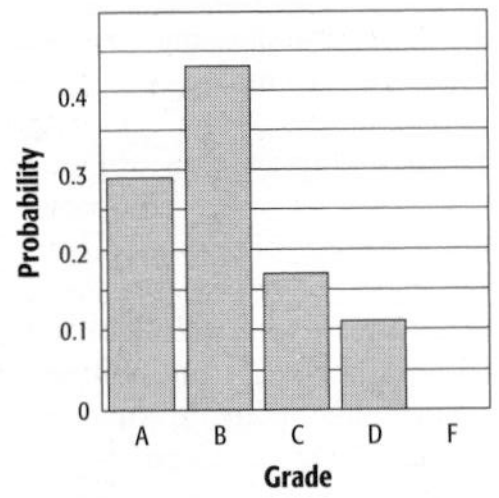

11a. $0.35 + 0.32 + 0.17 + 0.11 + 0.05 = 1$ so the distribution is valid.
b. $P = 0.17 + 0.11$
$= 0.28$ or 28%
c. Use the data from the probability distribution table to draw a graph. Remember to label each axis and give the graph a title.

Shopping Places

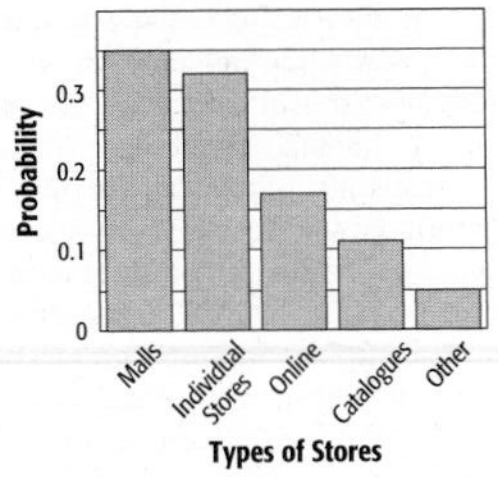

13a. $\frac{1}{6}, \frac{1}{3}, \frac{1}{2}$
13b. Sample answer: 1: 6; 2: 3; 3: 7; 4: 0; 5: 2; 6: 2
13c. Sample answer:

1	0.3
2	0.15
3	0.35
4	0
5	0.1
6	0.1

13d. $0.15 = \frac{3}{20} = 15\%$; $0.4 = \frac{2}{5} = 40\%$; $0.75 = \frac{3}{4} = 75\%$; The first set of probabilities were predictions based on everything being equal. The second set were based on what actually happened.
15. The sum 7 is most likely to happen.

X = Sum of Dice	2	3	4	5	6	7	8	9	10	11	12
Probability	$\frac{1}{36}$	$\frac{1}{18}$	$\frac{1}{12}$	$\frac{1}{9}$	$\frac{5}{36}$	$\frac{1}{6}$	$\frac{5}{36}$	$\frac{1}{9}$	$\frac{1}{12}$	$\frac{1}{18}$	$\frac{1}{36}$

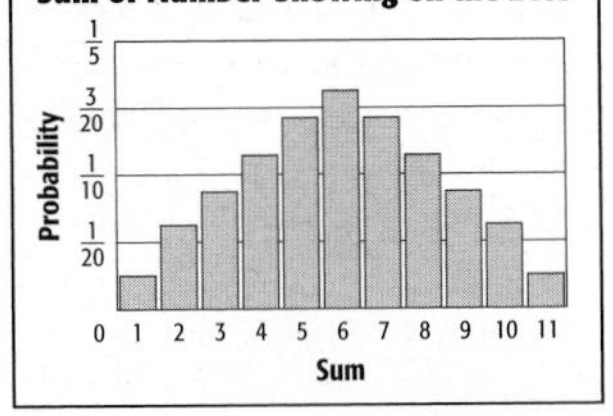

17. Sample answer: There are 870 students in a school: 179 freshmen, 215 sophomores, 211 juniors, and 265 seniors. Find the probability distribution for each class. What is the probability that a randomly chosen student is a sophomore?

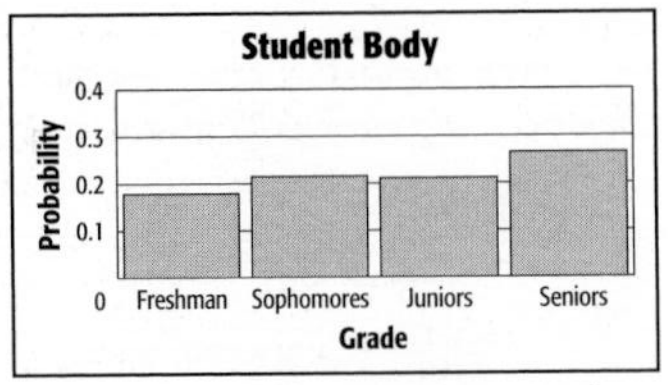

19. D **21.** J **23.** $\frac{10}{253}$ or about 4% **25.** $\frac{1}{8}$ **27.** $\frac{1}{8}$ **29.** $\frac{6a+4}{a^2}$ **31.** $\frac{9d+10}{(d+6)(d-5)}$ **33.** $\frac{9h(h-2)}{(h+6)(h-3)}$ **35.** $\frac{1}{2^n}$ **37.** $\frac{1}{2^n}$

Pages 789–792 Lesson 12-7

1a. $\frac{3}{10}$ or 30% **1b.** $\frac{47}{150}$ or about 31%
3a. You could flip a coin where heads represents true and tails represents false.
b. Flip a coin 20 times and record the results using heads for true and tails for false.
5a. $\frac{1}{5}$ or 20% **5b.** $\frac{16}{25}$ or 64% **5c.** $\frac{3}{10}$ or 30%
7 You could spin a spinner with 4 equal sections. The first section could represent the first choice, the second section could represent the second choice, the third section could represent the third choice and the fourth section could represent the fourth choice.
11 This will depend on students work. Sample answers are given:
a. $P(\text{3 heads}) = \frac{1}{4}$
b. $P(\text{2 heads}) = \frac{3}{8}$
c. $P(\text{1st and last heads}) = \frac{1}{16}$

13a. Sample answer:

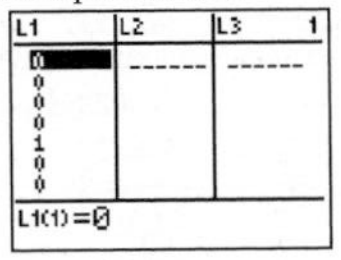

13b. Sample answer:

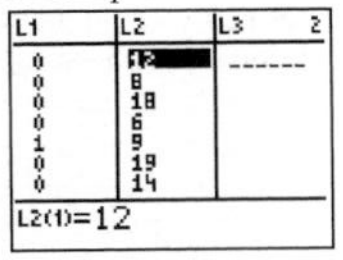

13c. A value of 1 in the third list means you won the cash prize because a 1 in the first list represents you won a prize and a 1 in the second list represents the cash prize.
13d. Sample answer:

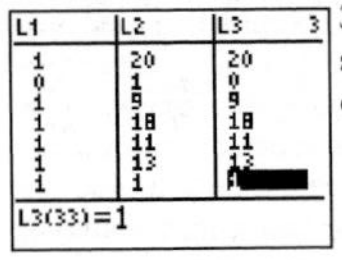

33 cards would have to be scratched in order to win the cash prize.

15. Never; the theoretical probability of getting tails from a coin toss is one half, or 7.5 times of 15 tosses. However, in an experiment you can never achieve 7.5 tails, only whole numbers. **17.** The theoretical probability of tossing a coin and showing heads or tails is 1, since it will always show one or the either. So when tossing a coin in an experiment, showing heads or tails will always happen, making the experimental probability always greater than 0. **19.** Theoretical probabilities are based on actual results, but experimental probabilities are based on trial results. The probabilities become closer and closer as more trials are done in the experiments. **21.** 24
23. C **25.** $\frac{10}{22}$ or about 45.5% **27.** $\frac{25}{484}$ or about 5.2% **29.** 60 **31.** $xy = 12.4$; -20 **33.** 3270 mi **35.** 44% **37.** 75% **39.** 27%

Pages 793–796 Chapter 12 Study Guide and Review

1. permutation **3.** 1 **5.** mutually exclusive **7.** unbiased **9.** median; 13 **11.** median; 3 **13.** 13.3 **15.** 11.4; 2; 1.4 **17.** 10.8, 0.6, 0.8 **19.** 3.1 **21.** 126 **23.** 120 **25.** $\frac{12}{325}$ **27.** $\frac{22}{325}$ **29.** $\frac{1}{2}$
31. For each X, the probability is greater than or equal to 0 and less than or equal to $0.18 + 0.36 + 0.34 + 0.08 + 0.04 = 1$, so the sum of the probabilities is 1. **33.** 0.25 **35.** 0.50

For Homework Help, go to Hotmath.com

Photo Credits

Cover: Michael Wong/CORBIS; **(bkrd.)** PhotoDisc; **vi–vii** VisionsofAmerica/Joe Sohm/Getty Images; **xv** Tim Bieber/Getty Images; **IL0** Radius Images/Masterfile; **P6** altrendo images/Altrendo/Getty Images; **P16** George Disario/CORBIS; **P28** Skyscan Photolibrary/Alamy; **P33** Eyewire/Getty Images; **P41** Martin Harvey/Gallo Images/Getty Images; **002–003** JUPITERIMAGES/Comstock Images/Alamy; **005** Gabe Palmer/CORBIS; **006** Masterfile; **008** Image Source/CORBIS; **010** Ken Biggs/Stone/Getty Images; **012** NOAA Photo by Will von Dauster; **014** guichaoua/Alamy; **016** JUPITERIMAGES/Brand X/Alamy; **018** Stewart Cohen/Blend Images/Getty Images; **020** Ariel Skelley/CORBIS; **023** SuperStock/AGE Fotostock; **024** Gail Mooney/Masterfile; **028** age fotostock/SuperStock; **031** Paul Rees/Imagestate; **035** Hola Images/Getty Images; **036** Matthew Mawson/Alamy; **038** Jeff Hunter/Photographer's Choice/Getty Images; **040** Masterfile; **042** blickwinkel/Alamy; **043** Robert Michael/CORBIS; **046** Rainer Raffalski/Alamy; **051** David P. Hall/CORBIS; **054** Chuck Pefley/Alamy; **057** AP Images; **058** AP Images; **068** fStop/Alamy; **072–073** Bob Daemmrich/PhotoEdit; **075** Doug Murray/Reuters/CORBIS; **076** SUNNYphotography.com/Alamy; **077** Art Resource, NY; **079** Ty Allison/Taxi/Getty Images; **083** Brian Bailey/Stone/Getty Images; **085** Ronnie Kaufman/Photolibrary; **087** Jim West/Alamy; **088** Stockbyte/Alamy; **092** William Thomas Cain/Getty Images; **095** YOSHIKAZU TSUNO/AFP/Getty Images; **097** Gen Nishino/Taxi/Getty Images; **101** David P. Hall/CORBIS; **104** Bill Aron/PhotoEdit; **107** Masterfile; **108** JUPITERIMAGES/Creatas/Alamy; **111** Digital Vision/Alamy; **113** Blend Images/SuperStock; **114** Rab Harling/Alamy; **115** Gary Crabbe/Alamy; **116** Gail Mooney/Masterfile; **118** Image Source/CORBIS; **120** Lloyd Sutton/Masterfie; **122** Jed Jacobsohn/Allsport/Getty Images; **123** ACE STOCK LIMITED/Alamy; **126** Stockbyte/SuperStock; **127** Erika Nelson/World's Largest Things, Lucas, KS; **129** Lisette Le Bon/SuperStock; **130** AP Images; **132** Photodisc/Getty Images; **134** David Young-Wolff/PhotoEdit; **137** Purcell Team/Alamy; **150–151** Wolfgang Kaehler; **153** Wesley Hitt/Alamy; **158** CORBIS; **159** Bill Aron/PhotoEdit; **163** Comstock/PunchStock; **164** Ausloser/zefa/CORBIS; **169 (cl)** Ed Imaging; **169 (cr)** Ed Imaging; **169 (bl)** PHOTOSPORT; **169 (tr)** The McGraw-Hill Companies; **170** J Silver/SuperStock; **176 (bc)** CORBIS; **176 (br)** Laura Hinshaw/Index Stock Imagery; **177** Artiga Photo/Masterfile; **180** NOVASTOCK/PhotoEdit; **182** Alamy Images; **184** Alamy Images; **185** Tom Grill/CORBIS; **187** Alamy Images; **188** Bettmann/CORBIS; **190** Stewart Cohen/Getty Images; **192** D. Hurst/Alamy Images; **194** Brooklyn Production/CORBIS; **196** CORBIS Super RF/Alamy; **199** Mark A. Johnson/Alamy; **206** Steven May/Alamy; **210–211** Alex Segre/Alamy; **213** Ed Imaging; **214** Image Source Pink/Getty Images; **217** Brand X Pictures/PunchStock; **219** Scott Tysick/Masterfile; **220** Sugar Gold Images/Photolibrary; **224** Blend Images/Alamy; **226** imagebroker/Alamy; **228** CORBIS; **229** Juliet Brauner/Alamy; **231** Chuck Savage/CORBIS; **235** Hermann Erber/LOOK/Getty Images; **237** Purestock/Getty Images; **238** Arcaid/Alamy; **242** Richard T. Nowitz/CORBIS; **246** AFP PHOTO/Stan HONDA/Getty Images; **249** George Rose/Getty Images; **250** Chuck Pefley/Alamy; **252** John Giustina/Photodisc/Getty Images; **254** AP Images; **255** Alan Thornton/Stone/Getty Images; **257** JUPITERIMAGES/Thinkstock/Alamy; **258** Courtesy of American Statistical Association; **259** Tracy Frankel/WireImage/Getty Images; **261** David J. Green/Alamy; **262** Yellow Dog Productions/Getty Images; **266** UpperCut Images/Alamy; **267** Visions of America, LLC/Alamy; **276** Chuck Franklin/Alamy; **280–281** Digital Vision Ltd./SuperStock; **283** JUPITERIMAGES/PIXLAND/Alamy; **285** IT Stock/PunchStock; **287** Jeff Greenberg/PhotoEdit; **290** Inti St Clair/Digital Vision/Getty Images; **291** blickwinkel/Alamy; **293** Brand X Pictures/PunchStock; **294** Chantelle Gorham - Northwest Fudge Factory; **296** Design Pics Inc./Alamy; **299** Masterfile; **300** Martin Harvey/CORBIS; **303 (cl)** George Grall/National Geographic/Getty Images; **303 (c)** Mike Randolph/Masterfile; **304** Joe Schwartz; **307** Larry Williams/CORBIS; **308** Laboratory for Atmospheres, NASA Goddard Space Flight Center; **310** David L. Moore/Alamy; **311** Stockbyte/Alamy; **313** Getty Images; 315 David Young-Wolff/PhotoEdit; **317** Spencer Grant/PhotoEdit; **319** David Young-Wolff/PhotoEdit; **326** Rob Gage/Taxi/Getty Images; **330–331** Masterfile; **335** Brand X Pictures/PunchStock; **337** Jason Horowitz/zefa/CORBIS; **338** JUPITERIMAGES/BananaStock/Alamy; **342** Colin Young-Wolff/PhotoEdit; **344** Michael Newman/PhotoEdit; **345** Rolf Bruderer/Masterfile; **346** WireImageStock/Masterfile; **348** Miles Ertman/Masterfile; **350** Photodisc/Alamy; **352** AP Images; **353** Science Source/Photo Researchers, Inc.; **355** Photodisc/SuperStock; **358** David M. Grossman/Phototake; **359** Wolfgang Kaehler/Alamy; **362** Mike Powell/Getty Images; **364** Tony Camacho/Photo Researchers, Inc.; **365** Spencer Grant/PhotoEdit; **366** JUPITERIMAGES/Creatas/Alamy; **368** David Young-Wolff/PhotoEdit; **370** Mark Richards/PhotoEdit; **373** foodfolio/Alamy; **374** AP Images; **376** Jonathan Nourok/PhotoEdit; **378** Jeff Henry/CORBIS; **380** JUPITERIMAGES/Brand X/Alamy; **383** Michael

Newman/PhotoEdit; **385** Patrick Olear/PhotoEdit; **394** CORBIS Premium RF/Alamy; **398–399** Roger Ressmeyer/CORBIS; **401** Zoomstock/Masterfile; **405** Steven Widoff/Alamy; **406** Deborah Betz Collection/CORBIS; **408** Taxi/Getty Images; **411** Blend Images/SuperStock; **412** Holt Studios International Ltd/Alamy; **414** Roger Ressmeyer/CORBIS; **416** StockTrek/Getty Images; **418** Michael Ochs Archives/CORBIS; **420** Bill Frymire/Masterfile **421** Nevada Wier/CORBIS; **424** JUPITERIMAGES/Creatas/Alamy; **426** FOUNDATION SKATEBOARD COMPANY; **428** CORBIS; **433** Jeff Greenberg/PhotoEdit; **435** Digital Vision/Alamy; **436** David R. Frazier Photolibrary, Inc./Alamy; **437** Marcel Mettelsiefen/Getty Images; **439** David Schmidt/Masterfile; **440** Noriyuki Yamagashira/ANYONE/amana images/Getty Images; **443** David Ashdown/Keystone/Getty Images; **447** Jo Katanigra/Alamy; **449** Roger Charity/Taxi/Getty Images; **451** Kevin C. Cox/Getty Images; **453** Alex Segre/Alamy; **456** Paul Sutherland/Digital Vision/Getty Images; **457** Yves Herman/Reuters/CORBIS; **464** Bob Daemmrich/PhotoEdit; **468–469** Jon Arnold Images Ltd/Alamy; **471** Spencer Grant/PhotoEdit; **473** Flying Colours Ltd/Digital Vision/Getty Images; **476** Dan Galic/Alamy; **479** Jeff Greenberg/PhotoEdit; **481** King's Dominion; **485** Image Source Black/Getty Images; **488** GLG3/Photodisc/Getty Images; **490** Getty Images; **493** Kim Karpeles/Alamy; **495** Gallo Images/CORBIS; **497** LWA/Dann Tardif/Blend Images/Getty Images; **499** David Young-Wolff/PhotoEdit; **502** David Young-Wolff/PhotoEdit; **505** Michael Newman/PhotoEdit; **509** Pictorial Press Ltd/Alamy; **510** JEFF HAYNES/Staff/AFP/Getty Images; **511** Joseph Barnell/SuperStock; **518** Michael Newman/PhotoEdit; **522–523** Stephen Chernin/Getty Images; **525** Bob Turner/Alamy; **530** Andy Lyons/Getty Image; **533** Tony Freeman/PhotoEdit; **536** Tsolo/Science Faction/Getty Images; **537** N.C. Department of Agriculture and Consumer Services; **539** moodboard/Alamy; **541** AP Images; **547** DOMINIQUE BRAUD/Animals Animals Earth Scenes; **548** Daniel Dempster Photography/Alamy; **552** Buzz Pictures/Alamy; **554** AP Images; **555** Raimund Koch/Photonica/Getty Images; **556** Stocktrek/age fotostock; **558** Creatas/PunchStock; **563** Digital Vision/Alamy; **568** Jonathan Nourok/PhotoEdit; **571** The Great Picture: Copyright 2006, The Legacy Project; **574** Digital Vision/Alamy; **576** Digital Vision/Alamy; **578** Karen Moskowitz/Taxi/Getty Images; **579** The Granger Collection, New York.; **580** Matt Sullivan/Reuters/CORBIS; **582** JUPITERIMAGES/Brand X/Alamy; **584** Tony Freeman/PhotoEdit; **586** PhotoAlto/SuperStock; **588** rubberball/Rubberball Productions/Royalty-Free/Getty Images; **598** Wright Group Stockdisc/PunchStock; **602–603** Stockbyte/PunchStock; **605** Louie Psihoyos/CORBIS; **607** Didier Dorval/Masterfile; **609** Glen Allison/Getty Images; **612** Cameron Davidson/Alamy; **615** Comstock/PunchStock; **616** V. Spencer Grant/PhotoEdit; **622** AP Images; **624** Digital Vision/Alamy; **626** Photo Courtesy of Silver Dollar City; **627** Johannes Rodach/StockFood Creative/Getty Images; **630** HANNSdribbling 10; **631** Gerry Walden/Alamy; **633** Blue Lantern Studio/CORBIS; **634** wendy connett/Alamy; **637** william casey/Alamy; **640** Jeff Greenberg/Alamy; **642** Jim Craigmyle/CORBIS; **645** Tommy Hindley/NewSport/CORBIS; **649** M Stock/Alamy; **651** Masterfile; **654** Comstock/JupiterImages; **662** JUPITERIMAGES/Polka Dot/Alamy; 666–667 Doug Pensinger/Getty Images; **670** Kim Karpeles/Alamy; **672** Trevor Lush/UpperCut Images/Getty Images; **674** Digital Vision; **675** David Young-Wolff/PhotoEdit; **678** Image Source Pink/Alamy; **679** Image Source/PunchStock; **680** Courtesy of Evelyn B. Granville; **682** Stockbyte; **684** Tatsuyuki Tayama Fujifotos/The Image Works; **688** Bettmann/CORBIS; **689** Will & Deni McIntyre/Photo Researchers, Inc.; **692** Mika/zefa/CORBIS; **696** Philip Gould/CORBIS; **697** GmbH & Co.KG/Alamy; **700** Juniors Bildarchiv/Alamy; **704** Tiziana and Gianni Baldizzone/CORBIS; **709** Gerolf Kalt/zefa/CORBIS; **711** Ingram Publishing/AGE Fotosearch; **712** Robert Michael/CORBIS; **714** David Allio/Icon SMI/CORBIS; **715** AP Images; 718 Rubberball Productions/Getty Images; **720** Creatas/PunchStock; **723** George Hall/CORBIS; **725** Glow Images/Alamy; **732** Will & Deni McIntyre/CORBIS; **736** Dex Image/Alamy; **740** Steve Prezant/CORBIS; **742** Jeff Greenberg/PhotoEdit; **744** Christian Schmidt/zefa/CORBIS; **748** Ryan McVay/Stone/Getty Images; **749** Robin Nelson/PhotoEdit; **753** Bob Daemmrich/PhotoEdit; **754** image100/CORBIS; **756** Halfdark/fStop/Getty Images; **757** Geoff A Howard/Alamy; **760** GARY CASKEY/Reuters/CORBIS; **761** Jeff Greenberg/Alamy; **764** Allan Munsie/Alamy; **766** Photodisc/Alamy; **769** Bob Daemmrich/PhotoEdit; **771** Spencer Grant/PhotoEdit; **772** Stock 4B RF; **775** JUPITERIMAGES/Thinkstock/Alamy; **776** A. Ramey/PhotoEdit; **780** Brand X Pictures; **782** Stockbyte/Getty Images; **783** David Young-Wolff/PhotoEdit; **787** Rana Faure/DigitalVision/Getty Images; **788** Bettmann/CORBIS; **790** Stewart Cohen/Taxi/Getty Image; **791** The Bridgeman Art Library International; **798** Jeff Greenberg/Alamy; **802** Eclipse Studios; **810** Judith Collins/Alamy

Glossary/Glosario

Math Online

A mathematics multilingual eGlossary is available at **glencoe.com**. The glossary includes the following languages:

Arabic	English	Portuguese	Urdu
Bengali	Haitian Creole	Russian	Vietnamese
Brazilian	Hmong	Spanish	
Cantonese	Korean	Tagalog	

Cómo usar el glosario en español:

1. Busca el término en inglés que desees encontrar.
2. El término en español, junto con la definición, se encuentran en la columna de la derecha.

English	Español

A

absolute value (p. P11) The distance a number is from zero on the number line.

valor aboluto Es la distancia que dista de cero en una recta numerica.

absolute value function (p. 242) A function written as $f(x) = |x|$, in which $f(x) \geq 0$ for all values of x.

función del valor absoluto Una función que se escribe $f(x) = |x|$, donde $f(x) \geq 0$, para todos los valores de x.

additive identity (p. 10) For any number a, $a + 0 = 0 + a = a$.

identidad de la adición Para cualquier número a, $a + 0 = 0 + a = a$.

additive inverse (p. P11) Two integers, x and $-x$, are called additive inverses. The sum of any number and its additive inverse is zero.

inverso aditivo Dos enteros x y $-x$ reciben el nobre de inversos aditivos. La suma de cualquier número y su inverso aditivo es cero.

algebraic expression (p. 5) An expression consisting of one or more numbers and variables along with one or more arithmetic operations.

expresión algebraica Una expresión que consiste en uno o más números y variables, junto con una o más operaciones aritméticas.

area (p. P26) The measure of the surface enclosed by a geometric figure.

área La medida de la superficie incluida por una figura geométrica.

arithmetic sequence (p. 187) A numerical pattern that increases or decreases at a constant rate or value. The difference between successive terms of the sequence is constant.

sucesión aritmética Un patrón numérico que aumenta o disminuye a una tasa o valor constante. La diferencia entre términos consecutivos de la sucesión es siempre la misma.

asymptote (p. 679) A line that a graph approaches but never crosses.

asíntota Una línea a que un gráfico acerca pero nunca cruza.

augmented matrix (p. 376) A coefficient matrix with an extra column containing the constant terms.

matriz aumentada una matriz del coeficiente con una columna adicional que contiene los términos de la constante

axis of symmetry (p. 525) The vertical line containing the vertex of a parabola.

eje de simetría La recta vertical que pasa por el vértice de una parábola.

B

bar graph (p. P40) A graphic form using bars to make comparisons of statistics.

gráfico de barra Forma gráfica usando barras para comparar estadísticas

base (p. 5) In an expression of the form x^n, the base is x.

base En una expresión de la forma x^n, la base es x.

best-fit line (p. 253) The line that most closely approximates the data in a scatter plot.

recta de ajuste óptimo La recta que mejor aproxima los datos de una gráfica de dispersión.

biased sample (p. 741) A sample in which one or more parts of the population are favored over others.

muestra sesgada Muestra en que se favorece una o más partes de una población en vez de otras partes.

binomial (p. 424) The sum of two monomials.

binomio La suma de dos monomios.

bivariate data (p. 245) Data with two variables.

datos bivariate Datos con dos variables.

boundary (p. 315) A line or curve that separates the coordinate plane into regions.

frontera Recta o curva que divide el plano de coordenadas en regiones.

box-and-whisker plot (p. P42) A diagram that divides a set of data into four parts using the median and quartiles. A box is drawn around the quartile values and whiskers extend from each quartile to the extreme data points.

diagrama de caja y patillas Diagram que divide un conjunto de datos en cuatro partes usando la mediana y los cuartiles. Se dibuja una caja alrededor de los cuartiles y se extienden patillas de cada uno de ellos a los valores extremos.

C

center (p .P24) The given point from which all points on the circle are the same distance.

centro Punto dado del cual equidistan todos los puntos de un circulo.

circle (p. P24) The set of all points in a plane that are the same distance from a given point called the center.

círculo Conjunto de todos los puntos del plano que están a la misma distancia de un punto dado del plano llamado centro.

circle graph (p. P41) A type of statistical graph used to compare parts of a whole.

gráfico del círculo Tipo de gráfica estadística que se usa para comparar las partes de un todo.

circumference (p. P24) The distance around a circle.

circunferencia Longitud del contorno de un círculo.

closed half-plane (p. 315) The solution of a linear inequality that includes the boundary line.

mitad-plano cerrado La solución de una desigualdad linear que incluye la línea de límite.

coefficient (p. 26) The numerical factor of a term.

coeficiente Factor numérico de un término.

combination (p. 765) An arrangement or listing in which order is not important.

combinación Arreglo o lista en que el orden no es importante.

common difference (p. 187) The difference between the terms in a sequence.

diferencia común Diferencia entre términos consecutivos de una sucesión.

common ratio (p. 580) The ratio of successive terms of a geometric sequence.

razón común El razón de términos sucesivos de una secuencia geométrica.

complements (p. P33 and 772) One of two parts of a probability making a whole.

completing the square (p. 552) To add a constant term to a binomial of the form $x^2 + bx$ so that the resulting trinomial is a perfect square.

complex fraction (p. 714) A fraction that has one or more fractions in the numerator or denominator.

composite number (p. 420) A whole number, greater than 1, that has more than two factors.

compound event (p. 771) Two or more simple events.

compound inequality (p. 304) Two or more inequalities that are connected by the words *and* or *or*.

compound interest (p. 574) A special application of exponential growth.

conclusion (p. 54) The part of a conditional statement immediately following the word *then*.

conditional probability (p. 777) The probability of an event under the condition that some preceding event has occurred.

conditional statements (p. 54) Statements written in the form *If A, then B*.

conjugates (p. 614) Binomials of the form $a\sqrt{b} + c\sqrt{d}$ and $a\sqrt{b} - c\sqrt{d}$.

consecutive integers (p. 92) Integers in counting order.

consistent (p. 333) A system of equations that has at least one ordered pair that satisfies both equations.

constant (p. 153, 401) A monomial that is a real number.

constant of variation (p. 180) The number k in equations of the form $y = kx$.

continuous function (p. 46) A function that can be graphed with a line or a smooth curve.

convenience sample (p. 643) A sample that includes members of a population that are easily accessed.

complementos Una de dos partes de una probabilidad que forma un todo.

completar el cuadrado Adición de un término constante a un binomio de la forma $x^2 + bx$, para que el trinomio resultante sea un cuadrado perfecto.

fracción compleja Fracción con una o más fracciones en el numerador o denominador.

número compuesto Número entero mayor que 1 que posee más de dos factores.

evento compuesto Dos o más eventos simples.

desigualdad compuesta Dos o más desigualdades que están unidas por las palabras y u o.

interés compuesto Aplicación especial de crecimiento exponencial.

conclusión Parte de un enunciado condicional que sigue inmediatamente a la palabra entonces.

probabilidad condicional La probabilidad de un acontecimiento bajo condición que ha ocurrido un cierto acontecimiento precedente.

enunciados condicionales Enunciados de la forma Si A, entonces B.

conjugados Binomios de la forma $a\sqrt{b} + c\sqrt{d}$ and $a\sqrt{b} - c\sqrt{d}$.

enteros consecutivos Enteros en el orden de contar.

consistente Sistema de ecuaciones para el cual existe al menos un par ordenado que satisface ambas ecuaciones.

constante Monomio que es un número real.

constante de variación El número k en ecuaciones de la forma $y = kx$.

función continua Función cuya gráfica puedes ser una recta o una curva suave.

muestra de conveniencia Muestra que incluye miembros de una población fácilmente accesibles.

converse (p. 631) The statement formed by exchanging the hypothesis and conclusion of a conditional statement.

coordinate (p. P8) The number that corresponds to a point on a number line.

coordinate plane (p. 53) The plane containing the x- and y-axes.

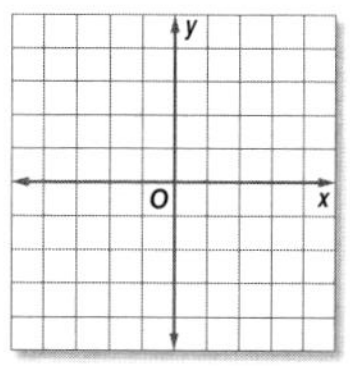

coordinate system (p. 38) The grid formed by the intersection of two number lines, the horizontal axis and the vertical axis.

correlation coefficient (p. 253) A value that shows how close data points are to a line.

cosine (p. 649) For an acute angle of a right triangle, the ratio of the measure of the leg adjacent to the acute angle to the measure of the hypotenuse.

counterexample (p. 56) A specific case in which a statement is false.

recíproco Enunciado que se obtiene al inter cambiar la hipótesis y la conclusión de un enucnciado condicional dado.

coordenada Número que corresponde a un punto en una recta numérica.

plano de coordenadas Plano que contiene los ejes x y y.

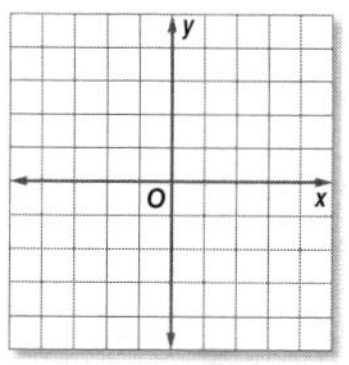

sistema de coordenadas Cuadriculado formado por la intersección de dos rectas numéricas: los ejes x y y.

coeficiente de correlación Un valor que demostraciones cómo los puntos de referencias cercanos están a una línea.

coseno Para un ángulo agudo de un triángulo derecho, el razón de la medida de la pierna adyacente al ángulo agudo de la medida de la hipotenusa.

contraejemplo Ejemplo específico de la falsedad de un enunciado.

D

deductive reasoning (p. 55) The process of using facts, rules, definitions, or properties to reach a valid conclusion.

defining a variable (p. P5) Choosing a variable to represent one of the unspecified numbers in a problem and using it to write expressions for the other unspecified numbers in the problem.

degree of a monomial (p. 424) The sum of the exponents of all its variables.

degree of a polynomial (p. 424) The greatest degree of any term in the polynomial.

dependent (p. 333) A system of equations that has an infinite number of solutions.

razonamiento deductivo Proceso de usar hechos, reglas, definiciones o propiedades para sacar conclusiones válidas.

definir una variable Consiste en escoger una variable para representar uno de los números desconocidos en un problema y luego usarla para escribir expresiones para otros números desconocidos en el problema.

grado de un monomio Suma de los exponentes de todas sus variables.

grado de un polinomio El grado mayor de cualquier término del polinomio.

dependiente Sistema de ecuaciones que posee un número infinito de soluciones.

dependent events (p. 771) Two or more events in which the outcome of one event affects the outcome of the other events.

eventos dependientes Dos o más eventos en que el resultado de un evento afecta el resultado de los otros eventos.

dependent variable (p. 40) The variable in a relation with a value that depends on the value of the independent variable.

variable dependiente La variable de una relación cuyo valor depende del valor de la variable independiente.

diameter (p. P24) The distance across a circle through its center.

diámetro La distancia a través de un círculo a través de su centro.

difference of two squares (p. 499) Two perfect squares separated by a subtraction sign. $a^2 - b^2 = (a + b)(a - b)$ or $a^2 - b^2 = (a - b)(a + b)$.

diferencia de cuadrados Dos cuadrados perfectos separados por el signo de sustracción. $a^2 - b^2 = (a + b)(a - b)$ or $a^2 - b^2 = (a - b)(a + b)$.

dilation (p. 24) A transformation that alters the size of a figure but not its shape.

homotecía Transformacióñ que altera el tamaño de una figure, pero no su forma.

dimension (p. 369) The number of rows, m, and the number of column, n, of a matrix written as $m \times n$.

dimension El número de filas, de m, y del número de la columna, n, de una matriz escrita como $m \times n$.

dimensional analysis (p. 128) The process of carrying units throughout a computation.

análisis dimensional Proceso de tomar en cuenta las unidades de medida al hacer cálculos.

direct variation (p. 180) An equation of the form $y = kx$, where $k \neq 0$.

variación directa Una ecuación de la forma $y = kx$, donde $k \neq 0$.

discrete function (p. 46) A function of points that are not connected.

función discreta Función de puntos desconectados.

discrete random variable (p. 779) A variable with a value that is a finite number of possible outcomes.

variable aleatoria discreta Variable cuyo valor es un número finito de posibles resultados.

discriminant (p. 562) In the Quadratic Formula, the expression under the radical sign, $b^2 - 4ac$.

discriminante En la fórmula cuadrática, la expresión debajo del signo radical, $b^2 - 4ac$.

Distance Formula (p. 636) The distance d between any two points with coordinates (x_1, y_1) and (x_2, y_2) is given by the formula

$$d = \sqrt{(x_2 - x_1)^2 + (y_2 - y_1)^2}.$$

Fórmula de la distancia La distancia d entre cualquier par de puntos con coordenadas (x_1, y_1) y (x_2, y_2) viene dada por la fórmula

$$d = \sqrt{(x_2 - x_1)^2 + (y_2 - y_1)^2}.$$

domain (p. 39) The set of the first numbers of the ordered pairs in a relation.

dominio Conjunto de los primeros números de los pares ordenados de una relación.

double root (p. 538) The roots of a quadratic function are the same number.

raíces dobles Las raíces de una función cuadrática son el mismo número.

E

element (p. 369) **1.** Each object or number in a set. (p. 715) **2.** Each entry in a matrix.

elemento **1.** Cada número u objeto de un conjunto. **2.** Cada entrada de una matriz.

elimination (p. 348) The use of addition or subtraction to eliminate one variable and solve a system of equations.

eliminación El uso de la adición o la sustracción para eliminar una variable y resolver así un sistema de ecuaciones.

empirical study (p. 787) Performing an experiment repeatedly, collecting and combining data, and analyzing the results.

estudio empírico Ejecución repetida de un experimento, recopilación y combinación de datos y análisis de resultados.

equally likely (p. P33) The outcomes of an experiment are equally likely if there are n outcomes and the probability of each is $\frac{1}{n}$.

igualmente probablemente Los resultados de un experimento son igualmente probables si hay resultados de n y la probabilidad de cada uno es $\frac{1}{n}$.

equation (p. 31) A mathematical sentence that contains an equals sign, =.

ecuación Enunciado matemático que contiene el signo de igualdad, =.

equivalent equations (p. 83) Equations that have the same solution.

ecuaciones equivalentes Ecuaciones que poseen la misma solución.

equivalent expressions (p. 16) Expressions that denote the same number.

expresiones equivalentes Expresiones que denotan el mismo número.

evaluate (p. 10) To find the value of an expression.

evaluar Calcular el valor de una expresión.

event (p. 650) Any collection of one or more outcomes in the sample space.

evento Cualquier colección de uno o más resultados de un espacio muestral.

excluded values (p. 678) Any values of a variable that result in a denominator of 0 must be excluded from the domain of that variable.

valores excluidos Cualquier valor de una variable cuyo resultado sea un denominador igual a cero, debe excluirse del dominio de dicha variable.

expected value (p. 791) The weighted average of all outcomes.

valor previsto El promédio cargado de todos los resultados.

experiment (p. 740) Data are recorded from outcomes involving characteristics of a sample.

experimento Los datos se registran de los resultados que implican características de una muestra.

experimental probability (pp. P35 and 787) What actually occurs when conducting a probability experiment, or the ratio of relative frequency to the total number of events or trials.

probabilidad experimental Lo que realmente sucede cuando se realiza un experimento probabilístico o la razón de la frecuencia relativa al número total de eventos o pruebas.

exponent (p. 5) In an expression of the form x^n, the exponent is n. It indicates the number of times x is used as a factor.

exponente En una expresión de la forma x^n, el exponente es n. Éste indica cuántas veces se usa x como factor.

exponential decay (p. 574) When an initial amount decreases by the same percent over a given period of time.

desintegración exponencial La cantidad inicial disminuye según el mismo porcentaje a lo largo de un período de tiempo dado.

exponential function (p. 567) A function that can be described by an equation of the form $y = a^x$, where $a > 0$ and $a \neq 1$.

función exponencial Función que puede describirse mediante una ecuación de la forma $y = a^x$, donde $a > 0$ y $a \neq 1$.

exponential growth (p. 573) When an initial amount increases by the same percent over a given period of time.

crecimiento exponencial La cantidad inicial aumenta según el mismo porcentaje a lo largo de un período de tiempo dado.

extraneous solutions (pp. 721, 624) Results that are not solutions to the original equation.

soluciones extrañas Resultados que no son soluciones de la ecuación original.

extremes (p. 112) In the ratio $\frac{a}{b} = \frac{c}{d}$, a and d are the extremes.

extremos En la razón $\frac{a}{b} = \frac{c}{d}$, a y d son los extremos.

F

factored form (p. 471) A monomial expressed as a product of prime numbers and variables in which no variable has an exponent greater than 1.

forma reducida Monomio escrito como el producto de números primos y variables y en el que ninguna variable tiene un exponente mayor que 1.

factorial (p. 764) The expression $n!$, read n factorial, where n is greater than zero, is the product of all positive integers beginning with n and counting backward to 1.

factorial La expresión $n!$, que se lee n factorial, donde n que es mayor que cero, es el producto de todos los números naturales, comenzando con n y contando hacia atrás hasta llegar al 1.

factoring (p. 476) To express a polynomial as the product of monomials and polynomials.

factorización La escritura de un polinomio como producto de monomios y polinomios.

factoring by grouping (p. 477) The use of the Distributive Property to factor some polynomials having four or more terms.

factorización por agrupamiento Uso de la Propiedad distributiva para factorizar polinomios que poseen cuatro o más términos.

factors (p. 6) In an algebraic expression, the quantities being multiplied are called factors.

factores En una expresión algebraica, los factores son las cantidades que se multiplican.

family of functions (p. 161) A group of functions that have one or more similar characteristics.

familia de funciones Un grupo de las funciones que tienen unas o más características similares.

family of graphs (pp. 197, 478) Graphs and equations of graphs that have at least one characteristic in common.

familia de gráficas Gráficas y ecuaciones de gráficas que tienen al menos una característica común.

FOIL method (p. 448) To multiply two binomials, find the sum of the products of the First terms, the Outer terms, the Inner terms, and the Last terms.

método FOIL Para multiplicar dos binomios, busca la suma de los productos de los primeros (First) términos, los términos exteriores (Outer), los términos interiores (Inner) y los últimos términos (Last).

formula (p. 76) An equation that states a rule for the relationship between certain quantities.

fórmula Ecuación que establece una relación entre ciertas cantidades.

four-step problem-solving plan (p. P5)
Step 1 Explore the problem.
Step 2 Plan the solution.
Step 3 Solve the problem.
Step 4 Check the solution.

plan de cuatro pasos para resolver problemas
Paso 1 Explora el problema.
Paso 2 Planifica la solución.
Paso 3 Resuelve el problema.
Paso 4 Examina la solución.

frequency table (p. P40) A chart that indicates the number of values in each interval.

Tabla de frecuencias Tabla que indica el número de valores en cada intervalo.

function (p. 45) A relation in which each element of the domain is paired with exactly one element of the range.

función Una relación en que a cada elemento del dominio le corresponde un único elemento del rango.

function notation (p. 48) A way to name a function that is defined by an equation. In function notation, the equation $y = 3x - 8$ is written as $f(x) = 3x - 8$.

notación funcional Una manera de nombrar una función definida por una ecuación. En notación funcional, la ecuación $y = 3x - 8$ se escribe $f(x) = 3x - 8$.

Fundamental Counting Principle (p. 764) If an event M can occur in m ways and is followed by an event N that can occur in n ways, then the event M followed by the event N can occur in $m \times n$ ways.

Principio fundamental de contar Si un evento M puede ocurrir de m maneras y lo sigue un evento N que puede ocurrir de n maneras, entonces el evento M seguido del evento N puede ocurrir de $m \times n$ maneras.

G

general equation for exponential decay (p. 511) $y = C(1 - r)^t$, where y is the final amount, C is the initial amount, r is the rate of decay expressed as a decimal, and t is time.

ecuación general de desintegración exponencial $y = C(1 - r)^t$, donde y es la cantidad final, C es la cantidad inicial, r es la tasa de desintegración escrita como decimal y t es el tiempo.

general equation for exponential growth (p. 510) $y = C(1 + r)^t$, where y is the final amount, C is the initial amount, r is the rate of change expressed as a decimal, and t is time.

ecuación general de crecimiento exponencial $y = C(1 + r)^t$, donde y es la cantidad final, C es la cantidad inicial, r es la tasa de cambio del crecimiento escrita como decimal y t es el tiempo.

geometric sequence (p. 580) A sequence in which each term after the first is found by multiplying the previous term by a constant r, called the common ratio.

secuencia geométrica Una secuencia en la cual cada término después de que la primera sea encontrada multiplicando el término anterior por un r constante, llamado el razón común.

graph (p. P8) To draw, or plot, the points named by certain numbers or ordered pairs on a number line or coordinate plane.

graficar Marcar los puntos que denotan ciertos números en una recta numérica o ciertos pares ordenados en un plano de coordenadas.

greatest common factor (GCF) (p. 471) The product of the prime factors common to two or more integers.

máximo común divisor (MCD) El producto de los factores primos comunes a dos o más enteros.

greatest integer function (p. 261) A step function, written as $f(x) = [\![x]\!]$, where $f(x)$ is the greatest integer less than or equal to x.

La función más grande del número entero Una función del paso, escrita como $f(x) = [\![x]\!]$, donde está el número entero $f(x)$ es el número más grande menos que o igual a x.

H

half-plane (p. 315) The region of the graph of an inequality on one side of a boundary.

semiplano Región de la gráfica de una desigualdad en un lado de la frontera.

histogram (p. P40) A graphical display that uses bars to display numerical data that have been organized into equal intervals.

histograma Una exhibición gráfica que utiliza barras para exhibir los datos numéricos que se han organizado en intervalos iguales.

hypotenuse (p. 630) The side opposite the right angle in a right triangle.

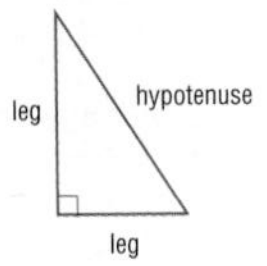

hypothesis (p. 54) The part of a conditional statement immediately following the word if.

I

identity (pp. 33, 98) An equation that is true for every value of the variable.

identity matrix (p. 377) A square matrix that, when multiplied by another matrix, equals that same matrix. If A is any $n \times n$ matrix and I is the $n \times n$ identity matrix, then $A \cdot I = A$ and $I \cdot A = A$.

if-then statements (p. 54) Conditional statements in the form *If A, then B.*

inclusive (p. 666) Two events that can occur at the same time.

inconsistent (p. 333) A system of equations with no ordered pair that satisfy both equations.

independent (p. 333) A system of equations with exactly one solution.

independent events (p. 771) Two or more events in which the outcome of one event does not affect the outcome of the other events.

independent variable (p. 40) The variable in a function with a value that is subject to choice.

inductive reasoning (p. 195) A conclusion based on a pattern of examples.

inequality (p. 16) An open sentence that contains the symbol $<, \leq, >$, or $\geq$.

integers (p. P7) The set $\{\ldots, -2, -1, 0, 1, 2, \ldots\}$.

interquartile range (p. P42) The range of the middle half of a set of data. It is the difference between the upper quartile and the lower quartile.

hipotenusa Lado opuesto al ángulo recto en un triángulo rectángulo.

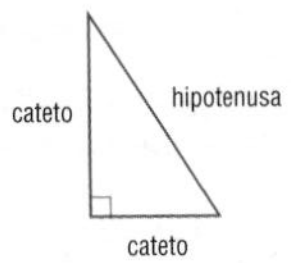

hipótesis Parte de un enunciado condicional que sigue inmediatamente a la palabra si.3

identidad Ecuación que es verdad para cada valor de la variable.

matriz de la identidad una matriz cuadrada que, cuando es multiplicada por otra matriz, iguala que la misma matriz. Si A es alguna de la matriz $n \times n$ e I es la matriz de la identidad de $n \times n$, entonces $A \cdot I = A$ e $I \cdot A = A$.

enunciados si-entonces Enunciados condicionales de la forma *Si A, entonces B.*

inclusivos Dos eventos que pueden ocurrir simultáneamente.

inconsistente Un sistema de ecuaciones para el cual no existe par ordenado alguno que satisfaga ambas ecuaciones.

independiente Un sistema de ecuaciones que posee una única solución.

eventos independientes El resultado de un evento no afecta el resultado del otro evento.

variable independiente La variable de una función sujeta a elección.

razonamiento inductivo Conclusión basada en un patrón de ejemplos.

desigualdad Enunciado abierto que contiene uno o más de los símbolos $<, \leq, >$, o $\geq$.

enteros El conjunto $\{\ldots, -2, -1, 0, 1, 2, \ldots\}$.

amplitud intercuartílica Amplitude de la mitad central de un conjunto de datos. Es la diferenccia entre el cuartil superior y el inferior.

intersection (p. 304) The graph of a compound inequality containing and; the solution is the set of elements common to both inequalities.

inverse (p. 145) The inverse of any relation is obtained by switching the coordinates in each ordered pair.

inverse cosine (p. 651) If $\angle A$ is an acute angle and the cosine of A is x, then the inverse cosine of x is the measure of $\angle A$.

inverse sine (p. 651) If $\angle A$ is an acute angle and the sine of A is x, then the inverse sine of x is the measure of $\angle A$.

inverse tangent (p. 651) If $\angle A$ is an acute angle and the tangent of A is x, then the inverse tangent of x is the measure of $\angle A$.

inverse variation (p. 670) An equation of the form $xy = k$, where $k \neq 0$.

irrational numbers (p. P7) Numbers that cannot be expressed as terminating or repeating decimals.

L

leading coefficient (p. 425) The coefficient of the term with the highest degree.

least common denominator (LCD) (p. 708) The least common multiple of the denominators of two or more fractions.

least common multiple (LCM) (p. 707) The least number that is a common multiple of two or more numbers.

legs (p. 549) The sides of a right triangle that form the right angle.

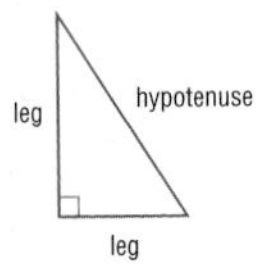

like terms (p. 25) Terms that contain the same variables, with corresponding variables having the same exponent.

intersección Gráfica de una desigualdad compuesta que contiene la palabra y; la solución es el conjunto de soluciones de ambas desigualdades.

inversa La inversa de una relación se halla intercambiando las coordenadas de cada par ordenado.

cosino inverso Si el $\angle A$ es un ángulo agudo y el coseno de A es x, entonces el coseno inverso de x es la medida de $\angle A$.

seno inverso Si $\angle A$ es un ángulo agudo y el seno de A es x, entonces el seno inverso de x es la medida de $\angle A$.

tangente inverso Si el $\angle A$ es un ángulo agudo y la tangente de A es x, entonces la tangente inversa de x es la medida de $\angle A$.

variación inversa Ecuación de la forma $xy = k$, donde $k \neq 0$.

números irracionales Números que no pueden escribirse como decimales terminales o periódicos.

coeficiente inicial El coeficiente del término con el grado más alto (el primer coeficiente inicial).

mínimo denominador común (mcd) El mínimo común múltiplo de los denominadores de dos o más fracciones.

mínimo común múltiplo (mcm) El número menor que es múltiplo común de dos o más números.

catetos Lados de un triángulo rectángulo que forman el ángulo recto del mismo.

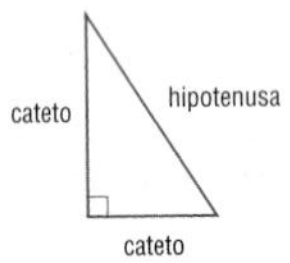

términos semejantes Expresiones que tienen las mismas variables, con las variables correspondientes elevadas a los mismos exponentes.

linear equation (p. 153) An equation in the form $Ax + By = C$, with a graph that is a straight line.

linear extrapolation (p. 226) The use of a linear equation to predict values that are outside the range of data.

linear function (p. 155) A function with ordered pairs that satisfy a linear equation.

linear interpolation (p. 247) The use of a linear equation to predict values that are inside of the data range.

linear regression (p. 253) An algorithm to find a precise line of fit for a set of data.

linear transformation (p. 760) One or more operations performed on a set of data that can be written as a linear funciton.

line of fit (p. 246) A line that describes the trend of the data in a scatter plot.

literal equation (p. 127) A formula or equation with several variables.

look for a pattern (p. 172) Find patterns in sequences to solve problems.

lower quartile (p. P38) Divides the lower half of the data into two equal parts.

ecuación lineal Ecuación de la forma $Ax + By = C$, cuya gráfica es una recta.

extrapolación lineal Uso de una ecuación lineal para predecir valores fuera de la amplitud de los datos.

función lineal Función cuyos pares ordenados satisfacen una ecuación lineal.

interpolación lineal Uso de una ecuación lineal para predecir valores dentro de la amplitud de los datos.

regresión linear Un algoritmo para encontrar una línea exacta del ajuste para un sistema de datos.

transformación lineal Una o más operaciones que se hacen en un conjunto de datos y que se pueden escribir como una función lineal.

recta de ajuste Recta que describe la tendencia de los datos en una gráfica de dispersión.

ecuación literal Un fórmula o ecuación con varias variables.

buscar un patrón Encontrar patrones en sucesiones para resolver problemas.

cuartil inferior Éste divide en dos partes iguales la mitad inferior de un conjunto de datos.

M

mapping (p. 38) Illustrates how each element of the domain is paired with an element in the range.

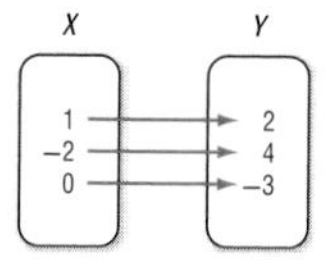

measures of central tendency (pp. P37, 746) Numbers or pieces of data that can represent the whole set of data.

matrix (p. 369) Any rectangular arrangement of numbers in rows and columns.

maximum (p. 525) The highest point on the graph of a curve.

aplicaciones Ilustra la correspondencia entre cada elemento del dominio con un elemento del rango.

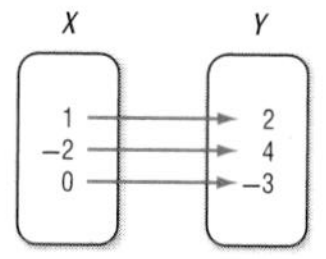

medidas de tendencia central Números o fragmentos que pueden representar el conjunto de datos total de datos.

matriz Disposción rectangular de numeros colocados en filas y columnas.

máximo El punto más alto en la gráfica de una curva.

mean (p. P37) The sum of numbers in a set of data divided by the number of items in the data set.

mean absolute deviation (p. 757) The average of the absolute values of differences between the mean and each value in a data set. It is used to predict errors and to judge equality.

means (p. 112) The middle terms of the proportion.

measures of central tendency (pp. P37, 746) Numbers or pieces of data that can represent the whole set of data.

measures of variation (p. P38) Used to describe the distribution of statistical data.

median (p. 37) The middle number in a set of data when the data are arranged in numerical order. If the data set has an even number, the median is the mean of the two middle numbers.

median fit line (p. 255) A type of best-fit line that is calculated using the medians of the coordinates of the data points.

midpoint (p. 638) The point halfway between the endpoints of a segment.

minimum (p. 525) The lowest point on the graph of a curve.

mixed expression (p. 714) An expression that contains the sum of a monomial and a rational expression.

mixture problems (p. 132) Problems in which two or more parts are combined into a whole.

mode (p. P37) The number(s) that appear most often in a set of data.

monomial (p. 401) A number, a variable, or a product of a number and one or more variables.

multiplicative identity (p. 17) For any number a, $a \cdot 1 = 1 \cdot a = a$.

multiplicative inverses (pp. P18, 17) Two numbers with a product of 1.

multi-step equation (p. 91) Equations with more than one operation.

mutually exclusive (p. 773) Events that cannot occur at the same time.

media La suma de los números de un conjunto de datos dividida entre el numero total de artículos.

desviación absoluta media El promedio de los valores absolutos de diferencias entre el medio y cada valor de un conjunto de datos. Ha usado para predecir errores y para juzgar igualdad.

medios Los términos centrales de una proporción.

medidas de tendencia central Números o fragmentos que pueden representar el conjunto de datos total de datos.

medidas de variación Números que se usan para describir la distribución o separación de un conjunto de datos.

mediana El número central de conjunto de datos, una vezque los datos han sido ordenados numéricamente. Si hay un número par de datos, la mediana es el promedio de los datos centrales.

línea apta del punto medio Tipo de mejor-cupo la línea se calcula que usando los puntos medios de los coordenadas de los puntos de referencias.

punto medio Punto que divide a un segmento separándolo en dos segmentos congruentes.

mínimo El punto más bajo en la gráfica de una curva.

expresión mixta Expresión que contiene la suma de un monomio y una expresión racional.

problemas de mezclas Problemas en que dos o más partes se combinan en un todo.

moda El número(s) que aparece más frecuencia en un conjunto de datos.

monomio Número, variable o producto de un número por una o más variables.

identidad de la multiplicación Para cualquier número $a \cdot 1 = 1 \cdot a = a$.

inversos multiplicativos Dos números cuyo producto es igual a 1.

ecuaciones de varios pasos Ecuaciones con más de una operación.

mutuamente exclusivos Eventos que no pueden ocurrir simultáneamente.

N

natural numbers (p. P7) The set {1, 2, 3, …}.

negative correlation (p. 227) In a scatter plot, as x increases, y decreases.

negative exponent (p. 410) For any real number $a \neq 0$ and any integer n, $a^{-n} = \frac{1}{a^n}$ and $\frac{1}{a^{-n}} = a^n$.

negative number (p. P7) Any value less than zero.

nonlinear function (pp. 48 and 525) A function with a variable term that has an exponent other than 1 or 0.

number theory (p. 92) The study of numbers and the relationships between them.

números naturales El conjunto {1, 2, 3, …}.

correlación negativa En una gráfica de dispersión, a medida que x aumenta, y disminuye.

exponiente negativo Para números reales, si $a \neq 0$, y cualquier número entero n, entonces $a^{-n} = \frac{1}{a^n}$ and $\frac{1}{a^{-n}} = a^n$.

número negativo Cualquier valor menor que cero.

función no lineal Una función con un término variable que tiene un exponente con excepción de 1 o de 0.

teoría del número El estudio de números y de las relaciones entre ellas.

O

observational study (p. 740) Data are recorded and made regarding certain activities within a sample.

odds (p. P35) The ratio of the probability of the success of an event to the probability of its complement.

open half-plane (p. 315) The solution of a linear inequality that does not include the boundary line.

open sentence (p. 31) A mathematical statement with one or more variables.

opposites (p. P11) Two numbers with the same absolute value by different signs.

ordered pair (p. 38) A set of numbers or coordinates used to locate any point on a coordinate plane, written in the form (x, y).

order of magnitude (p. 411) The order of magnitude of a quantity is the number rounded to the nearest power of 10.

order of operations (p. 10)
1. Evaluate expressions inside grouping symbols.
2. Evaluate all powers.
3. Do all multiplications and/or divisions from left to right.
4. Do all additions and/or subtractions from left to right.

origin (p. 38) The point where the two axes intersect at their zero points.

outliers (p. P42) Data that are more than 1.5 times the interquartile range beyond the quartiles.

estudio de observación Datos que se registran y se hacen con respecto a ciertas actividades dentro de una muestra.

probabilidades El cociente de la probabilidad del éxito de un acontecimiento a la probabilidad de su complemento.

abra el mitad-plano La solución de una desigualdad linear que no incluya la línea de límite.

enunciado abierto Un enunciado matemático que contiene una o más variables.

opuestos Dos números que tienen el mismo valor absolute, pero que tienen distintos signos.

par ordenado Un par de números que se usa para ubicar cualquier punto de un plano de coordenadas y que se escribe en la forma (x, y).

orden de magnitud de una cantidad Un número redondeado a la potencia más cercana de 10.

orden de las operaciones
1. Evalúa las expresiones dentro de los símbolos de agrupamiento.
2. Evalúa todas las potencias.
3. Multiplica o divide de izquierda a derecha.
4. Suma o resta de izquierda a derecha.

origen Punto donde se intersecan los dos ejes en sus puntos cero.

valores atípicos Datos que distan de los cuartiles más de 1.5 veces la amplitude intercuartílica.

P

parabola (p. 525) The graph of a quadratic function.

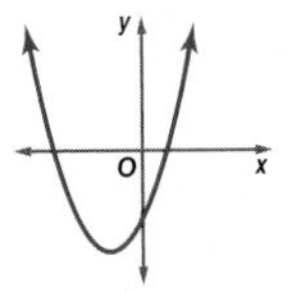

parallel lines (p. 237) Lines in the same plane that never intersect and have the same slope.

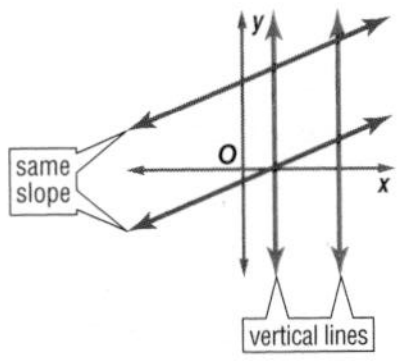

parameter (p. 756) A characteristic of the population as a whole.

parent function (p. 161) The simplest of functions in a family.

parent graph (p. 197) The simplest of the graphs in a family of graphs.

percent (p. P20) A ratio that compares a number to 100.

percent of change (p. 119) When an increase or decrease is expressed as a percent.

percent of decrease (p. 119) The ratio of an amount of decrease to the previous amount, expressed as a percent.

percent of increase (p. 119) The ratio of an amount of increase to the previous amount, expressed as a percent.

parábola La gráfica de una función cuadrática.

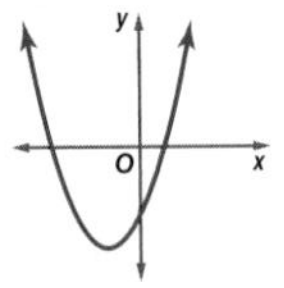

rectas paralelas Rectas en el mismo plano que no se intersecan jamás y que tienen pendientes iguales.

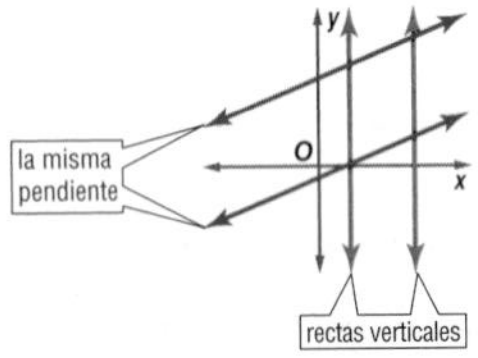

parámetro Una característica de la población en su totalidad.

función basíca La función más fundamental de un familia de funciones.

gráfica madre La gráfica más sencilla en una familia de gráficas.

porcentaje Razón que compara un numero con 100.

porcentaje de cambio Cuando un aumento o disminución se escribe como un tanto por ciento.

porcentaje de disminución Razón de la cantidad de disminución a la cantidad original, escrita como un tanto por ciento.

porcentaje de aumento Razón de la cantidad de aumento a la cantidad original, escrita como un tanto por ciento.

percent proportion (p. P20) $\frac{\text{part}}{\text{whole}} = \frac{\text{percent}}{100}$ or $\frac{a}{b} = \frac{p}{100}$

proporción porcentual $\frac{\text{parte}}{\text{todo}} = \frac{\text{por ciento}}{100}$ or $\frac{a}{b} = \frac{p}{100}$

perimeter (p. P23) The distance around a geometric figure.

perímetro Longitud alrededor una figura geométrica.

perfect square (p. P7) A number with a square root that is a rational number.

cuadrado perfecto Número cuya raíz cuadrada es un número racional.

perfect square trinomial (p. 505) A trinomial that is the square of a binomial.
$(a + b)^2 = (a + b)(a + b) = a^2 + 2ab + b^2$ *or*
$(a - b)^2 = (a - b)(a - b) = a^2 - 2ab - b^2$

trinomio cuadrado perfecto Un trinomio que es el cuadrado de un binomio.
$(a + b)^2 = (a + b)(a + b) = a^2 + 2ab + b^2$ *or*
$(a - b)^2 = (a - b)(a - b) = a^2 - 2ab - b^2$

permutation (p. 764) An arrangement or listing in which order is important.

permutación Arreglo o lista en que el orden es importante.

perpendicular line (p. 238) Lines that intersect to form a right angle.

recta perpendicular Recta que se intersecta formando un ángulo recto

piecewise-linear function (p. 261) A function written using two or more linear expressions.

función lineal por partes Función que se escribe usando dos o más expresiones lineales.

piecewise-defined function (p. 262) A function that is written using two or more expressions.

función definida por partes Función que se escribe usando dos o más expresiones.

point-slope form (p. 231) An equation of the form $y - y_1 = m(x - x_1)$, where m is the slope and (x_1, y_1) is a given point on a nonvertical line.

forma punto-pendiente Ecuación de la forma $y - y_1 = m(x - x_1)$, donde m es la pendiente y (x_1, y_1) es un punto dado de una recta no vertical.

polynomial (p. 424) A monomial or sum of monomials.

polinomio Un monomio o la suma de monomios.

population (p. 740) A large group of data usually represented by a sample.

población Grupo grande de datos, representado por lo general por una muestra.

positive correlation (p. 227) In a scatter plot, as x increases, y increases.

correlación positiva En una gráfica de dispersión, a medida que x aumenta, y aumenta.

positive number (p. P7) Any value that is greater than zero.

número positivos Cualquier valor mayor que cero.

power (p. 5) An expression of the form x^n, read *x to the nth power*.

potencia Una expresión de la forma x^n, se lee *x a la enésima potencia*.

prime factorization (p. 420) A whole number expressed as a product of factors that are all prime numbers.

factorización prima Número entero escrito como producto de factores primos.

prime number (p. 420) A whole number, greater than 1, with only factors that are 1 and itself.

número primo Número entero mayor que 1 cuyos únicos factores son 1 y sí mismo.

prime polynomial (p. 495) A polynomial that cannot be written as a product of two polynomials with integral coefficients.

polinomio primo Polinomio que no puede escribirse como producto de dos polinomios con coeficientes enteros.

principal square root (p. 49) The nonnegative square root of a number.

raíz cuadrada principal La raíz cuadrada no negativa de un número.

probability (p. P33) The ratio of the number of favorable equally likely outcomes to the number of possible equally likely outcomes.

probabilidad La razón del número de maneras en que puede ocurrir el evento al numero de resultados posibles.

probability distribution (p. 780) The probability of every possible value of the random variable x.

distribución de probabilidad Probabilidad de cada valor posible de una variable aleatoria x.

probability graph (p. 780) A way to give the probability distribution for a random variable and obtain other data.

gráfico probabilístico Una manera de exhibir la distribución de probabilidad de una variable aleatoria y obtener otros datos.

product (p. 5) In an algebraic expression, the result of quantities being multiplied is called the product.

producto En una expresión algebraica, se llama producto al resultado de las cantidades que se multiplican.

product rule (p. 671) If (x_1, y_1) and (x_2, y_2) are solutions to an inverse variation, then $y_1x_1 = y_2x_2$.

regla del producto Si (x_1, y_1) y (x_2, y_2) son soluciones de una variación inversa, entonces $y_1x_1 = y_2x_2$.

proportion (p. 111) An equation of the form $\frac{a}{b} = \frac{c}{d}$ stating that two ratios are equivalent.

proporción Ecuación de la forma $\frac{a}{b} = \frac{c}{d}$ que afirma la equivalencia de dos razones.

Pythagorean Theorem (p. 549) If a and b are the measures of the legs of a right triangle and c is the measure of the hypotenuse, then $c^2 = a^2 + b^2$.

Teorema de Pitágoras Si a y b son las longitudes de los catetos de un triángulo rectángulo y si c es la longitud de la hipotenusa, entonces $c^2 = a^2 + b^2$.

Pythagorean triple (p. 631) Whole numbers that satisfy the Pythagorean Theorem.

Triple pitagórico Números enteros que satisfacen el Teorema de Pitágoras.

Q

quadratic equation (pp. 485, 537) An equation of the form $ax^2 + bx + c = 0$, where $a \neq 0$.

ecuación cuadrática Ecuación de la forma $ax^2 + bx + c = 0$, donde $a \neq 0$.

quadratic expression (p. 448) An expression in one variable with a degree of 2 written in the form $ax^2 + bx + c$.

expression cuadratica Una expresión en una variable con un grado de 2, escritos en la forma $ax^2 + bx + c$.

Quadratic Formula (p. 558) The solutions of a quadratic equation in the form $ax^2 + bx + c$, where $a \neq 0$, are given by the formula $x = \frac{-b \pm \sqrt{b^2 - 4ac}}{2a}$.

Fórmula cuadrática Las soluciones de una ecuación cuadrática de la forma $ax^2 + bx + c$, donde $a \neq 0$, vienen dadas por la fórmula $x = \frac{-b \pm \sqrt{b^2 - 4ac}}{2a}$.

quadratic function (p. 525) An equation of the form $y = ax^2 + bx + c$, where $a \neq 0$.

función cuadrática Función de la forma $y = ax^2 + bx + c$, donde $a \neq 0$.

qualitative data (p. 746) Data that can not be given a numerical value

datos cualitativos Datos que no se pueden dar un valor numérico.

quantitative data (p. 746) Data that can be given as a numerical value

datos cuantitativos Datos que se pueden dar como numérico

quartile (p. P38) The values that divide a set of data into four equal parts.

cuartile Valores que dividen en conjunto de datos en cuarto partes iguales.

R

radical equations (p. 624) Equations that contain radicals with variables in the radicand.

ecuaciones radicales Ecuaciones que contienen radicales con variables en el radicando.

radical expression (p. 612) An expression that contains a square root.

expresión radical Expresión que contiene una raíz cuadrada.

radical function (p. 605) A function that contains radicals with variables in the radicand.

ecuaciones radicales Ecuaciones que contienen radicales con variables en el radicando.

radical sign (p. 49) The symbol $\sqrt{\ }$, used to indicate a nonnegative square root.

signo radical El símbolo $\sqrt{\ }$, que se usa para indicar la raíz cuadrada no negativa.

radicand (p. 605) The expression that is under the radical sign.

radicando La expresión debajo del signo radical.

radius (p. P24) Distance from the center to any point on the circle.

radio Distancia del centro cualquier punto de un círculo.

random sample (p. 741) A sample that is chosen without any preference, representative of the entire population.

muestra aleatoria Muestra tomada sin preferencia alguna y que es representativa de toda la población.

random variable (p. 779) A variable with a value that is the numerical outcome of a random event.

variable aleatoria Una variable cuyos valores son los resultados numéricos de un evento aleatorio.

range (p. 39) The set of second numbers of the ordered pairs in a relation.

rango Conjunto de los segundos números de los pares ordenados de una relación.

rate (p. 113) The ratio of two measurements having different units of measure.

tasa Razón de dos medidas que tienen distintas unidades de medida.

rate of change (p. 170) How a quantity is changing over time.

tasa de cambio Cómo cambia una cantidad con el tiempo.

rate problems (pp. 134, 725) Rational equations are used to solve problems involving transportal rates.

problemas de tasas Ecuaciones racionales que se usan para resolver problemas de tasas de transportación.

ratio (p. 111) A comparison of two numbers by division.

razón Comparación de dos números mediante división.

rational approximation (p. 50) A rational number that is close to, but not equal to, the value of an irrational number.

aproximación racional Número racional que está cercano, pero que no es igual, al valor de un número irracional.

rational equations (p. 720) Equations that contain rational expressions.

ecuaciones racionales Ecuaciones que contienen xpresiones racionales.

rational expression (p. 684) An algebraic fraction with a numerator and denominator that are polynomials.

expresión racional Fracción algebraica cuyo numerador y denominador son polinomios.

rational function (p. 678) An equation of the form $f(x) = \frac{p(x)}{q(x)}$, where $p(x)$ and $q(x)$ are polynomial functions, and $q(x) \neq 0$.

función racional Ecuación de la forma $f(x) = \frac{p(x)}{q(x)}$, donde $p(x)$ y $q(x)$ son funciones polinomiales y $q(x) \neq 0$.

rationalizing the denominator (p. 612) A method used to eliminate radicals from the denominator of a fraction.

racionalizar el denominador Método que se usa para eliminar radicales del denominador de una fracción.

rational numbers (p. P7) The set of numbers expressed in the form of a fraction $\frac{a}{b}$, where a and b are integers and $b \neq 0$.

números racionales Conjunto de los números que pueden escribirse en forma de fracción $\frac{a}{b}$, donde a y b son enteros y $b \neq 0$.

real numbers (p. P7) The set of rational numbers and the set of irrational numbers together.

números reales El conjunto de los números racionales junto con el conjunto de los números irracionales.

reciprocal (pp. P18, 17) The multiplicative inverse of a number.

recíproco Inverso multiplicativo de un número.

recursive formula (p. 188) Each term is formulated from one or more previous terms.

fórmula recursiva Cada tórmino proviene de uno o más terminos anteriores.

reflection (p. 545) A transformation where a figure, line, or curve, is flipped across a line.

reflexión Transformación en que cadapunto de una figura se aplica a través de una recta de simetría a su imagen correspondiente.

relation (p. 38) A set of ordered pairs.

relación Conjunto de pares ordenados.

relative frequency (p. 787) The number of times an outcome occurred in a probability experiment.

frecuencia relativa Número de veces que aparece un resultado en un experimento probabilístico.

replacement set (p. 31) A set of numbers from which replacements for a variable may be chosen.

conjunto de sustitución Conjunto de números del cual se pueden escoger sustituciones para una variable.

root (p. 161) The solutions of a quadratic equation.

raíces Las soluciones de una ecuación cuadrática

row reduction (p. 377) The process of performing elementary row operations on an augmented matrix to solve a system.

reducción de la fila El proceso de realizar operaciones elementales de la fila en una matriz aumentada para solucionar un sistema.

S

sample (p. 740) Some portion of a larger group selected to represent that group.

muestra Porción de un grupo más grande que se escoge para representarlo.

sample space (pp. P33, 764) The list of all possible outcomes.

espacio muestral Lista de todos los resultados posibles.

scalar (p. 371) A constant that is multiplied by a matrix.

escalar Una constante ques es multilicado por una matriz.

scalar multiplication (p. 371) Multiplication of a vector by a scalar.

multiplicación por escalare Multiplicación de un vector por una constante que es un vector.

scale (p. 108) A ratio or rate used when making a model of something that is too large or too small to be conveniently shown at actual size.

scale (p. 114) The relationship between the measurements on a drawing or model and the measurements of the real object.

scale model (p. 114) A model used to represent an object that is too large or too small to be built at actual size.

scatter plot (p. 245) Two sets of data plotted as ordered pairs in a coordinate plane.

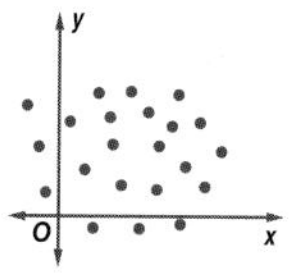

scientific notation (p. 416) A number in scientific notation is expressed as $a \times 10^n$, where $1 \leq a < 10$ and n is an integer.

sequence (p. 187) A set of numbers in a specific order.

set (p. 15) A collection of objects or numbers, often shown using braces { } and usually named by a capital letter.

set-builder notation (p. 284) A concise way of writing a solution set. For example, $\{t \mid t < 17\}$ represents the set of all numbers t such that t is less than 17.

similar triangles (p. 642) Triangles having the same shape but not necessarily the same size.

simple event (pp. 98, 663) A single event.

simple random sample (p. 742) A sample that is as likely to be chosen as any other from the population.

simplest form (p. 25) An expression is in simplest form when it is replaced by an equivalent expression having no like terms or parentheses.

escala Razón o tasa que se usa al construir un modelo de algo que es demasiado grande o pequeño como para mostrarlo de tamaño natural.

escala Relación entre las medidas de un dibujo o modelo y las medidas de la figura verdadera.

modelo a escala Modelo que se usa para representar un figura que es demasiado grande o pequeña como para ser construida de tamaño natural.

gráfica de dispersión Dos conjuntos de datos graficados como pares ordenados en un plano de coordenadas.

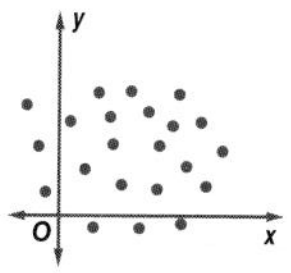

notación científica Un numero en notación científica se escribe con $a \times 10^n$, donde $1 \leq a < 10$ y n es un número entero.

sucesión Conjunto de números en un orden específico.

conjunto Colección de objetos o números, que a menudo se exhiben usando paréntesis de corchete { } y que se identifican por lo general mediante una letra mayúscula .

notación de construcción de conjuntos Manera concisa de escribir un conjunto solución. Por ejemplo, $\{t \mid t < 17\}$ representa el conjunto de todos los números t que son menores o iguales que 17.

semejantes Que tienen la misma forma, pero no necesariamente el mismo tamaño.

evento simple Un sólo evento.

muestra aleatoria simple Muestra de una población que tiene la misma probabilidad de escogerse que cualquier otra.

forma reducida Una expresión está reducida cuando se puede sustituir por una expresión equivalente que no tiene ni términos semejantes ni paréntesis.

simulation (p. 788) Using an object to act out an event that would be difficult or impractical to perform.

sine (p. 649) For an acute angle of a right triangle, the ratio of the measure of the leg opposite the acute angle to the measure of the hypotenuse.

slope (p. 172) The ratio of the change in the y-coordinates (rise) to the corresponding change in the x-coordinates (run) as you move from one point to another along a line.

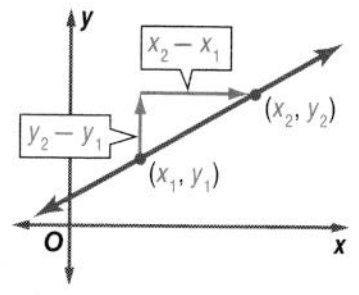

slope-intercept form (p. 214) An equation of the form $y = mx + b$, where m is the slope and b is the y-intercept.

solution (p. 31) A replacement value for the variable in an open sentence.

solution set (p. 31) The set of elements from the replacement set that make an open sentence true.

solve an equation (p. 83) The process of finding all values of the variable that make the equation a true statement.

solving an open sentence (p. 31) Finding a replacement value for the variable that results in a true sentence or an ordered pair that results in a true statement when substituted into the equation.

solving the triangle (p. 650) Finding the measures of all of the angles and sides of a triangle.

square root (p. P7) One of two equal factors of a number.

square root function (p. 605) Function that contains the square root of a variable.

standard deviation (p. 757) Is the square root of the variance.

simulación Uso de un objeto para representar un evento que pudiera ser difícil o poco práctico de ejecutar.

seno La razón entre la medida del cateto opuesto al ángulo agudo y la medida de la hipotenusa de un triángulo rectángulo.

pendiente Razón del cambio en la coordenada y (elevación) al cambio correspondiente en la coordenada x (desplazamiento) a medida que uno se mueve de un punto a otro en una recta.

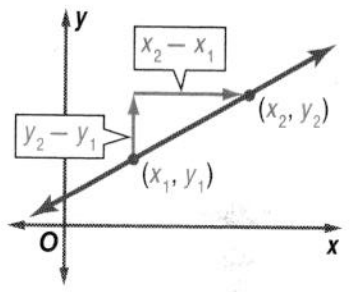

forma pendiente-intersección Ecuación de la forma $y = mx + b$, donde m es la pendiente y b es la intersección y.

solución Valor de sustitución de la variable en un enunciado abierto.

conjunto solución Conjunto de elementos del conjunto de sustitución que hacen verdadero un enunciado abierto.

resolver una ecuación Proceso en que se hallan todos los valores de la variable que hacen verdadera la ecuación.

resolver un enunciado abierto Hallar un valor de sustitución de la variable que resulte en un enunciado verdadero o un par ordenado que resulte en una proposición verdadera cuando se lo sustituye en la ecuación.

resolver un triángulo Hallar las medidas de todos los lados y todos los ángulos de un triángulo.

raíz cuadrada Uno de dos factores iguales de un número.

función radical Función que contiene la raíz cuadrada de una variable.

desviación tipica Calculada como la raíz cuadrada de la varianza.

standard form (p. 153) The standard form of a linear equation is $Ax + By = C$, where $A \geq 0$, A and B are not both zero, and A, B, and C are integers with a greatest common factor of 1.

forma estándar La forma estándar de una ecuación lineal es $Ax + By = C$, donde $A \geq 0$, ni A ni B son ambos cero, y A, B, y C son enteros cuyo máximo común divisor es 1.

standard form of a polynomial (p. 425) A polynomial that is written with the terms in order from greatest degree to least degree.

forma de estándar de un polinomio Un polinomio que se escribe con los términos en orden del grado más grande a menos grado.

statistic (p. 756) A quantity calculated from a sample.

estadística Una cantidad calculaba de una muestra.

statistical inference (p. 756) The statistics of a sample are used to draw conclusions about the population.

inferencia estadística La estadística de una muestra se utiliza para dibujar conclusiones sobre la población.

stratified random sample (p. 742) A sample in which the population is first divided into similar, nonoverlapping groups; a simple random sample is then selected from each group.

muestra aleatoria estratificada Muestra en que la población se divide en grupos similares que no se sobreponen; luego se selecciona una muestra aleatoria simple, de cada grupo.

stem-and-leaf plot (p. P41) A system used to condense a set of data where the greatest place value of the data forms the stem and the next greatest place value forms the leaves.

diagrama de tallo y hojas Sistema que se usa para condensar un conjunto de datos, en que el valor de posición máximo de los datos forma el tallo y el segundo valor de posiciós máximo forma las hojas. El valor de posición máximo de los datos forma eld tallo y el segundo valor de posición máximo forma las hojas.

step function (p. 261) A function with a graph that is a series of line segments.

funcion escalonada Función cuya gráfica es una serie de segmentos de recto.

substitution (p. 342) Use algebraic methods to find an exact solution of a system of equations.

sustitución Usa métodos algebraicos para hallar una solución exacta a un sistema de ecuaciones.

surface area (p. P31) The sum of the areas of all the surfaces of a three-dimensional figure.

área de superficie Suma de las áreas de todas las superficies (caras) de una figura tridimensional.

survey (p. 740) Data are from responses given by a sample of the population.

encuesta Datos son de las respuestas dadas por una muestra de la población.

symmetry (p. 526) A geometric property of figures that can be folded and each half matches the other exactly.

simetría Propiedad geométrica de figuras que pueden plegarse de modo que cada mitad corresponde exactamente a la otra.

system of equations (p. 333) A set of equations with the same variables.

sistema de ecuaciones Conjunto de ecuaciones con las mismas variables.

system of inequalities (p. 383) A set of two or more inequalities with the same variables.

sistema de desigualdades Conjunto de dos o más desigualdades con las mismas variables.

systematic random sample (p. 742) A sample in which the items in the sample are selected according to a specified time or item interval.

muestra aleatoria sistemática Muestra en que los elementos de la muestra se escogen según un intervalo de tiempo o elemento específico.

T

tangent (p. 649) For an acute angle of a right triangle, the ratio of the measure of the leg opposite the acute angle to the measure of the leg adjacent to the acute angle.

tangente La razón entre la medida del cateto opuesto al ángulo agudo y la medida del cateto adyacente al ángulo agudo de un triángulo rectángulo.

term (pp. 5, 187) A number, a variable, or a product or quotient of numbers and variables.

término Número, variable o producto, o cociente de números y variables.

terms (p. 187) The numbers in a sequence.

términos Los números de una sucesión.

theoretical probability (p. P35, 187) What should occur in a probability experiment.

probabilidad teórica Lo que debería ocurrir en un experimento probabilístico.

transformation (p. 544) A movement of a geometric figure.

transformación Desplazamiento de una figura geométrica.

translation (p. 544) A transformation where a figure is slid from one position to another without being turned.

translación Transformación en que una figura se desliza sin girar, de una posición a otra.

tree diagram (p. P34) A diagram used to show the total number of possible outcomes.

diagrama de árbol Diagrama que se usa para mostrar el número total de resultados posibles.

trigonometric function (p. 649) A function with a rule given by a trigonometric ratio.

funciónes trigonométricas Es una función con una regla dada por un razón trigonométrica.

trigonometric ratio (p. 649) A ratio of the lengths of sides of a right triangle.

razón trigonométrica Razón entre las longitudes de dos lados de un triángulo rectángulo.

trigonometry (p. 649) The study of the properties of triangles and trigonometric functions and their applications.

trigonométria Estudio de las relaciones entre los lados y ángulos de un triángulo rectángulo.

trinomials (p. 424) The sum of three monomials.

trinomios Suma de tres monomios.

U

uniform motion problems (p. 134) Problems in which an object moves at a certain speed, or rate.

problemas de movimiento uniforme Problemas en que el cuerpo se mueve a cierta velocidad o tasa.

union (p. 305) The graph of a compound inequality containing or; the solution is a solution of either inequality, not necessarily both.

unión Gráfica de una desigualdad compuesta que contiene la palabra o; la solución es el conjunto de soluciones de por lo menos una de las desigualdades, no necesariamente ambas.

unit analysis (p. 128) The process of including units of measurement when computing.

análisis de la unidad Proceso de incluir unidades de medida al computar.

unit rate (p. 113) A ratio of two quantities, the second of which is one unit.

tasa unitaria Tasa reducida que tiene denominador igual a 1.

univariate data (p. 757) Data with one variable.

datos univariate Datos con una variable.

upper quartile (p. P38) The median of the upper half of a set of data.

cuartil superior Mediana de la mitad superior de un conjunto de datos.

V

variable (p. 5) Symbols used to represent unspecified numbers or values.

variance (p. 757) The mean of the squares of the deviations from the arithmetic mean.

vertex (p. 525) The maximum or minimum point of a parabola.

vertical line test (p. 47) If any vertical line passes through no more than one point of the graph of a relation, then the relation is a function.

volume (p. P29) The measure of space occupied by a solid region.

voluntary response sample (p. 643) A sample that involves only those who want to participate.

variable Símbolos que se usan para representar números o valores no especificados.

varianza Media de los cuadrados de las desviaciones de la media aritmética.

vértice Punto máximo o mínimo de una parábola.

prueba de la recta vertical Si cualquier recta vertical pasa por un sólo punto de la gráfica de una relación, entonces la relación es una función.

volumen Medida del espacio que ocupa un solido.

muestra de respuesta voluntaria Muestra que involucra sólo aquellos que quieren participar.

W

weighted average (p. 132) The sum of the product of the number of units and the value per unit divided by the sum of the number of units, represented by M.

whole numbers (p. P7) The set {0, 1, 2, 3, …}.

work problems (p. 722) Rational equations are used to solve problems involving work rates.

promedio ponderado Suma del producto del número de unidades por el valor unitario dividida entre la suma del número de unidades y la cual se denota por M.

números enteros El conjunto {0, 1, 2, 3, …}.

problemas de trabajo Las ecuaciones racionales se usan para resolver problemas de tasas de trabajo.

X

x-axis (p. 38) The horizontal number line on a coordinate plane.

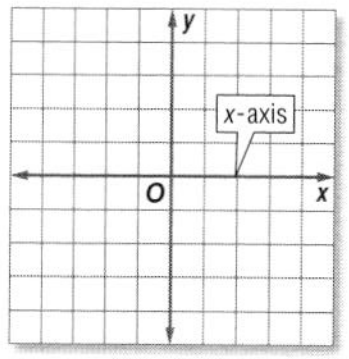

x-coordinate (p. 38) The first number in an ordered pair.

x-intercept (p. 154) The x-coordinate of a point where a graph crosses the x-axis.

eje x Recta numérica horizontal que forma parte de un plano de coordenadas.

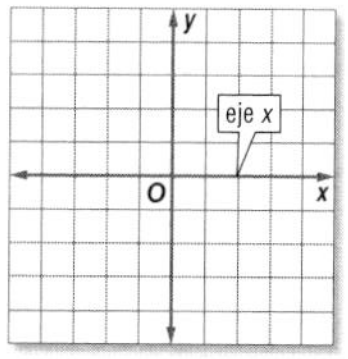

coordenada x El primer número de un par ordenado.

intersección x La coordenada x de un punto donde la gráfica corte al eje de x.

Y

y-axis (p. 38) The vertical number line on a coordinate plane.

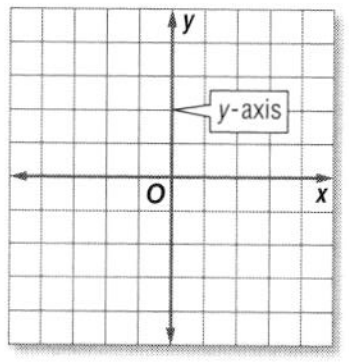

y-coordinate (p. 38) The second number in an ordered pair.

y-intercept (p. 154) The y-coordinate of a point where a graph crosses the y-axis.

eje y Recta numérica vertical que forma parte de un plano de coordenadas.

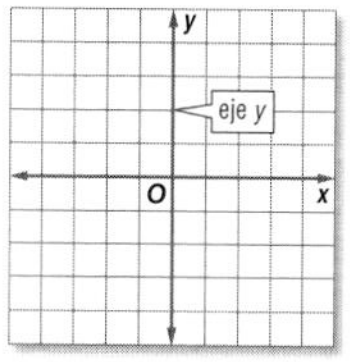

coordenada y El segundo número de un par ordenado.

intersección y La coordenada y de un punto donde la grafica corta al eje de y.

Z

zero (p. 161) The roots, or x-intercepts, of a quadratic function.

zero exponent (p. 410) For any nonzero number a, $a^0 = 1$. Any nonzero number raised to the zero power is equal to 1.

cero Las raíces o intersecciones x de una función cuadrática.

exponente cero Para cualquier número distinto a cero a, $a^0 = 1$. Cualquier número distinto a cero levantado al potente cero es igual a 1.

Index

Index

A

B

C

Index

F

H

Index

L

M

N

Index

O

P

Index

S

Index

Index

W

X

Y

Z

Symbols

$\neq$	is not equal to	AB	measure of $\overline{AB}$
$\approx$	is approximately equal to	$\angle$	angle
$\sim$	is similar to	$\triangle$	triangle
$>, \geq$	is greater than, is greater than or equal to	$^\circ$	degree
$<, \leq$	is less than, is less than or equal to	π	pi
$-a$	opposite or additive inverse of x	$\sin x$	sine of x
$\lvert a \rvert$	absolute value of a	$\cos x$	cosine of x
$\sqrt{a}$	principal square root of a	$\tan x$	tangent of x
$a : b$	ratio of a to b	!	factorial
(x, y)	ordered pair	$P(a)$	probability of a
$f(x)$	f of x, the value of f at x	$P(n, r)$	permutation of n objects taken r at a time
$\overline{AB}$	line segment AB	$C(n, r)$	combination of n objects taken r at a time

Algebraic Properties and Key Concepts

Identity	For any number a, $a + 0 = 0 + a = a$ and $a \cdot 1 = 1 \cdot a = a$.
Substitution (=)	If $a = b$, then a may be replaced by b.
Reflexive (=)	$a = a$
Symmetric (=)	If $a = b$, then $b = a$.
Transitive (=)	If $a = b$ and $b = c$, then $a = c$.
Commutative	For any numbers a and b, $a + b = b + a$ and $a \cdot b = b \cdot a$.
Associative	For any numbers a, b, and c, $(a + b) + c = a + (b + c)$ and $(a \cdot b) \cdot c = a \cdot (b \cdot c)$.
Distributive	For any numbers a, b, and c, $a(b + c) = ab + ac$ and $a(b - c) = ab - ac$.
Additive Inverse	For any number a, there is exactly one number $-a$ such that $a + (-a) = 0$.
Multiplicative Inverse	For any number $\frac{a}{b}$, where $a, b \neq 0$, there is exactly one number $\frac{b}{a}$ such that $\frac{a}{b} \cdot \frac{b}{a} = 1$.
Multiplicative (0)	For any number a, $a \cdot 0 = 0 \cdot a = 0$.
Addition (=)	For any numbers a, b, and c, if $a = b$, then $a + c = b + c$.
Subtraction (=)	For any numbers a, b, and c, if $a = b$, then $a - c = b - c$.
Multiplication and Division (=)	For any numbers a, b, and c, with $c \neq 0$, if $a = b$, then $ac = bc$ and $\frac{a}{c} = \frac{b}{c}$.
Addition (>)*	For any numbers a, b, and c, if $a > b$, then $a + c > b + c$.
Subtraction (>)*	For any numbers a, b, and c, if $a > b$, then $a - c > b - c$.
Multiplication and Division (>)*	For any numbers a, b, and c, 1. if $a > b$ and $c > 0$, then $ac > bc$ and $\frac{a}{c} > \frac{b}{c}$. 2. if $a > b$ and $c < 0$, then $ac < bc$ and $\frac{a}{c} < \frac{b}{c}$.
Zero Product	For any real numbers a and b, if $ab = 0$, then $a = 0$, $b = 0$, or both a and b equal 0.
Square of a Sum	$(a + b)^2 = (a + b)(a + b) = a^2 + 2ab + b^2$
Square of a Difference	$(a - b)^2 = (a - b)(a - b) = a^2 - 2ab + b^2$
Product of a Sum and a Difference	$(a + b)(a - b) = (a - b)(a + b) = a^2 - b^2$

*** *These properties are also true for $<$, $\geq$, and $\leq$.***

Formulas

Slope	$m = \frac{y_2 - y_1}{x_2 - x_1}$
Distance on a coordinate plane	$d = \sqrt{(x_2 - x_1)^2 + (y_2 - y_1)^2}$
Midpoint on a coordinate plane	$M = \left(\frac{x_1 + x_2}{2}, \frac{y_1 + y_2}{2}\right)$
Pythagorean Theorem	$a^2 + b^2 = c^2$
Quadratic Formula	$x = \frac{-b \pm \sqrt{b^2 - 4ac}}{2a}$
Perimeter of a rectangle	$P = 2\ell + 2w$ or $P = 2(\ell + w)$
Circumference of a circle	$C = 2\pi r$ or $C = \pi d$

Area

rectangle	$A = \ell w$	**trapezoid**	$A = \frac{1}{2}h(b_1 + b_2)$
parallelogram	$A = bh$	**circle**	$A = \pi r^2$
triangle	$A = \frac{1}{2}bh$		

Surface Area

cube	$S = 6s^2$	**regular pyramid**	$S = \frac{1}{2}P\ell + B$
prism	$S = Ph + 2B$	**cone**	$S = \pi r\ell + \pi r^2$
cylinder	$S = 2\pi rh + 2\pi r^2$		

Volume

cube	$V = s^3$	**regular pyramid**	$V = \frac{1}{3}Bh$
prism	$V = Bh$	**cone**	$V = \frac{1}{3}\pi r^2 h$
cylinder	$V = \pi r^2 h$		

Measures

Metric	Customary
Length	
1 kilometer (km) = 1000 meters (m)	1 mile (mi) = 1760 yards (yd)
1 meter = 100 centimeters (cm)	1 mile = 5280 feet (ft)
1 centimeter = 10 millimeters (mm)	1 yard = 3 feet
	1 foot = 12 inches (in.)
	1 yard = 36 inches
Volume and Capacity	
1 liter (L) = 1000 milliliters (mL)	1 gallon (gal) = 4 quarts (qt)
1 kiloliter (kL) = 1000 liters	1 gallon = 128 fluid ounces (fl oz)
	1 quart = 2 pints (pt)
	1 pint = 2 cups (c)
	1 cup = 8 fluid ounces
Weight and Mass	
1 kilogram (kg) = 1000 grams (g)	1 ton (T) = 2000 pounds (lb)
1 gram = 1000 milligrams (mg)	1 pound = 16 ounces (oz)
1 metric ton (t) = 1000 kilograms	